TEXTBOOK OF BIOCHEMISTRY

TEXTBOOK OF

THIRD EDITION

THE MACMILLAN COMPANY, NEW YORK

BIOCHEMISTRY

EDWARD STAUNTON WEST, Ph.D.

Professor of Biochemistry, University of

Oregon Medical School; Senior Scientist,

Oregon Primate Research Center

WILBERT R. TODD, Ph.D.

Professor of Biochemistry, University of

Oregon Medical School

SECOND PRINTING, 1962

LIBRARY OF CONGRESS CATALOG CARD NUMBER: 61-6423

THE MACMILLAN COMPANY, NEW YORK

PRINTED IN THE UNITED STATES OF AMERICA

Part of the material contained in this book has previously appeared in E. S. West's *Textbook of Biophysical Chemistry*, 2nd ed., © The Macmillan Company 1942, 1956.

Dedicated to DEAN DAVID W. E. BAIRD

Preface to the Third Edition

The objective of the authors, in this third edition of *Textbook of Biochemistry*, has been a careful and thorough revision of facts and theories, and changes in emphasis, necessitated by the exceedingly rapid advances in biochemical knowledge. The general organization of previous editions has been retained, but with changes in approach to various subjects designed to give the student a more thoroughly integrated understanding of biochemistry in its many relations. To do this has required that many chapters of the book be largely rewritten and the material extensively rearranged. Because of increased information relative to the metabolism of special tissues, and the importance of these tissues to medicine, a new chapter dealing with the composition and metabolism of special tissues has been added (Chap. 27). Also, the rapid advances in knowledge of the metabolism of nucleic acids, the relation of nucleic acids to protein synthesis, and the role of nucleic acids as carriers of hereditary information appeared to justify the discussion of nucleic acid metabolism in a separate chapter (Chap. 26).

The authors feel that a certain amount of well-organized elementary physical chemistry is essential for the student, preliminary to the study of biochemistry as such. As in previous editions this has been included, though in somewhat restricted detail. However, the aspects of physical chemistry related to special topics of biochemistry have been given particular attention, as will be observed in the discussions of protein chemistry, enzyme kinetics, bioenergetics, biological oxidations and reductions, and fluids and electrolytes.

The chapter dealing with acid-base balance and electrolyte and water balance (Chap. 17) has been introduced by a discussion of the mechanisms of kidney function, which provides a logical basis for better understanding the means by which the volume and composition of body fluids are maintained. Presentation of the material in this chapter has been drastically revised.

The discussion of plasma proteins, particularly with reference to blood coagulation, has been extensively revised (Chap. 15).

The chapters dealing with the organic chemistry of biochemistry, such as the chapters on the chemistry of lipids, carbohydrates, and proteins, have undergone much revision so as to present the material better and also to include new essential findings.

In the chapter on enzymes (Chap. 11) special attention has been given to enzyme kinetics, including the derivation and use of the Michaelis-Menten constant. Added sections in this chapter include intracellular enzyme distribution, Lineweaver-Burk treatment of enzyme reaction data, enzyme turnover numbers, enzyme synthesis and induction, and the clinical application of enzymes. Expansion of some sections and omission or shortening of others are among further changes in this chapter.

The discussion of gastric HCl production has been materially shortened to include, principally, substantiated concepts. Marked changes have been made in sections relating to the role of cholesterol in bile acid synthesis and in the digestion of phospholipids. The biosynthesis of heme and of bile pigments has been revised in keeping with recent advances. The fundamental chemistry of the van den Bergh reaction for determination of blood bilirubin has been clarified.

Much of the chapter on absorption from the intestine (Chap. 13) has been rewritten, and the discussion of detoxication mechanisms (Chap. 14) has been revised and expanded to include some of the newer drugs such as meprobamate and chloramphenicol.

While some sections of the chapter on the metabolism of inorganic elements (Chap. 30) have been shortened, new information on selenium and factor 3 and on cobalt, zinc, manganese, copper, molybdenum, and iron has been added.

The interesting place of polyunsaturated fatty acids in nutrition and a short discussion of the role of essential fatty acids have been added in the chapter dealing with the nutritional aspects of the lipids (Chap. 24).

New information relative to the amino acid requirements of humans (from the work of Rose and co-workers) has been added in the discussion of the nutritional aspects of proteins and amino acids (Chap. 28).

The principal change in the chapter on the vitamins (Chap. 18) consists in the addition of considerable new material relating to the role of these nutrients in metabolic reactions.

The extent to which formulas and other material should be repeated in a text such as this presents a difficult problem. The authors feel that from the standpoint of the bewildered student, confronted with the tremendous complexity of modern biochemistry, a certain amount of repetition is desirable in the treatment of a number of topics, in order that he may more readily maintain his orientation to the discussion at hand without having to piece-in critical information by referring back and forth through the text. The fact that so many of the vitamins are integral parts of enzyme systems necessitates considerable repetition of the material of Chapters 11 and 18 in order to present well-organized discussions. However, in sections of the book where repetition is not critical to maintenance of logical exposition, cross reference to pertinent material of other sections has been used to conserve space. Also to the end of conserving space, certain sections of the book have been put in small, but legible, print. These sections in fine print contribute to more complete treatment of special subjects, but may be omitted and still leave logical discussion of the subjects. The use of smaller-size formulas, and of word equations when readily understood, permits some conservation of space.

The authors feel a deep debt of gratitude to users of the book who have taken the time and trouble to point out errors in previous editions and to make suggestions for desirable changes. Without this help our task would have been much more difficult and the revision less complete. It is hoped that similar constructive criticism may be accorded the third edition.

The authors are particularly indebted to their friends and colleagues: Dr. John Van Bruggen, who revised the chapter on hormones and made many valuable suggestions throughout the revision; Dr. Howard Mason, Dr. Ruth Peterson, Dr. Clarissa Beatty, and Dr. Jack Fellman, who read manuscript and helped prevent errors of omission and commission; and Dr. David Jackson, who contributed much to the section on connective tissue.

Special thanks are due to Mrs. Mildred Cruz and Mrs. Beatrice Brunn, who typed the manuscript.

The authors wish to express their sincere appreciation to The Macmillan Company for their courteous and helpful aid throughout the revision process.

E. S. W.

W. R. T.

Preface to the
First Edition

Our understanding of living things is largely equivalent to what we know about the composition of protoplasm and the intricate biochemical reactions by which it is formed, broken down, and enabled to function. In particular, the recent marked advances and the future progress in the field of medicine depend upon an expanding knowledge of biochemistry. Biochemistry, which was only a fledgling twenty-five years ago, has now developed into a vastly complex science growing at an accelerated pace. This phenomenal development and its relation to the understanding of life processes is imposing ever-increasing demands upon students and the departments of biochemistry teaching them. It is also rendering increasingly difficult the writing of textbooks which encompass the current facts and theories of the general field of biochemistry.

In preparing this textbook of biochemistry the authors have attempted to outline in considerable detail the principles of physical and organic chemistry upon which biochemistry as such is based, and then to present the fundamental facts, principles, and theories which constitute biochemistry proper. Through the courtesy of The Macmillan Company large sections of West's *Physical Chemistry for Students of Biochemistry and Medicine** have been incorporated in various chapters of the text to provide such background for the student when this is necessary. Special consideration has been given to explanations designed to help the student understand the subject, and these explanations contribute materially to the length of the book. Repetition of

* Title changed in second edition (1956) to *Textbook of Biophysical Chemistry*.

important facts and theories will be found throughout the chapters. The authors feel that such repetition is invaluable to the learning process. Also, some facts and theories have various relations necessitating their repetition in order to present well-rounded discussions of different subjects. The book will be found to contain an unusual amount of the experimental evidence, with references, upon which the principles and theories of biochemistry are based. This the authors consider desirable in order to show the student how the science develops, to increase his critical judgment, and to stimulate his interest. The amount of material contained in the book is considerably greater than usually presented in courses in biochemistry. The authors consider this to be desirable for two reasons. In the first place, different instructors emphasize different phases of the subject, and a book of broad coverage enables the student to select the sections pertinent to the course he is taking. In the second place, a rather comprehensive text provides additional material to stimulate the interest and enthusiasm of the more capable students in a class. The book is liberally provided with summaries, charts, and diagrams which enable the student to obtain information quickly when necessary.

The principles of biochemistry related to medicine have been given special attention in the chapters of the book dealing with enzymes and digestion, blood, respiration, acid-base balance, salt and water balance, hormones, metabolism, and nutrition. An understanding of the theoretical basis of nutrition is extremely important to the medical student and physician; yet the presentation of a coherent body of information relative to it is often neglected in the medical course. The authors feel that the proper place for such material is in the biochemistry course and text immediately following intermediary metabolism. This arrangement is followed in the present text and comprises chapters on the nutritional aspects of proteins, carbohydrates, fats, and minerals. Due to their importance to medicine and the mechanisms of their action, antibiotics are properly considered in a book on biochemistry. This has been done briefly in a chapter on antimetabolic agents.

The use of isotopic atoms such as deuterium, N^{15}, and C^{14} to trace the chemical pathways of substances in the body has been largely responsible for many significant recent advances in our understanding of metabolism and other biochemical phenomena. The isotopic methods utilized and the results obtained have been particularly stressed in the book. The student should early become well acquainted with the method which has done so much and promises to do so much more for the advancement of biochemistry and medicine.

The authors have approached writing this book fully cognizant of the complexity and difficulty of the task and of their limitations. Their object has been to provide a comprehensive text of biochemistry similar to those current in the field of physiology, and written from the viewpoints of both student and teacher. In such a work many errors of both omission and commission are inevitable, and the authors will appreciate having these brought to their attention.

The authors are greatly indebted to their colleague, Dr. John T. Van

Bruggen, for preparation of the chapter on hormones. They also wish to express their deep appreciation to Dr. P. A. Shaffer of Washington University School of Medicine, Dr. E. A. Doisy, Saint Louis University School of Medicine, and Dr. C. G. Heller and Mr. K. B. Davison, University of Oregon Medical School, for reading portions of the manuscript and offering helpful suggestions; to Mrs. Nancy Moores, Mrs. Maxine Gross, and Mrs. Ruth West for typing the manuscript and other aid; to Mrs. Clarice Francone and Mrs. Kay Bittick for preparation of many of the illustrations and charts; and to the many authors and publishers who have kindly granted permission to use material from books and journals. The authors are particularly indebted to The Macmillan Company for their unfailing courtesy and aid given without stint in the preparation of the book.

E. S. W.
W. R. T.

Contents

TEXTBOOK OF BIOCHEMISTRY

1

Introduction

The scope of biochemistry. Biochemistry in its broad aspects is the most comprehensive of all the branches of chemistry. It includes inorganic, organic, and physical chemistry to the extent to which each of these is related to the chemistry of living things, both plant and animal. The chemical principles involved in the study of biochemistry are necessarily identical with those the student has learned in preliminary chemistry courses, but they are often posed in unique and intricate relationships.

The basis of all forms of life is the material called protoplasm, which in chemical composition, physical organization, and function is enormously complex; in fact, it is the most complex physicochemical system with which the chemist has to deal. The problem of biochemistry in general is to relate the properties and functions of protoplasm to its physicochemical organization. The protoplasm of each different kind of cell in each kind of animal or plant is different and characteristic, yet the similarities in chemical composition, organization, and chemical processes which take place in these many different forms of protoplasm are in many respects strikingly similar. The study of the biochemistry of one kind of protoplasm, therefore, is, in effect, the study of all kinds of protoplasm. The developments in animal biochemistry have been greatly aided by investigations of the chemical processes of plants and microorganisms, and vice versa. Various chemical reactions first observed in microorganisms or plants have later been sought and found in higher animals. The reverse also is true.

A knowledge of the broad chemical principles as they apply to protoplasm in general is desirable for the biochemist whether he be concerned with pure biology or with the more specialized fields relating to agriculture, industrial processes, or medicine. The objective of the present text is to provide a

1

broad foundation in biochemical facts and principles and, in addition, the specialized treatment of the subject desirable for students of medicine and the medical sciences.

Contents of a course in medical biochemistry. There are several particular phases of biochemistry with which the medical student is concerned. Among these may be listed the following:

1. The chemistry of tissues and foods. Foods are largely derived from animal or plant tissues, and the study of one is essentially identical with or closely supplementary to that of the other. Since most of the organic substances of both belong to the broad classes of carbohydrates, fatty materials, proteins, or related compounds, a rather thorough knowledge of the pure chemistry and physiological relations of these substances is of prime importance.

2. The chemistry of digestion and absorption. Much of our food is composed of large molecules, such as proteins and starch, which cannot be absorbed from the intestine into the blood stream and could not be utilized if they were absorbed. In fact, they might be definitely toxic, as in the case of undigested proteins. The proteins of foods contain about the same fundamental structural units (amino acids, etc.) as do the proteins of tissues, but the arrangement is different. Consequently, the various food proteins are broken into their constituent amino acids in the alimentary tract and are then absorbed into the blood stream and distributed to the various organs; there the amino acids are recombined into proteins of structure and characteristics peculiar to the proteins of our various tissues. Similarly, much of our carbohydrate food (such as starch) is broken into simpler molecules in the digestive tract before absorption and utilization. The same applies more or less to fatty foods also. In addition to digesting the larger food molecules to smaller utilizable ones, the alimentary tract provides a method of entry for water, mineral salts, vitamins, and many other diffusible molecules of the food supply. The study of the chemical and physiologic processes concerned in the digestion and absorption of food materials is a necessary part of medical biochemistry.

3. The chemistry of respiration. Respiration is an obligatory property of the living protoplasm of higher forms of life. In man oxygen is taken into the lungs and diffuses across the membranes into the blood, in which most of it combines loosely with the hemoglobin of the red cells; in this form it is carried to the tissues, where it is released for the oxidation of foods with the production of energy. In this process carbon dioxide is formed in volume about equal to that of the oxygen used. This carbon dioxide passes from the tissues to the blood stream and in various chemical combinations is transported to the lungs, from which it is exhaled. The gaseous exchange between air and tissues is composed of many chemical and physical mechanisms. Its importance is obvious.

4. The chemistry of tissue metabolism. Among the important problems of biochemistry is that concerned with the complicated reactions taking place within tissue cells by which protoplasm is synthesized or broken down and foods are oxidized to supply energy for the living processes. Since this problem involves a knowledge of the finer chemical composition of protoplasm as a basis for the understanding of many of the reactions, it is the most difficult phase of biochemistry and is as yet very imperfectly understood. It is commonly spoken of as intermediary metabolism and is as fundamental as life itself.

5. The chemistry of the glands of internal secretion. The regulation and coordination of the activity of the various organ systems of the body so that they function smoothly as an integrated whole are imperative. This is effected largely in two ways: by the hormonal control of the glands of internal secretion and by the nervous system. These systems may function either together or separately. The general process of nervous regulation of tissue functioning is well known. As an illustration of control through glands of internal secretion, consider the anatomically insignificant (in size only) pituitary gland located at the base of the brain. This gland produces a chemical substance (hormone) which regulates the activity of the thyroid gland, which in turn, among other things, controls the rate of energy production in the tissues. The pituitary gland produces hormones which regulate the development and functioning of the sex organs and is in this way vitally concerned with the process of reproduction. It secretes a hormone which determines the size to which an animal may grow and another concerned with the utilization of carbohydrates by the body. Various other hormones have been attributed to the pituitary. Additional glands of internal secretion are the thyroid, pancreas, testes, ovaries, adrenals, parathyroids, and possibly thymus, each producing one or more hormones concerned in the regulation of some organ or process. The biochemistry of the glands of internal secretion is one of the most brilliant and important chapters in the records of biologic achievement. This development has profoundly influenced the field of medicine both from the standpoint of understanding physiologic and pathologic processes and from that of furnishing effective agents of treating disease.

6. The chemistry of blood. The circulating blood represents the main transport system within and between the organs of the body. It carries foods to the tissues and waste products from them to the excretory organs. It transports the gases concerned in respiration. The hormones produced by the various glands of internal secretion pass into the blood and through its circulation reach the tissues for which they are specific. It serves as an efficient cooling system for the body and also for the distribution of heat from one part of the body to another. It is actively concerned in helping maintain the proper distribution of water and salts in tissues. It contains substances and cells which actively combat infection by microorganisms. The composition of blood is normally maintained relatively constant, but this constancy is a dynamic and not a static condition. For example, the quantity of glucose in the circulating blood represents a balance between that added to it from foods and body reserves and the amount removed by the tissues. In many pathologic conditions the amounts of one or more constituents of the blood may become definitely increased or decreased from normal and thereby furnish valuable information for clinical diagnosis and treatment. The chemistry of blood is better understood than that of any other tissue, and a knowledge of its normal composition and pathologic variations is an indispensable part of the physician's training.

7. The chemistry of excretion. The kidneys, lungs, intestines, and skin serve as excretory organs to remove decomposition products of tissues and foods in order that the composition of the body fluids and tissues may be kept approximately constant. Important among these decomposition products are the nitrogenous substances, urea, uric acid, and creatinine, which are formed from proteins. The metabolism of carbohydrates, fats, and proteins produces much carbon dioxide and water. The breakdown of sulfur- and phosphorus-containing proteins and other compounds leads to the formation of sulfates and phosphates. Excess salts (as NaCl), water, and various nonfood materials are taken with the food and absorbed into the blood and tissues. A certain range of concentration of the above substances in the body fluids and tissues is compatible with health, but much excess may lead to deranged function and illness.

The kidneys and lungs perform by far the more important roles in excretion from the body. Most of the organic waste products, mineral salts, and water are removed from the blood by the kidneys and passed in the urine. The lungs serve especially to remove carbon dioxide and considerable water, as well as some volatile substances such as alcohol, acetone (often present in the blood and tissues of a diabetic), and gases absorbed into the blood from the intestine. Most of the excretions from the intestine (feces) represent food and bacterial residues and intestinal secretions or products derived from them. However, some materials, especially certain metals such as calcium and iron, pass from the blood into the intestine and are excreted in the feces. Normally the skin functions to only a minor extent as an excretory organ, serving to remove chiefly water, with traces of salts and organic substances. In cases of prolonged profuse perspiration, however, the loss of sodium chloride may be so great as severely to deplete the body supply and cause violent illness.

Some special phases of excretion are of particular interest to the medical student. In various diseases the excretion of certain substances may be increased or decreased, or abnormal materials may be excreted as the result of disease. In the disease diabetes mellitus the body fails to use its sugar properly, and the blood sugar concentration rises. Consequently, the kidneys, in attempting to regulate the composition of the blood, excrete large amounts of sugar (in severe cases). In order to excrete much sugar, the kidneys must also excrete much water. As a result, the untreated severe diabetic is likely to be poorly nourished and continually hungry and thirsty. The well-trained physician quickly recognizes the significance of such facts.

A study of the chemistry of the excretions is of much importance in helping to unravel the chemical processes which take place in the body. If eating protein which contains unoxidized sulfur causes the excretion of more sulfates in the urine, it is only logical to conclude that the body can remove the sulfur from the protein and oxidize it to sulfuric acid. This is a very simple application of the use of a knowledge of excretory products in explaining metabolic processes. In most cases the problem is much more complex.

8. The physical chemistry of protoplasm. The body is composed of integrated organ systems which, in turn, are aggregates of cells and specialized membranes. The cells represent masses of protoplasm, jellylike in consistency, but in reality highly organized structurally, which are enclosed in membranes. The jellylike nature of protoplasm is due to the presence of colloidal particles, composed of proteins and other cellular substances, which make up by far the greater proportion of protoplasm, aside from water, which is the major component. These colloidal particles have rather specific and unique properties as a result of their size and composition, and represent not only important structural units, but also dynamic functional units of protoplasm. Some knowledge of the physicochemical principles related to the colloidal state of matter is necessary in the study of biochemistry.

It is evident that foods, hormones, and all substances necessary for the maintenance of cells, as well as the waste products formed in them, must pass through the cell membranes. These membranes are permeable to some materials and more or less impermeable to others, and different kinds of cells vary as to the substances which will diffuse through their membranes. The permeability of living membranes is often quite different from that of dead ones, so that the ordinary principles which apply to such things as collodion membranes apply only partially, for example, to the membranes of the cells of the intestinal tract. Maintenance of the normal permeability of cell membranes is necessary for normal physiologic processes, and abnormal permeability is often associated with pathologic conditions.

The large amount of water in protoplasm has already been stressed. A great deal of water is present in the blood and tissue fluids. Much is closely associated with protoplasmic structures, the colloidal molecules of proteins in particular holding large amounts. This protoplasmic water is an essential constituent; and when it is greatly increased or reduced, abnormal physiologic functioning occurs. The proper distribution of water between the blood, lymph, and tissue cells is one of the most important processes of the body and a rather complicated one. It is related to the osmotic pressure of the various dissolved colloids and crystalloids as well as to the blood pressure and membrane permeability to the dissolved substances. The water balance of the body is closely associated with the concentrations and kinds of electrolytes present, and the proper distribution of the latter is fundamental to the composition and functioning of tissues.

Normally the reaction of the blood and lymph is very slightly alkaline, and that of the protoplasmic mass within tissue cells is more nearly neutral or possibly faintly acid. A neutral reaction of the blood, if unrelieved, is associated with a comatose condition and death in a short time. On the other hand, a reaction slightly more alkaline than normal, if untreated, brings on a condition of hyperirritability of the tissues with tetanic contractions of the muscles and death. Such consequences of changes in reaction are not so unexpected if the relation of acidity and alkalinity (pH) to the action of enzymes, the properties of proteins, the permeability of membranes, etc., are understood. The body is equipped with various mechanisms for controlling the reaction of its tissues, and very important among these are its so-called buffer systems, which have the property of neutralizing acids and bases with only small changes in reaction. A thorough knowledge of the action of buffer systems is indispensable to an understanding of the acid-base balance of the body.

Various gases, such as oxygen, carbon dioxide, and nitrogen, are distributed throughout body fluids and tissues in physical solution and in some cases in chemical combination. A knowledge of the physical and chemical properties of these gases is essential.

Many other points of a physicochemical nature are concerned in tissue mechanisms such as the electrical potentials across membranes, the oxidation-reduction potentials within protoplasm, and the electric charges of colloid particles. The student will realize during his studies that while the physicochemical aspects of biochemistry are rather difficult, they are at the same time exceedingly fundamental.

Importance of biochemistry to medicine. Since all protoplasm is made up of chemical substances and the normal functioning of the body ultimately involves chemical processes, the basic importance of biochemistry to other medical subjects such as physiology is obvious. In fact, physiology and biochemistry overlap and merge, so that for practical consideration they are inseparable. Pathologic conditions in the body are often caused by deranged chemical composition and functioning of tissues, and many of the problems of pathology are most profitably approached from the chemical viewpoint. The bacteriologist is especially concerned with the chemical properties of bacteria and the chemical changes they produce in tissues, leading to various diseased conditions. He is also very much interested in such things as vaccines, serums, and antitoxins, which play such an important role in the treatment of disease. The pharmacologist must be acquainted with the chemical aspects of the body, because the action of his drugs nearly always involves some change in the biochemical events taking place in the tissues. Since the physician utilizes all these basic sciences in the diagnosis and treatment of disease, his dependence upon biochemistry, directly or indirectly, is far reaching. Medicine made important, but slow, progress before its disciples drafted the science of chemistry to its service. Within the last thirty years it has advanced at a most encouraging rate, and a major part of the credit is due to the contributions of the biochemist. He has given logical chemical explanations for physiologic and pathologic processes. He has worked out many of the complicated secrets of nutrition and enabled physicians to use foods intelligently in preventing and combating diseases. He has provided vitamins and hormones in pure condition for use in effectively treating many diseases. He has aided in the preparation of vaccines, antitoxins, serums, etc. Last, but not least, he has provided a large number of chemical tests as aids in the recognition of disease.

The literature of biochemistry. The subject is so vast and advances are being made so rapidly that the medical course in biochemistry cannot hope to do more than provide the student with an elementary knowledge of the facts and principles of the subject and, it is hoped, a realization of its increasing importance to medicine. The course should prepare the student with sufficient background for the successful study of his other medical courses, and it should also place him in position to read the medical literature that is becoming ever more chemical in nature.

In order that the student's training may be as broad as possible, it is desirable that he early form the habit of reading books on biochemistry other than the one adopted as a text for his class. By doing this, he will obtain knowledge of the subject from different angles. He should also become acquainted with current journals in which he may see the science in the making and learn how to weigh evidence and form his own opinions. Because the current literature of biochemistry is so vast, it is impossible to do more than read a very small fraction of the published original articles. In order that this handicap may be obviated as much as possible, review journals and books are published in which the status of important subjects at the time is summarized. These give references to the original literature for those who may wish to investigate a subject in detail. The abstract journals are among the most important publications in aiding the searcher to find any or all of the literature on a given subject, and the medical student should early become acquainted with those concerned with medicine and learn how to use them. There are various comprehensive treatises, monographs, and books dealing with the different phases of biochemistry that the student should know about and use as occasion demands. The point of the above admonitions is that unless the student learns how to use the literature of medicine and does so, he will regress, and the science, moving on, will leave him with an ever increasing deficiency, which after a time will become so great that he will be hopelessly out of date.

An abbreviated list of publications related to the field of biochemistry is given below.

Journals

Acta Chemica Scandinavica (Acta Chem. Scand.), Denmark.
American Journal of Physiology (Am. J. Physiol.).
Annalen der Chemie (Ann.), Germany.
Archives of Biochemistry and Biophysics (Arch. Biochem. and Biophys.).
Berichte der deutschen chemischen Gesellschaft (Ber.), Germany.
Biochimica et Biophysica Acta (Biochim. et Biophys. Acta), Holland.
Biochemical Journal (Biochem. J.), England.
Biochemische Zeitschrift (Biochem. Z.), Germany.
Biokhimiya (Biokhimiya), Russia.
British Medical Bulletin (Brit. Med. Bull.).
Bulletin de la société de chimie biologique (Bull. soc. chim. biol.), France.
Canadian Journal of Biochemistry and Physiology (Canad. J. Biochem. Physiol.).
Comptes rendus de la société chimie biologique (Compt. rend. soc. chim. biol.), France.
Diabetes (Diabetes).
Endocrinology (Endocrinology).
Enzymologia (Enzymologia), Holland.

Federation Proceedings (Federation Proc.).
Helvetica Chimica Acta (Helv. Chim. Acta), Switzerland.
Hoppe-Seyler's Zeitschrift für Physiologische Chemie (Z. Physiol. Chem.), Germany.
Journal of the American Chemical Society (J. Am. Chem. Soc.).
Journal of Bacteriology (J. Bact.).
Journal of Biochemistry (J. Biochem). Printed in English, French and German. Japan.
Journal of Biological Chemistry (J. Biol. Chem.).
Journal of Biophysical and Biochemical Cytology (J. Biophys. and Biochem. Cytol.).
Journal of Cellular and Comparative Physiology (J. Cellular Comp. Physiol.).
Journal of the Chemical Society (J. Chem. Soc.), England.
Journal of Clinical Investigation (J. Clin. Invest.).
Journal of Endocrinology (J. Endocrinol.).
Journal of Experimental Medicine (J. Exptl. Med.).
Journal of General Microbiology (J. Gen. Microbiol.).
Journal of General Physiology (J. Gen. Physiol.).
Journal of Immunology (J. Immunol.).
Journal of Molecular Biology (J. Molecular Biol.).
Journal of Neurochemistry (J. Neurochem.).
Journal of Nutrition (J. Nutrition).
Journal of Organic Chemistry (J. Org. Chem.).
Journal of Pharmacology and Experimental Therapeutics (J. Pharmacol. Exptl. Therap.).
Journal of Physical and Colloid Chemistry (J. Phys. and Colloid Chem.).
Journal of Physiology (J. Physiol.), England.
Metabolism (Metabolism).
Nature (Nature), England.
Naturwissenschaften (Naturwiss.), Germany.
Perspectives in Biology and Medicine (Perspectives Biol. Med.).
Plant Physiology (Plant Physiol.).
Proceedings of the National Academy of Sciences (Proc. Natl. Acad. Sci. U.S.).
Proceedings of the Royal Society, Series B (Proc. Roy. Soc. [London], Series B).
Proceedings of the Society for Experimental Biology and Medicine (Proc. Soc. Exptl. Biol. Med.).
Science (Science).
Yale Journal of Biology and Medicine (Yale J. Biol. Med.).
Zeitschrift für Naturforschung (Z. Naturforsch.), Germany.

Reviews and monograph series

Advances in Carbohydrate Chemistry. Books, issued yearly.
Advances in Enzymology. Books, issued yearly.
Advances in Protein Chemistry. Books, issued yearly.
American Scientist (Am. Scientist).
Annals of the New York Academy of Sciences (Ann. N.Y. Acad. Sci.).
Annual Reports of the Chemical Society (Ann. Reps.), England.
Annual Review of Biochemistry (Ann. Rev. Biochem.).
Annual Review of Microbiology (Ann. Rev. Microbiol.).
Annual Review of Physiology (Ann. Rev. Physiol.).
Annual Review of Plant Physiology (Ann. Rev. Plant Physiol.).
Bacteriological Reviews (Bact. Revs.).
Biochemical Society Symposia (Biochem. Soc. Symposia), England.
Biological Reviews of the Cambridge Philosophical Society (Biol. Revs. Cambridge Phil. Soc.), England.
Biological Symposia (Biol. Symposia).
Chemical Reviews (Chem. Revs.).
Cold Spring Harbor Symposia on Quantitative Biology (Cold Spring Harbor Symposia Quant. Biol.).
Ergebnisse der Physiologie, biologische Chemie und experimentellen Pharmakologie (Ergeb. Physiol. biol. Chem. exptl. Pharmakol.), Germany.
Harvey Lectures.
Nutrition Reviews (Nutrition Revs.).
Physiological Reviews (Physiol. Revs.).

Quarterly Review of Biology (Quart. Rev. Biol.).
Quarterly Reviews of the Chemical Society (Quart. Revs.), England.
Vitamins and Hormones. Books, issued yearly.

Textbooks of biochemistry

Baldwin, E.: *Dynamic Aspects of Biochemistry,* 3rd ed. Cambridge University Press, Cambridge, 1957.
Cantarow, A., and Schepartz, B.: *Biochemistry,* 2nd ed. W. B. Saunders Co., Philadelphia, 1957.
Fruton, J. S., and Simmonds, S.: *General Biochemistry,* 2nd ed. John Wiley & Sons, New York, 1958.
Gortner, R. A., Jr., and Gortner, W. A. (eds.): *Outlines of Biochemistry,* 3rd ed. John Wiley & Sons, New York, 1949.
Harrow, B., and Mazur, A.: *Textbook of Biochemistry,* 7th ed. W. B. Saunders Co., Philadelphia, 1958.
Hawk, P. B.; Oser, B. L.; and Summerson, W. H.: *Practical Physiological Chemistry,* 13th ed. McGraw-Hill Book Co., Inc., New York, 1954.
Kleiner, I. S., and Orten, J. M.: *Human Biochemistry,* 5th ed. C. V. Mosby Co., St. Louis, 1958.
Mitchell, P. H.: *Textbook of Biochemistry,* 2nd ed. McGraw-Hill Book Co., Inc., New York, 1950.
Walker, B. S.; Boyd, W. C.; and Asimov, I.: *Biochemistry and Human Metabolism,* 3rd ed. Williams & Wilkins Co., Baltimore, 1957.
White, A.; Handler, P.; Smith, E. L.; and Stetten, D., Jr.: *Principles of Biochemistry,* 2nd ed. McGraw-Hill Book Co., Inc., New York, 1959.

Books on the relation of biochemistry to medicine

Bodansky, M., and Bodansky, O.: *Biochemistry of Disease,* 2nd ed. The Macmillan Co., New York, 1952.
Cantarow, A., and Trumper, M.: *Clinical Biochemistry,* 5th ed. W. B. Saunders Co., Philadelphia, 1955.
Duncan, G. G.: *Diseases of Metabolism,* 3rd ed. W. B. Saunders Co., Philadelphia, 1952.
Grollman, A. (ed.): *Clinical Physiology.* McGraw-Hill Book Co., Inc., New York, 1957.
Hoffman, W. S.: *The Biochemistry of Clinical Medicine,* 2nd ed. Year Book Publishers, Inc., Chicago, 1959.
Peters, J. P., and Van Slyke, D. D.: *Quantitative Clinical Chemistry.* Vol. I, *Interpretations;* Vol. II, *Methods.* Williams & Wilkins Co., Baltimore, 1932. Vol. I. *Interpretations,* 2nd ed., 1946 (does not cover the whole field as did the 1st ed.); Vol. II, *Methods,* reprinted 1956 with some changes.
Thompson, R. H. S., and King, E. J.: *Biochemical Disorders in Human Disease,* Academic Press Inc., New York, 1957.

Abstract publications

Berichte über die gesammte Physiologie und experimentelle Pharmakologie (Ber. ges. Physiol u. exptl. Pharmakol.).
Biological Abstracts (Biol. Abstracts).
British Chemical and Physiological Abstracts (Brit. Chem. Physiol. Abstracts).
Chemical Abstracts (Chem. Abstracts).
Nutrition Abstracts and Reviews (Nut. Abstracts Revs.), England.
Quarterly Cumulative Index Medicus (Quart. Cum. Index Med.).

Encyclopedic references

Biochemisches Handlexikon (edited by Emil Abderhalden).

Chemical literature guides

Crane, E. J.; Patterson, A. M.; and Marr, E. B.: *A Guide to the Literature of Chemistry,* 2nd ed. John Wiley & Sons, New York, 1957.

Electrolytic dissociation and activity

METHODS OF EXPRESSING CONCENTRATIONS

Preliminary to discussing gases and solutions, a brief statement of the methods of indicating the concentration of solutions is desirable. Systems in common use in chemical laboratories are:

1. Per cent by weight indicates the grams of solute per 100 g of solution, and per cent by volume represents the grams of solute per 100 ml of solution. Commercial hydrochloric acid contains 38 per cent HCl by weight and has a density of 1.19. Each milliliter then contains $1.19 \times 0.38 = 0.45$ g of HCl, and 100 ml contain 45 g, or the solution is 45 per cent HCl by volume.

2. The mol or molar system of concentration gives the gram-molecular weights of solute in a liter of solution. It has been established that a gram symbol or formula weight of any substance contains 6.02×10^{23} (Avogadro number) particles. Thus, about 180 g of glucose, 46 g of ethyl alcohol, 23 g of Na^+, 35.46 g of Cl^-, 1 g of H^+, and 17 g of OH^- per liter of solution represent one molar concentration and at the same time 6.02×10^{23} particles in each case. Molar concentrations are commonly indicated as $1\ M$, $0.5\ M$, $0.1\ M$, etc., according to the number of gram mols (gram-molecular weights) present per liter of solution. Expressions in brackets, such as [1], [0.5], [0.1], are often used in expressing molar concentrations. Since reactions proceed between integral numbers of molecules or ions, molar solutions react according to integral volumes.

In biochemistry the terms millimol, mM, micromol, μM, milliosmol, and milliequivalent, meq, are commonly used.

1 millimol (mM) = 0.001 M = 1 formula weight in milligrams.

1 micromol (μM) = 0.001 mM = 1 formula weight in micrograms. A microgram (μg) = 0.001 mg.

The term "milliosmol" is used in connection with osmotic pressure, since osmotic pressure is proportional to the total number of particles in solution. In case of a nonelectrolyte such as glucose 1 millimol = 1 milliosmol, but this is not true with electrolytes. One millimol of NaCl is equivalent to two milliosmols ($Na^+ + Cl^-$).

A milliequivalent is one thousandth of an equivalent and is the same as a millimol when the valence is 1. However, a millimol of Zn^{++} ions represents 2 milliequivalents, and a millimol of Al^{+++} is 3 milliequivalents, etc.

Millimols may be calculated by dividing milligrams per liter by the formula weight. For example, 78 mg of K^+ ions per liter represent 78/39 = 2 millimols, 2 milliosmols, and 2 milligram equivalents. Also, 100 mg of Ca^{++} ions per liter represent 100/40 = 2.5 millimols, 2.5 milliosmols, and 5 milliequivalents. Similarly, 222 mg of $CaCl_2$ per liter represent 222/111 = 2 millimols of $CaCl_2$, and 6 milliosmols [$(Ca^{++} + 2Cl^-) \times 2$] of total particles.

Micromols are calculated similarly, substituting micrograms for milligrams.

3. Molal solutions contain a gram molecular weight of solute dissolved in 1000 g of solvent. The volume is not a liter and varies with the volume of the formula weight of dissolved solute. Molal solutions, in a given solvent, contain the same ratio of solute to solvent molecules. For example, if 46 g of ethyl alcohol and 342 g of cane sugar are each mixed with 1000 g of water, we have molal solutions. The ratio of alcohol molecules to water molecules is the same as the ratio of sugar molecules to water molecules. In molar solutions of these substances (one gram-molecular weight diluted to a liter) the alcohol solution contains much more water relative to a molecule of solute than does the sugar solution, because 342 g of cane sugar occupy several times the volume of 46 g of alcohol. The difference in water content is equal to the difference in volume represented by the dissolved solutes. Molal solutions provide a definite ratio of solute to solvent molecules.

4. At times it is desirable to know the so-called mol fractions of components in a solution. The solution is composed of the mol fractions of all constituents (solutes and solvent). The mol fraction of one constituent is equal to the number of mols of the constituent divided by the total number of mols present:

$$N_1 = \frac{n_1}{n_1 + n_2} \quad \text{and} \quad N_2 = \frac{n_2}{n_1 + n_2}$$

where N_1 and N_2 are the mol fractions of the two constituents in the solution, and n_1 and n_2 are the numbers of mols of the respective constituents present. For example, suppose 180 g of glucose are dissolved in 1000 g of water; the mol fraction of glucose is:

$$N_1 = \frac{\dfrac{180}{180}}{\dfrac{1000}{18} + \dfrac{180}{180}} = 0.0177$$

The mol fraction of water in the solution is:

$$N_2 = \frac{\dfrac{1000}{18}}{\dfrac{1000}{18} + \dfrac{180}{180}} = 0.982$$

5. The normal system of expressing concentrations is a special case of the molar system ordinarily applied to solutions of acids, bases, and often oxidizing solutions. When HCl is mixed with NaOH in solution, the reaction taking place is that of the combination of H^+ and OH^- to form very weakly dissociated HOH. Obviously, equal volumes of molar solutions of HCl and NaOH exactly neutralize each other. A given volume of 1 M H_2SO_4 would neutralize the same volume of 2 M NaOH because H_2SO_4 supplies $2H^+$ per formula weight. A normal solution of an acid contains the weight of acid per liter of solution which provides a formula weight of H^+ (6.02 × 10²³ H^+), and, similarly, a normal solution of alkali provides a formula weight of OH^- (6.02 × 10²³ OH^-) per liter.

A normal oxidizing solution contains sufficient oxidizing agent per liter to increase the positive valence or decrease the negative valence of a gram-formula weight of reducing agent by one unit. A normal reducing solution is the reverse of a normal oxidizing solution. Stated differently, a liter of normal oxidizing solution is capable of taking up 6.02 × 10²³ electrons from a reducing agent, and a normal reducing solution can give up 6.02 × 10²³ electrons to an oxidizing agent. Oxidation and reduction must proceed simultaneously.

In the reaction:

$$Cu^+ + I = Cu^{++} + I^-$$

gram-atomic weights of iodine and Cu^+ per liter of solution would represent normal oxidizing and reducing solutions, respectively.

In the reaction:

$$KIO_3 + 5KI + 6H_2SO_4 = 6KHSO_4 + 3H_2O + 3I_2$$

a gram-molecular weight of KIO_3 liberates $3I_2$ (6 atoms of I), and a normal oxidizing solution of KIO_3 contains one-sixth of a formula weight per liter.

ELECTROLYTIC DISSOCIATION AND THE MASS LAW

Much evidence has been accumulated that per cent dissociation, while valid in dealing with weak electrolytes such as acetic acid is entirely meaningless when applied to strong electrolytes (salts, strong bases, and strong acids). X-ray studies have shown that the crystals of salts, such as sodium chloride, do not contain molecules of the salts. Rather, the crystals of sodium chloride are composed of Na^+ and Cl^- ions arranged in perfectly ordered fashion in what is termed a space or ionic lattice. When a salt crystal is placed in water, the ions of the lattice structure are separated and distributed homogeneously throughout the water molecules. Accordingly, sodium chloride is completely ionized (100 per cent) in solutions of any concentration.

G. N. Lewis, in particular, has developed the theory of activity in order to account for the behavior of strong electrolytes. A simple illustration may help in understanding the theory. When a football player is surrounded closely on all sides by other players, his capacity to run and execute the maneuvers of football is greatly decreased as compared with this capacity when no one is near him. However, a certain few players on the field about him may cause him to show more activity than when the field is empty. In general, the activity of the player is conditioned by the other players surrounding him. The activity theory as applied to strong electrolytes considers these electrolytes to be 100 per cent ionized. Each ion possesses an activity or capacity to function as an ion according to the concentration of ions surrounding it. It is reasonable to suppose that an ion surrounded by other ions of both like and unlike charge and subjected to their attractions and repulsions will possess varying activities according to variations in the concentration of surrounding ions. Generally, the activity of an ion decreases as the ionic concentration about it increases. There are, however, some notable exceptions to this statement. The solvation of ions (combination with solvent molecules) and the activity of solvent molecules change, with changing concentration, to alter ionic activities.

The term "activity," designated by a, is used to indicate the apparent or effective concentration of a substance as shown by its properties in solution. For example, suppose a 0.2 M solution of an electrolyte exhibits an activity in lowering the freezing point corresponding to only 0.18 M as based on theoretical activity at great dilution (concentration = 0). In this case the value of the activity, a, is 0.18. If the solution were diluted to 0.00001 M, the electrolyte probably would show an activity indistinguishable from 0.00001. This demonstrates that, after a certain point at least, activity approaches concentration as the electrolyte solution is made infinitely dilute. Some electrolytes at certain concentrations possess activities considerably greater than indicated by their molal concentrations. For example, a 3 M solution of hydrochloric acid has an activity corresponding to a 3.96 M solution (calculated on basis of complete activity at infinite dilution).

Activity and ionic strength. Activities depend not only upon the concentrations of the ions concerned but upon the total ion concentration in the solution regardless of source. The activity of $NaCl$ mixed with KNO_3 in solution is a function of all ions present and not simply of the Na^+ and Cl^- concentrations. Since the ionic effect upon activity is electrostatic in nature, charges carried by the ions are a determining factor. Two divalent ions will attract or repel each other four times as strongly as two univalent ions; but since the ions are present in equivalent plus-minus pairs, the effect on any given ion is half the total electrostatic effect. Lewis uses the concept of ionic strength, designated μ (mu), to include the whole ionic effect. In order to obtain the ionic strength, μ, of a solution he multiplies the concentration of each ion by its valence squared, adds the products together, and takes half the sum.

The ionic strength of a uni-univalent compound, such as NaCl or KNO_3, is given by:

$$\mu = \frac{C(1)^2 + C(1)^2}{2} = C$$

The ionic strength of a uni-univalent compound is equal to the concentration, C. A di-divalent compound, such as $ZnSO_4$, has an ionic strength equal to $4C$:

$$\mu = \frac{C(2)^2 + C(2)^2}{2} = 4C$$

A di-univalent compound, such as $CaCl_2$, or a uni-divalent compound, such as K_2CO_3, has an ionic strength three times the concentration:

$$\mu = \frac{C(2)^2 + 2C(1)^2}{2} = 3C$$

Activity coefficients. The concept of activity coefficient is fundamental in dealing with activities. Lewis defines the activity coefficient designated γ (gamma), as the ratio of activity, a, to molal concentration, m:

$$\gamma = \frac{a}{m}$$

If a 0.2 molal electrolyte solution shows an activity of 0.18, the activity coefficient of the electrolyte at this concentration is:

$$\gamma = \frac{0.18}{0.20} = 0.90$$

In case of 3 molal hydrochloric acid, the activity coefficient is:

$$\gamma = \frac{3.96}{3.0} = 1.32$$

The values of both the activity coefficient and the activity related to it vary with conditions. It is apparent that as the concentration approaches 0 the activity coefficient approaches 1.

The activity coefficients of most electrolytes decrease with increasing concentration (Table 2.1). In some instances the activity coefficient decreases from 1 in infinitely dilute solution and reaches a minimum, then rises and, as the solutions become very strong, goes much above 1. This is true in the case of HCl. The activity coefficient of HCl is 1 in infinitely dilute solutions, 0.904 in 0.01 M solution, 1.019 in 2 M solution, 1.32 in 3 M solution, and 43.2 in 16 M solution.

The activity of an ionic compound, such as NaCl, is composed of the activities of the constituent Na^+ and Cl^- ions. The activities of the ions of an electrolyte are generally different. If we designate the activity of NaCl by a_2 and of Na^+ and Cl^- by a^+ and a^- (differ numerically), respectively, the total activity of NaCl is given by the equation:

$$a_2 = a^+ \times a^-$$

The activity of a binary electrolyte (gives two ions) such as NaCl and $ZnSO_4$ is equal to the product of the activities of the ions.

The equation:

$$\gamma = \frac{a}{m}$$

may be written:

$$a = \gamma m$$

which means that activity equals activity coefficient multiplied by concentration. The activity of a binary electrolyte, a_2, as given above, may also be written:

$$a_2 = \gamma^+ C \times \gamma^- C$$

where γ^+ and γ^- are the activity coefficients of the positive and negative ions and C is the molal concentration (equal for the two ions).

The activity of a uni-divalent electrolyte, such as Na_2SO_4, which dissociates into three ions, is given by the equation:

$$a_3 = a^+ \times a^+ \times a^- = (a^+)^2 a^-$$

Here the concentration of the positive ion is $2C$, and that of the negative ion is C. (These might be reversed.) If the activity coefficients corresponding to the positive and negative ions are γ^+ and γ^-, we may express the activity of the electrolyte, a_3, as follows:

$$a_3 = (2C\gamma^+)^2 C\gamma^-$$

The activities of electrolytes may be obtained from a variety of measurements. Measurement of any of the colligative properties of electrolyte solutions—namely, osmotic pressure, freezing point, boiling point, or vapor pressure—may be used. Measurements of one of these properties for a wide range of ionic strengths permit the calculation of activities and activity coefficients. In plotting curves relating to activity coefficients, it is customary to plot activity coefficients against ionic strength or some function of ionic strength such as the square root. According to definition of activity coefficient, it must equal unity at zero concentration. Since all other values are based upon this value of 1 for zero concentration, it is necessary to make measurements at very low concentrations and extrapolate (extend the curve) to zero concentration. It is often difficult to establish the position of unity on the curve axis with sufficient accuracy. Activity coefficients may often be obtained by measurements of the electromotive force of appropriate galvanic cells involving the electrolyte under consideration. Solubility measurements may also be used in certain cases. The subject of activity determination is complex, and for more detailed information the student should consult advanced works on physical chemistry.

Since the activities of the ions of an electrolyte are generally unequal the value of $a^+ \times a^-$ in the equation for the activity of an electrolyte, such as NaCl, is not a square:

$$a_2 = a^+ \times a^-$$

Generally, the mean activity, $a^\pm$, of an electrolyte is determined. For a uni-univalent electrolyte it is given by the equation:

$$a^\pm = \sqrt{a^+ \times a^-}$$

The mean activity coefficient of a uni-univalent electrolyte is defined as the mean activity divided by the molal concentration of the electrolyte:

$$\gamma^\pm = \frac{a^\pm}{m}$$

In general, the mean activity coefficient of the ions of a strong electrolyte ($\gamma^\pm$) is related to the activity coefficient of the strong electrolyte molecule (γ) by the relation:

$$\gamma^\pm = \gamma^{\frac{1}{n}}$$

where n is the total number of ions from the electrolyte molecule.

The mean activity coefficient ($\gamma^\pm$) of an electrolyte in solution (up to ionic strengths of about 0.3) may be calculated from the ionic strength (μ) by use of the Debye-Hückel equation:

$$- \log \gamma^\pm = \frac{(z_+ \times z_-)0.5 \sqrt{\mu}}{1 + \sqrt{\mu}}$$

in which z_+ and z_- are the numbers of charges on the positive and negative ions, respectively. The equation holds from 0° C to 60° C.

Suppose the ionic strength of a $ZnSO_4$ solution is 0.25. Calculate the mean activity coefficient, $\gamma^\pm$:

$$- \log \gamma^\pm = \frac{(2 \times 2) \times 0.5 \times 0.5}{1 + 0.5} = \frac{1}{1.5} = 0.66$$

$$\log \gamma^\pm = -0.66,$$

and

$$\gamma^\pm = 10^{-0.66} = 10^{-1} \times 10^{0.34} = 0.1 \times 2.19 = 0.219$$

In the case of relatively dilute solutions (such as 0.1 M) of weak electrolytes, where the ionic concentrations are low, the activity coefficients of the ions present are close to unity. Percentage ionizations of these substances calculated from electrical conductivity, freezing point, etc., are therefore taken to represent relatively correct values. In their more concentrated solutions the activity factor enters noticeably. Table 2.2 shows the calculated ionizations of a variety of weak electrolytes.

Table 2.1.   Mean Activity Coefficients of Representative Electrolytes at Round Concentrations (25° C)

Molal	0.01	0.05	0.10	0.50	1.00	1.50	2.00	3.00	4.00
KCl*	0.899	0.815	0.764	0.644	0.597	0.576	0.569	0.571	0.581
NaCl†	0.903	0.821	0.778	0.678	0.656	0.659	0.670	0.714	0.779
LiCl‡	0.901	0.819	0.779	0.725	0.757	0.819	0.919	1.174	1.544
HCl§	0.904	0.829	0.796	0.757	0.810	0.903	1.019	1.320	1.764
BaCl₂‖	0.723	0.554	0.495	0.395	0.398				
SrCl₂#	0.729	0.571	0.512	0.427	0.449	0.526	0.638	1.083	
CaCl₂#	0.732	0.582	0.528	0.510	0.725	1.065	1.555	3.385	
Na₂SO₄**	0.721	0.514	0.435	0.267	0.206	0.172	0.152		
H₂SO₄††	0.617	0.397	0.313	0.178	0.150		0.147	0.166	0.213

* Scatchard: *J. Am. Chem. Soc.*, **47**, 648, 1925. Harned: *ibid.*, **51**, 416, 1929. MacInnes and Parker: *ibid.*, **37**, 1445, 1915.
† Pearce and Hart: *J. Am. Chem. Soc.*, **43**, 2483, 1921; and * above.
‡ MacInnes and Beattie: *J. Am. Chem. Soc.*, **42**, 1117, 1921; and * above.
§ Randall and Young: *J. Am. Chem. Soc.*, **50**, 989, 1928.
‖ Lucasse: *J. Am. Chem. Soc.*, **47**, 743, 1925. Harned: *ibid.*, **48**, 326, 1926.
Harned and Åkerlöf: *Physik. Z.*, **27**, 411, 1926; and ‖ above.
** Åkerlöf: *J. Am. Chem. Soc.*, **48**, 1160, 1926. Harned and Åkerlöf: *Physik. Z.*, **27**, 411, 1926.
†† From *Thermodynamics and the Free Energy of Chemical Substances*, by Lewis and Randall. McGraw-Hill, New York, 1923.

Table 2.2.   Percentage Ionization of Some Weak Electrolytes in Water

Electrolyte	Conc. M	Ions	Percentage Ionization
HCN	0.1	H^+, CN^-	0.01
H_3BO_3	0.1	H^+, $H_2BO_3^-$	0.01
H_2S	0.1	H^+, SH^-	0.07
H_2CO_3	0.1	H^+, HCO_3^-	0.17
CH_3COOH	1.0	H^+, CH_3COO^-	0.42
CH_3COOH	0.1	H^+, CH_3COO^-	1.34
$HgCl_2$	0.05	Hg^{++}, Cl^-	1.00
Water		H^+, OH^-	0.0000018

The above discussion relative to ionization and activities of electrolytes has been applied especially to water solutions. Other solvents, such as formic acid, liquid HCN, and hydrogen peroxide, are excellent ionizing solvents because they, like water, have high dielectric constants. Generally the ionizing power of a solvent is greater the greater its dielectric constant. Organic solvents like chloroform, ether, and benzene, which have very low dielectric constants, are also very poor ionizing solvents.

While the concept of activity and activity coefficients has been applied particularly to solutions of electrolytes, it also applies to all types of substances in all three states of matter, though in many cases the determination of activity coefficients and activity may be difficult. In the case of nonelectrolytes, the interactions between molecules which affect activity coefficients are not so easily definable as those between ions of electrolytes. Such interactions of nonelectrolytes involve those with ions of electrolytes and also those with the molecules of other nonelectrolytes. The forces involved in these interactions of nonelectrolytes may be due to coordinate valence and hydrogen bonding, with formation of complexes such as hydrates, or may be the less understood Van der Waal forces.

As illustrations of the variation of activity coefficients in solutions, the following facts may be cited. In a mixture of ethanol and water the addition of salts increases the vapor pressure and activity coefficient of the ethanol but decreases the vapor pressure and activity coefficient of the water. When a salt, A, has a certain solubility in water at temperature T, this means that the quantity of salt in the solution possesses an activity capable of maintaining dynamic equilibrium with the solid salt A at temperature T. Now if a certain amount of ethanol is added to the water in which A is dissolved, some of A precipitates out, leaving a smaller quantity of A in the solution, which, however, is still capable of maintaining dynamic equilibrium with solid A at temperature T. This means that the mean activity coefficient of the salt is higher in the alcohol-water mixture than in water alone, because a smaller concentration is required to maintain equilibrium with the solid, the activity of which remains constant for a given temperature.

When the very soluble salt K_2CO_3 is dissolved to saturation in a mixture of alcohol and water, the solution separates into the two phases:

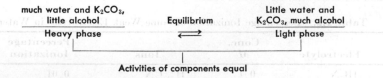

Since at equilibrium all of the components of the heavy phase are in dynamic equilibrium with all of the components in the light phase, the activities of water, K_2CO_3, and alcohol must be equal in the two phases despite great differences in concentration. This means the activity coefficients of the components in the two phases are very different. The presence of much K_2CO_3 lowers the activity coefficient of water in the heavy phase and increases it in the lighter phase. Also, in the light phase the high proportion of alcohol increases greatly the mean activity coefficient of K_2CO_3 and the activity coefficient of water. The vapor pressure of pure water and other liquids is a function of the activity of the molecules of the liquid. If to water a nonvolatile solute such as sucrose is added, the vapor pressure of the water over the solution is less than that over pure water. The presence of the sucrose molecules decreases the activity coefficient of the water molecules. Of course, electrolytes have larger effects because of their dissociation into ions.

EXERCISES *

1. Commercial sulfuric acid has a specific gravity of about 1.84 and contains approximately 95 per cent H_2SO_4. Calculate the molar concentration, normality, and per cent by volume of this acid.
2. Is the ratio of solute to solvent molecules constant in a molal solution? Is this true for a molar solution? Explain.

* For answers to problems, see Appendix I.

3. Calculate the weight of V_2O_5 required to prepare 1 l of 0.1 N oxidizing solution to be used in the following reaction with oxalic acid:

$$V_2O_5 + H_2C_2O_4 = V_2O_4 + 2CO_2 + H_2O$$

4. The activity coefficient of a 0.1 molal solution of HCl at 25° C is 0.796. Calculate the activity, a, of the HCl. The activity, a, of 16 M HCl is 691.8. Calculate the activity coefficient.

5. Calculate the total ionic strength of a solution containing 0.1 M $FeSO_4$, 0.4 M $Cr_2(SO_4)_3$, and 0.5 M glucose. Assume complete ionization of the salts.

GENERAL REFERENCES

Clark, W. M.: *Topics in Physical Chemistry*, 2nd ed. Williams & Wilkins Co., Baltimore, 1952.

Daniels, F., and Alberty, R. A.: *Physical Chemistry*. John Wiley & Sons, New York, 1955.

3

Acids, bases, and buffers

Brönsted's theory of acids and bases. Brönsted, Lowry, and others have developed a broad concept of acids and bases which is very useful. According to the older and conventional view, an acid is defined as a substance which yields H^+ ions in solution and a base as one which gives OH^- ions. The newer theory defines an acid as any substance that gives off protons (H^+ ions) and a base as any substance that combines with protons. Acids are proton donors, and bases are proton acceptors. This definition of an acid is equivalent to the older view, but the definition of a base is much broader in its implications. The following equations will illustrate the above points:

Acid		Base
HCl	$\rightleftharpoons$	$H^+ + Cl^-$
HCN	$\rightleftharpoons$	$H^+ + CN^-$
CH_3COOH	$\rightleftharpoons$	$H^+ + CH_3COO^-$
H_2CO_3	$\rightleftharpoons$	$H^+ + HCO_3^-$
HCO_3^-	$\rightleftharpoons$	$H^+ + CO_3^=$
H_2SO_4	$\rightleftharpoons$	$H^+ + HSO_4^-$
HSO_4^-	$\rightleftharpoons$	$H^+ + SO_4^=$
NH_4^+	$\rightleftharpoons$	$H^+ + NH_3$
NH_3	$\rightleftharpoons$	$H^+ + NH_2^-$
HOH	$\rightleftharpoons$	$H^+ + OH^-$
H_3O^+	$\rightleftharpoons$	$H^+ + H_2O$

All the above compounds listed as acids dissociate to yield protons (H^+ ions) plus ions or molecules capable of combining with protons—in other words, bases. Thus, HCN gives H^+ and CN^-, in which HCN is the acid and CN^- the base. The base corresponding to CH_3COOH is the acetate ion, CH_3COO^-. HSO_4^- is the base produced by the dissociation of H_2SO_4. However, HSO_4^- is also the acid corresponding to the base $SO_4^=$. According to this view, an acid dissociates into a proton and a base, whereas a base combines with a proton to form an acid. An acid and its corresponding base are said to be "conjugate," which means "joined in a pair." The CN^- ion is the

20

base conjugate to the acid HCN, and NH_3 is the base conjugate to the acid NH_4^+.

According to Brönsted's theory, the weakest acid has the strongest conjugate base, and the strongest acid has the weakest conjugate base. Thus, HCN is a very weak acid because its strong conjugate base, CN^-, combines firmly with protons, while HCl is a very strong acid because its conjugate base, Cl^-, combines loosely with protons.

It will be observed that the metallic hydroxides, such as NaOH and KOH, are not included in the new definition of bases because their molecules, as such, cannot combine with protons. They act as bases because they are ionic compounds and exist as metal ions and OH^- ions. The OH^- ion is a base because it combines with a proton to form H_2O. These substances will be referred to as alkalies instead of bases in this book.

A substance which can act both as an acid and as a base is said to be amphoteric. According to the old view, such substances were considered to give off both H^+ and OH^- ions. Both water and zinc hydroxide qualify under this definition. Water also qualifies under the Brönsted concept because it gives protons according to the equation:

$$HOH \rightleftarrows H^+ + OH^-$$

and it combines with protons according to the equation:

$$HOH + H^+ \rightleftarrows H_3O^+$$

Ammonia, as liquid NH_3, qualifies as an acid according to Brönsted:

$$NH_3 \rightleftarrows H^+ + NH_2^-$$

and also as a base:

$$NH_3 + H^+ \rightleftarrows NH_4^+$$

Salts are considered as compounds formed by replacing the ionizable hydrogen of acids by a metal or some positive group, such as NH_4^+. The modern tendency is to consider only ionic compounds as salts. Substances like mercuric chloride, which are little ionized, would not be classed as true salts. Bjerrum refers to all such compounds, both ionic and nonionic, as "acidates."

The ionization of acids. While it is customary to express the ionization of an acid by an equation such as the following:

$$HA \rightleftarrows H^+ + A^-$$

there is much reason for believing that H^+ ions, as such, do not exist in acid solutions, or that, if they do, their concentration is exceedingly small. In general, it is considered that H^+ ions combine with the solvent molecules to form what Bjerrum calls "lyonium" ions. For example, in water the H^+ ion combines with H_2O to form H_3O^+, which is called the hydronium, or oxonium, or hydroxonium, ion. In glacial acetic acid as solvent the H^+ ion forms the acetonium ion, $(H \cdot CH_3COOH)^+$; in alcohol it forms the ion, $(H \cdot C_2H_5OH)^+$; etc. When liquid ammonia is the solvent, the H^+ ion becomes ammoniated to form NH_4^+. The above associations of H^+ ions with solvent molecules are due to coordination of H^+ with free electron pairs in the oxygen and nitrogen atoms of the solvent molecules.

There are a number of reasons why the H^+ ions of acids are considered to be combined with the solvent. Among these may be mentioned the fact that x-ray analysis shows the presence of the H_3O group in the crystalline hydrate of perchloric acid. Also, neither HBr nor H_2O will conduct the electric current when dissolved in liquid SO_2, but if mixed in it, the current is readily conducted, and water accumulates at the negative electrode. This is due to the presence of H_3O^+ in solution from which H^+ is removed by the cathode with the formation of H_2O and hydrogen gas. Since the H^+ ion, or proton, is very small and has a very high ratio of positive charge to mass, it should exhibit high acitvity in coordinating with the unshared electrons of relatively negative oxygen and nitrogen atoms in the above solvents.

Both liquid HCl and H_2O are very poor conductors of the electric current and are little ionized. If they are mixed, the solution is an excellent conductor. This is best explained by assuming the following reaction to occur:

$$HCl + HOH \rightleftharpoons H_3O^+ + Cl^-$$

Similarly, the dissociation of acetic acid in water may be expressed:

$$CH_3COOH + HOH \rightleftharpoons H_3O^+ + CH_3COO^-$$

and the reaction of acids in general with water:

$$HA + HOH \rightleftharpoons H_3O^+ + A^-$$

Cl^- is the conjugate base of HCl, and CH_3COO^- the conjugate base of CH_3COOH. In the case of HCl dissolved in water, most of the H^+ ions are combined with H_2O as H_3O^+ and very few with the much weaker conjugate base Cl^-. Consequently, HCl in water is a very strong acid. For CH_3COOH the situation is quite different. Here the conjugate base, CH_3COO^-, is much stronger as a base than is Cl^-, and consequently most of the H^+ ions of the acetic acid solution are combined with it as CH_3COOH and relatively few with H_2O as H_3O^+. Accordingly, CH_3COOH in water is a relatively weak acid. However, the base NH_3 is just as strong as the base CH_3COO^-, and when acetic acid is dissolved in liquid ammonia:

$$CH_3COOH + NH_3 \rightleftharpoons NH_4^+ + CH_3COO^-$$

the ionization of CH_3COOH to produce CH_3COO^- and the acidic NH_4^+ ions is high, and CH_3COOH is a strong acid when dissolved in liquid ammonia.

It should be apparent from the above discussion that the strength of an acid in solution is dependent not only upon the chemical structure of the acid but also upon that of the solvent. An acid may be relatively weak in one solvent and strong in another. When the conjugate base of an acid is weak relative to the basic property of the solvent, then the acid is highly ionized in that solvent; and, conversely, when the conjugate base of the acid is strong relative to the solvent, the acid is poorly ionized.

The strength of an acid is determined by (a) the strength of its conjugate base, (b) the basic strength of the solvent, (c) and the dielectric constant of the solvent. Solvents of high dielectric constant greatly reduce the attraction between oppositely charged particles dissolved in them, which necessarily favors dissociation. The strength of the conjugate base of an acid is dependent upon, and controlled by, the structure of the acid.

The dissociation of water is of interest when considered in the light of the above theories. Ordinarily it is represented as:

$$HOH \rightleftharpoons H^+ + OH^-$$

but it is probable that the following takes place:

$$HOH + HOH \rightleftharpoons H_3O^+ + OH^-$$

Because OH^-, the conjugate base of HOH, combines with H^+ much more firmly than does H_2O, very little H_3O^+ exists, and water is slightly dissociated.

The strength of bases, according to Brönsted's theory, depends solely upon the readiness of their combination with protons and the strength of the valence bond formed. If all acids were tabulated from the weakest to the strongest, then the conjugate bases of these acids would represent a series, in reverse order, according to basic strength. Thus, Cl^- is a very weak base and CN^- a very strong one.

Brönsted's theory leads to a broad concept of neutralization, which is ordinarily considered as the reaction of H^+ with OH^- to form H_2O. Since OH^- is only one of many bases capable of combining with protons, the process of neutralization may be more completely defined as the combination of a base with protons. The completeness of neutralization depends upon the extent to which this combination occurs. When potassium is treated with liquid ammonia, the following action takes place:

$$2K + 2NH_3 \longrightarrow H_2 + 2KNH_2$$

Since KNH_2 is ionic, the solution contains K^+ and NH_2^- ions. If an ammonium salt, such as NH_4Cl, be added to the solution, the acid, NH_4^+, is neutralized by the base, NH_2^-, as follows:

$$NH_4^+ + NH_2^- \longrightarrow 2NH_3$$

This process is as truly neutralization as is the reaction:

$$H_3O^+ + OH^- \longrightarrow 2H_2O$$

While the broad concept of acids and bases in various solvents has been discussed in considerable detail, the biochemist is particularly concerned with the action of acids and bases in water solution. The acid ion of most concern to him is the hydronium ion, H_3O^+. To be sure, he also has occasion to deal with the acid ion, NH_4^+, and its many derivatives. The bases with which he is particularly concerned are OH^-, NH_3, and the ions of many weak acids, such as HCO_3^-, CH_3COO^-, and $H_2PO_4^-$. The hydration of the H^+ ion has been especially stressed, but the student should keep in mind that probably most ions and molecules in water are more or less hydrated through coordination. The electronic arrangements in such combinations may be pictured as follows:

$$\begin{bmatrix} & H & \\ & \cdot\cdot & \\ H & : O & : \\ & \cdot\cdot & \\ & H & \end{bmatrix}^{+} \qquad \begin{bmatrix} & \cdot\cdot & & \cdot\cdot & \\ H & : O & : H & : O & : H \\ & \cdot\cdot & & \cdot\cdot & \end{bmatrix}^{-} \qquad \begin{matrix} & \cdot\cdot & & \cdot\cdot & \\ C_2H_5 & : O & : H & : O & : H \\ & \cdot\cdot & & \cdot\cdot & \\ & & & H & \end{matrix}$$

$$H^+ + H_2O \qquad\qquad OH^- + H_2O \qquad\qquad C_2H_5OH + H_2O$$

Since in dealing with acids and alkalies it is simpler to use the expressions H^+ and OH^- rather than H_3O^+ and $H_3O_2^-$ (hydrated forms) and because most of the chemical literature follows this usage, H^+ and OH^- will be used in further discussions in this book. The student must never forget, however, that the hydrated forms are involved.

Titratable and actual acidity. Ten milliliters of 0.1 N HCl require 10 ml of 0.1 N NaOH for titration to the end point of phenolphthalein. The same volume of 0.1 N CH_3COOH also requires 10 ml of 0.1 N NaOH for titration. Both solutions have the same total acidities when phenolphthalein is used as indicator. The HCl solution is much more acid to the taste than is the CH_3COOH solution. Also, it conducts the electric current much better, and it freezes at a lower temperature. The reason for these differences is that HCl is completely ionized in the solution while CH_3COOH is slightly ionized. In the HCl solution we have:

$$HCl \longrightarrow H^+ + Cl^-$$

and all the hydrogen of the HCl exists as H^+ at any given instant, while in the CH_3COOH solution:

$$CH_3COOH \rightleftarrows CH_3COO^- + H^+$$

only about 1.3 per cent of the available hydrogen (from COOH) exists as H^+ at a given instant. Both acids give the same titratable acidity to an alkali:

$$HCl \longrightarrow Cl^- + H^+ \quad \text{Completely ionized}$$
$$+$$
$$NaOH \longrightarrow Na^+ + OH^- \quad \text{Completely ionized}$$
$$\downarrow$$
$$HOH \quad \text{One molecule in 550 million ionized}$$
$$\uparrow$$
$$NaOH \longrightarrow Na^+ + OH^-$$
$$+$$
$$CH_3COOH \rightleftarrows CH_3COO^- + H^+ \quad \text{Weakly ionized}$$

because the carboxyl hydrogen of the CH_3COOH molecules is quickly ionized in the solution as H^+ ions and these are removed by combination with OH^- ions. Since the water molecules formed are very little ionized, the H^+ ions are effectively removed, and the dissociation of CH_3COOH goes to completion as NaOH is added. Consequently, the total acidities of 0.1 N HCl and CH_3COOH are the same despite the fact that the actual number of H^+ ions present in the HCl solution is some seventy times greater than in the CH_3COOH solution. Judged by total acidity, the acids are of the same strength; but judged by properties dependent upon hydrogen ion concentration, the HCl is about seventy times stronger than the CH_3COOH. Now the action of an acid as an acid is dependent only upon the concentration of hydrogen ions per unit volume of its solution. This concentration determines how sour the acid is, how rapidly it will dissolve a metal such as zinc with the evolution of H_2, how effective it is in hydrolyzing a compound such as cane sugar, as well as many other properties. Pasteur was among the first to realize the difference between total, or titratable, acidity, and the "strength" of acids as related to biochemical processes. In his studies of the fermentation of fruit juices for the production of wine, he observed that "high" acidities favored the growth of certain types of microorganisms while inhibiting the growth of others. The Danish chemist, Sørensen, studied the effect of "acidity" upon the activity of enzyme systems and developed methods of determining the hydrogen ion concentrations of solutions. He originated a method of accurately expressing such concentrations in terms of pH values, which are the negative logarithms of the hydrogen ion concentrations. Later pH will be discussed in detail.

Evidently the activities of hydrogen and hydroxyl ions in solutions will vary with hydration as well as with total ionic concentration. For a given concentration and temperature the activity will be fixed. In dilute solutions, where interionic attractions are low and the proportion of water is relatively great (and the hydration practically constant), the activities of the ions are proportional to their concentrations. The expressions $[H^+]$ and $[OH^-]$ are commonly referred to as hydrogen and hydroxyl ion concentrations, respectively. They really indicate activities instead, because the methods by which they are determined give activities and not concentrations. However, in the following discussions, the terms hydrogen and hydroxyl ion concentrations and the symbols for them, $[H^+]$ and $[OH^-]$, will be used for simplicity and in accordance with general practice.

As previously pointed out, Sørensen first worked out methods of determining hydrogen ion concentration and developed a rational system of expression in terms of pH values. Michaelis and Clark have especially developed our knowledge of the subject, both as to methods and theory. Their respective books, referred to in the References, are classical treatises upon many phases of the subject and should be consulted by the student for full information. L. J. Henderson, of Harvard, and D. D. Van Slyke and associates, of the Rockefeller Institute, have especially worked out the relations between the acids and bases of the body fluids and pointed out their physiologic significance and importance. The discussion given below is an attempt to express to the student, as simply as possible, the fundamental principles concerned.

The dissociation of water, hydrogen ion concentration, and pH. That water dissociates into H^+ and OH^- ions has been shown by electrical conductivity, the hydrolysis of compounds, and other methods. The equation for the dissociation of water is:

$$HOH \rightleftharpoons H^+ + OH^-$$

and, according to the law of chemical equilibrium for weak electrolytes, we
have the mathematical expression:

$$\frac{[H^+][OH^-]}{[HOH]} = K \quad \text{and} \quad [H^+][OH^-] = K[HOH]$$

Now the concentration of water (figured as H_2O) per liter in pure water is
about $1000/18 = 55$ molar, and in the above equation $[HOH] = 55 = 0.55 \times 10^2$. The concentration of H^+ and of OH^-, however, is exceedingly
small, being about 10^{-7} mol per liter for each at ordinary temperatures.
This means that only about one molecule of water in 550 million molecules
is dissociated into H^+ and OH^- ions. The concentration of undissociated
water, $[HOH]$, is so enormous relative to $[H^+]$ and $[OH^-]$ that for all practical purposes $[HOH]$ is constant. We may write then:

$$[H^+][OH^-] = K[HOH] = K_w$$

or stated in words, the product of the hydrogen and hydroxyl ion concentrations in water is a constant for a given temperature. K_w is referred to as
the dissociation constant of water. Its value varies widely with temperature
but is constant at a given temperature. This is shown in Table 3.1.

Table 3.1   Values of K_w at Different Temperatures

Temp., degrees C	K_w
0	0.05×10^{-14}
18	0.8×10^{-14}
25	1.2×10^{-14}
37	3.13×10^{-14}
40	3.8×10^{-14}
75	16.9×10^{-14}
100	48.0×10^{-14}
306	166.0×10^{-14}

Values of $[H^+]$ and $[OH^-]$ in pure water can be calculated for any given
temperature from the values of K_w. Since $[H^+] = [OH^-]$ we may write:

$$[H^+][OH^-] = K_w = [H^+]^2 = [OH^-]^2$$

also $[H^+] = \sqrt{K_w} \quad \text{and} \quad [OH^-] = \sqrt{K_w}$

The value for both $[H^+]$ and $[OH^-]$ in pure water at $0°$ C is:

$$\sqrt{0.05 \times 10^{-14}} = 0.22 \times 10^{-7} \text{ g mol per liter}$$

At $100°$ C:

$$[H^+] \text{ and } [OH^-] = \sqrt{48 \times 10^{-14}} = 6.92 \times 10^{-7} \text{ g mol per liter}$$

The concentration of hydrogen and hydroxyl ions in pure water is about
thirty times greater at $100°$ C than at $0°$ C. In the case of superheated steam
at $306°$ C the concentrations are about fifty times as large as at $0°$ C. In
view of these facts it is not surprising that reactions involving the ions of
water are greatly increased by raising the temperature. Raising the temperature of water from $37°$ C to $40°$ C increases $[H^+]$ and $[OH^-]$ by about 10

per cent. A part of the effect of fever in patients may be related to the increased dissociation of water. It should be kept in mind that the reaction of pure water remains essentially neutral, regardless of the extent of dissociation, because [OH⁻] equals [H⁺].

Relation of [H⁺] and [OH⁻] in solutions; pH values. The equation $[H^+][OH^-] = K_w = 1 \times 10^{-14}$ (at ordinary temperature) applies not only to pure water but also to water solutions in which [H⁺] and [OH⁻] may be widely different. We may state, then, that in aqueous solutions the product of the hydrogen and hydroxyl ion concentrations is a constant, and at ordinary laboratory temperature is equal to about 1×10^{-14}. If we know either [H⁺] or [OH⁻], we may calculate the other as follows:

$$[H^+] = \frac{K_w}{[OH^-]} = \frac{1 \times 10^{-14}}{[OH^-]}$$

and

$$[OH^-] = \frac{K_w}{[H^+]} = \frac{1 \times 10^{-14}}{[H^+]}$$

Suppose we have 0.01 N HCl, which is completely dissociated into H⁺ and Cl⁻. Then [H⁺] will also be $0.01 = 1 \times 10^{-2}$ g mol per liter. The [OH⁻] of the solution will be:

$$[OH^-] = \frac{1 \times 10^{-14}}{1 \times 10^{-2}} = 1 \times 10^{-12} \text{ g mol per liter}$$

For an 0.000001 N HCl solution we would have:

$$[H^+] = 0.000001 = 1 \times 10^{-6} \text{ g mol per liter}$$

and

$$[OH^-] = \frac{1 \times 10^{-14}}{1 \times 10^{-6}} = 1 \times 10^{-8} \text{ g mol per liter}$$

Similarly, if we have 0.0001 N NaOH, which is completely dissociated, the $[OH^-] = 0.0001 = 1 \times 10^{-4}$ g mol per liter. The [H⁺] of the solution then is:

$$[H^+] = \frac{1 \times 10^{-14}}{1 \times 10^{-4}} = 1 \times 10^{-10} \text{ g mol per liter}$$

It will be seen that there is an inverse relationship between [H⁺] and [OH⁻] in solutions. As one increases, the other decreases, and they become equal when both are equal to 1×10^{-7} g mol per liter (at ordinary temperature). It is very convenient to express [H⁺] and [OH⁻] in powers of 10; for example, concentrations of 0.1, 0.01, 0.001, 0.0001, and 0.00001 g mol per liter may be expressed as 10^{-1}, 10^{-2}, 10^{-3}, 10^{-4}, 10^{-5}, etc. Now the exponents $-1, -2, -3, -4, -5$ are the logarithms of the concentrations. It is apparent that all variations of [H⁺] and [OH⁻] may be expressed in terms of either, because if one is known, the other may be easily calculated. It is customary to use the values for hydrogen ion concentration. To illustrate further how this works, the [H⁺] of 0.01 N HCl is 10^{-2} and that of 0.01 N NaOH is 10^{-12}. Sørensen used this system of expressing "acidity" and "alkalinity" and simplified it still further by indicating concentrations as the negative of their logarithms. For example, a hydrogen ion concentration of $0.01 = 10^{-2}$ g mol per liter. Sørensen indicated the acidity as 2, which is equal to $-(-2) =$ $-\log [H^+]$. Such numbers are referred to as pH values, and we may write:

$$pH = -\log [H^+] = \log \frac{1}{[H^+]}$$

Table 3.2 shows the relations between the concentrations of hydrogen and hydroxyl ions and pH in aqueous solutions.

Table 3.2.   Relation between Hydrogen Ions, Hydroxyl Ions, and pH in Aqueous Solutions

[OH⁻] Mols per Liter	[H⁺] Mols per Liter	$\log [H^+]$	$-\log [H^+]$ = pH	
$0.0_{13}1 = 1 \times 10^{-14}$	$1.0 = 1 \times 10^{0}$	0	0	↑
$0.0_{12}1 = 1 \times 10^{-13}$	$0.1 = 1 \times 10^{-1}$	-1	1	
$0.0_{11}1 = 1 \times 10^{-12}$	$0.01 = 1 \times 10^{-2}$	-2	2	increasing acidity
$0.0_{10}1 = 1 \times 10^{-11}$	$0.001 = 1 \times 10^{-3}$	-3	3	
$0.0_91 = 1 \times 10^{-10}$	$0.0_31 = 1 \times 10^{-4}$	-4	4	
$0.0_81 = 1 \times 10^{-9}$	$0.0_41 = 1 \times 10^{-5}$	-5	5	
$0.0_71 = 1 \times 10^{-8}$	$0.0_51 = 1 \times 10^{-6}$	-6	6	
$0.0_61 = 1 \times 10^{-7}$	$0.0_61 = 1 \times 10^{-7}$	-7	7	neutral
$0.0_51 = 1 \times 10^{-6}$	$0.0_71 = 1 \times 10^{-8}$	-8	8	
$0.0_41 = 1 \times 10^{-5}$	$0.0_81 = 1 \times 10^{-9}$	-9	9	
$0.0_31 = 1 \times 10^{-4}$	$0.0_91 = 1 \times 10^{-10}$	-10	10	increasing alkalinity
$0.001 = 1 \times 10^{-3}$	$0.0_{10}1 = 1 \times 10^{-11}$	-11	11	
$0.01 = 1 \times 10^{-2}$	$0.0_{11}1 = 1 \times 10^{-12}$	-12	12	
$0.1 = 1 \times 10^{-1}$	$0.0_{12}1 = 1 \times 10^{-13}$	-13	13	
$1.0 = 1 \times 10^{0}$	$0.0_{13}1 = 1 \times 10^{-14}$	-14	14	↓

From the table it can be seen that $[OH^-][H^+] = 1 \times 10^{-14}$ for all concentrations of OH⁻ and H⁺. At neutrality $[OH^-] = [H^+] = 1 \times 10^{-7}$. In acid solutions $[H^+] > [OH^-]$, and in alkaline solutions $[H^+] < [OH^-]$. The acidity or alkalinity of a solution is determined by the proportions of H⁺ and OH⁻ ions present. The pH of a solution containing 1 N H⁺ is 0, and that of one containing 1 N OH⁻ is 14. The pH scale expressing [H⁺] between 1 N strong acid and 1 N strong alkali extends from 0 to 14; pH 7 represents neutrality, and as the pH becomes smaller, the [H⁺] and acidity become greater. The [OH⁻] and the alkalinity of a solution increase as the pH rises above 7.

By taking the negative logarithm of the equation $[H^+][OH^-] = K_w = 10^{-14}$, we have:

$$-\log [H^+] - \log [OH^-] = -\log K_w = 14$$

Since $-\log [H^+] = pH$, $-\log [OH^-] = pOH$, and $-\log K_w = pK_w$, we may write:

$$pH + pOH = pK_w = 14 \text{ (at ordinary temperature)}$$

While pH values below 0 (which are negative) and above 14 are theoretically possible, the scale 0−14 covers the practical range of acidity and alkalinity of solutions commonly encountered. The reactions of tissues, tissue fluids, secretions, and excretions are rather characteristic and in some instances highly important. For example, the pH of normal blood serum is about 7.40, a reaction slightly on the alkaline side of neutrality. The body possesses complex chemical and physical mechanisms for controlling the pH of blood so that normally only slight variations occur. If the pH of blood falls to 7, death ensues as a result of acidotic coma, and at a pH of 7.8 life terminates in tetany. Variations in tissue pH accompany variations in blood pH, and vice versa. The dire consequences of more than slight variations in pH show the great importance of H^+ and OH^- in regulating the chemical processes of the body. In order that the student may at this time obtain a fair idea of the variations in pH found in biologic materials of different kinds, he should look over the data of Table 3.3.

Table 3.3.   pH Values of Various Materials

Material	pH Value
Body fluids and tissues	
Blood serum	7.35–7.45
Cerebrospinal fluid	7.35–7.45
Aqueous humor of eye	7.4
Saliva	6.35–6.85
Pure gastric juice	about 0.9
Pancreatic juice	7.5 –8.0
Intestinal juice	7.0 –8.0
Hepatic duct bile	7.4 –8.5
Gall bladder bile	5.4 –6.9
Urine	4.8 –7.5
Feces	7.0 –7.5
Tears	7.4
Milk	6.6 –6.9
Skin (intracellular, various layers)	6.2 –7.5
Liver (intracellular)	
Kupffer cells	6.4 –6.5
Peripheral cells	7.1 –7.4
Central cells	6.7 –6.9
Miscellaneous	
Distilled water, exposed to air from which it absorbs some CO_2	about 5.5
Sea water	8.0
Vinegar	3.0
Orange juice	2.6 –4.4
Grapefruit juice	3.2
Tomatoes (ripe)	4.3
Egg white (fresh)	8.0

It will be noted that all body fluids, excepting gastric juice (pH 0.9), have pH values lying essentially in the range of 5 − 8. Most of the values are within one pH unit of neutrality (pH 7). The pH of tissues is slightly lower than the value for blood. The actual concentration of H^+ and OH^- ions in most biologic materials is very small. For example, a pH of 5 for urine is rather acid, but this represents only 10^{-5}, or 0.00001 N H^+. Similarly, a pH of 8 is rather alkaline for body fluids, yet it represents 10^{-8} N H^+, and 10^{-6}, or 0.000001 N OH^-.

The student must remember that pH values are logarithmic functions of the actual hydrogen ion concentrations, and a pH difference of one unit represents a tenfold difference in actual H^+ concentrations. For example, pH 3 represents a hydrogen ion concentration of 0.001, and pH 4 a hydrogen ion concentration of 0.0001. Suppose the pH of blood serum should drop from 7.4 to 7.3, the change is 0.1 of a pH unit. The [H$^+$] corresponding to pH = 7.4 is 0.0000000398, while for pH = 7.3 the value of [H$^+$] is 0.00000005. There are about 25 per cent more H$^+$ in the serum at pH 7.3 than at pH 7.4.

Methods of calculating pH from [H$^+$] and the reverse. These calculations are very simple when expressions such as [H$^+$] = 0.001 g mol per liter and pH = 4 are encountered. From inspection it can be seen that [H$^+$] = 0.001 = 1 $\times$ 10^{-3} represents a pH of 3. Likewise, a pH of 4 represents a hydrogen ion concentration of 1 $\times$ 10^{-4} = 0.0001 g mol per liter.

Since the use of logarithms is involved in pH and other calculations encountered in this book, the following rules of logarithms are summarized for convenience.

1. The logarithm of a product is equal to the sum of the logarithms of the factors: log ab = log a + log b.

2. The logarithm of a fraction is equal to the logarithm of the numerator minus the logarithm of the denominator: log a/b = log a − log b.

3. The logarithm of the reciprocal of a number is equal to the negative logarithm of the number: log $1/a$ = log 1 − log a = 0 − log a = − log a.

4. The logarithm of a number raised to a power is equal to the logarithm of the number multiplied by the power: log a^b = b log a.

5. The logarithm of the root of a number is equal to the logarithm of the number divided by the index of the root: log $\sqrt[n]{a}$ = (log a)/n.

The following examples illustrate the calculation of pH when the values cannot be obtained by simple inspection:

1. Suppose the hydrogen ion concentration, [H$^+$], of a solution is 0.00456 g mol per liter. Calculate the pH of the solution. We may write:

[H$^+$] = 0.00456 = 4.56 $\times$ 10^{-3}. Since pH = − log [H$^+$], the pH of the solution is given by:

$$pH = - \log (4.56 \times 10^{-3})$$
$$= - (\log 4.56 + \log 10^{-3})$$
$$= - (\log 4.56 + (-3))$$
$$= - (0.6589 - 3)$$
$$pH = -0.6589 + 3 = 2.34$$

2. Suppose the pH of a solution is 5.3, calculate the [H$^+$]. Substituting in the equation

$$- \log [H^+] = pH$$

we have:

$$- \log [H^+] = 5.3$$
$$\log [H^+] = -5.3$$
$$[H^+] = 10^{-5.3} = 10^{0.7} \times 10^{-6} = 5.01 \times 10^{-6}$$
$$= 0.00000501 \text{ g mol per liter}$$

Dissociation of weak acids. The dissociation of weak acids takes place according to the law of mass action, and equilibrium equations can be formulated for their dissociation. Such equations do not apply to the dissociation of strong acids.

If we designate the general formula of any weak monobasic acid (such as acetic) by HA, its dissociation equation is:

$$HA \rightleftharpoons H^+ + A^-$$

and, according to the law of mass action, we may write the equilibrium mathematical expression for its dissociation as follows:

$$\frac{[H^+][A^-]}{[HA]} = \frac{k_1}{k_2} = K_a$$

in which K_a = what is called the "dissociation constant" of the acid. Dissociation constants of weak acids and bases may be calculated from data obtained by measuring the electrical conductivity of their solutions or by determining the pH values of their solutions. The value of K_w for water is generally calculated from conductivity measurements. It is obvious that the value of K_a is greater the more highly ionized the acid. For example, in the case of acetic acid, we have:

$$\frac{[H^+][CH_3COO^-]}{[CH_3COOH]} = K_a = 1.86 \times 10^{-5} - 0.0000186$$

and for hydrocyanic acid:

$$\frac{[H^+][CN^-]}{[HCN]} = K_a = 7.2 \times 10^{-10} = 0.00000000072$$

The value of K_a for acetic acid, 1.86×10^{-5}, is thousands of times greater than the value of K_a for hydrocyanic acid, 7.2×10^{-10}. Accordingly, one may look at a table of dissociation constants and readily determine the approximate relative strengths of acids.

Polybasic acids, which contain more than one ionizable hydrogen, dissociate in stages, and there is an equilibrium equation and a dissociation constant for each stage. This may be illustrated by the case of phosphoric acid:

$$H_3PO_4 \rightleftharpoons H^+ + H_2PO_4^-$$
$$H_2PO_4^- \rightleftharpoons H^+ + HPO_4^=$$
$$HPO_4^= \rightleftharpoons H^+ + PO_4^{\equiv}$$

The equilibrium equations for the three stages of dissociation are, respectively:

$$\frac{[H^+][H_2PO_4^-]}{[H_3PO_4]} = K_1 = 1.1 \times 10^{-2}$$

$$\frac{[H^+][HPO_4^=]}{[H_2PO_4^-]} = K_2 = 2 \times 10^{-7}$$

$$\frac{[H^+][PO_4^=]}{[HPO_4^=]} = K_3 = 3.6 \times 10^{-13}$$

K_1, K_2, and K_3 are referred to as the first, second, and third dissociation constants of the acid. The dissociation of the first H^+ from H_3PO_4 is opposed by the force of attraction of its linkage to the molecule. However, the second H^+, in dissociating from $H_2PO_4^-$, is held not only by its primary union with the molecule but also by the attraction of the negative charge left by the dissociation of the first H^+. The third H^+ must dissociate against the attraction of its primary linkage and of the two negative charges resulting from previous dissociations. It is not surprising, therefore, that the second and succeeding stages of dissociation take place with more difficulty than does the first, and the values of K_2, K_3, etc., are smaller than that of K_1.

The dissociation constant of a weak acid may be used for the approximate calculation of the pH of its solutions of known concentration. In the dissociation of a weak acid, HA:

$$HA \rightleftharpoons H^+ + A^-$$

the concentrations of H^+ and A^- are equal because they are formed in equal amounts. We may write the following expressions:

$$\frac{[H^+][A^-]}{[HA]} = K_a \quad \text{and} \quad [H^+][A^-] = K_a[HA]$$

Since $[H^+] = [A^-]$, we also have:

$$[H^+]^2 = K_a[HA] \quad \text{and} \quad [H^+] = \sqrt{K_a[HA]}$$

In the case of weak acids, which are slightly dissociated, most of the acid in solution exists in the undissociated form, HA, with no more than a per cent or two as H^+ and A^-. One may then assume, for approximate calculation, that [HA] is equal to the normality of the acid. For example, if we wish to calculate the pH of 0.1 N acetic acid (K_a for acetic acid $= 1.86 \times 10^{-5}$), we may assume that $[CH_3COOH] = 0.1$ g mol per liter and substitute in the equation:

$$[H^+] = \sqrt{K_a[CH_3COOH]} = \sqrt{1.86 \times 10^{-5} \times 0.1} = \sqrt{1.86 \times 10^{-6}}$$

Taking the logarithm of both sides of the equation, we may write:

$$\log [H^+] = \log \sqrt{1.86 \times 10^{-6}} = \frac{\log (1.86 \times 10^{-6})}{2}$$

$$= \frac{\log 1.86 + \log 10^{-6}}{2} = \frac{0.2695 - 6}{2} = -2.86$$

If $\log [H^+] = -2.86$, then pH $= -\log [H^+] = 2.86$. The pH of 0.1 N acetic acid solution is close to 2.86. The $[H^+]$ corresponding to this pH may be obtained in the usual way.

Since bases in the Brönsted sense are proton acceptors and, having accepted protons, become proton donors or acids, it is possible to calculate the dissociation constants for these acids. For example, the base NH_3 combines with H^+ in aqueous solution to form NH_4^+ which dissociates as a weak acid:

$$NH_4^+ \rightleftharpoons NH_3 + H^+$$

for which we have the equilibrium expression:

$$K_a = \frac{[NH_3][H^+]}{[NH_4^+]} = 5.5 \times 10^{-10}$$

Since NH_3 reacts with H_2O to form NH_4OH, which dissociates as follows:

$$NH_4OH \rightleftharpoons NH_4^+ + OH^-$$

the so-called basic dissociation constant, K_b, of the older literature is given by the expression:

$$K_b = \frac{[NH_4^+][OH^-]}{[NH_4OH]} = 1.8 \times 10^{-5}$$

K_a and K_b are related by the equation: $K_a K_b = K_w = 1 \times 10^{-14}$. If we take the negative logarithm of both sides, we have:

$$- \log K_a - \log K_b = - \log K_w = 14$$

Since $- \log K_a$, $- \log K_b$, and $- \log K_w$ are designated as pK_a, pK_b, and pK_w, we may write:

$$pK_a + pK_b = pK_w = 14$$

From the above relations it is possible to convert the so-called basic dissociation constants of ammonia and its derivatives, such as amines and amino acids, into the currently used acidic constants.

It is a well-known fact that salts such as NaCl and Na_2SO_4 react essentially neutral in water solution, while salts such as NH_4Cl and CH_3NH_3Cl react acid, and $NaHCO_3$ and CH_3COONa react alkaline. The reaction of a salt in water depends upon the extent to which the ions of the salt preferentially remove H^+ or OH^- ions from the solution. In the case of NaCl and Na_2SO_4, derived from strong acids and NaOH, none of their constituent ions remove either H^+ or OH^- ions appreciably. However, in the case of a salt such as NH_4Cl the following processes occur in water solution:

$$NH_4Cl \longrightarrow NH_4^+ + Cl^-$$
$$+$$
$$HOH \rightleftharpoons HO^- + H^+$$
$$\updownarrow$$
$$NH_4OH$$

The NH_4^+ ions act with OH^- ions of water to form NH_4OH, which is weakly dissociated, thus causing the $[H^+]$ to be greater than $[OH^-]$, and the solution to be acid.

In the case of salts such as CH_3COONa, the situation is as follows:

$$CH_3COONa \longrightarrow CH_3COO^- + Na^+$$
$$+$$
$$HOH \rightleftharpoons H^+ + OH^-$$
$$\updownarrow$$
$$CH_3COOH$$

Here the CH_3COO^- ions combine with H^+ ions of water to form weakly dissociated CH_3COOH, leaving $[OH^-]$ greater than $[H^+]$, and the solution alkaline.

The extent to which the unity ratio of [H⁺] and [OH⁻] of water is changed by the ions of the salt determines the degree of hydrolysis. If BA = the general formula of a salt, then the hydrolytic reaction in general is as follows:

$$BA + HOH \rightleftarrows BOH + HA$$

and is the reverse of neutralization.

It is interesting to note that ammonium acetate, formed from CH_3COOH and NH_4OH, both of which are weakly and about equally dissociated, gives an essentially neutral solution in water. This is because the H⁺ and OH⁻ ions are removed to about the same extent.

$$CH_3COONH_4 \longrightarrow CH_3COO^- + NH_4^+$$
$$+ \qquad\qquad +$$
$$HOH \rightleftarrows H^+ \quad + \quad OH^-$$
$$\Updownarrow \qquad\qquad \Updownarrow$$
$$CH_3COOH \quad NH_4OH$$

From the hydrolysis equation:

$$BA + HOH \rightleftarrows HA + BOH$$

it is evident that increasing the amount of water relative to salt will, according to the mass law, increase hydrolysis. In other words, salts are hydrolyzed more in dilute than in concentrated solutions. NH_4Cl is hydrolyzed 0.0075 per cent in 0.1 M and 0.024 per cent in 0.01 M solution at ordinary temperature. Hydrolysis in the 0.01 M is more than three times greater than in the 0.1 M solution. The extent of hydrolysis increases as the temperature rises. This is largely due to increased dissociation of water into H⁺ and OH⁻ ions at elevated temperatures.

The effect of salts upon the dissociation of acids; buffer solutions. When a salt of a weak acid is mixed with the weak acid in solution, the dissociation of the acid is decreased, and it shows less acidity and a higher pH than when the salt is absent. An explanation of this phenomenon is embodied in the following considerations. Salts of weak acids, as opposed to weak acids themselves, are generally highly ionized. In a solution containing acetic acid and sodium acetate, for example, we have the following dissociation equations:

$$CH_3COOH \rightleftarrows CH_3COO^- + H^+$$
$$CH_3COONa \longrightarrow CH_3COO^- + Na^+$$

The acetate ions from the dissociation of the acid are relatively few in comparison to the molecules of undissociated acid. Each hundred molecules of acetic acid produce less than two acetate and hydrogen ions. On the other hand, the number of acetate ions from the sodium acetate is equal to the number of sodium acetate molecules dissolved. Now, according to the mass law, if we wish to increase the rate of combination of H⁺ and CH_3COO^- ions in a solution, it is only necessary to increase the product of the concentrations of these ions. In other words, the point of equilibrium of the reaction:

$$CH_3COOH \rightleftarrows CH_3COO^- + H^+$$

can be shifted to the left by increasing the concentration of CH_3COO^- ions.

This will lead to a proportionate decrease in the concentration of H+ ions and a rise in pH. Evidently, then, the addition of a definite amount of acetate to a solution of acetic acid increases the concentration of CH_3COO^- ions by a definite value, and this causes the concentration of hydrogen ions and pH of the solution to be fixed. Thus, it is seen that the pH of a solution of a weak acid and its salt is determined by the ratio of salt to acid in the solution. The higher the salt concentration, the greater is the mass action in repressing the dissociation of the acid. In order that this may be better illustrated, the approximate pH values of solutions containing varying proportions of acetic acid and acetate are given in Table 3.4 below. For convenience in calculation the concentration of acid is held at 0.2 N and that of the salt varied. The

Table 3.4

| Concentration | | | Per Cent | |
CH₃COONa Molar	CH₃COOH Normal	Ratio Salt/Acid	Dissociation of Acid	pH
0.00	0.2	0.00	1.00	2.7
0.01	0.2	0.05	0.20	3.4
0.05	0.2	0.25	0.04	4.1
0.10	0.2	0.50	0.02	4.4
0.15	0.2	0.75	0.012	4.6
0.20	0.2	1.00	0.01	4.7
0.30	0.2	1.50	0.006	4.9

approximate percentage dissociation of the acid in the presence of different concentrations of salt is given. It will be observed that the presence of acetate in the solution with the acetic acid has a marked effect upon the dissociation of the acid and upon the pH. The 0.2 N acid alone is about 1 per cent dissociated and has a pH of about 2.7. When the solution contains 0.01 M acetate in addition to 0.2 N acid, the dissociation of the acid drops to 0.2 per cent, one-fifth of its value without salt. When the 0.2 N acid contains 0.2 M salt, the acid is dissociated only 1 per cent as much as it is in the absence of salt.

The above principles apply generally to solutions of weak acids in the presence of their salts. They also apply in the case of solutions of weak hydroxides and their salts, such as NH_4OH and NH_4Cl, where the dissociations are:

$$NH_4Cl \longrightarrow NH_4^+ + Cl^-$$
$$NH_4OH \rightleftarrows NH_4^+ + OH^-$$

The NH_4OH is slightly dissociated, while the NH_4Cl is completely dissociated. As the proportion of NH_4Cl is changed, the extent to which OH^- ions are converted to weakly dissociated NH_4OH changes. An increase in NH_4Cl increases NH_4^+ ions which decrease OH^- ions with a proportionate drop in pH. Similarly, a decrease in the ratio of NH_4Cl to NH_4OH leaves more OH^- ions in solution, with a proportionate rise in pH.

Solutions containing both weak acids and their salts are referred to as "buffer solutions." They have the capacity of resisting changes of pH when either acids or alkalies are added to them. For example, suppose 1 ml of 0.1

N HCl to be added to 99 ml of pure water of pH 7. The [H⁺] of the mixture
will be about 0.001 N and its pH about 3. The pH of the pure water changes
about four units (from 7 to 3) as a result of adding the acid. Suppose, however, 1 ml of 0.1 N HCl to be added to 99 ml of a buffer solution containing
0.1 N acetic acid and 0.1 M sodium acetate. The pH of the buffer solution
to begin with is 4.73. When the HCl is added, the pH becomes about 4.72, a
change of 0.01 pH, contrasted with a change of 4 pH units when the acid is
added to pure water. The mixture of acetic acid and sodium acetate is hundreds of times more resistant to pH change than is water alone. A similar
condition exists when alkali is added to water and to the buffer mixture.
One milliliter of 0.1 N NaOH added to 99 ml of pure water gives a pH of
about 11, whereas if it is added to 99 ml of the above acetate buffer solution
(pH 4.73), the pH becomes about 4.74.

The chemical mechanisms according to which buffers function may be
illustrated by what happens when NaOH and HCl are added to an acetate
buffer solution containing acetate ions, CH_3COO^-, and acetic acid molecules,
CH_3COOH. When NaOH is added to the buffer solution, OH^- ions from
NaOH take H^+ ions from CH_3COOH to form CH_3COO^- ions, and thus
increase the ratio of acetate to acid with a proportionate rise in pH:

$$OH^- + CH_3COOH \longrightarrow CH_3COO^- + H_2O$$

Upon the addition of HCl to the buffer solution, the H^+ ions from the HCl
combine with CH_3COO^- ions to form CH_3COOH and thus decrease the ratio
of acetate to acid and proportionately lower the pH:

$$H^+ + CH_3COO^- \longrightarrow CH_3COOH$$

In simple nonionic equations the above actions are as follows:
Upon the addition of NaOH:

$$\left\{ \begin{array}{l} CH_3COOH \\ CH_3COONa \end{array} \right. + NaOH \longrightarrow CH_3COONa + H_2O$$

The addition of the alkali decreases the CH_3COOH in the buffer and increases the CH_3COONa. The pH of the solution increases in proportion to
the change in ratio of salt to acid in the buffer solution.
Upon addition of HCl:

$$\left\{ \begin{array}{l} CH_3COOH \\ CH_3COONa \end{array} \right. + HCl \longrightarrow CH_3COOH + NaCl$$

In this case the HCl reacts to decrease CH_3COONa and increase CH_3COOH
in the buffer. The pH of the solution falls in proportion to the change in
ratio of salt to acid in the solution.

The Henderson-Hasselbalch equation for buffer solutions. The
pH of a buffer solution composed of a weak acid mixed with its salt can be
rather closely calculated by the use of the so-called Henderson-Hasselbalch
equation, derived in the following way. If, as previously, we designate a weak
acid by the general formula HA, then its salt may be indicated by the formula BA, in which B and A are positive and negative ions, respectively.

In the equilibrium reactions for the dissociation of HA and BA in a buffer solution, we have:

$$\text{HA} \rightleftharpoons \text{H}^+ + \text{A}^-, \text{ weakly dissociated}$$
$$\text{BA} \longrightarrow \text{B}^+ + \text{A}^-, \text{ highly dissociated}$$

As shown previously, the equilibrium mass law equation for the dissociation of a weak acid, HA, is:

$$\frac{[\text{H}^+][\text{A}^-]}{[\text{HA}]} = K_a$$

From this we have by simple transposition:

$$[\text{H}^+] = K_a \frac{[\text{HA}]}{[\text{A}^-]}$$

Now the weak acid, HA, is only slightly ionized, even when salt is absent. Most of the acid is present as HA with a very small fraction as H^+ and A^-. When the salt, BA, is added to the acid solution, practically all the A^- ions come from the highly dissociated salt. In a dilute buffer solution we may, as a close approximation, then assume that the concentration of undissociated acid, [HA], is equal to the total acid concentration and also that the concentration of acid ion, [A$^-$], is equal to the total salt concentration [BA]. If this is done, we may change the equation:

$$[\text{H}^+] = K_a \frac{[\text{HA}]}{[\text{A}^-]}$$

into the expression:

$$[\text{H}^+] = K_a \frac{[\text{HA}]}{[\text{BA}]} \quad \text{or} \quad [\text{H}^+] = K_a \frac{[\text{acid}]}{[\text{salt}]}$$

If one knows the dissociation constant, K_a, for the acid and the molecular ratio of acid to salt in the buffer solution, it is possible to calculate the hydrogen ion concentration, $[\text{H}^+]$, for the solution. This equation can be simply changed to calculate the pH of a buffer solution directly by taking the negative logarithm of both sides:

$$\text{pH} = -\log[\text{H}^+] = -\log K_a \frac{[\text{HA}]}{[\text{BA}]}$$
$$= -\left(\log K_a + \log \frac{[\text{HA}]}{[\text{BA}]}\right)$$
$$= -\log K_a - \log \frac{[\text{HA}]}{[\text{BA}]}$$

Since: $-\log K_a = pK_a$ and $-\log \dfrac{[\text{HA}]}{[\text{BA}]} = \log \dfrac{[\text{BA}]}{[\text{HA}]}$

we may rewrite the above equation:

$$\text{pH} = pK_a + \log \frac{[\text{BA}]}{[\text{HA}]} \quad \text{or} \quad \text{pH} = pK_a + \log \frac{[\text{salt}]}{[\text{acid}]}$$

Other equivalent forms of the equation are:

$$pH = pK_a + \log \frac{[A^-]}{[HA]} \quad \text{or} \quad pH = pK_a + \log \frac{[\text{conjugate base}]}{[\text{acid}]}$$

or
$$pH = pK_a + \log \frac{[\text{proton acceptor}]}{[\text{proton donor}]}$$

As to be expected, the equation applies more accurately when concentrations are converted to activities by multiplying by the appropriate activity coefficients, when these are available.

The equation is known as the Henderson-Hasselbalch equation for buffer solutions. By its use one may directly calculate the pH of a buffer solution if pK_a for the buffer acid and the molecular ratio of salt to acid in the solution are known. For example, suppose one were to have a solution containing 0.05 M sodium acetate and 0.1 N acetic acid. The value of pK_a for acetic acid is 4.73 at room temperature. To calculate the pH of this solution, we solve the equation:

$$pH = 4.73 + \log \frac{0.05}{0.1} = 4.73 + \log 0.5$$
$$= 4.73 - 0.30 = 4.43$$

If the solution contained 0.1 M acetate and 0.1 N acid, we would have:

$$pH = 4.73 + \log \frac{0.1}{0.1} = 4.73 + \log 1$$
$$= 4.73 + 0 = 4.73$$

This shows that when the molecular ratio of salt to acid in a buffer solution is unity, the pH of the solution is equal to the value of pK_a for the buffer acid. This is a very important fact, and use is made of it in experimentally determining the value of pK_a. To do this, it is only necessary to prepare a solution of the acid and one of its alkali salts, in which the concentrations of acid and salt are equal, and determine its pH. It is obvious that if a solution of an acid be half-neutralized with alkali, the molecular ratio of salt to acid in the solution is equal to 1 and the pH of the solution is equal to the pK_a of the buffer acid. If 5 ml of 0.1 N NaOH be added to 10 ml of 0.1 N CH_3COOH, one-half of the acid will be neutralized. The solution will contain the equivalent of 5 ml of 0.1 M CH_3COONa and 5 ml of 0.1 N CH_3COOH. The pH of the solution will be:

$$pH = 4.73 + \log \frac{5}{5} = 4.73 + \log 1$$
$$= 4.73 + 0 = 4.73$$

It is unnecessary to calculate the actual molecular concentrations of acid and salt in the half-neutralized solution (each would equal 0.0333), because the ratios are the same whether the actual molecular concentrations or the number of milliliter equivalents (of the same normality) are used in the equations. That is, the ratio of 5/5 = 1 just as the ratio of 0.0333/0.0333 = 1.

The Henderson-Hasselbalch equation does not apply with accuracy for the calculation of the pH of buffer solutions when the proportion of weak acid in the form of its salt is less than about 10 per cent of the total buffer concentration (salt plus acid). Also, the H^+ and OH^- ion concentrations of the buffer solutions must not be sufficiently great to constitute a significant proportion of the total ions present if the equation is to apply with accuracy. Generally, these conditions are satisfactorily met by the buffer solutions present in body fluids and tissues.

Buffer pH and capacity. According to the Henderson-Hasselbalch equation, $pH = pK_a + \log$ [salt]/[acid], the pH of a buffer solution is determined by two things. One of these is the value of pK_a. The smaller pK_a, the stronger is the acid. As shown above, pK_a represents the pH at which a weak acid is half-titrated, or half-converted, to its salt. If the pK_a of an acid is 3.5, the acid exists half as free acid and half as salt at pH 3.5. An acid with a pK_a of 8 would be half titrated to salt at pH 8. Evidently the acid of pK_a 3.5 is many times stronger as an acid than the one with a pK_a of 8. Thus, the lower the value of pK_a in the buffer equation, the lower is the pH of the solution. The second factor concerned in the pH of a buffer solution is, obviously, the ratio of salt to acid concentration. The higher the concentration of salt relative to acid, the higher is the pH of the solution. It will be observed that, according to the Henderson-Hasselbalch equation, the actual concentrations of salt and acid in a buffer solution may be varied widely, with no change in pH, so long as the ratio of the concentrations remains the same. For example, an acetate buffer containing 0.1 M acetate and 0.1 N acid should have the same pH after tenfold dilution, because the ratio of salt to acid will still be unity. Actually there is a slight increase in this case, amounting to less than 0.1 pH unit. Reasonable dilution of a well-buffered solution ordinarily causes only minor pH changes.

Van Slyke has pointed out that the buffer value, or capacity, of a solution is determined by the pH change caused by the addition of increments of strong acid or alkali to it. The smaller the pH change caused by the addition of a given amount of acid or alkali, the greater is the buffer capacity, and vice versa. According to Van Slyke, a solution has a buffer value of 1 when a liter requires one gram equivalent (1000 ml of 1 N solution) of strong acid or alkali per unit change in pH. For example, suppose 10 ml of a buffer require 5 ml of 0.1 N alkali to change the pH of the buffer 1 unit. Then 1000 ml of the buffer would require 500 ml of 0.1 N alkali or 50 ml of 1 N alkali. Fifty milliliters of 1 N alkali represent one-twentieth of one gram equivalent, or 0.05 gram equivalent. The buffer capacity of the solution toward strong alkali is 0.05. Its buffer capacity toward strong acid may be either greater or less than this. While the pH of a buffer solution is determined primarily by the pK_a value of the buffer acid and by the ratio of salt to acid in the solution, the buffer capacity is determined by the actual concentrations of salt and acid present, as well as by their ratio. For example, if 1 ml of 0.1 N HCl be added to a buffer solution containing 10 ml of 0.1 M CH_3COONa and

10 ml of 0.1 N CH$_3$COOH, the HCl will convert 1 ml of the salt to 1 ml of the acid and the pH of the solution will be (using pK_a = 4.73):

$$\text{pH} = 4.73 + \log \frac{9}{11} = 4.73 + \log 9 - \log 11$$

$$= 4.73 + 0.9542 - 1.0414 = 4.64$$

The pH of the buffer before addition of the HCl is calculated to be 4.73. One milliliter of 0.1 N HCl causes a decrease of about 0.09 pH unit. Suppose the buffer consists of 10 ml of 0.025 M CH$_3$COONa and 10 ml of 0.025 N CH$_3$COOH, and 1 ml of the 0.1 N HCl be added. Since 1 ml of 0.1 N HCl reacts with 4 ml of 0.025 M CH$_3$COONa to form 4 ml of 0.025 N CH$_3$COOH, the pH of the buffer solution, after adding the acid, is calculated to be:

$$\text{pH} = 4.73 + \log \frac{6}{14} = 4.36$$

The pH of the buffer before addition of the HCl is calculated to be 4.73, just as in the case of the first buffer, because the ratio of salt to acid is 1 in both buffers. One milliliter of 0.1 N HCl causes about four times the pH change in the second buffer (0.37) as it does in the first (0.09). The first buffer has more buffer capacity than the second, and this is true because it contains higher concentrations of salt and acid than does the second buffer. The addition of strong acid or alkali to the more concentrated buffer causes less change in the ratio of buffer salt to acid, and consequently less change in pH, than in case of the more dilute buffer solution.

In order to illustrate the effect of the ratio of salt to acid upon buffer capacity, suppose we have a buffer solution composed of 16 ml of 0.1 M CH$_3$COONa and 4 ml of 0.1 N CH$_3$COOH. The pH of the solution will be:

$$\text{pH} = 4.73 + \log \frac{16}{4}$$

$$= 4.73 + 1.2041 - 0.6020 = 5.33$$

Now suppose 1 ml of 0.1 N HCl be added to the buffer. This will convert the equivalent of 1 ml of 0.1 M CH$_3$COONa to 1 ml of 0.1 N CH$_3$COOH, and the pH of the solution becomes:

$$\text{pH} = 4.73 + \log \frac{15}{5} = 4.73 + 1.1760 - 0.6989 = 5.207$$

The pH of the buffer is lowered from 5.33 to 5.207 by the HCl, a drop of 0.123. As shown above, 1 ml of 0.1 N HCl added to the buffer composed of 10 ml of 0.1 M CH$_3$COONa and 10 ml of 0.1 N CH$_3$COOH causes a change of only 0.09 pH. Both buffer solutions contain the same total concentration of acetate (salt + acid), an amount equivalent to 20 ml of 0.1 M solution. In one case the ratio of salt to acid is 4; in the other the ratio is 1. The buffering capacity is higher in the case of the buffer with a salt to acid ratio of 1. The general principle may be stated that the maximum efficiency of a buffer with a given total concentration of salt plus acid is greatest when the ratio of salt to acid is equal to 1. The reason for this is shown in Table 3.5, in which the pH values of mixtures of 0.1 M CH$_3$COONa and 0.1 N CH$_3$COOH are calculated. The total volume in each case is 10 ml of 0.1 M solution (salt + acid). The ratio of salt to acid varies from 1/9 to 9/1. The pH interval differences between successive ratios are given and show that the rate of change of pH decreases the nearer the ratio of salt to acid approaches 1. One milliliter of 0.1 N HCl added to these buffer mixtures, thereby converting 1 ml equivalent of CH$_3$COO$^-$ to 1 ml equivalent of CH$_3$COOH, causes least pH change when the ratio of CH$_3$COONa to CH$_3$COOH is 5/5 = 1 before the HCl is added.

The efficient buffer range of a given buffer system is rather limited, as shown in Table 3.5. It consists of about 1 pH unit on either side of the pK_a value of the buffer acid. The acetate buffer of Table 3.5 is more or less efficient as a buffer from about pH 3.7 to pH 5.7, a total of 2 pH units. Should one wish to prepare a buffer solution to cover the pH range 6–8, it would be well, if possible, to select a buffer acid with pK_a value close to 7, and similarly for other pH ranges. Increasing the concentration of the buffer solution increases its effective range somewhat.

Table 3.5. Showing That the Efficiency of Buffer Mixtures of Constant Total Concentration Is Greatest When the Ratio of Salt to Acid Equals 1

0.1 M CH$_3$COONa	0.1 N CH$_3$COOH	pH Calculated	pH Differences
1	9	3.775	
2	8	4.127	0.35
3	7	4.362	0.23
4	6	4.553	0.19
5	5	4.730	0.17
6	4	4.906	0.17
7	3	5.097	0.19
8	2	5.332	0.23
9	1	5.684	0.35

Table 3.6 gives values for K_a and pK_a of a number of acids, most of which are approximate. It is impractical to give the conditions under which each value holds with accuracy. Edsall and Wyman give a table of more exact values in their *Biophysical Chemistry*.

Buffers are of primary importance in regulating the pH of the fluids and tissues of living organisms within limits consistent with life and normal function. They are widely used in the laboratory to control the pH of culture media for microorganisms and tissues. Many chemical reactions, including those catalyzed by enzymes, require pH control that is provided by appropriately buffered solutions. Standard buffer solutions are used with indicators for the determination of pH, which will be discussed later. They are also used to check the performance of electrodes used in pH determination.

Buffers of blood plasma (HCO$_3^-$/H$_2$CO$_3$, HPO$_4^=$/H$_2$PO$_4^-$, proteinate/protein). The bicarbonate-carbonic acid buffer system is present in greatest concentration (about 0.025 M HCO$_3^-$ and 0.00125 M H$_2$CO$_3$) and is of most

Table 3.6. Dissociation Constants, K_a and pK_a, of Acids
(Constants for Polybasic Acids are Indicated by K_1, K_2, K_3; pK_1, pK_2, pK_3)

Acid		K_a	$pK_a = -\log K_a$
Acetic		1.86×10^{-5}	4.73
Acetoacetic		1.6×10^{-4}	3.8
Barbital (Veronal)		3.7×10^{-8}	7.43
Benzoic		6.6×10^{-5}	4.18
Boric		6.4×10^{-10}	9.19
Butyric		1.48×10^{-5}	4.83
Carbonic	K_1	7.9×10^{-7}	pK_1 6.1
Carbonic	K_2	6×10^{-11}	pK_2 10.4
Chloroacetic		1.4×10^{-3}	2.86
Citric	K_1	8×10^{-4}	pK_1 3.1
Citric	K_2	2×10^{-5}	pK_2 4.7
Citric	K_3	4×10^{-7}	pK_3 6.4
Formic		2.14×10^{-4}	3.7
Glucose		1×10^{-12}	12
Glucose-1-phosphoric	K_1	7.9×10^{-2}	pK_1 1.1
Glucose-1-phosphoric	K_2	7.4×10^{-7}	pK_2 6.13
Glucose-6-phosphoric	K_1	1.15×10^{-1}	pK_1 0.94
Glucose-6-phosphoric	K_2	7.76×10^{-7}	pK_2 6.11
Glycerol-2-phosphoric	K_1	4.68×10^{-2}	pK_1 1.33
Glycerol-2-phosphoric	K_2	2.24×10^{-7}	pK_2 6.65
Hydrocyanic		7.2×10^{-10}	9.14
β-Hydroxybutyric		3.98×10^{-5}	4.4
Lactic		1.38×10^{-4}	3.86
Oxalic	K_1	3.8×10^{-2}	pK_1 1.42
Oxalic	K_2	4.9×10^{-5}	pK_2 4.31
Phosphoric	K_1	1.1×10^{-2}	pK_1 1.96
Phosphoric	K_2	2×10^{-7}	pK_2 6.7
Phosphoric	K_3	3.6×10^{-13}	pK_3 12.4
Propionic		1.35×10^{-5}	4.87
Succinic	K_1	6.31×10^{-5}	pK_1 4.2
Succinic	K_2	2.35×10^{-6}	pK_2 5.63
Tartaric	K_1	1.1×10^{-3}	pK_1 2.96
Tartaric	K_2	6.9×10^{-5}	pK_2 4.16
Ammonium ion		5.5×10^{-10}	9.26
Anilinium ion		2.5×10^{-5}	4.6
Dimethylammonium ion		1.74×10^{-11}	10.76
Ethanolammonium ion		3.24×10^{-10}	9.49
Methylammonium ion		2.46×10^{-11}	10.61
Trimethylammonium ion		1.62×10^{-10}	9.79
Tris (hydroxymethyl) aminomethane		8.51×10^{-9}	8.07

importance in maintaining the pH of blood within normal limits. The ratio $HC\bar{O}_3/H_2CO_3$ in blood plasma is normally about 20/1, which represents a pH of 7.4:

$$pH = pK + \log \frac{[HC\bar{O}_3]}{[H_2CO_3]}$$
$$= 6.1 + \log \frac{0.025}{0.00125} = 6.1 + \log \frac{20}{1}$$
$$= 6.1 + \log 20 - \log 1 = 6.1 + 1.30 - 0 = 7.4$$

The phosphate and protein buffers of plasma are relatively little importance, as compared with the bicarbonate buffer, in regulating pH.

Buffers of red blood cells. The red cells, or erythrocytes, of blood are heavily buffered, chiefly as a result of the presence of large amounts of the protein hemoglobin. This is an amphoteric substance and, at the pH of red cells (about 7.25), exists partly as salt. The HCO_3^-—H_2CO_3 buffer system is also present in the cells in considerable amounts and contributes much to the buffer capacity of the cells. Phosphate buffer in the cells is relatively insignificant.

The HCO_3^-—H_2CO_3 buffer system is peculiarly efficient in buffering the acids produced in the body. Some acids are continually being formed in the chemical reactions of tissue cells. These include sulfuric, phosphoric, lactic, acetoacetic, β-hydroxybutyric, and other acids. They react with the various buffer systems of the body and are converted into salts, which are then excreted or changed into other substances. In the disease diabetes mellitus, 50 or more grams of β-hydroxybutyric and acetoacetic acid per day may be produced. In order to prevent fatal acidosis, the acidity of these acids must be neutralized by the buffer systems of the body fluids and tissues. The HCO_3^-—H_2CO_3 system is the most efficient in this process. For example, consider what occurs when acetoacetic acid reacts with HCO_3^- in the blood or other body fluids:

$$CH_3 - CO - CH_2 - COOH + HCO_3^- \longrightarrow CH_3 - CO - CH_2 - COO^- + H_2CO_3$$

Here the acetoacetic acid decreases the concentration of HCO_3^- and increases the concentration of H_2CO_3 in the HCO_3^-—H_2CO_3 buffer system. The pH changes according to the change in ratio of HCO_3^- to H_2CO_3. However, the change in pH is actually not so great as this, because the H_2CO_3 formed in the action is blown off (as CO_2) when the blood containing it reaches the lungs. We may state, therefore, that the HCO_3^-—H_2CO_3 buffer system of the body is most important in buffering acids within the physiologic pH range because of the quantity of the buffer effective and also because the acid of the buffer, H_2CO_3, decomposes into CO_2, which can be quickly excreted through the lungs. All the other buffer systems of the body have acid components which cannot be removed in this way, and in equivalent amounts they are much less efficient.

Buffers of tissue fluids and tissues. The buffer systems present in lymph, spinal fluid, transudates, etc., are much the same as those of blood plasma, with the exception that these fluids contain much smaller quantities of protein buffers. The main buffer present in them is the HCO_3^-—H_2CO_3 system.

Tissues have much buffer capacity which is due chiefly to protein buffers and the HCO_3^-—H_2CO_3 buffer system. Buffers composed of various organic acids and their anions (salts) play some role in regulating the pH of body fluids.

As pointed out previously, there is a rather definite and limited pH range through which a given buffer functions efficiently, and this is determined by the pK_a of the buffer acid, as well as by the concentrations of buffer salt and acid. In the case of the buffer systems of the body fluids and tissues the pH ranges of efficient action for the buffers vary somewhat and overlap, thus tending to provide more efficient buffering than would be attained by having all of the buffer capacity present in only one buffer system.

Titration curves of acids and bases. Suppose 10 ml of 0.1 N HCl be mixed with varying amounts of 0.1 N NaOH and the pH determined after the addition of each increment of NaOH. It will be found that the pH changes in an orderly fashion as the OH$^-$ reacts with more and more of the H$^+$ of the acid. When the milliliters of NaOH added are plotted upon the abscissa and the pH values corresponding to each addition of NaOH upon the ordinate of a coordinate paper and the points are connected by a smooth line, a so-called titration curve of the acid is obtained (the coordinates may be reversed). A rather closely approximate curve may be obtained by assuming the HCl to be completely ionized and calculating the pH of the solution after the addition of each portion of NaOH. Before the addition of any NaOH, if we assume complete ionization, the [H$^+$] is $0.1 = 1 \times 10^{-1}$ g mol per liter. The pH of the solution is 1. After the addition of 1 ml of 0.1 N NaOH, which neutralizes the equivalent of 1 ml of 0.1 N HCl, there is the equivalent of 9 ml of 0.1 N HCl present in a total volume of 11 ml of solution. The normality of the HCl is no longer 0.1, because some of it has been used up and the volume has been increased. The normality of the acid is now calculated to be $9/11 \times 0.1 = 0.082$, and the [H$^+$] is 8.2×10^{-2}. The pH of this solution is calculated to be:

$$\text{pH} = -\log [\text{H}^+] = -\log (8.2 \times 10^{-2}) = -(\log 8.2 + (-2))$$
$$= -(0.9138 - 2) = -0.9138 + 2 = 1.09$$

Similarly, the pH may be calculated after the addition of 2, 3, 4, etc., ml of NaOH. Table 3.7 gives the pH values calculated throughout the titration. The student should check some of these calculations and plot the titration curve corresponding to them.

Table 3.7. Calculated pH Values of 10 ml of 0.1 N HCl Titrated with 0.1 N NaOH, Assuming Complete Ionization (Activity Coefficient of 1.00)

NaOH Added ml	Solution Volume ml	0.1 N HCl Remaining ml	[H$^+$] Calculated	pH Calculated
0	10	10	$1 \ \times 10^{-1}$	1.00
1	11	9	8.2×10^{-2}	1.09
2	12	8	6.6×10^{-2}	1.18
3	13	7	5.4×10^{-2}	1.27
4	14	6	4.3×10^{-2}	1.37
5	15	5	3.3×10^{-2}	1.48
6	16	4	2.5×10^{-2}	1.60
7	17	3	1.8×10^{-2}	1.74
8	18	2	1.1×10^{-2}	1.96
9	19	1	5.3×10^{-3}	2.27
9.9	19.9	0.1	$5 \ \times 10^{-4}$	3.30
9.95	19.95	0.05	2.5×10^{-4}	3.60
10.05	20.05	0.05 ml excess of 0.1 N NaOH	$4 \ \times 10^{-11}$	10.40

The striking thing about the pH curve for the titration of a strong acid, such as HCl, is the slow change in pH as NaOH is added, until almost all the acid has been used up. In the above case more than 80 per cent of the NaOH required for neutralization must be added to produce a change of 1 pH unit. In this region the HCl is exceptionally well buffered against pH change. While the reaction of the solution is still below pH 4, more than 99 per cent of the acid has been converted to NaCl + H_2O. When all but 0.05 ml of acid has been neutralized, the pH is still about 3.6. The addition of only 0.1 ml more of 0.1 N NaOH completely neutralizes the HCl and gives 0.05 ml excess of 0.1 N NaOH in the solution. Since this excess NaOH is not buffered, it represents (in a volume of 20 ml) an OH^- concentration of $0.00025 = 2.5 \times 10^{-4}$. This gives a calculated H^+ concentration of 4×10^{-11}, representing a pH of about 10.4. Close to the end point of the titration the addition of 0.1 ml of NaOH causes the pH to change by nearly 4 units. Thus the titration curve of a strong acid shows a very sharp break at the end point. In titrating such an acid, in order to determine its total acidity, one may use indicators which change color anywhere in the range of pH 4–10 with essentially correct results. Thus, either methyl orange, changing color around pH 4.5, or phenolphthalein, changing color around pH 9, may be used as an end-point indicator in titrating a strong acid with alkali. In any titration of an acid with alkali the object is to add sufficient alkali to convert the acid completely to its salt regardless of the pH of the resulting solution.

The titration curve of a weak acid, such as acetic, represents the variations in pH with different ratios of salt to acid in a buffer mixture. Before alkali is added, the pH is that due to the acid alone. As soon as any alkali is added, this reacts with an equivalent amount of acid and forms an equivalent quantity of salt and water. Now the weak acid plus its salt in solution constitute a buffer solution, the pH of which may be calculated fairly closely by the use of the Henderson-Hasselbalch equation: $pH = pK_a + \log R$, where R represents the ratio of salt to acid in the buffer solution. Since pK_a is a constant for a given acid (within certain limits) during its titration, the only variable is $\log R$. This changes with the addition of each increment of alkali. One may select a definite volume of a solution of a weak acid of known concentration and calculate the ratios of salt to acid after the addition of definite volumes of known alkali. The logarithms of these ratios added to the pK_a value for the acid give the calculated pH values during the titration. The pH values plotted against milliliters of alkali added yield the titration curve for the acid.

Table 3.8 gives the calculated values for the titration curves of CH_3COOH to $CH_3CO\bar{O}$, of H_2CO_3 to $HC\bar{O}_3$, and of $HC\bar{O}_3$ to $CO_3^=$. The student should check some of the calculations and plot the curves corresponding to these values upon his graph showing the titration curve of 0.1 N HCl (for comparison). It will be observed that the curve for the HCl is very different in shape from those for the weak acids. The curves for all the weak acids have similar shapes, as would be expected from the buffer equation. They differ in that they are located at different levels upon the pH scale. The position on the scale occupied by the curve of a given acid is determined by the pK value of the acid. Since the pK of an acid represents the pH of a solution containing salt and acid in equal concentrations, it is obvious that pK represents the pH at which the acid is half titrated. Most of the titration curve of a weak acid ordinarily extends over a range of 4 + pH units. If, then, an acid has a pK value of 6, it will begin to titrate at a little under pH 4, be half titrated at pH 6, and be completely converted into salt at a pH a bit above 8. Similarly, an acid with a pK of 10 begins to form salt at a pH near 8, is half titrated at pH 10, and is completely converted to salt at a pH above 12.

Table 3.8.   Data for Calculating the Titration Curve of a Weak Acid When 10 ml of 0.1 N Acids are Titrated with 0.1 N Alkali

pH Values Are Calculated by Adding pK to Values for Log R

0.1 N NaOH Added ml	0.1 N Acid Remaining ml equiv.	0.1 M Salt Formed ml equiv.	Salt/Acid Ratio, R	Log R	Calculated pH for:		
					CH_3COOH $pK_a = 4.73$	H_2CO_3 $pK_1 = 6.1$	H_2CO_3 $pK_2 = 10.4$
0.1	9.9	0.1*	0.1/9.9	−1.996	2.73*	4.10*	8.40*
1.0	9	1	1/9	−0.954	3.77	5.14	9.44
2.0	8	2	2/8	−0.602	4.13	5.50	9.80
3.0	7	3	3/7	−0.368	4.36	5.73	10.03
5.0	5	5	5/5	0.000	4.73 (pK)	6.10 (pK)	10.40 (pK)
7.0	3	7	7/3	+0.368	5.10	6.47	10.77
8.0	2	8	8/2	+0.602	5.33	6.70	11.00
9.0	1	9	9/1	+0.954	5.68	7.05	11.35
9.9	0.1	9.9	9.9/0.1	+1.996	6.73	8.10	12.40
9.95	0.05	9.95	9.95/0.05	+2.299	7.03	8.40	12.70

* Calculations inaccurate when less than 10 per cent of acid is present as salt.

It will be noted that the titration curves of weak acids (buffer curves) break sharply near both ends and are relatively flat in their center sections. They are poorly buffered when the concentrations of salt and acid are greatly different and well buffered when these concentrations approach in value. Consequently, one may look at a buffer curve and select salt and acid concentrations which will have good buffer capacity.

Titration curves of weak acids essentially represent dissociation curves of the acid. For example, in a 0.1 N solution of acetic acid less than 2 per cent of it is present as CH_3COO^-. This is true because CH_3COO^- ions have a relatively high affinity for H^+ in the reaction:

$$CH_3COOH \rightleftarrows CH_3COO^- + H^+$$

At a pH of 2.7 there are enough H^+ ions in solution to keep most of the acid in the undissociated form. Now as one adds NaOH the OH^- ions remove H^+ to form H_2O and thus permit the reaction to proceed to the right with the accumulation of more CH_3COO^- ions (salt form). When the pH corresponding to pK for the acid is reached, half of the acid exists as CH_3COO^- ions, and at a pH of about 8 all the acid is present as acetate ions. Likewise, an acid of pK 11 would be practically undissociated at pH 8, where acetic acid is completely dissociated. If one observes the titration curves of H_2CO_3 to HCO_3^- ($pK = 6.1$) and of HCO_3^- to $CO_3^=$ ($pK = 10.4$), the reason why little $CO_3^=$ exists in blood plasma (pH 7.4) or other body fluids is readily seen. The student should do this. Also it is obvious that at pH 7.4 a mixture of HCO_3^- and H_2CO_3 is present in plasma, and from the curve it is possible to calculate that the ratio of HCO_3^- to H_2CO_3 is 20/1 at this pH.

In the case of a weak acid, such as H_3PO_4, which has more than one pK value ($pK_1 = 1.96$, $pK_2 = 6.7$, $pK_3 = 12.4$) corresponding to the successive dissociation of H^+ ions, the complete titration curve is a composite of the three different curves corresponding to the different pK values. The first stage consists in the titration of H_3PO_4 to $H_2\bar{P}O_4$, the second in the titration of $H_2\bar{P}O_4$ to $HPO_4^=$, and in the third stage $HPO_4^=$ is converted to $PO_4^\equiv$. In terms of ions $H_3PO_4 \longrightarrow H_2PO_4^-$, $H_2PO_4^- \longrightarrow HPO_4^=$, and $HPO_4^= \longrightarrow PO_4^\equiv$. The H^+ ions in each case are removed by the OH^- of the added alkali to form H_2O. The student should use the data of Table 3.8 for log R and plot the complete titration curve for 10 ml of 0.1 M H_3PO_4 (equals 0.3 N for $3H^+$), using 0.1 N NaOH. After plotting the final milliliters of NaOH on the abscissa for the first stage of the titration ($pK = 1.96$), begin at this point for the milliliters of NaOH for the second stage, and so on through the third curve. Join the points with an even line. In this way the curve is continuous and shows the end-point inflections for each stage of the titration. When the different pK values are sufficiently separated, the breaks in the curve are quite sharp, and at these points the buffering capacity of the solution is very poor. In the case of a polybasic acid, such as citric, where the pK values are relatively close together ($pK_1 = 3.1$, $pK_2 = 4.7$, $pK_3 = 6.4$), the second H^+ is appreciably dissociated before the dissociation of the first is completed, and likewise the second stage of titration extends into the third. Because of this overlapping, the solution is well buffered throughout the titration and the curve shows no appreciable breaks in pH. A similar curve would be obtained by titrating an equivalent mixture of three different acids having pK values of 3.1, 4.7, and 6.4, respectively. As pointed out previously, the acids of the buffer systems of the body have pK values relatively close to each other, and their titration curves overlap. This enhances the buffer efficiency in the physiologic pH range.

It should now be apparent to the student why an indicator which changes color around pH 4.5 can be used as an end-point indicator in titrating a strong acid such as HCl (essentially all of the HCl is converted to salt at this pH) but cannot be used in titrating a weak acid, such as acetic. In the first place, at pH 4.5 the acetic acid solution is strongly buffered, and the color change of the indicator is gradual (owing to slow change in pH) so that a definite end point cannot be seen. In the second place, but of more importance, at a pH of 4.5 less than half of the acetic acid has been converted to salt. In determining the normality of weak acids by titration, an indicator must be used which changes color at a pH as high as or a bit higher than that at which the acid is completely converted to salt (titration-curve ends).

The titration curves of weak acids constructed from calculated data as given above are as accurate as the application of the Henderson-Hasselbalch equation to each case. The equation does not hold well when the acids are relatively strong, such as for the first dissociation of H_3PO_4 ($pK_1 = 1.96$). The calculated values for pH close to the ends of the curves are likely to be in considerable error, whereas those for the flat portions may be very close.

When a weak base, such as ammonia, is titrated with a strong acid, such as HCl, a buffer solution is produced ($NH_4OH + NH_4Cl$), and the pH varies throughout the addition of the HCl until all the NH_4OH is converted to salt.

Zwitterions and isoelectric pH. Many substances contain both acidic and basic groups and react with both alkalies and acids to form salts. Such substances are amphoteric and are called ampholytes. Notable among these substances are the amino acids of which proteins are composed. The action of amino acids as ampholytes may be represented by that of glycine, the simplest of the amino acids, which has the following formula:

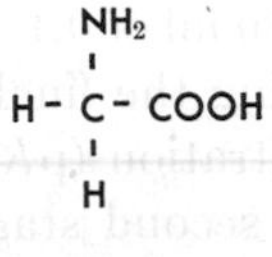

$$\begin{array}{c} NH_2 \\ | \\ H - C - COOH \\ | \\ H \end{array}$$

in which the —COOH group is the acidic group or proton donor, and the —NH_2 group is the basic group or proton acceptor. It has been found that such amino acids in the crystalline state exist as inner salts or zwitterions (hybrid ions) as the result of H^+ ions passing from the —COOH to the —NH_2 group:

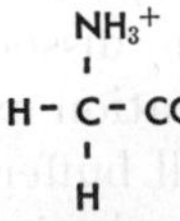

$$\begin{array}{c} NH_3{}^+ \\ | \\ H - C - COO^- \\ | \\ H \end{array}$$
Zwitterion

In acid solution the zwitterion combines with H^+ ions to form a cation:

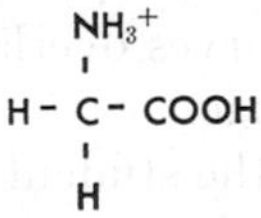

$$\begin{array}{c} NH_3{}^+ \\ | \\ H - C - COOH \\ | \\ H \end{array}$$

which dissociates H^+ ions in two stages:

$$^+H_3N - CH_2COOH \underset{}{\overset{K_1}{\rightleftarrows}} H^+ + {}^+H_3N - CH_2 - COO^- \underset{}{\overset{K_2}{\rightleftarrows}} H^+ + H_2N - CH_2 - COO^-$$
Cation   Zwitterion   Anion

The constants for these dissociations are:

$$K_1 = \frac{[\text{Zwitterion}][\text{H}^+]}{[\text{Cation}]} = 4.5 \times 10^{-3}$$

and

$$K_2 = \frac{[\text{Anion}][\text{H}^+]}{[\text{Zwitterion}]} = 1.6 \times 10^{-10}$$

It will be noted that the zwitterion is the ampholyte, since it is both a proton donor (acid) and proton acceptor (base).

When NaOH is added to the glycine cation solution, OH^- ions combine with the H^+ ions to form H_2O and shift the equilibria to the right, with the production of glycine anions $H_2N—CH_2—COO^-$. When an acid such as HCl is added to the glycine anion solution, H^+ ions cause the equilibria to shift to the left with the formation of glycine cations $^+H_3N—CH_2—COOH$. Thus, with NaOH the amino acid forms the sodium salt, and with HCl it forms the amino acid chloride.

Generally the acidic and basic strengths of the zwitterion are different, and a solution of the pure amino acid in water is not neutral.

$$
\begin{array}{l}
NH_3^+ \xrightarrow{\ acid\ } H^+ \\
\ \ |\qquad\qquad 1 \\
CH_2 \\
\ \ | \qquad\quad base \\
COO^- \xleftarrow{\quad} H^+ \\
\qquad\qquad 2
\end{array}
$$

The $—NH_3^+$ group of the zwitterion, acting as an acid, adds H^+ to the water and forms anions, $H_2N—CH_2—COO^-$, while the $—COO^-$ group, acting as a base, takes H^+ from the solution and forms cations $^+H_3N—CH_2—COOH$. If 1 exceeds 2, the solution is acid, whereas if 2 exceeds 1, the solution is alkaline. Process 1 can be repressed, according to the mass law, by adding H^+ to the solution (lowering pH), while process 2 can be repressed by adding OH^- (raising pH) to remove H^+. At some definite pH 1 equals 2, which means that the actions of the ampholyte as acid and base are equal. This is the so-called isoionic point or pH. At this pH the concentration of zwitterions is maximum, the concentrations of ampholyte anions and cations are minimum and equal, and the ampholyte shows minimum migration in an electric field. The latter is true because the net electric charge is least. While the zwitterion carries two charges, since one is positive and the other negative the net charge is zero, and the zwitterion does not move in an electric field.

In some cases ampholytes in solution with other substances combine with ions other than H^+, which influences the charges on the various components, and thus modifies ampholyte zwitterion, anion, and cation equilibria. Large and complex ampholytes, such as protein molecules in particular, tend to combine with ions other than H^+ to show this effect. However, in such cases also, there is a definite pH at which zwitterions are maximum, and the ampholyte does not migrate to either the positive or negative pole, or the ampholyte is isoelectric. This is the isoelectric pH. If the ampholyte does not combine with ions other than H^+, then the isoionic and isoelectric points are the same. For practical considerations in biochemistry the term "isoelectric" point or pH is used to include "isoionic" point or pH, and the custom will be followed in this book.

The isoelectric pH of an amino acid such as glycine can be calculated from the dissociation constants K_1 and K_2.

If K_1 is multiplied by K_2 we have:

$$K_1K_2 = \frac{[\text{Zwitterion}][\text{Anion}][H^+]^2}{[\text{Zwitterion}][\text{Cation}]}$$

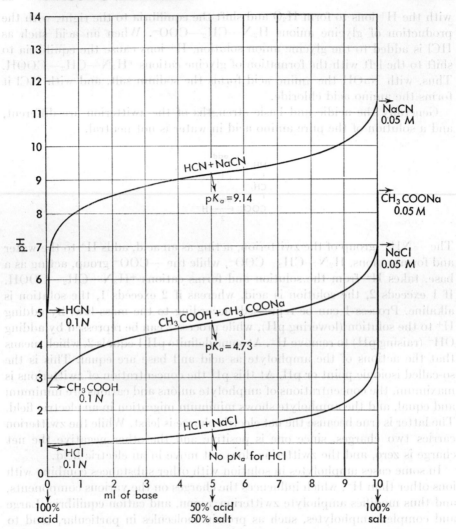

Figure 3.1. Calculated titration curves of monobasic acids. (From West, E. S.: *Textbook of Biophysical Chemistry*, 2nd ed. The Macmillan Co., New York, 1956.)

Since at the isoelectric pH [Anion] = [Cation], this equation simplifies to:

$$K_1 K_2 = [H^+]^2$$

or

$$[H^+] = \sqrt{K_1 K_2}$$

Since pH = − log [H$^+$]:

$$I \cdot pH = -\log[H^+] = -\frac{(\log K_1 + \log K_2)}{2} = \frac{-\log K_1 - \log K_2}{2}$$

Now: − log K_1 = pK_1 and − log K_2 = pK_2

then

$$I \cdot pH = \frac{pK_1 + pK_2}{2}$$

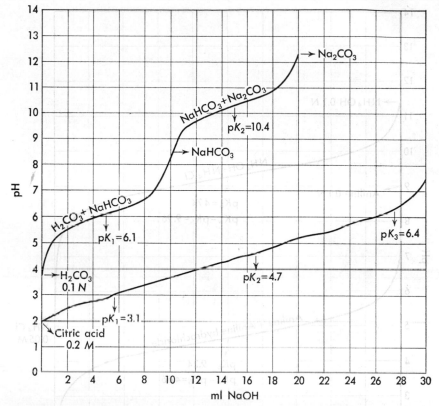

Figure 3.2. Titration curves of polybasic acids. Acids titrated with NaOH of equivalent strengths. H_2CO_3 curve calculated. Citric acid curve experimental by glass electrode. Note the flat curve of citric acid throughout the titration due to overlapping of first, second, and third stages of hydrogen ion dissociation. (From West, E. S.: *Textbook of Biophysical Chemistry*, 2nd ed. The Macmillan Co., New York, 1956.)

In the case of glycine $pK_1 = 2.35$ and $pK_2 = 9.78$; then:

$$1 \cdot pH = \frac{2.35 + 9.78}{2} = 6.06$$

The isoelectric pH of glycine is about 6.1.

From the above it can readily be seen that the more acidic the ampholyte (lower the pK values), the lower is the isoelectric pH, and the less acidic the ampholyte, the higher is the isoelectric pH.

It is important to keep in mind the fact that the ampholyte reacts as an acid at pH values above the isoelectric pH to form anions, whereas it reacts as a base below the isoelectric pH to form cations. Accordingly, an ampholyte titrates as an acid toward an alkali above the isoelectric pH, and as a base toward an acid below the isoelectric pH.

Proteins, like the amino acids of which they are composed, contain acidic and basic groups, exist in solution as zwitterions, and have isoelectric pH

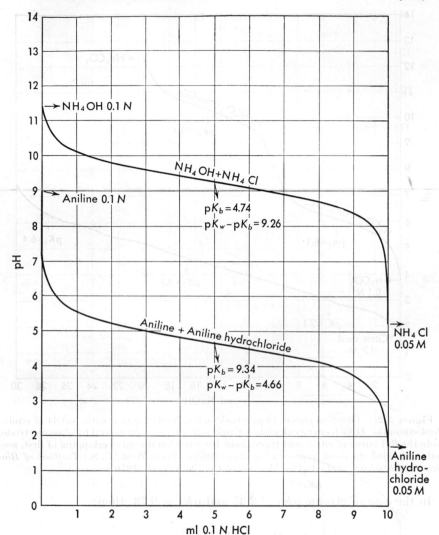

Figure 3.3. Calculated titration curves of bases. Ten milliliters of 0.1 N base titrated with 10 ml of 0.1 N HCl. (From West, E. S.: *Textbook of Biophysical Chemistry*, 2nd ed. The Macmillan Co., New York, 1956.)

values at which they are least soluble and migrate least in an electric field. Above the isoelectric pH they act as acids and form negative protein ions, whereas below the isoelectric pH they act as bases and form positive protein ions.

$$\text{protein}^+ \rightleftharpoons H^+ + {}^-\text{protein}^+ \rightleftharpoons H^+ + \text{protein}^-$$
$$\text{Cation} \qquad\qquad \text{Zwitterion} \qquad\qquad \text{Anion}$$

A number of titration curves are given in Figures 3.1–3.4, and the student is urged to study them until he understands their significance.

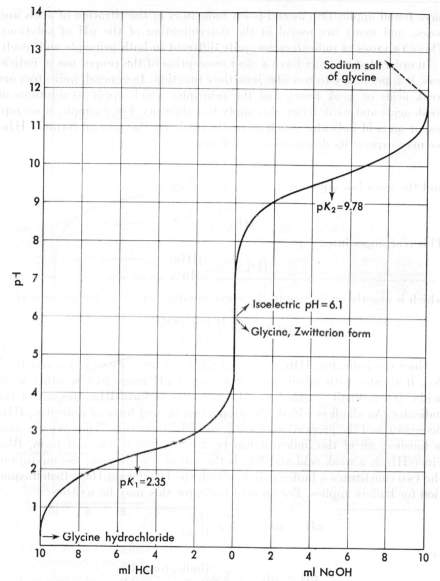

Figure 3.4.   Calculated titration curve of an amphoteric substance. Ten milliliters of 0.1 M isoelectric glycine combined with equivalent amounts of HCl and NaOH. (From West, E. S.: *Textbook of Biophysical Chemistry*, 2nd ed. The Macmillan Co., New York, 1956.)

THE DETERMINATION OF pH

COLORIMETRIC METHODS BASED UPON THE USE OF INDICATORS

There are various organic dyestuffs, of both natural and synthetic origin, that change color as the pH of their solutions is changed. Numbers of these have found application as end-point indicators in the titration of acids and bases, and many are useful in the determination of the pH of solutions. These two uses of indicators are quite different in both principle and result.

In order that we may have a clear conception of the proper use of indicators, it is necessary to consider how they function. In general, indicators are weak acids or weak bases, and the principles which apply to solutions of weak acids and weak bases also apply to indicators. For example, if we represent an acid indicator (such as methyl red) by the general formula HIn, we may express its dissociation as follows:

$$\text{HIn} \rightleftharpoons \text{H}^+ + \text{In}^-$$

and the mass law equation for the equilibrium is:

$$\frac{[\text{H}^+][\text{In}^-]}{[\text{HIn}]} = K_{\text{In}}$$

This rearranges into:

$$[\text{H}^+] = K_{\text{In}} \frac{[\text{HIn}]}{[\text{In}^-]}$$

which is exactly analogous to the corresponding equation for acetic acid:

$$[\text{H}^+] = K_a \frac{[\text{CH}_3\text{COOH}]}{[\text{CH}_3\text{COO}^-]}$$

Since the indicator, HIn, is an acid with a definite dissociation constant, K_{In}, it titrates with alkali through a certain pH range just as other weak acids. When alkali is added to HIn, it reacts to form BIn, the salt of the indicator. As alkali is added, the proportion of acid form of indicator, HIn, decreases, and the proportion of salt form, BIn, increases. When the titration is finished, all of the indicator has been converted to the salt form, BIn. Since HIn is a weak acid and BIn is the salt of a weak acid, the mixture of the two constitutes a buffer pair to which the Henderson-Hasselbalch equation for buffers applies. For an acid indicator this may be written:

$$\text{pH} = \text{p}K_{\text{In}} + \log \frac{[\text{In}^-]}{[\text{HIn}]}$$

or

$$\text{pH} = \text{p}K_{\text{In}} + \log \frac{[\text{indicator salt}]}{[\text{indicator acid}]}$$

When an indicator is half titrated, one-half of it is present as salt and one-half as acid, and the ratio of indicator salt to indicator acid is 1. The pH of the indicator solution at this point of half-neutralization is therefore equal to $\text{p}K_{\text{In}}$:

$$\text{pH} = \text{p}K_{\text{In}} + \log 1 = \text{p}K_{\text{In}} + 0 = \text{p}K_{\text{In}}$$

The value of $\text{p}K_{\text{In}}$ for indicators may be obtained by determining the pH of the indicator solution containing equal concentrations of indicator salt and indicator acid.

The indicator, methyl red, with $pK_{In} = 5.1$, begins to form salt (titrate) at a pH around 3, is half converted to salt at pH 5.1, and is practically completely in the salt form at pH 8. The form of its titration curve is similar to that for acetic and other weak acids. Now the acid form of methyl red (undissociated) has a red color, whereas the salt form (ionized) is yellow. Consequently, as one titrates methyl red with alkali, the color is first red and then passes through various shades of orange (red + yellow) and finally becomes yellow after all of the indicator has been converted to salt. It is obvious that the color of the indicator solution changes with pH according to the equation:

$$pH = pK_{In} + \log \frac{[\text{indicator salt}]}{[\text{indicator acid}]}$$

When all of the indicator is present as acid, the solution is red; when only salt is present, the solution is yellow; and at all intermediate pH values the color is composed of a mixture of red and yellow. Thus the *shade* of color of methyl red is fixed for any given pH value within its titration range, because the ratio of salt to acid form is constant for a given pH. The *intensity* of the color for a given pH and shade is determined by the *concentrations* of salt and acid forms present. In some instances, such as phenolphthalein, one form of the indicator is colorless. In such a case the color is dependent upon the concentration of the colored form present, and this is a function of the pH of the solution. The above principles apply to indicators in general.

The use of standard buffer solutions and indicators for pH determination. Suppose one were to prepare mixtures of sodium acetate and acetic acid in varying ratios so that a series of buffers would be obtained, each differing from the preceding and succeeding buffer by 0.1 pH unit. One might prepare such a series with pH values of 4.6, 4.7, 4.8, 4.9, 5.0, 5.1, 5.2, 5.3, 5.4, 5.5, etc. Now the pH of each of these buffers is given by:

$$pH = pK_a + \log \frac{[\text{CH}_3\text{COONa}]}{[\text{CH}_3\text{COOH}]}$$

Suppose one places 4 drops of 0.04 per cent methyl red in 10 ml of each of the above buffer solutions contained in test tubes of the same size and kind. The quantity of acetate buffer in each tube is so great relative to the methyl red added that no measurable change in pH occurs. In the buffer tube of pH 4.6 the ratio of methyl red salt to acid is given by:

$$4.6 = 5.1 + \log \frac{[\text{methyl red salt}]}{[\text{methyl red acid}]}$$

or $$\log \frac{[\text{methyl red salt}]}{[\text{methyl red acid}]} = 4.6 - 5.1 = -0.5$$

and $$\frac{[\text{methyl red salt}]}{[\text{methyl red acid}]} = 10^{-0.5} = 10^{-1} \times 10^{0.5} = 0.1 \times 3.16 = 0.316$$

In the acetate buffer of pH 5.1 the ratio of indicator salt to indicator acid will be 1.0, and in the buffer of pH 4.6 the ratio will be 0.316. Thus each buffer solution plus methyl red represents a definite ratio of indicator salt to indicator acid and consequently a definite shade of color.

If one now places 10 ml of a clear, colorless solution (pH 4.6 to 5.6) in a test tube like those used for the buffer solutions and adds 4 drops of 0.04 per cent methyl red, a color will be obtained which matches the color in one of the buffer tubes. The pH of the unknown solution is the same as that of the buffer tube, because the ratio of indicator salt to indicator acid is the same in both tubes. Obviously the amount of solution in the buffer tubes and unknown tubes, as well as the amount of indicator added to both, must be the same in order that the indicator concentration and the intensity of color may be the same.

Suppose one wishes to determine the pH of urine, which is colored yellow; what is the procedure? In this case the proper series of buffer standards with the proper indicator is prepared, and the urine sample is treated with the indicator as outlined above. The urine sample contains not only the color due to the indicator but also its own yellow color, while the standard buffer solutions contain only the indicator color. The problem can be solved by placing a tube containing only urine behind the buffer standard and a tube containing only water behind the tube of urine plus indicator and observing the color of light passing through the pairs of tubes. In this way the color of the urine is made constant for both the standard tubes and the unknown sample, and correct pH values may be obtained.

Obviously a given indicator can be used for pH determination only in a limited range. This range is determined by the pK_{In} of the indicator and also by the optical value of the colors of the indicator. Ordinarily the eye can observe the change in color of an indicator beginning about 1 pH unit below the pK_{In} value of the indicator and ending about 1 pH unit above pK_{In}. The useful range of most indicators for pH work is thus generally 2 pH units or less. However, there is considerable variation in the useful range of various indicators, and this must be determined by experiment. The relation of pK_{In} to the range of an indicator is easy to understand. Obviously one must choose an indicator which exists as both salt and acid in the pH range of the solutions to be tested. The standard buffer solutions for use with the indicators must also be selected on the same basis. For example, if one wishes to work in a pH range of 1.2 to 2.2, he may use an indicator such as thymol blue ($pK_{In} = 1.5$) and standard buffer solutions prepared by mixing HCl and KCl solutions of the proper concentrations. In the pH range 2.2 to 2.8 thymol blue may be used as indicator and phthalate mixtures as standard buffers. Table 3.9 lists indicators and buffer components which may be used in covering the pH range from 1.2 to 10.0. It will be seen from the table that, in general, a given indicator is satisfactory for pH determinations only through a range of 1 to 2 pH units. This represents the range in which the optical properties of the indicator are best. If one wishes to determine pH very closely, it is necessary to prepare buffered standards differing by small pH increments.

The indicators and buffers listed for pH determination in the table are

Table 3.9. Indicators and Buffer Components for pH 1.2–10

pH range	Indicator	pK_{In} of Indicator	Buffer Standards Prepared from
1.2–2.2	Thymol blue (acid)	1.5	HCl + KCl
2.2–2.8	Thymol blue (range)	1.5	Potassium acid phthalate + HCl
2.8–3.8	Brom phenol blue	3.98	Potassium acid phthalate + HCl
3.8–4.4	Brom phenol blue	3.98	Potassium acid phthalate + NaOH
4.4–5.8	Methyl red	5.1	Acetic acid + NaOH
5.8–6.8	Brom cresol purple	6.3	KH_2PO_4 + NaOH
6.8–8.0	Phenol red	7.9	KH_2PO_4 + NaOH
8.0–10.0	Thymol blue (alk. range)	8.9	H_3BO_3 + KCl + NaOH

among those in common use. Many others which are quite satisfactory have been developed. The student is referred to the books by Clark and Kolthoff and Furman, given in the references at the end of the chapter, for full discussion of both the theory and use of indicators.

Table 3.10 gives a list of frequently used indicators with their chemical and common names, pK_{In} values (if possible), acid-alkaline color changes, and their useful pH ranges. The student should study this table and become familiar with the characteristics of the indicators which he uses in the laboratory so that he may apply them to the best advantage.

Limitations in the colorimetric determination of pH. *1. Poorly buffered solutions.* Since indicators are weak acids or weak bases, their

Table 3.10. Some Commonly Used Indicators

Scientific Name	Common Name	pK_{In}	Acid and Alkali Colors and Useful pH Range
Thymolsulfonphthalein	Thymol blue	1.7	Red-Yellow (1.2–2.8)
p-Benzenesulfonic acid-azo-di-methylaniline	Methyl orange	3.5	Red-Yellow (3.1–4.4)
Tetrabromo-m-cresolsulfon-phthalein	Bromcresol green	4.7	Yellow-Blue (3.8–5.4)
Tetrabromophenolsulfon-phthalein	Bromphenol blue	4.0	Yellow-Blue (3.0–4.6)
Dimethylaminoazobenzene-o-carboxylic acid	Methyl red	5.1	Red-Yellow (4.2–6.3)
Dichlorophenolsulfonphthalein	Chlorphenol red	6.0	Yellow-Red (5.1–6.7)
Dibromo-o-cresolsulfonphthalein	Bromcresol purple	6.2	Yellow-Purple (5.4–7.0)
Dibromothymolsulfonphthalein	Bromthymol blue	7.0	Yellow-Blue (6.0–7.6)
Phenolsulfonphthalein	Phenol red	7.9	Yellow-Red (6.8–8.4)
o-Cresolsulfonphthalein	Cresol red	8.3	Yellow-Red (7.2–8.8)
Thymolsulfonphthalein	Thymol blue	8.9	Yellow-Blue (8.0–9.6)
Phenolphthalein	Phenolphthalein	9.7	Colorless-Red (8.3–10.0)
Thymolphthalein	Thymolphthalein	9.9	Yellow-Blue (9.3–10.5)
Diphenyl-disazo-bis-α-naphthylamine-4-sulfonic acid	Congo red		Blue-Violet Red (3.0–5.2)
Sodium alizarine sulfonate	Alizarine red		Yellow-Pink (3.7–4.2)
Azolitmin	Litmus		Red-Blue (5.0–8.0)
Dimethyldiamino-phenozine chloride	Neutral red	6.85	Yellow-Orange (6.8–8.0)

addition to pure water tends to change the pH of the water, and the pH observed is incorrect. The solution tested should be buffered sufficiently so that the very small amount of indicator added does not appreciably change the pH of the solution. Accordingly the pH of pure water or of solutions of salts of strong acids and alkalies (such as NaCl) is difficult to determine with accuracy. Very dilute solutions of bases and acids may suffer a change in pH upon the addition of indicator and give erroneous pH values.

2. *Other limitations.* There are many other limitations in the use of indicators for pH determination due to factors such as marked variations in temperature, the presence of proteins, organic solvents, heavy metal ions, or oxidizing and reducing agents, and high concentrations of neutral salts in the solutions to be tested. Since different indicators show different degrees of interference by different agents, it is often possible to select an indicator which can be used satisfactorily.

The use of indicators in titration. The use of indicators in quantitative neutralizations is of much importance. In this process the quantity of acid or alkali is measured without reference to the pH of the solution. The nature of the acid titrated is of first consideration in the choice of an endpoint indicator. The sharpness of the color change of the indicator and the optical properties of its color change are also important points.

1. *Titration of strong acids with alkalies.* If the student will refer to the titration curves for acids, the desirability of the following considerations in the use of indicators for titration will be apparent.

When the usual volume of a strong acid is titrated with alkali of 0.1 N concentration or more, most of the acid is converted to salt at pH values of 3 to 4. After this point is reached, the addition of a few drops of alkali solution causes a precipitate change in pH to values of 10 to 11. If a small amount of indicator, such as brom phenol blue ($pK_{In} = 3.98$), methyl red ($pK_{In} = 5.1$), brom cresol purple ($pK_{In} = 6.3$), or phenolphthalein ($pK_{In} = 9.7$), is present in such a solution, a sharp, easily observed color change occurs with the pH change. When the pH of the solution changes from pH 3 to pH 11, all the above indicators are converted into their salt forms and their colors change sharply. So little alkali is required to produce this large pH change that the various indicators give only small differences in titration values. Thus, HCl titrated with NaOH will give nearly the same titration with both methyl red and phenolphthalein. For precise work it is best to standardize the acid or alkali used with the indicator to be employed in the experimental work. Closely approximate values may be obtained by using various indicators with rather widely different pK_{In} values. If very dilute alkali is used in titrating, the pH change near the end point is obviously less abrupt because each drop of solution represents less $\overline{OH}$. As a consequence, the color change of the indicator is more gradual and the end point is not so sharp as when stronger alkali is employed.

2. *Titration of weak acids with alkalies.* In the titration of a weak acid, such as acetic, with alkali, a buffer solution is produced as soon as alkali is added, and the titration curve follows the Henderson-Hasselbalch equa-

tion. The pH range through which there is a rapid change of pH near the end point is much shorter than in case of a strong acid. Also, the weak acid is not completely converted to salt until an alkaline pH is reached (due to hydrolysis of the salt). If the concentration of sodium acetate at the end point is 0.1 M, the pH of the solution will be 9.07, whereas a salt concentration of 0.01 M gives a pH of 8.57. Obviously one must use an indicator, such as phenolphthalein ($pK_{In} = 9.7$), which changes color on the alkaline side when titrating a weak acid. If methyl red ($pK_{In} = 5.1$) were tried in titrating acetic acid, a color change would occur after very little alkali had been added and would gradually deepen until the full salt color of the indicator had been reached at a pH under 7. The pH range of useful color change for methyl red is about 4.2 to 6.3, which falls on the flat part of the buffer curve for acetic acid. Consequently, there is no sharp pH change and no sharp change in color. Under these conditions the eye cannot choose a definite end point. A more serious difficulty is that the color change of methyl red occurs at a pH below 7, while acetic acid is only completely converted to salt (purpose of the titration) at a pH of about 9. In general, when a weak acid is titrated, an indicator changing color at, or a little above, the pH of the salt formed in the titration should be used. HCN is too weak an acid ($pK_a = 9.1$) to be titrated with phenolphthalein or thymolphthalein, because these indicators change color long before the HCN is converted to its salt (pH of 0.1 M NaCN is about 11).

As pointed out above, there is no sharp color change of indicators while any appreciable amount of buffer mixture exists in the solution being titrated. The indicator color gradually changes from one shade to another, and it is difficult to titrate to a definite pH in such solutions. When such a titration is necessary, a proper buffer standard, containing the indicator used in the titration, should be prepared and the unknown titrated until its color matches that of the standard. As an illustration of such titrations we may consider the principle of Van Slyke's titration of HCO_3 in blood plasma. Plasma contains various buffer salts such as $BHCO_3$, B_2HPO_4, and B-protein, as well as the buffer acid components H_2CO_3, BH_2PO_4, and H-protein, in solution at pH 7.4. For the titration of HCO_3 one adds an excess of standard HCl, which causes the following reactions:

$$HCO_3^- + HCl \longrightarrow Cl^- + H_2CO_3 \longrightarrow CO_2 + H_2O$$
$$\downarrow \text{escapes}$$
$$HPO_4^= + HCl \longrightarrow H_2PO_4^- + Cl^-$$
$$Protein^- + HCl \longrightarrow H \cdot protein + Cl^-$$

The HCO_3^- is decomposed, and CO_2 liberated. In the next step phenol red indicator is added and the mixture titrated back to pH 7.4, thus reconstituting all of the buffer systems, except $HCO_3^- - H_2CO_3$, and neutralizing the excess HCl. From the standard acid added the equivalent of alkali required to titrate back to pH 7.4 is subtracted, and this gives the acid equivalent to the plasma HCO_3^-. The titration end point occurs when the solution is well buffered. There is no sharp color change. The end point is obtained by titrating the solution until its color matches that of a standard buffer of pH 7.4 containing the same concentration of phenol red as the sample titrated.

The titration of gastric contents and of urine is also generally more or less complicated by the presence of buffer systems at the pH of the desired end point.

3. The titration of a weak base with a strong acid. When a weak base, such as ammonia, is titrated with HCl, the base is completely converted to NH₄Cl only after an acid reaction is obtained. NH₄Cl, being the salt of a weak base and a strong acid, is hydrolyzed in solution to give an acid reaction. The pH of 0.1 M NH₄Cl is 5.1, while that of 0.01 M is 5.6. An indicator such as methyl red (pK_{In} = 5.1), which changes color in this region, must be used. Were phenolphthalein used, it would change on the alkaline side around pH 9, at which only a fraction of the ammonia is converted to NH₄Cl.

Exceedingly weak bases, such as aniline, are completely converted to their salts at such low pH values that their accurate titration is practically impossible. Normal aniline solution can be titrated with normal HCl in the presence of thymol blue (pK_{In} = 1.5) to give useful results. Excessive hydrolysis interferes when weak solutions are used.

The titration of a weak acid with a weak base is generally not very successful, because the salt formed is highly hydrolyzed. In the case of acetic acid and ammonia the titration may be carried out with considerable accuracy, because the pH of ammonium acetate is 7 and the titration curve breaks rapidly in this region. An indicator, such as neutral red, which changes color around the neutral point must be used.

A rather important and commonly used procedure consists in the titration of a strong acid in the presence of its salt with a weak base. For example, in the Kjeldahl determination of nitrogen, ammonia is distilled into an accurately measured volume of standard strong acid, such as HCl. The ammonia reacts with a definite amount of HCl to form NH₄Cl. From the quantity of HCl used up, one may calculate the ammonia and nitrogen. The problem is to titrate the excess HCl with NaOH without decomposing the NH₄Cl. If one uses an indicator like methyl red, which changes color near pH 5, all the HCl will be converted to NaCl, and the NH₄Cl will not decompose. If phenolphthalein is used as indicator, the HCl is converted to NaCl, but also, as the pH of the solution rises, the following reaction occurs:

$$NH_4Cl + NaOH \longrightarrow NaCl + NH_4OH \rightleftharpoons NH_3 + H_2O$$

and at the end-point color of phenolphthalein a large proportion of the NH₄Cl has been converted to NH₄OH. The results of such a titration are entirely worthless.

The following general rule may be stated relative to the selection of an indicator for titration. Select an indicator which changes color close to the pH of the salt solution formed in the titration. This principle is especially helpful in titrating weak acids and bases. As pointed out previously, a wide range of indicators may be used in titrating strong acids with alkalies (and vice versa) because of the rapid pH change over a wide range at the end point.

The electrometric determination of pH. The pH of solutions can generally be determined more accurately by potential measurements of certain electrodes than by the use of indicators. In fact, colorimetric methods are generally standardized against electrometric procedures. The electrical methods require relatively expensive equipment but afford rapid and accurate measurements after the apparatus is assembled. The common electrical methods for pH determination depend upon the use of the hydrogen, quinhydrone, or glass electrodes. The glass electrode method is most commonly used.

A few points relative to electrode potentials should be considered before discussing the electrometric methods of determining pH.

Solution tension and electrode potentials. When a strip of metal, such as zinc, copper, or silver, is placed in water or aqueous solution, the following reversible reaction occurs at the surface of the metal (using zinc as an example):

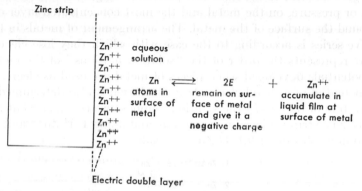

Some of the atoms of zinc in the surface of the metal strip give up two electrons and form Zn^{++} ions which pass into solution at the surface of the metal. The electrons remain on the metal and give it a negative charge. The process is reversible, and after a short time the rate at which Zn^{++} ions from the solution combine with electrons on the surface of the metal to form Zn atoms is equal to the rate at which Zn atoms lose electrons to form Zn^{++}. When the rates of both processes are equal, the reaction is at equilibrium, and the zinc strip contains a definite number of extra electrons, which give it a definite negative charge. Also, at equilibrium the concentration of Zn^{++} ions in the liquid has a fixed value. The surface of the metal remains constant for practical purposes. The tendency of the neutral Zn atoms to lose electrons and pass into solution as Zn^{++} ions is referred to as the "solution tension" of the metal. At equilibrium the "solution tension" of the Zn atoms is exactly balanced by the electrical attraction across the boundary of metal and solution. The diagram given with the above reaction shows the surface of the zinc covered with extra electrons, or negative charges, and surrounded by a layer of Zn^{++} ions in the liquid film. This combination of electron layer on the surface of the metal and ion layer in the liquid film is referred to as the "electric double layer." The magnitude of the electrical attraction across this layer determines the electrical voltage, or potential, of the metal in the solution. The potential developed depends upon the "solution tension" of the metal and also upon the concentration of metal ions in the solution. For example, in the reactions:

$$Na \rightleftharpoons 1E + Na^+$$
$$Zn \rightleftharpoons 2E + Zn^{++}$$
$$Cu \rightleftharpoons 2E + Cu^{++}$$

sodium loses electrons much more readily than does zinc, which in turn loses them more readily than does copper. The "solution tension" of sodium is greater than that of zinc, and that of zinc is greater than that of copper. Consequently, sodium will develop a greater potential in contact with an aqueous solution than will zinc, and copper will give the least potential. Sodium develops the strongest "electric double layer," while copper gives the weakest. All this simply means that of the above reactions the one for sodium goes farthest to the right and produces the greatest electron concentration, or pressure, on the metal and the most concentrated layer of metal ions around the surface of the metal. The arrangement of metals in the electromotive series is according to the ease with which they lose electrons. It therefore represents the order of the "solution tensions" of the metals and of the potentials developed when pieces of metal are used as electrodes.

The potential of a metal electrode in a solution is also determined by the concentration of its ions in the solution. Suppose we consider what happens when one zinc strip is placed in a solution containing 1 M Zn^{++} and another is placed in a solution of 0.1 M Zn^{++} (as salts):

$$\text{1. } Zn \rightleftharpoons 2E + Zn^{++}$$
$$\text{1 M}$$
$$\text{2. } Zn \rightleftharpoons 2E + Zn^{++}$$
$$\text{0.1 M}$$

According to the law of mass action, the rate at which Zn^{++} ions combine with electrons at the surface of electrode 1 is much greater than the rate of combination at electrode 2. This reduces the electron pressure of 1 as compared with that of 2, because the rate of the reaction to the right is the same in both cases. This means that electrode 2 is relatively negative in comparison to electrode 1.

Electrode potentials are also affected by changes in temperature and the nature of the solvent around the electrodes. Such changes alter the equilibrium points of the electrode reactions and consequently change the electron pressure of the electrodes.

Some implications of the above facts can be appreciated better from the diagram of Figure 3.5.

Zinc electrodes are represented as immersed in 1 M and 0.1 M solutions of Zn^{++} (as salts), respectively. These are connected by a copper wire and the solutions by a salt bridge so that a complete electric circuit is formed. This arrangement represents an electric battery, with an external circuit, through the copper wire, in which conduction is by the movement of electrons, and an internal circuit through the salt bridge, in which conduction is by the movement of ions. As pointed out above, the "electron pressure" of electrode 2 is higher than that of electrode 1. Consequently, electrons flow from 2 to 1, thereby decreasing the electron concentration upon electrode 2 and increasing it upon electrode 1. From the electrode equations it can be seen that an increase in electrons on electrode 1 will shift the reaction to the left and cause Zn^{++} ions to deposit on the electrode as Zn atoms. A decrease in electrons on electrode 2 will cause the reaction to shift to the right, and Zn atoms will pass from the surface of the electrode into solution as Zn^{++} ions. Thus Zn^{++} ions deposit from the $1\ M$ solution upon electrode 1 as atoms, and Zn atoms become Zn^{++} ions at electrode 2 and pass into the $0.1\ M$ solution. If the battery is permitted to operate, the Zn^{++} ion concentrations around electrodes 1 and 2 will eventually become equal, the electron

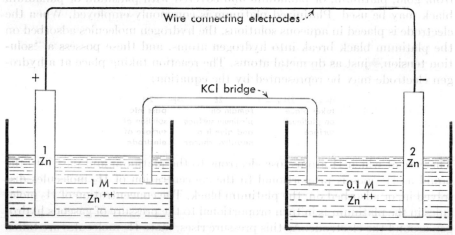

Figure 3.5. Zinc concentration cell. (From West, E. S.: *Textbook of Biophysical Chemistry*, 2nd ed. The Macmillan Co., New York, 1956.)

pressures of the two electrodes will become the same, and a state of equilibrium will be reached in which no current passes between the electrodes. Now suppose the electrodes are arranged as shown in the diagram with the exception that a voltage-measuring instrument (potentiometer) is connected between the electrodes. In this way no appreciable current flows between the electrodes, but the "electron pressure" difference, or voltage, between the electrodes is measured. If the Zn^{++} ion concentration around electrode 1 were maintained constant at $1\ M$ and that around electrode 2 varied and successively made $0.5\ M$, $0.2\ M$, $0.1\ M$, $0.01\ M$, $0.001\ M$, etc., a different voltage would be obtained in each case. The electron pressure of electrode 1 remains constant because $[Zn^{++}]$ around it remains constant, but the electron pressure of 2 changes by a definite amount with each change in the Zn^{++} ion concentration. Consequently, a definite voltage, or potential difference, is registered for each concentration of Zn^{++} ions around electrode 2. It is obvious that such an electrode arrangement could be used for the quantitative determination of Zn^{++} ions.

From the above discussion it should be apparent to the student that the absolute potential, or electron pressure, of a single electrode cannot be measured. Only potential differences between two electrodes can be obtained. One electrode must be used as a standard against which others are compared. As will be explained later, the so-called normal hydrogen electrode is the standard for comparison.

The hydrogen electrode. The principle of the operation of hydrogen electrodes is quite similar to that of the zinc electrodes discussed above. Of course, since hydrogen is a gas, it cannot be used directly as an electrode. However, if a piece of platinum, which itself is inert as an electrode, is covered with finely divided platinum (platinum black), it will take up hydrogen gas and then function as a hydrogen electrode. Inert electrodes prepared from gold, platinum, or palladium and covered with platinum or palladium black may be used. Platinized platinum is commonly employed. When the electrode is placed in aqueous solutions, the hydrogen molecules adsorbed on the platinum black break into hydrogen atoms, and these possess a "solution tension," just as do metal atoms. The reaction taking place at a hydrogen electrode may be represented by the equation:

$$H_2 \rightleftharpoons 2H \rightleftharpoons \quad 2E \quad + \quad 2H^+$$

| takes place on platinum surface | remain on platinum surface and give it a negative charge | pass into solution at surface of electrode |

The rate at which H atoms lose electrons to the platinum and pass into the liquid as H^+ ions is proportional to the concentration of H_2 molecules dissolved in, or adsorbed on, the platinum black. The concentration of H_2 molecules in the platinum is in turn proportional to the pressure of gaseous hydrogen around the electrode. As this pressure rises, more H_2 molecules are taken up by the platinum, and more H^+ ions pass into the solution. It is customary to bubble pure hydrogen gas around the platinum electrode at a pressure of one atmosphere, thereby fixing the "solution tension" of the H atoms at a constant value. In this way the reaction to the right:

$$H_2 \rightleftharpoons 2H \rightleftharpoons 2E + 2H^+$$

is fixed at a constant rate. In order to understand how the hydrogen electrode may be used for the determination of pH, consider the diagram of Figure 3.6. Electrode 1 is placed in a solution containing $1\ N\ H^+$ ions (1 g equivalent of "active" H^+ per liter), and electrode 2 in a solution with 0.1 $N\ H^+$ ions. The concentration of electrons on electrode 2 is greater than that on electrode 1, because the higher concentration of H^+ around 1 (1 N) drives the reaction farther to the left than does the lower H^+ concentration (0.1 N) around electrode 2. Electrode 2 is consequently negative to electrode 1, and the potential difference between the electrodes may be read with the potentiometer in the circuit. If electrode 1 is maintained constant by immersion in $1\ N\ H^+$ ions and the H^+ concentration of the solution around electrode 2 is varied, a different potential will be obtained for each H^+ concentration. Consequently, such an arrangement can be used for the determination of

hydrogen ion concentration and pH. The hydrogen electrode with H_2 gas at
one atmosphere pressure and immersed in a 1 N H^+ ion solution (1 g equivalent of "active" H^+ per liter) is called the normal hydrogen electrode. It is
arbitrarily assigned a potential, E_{h0}, of zero under all conditions and is used
as the standard of reference for other electrodes.

In order that the potentials developed between the normal hydrogen electrode and a hydrogen electrode immersed in an unknown solution may be
used for determining pH, the relation between these potentials and pH must
be known.

As stated above, the potential of the normal hydrogen electrode, E_{h0}, is
taken as zero. The potential of the hydrogen electrode in the unknown solution is designated as E_h. Now when these electrodes are connected in a circuit

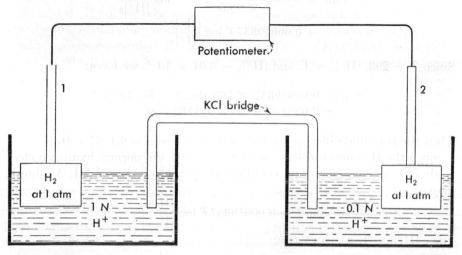

Figure 3.6.   Hydrogen concentration cell. (From West, E. S.: *Textbook of Biophysical
Chemistry*, 2nd ed. The Macmillan Co., New York, 1956.)

and the voltage read, the difference in potential, or electromotive force (emf),
is obtained. In this case we can therefore write:

$$\mathop{emf}_{volts} = E_h - E_{h0}$$

It can be shown that the potential difference, or emf, between two hydrogen electrodes placed in solutions of H^+ ion concentrations $[H^+]_1$ and $[H^+]_2$
is given by the expression:

$$emf = \frac{RT}{nF} \log_e \frac{[H^+]_1}{[H^+]_2}$$

where R = the gas constant (8.315 joules per degree), T = the absolute
temperature, n = the valence change, and F = faraday, representing the
quantity of electricity per gram-ion equivalent (96,500 coulombs). Log_e =
the natural logarithm. If we wish to calculate the emf which would be ob-

tained by connecting a normal hydrogen electrode with a hydrogen electrode placed in 0.01 N H^+ at 25° C (298° A), we proceed as follows:

According to the above equations the voltage, or potential difference, between the electrodes would be:

$$emf = E_h - E_{h0} = \frac{RT}{nF} \log_e \frac{[H^+]_1}{[H^+]_2}$$

In this case $R = 8.315$, $T = 298$, $n = 1$, $F = 96,500$, $[H^+]_1$ of normal hydrogen electrode $= 1$, $[H^+]_2$ of other electrode $= 0.01$, $\log_e = \log_{10} \times 2.30258$.

Upon partial substitution in the above equation, we have:

$$emf = \frac{8.315 \times T \times 2.30258}{1 \times 96,500} \log \frac{[H^+]_1}{[H^+]_2}$$

$$= 0.00019837 T \log \frac{[H^+]_1}{[H^+]_2}$$

Since $T = 298$, $[H^+]_1 = 1$, and $[H^+]_2 = 0.01 = 10^{-2}$, we have:

$$emf = 0.00019837 \times 298 \,(\log 1 - \log 10^{-2})$$
$$= 0.0591 \,(0 + 2) = 0.1182 \text{ volt}$$

Thus the potential difference between the electrodes is 0.1182 volt.

Since the H^+ concentration (activity) around the normal hydrogen electrode is 1, we may derive an equation for the calculation of pH. As shown above:

$$emf = 0.00019837 T \log \frac{[H^+]_1}{[H^+]_2}$$

Since $[H^+]_1 = 1$, we can write:

$$emf = 0.00019837 T \log \frac{1}{[H^+]_2}$$

but

$$\log \frac{1}{[H^+]_2} = \log 1 - \log [H^+]_2 = - \log [H^+]_2 = pH$$

and we have:

$$emf = 0.00019837 T \times pH$$

or

$$pH = \frac{emf}{0.00019837 T}$$

Thus, if the potential difference (emf) between the normal hydrogen electrode and the electrode in the unknown solution is known for a given temperature, the pH of the solution may be readily calculated.

As a matter of practice, a normal hydrogen electrode is very difficult to prepare and maintain, and a calomel electrode is substituted for it in making the voltage measurements. The calomel electrode consists of metallic mercury in contact with Hg_2Cl_2 in KCl solution (0.1 M, 1.0 M, or saturated KCl). The potential of the calomel electrode varies with the concentration of the KCl solution used in preparing it; but for a given temperature and concentration of KCl the potential of a calomel electrode against the normal hydrogen electrode is constant. For example, at 25° C the potential of the 0.1 M KCl calomel electrode against the normal hydrogen electrode is +0.3376 volt, for the 1.0 M KCl calomel electrode the potential is +0.2848 volt, and for the saturated calomel electrode the potential is +0.2458 volt. Now if a hydrogen electrode is placed in a solution of unknown pH at 25° C and connected in the appropriate circuit with a saturated KCl calomel electrode, a potential difference will be obtained. This potential will be larger than the potential obtained against the normal hydrogen electrode by 0.2458 volt. Consequently, we can calculate the voltage against the normal hydrogen electrode by subtracting 0.2458 volt from the potential obtained against the calomel electrode. The pH of the solution may accordingly be readily calculated.

The glass electrode. The glass-electrode method of determining pH is rapidly replacing other procedures. The principle according to which the glass electrode functions is relatively simple. The practical measurement of the potentials was a matter of considerable difficulty until radio amplifying tubes were used in the circuit. At present a number of compact, easily operated instruments are available with which pH may be measured quickly and accurately.

It has been found that thin membranes of the proper glass are selectively permeable to H+ ions, and if a cell is set up as follows:

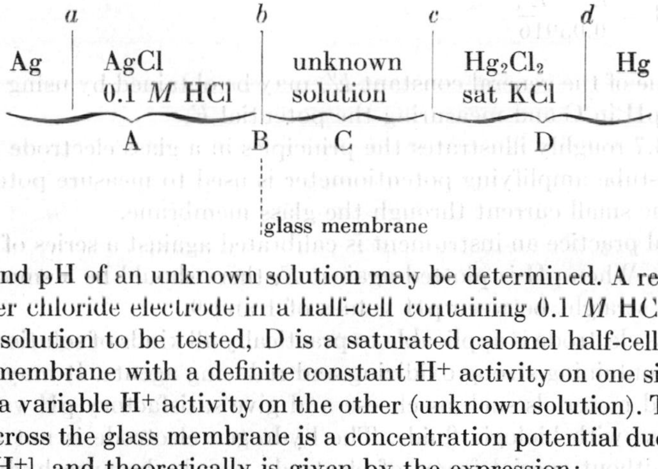

$$
\begin{array}{c|c|c|c|c}
a & b & c & d \\
\text{Ag} & \begin{array}{c}\text{AgCl}\\\text{0.1 }M\text{ HCl}\end{array} & \begin{array}{c}\text{unknown}\\\text{solution}\end{array} & \begin{array}{c}\text{Hg}_2\text{Cl}_2\\\text{sat KCl}\end{array} & \text{Hg} \\
\end{array}
$$

$$\underbrace{\qquad}_{A}\quad\underbrace{\qquad}_{B}\quad\underbrace{\qquad}_{C}\quad\underbrace{\qquad\qquad}_{D}$$

glass membrane

the [H+] and pH of an unknown solution may be determined. A represents a silver-silver chloride electrode in a half-cell containing 0.1 M HCl, C is the unknown solution to be tested, D is a saturated calomel half-cell, and B is the glass membrane with a definite constant H+ activity on one side (0.1 M HCl) and a variable H+ activity on the other (unknown solution). The potential at b across the glass membrane is a concentration potential due to differences in [H+], and theoretically is given by the expression:

$$E = \frac{RT}{F} \log_e \frac{[\text{H}^+]_1}{[\text{H}^+]_2}$$

There are potentials at the boundaries a, c, and d, but these are constant. Also, different glass membranes may give somewhat different potentials than expressed by the ideal equation above. However, for a given membrane the variation from the equation can be corrected by inserting a constant. For a given glass membrane, then, all these constants may be collected into a general constant E'_c, and the equation becomes:

$$E = E'_c + \frac{RT}{F} \log_e \frac{[H^+]_1}{[H^+]_2}$$

If $[H^+]_1$ is $1.0 = 10^0$, this expression becomes:

$$E = E'_c + \frac{RT}{F} \log_e 1 - \frac{RT}{F} \log_e [H^+]_2$$

$$E = E'_c + 0 - \frac{RT}{F} \log_e [H^+]_2$$

$$E = E'_c - \frac{RT}{F} \log_e [H^+]_2$$

Since $\log_e = 2.30258 \times \log_{10}$, this becomes:

$$E = E'_c - \frac{RT}{F} 2.30258 \log [H^+]_2$$

Substituting the values of R, 8.315 joules, and F, 96,500 coulombs, we have:

$$E = E'_c - 0.00019837T \log [H^+]_2, \text{ since } - \log [H^+] = pH$$
$$E = E'_c + 0.00019837T \text{ pH}$$
$$pH = \frac{E - E'_c}{0.00019837T}$$

At 25° C:

$$pH = \frac{E - E'_c}{0.05916}$$

The value of the general constant E'_c may be obtained by using a solution of known pH in C and measuring the potential E.

Figure 3.7 roughly illustrates the principles in a glass electrode assembly. A vacuum-tube amplifying potentiometer is used to measure potentials because of the small current through the glass membrane.

In actual practice an instrument is calibrated against a series of buffers of known pH. When pH is plotted against E, there should be a smooth curve, practically straight between pH values of 1 and 9.

The glass electrode is applicable to practically all kinds of solutions, including those containing strong oxidizing and reducing agents. It may be placed in semisolid materials such as cheese and give satisfactory pH values. It is ideal for use with biologic fluids. The hydrogen electrode is not applicable in blood without special forms of electrode vessels, because hydrogen gas, bubbling through the solution, sweeps out carbon dioxide and changes the pH. This objection does not apply to the glass electrode. Solutions tested by the glass electrode are not contaminated in the process and may be used for other determinations. Commercial glass-electrode equipment is calibrated to read directly in pH without requiring any calculations. The accuracy of the glass electrode is ordinarily within a few hundredths of a pH unit. The glass electrode, however, does not function so well in solutions of very high pH when appreciable quantities of certain metal ions are present. Under these conditions it begins to act as a Na^+ ion electrode because of the solubility of the sodium salts of the glass at high pH. Accordingly, the presence of Na^+ ions in solutions of high pH causes incorrect values. If one knows the Na^+ ion concentration of the solution to be tested, a correction may be applied and correct pH values obtained. For example, if the glass electrode gives a pH reading of 10.67 in a solution containing 1 M Na^+ ions, the value is too low. If one consults tables prepared for the purpose, he finds that 0.65 pH should be added as a correction. The pH of the solution is thus found to be 11.32.

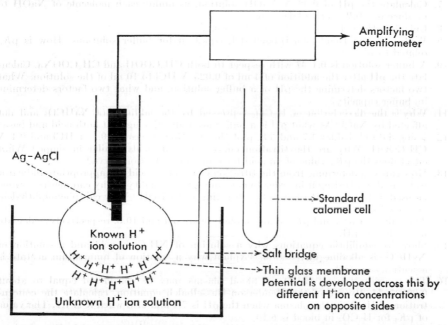

Figure 3.7. Diagram of glass electrode assembly. (From West, E. S.: *Textbook of Biophysical Chemistry*, 2nd ed. The Macmillan Co., New York, 1956.)

The presence of Li^+, K^+, NH_4^+, Ca^{++}, and Ba^{++} ions in the solution to be tested also interferes at high pH, but not so much as do Na^+ ions. The order of decreasing interference is: Na^+—Li^+—K^+—NH_4^+—Ca^{++}—Ba^{++}. Correction for various concentrations of these ions at different pH levels may be found in tables or charts.

The glass electrode also does not function well below pH 1.

With new glasses it is possible to obtain membranes which give good results up to pH 11 or 12; and, by making small corrections for Na^+ ions, these may be extended to pH 13 or 14.

EXERCISES

1. State Brönsted's definition of acids and bases. Show how a neutral molecule, a negative ion, and a positive ion may each act as an acid according to this definition. Indicate in each case the conjugate acid and base.

2. When is a substance amphoteric? Show how both H_2O and NH_3 act as amphoteric substances.

3. Bjerrum speaks of "lyonium" ions; to what does he refer? Write the formulas of the oxonium or hydronium ion and of the alcoholonium and acetonium ions. Show how H^+ coordinates with diethyl ether. Show how an acid, HA, reacts with H_2O and with NH_3.

4. State three factors which determine the strength of an acid according to Brönsted's theory. Upon what does the strength of a base depend?

5. Write out the mass law expression for the dissociation of water. How does the value of K_w vary with temperature? State one reason why superheated steam is much more effective in promoting hydrolytic reactions than is cold water.

6. What is the mathematical relation of $[H^+]$ and $[OH^-]$ in all aqueous solutions? Give the mathematical relation between $[H^+]$ and pH.

7. Calculate the pH of 0.02 N NaOH solution, assuming each molecule of NaOH to produce one fully active OH^- ion.

8. Calculate the $[OH^-]$ of a solution of pH 6.2.

9. Write out the Henderson-Hasselbalch equation for buffer solutions. How is pK_a related to K_a?

10. A buffer solution is 0.1 M with respect to both CH_3COOH and CH_3COONa. Calculate the pH after the addition of 4 ml of 0.025 N HCl to 10 ml of the solution. What two factors determine the pH of a buffer solution, and what two factors determine its buffer capacity?

11. Why is the dissociation of H_2CO_3 repressed by the addition of $NaHCO_3$ and not affected by NaCl? At what pH is a buffer most effective against both acid and base?

12. Using data of Tables 3.7 and 3.8, plot the titration curves for 0.1 N HCl and 0.1 N CH_3COOH. Why are the titration curves of weak acids similar in shape? What effect does the pK_a value of an acid have upon its titration curve?

13. How can you determine from the titration curve of an acid the appropriate indicator to be used in titrating it in order to determine its normality? Why can methyl orange be used in titrating HCl but not in titrating CH_3COOH? Why can phenolphthalein be used for either?

14. The values of pK_1 and pK_2 of an ampholyte are 3.4 and 10.8, respectively; calculate its isoelectric pH.

15. Show by equilibria equations why a solution of NH_4Cl is acid and a solution of $NaHCO_3$ is alkaline in reaction. Explain why a solution of ammonium acetate is essentially neutral.

16. The concentration of H_2CO_3 in blood plasma may be considered equal to about 0.00125 M. By use of the Henderson-Hasselbalch equation, calculate the concentration of HCO_3 in the plasma when the pH is 7.4 and also when it is 7.1. The value of pK_1 for H_2CO_3 in blood is 6.10

17. What principle is utilized in determining pH by means of standard buffer solutions and indicators? How is the proportion of indicator present as indicator salt related to the pH of the solution? What determines the color of a two-color indicator within its titration-curve range? What is the significance of the pK value of an indicator relative to the titration curve of the indicator? Can an indicator be used for pH determination throughout the entire pH range of its titration curve? Why?

18. What procedure is employed in the colorimetric determination of the pH of urine and other colored solutions?

19. Give the principle and some important advantages of the glass electrode as used for the estimation of pH.

20. In a determination of the pH of urine by the hydrogen electrode, potentials were read against a saturated calomel electrode at 25° C. A pH value of 5.5 was obtained. Calculate the potential in volts which correspond to this pH.

21. The hydrogen ion concentration $[H^+]_1$ on the inside of a glass electrode is 0.001. Calculate the pH on the outside of the electrode when the potential across the glass membrane is 0.1182 volt at 25° C $(E'_c = 0.05)$.

GENERAL REFERENCES

Bates, R. G.: *Electrometric pH Determinations*. John Wiley & Sons, New York, 1954.

Bell, R. P.: *Acids and Bases*. Methuen & Co., London; John Wiley & Sons, New York, 1952.

Clark, W. M.: *The Determination of Hydrogen Ion Concentration*, 3rd ed. Williams & Wilkins Co., Baltimore, 1928.

Clark, W. M.: *Topics in Physical Chemistry*, 2nd ed. Williams & Wilkins Co., Baltimore, 1952.

Dole, M.: *The Glass Electrode*. John Wiley & Sons, New York, 1941.

Edsall, J. T., and Wyman, J.: *Biophysical Chemistry*, Vol. I. Academic Press, New York, 1958.

Kolthoff, I. M., and Furman, N. H.: *Indicators*. John Wiley & Sons, New York, 1926.

Kolthoff, I. M., and Laitinen, H. A.: *pH and Electrotitrations*, 2nd ed. John Wiley & Sons, New York, 1941.

Kolthoff, I. M., and Rosenblum, C.: *Acid-Base Indicators*. The Macmillan Co., New York, 1937.

Michaelis, L.: *Hydrogen Ion Concentration*. Williams & Wilkins Co., Baltimore, 1926.

Tomicek, O.: *Indicators*. Academic Press, New York, 1951.

4

Osmotic pressure

Abbé Nollet in 1748 placed pure water and solutions of alcohol in water on opposite sides of animal membranes which were more permeable to the solvent than to the solute molecules and observed that the solvent (water) passed through the membrane from the water to the alcohol solution. This process is spoken of as "osmosis" (from the Greek word meaning push). Vierordt and Dutrochet placed an animal membrane (such as bladder) over the end of a glass tube and then put salt solution in the tube. When the membrane-covered end of this tube was placed in water, the level of the salt solution in the tube rose above that of the surrounding water until the hydrostatic pressure caused water to pass as rapidly from the salt solution into the water as the reverse. Since this hydrostatic pressure was caused by the process of osmosis (diffusion of water through the membrane), it was called "osmotic pressure." Osmotic pressure is the pressure which must be put upon a solution to keep it in equilibrium with the pure solvent when the two are separated by a semipermeable membrane. The apparatus used in these experiments was crude and unsuited to accurate osmotic pressure measurements. The membranes permitted both solute and water molecules to pass through, though the latter diffused much more rapidly. Also, the solution became diluted by the diffusing water, and the osmotic pressure observed was too low. Traube in 1867 found that the gelatinous precipitate of copper ferrocyanide is very effective as a semipermeable membrane, permitting the free passage of water but preventing the passage of dissolved material. Pfeffer, a botanist, conceived the idea of making the ferrocyanide membranes strong and capable of withstanding pressure by depositing them in the pores of clay cups. The American chemist Morse improved the construction of these membranes by placing potassium ferrocyanide solution inside the clay cup and a solution of copper sulfate outside the cup. A current of electricity was then passed through the solutions so that Cu^{++} ions and $Fe(CN)_6{}^{4-}$ ions migrated toward each other in the walls of the cup and upon contact precipitated the membrane of copper ferrocyanide. A diagram of the apparatus used by Pfeffer is shown in Figure 4.1. A is a porous cup with the ferrocyanide membrane deposited in its walls. B is a mercury manometer to measure the pressure. When used, the entire apparatus is filled through tube D with the solution to be tested so that the solution is in contact with mercury in tube C.

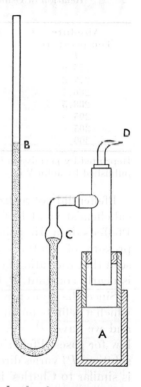

Figure 4.1. Pfeffer's osmotic pressure apparatus. (Reproduced by permission from *Second Year College Chemistry*, 5th ed., by W. H. Chapin and L. E. Steiner, published by John Wiley & Sons, New York, 1943.)

Tube D is sealed off. The cup is then surrounded by a bath of water at constant temperature. Water passes through the membrane, increasing the pressure in the cup, and the mercury in the manometer rises. When no further change takes place (equilibrium is reached), the pressure is read on the manometer and taken as the osmotic pressure of the solution. In the Pfeffer and Morse apparatus the solution is diluted by an amount equal to the volume of mercury displaced in the manometer tube. If this tube is small relative to the volume of the cup, the dilution causes little error. Apparatus in which the volume of solution is kept constant has been developed by the Earl of Berkley and Hartley.

Pfeffer in 1877, using the apparatus of Figure 4.1, made the first direct measurements of osmotic pressure. He observed the osmotic pressures of cane sugar solutions of different concentrations and also studied the effect of temperature upon these pressures. Some of his results are shown in Table 4.1.

Table 4.1.   Relation of Osmotic Pressure to the Concentration of Cane Sugar Solutions
Temperature 286.5° to 287.7° A

Per Cent Sugar C	Osmotic Pressure in Atmospheres P	Ratio of Osmotic Pressure to Sugar Concentrations P/C
1	0.70	0.70
2	1.34	0.67
4	2.74	0.68
6	4.10	0.68

Relation of Osmotic Pressure of a 1 Per Cent Cane Sugar Solution to
Absolute Temperature

Absolute Temperature T	Osmotic Pressure in Atmospheres P	Ratio of Pressure to Temperature $P/T \times 10^2$
273.0	0.649	0.238
279.8	0.664	0.237
286.7	0.691	0.241
288.5	0.684	0.237
295	0.721	0.244
305	0.716	0.235
309	0.746	0.241

Reprinted by permission from *Outlines of Theoretical Chemistry*, by Getman and Daniels, published by John Wiley & Sons.

Pfeffer did not realize the full significance of his findings. The Dutch physical chemist van't Hoff, however, deduced the laws of osmotic pressure from Pfeffer's data. He pointed out the striking resemblance between the osmotic pressure of solutions and the properties of gases. From Pfeffer's data it is seen that the ratio of osmotic pressure (P) to the concentration of solute (C) is nearly constant. $P/C = K$ and $P = KC$.

Since the concentration of a solution varies inversely as the volume in which a definite amount of solute is dissolved, $1/V$ may be substituted for C, and we have: $P = K/V$ or $PV = K$, which has the same form as Boyle's law for gases. Pfeffer's data also show that the osmotic pressure of a given solution (P) varies directly as the absolute temperature T, or $P/T = K$. This is similar to Charles' law for gas pressure.

Van't Hoff's laws of osmotic pressure. Van't Hoff's laws of osmotic pressure may be simply stated:

1. The osmotic pressure of a solution varies directly as the concentration of the solute in the solution and is equal to the pressure the solute would exert if it were a gas in the volume occupied by the solution, if the volume of solute molecules relative to volume of solvent be negligible.

2. The osmotic pressure of a solution varies directly as the absolute temperature in just the same way as the pressure of a gas varies when its volume is kept constant.

These laws of osmotic pressure, which were deduced from Pfeffer's data by van't Hoff, have been thoroughly verified by the more accurate observations of Morse and of Berkley and Hartley. As is the case with gases, the laws of osmotic pressure hold closely only for dilute solutions. Appropriate corrections must be made for concentrated solutions.

The following problem illustrates the simple application of the above laws to the calculation of osmotic pressure. Suppose 18 g of glucose (mol. wt. 180) to be contained in a liter of water solution. Calculate the osmotic pressure at 0° C and also at 20° C. One gram mol of a gas (6.02×10^{23} molecules) in a volume of 1 liter (1 molar concentration) at 0° C exerts a pressure of 22.4 atm. According to the laws of osmotic pressure, 1 M glucose solution (1 gram mol per liter) exerts an osmotic pressure of 22.4 atm. Eighteen grams of glucose in a liter of solution $= 18/180 = 0.1$ M. Consequently, the osmotic pressure of the glucose solution would be $0.1 \times 22.4 = 2.24$ atm at 0° C (273° A). The pressure at 20° C (293° A) is increased just as gas pressure is increased and so would be calculated: $P = 2.24 \times 293/273 = 2.4$ atm. Osmotic pressure is dependent only on the number of dissolved molecules (molecular concentration) and not upon the kind of molecules. Obviously, the osmotic pressure of a solution of a substance can be used to calculate the molecular weight of the substance. If 18 g of sugar in a liter of solution produce an osmotic pressure of 2.24 atm at 0° C, the molecular weight of the sugar is calculated as follows: If the osmotic pressure of the solution were 22.4 atm, the sugar solution would be 1 M. Since it is 2.24 atm, the concentration of the sugar solution is $2.24/22.4 = 0.1$ M. Therefore, 18 g of the sugar represents 0.1 g mol, and the molecular weight of the sugar $= 18 \times 10 = 180$.

When the statement is made that a molar solution (of a nonelectrolyte) has an osmotic pressure of 22.4 atm, reference is made to the theoretical osmotic pressure (calculated from observations upon dilute solutions). In other words, if the osmotic pressure of a 0.1 M solution at 0° C is observed, it is found to be about 2.24 atm, and theoretically a 1 M solution would have an osmotic pressure of 22.4 atm. Actually the osmotic pressure of a 1 M solution is a bit more than 22.4 atm, because the laws do not hold closely for the more concentrated solution. Obviously, the theoretical value of 22.4 atm for a 1 M solution may be used in calculating the osmotic pressure of dilute solutions where the laws do apply. The deviation of the osmotic pressure of strong solutions from the theoretical value is due to the fact that the volume occupied by the solute molecules is considerable in relation to the total volume of solution. In the case of dilute solutions, where the osmotic pressure laws apply, the volume occupied by the solute molecules relative to the total volume is negligible.

The mechanism of osmotic pressure. The mechanism of osmotic pressure may be illustrated by consideration of Figure 4.2. Suppose vessel A, with a semipermeable membrane over its lower end and containing a solution of sugar in water, is placed in the vessel of water, B. Water molecules can pass through the membrane in both directions, but sugar molecules cannot pass through. The rate at which water molecules pass through the membrane is determined by the concentration, or activity, of the water molecules in contact with the membrane.

There are more water molecules per unit volume in pure water than in the sugar solution, and consequently the diffusion pressure of water molecules from the pure water through the membrane is greater than the diffusion pressure of water molecules from the sugar solution through the membrane. The net result is that water passes from vessel *B* into vessel *A* and dilutes the solution, and the level of the sugar solution, *C*, rises above the level of the pure water, *D*. The level, *C*, continues to rise until the hydrostatic pressure, *CD*, equalizes the diffusion pressure of the water molecules in the sugar solution and in the pure water, at which point water passes through the membrane in opposite directions at the same rate and the system is in equilibrium. From a viewpoint such as this, solute molecules decrease the diffusion pressure of the solvent in direct proportion to their concentration, or number, and independently of the kind of molecules. The higher the osmotic pressure exhibited by a solution, the lower is the diffusion pressure of its

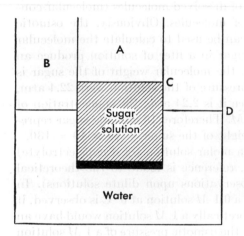

Figure 4.2. Mechanism of osmotic pressure. (From West, E. S.: *Textbook of Biophysical Chemistry*, 2nd ed. The Macmillan Co., New York, 1956.)

solvent molecules. The osmotic pressure thus represents the difference between the diffusion pressure of pure solvent molecules and the diffusion pressure of solvent molecules mixed with solute molecules. The more concentrated the solution, the greater is the difference in diffusion pressures and the greater is the osmotic pressure. The difference in diffusion pressures of solutions of different concentrations can be shown in various ways. If a 0.1 *M* solution is placed in one limb of a closed bent tube and a 1 *M* solution in the other limb so the surfaces of the two solutions are separated by a gas space, upon long standing the concentrations of the solutions will become the same. The vapor pressure (or diffusion pressure) of the solvent molecules in the more dilute solution is higher than that of the solvent molecules in the more concentrated solution, so the net result is that solvent molecules distill from the more dilute into the more concentrated solution until the concentrations and vapor pressures of the two solutions are equal. The use of a semipermeable membrane in determining osmotic pressure is only one way of estimating the diffusion or vapor pressure of solvent molecules. A viewpoint that the student should acquire is that in the case of gases and solutions or wherever there are mobile particles, diffusion takes place from the more concentrated solution to the less concentrated solution if this is physically possible. Suppose 1 *M* sugar solution to be carefully pipetted under a 0.1 *M* sugar solution so the more dilute solution overlays the more concentrated and there is a rather sharp interface between them. Since water molecules are more concentrated in the dilute solution, they will diffuse from the 0.1 M solution down into the 1 M solution. However, sugar molecules are more concentrated in the 1 M solution and will diffuse up into the 0.1 M solution. Both of these processes will go on until the solutions are of the same concentration and the liquid as a whole is homogeneous. If, however, a semipermeable membrane is placed between the solutions, only water molecules can pass, and we observe the phenomenon of osmotic pressure. If a membrane permeable to sugar molecules and not to water molecules could be used, we would have an osmotic pressure due to diffusion of sugar molecules and in a direction opposite to the osmotic pressure of water molecules. There are membranes of varying permeabilities for solutes. Different animal and vegetable membranes may be impermeable, slowly permeable, or rapidly permeable to a given solute. This is true of different kinds of parchment paper and cellophane. If a solution is separated from the solvent by a membrane readily permeable to the solvent and slowly permeable to the solute, a transitory rise of osmotic pressure, followed by a fall, is observed. If the membrane is equally readily permeable to both solute and solvent, no osmotic effect is observed, though it is present. For accurate osmotic pressure measurement a good semipermeable membrane must be used.

The importance of osmotic pressure, or diffusion pressure, in living organisms is hard to overemphasize. It is of primary importance in the distribution of water and permeable solutes throughout both plants and animals. Plant and animal tissues are composed of cells containing very complex solutions, and these cells are generally surrounded by, or suspended in, solutions. Cell membranes are generally permeable to water and some of the solutes but more or less impermeable to others and thereby maintain different concentrations of certain dissolved substances within and without the cell, even though the total molecular concentrations (and osmotic pressures) of the external and internal solutions may be the same. In general, water diffuses from the more dilute solution to the more concentrated solution in protoplasm because the membranes of the cells are permeable to it. Also, salts and other solutes diffuse from the more concentrated to the more dilute solutions in protoplasm if they can pass through the membranes. When the blood is diluted by drinking water, the diffusion pressure of water in the blood is increased (osmotic pressure is lowered), and more water passes from the blood to the tissues. In such a case the diffusion pressure of the water in the blood passing through the kidneys is also increased, and these organs put out a more dilute urine until the concentration of water in blood and tissues is returned to normal limits. At times a patient may lose much water from his tissues and blood as a result of fever or other cause, and his blood and tissue fluids become much more concentrated than normal. In such a case the diffusion pressure of water from the blood may be so low (blood osmotic pressure is high) that the kidneys are entirely unable to excrete water (and dissolved permeable solutes), and the patient suffers from anuria. The hydrostatic pressure of blood in the kidneys (depending upon the blood pressure) operates with the water diffusion pressure to cause filtration through the kidney glomerular membranes. For filtration the blood pressure must exceed the opposing osmotic pressure of the blood. Anuria may be caused by a low blood pressure as well as by an unusually high blood osmotic pressure (low water diffusion pressure).

The osmotic pressures of blood plasma, gastric juice, pancreatic juice, intestinal juice, liver bile, and cerebrospinal fluid are approximately equal. These fluids are roughly 0.3 M in total concentration of dissolved particles, including nonelectrolytes and ions. This means that the total number of particles per liter of fluid is approximately $0.3 \times 6.02 \times 10^{23}$.

The botanist De Vries first measured the osmotic pressure within living cells. He found that when certain plant cells, having a supporting wall of cellulose around the protoplasm, are placed in solutions of high osmotic pressure, water passes from protoplasm to the stronger solution outside. This causes the protoplasm to shrink away from the cellulose membrane, and the cells are said to be plasmolyzed. In such a case the external solution is hypertonic to the cells. If the osmotic pressure of the surrounding solution is lower than that within the cells, water flows into the cells, and they become turgid and may rupture. The external solution in this case is hypotonic to the cells. If the external solution is isotonic to the cells (has the same osmotic pressure), no flow of water takes place, and no effect upon the cell protoplasm is observed. By determining the osmotic pressure of a solution isotonic with a cell, the osmotic pressure within the cell is obtained. When red blood cells are placed in hypotonic solutions, they swell and may rupture (hemolyze). Hypertonic solutions cause them to shrink and assume an irregular, or crenated, appearance. A 0.16 M sodium chloride solution (about 0.95 per cent) or 0.3 M nonelectrolyte solution is approximately isotonic with blood cells. This is true for the other cells of the body also. The maintenance of the proper osmotic pressure within the cells and fluids of the body is essential for normal functioning.

Calculations involving osmotic pressure. Osmotic pressure is due to the difference in activity of pure solvent molecules and of solvent molecules associated with solute molecules. It is proportional to the number of and independent of the kind of dissolved particles present. The general equation for gases applies to osmotic pressure:

$$\pi V = nRT, \text{ or } \pi = \frac{nRT}{V}$$

where π = the osmotic pressure in atmospheres, n = the number of moles of solute, R = the molar gas constant (0.082 liter-atmosphere), T = the absolute temperature, and V = the volume in liters.

Since n is equal to g/M, where g = grams of solute and M = the molecular weight of the solute, the equation may be written:

$$\pi V = \frac{g}{M} RT$$

Suppose a solution contains 2 g of cane sugar (mol. wt. 342) per 100 ml at 25° C (298° A). One liter (V) of the solution contains 20 g of sugar, and the osmotic pressure is: $\pi V = \pi \times 1 = 20/342 \times 0.082 \times 298$, and $\pi = 0.0585 \times 0.082 \times 298 = 1.43$ atm.

It is obvious from the above equation that the molecular weight of a substance may be determined from its osmotic pressure. For example, suppose 2 g of cane sugar per 100 ml of solution at 25° C has an osmotic pressure of 1.43 atm; then its molecular weight will be:

$$1.43 = \frac{20}{M} \times 0.082 \times 298$$

$$1.43M = 488.72, \quad M = 342$$

The equation $\pi V = (g/M)RT$, given above, is for use only with relatively dilute molar solutions where the volume represented by the solute molecules relative to the total volume is very small and may be neglected. A more accurate equation for the calculation of osmotic pressure is:

$$\pi - CRT$$

where C = the molal concentration of the solution and corrects for the volume occupied by the solute molecules. The ratio of solute to solvent molecules is the same in all equimolal solutions, and it is this ratio which actually determines the osmotic pressure and other colligative properties of solutions—namely, elevation of the boiling point, depression of the freezing point, and lowering of the vapor pressure.

Suppose 18 g of glucose to be dissolved in 1000 g of water to give a 0.1 molal solution at 27° C (300° A); the osmotic pressure of the solution will be:

$$\pi = 0.1 \times 0.082 \times 300 = 2.46 \text{ atm}$$

The equation $\pi = CRT$ obviously may be used for molecular weight determinations from osmotic pressure measurements. Suppose 2 g of a substance dissolved in 50 g of water (40 g in 1000 g of water) gives an osmotic pressure of 2.54 atm at 37° C (310° A). Then the molal concentration C would be:

$$\pi = CRT, \quad C = \pi/RT = 2.54/0.082 \times 310 = 2.54/25.4 = 0.1$$

Thus, 40 g of the substance represents 0.1 mol, and the molecular weight of the substance accordingly is 400.

The direct measurement of osmotic pressure by use of apparatus involving semipermeable membranes presents technical difficulties and inconvenience. In dealing with biologic fluids such as urine, serum, etc., the osmotic pressure is generally arrived at indirectly through the total molal concentration determined from freezing point measurements. The lowering of the freezing point of a solvent by a solute is directly proportional to the ratio of solute to solvent molecules present. The relation may be expressed mathematically:

$$\Delta t = k_f M$$

where Δt is the depression of the freezing point, k_f is the molal freezing point or cryoscopic constant, and M is the molal concentration of the solute. A solution containing an Avogadro number (6.02×10^{23}) of total dissolved particles either as undissociated molecules or ions or a mixture of ions and undissociated molecules in 1000 g of water (1 M solution) freezes at $-1.858°$ C; or we say the cryoscopic constant, k_f, for water is $-1.858°$ C. This constant actually is calculated from the freezing points of dilute solutions where the relations hold well. Suppose a sample of blood serum freezes at $-0.56°$ C, then its molal concentration, C, is $0.56/1.858 = 0.3$. The osmotic pressure of such a solution at $37°$ C would be:

$$\pi = CRT = 0.3 \times 0.082 \times 310 = 7.6 \text{ atm}$$

Molal concentrations and osmotic pressures of solutions may also be obtained from measurements of boiling point elevation or vapor pressure lowering, colligative properties of solutions for which there are molal constants. However, neither of these methods is as convenient or applicable to biologic fluids as is determination from freezing point depression.

Of all the colligative properties (depression of freezing point, elevation of boiling point, lowering of vapor pressure, and osmotic pressure), only osmotic pressure offers a practical method for the determination of molecular weights above 10,000. For example, suppose a substance has a molecular weight of 20,000 and that 10 g are present in 1000 g of water at $27°$ C; then the osmotic pressure would be:

$$\pi = \frac{10}{20,000} \times 0.082 \times 300 = 0.0123 \text{ atm}$$
$$= 0.0123 \times 760, \text{ or } 9.35 \text{ mm Hg} = 9.35 \times 13.5, \text{ or } 126 \text{ mm of water}$$

which can be readily measured. However, the boiling point of the solution would be raised only about $0.00025°$ C and the freezing point would be lowered $0.001°$ C, which cannot be readily measured. Thus, the determination of the molecular weights of large molecules through osmotic pressure measurements assumes considerable importance.

Fluid secretion and osmotic work. Whenever substances in body fluids are raised from lower to higher concentrations (activities), osmotic work must be performed upon them. Of course, the reverse is also true: when substances pass from higher to lower concentrations, osmotic work is done by them. The relation between osmotic work and concentration change for a given substance is given by the equation:

$$W_{\text{min}} = NRT \ln \frac{C_2}{C_1} = 2.3 NRT \log \frac{C_2}{C_1}$$

where W_{min} equals minimum osmotic work in small calories involved in transferring N mols of substance from a molal concentration of C_1 to a molal concentration of C_2, R is the gas constant and equals 1.987 calories per mol per degree, T is the absolute temperature, ln is the natural logarithm, and

2.3 is the factor for the conversion of natural logarithms to logarithms of base 10.

This equation may be used for calculating the over-all osmotic work involved in the transfer of a substance from a solution of lower to one of higher concentration and vice versa. For example, the osmotic work done by the kidneys in forming urine may be calculated if one knows the concentrations of the various substances present in both plasma and urine. The total osmotic work is obtained as the sum of the osmotic work for all of the substances concerned, the osmotic work for each component being calculated according to the above equation. For example, suppose the Cl⁻ concentration in plasma is 0.104 molal, and in urine it is 0.166 molal, and you wish to calculate the work done by the kidneys in secreting 0.166 mols of Cl⁻ in one kilogram of urine water at 37° C. According to the above equation this would be:

$$W_{min} = \text{Osmotic work} = 2.3 \times 0.166 \times 1.987 \times 310 \times 0.2 = +47 \text{ cal}$$

In this case the kidneys do the work of concentrating the Cl⁻ in passing from plasma to urine, and the work sign is positive. However, since the concentration of water is higher in plasma than in urine, the water does work in passing from plasma to urine and the sign of the work becomes negative.

Distribution of a solute between two immiscible solvents. When a water solution of succinic acid is shaken with ether, the molecules of acid distribute themselves in such a way that the ratio of acid molecules dissolved in water to those dissolved in ether is constant, regardless of the total amount of acid dissolved. Table 4.2 illustrates this principle. The ratio of concentration of acid in water, C_1, to the concentration in ether, C_2, is relatively con-

Table 4.2.   Succinic Acid in Water and Ether at 15°C

Grams Acid in 10 ml of H₂O C_1	Grams Acid in 10 ml of Ether C_2	Ratio of Acid in H₂O to Acid in Ether $C_1/C_2 = K$
0.024	0.0046	5.2
0.070	0.013	5.2
0.121	0.022	5.4
0.236	0.041	5.7
0.420	0.067	6.3
0.486	0.073	6.6

Taken by permission from *Treatise on Physical Chemistry*, Vol. I, 2nd ed., by H. S. Taylor, published by D. Van Nostrand Co., Inc., 1931.

stant, or $C_1/C_2 = K$, where K is the distribution coefficient. The distribution coefficients for other solutes between immiscible liquids may similarly be obtained, and the value for a given solute and pair of liquids is relatively constant so long as the molecular weight of the solute is the same in the two solvents and the concentrations are rather low. The distribution coefficient varies with temperature changes. The distribution law may be stated: If the molecular weight of the solute is the same in both solvents, the ratio in which it distributes itself between them is constant at constant temperature. This is similar to Henry's law for gases, which states that the ratio of gas concentration over a liquid to gas dissolved in the liquid is constant at constant temperature. When a mixture of solutes is present, each solute distributes itself between the liquids according to its own distribution coefficient and independently of the other solutes. This is similar to Dalton's law of partial pressures for gases, which states that in a mixture of gases over a liquid each gas dissolves in proportion to its own partial pressure and independently of the other gases present.

When ether is poured upon a water solution of succinic acid and the system is allowed to stand, acid molecules pass from the water up into the ether layer. Also, acid molecules which have passed into the ether tend to pass back into the water. When the rate at which acid molecules pass from ether to water equals the rate of passage from water to ether, the system is in equilibrium. At equilibrium about five times as much acid is in water as in ether. When iodine is distributed between carbon disulfide and water at 18° C, about four hundred times as much iodine is in carbon disulfide as in water.

This principle of the distribution of solutes between immiscible solvents is of much importance in the body. In general, a substance which is more soluble in organic solvents than in water is also more soluble in lipids (the term "lipid" applies to fats, sterols, waxes, phospholipids, glycolipids, all of which are greasy, soluble in organic solvents, and generally dissolve molecules which are soluble in organic solvents). Consequently, drugs and other molecules which are more soluble in organic solvents than in water will tend to concentrate in the tissues and fluids of the body which contain more lipid material. On the other hand, molecules which are highly soluble in water and little soluble in lipids will be present in greater concentration in the body fluids and tissues which contain little lipid or fatlike material. For example, when ether is used as an anesthetic, the concentration in the brain and nervous tissue (rich in lipids) will be much greater than the concentration in the blood and tissues, which are much poorer in lipid material. Theoretically, the ether will be distributed in the body according to its distribution coefficients for the various fluids and tissues which serve as solvents for it.

EXERCISES

1. Assuming complete dissociation, calculate the osmotic pressure of 0.9 per cent NaCl solution at 38° C. How does this compare with the osmotic pressure of blood serum?
2. Concentrated urine may freeze as low as −2.3° C. Calculate its molal concentration and osmotic pressure at 38° C. What do you conclude about the osmotic work performed by the kidney in secreting this urine from blood?
3. Calculate the per cent by volume concentration of glucose which is isotonic with blood.
4. What effect does severe dehydration of the body have upon the diffusion pressure of water in the blood and upon the secretion of urine? What is the effect of excessive water intake?
5. Diagram the mechanism of osmotic pressure.
6. Equal volumes of ether and water are contained in a mixture of the two solvents at 15° C. An organic acid is added to the mixture, which is thoroughly agitated, and the layers of ether and water are permitted to separate. The distribution coefficient

for the acid between water and ether at 15° C is 0.4. Upon titration of 10 ml of the water layer, 0.05 g of acid is found to be present. Calculate the amount of acid in 10 ml of the ether layer.

7. Would cyclopropane, when used as an anesthetic, reach a higher concentration in brain tissue or in the blood stream?

GENERAL REFERENCES

Clark, W. M.: *Topics in Physical Chemistry*, 2nd ed. Williams & Wilkins Co., Baltimore, 1952.

Daniels, F., and Alberty, R. A.: *Physical Chemistry*. John Wiley & Sons, New York, 1955.

Gortner, R. A., Jr., and Gortner, W. A. (eds.): *Outlines of Biochemistry*, 3rd ed. John Wiley & Sons, New York, 1949.

OSMOTIC PRESSURE   83

for the acid between water and ether at 15° C. is 0.1. Upon titration of 10 ml of the
water layer, 0.05 g of acid is found to be present. Calculate the amount of acid in

Clark, W. M., Topics in Physical Chemistry, 2nd ed. William & Wilkins Co., Baltimore,
1952.
Daniels, F., and Alberty, R. A., Physical Chemistry. John Wiley & Sons, New York, 1955.
Gortner, R. A., Jr., and Gortner, W. A. (ed.), Outlines of Biochemistry, 3rd ed. John
Wiley & Sons, New York, 1949.

5

The colloidal state and membrane phenomena

COLLOIDAL SYSTEMS

Thomas Graham (1805–1869) is generally considered the father of colloid chemistry. He observed that solutions of certain substances such as proteins, polysaccharides, tannins, and gums do not diffuse through parchment and other membranes as do sugars, salts, and other common materials which crystallize. Solutions of the nondiffusible materials upon evaporation yield amorphous solids and are often sticky in character. Graham called these substances "colloids" (from the Greek words meaning gluelike). The crystalline substances which diffuse readily through membranes he called "crystalloids." Although Graham classified substances as "colloids" and "crystalloids," he realized that some substances may exist as either, depending upon the conditions.

The work of many investigators since the time of Graham has shown that the colloidal condition represents primarily a state of matter and not a special kind of matter. Some substances are always in the colloidal condition, while practically all crystalline substances can be made to assume the colloidal state under the proper conditions. A colloidal system comprises two phases, one of which is the continuous dispersions medium and the other the discontinuous dispersed phase of particles with diameters above and below certain limits. The colloidal state of matter is determined by the particle size of the dispersed phase, and by this only. Colloidal particles may represent single molecules, as in the case of various proteins and polysaccharides, or they may be aggregates of many smaller molecules.

84

All matter may be classified according to particle size. The relation of the colloidal state of matter to matter in general is given below.

Molecules and Ions Less than 0.000001 mm	Colloidal State 0.000001–0.0001 mm	Matter in Mass Greater than 0.0001 mm
Particle size less than 1 millimicron (mμ). Not visible in ultramicroscope.	Particle size 1–100 mμ. Visible in the ultramicroscope.	Particle size greater than 100 mμ. Visible in microscope.

In order that the student may better understand the relative sizes of particles, the following tabulation should be inspected.

1 micron (1 μ) = 0.001 mm = 10,000 Angstrom units (Å)
1 millimicron (1 mμ) = 0.000001 mm = 10Å
Wavelength of visible light = 3900–7700 Å
Wavelength of ultraviolet light = 2000–3900 Å
Wavelength of x-rays = 0.5 Å (varies)
Wavelength of gamma rays = 0.1 Å
Wavelength of radio waves = ordinarily many meters
Smallest particle visible in microscope has diameter of
   about 0.0001 mm = 0.1 μ = 100 mμ = 1000 Å
Diameter of: Human red cell = 0.008 mm = 8 μ = 80,000 Å
   Anthrax bacillus = 0.006 mm = 6 μ = 60,000 Å
   Micrococcus = 0.001 mm = 1 μ = 10,000 Å
   Colloidal particles = 0.000001–0.0001 mm = 1–100 mμ = 10–1,000 Å
   Starch molecule = 0.000008 mm = 8 mμ = 80 Å
   Cane sugar molecule = 0.0000007 mm = 0.7 mμ = 7 Å
   NaCl molecule = 0.00000028 mm = 0.28 mμ = 2.8 Å
   H_2 molecule = 0.0000001 mm = 0.1 mμ = 1 Å

The limits of colloidal size as given by various authorities differ somewhat. The lower limits are placed at 1 to 5 mμ and the upper at 100 to 500 mμ. There is a gradation of the colloidal state which extends both below and above the fixed limits.

The colloidal state in relation to surface forces and surface area. The student may properly wonder why colloidal matter, with particle sizes of about 1 to 100 mμ, is notably different from other states of matter. Every particle, whether a very small noncolloidal molecule or a very large colloidal particle, possesses certain fields of force about it which are probably largely electromagnetic. It may possess the property of coordination as the result of certain groupings and unshared electron pairs. It may be negatively or positively charged for various reasons. It may be highly polarized and act as a dipole and form associations with like or different particles. It may possess active chemical groups and undergo ordinary reactions characteristic of those groups. The forces about particles of colloidal size are less per unit mass than those around molecules of the same substance in true solution. However, because colloidal particles can often be observed with the ultramicroscope, can be flocculated from solution, can be separated from other molecules by dialysis through semipermeable membranes, often adsorb and hold other molecules and ions to their surfaces in a way that can be measured, and in general exhibit a relatively high activity of so-called surface forces as compared with primary chemical forces, the colloidal state of matter is studied as a separate branch of chemistry. The student must not forget that the fundamental properties of true and colloidal solutions are essentially the same qualitatively. Because of differences in particle size and structure, the properties differ largely from a quantitative standpoint. Particles of matter in mass exhibit at the surfaces the same qualitative properties as particles in the colloidal state. The activity per unit surface may be about as great as observed in the colloidal state; but, since the ratio of surface to mass is much less than in the colloidal state, the quantity of activity per unit mass of matter (above colloidal limits) is less.

In order that the student may have a more concrete picture of the relation of surface to various phenomena related to surface forces, some further discussion may help. As stated above, the surfaces of all atoms and molecules of whatever nature are surrounded by certain electric, or electromagnetic

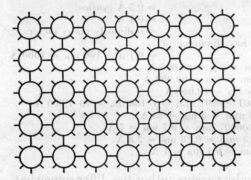

Figure 5.1. Diagram illustrating free surface forces around atoms of platinum. (From West, E. S.: *Textbook of Biophysical Chemistry*, 2nd ed. The Macmillan Co., New York, 1956.)

fields of force, which arise from the electric particles making up the structure of atoms. In some atoms and molecules the external, or surface, fields of force are relatively weak owing to effective neutralization within the particles. Other atoms and molecules have very strong surface fields of force because of poor internal neutralization. Consider the difference in the effective fields of force around the internal and surface atoms of a metal such as platinum. Figure 5.1 may aid in visualizing the situation.

The atoms of platinum are surrounded by external fields of force. However, these fields of force neutralize each other in the atoms located beneath the surface of the piece of metal, because each atom is attracted equally in all directions by the fields of force of the surrounding atoms. In the atoms in the surface of the metal the situation is quite different. The fields of force around these atoms are only partly neutralized by adjacent surface atoms and those beneath. Consequently, the surface of the metal has free fields of force, or attraction, which impart to it peculiar properties. A similar condition exists at all surfaces or interfaces of matter where the forces of attraction around the atoms are incompletely neutralized. In the above illustration the particles of air surrounding the metal surface tend partially to neutralize the fields of force around the platinum atoms. We may say that the fields of force of the air particles are attracted by those of the surface platinum atoms and thereby partially neutralize them. Air particles (N_2, O_2, etc.) are consequently adsorbed upon the surface of the platinum. All other kinds of molecules in contact with the platinum surface would be more or less held, or adsorbed, by the free fields of force around the atoms. These free surface forces are responsible for the powerful catalytic effect of platinum and other substances in certain chemical reactions. Benzene and water are not miscible, and benzene forms a separate layer over water. Where the two liquids meet, a so-called interface exists. Now, water molecules have stronger fields of force around them than do benzene molecules, and at the interface the forces of attraction are only partly neutralized. Consequently, there are more free forces of attraction at the interface between the liquids than elsewhere. However, there are stronger fields of force at the surface (or interface) of water and air than at the interface of water and benzene, because in the latter case the surface forces are more nearly neutralized. From the above discussion the student should understand that whenever particles of matter are surrounded by other particles in such a way that their fields of force do not mutually neutralize, there will result a region possessing free fields of attraction. This occurs at all surfaces or boundary phases (interfaces) between different kinds of matter. Two different solid surfaces, such as silver and gold, brought together show the effect. Similarly, a droplet of liquid suspended in air or other gas has unneutralized fields of force at the boundary or interface between the liquid and gas. A droplet of liquid suspended in an immiscible liquid has unneutralized fields of force at the interface. A particle of gold or other solid suspended in a gas or liquid possesses free surface forces.

It has been previously pointed out that the colloidal state of matter differs particularly from matter in mass by possessing a much greater surface area per unit of weight. The colloidal state of matter consequently possesses unneutralized surface forces to an extraordinary degree as compared with the coarse particles of matter in mass. In order to make this clear, let us consider the effect of particle size upon surface area. One gram mol of sodium chloride (58 g) in the shape of a cube would have an edge of about 3 cm and a surface area of 54 sq cm. If this cube were subdivided into cubes of 10 mμ diameter (colloidal size), the number of cubes obtained would be 27×10^{18}, and the total surface area would become 16,000 sq m! There would be about 20,000 molecules of sodium chloride in each particle. The surface area of the sodium chloride is increased three million times by subdivision into the colloidal state. This means also that unneutralized surface forces are increased three million times, and the material will possess marked surface properties which were hardly detectable before conversion to colloidal dimensions.

A physiologic example of the importance of surface area may be pointed out in case of the red blood corpuscles, which contain the oxygen-carrying pigment, hemoglobin. As blood circulates through the capillaries of the lungs, oxygen diffuses through the surface of the corpuscles and unites with hemoglobin to form oxyhemoglobin. This process must take place quickly, because the blood remains in the capillaries for only a short time. It is facilitated by the great surface area for taking up oxygen presented by the corpuscles. In a normal man the total corpuscle area amounts to some 1500 sq m, or 16,140 sq ft.

Colloid terminology. All colloid systems are composed of two phases of matter, one of which is represented by the colloidal particles and is called the "dispersed" or " internal" phase. The second phase is the "dispersions medium," which is also designated the "external" phase. The term "colloid sol," or simply "sol," is synonymous with "colloidal solution." A hydrosol represents a colloidal system in which water is the dispersions medium, while alcohol is the dispersions medium in an alcosol. A lyophobic colloid system (suspensoid) is one in which there is little attraction between the colloid particles and the dispersions medium. A hydrophobic colloid system is a lyophobic system in which the dispersions medium is water. A lyophilic colloid system (emulsoid) is one in which the colloidal particles have a high affinity for the dispersions medium and are combined with some of the medium, or are solvated. A hydrophilic colloid system is a lyophilic system in which the dispersions medium is water; in this case the colloid particles are hydrated. The particles in a lyophobic or suspensoid colloid system are generally solid, while the particles in a lyophilic or emulsoid colloid system appear to be more or less liquid.

A gel is a lyophilic colloid system which is more or less rigid. Gels generally are made up of "brush heap" fibrillar structures surrounded by dispersions medium. Good examples are gelatine and agar gels. Gels are freely permeable to noncolloid ions and molecules. The larger aggregates of colloidal particles formed in the process of gel formation are called "micelles."

DETERMINATION OF THE SIZE OF COLLOIDAL PARTICLES

1. By ultrafiltration. Colloidal particles readily pass through ordinary filter paper and porcelain filters. A series of collodion membranes with graded pore sizes may be prepared and used for the determination of colloidal particle size. The colloidal solution tested is filtered under pressure through the series of filters. The size of the colloidal particle is between the pore size of the first filter through which it will not pass and the next larger pore size through which it will pass. The method has a number of limitations.

2. By diffusion rate. The rate at which particles diffuse in solution has been used for the estimation of particle size and of molecular weights. The method is applicable to particles of colloidal and subcolloidal size, such as those of the sugars and amino acids. The rate of diffusion is best measured by optical methods, such as refractive index, light absorption, fluorescence, and Tyndall effect, in which the solution is not disturbed. Northrop and McBain have employed methods in which the rate of passage of particles in solution through a porous disk is measured.

3. By the ultracentrifuge. One of the most useful methods of determining the molecular weights of colloid particles was developed by Svedberg of Sweden; it is based upon use of the ultracentrifuge, in which materials may be subjected to centrifugal forces which are many thousands of times stronger than the force of gravity. Ultracentrifuges have been constructed in which the rotor revolves 60,000 times per minute, giving centrifugal forces of the order of 500,000 times gravity.

When solutions of proteins or other colloidal solutions are placed in glass or quartz cells in the rotor of the ultracentrifuge, they are subjected to a force depending upon the angular velocity of the centrifuge and the distance of the colloidal particles from the axis of rotation. The rate at which the particles move is dependent upon this force and also upon the shape, size, and density of the particles, and upon the density and viscosity of the suspending medium. In the case of homogeneous substances where the particles are all alike, the particles move under the centrifugal force as a sharp boundary in the medium. Since the particles absorb more light than the medium, their rate of movement may be determined by photographing the position of the particle boundary in the cells at various time intervals. However, since the refractive index of the particles is different from that of the medium, it is possible to follow the movement of the boundary by ingenious optical systems and techniques. These methods are based upon the fact that a light beam is bent most as it passes through the solution in the region of the boundary where the gradient of colloidal particle concentration is greatest. This refractive index effect is recorded photographically and indicates the distance of the boundary from the axis of rotation at different time intervals. The refractive index method gives not only the position of the particle boundary in the solution, but also an estimate of the concentration of a protein or other colloid. The refractive index method now is generally used.

The equation specifically applied in the calculation of molecular weights, M_s, from sedimentation velocity is:

$$M_s = \frac{RTs}{D(1 - V\rho)}$$

where R is the gas constant, T is the absolute temperature, D is the diffusion constant, V is the partial specific volume of the substance (the volume increment when 1 g of dry substance is added to a large amount of solvent; for proteins V is about 0.74), ρ is the density of the solution, and s is the sedimentation constant. It is customary to express sedimentation velocity in terms of the sedimentation constant, which represents the velocity of the particles in a unit centimeter-gram-second (cgs) field of force. If x represents the distance of the particles from the axis of rotation in the ultracentrifuge, then the rate at which they travel is:

$$\frac{dx}{dt} = s\omega^2 x, \text{ and } s = \frac{dx/dt}{\omega^2 x}$$

where ω is the velocity of revolution in radians per second ($\omega = 2\pi$ revolutions per second $= 6.2832 \cdot$ revolutions per second), and t is the time in seconds. The sedimentation constant, s, has the dimension of time. In the case of proteins, s varies from 1×10^{-13} sec to about 200×10^{-13} sec, and the unit 10^{-13} sec is called a svedberg. To illustrate the calculation of s, suppose at time t_1 the boundary of the particles in the colloidal solution is x_1 cm from the axis of the centrifuge and at time t_2 it is x_2 cm from the axis. Upon integration of the above equation between the limits x_2 and x_1 and t_2 and t_1, we have:

$$s = \frac{1}{\omega^2(t_2 - t_1)} \ln \frac{x_2}{x_1}$$

Suppose a protein solution is run in the ultracentrifuge at 840 rps at a constant temperature and that the first photograph shows the particle boundary to be 5.949 cm, x_1, from the axis of the ultracentrifuge at 0 time, t_1, and 6.731 cm, x_2, from the axis after 4200 seconds, t_2. Then:

$$s = \frac{1}{\omega^2(t_2 - t_1)} \ln \frac{x_2}{x_1} = \frac{1}{(2\pi 840)^2(4200)} \ln \frac{6.731}{5.949}$$

$$= \frac{2.303}{(6.2832 \times 840)^2(4200)} \log \frac{6.731}{5.949} = \frac{2.303(0.0531)}{(2.79 \times 10^7)(4200)}$$

$$= \frac{1.22 \times 10^{-1}}{1.17 \times 10^{11}} = 1.04 \times 10^{-12} = 10.4 \times 10^{-13} \text{ sec} = 10.4 \text{ svedbergs}$$

It is customary to use 20° C as the standard temperature in ultracentrifugal studies, and the sedimentation constant is commonly indicated as s_{20}. Table 5.1 gives s_{20} and other values for several proteins.

Table 5.1. Some Physical Constants at 20° C in Water and Molecular Weights of Proteins

Protein	$s_{20}x^*$ 10^{13} sec	$D_{20} \times 10^7$ cm² sec⁻¹	V_{20} cm³ g⁻¹	M g mol⁻¹
Insulin (monomer)	1.6	15	0.749	12,000
Ribonuclease	1.85	13.6	0.709	12,700
Cytochrome c	1.9	10.1	0.707	15,600
Pepsin	3.3	9.0	0.75	35,500
Ovalbumin	3.60	7.8	0.75	44,700
Fumarase	8.51	4.05	0.75	204,000
Urease	18.6	3.46	0.73	480,000
Actomyosin	12.0	0.30	0.75	3,900,000
Tobacco mosaic virus	174	0.3	0.727	59,000,000

* s_{20} = sedimentation constant; actual value = number in column $\times 10^{-13}$ sec.
D_{20} = diffusion coefficient in square cm per sec.; actual value = number in column $\times 10^{-7}$.
V_{20} = partial specific volume in cubic centimeters per g.
All of these values are at 20° C as indicated by s_{20}, etc.

The application of the sedimentation constant, s, in calculating the molecular weight of a protein from the equation:

$$M = \frac{RTs}{D(1 - V\rho)}$$

may be illustrated as follows: Suppose a water solution of ovalbumin is run in the ultracentrifuge at 20° C, and the value of the sedimentation constant, s, found to be 3.6×10^{-13} sec. The diffusion coefficient, D, is 7.8×10^{-7} cm² sec⁻¹; the partial specific volume, V, is 0.75 cm³ g⁻¹; the value of the gas constant, R, is 8.31×10^7 ergs per mol per degree; and the density of water, ρ, at 20° C is 0.9982 g per cubic centimeter. Substituting in the above equation, we have:

$$M = \frac{(8.31 \times 10^7 \text{ erg deg}^{-1} \text{ mol}^{-1})(293 \text{ deg})(3.6 \times 10^{-13} \text{ sec})}{(7.8 \times 10^{-7} \text{ cm}^2 \text{ sec}^{-1})[1 - (0.75 \text{ cm}^3 \text{ g}^{-1})(0.9982 \text{ g cm}^{-3})]}$$

$$= \frac{(8.31 \times 10^7)(293)(3.6 \times 10^{-13})}{(7.8 \times 10^{-7})[1 - (0.75)(0.9982)]} = \frac{8.765 \times 10^{-3}}{1.96 \times 10^{-7}}$$

or $\qquad M = 4.47 \times 10^4 = 44,700 \text{ g mol}^{-1}$

Thus, the formula weight of ovalbumin is found to be 44,700 g, and the molecular weight is 44,700.

Molecular weights may be determined also by centrifuging at a relatively low force until no further movement of the particles occurs (when the diffusion of the particles is balanced by their sedimentation velocity). The equation used in the calculation of molecular weights, M_E, by this method of sedimentation equilibrium is:

$$M_E = \frac{2RT \log_e(c_2/c_1)}{[\omega^2(1 - V\rho)(x_2^2 - x_1^2)]}$$

in which R and T have their usual significance, c_1 and c_2 are the concentrations of substances at distances x_1 and x_2 from the axis of rotation, ω is the angular velocity of the centrifuge, V is the partial specific volume, and ρ is the density of the solution.

The sedimentation velocity method of determining molecular weights is generally preferred because of its greater convenience.

Ultracentrifugation is valuable in determining the purity of colloids, and it has been applied especially in the case of proteins. If all particles are of the same kind, they move as a sharp single boundary in the medium, whereas mixtures of particles of different kinds give multiple boundaries and fuzzy zones.

Ultracentrifugation is used in the separation and purification of virus proteins mixed with tissue proteins. The virus proteins, of very large molecular size, are centrifuged to the bottom of the cell at a centrifuge speed at which the smaller tissue proteins are left suspended in the medium. Also, ultracentrifugation is used in the separation of mitochondrial, microsomal, and nuclear fractions from disrupted tissue cells.

4. By light scattering. The scattering of light by colloidal particles (Tyndall effect) affords a valuable method for the determination of particle size, and it has found particular application in estimating the molecular weights of proteins. When a beam of light is passed through a colloidal solution, a part of the light is transmitted and a part is scattered. The fractional decrease in the intensity of the transmitted light is related to the molecular weight, M, as follows:

$$M = -\left(\frac{\log_e I/I_0}{Hcl}\right)$$

in which I is the intensity of the transmitted light, I_0 is the intensity of the incident light, H is a proportionality constant, c is the concentration of the substance in grams per milliliter, and l is the length of the path through the scattering solution.

The value of the constant, H, is given by:

$$H = \frac{32\pi^3 n_0^2}{3N\lambda^4}\left(\frac{n - n_0}{c}\right)^2$$

in which λ is the wave length of the incident light, n_0 and n are the indices of refraction of the solvent and solution, respectively, and N is the Avogadro number.

Determination of molecular weights from light scattering is useful over a much wider range than determination from osmotic pressure. The lower limit for both methods is about 12,000, but for very high molecular weights light scattering is greatly superior, because while the intensity of scattering goes up with increasing molecular weight, osmotic pressure goes down.

5. By x-ray analysis. From the diffraction patterns of x-rays which have passed through particles of matter, it is possible to calculate particle size.

6. By osmotic pressure. In Chapter 4 of this book it was shown that molecular weights may be determined from osmotic pressure measurements. The method has been applied successfully to many proteins, as indicated by agreement of the values with those obtained by the ultracentrifuge. However, the procedure is most successful for molecular weights from about 30,000 to 100,000, because some of the smaller molecules may leak through the membranes used, while the very large molecules give a very low osmotic pressure relative to the weight concentration, and thus a large probable error of measurement. As will be shown later in this chapter, determination of the molecular weights of proteins from osmotic measurements may be complicated by the Donnan effect.

THE ELECTRIC CHARGE OF COLLOIDAL PARTICLES

The fact that colloidal particles are electrically charged has been previously pointed out. The charge upon such particles is of much importance in stabilizing colloidal solutions, because, since all the particles in a given sol are charged alike, they repel each other and remain in suspension. The neutralization of these charges is of importance in the precipitation or flocculation of colloids.

The charges on colloidal particles arise from ionization of groups in the particle surface, as in the case of proteins, and also through selective adsorption of ions from the medium upon the particle surface. Both mechanisms may operate simultaneously.

Helmholtz-Gouy double layer of colloidal particles. If the particles in a colloidal solution are charged as pointed out above, it seems that the solution should represent a statically charged electric system and, as pointed out by Von Smoluchowski, the solution should deflect an electroscope brought near it. The electroscope is not affected. In a solution of NaCl there are a great number of Na^+ ions, and if only these were present, the solution as a whole would be positively charged. However, the positive charge due to Na^+ ions is exactly balanced by the presence of an equal and opposite negative charge carried by the Cl^- ions associated with the Na^+ ions. If a colloidal solution does not show a net electric charge, the charge upon the surface of the particles must be balanced by an equal and opposite charge around the surface of the particles. The Helmholtz-Gouy double-layer theory gives the best explanation of the charge relations at the surface of a colloidal particle (and other surfaces also). According to this theory, the charged surface is surrounded by a layer of oppositely charged ions. There is an immobile layer of ions adsorbed upon the surface from the liquid followed by a more diffuse layer which is mobile, the mobility increasing with distance from the surface.

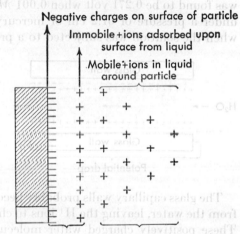

Negative charges on surface of particle

Immobile +ions adsorbed upon surface from liquid

Mobile +ions in liquid around particle

Figure 5.2. Diagram illustrating Helmholtz-Gouy double layer. (From West, E. S.: *Textbook of Biophysical Chemistry*, 2nd ed. The Macmillan Co., New York, 1956.)

Figure 5.2 may aid in visualizing the situation. If the colloid particle is positively charged, the double-layer relations are reversed and the surrounding liquid contains negative ions.

The potential drop across all the ionic layers from the surface of the particle into the solution is called the "electrochemical," or "epsilon" (ϵ), potential. The potential between the immobile layer of ions and the mobile layer is called the "electrokinetic," or "zeta" (ζ), potential. The potential between the immobile ion layer and the particle surface is referred to as the Stern potential and is equal to the electrochemical potential minus the electrokinetic potential:

$$\text{Stern potential} = \epsilon - \zeta$$

Accordingly, the electrochemical, or epsilon, potential is equal to the Stern potential plus the electrokinetic, or zeta, potential.

The magnitude of these various potentials varies with the density of charges in the layers concerned, which in turn is determined by the nature of the surface of the particle and of the surrounding liquid. The electrokinetic, or zeta, potential between the immobile and mobile ionic layers is of primary importance in connection with the properties of colloids. When this potential is lowered to a certain value, called the "critical" potential, by the addition of electrolytes, the double layers of the colloidal particles collapse, and the particles aggregate and precipitate.

Streaming potential or flow potential. When water is present in a glass capillary as shown in Figure 5.3, the walls of the capillary are negatively and the water positively charged. If water is forced to flow through the capillary from left to right, a potential develops between the ends of the capillary. This potential is referred to as the "streaming," or "flow," potential. It varies with the nature of the liquid and of the capillary, because different combinations give different charge values between capillary wall and liquid. It increases as the pressure forcing the liquid through the capillary increases. For example, the flow potential between the two ends of a glass capillary was found to be 0.271 volt when 0.001 M KCl solution was forced through it under a pressure of 61.2 cm of mercury. The potential rose to 0.315 volt when the solution was subjected to a pressure of 70.8 cm.

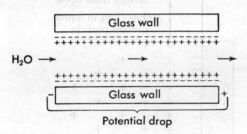

Figure 5.3. Diagram illustrating streaming potential. (From West, E. S.: *Textbook of Biophysical Chemistry*, 2nd ed. The Macmillan Co., New York, 1956.)

The glass capillary walls probably become negative by adsorbing OH^- ions from the water, leaving the H^+ ions to charge the water molecules positively. These positively charged water molecules are mobile, and as water flows through the capillary, the positive charges accumulate in excess at one end, leaving an excess of negative charges at the other. This causes a potential difference between the ends of the capillary, which opposes the flow. It is probable that the flow of fluids through the membranes of tissues develops streaming potentials which contribute to the potential differences across such membranes. The filtration of solutions through filters with fine pores may be very difficult owing to the development of powerful flow potentials in the membrane pores. This is especially true in the filtration of solutions containing low electrolyte concentrations. The presence of electrolytes tends to reduce the potentials at the pore surfaces just as the zeta potential is reduced on the surface of colloid particles by electrolytes. The fact that the pore surfaces of filters are electrically charged is an important influence in determining their impermeability to bacteria and other microorganisms (which are also charged, generally negatively).

Electroendosmosis. If a potential develops across the ends of a capillary when a liquid is forced through it, it is not surprising to find that the liquid flows through the capillary when a potential is applied across it. If the capillary of Figure 5.3 is placed in water between positive and negative electrodes, the water will flow through the capillary toward the negative pole because the water is positively charged and mobile. The movement of a liquid through a capillary under the influence of an electric potential is referred to as "electroendosmosis." Membranes prepared from collodion, parchment, tissue membranes, etc., may be considered structures containing great numbers of pores. The walls of the pores of these and most other membranes are negatively charged, and the water in the pores is positively charged. When such a membrane is placed in water between electrodes so that the liquid is separated into two compartments, water flows from the compartment containing the positive pole through the membrane into the compartment containing the negative pole. The process continues until the level of water in the negative electrode compartment is sufficiently above that in the positive electrode compartment to balance the rates of water movement through the membrane in opposite directions. Membranes with positively charged pore walls give electroendosmosis in the reverse direction, because in these the water is negatively charged and mobile. The addition of acids (H^+) causes negative pore walls to become less negative and positive pore walls more positive. Alkali (OH^-) has the reverse effect. Salts also tend to change the pore charge relative to the liquid, the change depending upon the selective adsorption of salt ions on the pore walls. The electroendosmotic effect is changed accordingly as the relative charges of pore walls and mobile liquid are changed.

THE PRECIPITATION OR FLOCCULATION OF COLLOIDAL PARTICLES

In order that a sol may be precipitated or flocculated, it is necessary that the stabilizing influences around the surfaces of the particles be removed or decreased to the point where they are no longer effective. Certain cohesive forces existing between colloidal particles tend to cause them to aggregate. This is prevented in lyophobic colloids (suspensoids) because the colloidal particles are electrically charged alike and repel each other. In lyophilic colloids (emulsoids) two factors operate to stabilize the solutions: the electric charge effect is one factor; the other is that the lyophilic colloid particle is combined with a layer of the surrounding liquid which is soluble in the suspension medium. In order to precipitate a suspensoid, all one needs to do is to add an electrolyte such as a salt, acid, or base. The ion of charge opposite to the charge on the colloid particle concentrates in the mobile layer around the particle and reduces the zeta potential to a value at which the colloidal particles aggregate into precipitable masses as a result of cohesive attraction. In emulsoids, which are stabilized by both combined liquid and electric charges, it is necessary to destroy stabilization due to both charge and liquid layer before efficient precipitation takes place.

Precipitation of emulsoids. Emulsoids are not precipitated by the addition of salts in amounts which readily flocculate suspensoids. In order to precipitate emulsoids by salts, sufficient salt must be added to dehydrate the colloid particles by combining with the layers of water surrounding them. At the same time the positive or negative ion of the salt reduces the charge upon the particles, leading to precipitation. The colloidal protein particles in blood serum may be precipitated by adding a large amount of ammonium sulfate. The precipitation occurs as a result of both dehydration of the protein particles and reduction of the zeta potential around the particles.

The precipitation of emulsoids by adding large amounts of soluble salts is referred to as "salting-out." The power of salting-out depends upon the nature of both the cation and the anion of the salt. Cations and anions arranged according to decreasing salting-out power are:

Cation series:

$$Li^+—Na^+—K^+—Rb^+—Cs^+ \quad \text{and} \quad Mg^{++}—Ca^{++}—Sr^{++}—Ba^{++}$$

Anion series:

$$SO_4^{--}—Cl^-—Br^-—NO_3^-—I^-—CNS^-$$

These arrangements of cations and anions in series according to their salting-out power are called "lyotropic," or Hofmeister, series. Such series of ions are observed in numerous other physicochemical relations. These series for salting-out probably represent the order of hydration of the ions; the more capable of hydration, the more efficient is the ion in dehydrating colloidal particles and causing their precipitation.

If considerable alcohol is added to an agar solution, which is an emulsoid, the water layers around the particles will be removed by the alcohol, and a suspensoid colloidal system will be produced. The particles are now easily precipitated by the addition of small amounts of electrolytes which would have been ineffective before dehydration with alcohol.

It should be pointed out that in emulsoids of proteins precipitation occurs when heavy-metal ions such as Pb^{++}, Hg^{++}, Fe^{+++}, and Ag^+ are added in relatively small amounts to the protein solutions made alkaline to the isoelectric pH. Dehydration is not necessary here. The heavy-metal ions combine with the negative protein ions to form insoluble complexes.

Mutual precipitation of colloids. When sufficient negative suspensoid is added to a positive suspensoid, their electric charges are decreased to the critical value, and flocculation occurs.

Protective colloids. When a gelatin solution is added to a gold sol, the particles of the emulsoid (gelatin) are adsorbed by the particles of suspensoid (gold), and the gold particles become much more resistant to precipitation. The combination of emulsoid particles with those of the suspensoid causes the resulting particles to have properties similar to those of an emulsoid. Gelatin, gum acacia, and other emulsoids are used extensively as protective colloids for suspensoids. Protective colloids undoubtedly play an important role physiologically. It is probable that some of the calcium phosphate of blood plasma is held in colloidal suspension by the protective action of the proteins present. The proteins of milk serve as protective colloids to calcium phosphate aggregates suspended in it. The bile salts and bile protein act as protective colloids to keep sparingly soluble cholesterol and the calcium salt of bilirubin in colloidal suspension. Gallstones may result from the precipitation of such substances in the absence of sufficient protective colloids. Protective colloids in urine may prevent bladder stone formation.

The precipitation of suspensoids is generally irreversible; that is, the precipitate cannot be resuspended in the colloidal state. Some of them, such as precipitated gold suspensoid, may be reversed by adding the proper solution. Precipitated gold is resuspended by adding dilute ammonia. Precipitated emulsoids such as agar, gelatin, and albumin may be resuspended by placing in water and dialyzing out adsorbed electrolytes.

SURFACE TENSION

The interior molecules of a homogeneous liquid are equally attracted in all directions by surrounding molecules. They are free to move in all directions, and free forces of attraction are not exhibited. The molecules of liquid in the surface, however, are attracted downward and sideways but not upward (except for the little attraction of air molecules). The result is that the molecules of the surface are not so free to move as the interior molecules are. They are held together and form a membrane over the surface of the liquid. The force with which the surface molecules are held is called the "surface tension" of the liquid. It is greater the stronger the attraction between the molecules of liquid. When finely powdered sulfur or other nonwetting powders are sprinkled upon water, they do not sink but are suspended on the surface film.

Surface tension, or, better, interfacial tension, exists wherever a liquid touches the walls of the container or the surface of solid particles in the liquid. There is also an interfacial tension at the boundary between immiscible liquids, for example, at the boundary of oil drops emulsified in water. In all these cases the tension is due to unequal attraction of the film molecules as compared with the molecules in the interior of the liquid. In colloidal solutions there is interfacial tension at the boundary of particle and liquid (at the interface).

There is a principle of thermodynamics according to which a physical or chemical system tends to assume the condition under which its free energy (energy capable of doing work) is at the minimum possible under the circumstances. Surface tension of a liquid multiplied by surface area of the liquid gives the free surface energy of the liquid. When the surface area is large, the free surface energy is large; and according to the above principle of thermodynamics, the surface of the liquid tends to decrease as much as possible so as to decrease surface energy. When a soap bubble is blown, energy is required to blow the bubble because molecules are forced from the interior of the soap solution into the surface layers of the films. The energy required to blow the bubble is stored in the surface films as free surface energy. This free surface energy can be maintained in the films of the bubble only by maintaining the air pressure energy inside the bubble. When this pressure is released, the free surface energy of the films causes them to contract and molecules move from the film surfaces into the interior of the liquid, with the result that the bubble disappears and a drop of soap solution is produced. Work is done upon the soap solution in forming the bubble, and the work energy is stored as free surface energy in the films of the bubble. This free surface energy is reconverted to work when the air is forced from the bubble by contraction of the films.

A falling drop of liquid assumes a spherical form, because in this shape the ratio of surface area and total free surface energy to the total mass of liquid is least. Water drops placed upon a paraffined surface (prevents wetting) assume a nearly spherical shape (slightly flattened by the pull of gravity) to decrease the free surface energy. Mercury drops are more nearly spherical because of the much higher surface tension and energy of mercury.

When a capillary glass tube is lowered into the surface of a liquid which wets the glass, the liquid spreads as a film over the glass surface in the capillary with an increase in free surface energy. This film of liquid tends to contract because of its free surface energy and in doing so pulls a column of liquid up into the capillary to a level above that of the surrounding liquid. The height to which the liquid rises is proportional to the surface tension of the liquid and to the bore of the capillary tube (height increases as bore decreases). The surface of the liquid in the capillary is concave in form. Some liquids, such as mercury, do not wet the walls of a capillary and, instead of rising, are depressed. In this case the surface of the liquid is convex in form. Both the concave surface of liquids that wet the capillary walls and the convex surface of those that do not wet them are expressions of the tendency for the free surface energy to reduce surface area to a minimum.

As pointed out above, energy as work is required to move molecules from the interior of a liquid into its surface. The higher the surface tension of the liquid, the greater is the energy necessary to accomplish this. The molecules in the surface attract each other so as to form a film of greater or less strength. The term "surface tension" is used to indicate this force of attraction. In order that surface tension may be defined in quantitative terms, it is necessary to express it in units of surface and force. If one linear centimeter of surface be considered and if the film on both sides of this line and at right angles to it be pulled until the surface breaks, the force in dynes required to effect the break is the surface tension of the liquid. The total amount of free surface energy (in ergs) is dependent upon the total surface area (expressed in square centimeters) and the surface tension (in dynes). Suppose a film of water (surface tension 72 dynes) is placed on a wire loop with a movable wire bar across one end as shown in Figure 5.4. The surface area of each side of the film on the loop as shown is 1 cm × 1 cm = 1 sq cm. Now suppose the movable bar is lowered 1 cm to the end of the loop, thereby increasing each surface by 1 sq cm. The work (force × distance), in ergs, to increase one surface by 1 sq cm then is:

$$W \text{ (ergs)} = 72 \text{ dynes} \times 1 \text{ cm} = 72 \text{ ergs}$$

The actual work in stretching the film is twice this, because the film has two surfaces.

It is obvious that the surface tension of a liquid is numerically equal to the work, in ergs, required to increase the surface by 1 sq cm.

From the above considerations it can be seen that the total free surface energy, in ergs, of a liquid is equal to its surface tension, in dynes, multiplied by its surface area, in square centimeters. For example, a water surface of 20 sq cm and surface tension of 72 dynes would have a total free surface energy of $72 \times 20 = 1440$ ergs.

It is not surprising that relatively great changes in free energy accompany marked changes in surface area. Factors which increase the surface of a liquid increase this energy in proportion to the area increase, and vice versa.

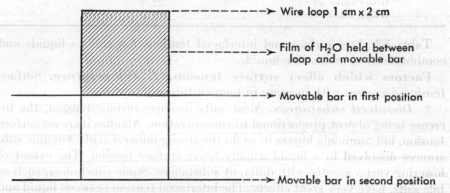

> Wire loop 1 cm x 2 cm

> Film of H_2O held between loop and movable bar

> Movable bar in first position

> Movable bar in second position

Figure 5.4. Film of liquid on wire loop. (From West, E. S.: *Textbook of Biophysical Chemistry*, 2nd ed. The Macmillan Co., New York, 1956.)

Methods of determining surface tension. The surface tension of a liquid may be determined by the height to which the solution rises in a capillary which the liquid wets (glass capillaries generally); it is given by the equation:

$$\gamma = \text{surface tension in dynes per centimeter} = \tfrac{1}{2}hdgr$$

in which h = height to which liquid rises in the capillary, d = density of the liquid, g = acceleration due to gravity, and r = capillary radius.

Another method is based upon the weight of liquid drops delivered from the tip of a tube calibrated against known liquids. The weight of the drop is proportional to the surface tension of the liquid. This is the drop-weight method.

Du Noüy devised a torsion balance in which a platinum loop is dipped into the liquid and the force, in dynes, required to separate the loop from the surface is measured. This instrument gives a direct reading of the surface tension on a calibrated scale.

For measuring interfacial tensions of liquids, modifications of methods for surface tension are used.

Table 5.2.   Surface Tensions at 20° C

Liquid	Surface Tension, in Dynes per Linear Centimeter
Water	72.8
Glycerol	65.2
Benzene	27.9
Ethyl acetate	23.3
Alcohol	21.7
Ether	16.5
Mercury	465.0

Interfacial Tensions between Liquids

Liquids	Interfacial Tension, in Dynes per Linear Centimeter of Interface
Water/benzene	32.6
Water/chloroform	27.7
Water/olive oil	22.9
Water/ether	9.7

Table 5.2 gives surface and interfacial tensions for various liquids and combinations of immiscible liquids.

Factors which affect surface tension. *1. Temperature.* Surface tension decreases with increase in temperature.

2. Dissolved substances. Most salts increase surface tension, the increase being almost proportional to concentration. Alkalies increase surface tension, but ammonia lowers it, as do the strong mineral acids. Organic substances dissolved in a liquid usually lower surface tension. The extent of lowering varies greatly with different substances. Some substances, such as bile salts, have very great effects. The interfacial tension between liquid and liquid is generally lowered by all dissolved substances.

Surface tension of colloidal solutions. Coarse suspensions and suspensoids produce little effect upon the air-liquid surface tension of the liquid in which the particles are suspended. There is an interfacial tension between the surfaces of the particles and surrounding liquid which cannot be measured. Emulsions and emulsoids, on the other hand, decrease the air-liquid surface tension of liquids in which they are suspended. When shaken, these solutions foam greatly, owing to the lowering of the surface tension of the suspending liquid. Suspensoid solutions do not foam appreciably.

When olive oil is shaken vigorously with water, it is broken into fine droplets, and a temporary emulsion is formed. The droplets soon coalesce, and the emulsion breaks. There is an interfacial tension of about 23 dynes (at ordinary temperature) between olive oil and water. If soap is added to the mixture and it is shaken, a permanent emulsion is formed. Soap molecules enter the interface between oil and water and lower the interfacial tension. This favors emulsion formation. As will be shown later, soap ions adsorb onto the oil droplet surfaces and give the droplets negative charges. This also stabilizes the emulsion.

Surface energy. The total free surface energy of a system is equal to the product of an intensity factor and a capacity factor. The intensity factor is the surface or interfacial tension. The capacity factor is the surface area.

The total free surface energy is given by the expression: $S = \gamma s$, where S = free surface energy, γ = surface or interfacial tension in dynes per centimeter, and s = surface area in square centimeters.

The Gibbs-Thomson principle in relation to surface tension. Willard Gibbs and Sir J. J. Thomson independently formulated a principle which determines the effect of substances upon surface and interfacial tension, as follows: Substances which lower the surface tension become concentrated in the surface layer, whereas substances which increase surface tension are more concentrated within the interior of the liquid than in the surface. The principle is of fundamental importance in relation to the phenomenon of adsorption and, consequently, to the field of biochemistry. Many characteristic properties of colloidal systems (protoplasm is a colloidal system), such as precipitation, electrical charges, surface tension, and viscosity, are connected with adsorption phenomena.

ADSORPTION

Surfaces of all kinds have unneutralized fields of force or free valences which have the power of more or less strongly attracting and holding other molecules upon the surface. Langmuir has especially contributed to the theory of adsorption on solids. He considers that each solid has a characteristic crystal lattice, or structure, and that the surface is like a checkerboard with atoms arranged in orderly fashion. Each atom at the surface has free valences or attractive forces which are capable of attaching one, and only one, molecule from a solution or gas. A dynamic condition exists at the surface with molecules continually passing into and away from it. At equilibrium the rate of adsorption is equal to the rate of desorption. According to Langmuir, the primarily adsorbed molecules on a surface are one molecule deep, because attractive forces on the surface are limited to distances of about one molecular thickness. A number of experiments tend to verify this theory.

The extent to which adsorption takes place is dependent upon the nature of both adsorbing agent and the substance adsorbed. The greater the surface of the adsorbing agent, the greater is the adsorption. Consequently, matter in finely divided or colloidal state exhibits great powers of adsorption. When charcoal is heated in steam and then at a temperature of 700° to 800° C in a closed container, it becomes "activated" and is the most powerful adsorbing agent (called "adsorbent") known. The activation process affects the surface of the charcoal and greatly increases its adsorbing power. Charcoal is exceedingly porous and consequently possesses enormous surface relative to mass. Harkins and Ewing state that the surface area (including the pore surfaces) of 1 g of charcoal is around 120 sq m. They state that water is adsorbed so powerfully upon this surface that its volume is compressed to 75 per cent of its original value. This would represent an adsorption pressure of about 37,000 atm. Gustaver considers that when a vapor is adsorbed by charcoal two processes occur: (*a*) the vapor is adsorbed at the surface; (*b*) the condensed vapor then collects as liquid in the capillary pores. He considers that, if the total surface represented by all the capillaries of charcoal is considered, the total surface area of 1 g is around 3000 sq m. We do not know definitely the surface area of charcoal, but we do know that it is relatively very great. The nature of the free valence or adsorbing forces upon the surface of charcoal is such as to make it an excellent adsorbing agent for many different substances. This is witnessed by its widespread use in the laboratory and industry for decolorizing all sorts of solutions, where the colored molecules are generally complex organic substances. It also adsorbs simple molecules, and there is generally some loss of practically all molecules from solutions decolorized by charcoal. Its great powers of adsorbing most gases make it an important component of the filling of gas masks.

Silica gel, alumina cream $Al(OH)_3$, kaolin, and fuller's earth are all excellent adsorbing agents which are commonly used in the laboratory and in industry.

Principles governing adsorption. 1. One of the most important principles is that of Gibbs-Thomson, which states, "those substances which decrease surface energy tend to concentrate at a liquid-air interface (in the surface), and those substances which decrease interfacial energy tend to concentrate at a liquid-solid or liquid-liquid interface."

It follows from this principle that adsorption is best from solvents of high surface tension, because here the solute causes the greatest decrease in surface energy at the interface of adsorbing solid and liquid solvent.

2. Freundlich proposed an empirical equation to describe the relation between amount of substance adsorbed and its equilibrium concentration at a given temperature. This equation is known as Freundlich's adsorption isotherm and may be written:

$$a = kC^{1/n}$$

or in logarithmic form:

$$\log a = \log k + \frac{1}{n} \log C$$

where a = the amount of substance adsorbed per gram of adsorbent, C = the equilibrium concentration of substance in solution (or pressure of gas in case of gas adsorption), and k and n are constants depending upon the natures of the adsorbent and the substance adsorbed and the temperature. When a is plotted against C, a curve of the general form shown in Figure 5.5 is obtained. If $\log a$ is plotted against $\log C$, a straight line is obtained such as is shown in Figure 5.6 if the process follows Freundlich's equation. The slope of the line is $1/n$ and the ordinate intercept is equal to $\log k$. Thus such a plot permits the values of the constants n and k to be evaluated.

Langmuir developed an adsorption equation from purely theoretical considerations:

$$a = \frac{\alpha\beta c}{1 + \alpha c}$$

in which a = the amount of substance adsorbed, c = the equilibrium concentration of the substance adsorbed, and α and β are constants. If c/a is plotted against c, a straight line should be obtained the slope of which is $1/\beta$ and the intercept $1/\alpha\beta$.

3. Adsorption is a reversible process. A condition of equilibrium is reached for any given concentration of solute in contact with the adsorbing agent.

4. Adsorption decreases with rise in temperature, as distinguished from chemical processes. This is due to the increased kinetic energy of the adsorbed molecules, which causes them to escape more readily from the adsorbing surface.

5. The adsorption process takes place relatively quickly. Equilibrium is generally reached within one hour.

6. The amount of adsorption is proportional to the surface area, and it varies with the nature of the surface of the adsorbent and of the substance adsorbed.

7. Adsorption is more nearly complete when the ratio of adsorbent to substance adsorbed is high; in other words, adsorption proceeds best from dilute solutions.

8. Narrow pores in the surface of the adsorbing agent are more effective than globular openings.

9. The heat of adsorption may be very great. Blench and Garner

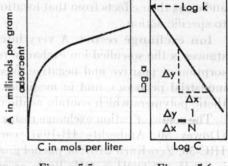

Figure 5.5   Figure 5.6

have determined that the heat of adsorption of oxygen on charcoal varies from 50,000 to 224,000 calories as compared with heats of combustion of 94,000 to 97,000 calories for the carbon which adsorbs this oxygen.

10. The molecules adsorbed on a surface are oriented and arranged in a definite manner relative to the adsorbing surface and to each other.

The importance of adsorption phenomena. *1. Adsorption and catalysts.* Many chemical reactions are speeded up by the presence of adsorptive surfaces. Oxygen and hydrogen are adsorbed together upon platinum black and combine rapidly at ordinary temperatures to form water. Charcoal, suspended in a solution of glycine, enables gaseous oxygen to oxidize the glycine at ordinary temperatures. Enzymes, which are organic catalysts of much importance in biologic processes, are proteins and consequently colloidal. They are known to combine with the substrate while acting upon it. Surface adsorption upon the colloidal enzyme particle is requisite for enzyme action. The tissues of the body are largely colloidal and interspersed with a network of membranes which possess enormous surfaces. It is probable that adsorption processes taking place at these membranes promote many vital chemical reactions and also cause changes in surface tension and cell consistency.

2. Purification of enzymes. As previously noted, adsorbing agents are widely used in purification processes in industry and in the laboratory. Adsorption processes are often applied in the purification of enzymes. The enzyme may be selectively adsorbed upon an agent, such as $Al(OH)_3$, from impure solution at one pH, the material washed, and then the enzyme liberated (desorbed) by placing it in a solution of different pH.

3. Protoplasmic organization. There are various more or less loosely joined complex compounds in protoplasm, such as combinations of proteins and lipids of various kinds, of proteins and salts, of proteins and carbohydrates, etc. It is probable that such compounds are being continually formed and broken down and that they enter vitally into the structure and function of living protoplasm. Adsorption processes very probably enter into the formation of some of these complexes.

4. Action of drugs. Adsorption plays a very important role in the action of certain drugs and poisons which are adsorbed upon cell surfaces and exert their effects from that location. Selective adsorption may be related to specific action.

Ion exchange resins. A very interesting and important group of substances is the so-called ion exchange resins that are widely used for the adsorption of positive and negative ions from solutions in the laboratory, in industrial processes, and in medicine. These substances are insoluble synthetic polymers which contain acidic or basic groups.

The acidic or cation exchange resins contain sulfonic acid groups, $-SO_3H$ (Dowex 50, Amberlite IR-105); carboxyl groups, $-COOH$ (Amberlite IRC-50, Zeo-Karb 216); or phenol groups, $-OH$. The order of acid strength is $SO_3H > COOH > OH$. Basic or anion exchange resins contain weakly basic amine groups, $-NH_2$ (Amberlite IR-4B), or strongly basic quaternary ammonium groups, $-(NR_3)^+ OH^-$ (Amberlite, IRA-400, Dowex I).

The acid groups present in the surfaces of acid resins dissociate as do other acid groups. For example, Resin $COOH \rightleftharpoons$ Resin $-COO + H^+$. Such resins may be titrated as other acids to give their salts (ionized forms), and they have pK values from the relation:

$$pH = pK + \log \frac{[\text{Resin COO}]}{[\text{Resin COOH}]}$$

The surfaces of acid resins bind cations such as H^+, Na^+, Ca^{++}, NH_4^+, and ions of organic bases, $R \cdot NH_3^+$, apparently through forces of adsorption in addition to the attraction of the negative charge. For each cation there is a definite adsorptive force binding it to the surface for a given set of conditions, some ions being bound much more firmly than others. For a number of cations the relative binding powers and replacement capacities are in the order:

$$Al^{+++} > Ba^{++} > Sr^{++} > Ca^{++} > Mg^{++} > Cs^+ > Rb^+ > K^+ > NH_4^+ > Na^+ > H^+ > Li^+$$

The adsorption of cations is markedly increased by an increase in valence.

A cation exchange resin may be prepared as the free acid form or as one of its salts. Suppose a cation exchange resin as its sodium salt, Resin—$\overset{-}{S}O_3\overset{+}{N}a$, is treated with a solution of the salt of an organic base, R—$\overset{+}{N}H_3\overset{-}{C}l$, the following reversible process takes place:

$$\underset{\substack{\text{Resin surface}}}{\text{Resin—}\overset{-}{S}O_3\overset{+}{N}a} + \underset{\substack{\text{Solution}}}{R—\overset{+}{N}H_3\overset{-}{C}l} \rightleftarrows \underset{\substack{\text{Resin surface}}}{\text{Resin—}\overset{-}{S}O_3\overset{+}{N}H_3 \cdot R} + \underset{\substack{\text{Solution}}}{\overset{+}{N}a + \overset{-}{C}l}$$

According to the mass law, the reaction can be pushed far to the right, with exchange of $R \cdot \overset{+}{N}H_3$ for $\overset{+}{N}a$ being most complete, by using a relatively large amount of resin and a relatively small amount of $R\overset{+}{N}H_3\overset{-}{C}l$. Conversely, Resin—$\overset{-}{S}O_3\overset{+}{N}a$ and $R \cdot \overset{+}{N}H_3\overset{-}{C}l$ can be regenerated by treating Resin—$\overset{-}{S}O_3\overset{+}{N}H_3 \cdot R$ with a large amount of $\overset{+}{N}a\overset{-}{C}l$ to reverse the reaction. In order that such exchanges may be as nearly complete as possible, the resins are generally packed in long vertical tubes and the solution containing the ion to be adsorbed is poured on the top of the column. As the solution passes over the resin, the ion exchanges as discussed above take place, and the solution emerging from the tube contains the ion originally on the resin surface. The solution remaining in the column may be washed out with a solvent or solution which does not remove the adsorbed ion. The adsorbed ion may then be obtained by in turn desorbing it from the resin by running the appropriate cation solution through the column.

The basic or anion exchange resins carry positive charges on the surface and thus adsorb negative ions. For example, a quaternary base resin, Resin—$(NR_3)\overset{+}{}\overset{-}{O}H$, undergoes exchange with the salt of an organic acid, $R\overset{-}{C}OO\overset{+}{N}a$, as follows:

$$\text{Resin}^-(NR_3)\overset{+}{}\overset{-}{O}H + R \cdot \overset{-}{C}OO\overset{+}{N}a \rightleftarrows \text{Resin}^-(NR_3)\overset{+}{}\overset{-}{O}OC \cdot R + \overset{+}{N}a + \overset{-}{O}H$$

Obviously a resin salt such as Resin—$(NR_3)\overset{+}{}\overset{-}{C}l$ functions in a like manner. The principles relating to the use of anion exchange resins are similar to those discussed for cation exchange resins.

For strong-base anion exchange resins of the quaternary type (Resin—$(NR_3)\overset{+}{}$) the binding powers and displacing capacities for anions are in the order: citrate > sulfate > oxalate > iodide > nitrate > chromate > bromide > thiocyanate > chloride > formate > hydroxyl > fluoride > acetate. In the case of weak-base anion exchange resins (Resin—$\overset{+}{N}H_3$) the order is a bit different, particularly in that OH has the highest combining power and displacement capacity: hydroxyl > sulfate > chromate > citrate > tartrate > nitrate > arsenate > phosphate > molybdate > acetate = iodide = bromide > chloride > fluoride. This means that other anions are readily displaced from the resins by hydroxyl ion.

All ions may be removed from solutions by passage of the solution through both a cation exchanger in the hydrogen (acid) form and an anion exchanger in the hydroxyl form. For example, the removal of NaCl from solution may be represented by:

$$\text{Resin} \cdot \overset{-}{H} + \overset{+\,-}{NaCl} \rightleftharpoons \text{Resin} \cdot \overset{-\ +}{Na} + \overset{+\ -}{HCl}$$
$$\text{Resin} \cdot \overset{+\ -}{OH} + \overset{+\ -}{HCl} \rightleftharpoons \text{Resin} \cdot \overset{+\ -}{Cl} + H_2O$$

Thus one resin removes $\overset{+}{Na}$ and the other $\overset{-}{Cl}$, and water is formed in the process.

The use of ion exchange resins has reached enormous proportions and is of very great importance. In the laboratory they are used widely in the preparation of deionized water, the removal of undesirable ions from many kinds of solutions, and the separation and purification of ionic substances in analytical and preparative procedures. Since different substances are held on a resin surface by different degrees of force, it is often possible to adsorb quantitatively a large number of cationic or anionic substances from a solution on the appropriate resin in a column and then to remove them selectively from the resin by running the proper eluting solution through the column. Such procedures are utilized in the separation and purification of amino acids, organic and inorganic phosphates, vitamins, hormones, and other biologic substances. Industrial processes by the hundreds utilize ion exchange resins for such purposes as water softening and demineralization, removal of electrolytes from foods and other products, and the separation and purification of metals. Ion exchange resins are used in medicine for such purposes as reducing the acidity of gastric juice in cases of peptic ulcer (oral administration of anion exchange resins), reduction of $\overset{+}{Na}$ and $\overset{+}{K}$ concentrations in body fluids in cases of congestive heart failure and renal failure (administration of cation exchange resins orally or by enema), and adsorption of toxic products of bacterial action in cases of diarrhea.

The zeolite minerals and several clays are naturally occurring cation exchangers which are used in the laboratory and in industry.

Orientation of molecules and ions in surfaces and interfacial films. The work of Hardy, Harkins, Langmuir, Adam, and others has shown that, whereas the molecules in the interior of a liquid are distributed in a random fashion relative to each other, the arrangement of the molecules in the surface or interface is more or less orderly. This orderly arrangement of molecules in surface films is commonly referred to as "molecular orientation." It is especially pronounced in molecules containing both polar and nonpolar groups. Polar groups are those such as —OH, —NH₂, —COOH, —CN, —CHO, —CONH₂, —SH, —NHCH₃, —NCS, —COOR, —NO₂ —CH=CH₂, —C≡CH, —SO₃H, and —COR. Also, halogens represent polar groups. These groups contain atoms which possess free pairs of electrons that can form coordinate linkages in many cases. They are surrounded by rather strong forces of attraction. Hydrocarbon radicals represent most of the nonpolar groups, and a saturated hydrocarbon radical is more nonpolar than an unsaturated one. A molecule such as hexane is symmetrical and nonpolar. The two ends of the molecule are identical in properties. The forces of attraction around the surface of the molecule are relatively weak. If an —OH group is placed on one end carbon of hexane, the molecule of hexyl alcohol is formed. It contains the polar —OH group and the nonpolar C_6H_{13}— (hexyl) radical. The two ends of the molecule have different chemical structures with different forces of attraction about them. The —OH group has forces of attraction and chemical properties similar to those of water, is strongly attracted by water, and is soluble in it. On the other hand, the forces of attraction about the hexyl radical are relatively weak compared with those of water; it is not attracted so strongly by water as the —OH group is, and it is not soluble in water.

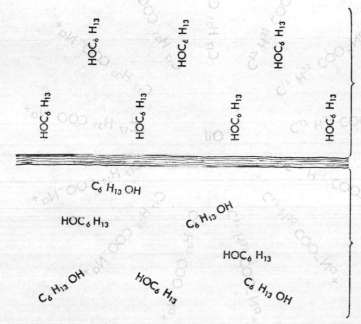

Figure 5.7. Orientation of hexyl alcohol molecules at surface of liquid. (From West, E. S.: *Textbook of Biophysical Chemistry*, 2nd ed. The Macmillan Co., New York, 1956.)

Suppose we consider the surface phenomena where molecules containing polar and nonpolar groups are concerned. In the first place, what condition exists in the surface (air-hexyl alcohol interface) of hexyl alcohol? Now, the forces of attraction within the alcohol are stronger than in the air above the surface. Around the —OH group of the hexyl alcohol molecule the forces of attraction are stronger than around the C_6H_{13}— radical. At the surface of the pure alcohol the molecules are more or less oriented so that the —OH groups are directed into the surface (where forces of attraction are stronger) and the hexyl radicals are directed above the surface in more or less parallel fashion at right angles to the surface. The diagram shown in Figure 5.7 may help illustrate the situation.

When hexyl alcohol is poured upon water, an interface is formed between the liquids. The —OH groups of the alcohol are more strongly attracted by the water molecules than the hexyl radicals are. Consequently, at the interface the alcohol molecules are oriented so that their —OH groups are directed into the water film and their hexyl radicals into the alcohol. The student should show these relations by diagram.

Suppose benzoic acid is dissolved in water and this is poured into benzene. The two liquids do not mix, and an interface is formed between them. The benzoic acid

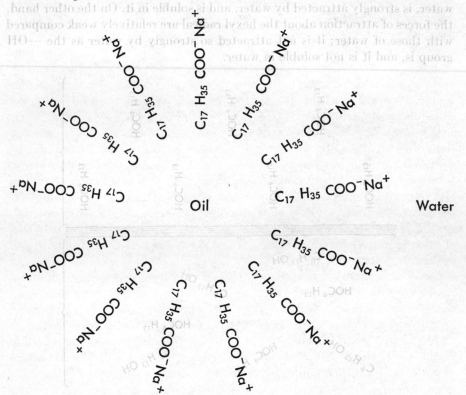

Figure 5.8. Emulsification of oil by sodium stearate. (From West, E. S.: *Textbook of Biophysical Chemistry*, 2nd ed. The Macmillan Co., New York, 1956.)

benzoic acid will be distributed between the liquids according to the distribution law. At the interface between the liquids, however, there will be orientation of benzoic acid molecules with the polar —COOH groups directed into the water and the less polar C_6H_5— groups into the benzene.

Consider what happens when mineral or other oil is emulsified with soap. If the oil is shaken vigorously with water, it is broken into droplets to form an emulsion which, however, is unstable. The droplets of oil coalesce and separate as a layer of oil on water. If a little soap, such as sodium stearate, is added before the oil is shaken with the water, a stable emulsion is formed. The diagram of Figure 5.8 will help in understanding the action of soap in stabilizing the emulsion.

The ionized soap molecules contain the hydrocarbon radical, $C_{17}H_{35}$—, which is soluble in oil but not in water, and the —COO⁻ group, which is soluble in water but not in oil. Consequently, the soap ions are oriented at the interface of oil and water with the hydrocarbon radicals in the oil and the carboxyl ions in the water. The negative carboxyl groups give the emulsion droplets a negative surface charge, which is balanced by the Na^+ ions in the surrounding water. The emulsion droplets thus have a Helmholtz double layer, across which there is a potential difference (zeta potential). Since the droplets are all charged alike, they repel each other and remain in suspension. Also, the layer of soap ions oriented in the interface causes the surface of the droplets to be strongly attracted by water (hydrophilic). This is due to the —COO⁻ groups for which the water has a high attraction. The soap thus stabilizes an oil emulsion both by imparting a charge to the droplets and by making the droplets hydrophilic. Various substances, such as high molecular weight alkyl sulfonic acids (or their salts), phospholipids, and bile salts, act as emulsifying agents upon this basis.

It is interesting to note that when calcium soaps are used in forming emulsions with oil and water an emulsion of water droplets in oil is obtained, as contrasted with oil droplets in water produced by sodium or potassium soaps. Calcium soaps are much more soluble in oil than in water, whereas sodium and potassium soaps are much more soluble in water. In general, emulsifying agents which are water-soluble give oil-in-water emulsions, whereas emulsifying agents which are soluble in oil give water-in-oil emulsions. The action of calcium soaps in producing water-in-oil emulsions and that of sodium and potassium salts in giving oil-in-water emulsions probably involve different ways of molecular orientation at the interfaces. An oil-in-water emulsion produced with a univalent metal soap may be reversed to a water-in-oil emulsion by adding a soluble calcium salt which, by double decomposition, produces the calcium soap. It should be pointed out that an emulsion is stable when the interfacial tension between the droplets and surrounding liquid is low, and that any agent which greatly lowers the interfacial tension of water and another liquid will tend to produce an emulsion. Molecular orientation takes place at these interfaces and is directly concerned in the emulsification. In emulsions of oil-in-water stabilized by sodium or potassium soaps, the carboxyl ion, with its associated metal, is oriented toward the water dispersions medium, and the hydrocarbon radical is oriented toward the oil droplet. With water-in-oil emulsions, stabilized by calcium soap, the carboxyl and metal ions are oriented toward the water droplet, and the hydrocarbon radicals are oriented toward the oil dispersions medium. Figure 5.9 illustrates the differences in orientation.

It has been found that calcium soaps increase the interfacial tension between oil and water, whereas sodium soaps decrease the tension. It is possible that effects upon interfacial tension are related to the production of oil-in-water emulsions by sodium soaps and water-in-oil emulsions by calcium soaps. Mixtures of sodium and calcium soaps in the proper proportion nullify the effects of both. This phenomenon is known as "ion antagonism." Various ions have antagonistic physiologic actions upon protoplasm. For example, calcium is antagonistic to sodium, magnesium to calcium, and sodium to potassium. These effects are probably due to complex causes. Interfacial tension phenomena and emulsifying action may play some role in physiologic ion antagonisms.

Where the oriented molecule has a hydrocarbon radical with a polar group attached at one end, the molecules tend to orient upon a water surface perpendicularly to the surface, with the polar groups in the water and the hydrocarbon groups directed up to the air. The lateral attraction between the hydrocarbon radicals tends to hold them together as a more or less compact film. However, if there are two or more polar groups in a molecule, these

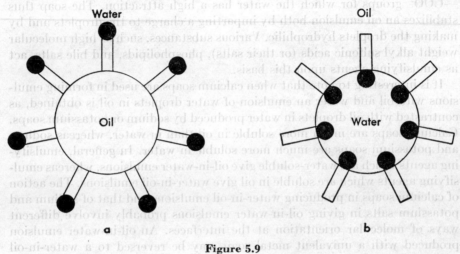

Figure 5.9

(*a*) Oil-in-water emulsion. Hydrocarbon group oriented to oil droplet; carboxyl and metal ions oriented to water dispersions medium. Produced by univalent metal soaps.

(*b*) Water-in-oil emulsion. Hydrocarbon group oriented to oil dispersions medium; carboxyl and metal ions oriented to water droplet. Produced by divalent metal soaps.

(From West, E. S.: *Textbook of Biophysical Chemistry*, 2nd ed. The Macmillan Co., New York, 1956.)

groups may pull the hydrocarbon group horizontally upon the surface with resultant packing into a horizontal oriented film.

It should be pointed out that the molecules in an oriented layer at an interface are in a dynamic condition. Molecules are continually leaving and entering it. The oriented layer of molecules may be saturated so that it cannot hold a greater number; or when a limited number of molecules are available, an incomplete layer may be present. An increase in temperature tends, through kinetic motion, to disrupt orientation. The addition of other molecules which are adsorbed into an interface or surface may change the orientation of molecules already there. Molecular orientation is evidently closely connected with surface and interfacial tensions and, consequently, with adsorption phenomena.

The methods of studying the orientation of molecules at interfaces involve various procedures which cannot be discussed in detail here. Harkins and coworkers have approached the problem especially through measurements of energies of surfaces and interfaces. Langmuir and associates have studied the spreading of films of various substances upon water; and, as these films are monomolecular in thickness, they have been able to calculate the area covered by each molecule in the film and from this the way in which the molecules are oriented. Langmuir also studied the energy relations in films of alcohols, organic acids, etc., by the use of his surface pressure balance. With this instrument one can apply lateral pressure to such films upon water and measure their spreading tendency or surface pressure. From such measurements many characteristics of the molecules in the films can be obtained.

VISCOSITY

The resistance experienced by one part of a liquid in moving over another part is called "viscosity." Viscosity varies greatly. Liquids such as ether and gasoline have little viscosity and are quite mobile, whereas others, such as honey and tar, have high viscosities. The unit of viscosity is the "poise," named after Poiseuille, the Frenchman who first devised methods of measuring viscosity. The poise may be defined, in centimeter-gram-second units, as the force, in dynes, necessary to be applied to an area of 1 sq cm between two parallel planes 1 sq cm in area and 1 cm apart, to produce a difference in streaming velocity between the liquid planes of 1 cm per second. The centipoise is one-hundredth of a poise. The absolute viscosity of water at 25° C is 0.00895 poise and is generally used as the unit in plotting the viscosity of liquid systems. Poiseuille discovered the law governing the rate of flow of liquids through capillary tubes. It is expressed mathematically as follows:

$$\eta = \frac{\pi P r^4}{8 V l} t$$

where η (eta) = viscosity, V = volume of liquid flowing through a capillary tube of length l, and radius r, in the time t, under pressure P. If the times of flow of equal volumes of two liquids through the same capillary are measured under the same head of liquid, the ratio of viscosities is given by:

$$\frac{\eta_1}{\eta_2} = \frac{d_1 t_1}{d_2 t_2}$$

where η_1 and η_2 represent the coefficients of viscosity of the two liquids, d_1 and d_2, their densities, and t_1 and t_2, their times of flow. If one chooses water as a standard with a viscosity of 1, the viscosities of other liquids relative to water may be determined by obtaining the time of flow of water and of these liquids through a capillary. The relative viscosity is obtained by using the equation:

$$\frac{\eta_1}{1} = \frac{d_1 t_1}{d_w t_w}$$

in which η_1 is the relative viscosity of the liquid, d_1 its density, and t_1 its time of flow. The assigned viscosity of water is 1, its density d_w, and its time of flow t_w. The relative viscosity values obtained in this way may be converted to absolute viscosities by multiplying by the absolute viscosity of water at the temperature of the experiment.

Fluidity expresses the tendency of a liquid to flow, whereas viscosity is a measure of the resistance which a liquid offers to flowing. Fluidity is equal to the reciprocal of viscosity.

Factors affecting viscosity. *1. Temperature.* The viscosity of liquids decreases about 2 per cent for each degree rise in temperature.

2. Dissolved substances. In general, small quantities of nonelectrolytes, such as sugar and alcohol, increase viscosity, whereas small amounts of highly ionized salts decrease it. Viscosity is generally increased by the solution of large quantities of solids.

3. Viscosity of colloid systems. Lyophobic colloids (suspensoids) in general have a viscosity that differs little from that of the pure dispersions medium and increases only slightly with increasing concentration of dispersed particles. In contrast, the viscosity of lyophilic colloid sols (emulsoids) is generally relatively high. When the emulsoid sol sets to a gel, the viscosity becomes so great that pressure is required to cause flow. This may be true also in the case of certain emulsoid sols.

4. Effect of suspended material. Suspended particles cause an increase in viscosity in proportion to the volume of suspended material relative to the total volume.

The viscosity of blood is of importance in relation to the resistance offered to the heart in circulating the blood. The heart muscle functions best when working against a certain resistance. The viscosity of blood is due largely to the emulsoid colloidal systems present in plasma (mainly protein solutions) and to the great proportion of suspended corpuscles.

The effect of metallic ions upon the viscosity of protoplasmic gel has been studied especially by Chambers and Reznikoff, who used the micromanipulation apparatus of Chambers. These workers injected solutions of the chlorides of sodium, potassium, calcium, and magnesium into amebae and observed the protoplasmic changes. Owing to decreased viscosity, sodium and potassium chlorides caused liquefaction of the protoplasm surrounding the injected area. The protoplasm tended to pass from the gel to the sol colloidal state. Injection of calcium chloride caused a local solidification of the protoplasmic mass, which the ameba "pinched off" and rejected, the remainder of the ameba appearing normal. Upon injection of magnesium chloride, local solidification occurred as in the case of calcium chloride. In this case no "pinching-off" occurred, and the solidification process gradually spread throughout the protoplasmic mass, leading to complete gelation and death. When proper mixtures of sodium or potassium chlorides and calcium chloride were injected, no effect was produced. The ions exerted an antagonistic effect upon the protoplasm. It is probable that the actions of these ions in protoplasm are related to changes in interfacial tension and the type of protoplasmic emulsions.

Heilbrunn and others have estimated the viscosity of protoplasm in eggs of the sea urchin Arbacia, of the clam Cumingia, and in ameba and other lower forms by determining the rate of fall of cellular granules through the hyaline protoplasm under centrifugal force. Protoplasmic viscosity also has been determined from the Brownian movement of cellular granules, to which the following equation of Einstein applies:

$$\eta = \frac{RTt}{D_x{}^2 N 3 \pi a}$$

in which η = the viscosity, R = the gas constant, T = the absolute temperature, N = the Avogadro number, D_x = the displacement of a particle in Brownian movement along one axis, t = the time, and a = the radius of the granule.

By the above methods the hyaline protoplasm showed viscosities ranging from 2 to 20 centipoises, which varied with species and conditions. The viscosity of the entire protoplasm is higher because of the inclusion granules and bodies.

MEMBRANE PHENOMENA

Membranes of parchment and collodion owe their permeability to pores passing through them. A membrane of rubber may be permeable to certain molecules, such as benzene, because the molecules pass through the membrane by solution in it. The living animal cell membrane surrounding protoplasm has properties not possessed by ordinary lifeless membranes. The cell membrane is an actual part of the living protoplasmic mass, and when the cell dies, so does the membrane. Protoplasm contains a complex mixture of proteins, phospholipids, cholesterol, some neutral fat, free fatty acids and soaps, carbohydrates, various inorganic ions, etc. The membrane of the cell is apparently formed from constituents of the protoplasm but in different proportions from those found within the cell. Because the cell membrane represents an interface, the substances which lower surface tension tend to concentrate there (principle of Gibbs). Accordingly, the membrane should contain more phospholipids, soaps, cholesterol, and other lipids than the interior of the protoplasm does. Such seems to be the case. According to the principle of molecular orientation the various molecules and ions in the surface of the cell membrane must be more or less oriented, giving it a characteristic type of structure and markedly influencing its permeability.

It appears rather well established that cell membranes generally are made up of organized and oriented lipid layers superposed upon a meshwork of protein layers, the lipid and protein layers being held together by forces of adsorption and by complex formations between them. The lipid layer of the erythrocyte membrane is about 50 Å thick, equal to the thickness of two to four lipid molecules. The thickness of the membrane lipid layers of other cells appears not to exceed 100 Å. While the thickness of the protein layers is less well known, it probably is something of the same order of magnitude.

Cell membranes contain holes or pores through which certain ions, small

molecules, and water may pass. The walls of the pores are generally negatively charged, with the result that the pores may show the phenomena of
streaming or flow potential and electroendosmosis.

The membrane surface possesses an electric charge due to selective adsorption of ions and the ionization of compounds in the membrane surface. Consequently, the membrane has a Helmholtz double ionic layer. Also, there is
a potential difference between the outside and inside of animal cell membranes which generally is of the order of $+0.1$ volt. This potential is in accord
with the differential distribution of K^+ ions in the intracellular and extracellular fluids in contact with the opposite sides of the membrane. There is
generally 36 to 40 times as much K^+ in intracellular, as in extracellular fluid.
According to the Nernst equation for a concentration cell this should give a
potential close to $+0.1$ volt at $37°$ C:

$$E = 0.061 \log C_2/C_1 = 0.061 \log 40/1 = 0.061 \times 1.6 = 0.097 \text{ volt}$$

where $C_2 = $ the concentration of K^+ in the intracellular fluid and $C_1 = $ the
concentration in extracellular fluid. It appears therefore that maintenance of
different concentrations of K^+ ions on the inside and outside of cell membranes is related to the potential across the membrane.

There is a potential drop across the membrane from the exterior to the
protoplasmic layer inside. Flexner and Stiehler found a potential drop as
high as 0.23 volt between the epithelium and stroma of the secreting choroid
plexus of the fetal pig. The potential in the epithelium was $+0.100$ volt, and
in the stroma -0.130 volt, as a maximum, under aerobic conditions. Under
anaerobiosis, which prevented cellular oxidations, this potential difference
between epithelium and stroma disappeared, both having a potential of
about -0.290 volt. Thus it is seen that cellular oxidation is necessary for
maintenance of the potential difference between the membrane and cytoplasmic layer. This potential difference causes an electric current between
the epithelium and stroma which promotes the movement of cations from
stroma to epithelium and anions from epithelium to stroma. Reversible oxidation-reduction processes involving cytochrome oxidase, dehydrogenases,
oxygen, and oxidizable substrates (food materials) furnish the electrons for
the current. The cytochrome oxidase is located in the epithelium. Acid dyes
(with negative charges) were found to pass from epithelium to stroma, and
basic dyes (with positive charges) from stroma to epithelium; neutral dyes
moved equally well in both directions, showing no selective effect due to the
membrane-stroma electric current. When oxidation processes were stopped
by asphyxia, the basic and acidic dyes showed no selective movement but
acted like neutral dyes. This showed that cellular oxidation is necessary for
maintenance of the membrane-stroma current and for the specific directional
movement of ions between epithelium and stroma.

Cattell and Civin found that if a cat is asphyxiated for a time, the potassium content of the blood increases greatly owing to passage of K^+ ions from
body cells across the cell membranes into the blood. Upon resumption of
respiration, the potassium passes back into the cells with restoration of the

normal ionic distribution. We must conclude that oxidation processes play an important role in regulating the structure, permeability, and functioning of cell membranes.

The purely physical forces which drive ions and molecules through membranes are those arising from differences in concentration and activity coefficients of substances on the opposite sides of membranes, differences in electric potential between phases in contact with opposite sides of membranes, and solvent drag forces by which substances are carried through membranes by the flow of solvent through the membranes. Such drag forces may arise from differences in osmotic pressure, electroendosmosis, etc.

The rate of penetration of a substance through a cell membrane at a given temperature is expressed as the net gram mols of substance passing through an area of one square micron in one second, with a concentration difference of one gram mol per liter across the membrane.

Since cell membranes contain a large proportion of lipid materials, they are more permeable to substances soluble in fats than they are to substances which are not fat-soluble. Since the surfaces of cell membranes and the pore walls of the membranes are electrically charged, neutral or uncharged molecules pass through better than do the ions of electrolytes. Thus, weakly dissociated organic acids pass into and out of cells more readily than their salts, which are highly ionized. Living membranes show great variation in permeability to different ions. The intestine absorbs Na^+, K^+, and Cl^- ions much more readily than it does Ca^{++}, Mg^{++}, and $SO_4^=$. In general, small molecules pass through living membranes better than do larger molecules of the same general type. A larger molecule may pass through much more readily than a smaller molecule of different chemical type. Cholesterol molecules are very little absorbed by the intestinal membranes into the blood, while these same molecules are readily absorbed when combined with bile salts to form much larger complex molecules. The intestine absorbs the sugar glucose more readily than it does the smaller molecules of the sugar xylose.

Some of the processes of passage through membranes involve chemical change. Galactose may be converted to glucose as it passes through intestinal membranes, and sucrose is split into glucose and fructose as it passes through.

There are a number of processes in the body in which membranes pass substances through from a lower to a higher concentration—that is, against a concentration gradient. This means that work is done at the expense of energy. For example, the membranes of the small intestine absorb glucose and sodium chloride into the blood from solutions in the lumen which are at much lower concentrations than in the blood. Such processes of passage through membranes requiring the expenditure of energy and the performance of work are referred to as "active transport." An outstanding example of active transport is found in muscle and other cells where the Na^+ concentrations within the cells are maintained at much lower concentrations than in the surrounding fluid.

While the total concentrations of ions in extracellular and intracellular compartments are generally quite different, the positive charges of the cations must equal the negative charges of the anions in each compartment in order to maintain electrical neutrality. The interior of the cell contains a relatively very high concentration of negatively charged protein anions (proteiñ), which exert a powerful Donnan effect across the membrane, and which must be balanced by equivalents of cations (mainly Na^+ and K^+). The total quantity of Na^+ and K^+ which the cell can hold is determined primarily by the quantity of proteiñ present. The quantity of proteiñ (and other anions) present within cells (also in extracellular fluids) is determined by the pH. As the pH rises, the proteins and other acids undergo more ionization to increase the negative charges, while when the pH decreases, the reverse takes place. In an alkalosis (pH above normal) the body tissues and fluids require more cations to balance the negative charges, while in an acidosis (pH below normal) fewer cations are required. Thus, the total electrolyte content of the body varies with the pH.

In order to maintain electrical neutrality, when ions such as K^+ and H^+ pass from the cell across the membrane to the extracellular fluid, a cation such as Na^+ passes from the extracellular fluid into the cell. Vice versa, when Na^+ moves into the cell, equivalent amounts of K^+ and H^+ pass out of it.

Tissue cell membranes generally are permeable to both K^+ and Na^+; however, the concentration of K^+ inside the cell is some forty times greater than in the surrounding interstitial fluid while the concentration of Na^+ in the cell is only about one-twelfth that of the interstitial fluid. The distribution of K^+ between cellular and interstitial fluids is in accord with the Donnan equilibrium principle and the potential across the cell membrane (0.1 volt). However, the distribution of Na^+ is strikingly opposite to the Donnan distribution. Since Na^+ readily enters the cell from extracellular fluid, maintenance of the very low Na^+ concentration within the cell appears to depend upon active transport of the Na^+ from the intracellular to the extracellular fluid across the cell membrane, which represents extrusion of Na^+ from the cell to maintain proper ionic balance. While this so-called sodium pump mechanism appears to operate, there is no conclusive evidence as to what constitutes the sodium pump, though several explanations have been proposed. The hypothesis most in favor at present is something as follows. A substance, P, is produced within the cell which forms a complex with sodium ions, PNa^+, which is more soluble in the lipid rich cell membrane than either free P or Na^+ and can pass through the membrane more rapidly than either. After passage through the cell membrane PNa^+ dissociates in the extracellular fluid into Na^+ and P, the latter being destroyed or otherwise inactivated. In essence, then, the sodium pump is envisaged as a stream of carrier passing from the cell through the cell membrane and carrying with it Na^+ in the form of a complex, PNa^+, which then dissociates to deliver Na^+ to the extracellular fluid.

The nature of the pump substance, or Na^+ carrier, is unknown, though some indirect evidence suggests that histamine, formed by decarboxylation of the amino acid histidine in cells generally, may be involved. Pyridoxal phosphate, a chelating agent, and phosphatidyl serine have also been suggested as carrier molecules for Na^+. It is probable that there are a number of pump substances. Also, substances other than Na^+ ions must be pumped. This apparently is true in the distribution of K^+ between erythrocytes and plasma, and in other cases where substances are moved across membranes against concentration gradients.

The operation of a pumping mechanism requires the expenditure of energy; in fact, it has been estimated that as much as 10 per cent of the energy of resting muscle cells is utilized in running the sodium pump. The necessity for metabolic processes to supply energy to run the pump is seen from experiments with human erythrocytes. When such cells, suspended in serum, are held at 0° C, which markedly decreases cellular metabolism, they lose K^+ and equilibrate with the Na^+ of the surrounding medium. Now if the temperature is raised to 37° C, which increases the cellular metabolism, Na^+ leaves the cell and K^+ re-enters until the normal distribution is established. If the cells at 0° C are suspended in salt solution without glucose and then rewarmed to 37° C, the ionic balance is not re-established; however, if glucose also is added to the suspension medium, the ionic shift takes place in proportion to the metabolism of glucose by the cells.

It appears that in most cases the movement of K^+ and H^+ from extracellular to intracellular fluid and the reverse across the cell membrane takes place by free diffusion, and that their quantitative distributions are determined by the extent to which the sodium pump creates a deficiency of positive ions within the cell to balance the total negative charges present (largely protein).

Donnan membrane equilibrium. Suppose a vessel is separated into two compartments by a semipermeable membrane which permits water and crystalloids, but not colloidal particles, to pass through. If water is placed in both compartments and then some NaCl is added to one compartment, the NaCl will diffuse through the membrane and after a time become equally distributed in the water of both compartments. Donnan, in 1911, showed that, if an ion which cannot pass through is placed on one side of the membrane, the distribution of NaCl, or other electrolyte, is unequal in the solutions on the opposite sides of the membrane. Donnan used sodium salts of nondiffusible ions such as Congo red, which may be represented by the general formula NaR. R^- may also be a protein or other nondiffusible ion. The membrane is impermeable to R^- and also to undissociated NaR. Donnan derived his theory on the basis of thermodynamics. A simpler derivation based upon kinetics may also be used and is given below.

Suppose we have a solution of NaR on one side of a membrane which is impermeable to R^- or undissociated NaR and that the concentration of NaR is equal to a. Suppose a solution of NaCl of concentration b is on the other side of the membrane and that the membrane is freely permeable to NaCl. The initial situation may be shown diagrammatically as follows:

	(1)		(2)	
a	Na^+		Na^+	b
a	R^-		Cl^-	b

Na$^+$ and Cl$^-$ ions diffuse in pairs, to maintain electrical neutrality of the solutions, from solution (2) through the membrane to solution (1). Upon passing into (1), they may reversely diffuse back into (2). After a certain period of time the rate of diffusion from (1) to (2) equals the rate from (2) to (1), and the system is at equilibrium. The net process involves the loss of NaCl from (2) and its addition to (1). Let x represent the net concentration of NaCl which has passed from (2) to (1) at equilibrium. Also, x equals the concentrations of Na$^+$ and Cl$^-$ ions which have passed from (2) to (1) (xNaCl $= x$Na$^+ + x$Cl$^-$). Then $b - x$ represents the concentration of NaCl and of Na$^+$ and Cl$^-$ remaining in (2) at equilibrium. The ionic distributions and concentrations at equilibrium are:

	(1)		(2)	
$a + x$	Na$^+$		Na$^+$	$b - x$
a	R$^-$			
x	Cl$^-$		Cl$^-$	$b - x$

In order that Na$^+$ and Cl$^-$ ions may pass through the membrane together, they must arrive simultaneously at a given point on the membrane. The probability that they will do this is directly proportional to the product of the ion concentrations (activities in more concentrated solutions). The rate of diffusion of NaCl from (2) to (1) is proportional to the product of the concentrations of Na$^+$ and Cl$^-$ in (2), namely, $(b - x)^2$. The rate of diffusion of NaCl from (1) to (2) is proportional to the product of the concentrations of Na$^+$ and Cl$^-$ in (1); namely, $(a + x)x$. Since the rates of diffusion are equal at equilibrium, we have:

$$(b - x)^2 = (a + x)x$$
$$ (2) \qquad\qquad (1)$$

This is the fundamental Donnan equation and may be written for the above example in the form:

$$[Na^+]_2 \cdot [Cl^-]_2 = [Na^+]_1 \cdot [Cl^-]_1$$

It states that at equilibrium the product of the concentrations of Na$^+$ and Cl$^-$ ions in compartment (2) equals the product of the concentrations of Na$^+$ and Cl$^-$ ions in compartment (1), which contains the nondiffusible ion.

It can be seen from the equation:

$$(b - x)(b - x) = (a + x)x$$
$$[Na^+]_2 \, [Cl^-]_2 = [Na^+]_1 \, [Cl^-]_1$$

that the concentration of Na$^+$ in (1) is greater than the concentration of Cl$^-$ in (1), whereas the concentrations of Na$^+$ and Cl$^-$ in (2) are equal. Also, since this is true, the product of the concentrations of Na$^+$ and Cl$^-$ in (2) represents a square, while the product of the concentrations of Na$^+$ and Cl$^-$ in (1) does not. This means that the concentration of Na$^+$ ions in (1) is greater than in (2) and the concentration of Cl$^-$ ions in (2) is greater than in (1). This is true because the sum of the factors in a square is less than the sum of the factors in the same product which is not a square. In order to illustrate this, suppose the concentrations of Na^+ and Cl^- in (2) are represented by 8; then the concentrations of Na^+ and Cl^- in (1) may be 8.1 and 7.90123, respectively, and we have:

$$[Na^+]_2 \cdot [Cl^-]_2 = [Na^+]_1 \cdot [Cl^-]_1$$
$$8 \times 8 = 64 \qquad 8.1 \times 7.90123 = 64$$
$$8 + 8 = 16 \qquad 8.1 + 7.90123 = 16.0123$$

Of course, for illustration, various factors other than 8.1 and 7.90123 might be used to give a product of 64. Their sum would always be greater than 16, and the concentration of Na^+ in (1) would be greater than in (2), while the concentration of Cl^- in (2) would be greater than in (1).

These ionic relations for the Donnan equilibrium may be summarized:

(a) The concentration of a diffusible positive ion is greater on the side of the membrane containing a nondiffusible negative ion $[Na^+]_1 > [Na^+]_2$.

(b) The concentration of a diffusible negative ion is greater on the side of the membrane not containing the nondiffusible negative ion $[Cl^-]_2 > [Cl^-]_1$. The above distributions are reversed when the nondiffusible ion is positive, as in case of protein chloride.

The equation:

$$[Na^+]_2 \cdot [Cl^-]_2 = [Na^+]_1 \cdot [Cl^-]_1$$

may be written:

$$\frac{[Na^+]_2}{[Na^+]_1} = \frac{[Cl^-]_1}{[Cl^-]_2}$$

It can be shown that if a series of uni-univalent diffusible electrolytes such as $NaCl$, KNO_3, $LiBr$, and HI be present in a Donnan system, as described above, the following relations hold:

$$\frac{[Na^+]_2}{[Na^+]_1} = \frac{[K^+]_2}{[K^+]_1} = \frac{[Li^+]_2}{[Li^+]_1} = \frac{[H^+]_2}{[H^+]_1}$$
$$= \frac{[Cl^-]_1}{[Cl^-]_2} = \frac{[NO_3^-]_1}{[NO_3^-]_2} = \frac{[Br^-]_1}{[Br^-]_2} = \frac{[I^-]_1}{[I^-]_2}$$

When a nondiffusible ion is present on one side of a membrane, it causes unequal distribution of each diffusible ion on the opposite sides of the membrane. The positive diffusible ions are more concentrated in the solution containing a nondiffusible negative ion than they are in the solution on the opposite side of the membrane. The reverse is true of the negative diffusible ions. However, if a positive nondiffusible ion be present, the positive diffusible ions are more concentrated in the solution on the opposite side of the membrane, and the reverse is true of negative diffusible ions.

Jacques Loeb, from his studies on the behavior of proteins in solution, did much to establish thoroughly the validity of Donnan's theory of membrane equilibrium. Today this theory is recognized as having wide physiologic implications.

In the Donnan equation given above:

$$(b - x)^2 = (a + x)x$$

in which x = the mols of Na^+ and Cl^- ions transferred from pure NaCl solution (2) to solution (1) containing nondiffusible negative ions, R^-, we may solve for x and obtain its value in terms of a and b. The equation may be written:

$$b^2 - 2bx + x^2 = ax + x^2$$

which becomes

$$b^2 - 2bx = ax$$

or

$$b^2 = ax + 2bx$$

and

$$b^2 = (a + 2b)x$$

and

$$x = \frac{b^2}{a + 2b}$$

From this equation it is seen that the amount of electrolyte (NaCl above), x, diffusing from (2) to (1) is inversely proportional to the concentration of nondiffusible ion, a, in (1). When b is large relative to a, the value of x is relatively large, which means that much NaCl diffuses from (2) to (1). When however, b is small relative to a, the value of x is small, indicating that little diffusion of NaCl from (2) to (1) occurs. These relations may be seen by referring to the data of Table 5.3.

Relation of Donnan effect to osmotic pressure. The Donnan effect, which leads to unequal distribution of diffusible ions across a membrane, also causes an osmotic pressure difference between the solutions across the membrane. This is due to the fact that the solution containing the nondiffusible ion also contains the greater number of dissolved particles. In the diagram representing a Donnan system at equilibrium:

(1)	(2)
Na^+	Na^+
$a + x$ mols	$b - x$ mols
Cl^-	Cl^-
x mols	$b - x$ mols
R^-	
a mols	

the value of x, the amount of NaCl diffusing from (2) to (1), is:

$$x = \frac{b^2}{a + 2b}$$

For illustration, let $a = 1$ mol and $b = 2$ mols; then:

$$x = \frac{4}{1 + 4} = \frac{4}{5} = 0.80$$

If we add up the concentrations in (1) and (2) above, we have:

(1)		(2)	
Na$^+$	1.8	Na$^+$	1.2
Cl$^-$	0.8	Cl$^-$	1.2
R$^-$	1.0		
3.6	mols	2.4	mols

Since osmotic pressure is given by the equation:

$$P = cRT$$

where c = concentration, the osmotic pressure across the membrane in the Donnan system will be:

$$P = (3.6 - 2.4)RT$$
$$= 1.2RT$$

At 27° C (300° A) the osmotic pressure would be:

$$P = 1.2 \times 0.082 \times 300 = 29.52 \text{ atm}$$

It is obvious that when the osmotic pressure of a solution is being directly determined by the use of a membrane, the presence of nondiffusible ions may vitiate the results unless precautions are taken to minimize or correct for the osmotic error due to the Donnan effect. Such errors are particularly likely to occur when working with protein solutions (such as serum) in which considerable of the protein exists as nondiffusible negative or positive ions and salts are present. Under these conditions a membrane freely permeable to the salt ions and impermeable to the protein must be used in order to measure only the colloidal osmotic pressure due to the protein. To minimize the Donnan effect, the measurements are made, when possible, at the isoelectric pH of the protein, and in the presence of fairly high salt concentrations.

When a protein gel, such as that of gelatin, is in contact with a water solution at a pH above or below its isoelectric pH, an interesting situation exists. The presence of electrolytes in the solution about the gel causes it to take up more water and swell. This swelling may be due in part to some specific effect of the ions present, but undoubtedly it is partly caused by a Donnan osmotic effect between the gel and the surrounding solution. The gel surface acts as a semipermeable membrane to any diffusible electrolyte in the solution surrounding the gel. Some of the protein exists as P$^+$ or P$^-$ ions (depending upon pH) within the gel structure. These protein ions cannot diffuse through the gel surface into the solution. The result is that a Donnan equilibrium is set up between the gel and the surrounding electrolyte solution. As pointed out above, the concentration of dissolved particles is greatest in the solution containing the nondiffusible ions. This means that the total concentration of dissolved particles is higher within the gel than in the surrounding solution. Accordingly, water diffuses from the solution into the gel, with the result that the gel swells. The amount of swelling depends

upon the concentration of electrolyte, the pH, and to a certain extent upon
the valence and nature of the diffusible ions present. The Donnan osmotic
effect is therefore seen to be one factor concerned in the swelling of proteins
due to electrolytes. The abnormal swelling of tissues of the body in certain
diseases is undoubtedly due in part to the Donnan osmotic effect.

Membrane hydrolysis. According to the Donnan principle, the presence
of a nondiffusible ion on one side of a membrane produces hydrolysis and a
difference in pH on the two sides of the membrane. If a salt, NaR, is placed
in water on one side of a membrane, we will have at equilibrium:

Na^+	Na^+
R^-	OH^-
H^+	H^+
OH^-	
(1)	(2)

Since R^- causes a higher concentration of diffusible negative ions on the
opposite side of the membrane, OH^- ions (from H_2O) move through the
membrane with associated Na^+ ions (to maintain electrical neutrality), solution (2) becomes alkaline, and the pH of solution (1) falls. The membrane
permits the hydrolysis reaction:

$$NaR + HOH \longrightarrow NaOH + HR$$

to proceed with separation of NaOH and HR across the membrane.

Suppose that instead of NaR we have RCl (protein hydrochloride) in one
compartment:

R^+	H^+
Cl^-	Cl^-
H^+	OH^-
OH^-	
(1)	(2)

In this case H^+ ions, with associated Cl^- ions, will move from (1) to (2),
because the nondiffusible R^+ ions in (1) cause a greater concentration of H^+
ions in compartment (2). The solution in (2) will become acid, and the pH of
the solution in (1) will rise. The membrane permits the hydrolysis reaction:

$$RCl + HOH \longrightarrow ROH + HCl$$

to proceed with retention of ROH on one side of the membrane and secretion
of HCl through the membrane to the opposite side.

The pH within red cells is lower than that of the surrounding plasma and
is due, in part, to the very high concentration of negative nondiffusible hemoglobin ions. These cause unequal distribution of H^+ ions on the opposite
sides of the red cell membrane, with a higher concentration within the cell.
The lower pH values within tissue cells in general than in the surrounding
fluids are partly due to the concentrations of negative protein ions within
the cells being higher than in the surrounding fluids.

As pointed out above, the Donnan effect applies to all diffusible ions regardless of kind.

The magnitude of the Donnan effect is shown in Table 5.3, where the
concentrations of nondiffusible and diffusible ions are varied.

Table 5.3

Initial Conc. NaR in (1) a	Initial Conc. NaCl in (2) b	Initial Ratio $[NaR]_1/[NaCl]_2$ a/b	Per Cent NaCl Transferred from (2) to (1)	Distribution Ratio of NaCl between (2) and (1) $[NaCl]_2/[NaCl]_1$
0.01	1.0	0.01	49.7	1.01
0.1	1.0	0.1	47.6	1.1
1.0	1.0	1.0	33.0	2.0
1.0	0.1	10.0	8.3	11.0
1.0	0.01	100.0	1.0	99.0

Taken by permission from *Treatise on Physical Chemistry*, Vol. I, 2nd ed., by H. S. Taylor, published by D. Van Nostrand Co., Inc., 1931.

The results show that, when the ratio of NaR in (1) to NaCl in (2) is initially 100, only 1 per cent of the NaCl passes through the membrane into solution (1). If the NaR and NaCl in this ratio were both placed in (1), 99 per cent of the NaCl would pass into solution (2). This would be equivalent to the excretion of NaCl through the membrane caused by the presence of a nondiffusible negative ion. The apparent impermeability of living cell membranes to certain electrolytes may be partly due to the Donnan effect (most of the cytoplasmic proteins have isoelectric pH values below the pH of cells and consequently exist partly as negative ions). Should a cell membrane be impermeable to any ordinary diffusible ion such as K^+ or Ca^{++}, this ion would cause a Donnan effect across the membrane.

That the Donnan principle operates to regulate the distribution of electrolyte ions across the membranes of living organisms is obvious. However, owing to the limited permeability of some of these membranes to certain ions, the extent to which the Donnan effect determines the ionic distribution between certain body fluids may be of secondary importance and impossible of quantitative evaluation. For example, the relatively low permeability of the red cell membrane to Na^+, K^+, Ca^{++}, and Mg^{++} permits the maintenance of high concentrations of Na^+ and Ca^{++} in the serum relative to their concentrations inside the red cell, and of high concentrations of K^+ and Mg^{++} within the red cell fluid relative to their concentrations in the plasma. In fact, these electrolyte ions themselves exert Donnan effects across membranes in proportion to the extent to which the membranes are impermeable to them.

The distribution of HCO_3^- and Cl^- ions between plasma water and red cell water, if according to the Donnan principle, should correspond with the ratios:

$$\frac{[HCO_3^-] \text{ cells}}{[HCO_3^-] \text{ plasma}} = \frac{[Cl^-] \text{ cells}}{[Cl^-] \text{ plasma}}$$

if the ionic activity coefficients are the same in the different media. Apparently, however, they are not equal, and the above equation is valid only when a proportionality factor, f, equal to 0.8 to 0.9, is introduced:

$$\frac{[HCO_3^-] \text{ cells}}{[HCO_3^-] \text{ plasma}} = f \frac{[Cl^-] \text{ cells}}{[Cl^-] \text{ plasma}}$$

The distributions of the cations Na^+, K^+, Ca^{++}, and Mg^{++} between plasma and lymph qualitatively are, according to the Donnan principle, higher in plasma (higher protein negative ion concentration) than in lymph.

The ratios of these concentrations as obtained from their average concentrations in millimols per kilogram of water are:

$$\frac{[Na^+]_P}{[Na^+]_L} = \frac{155}{153} = 1.01; \frac{[K^+]_P}{[K^+]_L} = \frac{5.3}{3.5} = 1.5$$

$$\frac{[Ca^{++}]_P}{[Ca^{++}]_L} = \frac{2.5}{2.0} = 1.25; \frac{[Mg^{++}]_P}{[Mg^{++}]_L} = \frac{1.4}{1.0} = 1.4$$

and are not equal as required quantitatively by the Donnan principle. However, if ion activities in plasma and lymph could be substituted for concentrations, it is probable that agreement would be closer.

Peculiarly, while the concentration of Cl^- ions is higher in lymph than in plasma, as required by the Donnan principle, the concentration of HCO_3^- ions in plasma is a bit higher than in lymph, contrary to the Donnan principle.

From the above discussion the student will realize that application of the Donnan principle to biologic systems is a complex problem.

EXERCISES

1. Define "colloidal state."
2. How is the colloidal state related to surface area? Do surface forces play an important role in colloidal phenomena?
3. Enumerate the kinds of colloidal systems and give an example of each. Which are of most importance from a physiological standpoint?
4. Define the following terms and give examples: (a) phase, (b) dispersions medium, (c) micelle, (d) lyophobic colloidal system, (e) hydrophobic colloidal system, (f) lyophilic colloidal system, (g) hydrophilic colloidal system, (h) sol, (i) gel, (j) emulsoid, (k) suspensoid.
5. Give the principles of two methods used for the determination of colloidal particle size. State three ways in which the charges upon colloidal particles may originate. Diagram the Helmholtz-Gouy double layer. What is the electrochemical, or epsilon, potential; what is the electrokinetic, or zeta, potential? Which is of more importance relative to the properties of colloidal systems? What is the "critical potential"? Explain the meaning of streaming potential (flow potential) and electroendosmosis. How are they related? Are both probably operative in protoplasm?
6. What is necessary in order to precipitate a suspensoid, an emulsoid? What is meant by mutual precipitation of colloids? Why may electronegative acacia particles be safely injected into the blood stream, while positively charged colloidal particles may cause thrombosis? At blood pH (7.4) the protein hormone insulin is negatively charged, while the protein protamin is positively charged. What would you expect to happen when protamin and insulin are brought together at pH 7.4? Give examples of the importance of protective colloids in the body. How do they function?
7. Define "surface tension." How is total free surface energy calculated? What is interfacial tension? What is the Gibbs-Thomson principle in relation to surface tension? What is the relation between emulsification and interfacial tension?
8. Contrast the meanings of the terms adsorption and absorption. Write out six principles governing the adsorption process. How does the Gibbs-Thomson principle apply? What is the adsorption isotherm equation of Freundlich? Give four examples of the importance of adsorption processes.
9. What is meant by "molecular orientation"? Show by diagrams the orientation of sodium benzoate at the interface of oil and water, of alcohol molecules at the interface of air and alcohol.

10. What is the unit of viscosity called? What is relative viscosity? The density of liquid A is 1.102 g per cubic centimeter, and 5 ml of it flows through a capillary in 60 sec. Five cubic centimeters of water (density 0.99823 g per cubic centimeter) flows through the same capillary in 40 sec. Calculate the relative viscosity of liquid A. What causes most of the viscosity of blood, and of what importance is blood viscosity?

11. What are the factors concerned with the permeability of membranes? What is your view about the composition of protoplasmic membranes? What did the experiments of Flexner and Stiehler and of Cattell and Civin suggest about the functioning of animal membranes?

12. Write out a general Donnan membrane equilibrium equation. The product of equal concentrations of Na^+ and Cl^- ions on one side of a membrane is 0.16. The concentration of Na^+ ions on the other side of the membrane is 0.45 and is greater than the concentration of Cl^- ions. Calculate the concentration of Cl^- ions. On which side of the membrane would you expect to find nondiffusible negative ions?

13. State why the osmotic pressure of a protein solution measured by the use of a semipermeable membrane may be correct when the solution pH is 6 but very erroneous when the solution pH is 8.

14. Large neutral glycogen molecules break into many small lactic acid molecules within protein-rich muscle cells during muscle contraction. Explain how this may tend to cause a redistribution of diffusible positive and negative ions between muscle cells and the surrounding fluid. What would be the effect upon intracellular osmotic pressure?

GENERAL REFERENCES

Clark, W. M.: *Topics in Physical Chemistry*, 2nd ed. Williams & Wilkins Co., Baltimore, 1952.

Daniels, F., and Alberty, R. A.: *Physical Chemistry*. John Wiley & Sons, New York, 1955.

Gortner, R. A., Jr., and Gortner, W. A. (eds.): *Outlines of Biochemistry*, 3rd ed. John Wiley & Sons, New York, 1949.

Kruyt, H. R.: *Colloid Science*, 2 vols. Elsevier Press, New York, 1949, 1952.

Kunin, R., and Myers, R. J.: *Ion Exchange Resins*. John Wiley & Sons, New York, 1950.

Martin, G. J.: *Ion Exchange and Adsorption Agents in Medicine*. Little, Brown & Co., Boston, 1955.

Neurath, H., and Bailey, K.: *The Proteins*, Vol. I, Part B. Academic Press, New York, 1953.

Samuelson, O.: *Ion Exchangers in Analytical Chemistry*. John Wiley & Sons, New York, 1953.

Schachman, H. K.: *Ultracentrifugation in Biochemistry*. Academic Press, New York, 1959.

6

Lipids

FATS, WAXES, PHOSPHOLIPIDS, GLYCOLIPIDS, AND STEROLS

Three great classes of organic substances—lipids, carbohydrates, and proteins—make up most of the solid material of all protoplasm, both plant and animal. Animals eat plants and plant products and the tissues of other animals, and, consequently, carbohydrates, lipids, and proteins represent the bulk of food for animals. Each of these classes of substances is composed of many and diverse members and constitutes a very large section of organic and biochemistry. Considerable knowledge of these classes of compounds is necessary as an introduction to the study of biochemistry.

General occurrence. The greasy material which may be extracted from animal and plant tissues by solvents such as hot alcohol or ether generally represents a complex mixture. This mixture, depending upon the tissue extracted, usually contains representatives of several or all of the classes of organic compounds known as fats, waxes, phospholipids, glycolipids, and sterols, as well as hydrolytic products of some of them. These substances, though often very different in chemical structure and properties, are commonly called, as a group, the "lipids."

The distribution of lipids in different animal tissues is widely variable in both quantity and type of lipid. A nondepot tissue may contain 1 to 10 per cent of total lipid, the lowest content, 1 to 2 per cent, occurring in rapidly growing embryonic tissue. Lipids generally constitute 7.5 to 30 per cent of sperm, egg, and brain tissue. Storehouse or depot tissues, such as subcutaneous tissue, mesenteric tissue, the fatty tissue around the kidneys and other organs, and yellow bone marrow, contain very large amounts of lipid,

126

which may represent as much as 90 per cent of the tissue. This lipid is almost exclusively fat. The lipids present in the nonfat tissues such as muscle, glandular organs, and brain generally contain relatively little fat, but larger proportions of phospholipids, sterols, and glycolipids.

According to Bloor, the lipids are substances possessing the following characteristics as a group: (a) They are insoluble in water and soluble in fat solvents such as chloroform, ether, and benzene. (b) They are esters of fatty acids, either actual or potential. (c) They are utilized by living organisms.

FATTY ACIDS

In the following discussion of the chemistry of the various groups of lipids it will be noted that most lipids may be hydrolyzed into simpler components. Fats yield glycerol and fatty acids when hydrolyzed. Hydrolysis of waxes produces long-chain fatty acids and monohydroxy alcohols of high molecular weight. Phospholipids yield fatty acids, phosphoric acid, a nitrogenous compound, and often glycerol. Glycolipids are decomposed into fatty acids, a nitrogen-containing alcohol, and a sugar. A sterol such as cholesterol may occur in tissues in the free condition and also as esters of fatty acids. The common component of most lipid structures is fatty acid of some type. It is often true that the identity of a lipid is determined by the kind of fatty acid or acids present in the molecule. The number of acids present in the lipids as a group is very large, and the chemical composition of these acids shows considerable variation. Some knowledge of the chemistry of the fatty acids is essential to an understanding of the chemistry of the lipids containing them.

The acids known to be present in the lipids of various kinds vary in carbon content from C_2 to C_{34} and nearly always contain an even number of carbon atoms. Many of these acids belong to the saturated aliphatic series, while others contain from one to six double bonds. Recently, fatty acids containing both double and triple bonds have been discovered in certain seed fats. A few fatty acids, especially those from chaulmoogra oil, have cyclic structures attached to the carbon chain. Table 6.1 lists many of the fatty acids which enter into the composition of various lipids. Of these acids the ones most common in animal and plant fats are lauric, myristic, palmitic, stearic, and arachidic among the saturated acids, and oleic, erucic, linoleic, linolenic, arachidonic, and clupanodonic among the unsaturated acids. Oleic acid is by far the most abundant fatty acid in nature; it forms more than half of the total fatty acids in many fats and is seldom present in amounts less than 10 per cent. So far, oleic acid has been found in all natural fats and phospholipids investigated. The saturated acid, palmitic, ranks next to oleic acid in its widespread occurrence. It constitutes 15 to 50 per cent of the total acids in many fats and is present in most, if not all, of them. Myristic and stearic acids of the saturated series also occur frequently in fats.

It is of some interest to note the number of important fatty acids which contain 18 carbon atoms. Several may be considered derivatives of stearic

Table 6.1. Classification of Lipid Fatty Acids
(The acids which occur more commonly are indicated by asterisks.)

Name	Formula	Some Sources
I. Saturated Acids, $C_nH_{2n+1}COOH$		
a. Unbranched chain		
Acetic	CH_3COOH	Oil of spindle tree
Butyric	C_3H_7COOH	Butter
Caproic (hexanoic)	$C_5H_{11}COOH$	Butter, coconut, and palm nut oils
Caprylic (octanoic)	$C_7H_{15}COOH$	Butter, coconut, and palm nut oils
Capric (decanoic)	$C_9H_{19}COOH$	Butter, coconut, and palm nut oils
*Lauric (dodecanoic)	$C_{11}H_{23}COOH$	Laurel oil, coconut oil, spermaceti
*Myristic (tetradecanoic)	$C_{13}H_{27}COOH$	Coconut oil, nutmeg oil, animal fats
*Palmitic (hexadecanoic)	$C_{15}H_{31}COOH$	Plant and animal fats
*Stearic (octadecanoic)	$C_{17}H_{35}COOH$	Plant and animal fats
*Arachidic (eicosanoic)	$C_{19}H_{39}COOH$	Peanut oil, rape oil, butter, lard
Behenic (docosanoic)	$C_{21}H_{43}COOH$	Oil of ben, peanut oil
Lignoceric (tetracosanoic)	$C_{23}H_{47}COOH$	Peanut oil, glycolipids, phospholipids
Cerotic (hexacosanoic)	$C_{25}H_{51}COOH$	Chinese wax, beeswax, wool fat
Montanic (octacosanoic)	$C_{27}H_{55}COOH$	Carnauba wax, beeswax
Melissic (triacontanoic)	$C_{29}H_{59}COOH$	Beeswax
b. Branched chain		
Tuberculostearic (10-methyl stearic)	$C_{18}H_{37}COOH$	Human tubercle bacillus
II. Unsaturated Acids		
a. One double bond, $C_nH_{2n-1}COOH$		
Crotonic$\Delta^{2:3}$(2-butenoic)	C_3H_5COOH	Croton oil
Myristoleic$\Delta^{9:10}$- (9-tetradecenoic)	$C_{13}H_{25}COOH$	Butter, sperm oil, fish liver oils
Palmitoleic$\Delta^{9:10}$- (9-hexadecenoic)(cis)	$C_{15}H_{29}COOH$	Butter, fish oils, animal fats
*Oleic$\Delta^{9:10}$- (9-octadecenoic)(cis)	$C_{17}H_{33}COOH$	Plant and animal fats
Vaccenic$\Delta^{11:12}$(11-octadecenoic)(cis and trans)	$C_{17}H_{33}COOH$	Butter
Gadoleic$\Delta^{9:10}$- (9-eicosenoic)	$C_{19}H_{37}COOH$	Brain phospholipids, fish liver oils
*Erucic$\Delta^{13:14}$- (13-docosenoic)(cis)	$C_{21}H_{41}COOH$	Rape-seed oil, various seed oils
Nervonic$\Delta^{15:16}$- (15-tetracosenoic)(cis)	$C_{23}H_{45}COOH$	Brain phospholipids and glycolipids
b. Two double bonds, $C_nH_{2n-3}COOH$		
*Linoleic$\Delta^{9:10,12:13}$- (9,12-octadecadienoic)	$C_{17}H_{31}COOH$	Plant and animal fats
c. Three double bonds, $C_nH_{2n-5}COOH$		
*Linolenic$\Delta^{9:10,12:13,15:16}$- (9,12,15-octadecatrienoic)	$C_{17}H_{29}COOH$	Linseed oil, mammal fats, fish liver oils
Eleostearic(9,11,13-octadecatrienoic)(cis, trans, trans)	$C_{17}H_{29}COOH$	Chinese wood oil, seed fats

Table 6.1.   Classification of Lipid Fatty Acids (*Continued*)

Name	Formula	Some Sources
γ-Linolenic(6,9,12-octa-decatrienoic)	$C_{17}H_{29}COOH$	Primrose seed oil
5,8,11-eicosatrienoic	$C_{19}H_{33}COOH$	Fats of fat-deficient rats
d. Four double bonds, $C_nH_{2n-7}COOH$		
Moroctic(4,8,12,15-octa-decatetraenoic)	$C_{17}H_{27}COOH$	Fish oil
*Arachidonic(5,8,11,14-eicosatetraenoic)	$C_{19}H_{31}COOH$	Animal phospholipids, liver fats
e. Five double bonds, $C_nH_{2n-9}COOH$		
Timnodonic(4,8,12,15,18-eicosapentaenoic)	$C_{19}H_{29}COOH$	Sardine oil
*Clupanodonic(4,8,12,15,-19-docosapentaenoic)	$C_{21}H_{33}COOH$	Brain and liver phospholipids
f. Six double bonds, $C_nH_{2n-11}COOH$		
Nisinic(4,8,12,15,18,21-tetracosahexaenoic)	$C_{23}H_{35}COOH$	Sardine oil
III. Hydroxy Acids		
a. Saturated		
Dihydroxystearic(9,10-dihydroxyoctadecanoic)	$C_{17}H_{33}(OH)_2COOH$	Castor oil
Cerebronic(2-hydroxy-tetracosanoic)	$C_{23}H_{46}(OH)COOH$	Brain glycolipids
b. Unsaturated		
Ricinoleic(12-hydroxy-9-octadecenoic)(cis)	$C_{17}H_{32}(OH)COOH$	Castor oil
Hydroxynervonic(2-hydroxy-9-tetracosenoic)	$C_{23}H_{44}(OH)COOH$	Brain glycolipids
IV. Cyclic Acids		
Hydnocarpic	$C_{16}H_{28}O_2$	Chaulmoogra oil
Chaulmoogric	$C_{18}H_{32}O_2$	Chaulmoogra oil

acid through introduction of double bonds or hydroxyl groups or both. The structural formulas of a number of these acids are tabulated below.

Stearic	$CH_3(CH_2)_7 - CH_2 - CH_2 - (CH_2)_7COOH$
Oleic	$CH_3(CH_2)_7 - CH = CH(CH_2)_7COOH$
Linoleic	$CH_3(CH_2)_4 - CH = CHCH_2CH - CH(CH_2)_7COOH$
Linolenic	$CH_3CH_2CH = CHCH_2CH = CHCH_2CH = CH(CH_2)_7COOH$
Ricinoleic	$CH_3(CH_2)_5CHOHCH_2CH = CH(CH_2)_7COOH$

Many of the unsaturated acids have a double bond between carbon atoms 9 and 10. Two hydrogen atoms are dropped from the acid molecule upon the introduction of each double bond. Consequently, the formulas of stearic acid and its unsaturated derivatives are: stearic, $C_{17}H_{35}COOH$; oleic, $C_{17}H_{33}$-COOH; linoleic, $C_{17}H_{31}COOH$; and linolenic, $C_{17}H_{29}COOH$.

Two types of isomers are possible among the unsaturated fatty acids. Variation in the position of the double bond or bonds is one cause of isomerism. For example, oleic acids with the double bond between carbon atoms 2, 3; 3, 4; and 9, 10 have different properties and are isomeric compounds. The second type of isomerism involved is so-called cis-trans isomerism about the double bond, a form of geometrical isomerism. For example, when oleic acid is treated with nitrous acid, an isomer, elaidic acid, is produced. The formulas of these acids are:

$$CH_3(CH_2)_7 - C - H$$
$$||$$
$$HOOC(CH_2)_7 - C - H$$

Cis form, oleic acid *liquid*
m.p. 13° C

$$CH_3(CH_2)_7 - C - H$$
$$||$$
$$H - C - (CH_2)_7COOH$$

Trans form, elaidic acid *solid*
m.p. 45° C

Theoretically 31 isomers of oleic acid are possible, of which several are known.

Tuberculostearic and phthioic acids are of interest because they occur in the lipids of human tubercle bacilli. Tuberculostearic acid is 10-methyl stearic acid and has the formula:

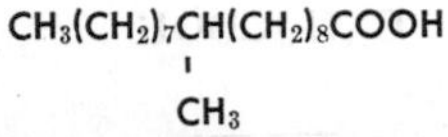

$$CH_3(CH_2)_7CH(CH_2)_8COOH$$
$$|$$
$$CH_3$$

Phthioic acid, $C_{26}H_{52}O_2$, is a saturated acid and is unique in being a liquid at ordinary temperature and in possessing optical activity, $[\alpha]_D = +12.56°$. Polgar and Robinson (1) consider it to be 3,13,19-trimethyltricosanoic acid:

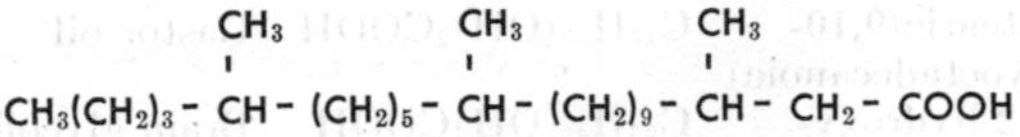

$$CH_3 \quad\quad CH_3 \quad\quad CH_3$$
$$| \quad\quad\quad | \quad\quad\quad |$$
$$CH_3(CH_2)_3 - CH - (CH_2)_5 - CH - (CH_2)_9 - CH - CH_2 - COOH$$

Phthioic acid is probably of importance in causing some of the manifestations of tuberculosis, since it has the property of stimulating proliferation of epitheloid cells and epitheloid giant cells.

The cyclic acids, hydnocarpic and chaulmoogric, occur as the glycerol esters in chaulmoogra oil. They have the structures:

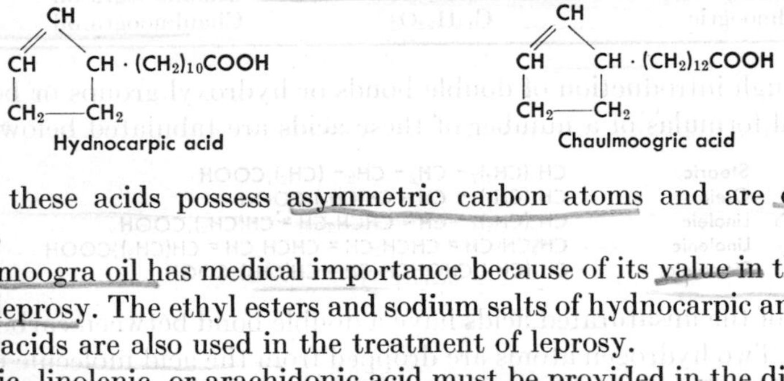

$$
\begin{array}{cc}
CH & \\
\| & \\
CH \quad CH \cdot (CH_2)_{10}COOH & \\
| \quad\quad | & \\
CH_2 \!-\!\!-\! CH_2 &
\end{array}
$$
Hydnocarpic acid

$$
\begin{array}{cc}
CH & \\
\| & \\
CH \quad CH \cdot (CH_2)_{12}COOH & \\
| \quad\quad | & \\
CH_2 \!-\!\!-\! CH_2 &
\end{array}
$$
Chaulmoogric acid

Both of these acids possess asymmetric carbon atoms and are optically active.

Chaulmoogra oil has medical importance because of its value in the treatment of leprosy. The ethyl esters and sodium salts of hydnocarpic and chaulmoogric acids are also used in the treatment of leprosy.

Linoleic, linolenic, or arachidonic acid must be provided in the diet of the rat for adequate nutrition. Without one of these acids the animals develop a characteristic deficiency disease. It is probable that these acids are similarly required by other animals, including human beings.

The common names of the fatty acids do not indicate chemical composition. Occasionally the systematic chemical names are employed, and the student should understand the meaning of these. For example, caproic acid is hexanoic acid, caprylic is octanoic, capric is decanoic, lauric is dodecanoic, myristic is tetradecanoic, palmitic is hexadecanoic, and stearic is octadecanoic acid. The first part of these names indicates the number of carbon atoms present and the ending "-anoic" that the acids are saturated. Unsaturated acids are given similar systematic names with appropriate modifications to indicate the numbers and positions (if known) of the unsaturated bonds present. For example, oleic acid with 18 carbon atoms and a double bond between the ninth and tenth carbons is systematically 9-octadecenoic acid, the ending "-enoic" indicating a double bond and the prefix 9- that this bond is between carbon atoms 9 and 10. Similarly, linoleic acid is 9,12-octadecadienoic acid, and linolenic acid is 9,12,15-octadecatrienoic acid, the endings "-dienoic" and "-trienoic" designating two and three double bonds respectively. The prefix "9,12-" shows that the double bonds are between carbon atoms 9 and 10 and 12 and 13 in linoleic acid. Similarly, these bonds come between carbon atoms 9 and 10, 12 and 13, and 15 and 16 in linolenic acid.

Another system of indicating double-bond position in unsaturated fatty acids is by use of the symbol Δ with a superscript denoting both of the carbon atoms joined by the double bond. For example, oleic acid may be designated $\Delta^{9:10}$-octadecenoic acid and linolenic acid $\Delta^{9:10,12:13,15:16}$-octadecatrienoic acid.

A. PHYSICAL PROPERTIES OF FATTY ACIDS

All the saturated fatty acids up to and including capric acid with 10 carbon atoms are liquids at ordinary temperatures, whereas the higher members are solids. The melting points of the fatty acids increase with chain length. Lauric acid (C_{12}) melts at 48° C, and stearic (C_{18}) melts at 69° C. Acetic and butyric acids mix with water in all proportions, and the solubility of the higher acids rapidly decreases with increasing chain length, caproic acid dissolving only to the extent of 0.9 per cent at 15° C. Above C_{10} the acids are essentially insoluble in water. The liquid acids from C_2 to C_{10} are also volatile with steam, the volatility decreasing as the carbon chain increases. These shorter chain acids may accordingly be separated from the higher solid acids by steam distillation.

All the naturally occurring unsaturated acids are liquids at room temperature; this fact indicates the influence of unsaturation. They are generally insoluble in water and are not volatile with steam.

Most of the fatty acids are soluble in hot alcohol. In general they are soluble in ether, benzene, and chloroform, and all except hydroxylated acids are soluble in low-boiling petroleum ether. Highly hydroxylated acids, such as octahydroxyarachidic acid, are relatively soluble in water but are insoluble in ether and relatively insoluble in alcohol.

With the exception of acetic, fatty acids are lighter than water.

B. CHEMICAL PROPERTIES OF FATTY ACIDS

Salts. The metallic salts of the fatty acids above C_6 are known as soaps. The alkali metal soaps are soluble in water and serve as efficient emulsifying and cleansing agents. Other soaps are generally insoluble in water and are not useful as cleansing agents. Commercial soaps are mixtures of the sodium salts of higher acids such as palmitic, stearic, and oleic. Potassium soaps are softer than sodium soaps and are more soluble in water and alcohol. Potassium and sodium soaps are insoluble in ether, benzene, chloroform, etc.

The lead salts of unsaturated acids are soluble in ether and alcohol; those of saturated acids are insoluble. This property affords a method of separating the saturated and unsaturated acids in a mixture.

The carboxyl group of a fatty acid may be reduced to the corresponding alcohol by treatment with hydrogen at 200 atm pressure and 320° C in the presence of a nickel catalyst:

$$R \cdot COOH + 2H_2 \longrightarrow R \cdot CH_2OH + H_2O$$

Fatty acid   Higher alcohol

These higher alcohols derived from the fatty acids by reduction may then be converted into the sulfuric acid esters by treatment with fuming H_2SO_4 or other means:

$$R \cdot CH_2OH + HO \cdot SO_3H \longrightarrow R \cdot CH_2 - O - SO_3H + H_2O$$

The salts of these sulfuric acid derivatives such as the sodium salts, $R \cdot CH_2\text{-}O\text{—}SO_3Na$, are excellent wetting agents and detergents and are being widely used in place of ordinary soap for cleaning. They may be used in hard water because the calcium and magnesium salts are soluble. Another advantage over ordinary soaps is that the sulfuric acid esters are strong acids and their salts are not decomposed in acid solutions.

Esters. The glycerol esters of the fatty acids constitute the natural fats. Methyl and ethyl esters of the acids are used in separating the acids by fractional distillation.

Reactions of unsaturated acids. Besides the chemical properties characteristic of the carboxyl group, the unsaturated acids show important reactions of the double bond. These reactions involve the addition of hydrogen and halogens and oxidation. Examples of such reactions are given below:

Hydrogenation.

$$CH_3(CH_2)_7 - CH = CH(CH_2)_7COOH + H_2 \longrightarrow CH_3(CH_2)_7CH_2CH_2(CH_2)_7COOH$$

Oleic acid   Stearic acid

The reaction is generally catalyzed by finely divided nickel. Two hydrogen atoms may be added for each double bond present. Linolenic acid will take up as a maximum three molecules of hydrogen per molecule of acid, though by careful technique only one or two of the three double bonds may be saturated.

Halogenation.

$$CH_3(CH_2)_7 - CH = CH - (CH_2)_7COOH + Br_2 \longrightarrow CH_3(CH_2)_7 - CH - CH - (CH_2)_7COOH$$

Oleic acid   Br Br

Dibromostearic acid

Chlorine and iodine or iodine chloride may be added in a similar manner. The bromine derivatives of the more unsaturated acids (three to five double bonds) are insoluble in most fat solvents and are used for separation and identification of the acids. The iodine absorption of a fatty acid may be measured quantitatively; it indicates the number of double bonds present, or the degree of unsaturation.

Oxidation. Oxidation of unsaturated acids at the double bond yields a variety of products, depending upon the oxidizing agent and conditions employed. When oleic acid is carefully oxidized with alkaline permanganate at low temperature, two hydroxyl groups are added at the double bond with the formation of dihydroxystearic acid. At higher temperatures the molecule is further oxidized and broken into two acids of nine carbon atoms each:

$$CH_3(CH_2)_7CH = CH(CH_2)_7COOH + HOH + O \longrightarrow CH_3(CH_2)_7CH - CH - (CH_2)_7COOH + 3O \longrightarrow$$

Oleic acid

$$\underset{OH\quad OH}{|\qquad |}$$

Dihydroxystearic acid

$$CH_3(CH_2)_7COOH + HOOC(CH_2)_7COOH + H_2O$$

Pelargonic acid   Azelaic acid

The reaction of unsaturated acids with oxygen is exceedingly complex, and it involves the preliminary formation of unstable peroxides that decompose into a mixture of shorter-chain acids and aldehydes. Although addition of O_2 at the double bond to form a structure such as:

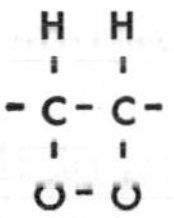

$$\begin{array}{cc} H & H \\ | & | \\ -C- & C- \\ | & | \\ O- & O \end{array}$$

may occur, it appears that most of the peroxide is a hydroperoxide of the type:

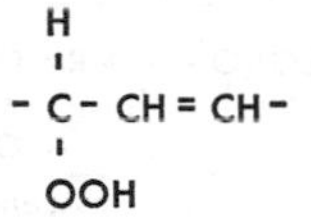

$$\begin{array}{c} H \\ | \\ -C- CH = CH- \\ | \\ OOH \end{array}$$

Ozone adds to the double bonds of unsaturated acids forming ozonides which are split by water into two molecules containing aldehyde groups:

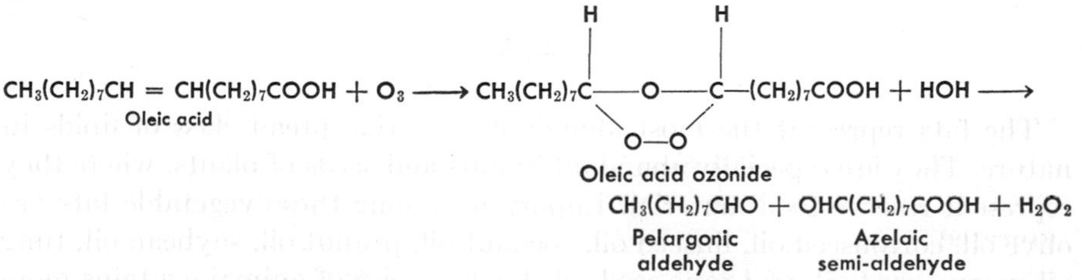

$$CH_3(CH_2)_7CH = CH(CH_2)_7COOH + O_3 \longrightarrow CH_3(CH_2)_7C \overset{H}{\underset{}{—}} O \overset{H}{\underset{}{—}} C-(CH_2)_7COOH + HOH \longrightarrow$$

Oleic acid

$$\underset{O—O}{}$$

Oleic acid ozonide

$$CH_3(CH_2)_7CHO + OHC(CH_2)_7COOH + H_2O_2$$

Pelargonic   Azelaic
aldehyde   semi-aldehyde

This reaction with ozone is of value in establishing the position of double bonds in fatty acid chains.

Alpha and beta oxidation of saturated fatty acids. When saturated fatty acids are carefully oxidized with permanganate or hydrogen peroxide in slightly alkaline solution, alpha and beta oxidations occur with the final removal of two carbon atoms from the carboxyl end of the chain. Witzemann (2) explains the oxidation as occurring in stages:

$$
\begin{array}{llll}
\text{COONa} & \text{COONa} & \text{COONa} + H_2O & \text{COONa} \\
| & | & | & | \\
CH_2 + O \rightarrow HCOH + O \rightarrow C = O & & C^- OH + 4O \rightarrow 2CO_2 + RCOONa + H_2O \\
| & | & | & \| \\
CH_2 & CH_2 & HCH & CH \\
| & | & | & | \\
R & R & R & R \\
\underline{\text{Salt of}} & \text{Hydroxy} & \alpha\text{-Ketonic} & \text{Enol} \\
\underline{\text{fatty acid}} & \text{acid salt} & \text{acid salt} & \text{form}
\end{array}
$$

(enoli-zation) above the third arrow; "Salt of fatty acid with 2 less C atoms" under the final term.

An interesting oxidation of fatty acids is produced by a peroxidase enzyme present in certain molds such as *Penicillium glaucum*, which, acting at moderately warm temperatures in the presence of traces of moisture and in the absence of light, produces β-ketonic acids which then decompose into ketones:

$$R^- CH_2 ^- CH_2COOH + O \longrightarrow R^- CHOH ^- CH_2 ^- COOH + O \longrightarrow$$

Fatty acid   Hydroxy acid

$$H_2O + R^- CO ^- CH_2COOH \longrightarrow CO_2 + R^- \overset{O}{\overset{\|}{C}} ^- CH_3$$

β-Ketonic acid   Ketone

Reactions of hydroxylated acids. These acids, in addition to possessing chemical groups characteristic of other fatty acids previously discussed, also contain one or more alcoholic hydroxyl groups in the hydrocarbon chain and consequently give the reactions of this group. The most important of these reactions is the formation of esters, in particular the acetic acid esters. When hydroxylated acids are treated with acetic anhydride, the reaction proceeds as follows:

$$R^- CH ^- (CH_2)_xCOOH + (CH_3CO)_2O \longrightarrow R^- CH ^- (CH_2)_xCOOH + CH_3COOH$$

OH   O $^-$ CO $^-$ CH$_3$

Hydroxylated acid   Acetic ester, or acetylated fatty acid

The amount of acetyl group taken up by these acids may be quantitatively determined, and it indicates the degree of hydroxylation of the acids.

FATS

The fats represent the most abundant and widespread class of lipids in nature. They are especially abundant in nuts and seeds of plants, where they represent reserve food material. Important among these vegetable fats are olive oil, cottonseed oil, linseed oil, coconut oil, peanut oil, soybean oil, tung oil, poppy-seed oil, and rape-seed oil. Each species of animal contains more or less characteristic fats in its various tissues in greater or lesser amounts. Fats such as lard, tallow, butter, neat's foot oil, and fish oils are common representatives of important animal fats differentiated by both source and chemical properties. Fat deposits serve three major physiologic functions in the animal body: they are reserve food material, they serve as insulation against the loss of body heat, and they are important as padding material to support and protect internal organs.

A. CHEMICAL COMPOSITION OF THE FATS

Animal and vegetable fats are generally rather complex mixtures of the glycerol esters of fatty acids (glycerides). Fats from different sources differ because of differences in the glycerides composing them. The fat from a given source consists of a rather characteristic mixture of glycerides, although considerable variation may be found in certain cases.

The glycerides composing fats are of two types, simple and mixed. General and specific formulas of such glycerides and their names are given below:

$$H_2C - O - CO - R$$
$$HC - O - CO - R$$
$$H_2C - O - CO - R$$
Simple glyceride

$$H_2C - O - CO - R_1$$
$$HC - O - CO - R_2$$
$$H_2C - O - CO - R_3$$
Mixed glyceride

The fatty acid groups in a simple glyceride are all alike, while two or more of them are different in mixed glycerides:

$$H_2C - O - CO - C_{17}H_{35}$$
$$HC - O - CO - C_{17}H_{35}$$
$$H_2C - O - CO - C_{17}H_{35}$$
Glyceryl tristearate
Tristearin
Stearin
Simple glyceride
i

$$H_2C - O - CO - C_{17}H_{33}$$
$$HC - O - CO - C_{17}H_{33}$$
$$H_2C - O - CO - C_{17}H_{33}$$
Glyceryl trioleate
Triolein
Olein
Simple glyceride
ii

$$\alpha\text{-}H_2C - O - CO - C_{17}H_{35}$$
$$\beta\text{-}HC - O - CO - C_{17}H_{33}$$
$$\alpha'\text{-}H_2C - O - CO - C_{15}H_{31}$$
β-Oleo-α-α'-stearopalmitin
An oleopalmitostearin
Mixed glyceride
III

$$H_2C - O - CO - C_{17}H_{33}$$
$$HC - O - CO - C_{17}H_{35}$$
$$H_2C - O - CO - C_{15}H_{31}$$
α-Oleo-α'-β-palmitostearin
An oleopalmitostearin
Mixed glyceride
IV

$$H_2C - O - CO - C_{17}H_{35}$$
$$HC - O - CO - C_{17}H_{35}$$
$$H_2C - O - CO - C_{17}H_{33}$$
α-Oleodistearin
Mixed glyceride
V

$$H_2C - O - CO - C_{17}H_{35}$$
$$HC - O - CO - C_{15}H_{31}$$
$$H_2C - O - CO - C_{17}H_{35}$$
β-Palmitodistearin
Mixed glyceride
VI

These formulas of mixed glycerides containing different fatty acids show isomerism due to different positions of attachment of the different acid groups to the glycerol molecule.

Hilditch and associates (3) have demonstrated that natural fats usually are largely composed of mixed glycerides with only small amounts or traces of simple glycerides. Their method of separation involves fractional crystallization from acetone at controlled temperatures, since different glycerides show different solubilities. Only a substantial beginning has been made in this work, but the glyceride composition of a number of fats has been worked out. Table 6.2, compiled by Hilditch, shows the component glycerides and also fatty acids present in fats of the pig, sheep, and ox. The preponderance of mixed glycerides in the fats is striking.

These workers have studied extensively the composition of fats from various animal and plant sources. Table 6.3 shows in a general way the distribution of fatty acids according to carbon content in five groups of animal and vegetable fats. Table 6.4 gives data on the composition of fatty acids from human fat, and Table 6.5 values for the fatty acids of phospholipid-free beef plasma.

Table 6.2. Component Acids and Glycerides of Pig, Sheep, and Ox Depot Fats (Molar per cent)*

Component Acids	Pig (Back Fat)	Sheep (External Fat)	Ox
Myristic + lauric	1.3	3.8	2.6
Palmitic	29.0	31.5	33.4
Stearic	13.8	14.5	21.4
Arachidic	....	0.4	1.3
Hexa + tetradecenoic	2.7	1.2	2.5
Oleic	43.9	45.8	35.2
Octadecadienoic	7.2	2.1	3.5
Unsaturated C_{20-22}	2.1	0.7	0.1
Component Glycerides (Approximate)			
Fully saturated:			
Tripalmitin	1	Trace	3
Dipalmitostearin	2	3	8
Palmitodistearin	2	2	6
Tristearin	....	....	....
Mono-oleo-disaturated:			
Oleodipalmitin	5	13	15
Oleopalmitostearin	27	28	32
Oleodistearin	....	1	2
Dioleo-monosaturated:			
Palmitodiolein	53	46	23
Stearodiolein	7	7	11
Trioleins	3	0	0

From Hilditch, T. P.: *Ann. Rev. Biochem.*, 11, 95, 1942.

Table 6.3. Chief Qualitative Distribution of Fatty Acids According to Carbon Content in Five Groups of Fats

Fat	Saturated	Unsaturated
Seed fats of cocoa butter	C_{16}, C_{18}	C_{18}
Palm oil, tallow, lard, and many vegetable oils	C_{14}, C_{16}, C_{18}	C_{18}
Seed fats of palmae	C_8, C_{10}, C_{12}, C_{14}, C_{16}	C_{18}
Milk fats	C_4, C_6, C_8, C_{10}, C_{12}, C_{14}, C_{16}, C_{18}	C_{18}
Marine fats	C_{14}, C_{16}, C_{18}	C_{14}, C_{16}, C_{18}, C_{20}, C_{22}, C_{24}

Reprinted by permission from *Biochemistry of the Lipids* by H. B. Bull, published by John Wiley & Sons, 1937.

Table 6.4. Per Cent of Fatty Acids in the Mixture of Acids from Human Fat

Acids	Specimen No.				
	XIII	XII	III	XX	H-XIV
Lauric	0.1	0.6	....	....	0.9
Myristic	2.7	5.9	2.6	2.6	3.9
Tetradecenoic	0.2	0.6	0.4	0.4	0.5
Palmitic	24.0	25.0	24.7	25.4	25.7
Hexadecenoic	5.0	6.7	7.3	5.6	7.6
Stearic	8.4	5.8	7.7	7.7	5.2
Octadecenoic (chiefly oleic)	46.9	45.4	45.8	44.8	46.6
Octadecadienoic (chiefly linoleic)	10.2	8.2	10.0	11.0	8.7
Arachidonic	1.0	1.0	0.4	0.3	0.6
Other C_{20}	1.5	0.8	1.1	2.2	0.3

From Cramer, D. L., and Brown, J. B.: *J. Biol. Chem.*, **151**, 428, 1942.

Table 6.5. Fatty Acid Composition of Acetone-Soluble Beef Plasma Lipids
(Molar per cent)

Acids	Free Fatty Acids	Glyceride Acids	Cholesterol Ester Acids
Myristic	0.8	0.2	....
Palmitic	34.4	33.7	11.1
Stearic	5.2	22.2	3.3
Arachidic	2.7	0.5	0.3
Hexadecenoic	....	2.6	4.2
Oleic	40.5	21.3	7.9
Linoleic	16.4	18.4	61.7
Linolenic	....	....	9.2
Arachidonic	....	1.1	2.3

Note: The large proportion of octadecadienoic acids (linoleic) in cholesterol esters is noteworthy.
From the work of Kelsey, F. E. and Longenecker, H. E.: *J. Biol. Chem.*, **139**, 727–739, 1941. Table from article by Hilditch, T. P.: *Ann. Rev. Biochem*, **11**, 88, 1942.

Mattson and Lutton (4) have studied the position (α, α', β) distribution of fatty acids in the glycerides of a number of vegetable and animal fats. Pancreatic lipase hydrolyzes off rather specifically fatty acids attached to glycerol at the end positions (α, α'; or 1 and 3) and forms monoglycerides, with the fatty acid in the 2, or β, position. The above workers, by studying the free fatty acids liberated from glycerides by pancreatic lipase and the fatty acid remaining in the monoglycerides formed, found a high degree of position specificity for fatty acid distribution in the glycerides of a given vegetable or animal fat. In the vegetable fats as a class the saturated fatty acids are predominantly esterified at the end positions (α, α') of glycerol. For each animal fat a rather characteristic fatty acid distribution in the glycerol group was found, though there is no general pattern for animal fats as a class. Lard is unique in that of all fats studied the saturated fatty acids are predominantly in the β position.

B. PHYSICAL PROPERTIES OF THE FATS

The glycerides of lower fatty acids, such as butyric, are somewhat soluble in water, whereas those of the higher acids are insoluble. All glycerides are soluble in ether, chloroform, and benzene. They are only slightly soluble in cold methyl and ethyl alcohol and acetone, but much more soluble in these solvents when hot. Boiling ethyl alcohol is one of the best solvents for the extraction of fats as well as all other lipids from tissues. Glycerides, except those of hydroxylated acids, are soluble in petroleum ether.

The specific gravity of fats is generally lower than that of water.

The melting point of a fat depends upon its component glycerides. The melting points of the glycerides are generally higher than those of the fatty acids present and vary with the acids. Glycerides of the higher saturated fatty acids have the highest melting points, and those of unsaturated acids have the lowest. The presence of a large proportion of unsaturated acids or of short-chain acids in the glycerides of a fat accordingly lowers the melting point and causes the fat to be liquid (an oil) at room temperature. In most fatty oils unsaturation is the dominant factor. Since natural fats are mixtures, their melting points are not sharp as is the case with pure compounds.

Pure glycerides have no color, odor, or taste. The presence of these properties in a fat are the result of foreign substances mixed with or dissolved in the glycerides. For example, the yellow color of butter is due to the presence of the plant pigments carotene and xanthopyll, chiefly carotene. Such pigments also generally give the color to the fats of animal tissues and egg yolk.

Although many of the mixed glycerides of the natural fats contain asymmetric carbon atoms in the glyceryl carbon chain, only those which contain optically active acids, such as chaulmoogric, show demonstrable optical activity.

C. CHEMICAL PROPERTIES OF THE FATS

The chemical properties of the fats are the properties of their component glycerides, and these in turn depend in particular upon the character of the fatty acids present. Since all the glycerides are esters, they give the reactions of esters. Those which contain double bonds in the fatty acid chains show the characteristic properties of unsaturation. The presence of hydroxylated fatty acids in glycerides causes them to give reactions of the alcoholic hydroxyl group. These chemical properties are outlined below.

Hydrolysis. The hydrolysis of the glycerides of a fat may be readily accomplished by heating with water at high temperatures and pressures in an autoclave, preferably with addition of catalysts such as acids. When boiled at ordinary pressure the action is very slow:

$$
\begin{array}{lll}
H_2C-O- & -CO-R \quad HO|H & H_2C-OH \\
HC-O- & -CO-R + HO|H \longrightarrow 3RCOOH + & HC-OH \\
H_2C-O- & -CO-R \quad HO|H \quad \text{Fatty acid} & H_2C-OH \\
& & \text{or acids} \\
\text{Glyceride} & & \text{Glycerol}
\end{array}
$$

This reaction of hydrolysis may be efficiently accomplished also by a lipase enzyme such as steapsin of pancreatic juice or the lipase of castor bean.

Lipases are widespread in both plants and animals, and the keeping qualities of animal and vegetable fats which often contain some lipase may be improved by heating to inactivate the enzyme.

Saponification. The glycerides of the fats may be readily decomposed into glycerol and salts of the constituent fatty acids (soaps) by boiling with strong bases such as sodium or potassium hydroxide. Since fats are insolube in water, the process is facilitated by the addition of alcohol which dissolves the fat:

$$
\begin{array}{ll}
H_2C-O-CO-C_{17}H_{35} & KOH \\
| & \\
HC-O-CO-C_{17}H_{35} + KOH & \longrightarrow 3C_{17}H_{35}COOK + HC-OH \\
| & \text{Potassium stearate,} \\
H_2C-O-CO-C_{17}H_{35} & KOH \quad\quad \text{a soap} \\
\text{Stearin} &
\end{array}
$$

$$
\begin{array}{l}
H_2C-OH \\
| \\
HC-OH \\
| \\
H_2C-OH \\
\text{Glycerol}
\end{array}
$$

The soap and glycerol are soluble in water, but the soap may be separated out by the addition of salt. The glycerol may be recovered from the aqueous solution by careful evaporation of the water followed by vacuum distillation.

Since glycerol is a component of fats and some other lipids, a few of its properties may be mentioned. It is a sweet, heavy liquid (sp. gr. 1.26 at 20° C), miscible with water and alcohol in all proportions but insoluble in ether, chloroform, and benzene. When carefully oxidized with H_2O_2 in slightly alkaline solution in the presence of an iron salt, a mixture of glyceric aldehyde and dihydroxy acetone is formed. Either a primary or the secondary alcohol group of the glycerol may be oxidized to give an aldehyde or ketone, respectively:

$$
\begin{array}{lll}
H_2COH + O & HCO & H_2COH \\
| & | & | \\
HCOH \quad\longrightarrow & HCOH \quad\quad \text{and} & C=O + H_2O \\
| & | & | \\
H_2COH & H_2COH & H_2COH \\
\text{Glycerol} & \text{Glyceric} & \text{Dihydroxy} \\
& \text{aldehyde} & \text{acetone}
\end{array}
$$

Both glyceric aldehyde and dihydroxy acetone are sugars (trioses), and the mixture produced in the reaction reduces alkaline copper reagents such as those of Fehling and Benedict. These properties are occasionally used in testing for the presence of glycerol.

A second important chemical property of glycerol is the production of the unsaturated aldehyde acrolein when glycerol is heated, preferably with a dehydrating agent such as $KHSO_4$ or P_2O_5:

$$
\begin{array}{ll}
H_2COH & CHO \\
| & | \\
HCOH + KHSO_4 \longrightarrow & CH \quad + 2H_2O \\
| & \| \\
H_2COH & CH_2 \\
\text{Glycerol} & \text{Acrolein,} \\
& \text{acrylic aldehyde}
\end{array}
$$

The acrolein is given off from the hot mixture as an exceedingly irritating vapor which can be readily detected. If fats are heated to a sufficiently high temperature, they may be broken down with subsequent formation of acrolein from glycerol, which accounts for the irritating odor from the hot fat.

Glycerol, in common with many other polyhydroxy compounds, has the property of dissolving metallic hydroxides such as $Cu(OH)_2$. Glycerol combines with the positive metallic ions through coordination of the ions with free electron pairs of the hydroxyl oxygen atoms to form slightly dissociated soluble complexes. The reaction proceeds in alkaline solution, and the complexes are broken up by acidification.

Glycerol is an excellent solvent for many substances. It is used widely in cosmetics and medicines, as a solvent, and, because of its capacity to take up and hold water, as a moistening agent. Large quantities are employed in the manufacture of nitroglycerin. Glycerol is nontoxic to animals and is readily utilized by the animal body.

The saponification of fats is important not only in the preparation of commercial soaps but also in the chemical examination of fats. The separation of the glycerides in a fat is a laborious and difficult operation which has only recently been accomplished for a number of fats. The more common procedure is to investigate the total fatty acids contained in the glycerides of a fat. For this purpose the first procedure is saponification with NaOH or KOH to form the soluble soaps of the acids. The hot saponification mixture is then acidified with mineral acid which takes the metal from the soaps and frees the fatty acids:

$$R - CO - O - Na + HCl \longrightarrow R - COOH + NaCl$$

Soaps of fatty acids   Free fatty acids

Separation of fatty acids. When a fat is saponified and the mixture acidified, the insoluble fatty acids float on the surface of the solution and may be removed. The water-soluble shorter chain acids (C_2—C_{10}) are separated from the cooled aqueous layer by extraction with ether. Saturated and unsaturated fatty acids may be separated by crystallization of the former from cold acetone, or by preparing the lead salts of the mixed acids and precipitating with ethanol, in which the lead salts of the saturated acids are relatively insoluble. Unsaturated fatty acids may be further separated by fractional crystallization of their bromine derivatives. Careful fractional vacuum distillation of the mixed methyl esters of fatty acids has been very helpful for separation.

The above procedures are laborious and seldom afford sharp separations; they are being rapidly replaced by methods utilizing paper and column chromatography. In particular, the application of liquid-gas-column chromatography has greatly facilitated the separation of fatty acids as well as various other substances. In this procedure a long tube is filled with an inert solid material coated with a nonvolatile oil in which the methyl esters of the fatty acids exhibit differential solubility. A mixture of the esters is introduced at one end of the heated tube and the vapors carried through the tube by an inert gas. Each ester migrates through the tube according to its vapor pressure and solubility in the oil, and may be identified by the thermal conductance of its vapor as it emerges from the tube prior to condensation back to the liquid state. This process gives a sharp fractional distillation and permits good resolution of closely related fatty acids from complex mixtures.

Saponification number. The amount of alkali required to saponify a given weight of fat can be accurately determined. Each molecule of glyceride requires three molecules of alkali regardless of the molecular size of the fatty acids present. Thus, one molecule of butyrin (mol. wt. 302) requires the same quantity of alkali as does one molecule of stearin (mol. wt. 891). However, in a given weight of butyrin there are 2.95 times as many molecules as in the same weight of stearin $(891/302 = 2.95)$. This means that 2.95 times as much alkali is required to saponify 1 g of butyrin as to saponify 1 g of stearin. The saponification number is defined as the milligrams of KOH required to saponify 1 g of fat. One gram of stearin requires 189 mg of KOH for saponification, while 1 g of butyrin requires 557 mg (2.95×189). Accordingly, the saponification number of stearin is 189 and that of butyrin 557. Since fats are mixtures of glycerides, most of which are of the mixed type, the saponification number of a fat gives information about the average molecular size of the fatty acids present in the glycerides of the fat.

Reactions of fats due to unsaturation. The double bonds of unsaturated acids in glycerides undergo the reactions characteristic of these bonds in the free acids.

Hydrogenation. The unsaturated glycerides of fats may be hydrogenated by treatment with hydrogen in the presence of nickel catalyst:

$$H_2C - O - CO - (CH_2)_7CH = CH(CH_2)_7CH_3 \quad H_2 \qquad H_2C - O - CO - (CH_2)_{16}CH_3$$
$$HC - O - CO - (CH_2)_7CH = CH(CH_2)_7CH_3 + H_2 \longrightarrow HC - O - CO - (CH_2)_{16}CH_3$$
$$H_2C - O - CO - (CH_2)_7CH = CH(CH_2)_7CH_3 \quad H_2 \qquad H_2C - O - CO - (CH_2)_{16}CH_3$$
$$\text{Olein, unsaturated} \qquad\qquad\qquad \text{Stearin, saturated}$$

The hydrogenation of oils such as cottonseed to prepare commercial cooking fats (Crisco, etc.) and margarines is an important food industry. In the process the glycerides are only partially saturated to form a soft fat. If completely hydrogenated, the fat would be too hard for convenient use and would not be digested and absorbed efficiently.

Halogenation. Chlorine, bromine, iodine, iodine chloride, and iodine bromide may be added to the double bonds of the unsaturated glycerides in fats. One atom of halogen adds to each side of the double bond, producing a saturated halogenated glyceride.

Olein adds six halogen atoms, linolein adds 12, and linolenin adds 18. The halogenation of the mixture of glycerides composing a fat is not represented so simply, but the amount of halogen absorbed is proportional to the total number of double bonds present in the glyceride mixture.

Iodine number. Since the quantity of halogen absorbed by the glycerides of a fat can be measured accurately, it is possible to calculate the relative unsaturation of fats. This is done by determining the so-called iodine number, which is defined as the per cent of iodine absorbed by the fat, or the grams of iodine absorbed by 100 g of fat. In actual practice, solutions containing iodine monobromide (Hanus method) or iodine monochloride (Wijs

method) or bromine (Rosenmund-Kuhnehenn method) are used in preference to iodine solutions, because they are more active and give more nearly
correct results. Regardless of the halogenating solution used, the results are
always calculated in terms of iodine and are expressed as iodine numbers.

Certain iodized oils, such as iodized poppy-seed oil, are used in medicine
for injection into body cavities to be x-rayed. The iodine stops the rays and
causes the cavities to be outlined in the photographs.

Acetylation. The glycerides of fats containing hydroxylated fatty acids
react with acetic anhydride and other acylating agents to form the corresponding esters:

$$
\left(R - \underset{\underset{OH}{|}}{\overset{\overset{H}{|}}{C}} - (CH_2)_x - COO\right)_3 C_3H_5 + 3(CH_3CO)_2O \longrightarrow \left(R - \underset{\underset{O-CO-CH_3}{|}}{\overset{\overset{H}{|}}{C}} - (CH_2)_x COO\right)_3 C_3H_5 + 3CH_3COOH
$$

Hydroxylated glyceride   Acetic anhydride   Acetylated glyceride

Acetyl number. The "acetyl number" is defined as the milligrams of
KOH required to combine with the acetic acid liberated by the saponification of 1 g of acetylated fat. When a fat containing hydroxylated acid is
boiled with acetic anhydride and the excess anhydride decomposed and
washed out with water and the fat dried, the product contains the acetyl
derivatives (esters) of the hydroxylated acids of the glycerides. A weighed
amount of this acetylated fat may be saponified with alkali, the soaps decomposed by acidification with H_2SO_4, and the volatile acid removed by steam
distillation and then titrated. Generally a correction for the volatile short-
chain fatty acids present in the glycerides of the fat must be made. Of the
natural fats, only castor oil contains sufficient hydroxylated acids (chiefly
ricinoleic) to give a high acetyl number (146–150). Butter has an acetyl value
of 1.9 to 8.6, indicating the presence of very small amounts of hydroxylated
acids.

Oxidation of unsaturated glycerides of fats. Oxidation of unsaturated
bonds in the glycerides of fats proceeds as previously outlined for the fatty
acids. Ozone and oxygen may add at the double bonds to form ozonides and
peroxides, respectively, which may then decompose into other substances.
Certain of the natural oils containing large proportions of highly unsaturated
acids such as linseed, when exposed to the air and light, absorb oxygen (auto-
oxidize) and form products which polymerize to produce insoluble hard films.
Such oils are used in the production of paints and varnishes. The chemical
processes occurring in the hardening or drying of oils are very complex, but
it is probable that peroxide formation at the double bond is the primary
reaction.

Rancidity of fats. The unpleasant odor and taste developed by most
natural fats upon aging is referred to as "rancidity." Rancidity may be due
to hydrolysis of component glycerides of a fat into free fatty acids and glycerol or mono- and diglycerides. This is often hastened by the presence of
lipolytic enzymes (fat-splitting enzymes or lipases) in the fats, which in the
presence of moisture and at warm temperature bring about hydrolysis. Ran-

cidity may also be caused by various oxidative processes. For example, oxidation at the double bonds of unsaturated glycerides may form peroxides which then decompose to form aldehydes of objectionable odor and taste. This process is greatly increased by exposure to light. A third type of rancidity may be caused by beta oxidation of free saturated fatty acids, as previously indicated in the discussion of fatty acid oxidation.

It has been observed that highly refined fats and distilled fatty acids or their esters begin to absorb atmospheric oxygen almost immediately upon exposure to it, whereas natural fats often exhibit an "induction period" of variable duration before oxidation begins. This resistance of natural fats to oxidation has been shown to be due to the presence therein of small quantities of nonfatty compounds concerning the exact chemical nature of which little is known. These substances are called "antioxygens" or "antioxidants," and they prevent the oxidation of unsaturated glycerides until they themselves have been destroyed. The addition of minute amounts of certain reducing compounds such as hydroquinone to fats has been found to retard oxidative rancidity.

Acid number. This represents, by definition, the milligrams of KOH required to neutralize the free fatty acids present in 1 g of fat, and is of value in determining rancidity due to free fatty acids.

Reichert-Meissl number or volatile fatty acid number. This represents the cubic centimeters of 0.1 N alkali required to neutralize the volatile acid obtained from 5 g of fat which has been saponified, acidified to liberate the fatty acids, and then steam distilled. Butter fat, which contains a considerable proportion of glycerides of the shorter-chain fatty acids, has a Reichert-Meissl value of 26–33, whereas the number for lard is only about 0.6.

D. CHARACTERIZATION OF FATS

The chemical analysis and identification of fats is important both in industry and in biochemical investigations. The methods used are numerous and often involved and cannot be given in detail here. Works such as those of Lewkowitsch, *Chemical Technology and Analysis of Oils, Fats, and Waxes,* and of Allen, *Commercial Organic Analysis* and the *Official Methods of the Association of Agricultural Chemists*, should be consulted for comprehensive and detailed information.

The identification of fats is generally based upon physical properties such as specific gravity, melting point, refractive index, and viscosity, and upon determination of saponification number, iodine number, acetyl value, and Reichert-Meissl number.

The various constants provide information about the nature of the fatty acids present in the mixture of glycerides composing a fat. Since the fat from a given source is made up of a rather characteristic mixture of glycerides, it may generally be definitely identified by determining its physical and chemical constants. The presence of impurities and adulterations in food fats may

Table 6.6. Chemical Constants of Some Common Fats

Name	Acid No.	Reichert-Meissl No.	Saponif. No.	Iodine No.	Acetyl No.
Lard	0.5–0.8	0.5–0.8	195–203	47–66.5	2.6 Ave.
Human Fat		0.25–0.55	194–198*	65–69*	
Tallow, beef	0.25		196–200	35–42	2.7–8.6
Butter fat	0.45–35	17–35	210–230	26–28	1.9–8.6
Olive oil	0.3–1	0.6–1.5	185–196	79–88	10–11
Cottonseed oil	0.6–0.9	0.95	194–196	103–111	21–25
Linseed oil	1–3.5	0.95	188–195	175–202	4.0
Castor oil	0.12–0.8	1.4	175–183	84	146–150
Coconut oil	1.1–1.9	6.6–7.5	253–262	6–10	2.0

* Data of Cramer, D. S., and Brown, J. B.: *J. Biol. Chem.*, **151**, 429, 1943.

also be indicated by variations in these values. Table 6.6 shows some common fats and their chemical constants. Detailed values for both physical and chemical constants are available in the various handbooks of chemistry. It is seldom that any fat can be identified by a single constant, but most fats may be identified by a group of constants.

WAXES

Waxes are widespread in nature as the secretions of certain insects and as protective coatings of the skins and furs of animals and the leaves and fruit of plants. Certain animal oils, such as that of the sperm whale, are composed largely of waxes rather than of fats.

Waxes commonly are defined chemically as the esters of higher fatty acids and of higher monohydroxy alcohols. Dihydroxy alcohols may occasionally be present. As a matter of fact, although such esters generally make up the larger proportion of waxes, there may be present appreciable quantities of free higher fatty acids and higher alcohols as well as saturated hydrocarbons of high molecular weight.

Beeswax. This insect wax is a complex mixture of esters, some free fatty acids, alcohols, and hydrocarbons. The ester of myricyl alcohol ($C_{30}H_{61}OH$) and palmitic acid ($C_{15}H_{31}COOH$) is an important constituent and has the formula $C_{15}H_{31}COOC_{30}H_{61}$ (myricyl palmitate). Even carbon fatty acids from C_{24} to C_{34} and primary monohydroxy alcohols from C_{24} to C_{34} are present as esters or in the free condition. Odd carbon paraffin hydrocarbons from C_{25} to C_{31} are also present.

Carnauba wax. This is an important plant wax (leaf cuticle) and is also a rather complex mixture. The fatty acids and alcohols of carnauba wax have even carbon chains ranging from C_{26} to C_{34}. A C_{27} paraffin hydrocarbon has also been identified as a constituent.

Sperm oil. This oil from the head of the sperm whale consists of about three-fourths wax esters and one-fourth triglycerides. Saturated acids present range from C_{10} to C_{18}, and unsaturated from C_{12} to C_{20}. Saturated alcohols from C_{14} to C_{18} and unsaturated from C_{16} to C_{20} are present.

Lanolin or wool fat. This material forms a protective coating over the wool fibers and is a wax rather than a fat. It is a very complex mixture and is characterized among waxes by containing both free and esterified cholesterol ($C_{27}H_{45}OH$), as well as the sterols lanosterol ($C_{30}H_{49}OH$) and agnosterol ($C_{30}H_{47}OH$). Lanolin has the property of taking up much water without dissolving, which makes it valuable as a medium in the preparation of ointments and cosmetics.

Waxes are used chiefly in the manufacture of polishes (carnauba wax), lubricants (sperm oil), candles (spermaceti), and ointments (lanolin).

PHOSPHOLIPIDS OR PHOSPHATIDES

The phospholipids or phosphatides are lipids which contain phosphorus, the latter being present as esterfied phosphoric acid. Gobley (1846, 1847) isolated a phospholipid from egg yolk which he called "lecithin" (Greek *lekithos*, egg yolk). Couerbe, Fremy, and Valencienne (1834–1857) found phospholipids in a variety of animal sources, and in 1861 Töpler found them in plant seeds. Thus, by the middle of the nineteenth century the widespread occurrence of phosphorus containing lipids in both plant and animal tissues and products had been established. During the latter half of the nineteenth century, Thudichum made an exhaustive and careful study of the chemistry of the brain, much of which dealt with the phospholipids, that was summarized in his classical monograph "A Treatise on the Chemical Constitution of the Brain" (London, 1884).

The phospholipids or phosphatides as a group are separated from fats and other lipids by precipitation from ether solution with acetone, the phospholipids being insoluble in acetone. It was discovered early that egg yolk lecithin and so-called lecithins from other sources upon hydrolysis yield glycerol, fatty acids, phosphoric acid, and the quaternary nitrogen base choline. The so-called lecithins are soluble in alcohol and ether and insoluble in acetone. Another group of phospholipids, called "cephalins," is generally associated with the lecithins and is characterized by being soluble in ether but insoluble in both alcohol and acetone. Thus, they may be separated from lecithins by differential solubility in alcohol. A cephalin fraction was first isolated from brain and characterized as a separate entity by Thudichum. It yielded glycerol, fatty acids, phosphoric acid, and the nitrogen base ethanolamine upon hydrolysis, thus differing from lecithin only in the nitrogenous compound present. Thudichum also obtained from a concentrated alcohol extract of brain tissue a third type of phospholipid, which he called "sphingomyelin." The sphingomyelin phospholipid fraction is characterized by being soluble in hot alcohol and insoluble in ether and acetone. Sphingomyelins, when hydrolyzed, yield a complex nitrogen containing alcohol, sphingosine, fatty acid, phosphoric acid, and choline; glycerol is absent. Thus, the phospholipids or phosphatides were differentiated into the lecithins, cephalins, and sphingomyelins. More recently a fourth group of phospholipids, called "acetal phospholipids" or "phosphoglyceracetals" (originally "plasmalogens") has been discovered. These substances yield a long-chain aliphatic aldehyde, glycerol, fatty acid, phosphoric acid, and a nitrogen compound (choline, ethanolamine, or serine) upon hydrolysis.

Phospholipids are, so far as known, present in all vegetable and animal cells. They undoubtedly enter into the fundamental structure of protoplasm itself as well as contribute to the chemical processes concerned with cell metabolism. Phospholipids are more abundant in eggs, brain, liver, kidney, pancreas, lung, and heart muscle than in other common tissues. Bloor found the following percentages of phospholipid (lecithin + cephalin) in fresh organs of beef: brain, 4.58; liver, 3.06; pancreas, 1.86; heart muscle, 1.64; kidney, 1.62; lung, 1.25; jaw muscle, 1.06; diaphragm, 0.76; neck muscle, 0.63; round muscle, 0.42. The white matter contains most of the phospholipid of brain. An important source of commercial vegetable lecithin (a mixture) is the soybean.

Since the phospholipid fraction is a complex mixture from which the separation of analytically pure substances is difficult and fraught with uncertainties, the elucidation of the chemistry of the phospholipids has been slow and tedious and is still in progress. Application of the techniques of paper and column chromatography in the separation and identification of the phospholipids and their derivatives is now facilitating greatly developments in this field of lipid biochemistry.

Recent reviews on the chemistry of the phospholipids have been written by Celmer and Carter (5), Baer (6), and Folch (7). Much of the modern work on phosphatides is outlined in the report of a Symposium on Chemistry and Metabolism of Phosphatides in *Federation Proceedings* (**16**, 816, 1957). Wittcoff has published a comprehensive monograph on the phospholipids (8).

In recent years it has been found by Folch (7) that the cephalin fraction from beef brain is a complex mixture containing not only ethanolamine cephalins, but cephalins with serine or inositol in them. The phospholipids known as sphingomyelins are derivatives of sphingosine, but the cerebroside glycolipids, which are present in large amounts in brain, also are sphingosine derivatives. The old terms "lecithin," "cephalin," and "sphingomyelin" have been used to designate not only definite chemical substances, but also lipid fractions which are grossly impure. Thus, it is desirable to have a more definitive classification. Folch and Sperry (9), Folch (7), and Celmer and Carter (5) have proposed classifications of phosphatides based upon chemical relations. The classification given below is essentially that proposed by Carter and is based upon the alcoholic compound present in the molecule. For example, the lecithins and cephalins are glycerol derivatives and are designated "glycerophosphatides" or "phosphoglycerides." Similarly, the phospholipids which are derivatives of the alcohol inositol are the "phosphoinositides" or "inositol lipids." The sphingomyelins which are derived from the complex amino alcohol sphingosine are "sphingolipids." However, the cerebrosides which are glycolipids and not phospholipids also are sphingolipids, because they are derivatives of sphingosine. Since both the lecithins and cephalins are derivatives of phosphatidic acid, and contain the phosphatidyl group specifically, they are designated by such names as "phosphatidyl choline" and "phosphatidyl ethanolamine."

Phosphatides Yielding Glycerol upon Hydrolysis:

I. Glycerophosphatides or phosphoglycerides
   A. Phosphatidyl cholines (lecithins)
   B. Phosphatidyl ethanolamines (cephalins)
   C. Phosphatidyl serines (in cephalin fraction)
   D. Acetal phospholipids or phosphoglyceracetals
   E. Cardiolipins

Phosphatides Yielding Inositol upon Hydrolysis:

II. Phosphoinositides or inositol lipids
   A. Monophosphoinositide
   B. Diphosphoinositide (from brain)

Lipids Yielding Sphingosine upon Hydrolysis:

III. Sphingolipids*
   A. Phosphosphingosides (sphingomyelins) – *only phospholipid of this group*
   B. Glycosphingosides (cerebrosides)
   C. Sulfolipids
   D. Gangliosides
   E. Hematosides and globosides
   F. Strandin

I. GLYCEROPHOSPHATIDES OR PHOSPHOGLYCERIDES

A. PHOSPHATIDYL CHOLINES OR LECITHINS

The lecithins are derivatives of phosphatidic acid which is equivalent to a triglyceride in which a fatty acid group has been replaced by a phosphate group:

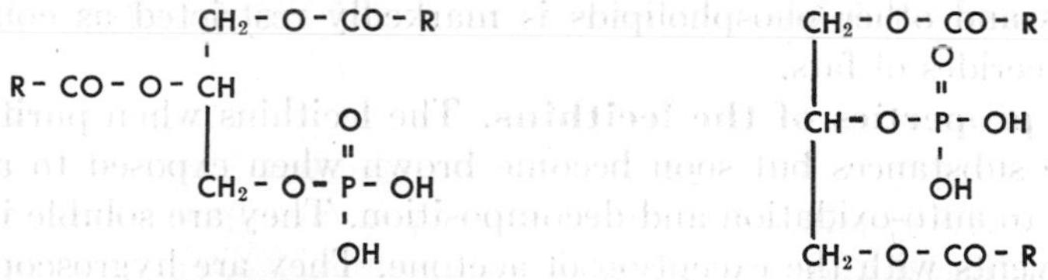

$$CH_2 - O - CO - R$$
$$R - CO - O - CH$$
$$CH_2 - O - P - OH$$
$$OH$$

L-α-Phosphatidic acid

$$CH_2 - O - CO - R$$
$$\overset{O}{CH - O - P - OH}$$
$$OH$$
$$CH_2 - O - CO - R$$

β-Phosphatidic acid

Both α- and β-phosphatidic acids are possible, though only lecithins containing α-phosphatidic acid have been found. The central glycerol carbon atom of natural α-phosphatidic acid is asymmetric and has the same configuration about it as the asymmetric carbon of L-glyceraldehyde and conse-

---

* Only the phosphosphingosides or sphingomyelins are phospholipids in group III of the classification.

quently belongs to the L-series. The lecithins, then, are L-α-phosphatidyl cholines of the general formula:

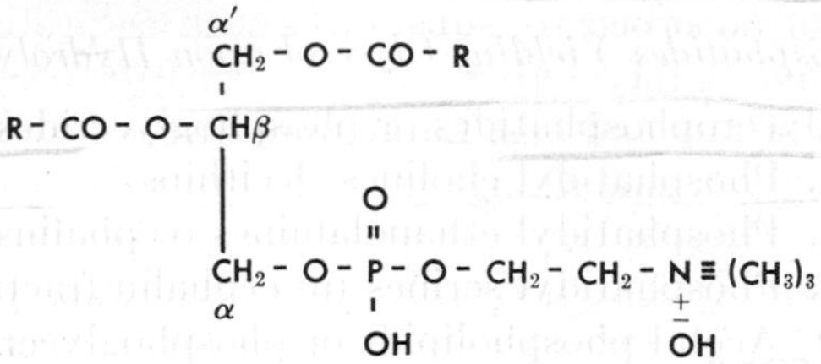

$$\alpha'$$
$$CH_2 - O - CO - R$$
$$|$$
$$R - CO - O - CH\beta$$
$$|$$
$$\quad\quad O$$
$$\quad\quad \|$$
$$CH_2 - O - P - O - CH_2 - CH_2 - N \equiv (CH_3)_3$$
$$\alpha \quad\quad | \quad\quad\quad\quad\quad\quad +$$
$$\quad\quad OH \quad\quad\quad\quad\quad OH$$

L-α-phosphatidyl choline
α-Lecithin

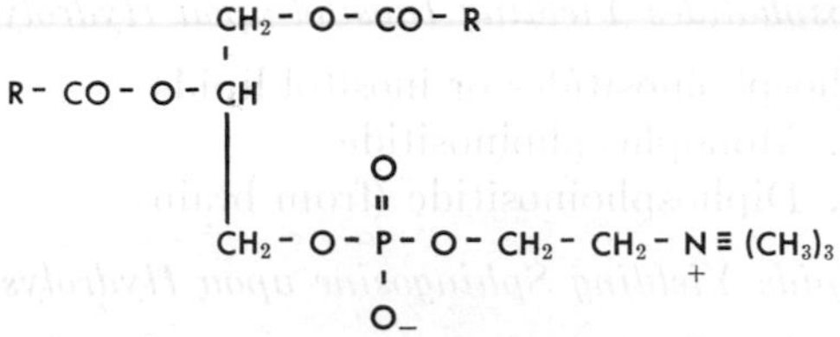

$$CH_2 - O - CO - R$$
$$|$$
$$R - CO - O - CH$$
$$|$$
$$\quad\quad O$$
$$\quad\quad \|$$
$$CH_2 - O - P - O - CH_2 - CH_2 - N \equiv (CH_3)_3$$
$$\quad\quad | \quad\quad\quad\quad\quad\quad +$$
$$\quad\quad O_-$$

Zwitterion form of an
α-Lecithin

Since the lecithins contain the acidic OH of phosphoric acid and the very basic OH⁻ of choline, they exist as internal salts or zwitterions, as shown in the lower formula above. The isoelectric pH of a pure lecithin is usually 6.7 or higher, which is in agreement with the zwitterion structure.

Variations in the fatty acid components give rise to different lecithins. For example, a lecithin containing stearic and oleic acids is different from one containing palmitic and oleic acids. Various combinations of saturated and unsaturated acids occur in lecithins. Many contain both saturated and unsaturated acids. There are others in which both acids are unsaturated, and some in which both acids are saturated. Liver lecithins have been found to contain the saturated acids palmitic and stearic, and the unsaturated acids oleic, linoleic, and arachidonic. Stearic, palmitic, oleic, linoleic, and linolenic acids have been found in soybean lecithins. The variety of acids occurring in the lecithins and other phospholipids is markedly restricted as compared with the glycerides of fats.

Physical properties of the lecithins. The lecithins when purified are waxy, white substances but soon become brown when exposed to air and light, owing to auto-oxidation and decomposition. They are soluble in ordinary fat solvents with the exception of acetone. They are hygroscopic and mix well with water to form cloudy, colloidal solutions from which they can be precipitated with acetone. They do not have definite melting points but decompose when heated.

Lecithin molecules, owing to their highly polar structure, tend to associate in definite orderly fashion even in colloidal aqueous suspensions. This capacity of orientation probably gives to the lecithins (and also other phospholipids) the function, in conjunction with proteins and other substances, of organizing protoplasm into its orderly and characteristic structure.

Purified lecithin preparations are moderately effective in lowering the surface tension of aqueous solutions, but when lecithins are either combined chemically with, or adsorbed to, substances such as proteins and carbohydrates, they are remarkably active and they constitute valuable agents for the emulsification of fats and oils. Large quantities of soybean lecithins are used as emulsifying and smoothing agents in the food industries.

Chemical properties of the lecithins. When aqueous lecithin emulsions are shaken with sulfuric acid, choline is split off, forming phosphatidic acid:

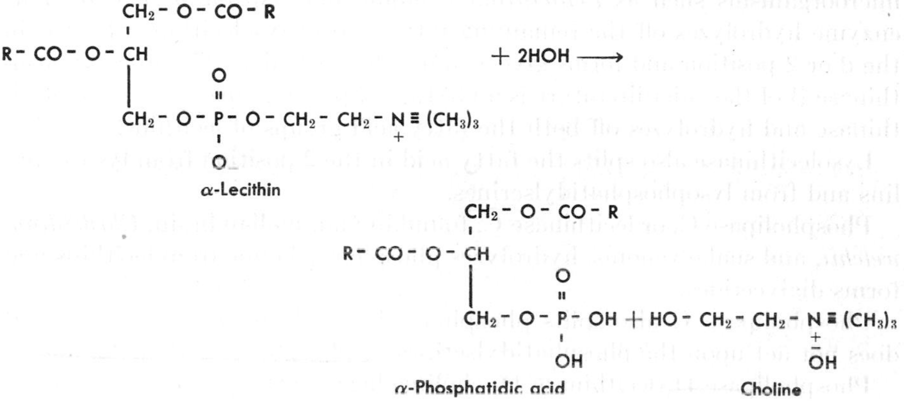

$$CH_2 - O - CO - R$$
$$R - CO - O - CH \qquad\qquad + 2HOH \longrightarrow$$
$$CH_2 - O - \underset{\underset{O}{\underset{|}{\|}}}{P} - O - CH_2 - CH_2 - \overset{+}{N} \equiv (CH_3)_3$$

α-Lecithin

$$CH_2 - O - CO - R$$
$$R - CO - O - CH$$
$$CH_2 - O - \underset{\underset{OH}{|}}{\overset{O}{\overset{\|}{P}}} - OH + HO - CH_2 - CH_2 - \overset{+}{\underset{OH}{N}} \equiv (CH_3)_3$$

α-Phosphatidic acid   Choline

When lecithins are boiled with alkalies or mineral acids, not only is choline split off as above, but the phosphatidic acid is hydrolyzed to give glycerophosphoric acid and fatty acids:

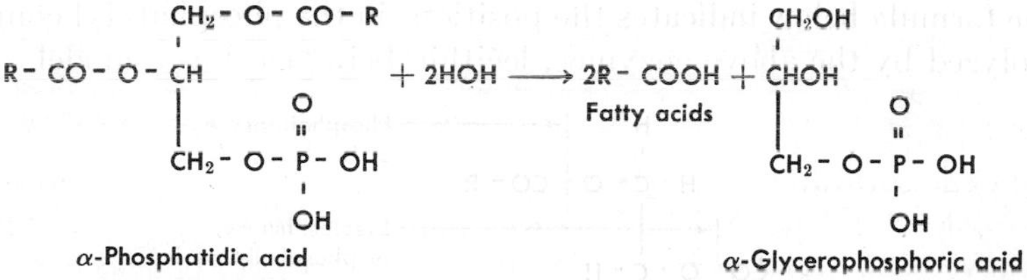

$$CH_2 - O - CO - R \qquad\qquad\qquad CH_2OH$$
$$R - CO - O - CH \qquad + 2HOH \longrightarrow 2R - COOH + CHOH$$
$$CH_2 - O - \underset{\underset{OH}{|}}{\overset{O}{\overset{\|}{P}}} - OH \qquad\qquad\qquad Fatty\ acids \qquad CH_2 - O - \underset{\underset{OH}{|}}{\overset{O}{\overset{\|}{P}}} - OH$$

α-Phosphatidic acid   α-Glycerophosphoric acid

Thus, the lecithins are hydrolyzed by boiling alkalies or strong acids to give choline, fatty acids (or soaps) and glycerophosphoric acid. The fatty acid groups are more readily hydrolyzed from lecithins than they are from the triglycerides of fats.

Glycerophosphoric acid is very difficult to hydrolyze into glycerol and phosphoric acid. It is not decomposed by boiling alkali and only very slowly by boiling dilute mineral acids. However, it is hydrolyzed readily by a phosphatase enzyme found in yeast and many plant and animal tissues. Glycerophosphoric acid is a stronger acid than phosphoric acid, its pK_1 and pK_2 values being 1.4 and 6.32, respectively.

Certain enzymes—the phospholipases, or the lecithinases—hydrolyze lecithins, the nature of the hydrolysis depending upon the kind of phospholipase acting. Hanahan (10) has shown that phospholipase A (lecithinase A) found in certain snake venoms (cobra, cottonmouth moccasin) poisons of scorpions and bees, and various mammalian tissues, specifically hydrolyzes off the fatty acid in the α or 1 position of glycerol in the lecithins to form lysolecithins. The lysolecithins are powerful hemolytic agents which rapidly hemolyze blood erythrocytes, and are considered to be responsible for harmful physiologic effects of venoms containing phospholipase A.

Phospholipase A also acts upon the cephalins in the same manner as upon the lecithins to form lysocephalins.

Lysolecithinase, or phospholipase B, is found in rice hulls and certain microorganisms such as *Penicillium notatum* and *Aspergillus oryzai*. This enzyme hydrolyzes off the remaining fatty acid of lysolecithin, which is in the β or 2 position and forms glycerylphosphorylcholine. The so-called lecithinase B of the older literature is a mixture of phospholipase A and lysolecithinase and hydrolyzes off both the fatty acid groups of lecithins.

Lysolecithinase also splits the fatty acid in the 2 position from lysocephalins and from lysophosphatidylserines.

Phospholipase C, or lecithinase C, found in mammalian brain, *Clostridium welchii*, and snake venoms, hydrolyzes phosphorylcholine from lecithins and forms diglycerides.

Phospholipase C also splits phosphorylcholine from sphingomyelins but does not act upon the phosphatidylserines or phosphatidylethanolamines.

Phospholipase D (lecithinase D, cholinephosphatase, phosphatidase C)—found in the tissues of higher plants such as cabbage leaves, carrots, and cottonseed—hydrolyzes the choline off of lecithins to form α-phosphatidic acids. It also splits choline from phosphatidylethanolamines (cephalins) and from phosphatidylserines.

The formula below indicates the positions in the phosphatidyl compounds hydrolyzed by the above enzymes, lecithin being used as a model.

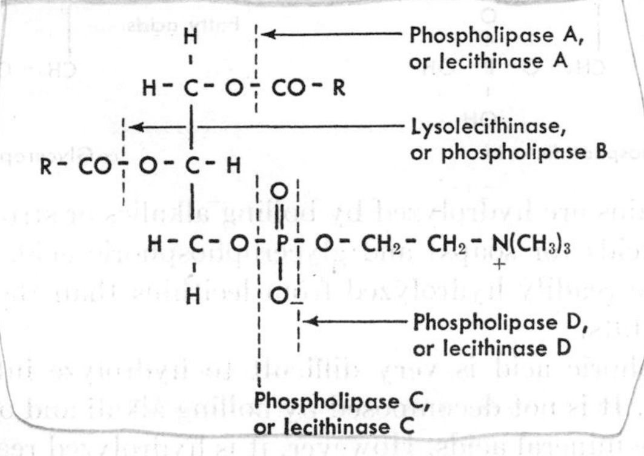

Hanahan (11) has made the very interesting discovery that the liver lecithins of beef, rabbit, guinea pig, rat, and dog have only unsaturated fatty acids on the α'-ester, or 1 position, and only saturated fatty acids on the β-ester, or 2 position. This fact may be related to some of the important biochemical functions of the lecithins.

Lecithins have the property of forming more or less stable combinations or complexes with many different substances, especially with other lipids,

proteins, carbohydrates, and various heavy metal salts. This property undoubtedly is concerned in the organization and function of many macromo-
lecular cellular components.

As indicated above, fatty acid groups are hydrolyzed from lecithins more
readily than they are from triglycerides. Also, unsaturated fatty acid groups
of lecithins more readily take up oxygen from the air and oxidize at the
double bond than these acid groups do when present in triglycerides. In fact,
the auto-oxidizability and instability of lecithins when exposed to air and
light is a dominant characteristic. This increase in the chemical reactivity of
the acid residues of lecithins is attributable to the influence of the phosphoric
acid-choline group in the molecule.

Since choline is a quaternary base, it is about as alkaline as sodium or
potassium hydroxide. Choline forms an insoluble salt with platinum chloride
and also an insoluble iodide. Both compounds have been used for the quantitative estimation of choline. When choline is heated, it decomposes into trimethylamine and ethylene glycol:

$$HO-CH_2-CH_2-\underset{\underset{OH}{+}}{N(CH_3)_3} \xrightarrow{\Delta} (CH_3)_3N + HOCH_2CH_2OH$$

When lecithin is boiled with alkali, choline is split off, and this gives trimethylamine according to the above reaction. Trimethylamine may be detected by its fishy odor.

Putrefying bacteria acting upon tissues often produce the very poisonous
base, neurine, by splitting water from the choline molecule:

$$HO-CH_2-CH_2-\underset{\underset{OH}{+}}{N}\equiv(CH_3)_3 \longrightarrow CH_2=CH-\underset{\underset{OH}{+}}{N}\equiv(CH_3)_3 + H_2O$$

Choline   Neurine

When the alcoholic hydroxyl group of choline is acetylated, a very important physiologic substance, acetylcholine, is formed.

$$CH_3CO-O-CH_2-CH_2-\underset{\underset{OH}{+}}{N}\equiv(CH_3)_3$$

Acetylcholine

Acetylcholine is of peculiar interest because it plays an important role in
the transmission of nerve impulses across synapses and from nerve endings
to the muscles innervated. This applies especially to the action of the so-
called cholinergic nerves, which are composed largely of parasympathetics.
It seems probable that all nerve cells have the capacity to form acetylcholine
to a greater or lesser degree.

B. PHOSPHATIDYL ETHANOLAMINES OR CEPHALINS

The cephalins are structurally identical with the lecithins, with the exception that the base ethanolamine (colamine), instead of choline, is present:

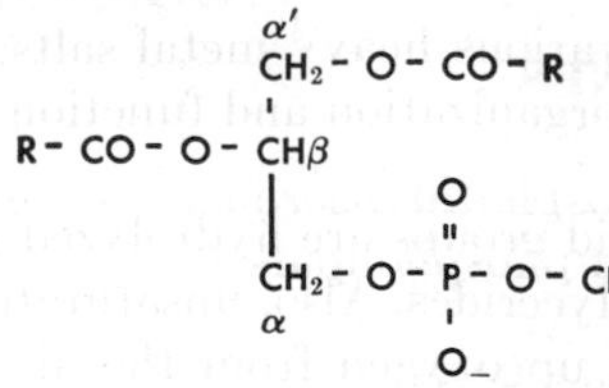

$$\begin{array}{c}
\overset{\alpha'}{CH_2} - O - CO - R \\
| \\
R - CO - O - CH\beta \\
| \\
\overset{}{CH_2} - O - \overset{O}{\overset{||}{P}} - O - CH_2 - CH_2 - NH_3{}^+ \\
\underset{\alpha}{} \quad | \\
O_-
\end{array}$$

L-α-Phosphatidyl ethanolamine
α-Cephalin
Zwitterion form

The cephalins, like the lecithins, form internal salts or zwitterions.

The separation and purification of the cephalins has been exceedingly difficult, and only in recent years have suitable methods, based largely upon chromatography, been developed (12).

Baer and Maurukas (13) found that diazomethane reacts with cephalins, but not lecithins, to split out the nitrogenous group and form the dimethyl esters of L-α-phosphatidic acids, thus proving that the cephalins are ethanolamine derivatives of L-α-phosphatidic acid and, thus, like the lecithins, belong to the L-series of compounds:

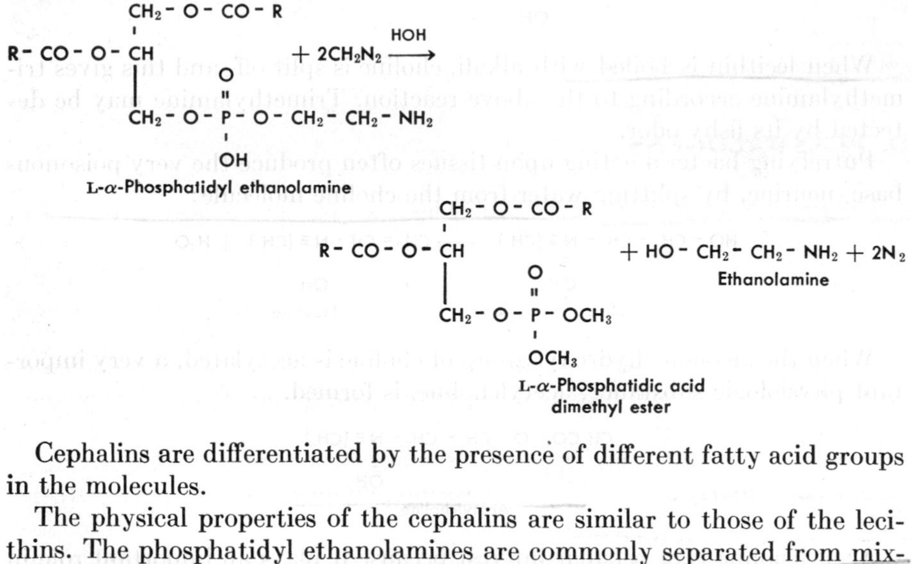

$$\begin{array}{c}
CH_2 - O - CO - R \\
| \\
R - CO - O - CH \qquad + 2CH_2N_2 \xrightarrow{\text{HOH}} \\
| \\
CH_2 - O - \overset{O}{\overset{||}{P}} - O - CH_2 - CH_2 - NH_2 \\
| \\
OH
\end{array}$$

L-α-Phosphatidyl ethanolamine

$$\begin{array}{c}
CH_2 - O - CO - R \\
| \\
R - CO - O - CH \qquad\qquad + HO - CH_2 - CH_2 - NH_2 + 2N_2 \\
| \qquad\qquad\qquad\qquad\qquad\qquad \text{Ethanolamine} \\
CH_2 - O - \overset{O}{\overset{||}{P}} - OCH_3 \\
| \\
OCH_3
\end{array}$$

L-α-Phosphatidic acid
dimethyl ester

Cephalins are differentiated by the presence of different fatty acid groups in the molecules.

The physical properties of the cephalins are similar to those of the lecithins. The phosphatidyl ethanolamines are commonly separated from mixtures of phospholipids by alcohol extraction, in which the crude phosphatidyl ethanolamines, contaminated with other phosphatides, are insoluble. However, Folch (14) found the highly purified phosphatidyl ethanolamine isolated from a mixture of brain phosphatides to be readily soluble in alcohol. This illustrates the possible effect of the presence of related compounds upon the solubility of a substance.

The cephalins are hydrolyzed by boiling with alkalies and dilute mineral acids according to the reactions outlined above for the lecithins. Lecithinase from snake venom hydrolyzes cephalins to lysocephalins which are similar to the lysolecithins formed from lecithins.

C. PHOSPHATIDYL SERINES

Folch (15) first isolated a phosphatidyl serine containing oleic and stearic acids from the mixture of brain phospholipids:

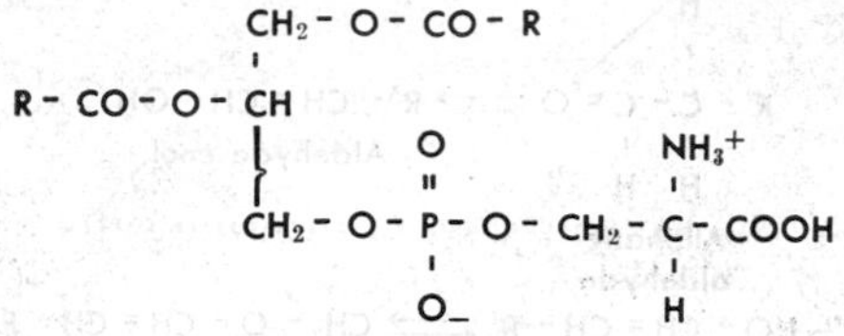

$$
\begin{array}{l}
CH_2 - O - CO - R \\
| \\
R - CO - O - CH \\
|\quad\quad\quad\quad O\quad\quad\quad NH_3^+ \\
|\quad\quad\quad\quad || \quad\quad\quad\quad | \\
CH_2 - O - P - O - CH_2 - C - COOH \\
\quad\quad\quad\quad | \quad\quad\quad\quad | \\
\quad\quad\quad\quad O_- \quad\quad\quad H
\end{array}
$$

L-α-Phosphatidyl serine

The phosphatidyl serines possess structures analogous to those of the lecithins and cephalins in which the amino acid serine is esterified through its hydroxyl group (HO—CH$_2$—CH(NH$_2$)COOH) to the phosphate group of phosphatidic acid. Baer and associates (16) have synthesized L-α-Distearoyl-phosphatidyl-L-serine and shown it to be identical with the hydrogenated phosphatidyl serine of ox brain which contains oleic and stearic acid groups.

The phosphatidyl serines show hydrolytic reactions similar to those of the other phosphatidyl phosphatides.

D. PLASMALOGENS

The plasmalogens make up an appreciable proportion (about 10 per cent) of the phospholipids of muscle and brain. They were first discovered in tissues by Feulgen in 1924 by a histochemical test, the plasmal reaction, in which the phosphatide, after treatment with HgCl$_2$, gave an aldehyde reaction with Schiff's reagent (fuchsin sulfurous acid).

The plasmalogens yield one mol each of long-chain aliphatic aldehyde, fatty acid, glycerol, and nitrogen-containing base (ethanolamine or choline) upon hydrolysis.

Determination of the structure of plasmalogens has presented many difficulties, particularly because no adequate method for separating plasmalogens from associated phosphatides is available. The more recent work indicates that the plasmalogens differ in structure from the lecithins and cephalins in having one fatty acid group replaced by a long unsaturated aliphatic chain joined to glycerol by an ether linkage (17).

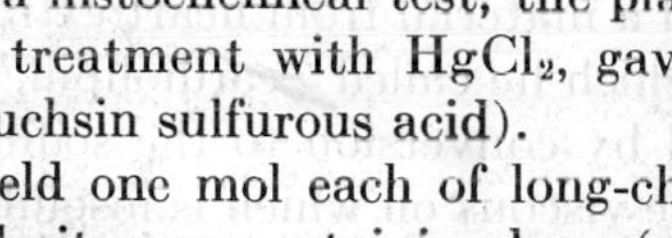

$$
\begin{array}{l}
\alpha\ CH_2 - O - CH = CH - R \\
| \\
\beta\ CH - O - CO - R' \\
|\quad\quad\quad\quad O \\
|\quad\quad\quad\quad || \\
CH_2 - O - P - O - CH_2 - CH_2 - NH_2 \\
\quad\quad\quad\quad | \\
\quad\quad\quad\quad OH
\end{array}
$$

Phosphatidal ethanolamine
Plasmalogen structure

When hydrolyzed, the unsaturated ether group at the α position yields a saturated aldehyde such as palmitic or stearic aldehyde. This group may be considered, in effect, to represent the condensation of the enol form of an aliphatic aldehyde with a glycerol hydroxyl group:

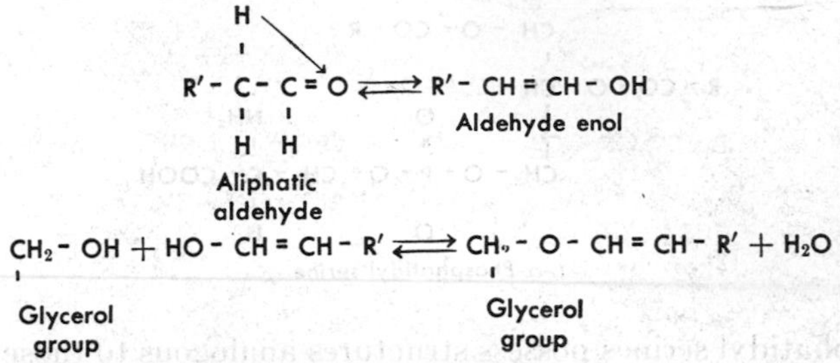

$$R' - C - C = O \rightleftarrows R' - CH = CH - OH$$

Aldehyde enol

Aliphatic aldehyde

$$CH_2 - OH + HO - CH = CH - R' \rightleftarrows CH_2 - O - CH = CH - R' + H_2O$$

Glycerol group   Glycerol group

Upon hydrolysis, the above reactions are reversed with formation of the aldehyde corresponding to a fatty acid.

Research up to the present indicates that there probably are two types of plasmalogens, those with the unsaturated ether linkage in the α position of glycerol and those with this linkage in the β position. Recent work of Stotz and associates [18] indicates that at least 70 per cent of beef heart plasmalogens have the α-unsaturated ether linkage. More work is necessary for full clarification of the structure of plasmalogens, and for determination of their biochemical importance.

E. CARDIOLIPINS

Pangborn [19] isolated a material from heart extract, serologically active in the test for syphilis, which he called "cardiolipin." It was isolated as the barium salt and purified by conversion to the sodium salt. The free acid, cardiolipin, is an unstable viscous oil which is insoluble in water but readily soluble in alcohol and acetone. It is optically active $[\alpha]_D = 5.8°$ (in ethanol), has an apparent molecular weight by titration of 726, and an iodine number of 119. Oleic and linoleic acids (1:5 ratio) are the chief fatty acid components. After hydrolysis with alcoholic KOH, Pangborn isolated fatty acids, glycerol, glycerol phosphate, glyceryl triglycerophosphate, and possibly glyceryl glycerophosphate. These products suggest that cardiolipin is made up of condensed phosphatidic acid molecules; that is, it appears to be a polyphosphatidic acid, and the apparent molecular weight of 726, obtained by titration, is probably too low to represent the true molecular weight.

II. PHOSPHOINOSITIDES OR INOSITOL LIPIDS

A. MONOPHOSPHOINOSITIDE

Folch [20] first separated a phosphoinositide from the crude cephalin fraction from ox brain. Two different types of phosphoinositides have been described which are differentiated by the inositol derivatives yielded upon hydrolysis. One type found in heart, liver, soybean, and wheat germ yields inositol monophosphate, fatty acids, and α-glycerol phosphate upon hydrolysis; it has a structure similar to the structures of other glycerophosphatides (21) and is phosphatidyl inositol:

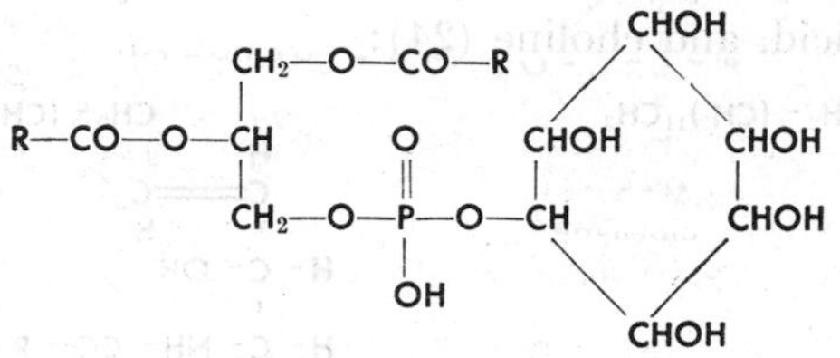

$$
\begin{array}{l}
\text{CH}_2\text{—O—CO—R} \\
\text{R—CO—O—CH} \quad\quad \text{O} \\
\text{CH}_2\text{—O—P—O—CH} \\
\quad\quad\quad\quad \text{OH}
\end{array}
\quad
\begin{array}{c}
\text{CHOH} \\
\text{CHOH} \quad \text{CHOH} \\
\text{CHOH} \quad \text{CHOH} \\
\text{CHOH}
\end{array}
$$

Phosphatidyl inositol
Monophosphoinositide

The inositol present in the inositol lipids is the inactive isomer meso-inositol.

B. DIPHOSPHOINOSITIDE

Another type of phosphoinositide found in brain (22) yields inositol-meta-diphosphate, glycerol, and fatty acids in equimolecular proportions. Folch named the compound diphosphoinositide and found the following structure in its molecule (R and R' are unknown groups):

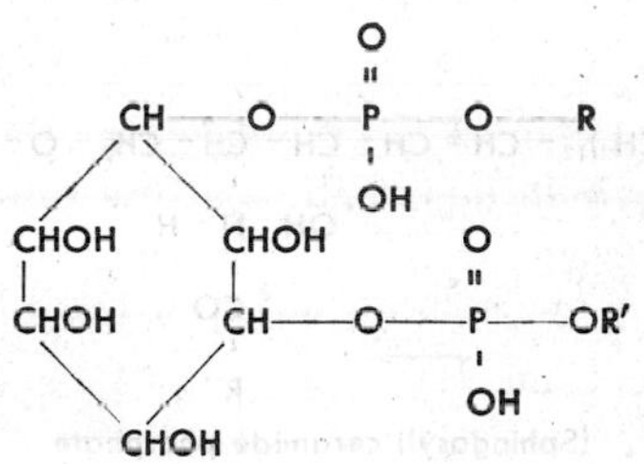

$$
\begin{array}{c}
\text{O} \\
\text{CH—O—P—O—R} \\
\text{OH} \\
\text{CHOH} \quad \text{CHOH} \quad \text{O} \\
\text{CHOH} \quad \text{CH—O—P—OR'} \\
\text{OH} \\
\text{CHOH}
\end{array}
$$

Diphosphoinositide

A plausible formula for the substance is the structure suggested by Fruton and Simmonds (23):

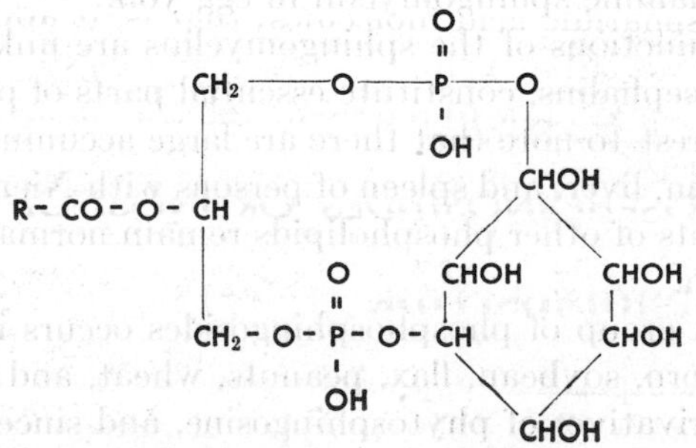

$$
\begin{array}{l}
\text{O} \\
\text{CH}_2\text{—O—P—O} \\
\quad\quad \text{OH} \\
\text{R—CO—O—CH} \\
\quad\quad \text{O} \\
\text{CH}_2\text{—O—P—O—CH} \\
\quad\quad \text{OH}
\end{array}
\quad
\begin{array}{c}
\text{CHOH} \\
\text{CHOH} \quad \text{CHOH} \\
\text{CHOH} \quad \text{CHOH} \\
\text{CHOH}
\end{array}
$$

III. SPHINGOLIPIDS

A. PHOSPHOSPHINGOSIDES

Sphingosine-choline sphingolipids, sphingomyelins. The sphingomyelins upon hydrolysis yield the unsaturated nitrogen alcohol, sphingosine, phosphate, fatty acid, and choline (24):

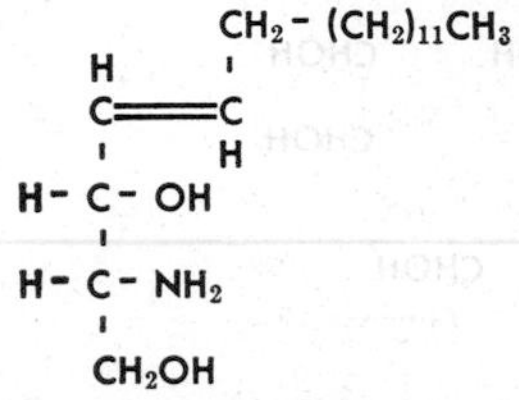

$$CH_2 - (CH_2)_{11}CH_3$$
$$H \quad | $$
$$C \!=\!=\! C$$
$$| \quad H$$
$$H - C - OH$$
$$|$$
$$H - C - NH_2$$
$$|$$
$$CH_2OH$$

Sphingosine
1,3-Dihydroxy-2-amino-
4-trans-octadecene

$$CH_2 - (CH_2)_{11}CH_3$$
$$H \quad |$$
$$C \!=\!=\! C$$
$$| \quad H$$
$$H - C - OH$$
$$|$$
$$H - C - NH - CO - R \longleftarrow Fatty\ acid\ group$$
$$| \qquad O$$
$$\qquad \quad \|$$
$$CH_2 - O - P - O - CH_2 - CH_2 - N \equiv (CH_3)_3$$
$$| \qquad\qquad\qquad\qquad +$$
$$O_-$$

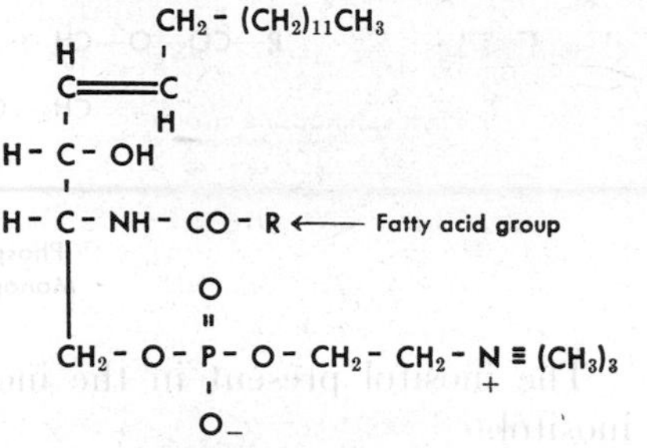

Sphingomyelin

The configuration about the amino and adjacent secondary alcoholic carbon atoms in sphingosine is that found in D-erythrose and the configuration about the double bond is trans. Accordingly, sphingosine is D-erythro-1,3-dihydroxy-2-amino-4-trans-octadecene (25).

The sphingosine molecule in which a fatty acyl group is substituted in the amino group is called a "ceramide." When the choline group is removed from a sphingomyelin, a ceramide phosphate is formed:

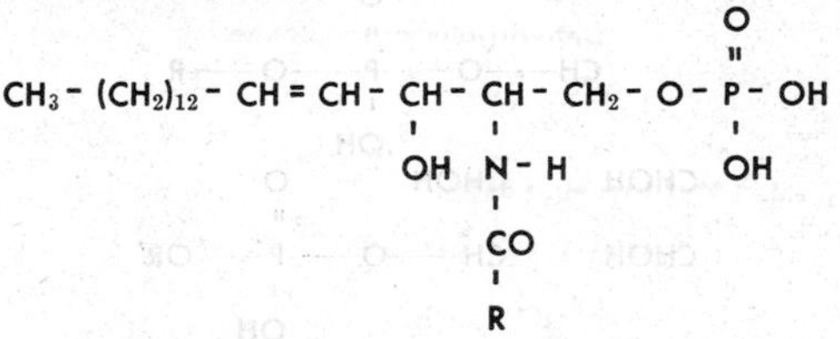

$$\qquad\qquad\qquad\qquad\qquad\qquad O$$
$$\qquad\qquad\qquad\qquad\qquad\qquad \|$$
$$CH_3 - (CH_2)_{12} - CH = CH - CH - CH - CH_2 - O - P - OH$$
$$\qquad\qquad\qquad\qquad\quad | \quad | \qquad\qquad\quad |$$
$$\qquad\qquad\qquad\qquad\; OH \; N - H \qquad\qquad OH$$
$$\qquad\qquad\qquad\qquad\qquad\quad |$$
$$\qquad\qquad\qquad\qquad\qquad\quad CO$$
$$\qquad\qquad\qquad\qquad\qquad\quad |$$
$$\qquad\qquad\qquad\qquad\qquad\quad R$$

(Sphingosyl) ceramide phosphate

Sphingomyelins are present in large amounts in brain and nerve tissues and in smaller quantities in other tissues and blood.

Carter and associates (26) have recently obtained evidence for the presence of an ethanolamine sphingomyelin in egg yolk.

While specific functions of the sphingomyelins are unknown, they must, like lecithins and cephalins, constitute essential parts of protoplasmic structure. It is of interest to note that there are large accumulations of sphingomyelins in the brain, liver, and spleen of persons with Niemann-Pick disease, though the amounts of other phospholipids remain normal. The significance of this is unknown.

A very complex group of phosphosphingosides occurs in many vegetable sources, such as corn, soybean, flax, peanuts, wheat, and cottonseed. These substances are derivatives of phytosphingosine, and since they contain carbohydrate groups, they are both phospholipids and glycolipids (26). They are called "phytoglycolipids." Phytosphingosine has the structure:

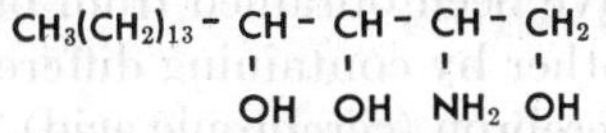

$$CH_3(CH_2)_{13} - CH - CH - CH - CH_2$$
$$\phantom{CH_3(CH_2)_{13} - }OH OH NH_2 OH$$

Phytosphingosine
1,3,4-Trihydroxy-2-amino-octadecane

and the following type of partial structure has been proposed for the phytoglycolipids:

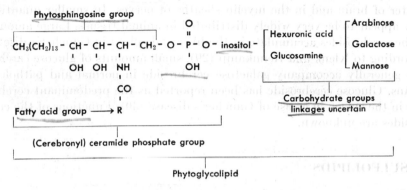

Phytoglycolipid containing dehydrophytosphingosine, an unsaturated derivative (one double bond) has been found in soybean (26):

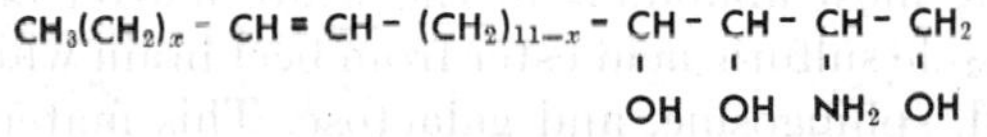

$$CH_3(CH_2)_x - CH = CH - (CH_2)_{11-x} - CH - CH - CH - CH_2$$
$$\phantom{CH_3(CH_2)_x - CH = CH - (CH_2)_{11-x} - }OH OH NH_2 OH$$

Dehydrophytosphingosine
Position of double bond uncertain

B. GLYCOSPHINGOSIDES OR CEREBROSIDES OR GLYCOLIPIDS

This group of lipids was prepared from brain and studied first by Thudichum and later by Thierfelder and Klenk (27). When hydrolyzed, the cerebrosides were found to yield sphingosine, a fatty acid, and the sugar galactose. Carter and Greenwood (28) worked out the structure of these substances:

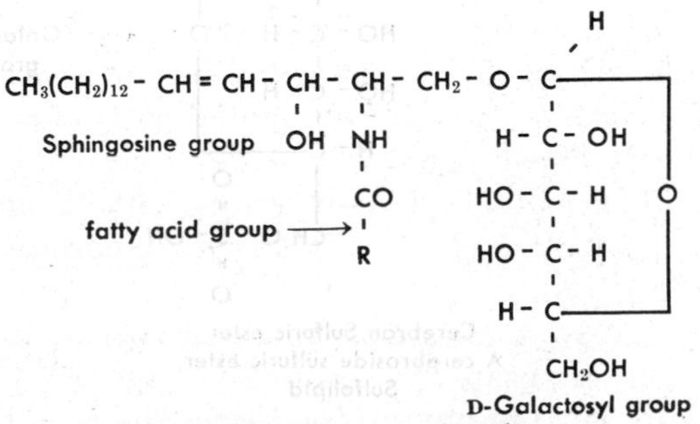

$$CH_3(CH_2)_{12} - CH = CH - CH - CH - CH_2 - O - C \overset{H}{}$$

Sphingosine group OH NH

                    CO
fatty acid group ⟶ |
                    R

H – C – OH

HO – C – H   O

HO – C – H

H – C –

CH₂OH

D-Galactosyl group

Glycosphingoside or cerebroside

It is uncertain as to whether the sugar linkage to sphingosine is α or β. The configuration about the double bond of sphingosine is trans.

Various cerebrosides have been obtained from brain and nerve which are differentiated from each other by containing different fatty acids. Such substances are phrenosin or cerebron (cerebronic acid), kerasin (lignoceric acid), nervon (nervonic acid), and oxynervon (oxynervonic acid).

Cerebroside containing dihydrosphingosine, the saturated reduction product of sphingosine, has been obtained from beef brain.

The sphingoglycosides or cerebrosides occur in large amounts in the white matter of brain and in the myelin sheaths of nerves. In smaller quantities they appear to be very widely distributed in animal tissues. Large amounts of the cerebrosides accumulate in the liver and spleen in Gaucher's disease. According to Klenk and Rennkamp (29), small amounts of glucose cerebroside generally accompany galactose cerebroside in normal and pathologic organs. Glucose cerebroside has been reported as the predominant cerebroside in the spleen in a case of Gaucher's disease (30). Functions of the cerebrosides are unknown.

C. SULFOLIPIDS

Lipid material containing sulfur has long been known to be present in tissues, and has been found in liver, kidney, testicle, salivary gland, brain, and tumors, being most abundant in the white matter of brain. Blix (31) isolated a cerebroside sulfuric acid ester from beef brain which was composed of cerebronic acid, sphingosine, and galactose. This material has been prepared as a pure substance, and its structure was determined by Thannhauser and associates (32).

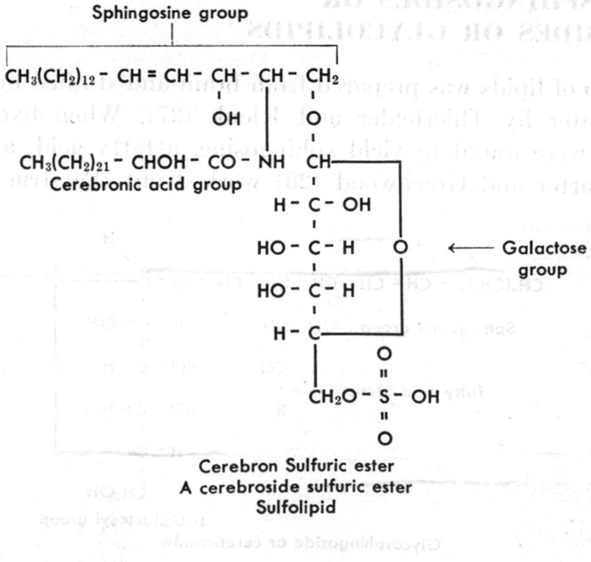

Cerebron Sulfuric ester
A cerebroside sulfuric ester
Sulfolipid

The sphingolipid composed of sphingosine cerebronic acid and galactose is called "cerebron," and the above sulfolipid accordingly is the sulfuric ester of cerebron.

D. GANGLIOSIDES, HEMATOSIDES, STRANDIN

These are complex derivatives of sphingosine or an analogous amino alcohol.

The gangliosides are present in the ganglion cells of nervous tissue, and in the spleen. Large amounts occur in the brain in cases of Tay-Sachs disease and Niemann-Pick's disease. The gangliosides contain sphingosine, fatty acid, both the hexose sugars glucose and galactose, N-acetylgalactosamine, and the unusual amino sugar acid N-acetyl-neuraminic acid, or sialic acid:

$$\begin{array}{c}
\text{CO-CH}_3\\
|\\
\text{OH} \quad \text{OH} \quad \text{NH} \quad \text{OH} \quad \text{OH}\\
| \quad\quad | \quad\quad | \quad\quad | \quad\quad |\\
\text{HOOC-C-CH}_2\text{-CH-CH-CH-CH-CH-CH}_2\text{OH}\\
\underline{\qquad\qquad}\text{O}\underline{\qquad\qquad}
\end{array}$$

N-Acetylneuraminic acid, Sialic acid

Svennerholm (33) has proposed the following general structure for the gangliosides:

$$\begin{array}{c}
\text{CH}_3\text{(CH}_2\text{)}_{12}\text{-CH=CH-CH-CH-CH}_2\text{-O-hexose-hexose-N-acetylgalactosamine-}\\
\qquad\qquad\qquad\quad |\quad\quad\ |\qquad\qquad\qquad\qquad\qquad\text{N-acetylneuraminic acid}\\
\qquad\qquad\qquad \text{OH} \quad \text{NH}\\
\qquad\qquad\qquad\qquad\quad |\\
\qquad\qquad\qquad\qquad\quad \text{CO}\\
\qquad\qquad\qquad\qquad\quad |\\
\qquad\qquad\qquad\qquad\quad \text{R}
\end{array}$$

Ceramide group

Proposed Ganglioside Structure

This structure may be written more simply ceramide—hexose—hexose—N-acetylgalactosamine—N-acetylneuraminic acid.

Complex substances called "hematosides" and "globosides" have been isolated from erythrocyte stroma of different animals (34). These substances are sphingolipids which appear to have structures similar to the gangliosides. The hematosides contain neuraminic acid, but the globosides do not. Some of the hematosides do not contain a hexosamine. The hexosamine when present may be glucosamine or galactosamine. The following tentative structures have been proposed:

Globosides: ceramide-(hexose)$_x$-hexosamine
Hematosides: ceramide-(hexose)$_x$-hexosamine-neuraminic acid

Globosides have been found in human, sheep, goat, and hog red cell stroma, and hematosides in dog, rabbit, and beef stroma. Chicken erythrocyte stroma contains a complex sphingolipid without either hexosamine or neuraminic acid. Much work remains to be done in clarifying the chemistry of these complex lipids.

Folch and associates (35) isolated a lipid from brain tissue of high molecular weight (minimum 250,000) which they called "strandin" because when aqueous solutions are evaporated, the substance forms well-oriented strands. Its concentration is much higher in gray than in white matter of brain. Strandin is present in very low concentrations in lung, heart, liver, kidney, and skeletal muscle. Strandin when hydrolyzed yields fatty acid, sphingosine or a similar compound, carbohydrate, a primary amine, small amounts of neuraminic acid, and an unidentified chromogenic substance. Obviously, the strandin molecule is very large and complex.

E. MALIGNOLIPIN

Kosaki and associates (36) reported a new and peculiar type of phospholipid, called "malignolipin," which appears to be present only in malignant tumors and not in normal tissues. The substance is composed of fatty acid, choline, spermine, and phosphoric acid. The following tentative formula was proposed:

$$
\begin{array}{c}
\quad\quad\quad\quad\quad\quad\quad\quad O \\
\quad\quad\quad\quad\quad\quad\quad\quad \| \quad\quad\quad\quad \text{Spermine group} \\
(CH_3)_3 \equiv N - CH_2 - CH_2 - O - P \div NH - (CH_2)_3 - N - (CH_2)_4 - NH - (CH_2)_3 - NH_2 \\
\quad + \quad\quad\quad\quad\quad\quad\quad\quad\quad | \quad\quad\quad\quad\quad\quad\quad\quad\quad | \\
\text{Choline group} \quad\quad\quad\quad O\_ \quad\quad\quad\quad\quad\quad CO \\
\quad\quad\quad\quad\quad\quad\quad\quad\quad\quad\quad\quad\quad\quad\quad | \quad \longleftarrow \text{ Fatty acid group} \\
\quad\quad\quad\quad\quad\quad\quad\quad\quad\quad\quad\quad\quad\quad\quad R \\
\quad\quad\quad\quad\quad\quad\quad \text{Malignolipin}
\end{array}
$$

Spermine is the very basic substance H_2N—CH_2—CH_2—CH_2—NH—CH_2—CH_2—CH_2—CH_2—NH—CH_2—CH_2—CH_2—NH_2.

Malignolipin has been obtained from human cancers, such as the following: seminoma: stomach, colon, breast, and uterine cancers; and Hodgkin's malignant granuloma. The malignolipin content was found to be highest in tumors of high malignancy and in the rapidly growing part of a tumor, and very little was present in necrotic tumors or the degrading part of a tumor. Malignolipin thus appears to be closely related to the malignancy of tumor cells.

F. PROTEOLIPIDS

Folch and Lees (37) extracted brain with a mixture of chloroform and methanol and from the extract obtained a new type of lipid containing protein, called "proteolipid," which peculiarly was soluble in organic solvents, but insoluble in water, being thus distinguished from the class of substances known as lipoproteins. Proteolipids have been found in animal tissues such as heart, kidney, brain, liver, lung, and muscle. Brain white matter is richest in proteolipid, from which three proteolipid fractions (A, B, C) have been separated.

Proteolipid B has been obtained as a crystalline material, but may not be pure. It is composed of 50 per cent protein, 20 per cent cerebroside, and 30 per cent phosphatide, about half of which appears to be sphingomyelin.

Proteolipid fractions A and C are not crystalline, but birefringent powders. Proteolipid A contains about 20 per cent protein, 65 to 75 per cent cerebroside, and little phosphatide. Proteolipid C consists mainly of protein (70 to 75 per cent) and phosphatide (25 per cent). The lipid-protein bonds in proteolipids are weak and easily broken into their protein and lipid moieties.

STEROLS

A very large number of substances occurring widespread in animals and plants contain the cyclopentanoperhydrophenanthrene ring system or a modification of it.

The phenanthrene ring system is a composite of three benzene rings as follows:

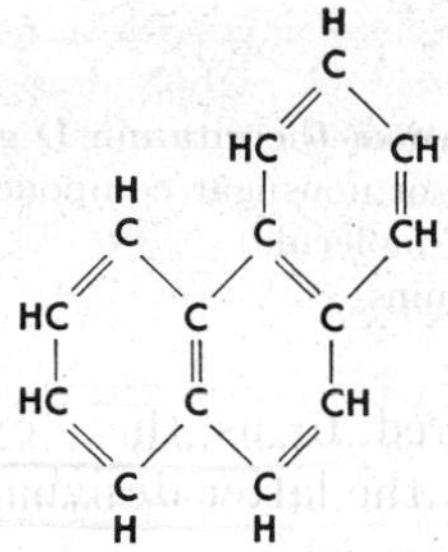

$$\begin{array}{c}
\text{H} \\
\text{C} \\
\text{HC} \qquad \text{CH} \\
\text{H} \qquad\qquad \text{CH} \\
\text{C} \quad \text{C} \quad \text{C} \\
\text{HC} \quad \text{C} \quad \text{C} \\
\text{HC} \quad \text{C} \quad \text{CH} \\
\text{C} \quad \text{C} \\
\text{H} \quad \text{H}
\end{array}$$

When an additional hydrogen is attached to each of the carbon atoms of the phenanthrene ring, the double bonds disappear and the perhydrophenanthrene ring is formed:

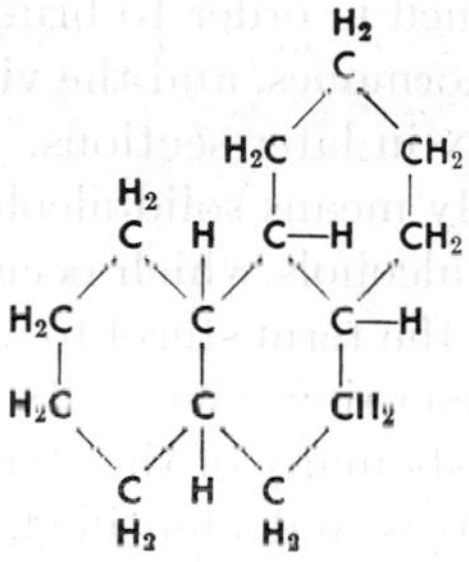

$$\begin{array}{c}
\text{H}_2 \\
\text{C} \\
\text{H}_2\text{C} \qquad \text{CH}_2 \\
\text{H}_2 \\
\text{C} \quad \text{H} \quad \text{C}-\text{H} \quad \text{CH}_2 \\
\text{H}_2\text{C} \quad \text{C} \quad \text{C}-\text{H} \\
\text{H}_2\text{C} \quad \text{C} \quad \text{CH}_2 \\
\text{C} \quad \text{H} \quad \text{C} \\
\text{H}_2 \qquad \text{H}_2
\end{array}$$

The cyclopentane ring has the structure:

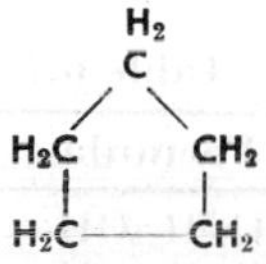

$$\begin{array}{c}
\text{H}_2 \\
\text{C} \\
\text{H}_2\text{C} \qquad \text{CH}_2 \\
\text{H}_2\text{C}\text{---}\text{CH}_2
\end{array}$$

The cyclopentanoperhydrophenanthrene ring system is a combination of the cyclopentane and perhydrophenanthrene rings as follows, with the carbon atoms numbered as shown:

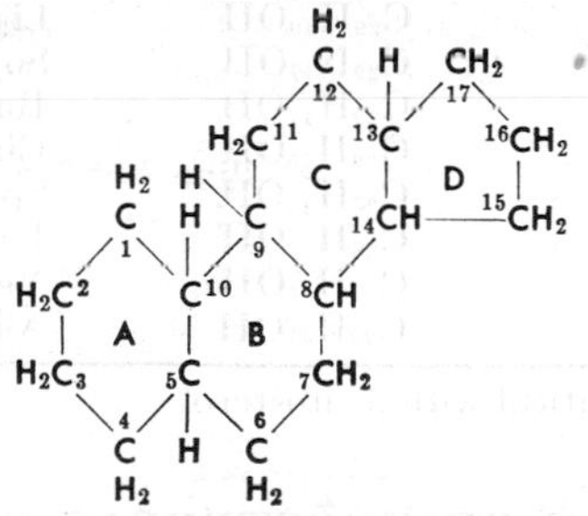

$$\begin{array}{c}
\text{H}_2 \\
\text{C} \quad \text{H} \quad \text{CH}_2 \\
12 \qquad 17 \\
\text{H}_2\text{C}^{11} \quad {}^{13}\text{C} \quad {}^{16}\text{CH}_2 \\
\text{H}_2 \quad \text{H} \qquad \text{C} \qquad \text{D} \\
\text{C} \quad \text{H} \quad \text{C} \quad {}_{14}\text{CH}\text{---}{}^{15}\text{CH}_2 \\
1 \qquad 9 \\
\text{H}_2\text{C}^2 \quad \text{C}^{10} \quad {}^8\text{CH} \\
\text{A} \qquad \text{B} \\
\text{H}_2\text{C}_3 \quad {}_5\text{C} \quad {}_7\text{CH}_2 \\
4 \qquad 6 \\
\text{C} \quad \text{H} \quad \text{C} \\
\text{H}_2 \qquad \text{H}_2
\end{array}$$

Cyclopentanoperhydrophenanthrene

Some of the biologically important groups of substances which contain this ring system or modifications of it are:

1. Sterols
2. Bile acids

3. Sex hormones
4. Adrenal cortical hormones
5. Vitamins related to calcification, the vitamin D group
6. Cardiac glycosides (aglucon or nonsugar component)
7. Toad poisons (genin part of molecule)
8. Sapogenins of digitalis saponins

These substances are referred to as the "cyclopentanoperhydrophenan-threne" or "steroid" group, the latter designation being generally used because of its convenience.

Since this discussion is concerned primarily with substances functioning as lipids in physiologic processes, only the sterol group among the steroids will be treated in some detail in this chapter. However, specific examples of other groups will be mentioned in order to bring out chemical relationships. Bile acids, sex and adrenal hormones, and the vitamin D group of substances will be considered more fully in later sections.

The term "sterol" literally means solid alcohol. However, since there are a number of solid aliphatic alcohols which occur as lipids (especially in the waxes), present usage limits the term sterol to alcohols containing the cyclopentanoperhydrophenanthrene ring. Generally the sterols contain only one hydroxyl group. Table 6.7 lists many of the sterols which have been isolated from animal and plant sources and identified. Although some of the hormones are sterols, they are classified separately because of their special physiologic functions.

Table 6.7

Sterol	Formula	Occurrence
Cholesterol	$C_{27}H_{45}OH$	All animal cells
Dihydrocholesterol	$C_{27}H_{47}OH$	Accompanies cholesterol
7-Dehydrocholesterol	$C_{27}H_{43}OH$	Skin, brain, other tissues
Coprostanol	$C_{27}H_{47}OH$	Feces
Ostreasterol	$C_{29}H_{47}OH$	Oysters, gastropods
β-Equistanol	$C_{30}H_{53}OH$	Urine of pregnancy
Sitosterols	$C_{29}H_{49}OH$	Lipids of higher plants
Stigmasterol	$C_{29}H_{47}OH$	Soy and calabar beans
Brassicasterol	$C_{29}H_{47}OH$	Rapeseed oil
Cinchol*	$C_{29}H_{49}OH$	Cinchona bark
Spinasterols	$C_{27}H_{45}OH$	Spinach, alfalfa
Ergosterol	$C_{28}H_{43}OH$	Ergot, yeast
Zymosterol	$C_{27}H_{43}OH$	Yeast
Fucosterol	$C_{29}H_{47}OH$	Algae

* Cinchol is apparently identical with β-sitosterol.

A. ANIMAL STEROLS OR ZOÖSTEROLS:
CHOLESTEROL AND RELATED SUBSTANCES

Cholesterol. Cholesterol has been found in all animal tissues and in no plant tissues examined. It is accompanied by its derivatives, dihydrocholesterol and 7-dehydrocholesterol.

Cholesterol, literally meaning bile solid-alcohol, derives its name from the fact that it was first isolated from human gallstones, of which it is generally the chief component. The amount of cholesterol in animal tissues varies widely. It is particularly abundant in brain and nerve tissue, adrenal glands, and egg yolk. Dry white matter of brain contains about 14 per cent of cholesterol, and spinal cord 10 to 15 per cent. The cholesterol content of glandular organs is generally higher than that of muscles, and heart and smooth muscle contain more than skeletal muscle. Bloor (*Biochemistry of the Fatty Acids*, p. 33) gives the following percentage values for the average cholesterol content of dry tissues:

White matter of brain	14
Gray matter of brain	6
Kidney	1.6
Spleen	1.5
Skin	1.3
Liver	0.93
Mammary gland	0.70
Whole blood	0.65
Smooth muscle	0.55
Diaphragm	0.35
Skeletal muscle	0.25

The cholesterol content of fetal muscles is much higher than that of adult muscles. The cholesterol of tissues includes both free cholesterol and cholesterol esters of fatty acids. The proportions of free and ester cholesterol vary with the tissue.

Structure of cholesterol and related compounds. The chemical structure of cholesterol and other sterols has been the subject of investigation by able workers for many years. Windaus (38) in 1932 proposed a structure for cholesterol which is now generally accepted as correct:

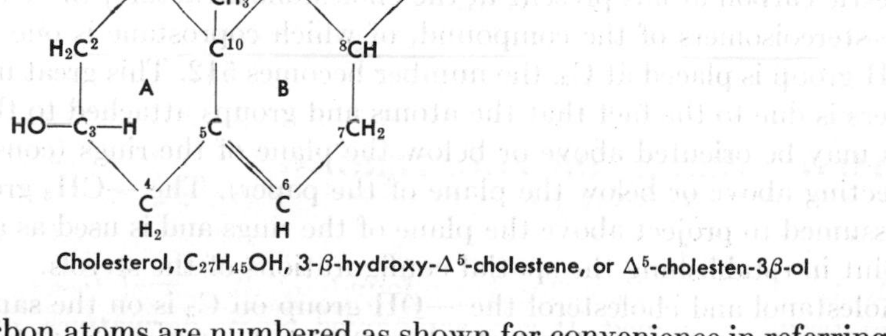

Cholesterol, $C_{27}H_{45}OH$, 3-β-hydroxy-Δ⁵-cholestene, or Δ⁵-cholesten-3β-ol

The carbon atoms are numbered as shown for convenience in referring to the specific structure of the compound and its derivatives.

If hydrogen atoms are added to saturate the double bond, two isomeric sterols are formed:

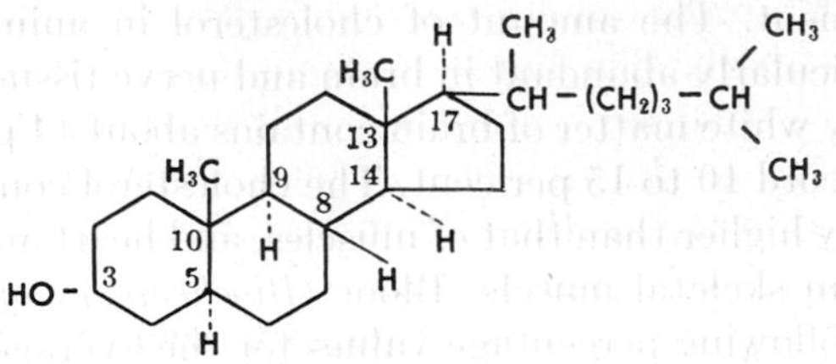

Cholestanol

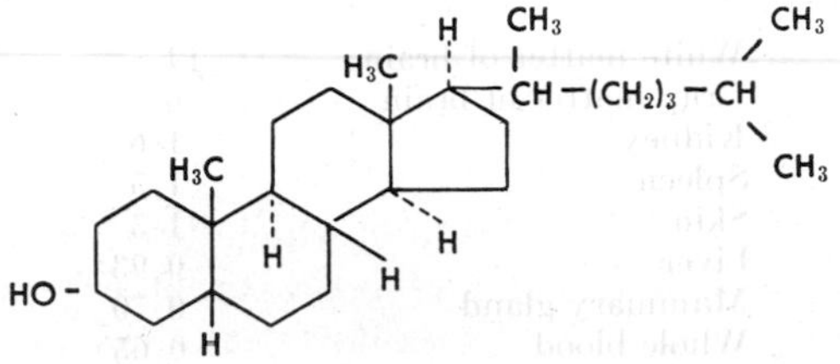

Coprostanol

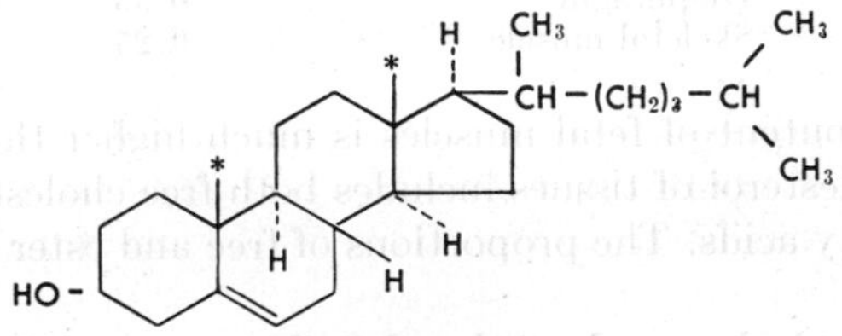

Cholesterol

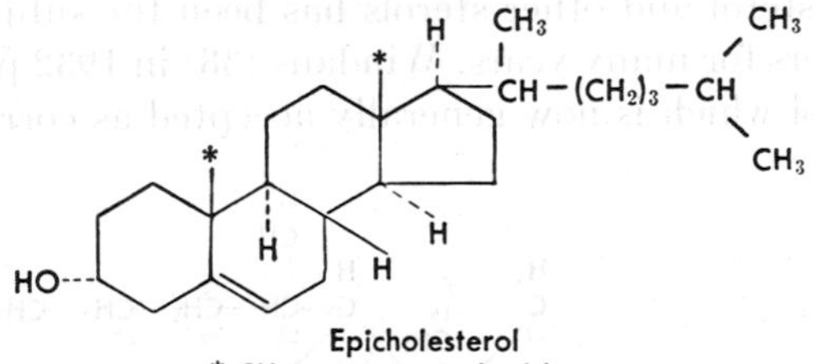

Epicholesterol
* CH₃ groups attached here

Cholestanol and coprostanol are derivatives of the hydrocarbons cholestane and coprostane, as are all the sterols. Because of the large number of asymmetric carbon atoms present in the cholestane structure, there are 256 possible stereoisomers of the compound, of which coprostane is one. When an —OH group is placed at C_3, the number becomes 512. This great number of isomers is due to the fact that the atoms and groups attached to the ring carbons may be oriented above or below the plane of the rings (considered as projecting above or below the plane of the paper). The —CH₃ group on C_{10} is assumed to project above the plane of the rings and is used as a reference point in establishing the spatial configurations of the sterols.

In cholestanol and cholesterol the —OH group on C_3 is on the same side as the —CH₃ group on C_{10}; that is, both —CH₃ and —OH project above the plane of the paper. This is designated as the "cis," or "β," configuration.

When the —OH group of C_3 lies on the side of the ring opposite the —CH$_3$ on C_{10}, the configuration is designated as the "trans," or "α," configuration. The relations of H atoms (on asymmetric carbon atoms) to the —CH$_3$ on C_{10} are treated similarly. The bonds to atoms and groups of β (cis) configuration are drawn as solid lines, and the bonds to atoms and groups of the α (trans) configuration are drawn as dotted lines. Coprostanol and cholestanol differ in that the H of C_5 has the α (trans) configuration in cholestanol and the β (cis) configuration in coprostanol.

The isomerism of natural sterols is limited to that represented by derivatives of cholestane and coprostane, with the cholestane type predominating. In natural sterols the H at C_8, the —CH$_3$ at C_{13}, and the side chain at C_{17} have the same orientation as that of the —CH$_3$ at C_{10} (β, or cis, configuration), while the H atoms at C_9, C_{14}, and C_{17} have the opposite orientation (α, or trans, configuration).

Isomers of cholestanol and coprostanol which have the —OH of C_3 opposite the positions in cholestanol and coprostanol are epimers; they are epicholestanol and epicoprostanol. Similarly, the epimer of cholesterol is epicholesterol.

When the above principles are applied to the systematic naming of sterols, cholestanol becomes 3-β-hydroxycholestane or cholestan-3-β-ol, epicholestane is 3-α-hydroxycholestane or cholestan-3-α-ol, and coprostanol is 3-β-hydroxycoprostane or coprostan-3-β-ol. Since cholesterol contains a double bond, it may be considered a derivative of the unsaturated hydrocarbon Δ^5-cholestene Systematically, cholesterol is 3-β-hydroxy-Δ^5-cholestene, or Δ^5-cholesten-3-β-ol, and epicholesterol is 3-α-hydroxy-Δ^5-cholestene or Δ^5-cholesten-3-α-ol.

The spatial relations of the rings, A, B, C, and D, to each other in cholestane and coprostane and their derivatives are determined by the manner of ring fusion along the common valence bonds. These relations are shown in Figure 6.1.

Properties of cholesterol. Cholesterol generally crystallizes as white, shining rhombic plates. It melts at 150° to 151° C. It is tasteless and odorless. Upon exposure to air and light, cholesterol slowly oxidizes to form a mixture of products resulting in a lowered melting point and changed solubility and reactions. Cholesterol is insoluble in water, acids, and alkalies, somewhat soluble in soap solutions, and much more soluble in solutions of bile salts. It is readily soluble in ether, benzene, chloroform, petroleum ether, carbon bisulfide, and acetone. It is readily soluble in hot alcohol, but only slightly soluble in cold. It dissolves readily in oleic acid and liquid fats. Cholesterol shows a specific rotation, $[\alpha]_D$, of $-39.5°$ when dissolved in chloroform. Cholesterol may be readily prepared in the laboratory by extraction from cholesterol gallstones or brain tissue. It is produced commercially from the spinal cords of cattle.

Cholesterol has the important property, when mixed with a fat or oil, of enabling the fat or oil to absorb relatively large amounts of water. Since cholesterol is not soluble in water, it is probable that this property is related

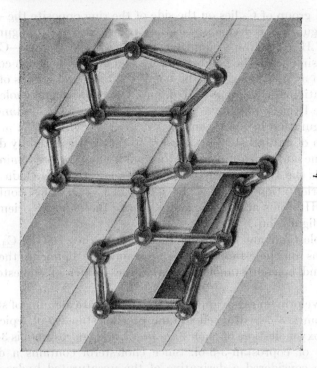

b
Coprostane ring
Cis, cis, trans, trans

Figure 6.1

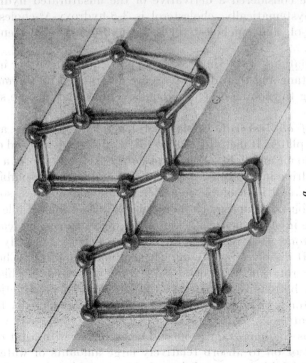

a
Cholestane ring
Trans, trans, trans, trans

to its tendency to form water-in-oil emulsions. Wool fat, or lanolin, which contains much cholesterol, readily absorbs water. It is often used in pharmacy as the grease vehicle in the preparation of ointments containing water-soluble constituents. While cholesterol is not saponifiable with alkali, prolonged heating with alkali slowly decomposes it.

Since cholesterol is a poor conductor of electricity and has a high dielectric value, it is a good insulator against electric discharge. Possibly, as an abundant constituent of brain, nerves, and spinal cord, it functions as an insulating covering of impulse-generating and transmitting structures. It is well established that brain and nerve impulses are electrical in character.

It is of interest to note that cholesterol serves as the precursor of cholic acid of bile, of the female sex hormone pregnanediol, and also of the steroid hormones of the adrenal cortex. These relations are pointed out in more detail in the chapters on lipid metabolism and on hormones.

The chemical properties of cholesterol are particularly related to the secondary hydroxyl group and the double bond present in the molecule. When cholesterol is oxidized under the proper conditions, the corresponding ketone, cholestenone, is formed. The hydroxyl group readily forms esters with acids, the fatty acid esters being widespread in blood and tissues. Cholesterol gives an insoluble precipitate, cholesterol digitonide, when treated with the saponin digitonin. This reaction in general is given by those sterols in which the C_3 hydroxyl and the C_{10} methyl lie on the same side of the molecule plane (cishydroxy sterols). Epicholesterol, which has the C_3 hydroxyl in the trans position, does not react. Although the exact nature of the reaction is obscure, the C_3 hydroxyl must be free. Sterol esters do not react. The digitonin reaction is of importance in the separation and quantitative determination of cholesterol and other sterols.

On account of the presence of a double bond, cholesterol gives the addition reactions characteristic of unsaturated compounds. The addition of hydrogen produces dihydrocholesterol. This substance occurs with cholesterol in animal tissues. Cholesterol takes up halogens at the double bond to form cholesterol dihalides. It has an iodine number of 65.8.

Upon oxidation, cholesterol gives various ketones, hydroxy compounds, and acids, the products depending upon the oxidizing agents and conditions used.

Other animal sterols. The derivatives of cholesterol, dihydrocholesterol and 7-dehydrocholesterol, are associated with cholesterol in animal tissues. 7-Dehydrocholesterol is the precursor of vitamin D_3. Lanosterol and agnosterol are present in wool lipids.

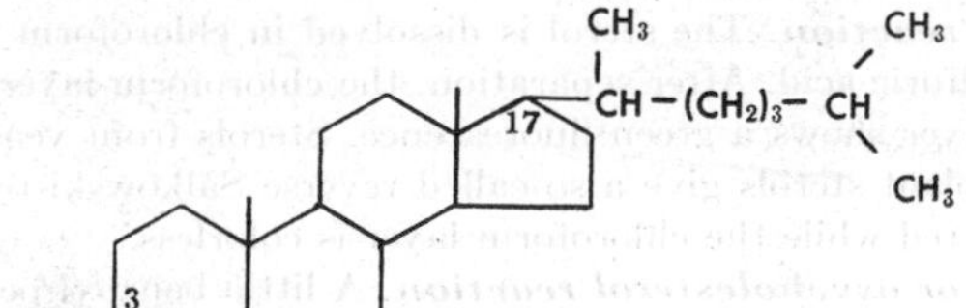

Dihydrocholesterol

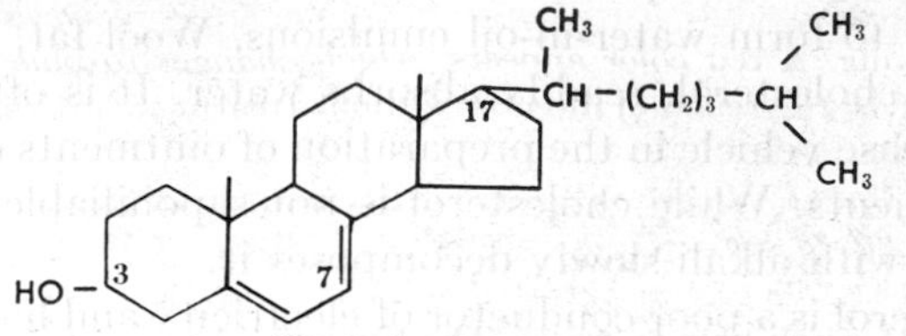

CH₃   CH₃
CH–(CH₂)₃–CH
                CH₃

7-Dehydrocholesterol

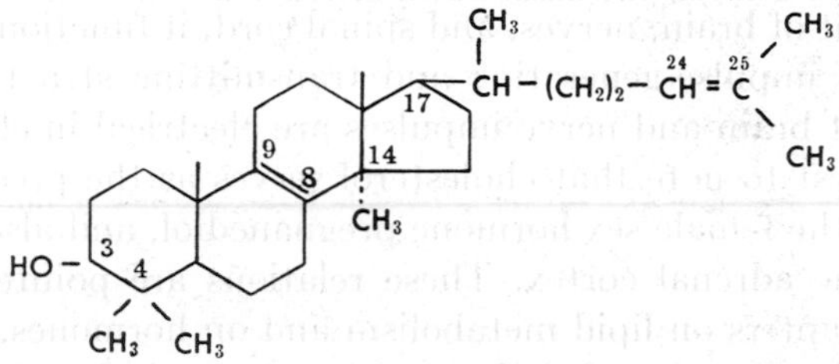

CH₃   CH₃
CH–(CH₂)₂–CH=C
                CH₃
CH₃

Lanosterol

CH₃   CH₃
CH–(CH₂)₂–CH=C
                CH₃
CH₃

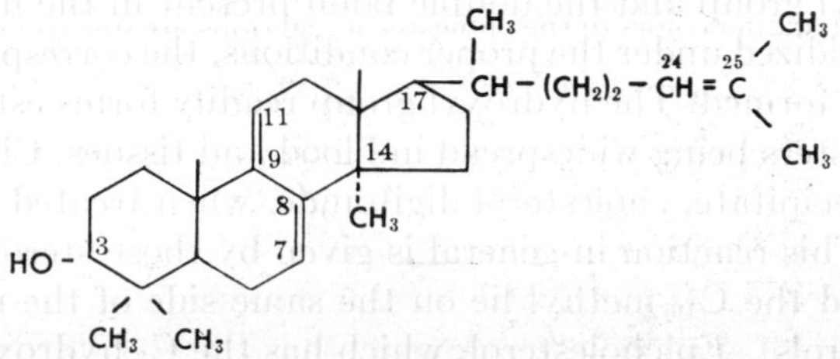

Agnosterol

The sterol mixture in the feces of man and the carnivora is composed largely of coprostanol with small amounts of dihydrocholesterol and traces of cholesterol. Superficially coprostanol appears to be a simple reduction product of cholesterol involving only the addition of hydrogen at the 5,6 double bond. However, it must be remembered that the spatial relations of rings A/B in cholesterol from cholestane and coprostanol from coprostane are different, and consequently the conversion of cholesterol to coprostanol must involve not only reduction by hydrogen but also change in the A/B ring fusion from the cholestane to the coprostane type.

The sterols have the characteristic property of forming molecular complexes and mixed crystals with other sterols, which may cause much trouble in their separation and purification.

Color reactions of sterols. Cholesterol and other sterols are characterized by giving numerous color reactions, a few of which are commonly used for the qualitative detection or quantitative determination of sterols.

The Salkowski reaction. The sterol is dissolved in chloroform and shaken with an equal volume of sulfuric acid. After separation, the chloroform layer is generally colored red and the acid layer shows a green fluorescence. Sterols from yeast and fungi (mycosterols) and some plant sterols give a so-called reverse Salkowski reaction in which the acid layer becomes red while the chloroform layer is colorless.

The Lipschütz or oxycholesterol reaction. A little benzoyl peroxide is added to a few milligrams of cholesterol dissolved in 2 to 3 ml of glacial acetic acid. The solution is heated to the boiling point for a short time. This process converts some of the cholesterol to oxycholesterol. The solution is cooled, and four drops of concentrated sulfuric acid added, with shaking. A red color appears, which changes to blue and finally to green. Oxycholesterol gives the reaction directly without treatment with benzoyl peroxide. The reaction is very sensitive.

The Lieberman-Burchard or acetic anhydride reaction. A little of the sterol is dissolved in 2 ml of chloroform followed by the addition of 10 drops of acetic acid anhydride and a drop or two of concentrated sulfuric acid. A rose red color develops which quickly changes through blue to green. The time of color appearance is characteristic of the sterol used. In general, the unsaturated sterols react much more rapidly than the saturated ones do. This reaction has been made the basis of a widely used quantitative method of determining cholesterol in biological materials.

Zlatkis and associates (39) have developed an improved method for the quantitative determination of cholesterol based upon a reagent containing ferric chloride, glacial acetic acid, and concentrated sulfuric acid. Cholesterol gives a purple color with the reagent.

It appears that color reactions of cholesterol such as outlined above are due to preliminary dehydration to form a 3,5-cholestadiene or a 2,4-cholestadiene, which polymerizes to a dimer or trimer. The cholestadiene and its polymers react with sulfuric acid to form sulfonic acids, which may represent intermediate or final products in the reactions. The evanescent changing colors in the cholesterol reactions are due to various stages in the process (40).

B. STEROLS OF YEAST AND FUNGI: MYCOSTEROLS

Ergosterol. This sterol is the principal sterol of fungi and yeast and is classed as a mycosterol. Its name derives from the fact that it was first discovered in ergot bodies which form on rye and other cereal plants diseased with ergot fungi. It is produced commercially in large quantities from certain strains of yeast. Ergosterol has the formula:

Ergosterol, $C_{28}H_{43}OH$
3-β-Hydroxy-24-methyl-$\Delta^{5,7,22}$-cholestatriene

The C_3 hydroxyl of ergosterol is in the β (cis) position relative to the C_{10} methyl group. The spatial relations of the rings in ergosterol are of the cholestane type. There are double bonds between C_5-C_6, C_7-C_8, and C_{22}-C_{23}. Ergosterol therefore is a cholestatriene derivative, and specifically it is 3-β-hydroxy-24-methyl-$\Delta^{5,7,22}$-cholestatriene.

Ergosterol is an important substance because when irradiated with ultraviolet light a series of substances is formed which includes calciferol (vitamin D$_2$) and tachysterol, from which another member of the vitamin D group, dihydrotachysterol (AT10), is derived.

C. STEROLS OF HIGHER PLANTS: PHYTOSTEROLS

Stigmasterol. This sterol occurs especially in calabar and soybean oils. It possesses a ring system of cholestane type, and its structure is:

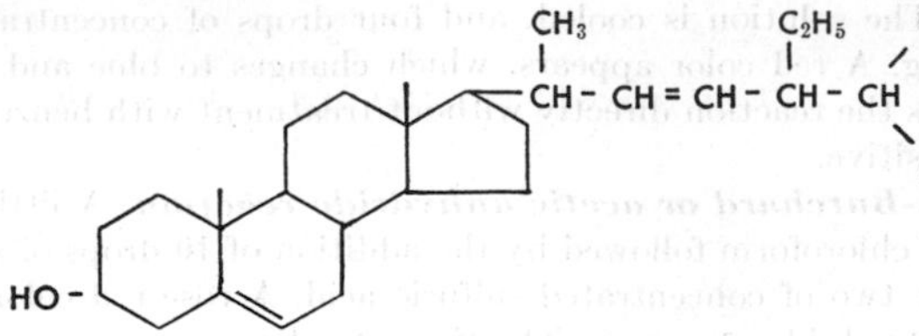

Stigmasterol, $C_{29}H_{47}OH$
3-β-Hxdroxy-24-ethyl-$\Delta^{5,22}$-cholestadiene

The formula of stigmasterol is identical with that of cholesterol with the exception of the side chain attached to C_{17}, stigmasterol having an ethyl group on C_{24} and a double bond between C_{22} and C_{23} of the side chain. Stigmasterol is of interest because it can be converted in the laboratory into the hormone of the corpus luteum, progesterone.

Sitosterols. The sitosterols constitute a complex mixture of sterols occurring in the oils of higher plants, being especially abundant in wheat germ oil. Seven sterols of this group have been reported. Only the structures of β-sitosterol and γ-sitosterol have been established. A number of the sitosterols appear to be isomers of stigmasterol or derivatives of it. β-Sitosterol has been identified as 22-dihydrostigmasterol in which the double bond between C_{22} and C_{23} of stigmasterol has been saturated with two hydrogen atoms.

γ-Sitosterol apparently differs from β-sitosterol only in the spatial arrangement of the side chain attached to C_{17} relative to the methyl group on C_{13}.

D. BILE ACIDS

The bile acids—cholic, deoxycholic, and lithocholic—are found in the bile of higher animals, where they are largely conjugated with glycine and taurine to form compounds such as glycocholic and taurocholic acids.

The bile acids may be considered derivatives of cholanic acid, in which the spatial relations of the rings are the same as in coprostane. The C_3 hydroxyl group of the bile acids has the α (trans) configuration relative to the C_{10} methyl group. If other hydroxyl groups are present, they also have this configuration.

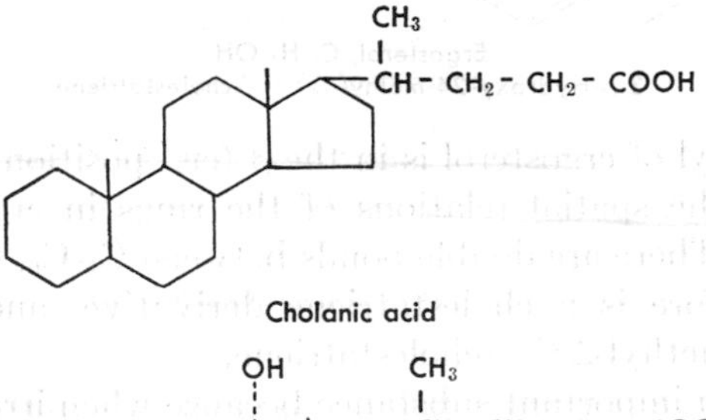

Cholanic acid

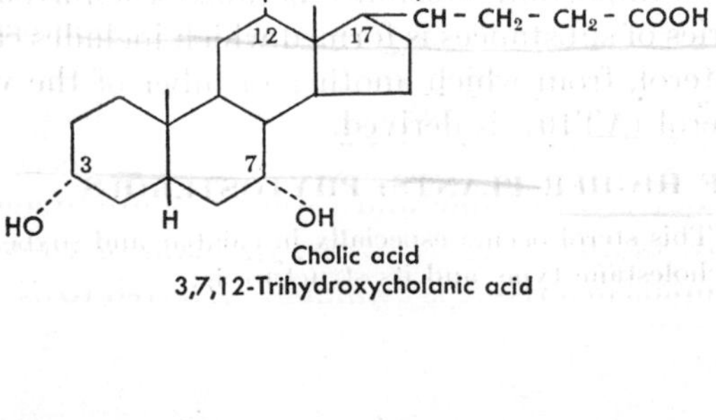

Cholic acid
3,7,12-Trihydroxycholanic acid

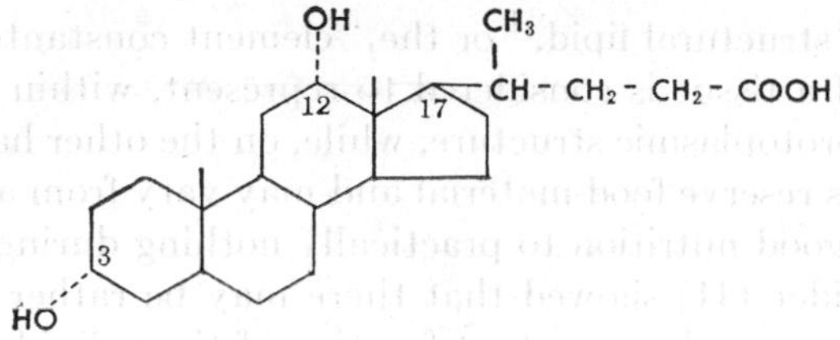

Deoxycholic acid
3,12-Dihydroxycholanic acid

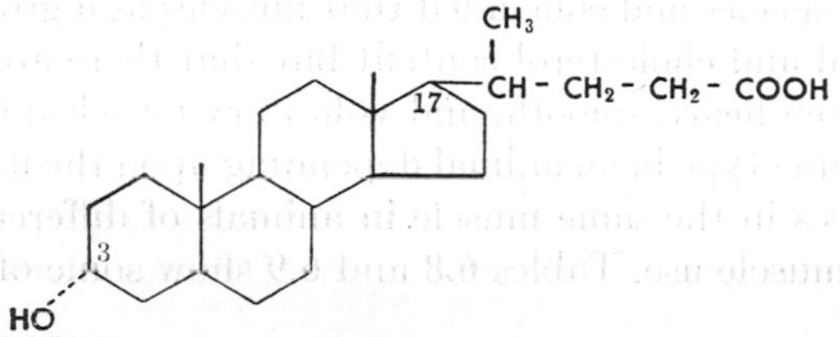

Lithocholic acid
3-Hydroxycholanic acid

Other bile acids also found in animal biles are hyodeoxycholic acid (3,6-dihydroxycholanic acid) and chenodeoxycholic acid (3,7-dihydroxycholanic acid). Python sebae bile contains pythonic acid, which appears to be 3,12,15-trihydroxycholanic acid.

The bile acids are conjugated with glycine and taurine through the side chain carboxyl groups as follows:

$$-\underset{\displaystyle CH_3}{\overset{}{CH}}-CH_2-CH_2-CO-NH-CH_2COOH$$

Glycocholic acid
Glycodeoxycholic acid
Glycolithocholic acid

$$-\underset{\displaystyle CH_3}{\overset{}{CH}}-CH_2-CH_2-CO-NH-CH_2-CH_2-SO_3H$$

Taurocholic acid
Taurodeoxycholic acid
Taurolithocholic acid

The salts of the bile acids lower surface tension and are good emulsifying agents. They play an important role in the absorption of lipids from the intestine.

THE GENERAL LIPID CONTENT OF TISSUES

It has been well established that, although the total lipid content of a given tissue may vary within wide limits, this variation generally is largely due to changes in the glyceride or fat content. The lipid fraction composed of cholesterol, phospholipids, and glycolipids is relatively more constant in amount. The tissues of animals starving to death have been found to contain little or no fat, but considerable and rather definite amounts of the other lipids. As a result of these observations, the sum of cholesterol, phospholipids, and glycolipids in a tissue is commonly referred to as "essential lipid," "tissue lipid," "structural lipid," or the "element constant." The so-called essential lipid of a tissue is considered to represent, within limits, essential components of protoplasmic structure, while, on the other hand, the fat content of a tissue is reserve food material and may vary from a relatively large amount during good nutrition to practically nothing during starvation.

Bloor and Snider (41) showed that there may be rather wide variations in the so-called essential or constant fraction of tissue lipids. These workers studied the cholesterol and phospholipid content of the muscles of many different animal species and concluded that muscles as a group have no definite phospholipid and cholesterol content but that there are: (a) differences in content between heart, smooth, and voluntary muscles; (b) differences in muscles of the same type in an animal depending upon the use of the muscle; and (c) differences in the same muscle in animals of different species which may vary with muscle use. Tables 6.8 and 6.9 show some of these relations.

Table 6.8.   Average Phospholipid, Cholesterol, and P/C* Ratios for
Muscles of Different Types
(Values represent per cent of dry weight)

Muscle	Phospholipid	Cholesterol	P/C
Mammalian			
Heart	7.65	0.51	15
Skeletal	4.59	0.27	17
Bird			
Heart	7.56	0.54	14
Skeletal	4.34	0.31	14
Cold-blooded animals			
Heart	6.00	0.75	8
Skeletal	4.14	0.23	18
All smooth muscle	3.08	0.77	4

* Phospholipid/cholesterol.
Data of table taken by permission from *Biochemistry of the Fatty Acids*, by W. R. Bloor, published by Reinhold Publishing Corp., 1943, pp. 200–210.

In general, the phospholipid content of heart muscle is decidedly the highest, and that of voluntary muscle a bit higher than of smooth muscle. On the other hand, smooth muscle generally contains the most cholesterol and skeletal muscle the least, with heart muscle in between. It is interesting to note, as pointed out by Bloor, that the phospholipid content of the muscle increases with activity. Heart muscle in general is most active and contains the most phospholipid on the average. The thigh muscle of the domestic rabbit contained only 1.7 per cent phospholipid, as contrasted with 3.75 per cent in the same muscle of the much more active wild rabbit. A high cholesterol content is correlated with the automatic action of smooth and heart muscle.

Yasuda and Bloor (42) found both cholesterol and phospholipid to be much higher in malignant than in benign tumors.

Kaucher, Galbraith, Button, and Williams (43) published the results of an extensive investigation of the lipids of tissues including glycolipids (cerebrosides), and also the distribution of phospholipids as lecithin, cephalin, and sphingomyelins. Results of their work are summarized in Tables 6.10 and 6.11. A number of interesting conclusions may be drawn from the data of these tables.

Table 6.9. Phospholipid and Cholesterol Content of Dry Muscle in Per Cent

Animal	Muscle	Phospholipid	Cholesterol	P/C*
Man	Heart (ventricle)	7.0	0.70	10
Man	Uterus	3.5	1.0	3.5
Dog	Heart	8.54	0.61	14
Dog	Thigh	8.0	0.32	25
Dog	Uterus	3.0	1.0	3
Cat	Heart	5.72	0.44	13
Cat	Thigh	2.47	0.19	13
Cat	Intestine	3.24	0.81	4
Rat	Heart	7.95	0.53	15
Rat	Thigh	3.50	0.25	14
Rabbit				
Laboratory	Heart	9.12	0.57	16
Laboratory	Thigh	1.70	0.17	10
Wild	Heart	7.65	0.45	17
Wild	Thigh	3.75	0.25	15
Wild	Stomach	2.50	0.50	5
Pigeon	Heart	7.28	0.52	14
Pigeon	Breast	4.7	0.25	18.8
Pigeon	Thigh	4.51	0.41	11
Pigeon	Gizzard	2.52	0.63	4
Turtle	Heart	6.40	0.80	8
Turtle	Thigh	3.50	0.35	10
Frog	Heart	4.20	0.70	6
Frog	Thigh	3.80	0.20	19
Grasshopper	Thigh	5.40	0.18	30

* Phospholipid/cholesterol.
Data of table taken by permission from *Biochemistry of the Fatty Acids*, by W. R. Bloor, published by Reinhold Publishing Corp., 1943, p. 200.

Table 6.10. Lipid Content of Beef Organs*
(Per cent of dry weight)

Organ	Fat	Glyco-lipid	Free Choles-terol	Choles-terol Esters	Total Choles-terol	Leci-thin	Cepha-lin	Sphin-gomyelin	Total Phos-pho-lipid	Total Lipid	Nonfat or Es-sential Lipid
Brain	2.97	12.01	10.0	0.25	10.25	7.05	14.35	4.96	26.37	51.59	48.62
Liver	5.79	0.00	0.44	0.53	0.97	8.86	6.59	0.76	16.22	22.99	17.18
Kidney	5.45	0.71	1.44	0.34	1.78	5.62	3.02	1.66	10.32	17.25	12.80
Heart	4.05	2.00	0.34	0.23	0.57	3.96	5.34	0.52	9.83	16.45	12.39
Lung	2.41	0.44	1.34	0.86	2.20	3.60	3.90	2.27	9.78	14.83	12.43
Thymus	11.99	0.42	0.44	0.85	1.29	3.28	2.72	0.70	6.71	20.42	8.42

* Averaged values. Compiled from data of Kaucher, Galbraith, Button, and Williams, *Arch. Biochem.*, **3**, 203, 1943.

"Essential" or nonfat lipids constitute nearly all the lipids of brain and represent nearly half of the brain solids. While cholesterol and glycolipids are much more abundant than in any other tissue, the amount of phospholipids is especially striking, making up more than half of the total brain lipids. Cephalin represents more than half of brain phospholipid. The proportion of free cholesterol in brain is noteworthy.

Table 6.11. Lipid Content of Muscle and Egg*
(Per cent of dry weight)

Muscle	Fat	Glyco-lipid	Free Choles-terol	Choles-terol Esters	Total Choles-terol	Leci-thin	Cepha-lin	Sphin-gomyelin	Total Phos-pho-lipid	Total Lipid	Nonfat or Es-sential Lipid
Frog	1.72	1.76	0.18	0.08	0.26	2.79	4.16	0.19	7.14	10.88	9.16
Turtle	10.89	0.91	0.26	0.11	0.37	2.98	2.27	0.00	5.25	17.42	6.53
Veal	5.86	0.62	0.16	0.16	0.32	2.70	2.15	0.19	5.04	11.84	5.98
Lamb	4.19	1.95	0.13	0.18	0.31	2.55	1.90	0.29	4.74	11.19	7.00
Salmon	9.76	3.96	0.11	0.08	0.19	2.53	1.86	0.00	4.39	18.30	8.54
Chicken (dark)	6.65	1.26	0.28	0.12	0.40	1.70	2.39	0.27	4.36	12.67	6.02
Chicken (light)	1.99	1.99	0.17	0.08	0.25	1.91	0.81	0.00	2.72	6.95	4.96
Codfish	2.20	2.64	0.22	0.13	0.35	3.31	0.49	0.48	4.28	9.47	7.27
Shrimp	2.24	1.22	0.70	0.07	0.77	2.63	1.03	0.23	3.89	8.12	5.88
Beef	9.97	0.94	0.19	0.03	0.22	1.72	1.12	0.24	3.08	14.21	4.24
Pork	17.97	1.17	0.14	0.06	0.20	1.69	1.25	0.12	3.06	22.40	4.43
Intestine (beef)	2.89	0.32	0.76	0.73	1.49	3.81	1.86	1.26	6.93	11.63	8.74
Stomach (beef)	3.60	0.39	0.64	0.25	0.89	1.60	0.88	0.62	3.10	7.98	4.38
Egg:											
Chicken	33.15	1.35	1.69	0.35	2.04	9.95	3.44	0.34	13.73	50.27	17.12
Turtle	27.22	0.00	0.76	0.31	1.07	4.84	1.85	0.25	6.94	35.23	8.01

* Average of values. Compiled from data of Kaucher, Galbraith, Button, and Williams, *Arch. Biochem.*, **3**, 203, 1943.

Organ tissues such as liver, heart, kidney, and lung contain relatively large amounts of nonfat lipids, though less than brain. These tissues, like brain, contain more phospholipid than all other essential lipid combined.

Liver is noteworthy for the absence of glycolipid and the presence of large amounts of lecithin and cephalin.

Muscles in general contain less total lipid, less essential or nonfat lipid, and more fat than organ tissues do. Cholesterol is generally lower, and glycolipid higher, in muscles than in organs.

Phospholipids constitute the bulk of essential lipids in muscle, as they do in organs. The sphingomyelin of skeletal or voluntary muscle is notably low compared to that of smooth or involuntary muscles and organs.

Skeletal muscle generally contains more glycolipid than cholesterol, while the reverse is true for smooth muscle. The glycolipid of skeletal muscle is relatively high.

The cholesterol of both organs and muscles is distributed between free and ester forms with free cholesterol generally in excess, but wide variations occur in different tissues. It is interesting to note the equal distribution of free and ester cholesterol in veal muscle as compared with the preponderance of free cholesterol in beef muscle. The young tissue has more essential lipid and less fat than the older tissue.

Eggs are generally comparable to brain in total lipid but contain much less essential lipid and large amounts of fat. Here also phospholipids constitute most of the essential lipid.

Phospholipids, as pointed out above, represent the most abundant of the nonfat lipids of tissues amd must occupy a very important place as essential constituents of protoplasm from both a structural and a functional viewpoint, though very little is known of the details. Here, as in the case of both carbohydrates and proteins, phosphoric acid in ester combination serves in the vital structures and functions of tissues.

Bloor and associates (44) have pointed out that tissues highest in essential lipids are those possessing the greatest extent and variety of physiologic functions. In tissues such as heart, liver, brain, and kidney the essential lipid is high and the ratio of essential lipid to protein in the tissue is high. The physiologic function of these tissues is very diversified as compared to muscle in which essential lipid is much lower and protein much higher.

GENERAL REFERENCES

Annual Reviews of Biochemistry. These yearly volumes contain up-to-date reviews on lipids.

Bloor, W. R.: *Biochemistry of the Fatty Acids.* Reinhold, New York, 1943.

Bull, H. B.: *Biochemistry of the Lipids.* John Wiley & Sons, New York, 1943.

Cook, R. P.: *Cholesterol: Chemistry, Biochemistry and Pathology.* Academic Press, New York, 1958.

Deuel, H. J., Jr.: *The Lipids,* Vols. I, II, III. Interscience, New York, 1951, 1955, 1957.

Fieser, L. F., and Fieser, M.: *Natural Products Related to Phenanthrene,* 3rd ed. Reinhold, New York, 1949.

Fieser, L. F., and Fieser, M.: *Steroids.* Reinhold, New York, 1959.

Hanahan, D. J.: *Lipide Chemistry.* John Wiley & Sons, New York, 1960.

Hilditch, T. P.: *The Chemical Constitution of Natural Fats,* 3rd ed. John Wiley & Sons, New York, 1956.

Jamieson, G. S.: *Vegetable Fats and Oils,* 2nd ed. Reinhold, New York, 1943.

Klyne, W.: *The Chemistry of the Steroids.* John Wiley & Sons, New York, 1957.

Kritchevsky, D.: *Cholesterol.* John Wiley & Sons, New York, 1958.

Lovern, J. A.: *The Chemistry of Lipids of Biochemical Significance.* Methuen, London 1955.

Popják, G., and Le Breton, E. (eds.): *Biochemical Problems of Lipids.* Interscience, New York, 1956.

Shoppee, C. W.: *Chemistry of the Steroids.* Academic Press, New York, 1958.

Sinclair, H. M., (ed.): *Essential Fatty Acids.* Academic Press, New York, 1958.

Sobotka, H.: *The Chemistry of the Steroids.* Wood, Baltimore, 1938.

Thierfelder, H., and Klenk, E.: *Chemie der Cerebroside und Phosphatide.* Berlin, 1930.

Wittcoff, H.: *The Phosphatides.* Reinhold, New York, 1951.

SPECIAL REFERENCES

1. Polgar, N., and Robinson, R.: *J. Chem. Soc.,* 389, 1945.
2. Witzemann, E. J.: *J. Biol. Chem.,* 95, 219, 1932.
3. Hilditch, T. P.: *The Chemical Constitution of Natural Fats.* John Wiley & Sons, New York, 1940.
4. Mattson, F. H., and Lutton, E. S.: *J. Biol. Chem.,* 233, 869, 1958.
5. Celmer, W. D., and Carter, H. E.: *Physiol. Revs.,* 32, 167, 1952.
6. Baer, E.: *Ann. Rev. Biochem.,* 24, 135, 1955.
7. Folch, J.: *Phosphorus Metabolism,* II, 186, 1952.
8. Wittcoff, H.: *The Phosphatides.* Reinhold, New York, 1951.
9. Folch, J., and Sperry, W. M.: *Ann. Rev. Biochem.,* 17, 147, 1948.
10. Hanahan, D. J.: *J. Biol. Chem.,* 207, 879, 1954.
11. Hanahan, D. J.: *J. Biol. Chem.,* 211, 313, 1954.
12. Olley, J.: *Federation Proc.,* 16, 845, 1957.
13. Baer, E., and Maurukas, J.: *J. Biol. Chem.,* 212, 25, 39, 1955.
14. Folch, J.: *J. Biol. Chem.,* 146, 34, 1942.
15. Folch, J.: *J. Biol. Chem.,* 146, 34, 1942; 174, 439, 1948.
16. Baer, E., and Maurukas, J.: *J. Biol. Chem.,* 212, 25, 39, 1955. Baer, E., *et al.: J. Am. Chem. Soc.,* 78, 232, 1956.

17. Klenk, E., and Debuch, H.: *Ann. Rev. Biochem.*, **28**, 53, 1959. Marinetti, G. V.; Erbland, J.; and Stotz, E.: *J. Am. Chem. Soc.*, **81**, 861, 1959.
18. Marinetti, J. V.; Erbland, J.; and Stotz, E.: *J. Am. Chem. Soc.*, **81**, 861, 1959.
19. Pangborn, M. C.: *J. Biol. Chem.*, **153**, 343, 1948; **161**, 71, 1945; **168**, 351, 1947.
20. Folch, J.: *J. Biol. Chem.*, **146**, 35, 1942.
21. Okuhara, E., and Nakayama, T.: *J. Biol. Chem.*, **215**, 295, 1955.
22. Folch, J.: *J. Biol. Chem.*, **177**, 505, 1949. Hawthorne, J. N.: *Biochim. et Biophys. Acta*, **18**, 389, 1955.
23. Fruton, J. S., and Simmonds, S.: *General Biochemistry*, 2nd ed. John Wiley & Sons, New York, 1957.
24. Carter, H. E., *et al.*: *J. Biol. Chem.*, **170**, 285, 1947; **191**, 727, 1951; *J. Am. Chem. Soc.*, **75**, 1007, 1953; *Federation Proc.*, **16**, 817, 1957.
25. Carter, H. E.; Galanos, D. S.; and Fujino, Y.: *Can. J. Biochem. and Physiol.*, **34**, 320, 1956.
26. Carter, H. E., *et al.*: *Federation Proc.*, **16**, 817, 1957.
27. Thierfelder, H., and Klenk, E.: *Chemie der Cerebroside und Phosphatide*. Springer Verlag, Berlin, 1930.
28. Carter, H. E., and Greenwood, F. L.: *J. Biol. Chem.*, **199**, 283, 1952.
29. Klenk, E., and Rennkamp, F.: *Z. physiol. Chem.*, **273**, 253, 1942.
30. Halliday, N.: *Proc. Soc. Exptl. Biol. Med.*, **75**, 659, 1950.
31. Blix, A.: *Z. physiol. Chem.*, **219**, 8, 1933.
32. Thannhauser, S. J., and Boncoddo, N.: *Federation Proc.*, **12**, 280, 1953. Thannhauser, S. J.; Fellig, J.; and Schmidt, G.: *J. Biol. Chem.*, **215**, 211, 1955.
33. Svennerholm, L.: *Nature*, **177**, 524, 1956.
34. Carter, H. E., *et al.*: *Federation Proc.*, **16**, 817, 1957.
35. Folch, J.; Arsone, S.; and Meath, J. A.: *J. Biol. Chem.*, **191**, 819, 1951.
36. Kosaki, T.; Ikoda, T.; Kotani, Y.; Nakagawa, S.; and Saka, T.: *Science*, **127**, 1176, 1958.
37. Folch, J., and Lees, M.: *J. Biol. Chem.*, **191**, 807, 1951.
38. Windaus, A.: *Z. physiol. Chem.*, **213**, 147, 1932.
39. Zlatkis, A.; Zak, B.; and Boyle, A. J.: *J. Lab. Clin. Med.*, **41**, 486, 1953. Zak, B.; Moss, N.; Boyle, A. J.; and Zlatkis, A.: *Anal. Chem.*, **26**, 776, 1954.
40. Kritchevsky, D.: *Cholesterol*, p. 235. John Wiley & Sons, New York, 1958.
41. Bloor, W. R., and Snider, R. H.: *J. Biol. Chem.*, **107**, 459, 1934. Bloor, W. R.: *ibid.*, **114**, 639, 1936.
42. Yasuda, M., and Bloor, W. R.: *J. Clin. Invest.*, **11**, 677, 1932.
43. Kaucher, M.; Galbraith, H.; Button, V.; and Williams, H. H.: *Arch. Biochem.*, **3**, 203, 1943.
44. Bloor, W. R.; Okey, R.; and Corner, G. W.: *J. Biol. Chem.*, **86**, 291, 1930.

7

Carbohydrates, or the saccharides

INTRODUCTION

Occurrence and general importance of carbohydrates. There is more carbohydrate material in nature than all other organic substances combined. This is due to the fact that carbohydrates make up most of the organic structure of all plants, as well as being present to some extent in all animals. The most abundant carbohydrate is cellulose, found in the woody structures and fibers of plants.

The starches are abundant and widespread, especially in grains, tubers, and roots, where they serve as reserve food material for plants and are utilized as the chief carbohydrate food of man.

Cane sugar or sucrose is present in the nectar of flowers, in fruits, and in the juices of various plants. The annual production of sucrose, largely for food, is about 30,000,000 tons, approximately two-thirds from sugar cane and one-third from sugar beets.

Large quantities of pentosans, so called because they are composed of simple sugars called pentoses, are found in plants, especially in seed husks, corn cobs, and other fibrous structures, and in plant gums and mucilages.

The glucosides are a class of carbohydrate derivatives which are frequent constituents of plants. A number of these substances are important drugs, among which are the glucosides of digitalis used in the treatment of heart disease.

The simple sugars, glucose and fructose, occur in small amounts widely distributed in plants.

Carbohydrates and their derivatives are present in all animal tissues and tissue fluids, blood, and milk. To a greater or lesser extent they are found in animal secretions and excretions.

Although a variety of carbohydrates, such as starch, dextrins, sucrose, and lactose or milk sugar, are taken in the food, all these substances are eventually converted to the simple sugar, glucose, which is the primary carbohydrate utilized by the body tissues.

Glucose is the sugar of blood and other body fluids. Blood normally contains from 60 to 90 mg of glucose in each 100 ml, but in the diabetic condition more than 1,000 mg may be present.

Blood glucose serves a number of purposes. The liver removes it and combines many molecules to form the polysaccharide glycogen, which normally is present in liver to the extent of a few per cent. Liver glycogen helps keep up the blood glucose level by breaking down to glucose again when absorption of sugar from the intestine falls off after a meal. Muscles and other tissues remove glucose from blood to form glycogen, which by breaking down through many and complex reactions provides energy to operate the tissue machinery. Blood glucose serves as the direct food for brain tissue, which removes it from the circulating blood as needed. Mammary glands remove glucose from the blood, convert some of it to another simple sugar, galactose, and then combine a molecule of galactose with a molecule of glucose to form lactose, which is milk sugar. Other sugars or sugar derivatives are formed from blood glucose and combined with proteins and other substances to make essential tissue constituents. Glucose is oxidized preferentially by all the tissues of the body to provide energy. Ordinarily, more than half of the energy of the body is provided by the oxidation of glucose. Excess glucose is readily converted to fats in the body and stored in the fat depots. A very large proportion of all the chemical changes occurring in tissues involve glucose or substances derived from it.

Chemical characteristics of the carbohydrates. The carbohydrates are all compounds of carbon, hydrogen, and oxygen, as are thousands of compounds which are not carbohydrates. Generally, but not always, the hydrogen and oxygen in carbohydrates are present in the proportion of two hydrogen atoms to one oxygen atom as in H_2O, from which fact the term "carbohydrate" (carbon hydrate) was derived. Glucose has the molecular formula $C_6H_{12}O_6$ and can be written as carbon hydrate, $C_6(H_2O)_6$, which, however, is entirely erroneous from a structural standpoint. Many substances not carbohydrates contain hydrogen and oxygen in the proportion of H_2O such as acetic and lactic acids, $C_2H_4O_2$ and $C_3H_6O_3$. Also, some carbohydrates, such as rhamnose, $C_6H_{12}O_5$, do not contain hydrogen and oxygen in the proportion of H_2O. The carbohydrates are actually or potentially (convertible into) hydroxy aldehydes or ketones, and in most cases they are polyhydroxy aldehydes or ketones. All the simple sugars contain a free sugar

group, $-\underset{\underset{H}{|}}{\overset{\overset{OH}{|}}{C}}-\overset{\overset{O}{\|}}{C}-$, in which the carbonyl group is part of an aldehyde or ketone

group. All the compound sugars, which are made up of simple sugar molecules, contain the sugar group in combined form, though a number also possess one free sugar group. The importance of a free sugar group in determining many of the chemical properties of carbohydrates will become evident later in the discussion.

Classification of the carbohydrates. The carbohydrates are sometimes referred to as the saccharides. The word "saccharide" comes from the Greek word *sakcharon*, meaning sugar. Those carbohydrates such as glucose and fructose which cannot be hydrolyzed into simpler compounds are called "simple sugars," or "monosaccharides," or "monosaccharoses," or at times simply "monoses." Certain carbohydrates are made up of two molecules of monosaccharide such as sucrose, lactose, and maltose. These carbohydrates are called "disaccharides," or "disaccharoses." Similarly, trisaccharides are composed of three, and tetrasaccharides of four, monosaccharide molecules. Those carbohydrates made up of many monosaccharide molecules (starches, glycogens, celluloses, etc.) are called "polysaccharides," or " polysaccharoses." All these compound carbohydrates may be readily hydrolyzed into their constituent monosaccharides by heating with dilute acids or by the action of specific enzymes.

Monosaccharides containing from two to ten carbon atoms have been synthesized, and many occur in natural sources. They are either hydroxy aldehydes or hydroxy ketones and are named systematically to indicate both the number of carbon atoms present and the aldehyde or ketone structure. For example, glycol aldehyde, $CH_2OH \cdot CHO$, the simplest compound to be classed as a carbohydrate, contains two carbon atoms and is referred to as a "diose." Since it contains an aldehyde group, it is called an "aldose." To indicate the presence of two carbon atoms and an aldehyde group in a single term it is called an "aldodiose." Similarly, glyceric aldehyde, $CH_2OH \cdot CHOH \cdot CHO$, contains three carbon atoms, is an aldehyde, and is called an "aldotriose." Glucose, $C_6H_{12}O_6$, contains an aldehyde group and is an aldohexose. Sugars possessing a ketone group are "ketoses." Dihydroxyacetone, $CH_2OH \cdot CO \cdot CH_2OH$, with three carbon atoms and a ketone group, is a "ketotriose," and fructose, $C_6H_{12}O_6$, since it has a ketone group and six carbons, is a "ketohexose."

The several ways of classifying carbohydrates vary in minor details and completeness. Since one group of carbohydrates cannot be hydrolyzed into anything simpler, it is logical to refer to these substances as the simple carbohydrates, or simple sugars, or monosaccharides, or monosaccharoses. However, many carbohydrates are made up of from two to a thousand or more molecules of simple sugar into which they may be split by hydrolysis.

These carbohydrates may be referred to as the "compound carbohydrates." The classification given below is based upon these considerations.

CLASSIFICATION OF THE CARBOHYDRATES

A. MONOSACCHARIDES, OR SIMPLE SUGARS

Monosaccharides which are marked with an asterisk occur in nature; others are synthetic. The hexoses and pentoses are the most important of the simple sugars. The monosaccharides or simple sugars are generally well-crystallized solids, soluble in water, and have a more or less sweet taste. They all have the property of reducing alkaline copper solutions and giving other reactions characteristic of the free sugar group such as reactions with phenylhydrazine, hydrogen cyanide, and hydroxylamine.

	Aldoses	Ketoses
1. Dioses, $C_2H_4O_2$	Glycolaldehyde	
2. Trioses, $C_3H_6O_3$	D*- and L-glycerose or glyceric aldehyde	*Dihydroxyacetone
3. Tetroses, $C_4H_8O_4$	D- and L-erythrose	Erythrulose
	D- and L-threose	
4. Pentoses, $C_5H_{10}O_5$	D*- and L*-arabinose	D- and L*-xyloketose
	D*- and L-xylose	
	D*- and L-ribose	
	D- and L-lyxose	
5. Hexoses, $C_6H_{12}O_6$	D*- and L-glucose	D*- and L-fructose
	D*- and L-mannose	D- and L-sorbose
	D*- and L*-galactose	D-tagatose
	D- and L-gulose	
	D- and L-idose	
	D- and L-talose	
	D- and L-altrose	
	D- and L-allose	
6. Heptoses, $C_7H_{14}O_7$	Glucoheptose	D*-altroheptulose or sedoheptose
	Mannoheptose	D*-mannoketoheptose
	Galactoheptose	D-glucoheptulose
		L-glucoheptulose
		L-galactoheptulose or perseulose
7. Octoses, $C_8H_{16}O_8$	Glucooctose	
	Mannooctose	
	Galactooctose	
8. Nonoses, $C_9H_{18}O_9$	Gluconone	
	Mannononose	
9. Decoses, $C_{10}H_{20}O_{10}$	Glucodecose	

B. COMPOUND CARBOHYDRATES

The compound carbohydrates are composed of two or more molecules of monosaccharide. Although they apparently are not produced in nature by condensation of monosaccharide molecules with the loss of a molecule of water for each linkage formed, this is the net effect in their formation.

$$2C_6H_{12}O_6 \longrightarrow H_2O + C_{12}H_{22}O_{11} \quad \text{(disaccharide)}$$
$$3C_6H_{12}O_6 \longrightarrow 2H_2O + C_{18}H_{32}O_{16} \quad \text{(trisaccharide)}$$
$$4C_6H_{12}O_6 \longrightarrow 3H_2O + C_{24}H_{42}O_{21} \quad \text{(tetrasaccharide)}$$
$$nC_6H_{12}O_6 \longrightarrow (n-1)H_2O + (C_6H_{10}O_5)_n \quad \text{(polysaccharide)}$$

STEREOISOMERISM AND OPTICAL ISOMERISM

Many of the carbohydrates contain the same number of atoms and the same kinds of groups, yet are definitely distinct substances. For example, the formula $C_6H_{12}O_6$ represents 16 different simple sugars, all possessing the structure $CH_2OH \cdot CHOH \cdot CHOH \cdot CHOH \cdot CHOH \cdot CHO$. This is due to different arrangements of the constituent groups of the molecules in space. This phenomenon represents what is called "stereoisomerism" (space isomerism), and these sugars are "stereoisomers." The space formulas of three of the above sugars are illustrative.

CHO	CHO	CHO
H‑ C‑ OH	HO ‑ C‑ H	H‑ C‑ OH
HO ‑ C‑ H	HO ‑ C‑ H	HO ‑ C‑ H
H‑ C‑ OH	H‑ C‑ OH	HO ‑ C‑ H
H‑ C‑ OH	H‑ C‑ OH	H‑ C‑ OH
CH_2OH	CH_2OH	CH_2OH
Glucose	Mannose	Galactose

The arrangement of the groups of the end carbon atoms is not significant.

The carbohydrates also exhibit the property of optical activity and exist as optical isomers, as do amino acids and various other biologically important substances. The subjects of stereoisomerism, optical activity, and optical isomerism are of so much importance in the study of biochemistry that they are considered in the following pages before the carbohydrates are discussed systematically.

Polarized light and optical activity. According to the modern wave theory, light consists of electromagnetic disturbances propagated as trains of waves oscillating transversely to the direction of propagation. By reflection or refraction it is possible to separate out the component of the light vibrating in a single plane, and this is plane polarized light.

When a beam of light is passed through a crystal of Iceland spar (transparent calcite, $CaCO_3$), it is split into two components, an ordinary ray which obeys the usual laws of refraction and an extraordinary ray which is not normally refracted. The light in each ray is plane polarized, and the planes of polarization of the rays are perpendicular to each other.

A Nicol prism provides a mechanism for rejecting the ordinary, and transmitting the extraordinary, ray. In preparing it, an Iceland spar crystal is cut along a certain plane, and the pieces are cemented together with Canada balsam so that, when unpolarized light is passed through it at the proper angle to the optic axis, the ordinary ray is completely reflected at the junction of the two halves while the extraordinary ray passes through. The figures below diagrammatically illustrate cross sections of beams of ordinary light and plane polarized light.

Biot, in 1815, found that certain substances, such as turpentine and solutions of tartaric acid and sugars, rotate the plane of polarized light when it is passed through them. Since that time it has been found that thousands of substances in liquid form or in solution rotate the plane of polarized light.

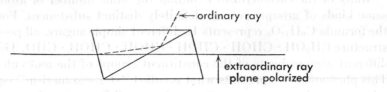

Diagram of Nicol prism.

Ordinary light. Oscillations in all planes of beam.

Plane polarized light. Oscillations in one plane of beam.

The following figures illustrate optical rotation.

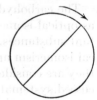

Plane polarized light rotated counterclockwise or levo.

Plane polarized light before rotation.

Plane polarized light rotated clockwise or dextro.

Substances which rotate the plane of polarized light clockwise, or to the right, are said to be dextrorotatory. Similarly, substances rotating counterclockwise, or to the left, are levorotatory.

The phenomenon of optical rotation is due to asymmetry, and in the case of the carbon compounds it is related to the presence of so-called asymmetric carbon atoms in the molecules. These asymmetric carbon atoms have their valence bonds attached to four different atoms or groups. In the tetrahedral model of the carbon atom the carbon is considered to be at the center of the tetrahedron with its four valence bonds directed to the corners of the tetrahedron. The figures below illustrate asymmetrical and symmetrical carbon atoms in which *a*, *b*, *c*, and *d* are different atoms or groups. When there are four different atoms or groups attached to a carbon atom, the molecule is asymmetric and exists in two forms, 1 and 2, which are mirror images. If two or more of the groups attached to carbon are alike, as in 3, the molecule is symmetrical, and a plane of symmetry can be passed through it (assuming atoms and groups can be divided by the plane) dividing it into two mirror-image halves. Structures 1 and 2 cannot be divided into mirror-image halves.

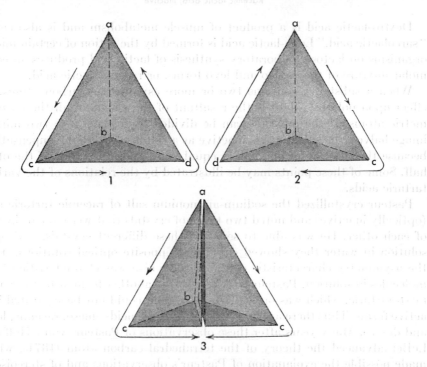

The electromagnetic fields of the atoms and groups in a molecule act upon polarized light passing through them to cause rotation of the plane of polarization. In the case of a symmetrical molecule, such as 3, the net effect of the groups is zero and the light emerges unchanged. However, in the case of unsymmetrical molecules, such as 1 and 2, there is a net rotation of the plane of polarization and such molecules are optically active. If the tetrahedra, 1 and 2, are viewed from a, the direction from b to c to d is counterclockwise in 1 and clockwise in 2. Since the groups present in 1 and 2 are identical but oppositely arranged in space, the effects upon polarized light are equal and opposite. If 1 rotates the plane of polarization to the right, then 2 will rotate it equally to the left; 1 is dextrorotatory, and 2 is levorotatory. Substances possessing equal and opposite optical rotations and bearing mirror image relations to each other are optical isomers or optical enantiomorphs. When equal molecular quantities are mixed, a racemic mixture is obtained which is optically inactive.

The lactic acids were among the first optically active substances of biochemical importance examined. Dextro, levo, and racemic forms were found. The projection formulas of the two active forms are:

$$\begin{array}{cc}
\text{COOH} & \text{COOH} \\
| & | \\
\text{H} - \text{C} - \text{OH} & \text{HO} - \text{C} - \text{H} \\
| & | \\
\text{CH}_3 & \text{CH}_3 \\
\text{Levo-lactic acid} & \text{Dextro-lactic acid}
\end{array}$$

Racemic lactic acid, inactive

Dextro-lactic acid is a product of muscle metabolism and is also called "sarcolactic acid." Levo-lactic acid is formed by the action of certain microorganisms on lactose. Laboratory synthesis of lactic acid produces an equimolar mixture of the dextro and levo forms, or racemic lactic acid.

When a substance contains two or more asymmetric carbon atoms, its effect upon polarized light is the resultant of the effects of all these asymmetric atoms. If the molecule can be divided by a plane into two mirror-image halves, the substance is inactive as a result of internal compensation, because the rotation of one half is equal and opposite to that of the other half. Some of these points may be illustrated by the relations of the various tartaric acids.

Pasteur crystallized the sodium-ammonium salt of racemic tartaric acid (optically inactive) and noted two types of crystals that were mirror images of each other. He was able to separate these different crystals, and upon solution in water they showed equal and opposite optical rotations. Thus the asymmetry characteristic of the crystals also was characteristic of the molecules in solution. Pasteur later discovered another form of tartaric acid, meso-tartaric, which was optically inactive and could not be separated into active forms. Thus there are four forms of tartaric acid—meso, racemic, levo, and dextro. Many years after these observations of Pasteur, van't Hoff and LeBel advanced the theory of the tetrahedral carbon atom (1874), which made possible the explanation of Pasteur's observations and of stereoisomerism in general.

The projection formulas of the tetrahedral structures of dextro-, levo-, and meso-tartaric acids may be represented:

$$\begin{array}{ccc}
\text{A} \quad \text{COOH} & \text{B} \quad \text{COOH} & \text{A} \quad \text{COOH} \\
| & | & | \\
\text{HO} - \text{C} - \text{H} & \text{H} - \text{C} - \text{OH} & \text{HO} - \text{C} - \text{H} \\
| & | & | \\
\hline
| & | & | \\
\text{H} - \text{C} - \text{OH} & \text{HO} - \text{C} - \text{H} & \text{HO} - \text{C} - \text{H} \\
| & | & | \\
\text{A} \quad \text{COOH} & \text{B} \quad \text{COOH} & \text{B} \quad\quad \text{COOH} \\
\text{I} & \text{II} & \text{III} \\
\text{Levo-tartaric} & \text{Dextro-tartaric} & \text{Meso-tartaric} \\
l\text{-Tartaric} & d\text{-Tartaric} & m\text{-Tartaric} \\
\text{D-Tartaric} & \text{L-Tartaric} &
\end{array}$$

All these molecules contain the same atoms and groups, but with different relative positions in space. Two asymmetric carbon atoms are present. Structures I and II are mirror images. Both A groups in I are configurationally alike, as can be seen by rotating the lower group A in the plane of the paper when it superposes upon the top group A. Similarly, both B groups are alike in II and are mirror images of the A groups in I. Groups A and B in III are exactly reversed in space and are mirror images. If group A rotates the plane of polarized light to the left and group B rotates an equal amount to the right, then I is levorotatory, II is dextrorotatory, and III is optically inactive, because the A and B groups present rotate equally but in opposite directions. III is optically inactive because of internal compensation and is called a "meso compound." An equimolecular mixture of the active forms, I and II, is a racemic mixture and is optically inactive.

When there are several asymmetric carbon atoms in a chain molecule and the end groups are not identical, the number of stereoisomers possible is equal to 2^n, where n is the number of asymmetric carbon atoms. Thus there are $2^4 = 16$ stereoisomeric sugars corresponding to the formula CH_2OH—$CHOH$—$CHOH$—$CHOH$—$CHOH$—CHO, which contains four asymmetric carbon atoms.

It will be noted that the structures of glucose and mannose, previously given, contain four asymmetric groups, and that all these groups are identical except those at the top, which are opposite in space. Such isomers are called "epimers."

The D and L forms of optical isomers. It has been possible to relate the spatial configurations of sugars, amino acids, and many other optically active substances of biologic importance to the configurations of the dextro and levo forms of glyceraldehyde:

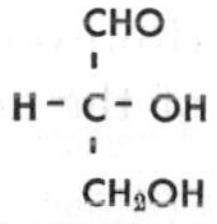

CHO	CHO
H – C – OH	HO – C – H
CH₂OH	CH₂OH
D-Glyceraldehyde	L-Glyceraldehyde
$[\alpha]_D = +13.5°$	$[\alpha]_D = -13.5°$

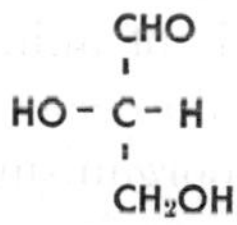

Sugars, amino acids, etc., related to dextro-glyceraldehyde are designated "D" compounds; substances related to levo-glyceraldehyde are "L" compounds.

Although the optical rotations of the glyceraldehydes upon which the D and L configurations are based are dextro and levo, respectively, the rotations of many members of the D-series are levo, and of the L-series are dextro. Accordingly, the prefixes "D" and "L" have no significance relative to the direction of optical rotation. They simply designate spatial relations of the compounds to the two forms of glyceraldehyde. The configurations originally assigned to the two forms of glyceraldehyde necessarily were arbitrarily chosen but agreed with the configurations assigned to the corresponding optical isomers of glucose. It is of interest and importance that the absolute configurations of the tartaric acids appear to have been established by a physical method (1) and agree with the arbitrary configurations shown above in I and II. Since the configurations of levorotatory and dextrorotatory tartaric acids are related to the configurations of the dextrorotatory (D) and levorotatory (L) forms of glyceric aldehyde, respectively, the absolute configurations of D- and L-glyceric aldehyde, D- and L-glucose, and all other compounds belonging to the D- and L- series seem to be established as the configurations already assigned arbitrarily.

Although in general the direction of optical rotation of substances may be indicated by the prefixes "d" and "l," in the case of compounds belonging to the D and L series the direction of rotation is designated by prefixes such as "$D(-)$," "$D(+)$," "$L(-)$," and "$L(+)$." Thus, ordinary fructose is $D(-)$-fructose, and glucose is $D(+)$-glucose.

Racemic mixtures may be designated in general by the prefix "dl" and, in the case of substances of the D- and L- series, by the prefix "DL."

An example of the method used in correlating the configuration of a compound with a form of glyceraldehyde is the following:

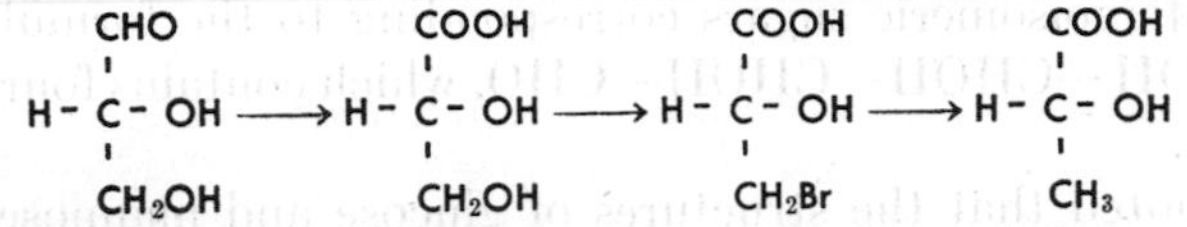

$$
\begin{array}{cccc}
\text{CHO} & \text{COOH} & \text{COOH} & \text{COOH} \\
| & | & | & | \\
\text{H}-\text{C}-\text{OH} \longrightarrow & \text{H}-\text{C}-\text{OH} \longrightarrow & \text{H}-\text{C}-\text{OH} \longrightarrow & \text{H}-\text{C}-\text{OH} \\
| & | & | & | \\
\text{CH}_2\text{OH} & \text{CH}_2\text{OH} & \text{CH}_2\text{Br} & \text{CH}_3 \\
\text{D(+)-Glycer-} & \text{D(-)-Glyceric} & \text{D(+)-}\beta\text{-Bromo-} & \text{D(-)-Lactic} \\
\text{aldehyde} & \text{acid} & \text{lactic acid} & \text{acid}
\end{array}
$$

Thus the lactic acid of levo rotation belongs to the D-series.

Most of the organic substances involved in the structure and metabolism of living organisms belong to the D- or L-series. An enzyme system will act only upon one form of a substance (D or L). For example, certain of the D-sugars are utilized in the animal body and by microorganisms, whereas the corresponding L-sugars are not utilized. Also, only L-amino acids are utilized in the synthesis of animal and vegetable proteins. However, some of the D-amino acids do occur in nature, notably in some of the antibiotics produced by microorganisms.

Separation or resolution of racemic forms. Although enzymatic synthesis in animals and plants produces only the d or l isomer of a substance, laboratory synthesis yields a mixture of the d and l forms, or the racemic mixture. Accordingly, methods for the separation or resolution of the d and l forms from such mixtures are necessary. Some of these methods are outlined below.

1. Mechanical separation of crystals. This method was used by Pasteur in separating the salts of d- and l-tartaric acids from the racemic mixture. It can be applied only when it is possible to have the isomers crystallize out in forms that can be distinguished and separated. This is seldom possible, and the method has been used in very few cases.

2. Preferential crystallization due to inoculation. In some cases a supersaturated solution of the racemic mixture upon seeding with a crystal of one of the active forms present in the mixture will deposit more or less pure crystals of the inoculating form. Strangely, some mixtures may be separated by inoculation with crystals of the same form but entirely different composition. For example, when a crystal of l-asparagine is added to a solution of dl-sodium ammonium tartrate, pure d-sodium ammonium tartrate crystallizes out.

3. Resolution by conversion to diastereoisomers. This method was also devised by Pasteur. It consists in treating the racemic modification with an optically active reagent which forms derivatives that are no longer mirror images and which possess different solubilities.

For example, if a racemic acid is composed of d-A and l-A and this is treated with an optically active base, l-B, such as quinine, strychnine, or brucine, the following reaction will occur:

$$dl\text{-A} + 2l\text{B} \longrightarrow d\text{-A}\cdot l\text{-B} + l\text{-A}\cdot l\text{-B}$$

d-A · *l*-B and *l*-A · *l*-B are called "diastereoisomers," are not mirror images, have different solubilities, and can be separated by fractional crystallization. Optically active acids are similarly used in separating racemic bases. After separation of the active derivatives, these are decomposed into the active isomers.

4. Resolution by biochemical processes. Pasteur also originated this method of separating racemic forms, which is based upon the selective utilization of one isomer, the other remaining. Pasteur found that the mold *Penicillium glaucum* destroys *d*-ammonium tartrate more rapidly than *l*-ammonium tartrate in a solution of *dl*-ammonium tartrate. Higher organisms also often show selectivity in the utilization of the isomers in a racemic form. For example, when a salt of *dl*-malic acid is injected subcutaneously into a rabbit, the salt of *d*-malic acid is excreted in the urine. Specific enzymes in the absence of living cells may also show selective action upon the isomers of the racemic form. For example, the enzyme emulsin from bitter almonds acts upon *dl*-mandelonitrile to destroy the *d* form more rapidly.

Biochemical resolution of the racemic forms of amino acids is exceedingly important and may be accomplished in several ways. These methods depend upon the use of specific enzymes which differentiate in their action upon optical enantiomorphs or their derivatives. Examples are outlined below.

a). Asymmetric hydrolysis. In this procedure a derivative of the amino acid enantiomorphs is prepared and treated with an enzyme that selectively hydrolyzes the derivative of one form. For example, it has been found that in the N-acyl derivatives of amino acids, the enzymes acylase of kidney and carboxypeptidase of pancreas hydrolyze one form much more readily than the other:

COOH   COOH

H – C – NH – CO – R   R – CO –⋮– HN – C – H

R′   HO⋮H R′

Hydrolyzed preferentially

The free amino acid may be separated from the unhydrolyzed acyl derivative by precipitation with alcohol.

b). Asymmetric synthesis by enzymes. This method depends upon the fact that the enzyme papain will selectively effect the condensation of the N-acyl derivative of one form of the amino acid with certain nitrogenous bases, such as aniline, to produce an insoluble product which can be separated.

c). Asymmetric degradation. This procedure is based upon the selective destruction of one amino acid isomer by a suitably chosen enzyme. For example, D-amino acid oxidase selectively decomposes D-methionine and leaves L-methionine. This method is less effective than the first two, since it entails the loss of one isomer and it is much less general in application.

The polariscope and specific rotation. The actual measurement of the rotation of polarized light involves the use of an instrument called the "polariscope" or polarimeter. The essential action of a polariscope may be simply explained from the diagram of Figure 7.1.

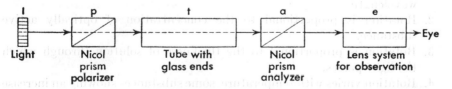

Figure 7.1

Because different wavelengths of polarized light are rotated differently, it is necessary to use monochromatic light. Ordinarily the light from incandescent sodium or mercury is used. Special electric lamps as sources of these lights are available. Polariscopes often have special filters designed to purify the beam of light as it passes through. The sodium-D spectral line is really composed of two wavelengths, D_1 (5896 Å) and D_2 (5890 Å) and, except for work of high precision, is commonly used. The most satisfactory light for polariscopic work is the yellow-green mercury line (5461 Å), since only one wavelength is involved. Because of its shorter wavelength, the mercury line gives slightly greater rotation than sodium-D light.

In Figure 7.1, p represents the polarizing Nicol prism which converts the beam of monochromatic light into plane polarized light. This light passes through tube, t, then through the analyzing Nicol prism, a, and finally through the lens system, e. The analyzing Nicol is mounted in the center of a large disk with a vernier scale on the edge, so that the prism may be rotated about its optical axis and the angle of rotation in degrees and fractions may be read from the scale. When prism a is turned so that its optical axis exactly corresponds to that of prism p, polarized light passes from p through a. However, if a is now turned about its optical axis, light from p cannot pass through a, and an observer looking through e sees a dark field. If prism a is set so that it is lined up with prism p and water or an optically inactive solution is placed in tube t, the observer at e sees a light field. Suppose, however, that a solution of dextro-tartaric acid be placed in t; then the polarized light from p, on passing through the solution, is rotated to the right and does not pass through a, and the observer sees a dark field. If now the disk supporting a is rotated through an angle to the right, corresponding to the rotation of the polarized light by the solution, the light passes through a, and the observer sees a light field. Similarly, levorotating substances necessitate rotation of a to the left to permit passage of light to the eye.

In the construction of a polariscope the polarizing prism is cut and cemented together so as to give a divided optical field, which greatly increases the accuracy of observation. Some instruments accomplish this by using a multiple polarizing prism system. In adjusting the instrument for a reading, the analyzer is rotated until all segments of the divided field are equally illuminated.

Practically all the principles of optical rotation were formulated by Biot. Among these the following are of direct application:

1. An optically active substance has a definite rotation for a given wavelength.
2. Rotation is proportional to the concentration of optically active substance.
3. Rotation is proportional to the thickness of solution through which the light passes.
4. Rotation varies with temperature, some substances showing an increase and others a decrease with rising temperature.

5. Rotation varies with wavelength of light, being greater the shorter the wavelength.

6. Rotation varies with the nature of the solvent in which the substance is dissolved.

In view of these principles, it is necessary to express the rotation of all substances according to a single definition in order that the values may be comparable. This is done by expression as specific rotation, which is defined as the rotation in degrees of 1 g of substance per milliliter in a tube 1 dm (10 cm) in length.

Most substances cannot be used in the pure state for rotation measurements but must be dissolved in an appropriate solvent. The specific rotation of a pure substance is calculated from the rotation of its solution according to the equation:

$$[\alpha]_D^T = \frac{\alpha_{obs} \times 100}{l \times c}$$

in which $[\alpha]_D^T$ = specific rotation at temperature T and with sodium-D light (if the mercury 5461 wavelength is used, the expression is $[\alpha]_{5461}^T$); α_{obs} = observed rotation; l = length of polariscope tube, in decimeters; c = grams of substance in 100 ml of solution. Observations are usually made at 20° C. The solvent should be specified.

If the specific rotation of a substance is known, its concentration in a solution may be calculated by rearranging the above equation:

$$c = \frac{\alpha_{obs} \times 100}{l \times [\alpha]_D^T}$$

Suppose a solution of an active substance contains 5 g per 100 ml, and the rotation is observed to be +0.8° in a 2-dm tube at 20° C using sodium-D light. The specific rotation is calculated as follows:

$$[\alpha]_D^{20} = \frac{+0.8 \times 100}{2 \times 5} = \frac{+80}{10} = +8°$$

The molecular rotation of a substance is the product of its specific rotation and molecular weight.

MONOSACCHARIDES, OR SIMPLE SUGARS

The structures of the monosaccharides. The determination of the structural relations of the monosaccharides by Emil Fischer and others represents complex and beautiful research. Discussions of the details of this work may be found in Volume II of Gilman's *Organic Chemistry; in Structural*

Carbohydrate Chemistry, by Percival; in *The Carbohydrates*, by Pigman; and in other advanced treatises.

Fischer worked out the structural configurations of the monosaccharides in reference to the configurations of the dextro and levorotatory forms of glucose. Since he had no evidence as to which of the mirror-image configurations of glucose represents the levo and which the dextrorotatory form, he arbitrarily assigned the following configurations:

$$
\begin{array}{cc}
\text{A} & \text{B} \\
\begin{array}{l}
\text{H} - \text{C} = \text{O} \\
\text{H} - \text{C} - \text{OH} \\
\text{HO} - \text{C} - \text{H} \\
\text{H} - \text{C} - \text{OH} \\
\text{H} - \text{C} - \text{OH} \\
\text{CH}_2\text{OH}
\end{array}
&
\begin{array}{l}
\text{H} - \text{C} = \text{O} \\
\text{HO} - \text{C} - \text{H} \\
\text{H} - \text{C} - \text{OH} \\
\text{HO} - \text{C} - \text{H} \\
\text{HO} - \text{C} - \text{H} \\
\text{CH}_2\text{OH}
\end{array}
\end{array}
$$

Dextro-glucose   Levo-glucose
D-Glucose   L-Glucose

Sugars related configurationally to dextro- and levorotatory glucose were designated D- and L-sugars, respectively.

Fischer was fortunate in his selection, since proof of the absolute configurations of the D- and L- forms of tartaric acid established A and B as the absolute configurations of D- and L-glucose.

$$
\begin{array}{cc}
\begin{array}{l}
\text{H} - \text{C} = \text{O} \\
\text{H} - \text{C} - \text{OH} \\
\text{CH}_2\text{OH}
\end{array}
&
\begin{array}{l}
\text{H} - \text{C} = \text{O} \\
\text{HO} - \text{C} - \text{H} \\
\text{CH}_2\text{OH}
\end{array}
\end{array}
$$

D-Glyceric aldehyde   L-Glyceric aldehyde

The configurations of H and OH groups on the asymmetric carbon atoms of D- and L-glyceric aldehyde are identical with the configurations of these groups on asymmetric carbon 5 of D- and L-glucose, respectively.

All the D-aldose sugars may be considered derivatives of D-glyceric aldehyde, and all the L-aldose sugars derivatives of L-glyceric aldehyde.

This system is all the more reasonable because the tetroses, pentoses, hexoses, etc., may be formed from D- and L-glyceric aldehyde by the cyanhydrin synthesis as outlined below.

When HCN is added to an aldehyde group, an asymmetric carbon is formed, giving two cyanhydrins:

$$
\text{H} - \text{C} = \text{O} + \text{HCN} \longrightarrow
\begin{array}{l}
\text{C} \equiv \text{N} \\
\text{H} - \text{C} - \text{OH} \\
\text{R}
\end{array}
\quad \text{and} \quad
\begin{array}{l}
\text{C} \equiv \text{N} \\
\text{HO} - \text{C} - \text{H} \\
\text{R}
\end{array}
$$

Suppose HCN is added to D-glyceric aldehyde; two cyanhydrins will be formed as follows:

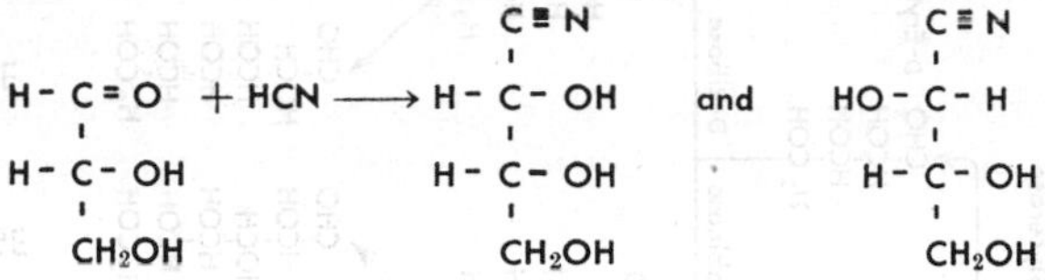

$$
\begin{array}{ccc}
& & C \equiv N & & C \equiv N \\
& & | & & | \\
H-C=O \;+\; HCN \longrightarrow & H-C-OH & \text{and} & HO-C-H \\
| & | & & | \\
H-C-OH & H-C-OH & & H-C-OH \\
| & | & & | \\
CH_2OH & CH_2OH & & CH_2OH
\end{array}
$$

When these cyanhydrins are hydrolyzed, the corresponding acids are formed:

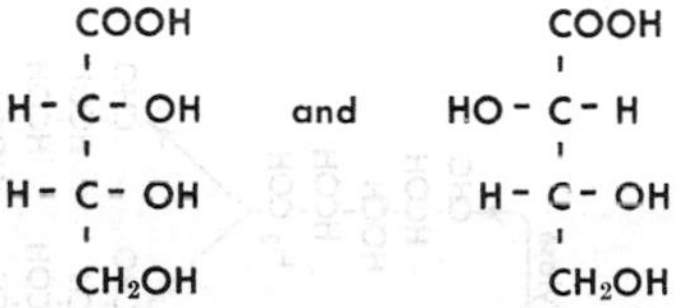

$$
\begin{array}{ccc}
COOH & & COOH \\
| & & | \\
H-C-OH & \text{and} & HO-C-H \\
| & & | \\
H-C-OH & & H-C-OH \\
| & & | \\
CH_2OH & & CH_2OH
\end{array}
$$

The carboxyl groups of these acids may be reduced to aldehyde groups, forming the two aldotetroses:

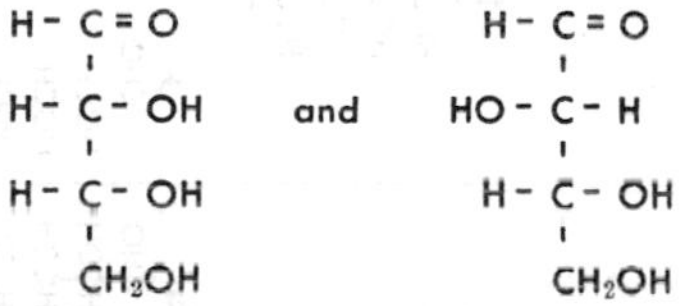

$$
\begin{array}{ccc}
H-C=O & & H-C=O \\
| & & | \\
H-C-OH & \text{and} & HO-C-H \\
| & & | \\
H-C-OH & & H-C-OH \\
| & & | \\
CH_2OH & & CH_2OH \\
\text{D-Erythrose} & & \text{D-Threose}
\end{array}
$$

D-Erythrose may be treated with HCN and the process repeated to form the pentoses:

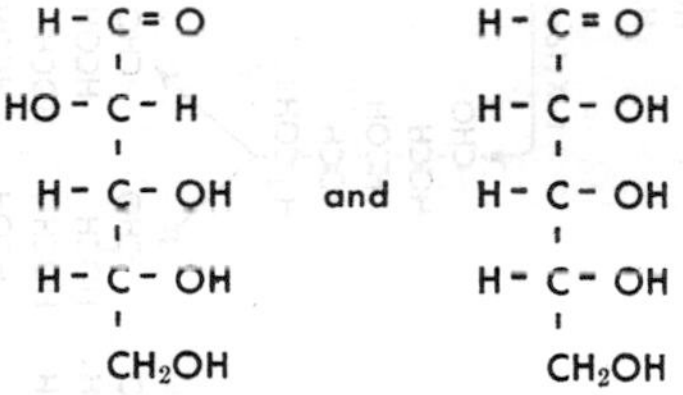

$$
\begin{array}{ccc}
H-C=O & & H-C=O \\
| & & | \\
HO-C-H & & H-C-OH \\
| & & | \\
H-C-OH & \text{and} & H-C-OH \\
| & & | \\
H-C-OH & & H-C-OH \\
| & & | \\
CH_2OH & & CH_2OH \\
\text{D-Arabinose} & & \text{D-Ribose}
\end{array}
$$

Similarly, D-threose gives two pentoses:

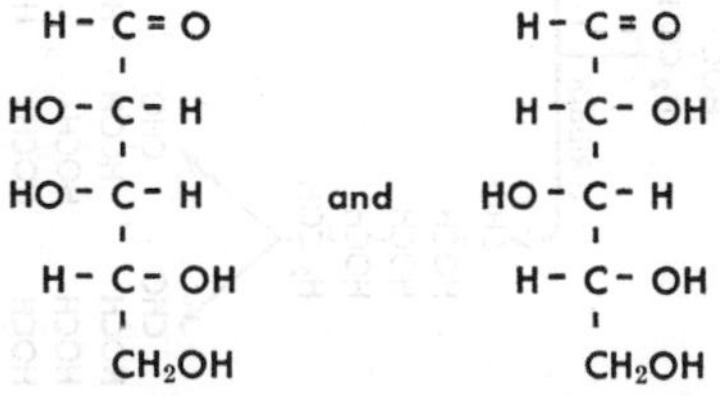

$$
\begin{array}{ccc}
H-C=O & & H-C=O \\
| & & | \\
HO-C-H & & H-C-OH \\
| & & | \\
HO-C-H & \text{and} & HO-C-H \\
| & & | \\
H-C-OH & & H-C-OH \\
| & & | \\
CH_2OH & & CH_2OH \\
\text{D-Lyxose} & & \text{D-Xylose}
\end{array}
$$

CONFIGURATIONS OF THE ALDOSES

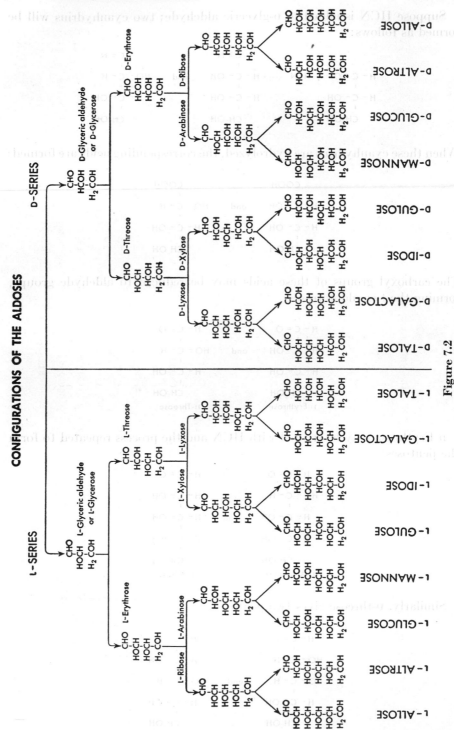

Figure 7.2

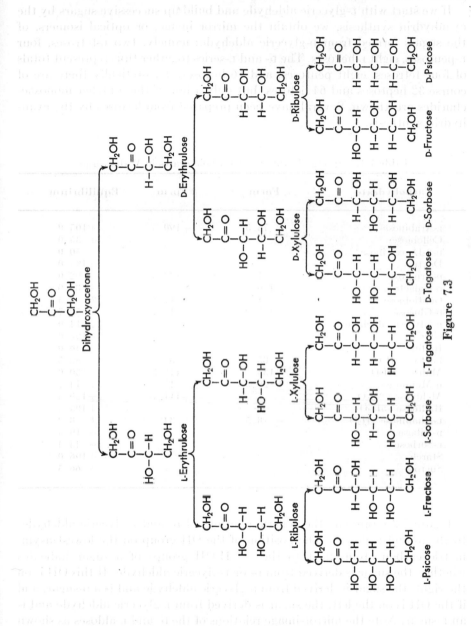

Figure 7.3

Each of the above four D-pentoses may be converted to two D-hexoses, giving a total of eight D-hexoses.

If we start with L-glyceric aldehyde and build up successive sugars by the cyanhydrin synthesis, we obtain the mirror image, or optical isomers, of the sugars formed from D-glyceric aldehyde; namely, two L-tetroses, four L-pentoses, eight L-hexoses. The D- and L-series together thus represent totals of four tetroses, eight pentoses, and 16 hexoses. Theoretically there are of course 32 heptoses and 64 octoses, but only a few of these higher monosaccharides are known. Several have been prepared from hexoses by the cyanhydrin synthesis.

Table 7.1.   Specific Rotations of Carbohydrates in Water, $[\alpha]_D^{20}$

Carbohydrate	α Form	β Form	Equilibrium
L-Arabinose	+ 75.5	+190.5	+105.0
Cellobiose			+ 35.0
D-2-Deoxyribose			− 50.0
Dextrin			+195.0
D-Fructose	− 21	−133.5	− 92.0
D-Galactose	+150.7	+ 43	+ 80.0
Gentiobiose	+ 31	− 11	+ 9.5
D-Glucose	+112.2	+ 18.7	+ 52.7
D-Glyceric aldehyde			+ 14.0
Glycogen			+196.0
Inulin			− 40.0
Lactose · H_2O	+ 85	+ 35	+ 52.5
Maltose · H_2O	+133	+112.5	+130.0
D-Mannose	+ 29.3	− 17	+ 14.2
Melibiose · $2H_2O$		+111.7	+129.5
Raffinose · $5H_2O$			+105.2
L-Rhamnose · H_2O	− 8.5	+ 34	+ 8.2
D-Ribose			− 19.5
L-Sorbose			− 43.4
Starch			+196.0
Sucrose			+ 66.5

Figure 7.2 represents the generic relations of D- and L-glyceric aldehydes to the D- and L-aldoses. The position of the OH group on the lowest asymmetric carbon atom (next to the —CH₂OH group) of a sugar indicates whether the sugar is derived from D- or L-glyceric aldehyde. If this OH is on the right, the sugar is derived from D-glyceric aldehyde and is a D-sugar, and if the OH is on the left, the sugar is derived from L-glyceric aldehyde and is an L-sugar. Note the mirror-image relations of the D- and L-aldoses as shown in Figure 7.2.

The ketose sugars may be considered derivatives of D- and L-erythrulose, as shown in Figure 7.3.

Several ketoheptoses are natural products. Some of them are named according to the hexose sugars having similar configurations on the lower five carbon atoms.

```
CH₂OH          CH₂OH          CH₂OH          CH₂OH          CH₂OH
 |              |              |              |              |
 C=O            C=O            C=O            C=O            C=O
 |              |              |              |              |
HO-C-H         HO-C-H         H-C-OH         HO-C-H         HO-C-H
 |              |              |              |              |
H-C-OH         H-C-OH         HO-C-H         H-C-OH         HO-C-H
 |              |              |              |              |
H-C-OH         H-C-OH         H-C-OH         HO-C-H         H-C-OH
 |              |              |              |              |
H-C-OH         HO-C-H         H-C-OH         HO-C-H         H-C-OH
 |              |              |              |              |
CH₂OH          CH₂OH          CH₂OH          CH₂OH          CH₂OH
D-Sedo-        L-Per-         D-Gluco-       L-Gluco-       D-Manno-
heptulose      seulose        heptulose      heptulose      heptulose
```

Sugars and deoxy sugars with branched chains are natural products. The structures of several are given below:

```
                              H-C=O                    H-C=O
                               |                        |
     H-C=O               HOH₂C-C-OH                H-C-OH
      |                        |                        |
     H-C-OH                H-C-OH                OHC-C-OH
      |                        |                        |
      C-OH                  H-C-OH                 HO-C-H
    /    \                     |                        |
 HOH₂C   CH₂OH              CH₂OH                     CH₃
    Apiose                 Hamamelose                Streptose

                              H-C=O                    H-C=O
                               |                        |
                              CH₂                      CH₂
                               |  ,CH₃                  |  ,CH₃
     H-C=O                     C                        C
      |                        |  `OH                   |  `OCH₃
     CHOH                    CHOH                      CHOH
      |                        |                        |
      CH                     CHOH                      CHOH
    /    \                     |                        |
 HOH₂C   CH₂OH               CH₃                       CH₃
   Cordycepose              Mycarose                  Cladinose
```

Apiose and hamamelose are plant products, while streptose, cordycepose, mycarose, and cladinose occur as constituents of antibiotic substances.

D-Glucose and L-glucose rotate polarized light dextro and levo, respectively, as D- and L-glyceric aldehyde do. However, the direction of rotation of a sugar may be opposite to the prefix. This is true, for example, in case of D- and L-arabinose and D- and L-fructose. D-Fructose is commonly called "levulose" because of its strong levorotation. The point to be emphasized is that the "D" or "L" prefix before a sugar designates it as configurationally related to the D or L form of glyceric aldehyde and is not intended to indicate the direction of rotation of the sugar. The rotations of a number of carbohydrates are given in Table 7.1.

REACTIONS OF MONOSACCHARIDES CHARACTERISTIC OF THE ALDEHYDE AND KETONE GROUPS

1. Reaction with hydrazines to form hydrazones and osazones. Phenylhydrazine and other substituted hydrazines react with the monosaccharides and other carbohydrates containing a free sugar group to form hydrazones and osazones. The reactions of glucose with phenylhydrazine may be used for illustration; as commonly given, they are:

$$
\begin{array}{c}
\text{H}-\text{C}=\text{O} \\
| \\
\text{H}-\text{C}-\text{OH} \\
| \\
\text{HO}-\text{C}-\text{H} \quad + \text{H}_2\text{N}-\text{NHC}_6\text{H}_5 \longrightarrow \text{H}_2\text{O} + \\
| \\
\text{H}-\text{C}-\text{OH} \\
| \\
\text{H}-\text{C}-\text{OH} \\
| \\
\text{CH}_2\text{OH} \\
\text{D-Glucose}
\end{array}
\qquad
\begin{array}{c}
\text{H}-\text{C}=\text{N}-\text{NHC}_6\text{H}_5 \\
| \\
\text{H}-\text{C}-\text{OH} \\
| \\
\text{HO}-\text{C}-\text{H} \quad + \text{H}_2\text{N}-\text{NHC}_6\text{H}_5 \longrightarrow \\
| \\
\text{H}-\text{C}-\text{OH} \\
| \\
\text{H}-\text{C}-\text{OH} \\
| \\
\text{CH}_2\text{OH} \\
\text{D-Glucose} \\
\text{phenylhydrazone}
\end{array}
$$

$$
\begin{array}{c}
\text{H}-\text{C}=\text{N}-\text{NHC}_6\text{H}_5 \\
| \\
\text{C}=\text{O} \\
\text{C}_6\text{H}_5\text{NH}_2 \quad | \\
\text{NH}_3 \quad + \text{HO}-\text{C}-\text{H} \quad + \text{H}_2\text{N}-\text{NHC}_6\text{H}_5 \longrightarrow \text{H}_2\text{O} + \\
| \\
\text{H}-\text{C}-\text{OH} \\
| \\
\text{H}-\text{C}-\text{OH} \\
| \\
\text{CH}_2\text{OH} \\
\text{Intermediate} \\
\text{product}
\end{array}
\qquad
\begin{array}{c}
\text{H}-\text{C}=\text{N}-\text{NHC}_6\text{H}_5 \\
| \\
\text{C}=\text{N}-\text{NHC}_6\text{H}_5 \\
| \\
\text{HO}-\text{C}-\text{H} \\
| \\
\text{H}-\text{C}-\text{OH} \\
| \\
\text{H}-\text{C}-\text{OH} \\
| \\
\text{CH}_2\text{OH} \\
\text{D-Glucose} \\
\text{phenylosazone}
\end{array}
$$

However, it appears that, although the above sequence of reactions represents the net result, the conversion of the phenylhydrazone to the phenylosazone actually involves a more complex mechanism because phenylhydrazine is a reducing rather than an oxidizing agent. Weygand (2) proposed that osazone formation may involve an Amadori rearrangement:

$$
\begin{array}{c}
\text{H} \\
| \\
\text{C}=\text{N}-\text{NH}-\text{C}_6\text{H}_5 \\
| \\
\text{H}-\text{C}-\text{OH} \\
| \\
\text{R} \\
\text{Phenylhydrazone}
\end{array}
\xrightleftharpoons[\text{rearrangement}]{\text{Amadori}}
\begin{array}{c}
\text{H} \\
| \\
\text{H}-\text{C}-\text{NH}-\text{NH}-\text{C}_6\text{H}_5 \\
| \\
\text{C}=\text{O} \\
| \\
\text{R}
\end{array}
\xrightleftharpoons{\text{H}_2\text{N}-\text{NH}-\text{C}_6\text{H}_5}
$$

$$
\begin{array}{c}
\text{H} \\
| \\
\text{H}-\text{C}-\text{NH}-\text{NH}-\text{C}_6\text{H}_5 \\
| \\
\text{C}=\text{N}-\text{NH}-\text{C}_6\text{H}_5 \\
| \\
\text{R}
\end{array}
\rightleftharpoons
\begin{array}{c}
\text{C}-\text{NH}-\text{NH}-\text{C}_6\text{H}_5 \\
\| \\
\text{C}-\text{NH}-\text{NH}-\text{C}_6\text{H}_5 \\
| \\
\text{R}
\end{array}
\longleftrightarrow \text{C}_6\text{H}_5\text{NH}_2 +
$$

$$
\begin{array}{c}
\text{H} \\
| \\
\text{C}=\text{NH} \\
| \\
\text{C}=\text{N}-\text{NH}-\text{C}_6\text{H}_5 \\
| \\
\text{R}
\end{array}
\xrightleftharpoons[-\text{H}_2\text{O}]{+\text{H}_2\text{O}}
\begin{array}{c}
\text{H} \\
| \\
\text{C}=\text{O} \\
| \\
\text{C}=\text{N}-\text{NH}-\text{C}_6\text{H}_5 \\
| \\
\text{R} \quad +\text{NH}_3
\end{array}
\xrightleftharpoons{\text{H}_2\text{N}-\text{NH}-\text{C}_6\text{H}_5}
\begin{array}{c}
\text{H} \\
| \\
\text{C}=\text{N}-\text{NH}-\text{C}_6\text{H}_5 \\
| \\
\text{C}=\text{N}-\text{NH}-\text{C}_6\text{H}_5 \\
| \\
\text{R} \\
\text{Phenylosazone}
\end{array} + \text{H}_2\text{O}
$$

Other mechanisms have been proposed. The chemistry of the hydrazones and osazones is discussed by Pigman in *The Carbohydrates*.

Fructose and other ketoses react similarly to form the hydrazones and osazones:

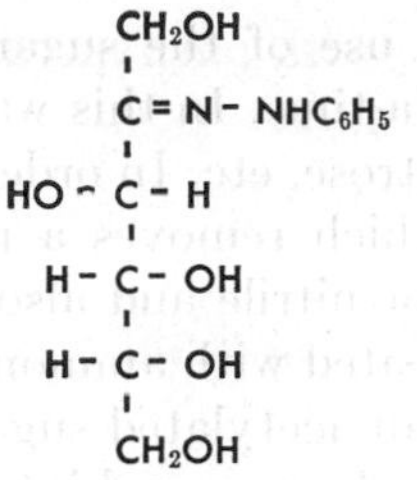

$$
\begin{array}{c}
CH_2OH \\
| \\
C = N - NHC_6H_5 \\
| \\
HO - C - H \\
| \\
H - C - OH \\
| \\
H - C - OH \\
| \\
CH_2OH
\end{array}
\qquad
\begin{array}{c}
H - C = N - NHC_6H_5 \\
| \\
C = N - NHC_6H_5 \\
| \\
HO - C - H \\
| \\
H - C - OH \\
| \\
H - C - OH \\
| \\
CH_2OH
\end{array}
$$

D-Fructose
phenylhydrazone

D-Fructose
 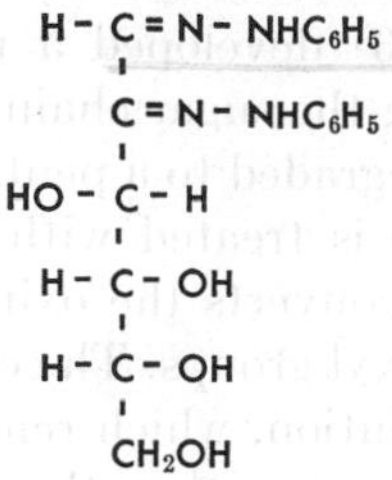
phenylosazone

With few exceptions the hydrazones are soluble and difficult to isolate. On the other hand, the osazones are relatively insoluble and crystallize in beautiful and characteristic forms for different sugars. It will be noted that the osazones formed from glucose, mannose, and fructose are identical, and by this fact Fischer demonstrated that the glucose, mannose, and fructose molecules are identical in the lower four carbon atoms. Similar relations were found for other groups of sugars, and thus the osazones became of prime importance in helping to determine the structural configurations of the sugars.

Osazones are hydrolyzed to the corresponding osones when treated with strong hydrochloric acid:

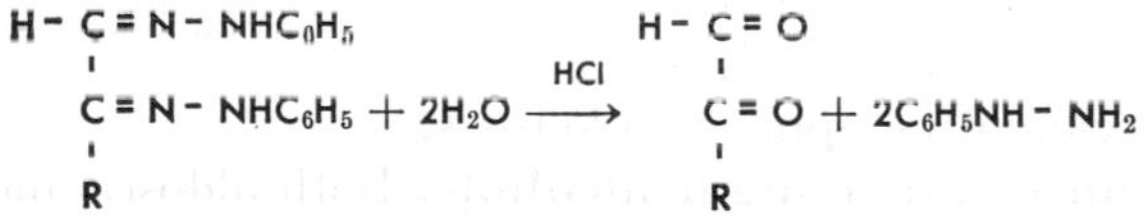

$$
\begin{array}{c}
H - C = N - NHC_6H_5 \\
| \\
C = N - NHC_6H_5 + 2H_2O \\
| \\
R
\end{array}
\xrightarrow{HCl}
\begin{array}{c}
H - C = O \\
| \\
C = O + 2C_6H_5NH - NH_2 \\
| \\
R
\end{array}
$$

Osazone   Osone

When osones are treated with zinc and acetic acid, the aldehyde group is preferentially reduced to form the corresponding ketose:

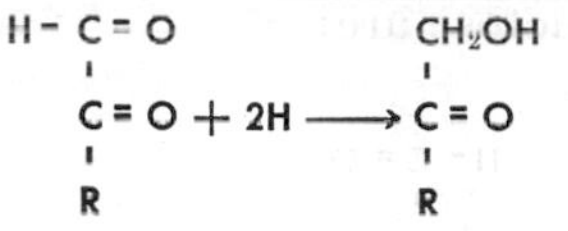

$$
\begin{array}{c}
H - C = O \\
| \\
C = O + 2H \\
| \\
R
\end{array}
\longrightarrow
\begin{array}{c}
CH_2OH \\
| \\
C = O \\
| \\
R
\end{array}
$$

Osone   Ketose

These reactions provide a method of converting an aldose into a ketose— for example, the conversion of glucose to fructose.

2. **Reaction with hydrogen cyanide to form cyanhydrins.** This reaction has been previously discussed and its importance in the synthesis of sugars pointed out (page 191).

3. **Reaction with hydroxylamine to form oximes.** Hydroxylamine condenses with aldoses and ketoses, as it does with ordinary aldehydes and ketones, to form oximes:

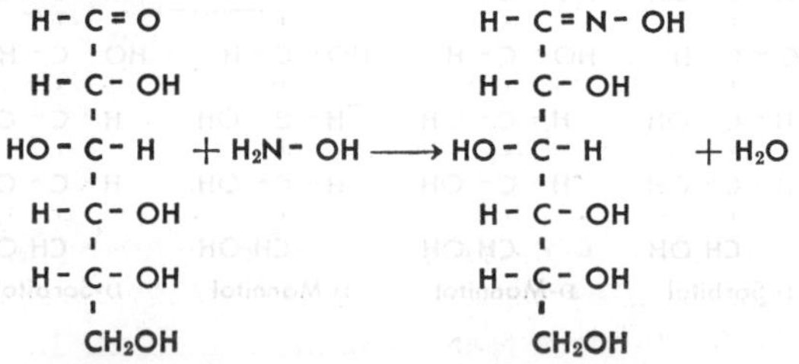

$$
\begin{array}{c}
H - C = O \\
| \\
H - C - OH \\
| \\
HO - C - H \\
| \\
H - C - OH \\
| \\
H - C - OH \\
| \\
CH_2OH
\end{array}
+ H_2N - OH \longrightarrow
\begin{array}{c}
H - C = N - OH \\
| \\
H - C - OH \\
| \\
HO - C - H \\
| \\
H - C - OH \\
| \\
H - C - OH \\
| \\
CH_2OH
\end{array}
+ H_2O
$$

D-Glucose   D-Glucose oxime

Wohl (3) developed a method, based upon use of the sugar oxime, of shortening the sugar chain one carbon atom at a time. In this way a hexose may be degraded to a pentose, a pentose to a tetrose, etc. In order to do this the oxime is treated with acetic anhydride, which removes a molecule of H_2O and converts the oxime to a cyanhydrin or nitrile and also acetylates the hydroxyl groups. The cyanhydrin is then treated with ammoniacal silver nitrate solution, which removes HCN to form an acetylated sugar with one less carbon atom than the original, which can be decomposed into the sugar. The process is shown in outline form as follows, the acetyl groups being omitted.

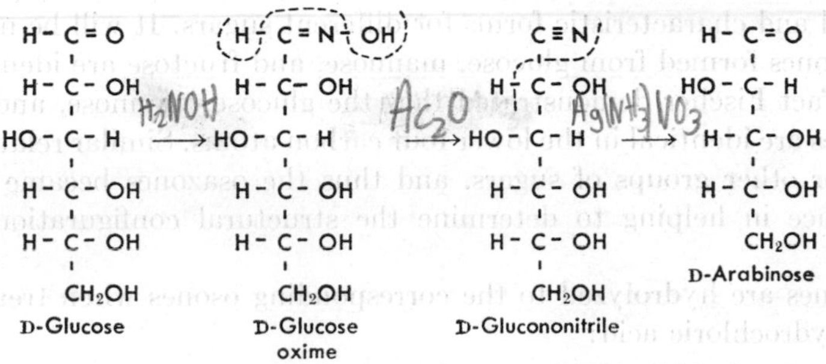

$$
\begin{array}{ccccc}
\text{H-C=O} & \text{H-C=N-OH} & \text{C}\equiv\text{N} & \text{H-C=O} \\
\text{H-C-OH} & \text{H-C-OH} & \text{H-C-OH} & \text{HO-C-H} \\
\text{HO-C-H} & \text{HO-C-H} & \text{HO-C-H} & \text{H-C-OH} \\
\text{H-C-OH} & \text{H-C-OH} & \text{H-C-OH} & \text{H-C-OH} \\
\text{H-C-OH} & \text{H-C-OH} & \text{H-C-OH} & \text{CH}_2\text{OH} \\
\text{CH}_2\text{OH} & \text{CH}_2\text{OH} & \text{CH}_2\text{OH} & \text{D-Arabinose} \\
\text{D-Glucose} & \text{D-Glucose} & \text{D-Glucononitrile} \\
 & \text{oxime}
\end{array}
$$

with reagents H_2NOH, Ac_2O, $AgNH_3NO_3$ between steps.

The process cannot be applied to ketoses.

4. Reduction to form sugar alcohols. Both aldoses and ketoses may be reduced to the corresponding polyhydroxy alcohols. This may be accomplished with sodium amalgam or, better, electrolytically or by hydrogen under high pressure in the presence of a catalyst. The alcohols formed from glucose, mannose, and fructose are:

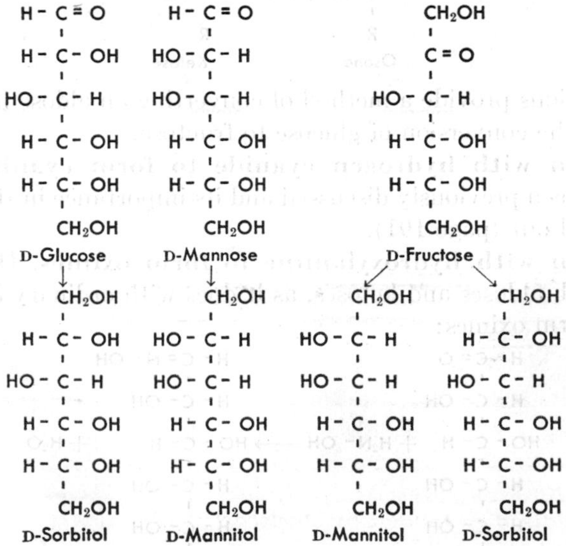

$$
\begin{array}{cccc}
\text{H-C=O} & \text{H-C=O} & & \text{CH}_2\text{OH} \\
\text{H-C-OH} & \text{HO-C-H} & & \text{C=O} \\
\text{HO-C-H} & \text{HO-C-H} & \text{HO-C-H} \\
\text{H-C-OH} & \text{H-C-OH} & \text{H-C-OH} \\
\text{H-C-OH} & \text{H-C-OH} & \text{H-C-OH} \\
\text{CH}_2\text{OH} & \text{CH}_2\text{OH} & \text{CH}_2\text{OH} \\
\text{D-Glucose} & \text{D-Mannose} & \text{D-Fructose} \\
\downarrow & \downarrow & \swarrow \qquad \searrow
\end{array}
$$

$$
\begin{array}{cccc}
\text{CH}_2\text{OH} & \text{CH}_2\text{OH} & \text{CH}_2\text{OH} & \text{CH}_2\text{OH} \\
\text{H-C-OH} & \text{HO-C-H} & \text{HO-C-H} & \text{H-C-OH} \\
\text{HO-C-H} & \text{HO-C-H} & \text{HO-C-H} & \text{HO-C-H} \\
\text{H-C-OH} & \text{H-C-OH} & \text{H-C-OH} & \text{H-C-OH} \\
\text{H-C-OH} & \text{H-C-OH} & \text{H-C-OH} & \text{H-C-OH} \\
\text{CH}_2\text{OH} & \text{CH}_2\text{OH} & \text{CH}_2\text{OH} & \text{CH}_2\text{OH} \\
\text{D-Sorbitol} & \text{D-Mannitol} & \text{D-Mannitol} & \text{D-Sorbitol}
\end{array}
$$

Each aldose yields the corresponding alcohol upon reduction, while a ketose forms two alcohols because of the appearance of a new asymmetric carbon atom in the process.

It is interesting to note that reduction of the ketohexose L-sorbose forms D-sorbitol and L-iditol:

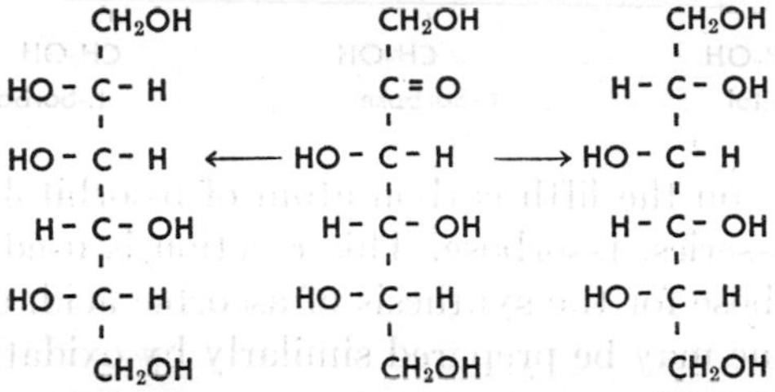

$$
\begin{array}{ccc}
\text{CH}_2\text{OH} & \text{CH}_2\text{OH} & \text{CH}_2\text{OH} \\
\text{HO—C—H} & \text{C}=\text{O} & \text{H—C—OH} \\
\text{HO—C—H} \longleftarrow & \text{HO—C—H} \longrightarrow & \text{HO—C—H} \\
\text{H—C—OH} & \text{H—C—OH} & \text{H—C—OH} \\
\text{HO—C—H} & \text{HO—C—H} & \text{HO—C—H} \\
\text{CH}_2\text{OH} & \text{CH}_2\text{OH} & \text{CH}_2\text{OH} \\
\text{D-Sorbitol} & \text{L-Sorbose} & \text{L-Iditol}
\end{array}
$$

If the above formula of D-sorbitol is rotated through 180 degrees in the plane of the paper, it will appear as the conventionally written formula of D-sorbitol.

Reduction of glyceric aldehyde and dihydroxyacetone forms the trihydroxy alcohol glycerol.

Erythritol is the reduction product of the aldotetrose erythrose.

Ribitol is the alcohol formed from the aldopentose ribose.

Reduction of galactose gives dulcitol.

The formulas of these sugar alcohols are:

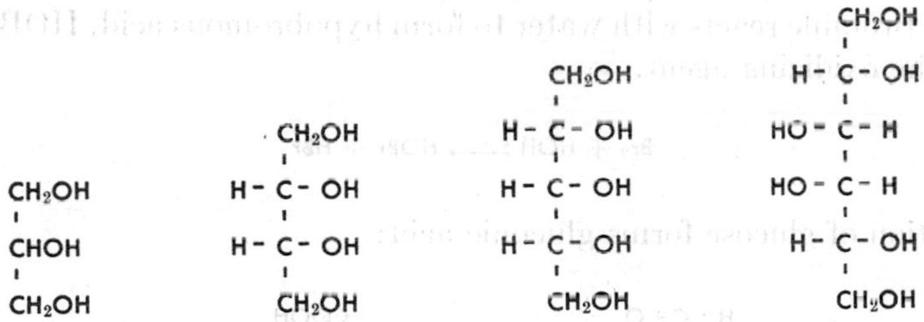

$$
\begin{array}{cccc}
 & & & \text{CH}_2\text{OH} \\
 & & \text{CH}_2\text{OH} & \text{H—C—OH} \\
 & \text{CH}_2\text{OH} & \text{H—C—OH} & \text{HO—C—H} \\
\text{CH}_2\text{OH} & \text{H—C—OH} & \text{H—C—OH} & \text{HO—C—H} \\
\text{CHOH} & \text{H—C—OH} & \text{H—C—OH} & \text{H—C—OH} \\
\text{CH}_2\text{OH} & \text{CH}_2\text{OH} & \text{CH}_2\text{OH} & \text{CH}_2\text{OH} \\
\text{Glycerol} & \text{Erythritol} & \text{Ribitol} & \text{Dulcitol}
\end{array}
$$

Each of these sugar alcohols is formed by reduction of both the D- and L-corresponding sugar, and the alcohols are not designated by either the "D" or the "L" prefix. They are optically inactive, though erythritol, ribitol, and dulcitol contain asymmetric carbon atoms. This is due to the fact that the molecules are symmetrical and are internally compensated relative to polarized light just as meso-tartaric acid is.

All the sugar alcohols discussed above are natural products.

As a class, the sugar alcohols are well-crystallized compounds, soluble in water and alcohol, and they have a sweet taste.

A number of the sugar alcohols may be oxidized to the corresponding ketoses by appropriate bacteria in the presence of oxygen. For example, D-sorbitol is oxidized as follows by *Acetobacter suboxidans:*

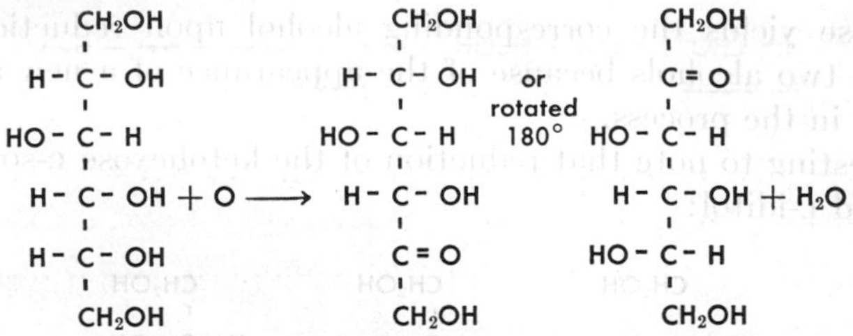

$$
\begin{array}{ccc}
\text{CH}_2\text{OH} & \text{CH}_2\text{OH} & \text{CH}_2\text{OH} \\
| & | & | \\
\text{H}-\text{C}-\text{OH} & \text{H}-\text{C}-\text{OH} \quad \text{or} & \text{C}=\text{O} \\
| & | \quad \text{rotated} & | \\
\text{HO}-\text{C}-\text{H} & \text{HO}-\text{C}-\text{H} \quad 180° & \text{HO}-\text{C}-\text{H} \\
| & | & | \\
\text{H}-\text{C}-\text{OH} + \text{O} \longrightarrow & \text{H}-\text{C}-\text{OH} & \text{H}-\text{C}-\text{OH} + \text{H}_2\text{O} \\
| & | & | \\
\text{H}-\text{C}-\text{OH} & \text{C}=\text{O} & \text{HO}-\text{C}-\text{H} \\
| & | & | \\
\text{CH}_2\text{OH} & \text{CH}_2\text{OH} & \text{CH}_2\text{OH} \\
\text{D-Sorbitol} & \text{L-Sorbose} & \text{L-Sorbose}
\end{array}
$$

Oxidation occurs on the fifth carbon atom of D-sorbitol to form a ketose belonging to the L-series, L-sorbose. This reaction is used to produce large quantities of L-sorbose for the synthesis of ascorbic acid, or vitamin C.

Dihydroxyacetone may be prepared similarly by oxidation of glycerol:

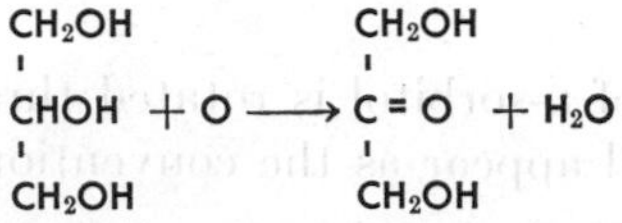

$$
\begin{array}{cc}
\text{CH}_2\text{OH} & \text{CH}_2\text{OH} \\
| & | \\
\text{CHOH} + \text{O} \longrightarrow & \text{C}=\text{O} + \text{H}_2\text{O} \\
| & | \\
\text{CH}_2\text{OH} & \text{CH}_2\text{OH} \\
\text{Glycerol} & \text{Dihydroxyacetone}
\end{array}
$$

5. Oxidation to produce sugar acids. When oxidized under the proper conditions, the aldoses may form monobasic aldonic acids, or dibasic saccharic acids, or monobasic uronic acids containing the aldehyde group.

a) Aldonic acids. Oxidation of an aldose with bromine water converts the aldehyde group to a carboxyl group and thereby forms the corresponding acid. Bromine reacts with water to form hypobromous acid, HOBr, which acts as the oxidizing agent.

$$ \text{Br}_2 + \text{HOH} \rightleftharpoons \text{HOBr} + \text{HBr} $$

Oxidation of glucose forms gluconic acid:

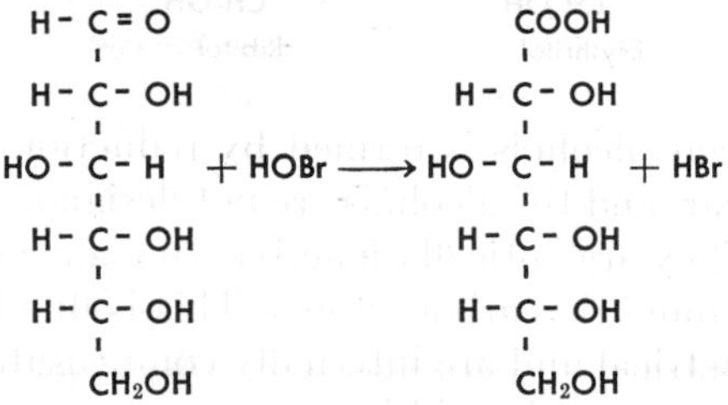

$$
\begin{array}{cc}
\text{H}-\text{C}=\text{O} & \text{COOH} \\
| & | \\
\text{H}-\text{C}-\text{OH} & \text{H}-\text{C}-\text{OH} \\
| & | \\
\text{HO}-\text{C}-\text{H} + \text{HOBr} \longrightarrow & \text{HO}-\text{C}-\text{H} + \text{HBr} \\
| & | \\
\text{H}-\text{C}-\text{OH} & \text{H}-\text{C}-\text{OH} \\
| & | \\
\text{H}-\text{C}-\text{OH} & \text{H}-\text{C}-\text{OH} \\
| & | \\
\text{CH}_2\text{OH} & \text{CH}_2\text{OH} \\
\text{D-Glucose} & \text{D-Gluconic acid}
\end{array}
$$

Similarly, mannose, galactose, and arabinose give mannonic, galactonic, and arabonic acids, respectively. Other aldoses form the corresponding aldonic acids. Ketoses are not readily oxidized by bromine water.

Aldoses are readily oxidized to aldonic acids by alkaline iodine solution, but ketoses are not oxidized. The reactions may be represented:

$$I_2 + 2NaOH \rightleftharpoons NaOI + NaI + H_2O$$
$$R-CHO + NaOI + NaOH \longrightarrow R-COONa + NaI + H_2O$$

An aldose   Aldonic acid
                                salt

Willstätter and Schudel (4) developed a method for the quantitative determination of aldoses based upon this oxidation.

When gluconic acid is heated, water is readily lost, and it forms a mixture of gamma (γ) and delta (δ) lactones:

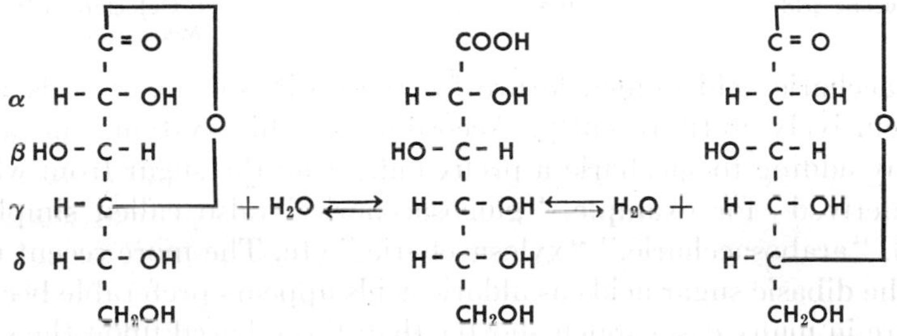

γ Gluconolactone   Gluconic acid   δ-Gluconolactone

In aqueous solutions an equilibrium is established between gluconic acid and its two lactones. Other sugar acids containing five or more carbon atoms similarly form two lactones. Acids with four carbon atoms can form only the gamma lactone.

Sugar acid lactones may be reduced to the corresponding sugars by treatment with sodium amalgam in the presence of dilute sulfuric acid.

When the calcium salts of aldonic acids are oxidized with hydrogen peroxide in the presence of Fe^{+++} ions as catalyst, carbon dioxide is split out and sugars of one less carbon are formed.

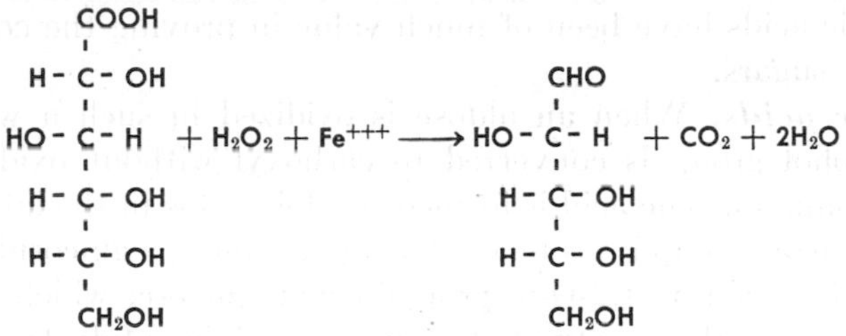

D-Gluconic acid   D-Arabinose
(as calcium salt)

A sugar may be oxidized to the corresponding aldonic acid, and this then converted to the sugar with one less carbon atom.

Calcium gluconate is often administered as a source of calcium. Solutions of it are given intravenously to raise the blood calcium.

b) *Saccharic or aldaric acids.* Oxidation of aldoses with nitric acid under the proper conditions converts both aldehyde and primary alcohol groups to carboxyl, forming dibasic sugar acids, the saccharic or aldaric acids:

```
        COOH                    COOH                    COOH
         |                       |                       |
   H - C - OH             HO - C - H              H - C - OH
         |                       |                       |
  HO - C - H              HO - C - H             HO - C - H
         |                       |                       |
   H - C - OH              H - C - OH             HO - C - H
         |                       |                       |
   H - C - OH              H - C - OH              H - C - OH
         |                       |                       |
        COOH                    COOH                    COOH
   D-Glucosaccharic acid   D-Mannosaccharic acid   D-Galactosaccharic acid
   D-Glucaric acid         D-Mannaric acid         D-Galactaric acid
                                                   Mucic acid
```

The saccharic acid nomenclature for these dibasic sugar acids has been used exclusively until recently. According to this system, the acids are named by adding to saccharic a prefix indicating the sugar from which the acid is derived—for example, "glucosaccharic" (also called simply "saccharic"), "arabosaccharic," "xylosaccharic," etc. The more recent designation of the dibasic sugar acids as aldaric acids appears preferable because the names are in many cases much shorter than those based upon the saccharic nomenclature. According to the aldaric acid system, the name of the acid from a sugar is the name of the sugar with the ending "-aric" replacing "-ose"—for example, "glucaric," "xylaric," "arabaric," "threaric," "hexaric" (from a hexose), "pentaric" (from a pentose), etc.

The aldaric acids form more complex mixtures of lactones than do the aldonic acids, due to the presence of two carboxyl groups.

The acid salts of the aldaric acids are often used in the identification of sugars because of their low solubility in water.

Galactaric (galactosaccharic) or mucic acid, produced by oxidation of galactose, is relatively insoluble in water and well crystallized, and its formation is used as a test for galactose in both the free and combined states.

The aldaric acids have been of much value in proving the configurations of the aldose sugars.

c) *Uronic acids.* When an aldose is oxidized in such a way that the primary alcohol group is converted to carboxyl without oxidation of the aldehyde group, a uronic acid is formed. In doing this in the laboratory, the aldehyde or sugar group is protected by conversion to a glucoside or the acetone derivative such as 1,2-O-isopropylidene-D-glucose, which may be oxidized by oxygen with an activated-platinum carbon catalyst:

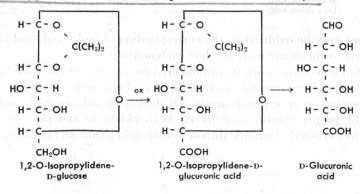

```
     H - C - O                  H - C - O                  CHO
             \                          \                   |
              C(CH3)2                     C(CH3)2      H - C - OH
             /                          /                   |
     H - C - O                  H - C - O             HO - C - H
         |                          |                       |
  HO - C - H           ox    HO - C - H                H - C - OH
         |             O ——>      |              O         |
   H - C - OH                 H - C - OH    ——>       H - C - OH
         |                          |                       |
   H - C                       H - C                       COOH
         |                          |
       CH2OH                      COOH
  1,2-O-Isopropylidene-     1,2-O-Isopropylidene-D-    D-Glucuronic
      D-glucose                glucuronic acid            acid
```

The isopropylidene group may be removed as acetone by careful acid hydrolysis to yield D-glucuronic acid:

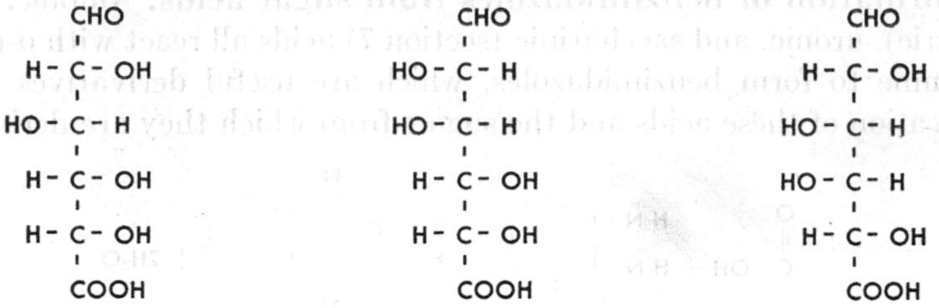

$$
\begin{array}{ccc}
\text{CHO} & \text{CHO} & \text{CHO} \\
\text{H}-\text{C}-\text{OH} & \text{HO}-\text{C}-\text{H} & \text{H}-\text{C}-\text{OH} \\
\text{HO}-\text{C}-\text{H} & \text{HO}-\text{C}-\text{H} & \text{HO}-\text{C}-\text{H} \\
\text{H}-\text{C}-\text{OH} & \text{H}-\text{C}-\text{OH} & \text{HO}-\text{C}-\text{H} \\
\text{H}-\text{C}-\text{OH} & \text{H}-\text{C}-\text{OH} & \text{H}-\text{C}-\text{OH} \\
\text{COOH} & \text{COOH} & \text{COOH} \\
\text{D-Glucuronic} & \text{D-Mannuronic acid} & \text{D-Galacturonic acid} \\
\text{or D-glycuronic acid} & &
\end{array}
$$

All three of these uronic acids are natural products.

D-Glucuronic acid occurs combined in plant materials. It is also a constituent of the chondroitin and mucoitin sulfuric acids of glycoproteins. Glucuronic acid is formed in the animal body in the process of detoxifying substances such as borneol, camphor, and benzoic acid, the glucuronic acid compounds of these substances being excreted in the urine. Glucuronic acid may be prepared in the laboratory by feeding borneol to a dog and hydrolyzing the borneol compound of glucuronic acid which is excreted in the urine.

D-Galacturonic acid is widely distributed as a constituent of pectins and many plant gums and mucilages. It may be conveniently prepared from pectin.

D-Mannuronic acid occurs as a polymer anhydride in alginic acid.

The decarboxylase enzyme of certain bacteria acts upon D-glucuronic acid to form the pentose D-xylose:

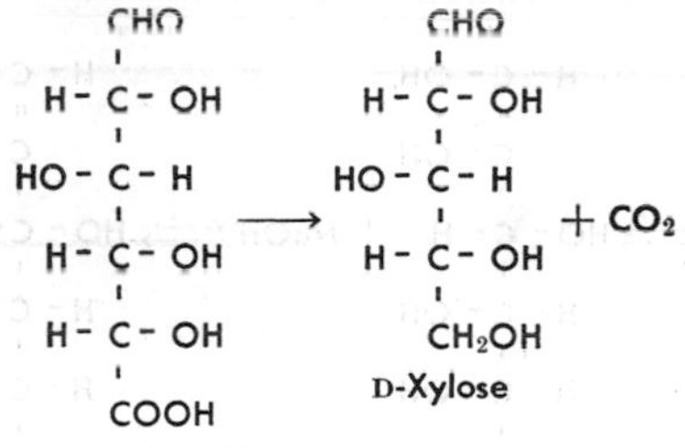

$$
\begin{array}{ccc}
\text{CHO} & \text{CHO} & \\
\text{H}-\text{C}-\text{OH} & \text{H}-\text{C}-\text{OH} & \\
\text{HO}-\text{C}-\text{H} & \text{HO}-\text{C}-\text{H} & \\
\text{H}-\text{C}-\text{OH} & \longrightarrow \quad \text{H}-\text{C}-\text{OH} & +\,CO_2 \\
\text{H}-\text{C}-\text{OH} & \text{CH}_2\text{OH} & \\
\text{COOH} & \text{D-Xylose} & \\
\text{D-Glucuronic acid} & &
\end{array}
$$

It is probable that at least some of the pentoses of plants are formed from hexoses through uronic acids in this way. Decarboxylation of D-galacturonic acid forms L-arabinose:

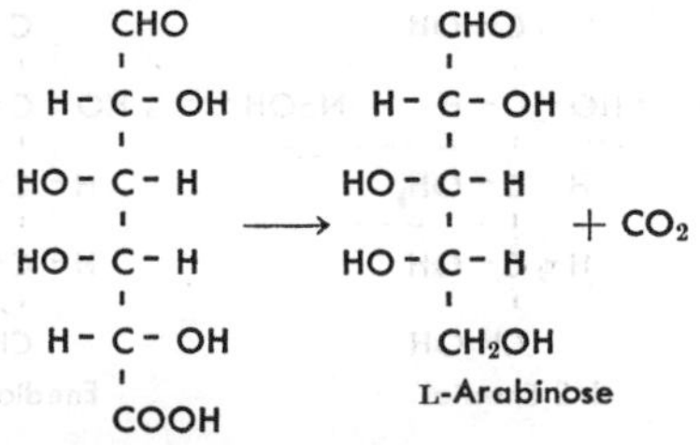

$$
\begin{array}{ccc}
\text{CHO} & \text{CHO} & \\
\text{H}-\text{C}-\text{OH} & \text{H}-\text{C}-\text{OH} & \\
\text{HO}-\text{C}-\text{H} & \text{HO}-\text{C}-\text{H} & \\
\text{HO}-\text{C}-\text{H} & \longrightarrow \quad \text{HO}-\text{C}-\text{H} & +\,CO_2 \\
\text{H}-\text{C}-\text{OH} & \text{CH}_2\text{OH} & \\
\text{COOH} & \text{L-Arabinose} & \\
\text{D-Galacturonic acid} & &
\end{array}
$$

In this connection it is interesting to note that D-xylose is generally associated with D-glucose in plants, while L-arabinose and D-galactose are associated.

6. Formation of benzimidazoles from sugar acids. Aldonic, aldaric (saccharic), uronic, and saccharinic (section 7) acids all react with o-phenylenediamine to form benzimidazoles, which are useful derivatives for the identification of these acids and the sugars from which they are derived (5).

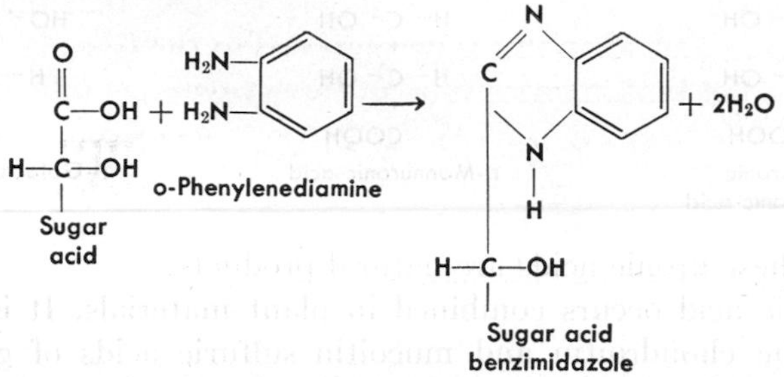

The reaction is carried out in the presence of hot acid.

7. Action of alkalies upon sugars. Sugars behave as very weak acids and form salts at high alkalinities. The pK values (pH at which acid is half converted to salt) of four common sugars are given below.

Sugar	pK_1	pK_2
Glucose	12.09	13.85
Fructose	11.68	13.24
Sucrose	12.60	13.52
Lactose	11.92	13.44

Monosaccharides, both aldoses and ketoses, and compound carbohydrates containing a free sugar group tautomerize and form the enol salt in alkaline solution.

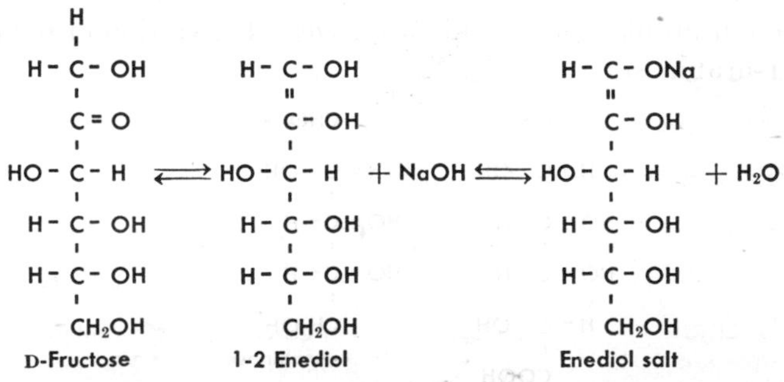

The enol forms of the sugars are enediols, because two hydroxyl groups are attached to the double-bonded carbon system. It is uncertain which enolic hydroxyl first reacts to form the salt.

It will be noted that glucose, mannose, and fructose form the same enediol and enediol salt forms. When a solution of any one of these sugars is allowed to stand in dilute alkali (0.05 N) for some time and then acidified, a mixture of all three sugars is obtained. This is due to the fact that they all give the same enediol salt, and when this is decomposed to the free enediol by acidification, the enediol tautomerizes into all three sugars as follows:

```
   H - C = O            H - C - OH           H - C = O
     |                      ‖     ⤡             |
  HO - C - H             C - OH             H - C - OH
     |                      |                   |
  HO - C - H  ⇌  HO - C - H  ⇌  HO - C - H
     |                      |                   |
   H - C - OH            H - C - OH           H - C - OH
     |                      |                   |
   H - C - OH            H - C - OH           H - C - OH
     |                      |                   |
    CH₂OH                 CH₂OH                CH₂OH
  D-Mannose          1-2 Enediol form        D-Glucose
```

$$CH_2OH$$

```
                          ⇅
                          H
                          |
                       H - C - OH
                          |
                        C = O
                          |
                      HO - C - H
                          |
                       H - C - OH
                          |
                       H - C - OH
                          |
                        CH₂OH
                      D-Fructose
```

This interconversion of related sugars by the action of dilute alkali is referred to as the Lobry de Bruyn-van Ekenstein reaction; it has been used for the synthesis of certain sugars.

When sugars with free sugar groups are treated with stronger alkali (0.5 N and stronger), enolization occurs to form not only 1-2, but also 2-3 and 3-4 enediols. The 2-3 and 3-4 enediols are apparently produced from the ketose sugars present in the mixture. An outline of the probable process is given below, glucose being used as the initial sugar:

```
                                          H                    H
                                          |                    |
   H - C = O         H - C - OH       H - C - OH           H - C - OH
     |                   ‖                |                    |
   H - C - OH          C - OH           C = O               C - OH
     |                   |                |                    |
  HO - C - H  ⇌  HO - C - H  ⇌  HO - C - H  ⇌  C - OH  ⇌
     |                   |                |                    |
   H - C - OH          H - C - OH       H - C - OH           H - C - OH
     |                   |                |                    |
   H - C - OH          H - C - OH       H - C - OH           H - C - OH
     |                   |                |                    |
    CH₂OH              CH₂OH             CH₂OH               CH₂OH
  D-Glucose         1-2 Enediol        D-Fructose         2-3 Enediol
```

$$
\begin{array}{ccc}
\text{H} & & \text{H} \\
| & & | \\
\text{H}-\text{C}-\text{OH} & & \text{H}-\text{C}-\text{OH} \\
| & & | \\
\text{H}-\text{C}-\text{OH} & & \text{H}-\text{C}-\text{OH} \\
| & & | \\
\text{C}=\text{O} & \rightleftharpoons & \text{C}-\text{OH} \\
| & & || \\
\text{H}-\text{C}-\text{OH} & & \text{C}-\text{OH} \\
| & & | \\
\text{H}-\text{C}-\text{OH} & & \text{H}-\text{C}-\text{OH} \\
| & & | \\
\text{CH}_2\text{OH} & & \text{CH}_2\text{OH} \\
\text{3-Ketose,} & & \text{3-4 Enediol} \\
\text{glutose} & &
\end{array}
$$

In strong alkali the enediol forms are very unstable and reactive. The enediols break at the double bond, forming a complex mixture of products. For example, a 1-2 enediol decomposes to give formaldehyde and a pentose; a 2-3 enediol gives glycollic aldehyde, $CH_2OH \cdot CHO$, and a tetrose; and a 3-4 enediol forms glyceric aldehyde, which is a triose. However, since aldoses formed by scission of the parent enediol may also enolize and rearrange, an extremely complicated mixture of sugars is produced. In the presence of oxygen or other oxidizing agent such as Cu^{++} (Fehling's solution) the acids corresponding to the various scission products of the alkaline mixture are obtained. For example, the following acids have been isolated from an oxidized alkaline sugar solution and identified: carbon dioxide, formic acid, glycollic acid, oxalic acid, DL-glyceric acid, four trihydroxybutyric acids, eight tetrahydroxyvaleric acids, and eight pentahydroxyhexoic acids.

Oxidation of the enediols involves rupture of the double bond with formation of shorter-chain acids:

$$
\begin{array}{ccc}
\text{H}-\text{C}-\text{OH} & & \text{H}\cdot\text{COOH} \\
|| & & \text{Formic acid} \\
\text{C}-\text{OH} & & \text{COOH} \\
| & \xrightarrow{\text{ox}} & | \\
\text{HO}-\text{C}-\text{H} & & \text{HO}-\text{C}-\text{H} \\
| & & | \\
\text{H}-\text{C}-\text{OH} & & \text{H}-\text{C}-\text{OH} \\
| & & | \\
\text{H}-\text{C}-\text{OH} & & \text{H}-\text{C}-\text{OH} \\
| & & | \\
\text{CH}_2\text{OH} & & \text{CH}_2\text{OH} \\
\text{D-Glucose} & & \text{D-Arabonic} \\
\text{enediol} & & \text{acid}
\end{array}
$$

When strongly alkaline solutions of sugars are permitted to stand in the absence of an oxidizing agent, a complex mixture of saccharinic acids is formed as a result of intramolecular oxidation-reduction and rearrangement. The formulas of a number of those that have been identified are:

$$
\begin{array}{cccc}
 & & \text{COOH} & \text{COOH} \quad \text{CH}_2\text{OH} \\
 & & | & \diagdown \diagup \\
 & & \text{CHOH} & \text{C(OH)} \\
 & & | & | \\
 & & \text{CH}_2 & \text{CH}_2 \\
\text{COOH} & & | & | \\
| & & \text{CHOH} & \text{CHOH} \\
\text{CHOH} & & | & | \\
| & & \text{CHOH} & \text{CH}_2\text{OH} \\
\text{CH}_3 & & | & \\
 & & \text{CH}_2\text{OH} & \\
\text{DL-Lactic} & & \text{meta-Saccharinic,} & \text{iso-Saccharinic,} \\
 & & \text{8 possible} & \text{4 possible}
\end{array}
$$

$$
\begin{array}{c}
\text{COOH CH}_3 \\
\diagdown \diagup \\
\text{C(OH)} \\
| \\
\text{CHOH} \\
| \\
\text{CHOH} \\
| \\
\text{CH}_2\text{OH}
\end{array}
$$

Saccharinic,
8 possible

$$
\begin{array}{c}
\text{COOH CH}_2\text{CH}_2\text{OH} \\
\diagdown \diagup \\
\text{C(OH)} \\
| \\
\text{CHOH} \\
| \\
\text{CH}_2\text{OH}
\end{array}
$$

para-Saccharinic,
4 possible

Lactic acid is apparently formed from glyceric aldehyde by intramolecular oxidation-reduction involving the first and third carbon atoms. It is generally formed in rather large amounts.

Lime water at ordinary temperature causes formaldehyde to polymerize to a sweet syrup, $C_6H_{12}O_6$, which Fischer called "formose." Fischer showed formose to be a complex mixture. Fischer and Tafel oxidized glycerol to form a mixture of dihydroxyacetone and glyceric aldehyde, treated the mixture with dilute alkali, and obtained a sweet syrup which was called "α-acrose." DL-Fructose was identified as a constituent of α-acrose.

$$
\begin{array}{c}
\text{CH}_2\text{OH} \\
| \\
\text{C = O} \\
| \\
\text{CH}_2\text{OH}
\end{array}
\quad + \quad
\begin{array}{c}
\text{CHO} \\
| \\
\text{CHOH} \\
| \\
\text{CH}_2\text{OH}
\end{array}
\quad \longrightarrow \quad
\begin{array}{c}
\text{CH}_2\text{OH} \\
| \\
\text{C = O} \\
| \\
\text{CHOH} \\
| \\
\text{CHOH} \\
| \\
\text{CHOH} \\
| \\
\text{CH}_2\text{OH}
\end{array}
$$

Dihydroxy-   DL-Glyceric   DL-Fructose
acetone   aldehyde

Three molecules of glycollic aldehyde, $CH_2OH \cdot CHO$, have also been found to polymerize to α-acrose when treated with dilute alkali.

The action of alkali upon formaldehyde and the lower sugars produces a very complex mixture of sugars.

Carbohydrates such as sucrose, which do not contain a free sugar group, are not enolized by alkali and are relatively stable in alkaline solution.

When sugars containing a free sugar group are heated with alkali, the solutions turn yellow to reddish brown as a result of the formation of complex resinous substances. This is known as Moore's test.

The sugar enediols exist in the cis and trans configurations about the double bond. Topper (6) has obtained evidence that the enzyme phosphoglucose isomerase acts stereospecifically upon H on C-2 of glucose-6-phosphate to form the cis-1,2-enediol, while the enzyme phosphomannose isomerase acts upon the H on C-2 of Mannose-6-phosphate to form the trans-1,2-enediol:

$$
\begin{array}{c}
\text{H - C = O} \\
| \\
\text{H - C - OH} \\
| \\
\text{HO - C - H} \\
| \\
\text{H - C - OH} \\
| \\
\text{H - C - OH} \quad \text{O} \\
| \qquad\qquad \| \\
\text{CH}_2 - \text{O - P - OH} \\
| \\
\text{OH}
\end{array}
$$

D-Glucose-6-PO$_4$
chain form

phosphoglucose
isomerase
$\xrightarrow{\qquad}$
$\xleftarrow{\qquad}$

$$
\begin{array}{c}
\text{H - C - OH} \\
\| \\
\text{C - OH} \\
| \\
\text{HO - C - H} \\
| \\
\text{H - C - OH} \\
| \\
\text{H - C - OH} \quad \text{O} \\
| \qquad\qquad \| \\
\text{CH}_2 - \text{O - P - OH} \\
| \\
\text{OH}
\end{array}
$$

D-Glucose-6-PO$_4$
cis-1,2-enediol

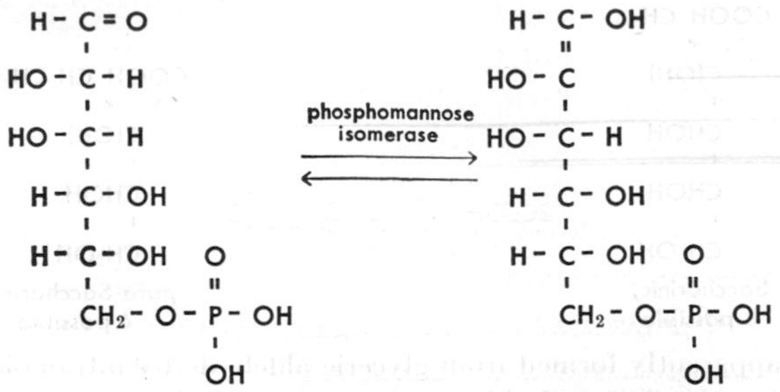

H – C = O   H – C – OH
  | ||
HO – C – H   HO – C
  | phosphomannose |
HO – C – H   isomerase   HO – C – H
  | ─────────────────────────▶ |
  | ◀───────────────────────── |
H – C – OH   H – C – OH
  | |
H – C – OH   O   H – C – OH   O
  | || | ||
CH$_2$ – O – P – OH   CH$_2$ – O – P – OH
             | |
            OH   OH

D-Mannose-6-PO$_4$ D-Mannose-6-PO$_4$
chain form   trans-1,2-enediol

Phosphoglucose isomerase will not act upon D-mannose-6-PO$_4$, and phosphomannose isomerase will not act upon D-glucose-6-PO$_4$.

8. Reducing action of sugars in alkaline solution. *Determination of sugars.*

All the sugars which contain the free sugar group undergo enolization and various other changes when placed in alkaline solution, as discussed in the previous section. There it was also pointed out that the enediol forms of the sugars are highly reactive and are easily oxidized by oxygen and other oxidizing agents. This means that these sugars in alkaline solution are very powerful reducing agents. As a consequence, they readily reduce oxidizing ions such as Ag$^+$, Hg^{++}, Bi^{+++}, Cu^{++}, and Fe(CN)$_6^{\equiv}$, and the sugars are oxidized to complex mixtures of acids. This reducing action of sugars in alkaline solution is utilized for both the qualitative and quantitative determination of sugars. Reagents containing Cu^{++} ions are most commonly used. These are generally alkaline solutions of cupric sulfate containing sodium potassium tartrate (rochelle salt) or sodium citrate. Sodium or potassium hydroxide is used as the alkali in the older reagents, such as Fehling's solution; but weaker alkalies, such as sodium carbonate and sodium bicarbonate, are used in the more recent reagents, such as those of Benedict, Folin, and Shaffer and Hartmann. The student should consult laboratory manuals of biochemistry for the details of these reagents and their use. The general principles upon which they function are the same.

Citrate and rochelle salt in the reagents prevent precipitation of cupric hydroxide or carbonate by forming soluble, slightly dissociated complexes with the Cu^{++} ions. These complexes dissociate sufficiently to provide a continuous supply of readily available Cu^{++} ions for oxidation but at concentrations which prevent the solubility products of cupric hydroxide and carbonate being exceeded.

The alkali of the sugar reagents enolizes the sugars and thereby causes them to be strong reducing agents.

When a reducing sugar is heated with one of the alkaline copper reagents, the processes shown below occur:

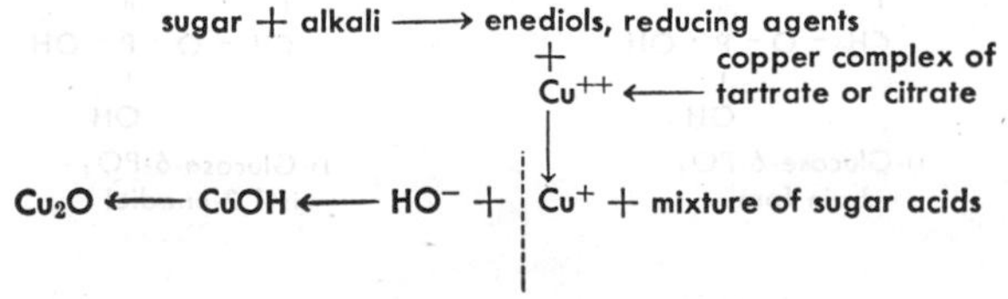

sugar + alkali ⟶ enediols, reducing agents
                              +   copper complex of
                           Cu^{++} ◀──── tartrate or citrate
                              │
                              ▼
Cu$_2$O ◀──── CuOH ◀──── HO$^-$ + Cu$^+$ + mixture of sugar acids

The Cu^{++} ions take electrons from the enediols and oxidize them to sugar acids and are in turn reduced to cuprous ions, Cu$^+$. The cuprous ions combine with hydroxyl ions to form yellow cuprous hydroxide, which upon heating is converted to red cuprous oxide, Cu$_2$O:

$$2CuOH \longrightarrow Cu_2O + H_2O$$

The appearance of a yellow-to-red precipitate indicates reduction, and the quantity of sugar present can be roughly estimated from the amount of precipitate. In quantitative determinations the amount of copper reduced is obtained by iodometric titration or colorimetric methods, and from this the amount of sugar is calculated.

Alkaline solutions of ferricyanide, K$_3$Fe(CN)$_6$, are also used in the quantitative determination of sugars, the most common reagent being that of Hagedorn and Jensen. These are stronger oxidizing solutions than the copper reagents and are more liable to oxidize nonsugars present than the copper reagents are. Their action involves oxidation of the sugar enediols by the ferricyanide ion, Fe(CN)$_6^\equiv$, which is reduced to the ferrocyanide ion, Fe(CN)$_6^\equiv$. The amount of ferricyanide reduced is easily determined by iodine titration, and from this the quantity of sugar is obtained.

Polysaccharides such as glycogen and starch are generally quantitatively determined by preliminary hydrolysis with acid to the constituent monosaccharides, which are then estimated by one of the above reduction methods.

An interesting determination of D-glucose is based upon its quantitative oxidation to D-gluco-δ-lactone in the presence of molecular oxygen by the enzyme D-glucose oxidase. The lactone is converted to D-gluconic acid, which is then titrated with alkali (7).

Hydrogen peroxide also is formed in the oxidation which is used as the basis of a very sensitive colorimetric method for glucose determination (8):

$$Glucose + O_2 \xrightarrow[\text{oxidase}]{\text{glucose}} gluconolactone + H_2O_2$$

$$\downarrow +H_2O$$

D-Gluconic acid

$$H_2O_2 + \text{o-dianisidine} \xrightarrow{\text{peroxidase}} \text{yellow compound}$$

A very useful method for the colorimetric determination of carbohydrates is based upon the reaction of anthrone with a carbohydrate in the presence of strong sulfuric acid (9). The carbohydrate is decomposed by the acid to give a substance, probably a furfural derivative, which reacts with anthrone to form a blue compound. The reaction is given by both free and combined sugars and is very sensitive:

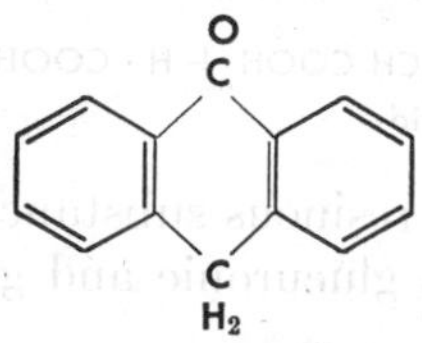

Anthrone

Various other colorimetric methods for the determination of sugars have been developed based upon reaction in acid solution with reagents such as carbazole and orcinol (see Pigman, *The Carbohydrates*).

9. Action of acids upon carbohydrates. Polysaccharides and the compound carbohydrates in general are hydrolyzed into their constituent monosaccharides by boiling with dilute (0.5–1.0 N) mineral acids, such as hydrochloric or sulfuric.

In general the monosaccharides are relatively stable to these hot dilute acids, though the ketoses are appreciably decomposed by prolonged action. When the concentration of acid is increased to several normalities, the monosaccharide molecules are decomposed. Pentoses yield the cyclic aldehyde furfural, as illustrated by the reaction for ribose:

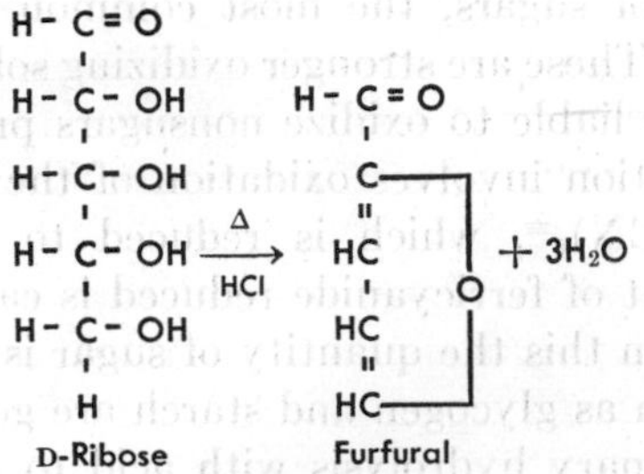

$$H-C=O$$
$$H-C-OH \qquad H-C=O$$
$$H-C-OH \qquad\quad C$$
$$H-C-OH \xrightarrow[HCl]{\Delta} HC \quad\bigg| \quad + 3H_2O$$
$$H-C-OH \qquad\quad HC \quad O$$
$$H \qquad\qquad HC$$
$$\text{D-Ribose} \qquad \text{Furfural}$$

This reaction is used for the quantitative determination of pentoses and compound carbohydrates containing pentoses (pentosans, etc.). Twelve per cent hydrochloric acid has been found the most satisfactory acid for decomposition. Furfural forms, with phloroglucinol, a relatively insoluble compound, furfural-phloroglucide, which may be used in estimating the furfural formed in the reaction as a measure of the pentose present. The furfural may also be determined by use of its color reaction with aniline acetate or by a titrimetric reaction.

Hexoses are decomposed by hot strong acid to give hydroxymethylfurfural, which decomposes into levulinic acid and other products:

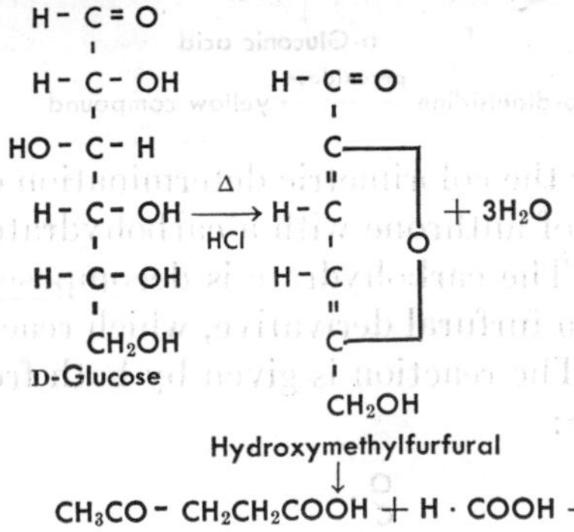

$$H-C=O$$
$$H-C-OH \qquad H-C=O$$
$$HO-C-H \qquad\quad C$$
$$H-C-OH \xrightarrow[HCl]{\Delta} H-C \quad\bigg| \quad + 3H_2O$$
$$H-C-OH \qquad\quad H-C \quad O$$
$$CH_2OH \qquad\quad C$$
$$\text{D-Glucose} \qquad CH_2OH$$
$$\text{Hydroxymethylfurfural}$$
$$\downarrow$$
$$CH_3CO-CH_2CH_2COOH + H\cdot COOH + CO + CO_2$$
$$\text{Levulinic acid}$$

Considerable brown or black resinous substances are also formed.

When uronic acids such as glucuronic and galacturonic acids are heated with acid, they lose carbon dioxide and form the corresponding pentose, which in turn is converted to furfural:

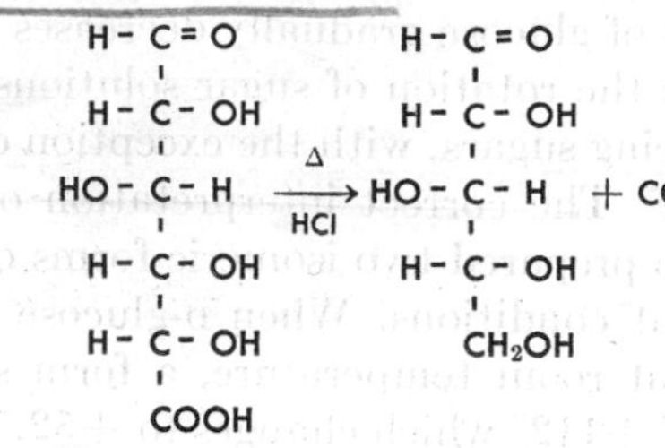

$$
\begin{array}{ccc}
\text{H} - \text{C} = \text{O} & & \text{H} - \text{C} = \text{O} \\
| & & | \\
\text{H} - \text{C} - \text{OH} & & \text{H} - \text{C} - \text{OH} \\
| & \overset{\Delta}{\underset{\text{HCl}}{\longrightarrow}} & | \\
\text{HO} - \text{C} - \text{H} & & \text{HO} - \text{C} - \text{H} \quad + \text{CO}_2 \\
| & & | \\
\text{H} - \text{C} - \text{OH} & & \text{H} - \text{C} - \text{OH} \\
| & & | \\
\text{H} - \text{C} - \text{OH} & & \text{CH}_2\text{OH} \\
| & & \\
\text{COOH} & & \\
\text{D-Glucuronic acid} & & \text{D-Xylose}
\end{array}
$$

The yield of carbon dioxide is quantitative, and uronic acids are determined by estimating the amount liberated in the above reaction. The yield of furfural from the pentose in this reaction is not quantitative.

RING STRUCTURES AND TAUTOMERIC FORMS OF THE SUGARS

The preceding discussion of the monosaccharides has considered them chain compounds containing the aldehyde or ketone group. It is now well established that in the crystalline state the monosaccharides containing five or more carbon atoms exist in tautomeric ring forms. Even in solution these sugars exist almost entirely in ring forms, which are in dynamic equilibria with very small amounts of the chain forms.

Ring forms and mutarotation of sugars. Schiff's reagent for aldehydes consists of a solution of the dye fuchsine to which just sufficient sulfurous acid has been added to combine with and decolorize the dye. When an aldehyde is added to the reagent, the aldehyde removes the sulfurous acid from the dye and restores its color. The aldoses containing four or more carbons do not restore the color to Schiff's reagent, because they exist chiefly in ring forms and not enough aldehyde form is present to give a positive test.

Fischer treated glucose with methyl alcohol and hydrogen chloride and obtained a product which van Ekenstein showed consisted of two isomeric methyl derivatives of glucose. These substances had specific rotations of +159° and −34° and were named "α-methyl-D-glucoside" and "β-methyl-D-glucoside," respectively. They have been shown to possess ring structures as follows:

$$
\begin{array}{cc}
\begin{array}{l}
\quad \text{H} \quad\quad \text{OCH}_3 \\
\quad\quad \text{C} \\
| \\
\text{H} - \text{C} - \text{OH} \\
| \\
\text{HO} - \text{C} - \text{H} \quad \text{O} \\
| \\
\text{H} - \text{C} - \text{OH} \\
| \\
\text{H} - \text{C} \\
| \\
\quad \text{CH}_2\text{OH} \\
\text{α-Methyl-D-glucoside} \\
(\alpha)_\text{D} = +159°
\end{array}
&
\begin{array}{l}
\quad \text{CH}_3\text{O} \quad\quad \text{H} \\
\quad\quad \text{C} \\
| \\
\text{H} - \text{C} - \text{OH} \\
| \\
\text{HO} - \text{C} - \text{H} \quad \text{O} \\
| \\
\text{H} - \text{C} - \text{OH} \\
| \\
\text{H} - \text{C} \\
| \\
\quad \text{CH}_2\text{OH} \\
\text{β-Methyl-D-glucoside} \\
(\alpha)_\text{D} = -34°
\end{array}
\end{array}
$$

It will be seen that carbon 1 has become asymmetric; this accounts for the two isomers. Dubrunfaut first noticed that the optical rotation of a freshly prepared solution of glucose gradually decreases and finally becomes constant. This change in the rotation of sugar solutions upon standing is a general property of reducing sugars, with the exception of some ketoses, and is called "mutarotation." The correct interpretation of mutarotation was provided by Tanret, who prepared two isomeric forms of D-glucose by crystallization under different conditions. When D-glucose is crystallized from water or dilute alcohol at room temperature, a form separates having an initial specific rotation of +112° which changes to +52.5°. If, however, crystallization takes place from water at temperatures above 98° C, a different form of glucose, having an initial specific rotation of +19° which changes to +52.5°, is obtained. The first of these isomers of glucose was called "α-D-glucose" and the second "β-D-glucose":

$$\alpha\text{-D-Glucose} \qquad \beta\text{-D-Glucose}$$
$$+112° \longrightarrow +52.5° \longleftarrow +19°$$

This work of Tanret showed that glucose exists in isomeric forms which in solution change into the same equilibrium mixture regardless of which form is dissolved:

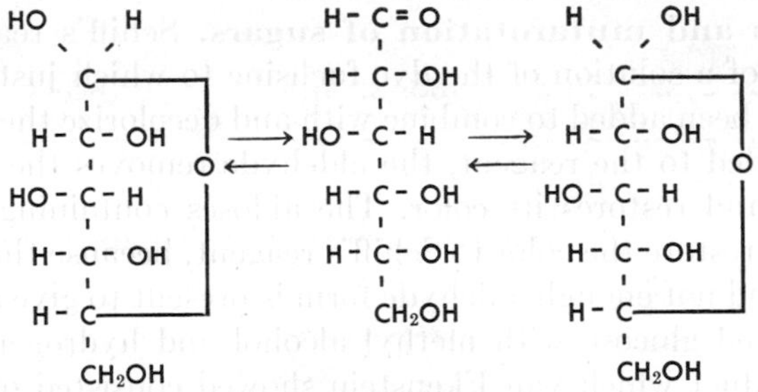

β-D-Glucose +19°   Chain form of D-glucose, only trace present   α-D-Glucose +112°

In glucose solutions approximately two-thirds of the sugar exists as the β form at equilibrium. While hours may be required for the completion of mutarotation and the attainment of equilibrium in pure solution, the addition of hydroxyl or hydrogen ions catalyzes the process. Hydroxyl ions are about 40,000 times as efficient as hydrogen ions as catalyst.

The α- and β-methyl-D-glucosides are the methyl derivatives of α- and β-D-glucose, respectively.

An equilibrium between the ring forms and the chain form exists in solutions of all aldose sugars containing four or more carbon atoms. The keto-hexose, fructose, mutarotates, and benzoyl derivatives of ring and chain forms have been obtained. It appears that the equilibrium for fructose in aqueous solution is:

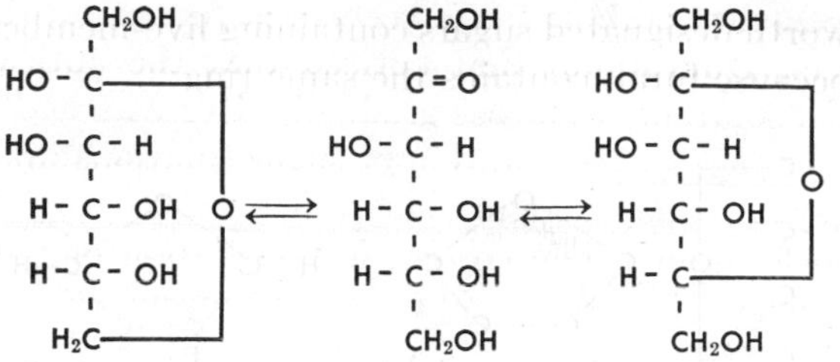

β-D-Fructose or β-D-fructopyranose six-membered ring   D-Fructose keto form   β-D-Fructofuranose five-membered ring

It will be noted that both ring forms of fructose are β forms, but that one ring contains five carbon atoms and the other four. The α form of fructose containing a five-carbon ring and corresponding to β-D-fructopyranose has been prepared.

The α and β forms of the sugars are also called "anomers." Thus we have the α and β anomeric forms, or the α and β anomers. The asymmetric carbon atom giving rise to the α and β forms, carbon number 1, is called the "anomeric carbon atom."

Evidence has been presented that the sugar osazones as well as the sugars exist in both chain and ring forms (see Percival in *Advances in Carbohydrate Chemistry*, Vol. 3, 1948):

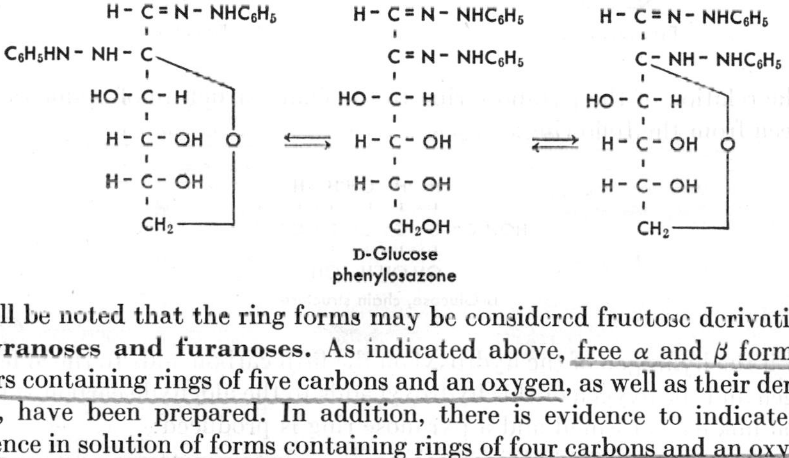

D-Glucose phenylosazone

It will be noted that the ring forms may be considered fructose derivatives.

Pyranoses and furanoses. As indicated above, free α and β forms of sugars containing rings of five carbons and an oxygen, as well as their derivatives, have been prepared. In addition, there is evidence to indicate the presence in solution of forms containing rings of four carbons and an oxygen, and derivatives containing such rings have been prepared.

Haworth (10) has suggested that the six-membered ring forms of the sugars be called "pyranoses," because pyran possesses the same ring of five carbons and an oxygen:

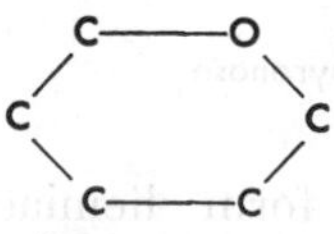

Pyranose structure 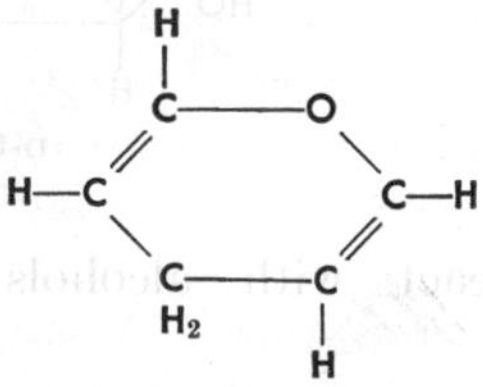   Pyran

Similarly, Haworth designated sugars containing five-membered rings as the "furanoses" because furan contains the same ring:

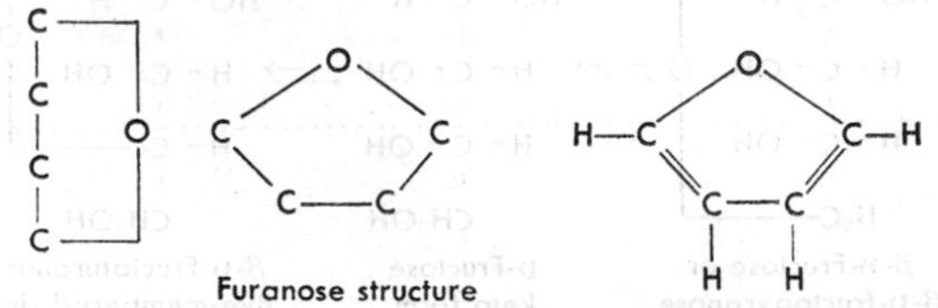

Furanose structure   Furan

The pyranose and furanose ring structures of the sugars proposed by Haworth more accurately represent their actual configurations than do the older structures used by Fischer and other early workers, though the older ring forms are still used extensively in writing reactions of the sugars because of their convenience in writing and the greater ease of interpreting the configurations. It is customary in writing pyranose and furanose rings to leave out the C atoms and write them as follows:

Pyranose ring 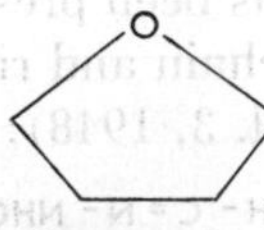   Furanose ring

The relation of the pyranose ring to the chain structure of D-glucose may be seen from the following:

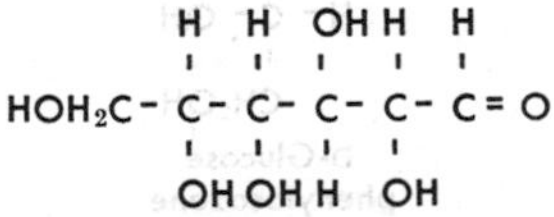

$$\underset{\text{OH OH H\quad OH}}{\overset{\text{H\quad H\quad OH H\quad H}}{\text{HOH}_2\text{C}-\text{C}-\text{C}-\text{C}-\text{C}-\text{C}=\text{O}}}$$

D-Glucose, chain structure

Now if the hydrogen of the hydroxyl on the fifth carbon adds to the aldehyde oxygen and the oxygen of this hydroxyl adds to the aldehyde carbon, a hemiacetal linkage is formed and a pyranose ring is produced:

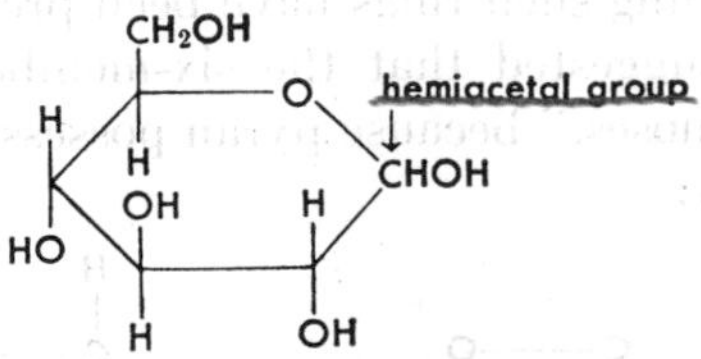

D-Glucopyranose

Aldehydes react with alcohols to form hemiacetals and acetals as follows:

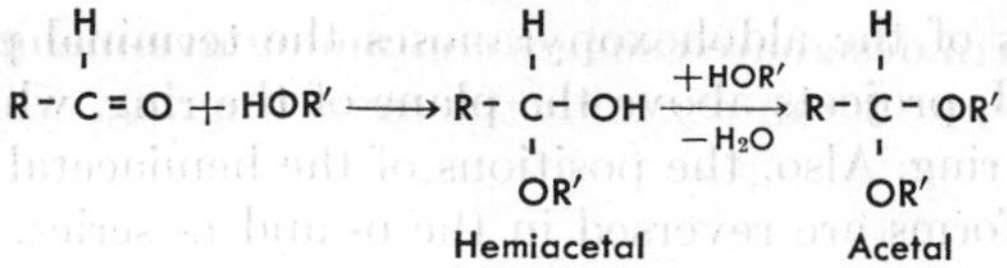

$$\overset{\text{H}}{\underset{}{\text{R}-\text{C}=\text{O}}} + \text{HOR}' \longrightarrow \overset{\text{H}}{\underset{\overset{|}{\text{OR}'}}{\text{R}-\text{C}-\text{OH}}} \xrightarrow[-\text{H}_2\text{O}]{+\text{HOR}'} \overset{\text{H}}{\underset{\overset{|}{\text{OR}'}}{\text{R}-\text{C}-\text{OR}'}}$$

Hemiacetal   Acetal

Thus it can be seen that the reaction of a hydroxyl hydrogen in a sugar with

the aldehyde group forms a hemiacetal group, $\overset{\text{H}}{\underset{\overset{|}{\text{O}}}{\text{R}-\text{C}-\text{OH}}}$.

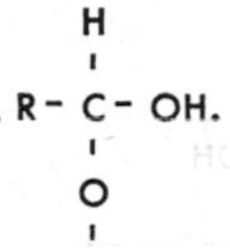

The formulas of a number of sugars according to both the older Fischer ring structures and the pyranose and furanose structures of Haworth are given below for comparison:

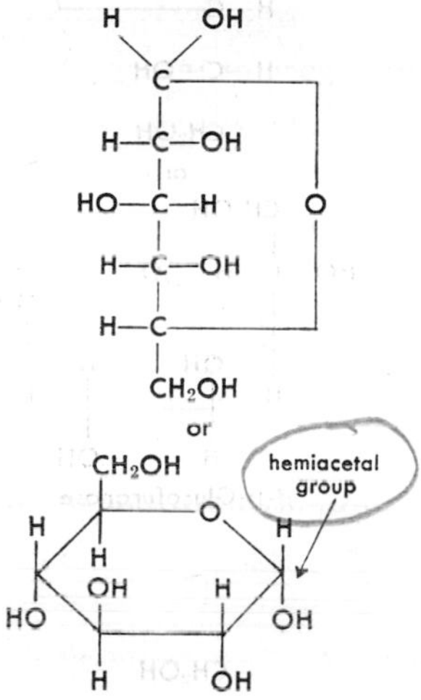

α-D-Glucopyranose

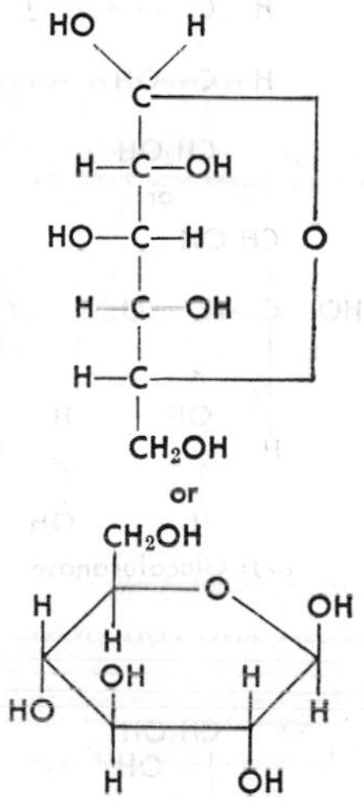

β-D-Glucopyranose

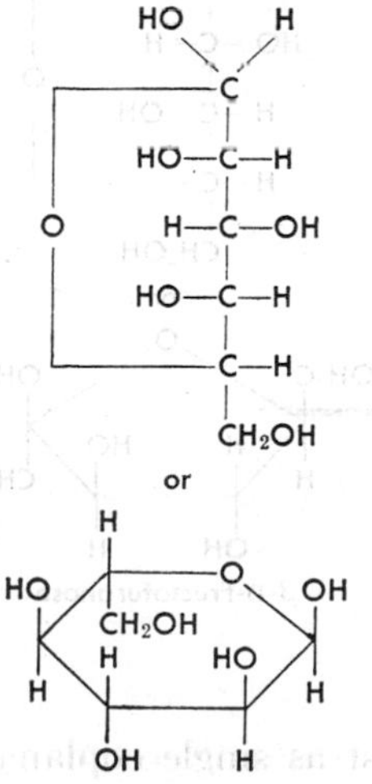

α-L-Glucopyranose

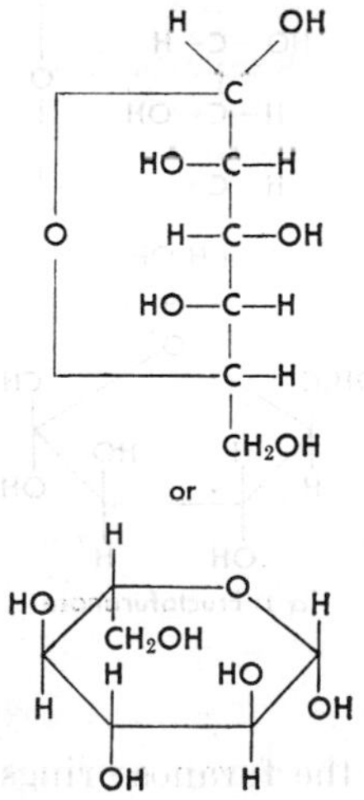

β-L-Glucopyranose

In the D-series of the aldohexopyranoses the terminal primary alcoholic group, —CH₂OH, projects above the plane of the ring, while in the L-series it lies below the ring. Also, the positions of the hemiacetal hydroxyl groups in the α and β forms are reversed in the D- and L- series. The α-D and β-L hydroxyl groups lie below the plane of the ring, while the β-D and α-L hydroxyls are above the plane of the ring:

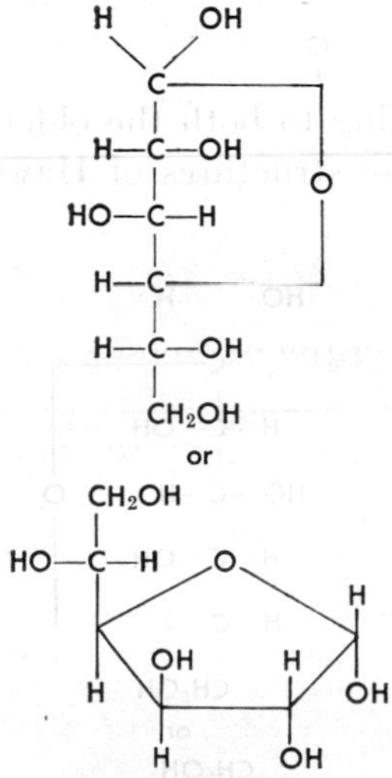

α-D-Glucofuranose

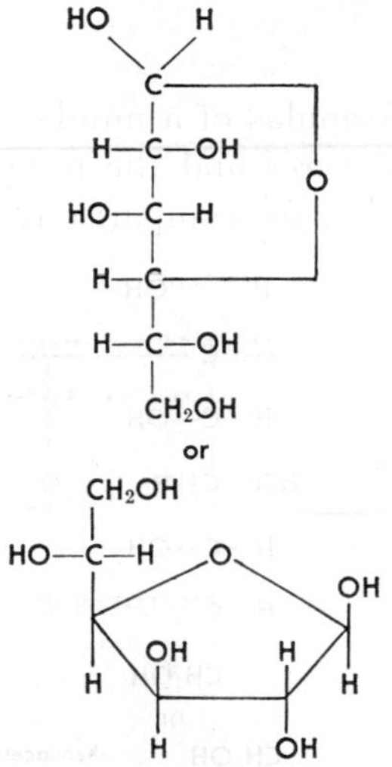

β-D-Glucofuranose

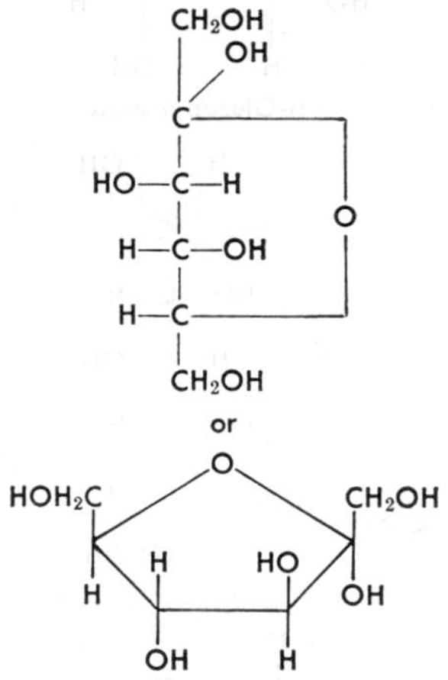

α-D-Fructofuranose

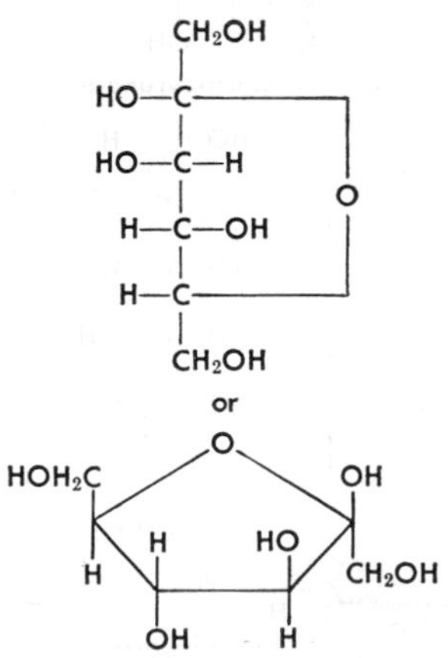

β-D-Fructofuranose

While the furanose rings of the sugars exist as single coplanar strained rings, the pyranose rings are puckered strainless rings (11). There are eight strainless rings possible for each α- and β-pyranose, representatives of which are illustrated below:

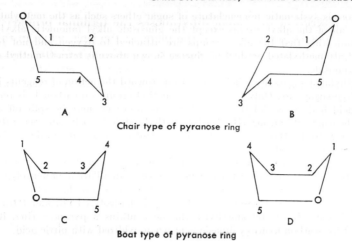

Chair type of pyranose ring

Boat type of pyranose ring

It appears that the common configurations of the pyranose rings are chair forms such as A and B. In solutions of the free sugars, where the ring form is in equilibrium with the aldehyde form, there is a mixture of the various ring types in equilibrium; but sugar derivatives, such as the glucosides in which the ring is fixed, probably are stabilized usually in chair forms.

Proof of ring structures of sugars by the use of methylated sugars. Purdie and Irvine showed that the glucosides of sugars may be completely methylated by treatment with methyl iodide and silver oxide. In this process a methyl group replaces the hydrogen of each hydroxyl group:

$$H-\overset{|}{\underset{|}{C}}-OH + ICH_3 \longrightarrow H-\overset{|}{\underset{|}{C}}-O-CH_3 + HI$$

$$2HI + Ag_2O \longrightarrow 2AgI + H_2O$$

The silver oxide promotes the reaction by removing the HI. Haworth (12) devised a better methylation procedure based upon reaction of the sugar glucosides or the free sugars with dimethyl sulfate and alkali. The methylation of a hydroxyl group by these reagents proceeds as follows:

$$H-\overset{|}{\underset{|}{C}}-OH + \overset{CH_3}{\underset{CH_3}{\diagup}}SO_4 + NaOH \longrightarrow H-\overset{|}{\underset{|}{C}}-OCH_3 + CH_3-S\bar{O}_4Na^+ + H_2O$$

When α- or β-methyl glucoside or the free sugar is treated with alkali and dimethyl sulfate under proper conditions, all the free hydroxyl groups are methylated to form pentamethylated glucose, which is a mixture of the α and β forms when the free sugar is methylated:

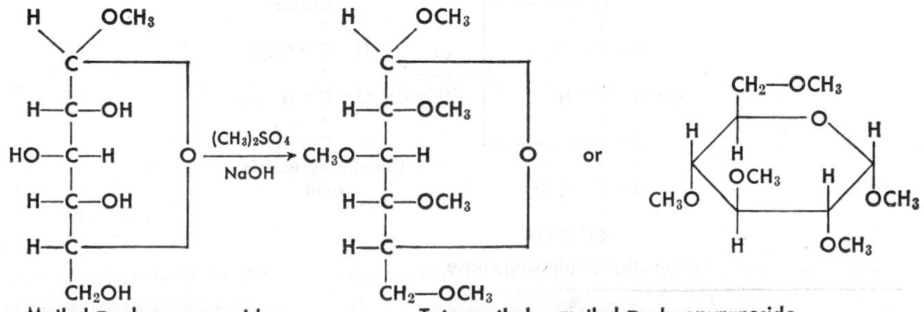

H OCH₃		H OCH₃		CH₂—OCH₃

$$
\begin{array}{c}
H \quad OCH_3 \\
\diagdown C \diagup \\
| \\
H-C-OH \\
| \\
HO-C-H \\
| \\
H-C-OH \\
| \\
H-C \\
| \\
CH_2OH
\end{array}
\quad
\xrightarrow[\text{NaOH}]{(CH_3)_2SO_4}
\quad
\begin{array}{c}
H \quad OCH_3 \\
\diagdown C \diagup \\
| \\
H-C-OCH_3 \\
| \\
CH_3O-C-H \\
| \\
H-C-OCH_3 \\
| \\
H-C \\
| \\
CH_2-OCH_3
\end{array}
\quad \text{or}
$$

α-Methyl-D-glucopyranoside

Tetramethyl-α-methyl-D-glucopyranoside
Pentamethyl-D-glucopyranose
Tetra-O-methyl-α-methyl-D-glucopyranoside

The rigorous systematic nomenclature of sugar ethers such as the methylated sugars designates all of the alkyl groups except the glucoside alkyl (anomeric alkyl) as "-O-alkyls," indicating that the alkyl groups are attached to oxygen and not to carbon. Thus the fully methylated product of glucose shown above is tetra-O-methyl-α-methyl-D-glucopyranoside.

The methylated sugars are much more stable toward the action of reagents in general than the free sugars are. Only the glucoside methyl group (on carbon I) is removed by ordinary acid hydrolysis. All the methyl groups, however, may be split off as methyl iodide by heating with strong HI, and the methyl iodide is easily and accurately determined quantitatively, thereby affording an excellent method of determining the number of methyl groups present.

The methylated sugars are readily soluble in organic solvents and may be purified by crystallization from them. They also may be purified by distillation, preferably in vacuum.

When pentamethyl glucose, which is tetramethyl-methyl-D-glucoside, is boiled with dilute mineral acid, the glucoside methyl group is hydrolyzed off, and tetramethyl-D-glucose is formed. If the tetramethyl-D-glucose contains a pyranose ring, it forms a methylated five-carbon hydroxy dibasic acid when oxidized with nitric acid.

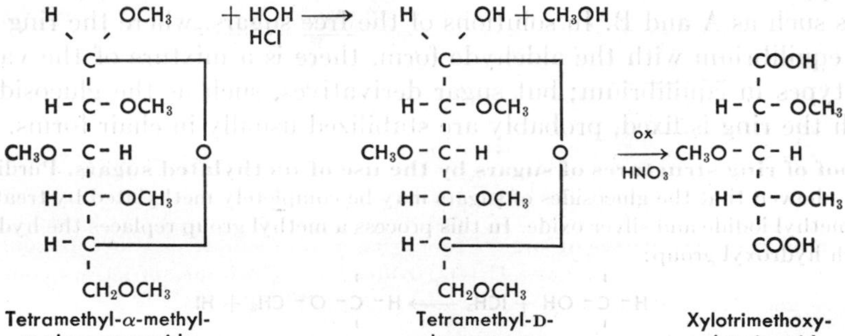

$$
\begin{array}{l}
\text{H} \quad\quad \text{OCH}_3 \quad + \text{HOH} \xrightarrow{\text{HCl}} \\
\quad\text{C} \\
\text{H}-\text{C}-\text{OCH}_3 \\
\text{CH}_3\text{O}-\text{C}-\text{H} \quad\quad \text{O} \\
\text{H}-\text{C}-\text{OCH}_3 \\
\text{H}-\text{C} \\
\quad\text{CH}_2\text{OCH}_3
\end{array}
$$

Tetramethyl-α-methyl-
D-glucopyranoside

Tetramethyl-D-
glucopyranose

Xylotrimethoxy-
glutaric acid

Since oxidation of the methylated sugar as above converts the end ring carbon atoms to carboxyl groups, the production of a five-carbon dibasic acid shows that five carbon atoms are present in the sugar ring and that the corresponding sugar has the amylene oxide or pyranose structure.

If oxidation of the methylated sugar produces a methylated four-carbon hydroxy dibasic acid, this indicates the presence of only four carbon atoms in the ring, and the corresponding sugar has the butylene oxide or furanose ring structure:

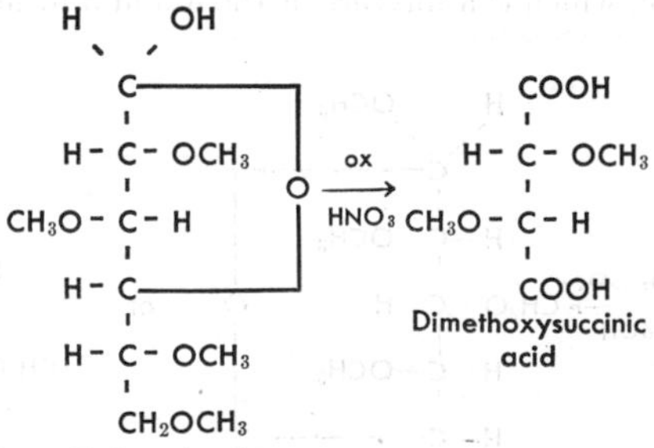

Dimethoxysuccinic
acid

Tetramethyl-D-glucofuranose

Haworth and associates have used the methylated sugars extensively in establishing the ring structures of sugars and have found that the ordinary forms of the simple aldose sugars containing five or more carbon atoms have amylene oxide or pyranose ring structures. Also, the ketose simple sugars with six or more carbon atoms contain pyranose rings. As pointed out previously furanose forms of both aldoses and ketoses exist in solution in traces, and derivatives of furanose sugars, such as the glucosides, may be prepared. The furanose sugar derivatives are much less stable and generally more reactive chemically than the corresponding pyranose compounds are.

It is obvious that a glucoside such as α-methyl-D-glucoside may have either the pyranose or the furanose structure, and in order to differentiate between such substances, they are referred to as "pyranosides" or "furanosides," respectively:

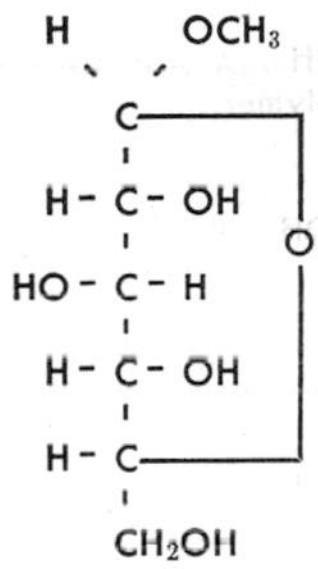

α-Methyl-D-glucopyranoside

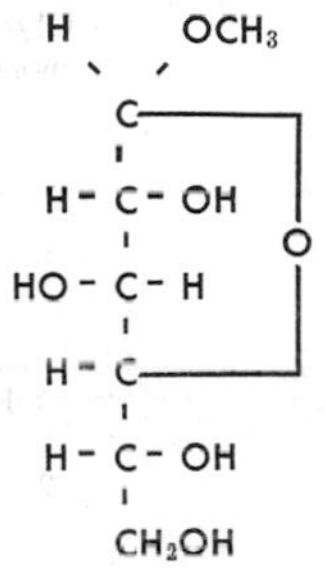

α-Methyl-D-glucofuranoside

Proof of ring structures of sugars by periodic acid oxidation. Jackson and Hudson (12) found that periodic acid, H_5IO_6, oxidizes the glucosides of sugars containing pyranose and furanose rings to give characteristic products:

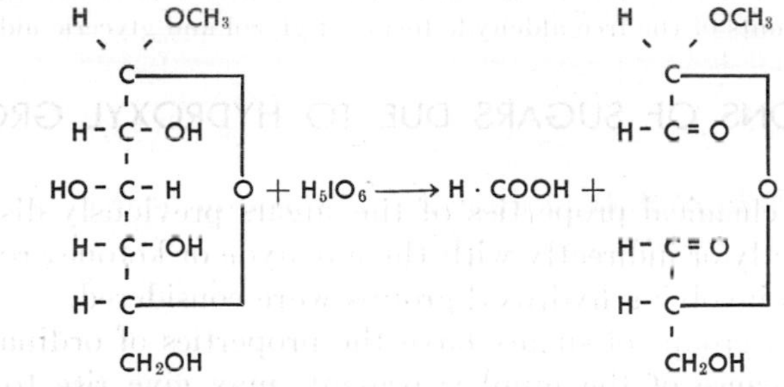

α-Methyl-D-glucopyranoside   A dialdehyde

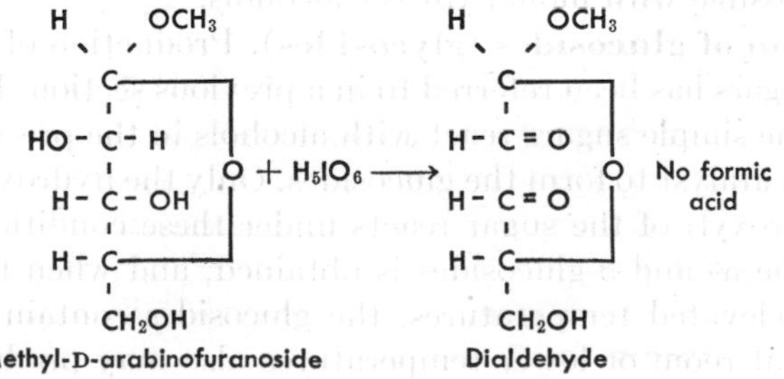

α-Methyl-D-arabinofuranoside   Dialdehyde

From the above it is seen that both glucosides give the same dialdehyde, but α-methyl-D-arabinofuranoside yields no formic acid. The dialdehydes are oxidized with bromine to give the corresponding dibasic acids which are readily isolated as the strontium salts. From the optical rotations of the dibasic acids the configurations about carbons 1 and 4 of the pentose furanosides, carbon 1 of the pentose pyranosides, and about carbons 1 and 5 of the hexose pyranosides may be determined (see Pigman, *The Carbohydrates*).

The monosaccharides glycol aldehyde and glyceric aldehyde, with two and three carbon atoms, respectively, exist as polymers containing two molecules each of the simple sugar. The following equations probably represent these polymerizations:

$$
\begin{array}{ccc}
\text{H} - \text{C} = \text{O} & \rightleftharpoons & \text{HOCH} \text{\textemdash} \text{CH}_2 \\
2 \quad | & & | \quad\quad | \\
\quad \text{CH}_2\text{OH} & & \text{O} \quad\quad \text{O} \\
\text{Glycol aldehyde} & & | \quad\quad | \\
\text{monomeric form} & & \text{CH}_2 \text{\textemdash} \text{CHOH} \\
& & \text{Glycol aldehyde polymer} \\
& & \text{dimeric form}
\end{array}
$$

$$
\begin{array}{ccc}
& & \text{CH}_2\text{OH} \\
& & | \\
& & \text{HOCH} \text{\textemdash} \text{CH} \\
\text{H} - \text{C} = \text{O} & \rightleftharpoons & | \quad\quad | \\
2 \quad\; \text{CHOH} & & \text{O} \quad\quad \text{O} \\
\quad\; | & & | \quad\quad | \\
\quad \text{CH}_2\text{OH} & & \text{CH} \text{\textemdash} \text{CHOH} \\
\text{Glyceric aldehyde} & & | \\
\text{monomeric form} & & \text{CH}_2\text{OH} \\
& & \text{Glyceric aldehyde} \\
& & \text{polymer dimeric} \\
& & \text{form}
\end{array}
$$

The polymers of glycol aldehyde and glyceric aldehyde spontaneously depolymerize into the monomeric forms in aqueous solution. They show the characteristic aldehyde properties and are very reactive. Their solutions restore the color to Schiff's aldehyde reagent; the higher aldoses fail to do this. This restoration indicates the presence of considerable amounts of the free aldehyde forms of glycol and glyceric aldehydes.

REACTIONS OF SUGARS DUE TO HYDROXYL GROUPS

Most of the chemical properties of the sugars previously discussed were concerned directly or indirectly with the aldehyde or ketone groups, though a few reactions involving hydroxyl groups were considered.

The hydroxyl groups of sugars have the properties of ordinary alcoholic groups but, because of the number present, may give rise to derivatives which are impossible with monohydroxy alcohols.

1. Formation of glucosides (glycosides). Production of the glucosides of the simple sugars has been referred to in a previous section. In general, the ring forms of the simple sugars react with alcohols in the presence of hydrogen chloride as catalyst to form the glucosides. Only the hydroxyl on carbon 1 (glucosidic hydroxyl) of the sugar reacts under these conditions. Generally a mixture of the α- and β-glucosides is obtained, and when the reaction is carried out at elevated temperatures, the glucosides contain the pyranose ring. Reaction at room or lower temperatures also may produce glucosides with the furanose ring.

The general reaction may be represented as follows:

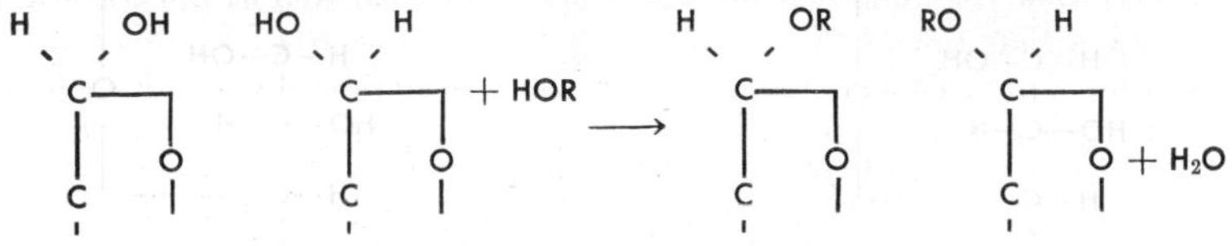

$$\text{H} \quad \text{OH} \quad \text{HO} \quad \text{H} \qquad \qquad \text{H} \quad \text{OR} \quad \text{RO} \quad \text{H}$$

α Form of sugar   β Form of sugar   + HOR ⟶   α-Glucoside   β-Glucoside   + H₂O

The pyranose glucosides are called "pyranosides," whereas the furanose glucosides are "furanosides." The formulas and names below will illustrate:

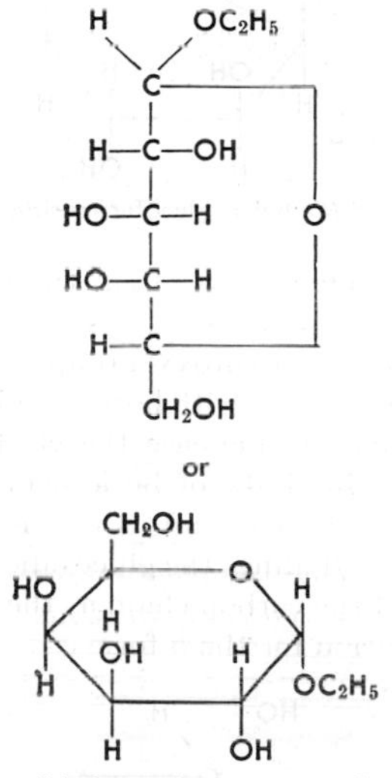

α-Ethyl-D-galactopyranoside

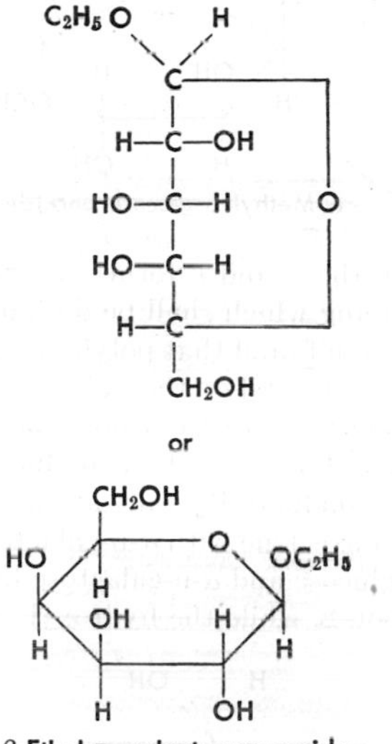

β-Ethyl-D-galactopyranoside

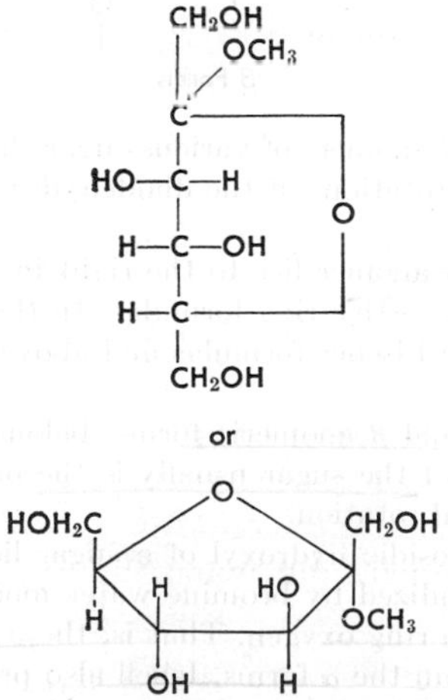

α-Methyl-D-fructofuranoside

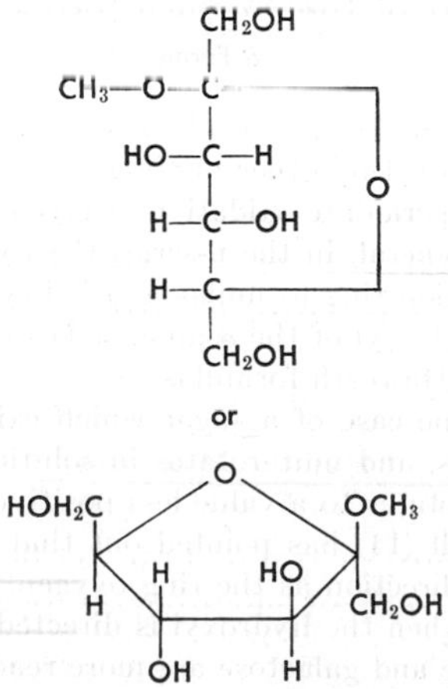

β-Methyl-D-fructofuranoside

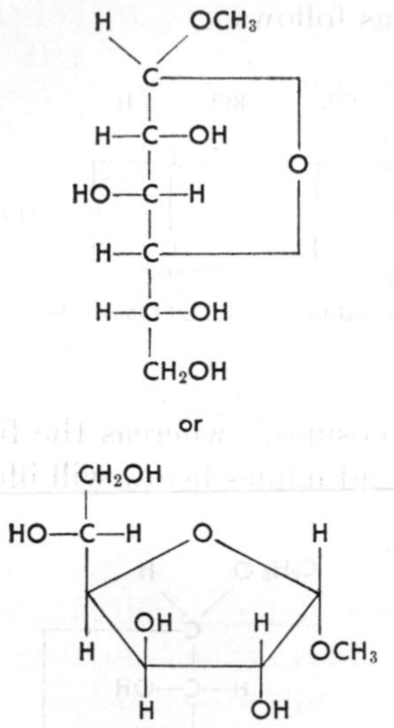

α-Methyl-D-glucofuranoside 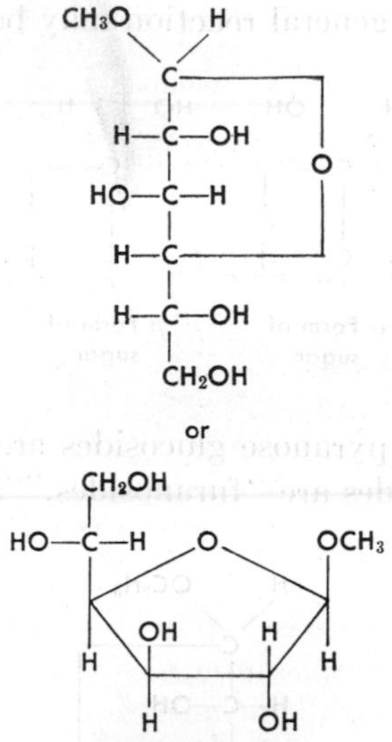   β-Methyl-D-glucofuranoside

When the α and β forms of a free sugar or a glucoside are prepared, the problem of determining which shall be designated as α and which as β arises.

Boeseken found that polyhydroxy compounds having two hydroxyl groups on adjacent carbon atoms and on the same side of the chain form complexes with boric acid in solution which ionize more than boric acid alone and consequently increase the electrical conductivity. For example, α-D-glucose increases the conductivity of boric acid solutions, but the conductivity falls as the sugar mutarotates and passes into the β isomer. The same thing is true with α-D-galactose. According to these findings the glucosidic hydroxyls of α-D-glucose and α-D-galactose lie on the same side of the carbon chain as the hydroxyls on carbon 2, while the hydroxyls are in the trans position for the β forms.

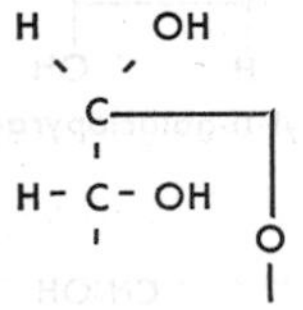

α Forms 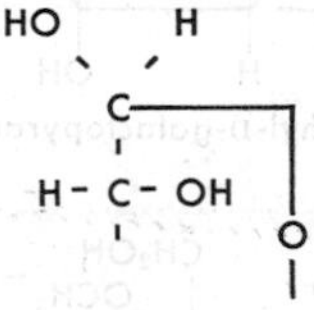   β Forms

The configurations about carbon 1 of the α and β anomers of various sugars have been established by other methods, especially from the rotations of the dialdehydes obtained in the periodate oxidation of glycosides (13).

In general, in the D-series the hydroxyl of the α anomer lies to the right in Fischer's projection ring formulas and below the ring in Haworth's ring formulas. In the L-series the hydroxyl of the α-anomer lies to the left in the Fischer formulas and above the ring in the Haworth formulas.

In the case of a sugar which exists as both α and β anomeric forms, belongs to the D-series, and mutarotates in solution, the α form of the sugar usually is the one which mutarotates to a value less positive than the initial rotation.

Isbell (14) has pointed out that, when the glucosidic hydroxyl of a sugar lies in the same direction as the ring oxygen, the sugar is oxidized by bromine water more slowly than when the hydroxyl is directed away from the ring oxygen. That is, the β forms of glucose and galactose are more readily oxidized than the α forms. Isbell also proposed a general rule for differentiating the α and β pairs of a sugar, or its glucosides, or other derivatives, based upon optical rotation: "When the oxygen ring lies to the right, as in D-glucose, the more dextrorotatory member of the α-β pair shall be designated α, and the less dextrorotatory member β; when the oxygen ring lies to the left, as in L-glucose, the more levorotatory member shall be designated α, and the less levorotatory β. This rule is applicable to the furanoses as well as to the pyranoses and to the derivatives of both."

The glucosides do not reduce alkaline copper solutions, because the sugar group is combined. For the same reason, they are resistant to the action of alkali. They may be hydrolyzed to the constituent reducing sugars by boiling with dilute mineral acids. α-Glucosides are hydrolyzed by maltase, an enzyme from yeast, while β-glucosides are hydrolyzed by the enzyme emulsin, from bitter almonds. Enzyme hydrolysis thus affords a method of distinguishing between the two forms.

Many glucosides occur in the roots, bark, and fruit, and frequently the leaves of various plants. Glucosides are usually well-crystallized, colorless, bitter solids, soluble in water and alcohol. A number of the natural glucosides are important in medicine or otherwise. The groups attached to the sugars in the natural glucosides are frequently quite complex, but the union is always through condensation of an alcoholic or phenolic hydroxyl with the glucosidic hydroxyl of the sugar.

Table 7.2 lists a number of the natural glucosides, with their hydrolytic products and source.

Table 7.2. Some Natural Glucosides

Glucoside	Hydrolytic Products	Source
Arbutin	Glucose + hydroquinone	Arbutus
Phlorizin	Glucose + phloretin	Rose bark
Amygdalin	2 Glucose + D-mandelonitrile	Seeds of bitter almond
Digitonin	4 Galactose + xylose + digitogenin ($C_{27}H_{44}O_5$)	Leaves of foxglove
Saponin	Sugar + sapogenin	Soapwort
Indican	Glucose + indoxyl	Leaves of indigofera

The group attached to the sugar in a glucoside is often referred to as the "aglucone" or "aglycone"; thus mandelonitrile is the aglucone of amygdalin, and digitogenin is the aglucone of digitonin.

2. Formation of ethers. The hydrogen of hydroxyl groups of sugars and of carbohydrates in general may be replaced by alkyl groups to form ethers. The methylated sugars which have already been discussed in some detail are methyl ethers of the sugars. Ethylated sugars, or ethyl ethers of the sugars, may be prepared by reactions analogous to those for the preparation of the methylated sugars.

3. Formation of esters. The hydroxyl groups of the sugars may be esterified to give esters such as the sugar acetates, propionates, stearates, and benzoates. This is generally accomplished by treating the sugar with the appropriate acid anhydride or chloride under the proper conditions.

For example, when glucose is treated with acetic anhydride, pentaacetyl glucose or glucose pentaacetate is formed. By varying the conditions the α or β form may be obtained as the chief product:

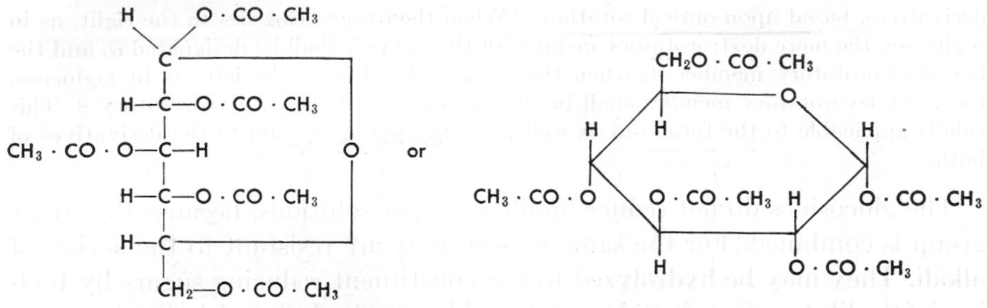

α-D-Glucopyranose pentaacetate
Penta-O-acetyl-α-D-glucopyranose

In the case of sugar esters rigid systematic nomenclature requires that the acyl groups be designated "-O-acyl" as in "penta-O-acetyl-α-D-glucopyranose."

The acetyl group on the first carbon is readily hydrolyzed off, leaving tetraacetyl glucose with a free sugar group. All the acetyl groups may be removed by mild alkaline hydrolysis to re-form the sugar. The sugar acetates and other esters are used especially in the preparation of other sugar derivatives. They are generally insoluble in water and soluble in organic solvents.

While sugars form various inorganic esters such as sulfates and nitrates, the sugar phosphates are outstanding in biologic importance. The breakdown or metabolism of glucose and other sugars by animal tissues and by yeast and other microorganisms involves a succession of the phosphates of sugars and sugar derivatives. Nucleoproteins of cell nuclei also contain sugar phosphates in combination. Sugar phosphates have been found as intermediate products in the carbohydrate metabolism of plants. Many of these substances have been isolated and identified, and a number have been synthesized. Table 7.3 gives the structures of phosphates of glucose and fructose which are of biologic importance.

It will be observed that, whereas glucose phosphates have pyranose rings, the phosphates of fructose are of the furanose type.

Table 7.3. Structures of Sugar Phosphates

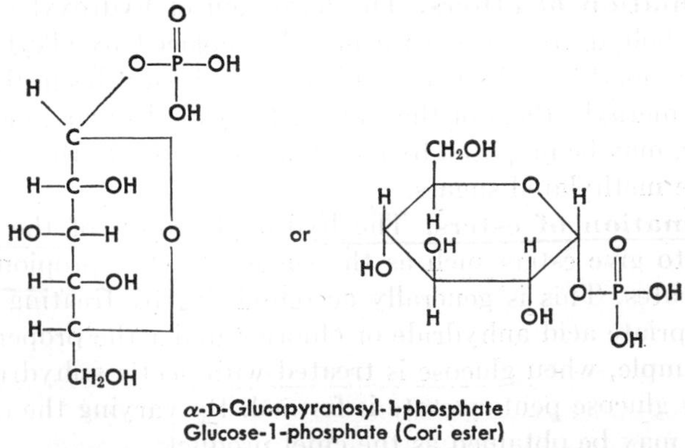

α-D-Glucopyranosyl-1-phosphate
Glucose-1-phosphate (Cori ester)

Table 7.3.   Structures of Sugar Phosphates (*Continued*)

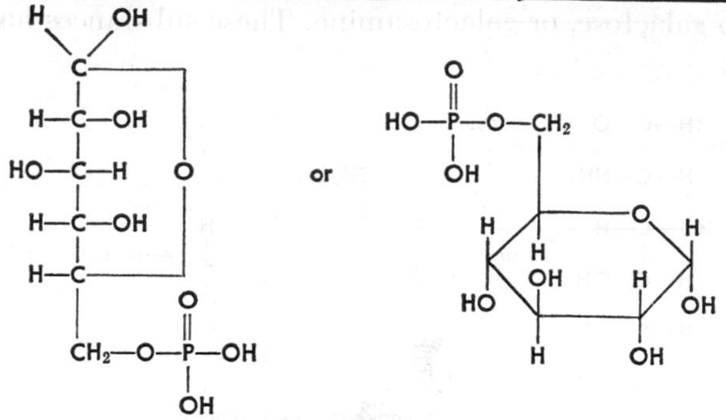

D-Glucopyranosyl-6-phosphate
Glucose-6-phosphate (Robison ester)

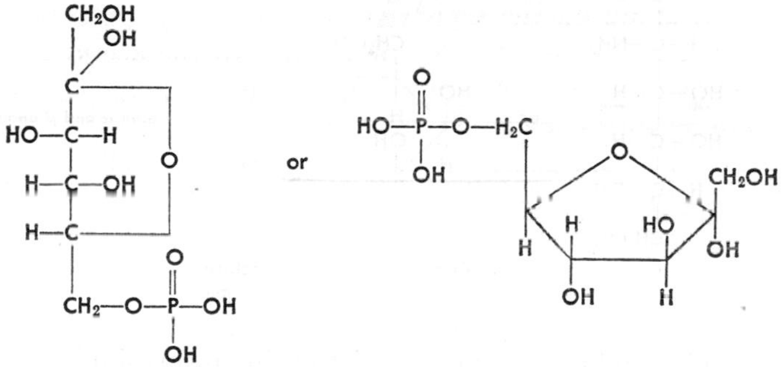

D-Fructofuranosyl-6-phosphate
Fructose-6-phosphate (Neuberg ester)

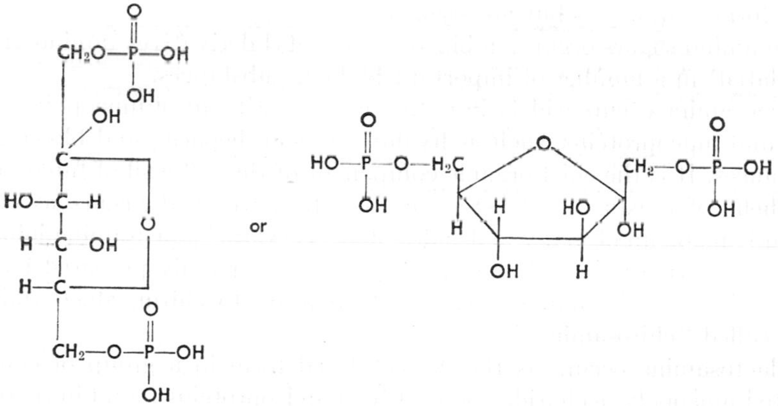

D-Fructofuranosyl-1,6-diphosphate
Fructose diphosphate (Harden-Young ester)

OTHER SUGAR DERIVATIVES OF BIOLOGIC IMPORTANCE

1. **Amino sugars.** Amino groups may be substituted for various hydroxyl groups of sugars to give amino sugars. Although many of these substances have been synthesized, relatively few are natural products, among which

the best known are 2-amino-2-deoxy-D-glucose, or glucosamine, and 2-amino-2-deoxy-D-galactose, or galactosamine. These substances have the following formulas:

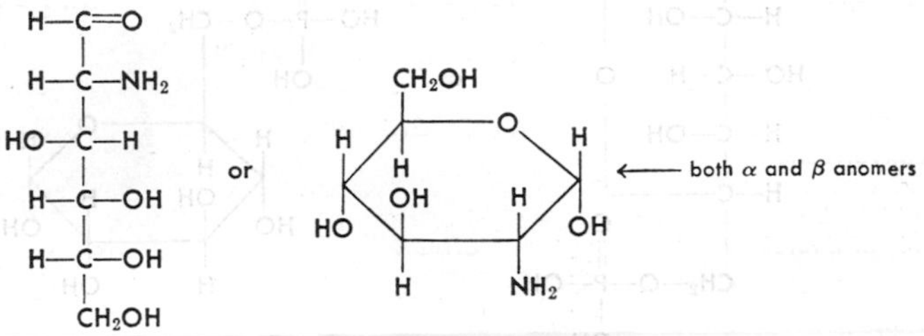

$$
\begin{array}{l}
H-C=O \\
H-C-NH_2 \\
HO-C-H \\
H-C-OH \\
H-C-OH \\
CH_2OH
\end{array}
$$

or

← both α and β anomers

2-Amino-2-deoxy-D-glucose
Glucosamine or chitosamine

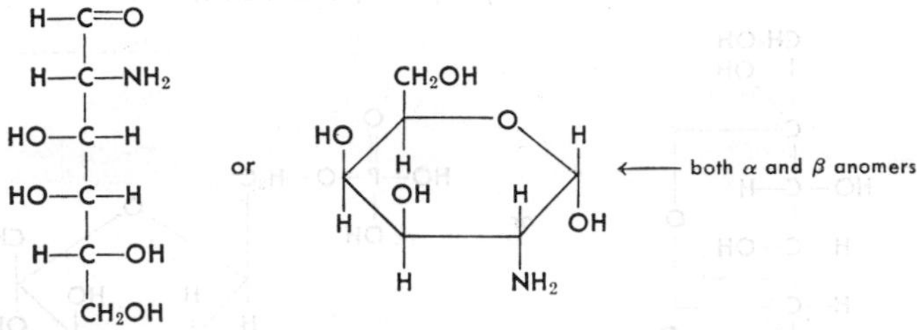

$$
\begin{array}{l}
H-C=O \\
H-C-NH_2 \\
HO-C-H \\
HO-C-H \\
H-C-OH \\
CH_2OH
\end{array}
$$

or

← both α and β anomers

2-Amino-2-deoxy-D-galactose
Galactosamine or chondrosamine

Glucosamine and galactosamine exist in ring forms similar to those of glucose and galactose. They give chemical reactions characteristic of the sugars. They form hydrazones but not osazones.

The amino sugars occur combined as N-acetyl derivatives (amino groups acetylated) in a number of important biologic substances.

Glucosamine occurs widely in nature as a constituent of mucopolysaccharides and mucoproteins, such as hyaluronic acid, heparin, and blood group substances. It is the chief organic component of the cell wall of fungi and of the shells of crustaceae (lobsters, crabs, etc.), where it occurs as chitin. Chitin is made up of many molecules of N-acetylated glucosamine joined in a polysaccharide type of linkage. Glucosamine is readily prepared by acid hydrolysis of chitin and, because of its relation to chitin, glucosamine is often called "chitosamine."

Galactosamine occurs as the N-acetylated form in a group of complex sulfated mucopolysaccharides present in chondroproteins found in cartilage, adult bone, cornea, skin, tendons, and heart valves. Upon mild hydrolysis the chondroproteins yield protein plus chondroitin sulfate. When chondroitin sulfate is completely hydrolyzed, galactosamine, a uronic acid, and acetic and sulfuric acids are obtained. Because of its presence in chondroitin, galactosamine is also called "chondrosamine."

The student is referred to *Biochemistry of the Aminosugars* by Kent and Whitehouse for a thorough discussion of the amino sugars (14).

2. **Deoxy sugars.** Deoxy sugars represent sugars in which the oxygen of a hydroxyl group has been removed, leaving the hydrogen. The —CHOH—

or —CH₂OH group thus becomes a —CH₂— or —CH₃ group. Several of the deoxy sugars have been synthesized, and others are natural products. Some of the naturally occurring deoxy sugars are given below:

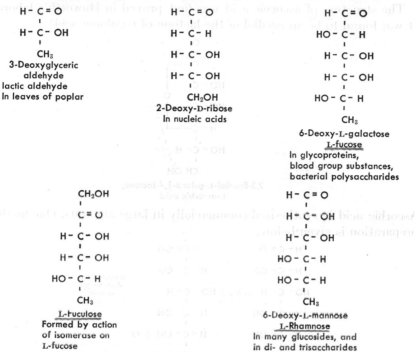

H - C = O
|
H - C - OH
|
CH₃
3-Deoxyglyceric
aldehyde
lactic aldehyde
In leaves of poplar

H - C = O
|
H - C - H
|
H - C - OH
|
H - C - OH
|
CH₂OH
2-Deoxy-D-ribose
In nucleic acids

H - C = O
|
HO - C - H
|
H - C - OH
|
H - C - OH
|
HO - C - H
|
CH₃
6-Deoxy-L-galactose
L-fucose
In glycoproteins,
blood group substances,
bacterial polysaccharides

CH₂OH
|
C = O
|
H - C - OH
|
H - C - OH
|
HO - C - H
|
CH₃
L-Fuculose
Formed by action
of isomerase on
L-fucose

H - C = O
|
H - C - OH
|
H - C - OH
|
HO - C - H
|
HO - C - H
|
CH₃
6-Deoxy-L-mannose
L-Rhamnose
In many glucosides, and
in di- and trisaccharides

2-Deoxy sugars give most of the sugar reactions, though they cannot form osazones. They are very unstable, and they easily form resins. Unlike the corresponding sugars, they restore the color to fuchsin-sulfurous acid (Schiff's reagent), indicating the presence of considerable aldehyde form in solution. ω-Deoxy sugars (methyl on end of chain) are not unstable as are the 2-deoxy compounds, and they behave chemically much as the corresponding monosaccharides.

It is interesting to note that 2-deoxy-D-ribose and other 2-deoxy pentoses yield levulinic acid when heated with 12 per cent hydrochloric acid:

H - C = O   COOH
| |
H - C - H   CH₂
| |
H - C - OH ——→   CH₂   + H₂O
| |
H - C - OH   C = O
| |
CH₂OH   CH₃
2-Deoxy-D-   Levulinic
ribose   acid

It will be recalled that hexoses also yield levulinic acid, as well as other products, under these conditions.

3. **Ascorbic acid or vitamin C.** This is a very interesting sugar derivative found widespread in plant and animal tissues and is especially abundant

in citrus juices, Hungarian paprika, and green walnuts. Its presence in the diet is essential for the prevention of scurvy in man and some animals. It is referred to as the antiscorbutic vitamin and vitamin C.

The structure of ascorbic acid was first proved in Haworth's laboratory. It was found to be an enediol of the lactone of L-gulonic acid:

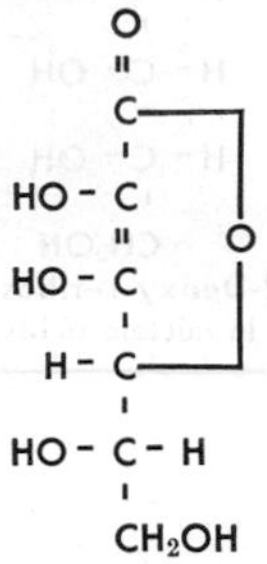

$$
\begin{array}{c}
\text{O} \\
\parallel \\
\text{C} \\
| \\
\text{HO} - \text{C} \\
\parallel \quad\quad \text{O} \\
\text{HO} - \text{C} \\
| \\
\text{H} - \text{C} \\
| \\
\text{HO} - \text{C} - \text{H} \\
| \\
\text{CH}_2\text{OH}
\end{array}
$$

2,3-Enediol-L-gulono-1,4-lactone,
L-ascorbic acid

Ascorbic acid is synthesized commercially in large amounts. One method of preparation is given below.

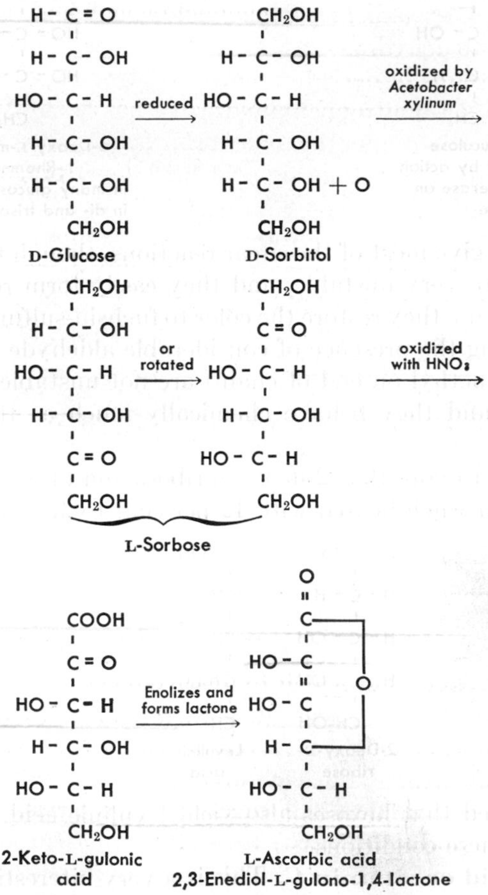

$$
\begin{array}{ccc}
\text{H} - \text{C} = \text{O} & \quad & \text{CH}_2\text{OH} \\
| & & | \\
\text{H} - \text{C} - \text{OH} & & \text{H} - \text{C} - \text{OH} \\
| & \text{reduced} & | \\
\text{HO} - \text{C} - \text{H} & \xrightarrow{\quad} & \text{HO} - \text{C} - \text{H} \\
| & & | \\
\text{H} - \text{C} - \text{OH} & & \text{H} - \text{C} - \text{OH} \\
| & & | \\
\text{H} - \text{C} - \text{OH} & & \text{H} - \text{C} - \text{OH} + \text{O} \\
| & & | \\
\text{CH}_2\text{OH} & & \text{CH}_2\text{OH} \\
\text{D-Glucose} & & \text{D-Sorbitol}
\end{array}
$$

oxidized by
Acetobacter
xylinum

$$
\begin{array}{ccc}
\text{CH}_2\text{OH} & \quad & \text{CH}_2\text{OH} \\
| & & | \\
\text{H} - \text{C} - \text{OH} & & \text{C} = \text{O} \\
| & \text{or} & | \\
\text{HO} - \text{C} - \text{H} & \xrightarrow{\text{rotated}} & \text{HO} - \text{C} - \text{H} \\
| & & | \\
\text{H} - \text{C} - \text{OH} & & \text{H} - \text{C} - \text{OH} \\
| & & | \\
\text{C} = \text{O} & & \text{HO} - \text{C} - \text{H} \\
| & & | \\
\text{CH}_2\text{OH} & & \text{CH}_2\text{OH}
\end{array}
$$

oxidized
with HNO₃

L-Sorbose

$$
\begin{array}{ccc}
\text{COOH} & \quad & \text{O} \\
| & & \parallel \\
\text{C} = \text{O} & & \text{C} \\
| & & | \\
\text{HO} - \text{C} - \text{H} & \xrightarrow[\text{forms lactone}]{\text{Enolizes and}} & \text{HO} - \text{C} \\
| & & \parallel \quad\quad \text{O} \\
\text{H} - \text{C} - \text{OH} & & \text{HO} - \text{C} \\
| & & | \\
\text{HO} - \text{C} - \text{H} & & \text{H} - \text{C} \\
| & & | \\
\text{CH}_2\text{OH} & & \text{HO} - \text{C} - \text{H} \\
& & | \\
& & \text{CH}_2\text{OH}
\end{array}
$$

2-Keto-L-gulonic   L-Ascorbic acid
acid   2,3-Enediol-L-gulono-1,4-lactone

Ascorbic acid is a fairly strong organic acid ($pK = 4.21$), and it owes its acidic property to the enolic hydroxyl groups. It is stable in the crystalline state but is readily oxidized in aqueous solution by oxygen and other oxidizing agents because of its enediol structure. The first product of oxidation is dehydroascorbic acid:

$$
\begin{array}{ccc}
\underset{\text{L-Ascorbic acid}}{
\begin{array}{l}
O \\
\parallel \\
C- \\
HO-C \\
\parallel \\
HO-C \\
\mid \\
H-C- \\
\mid \\
HO-C-H \\
\mid \\
CH_2OH
\end{array}
} O + O & \longrightarrow &
\underset{\substack{\text{L-Dehydroascorbic} \\ \text{acid}}}{
\begin{array}{l}
O \\
\parallel \\
C- \\
O=C \\
\mid \\
O=C \\
\mid \\
H-C- \\
\mid \\
HO-C-H \\
\mid \\
CH_2OH
\end{array}
} O + H_2O
\end{array}
$$

Further oxidation disrupts the carbon chain to form oxalic and L-threonic acids.

Iodine and the dye 2,6-dichlorophenolindophenol both quantitatively oxidize ascorbic acid to dehydroascorbic acid and are used for its determination.

The carbonyl groups of dehydroascorbic acid react with hydrazines, and this reaction with 2,4-dinitrophenylhydrazine has been utilized in an excellent method for the determination of ascorbic acid by Roe and Kuether (16).

A number of analogs of ascorbic acid have been prepared from various sugars.

Fermentation of monosaccharides. The common monosaccharides, D-glucose, D-fructose, and D-mannose, are readily fermented by ordinary yeast, and D-galactose is fermented by specially cultured yeasts. One nonose, 5-ketofructose, α-glucosan, and the trioses D-glyceric aldehyde and dihydroxyacetone are also fermentable.

The process of yeast fermentation is exceedingly complicated. In ordinary fermentation alcohol and carbon dioxide represent the main products as shown by the following equation:

$$C_6H_{12}O_6 \longrightarrow 2CO_2 + 2C_2H_5OH$$
Glucose

However, this equation is only an approximate over-all expression. The actual process involves the formation of sugar phosphates which then break down into three-carbon sugar phosphates and sugar acid phosphates, and the latter yield pyruvic acid which by decarboxylation forms acetaldehyde and carbon dioxide. The acetaldehyde is then reduced to alcohol. A detailed outline of the chemical changes involved in yeast fermentation will be found in the discussion of carbohydrate metabolism in Chapter 24.

It is interesting to note that only sugars of the D-series, and relatively few of those, are fermentable by yeast. However, many carbohydrates are fermented by bacteria and fungi to form a variety of products. The commercial production of a large number of important substances is effected through the action of selected microorganisms upon the appropriate carbohydrate. Citric acid, butyl alcohol, and glycerol are representative of such substances. The selective fermentation of certain carbohydrates by different bacteria affords an important means of bacterial identification. The reverse of this has also been applied in the identification of sugars.

Inositols or cyclitols or cyclohexanehexols. The cyclitols or inositols are derivatives of cyclohexane in which one hydrogen to each carbon is re-

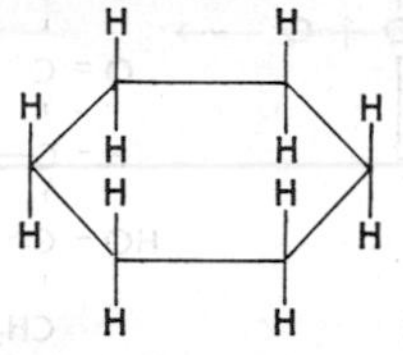

placed by a hydroxyl group. Consequently, they are cyclohexanehexols and, because they are cyclic alcohols, are called "cyclitols." The inositol rings are similar to the Haworth pyranose sugar rings and, like pyranose rings, are not planar but assume chair or boat forms.

There are nine possible isomeric inositols, depending upon the arrangements of the hydrogen and hydroxyl groups about the ring carbon atoms. Only four of the inositols occur naturally: D-inositol, L-inositol, myo-inositol (meso-inositol), and scyllo-inositol (scyllitol, cocositol, quercin). Various derivatives of the inositols are natural products such as deoxy-inositols:

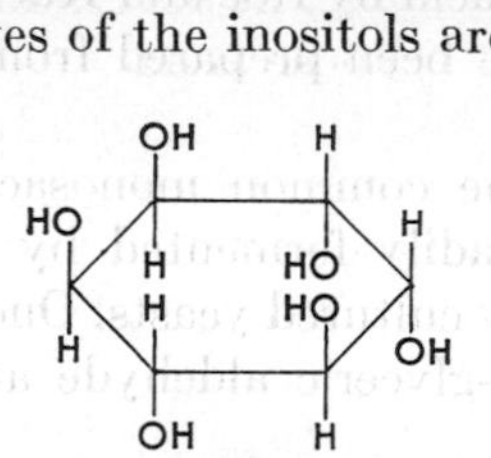

D-Inositol

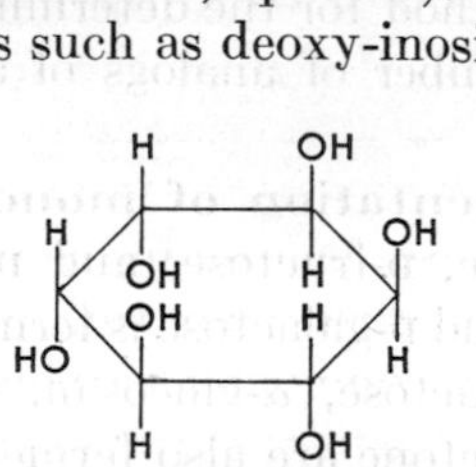

L-Inositol

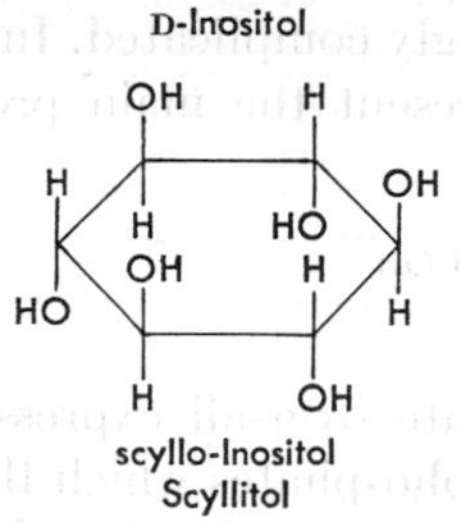

scyllo-Inositol
Scyllitol

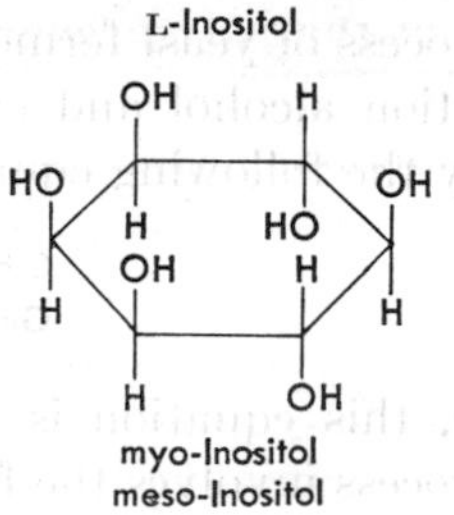

myo-Inositol
meso-Inositol

All but two of the possible inositols are optically inactive.

D-, L-, and scyllo-inositols are plant products. Myo-inositol, or meso-inositol, is a very important biochemical substance, occurring widespread in animals, plants, bacteria, yeasts, and molds. It is a member of the B-complex vitamins. It is generally present in animal tissues.

An excellent discussion of the inositols may be found in *The Carbohydrates* by Pigman.

COMPOUND CARBOHYDRATES

The compound carbohydrates are derivatives of the monosaccharides, and their molecular complexity varies from those made up of two monosaccharide units, such as sucrose, to those containing hundreds or thousands of monosaccharide units, as in the case of glycogen.

The simpler compound carbohydrates containing only a few monosaccharide units are crystalline substances with a sweet taste, form true solutions in water, and give the characteristic sugar reactions if a free sugar group is present in the molecule. These carbohydrates are called "oligosaccharides" because they are composed of only a few (oligos) monosaccharide units.

The more complex compound carbohydrates, such as celluloses, starches, glycogen, and dextrins, are composed of many monosaccharide units, and most of them do not crystallize but are amorphous solids. Those that are soluble form colloidal solutions. Most of them are tasteless, though the dextrins are mildly sweet. Some contain the free sugar group and give its characteristic reactions, though the quantity of reagent used per unit weight of carbohydrate is small owing to the high molecular weights of these carbohydrates. The complex compound carbohydrates are called "polysaccharides" because their structures contain many (poly) monosaccharide units.

All the compound carbohydrates are hydrolyzed by hot dilute mineral acids into their constituent monosaccharides. Alkalies, however, do not hydrolyze them and do not otherwise readily decompose them unless a free sugar group is present in their structures. Many of them are hydrolyzed by specific glycosidase enzymes. For example, sucrose is hydrolyzed by sucrase, or invertase; lactose by lactase; maltose by maltase; cellulose by cellulase; and the starches, dextrins, and glycogens by the amylases or diastases.

All the compound carbohydrates are optically active as a result of the optical activity of their constituent monosaccharides. In general, the specific rotations of the polysaccharides are much higher than those of the monosaccharides.

The compound carbohydrates represent an exceedingly important group of substances biochemically. Sucrose, lactose, maltose, starches, and dextrins constitute the bulk of man's carbohydrate food. Glycogen is the form in which reserve carbohydrate is stored in the liver and muscles and is the primary carbohydrate involved in supplying energy for muscle contraction. The celluloses make up the larger proportion of the woody and fibrous structures of plants and are used directly and as derivatives for many purposes. The celluloses are by far the most abundant of all organic compounds in nature.

A. OLIGOSACCHARIDES

The oligosaccharides are composed of the disaccharides, trisaccharides, and tetrasaccharides and are so designated to indicate the number of monosaccharide units involved in their structures. Those which contain free sugar groups exist in the α and β forms, just as the monosaccharides do.

1. Disaccharides. The following tabulation gives the better-known disaccharides with their component monosaccharides. Those possessing a free sugar group, which consequently are reducing sugars and give the other characteristic sugar reactions, are indicated as reducing sugars.

Disaccharides $C_{12}H_{22}O_{11}$	Constituent Monosaccharides
I. Reducing Sugars	
Maltose	glucose, glucose
Lactose	glucose, galactose
Cellobiose	glucose, glucose
Gentiobiose	glucose, glucose
Melibiose	glucose, galactose
Turanose	glucose, fructose
II. Nonreducing Sugars	
Sucrose	glucose, fructose
Trehalose	glucose, glucose

Sucrose, lactose, and maltose are the most important disaccharides.

a) Sucrose. Sucrose occurs especially in the juices of plants such as sugar beets, sugar cane, sorghum, sugar maple, and pineapple, and in smaller quantities in the juices of many other plants. Ripe fruits are rich in sucrose. It is by far the most abundantly distributed of the sugars.

Hydrolysis of sucrose by dilute acid or by the enzyme invertase or sucrase produces one molecule each of glucose and fructose, with a change in optical rotation from positive to negative because D-fructose is more levorotatory than D-glucose is dextrorotatory:

$$C_{12}H_{22}O_{11} + H_2O \longrightarrow C_6H_{12}O_6 + C_6H_{12}O_6$$
$$+66.5° \qquad\qquad +52.5° \quad -92°$$

Because of the inversion of the sign of rotation in the reaction, the process is referred to as "inversion," and the mixture of glucose and fructose obtained is called "invert sugar." Honey contains a large proportion of invert sugar.

Sucrose is not a reducing sugar, is relatively stable toward the action of alkali, and in general does not give the reactions characteristic of the sugar group.

The fact that sucrose has no free sugar group indicates that the linkage of glucose to fructose in the molecules involves the 1 hydroxyl of glucose and the 2 hydroxyl of fructose (the sugar group hydroxyls).

Haworth and associates prepared octamethyl sucrose and hydrolyzed it. The products were 2,3,4,6-tetramethyl glucopyranose and 1,3,4,6-tetramethyl fructofuranose.

Hudson followed the optical rotation of sucrose solutions hydrolyzed by concentrated invertase at low temperatures. The sucrose was hydrolyzed almost instantly at 0° C. The specific rotation of sucrose is +66.5°, and of stable invert sugar −28.2° when measured at 0° C. Despite the fact that Hudson found sucrose to be very quickly converted by invertase to glucose and fructose at 0° C, the specific rotation did not quickly fall to −28.2° as expected. Instead it dropped moderately rapidly for the first few minutes and then decreased slowly for many hours. After 25 minutes the rotation was still +1.1°. Hudson has pointed out that only an α–β glucose-to-fructose linkage in sucrose can explain these rotatory changes.

It appears that the above phenomena are explainable on the basis of the following processes:

$$\text{Sucrose} + \text{HOH} \xrightarrow{\text{0° C}} \underset{(+ \text{ rotation})}{\text{D-glucopyranose}} + \underset{(+ \text{ rotation})}{\text{D-fructofuranose}}$$

$$\downarrow$$

$$\underset{(- \text{ rotation})}{\text{D-fructopyranose}}$$

The sucrose is first split into α-D-glucopyranose and β-D-fructofuranose, both of which are dextrorotatory. However, the less stable β-D-fructofuranose then sets up an equilibrium with its more stable isomer, β-D-fructopyranose, which is strongly levorotatory. The rate of this change increases rapidly with rising temperature.

It is of interest that Koshland and Stein (17) by hydrolyzing sucrose with invertase in the presence of O^{18}-labeled water have shown the point of cleavage to be between the C-1 carbon of fructose and the bridge oxygen:

$$\underset{\text{Sucrose}}{\text{Gl} - \text{O} - \text{Fr}} + \text{HO}^{18}\text{H} \xrightarrow{\text{invertase}} \underset{\text{Glucose}}{\text{Gl} - \text{OH}} + \underset{\text{Fructose}}{\text{Fr} - \text{O}^{18}\text{H}}$$

According to findings on the previous page sucrose has the configuration:

1-α-D-Glucopyranosyl group β-D-Fructofuranoside group

1-α-D-Glucopyranosyl-β-D-fructofuranoside

Sucrose

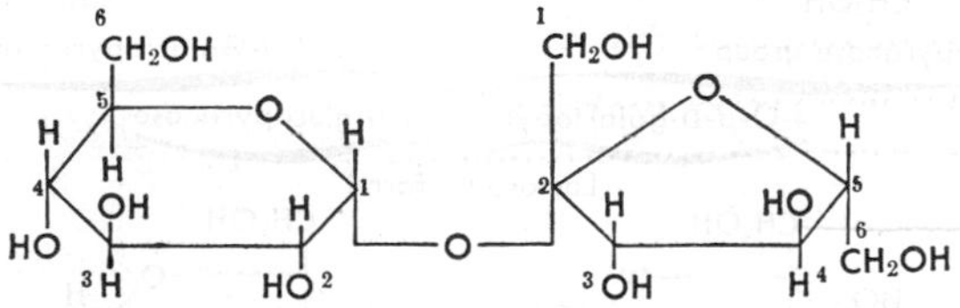

Sucrose is hydrolyzed by dilute acids more easily than any other sugar. Normal sulfuric acid hydrolyzes it rapidly at 20° C, whereas lactose must be heated for a long time at 80° C for the same degree of hydrolysis. Armstrong states that if the rate of acid hydrolysis of lactose is taken as 1.00, the rate for maltose is 1.27 and for sucrose 1,240.

Through its hydroxyl groups sucrose forms salts with bases, such as the calcium sucrates. All its hydroxyl groups may be methylated or acetylated to form octa-O-methyl sucrose and octa-O-acetyl sucrose. When sucrose is heated to about 200° C, it loses water and forms a brown amorphous mass called "caramel."

The presence of the furanose ring in the fructose component of sucrose apparently is related to the ease of hydrolysis of the glycosidic bond of sucrose. The free energy of hydrolysis of this bond is 6570 cal (18), which represents a relatively high potential for chemical reaction.

Sucrose is readily fermented by yeast. It is apparently first split into glucose and fructose by invertase, and the monosaccharides are then fermented by the zymase system of enzymes.

b) Lactose. Lactose is formed by the mammary glands and occurs to the extent of about 5 per cent in milk (Latin *lac*); hence its name. It is prepared commercially from milk whey.

Lactose is hydrolyzed by acids and the specific enzyme lactase into its constituent monosaccharides, glucose and galactose.

Lactose is a reducing sugar, forms osazones, a cyanhydrin, and an oxime, and is decomposed by alkali. It accordingly contains a free sugar group in its structure.

When lactose is carefully oxidized with bromine, the free sugar group is oxidized to a carboxyl giving lactobionic acid. Hydrolysis of lactobionic acid forms gluconic acid and galactose, showing that the sugar group of the glucose unit in lactose is free, while that of the galactose unit is combined. Lactose is thus a glucose galactoside.

The enzyme emulsin, a β-glycosidase found in bitter almonds, selectively splits β-glucoside linkages. This enzyme hydrolyzes lactose, proving that the sugar is a glucose β-galactoside.

The structure of lactose has been established by the work of Haworth and Long on methylated lactose. It was shown to be:

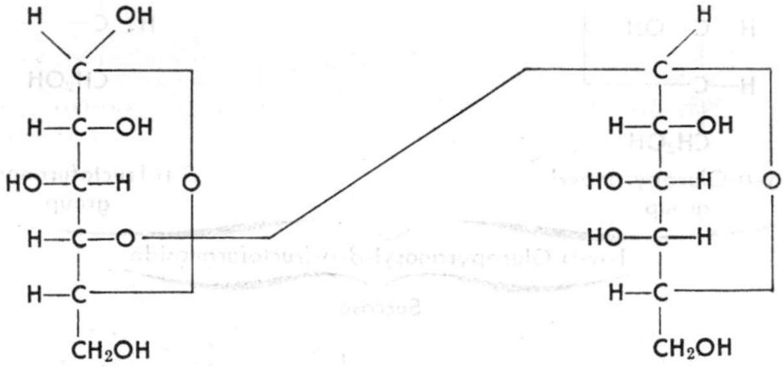

D-Glucopyranose group   β-D-Galactopyranosyl group

4-O-β-D-galactopyranosyl-D-glucopyranose

Lactose (α-form)

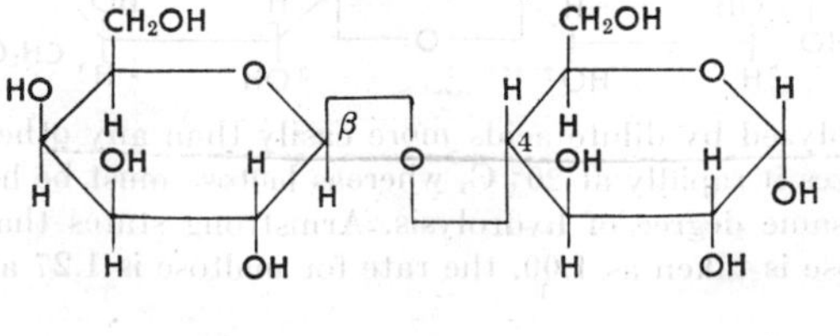

It is of interest that human milk differs from cow's milk in containing, in addition to regular lactose, other oligosaccharides, such as L-fucosyl-lactose, in which the deoxy sugar L-fucose is linked to galactose at carbon 2 (19).

Lactose generally crystallizes as the α form. It is not fermented by yeast.

c) Maltose. Maltose is composed of two glucose units and is formed when the enzyme amylase or diastase hydrolyzes starch. It is a product of the action of salivary amylase (ptyalin) and pancreatic amylase (amylopsin) upon starch in the processes of digestion. Maltose is formed as an intermediate product in the acid hydrolysis of starch and consequently is an important constituent of corn syrups, which are prepared by partial hydrolysis of starch with dilute acid. These syrups are complex mixtures of dextrins, maltose, and glucose. Commercial malt sugar is a mixture of maltose and dextrins formed from starch by hydrolysis with amylase.

Maltose contains a free sugar group, since it is a reducing sugar and gives the other reactions characteristic of the sugar group. Maltase, an α-glycosidase which splits α-glucoside linkages only and which is abundant in yeast, hydrolyzes maltose to give two molecules of glucose. These facts show that the linkage of glucose units in maltose involves only one sugar group, and that maltose is a glucose α-glucoside. Maltose generally crystallizes as the β form.

Haworth and Peat have shown maltose to have the following structure:

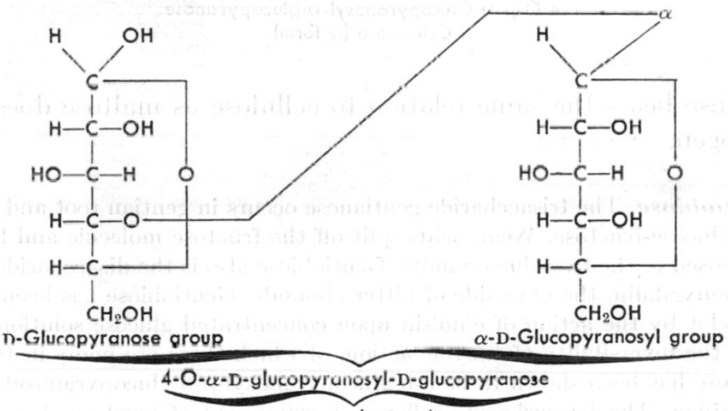

D-Glucopyranose group α-D-Glucopyranosyl group

4-O-α-D-glucopyranosyl-D-glucopyranose

Maltose (α form)

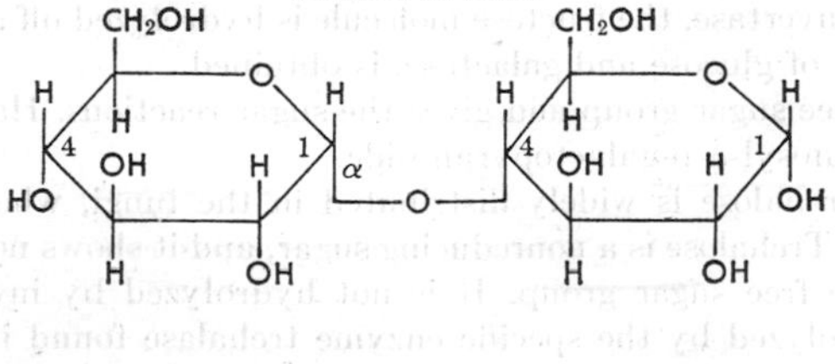

Maltose is readily fermented by yeast.

Isomaltose is 6-O-α-D-glucopyranosyl-D-glucopyranose. It exists as a disaccharide unit in glycogens, amylopectins, and especially certain bacterial dextrans, from which it may be obtained by partial hydrolysis. It is hydrolyzed to glucose in the intestinal tract by the enzyme oligo-1,6-glucosidase (19).

CH₂OH

6-O-α-D-Glucopyranosyl-D-glucopyranose
Isomaltose (α form)

d) **Cellobiose.** Cellobiose is <u>obtained as a product of the incomplete</u>
hydrolysis of cellulose. It is composed of two molecules of glucose into which
it is <u>split by either acids or the enzyme emulsin</u>. Cellobiose is <u>a reducing</u>
<u>sugar</u> and gives the reactions generally characteristic of the free sugar group.

CH₂OH   CH₂OH

4-O-β-D-Glucopyranosyl-D-glucopyranose
Cellobiose (α form)

<u>Cellobiose bears the same relation to cellulose as maltose does to starch</u>
<u>and glycogen.</u>

e) **Gentiobiose.** The <u>trisaccharide gentianose</u> occurs in gentian root and is composed
of <u>glucose-glucose-fructose</u>. <u>Weak acids split off the fructose molecule and leave gentio-</u>
<u>biose</u>, composed of the two glucose units. Gentiobiose also is the disaccharide component
present in amygdalin, the glucoside of bitter almonds. Gentiobiose has been synthesized
by Bourquelot by the action of emulsin upon concentrated glucose solution. This is an
example of the reversibility of enzyme action, of which there are many instances.
    Gentiobiose has been shown to be 6-D-glucopyranosyl-β-D-glucopyranoside.
    f) **Melibiose.** The <u>trisaccharide raffinose</u> is composed of <u>fructose-glucose-galactose.</u>
When treated with <u>invertase</u>, the <u>fructose molecule is hydrolyzed off</u> and the disaccharide
melibiose, composed of glucose and galactose, is obtained.
    Melibiose has a free sugar group and gives the sugar reactions. Haworth has shown it
to be <u>6-D-glucopyranosyl-α-D-galactopyranoside.</u>
    g) **Trehalose.** Trehalose is widely distributed in the fungi, where it is stored as a
reserve food supply. Trehalose is <u>a nonreducing sugar</u>, and it shows none of the properties
characteristic of the free sugar group. It is not hydrolyzed by invertase, maltase, or
emulsin but is <u>hydrolyzed by the specific enzyme trehalase</u> found in yeast and certain
fungi, such as *Aspergillus niger*. Trehalose is <u>difficultly hydrolyzable by acids</u>.
    Trehalose has been shown to be 1-α-D-glucopyranosyl-α-D-glucopyranoside.
    h) **Turanose.** The <u>trisaccharide melezitose</u> is composed of glucose-fructose-glucose.
By partial hydrolysis one glucose unit is removed and the disaccharide turanose is formed.
Turanose contains a free sugar group and gives the characteristic sugar reactions. It has
the structure represented by 3-D-fructofuranosyl-α-D-glucopyranoside.

2. Trisaccharides. Several oligosaccharides containing three monosaccharide units occur in nature. These are given in the following tabulation:

Trisaccharides	Constituent Monosaccharides with Order of Linkage
I. Reducing sugars	
Mannotriose	galactose, galactose, glucose
Robinose	galactose, rhamnose, rhamnose
Rhamninose	galactose, rhamnose, rhamnose
II. Nonreducing sugars	
Raffinose	fructose, glucose, galactose
Gentianose	fructose, glucose, glucose
Melezitose	glucose, fructose, glucose

a) **Raffinose.** Raffinose is the most important of the trisaccharides. It occurs in sugar beets and is concentrated in sugar beet molasses. Cottonseed meal contains about 8 per cent of raffinose and is the material generally used for its preparation. Raffinose is also frequently found in the higher plants and fungi.

When hydrolyzed completely, raffinose yields one molecule each of fructose, glucose, and galactose. It has been shown that the fructose and glucose components are joined in a sucrose linkage and that the galactose molecule is attached to glucose. Accordingly raffinose may yield the disaccharide melibiose (galactose, glucose) and fructose, or sucrose (glucose, fructose) and galactose by appropriate hydrolysis. Examples of such hydrolyses are:

1. Hydrolysis by weak acids (low hydrogen ion concentration):

fructose − ¦ − glucose-galactose + HOH ⟶ fructose + glucose-galactose

  Raffinose   Melibiose

2. Hydrolysis by sucrase:

fructose − ¦ − glucose-galactose + HOH ⟶ fructose + glucose-galactose

  Raffinose   Melibiose

3. Hydrolysis by maltase:

fructose-glucose − ¦ − galactose + HOH ⟶ galactose + fructose-glucose

  Raffinose   Sucrose

Bottom yeasts contain both sucrase and melibiase and consequently hydrolyze raffinose completely to glucose, fructose, and galactose.

The fact that raffinose fails to give the characteristic sugar reactions means that all the sugar groups of glucose, fructose, and galactose are combined in its structure. Hydrolysis of raffinose by sucrase to form fructose and melibiose (glucose-galactose) shows that glucose and galactose are linked and also indicates the presence of a sucrose type of linkage. Maltase, which hydrolyzes α-glucoside linkages, converts raffinose into galactose and sucrose (fructose-glucose), showing that fructose and glucose are linked, and that galactose is joined by an α-glucoside linkage. The sequence of sugars in raffinose accordingly is fructose-glucose-galactose. Haworth and associates, through studies on methylated raffinose, have assigned the following structure:

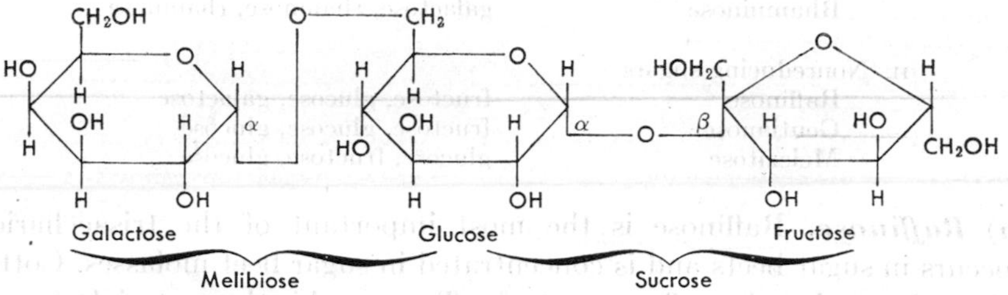

O-α-D-Galactopyranosyl-(1 ⟶ 6)-O-α-D-glucopyranosyl-(1 ⟶ 2)-β-D-fructofuranoside
Raffinose

Raffinose is fermented by yeast. It is hydrolyzed by enzymes of the gastro-intestinal bacteria of herbivorous animals and serves as food for these animals. Raffinose is not well utilized as food by man.

b) ***Gentianose.*** The trisaccharide gentianose occurs in gentian root. When hydrolyzed, it yields fructose and two molecules of glucose, and the order of linkage is fructose-glucose-glucose. The fructose and glucose are joined by a sucrose type of linkage, and the two glucose molecules are linked as in gentiobiose:

Fructose-glucose-glucose
Sucrose Gentiobiose
Gentianose

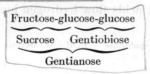

c) ***Melezitose.*** Melezitose is a very rare sugar. It occurs in the sap of the larch, scrub pine, and Douglas fir. When hydrolyzed completely, it yields two molecules of glucose and one molecule of fructose. Partial hydrolysis gives the disaccharide turanose, and glucose. The order of linkage is glucose-fructose-glucose.

Melezitose has the structure:

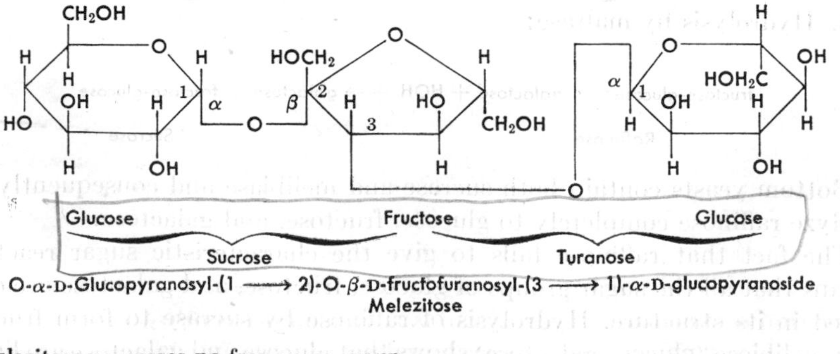

O-α-D-Glucopyranosyl-(1 ⟶ 2)-O-β-D-fructofuranosyl-(3 ⟶ 1)-α-D-glucopyranoside
Melezitose

Melezitose possesses no free sugar group.

d) Robinose. Robinose is a reducing trisaccharide composed of galactose and two molecules of the deoxy sugar rhamnose. It is present in combination in the glucoside robinine. Robinose is reported to reduce Fehling's solution in the cold.

e) Mannotriose. Mannotriose is formed by partial hydrolysis of the tetrasaccharide stachyose and is composed of glucose and two molecules of galactose linked in the order galactose-galactose-glucose. The glucose unit possesses a free sugar group.

3. Tetrasaccharides. Two tetrasaccharides are known: stachyose (lupeose, β-galactan, Manneotetrose), found in *Stachys tuberifera* and many other plant sources, and scorodose, found in the bulbs of onion and garlic.

Stachyose is composed of D-galactose, D-glucose, and D-fructose, and is O-α-D-galactopyranosyl-(1 $\longrightarrow$ 6)-O-α-D-galactopyranosyl-(1 $\longrightarrow$ 6)-O-α-D-glucopyranosyl-(1 $\longrightarrow$ 2)-β-D-fructofuranoside.

4. Pentasaccharides. One pentasaccharide, verbascose, is known: O-α-D-galactopyranosyl-(1 $\longrightarrow$ 6)-O-α-D-galactopyranosyl-(1 $\longrightarrow$ 6)-O-α-D-galactopyranosyl-(1 $\longrightarrow$ 6)-O-α-D-glucopyranosyl-(1 $\longrightarrow$ 2)-β-D-fructofuranoside. Verbascose has been found in the roots of the mullein *Verbascum thapsus.*

B. POLYSACCHARIDES

The polysaccharides are composed of many molecules of monosaccharides. Their molecules are very large and are classed as colloids. The most important polysaccharides are the starches, the glycogens, the dextrins obtained from starch and glycogen, and the celluloses. All these substances are formed of many molecules of D-glucose and are referred to as "glucosans." The polysaccharide inulin is a compound made up of fructose units. Chitin is composed of the amino sugar glucosamine. There are various complex carbohydrate substances containing sugars and uronic acids, such as the plant gums.

The polysaccharides are hydrolyzed by the group of enzymes called the "polysaccharidases."

STARCHES

1. Occurrence. The starches occur widespread as reserve carbohydrate in tubers such as potatoes, in grains and seeds, in many fruits, and in the rhizomes and pith of plants. The starches occur as grains which may be spherical, oval, lens-shaped, or irregular in form. Starch may be arranged in concentric layers in the grains, as is common for cereal starches, or it may be in eccentric layers, as in potato starch. These layers may be clearly seen in starch grains which have been heated. The starch grains from a given source have a definite characteristic shape, and this fact is utilized in identifying starches microscopically. Starch in the grains contains 14 to 19 per cent of water, with 10 per cent bound chemically, giving a composition corresponding to $(C_6H_{10}O_5 \cdot H_2O)n$. The hydrated starch molecules are arranged in a crystalline lattice, but the structure becomes amorphous when the water of hydration is expelled by heat. From 0.01 to 0.05 per cent nitrogen and some fatty acids and phosphoric acid are found associated with starch in the grains.

The nitrogenous material can be removed by treatment with alcoholic HCl. The resulting starch may contain up to 0.6 per cent fatty acids, among which oleic, palmitic, and linoleic have been identified. Some of these acids may be present as phosphatides. The fatty acids can be removed from starch by extraction with alkalies.

The chief constituent of the starch grain yields glucose when hydrolyzed and is called starch. As a matter of fact, the material is a mixture of substances of different structures and properties. When starch is treated with boiling water, a substance in the center of the grain passes into solution, but the greater part of the grain is not soluble. This insoluble portion absorbs water and swells to form an elastic sphere, and the whole mass becomes starch paste. While both the soluble and the insoluble fractions are mixtures, it is customary to refer to the soluble component as "amylose" and to the insoluble fraction as "amylopectin." Starches generally contain 80 to 90 per cent amylopectin and 10 to 20 per cent amylose, though in a few instances the amylose content is higher.

Amylopectin as obtained by separation with hot water is often combined with phosphoric acid, while the amylose fraction is not.

Both amylose and amylopectin are hydrolyzed by acids to D-glucose. Partial acid hydrolysis gives complex mixtures of dextrins, maltose, and glucose.

2. Structure of starch and related properties. The structure of starch from the viewpoint of both the glucose linkages and molecular arrangement has been the subject of investigation for many workers. Studies of methylated starches by Irvine and associates, Haworth and associates, Freudenberg, Hess, and K. H. Meyer have contributed much in establishing the positions of glucose linkages and the degree of glucose chain branching. The student is referred to the monograph *Natural and Synthetic High Polymers*, by K. H. Meyer, for an exhaustive discussion of the chemistry of starch.

Work on the structure of starch has been concerned essentially with the structures of amylose and amylopectin. Both are composed of many glucose units joined through the α-glucoside linkage, chiefly as found in maltose.

The glucose units of amylose are linked in an unbranched chain. The amylose structure may be considered an expanded maltose structure with a free sugar group on one end:

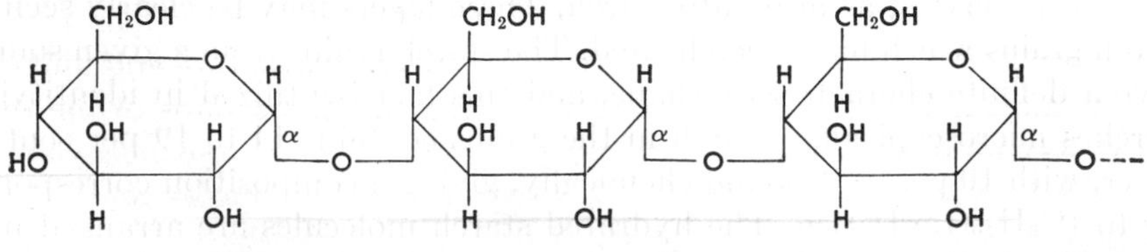

Amylopectin, while containing chains of glucose units like those of amylose, also has branches of these glucose chains linked through the 6-OH of glucose in the manner shown below:

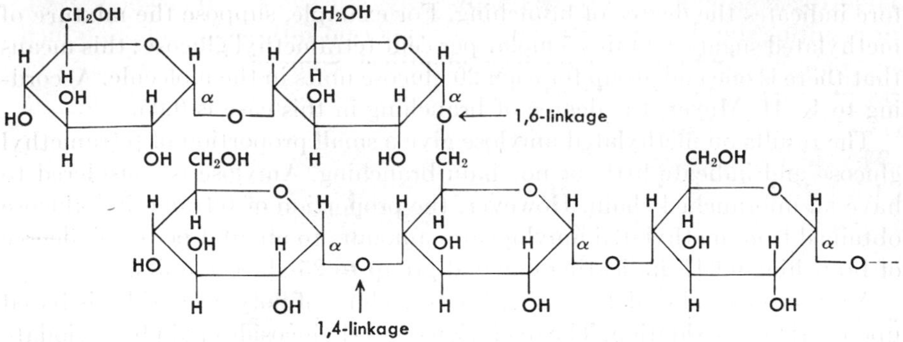

CH₂OH ... 1,6-linkage ... 1,4-linkage

The following figures represent diagrammatically the difference in the glucose chains of amylose and amylopectin molecules:

OOOOOOOOOOOOOOOOOOOOOOOOOOOOOOOOOOOOOOOO
Amylose type of structure, glucose units in a chain

O O
O O
O O
O O
O O
O O

OOOOOOOOOOOOOOOOOOOOOOOOOOOOOOOOOOOOOOOO

O O
O O
O O
O O
O O
OOOOOOOO O
O

Amylopectin type of structure with branched
chains of glucose units

The study of methylated starches has given evidence of the degree of chain branching. Methylation replaces all the hydroxyl hydrogen with methyl groups. Acid hydrolysis of the methylated products produces the free methylated sugars. Each end glucose unit with a combined sugar group in the methylated starch, such as unit 1 in the amylose structure and units 1 and 8 in the amylopectin structure, contains four methyl groups, while the other units contain only three or two methyl groups. When these methylated starches are hydrolyzed, mixtures of 2,3,4,6-tetramethyl glucose and 2,3,6-trimethyl glucose are obtained, and also 2,3-dimethyl glucose when branched chains as in amylopectin are present. The greater the number of branched chains in the starch molecule, the greater is the proportion of tetramethyl glucose obtained upon hydrolysis of the methylated starch. The amount of tetramethyl glucose in the hydrolysis mixture of a methylated starch therefore indicates the degree of branching. For example, suppose the mixture of methylated sugars contains 5 molar per cent tetramethyl glucose; this means that there is one end group for each 20 glucose units in the molecule. According to K. H. Meyer, the degree of branching in this case is 0.05.

The results on methylated amylose give a small proportion of tetramethyl glucose and indicate little or no chain branching. Amylose is considered to have an unbranched chain. However, the proportion of tetramethyl glucose obtained from methylated amylopectin amounts to about 4 per cent (degree of branching 0.04), indicating one end group to 25 glucose units.

Another method of determining the branching of polysaccharides is based upon periodate oxidation. The oxidation of a 1-4 glucoside chain by periodate yields three moles of formic acid per chain:

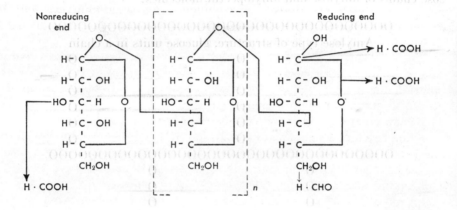

In the case of amylopectins and glycogens, which possess many branches and nonreducing end groups, the ratio of nonreducing to reducing end groups is very high, and practically all the formic acid arises from the nonreducing branches, one mol of formic acid per nonreducing end group. Consequently, oxidation of such substances with periodate, followed by titration of the formic acid formed, permits calculation of the degree of branching. The method is much less time-consuming and more convenient than the methylation procedure, and it gives essentially the same results.

The amylose extracted from starch grains is a mixture of molecules of different sizes. Amylose fractions with molecular weights from 4000 to 400,000 have been obtained.

The amylopectin molecules differ from amylose molecules not only in possessing many branched chains, but also in being larger. The molecular weights of the amylopectins apparently vary from 50,000 to about 1,000,000.

Great care must be exercised in isolating and working with amyloses and amylopectins to prevent hydrolysis and reduction in molecular size. Many relatively low molecular weight values have been reported, which were probably due in large part to splitting of the original molecules into smaller ones during the experimental procedures.

3. Action of amylases upon starch. The enzymes which hydrolyze starch are known as the "amylases" and are of plant or animal origin. The plant amylases are especially abundant in grains, potatoes, and in all germinating seeds. The animal amylases are represented by ptyalin of saliva and amylopsin of pancreatic juice.

The smallest molecule formed by the action of amylase on starch is the disaccharide maltose. Pancreatic amylase acting upon starch liberates products of the α-configuration, while malt amylase liberates β-maltose. The amylases are accordingly classified as α- and β-amylases. Malt amylase has been shown to contain a small amount of α-amylase mixed with β-amylase.

The α-amylases include pancreatic amylase, salivary amylase, takadiastase (from mold), and the small amount of α-amylase in malt. β-Amylase accompanies vegetable starch and is especially abundant in all germinating seeds, in potatoes, etc. Malt is the commonest source of β-amylase, but, on account of the presence of a small amount of α-amylase, pure β-amylase is best prepared from nongerminated barley or wheat.

The action of the amylases upon starch mixtures generally causes characteristic changes in properties. These include a decrease in viscosity of the solution due to decreased molecular size, appearance of reducing groups due to the formation of maltose and dextrins, and loss of capacity to give the blue color reaction with iodine.

α-Amylase first acts upon amylose to split the more central linkages, forming a mixture of smaller dextrins but only a little maltose. As the action proceeds, these dextrins are partially hydrolyzed to maltose.

β-Amylases hydrolyze amylose completely to maltose.

β-Amylase splits maltose molecules from the ends of the branches of amylopectin until its action is blocked at the 1-6 glucoside linkages or branch points, leaving branched large molecules of so-called grenzdextrin (residual dextrin). β-Amylase forms only 50 to 60 per cent of the theoretical maximum of maltose from amylopectin. The 1-6 glucoside linkages are split by a 1-6 glucosidase from yeast, after which the action of β-amylase will proceed. α-Amylase splits the more central 1-4 glucoside linkages of amylopectin to liberate end groups. Thus α- and β-amylase supplement each other's action upon amylopectin, the β-amylase splitting maltose from the end groups and α-amylase splitting central linkages to form more end groups. However, even after the joint action of the amylases upon amylopectin, some 25 per cent remains as unidentified disaccharides and trisaccharides which have been formed at the 1-6 glucoside branch points. The action of 1-6 glucosidase with the amylases is necessary for the more complete hydrolysis of amylopectin.

Since the chief action of α-amylase on starch components is to form dextrins, it is called "dextrinogenic amylase," while β-amylase, which forms much maltose, is referred to as "saccharogenic amylase."

From the above discussion it is evident that incomplete hydrolysis of starch by the amylases is due to the 1-6 branched structure of the amylopectin component. However, it has been found that old starch solutions and pastes are less completely hydrolyzed than fresh preparations. This apparently is due to association of starch molecules into aggregates which are resistant to enzyme action; it applies to solutions of both amylose and amylopectin.

Larner and McNickle (20) have shown that in the digestion of starch in the intestine an enzyme, oligo-1,6-glucosidase, splits the 1,6 linkages of the dextrins formed by the action of α-amylase and thus permits α-amylase action to continue and form maltose. Oligo-1,6-glucosidase also hydrolyzes the 1,6 linkage of isomaltose, converting it to glucose. The three intestinal enzymes—α-amylase, oligo-1,6-glucosidase, and maltase—catalyze the practically complete digestion of starch in the gastrointestinal tract.

4. Comparison of amyloses and amylopectins. When amylose solutions are prepared and allowed to stand for some time (three or four weeks), an insoluble precipitate settles out. This process is called "retrograding," and the precipitate is retrograded amylose. The precipitate is made up of small crystallites formed by coherence of the unbranched amylose chains. Air-dried amylose fractions are free from phosphorus and contain water of hydration $(C_6H_{10}O_5 \cdot H_2O)_n$. When the water is removed, the crystalline structure disappears. Rehydration restores it.

Although amylopectin combines with water, when warmed, to swell and form pastes, it does not go entirely into solution. Water at 130° C dissolves amylopectin with partial hydrolysis forming so-called erythroamyloses (red reaction with iodine). These erythroamyloses show molecular weights of around 300,000. In starch pastes the large branched amylopectin molecules are highly hydrated and mat together as a network. The chains are linked together through coordinate linkages (hydrogen bonding) at various points. These linkages may be broken by treatment with hydrazine hydrate at room temperature or 40 per cent aqueous chloral hydrate at 90°, giving nearly clear solutions. Hydrated amylopectin has a crystalline structure.

Both amylose and amylopectin give characteristic color reactions with iodine. Amylose produces a blue-black color, whereas amylopectin gives a violet to red-violet color. The colors disappear on heating the solutions and reappear upon cooling. These phenomena seem to be best explained by means of the following considerations. In solutions of starch a complex equilibrium between molecules, associated molecules, and complexes of associated molecules (micells) exists. Iodine reacts with the starch micells through secondary valences (coordinate) to form the colored complexes. When the mixtures are heated, the micells are broken up to shift the equilibrium toward the smaller aggregates and molecules with disruption of the iodine micell complexes. Upon cooling, the micells and iodine-micell complexes re-form and the color returns:

$$
\begin{array}{ccccc}
 & & & & \text{micells} \\
\text{amylose or} & & \text{small} & & \text{large} \\
\text{amylopectin} & \rightleftharpoons & \text{molecular} & \rightleftharpoons & \text{molecular} \\
\text{molecules} & & \text{aggregates} & & \text{aggregates} \\
 & & & & + \\
 & & & & I_2 \\
 & & & & \Updownarrow \\
 & & & & \text{micell-}I_2 \\
 & & & & \text{colored}
\end{array}
$$

Starches with unbranched chains (amyloses) give a blue color with iodine, whereas those with branched chains (amylopectins) give a violet to red-violet color. Dextrins formed from starch by the action of β-amylase upon amylopectin are highly branched and give a red color. These dextrins are called "erythrodextrins." Dextrins of relatively small molecular size do not give a color with iodine and are called "achroodextrins" ("achro-" meaning colorless). The color produced by reaction with iodine is used as an indication of the degree of branching of starch components.

5. **Action of various agents on starch.** Alkalies such as NaOH, KOH, and LiOH react with the alcoholic hydroxyl groups of starches to form alcoholates. The starches first swell in alkaline solution and may, as in the case of corn starch, go into solution and then set to a gel. Alkaline solutions of starch are rapidly oxidized and broken down upon exposure to oxygen, with a rapid decrease in viscosity.

Starches swell in the presence of concentrated acids and salts such as H_3PO_4, HCl, LiBr, and $ZnCl_2$. The cations form coordinate compounds with the alcoholic hydroxyl groups.

The starches give all the reactions with organic reagents characteristic of alcoholic groups. They may be treated with acid anhydrides and chlorides to form esters such as the acetates, with methylating and ethylating agents to form ethers such as the methylated starches, and they may be nitrated and phosphorylated to form starch nitrates and phosphates.

6. **Enzymatic synthesis of starch.** Cori (21) and Hanes (22) have synthesized starch by the action of the enzyme, phosphorylase, present in plant and animal tissues, upon glucose-1-phosphate:

$$\text{glucose-1-phosphate} + \text{phosphorylase} \rightleftharpoons \text{starch} + \text{inorganic phosphate}$$

The product obtained gave a blue iodine reaction indicating the presence of amylose. The above reaction is reversible. It is necessary to prime the reaction by adding a little starch, glycogen, or dextrin. It is probable that the synthesis of starch in plants is effected chiefly by a different process, which is similar to that of glycogen synthesis (Chapter 24).

7. **Quantitative determination of starch.** Starches may be quantitatively determined by acid hydrolysis to form glucose, which is then determined by any of the established procedures.

DEXTRINS

As previously indicated, the partial hydrolysis of starches by acids, or α- and β-amylase, produces substances known as "dextrins." These substances consist of a very complex mixture of molecules of different sizes and structures. Dextrins formed from amylose have unbranched chains, while those from amylopectin are branched. The larger branched dextrins give a red color with iodine and are called "erythrodextrins."

Dextrins occur in the leaves of all starch-producing plants, where they represent intermediates in the synthesis of starch from glucose, or the breakdown of starch. Dextrins also occur in honey.

The dextrins are generally soluble in water, and their solutions do not gel as starch solutions do. Dextrin fractions may be precipitated from water solutions by the addition of alcohol. Dextrins generally have a sweet taste.

All dextrins have free sugar groups and accordingly reduce alkaline copper solutions and give other sugar reactions. They are not fermented by yeast.

Dextrins are important constituents of various food products, such as corn syrups. They are also used extensively as adhesives and binders.

GLYCOGENS

1. **Occurrence.** The term "glycogen," like the terms "starch" or "dextrin," refers to no specific chemical compound. The polysaccharides occurring widespread in animal tissues, especially liver and muscle, which give a red-brown, red, or at times violet color with iodine, and which yield D-glucose upon complete hydrolysis, are referred to collectively as "glycogen." This group of polysaccharides occurs in most animal cells, as well as in certain plants, such as varieties of rice, and in yeasts. Mollusks such as oysters and clams are usually rich in glycogen.

Biochemically glycogen is one of the most important substances in the body. Liver glycogen is broken down to glucose and passed into the blood stream for use by the tissues. Muscle glycogen is a source of energy for muscle contractions.

2. **Isolation from tissues.** Glycogen may be extracted from tissues by quickly mincing the fresh tissue and boiling with water. The glycogen forms an opalescent solution from which it can be precipitated with alcohol. Such a procedure removes only part of the glycogen and does not yield a pure product. For the quantitative separation of glycogen from tissues the procedure of Pflüger, or some modification of it, is generally used. Pflüger's procedure consists in heating the tissue with 60 per cent KOH, which disintegrates it and leaves the glycogen in solution, from which it is precipitated by alcohol and centrifuged down. It is then washed with alcoholic KOH and finally with alcohol. The amount of glycogen is determined by acid hydrolysis to glucose, followed by determination of the glucose. Pflüger's procedure, while giving quantitative values for the glycogen of tissues, does not produce unaltered glycogen. Unless oxygen is excluded from KOH solution, glycogen molecules are broken into simpler structures. Commercial glycogen is ordinarily prepared by Pflüger's method and consequently does not represent the unaltered material.

Various methods have been devised for the extraction and purification of glycogen with as little alteration as possible. Among these may be mentioned the methods of Bell and Young (23) and Meyer and Jeanloz (24). In these methods glycogen is extracted from the tissue with hot water and purified by special procedures. These methods avoid treatment with alkali. Crude glycogen as obtained from tissues may be separated by electrodialysis, by fractional precipitation with alcohol, or by rapid centrifugation into different fractions. Meyer and Jeanloz separated their glycogen into three fractions by electrodialysis. Fraction I dissolved in water to a clear solution, fraction II gave a turbid solution, and fraction III gave a suspension from which the glycogen could be centrifuged. Fraction III was soluble in dilute sodium hydroxide and aqueous chloral hydrate. The cloudy solutions undoubtedly contained very large aggregates of many single molecules. The viscosities of the acetates of the three fractions were different, indicating different molecular weights.

3. Structure of glycogen. Glycogen, like starch, yields D-glucose upon acid hydrolysis. β-Amylase acts upon glycogen to give considerable amounts of maltose, indicating the presence of α-1-4 glucoside linkages. Haworth and associates have contributed much to the knowledge of the structure of glycogen through their studies of methylated glycogen. They found that when methylated glycogen is hydrolyzed a mixture of 2,3,4,6-tetramethyl glucose, 2,3,6-trimethyl glucose, and 2,3-dimethyl glucose is obtained as is the case with methylated starch. However, the proportions of 2,3,4,6-tetramethyl glucose (from end glucose units) and of 2,3-dimethyl glucose (from glucose units where branching occurs) were higher than for methylated starch. About 9 molar per cent of 2,3,4,6-tetramethyl glucose was present in the mixture, indicating one end glucose unit for each 11 glucose units in the molecule, as compared with one end unit for each 25 glucose units in amylopectin. These results showed that the glucose chains in glycogen are much more branched than in amylopectin. The degree of branching in glycogen is about 0.09, as compared with 0.04 for amylopectin. The presence of 2,3-dimethyl glucose in the mixture of methylated sugars showed that the branched chains are linked through position 6 of the glucose molecule as they are in amylopectin. Haworth and coworkers have found that the degree of branching differs for different glycogen samples. For example, two different samples of rabbit liver glycogen showed 7 and 9 per cent of terminal glucose groups (0.07 and 0.09 degree of branching).

Meyer and Bernfeld (25) have studied the hydrolysis of glycogen with β amylase. It will be recalled from the discussion of starch that β-amylase splits off maltose only from the ends of the glucose unit branches which do not possess the free sugar group, and its action does not split the 1-6 glucose linkage at the branch points. This leaves at least one end glucose unit attached to the branch points. Meyer and associates found that β-amylase acts upon glycogen to form maltose and a residual dextrin (grenzdextrin) of high molecular weight. Only 47 per cent of the original glycogen was converted to maltose, leaving 53 per cent of residual dextrin. The original glycogen contained 9 molar per cent of end groups, one end group for 11 glucose units. The residual dextrin, however, contained 18 molar per cent of end groups, or one end group for an average of 5.5 glucose units. From these results the above workers calculated that glycogen molecules are made up of branched structures in which the exterior branches are six to seven glucose units long, while the chain fragments between branches average only about three glucose units in length. In amylopectin the exterior branches contain 15 to 18 glucose units, and the chain fragments between branches eight to nine units, on the average. The glycogen molecule is thus seen to be much more highly branched and more compactly organized than the amylopectin molecule. Figure 7.4 shows a section of glycogen molecule with various types of linkages according to Haworth.

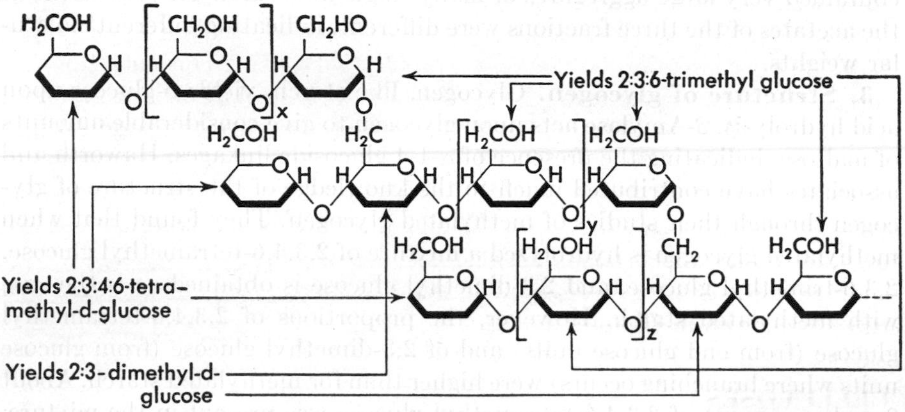

Figure 7.4. Types of linkage in the glycogen molecule according to Haworth. (From Meyer, K. H.: *Natural and Synthetic High Polymers.* Interscience Publishers, Inc., New York, 1942, p. 419.)

Meyer considers the branched glycogen molecule to have a treelike structure; the enzymatic studies of Cori and associates discussed in Chapter 24 proved that it has this type of structure.

The molecular weight of glycogen has been the subject of many investigations. Apparently the most reliable results have been obtained by measurements of the osmotic pressure of methylated and acetylated glycogens in appropriate solvents. Widely different values have been obtained which were apparently related to different degrees of breakdown of the glycogen molecule during isolation. Van der Wyk and Jeanloz (24) obtained, from osmotic measurements on very carefully prepared acetylated glycogen dissolved in benzyl alcohol a lower limiting molecular weight of about 5,000,000. According to K. H. Meyer, available evidence indicates that undecomposed glycogen from all sources has molecular weights in excess of 4,000,000, and the larger molecules have molecular weights several times this value.

The shape of glycogen particles has been indicated by viscosity studies. The specific viscosity of solutions containing very large spherical molecules is independent of molecular size and concentration in dilute solutions. Specific viscosity, η_{sp}, for spherical particles is given by the equation of Einstein:

$$\eta_{sp} = 2.5 \frac{\text{volume of suspended particles}}{\text{volume of suspension}}$$

For nonspherical molecules the specific viscosity increases with both molecular weight and concentration. Measurements upon glycogen fractions with molecular weights from 66,000 to 800,000 gave constant values according to Staudinger and associates (26), indicating spherical particles. Meyer and Jeanloz (24), however, found that for undecomposed glycogens the higher molecular fractions gave higher specific viscosities, indicating that the molecular form deviates from spherical.

The osmotic pressure of large spherical molecules is directly proportional to concentration; that is, osmotic pressure divided by concentration equals a constant $(\pi/c = k)$. The osmotic pressure of chain molecules is not proportional to concentration but increases rapidly with rising concentration $(\pi/c$ increases). Measurements on glycogen acetate in benzyl alcohol show a gradual and small increase in π/c with increasing concentration, indicating a nearly spherical molecule.

The sphericity of glycogen molecules means that the branched chains of the molecule are aggregated into a compact nearly round structure and held together by hydrogen bonds between alcoholic hydroxyl groups.

4. Synthesis of glycogen. The detailed mechanisms of glycogen synthesis are given in Chapter 24.

CELLULOSES

1. Occurrence. Cellulose is the chief constituent of the fibrous parts of plants and is consequently the most abundant organic material in nature. The cellulose content of flax, ramie, and cotton amounts to 97 to 99 per cent, while the content in woods varies from 41 to 53 per cent. Cereal straws contain from 30 to 43 per cent cellulose. The purest cellulose used for experimental studies is prepared from raw cotton by extraction with organic solvents to remove lipids and other soluble impurities, followed by careful treatment with dilute alkali to remove pectin and other noncellulose substances.

Although usually considered to be only a plant product, cellulose (tunicin) is found in certain marine animals (*Tunicata, Polycarpa varians, Phallusia mamillata*).

Cellulose yields D-glucose as the final product of hydrolysis. It is resistant to hydrolysis and requires the action of strong acids. Various bacteria and other lower forms possess enzymes, cellulases, capable of hydrolyzing cellulose. The snail, *Helix pomatia*, produces a cellulase which completely hydrolyzes cellulose to glucose. Cellulases are absent from animal digestive juices. Herbivorous animals utilize cellulose as food by virtue of the action of gastrointestinal bacteria and fungi which split it into glucose and other utilizable products.

Partial hydrolysis of cellulose by acids yields a mixture of cellodextrins (analogous to dextrins), various oligosaccharides, cellobiose (analogous to maltose), and glucose.

2. Structure of cellulose. The term "cellulose" represents a group of high molecular weight substances, just as the terms "starch" and "glycogen" do. The fact that cellobiose is the disaccharide obtained in the hydrolysis of cellulose indicates that the linkages of the glucose units in cellulose are as they are in cellobiose.

Methylation of cellulose followed by hydrolysis gives chiefly 2,3,6-trimethyl glucose mixed with some 2,3,4,6-tetramethyl glucose from end groups. The evidence indicates that the cellulose molecules are not branched as those of amylopectin and glycogen are, but consist essentially of glucose units linked in repeating sequence as they are in cellobiose, with a free sugar group on one end:

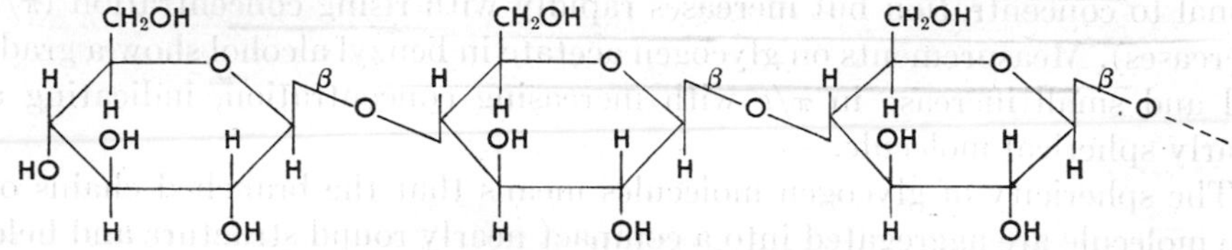

Cellulose type structure,
4-D-glucopyranosyl-β-D-glucopyranoside linkages

X-ray analysis of cellulose fibers indicates that they are composed of bundles of parallel cellulose chains. The chains are held together horizontally by hydrogen bonds between the alcoholic hydroxyl groups.

The molecular weights of cellulose molecules have been determined by numerous chemical and physical methods and found to be high. Here, as with starch and glycogen, care must be taken to prevent splitting and decomposition of the cellulose during its preparation and the preparation of its derivatives. Probably the most reliable molecular weight values have been obtained by the ultracentrifugal method of Svedberg. According to this method, the average molecular weight of native cellulose is about 570,000, and that of purified cellulose (partly broken down) 150,000 to 500,000.

3. Properties of cellulose. The chemistry of cellulose is exceedingly complex. The student is referred to *The Chemistry of Cellulose*, by E. Heuser, for an exhaustive discussion.

Cellulose is not soluble in water. It may be dissolved in an ammoniacal solution of cupric hydroxide (Schweitzer's reagent) and in a hydrochloric acid solution of zinc chloride. Cellulose is also dissolved by aqueous solutions (35 to 40 per cent) of various quaternary ammonium bases. Cellulose is dissolved by fuming hydrochloric acid, anhydrous hydrogen fluoride, concentrated sulfuric acid, and concentrated phosphoric acid. By quickly diluting such solutions with water and cooling, much of the cellulose may be precipitated in a modified form. The action of alkalies causes partial solution of cellulose with the formation of cellulose alcoholates (alkali cellulose) in which the metal ion replaces hydroxyl hydrogen.

When alkali cellulose is treated with CS_2, water-soluble cellulose xanthates are formed. The reaction may be represented in outline:

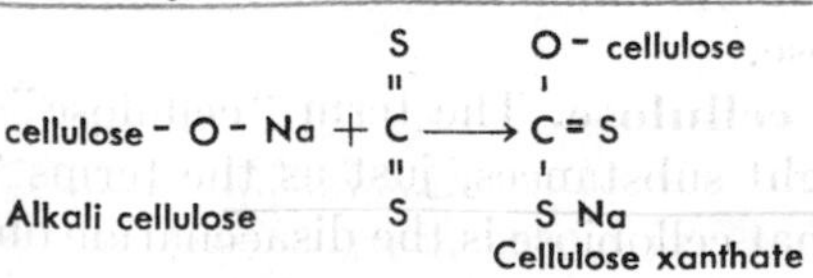

$$\text{cellulose} - O - Na + C\overset{S}{\underset{S}{\parallel}} \longrightarrow C\overset{O - \text{cellulose}}{\underset{S\ Na}{\parallel}}$$

Alkali cellulose   Cellulose xanthate

Solutions of the xanthates in water are very viscous and are called "viscose." Viscose is used in the production of one type of rayon.

Cellulose may be nitrated to form cellulose nitrates or nitrocelluloses which are of much importance in the manufacture of explosives, celluloid, and other substances. Cellulose acetates are used in making photographic film, rayon, and various plastic materials.

Cellulose ethers, such as the methylated celluloses, are prepared by treatment of cellulose with alkali and dimethyl sulfate or other alkyl sulfate. They may also be prepared by treating alkali cellulose with alkyl halides.

Cellulose does not give a characteristic reaction with iodine.

INULIN

Inulin is a polysaccharide composed of D-fructose units. It occurs as the reserve carbohydrate in the tubers of chicory, Jerusalem artichoke, and dahlia, and in the bulb of onion and garlic. Inulin is a white, more or less crystalline powder. Owing to the presence of fructofuranose units, it is very easily hydrolyzed by acids. Inulin is readily soluble in hot, but slightly soluble in cold, water. When heated with water, it does not gelatinize as starch does. It does not give a characteristic color with iodine. Inulin is not hydrolyzed by amylase but is split by inulinase. It is levorotatory.

The structure of inulin has been worked out especially by Haworth and associates from studies of methylated inulin. When hydrolyzed, methylated inulin gives chiefly 3,4,6-trimethyl fructofuranose with some 2,3,4,6-tetramethyl fructofuranose. The amount of tetramethyl fructose corresponds to one glucosidic fructose end group for about 30 fructose units. Since inulin apparently is not a branched structure, this corresponds to a molecular weight of approximately 5000. The type of linkage in the inulin molecule is:

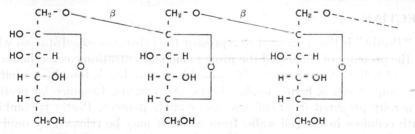

Inulin is used as a source of commercial fructose. It is also administered to animals in studies of glomerular membrane filtration rates.

Inulin is not hydrolyzed by any of the enzymes of the gastrointestinal tract and is not utilized as food.

AGAR

Agar is a vegetable mucilage obtained from seaweeds. It is a sulfuric acid ester of a complex galactose polysaccharide. Agar is odorless and tasteless. It swells strongly in cold water but does not dissolve. It dissolves in hot water to form a sol which upon cooling sets to a gel. Agar is ordinarily combined with metal ions such as Na$^+$, K$^+$, Ca^{++}, and Mg^{++}; that is, it is a salt. The metals are combined with the sulfuric acid groups of the agar molecule and are necessary for gelation. The free agar acid is a relatively strong acid (a 1 per cent solution having a pH of about 2.0) and will not form gels. A 1 per cent agar gel is fairly rigid, and a 2 per cent gel is very rigid. These agar gels are not liquefied by organisms that digest gelatin and are very valuable as a supporting agent in bacterial culture media. Agar is nondigestible and is at times given to provide bulk to the feces in the treatment of constipation.

Carrageen, or "Irish Moss," is similar to agar in composition.

Both D- and L-galactose units are present in the agar molecule, but the complete structure has not been established.

GUM ARABIC OR GUM ACACIA

The vegetable gums are carbohydrate materials containing hexoses or pentoses or both in glucoside union and a carbohydrate acid group. Hydrolysis of gums usually yields galactose and arabinose or xylose, alone or in mixtures. Gum arabic, or gum acacia, is one of the most important and best-known gums. Gum arabic appears to be the salt of a high polymer of arabic acid which upon complete hydrolysis yields galactose, arabinose, rhamnose, and glucuronic acid. Upon careful partial hydrolysis an aldobionic acid composed of D-galactose and D-glucuronic acid is obtained which is 6-D-galactopyranosyl-β-D-glucuroniside. Arabic acid appears to have a molecular weight of about 1200 and is a relatively strong acid (pH of 1 per cent solution = 2.70).

Gum arabic is used in the preparation of pharmaceuticals, in confections, and as an adhesive.

PECTINS

"Pectin" is the term used to represent the substance or substances which in the presence of sugar and the proper acid concentration causes the formation of jellies. Pectin occurs widespread in nature but is found especially in the pulp of citrus fruits, apples, beets, and carrots. Commercial pectin is generally prepared from cull lemons or apple pomace. Pectin is combined with cellulose in the cell walls, from which it may be released by mild hydrolysis or other means and converted into soluble pectin. The combined, insoluble pectin is referred to as "protopectin." When soluble pectin is boiled with dilute acid, it is slowly hydrolyzed to pectic acid and methyl alcohol. Dilute alkali at room temperature quickly decomposes pectin into alkali pectate and methyl alcohol. Purified pectin yields 10 to 12 per cent methyl alcohol. Pectin accordingly is the methyl ester (many methyl groups per molecule) of pectic acid. Pectic acid is a chain of at least 200 1 $\longrightarrow$ 4 linked α-D-galactopyranosyluronic acid units.

In order for pectin to form a gel, the mixture must contain 65 to 70 per cent sugar, 0.3 to 0.7 per cent pectin, and the pH must be 3.2 to 3.5.

Large amounts of pectin are used in the fruit-conserving industry and for other purposes.

"Pectin" is a group term, and a number of different pectins are known, some of which are insoluble and useless for gelation.

ALGINIC ACIDS

Alginic acids consist chiefly of linear polymers of D-mannuronic acid units with β-1 $\longrightarrow$ 4 linkages and molecular weights ranging from 50,000 to 185,000. Alginic acids are found in many marine algae and in giant kelp, which is a commercial source. Large amounts are used as emulsifier and smoothing agent in the food industries. The alginic acids gel easily and form salts, as do the pectins.

CHITIN

The amino sugars, such as glucosamine, galactosamine, and mannosamine, are rather widely distributed in nature in combination with proteins, and glucosamine occurs in a polysaccharide type of substance called "chitin." All the naturally occurring amino sugars appear to be 2-hexosamines, in which the amino group has the same configuration as the 2-OH in the parent sugar.

Chitin is the structural material of the skeletons of the arthropoda. With few exceptions chitin occurs only in the invertebrates. It forms the exoskeletons of crustaceans (crabs, lobsters, etc.), insects, etc., and is an important constituent of the lenses of the eyes, of the tendons, and of the linings of the digestive, excretory, and respiratory tracts of these animals. Chitin bears the same relation to invertebrates as cellulose does to plants.

When chitin is hydrolyzed by acids, it yields glucosamine and acetic acid. The acetic acid is combined with the amino group of glucosamine as acetylglucosamine. Chitin is a condensation product of acetylglucosamine, just as cellulose is a condensation product of glucose. When chitin is partially hydrolyzed, chitobiose, composed of two molecules of acetylglucosamine, is obtained. The linkage of the acetylglucosamine units in chitobiose is exactly the same as that of glucose units in cellobiose, the disaccharide from cellulose. The chitin molecules are chains of acetylglycosamine units linked similarly as the glucose units in cellulose (β-1-4 linkages). X-ray diffraction studies show that chitin is beautifully crystalline. Chitin is highly resistant to the action of solvents and of bacteria:

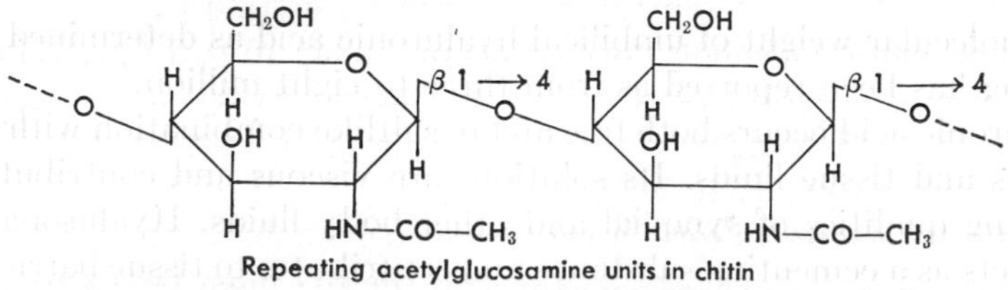

Repeating acetylglucosamine units in chitin

MUCOPOLYSACCHARIDES

The substances referred to as "mucopolysaccharides" often are composed of amino sugar and uronic acid units as the principal components, though some are chiefly made up of amino sugar and monosaccharide units without the presence of uronic acid (27). The hexosamine present is generally acetylated.

The mucopolysaccharides are essential components of tissues, where they are generally present, at least in part, combined with protein as mucoproteins or mucoids.

Included among the mucopolysaccharides are such biologically important substances as hyaluronic acid, heparin, the chondroitin sulfuric acids, and the blood-group polysaccharides.

HYALURONIC ACID

Hyaluronic acid was first isolated from vitreous humor by Meyer and Palmer (28) and later from synovial fluid, skin, umbilical cord, hemolytic streptococci, and other sources. Hyaluronic acid appears to serve as an integral part of the gel-like ground substance of connective and other tissues, and as lubricant and shock absorbent in joints.

Hyaluronic acid upon hydrolysis yields equimolecular quantities of D-glucosamine, D-glucuronic acid, and acetic acid. When acted upon by the enzyme testicular hyaluronidase followed by mineral acid hydrolysis, hyalobiuronic acid is obtained. Hyalobiuronic acid is 3-(β-D-glucopyranosyluronic acid)-2-amino-2-deoxy-D-glucose; that is, a combination of D-glucuronic acid and D-glucosamine. Hyaluronic acid appears to be an unbranched or nearly unbranched chain polymer of N-acetylated hyalobiuronic acid units:

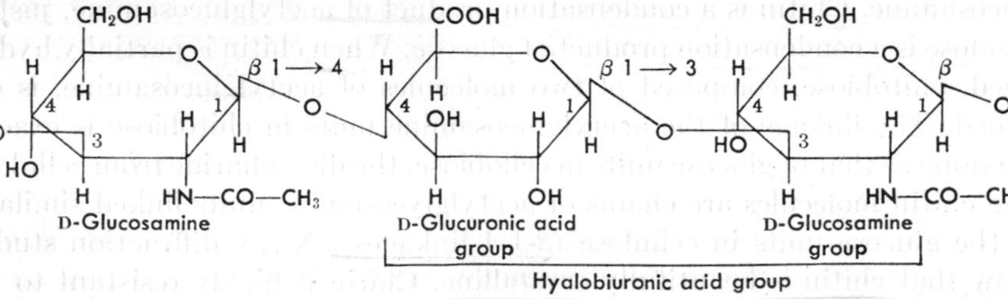

Repeating units in hyaluronic acid structure

The molecular weight of umbilical hyaluronic acid as determined by light scattering has been reported as from three to eight million.

Hyaluronic acid occurs both free and in saltlike combination with proteins of tissues and tissue fluids. Its solutions are viscous and contribute to the lubricating qualities of synovial and other body fluids. Hyaluronic acid in tissues acts as a cementing substance and contributes to tissue barriers which permit metabolites to pass through but resist penetration by bacteria and other infective agents.

The substances which Levene (29) classified as mucoitin sulfates appear to have been mixtures of several substances. In current practice "mucoitin" as used earlier is known as "hyaluronic acid." It appears desirable to discard the terms "mucoitin" and "mucoitin sulfate."

HEPARIN   *α 1-4, α 1-3 linkages*

Heparin (α-heparin) is a blood anticoagulant present in liver (from which it was originally isolated), lung, thymus, spleen, and blood.

Heparin is a polymer of D-glucuronic acid and D-glucosamine. The amino groups and some of the hydroxyl groups are combined with sulfuric acid. The probable repeating unit is given below:

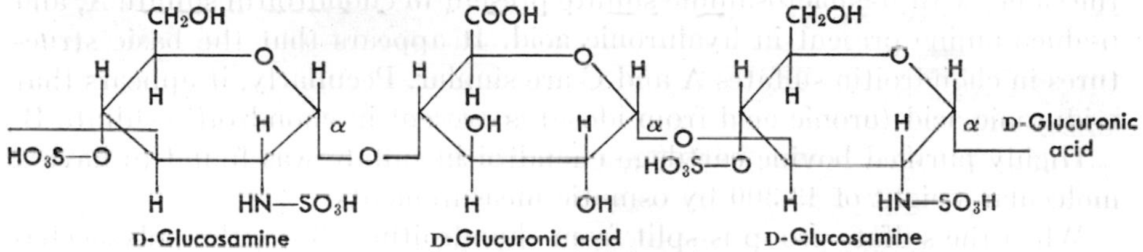

CH₂OH   COOH   CH₂OH

HO₃S—O   OH   HO₃S—O   α D-Glucuronic acid

D-Glucosamine   HN—SO₃H   OH   HN—SO₃H
D-Glucosamine   D-Glucuronic acid   D-Glucosamine
Repeating units in heparin

The molecular weight of heparin appears to be in the range 17,000 to 20,000. It is strongly acidic, due to the sulfuric acid groups, and readily forms salts. The barium salt is used in its isolation.

CHONDROITIN SULFATES   *β 1-4, β 1-3 linkages*

The chondroitin sulfates are among the principal mucopolysaccharides in the ground substance of mammalian tissues and cartilage, and occur combined with proteins. Three chondroitin sulfates have been isolated and designated A, B, and C. Chondroitin sulfate A is the chief one present in cartilage, adult bone, and cornea; chondroitin sulfate B is present in skin, heart valves, and tendons; and chondroitin sulfate C is found in cartilage and tendons. The chondroitin sulfates have been differentiated on the basis of optical rotation and their behavior toward testicular hyaluronidase.

Chondroitin sulfates A and C appear to be made up of equimolar quantities of N-acetyl-2-amino-2-deoxy-D-galactose (N-acetyl-D-galactosamine or N-acetylchondrosamine), D-glucuronic acid, and sulfuric acid. A deacetylated disaccharide, called "chondrosine," has been obtained by acid hydrolysis of chondroitin sulfate A. Chondrosine is 3-O-β-D-glucopyranosyluronic acid-2-amino-2-deoxy-D-galactopyranose. Its structure is the same as that of hyalobiuronic acid obtained from hyaluronic acid except that D-galactosamine replaces D-glucosamine. It appears that the basic structure of chondroitin sulfate A consists of repeating units of glucuronic acid and N-acetylated glucosamine with esterfied sulfate on position 4 or 6 of galactosamine:

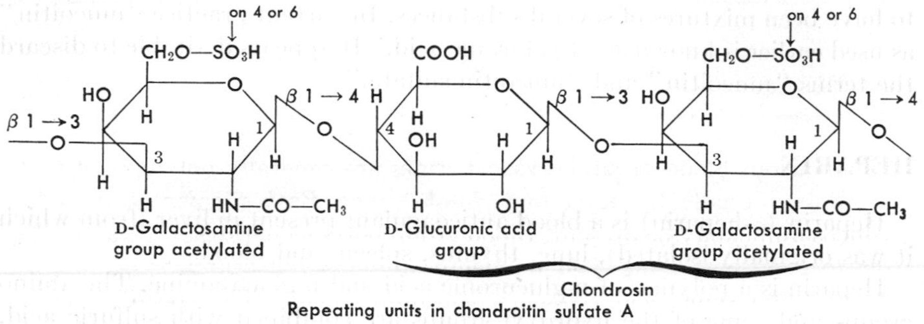

Chondrosin

Repeating units in chondroitin sulfate A

Thus, the basic structures of hyaluronic acid and chondroitin sulfate A are the same, with D-galactosamine sulfate present in chondroitin sulfate A, and D-glucosamine present in hyaluronic acid. It appears that the basic structures in chondroitin sulfates A and C are similar. Peculiarly, it appears that L-iduronic acid (uronic acid from idose) is present in chondroitin sulfate B.

Highly purified bovine cartilage chondroitin sulfate was found to have a molecular weight of 43,300 by osmotic measurements.

When the sulfate group is split from chondroitin sulfate, the polysaccharide chondroitin is obtained.

An anticoagulant isolated from lung, and called "β-heparin," appears to be chondroitin sulfate B, since it yields approximately equimolar quantities of N-acetyl-D-galactosamine, L-iduronic acid, and sulfuric acid.

Chondroitin, which appears to be desulfated chondroitin sulfate A or C, has been isolated from the polysaccharide components of the cornea (17, p. 720). Keratosulfate, also a corneal polysaccharide, is composed of N-acetyl-D-glucosamine, D-galactose, and sulfuric acid, apparently in equimolecular proportions (17, p. 722).

BLOOD-GROUP POLYSACCHARIDES

The so-called blood-group polysaccharides are present in erythrocytes, saliva, gastric mucin, cystic fluids, and other body secretions. When combined with proteins, they constitute the A, B, O (H), Rh, and other antigens of the erythrocytes and differentiate the blood groups or types. When red cells containing a specific type polysaccharide antigen are mixed with specific antibodies of serum, agglutination of the cells takes place: the erythrocytes of type A blood are agglutinated by antibodies (isoagglutinins) found in serum of type B or O blood; group A serum agglutinates red cells of blood types B and AB; etc. Thus, by working out the agglutination characteristics of cells and sera, it is possible to determine whether or not a given blood is of the proper type for transfusion into a particular patient so that agglutination and disastrous results will not follow.

Table 7.4

Blood Type	Serum Isoagglutinins	Agglutination of Red Cells of Blood Type			
		A	B	AB	O (H)
A	β	−	+	+	−
B	α	+	−	+	−
AB	none	−	−	−	−
O (H)	α and β	+	+	+	−

The various blood group polysaccharides are generally polymers of D-glucosamine or D-galactosamine and simple sugar. Both D-galactosamine and D-glucosamine may be present. Blood group polysaccharides A, B, and O (H) from ovarian cyst fluid yield D-galactosamine, D-glucosamine, D-galactose, L-fucose, and sialic acid (N-acetylneuraminic acid). The specific polysaccharides from hog gastric mucin are made up of D-galactose, N-acetyl-D-glucosamine, and L-fucose.

SIALIC ACIDS

The sialic acids represent a group of naturally occurring substances widely distributed in tissues, particularly in mucins and blood group substances. They are components of complex lipids and carbohydrates (mucopolysaccharides of mucoproteins).

The sialic acids are acetyl derivatives of a 9-carbon 3-deoxy-5-amino sugar acid called "neuraminic acid," in which the amino group is acetylated, and in some cases a hydroxyl group also is acetylated. Neuraminic acids may be considered to be derived from an amino sugar (D-mannosamine) and pyruvic acid by an aldol condensation. Certain bacterial enzymes hydrolyze neuraminic acids to an amino sugar and pyruvic acid:

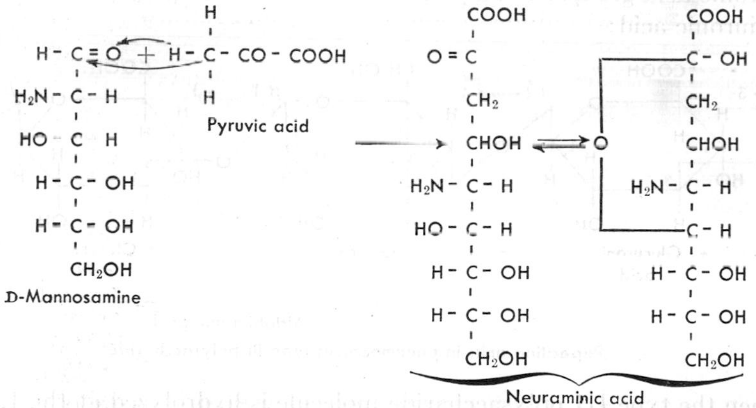

The sialic acids present in mucopolysaccharides are linked with a sugar by a glycosidic bond at carbon 2 of the sialic acid.

Sialic acid containing the glycolyl group CH_2OH—CO—, substituted in neuraminic acid in place of the acetyl group CH_3—CO—, has been found in salivary mucin and erythrocytes.

It seems probable that the neuraminic acids and the sialic acids derived from them represent a group of compounds in which either mannosamine or glucosamine may be a constituent. However, up to the present only mannosamine has been found.

The neuraminic and sialic acids have been reviewed by Roseman (30).

BACTERIAL POLYSACCHARIDES

SPECIFIC POLYSACCHARIDES

Complex carbohydrate substances have been isolated from many different species of bacteria. A number of these carbohydrates have been found to be responsible for the specificity of immune reactions. They are commonly referred to as "specific polysaccharides."

While the hydrolytic products of the different polysaccharides vary, the following substances have been obtained from the group as a whole: uronic acids, especially glucuronic and galacturonic; monosaccharides, such as glucose, galactose, arabinose, mannose, rhamnose; inositol; amino sugars, notably glucosamine and galactosamine; and acetic acid. The amino sugars present are N-acetylated.

Heidelberger and Avery (31) first demonstrated the presence of specific bacterial polysaccharides by their work on pneumococcus types II and III, where the polysaccharides are found in the bacterial capsules. Type II polysaccharide is composed of D-glucose, L-rhamnose (40 per cent), and D-glucuronic acid units, while type III polysaccharide contains only D-glucose and D-glucuronic acid groups. By careful hydrolysis of type III polysaccharide an aldobiuronic acid has been obtained composed of D-glucose and D-glucuronic acid units, 3-O-β-D-glucopyranosyl-D-glucopyranosyluronic acid. The structure of the polysaccharide is a linear chain with alternate glucose and glucuronic acid groups. It may be considered a chain polymer of the above aldobiuronic acid:

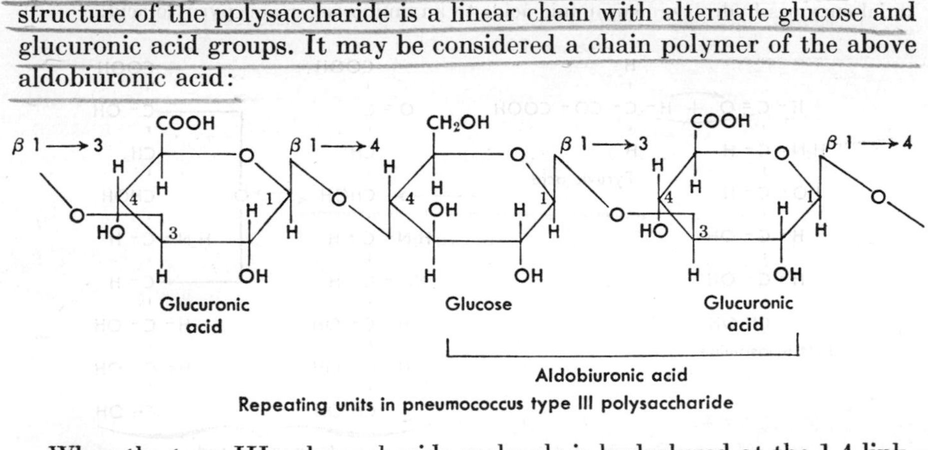

Repeating units in pneumococcus type III polysaccharide

When the type III polysaccharide molecule is hydrolyzed at the 1,4 linkages an aldobiuronic acid with D-glucose linked to D-glucuronic acid by 1 ⟶ 3 linkage is obtained, 3-O-β-D-glucopyranosyl-D-glucopyranosyluronic acid. If, however, the 1,3 linkages are hydrolyzed, leaving the glucuronic acid and glucose joined by 1 ⟶ 4 bonds, a different aldobiuronic acid is formed, cellobiuronic acid, 4-O-β-D-glucopyranosyluronic acid-D-glucopyranose.

The polysaccharide of type I pneumococcus is composed of D-galacturonic acid (28 per cent) and N-acetyl-D-glucosamine, while type VIII polysaccharide is made up of D-glucose and D-glucuronic acid (in 7:2 ratio), and type

XIV polysaccharide has D-galactose and N-acetyl-D-glucosamine as constituent units. Only the type III polysaccharide structure has been definitely established.

The immunologically active polysaccharide of tubercle bacillus has been found to contain D-galactose, D-mannose, D-arabinose, and inositol.

The so-called Vi antigen of *Salmonella typhosa* and other bacterial species appears to be largely a polymer of an N-acetyl-aminohexuronic acid, possibly of N-acetyl-D-glucosaminuronic acid (32).

DEXTRANS

[handwritten: branch 1-4, 1-3 ; straight chain 1-6]

Polysaccharides called "dextrans" are formed when various strains of *Leuconostoc mesenteroides* and some other microorganisms are grown in sucrose solutions. The dextrans form ropy slimes and have various molecular weights, some as high as 4,000,000. They are all D-glucopyranose polymers, but the molecular structure varies with the type and strain of organism forming them. They have branched structures involving $1 \longrightarrow 6$, $1 \longrightarrow 4$, and $1 \longrightarrow 3$ linkages between the glucose units, though α-$1 \longrightarrow 6$ bonds generally predominate.

Dextran synthesis by microorganisms consists in a series of transglycosylations. Apparently the process starts something as follows, assuming a $1 \longrightarrow 6$ linkage to be formed at first:

$$\text{Glucose-1-fructoside} + \text{glucose-1-fructoside} \xrightarrow{\text{Enzyme system}} \text{Glucose-1,6-glucoside} + 2 \text{ fructose}$$
$$\text{Sucrose} \qquad\qquad \text{Sucrose}$$

Sucrose then continues to add glucose units to the new disaccharide with varying linkages to build up the exceedingly complex dextran structures. The over-all process may be represented approximately as follows:

$$n \text{ Sucrose} \longrightarrow (C_6H_{10}O_5)_n + n \text{ fructose}$$
$$\text{Dextran}$$

Dextran is of importance in medicine because of its use as plasma substitute or extender in the treatment of shock. The very great particle size of native dextran makes it unsuitable for this purpose. Good preparations are obtained by hydrolyzing it with acid or enzymes to an average molecular weight of about 76,000.

COLOR REACTIONS OF CARBOHYDRATES

A very large number of color reactions more or less characteristic of carbohydrates is known. Most of these reactions are carried out in strongly acid solution; this hydrolyzes the polysaccharides present to monosaccharides, which give the color reactions. The basis of these color tests involving strongly acid reagents appears to be conversion of the monosaccharide to furfural (pentose), hydroxymethylfurfural (hexose), methylfurfural (methyl-pentose as rhamnose), or other aldehydic compound. The aldehyde formed by action of the acid is then condensed with a phenol or other aromatic substance to give the color. A few of the more commonly used color reactions are given below.

a) *Molisch test.* This is a very sensitive general reaction for carbohydrates. It is performed by mixing a dew drops of an alcoholic solution of α-naphthol with the sugar solution and stratifying the mixture over concentrated sulfuric acid. A red or violet ring appears at the junction of the liquids. Amino sugars, sugar alcohols, and carboxylic acids do not give the test. 2-Ketoaldonic acids give green colors.

b) *Bial's test, orcinol-hydrochloric acid test.* This is a sensitive reaction for the detection of pentoses and certain uronic acids which decompose upon heating with acid to form pentoses (glucuronic, galacturonic acids, etc.). A dilute solution of orcinol in 30 per cent hydrochloric acid containing a little ferric chloride constitutes Bial's reagent. The reagent is heated to boiling, and several drops of the sugar solution are added immediately after removing from the flame. Pentoses give a green color, as do aldohexuronic acids (glucuronic, etc.). Trioses and 5-ketoaldonic acids give a positive test. Ketoheptoses give a purple color, and ketohexoses and methylpentoses produce orange-colored solutions which separate dark green precipitates on standing.

c) *Phloroglycinol-hydrochloric acid test.* When pentoses are boiled with a solution of phloroglucinol in hydrochloric acid, a cherry red color is formed. Galactose also gives this test.

d) *Seliwanoff's test* (*Resorcinol hydrochloric acid test*). This test is given by ketohexoses. Seliwanoff's reagent is a solution of resorcinol in hydrochloric acid. When heated with the reagent, ketohexoses give a red color.

e) *Naphthoresorcinol test.* This test is used for the detection of the common uronic acids, such as glucuronic, galacturonic, and mannuronic. The sugar is dissolved in 1 *N* hydrochloric acid containing a small amount of naphthoresorcinol and heated for five minutes in a boiling water bath. The mixture is cooled and extracted with ether. The ether solution is colored purple, violet, or pink when the test is positive.

f) *Test for deoxy sugars.* When a pine splinter is placed in concentrated hydrochloric acid containing a 2-deoxy sugar, the splinter develops a green color. Kiliani's test consists in placing the sugar in glacial acetic acid containing a ferrous salt and sulfuric acid; a blue color is produced.

g) *Barfoed's test.* This test is used in distinguishing monosaccharides from reducing disaccharides. Barfoed's reagent is a solution of cupric acetate in dilute acetic acid. When monosaccharides are boiled with this reagent, it is reduced and Cu_2O separates. The reducing disaccharides (reduce Fehling, Benedict, Shaffer-Hartman reagents) reduce Barfoed's reagent very slowly as compared with the monosaccharides. In using this test the concentrations of the sugar solutions compared should be not too different, since a more concentrated disaccharide solution will reduce faster than a dilute monosaccharide solution.

h) Moore's test. This test consists in heating the carbohydrate with dilute alkali, a yellow to brown or reddish brown color being produced if the carbohydrate contains a free sugar group.

Table 7.5.   Relative Sweetness of Sugars and Other Substances
Sucrose is assigned a value of 100 for comparison

Substance	Sweetness
Lactose	16
Raffinose	22
Galactose	32
Rhamnose	32
Maltose	32
Xylose	40
Sorbitol	54
Mannitol	57
Glucose	74
Sucrose	100
Glycerol	108
Invert sugar	130
Ethylene glycol	130
Fructose	173
Dulcin (aromatic)	20,000
Saccharin (aromatic)	55,000
1-N-Propoxy-2-amino-4-nitrobenzene	200,000

GENERAL REFERENCES

Advances in Carbohydrate Chemistry. Academic Press, New York, 1945—. Annual monographs on carbohydrate chemistry.

Annual Review of Biochemistry. Annual Reviews, Inc., Palo Alto, California. These annual volumes contain up-to-date reviews on carbohydrates.

Bates, F. J., and associates: "Polarimetry, Saccharimetry and the Sugars," *Natl. Bur. Standards (U.S.) Circ. C 440,* U.S. Government Printing Office, Washington, D.C., 1942.

Browne, C. A., and Zerban, F. W.: *Physical and Chemical Methods of Sugar Analysis.* John Wiley & Sons, New York, 1941.

Burger, M.: *Bacterial Polysaccharides.* Charles C Thomas, Springfield, Ill., 1950.

Fieser, L. F., and Fieser, M.: *Organic Chemistry,* 3rd ed. Reinhold, New York, 1956.

Fischer, E.: *Untersuchungen über Kohlenhydrate und Fermente.* Berlin, 1909.

Haworth, W. N.: *The Constitution of Sugars.* Longmans, New York, 1929.

Heuser, E.: *The Chemistry of Cellulose.* John Wiley & Sons, New York, 1944.

Hudson, C. S.: "Relations between Rotatory Power and Structure in the Sugar Group," *Natl. Bur. Standards Bull. 21.* U.S. Government Printing Office, Washington, D.C., 1926.

Meyer, K. H.: *Natural and Synthetic High Polymers,* 2nd ed. Interscience, New York, 1950.

Pigman, W.: *The Carbohydrates.* Academic Press, New York, 1957.

Whistler, R. L., and Smart, C. L.: *Polysaccharide Chemistry.* Academic Press, New York, 1953.

SPECIAL REFERENCES

1. Bijovet, J. M.: *Endeavour,* **14,** 71, 1955. Trommel, J., and Bijovet, J. M.: *Acta Cryst.,* **7,** 703, 1954.
2. Weygand, F.: *Ber.,* **73,** 1284, 1940.
3. Wohl, A.: *Ber.,* **26,** 730, 1893.
4. Willstätter, R., and Schudel, G.: *Ber.,* **51,** 780, 1918. *Ind. Eng. Chem., Anal. Ed.,* **2,** 413, 1930.

5. Moore, S., and Link, K. P.: *J. Biol. Chem.*, **133**, 293, 1940. Richtmyer, N. K.: *Advances in Carbohydrate Chem.*, **6**, 175, 1951. Sowden, J. C., and Kuenne, D. J.: *J. Am. Chem. Soc.*, **75**, 2788, 1953.
6. Topper, Y. J.: *J. Biol. Chem.*, **225**, 419, 1957.
7. Whistler, R. L.; Hough, L.; and Hylin, J. W.: *Anal. Chem.*, **25**, 1215, 1953.
8. Saifer, A., and Gerstenfeld, S.: *J. Lab. Clin. Med.*, **51**, 448, 1958.
9. Morris, D. L.: *Science*, **107**, 254, 1948.
10. Haworth, W. N.: *J. Soc. Chem. Ind.*, **46**, 295, 1927; **54**, 859, 1935.
11. Haworth, W. N.: *The Constitution of Sugars.* Edward Arnold, London, 1929. Sponsler, O. L., and Dore, W. H.: *Ann. Rev. Biochem.*, **5**, 66, 1936. Reeves, R. E.: *Advances in Carbohydrate Chem.*, **6**, 123, 1951.
12. Haworth, W. N.: *J. Chem. Soc.*, **107**, 8, 1915. For an improved method see West, E. S., and Holden, R. F.: *J. Am. Chem. Soc.*, **56**, 930, 1934.
13. Jackson, E. L., and Hudson, C. S.: *J. Am. Chem. Soc.*, **59**, 994, 1937.
14. Isbell, H. S.: *J. Chem. Education*, **12**, 96, 1935.
15. Kent, P. W., and Whitehouse, M. W.: *Biochemistry of the Aminosugars.* Academic Press, New York, 1955.
16. Roe, J. H., and Kuether, C. A.: *J. Biol. Chem.*, **147**, 399, 1943. Bolin, D. W., and Book, L.: *Science*, **106**, 451, 1947.
17. Koshland, D. E., and Stein, S. F.: *J. Biol. Chem.*, **208**, 139, 1954.
18. Pigman, W.: *The Carbohydrates*, p. 523. Academic Press, New York, 1957.
19. Bell, D. J.: *Ann. Repts.*, **52**, 333, 1956.
20. Larner, J., and McNickle, C. M.: *J. Biol. Chem.*, **215**, 723, 1955.
21. Cori, G. T., and Cori, C. F.: *J. Biol. Chem.*, **131**, 397, 1939; **135**, 733, 1940. Bear, R. S., and Cori, C. F.: *ibid.*, **140**, 111, 1941.
22. Hanes, C. S.: *Nature*, **145**, 348, 1940.
23. Bell, D. J., and Young, F. G.: *Biochem. J.*, **28**, 882, 1934.
24. Meyer, K. H., and Jeanloz, R.: *Advances in Enzymol.*, **3**, 112, 1943.
25. Meyer, K. H., and Bernfeld, P.: *Helv. Chim. Acta*, **23**, 875, 1940.
26. Staudinger, H., and Husemann, E.: *Ann.*, **530**, 1, 1937. Staudinger, H., and Zapf, F.: *J. prakt. Chem.*, **157**, 1, 1941.
27. Meyer, K. H.: *Harvey Lectures*, **51**, 88, 1957. *Advances in Protein Chem.*, **2**, 249, 1945. Stacey, M.: *Advances in Carbohydrate Chem.*, **2**, 161, 1946.
28. Meyer, K., and Palmer, J. W.: *J. Biol. Chem.*, **107**, 629, 1934.
29. Levene, P. A.: *The Hexosamines and Mucoproteins.* Longmans, Green, London, 1925.
30. Roseman, S.: *Ann. Rev. Biochem.*, **28**, 545, 1959.
31. Heidelberger, M., and Avery, O. T.: *J. Exptl. Med.*, **38**, 73, 1923; **40**, 301, 1924. Goebel, W. F.: *ibid.*, **42**, 727, 1925. Heidelberger, M., and Goebel, W. F.: *J. Biol. Chem.*, **70**, 613, 1926.
32. Clark, W. R.; McLaughlin, J.; and Webster, M. E.: *J. Biol. Chem.*, **230**, 81, 1958.

8

Proteins

OCCURRENCE, IMPORTANCE, AND GENERAL PROPERTIES OF PROTEINS

The term "protein" is derived from the Greek word *proteios*, meaning primary or holding first place, and is well chosen. It represents an enormous group of complex nitrogenous compounds, members of which occur in all animal and plant protoplasm.

There is greater diversity in the chemical composition of proteins than in that of any other group of biologically important compounds.

The proteins of the protoplasm of all different kinds of animals and plants are chemically different and characteristic. This difference in proteins extends to the composition of different tissues within the organism. For example, the proteins of muscle, liver, brain, spleen, kidney, and blood differ in composition and properties. The differentiation of tissues within the organism, as well as the differentiation of species, is basically related to the specific proteins present in the protoplasm. The nuclear material of cells is composed chiefly of nucleoproteins. The nucleoproteins of the germ cells are largely the physical basis for the transmission of hereditary characteristics from generation to generation.

The protein content of tissues varies widely. Fresh mammalian striated and unstriated muscle generally contains 18 to 20 per cent protein, blood plasma 6.5 to 7.5 per cent, and brain about 8 per cent. Egg yolk is about 15 per cent and egg white 12 per cent protein. The average protein content of cow's milk is about 3.3 per cent, while the protein of cheese varies, according to kind, from 14 to 49 per cent. The quantity of protein in the leaves, stems, roots, and tubers of plants is relatively small, while the seeds of plants

often contain large amounts of protein. For example, lettuce contains about
1.2 per cent, asparagus 1.8 per cent, cabbage 1.6 per cent, potatoes 2 per cent,
and beets 1.6 per cent of protein. The protein content of cereal grains generally varies between 10 and 15 per cent. The protein content of dried beans
and nuts is generally high. Values for some of these are: navy beans, 22 per
cent; lima beans, 18 per cent; soybeans, 37 per cent; peanuts, 26 per cent;
and almonds, 21 per cent. The protein content of fruits such as apples, ber-
ries, citrus fruits, peaches, pears, and plums varies from 0.4 to 1.5 per cent.

Plants readily synthesize proteins from simple substances such as carbon
dioxide, water, and inorganic nitrogen compounds. Animals, however, cannot
do this, but are directly or indirectly dependent upon plants for their protein
supply.

Although animals utilize food carbohydrates and lipids to a small extent
as structural components of protoplasm, their chief utilization is as sources
of energy for operating the body machinery. On the other hand, the main
function of food proteins is to provide the major organic structures of the
protoplasmic machine itself, although excess is utilized as a source of energy.

Much of the regulation and integration of physiologic processes in the
body is accomplished through the hormones, which are secreted by the endocrine glands. Several of these hormones are specific proteins, such as insulin
of the pancreas and the hormones of the anterior pituitary gland.

The chemical processes involved in the digestion of foods and also in the
utilization or metabolism of foods in animal tissues are in general catalyzed
and directed by substances known as "enzymes." The chemical processes
of plants are similarly under the control of enzymes. Many enzymes have
been isolated, purified, and analyzed. Without exception, they have all been
found to be protein in character.

Certain diseases in both plants and animals are caused by substances
called "viruses." A few of these have been isolated and purified and have
been identified as very complex proteins.

All proteins contain C, H, O, N, and generally S. Many contain P. Elements such as I, Fe, Cu, and Zn are also occasionally present. The approximate average elementary composition of proteins is as follows:

Element	Per Cent
C	50
H	7
O	23
N	16
S	0–3
P	0–3

Other elements may be present in small amounts.

The amount of total protein in a tissue, foodstuff, or other material is
commonly estimated from a determination of nitrogen by the Kjeldahl procedure or a modification of it. In this procedure a sample of material is
digested with boiling concentrated sulfuric acid to which a catalyst such as
copper, selenium, or mercury has been added. Sodium or potassium sulfate

generally is also added to raise the boiling point of the "digestion mixture." The digestion process causes oxidation and destruction of the protein and conversion of the nitrogen to ammonia, which remains in the acid mixture as ammonium sulfate. The amount of ammonia nitrogen is determined by making the digest alkaline, followed by distillation of the liberated ammonia into standard acid and titration of excess acid with standard base. Most proteins contain about 16 per cent nitrogen, which means that the weight of protein nitrogen multiplied by 6.25 ($100 \div 16 = 6.25$) equals the weight of protein. Suppose a sample to be analyzed yields 0.1 g of nitrogen by the Kjeldahl process; then the weight of protein represented is $0.1 \times 6.25 = 0.625$ g. If the material analyzed contains nonprotein nitrogenous substances, these must be removed, or analysis must be made of the nonprotein nitrogen content, which is subtracted from the total nitrogen before the protein calculation. In a few cases the nitrogen content of a protein varies sufficiently from 16 per cent to necessitate the use of a factor other than 6.25. The Kjeldahl method of nitrogen determination is one of the most valuable and most used procedures of analysis employed by biochemists.

Protein molecules, like those of the glycogens, starches, and celluloses, are very large and are classed among the colloids. The molecular weights of proteins vary over a wide range. For example, the molecular weight of lactalbumin of milk is about 17,000, of gliadin from wheat 27,000, of human hemoglobin 66,700, of serum globulin 170,000, of edestin from hemp seed 300,000 of thyroglobulin from pig's thyroid 630,000, and of hemocyanin from snail blood 6,600,000; the molecular weight of tobacco mosaic virus protein has been estimated at 60,000,000.

Proteins do not melt when heated but decompose and char with the evolution of gases possessing a characteristic odor of burning feathers.

Different kinds of proteins are soluble in different solvents. Solvents for proteins include water, dilute neutral salt solutions, dilute acids and bases, 70 to 80 per cent alcohol, and strong solutions of salicylates, urea, and glycerol. Some proteins, such as the albuminoids, are insoluble in any of the above solvents. Solutions of proteins are colloidal and generally opalescent in appearance. When solutions of many of the proteins are heated, the protein molecules are rendered insoluble and coagulate.

HYDROLYSIS OF PROTEINS

All proteins yield amino acids when hydrolyzed, and all these acids but two have an amino group attached to the carbon atom next to the carboxyl group (α position); that is, they are α-amino acids. The general formula for these acids is:

$$\begin{array}{c} \text{COOH} \\ | \\ \text{H}_2\text{N}-\text{C}-\text{H} \\ | \\ \text{R} \end{array}$$

where R—represents a great variety of structures.

Some proteins yield only amino acids when hydrolyzed (simple proteins) whereas others produce amino acids plus other types of molecules (conjugated proteins).

Proteins are composed of amino acids united through an acid-amide type of bond called a "peptide linkage," and hydrolysis of proteins involves hydrolysis of many peptide linkages, since a protein molecule may contain hundreds or thousands of amino acid groups. The nature of the peptide linkage between the amino acids of proteins is shown below:

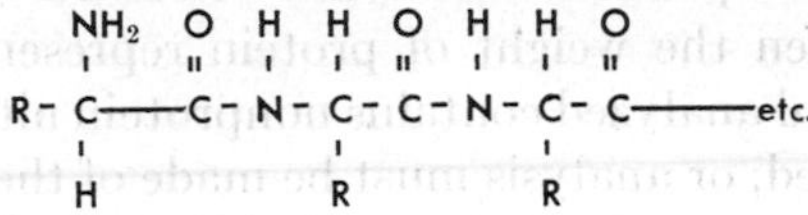

$$\begin{array}{c} NH_2 \quad O \quad H \quad H \quad O \quad H \quad H \quad O \\ R-C\!-\!-\!-\!C-N-C-C-N-C-C\!-\!-\!-\!etc. \\ H \qquad R \qquad R \end{array}$$

Just as is the case with acid amides, the peptide linkages in proteins are resistant to hydrolysis and require prolonged boiling with relatively strong acids or alkalies for completion of the process. The acids most commonly used are hydrochloric 3 to 12 N (commonly 6 N), sulfuric 4 to 8 N (commonly 8 N), and hydriodic 57 per cent. Among bases, 5 N sodium hydroxide and 14 per cent barium hydroxide are commonly used.

An interesting reagent for the acid hydrolysis of proteins is a synthetic resin containing sulfonic acid groups substituted into its structure (1).

Acid hydrolysis of proteins is generally preferred. Alkaline hydrolysis, although efficient in liberating the amino acids, partly converts the pure optically active forms which exist in proteins into racemic mixtures (mixtures of D and L forms). Acid hydrolysis is essentially free from this objection. Both acid and alkaline hydrolysis lead to decomposition and loss of some of the more unstable amino acids.

Proteolytic enzymes, such as trypsin, are frequently used for the hydrolysis of proteins. The process is generally slow and incomplete, but enzymatic hydrolysis causes neither racemization nor decomposition of sensitive amino acids.

About two dozen amino acids have been definitely established as occurring in proteins, and most proteins contain a large proportion of these amino acids. According to Vickery and Schmidt (2), an amino acid to be classified as occurring in proteins should have been isolated from protein hydrolysates by two independent workers and its structure proved by synthesis. A number of amino acids have been reported which as yet have not been established according to these requirements.

Amino acids have been classified in various ways. One system classifies them according to the number of amino and carboxyl groups present in the molecule as monoamino monocarboxylic acids and monoaminodicarboxylic acids, etc. Another system designates them as aliphatic, aromatic, and heterocyclic amino acids, depending upon the presence of chain and ring structures. Again they are classified according to reaction in solution as neutral, acidic, and basic amino acids. Classifications often utilize two or more of the above systems. The classification given below divides the amino acids into aliphatic, aromatic and heterocyclic with subdivisions indicating the relations between the amino and carboxyl groups present in the molecule.

All the amino acids except glycine possess at least one asymmetric carbon atom, and accordingly they may be obtained in optically active dextro and levo and optically inactive racemic forms. In all the amino acids (except glycine) the carbon atom attached to nitrogen and alpha to the carboxyl group is asymmetric. It has been found in general that the configuration of the asymmetric groups of the amino acids naturally occurring in plant and animal proteins is the same as found in L-glyceric aldehyde, to which the configuration of the L-series of sugars is referred. However, several amino acids with the D configuration occur in natural peptides, most of which are antibiotics. For example, D-phenylalanine is a constituent of gramicidin S and tyrocidine; D-leucine is present in gramicidin D, polymixins, and circulin; and D-proline is found in ergocornine (3).

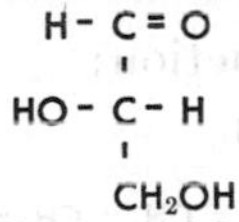

$$
\begin{array}{cc}
H-C=O & COOH \\
| & | \\
HO-C-H & H_2N-C-H \\
| & | \\
CH_2OH & R \\
\text{L-Glyceric aldehyde} & \text{L-Amino acid}
\end{array}
$$

In general, the natural amino acids are represented as the L-series and the unnatural acids as the D-series. The small capital D and L prefixes are used for the amino acids, just as they are for the sugars, and, as in case of the sugars, refer only to sugar series configurational relationships and not to the direction of optical rotation. In this book the small capital D and L prefixes will be used when designation is required. In the classification to follow it is to be understood that the optically active amino acids listed belong to the L-series and individually are designated as L-acids.

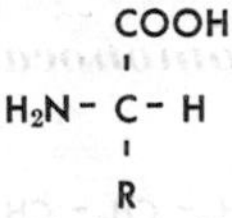

CLASSIFICATION AND FORMULAS OF AMINO ACIDS

A. AMINO ACIDS WHICH HAVE BEEN ESTABLISHED AS PROTEIN CONSTITUENTS

1. **Aliphatic amino acids.** Chain compounds.

a) *Monoaminomonocarboxylic acids.* Neutral in reaction:

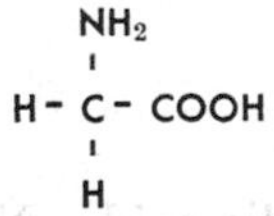

$$
\begin{array}{ccc}
NH_2 & NH_2 & NH_2 \\
| & | & | \\
H-C-COOH & CH_3-C-COOH & HO-CH_2-C-COOH \\
| & | & | \\
H & H & H \\
\text{Glycine, or glycocoll} & \text{Alanine} & \text{Serine} \\
\text{Aminoacetic acid} & \alpha\text{-Aminopropionic acid} & \alpha\text{-Amino-}\beta\text{-hydroxypropionic} \\
& & \text{acid}
\end{array}
$$

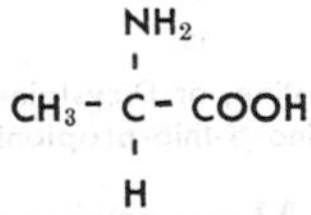

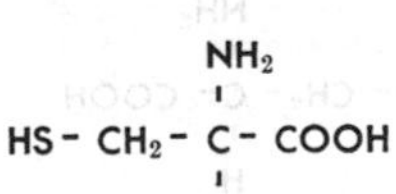

$$
\begin{array}{ccc}
NH_2 & H\ \ NH_2 & NH_2 \\
| & |\ \ | & | \\
HS-CH_2-C-COOH & CH_3-C-C-COOH & CH_3-S-CH_2-CH_2-C-COOH \\
| & |\ \ | & | \\
H & OH\ H & H \\
\text{Cysteine} & \text{Threonine} & \text{Methionine} \\
\alpha\text{-Amino-}\beta\text{-thiopropionic} & \alpha\text{-Amino-}\beta\text{-hydroxy-n-butyric} & \alpha\text{-Amino-}\gamma\text{-methylthio-n-butyric} \\
\text{acid} & \text{acid} & \text{acid}
\end{array}
$$

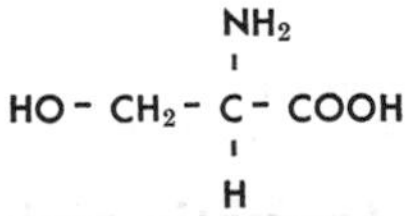

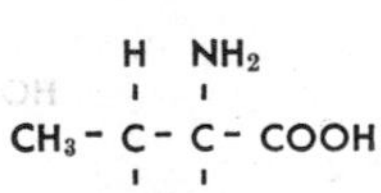

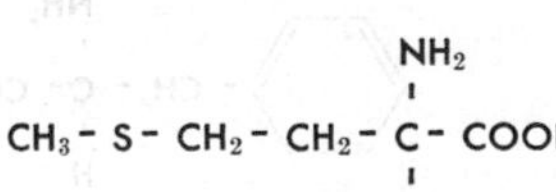

Valine
α-Aminoisovaleric acid

Leucine
α-Aminoisocaproic acid

Isoleucine
α-Amino-β-methyl-n-valeric acid

b) Monoaminodicarboxylic acids. Acid in reaction:

COOH
|
H₂N - C - H
|
CH₂
|
COOH

Aspartic acid
α-Aminosuccinic acid

COOH
|
H₂N - C - H
|
CH₂
|
CH₂
|
COOH

Glutamic acid
α-Aminoglutaric acid

c) Diaminomonocarboxylic acids. Basic in reaction:

$$H_2N - CH_2 - CH_2 - CH_2 - CH_2 - \underset{\underset{H}{|}}{\overset{\overset{NH_2}{|}}{C}} - COOH$$

Lysine
α-ε-Diamino-n-caproic acid

$$H_2N - CH_2 - \underset{\underset{OH}{|}}{\overset{\overset{H}{|}}{C}} - CH_2 - CH_2 - \underset{\underset{H}{|}}{\overset{\overset{NH_2}{|}}{C}} - COOH$$

Hydroxylysine
α-ε-Diamino-δ-hydroxy-n-caproic acid

$$H_2N - \underset{\underset{}{}}{\overset{\overset{NH}{||}}{C}} - \underset{\underset{}{}}{\overset{\overset{H}{|}}{N}} - CH_2 - CH_2 - CH_2 - \underset{\underset{H}{|}}{\overset{\overset{NH_2}{|}}{C}} - COOH$$

Arginine
α-Amino-δ-guanidino-n-valeric acid

d) Diaminodicarboxylic acids:

NH₂
|
CH₂ - C - COOH
| |
S   H
|
S   NH₂
| |
CH₂ - C - COOH
|
H

Cystine, or Dicysteine
Di-[α-amino-β-thio-propionic acid]

2. Aromatic amino acids. Monoaminomonocarboxylic acids. Neutral in reaction:

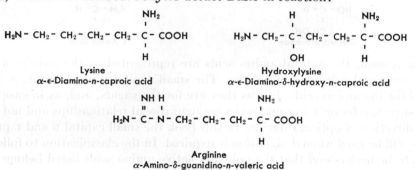

Phenylalanine
α-Amino-β-phenylpropionic acid

Tyrosine
α-Amino-β-parahydroxyphenylpropionic acid

3. Heterocyclic amino acids. Monoaminomonocarboxylic acids. Neutral in reaction, except histidine is slightly basic:

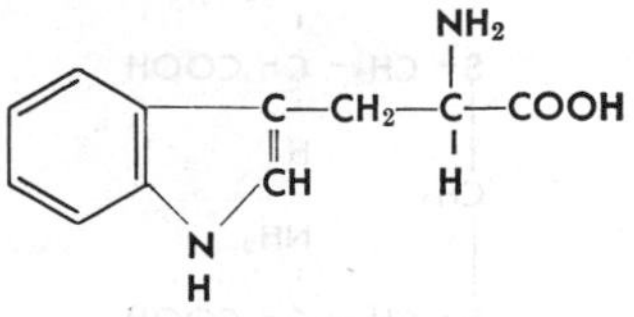

Tryptophane
α-Amino-β-indolepropionic acid

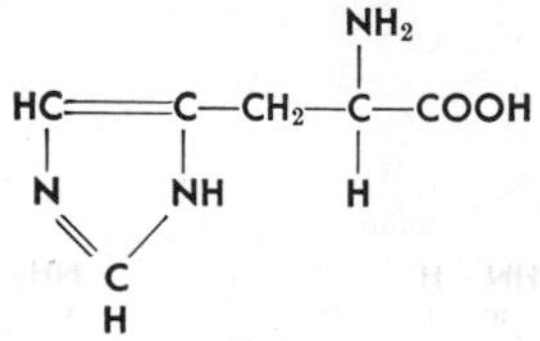

Histidine
α-Amino-β-imidazolepropionic acid

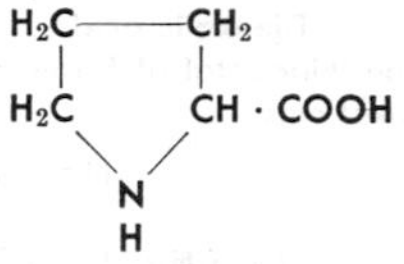

Proline
α-Pyrrolidinecarboxylic acid

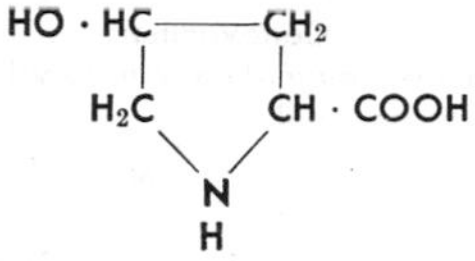

Hydroxyproline
γ-Hydroxy-α-pyrrolidinecarboxylic acid

B. AMINO ACIDS FOUND IN SPECIAL SOURCES:

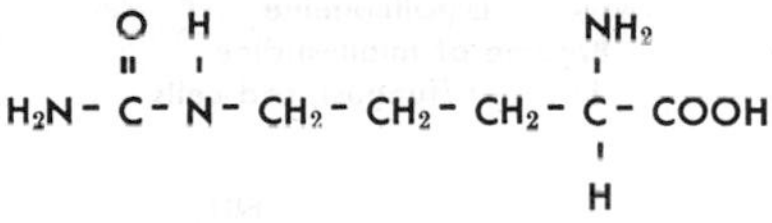

$$H_2N - \overset{O}{\overset{\|}{C}} - \overset{H}{\overset{|}{N}} - CH_2 - CH_2 - CH_2 - \overset{NH_2}{\overset{|}{C}} - COOH$$
$$|$$
$$H$$

Citrulline
α-Amino-δ-carbamido-n-valeric acid
In watermelon juice, liver

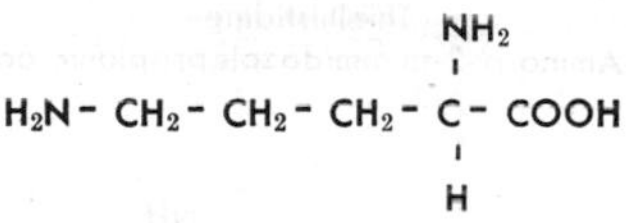

$$H_2N - CH_2 - CH_2 - CH_2 - \overset{NH_2}{\overset{|}{C}} - COOH$$
$$|$$
$$H$$

Ornithine
α-δ-Diamino-n-valeric acid
In liver

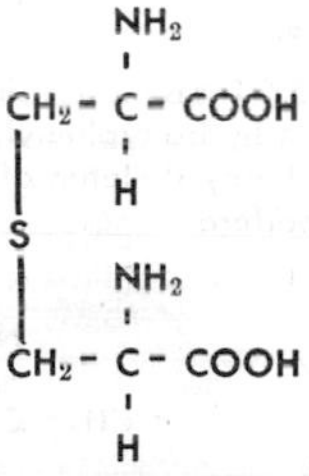

$$CH_2 - \overset{NH_2}{\overset{|}{C}} - COOH$$
$$|$$
$$H$$
$$|$$
$$S$$
$$|$$
$$CH_2 - \overset{NH_2}{\overset{|}{C}} - COOH$$
$$|$$
$$H$$

Lanthionine
β-Amino-β-carboxyethyl sulfide
Formed in acid hydrolysis of keratin proteins
previously boiled with Na_2CO_3

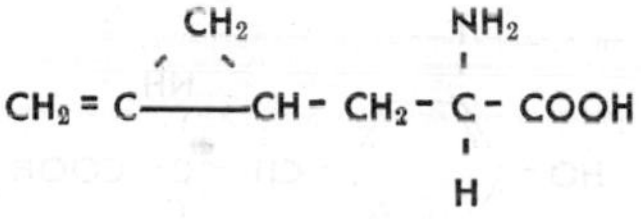

$$CH_2 = C \overset{CH_2}{\underset{}{\diagdown}} CH - CH_2 - \overset{NH_2}{\overset{|}{C}} - COOH$$
$$|$$
$$H$$

Hypoglycin A
α-Amino-methylenecyclopropane
propionic acid
Seeds of Blighia sapida
(J. Am. Chem. Soc., 80, 1002, 1004, 1958)

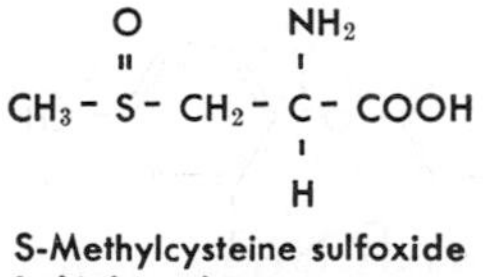

$$CH_3 - S - CH_2 - \overset{O}{\overset{\|}{}}\overset{NH_2}{\overset{|}{C}} - COOH$$
$$|$$
$$H$$

S-Methylcysteine sulfoxide
In higher plants

$$CH_2 = CH - CH_2 - S - CH_2 - \overset{O}{\overset{\|}{}}\overset{NH_2}{\overset{|}{C}} - COOH$$
$$|$$
$$H$$

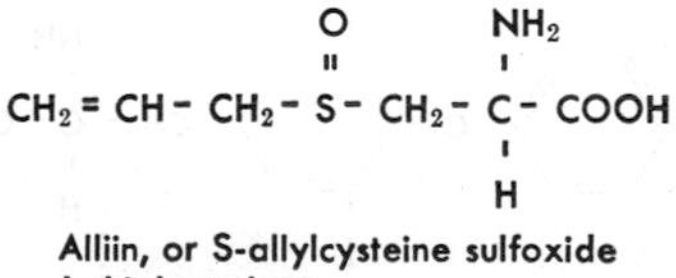

Alliin, or S-allylcysteine sulfoxide
In higher plants

$$H_2N - CH_2 - CH_2 - COOH$$

β-Alanine
β-Aminopropionic acid
Constituent of pantothenic acid

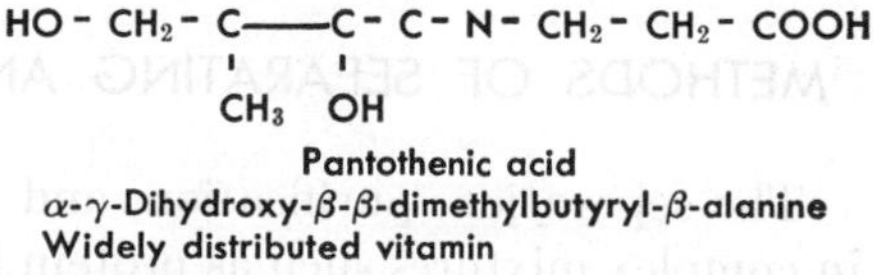

$$HO - CH_2 - \overset{CH_3}{\underset{CH_3}{\overset{|}{C}}} - \overset{H}{\overset{|}{\underset{OH}{C}}} - \overset{O}{\overset{\|}{C}} - \overset{H}{\overset{|}{N}} - CH_2 - CH_2 - COOH$$

Pantothenic acid
α-γ-Dihydroxy-β-β-dimethylbutyryl-β-alanine
Widely distributed vitamin

$$H_2N - CH_2 - CH_2 - CH_2 - COOH$$
γ-Aminobutyric acid
In plants, brain, and other animal tissues

HN H   NH₂
‖   │   │
H₂N – C – N – O – CH₂ – CH₂ – C – COOH   S – CH₂ – C – COOH
                          │   │   │
                          H   CH₂   H
                                              │
                                              NH₂
                                              │
                                              S – CH₂ – C – COOH
                                                          │
                                                          H

Canavanine   **Djenkolic acid**
α-Amino-γ-guanidinoxy-n-butyric acid   Cysteine thioacetal of formaldehyde
In soybean meal   In djenkol nuts

                    NH₂   ⁺N≡(CH₃)₃
                     │   │
HC═══════C–CH₂–C–COOH   HC═══════C–CH₂–C–COO⁻
│   │   │   │   │   │
N   NH   H   N   NH   H
 \   /   \   /
   C   C
   │   │
   SH   SH

Thiolhistidine   **Ergothioneine**
α-Amino-β-2-thioimidazolepropionic acid   Betaine of thiolhistidine
                                             In ergot (fungus), red cells

                         NH₂   Br
                          │   │   NH₂
HO –⟨ ⟩– CH₂ – C – COOH   HO –⟨ ⟩– CH₂ – C – COOH
        │   │   │   │
        OH   H   Br   H

Dihydroxyphenylalanine   **3,5-Dibromotyrosine**
α-Amino-β-3,4-dihydroxyphenylpropionic acid 3,5-Dibromo-4-hydroxyphenylpropionic acid
In sprouts and seedlings of velvet bean   In protein of horny skeleton of coral
                                             Primnoa lepadifera

        I   I
        │   NH₂   │   NH₂
HO –⟨ ⟩– CH₂ – C – COOH   HO –⟨ ⟩– CH₂ – C – COOH
                       │   │   │
                       H   I   H

3-Iodotyrosine   **3,5-Diiodotyrosine, or iodogorgoic acid**
In thyroid gland   In thyroid gland

    I   I   I   I
    │   │   NH₂   │   │   NH₂
HO –⟨ ⟩– O –⟨ ⟩– CH₂ – C – COOH HO –⟨ ⟩– O –⟨ ⟩– CH₂ – C – COOH
                            │   │
    I   H   I   I   H

3,5,3′-Triiodothyronine   **Thyroxine**
In thyroid gland   3,5,3′,5′-Tetraiodothyronine
                                             In thyroid gland

METHODS OF SEPARATING AND DETERMINING AMINO ACIDS

The separation, purification, and quantitative estimation of amino acids
in complex mixtures such as protein hydrolysates have in the past presented
laborious and difficult problems. These problems in recent years have been

greatly simplified and improved by application of new methods, such as paper and column chromatography, countercurrent distribution, microbial analysis, and spectrophotometric analysis.

Among the earlier methods of separating amino acids from protein hydrolysates was Fischer's esterification method, in which the amino acids were converted to ethyl esters and the esters fractionally distilled in vacuo. The separations were incomplete, and large losses occurred. Dakin's butyl alcohol extraction method depended upon the differential distribution of amino acids between water saturated with butanol and butanol saturated with water. By this method it was possible to effect approximate separation of the monoaminomonocarboxylic acids (in butyl alcohol layer) from the acidic and basic amino acids (in the aqueous layer).

Humin or melanin formation. Humin nitrogen. Acid hydrolysis of proteins generally causes the formation of a black or brownish-black amorphous precipitate called "humin" or "melanin." The production of humin is a complex process as yet incompletely understood. Gortner and associates (4) have presented evidence indicating that humin production is largely the result of the condensation of the indole group of tryptophan with an unknown aldehyde. The source of the aldehyde may be carbohydrate present in the protein molecule or mixed with the protein sample which, when heated with the strong acid, produces a furfural or other aldehyde. Gortner and Blish (5) found that zein, a protein of corn that contains neither tryptophan nor carbohydrate, yields very little humin upon acid hydrolysis. However, when they hydrolyzed zein with the addition of tryptophan and carbohydrate, they recovered 86.6 per cent of the tryptophan nitrogen in the humin produced. As much as 15 per cent of tyrosine nitrogen has been found in the brown soluble humin formed by acid hydrolysis. The amino acids arginine, lysine, histidine, and cystine may contribute 2 to 3 per cent of their nitrogen to humin formation.

The insoluble humin formed in acid hydrolysis of proteins may be separated off, and its nitrogen content may be determined. This nitrogen is referred to as "humin nitrogen."

Obviously acid hydrolysis cannot be used for the preparation of tryptophan. It is generally prepared by the tryptic digestion of casein.

Ammonia formation. Amide nitrogen. Hydrolysis of proteins by acids and alkalies splits off more or less ammonia, the amount depending upon the particular protein concerned. In alkaline hydrolysis the liberated ammonia is boiled out of the solution. If the protein is hydrolyzed with acid, the ammonia is retained in solution as the ammonium salt and can be quantitatively estimated by neutralization and rendering alkaline with a mild alkali, such as magnesium oxide or calcium hydroxide, followed by distillation (under vacuum) into standard acid and titration. Since boiling with acid has little effect in splitting off the amino groups of amino acids, the ammonia arises largely from another source. It is formed from acid amide groups of the dicarboxylic amino acids, aspartic and glutamic, present in the protein molecules. Amino acids are linked together in proteins through the

so-called peptide linkage formed in effect, by condensation of the carboxyl
of one amino acid and the amino group of another:

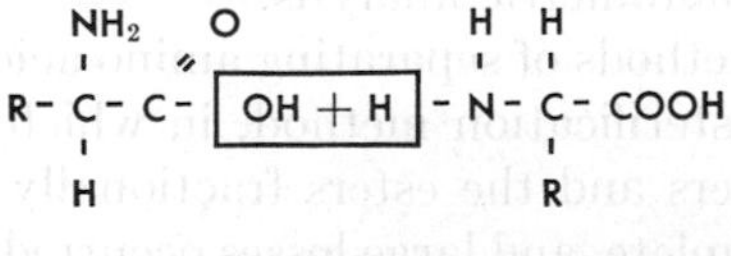

$$\begin{array}{ccccccc}
NH_2 & O & & & H & H \\
| & \nearrow & & & | & | \\
R- C- C- & \boxed{OH + H} & - N- & C- & COOH \\
| & & & | \\
H & & & R
\end{array}$$

Dicarboxylic acids present in protein molecules have only one carboxyl
involved in the peptide linkage, leaving one which may be free or combined
with ammonia as an acid amide group. This is illustrated in the following
formula showing the linkage of aspartic acid in a peptide chain:

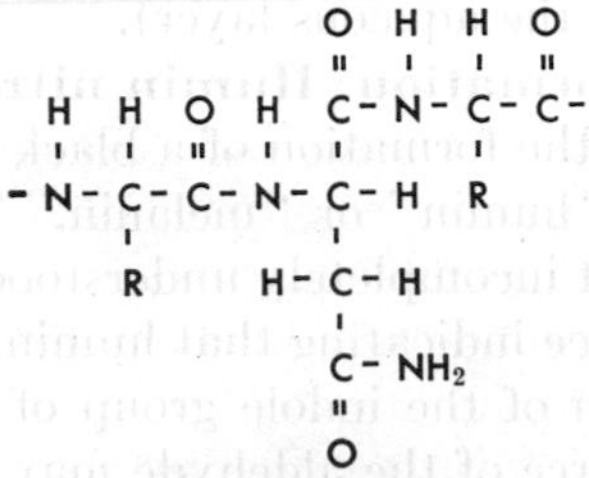

$$\begin{array}{ccccccccc}
& & & & & O & H & H & O \\
& & & & & || & | & | & || \\
H & H & O & H & & C- N- C- C- \\
| & | & || & | & & | \\
- N- C- C- N- & C- H & & R \\
| & | & & \\
R & H- C- H \\
& | \\
& C- NH_2 \\
& || \\
& O
\end{array}$$

Amide group

These acid-amide groups are split by acid and alkaline hydrolysis to form
ammonia and the carboxyl group, just as the peptide linkages are broken to
give carboxyl and amino groups. The ammonia so formed is referred to as
"amide nitrogen," and the amount obtained in the hydrolysis of a protein
is proportional to the quantity of dicarboxylic amino acids present.

Electrical transport method of separating amino acids. The principle of the method is based upon the fact that at a pH of about 5.5 the
acidic amino acids (aspartic and glutamic) exist as negative ions, the basic
amino acids (arginine, lysine, and histidine) exist as positive ions, while the
monoaminomonocarboxylic acids are present as zwitterions, without net
positive or negative charge; so that these three groups of amino acids show
different migration behavior when an electric current is passed through the
solution. In actual practice a cell of three compartments is used, with electrodes in the end compartments. The amino acid mixture at pH 5.5 is placed
in the center compartment and the current started. The acidic amino acids
(negatively charged) migrate to the anode compartment, the basic amino
acids (positively charged) pass into the cathode compartment, while the
monoaminomonocarboxylic acids remain in the center compartment. The
solutions are removed from the respective compartments, and the amino
acids are separated by special procedures for each acid. Electrical transport
may be used in the further separation of arginine, histidine, and lysine at
pH 7.5, at which arginine and lysine pass to the cathode and histidine remains in the center compartment.

Separation by countercurrent distribution. Craig (6) developed a
technique and apparatus with which a solute in one solvent (such as water)
may be subjected to many successive extractions by another immiscible

solvent (such as heptane) while maintaining the different fractions in separate compartments so they may be isolated and examined. Apparatus has been devised that permits more than 100 nearly quantitative extractions to be made in a single operation. This method has been applied to the isolation of amino acids obtained in the hydrolysis of antibiotics and other substances of biologic importance.

Separation of amino acids by paper chromatography. The separation of mixtures of amino acids and many other biologic substances by the process of paper chromatography has been found very helpful and is widely used. When a strip of filter paper is suspended vertically with the lower end dipping into a mixture of water and an organic solvent, such as n-butyl alcohol, n-propyl alcohol, phenol, isobutyric acid, or collidine, the mixture of water and organic solvent moves up the filter paper. The water being strongly held by the paper represents a stationary solvent phase, while the organic solvent for which the paper has little attraction represents a mobile phase. The paper and solvent mixture is enclosed in a covered glass cylinder or other container, and the temperature is maintained constant, so that the solvent moves up the paper in an atmosphere saturated with the vapor of both water and organic solvent at the temperature used. When a solute is spotted on the paper close to the end dipping in the solvent, as the solvent moves up the strip and over the solute, the solute is partitioned between the stationary water phase on the paper and the moving organic phase. As the moving organic phase reaches a section of paper containing no solute, partition again takes place, and solute is transferred from the organic to the stationary water phase. As the solvent continually moves up the paper, the net effect of this partition between the two phases is the transfer of the solute from the point of its application to the paper to a point some distance along the paper in the direction of solvent flow. The solute is present as a characteristically localized spot on the paper.

In carrying out the procedure, a pencil line is drawn about 5 cm from the end of a dry strip of filter paper, 1.5 by 50 cm, and a very small sample of amino acid solution (5 to 15 μg of amino acid) is applied at the pencil line. The strip is then supported with the sample end dipping into the solvent in the covered vessel, and the solvent begins to move up the strip. After the solvent front has run a convenient distance in 15 to 20 hours (depending on solvent, paper, and temperature), the strip is removed and the position of the solvent front is marked. The strip is dried and sprayed with a solution of ninhydrin which with amino acids gives a color (purple to orange). The amino acid is found localized as a spot at some position up the strip. The ratio of the distance of the spot from the pencil line to the distance of the solvent front from the pencil line is the R_F value. The R_F values are characteristic for the different amino acids when run under the same experimental conditions.

When a mixture of amino acids is chromatographed, a vertical series of spots representing the different amino acids is obtained unless the R_F values are too close; then the spots may overlap. If a sheet of filter paper is used instead of a strip, a first chromatograph may be run at one corner of the sheet to give as much vertical separation as possible; this may be rechromatographed with a different solvent mixture at right angles to the original chromatograph to give a two-dimensional dispersion of the amino acid spots. This is called two-dimensional chromatography. Two-dimensional separation of electrolytes may be achieved by applying a direct current across the paper at right angles to the chromatographic flow. This technique, called "electrophoretic chromatography," has been applied in the separation of blood serum proteins.

Sample and solvent may be applied at the top of the strip to give descending chromatographs instead of at the bottom to give ascending chromatographs.

After the components of a mixture have been localized in spots on the paper, the spots may be cut out, extracted with proper solvents, and often

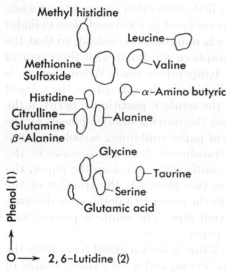

Figure 8.1.   Two dimensional chromatogram of amino acids in human urine. (From *Univ. Texas Pub. No.* 5109, p.157.)

determined quantitatively by suitable micromethods. Occasionally a substance may be determined quantitatively in the spot on the chromatograph through a suitable color reaction applied simultaneously to the spot and a spot developed from a known amount of the same material.

The selection of proper solvent mixtures, filter paper, and other conditions for paper chromatography is very important, because these determine the R_F values and degrees of separation.

Separation and estimation of amino acids by column chromatography. The adsorption of amino acids upon different solid adsorbing agents arranged as columns in glass tubes, followed by differential elution of the amino acids from the columns with appropriate solutions, has proved to be the most powerful tool in the separation of the amino acids of a protein hydrolysate. This procedure is referred to as "column chromatography" and is used for the separation of many substances other than amino acids from mixtures.

The chromatographic method of separating and estimating amino acids was introduced first by Martin and Synge (7). Moore and Stein (8) have perfected the procedure so that only a few milligrams of sample are required. These workers initially used starch columns, through which a solvent such as aqueous butanol is first run to equilibration. The amino acid mixture dissolved in the same solvent is then poured on the column, and more solvent is passed through the column. The individual amino acids are adsorbed at the surfaces of the starch grains, from which they are eluted by the solvent and move slowly down and from the column at rates determined largely by their chemical natures and the kind of solvent system used. When the conditions are proper, the individual amino acids emerge from the column at rates sufficiently different that each may be collected separately in a definite volume and fraction of the solution emerging from the column.

A useful apparatus has been developed—a fraction collector—which automatically collects the column effluent as successive aliquots of definite volume. The aliquots are then analyzed for their amino acid content by the ninhydrin colorimetric method to establish the fractions of effluent in which the different amino acids appear. The identity of the amino acids present in the different fractions may be established by paper chromatography or other methods. When two or three amino acids are present in a fraction, this can be rechromatographed using a different solvent system found to separate these amino acids. The quantity of each individual amino acid is plotted against the effluent fraction in which it is found to give a typical chromatogram curve for a given amino acid mixture.

In the operation of a starch column for the separation of amino acids it appears that both adsorption of the highly polar amino acids by the polar starch surface and also partition of the amino acids between the polar solvent (water) held stationary on the starch and the less polar organic solvent (such as butanol) moving over the starch surface occur. We might say the process is a combination of repetitive differential adsorption and partition between solvents throughout the starch column.

The use of starch columns has been largely superseded by the use of synthetic resin columns (see Chapter 3).

In the use of resin columns for the chromatographic analysis of protein hydrolysates the resin is first equilibrated with a suitable buffer solution, and then a sample of the amino acid mixture in the buffer is added to the column. The chromatogram is developed by a continuous flow of buffer through the column, with changes in column temperature, buffer pH, and ionic strength at intervals throughout the process. Figure 8.2 shows the chromatogram obtained (9) from a sample of only 2 mg of a mixture of 17 amino acids, using a column of Dowex 50.

The ion exchange chromatography of the amino acid mixture of protein hydrolysates is based upon differential adsorption of the amino acids on the resin and differential elution of them from it. The forces binding the amino acids to the ionized groups of the resin surface vary with the ionized groups of the amino acids, and the elution of the amino acids from the resin is

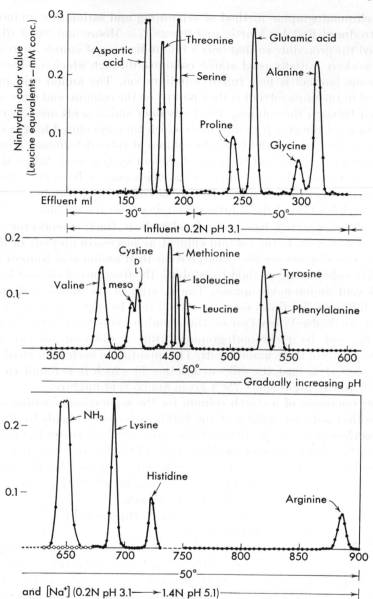

Figure 8.2. Amino acids were eluted from the column initially (upper row) with 0.2 N sodium citrate buffer at pH 3.1; then the concentration of buffer was gradually raised to 1.4 N and the pH to 5.1. (From Hirs, C. H. W.; Stein, W. H.; and Moore, S.: *J. Biol. Chem.*, **211**, 944, 1954.)

dependent upon competition of the eluting buffer ions with the amino acid ions for the charged resin surface. The ionic resin columns are far superior to starch columns in the separation and quantitative estimation of amino acids, and provide the best general method now available for this purpose. It has been applied in the amino acid analysis of a large variety of proteins.

In the determination of the amino acid content of a protein hydrolysate the weight of total amino acids exceeds the weight of protein hydrolyzed because water is added in the process. Thus 100 g of protein may yield a total of 117 g of amino acids. When the molecular weight of the protein is known, the molar equivalents of each amino acid per mol of protein may be calculated. Methods commonly used in expressing the amino acid composition of proteins include: (*a*) Grams of amino acid from 100 g of protein; (*b*) Residues of amino acid per molecule of protein (generally applied only when the protein molecular weight is not over 100,000); (*c*) Residues of amino acid per 10^5 g of protein; (*d*) Per cent of total protein nitrogen.

The application of ion exchange chromatography to the analysis of a protein is well illustrated by the results obtained by Hirs and associates (10) in the analysis of the enzyme pancreatic ribonuclease, which has a molecular weight of about 13,700. The results of this analysis are given in Table 8.1.

Table 8.1. Amino Acid Composition of Pancreatic Ribonuclease

Amino Acid	Grams Per 100 g Protein	Grams Amino Acid Residue per 100 g Protein	N as Per cent of Protein N	Calculated Number of Residues*
Aspartic acid	15.0	13.0	8.9	15
Glutamic acid	12.4	10.9	6.6	12
Glycine	1.6	1.25	1.7	3
Alanine	7.7	6.1	6.8	12
Valine	7.5	6.3	5.0	9
Leucine	2.0	1.7	1.2	2
Isoleucine	2.7	2.3	1.6	3
Serine	11.4	9.4	8.5	15
Threonine	8.9	7.6	5.9	10
Cystine/2	7.0	5.95	4.6	8
Methionine	4.0	3.5	2.1	4
Proline	3.9	3.3	2.7	4
Phenylalanine	3.5	3.1	1.7	3
Tyrosine	7.6	6.8	3.3	6
Histidine	4.2	3.7	6.4	4
Lysine	10.5	9.2	11.3	10
Arginine	4.9	4.4	8.9	4
Amide NH₃	2.1		9.6	17†
Total	116.9	98.8	96.8	124

* Number of residues per unit molecular weight of 13,700, calculated from analytical data and rounded off to the nearest integer.
† Not included in the total.
Data from Hirs, C. H. W.; Stein, W. H.; and Moore, S.: *J. Biol. Chem.*, **211**, 948, 1954. Hirs, C. H. W.; Moore, S.; and Stein, W. H.: *J. Biol. Chem.*, **235**, 634, 1960.

Ion exchange resins are used on a macro scale in the preparation of amino acids in the laboratory and commercially.

Microbial assay of amino acids. An important development in the quantitative determination of amino acids is based upon the use of microorganisms that require certain amino acids for growth. A culture medium is prepared which contains all essential substances except the amino acid to be determined. When this amino acid is added under proper conditions, the amount of growth is proportional to the amount of amino acid. The growth may be estimated by turbidometric or other procedures with good accuracy. An excellent illustration of the application of this method was the determination in proteins of the so-called essential amino acids—histidine, arginine, lysine, leucine, isoleucine, valine, methionine, threonine, tryptophan, and phenylalanine—by Stokes and associates (11). Nine of the amino acids were determined with only one organism, *Streptococcus faecalis*. *Lactobacillus delbrückii* was used for the determination of phenylalanine.

Spectrophotometric analysis. The determination of amino acids by spectrophotometric analysis based upon specific light absorption has received considerable attention. Such analysis of the amino acids generally depends upon absorption exhibited by their colored derivatives. Tryptophane and tyrosine may be directly determined.

Isotope dilution analysis of amino acids in mixtures. This method, devised by Rittenberg and Foster (12), is ingenuous in principle but is limited in practical application because it requires pure isotopically labeled amino acids, isotope measurement facilities, and rigorous control of conditions. To illustrate the method, suppose a definite weight of glycine containing a known amount of N^{15} is added to a definite volume of an amino acid mixture containing glycine, in which the nitrogen is the ordinary isotope N^{14}. If pure crystalline glycine is now isolated from the mixture, it will be composed of N^{15}-glycine and N^{14}-glycine in the ratio of the two compounds in solution. Since the amount of N^{15}-glycine added is known and the quantity of N^{15} present in the crystalline glycine shows how much the N^{14}-glycine has been diluted by the N^{15}-glycine, it is possible to calculate the amount of ordinary glycine present. Of course, the principle of isotope dilution may be applied to many substances other than amino acids.

Special reagents used in the separation of amino acids. A number of metal ions and various organic compounds form characteristic derivatives of amino acids which at times are useful in their isolation.

   1. Picric acid:

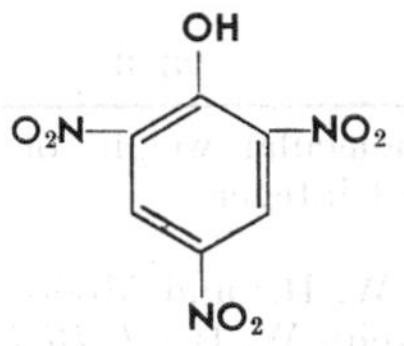

Forms well-characterized picrates of lysine, histidine, arginine, glycine, and proline.

   2. Flavianic acid:

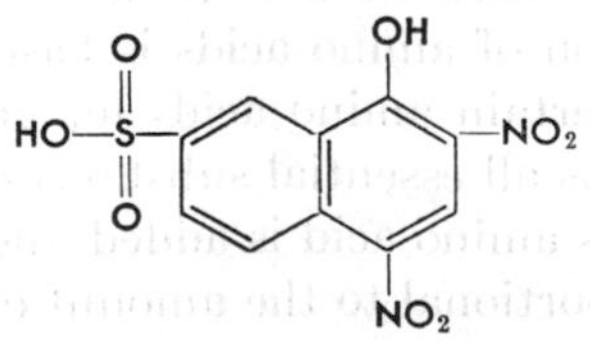

Table 8.2

Amino Acid	Per Cent	Number of Amino Acid Residues per Mol of β-Lactoglobulin
Glycine	1.4	8
Alanine	6.2	29
Valine	5.83	21
Leucine	15.6	50
Isoleucine	8.4	27
Proline	4.1	15
Phenylalanine	3.54	9
Cysteine	1.11	4
Half cystine	2.29	8 Cy-S-½ mols
Methionine	3.22	9
Tryptophan	1.94	4
Arginine	2.88	7
Histidine	1.58	4
Lysine	11.4	33
Aspartic acid	11.4	36
Amide NH_3	1.31	32
Glutamic acid, free and as glutamine	19.5	
Free glutamic acid		24
Glutamine		32
Serine	5.0	20
Threonine	5.85	21
Tyrosine	3.78	9
Total	116.33	402

Taken from Brand, E., Saidel, L. J., Goldwater, W. H., Kassell, B., and Ryan, F. J.: *J. Am. Chem. Soc.*, **67**, 1525, 1945.

Precipitates the flavianates of arginine and histidine. Arginine flavianate is so insoluble that it precipitates almost quantitatively from solutions containing all of the other amino acids.

3. Picrolonic acid:

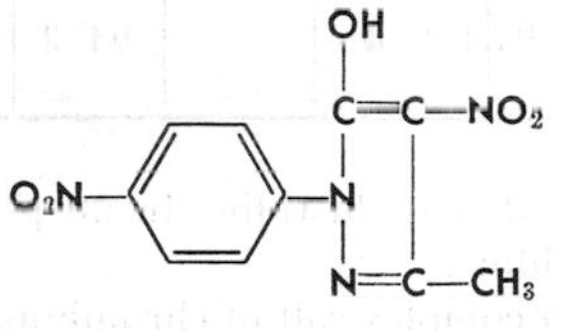

Precipitates the picrolonates of the basic amino acids. All the monoaminomono-carboxylic acids form picrolonates, most of which are insoluble in water. Tryptophan and phenylalanine form very insoluble picrolonates. Proline and hydroxyproline do not form definite salts with picrolonic acid.

4. Nitranilic acid:

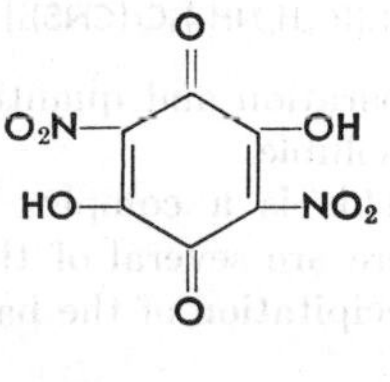

Table 8.3.   Amino Acid
The values represent grams of amino

Per cent N	15.6	15.95	15.63	18.6	18.55	16.9	18.0	17.66	16.03
	ACTH sheep	Albumin, human serum	Casein	Collagen	Edestin	Fibrinogen, human	Gelatin	Gliadin	γ Globulin, human
Alanine	—	—	3.2	9.5	4.31	3.7	9.3	2.13	—
Arginine	8.7	6.2	4.1	8.59	16.7	7.8	8.55	2.74	4.8
Aspartic acid	6.7	8.95	7.1	6.3	12.0	13.1	6.7	1.34	8.8
Cysteine	—	0.70		0	0.5	0.4	0	} 2.58	0.7
Cystine/2	7.2	5.6	0.34	0	0.93	2.3	0		2.4
Glutamic acid	15.6	17.0	22.4	11.3	20.7	14.5	11.2	45.7	11.8
Glycine	8.0	1.6	2.0	27.2	—	5.6	26.9		4.2
Histidine	1.3	3.5	3.1	0.74	2.5	2.6	0.73	1.82	2.5
Hydroxylysine				1.1					
Hydroxyproline				14.0					
Isoleucine	3.1	1.7	6.1 }	5.6	4.7	4.8	1.8 }	11.9	2.7
Leucine	7.8	11.0	9.2		7.5	7.1	3.4		9.3
Lysine	5.0	12.3	8.2	4.47	2.4	9.2	4.6	0.65	8.1
Methionine	1.9	1.3	2.8	0.8	2.4	2.6	0.9	1.69	1.1
Phenylalanine	4.0	7.8	5.0	2.5	5.45	4.6	2.55	6.44	4.6
Proline	8.2	5.1	10.6	15.1	4.25	5.7	14.8	13.55	8.1
Serine	6.0	3.34	6.3	3.37	6.30	7.0	3.18	4.9	11.4
Threonine	3.2	4.6	4.9	2.28	3.85	6.1	2.2	2.1	8.4
Tryptophan	—	0.2	1.2	0	1.48	3.3	0	6.6	2.9
Tyrosine	2.4	4.7	6.3	1.0	4.34	5.5	1.0	3.2	6.8
Valine	3.4	7.7	7.2	3.4	6.5	4.1	3.3	2.66	9.7
Amide N	1.2	0.88	1.6	0.66	1.77	1.49	0.07	4.5	1.11
Total	92.5	103.3	110	117.3	106.8	110	116.83	103.8	108.3
Per cent total N recovered	91.5	92.97	100.3		94.3	99.34			96.13

Forms an insoluble compound with histidine in 50 per cent methanol. Used in the quantitative estimation of histidine.

   5. *Reinecke salt.* This is a complex salt of chromium, ammonium tetrathiocyanodiamminochromate:

$$NH_4[(NH_3)_2Cr(CNS)_4]$$

   Reinecke salt precipitates proline and hydroxyproline as the reineckates from which pure proline and hydroxyproline may be separated.

   6. *Rhodanilic acid.* This substance is reinecke acid with the ammonia replaced by aniline groups:

$$H[(C_6H_5NH_2)_2Cr(CNS)_4]$$

   It is especially useful in the separation and quantitative estimation of proline, since proline rhodanilate is relatively insoluble.

   7. *Phosphotungstic acid.* This is a complex acid formed from tungstic acid, H_2WO_4, and phosphoric acid. There are several of these acids. The so-called phospho-24-tungstic acid is used for the precipitation of the basic amino acids and cystine.

Composition of Proteins
acids obtained from 100 grams of proteins.

15.65	16.8	18.5	15.78	16.3	16.9	16.7	15.76	14.65	15.86	30.7	16.2
Growth hormone, bovine	Hemoglobin, horse	Histone, fowl erythrocyte	Insulin, bovine	Keratin, wool	Myoglobin, horse	Myosin, rabbit	Ovalbumin, hen egg	Pepsin	Prolactin, sheep	Salmine	Zein
—	7.4	8.6	4.5	4.14	7.95	6.5	6.72	—	—	1.12	10.52
9.1	3.65	14.7	3.07	10.4	2.2	7.36	5.72	1.0	8.6	85.2	1.71
9.0	10.6	6.13	6.8	7.2	8.2	8.9	9.3	16.0	11.6	0	4.61
—	0.56	0	0	—	0	—	1.35	0.5	—	0	
2.5	0.45		12.5	11.9	0	1.4	0.51	1.64	3.1	0	0.83
13.0	8.5	11.2	18.6	14.1	16.48	22.1	16.5	11.9	14.1	0	26.9
3.8	5.6	5.78	4.3	6.53	5.85	1.9	3.05	6.4	4.0	2.95	
2.65	8.71	2.33	4.91	1.1	8.5	2.41	2.35	0.9	4.5	0	1.32
			0								
			0								
4.0	0	6.38	2.77			$\left.\begin{array}{c} \\ \end{array}\right\}$ 15.6	7.0	10.8	7.2	1.64	5.0
12.1	15.4	10.04	13.2	11.3	16.8		9.2	10.4	12.5	0	21.1
7.1	8.51	12.1	2.51	2.76	15.5	11.92	6.3	0.9	5.3	0	0
2.9	1.0	0	0	0.7	1.71	2.4	5.2	1.7	3.6	0	2.41
7.9	7.7	3.55	8.14	3.65	5.09	4.3	7.66	6.4	4.1	0	7.3
3.4	3.9	4.08	2.53	9.5	3.34	1.9	3.6	5.0	6.2	5.8	10.53
5.7	5.8	6.3	5.23	10.01	6.46	4.33	8.15	12.2	6.5	9.1	7.05
6.1	4.36	5.31	2.08	6.42	4.56	5.1	4.03	9.6	4.8	0	3.45
0.84	1.7	0	1.8	2.34	0.8	1.2	2.4	1.2	0		0.16
5.2	3.03	3.87	13.0	4.65	2.4	3.4	3.68	8.5	4.7	0	5.25
3.9	9.1	6.09	7.75	4.64	4.09	2.6	7.05	7.1	5.9	3.14	3.98
0.99	0.87	0.95	1.39	1.17	0.66	1.2	1.02	1.32	1.0	0	2.98
99.19	105.97	107.6	113.6	110.8	108.49	103.96	108.6	113.34	107.9	108.94	112.1
94.0	97.3	96.2	97.8	99.5	98.02	93.04	96.8	98.31	99.9	99.92	

8. Cuprous oxide. Used for the precipitation of cystine.

9. Zinc acetate or chloride. Used for the precipitation of leucine, phenylalanine, histidine, and glutamic acid.

10. Calcium and barium hydroxides. Used to precipitate the calcium and barium salts of glutamic and aspartic acids.

11. Silver sulfate. Used to precipitate the silver salts of arginine, histidine, and glutamic and aspartic acids.

12. Mercuric sulfate. Used for the precipitation of tryptophan and histidine.

Lead and copper salts of the amino acids are frequently used for isolation purposes.

Improvement in the methods for the quantitative determination of amino acids is progressing rapidly, as illustrated by the work of Brand and associates, who have carried out a most careful and complete analysis of crystalline β-lactoglobulin. They established its molecular weight as $42,020 \pm 105$ and its empirical formula as $C_{1864}H_{3012}N_{468}S_{21}O_{576}$. Upon hydrolysis 100 g of the protein took up 17 g of water, corresponding to 397 mols of H_2O per mol of protein (42,020 g). This quantity of water would hydrolyze 397 peptide or amide linkages. These workers determined very carefully all the amino acids present in the protein by the best methods available and from these results calculated the number of amino acid residues for each amino acid present in the molecule. They also determined the amide groups, which were assumed to be present as glutamine. The results are given in Table 8.2.

Although the assumption was made that all the amide nitrogen is present in the amide group of glutamine, it is probable that a part of the amide nitrogen is present combined with the second carboxyl of aspartic acid as asparagine.

The above data indicate that β-lactoglobulin is composed of 370 amino acid residues (402-32 acid amide groups). There are four cystine—S—S— linkages in the molecule, each representing two peptide linkages. The free α-amino nitrogen (0.155 per cent) represents four free α-amino groups per molecule. However, since a peptide chain contains only one free α-amino group, it is assumed that the β-lactoglobulin molecule is made up of four subpeptide chains.

Table 8.3 gives the amino acid composition of a number of proteins.

PHYSICAL PROPERTIES OF AMINO ACIDS

Solubility. In general, the amino acids are readily soluble in water, insoluble or slightly soluble in alcohol, and insoluble in ether. Tyrosine is only slightly soluble in cold water and more soluble in hot water; and cystine is difficultly soluble in both hot and cold water. Proline and hydroxyproline are soluble in alcohol and ether.

The amino acids are generally soluble in dilute acids and bases, in which they form the amino acid salts. Tyrosine is only moderately soluble in dilute acids and bases. Cystine is soluble in solutions of strong mineral acids, such as hydrochloric, but only slightly soluble in solutions of acetic acid. It is also only slightly soluble in dilute ammonia.

Melting points. The amino acids are outstanding among organic compounds in possessing high melting points. Many of the amino acids undergo more or less decomposition at or near the melting point, which, as a result, is not sharp. In general, the melting points are above 200° C, and in some instances above 300° C.

Taste of amino acids. Amino acids are usually sweet, tasteless, or bitter. For examples, glycine, alanine, valine, proline, hydroxyproline, serine, tryptophan, and histidine are sweet; leucine is tasteless; and isoleucine and arginine are bitter. The sodium salt of glutamic acid, sodium glutamate, is valuable as a flavoring agent for certain sauces and foods, since it enhances the flavor. It is manufactured in large quantities for this purpose, usually by hydrolysis of proteins which contain much glutamic acid.

Amino acids as ampholytes. Zwitterion structures and acidic and basic properties. The zwitterion structures and the acidic and basic properties of amino acids have been considered in detail in Chapter 3, and the student should review carefully that material at this time. It is pointed out there that the pure amino acids exist as dipolar ions or zwitterions, and in solution the following relations of the zwitterion structure to H^+ ions exist:

$$\underset{\substack{\text{Amino acid} \\ \text{cation} \\ \text{in acid solution}}}{\overset{1}{+H_3N - CH(R) - COOH}} \rightleftarrows H^+ + \underset{\substack{\text{Zwitterion}}}{\overset{2}{+H_3N - CH(R) - COO^-}} \rightleftarrows H^+ + \underset{\substack{\text{Amino acid} \\ \text{anion} \\ \text{in alkaline solution}}}{\overset{3}{H_2N - CH(R) - COO^-}}$$

For these equilibria dissociation constants, K_1 and K_2, may be calculated for the processes 1 to 2 and 2 to 3 respectively. When more than one amino or carboxyl group is present in the amino acid, there may be in addition constants K_3, etc.

Also, it is shown in the previous discussion that for an amino acid the isoelectric pH is given by the expression:

$$\text{Isoelectric pH} = \tfrac{1}{2}(pK_1 + pK_2)$$

If an amino acid has more than two ionizable groups, theoretically all the ionization constants—K_1, K_2, K_3, etc.—will participate in determining the isoelectric pH, and the equation should be modified accordingly. Often, however, two of the constants have the major effect, and, for practical purposes, the isoelectric pH of such an amino acid can be calculated according to the equation given above or a slightly modified form of it. For example, the isoelectric pH of arginine is obtained by taking half the sum of $pK_2 + pK_3$ (see Table 8.4).

Table 8.4. Dissociation Constants and Isoelectric pH Values of Some Amino Acids Constants are expressed in terms of negative logarithms, or pK values, at 25° C

Amino Acids	pK_1	pK_2	pK_3	IpH
Glycine	2.35	9.78		6.1
Alanine	2.34	9.87		6.1
Serine	2.21	9.15		5.7
Cysteine (30°)	1.96	8.18	$10.28 \left(\begin{matrix}pK_4\end{matrix}\right.$	5.1
Cystine (30°)	1.0	1.7	$7.48 \left.\begin{matrix}9.02\end{matrix}\right)$	5.6
Methionine	2.28	9.21		5.8
Valine	2.32	9.62		6.0
Leucine	2.36	9.60		6.0
Isoleucine	2.36	9.68		6.0
Norleucine	2.39	9.76		6.1
Tyrosine	2.20	9.1	10.1	5.7
Diiodotyrosine	2.12	6.48	7.82	4.3
Phenylalanine	2.58	9.24		5.9
Tryptophan	2.38	9.39		5.9
Proline	2.00	10.60		6.4
Hydroxyproline	1.92	9.73		5.8
Glutamic acid	2.19	4.28	9.66	3.2
Aspartic acid	2.09	3.87	9.82	3.0
Histidine	1.77	6.10	9.18	7.6
Lysine	2.18	8.95	10.53	9.7
Arginine	2.02	9.04	12.48	10.8

It has been found that the isoelectric pH values of many simple amino acids are not sharp but may extend over a range of several pH units. Michaelis has shown that an amino acid possesses a sharp isoelectric pH only if the value of K_1 is less than 10,000 times that of K_2; that is, if pK_1 and pK_2 differ by not more than four units. Since most amino acids do not meet this condition, they do not possess sharp isoelectric values.

It should be pointed out that peptides and proteins, which are derivatives of amino acids, also behave as zwitterions in the isoelectric condition. The general theories relating to amino acids may also be applied to these substances.

Table 8.4 lists a number of amino acids with their corresponding dissociation constants and isoelectric pH values. These constants may be due to the ionization of $-COOH$, $-NH_2$, $= NH$, $-OH$, and $-SH$ groups, depending upon their presence in the amino acids concerned.

Optical properties of amino acids. The α-amino carbon atoms of all the amino acids except glycine are asymmetric. A second asymmetric carbon is also present in isoleucine, threonine, hydroxylysine, and hydroxyproline. All of the amino acids except glycine show optical activity.

The amino acids form salts with acids and bases, such as:

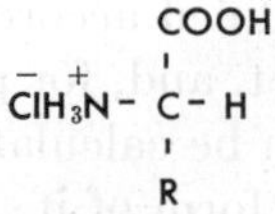

$$
\begin{array}{ccc}
\text{COOH} & & \text{COO}^-\text{Na}^+ \\
| & & | \\
\text{ClH}_3\overset{-}{\underset{+}{N}}-\text{C}-\text{H} & & \text{H}_2\text{N}-\text{C}-\text{H} \\
| & & | \\
\text{R} & & \text{R}
\end{array}
$$

Amino acid hydrochloride cation form   Sodium salt of amino acid anion form

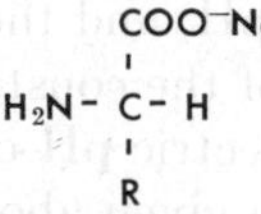

and exist as zwitterions:

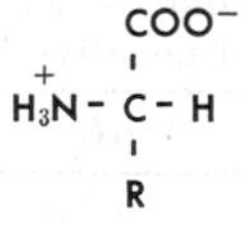

$$
\begin{array}{c}
\text{COO}^- \\
| \\
\overset{+}{\text{H}_3\text{N}}-\text{C}-\text{H} \\
| \\
\text{R}
\end{array}
$$

The optical rotations of these forms—cation, anion, and zwitterion—are different, and the rotations of the amino acids vary according to the pH of the solution, which determines the ionic state of the amino acid. For example, the specific rotation of L-alanine in H_2O at 25° C is $+2.4$, while in 6 N HCl it is $+14.5$; and the specific rotation of L-leucine in H_2O at 25° C is -10.7, while in 6 N HCl at 25° C it is $+15.1$.

It is obvious that for consistent comparison of the rotations of the different amino acids it is essential to measure the rotations under conditions such that the rotation of a given definite amino acid ion is measured. Consequently, the rotations of amino acids are generally measured in HCl solutions, with the amino acid present as cation.

When the rotation of an amino acid is measured in HCl solutions of progressively increasing concentration, the rotation increases up to a certain point and represents the progressive conversion of the amino acid to the cation form. In the case of an L-amino acid the rotation always becomes more positive (or less negative) as the HCl concentration is increased, while the rotation of a D-amino acid becomes more negative (or less positive).

The rotations of amino acids are in some cases changed by the addition of neutral salts, and may be somewhat dependent upon the amino acid concentration.

Optically active amino acids may be converted into the racemic forms (DL mixtures) by heating with alkalies, by heating with acids under pressure (160°–180° C), and by treating the amino acids with acetic anhydride under the proper conditions, which converts the optically active acids into the DL-acetylated acids (racemic form) from which the acetyl groups may be hydrolyzed to yield the racemic DL mixture of amino acids.

Synthesis of amino acids from optically inactive substances in the laboratory leads to DL forms, from which the D and L isomers must be separated or resolved in case these are desired.

CHEMICAL PROPERTIES OF AMINO ACIDS

A. CHEMICAL PROPERTIES DUE TO THE CARBOXYL GROUP

The amino acids in general give the reactions characteristic of the carboxyl group. Some of these reactions take place with more difficulty or under more restricted conditions than in the case of ordinary organic acids because of participation of the carboxyl group of amino acids in the zwitterion structure.

Salt formation and titration. As previously indicated, both the acidic and basic groups of amino acids form salts. However, owing to zwitterion formation the titration of amino acids with alkalies or acids in aqueous solution is impossible because no sharp end point is obtained. The carboxyl groups of amino acids may be titrated with alkali in alcoholic or acetone solution, in which the end point of the indicator such as phenolphthalein is shifted to a more alkaline pH. The basic groups of amino acids may be titrated in glacial acetic acid solution with standard sulfuric, hydrobromic, or perchloric acid using an indicator such as crystal violet.

The titration curves of amino acids in aqueous solution may be run with the glass or hydrogen electrodes (see Chapter 3). Theoretical curves may be calculated by the Henderson-Hasselbalch equation from pK values. The student should refer to Figure 3.4 (page 53).

Formation of esters. Amino acids react with alcohols in the presence of dry HCl to form the corresponding esters. The HCl first breaks up the zwitterion structure to form the amino acid hydrochloride which then reacts with the alcohol:

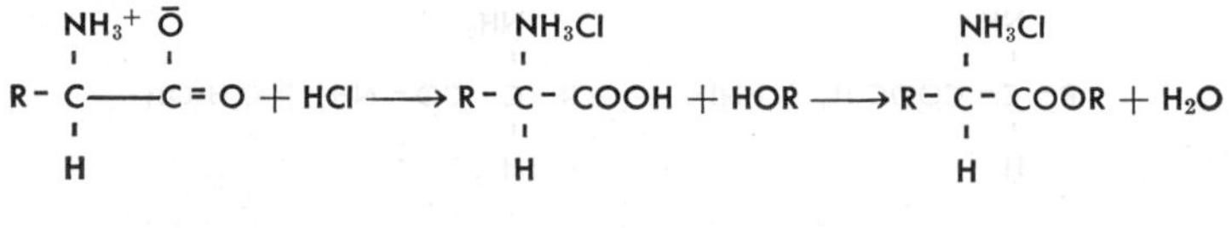

$$\underset{\underset{H}{|}}{\overset{\overset{NH_3^+}{|}}{R-C}}\underset{}{\overset{\overset{\bar{O}}{|}}{---C}}=O + HCl \longrightarrow \underset{\underset{H}{|}}{\overset{\overset{NH_3Cl}{|}}{R-C}}-COOH + HOR \longrightarrow \underset{\underset{H}{|}}{\overset{\overset{NH_3Cl}{|}}{R-C}}-COOR + H_2O$$

The ester hydrochloride is decomposed by mild alkali in the cold to give the free ester.

Both free amino acids and their esters are readily reduced by lithium aluminum hydride, $LiAlH_4$, dissolved in ether, to the corresponding alcohols without racemization:

$$R-CH(NH_2)-COOH + LiAlH_4 \longrightarrow R-CH(NH_2)-CH_2OH + H_2O$$

Amino acid   Amino alcohol

Formation of amino acyl chlorides. The amino group is first acetylated for protection, and the acetylated amino acid is treated with $SOCl_2$ or PCl_5. The acetyl group may be removed by treatment with dry HCl:

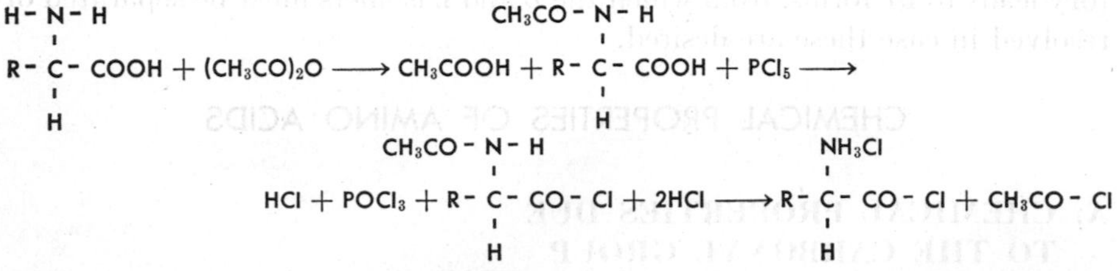

H–N–H $CH_3CO-N-H$
  |
R–C–COOH + $(CH_3CO)_2O \longrightarrow CH_3COOH + R-C-COOH + PCl_5 \longrightarrow$
  |
H   H

                    $CH_3CO-N-H$ NH_3Cl

$$HCl + POCl_3 + R-C-CO-Cl + 2HCl \longrightarrow R-C-CO-Cl + CH_3CO-Cl$$

                               H   H

The amino acyl chlorides exist as the hydrochloride salts.

Decarboxylation. When amino acids are heated, preferably in the presence of barium hydroxide or diphenylamine, carbon dioxide is lost and an amine is formed. The decarboxylation of histidine may be taken as an example:

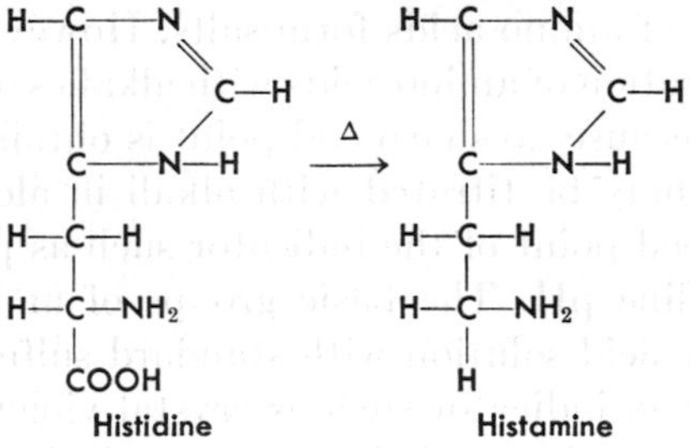

Histidine   Histamine

Decarboxylation of amino acids is caused also by decarboxylase enzymes of bacteria. This occurs in the large intestine as a result of the action of putrefactive organisms. Some of the amines produced, such as histamine and tyramine (from tyrosine), are pharmacologically active.

Amide formation. Amino acid amides may be prepared by treatment of the amino acid esters with alcoholic or anhydrous ammonia:

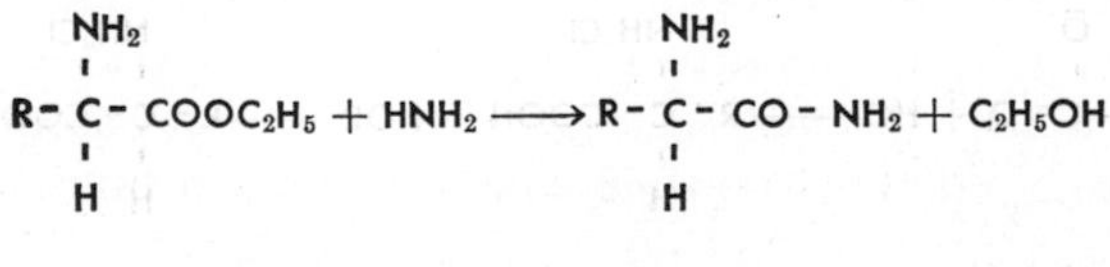

       NH_2 NH_2

$$R-C-COOC_2H_5 + HNH_2 \longrightarrow R-C-CO-NH_2 + C_2H_5OH$$

        H   H

B. CHEMICAL PROPERTIES DUE TO THE AMINO GROUP

Salt formation. As previously indicated, the amino acids act as bases toward acids and form salts.

The α-amino acids, under the proper conditions, will undergo all the reactions given by primary aliphatic amines.

Acylation of the amino acids. The amino groups of the amino acids may be acylated by treatment with acid anhydrides or chlorides under the proper conditions. The action takes place best under conditions in which the amino acid is not largely in the zwitterion form. For example, amino acids may be acetylated when dissolved in cold acetic acid or cold alkali by addition of the theoretical quantity of acetic anhydride:

$$R-\overset{\overset{\displaystyle H}{|}}{\underset{\underset{\displaystyle COONa}{|}}{C}}-\overset{\overset{\displaystyle H}{|}}{N}-H + (CH_3CO)_2O + NaOH \longrightarrow CH_3COONa + H_2O + R-\overset{\overset{\displaystyle H}{|}}{\underset{\underset{\displaystyle COONa}{|}}{C}}-\overset{\overset{\displaystyle H}{|}}{N}-\overset{\overset{\displaystyle O}{||}}{C}-CH_3$$

Upon acidifying the solution, the free acetylated amino acid is obtained.

If optically active acetylated amino acids are heated in acetic acid solution with a small amount of acetic anhydride, they are racemized into inactive DL-acetylated amino acids.

Benzoylation of glycine is readily accomplished in the animal body as a process for the detoxication of benzoic acid:

$$C_6H_5COOH + H-\overset{\overset{\displaystyle H}{|}}{N}-CH_2COOH \longrightarrow H_2O + C_6H_5-\overset{\overset{\displaystyle O}{||}}{C}-\overset{\overset{\displaystyle H}{|}}{N}-CH_2COOH$$
Benzoyl glycine
(hippuric acid)

Hydroxyl groups which may be present in amino acids (serine, threonine, tyrosine) are esterified upon treatment with acid chlorides and anhydrides.

N-acyl amino acids when dissolved in absolute sulfuric acid lose water and form ring compounds, the azlactones, or oxazolones which in reality are internal anhydrides of the N-acyl amino acids.

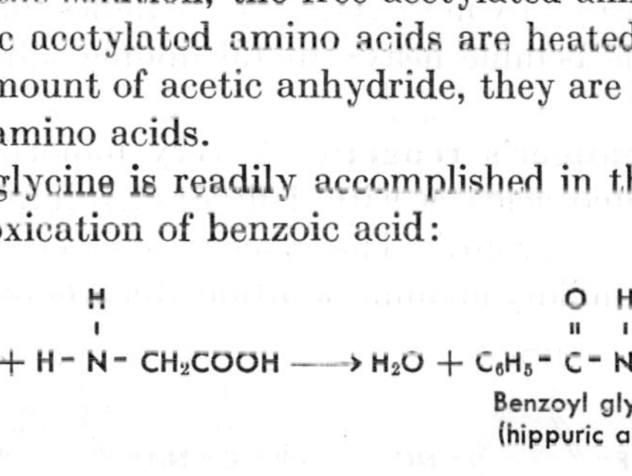

$$\begin{array}{ccc}
R-CH-COOH & & R-CH-\!-\!-CO \\
\;\;\;|\;\;\;\; & \longrightarrow & \;\;\;|\;\;\;\;\;\;\;\;| \quad + H_2O \\
N-H & & N \qquad O \\
\;|\; & & \;\;\backslash\!\!\nearrow \\
CO & & C \\
\;|\; & & \;|\; \\
R' & & R'
\end{array}$$

N-Acyl amino acid   Azlactone or
oxazolone, an
internal anhydride

The azlactones are of importance in the synthesis of peptides (13).

Methylation of the amino acids. The amino groups of the amino acids may be exhaustively methylated by treatment with methyl iodide or dimethyl sulfate in alkaline solution. The methylation takes place in stages, but the final product is a betaine of the amino acid. The reaction may be represented:

$$
\begin{array}{c}
\text{H} \quad \text{H} \\
| \quad \nearrow \\
\text{R} - \text{C} - \text{N} \\
| \quad \searrow \\
\text{H} \\
\text{COONa}
\end{array}
+ 2CH_3I + 2NaOH \longrightarrow 2NaI + 2H_2O +
\begin{array}{c}
\text{H} \quad \text{CH}_3 \\
| \quad \nearrow \\
\text{R} - \text{C} - \text{N} \\
| \quad \searrow \\
\text{CH}_3 \\
\text{COONa}
\end{array}
+ CH_3I \longrightarrow
$$

$$
\begin{array}{c}
\text{H} \quad \text{CH}_3 \\
| \quad \nearrow \\
\text{R} - \text{C} - \text{N} - \text{CH}_3 \\
| \quad + \searrow \\
\text{I} \quad \text{CH}_3 \\
\text{COONa}
\end{array}
\longrightarrow NaI +
\begin{array}{c}
\text{H} \quad \text{CH}_3 \\
| \quad \nearrow \\
\text{R} - \text{C} - \text{N} - \text{CH}_3 \\
| \quad + \searrow \\
\text{CH}_3 \\
\text{COO}^{\bar{}}
\end{array}
$$

Betaine of an amino acid

The basicity of the amino group is greatly increased by methylation to the quaternary nitrogen stage of the betaine structure, and the betaines represent internal salt or zwitterion structures. The betaines form well-crystallized double salts with the chlorides of platinum, gold, and mercury, which are useful in their separation and purification. Mixtures of amino acids have been separated by methylation to betaines followed by formation and separation of the betaine heavy metal double salts. Various betaines occur in plants.

Reaction with Sanger's reagent. A very important reaction of the amino groups of amino acids is with 1-fluoro-2,4-dinitrobenzene, FDNB, also called "Sanger's reagent." The reagent condenses with free amino groups in the cold in mildly alkaline solution (bicarbonate):

$$
\begin{array}{c}
\text{H} \\
| \\
\text{R} - \text{C} - \text{NH}_2 \\
| \\
\text{COOH}
\end{array}
+ \text{F} - \underset{}{\bigcirc} - NO_2
\longrightarrow
\begin{array}{c}
\text{H} \\
| \\
\text{R} - \text{C} - \text{NH} - \\
| \\
\text{COOH}
\end{array}
\underset{}{\bigcirc} - NO_2 + HF
$$

Amino acid   1-Fluoro-2,4-dinitrobenzene   Dinitrophenylamino acid, or DNP-amino acid

Most of the DNP-amino acids are colored bright yellow, and most are soluble in ether. The DNP bond is generally more stable in acid hydrolysis than peptide bonds. The importance of the reaction is largely due to the fact that the terminal amino acid group, having a free amino group in a peptide or protein chain, forms a DNP-derivative which may be hydrolyzed with acid to give the DNP-amino acid. In this way it is possible to identify one of the terminal amino acids in a peptide or protein.

Reaction of amino acids with nitrous acid. Nitrous acid reacts with the amino group of amino acids to form the corresponding hydroxy acids, with the liberation of nitrogen gas:

$$
\begin{array}{c}
\text{NH}_2 \\
| \\
\text{R} - \text{C} - \text{COOH} \\
| \\
\text{H}
\end{array}
+ HONO \longrightarrow
\begin{array}{c}
\text{OH} \\
| \\
\text{R} - \text{C} - \text{COOH} \\
| \\
\text{H}
\end{array}
+ N_2 + H_2O
$$

Since each amino group gives one molecule of nitrogen, which can be accurately measured, Van Slyke (14) has utilized the reaction in an excellent method for the estimation of free amino groups in amino acids, peptides, and proteins. As commonly carried out, the amino acid, peptide, or protein solution is treated with sodium nitrite and acetic acid, which react to form nitrous acid in a mildly acid solution. Under these conditions the α-amino groups react quantitatively in three to four minutes at room temperature, while the ϵ-amino group of lysine reacts more slowly.

The Van Slyke amino nitrogen method may be used conveniently to follow the rate of hydrolysis of proteins, since for each peptide linkage hydrolyzed an α-amino group is liberated. The amount of amino nitrogen thus progressively increases until hydrolysis of the protein is complete.

Oxidative deamination of amino acids. The ninhydrin reaction for the qualitative detection and quantitative estimation of amino acids. The amino groups of amino acids are very resistant to hydrolysis but may be easily removed by oxidation. The oxidative enzyme systems of tissues, especially liver and kidney, effect the oxidative deamination of amino acids to form keto acids and ammonia. The reaction apparently proceeds as follows:

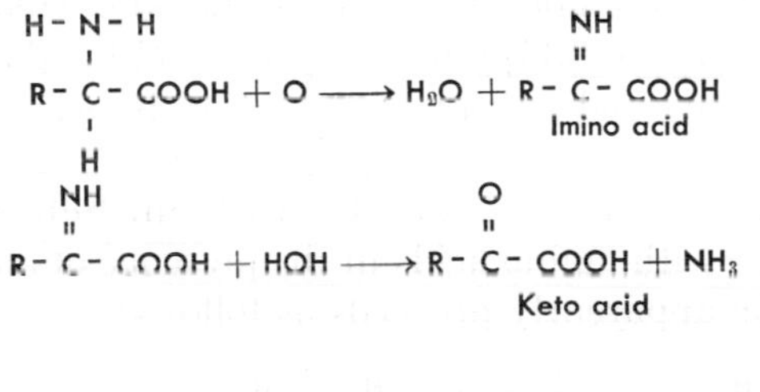

$$
\begin{array}{c}
\text{H--N--H}\\
|\\
\text{R--C--COOH} + \text{O} \longrightarrow \text{H}_2\text{O} + \overset{\text{NH}}{\underset{}{\text{R--C--COOH}}} \\
|\\
\text{H}
\end{array}
\qquad \text{Imino acid}
$$

$$
\overset{\text{NH}}{\text{R--C--COOH}} + \text{HOH} \longrightarrow \overset{\text{O}}{\text{R--C--COOH}} + \text{NH}_3
$$
Keto acid

Similar oxidation may be effected by oxidizing agents such as hydrogen peroxide, permanganate, and oxygen in the presence of charcoal.

When amino acids are heated with ninhydrin they are quantitatively deaminized and a beautiful blue color appears, which is of value in the qualitative detection of amino acids and proteins. The keto acid formed in the oxidative deamination is decomposed by heat into an aldehyde and carbon dioxide, the latter being evolved in quantitative amounts from an acid solution. The sequence of reactions may be represented as follows:

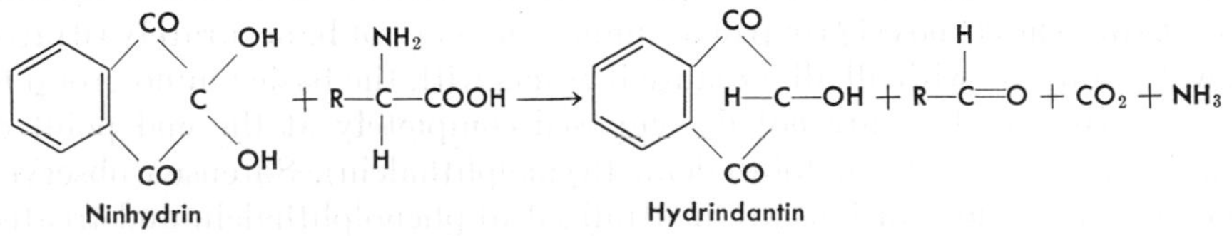

Ninhydrin   Hydrindantin

The blue-colored substance (Ruhemann's purple) is formed by reaction of some of the ninhydrin with its reduction product, hydrindantin, and ammonia:

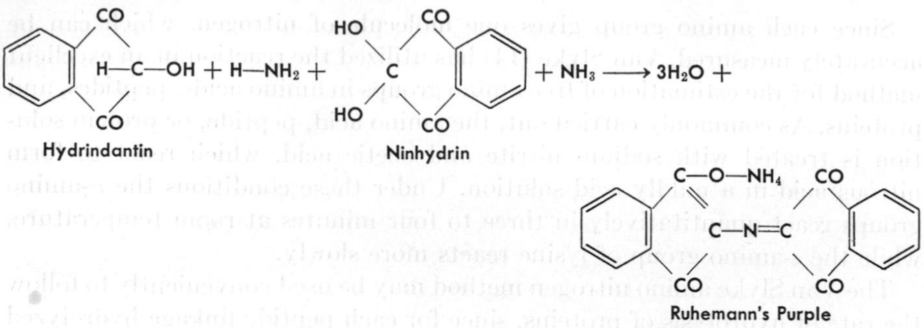

The blue-colored substance is formed whenever ninhydrin is heated with solutions of amino acids or of peptides or proteins which contain the α-amino acyl group:

$$R - \underset{\underset{H}{|}}{\overset{\overset{NH_2}{|}}{C}} - CO -$$

Proline and hydroxyproline, which contain no α-amino group, give condensation products with ninhydrin of a different type and color. Both, however, yield quantitative amounts of carbon dioxide. Moore and Stein (15) have developed a very useful quantitative method for the colorimetric estimation of amino acids and peptides in solution based upon the ninhydrin reaction.

Reaction with aromatic aldehydes to form Schiff bases. Aromatic aldehydes condense with amino acids in the presence of alkali to form Schiff bases. The reaction apparently proceeds as follows:

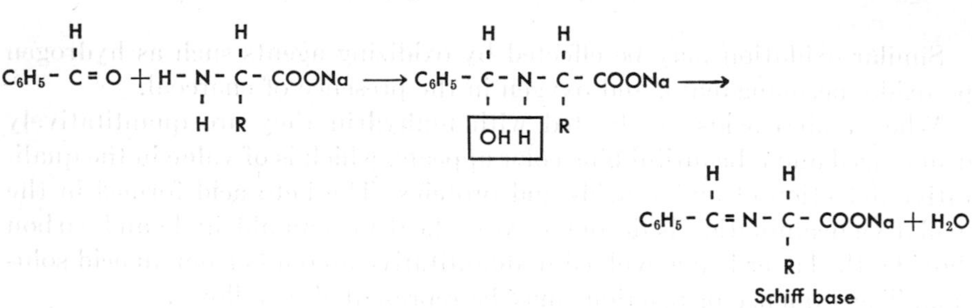

Reaction of amino acids with formaldehyde. Sørensen's formal titration. The carboxyl group of α-amino acids cannot be accurately titrated in water solution with alkali, because it reacts with the basic amino group to form zwitterions that are not decomposed completely at the end point of alkaline indicators (phenolphthalein, thymolphthalein). Sørensen observed that if amino acid solutions are neutralized to phenolphthalein and treated with a large excess of neutralized formaldehyde solution, the mixture becomes acid and can be titrated sharply to phenolphthalein with standard alkali. The amount of alkali required for this titration was found to correspond to the complete titration of the carboxyl group of the amino acid.

Levy (16) has shown that the reaction of formaldehyde with amino acids in the Sørensen titration is complex. Under these conditions it appears that formaldehyde adds to the amino groups with the formation of dimethylol amino acids. Addition of formaldehyde to the amino group occurs as the titration with alkali proceeds until two molecules of the aldehyde have reacted and titration of the compound is complete. The reactions are reversible, and a large excess of formaldehyde must be present to convert all the amino acid into the dimethylol derivative and to give accurate titration. The reactions apparently proceed as follows:

$$
\begin{array}{cc}
\text{NH}_3{}^+ & \text{HOH}_2\text{C} - \text{N} - \text{CH}_2\text{OH} \\
| & | \\
\text{R} - \text{C} - \text{COO}^{\bar{}} \qquad + \text{OH}^- \qquad \text{R} - \text{C} - \text{COO}^- \qquad + \text{H}_2\text{O} \\
| \qquad + 2\text{CH}_2\text{O} \rightleftharpoons \qquad | \\
\text{H} & \text{H} \\
\text{Zwitterion} & \text{Dimethylol} \\
& \text{amino acid}
\end{array}
$$

The H$^+$ is removed from the $-\text{NH}_3{}^+$ by the addition of OH$^-$ as the reaction with formaldehyde proceeds. The addition of formaldehyde to it thus causes the zwitterion to titrate sharply as a monobasic acid.

Reaction of amino acids with carbon dioxide. Siegfried's carbamino reaction. N-carboxyamino acids. When carbon dioxide is passed into the alkaline solution of an amino acid, the carbon dioxide adds to the amino group to form a carbamino or N-carboxyamino acid:

$$
\begin{array}{ccc}
\text{H} - \text{N} - \text{H} \quad + \text{O} = \text{C} = \text{O} & \text{H} - \text{N} - \text{COOH} + {}^-\text{OH} & \text{H} - \text{N} - \text{COO}^- + \text{H}_2\text{O} \\
| & \longrightarrow \quad | & \longrightarrow \quad | \\
\text{R} - \text{C} - \text{COO}^- & \text{R} - \text{C} - \text{COO}^- & \text{R} - \text{C} - \text{COO}^- \\
| & | & | \\
\text{H} & \text{H} & \text{H} \\
\text{Amino acid in} & & \text{N-Carboxyamino} \\
\text{alkaline solution} & & \text{acid ion}
\end{array}
$$

If the carbamino acid is prepared in the presence of calcium or barium hydroxide, a solution of the calcium or barium salt of the acid is obtained, which may be precipitated by the addition of alcohol. When a solution of the salt is boiled, the amino acid is regenerated and the metal carbonate precipitated:

$$
\begin{array}{ccc}
\text{R—CH—COO} & & \text{NH}_2 \\
| \qquad \diagdown \qquad \text{H}_2\text{O} & | \\
| \qquad \qquad \text{Ca} \longrightarrow \text{R—C—COOH} + \text{CaCO}_3 \\
| \qquad \diagup & | \\
\text{NH—COO} & \text{H}
\end{array}
$$

Carbamino salts, especially those of barium, have been used for the separation of amino acids in mixtures by Schryver and associates (17).

Hemoglobin contains an amino group which reacts with carbon dioxide to form carbamino hemoglobin. The reaction is easily reversible and is important in the transport of carbon dioxide from the tissues to the lungs.

The anhydrides of the N-carboxyamino acids are important in the synthesis of peptides. One way in which these anhydrides may be prepared is by heating the amino acids with phosgene (18):

$$
\begin{array}{ccc}
\underset{\substack{|\\ \text{COOH}}}{\overset{\substack{H\\ |}}{\text{R---CH---N---H}}}
\quad + \quad
\underset{\substack{|\\ Cl}}{\overset{\substack{Cl\\ |}}{\text{CO}}}
& \longrightarrow &
\underset{\substack{|\\ OC\text{---}O}}{\overset{\substack{H\\ |}}{\text{R---CH---N}}} + 2HCl
\\
\text{Amino acid} & & \text{N-Carboxyamino}\\
& & \text{acid anhydride}
\end{array}
$$

These anhydrides are stable in aqueous solution below 10° C, but when the temperature is raised to 15° C, they hydrolyze quickly into CO_2 and the amino acids. When heated in the dry state, they split out CO_2 and leave the active residues —NH · CHR · CO—, which polymerize to form large peptide chain structures:

$$
\underset{R}{-NH-CH-CO}-\underset{R}{NH-CH-CO}-\underset{R}{NH-CH-CO}-
$$

Polymers such as polyarginine, polyaspartic acid, polycysteine, and a mixed polymer (copolymer) of lysine and glutamic acid have been prepared.

The anhydrides also are useful in the addition of specific amino acids to native proteins.

Formation of diketopiperazines. The esters of the amino acids condense to form anhydride ring structures containing two amino acid groups. These substances are called "diketopiperazines":

$$
\begin{array}{ccc}
\underset{\substack{|\\ \text{H-N-H}}}{\overset{\substack{H \quad O\\ |\quad\ ||}}{\text{R- C- C- OC}_2\text{H}_5}}
\; + \;
\underset{\substack{|\\ \text{C}_2\text{H}_5\text{O- C = O}}}{\overset{\substack{H \quad H\\ |\quad |}}{\text{H- N- C- R}}}
& \longrightarrow 2\text{C}_2\text{H}_5\text{OH} + &
\underset{\substack{|\\ \text{H- N}\rule[0.5ex]{3em}{0.4pt}\text{C = O}}}{\overset{\substack{H \quad O \quad H \; H\\ |\quad\ ||\quad |\ \ |}}{\text{R- C- C- N- C- R}}}
\\
& & \text{Diketopiperazine}
\end{array}
$$

When diketopiperazines are carefully hydrolyzed, only one peptide bond may be broken to yield a dipeptide. In the case of a mixed diketopiperazine hydrolysis yields a mixture of two dipeptides.

Chelation of amino acids with metal ions. A number of the heavy metal ions, such as Cu^{++}, Co^{++}, Mn^{++}, Fe^{++}, etc., form chelated (Greek *chela*, claw) complexes with amino acids in which both carboxyl and other groups, such as —NH_2 and —SH, are involved. Examples are:

$$
\begin{array}{cc}
\begin{array}{c}
\overset{\displaystyle COO^-}{\diagdown}\qquad\overset{\displaystyle ^-OOC}{\diagup}\\
\underset{++}{Cu}\\
\diagup\qquad\qquad\diagdown\\
\underset{\substack{\\ H_2}}{CH_2- N}\qquad\underset{\substack{\\ H_2}}{N\text{---}CH_2}\\
\text{Copper diglycinate}
\end{array}
&
\begin{array}{c}
\overset{\displaystyle COO^-}{\diagdown}\qquad\qquad\overset{\displaystyle ^-OOC}{\diagup}\\
\underset{\substack{|\\ CH_2}}{H_2N - CH}\qquad\underset{\substack{|\\ CH_2}}{HC- NH_2}\\
\underset{++}{Co}\\
S\qquad\qquad S\\
\diagdown\qquad\diagup\\
\underset{++}{Co}\\
\text{Cobalt complex of cysteine}
\end{array}
\end{array}
$$

SYNTHESIS OF PEPTIDES

The combination of amino acids through the carboxyl group of one and the amino group of another to form amide or peptide bonds, linking great numbers of amino acids into peptide chains in the proper sequence, represents the most complex type of synthesis in plants and animals. Needless to say, it is of immense interest and importance and will be considered specifically later in the discussion of protein metabolism.

The synthesis of peptide structures in the laboratory has been a major problem for many years. While relatively simple peptides have been prepared, the synthesis of a natural protein has not been achieved. In most of the practical laboratory methods of peptide synthesis the carboxyl group of an amino acid is converted into a form which will react with an amino group of another acid to form the peptide bond, such as the amino acyl chlorides (—CO—Cl), the azides (—CO—N₃), or the anhydrides (—CO—O—CO—R). In order to make such reactive carboxyl derivatives of amino acids, it is generally necessary to introduce a protective group into the amino group to prevent undesirable changes in it. This protective group must be readily removable, so that the amino group may be regenerated after the peptide bond is formed.

Synthesis of peptides by reaction of halogen-substituted acyl halides with amino acids and peptides. In this method the halogen acyl halide corresponding to an amino acid is reacted with the free amino group of another amino acid molecule or peptide, and then the substituted halogen is removed by treatment with ammonia:

$$CH_3 - \overset{\overset{\text{Br}}{|}}{\underset{\underset{\text{H}}{|}}{C}} - CO - Br + H - \overset{\overset{\text{H}}{|}}{\underset{\underset{\text{CH}_2}{|}}{N}} - \overset{\overset{\text{H}}{|}}{\underset{\underset{\text{C}_6\text{H}_4\text{OH}}{|}}{C}} - COOH \longrightarrow HBr + CH_3 - \overset{\overset{\text{Br}}{|}}{\underset{\underset{\text{H}}{|}}{C}} - CO - N - \overset{\overset{\text{H}}{|}}{\underset{\underset{\text{C}_6\text{H}_4\text{OH}}{|}}{C}} - COOH \xrightarrow{2NH_3}$$

L-α-Bromo-propionyl bromide   L-Tyrosine

$$CH_3 - \overset{\overset{\text{NH}_2}{|}}{\underset{\underset{\text{H}}{|}}{C}} - CO - N - \overset{\overset{\text{H}}{|}}{\underset{\underset{\text{C}_6\text{H}_4\text{OH}}{|}}{C}} - COOH + NH_4Cl$$

L-Alanyl-L-tyrosine

The process may be repeated by reaction of another molecule of halogen acyl halide with the free amino group of the alanine residue, etc.

The application of this method of peptide synthesis is excellent in theory but severely handicapped practically. One of the chief difficulties lies in the preparation of the optically active halogen acyl halides corresponding to the various amino acids. Only peptides of monoaminomonocarboxylic acids can be prepared by the method, and the peptide chain can be lengthened at only one end. This method of synthesis was originated by Fischer and Otto

(19). Fischer made many peptides by this process, one the octadecapeptide L-leucyl-(triglycyl)-L-leucyl-(triglycyl)-L-leucyl-(octaglycyl)-glycine.

The carbobenzoxy chloride synthesis of peptides. Bergmann and Zervas (20) developed an excellent method of peptide synthesis which has proved applicable to the synthesis of peptide chains containing both simple and complex amino acids. These workers found that the amino group of an amino acid reacts with carbobenzoxy chloride to give the carbobenzoxy amino acid, which in turn may be converted to the carbobenzoxy amino acid chloride by treatment with phosphorus pentachloride. The carbobenzoxy amino acid chloride in turn will react with an amino acid or peptide to form a carbobenzoxy peptide from which the carbobenzoxy group may be removed by reduction with hydrogen on palladium black to give the free peptide.

Carbobenzoxy chloride—or, more correctly, benzyloxycarbonyl chloride—is prepared from benzyl alcohol and phosgene:

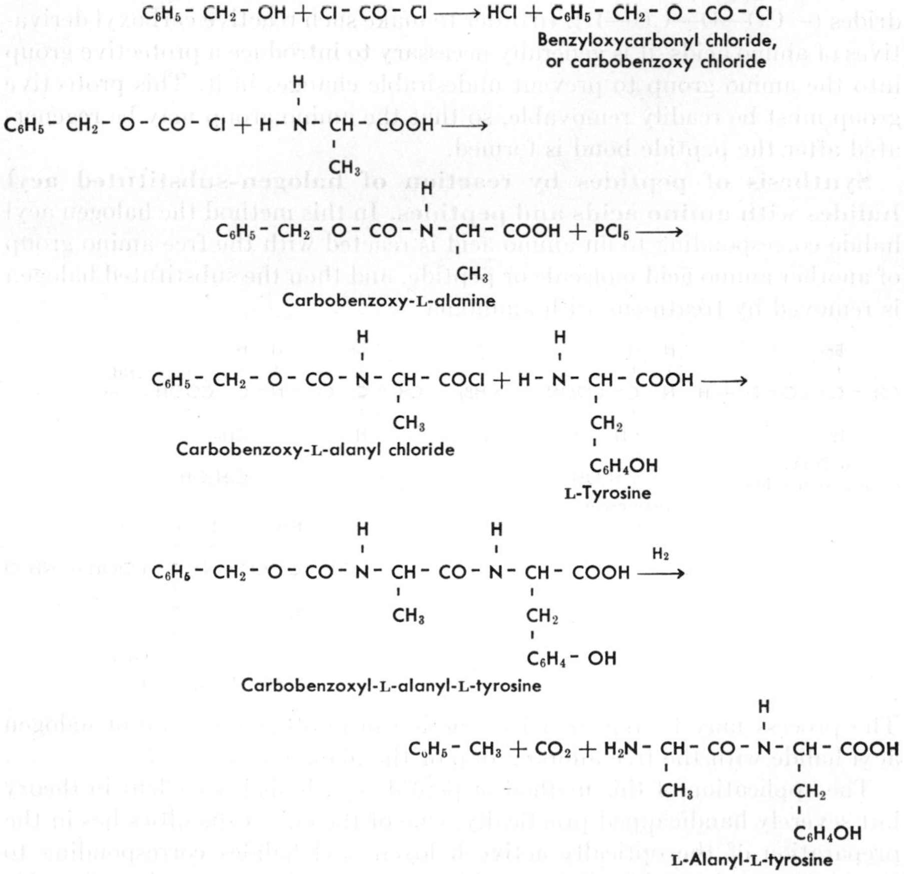

$$C_6H_5 - CH_2 - OH + Cl - CO - Cl \longrightarrow HCl + C_6H_5 - CH_2 - O - CO - Cl$$

Benzyloxycarbonyl chloride,
or carbobenzoxy chloride

$$\overset{\displaystyle H}{C_6H_5 - CH_2 - O - CO - Cl + H - N - CH - COOH} \longrightarrow$$
$$\underset{\displaystyle CH_3}{|}$$

$$\overset{\displaystyle H}{C_6H_5 - CH_2 - O - CO - N - CH - COOH + PCl_5} \longrightarrow$$
$$\underset{\displaystyle CH_3}{|}$$

Carbobenzoxy-L-alanine

$$\overset{\displaystyle H}{C_6H_5 - CH_2 - O - CO - N - CH - COCl} + \overset{\displaystyle H}{H - N - CH - COOH} \longrightarrow$$
$$\underset{\displaystyle CH_3}{|} \qquad \underset{\displaystyle CH_2}{|}$$
$$\underset{\displaystyle C_6H_4OH}{|}$$

Carbobenzoxy-L-alanyl chloride   L-Tyrosine

$$\overset{\displaystyle H}{C_6H_6 - CH_2 - O - CO - N - CH - CO - } \overset{\displaystyle H}{N - CH - COOH} \overset{\displaystyle H_2}{\longrightarrow}$$
$$\underset{\displaystyle CH_3}{|} \qquad \underset{\displaystyle CH_2}{|}$$
$$\underset{\displaystyle C_6H_4 - OH}{|}$$

Carbobenzoxyl-L-alanyl-L-tyrosine

$$C_uH_5 - CH_3 + CO_2 + H_2N - CH - CO - \overset{\displaystyle H}{N - CH - COOH}$$
$$\underset{\displaystyle CH_3}{|} \qquad \underset{\displaystyle CH_2}{|}$$
$$\underset{\displaystyle C_6H_4OH}{|}$$

L-Alanyl-L-tyrosine

The secret of the success of this method is that the carbobenzoxy group is easily introduced into the amino group to protect it when the acid chloride is formed and it is readily removed without hydrolysis of the peptide linkage. In the synthesis of cystine peptides it is necessary to remove the carbobenzoxy group by reduction with sodium in liquid ammonia or with phosphonium iodide.

Synthesis by use of amino acid carboxyanhydrides. Bailey (21) has worked out the conditions under which a single amino acid group may be added to the amino group of an amino acid or peptide chain by the use of an amino acid carboxyanhydride (preparation given previously). The reaction is carried out in anhydrous media in the presence of a tertiary base (triethylamine) at low temperature:

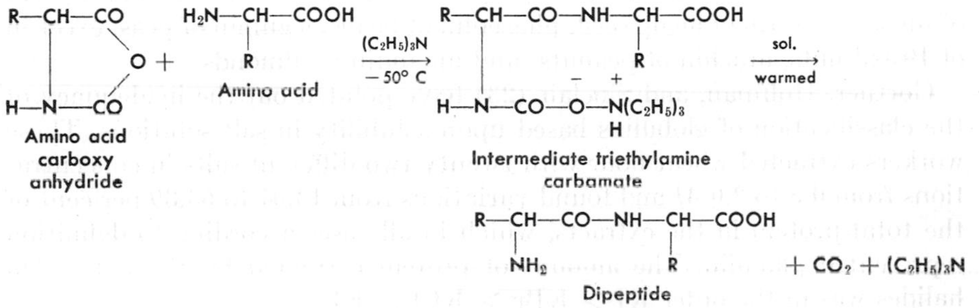

Many additional methods of peptide synthesis have been developed. Goodman and Kenner (22) give a comprehensive review.

CLASSIFICATION OF THE PROTEINS

Proteins cannot be classified on a purely chemical basis at the present time because of deficiencies in our knowledge of their composition and structure, and they must be classified on the basis of both physical and chemical properties. The physical properties of most value for classification purposes are those of solubility and heat coagulability. The classification given below is based upon the recommendations of a joint committee of the American Society of Biological Chemists and the American Physiological Society.

According to this system, proteins are classified into the three main groups of simple, conjugated, and derived proteins, and each of these main groups is subdivided into a number of classes.

A. SIMPLE PROTEINS

Simple proteins are defined as those proteins which upon hydrolysis yield only amino acids or their derivatives.

1. Albumins. The albumins are soluble in water, coagulated by heat, and usually deficient in glycine. They are products of both plants and animals. Examples include egg albumin, myogen of muscle, serum albumin of blood, lactalbumin of milk, legumelin of peas, and leucosin of wheat.

Some of the albumins contain carbohydrate residues, according to which they are conjugated proteins of the glycoprotein class. However, since they were originally classed as simple proteins before their conjugated nature was discovered, they are still retained in the simple protein group.

Albumins may be precipitated from solution by saturation with ammonium sulfate.

2. Globulins. The globulins are insoluble in pure water, but they are soluble in dilute neutral solutions of salts of alkalies and acids and are heat coagulable. Globulins are precipitated from solution by half saturation with ammonium sulfate. They generally contain glycine. The globulins constitute an important and widely distributed group of animal and plant proteins. Examples include ovoglobulin of egg yolk, serum globulin of blood, myosin of muscle, edestin of hemp seed, phaseolin of beans, legumin of peas, excelsin of Brazil nuts, arachin of peanuts, and amandin of almonds.

Gortner, Hoffman, and Sinclair (23) have pointed out the inadequacy of the classification of globulins based upon solubility in salt solutions. These workers extracted wheat flour with twenty-two different salts in concentrations from 0.5 to 2.0 M and found variations from 13.07 to 63.89 per cent of the total protein in the extracts, which in all cases according to definition represented globulin. The amount of protein extracted by the potassium halides was in the order KI > KBr > KCl > KF.

3. Glutelins. The glutelins are soluble in very dilute acids and alkalies, but they are insoluble in neutral solvents. They are plant proteins. Examples include glutenin of wheat, and oryzenin of rice.

4. Prolamins or alcohol-soluble proteins. The prolamins are soluble in 70 to 80 per cent alcohol, but they are insoluble in water, neutral solvents, or absolute alcohol. The prolamins generally yield much proline and amide nitrogen upon hydrolysis but are deficient in lysine. The prolamins are plant proteins found principally in seeds. Examples include zein of corn, hordein of barley, gliadin of wheat, and kafirin of kafir corn.

5. Albuminoids or scleroproteins. The albuminoids are the least soluble of all the proteins. They are generally insoluble in water, salt solutions, dilute acids and alkalies, and alcohol. The albuminoids constitute a very diverse group of proteins, the members of which show widely different physical and chemical properties. The albuminoids are entirely animal proteins and are the chief constituents of exoskeletal structures, such as hair, horn, hoofs, and nails, as well as of supporting and connecting fibrous tissues, and of the organic material of cartilage and bone. Examples include keratins of hair, horn, hoofs, nails; elastin of connective tissue and ligaments; collagen of bones, cartilage, and tendons; spongin of sponges; and fibroin and sericin of silk.

6. Histones. The histones are soluble in water and insoluble in dilute ammonia. They are readily soluble in dilute acids and alkalies. They are not readily coagulated by heat. Histones are basic proteins. They yield a large proportion of basic amino acids upon hydrolysis. They often precipitate other proteins from solution. The histones, being basic, usually occur in tissues in salt combinations with acidic substance, such as heme of hemoglobin, and nucleic acids. Such combinations of simple proteins with non-protein groups are conjugated proteins. Examples of histones include globin of hemoglobin, thymus histone, scombrone of mackerel sperm, and gadus histone of codfish sperm.

7. **Protamins.** The protamins are the simplest of the proteins and may be regarded as large polypeptides. They are strongly basic and yield chiefly basic amino acids upon hydrolysis, particularly arginine. The protamins are soluble in water, dilute ammonia, acids, and alkalies. They are not coagulated by heat. They precipitate other proteins from their solutions. Like the histones, they usually occur in tissues in salt combination with acids, particularly with nucleic acids as nucleoproteins of sperm. Examples include salmine of salmon sperm, clupeine of herring sperm, sturine of sturgeon sperm, scombrine of mackerel sperm, and cyprinine of carp sperm.

It is of interest to note that salmine contains 88 per cent of arginine in its structure. Kossel has subdivided the protamins into four groups based upon their content of the basic amino acids: (*a*) monoprotamins, those which contain only arginine; (*b*) lysine diprotamins, those which contain arginine and lysine; (*c*) histidine diprotamins, those which contain arginine and histidine; (*d*) triprotamins, those which contain arginine, lysine, and histidine.

B. CONJUGATED PROTEINS

Conjugated proteins are composed of simple protein combined with some nonprotein substance. The nonprotein group is referred to as the prosthetic (addition) group.

1. **Nucleoproteins.** The nucleoproteins are composed of simple basic proteins (protamin or histone) in salt combinations with nucleic acids as the prosthetic groups. They are the proteins of cell nuclei and apparently are the chief constituents of chromatin. They are most abundant in tissues, both plant and animal, having a large proportion of nuclear material, such as yeast, asparagus tips, thymus and other glandular organs, and sperm. Examples include nucleohistone and nucleoprotamin.

2. **Mucoproteins or mucoids.** The mucoproteins are composed of simple proteins combined with mucopolysaccharides such as hyaluronic acid and the chondroitin sulfates (see Chapter 7). They generally contain rather large amounts of N-acetylated hexosamine (more than 4 per cent) and, in addition, more or less of such substances as uronic acid, sialic acid, and monosaccharides.

Water-soluble mucoproteins have been obtained from serum, egg white (ovomucoid α) and human urine. These water-soluble mucoproteins are not easily denatured by heat or readily precipitated by agents such as picric and trichloroacetic acids. Their mucopolysaccharides are composed of hexosamine and hexose sugars.

Mucoproteins are important constituents of the ground substance of connective tissues. They are present as tendomucoid, osseomucoid, and chondroproteins in tendons, bones, and cartilage, respectively. Large amounts are present in the umbilical cord. They are generally present in all kinds of animal mucins and in the blood-group substances. Several gonadotropic hormones, such as interstitial cell-stimulating hormone (ICSH), follicle-stimulating hormone (FSH), pregnant mares' serum gonadotropin (PMSG), and human chorionic gonadotropin (HCG), are mucoproteins.

Insoluble mucoproteins or mucoids have been obtained from egg white (ovomucoid β), egg chalazae, vitreous humor, and submaxillary glands.

The term "glycoprotein" has been generally used in the past to include the mucoproteins and other carbohydrate-containing proteins. However, Karl Meyer has made the sensible suggestion that the term "glycoprotein" be limited to those proteins which contain only small amounts of carbohydrate, such as the serum albumins and globulins and ovalbumin, and that the term "mucoprotein" be limited to proteins containing more than 4 per cent hexosamine.

The carbohydrate is generally bound much more firmly in the glycoproteins than in the mucoproteins.

Table 8.5 gives the carbohydrate content of a number of glycoproteins.

Table 8.5.   Carbohydrate Content of Proteins

Protein	Per Cent Carbohydrate
Ovalbumin	1.7 ; mannose
Serum albumin	
Easily soluble fraction	0.47; mannose + galactose
Sparingly soluble fraction	0.02
Horse serum globulin	1.82; mannose + galactose
Casein	0.31; galactose, no lactose
Lactalbumin	0.44; galactose, no lactose
Wheat gliadin	
Sparingly soluble fraction	0.20; mannose
Egg white proteins	
Globulin	4.0 ; mannose
Albumin	1.7 ; mannose
Conalbumin	2.8 ; 3 mannose + 1 galactose
Mucin	14.9 ; mannose + galactose
Mucoid	9.2 ; 3 mannose + 1 galactose

Taken from C. Rimington, *Ann. Rev. Biochem.*, **5**, 138, 1936.

The mucoproteins are reviewed by Kent and Whitehouse in *Biochemistry of the Amino Sugars.*

3. Chromoproteins. The chromoproteins are composed of simple proteins united with a colored prosthetic group. Many proteins of important biologic functions belong to this group.

The following are examples of chromoproteins:

Hemoglobins, respiratory proteins in which the prosthetic group is the iron-containing, porphyrin complex, heme.

Chromoproteins similar to the hemoglobins in function, and apparently in chemical constitution, found in certain mollusks (helicorubin), marine worms (chlorocruorin), and anemones (actiniohematin).

Cytochromes, cellular oxidation-reduction proteins in which the prosthetic group is heme.

Flavoproteins, cellular oxidation-reduction proteins in which the prosthetic group is riboflavin.

Chromoproteins of certain animal fibers, such as black wool and hair, in which the prosthetic group is melanin.

Visual purple of the retina, a chromoprotein in which the prosthetic group is a carotenoid pigment.

Catalase, the enzyme which decomposes hydrogen peroxide into water and oxygen, a chromoprotein in which the prosthetic group is heme. The oxidative enzyme, peroxidase, has a similar composition.

There is evidence to indicate that chlorophyll occurs in the chloroplasts in combination with protein constituting a chromoprotein.

4. Phosphoproteins. Phosphoric acid is the prosthetic group of the phosphoproteins. Phosphoserine has been isolated from casein and vitellin by Lipmann and Levene (24).

Lipmann considers phosphoserine to represent the only phosphate containing group of phosphoproteins:

$$(HO)_2OPO \cdot CH_2CH(NH_2)COOH$$
Phosphoserine

Casein of milk and vitellin of egg yolk are the best known phosphoproteins.

5. Lipoproteins. The lipoproteins are formed by combination of protein with a lipid, such as lecithin, cephalin, fatty acid, etc. Phospholipid protein complexes (also called "lecithoproteins") are widely distributed in animal and plant material. They occur in milk, blood, cell nuclei, egg yolk, cell membranes, and chloroplasts of plants. They are also found in bacterial antigens and viruses.

Lipoproteins may be prepared by adding alcoholic solutions of lecithins to egg albumin solutions.

The lipoproteins are distinguished from the proteolipids in that the proteolipids are soluble in organic solvents and insoluble in water. They also contain less lipid component than the proteolipids.

6. Metalloproteins. A large group of enzyme proteins contain metallic elements, such as Fe, Co, Mn, Zn, Cu, Mg, etc., which are parts of their essential structures. The heme proteins, which contain iron and are classed as chromoproteins above, also are metalloproteins.

C. DERIVED PROTEINS

This class of proteins, as the name implies, includes those substances formed from simple and conjugated proteins. It is the least well defined of the protein groups. Derived proteins are subdivided into primary derived proteins and secondary derived proteins.

1. Primary derived proteins. These protein derivatives are formed by processes which cause only slight changes in the protein molecule and its properties. There is little or no hydrolytic cleavage of peptide bonds. The primary derived proteins are synonymous with denatured proteins.

a) *Proteans.* The proteans are insoluble products formed by the incipient action of water, very dilute acids, and enzymes. They are particularly formed from certain globulins, and differ from globulins in being insoluble in dilute salt solutions. In general, they have the physical characteristics of the naturally occurring glutelins. Examples include myosan from myosin, edestan from edestin, and fibrin from fibrinogen.

b) *Metaproteins.* The metaproteins are formed by further action of acids and alkalies upon proteins. They are generally soluble in very dilute acids and alkalies but insoluble in neutral solvents. Examples include acid and alkali metaproteins such as acid and alkali albuminates.

c) *Coagulated proteins.* The coagulated proteins are insoluble products formed by the action of heat or alcohol upon natural proteins. Similar substances may also be formed by action of ultraviolet light, x-rays, very high pressure, and mechanical shaking upon protein solutions at the iso-electric pH. Examples include cooked egg albumin, cooked meat and other proteins, and alcohol-precipitated proteins.

2. Secondary derived proteins. These substances are formed in the progressive hydrolytic cleavage of the peptide unions of protein molecules. They represent a great complexity of molecules of different sizes and amino acid composition. They are roughly grouped into proteoses, peptones, and peptides, according to relative average molecular complexity. Each group is composed of many different substances.

a) *Proteoses or albumoses.* Proteoses are hydrolytic products of proteins which are soluble in water, are not coagulated by heat, and are precipitated from their solutions by saturation with ammonium sulfate.

b) *Peptones.* Peptones are hydrolytic products of simpler structure than the proteoses. They are soluble in water, are not coagulated by heat, and are not precipitated by saturation with ammonium sulfate. They are precipitated by phosphotungstic acid.

c) *Peptides.* Peptides are composed of only a relatively few amino acids united through peptide bonds. They are named according to the number of amino acid groups present as "di-," "tri-," "tetrapeptides," etc. They are water-soluble, are not coagulated by heat, are not salted out of solution, and are often precipitated by phosphotungstic acid. Various definitely characterized peptides have been isolated from protein hydrolytic products, and many have been synthesized.

Mixtures of proteoses, peptones, and peptides are prepared commercially by both acid and enzymatic digestion of proteins. The so-called peptones used for bacteriologic culture media are such mixtures. Various mixtures of this type are prepared by the enzymatic digestion of casein for nutritional purposes.

The complete hydrolytic decomposition of a natural protein molecule into amino acids generally progresses through successive stages as follows:

protein ⟶ protean ⟶ metaprotein ⟶
proteose ⟶ peptone ⟶ peptides ⟶ amino acids

The synthesis of proteins by plants and animals consists of a progressive process in which amino acid groups are successively joined by peptide linkages until the molecular size and structure is that of a specific plant or animal protein. Also, the proteins of tissues are continually being broken down to amino acids through the various hydrolytic stages. Accordingly, substances belonging to the classes of proteoses, peptones, and peptides are constituents of tissue, though often in very small amounts.

ORGANIZATION OF AMINO ACIDS IN PEPTIDE CHAINS

One of the most striking and important facts about proteins is their chemical and biologic specificity relative to tissue composition and function, with each kind of plant and animal tissue containing proteins of characteristic properties. This differentiation of proteins is determined chiefly by the number and sequence of amino acids in the peptide chains and the organization of the peptide chains in the protein structures.

Three types of polypeptide chains are possible: open, cyclic, and branched.

Open chains contain a free α-amino group at one end of the chain and a free α-carboxyl group at the other end:

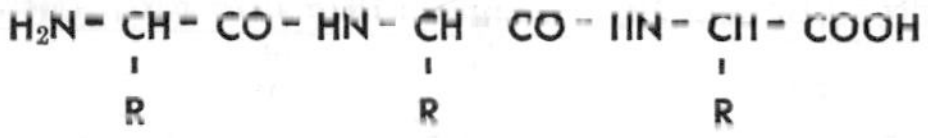

H₂N = CH = CO = HN = CH   CO = HN = CH = COOH
     | | |
     R   R   R

An open polypeptide chain may produce a cyclic chain through peptide bond formation from the terminal α-amino and α-carboxyl groups. The antibiotics tyrocidine and gramicidin S are cyclic polypeptides. The fact that no free α-amino groups have been found in ovalbumin and certain muscle proteins suggests that these are composed of cyclic chains.

The presence of two amino groups in lysine and of two carboxyl groups in aspartic and glutamic acids suggests the possibility of peptide bond branching from the additional amino and carboxyl groups in proteins that contain these amino acids. So far the ϵ-amino group of lysine always has been found free in the proteins studied. Peptide bond branching is possible between the β- and γ-carboxyl groups of aspartic and glutamic acids in a peptide chain and a free α-amino group at the end of another peptide chain. The extent to which this may occur is unknown. Branching by union of two peptide chains through the disulfide linkage —S—S— formed from cysteine groups present in the peptide chains is well established.

Owing to the presence, generally, of a free α-amino group and an α-carboxyl group in a peptide chain, it is possible to have these groups react with certain reagents to give derivatives of the end amino acid which are stable to peptide bond hydrolysis. The derivative of the end amino acid may then be isolated and identified.

Although a number of reagents have been used to form derivatives with the α-amino end of the chain, Sanger's reagent, 1-fluoro-2,4-dinitrobenzene (FDNB), is one of the best. This reagent readily reacts in mildly alkaline solution that does not hydrolyze peptide bonds:

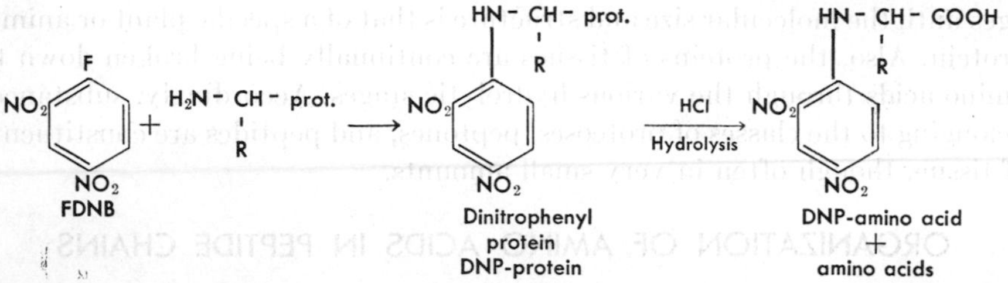

The amino acid at the other end of the peptide chain containing the free α-carboxyl group may be split off by the specific action of the enzyme carboxypeptidase, isolated, and identified. Carboxypeptidase specifically splits peptide bonds adjacent to a free α-carboxyl group, with the possible exception of those involving glycine.

It has been found that the α-carboxyl group of the end amino acid may be reduced to a primary alcohol group by lithium aluminum hydride, forming a β-amino alcohol group:

$$\text{prot.} - \text{HN} - \text{CH} - \text{COOH} \xrightarrow{4H} \text{prot.} - \text{HN} - \text{CH} - \text{CH}_2 - \text{OH} + \text{H}_2\text{O}$$

$$\underset{\text{Protein}}{|} \qquad\qquad\qquad \underset{\text{Protein amino alcohol}}{|}$$

The protein amino alcohol is hydrolyzed and the amino alcohol separated and identified, thus establishing the nature of the end amino acid group containing the free α-carboxyl group.

Chibnall and Rees improved this procedure by converting the free α-carboxyl group to the methyl ester and reducing it with lithium borohydride.

Through determination of the end amino acids of proteins and of series of peptides obtained by the partial hydrolysis of proteins it has been possible to obtain considerable information relative to the sequence of amino acids. As a simple illustration of how the method works, suppose a peptide chain of a protein is made up of a sequence of amino acids represented by the letters A, B, C, etc.:

$$\text{A} - \text{B} - \text{C} - \text{D} - \text{E} - \text{F} - \text{G} - \text{H} - \text{I} - \text{J}$$

and suppose by end-group analysis it is found that A and J represent the end amino acids of the original molecule. Now suppose the peptide is partially hydrolyzed by proteolytic enzymes and acid into a series of simpler peptides and the end amino acids determined. The peptides may be further hydrolyzed to the stage where maybe only two or three amino acids are

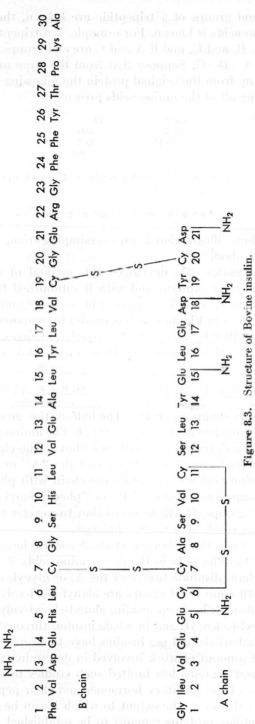

Figure 8.3. Structure of Bovine insulin.

present. If the end groups of a tripeptide are known, then the complete sequence of amino acids is known. For example, if a tripeptide is composed of amino acids A, B, and C, and if A and C are end groups, then the amino acid sequence is A—B—C. Suppose that from the large number of simple peptides worked up from the original protein the following peptides are obtained representing all of the amino acids present:

ABCD	EF
BCD	GH
CDEF	GHI
DEF	HIJ

Then the complete sequence of amino acids in the original molecule must have been:

$$A- B- C- D- E- F- G- H- I- J$$

Of course, the above illustration is an oversimplification, but it gives the principle of the method.

Sanger and associates (25) developed this method of determining the amino acid sequence in proteins and with it established the structures of insulins from various species. The amino acid sequence and arrangement in bovine insulin is given in Figure 8.3; this insulin is composed of two peptide chains bonded together by two —S—S— cystine linkages. In determining the insulin structure, these bonds were broken by oxidation with performic acid:

$$R- S- S- R' + H \cdot COOOH \longrightarrow R- SO_3H + R'- SO_3H$$

and the two peptide chains separated. The half-cystine group of each chain was converted to a cysteic acid group, —SO_3H. The amino acid sequence of each chain was then determined as outlined above. The chain with glycine and asparagine as end groups was designated the "A" or "glycyl chain," containing 21 amino acid groups, while the chain with phenylalanine and alanine as end groups was called the "B" or "phenylalanyl chain," containing 30 amino acid groups. It will be noted that two cycles are formed in the structure, both the result of —S—S— linkages.

The structures of pig, sheep, horse and whale insulins have also been determined and found to differ only in the three amino acids, 8, 9, 10, contained within the intrachain disulfide bridge of the A, or glycyl, chain. In bovine insulin these 8-9-10 amino acid groups are alanyl-seryl-valyl; in pig insulin, threonyl-seryl-isoleucyl; in sheep insulin, alanyl-glycyl-valyl; in horse insulin, threonyl-glycyl-isoleucyl; and in whale insulin, threonyl-seryl-isoleucyl. Thus it is seen that whale and pig insulins have the same structures.

The very great amount of work involved in determining the amino acid sequence in natural proteins has limited such studies to simpler proteins, such as a number of the pituitary hormones and their peptide derivatives (see Chapter 34). However, the extent to which it can be applied successfully to more complex proteins remains to be established. The techniques of paper chromatography, column chromatography, and countercurrent distribution have been of paramount aid in the isolation and identification of the peptides involved in the determination of amino acid sequence in proteins.

ORGANIZATION OF PEPTIDE CHAINS IN PROTEINS

The sequence of amino acids in the peptide chains of natural proteins is one of the fundamental aspects of protein structure. The other is the configuration of the peptide chains and their organization into the protein structures which are characteristic in both properties and biologic function.

The physical forms of natural proteins are fibrous—represented by hair, wool, epidermin of epidermis, silk fibroin, fibrin, collagen, and myosin of muscle fibers—and globular—represented by proteins such as insulin, hemoglobins, albumins, globulins, etc.

Evidence as to the organization of peptide chains in proteins has been obtained from both chemical and physical properties. X-ray studies of fibrous proteins have yielded much revealing information. Some reviews of the subject are listed in reference 26.

It has been found that all of the fibrous proteins consist of long peptide chains organized into submicroscopic crystalline bundles lying approximately parallel to the fiber axis or inclined at a roughly constant angle to it.

X-ray studies of fibrous proteins have shown that certain types of configuration are characteristic of silk fibroin, of the keratin-epidermin-myosin-fibrinogen group of proteins, and of collagen.

The peptide chains of silk fibroin are considered to be arranged as follows:

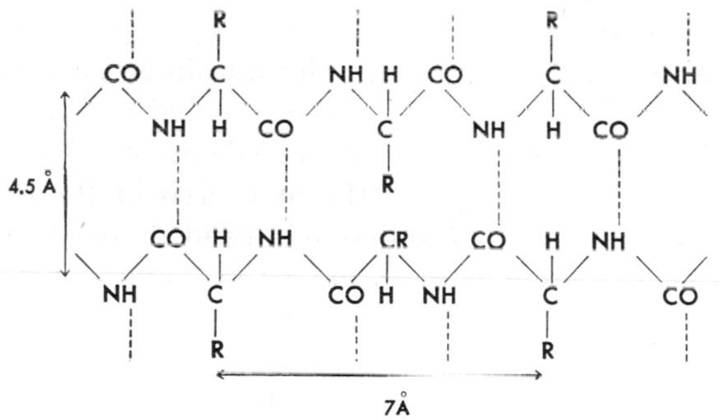

The peptide linkages of the diagram lie in the plane of the paper (are coplanar), while the R groups lie at right angles to the plane of the paper and alternate along the sides of the chain. The peptide chains are united by hydrogen bonds between the —NH and —CO groups, and also by cross linkages between the R groups. The cross linkages between the R groups are of various types, such as —S—S— formed by oxidation of two —SH groups, salt linkages formed by reaction of acidic and basic groups (a type of hydrogen bonding), and ester linkages. The diagram below illustrates the linkages between the R groups.

```
      NH                              NH
      |                               |
      CO                              CO
      |                               |
     HC - CH₂————————S————————S————————CH₂ - CH  ◄———— cystine linkage
      |                               |
      NH                              NH
      |                               |
      CO              O               CO
      |               ‖               |
     HC - CH₂———————O - P - O————————CH₂ - CH  ◄———— diester phosphate linkage
                      |
                      OH
      HN                              NH
      |                               |
      CO              O               CO
      |               ‖               |
     HC - (CH₂)₃CH₂ - NH₃⁺    Ō - C - CH₂ - CH₂ - CH  ◄———— salt linkage
      |                               |
      NH                              NH
      |                               |
      CO              OH              CO
      |               |               |
     HC - CH₂ - OH --------O = C - CH₂————CH₂————CH  ◄———— hydrogen bond
      |                               |
      NH                              NH
      |                               |
      CO   ◄————————————————————————► CO
              9.6 to 11.5 Å
              average 10 Å
```

The fibers of hair and wool (keratin proteins) and myosin of muscle are different from those of silk fibroin in that they may be reversibly stretched when wet. X-ray diagrams of the stretched and unstretched fibers are distinctly different, showing that stretching causes intramolecular transformation. Unstretched normal keratin is designated as "α-keratin," while the stretched keratin is called "β-keratin." Silk fibroin is a β-keratin.

Pauling, Corey, and Branson (27) have presented evidence that the peptide chains in the α-keratin fibers (unstretched) are arranged in a spiral or helix designated the "α-helix," with the main axis of the helix parallel to the fiber axis and containing 3.7 amino acid residues per turn. The helix is formed by hydrogen bonding between the —CO— and —NH groups to give 13 atoms in the ring:

```
       H----------------O
       |       H        ‖
       |       |        |
       N - (C - C - N)₃ - C
           ‖   |   |
           O   R   H
```

Figure 8.4 shows the bond distances and angles in the peptide chain, and Figure 8.5 is a drawing of the α-helix with 3.7 residues per turn. The α-helix chains in the α-keratin structure are held together by hydrogen bonding and other linkages between the R groups, as in the case of silk fibroin.

Myosin of muscle and both fibrinogen and the fibrin formed from it in blood coagulation are elastic fibrous proteins of the α-keratin type, just as are hair and wool.

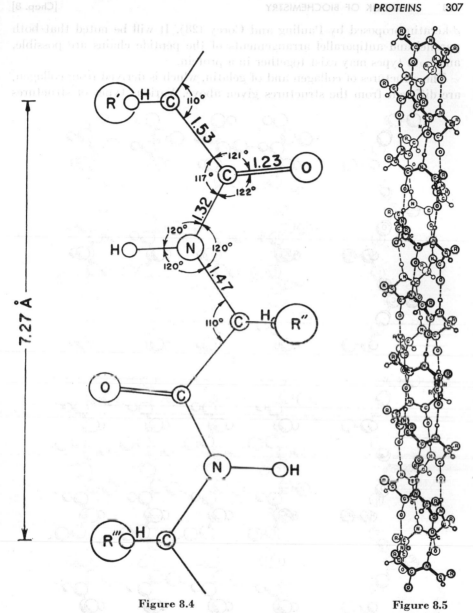

Figure 8.4

Figure 8.5

Figure 8.4.   Dimensions of the polypeptide chain. (From Pauling, L.; Corey, R. B.; and Branson, H. R.: *Proc. Natl. Acad. Sci.*, **37**, 206, 1951.)

Figure 8.5.   The helix with 3.7 residues per turn. (From Pauling, L.; Corey, R. B.; and Branson, H. R.: *Proc. Natl. Acad. Sci.*, **37**, 207, 1951.)

When an α-keratin is treated with water, the hydrogen bonds between the —CO— and —NH groups holding the peptide chain in the α-helix structure are broken and the fibers may be stretched out, with disruption of the α-helices. Drying the fibers permits the α-helices to reform, with reversal to α-keratin. Figure 8.6 shows a drawing of the pleated-sheet structure for β-keratin proposed by Pauling and Corey (28). It will be noted that both parallel and antiparallel arrangements of the peptide chains are possible, and both types may exist together in a protein.

The structures of collagen and of gelatin, which is derived from collagen, are different from the structures given above. Various types of structures

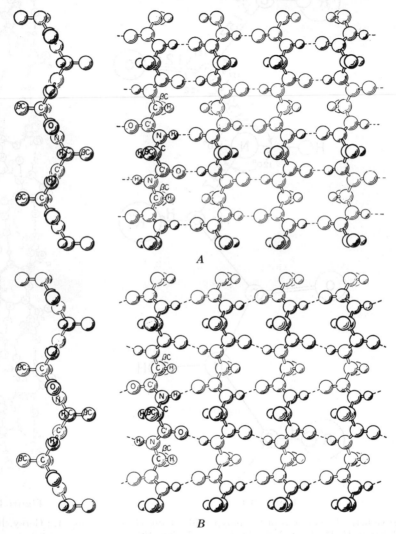

Figure 8.6. *A*, Drawing representing the parallel-chain pleated sheet structure. *B*, Drawing representing the anti-parallel-chain pleated sheet structure. (From Pauling, L., and Corey, R. B.: *Proc. Natl. Acad. Sci.*, **37,** 738, 739, 1951).

have been proposed for these proteins, ranging from two-dimensional sheet to helical arrangements of peptide chains. The most promising structure so far proposed appears to be that of Rich and Crick (29), which considers the collagen unit to be made up of three peptide chains joined together by hydrogen bonds into a helix with a gradual right-handed twist.

It is interesting to note that the carbon, nitrogen, and oxygen atoms of a peptide bond lie in the same plane (coplanar).

The organization of globular proteins is much less understood than that of fibrous proteins. Many proteins classed as globular are not strictly round in form, but are more or less ellipsoidal in shape. For example, the axis ratio of the hemoglobin molecule is about 4:1; of serum albumin, 4:1; and of serum γ-globulin, 10:1. The insulin molecule, however, is approximately round.

It is well established that in the organization of globular proteins the peptide chains are coiled and folded into well-defined patterns, the chains probably constituting thin layers with interspersed layers of water molecules between when the protein is in solution. The coiled or rolled-up structure is maintained by definite cross linkages of the types operative in fibrous proteins. When a globular protein is denatured by the action of heat, acids, alkalies, and other agents, x-ray analysis indicates a change in structure toward the fibrous keratin type. The denaturing agents break cross linkages and permit the peptide chains to uncoil and assume a more fibrous and crystalline form.

The x-ray studies of Perutz and associates on carbon monoxide hemoglobin have been interpreted as indicating the presence of α-helix peptide chains in the hemoglobin molecule (30), and it appears probable that the α-helix is present in various globular proteins.

The proteins of tissues represent latticework continuous structures with holes of varying size through which there is transport of water and various molecules and ions.

It seems probable that what is ordinarily considered to be the protein molecule may in certain cases be composed of two or more peptide chains organized and held together by loose cross linkages. This is suggested by the fact that when certain proteins are dissolved in solvents such as strong urea solution, the molecular weight becomes less, indicating the rupture of loose linkages (nonpeptide) and the formation of smaller particles. For example, Burk and Greenberg (31) found the molecular weight of horse hemoglobin to be 34,300 when dissolved in 6.66 M urea solution, as compared with the ordinarily accepted value of about 68,000 determined in dilute salt solution. Edestin has a molecular weight of 300,000 in aqueous solution and of 50,000 in urea solution.

The molecules of some proteins are dissociated into smaller particles by pH change. Phycocyan has a molecular weight of 273,000 at pH 7 to 8.2, which is reduced to half this value at pH 2.5 to 6. Particles of both molecular weights are present at pH 6 to 7. In relatively acid solutions insulin has a molecular weight of 12,000. As the pH is raised, aggregates of 2, 3, and 4 of these smaller units are formed.

Strong salt solutions may cause dissociation into smaller molecules or association into larger ones. Thyroglobulin has a molecular weight of 640,000 which changes to about 16,000,000 in 4 M sodium chloride solution.

The biologic specificity of proteins is determined by two major factors.

The first of these is the number of each specific amino acid residues present in the peptide chains and the order of arrangement of these residues in the chains. The second factor is represented by the manner in which the peptide chains are organized in the protein; that is, as specific globular or fibrous structures. It is interesting to note that the solubility and digestibility of fibrous proteins may be markedly altered by changing the physical organization of the fibers. Thus, silk is an insoluble fibrous protein which is not digested by proteolytic enzymes. However, when it is finely ground, it becomes both soluble and digestible.

Proteins, as they exist in living cells, are intimately associated with various types of lipids, carbohydrates and their derivatives, hormones, vitamins, inorganic ions, and many other diverse substances. In view of the reactive groups present in proteins, it is highly probable that many of these associated substances are loosely united to the cell proteins by hydrogen bonds, salt linkages, etc., in constituting the biologic units of living protoplasm.

THE SHAPE OF PROTEIN MOLECULES

Determination of the shapes of protein molecules in solution is an important problem. These shapes vary widely from spherical, as in the case of horse heart cytochrome c, to very elongated spheroids, as in the case of fibrinogen. The methods used for arriving at the shape of protein molecules in solution are based upon properties such as rate of diffusion; viscosity; double refraction of flow, or birefringence; and orientation in an alternating-current field.

In determining the rate of diffusion of a protein, a sharp boundary is formed between the protein solution and the solvent, and the rate at which the protein moves into the solvent is determined by the change in refractive index, obtained by an optical technique. From the rate of diffusion, the diffusion constant, D, may be calculated from the equation:

$$D = \frac{KT}{f} = \frac{RT}{Nf}$$

or

$$f = \frac{RT}{ND}$$

where K, the gas constant per molecule $= R/N$; $R =$ the gas constant per mol; $T =$ the absolute temperature, $N =$ the Avogadro number; and $f =$ a constant characteristic of the particles and the solution, equivalent to the force required to give a molecule a velocity of 1 cm per second. If the molecules are spherical then the force required, f_0, is obtained from Stoke's law:

$$f_0 = 6\pi n r$$

where $r =$ the radius of the dissolved particle and $n =$ the viscosity of the solution. The radius, r, of a spherical particle is equal to $(3MV/4\pi N)^{1/3}$, and:

$$f_0 = 6\pi n \left(\frac{3MV}{4\pi N}\right)^{1/3}$$

where $V =$ the partial specific volume of the particles and $M =$ the molecular weight. Since M and V can be determined for a protein, the theoretical value of f_0, assuming a spherical shape, can be calculated and compared with the actual value of f determined from the diffusion constant. The ratio f/f_0 is termed the "frictional ratio" or "dyssymmetry constant." This ratio is a measure of the degree to which the shape of a protein molecule deviates from that of a perfect sphere. The frictional ratio f/f_0 is unity for a purely spherical protein molecule, such as that of horse heart cytochrome c, but is progressively greater than unity as the shape of the molecule becomes more and more elongated. It cannot be less than unity. For example, some frictional ratios of proteins are: horse heart cytochrome, c, 1.0; ribonuclease, 1.04; insulin monomer, 1.1; human hemoglobin, 1.16; human fibrinogen, 1.98; and myosin of muscle 4. The values for the diffusion constant D and of the frictional ratios are for the hydrated protein molecules as they occur in solution. The axial dyssymmetry of such a molecule may be due both to the binding of water by the protein (hydration) and the intrinsic asymmetry of the anhydrous molecule.

Another approach to the shape of protein molecules is through viscosity measurements on their solutions (see Chapter 5). Einstein found that a dilute solution of rigid spherical particles obeys the equation:

$$n_{sp} = n_r - 1 = 2.5\phi$$

or

$$2.5 = \frac{n_{sp}}{\phi}$$

where n_{sp} = the specific viscosity, which is equal to the relative viscosity $n_r - 1$, and ϕ = the volume fraction of the solute. As protein molecules become more elongated or flattened, the viscosity of their solutions increases. The value of n_{sp}/ϕ for a protein solution is greater than 2.5 as ϕ approaches zero (as the protein solution becomes infinitely dilute), and this increase or increment above 2.5 may be used to calculate the axial ratio of the protein molecules. Values obtained in this way are for the hydrated protein molecules.

For a given shape larger protein molecules give higher viscosities than do smaller ones. Viscosity is least at the isoelectric pH, which means that protein ions orient in solution to increase frictional resistance to flow more than do electrically neutral molecules.

When a protein solution is subjected to an alternating-current field of sufficiently low frequency, the protein ions rotate to follow the field alternations. However, when the frequency of the field is progressively increased, a frequency is reached where the charged protein molecules cannot follow the field and are unoriented. The longer protein molecules orient less readily than the shorter ones. The dielectric constant of protein solutions containing oriented molecules (at low field frequencies) is high, while it is lower with unoriented molecules (at high field frequencies). When the dielectric constant values for a protein solution are plotted against field frequencies, curves are obtained from which it is possible to draw conclusions relative to the axial ratios of the molecules.

When a beam of polarized light is passed through a protein solution in which the molecules are unoriented (solution at rest), the beam is not affected. If the solution is passed rapidly through a narrow tube or is placed between concentric glass cylinders one of which is at rest while the other is rotated so the solution comes into rapid circular motion, the protein molecules become lined up or oriented relative to each other in the direction of flow, and the orientation becomes more complete the more rapid the flow. Longer molecules orient more readily than do shorter ones. When the rapidly moving solution is viewed at right angles to the flow with polarized light (between crossed polarizers) the flowing liquid appears optically just like a uniaxial spherocrystal, due to birefringence, or double refraction of the polarized light by the oriented protein molecules. The phenomenon is called "double refraction of flow," or "flow birefringence." The value of the birefringence is proportional to the degree of orientation of the protein molecules, which in turn is proportional to the velocity of flow and asymmetry of the molecules. From measurements of the double refraction of flow at different velocities of flow it is possible to calculate the axial ratios and asymmetry of protein molecules in solution. This method is applicable only to molecules with a long axis of 200 Å or greater, but with highly elongated molecules, such as actomyosin of muscle, it is a powerful method of investigation.

Another method of studying the shape of protein molecules utilizing birefringence due to orientation is due to Benoit (32). In this method the protein molecules in solution are oriented by applying a strong electric field to the solution for a brief interval (10^{-2} sec.). When the field is suddenly cut off, the molecules disorient, and the rate of disorientation is followed by measuring the change in birefringence of the solution at different time intervals. From such measurements the axial ratios or asymmetry of the molecules may be calculated. The reorientation rate of longer molecules is slower than that of the shorter molecules.

X-ray and electron microscopic studies contribute information as to the shapes and sizes of globular as well as of fibrous proteins. X-ray data in particular have permitted calculation of the dimensions of protein molecules in crystals and in the dry state. Viscosity, diffusion, double refraction of flow studies, etc., outlined above, give information as to the shape of protein molecules and their axial ratios when in solution.

Table 8.6 gives some idea of the approximate sizes and shapes of several proteins.

Table 8.6

Protein	Mol. wt.	Molecular dimensions, Å	Axial ratio
Serum albumin (human)	65,600	145 × 50 × 22	2.9
Hemoglobin*	66,800	65 × 55 × 55	1.18
Fibrinogen	340,000	700 × 39	18
Myosin	840,000	2000 × 20	100
Tropomyosin	53,000	385 × 14.5	2.65

* It is of interest that the volumes of anhydrous and hydrated hemoglobin molecules have been estimated as 83,000 and 116,000 cubic angstroms respectively. The dimensions of protein molecules obtained by x-ray studies of crystals may be considerably different from the dimensions of the hydrated molecules in solution, with different axial ratios.

A rigorous discussion of the size, shape, and hydration of protein molecules is given by Edsall in *The Proteins*, edited by H. Neurath and K. Bailey, Vol. I, Part B, p. 549.

PHYSICAL AND CHEMICAL PROPERTIES OF THE PROTEINS

Taste. Pure proteins are generally tasteless, though the predominant taste of protein hydrolysates (proteoses, peptones, peptides, amino acids) is bitter.

Odor. Pure proteins are odorless. When heated, they turn brown and char and give off the odor of burning feathers or hair.

Molecular weights of proteins. As previously indicated, protein molecules are exceedingly complex in structure and are very large. Because of the size of their molecules, proteins belong to the so-called colloidal state of matter.

The most important method for the determination of protein molecular weights is based upon the ultracentrifuge, which was considered in Chapter 5. The student should review that discussion at this time.

The minimal molecular weight of a protein may be calculated from the content of some characteristic component, if this is known. For example, horse hemoglobin contains 0.335 per cent iron. At least one iron atom must be present per molecule of hemoglobin. Since an atom of iron represents 55.85 units of weight and this is 0.335 per cent of the total molecular weight of hemoglobin (if only one Fe is present), the minimal molecular weight of hemoglobin is given by the expression:

$$0.335 \text{ per cent}:100 \text{ per cent}::55.85:\text{mol. wt.}$$
$$\text{mol. wt.} = 16,671$$

Actually the molecular weight of hemoglobin is four times the minimal molecular weight as calculated on the assumption of one iron atom per molecule, which means that there are four iron atoms in each hemoglobin molecule. The true molecular weight is $4 \times 16,671 = 66,684$.

The amino acid content of a protein may also be used for calculating minimal molecular weights. The methods of analysis for tyrosine, cystine, and tryptophan give quite accurate results, and determination of these acids in proteins may be used for the calculation of minimal molecular weights. Minimal molecular weights are of value in checking on actual molecular weights determined by the ultracentrifuge or other physical methods. In some instances, by calculating the minimal molecular weight for several constituents, it is possible to calculate the actual molecular weight.

The molecular weights of proteins also may be obtained from osmotic pressure measurements and light scattering which are discussed in Chapter 5, to which the student is referred.

Table 8.7 gives the molecular weights of a number of proteins, most of which were obtained by the ultracentrifugal method.

A number of the naturally occurring proteins designated by a definite name really represent complex mixtures of different proteins with molecules of widely different sizes. The crude material isolated from milk and known as "casein" is shown by the ultracentrifuge to be a complex mixture of molecules varying in molecular weight from 75,000 to 375,000. If the casein is exhaustively purified according to Hammarsten's method, a fraction of molecular weight 375,000 is obtained. Von Hippel and Waugh (33) found that soluble casein at pH 12 and 0° C exists as monomeric units, α- and β-casein monomers, with molecular weights in the range of 15,000 to 25,000. As the temperature is raised and the pH decreased to 7, these monomers polymerize into larger aggregates. The molecules of gelatin vary in mass from 10,000 to 100,000. Myoglobin of muscle apparently is composed of 17,000, 34,000, and 68,000 molecular weight fractions. The globulin fraction of blood serum is complex.

The molecular weights of proteins cannot be determined with a high degree of accuracy in most cases, and the values reported are more or less approximate.

Proteins as ampholytes. Isoelectric pH values of proteins. The properties of proteins as electrolytes are determined by the ionizable groups present. Since each open peptide chain contains only one free α-amino group and one free α-carboxyl group, those groups contribute relatively little to these properties. However, a number of the constituent amino acids contain ionizable groups not involved in peptide bond formation. These groups include the ϵ-amino group of lysine, the guanidine group of arginine, the imid-

Table 8.7. Some Physical Properties of Proteins

Protein	S_{20}*	D_{20} (cm²/sec)†	f/f_0‡	V_{20} ml/g§	M_s‖	IpH approximate
Actomyosin	12.0	0.30		(0.75)	3,900,000	
Adrenocorticotropic hormone (sheep)	2.1	10.5		(0.75)	20,000	
Albumin (serum, horse)	4.46	6.1	1.27	0.748	70,000	
Albumin (serum, human)	4.6	6.1	1.28	0.733	69,000	4.7
Aldolase	7.3	4.63	1.31	0.74	147,000	
β-Amylase (sweet potato)	8.9	5.77		(0.749)	152,000	
Carbonic anhydrase	2.8	9.0		0.749	30,000	5.3
Carboxyhemoglobin (cow)	4.6			0.749		
Catalase	11.3	4.1	1.25	0.73	250,000	
Chymotrypsinogen	2.54	9.5	1.19	0.72	23,200	9.5
Cytochrome c (horse heart)	1.9	10.1	1.29	0.707	15,600	10.65
Diphtheria toxin	4.6	6.0	1.22	0.736	74,000	
Enolase	5.59	8.08	1.01	0.735	63,700	
Fibrinogen (cow)	7.9	2.02	2.34	0.706	330,000	
Fumarase	8.51	4.05		(0.75)	204,000	
γ-Globulin (man)	7.1	3.84		(0.745)	176,000	6.4
Growth hormone (pituitary)	3.60	7.15	1.31	0.76	49,000	6.85
Hemoglobin (man)	4.46	6.9		(0.749)	63,000	6.7
Hexokinase	3.1	2.9	2.37	0.740	96,600	
Insulin (monomer)	1.6	15.0		0.749	12,000	
Insulin (tetramer)	3.68	7.45	1.18		47,800	5.3
Lactalbumin (cow)	1.9	10.6		0.751	17,400	5.12
β-Lactoglobulin	3.12	7.3	1.26	0.7514	41,500	5.19
Lysozyme (chicken)	2.11	10.2–11.2	1.14–1.21	0.722	17,200	11.0
Myoglobin	2.04	11.3	1.11	0.741	16,900	7.0
Myosin	7.2	0.87	4.0	0.74	829,000–880,000	6.2–6.6
Ovalbumin	3.55	7.76	1.16	0.749	44,000	4.6
Pepsin	3.3	9.0	1.08	0.750	35,500	<1.1
Peroxidase	3.48	7.05	1.36	0.699	39,800	
Phosphorylase (rabbit muscle)	13.7	3.2–3.8		(0.74)	340,000–400,000	5.8
Pyruvic oxidase	40.4	0.91	1.51	(0.74)	4,000,000	
Urease	18.6	3.46	1.19	0.73	480,000	5.0–5.1
Virus (rabbit papilloma)	280.0	0.51	1.65	0.756	47,100,000	
Virus (tobacco mosaic, ordinary)	174.0	0.3	2.9	0.727	59,000,000	
Zein	1.9	4.0	2.7	0.776	50,000	

* S_{20} = sedimentation constant in Svedberg units reduced to water at 20° C.

† D_{20} = diffusion constant in units of 1×10^{-7} reduced to water at 20° C.

‡ f/f_0 = frictional ratio; the ratio of determined molar frictional constant, f, to the calculated molar frictional constant, f_0, for nonsolvated spherical molecules of the same mass.

§ V_{20} = partial specific volume of the protein at 20° C. The partial specific volume of a protein represents the volume increment when 1 g of dried protein is added to a very large volume of water (solvent). Values in brackets in the table are assumed values based upon determinations on closely related proteins. One gram of protein in solution generally occupies a volume of 0.70–0.75 ml, representing a protein density of 1.33–1.43 in water solution.

‖ M_s = molecular weight by sedimentation velocity and diffusion measurements.

azole group of histidine, the β-carboxyl of aspartic acid, the γ-carboxyl of glutamic acid, the phenolic hydroxyl of tyrosine, and the sulfhydryl group of cysteine. The extra carboxyl groups of aspartic and glutamic acids occur both free and combined with ammonia as the amide group (asparagine and glutamine). The acidic properties of phosphoproteins such as casein are partly due to the phosphoric acid groups present.

In Chapter 3, to which the student is referred, it was shown that the amino acids in acid solutions exist as cations which dissociate to give H⁺ ions in stages to which acid dissociation constants K_1, K_2, K_3, etc., may be assigned. The zwitterion form of the amino acid is an intermediate stage in the process. Proteins in a similar manner exist as complex cations in acid solution and when titrated with alkali show successive overlapping stages of H⁺ ion dissociation with the formation of zwitterions, and finally protein anions. Although the processes of protein dissociation represent many ionizable groups, numbers of which may be functioning simultaneously, the general process may be represented as follows, in which the numbers of charges and H⁺ ions involved are not indicated:

$$\text{protein}^+ \rightleftharpoons H^+ + {}^+\text{protein}^- \rightleftharpoons H^+ + \text{protein}^-$$

Cation   Zwitterion   Anion

Because protein molecules contain numbers of groups that interact reversibly with H⁺ ions over a wide pH range, their solutions have excellent buffer

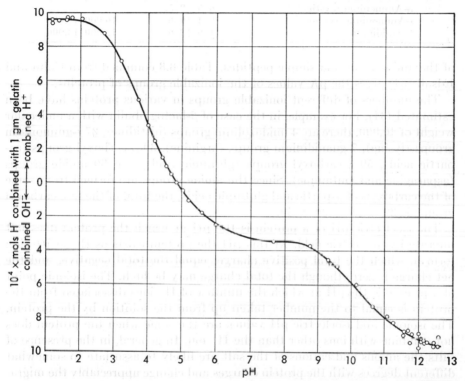

Figure 8.7. Dissociation curve of a standard gelatin preparation in hydrochloric acid or sodium hydroxide solution, as obtained from pH measurements at 30° C. The curve was drawn to fit the experimental points. (From Hitchcock, D. I.: *J. Gen. Physiol.*, **15**, 125, 1932.)

action, and much of the buffer capacity of body tissues is due to the protein buffers.

The dissociation curves, or titration curves, of proteins corresponding to the above equilibria with H⁺ ions may be determined, and an example is given in Figure 8.7. These curves extend over a wide range of pH and do not show the sharp breaks characteristic of the curves of monobasic weak acids. This is due to the large number of groups which ionize successively and simultaneously throughout most of the pH range.

The nature of the ionizing groups in proteins may be determined from the titration curves under various conditions, and the heats of ionization, ΔH,

Table 8.8.   Characteristic pK Values and Heats of Ionization (ΔH) of Groups Found in Proteins

Group	pK(25° C)	ΔH, cal/mol
α-Carboxyl	3.0– 3.2	±1,500
β-Carboxyl (aspartic acid)	3.0– 4.7	±1,500
γ-Carboxyl (glutamic acid)	ca 4.4	±1,500
Phenolic hydroxyl (tyrosine)	9.8–10.4	6,000
Sulfhydryl	9.1–10.8	
Imidazolium (histidine)	5.6– 7.0	6,900– 7,500
α-Ammonium	7.6– 8.4	10,000–13,000
α-Ammonium (cystine)	6.5– 8.5	
ε-Ammonium (lysine)	9.4–10.6	10,000–12,000
Guanidinium	11.6–12.6	12,000–13,000

of the amino acids and simple peptides. Table 8.8 compiled from Cohn and Edsall (34) gives the pK values of the ionizable groups of proteins.

The numbers of different ionizable groups in various proteins have been estimated (34). For example, in the case of β-lactoglobulin with a molecular weight of 40,000, there are 4 imidazolium groups (histidine), 27 ε-ammonium groups (lysine), 7 guanidinium groups (arginine), 30 β-carboxyl groups (aspartic acid), 59 γ-carboxyl groups (glutamic acid), and 30 amide groups (asparagine and glutamine). Since the amide groups are formed from some of the carboxyls of aspartic and glutamic acids, the total of the free carboxyl groups is $30 + 59 - 30 = 59$.

The isoelectric pH of a protein is the pH at which the protein does not migrate in an electric field. At this pH the protein exists as the zwitterion form in which the total positive charges equal the total negative, and the net charge is zero, though the total charge may be high. The isoionic point of a protein is the pH at which the number of H+ ions dissociated from the protein is equal to the number taken up from the solution by the protein. The isoionic and isoelectric pH values are the same when the protein does not combine with ions other than the H+ ion. In general, in the presence of salts the anions and cations of the salt are likely to associate to somewhat different degrees with the protein charges and change appreciably the migration in an electric field and the isoelectric pH; consequently, accurate isoelectric pH values can be given for proteins only under specified conditions of salt concentration and ionic strength.

The isoelectric pH of a protein is of great importance in relation to the physical and chemical properties of the protein. In general, the properties of a protein are minimal at the isoelectric pH. At this pH the net charge on the protein is least and the electrical conductivity is least. Also, at this pH the osmotic pressure, swelling capacity, viscosity, and solubility are minimum. Proteins exist as cations on the acid side and as anions on the alkaline side of the isoelectric pH.

A number of methods are used for the determination of the isoelectric pH values of proteins. These methods are generally based upon determination of minima in properties, such as the pH at which electrical migration is least or the pH of minimum solubility.

The migration of particles in a solution between electrodes is referred to as "electrophoresis." Tiselius (35) has developed a very useful electrophoretic apparatus for studying the migration of proteins and other colloids. The solution to be examined is well buffered and is placed in a special square U-tube provided with compartments and with electrodes attached to the ends. Upon passage of a current, the charged protein particles migrate toward the electrode of opposite charge. If the buffer solution is alkaline to the isoelectric pH of the protein, the particles migrate toward the positive electrode, while they migrate toward the negative electrode when the buffer solution is acid to the isoelectric pH of the protein. Migration of the particles ceases or is minimal when the pH of the buffer solution is the same as the isoelectric pH of the protein. The moving boundaries of the migrating protein particles are observed by photographing them through a special optical system. If the protein particles under observation possess the same isoelectric pH and are of the same size and shape, they migrate at the same speed and a sharp boundary is obtained. On the other hand, if a mixture of proteins in which the components have different isoelectric pH values, molecular sizes, etc., is observed in the apparatus, each molecular species will migrate at a different rate and become concentrated in different compartments of the cell, from which they can be removed. The Tiselius apparatus is of much importance in the separation and purification of proteins, and in the determination of isoelectric pH values. See discussion in Chapter 15.

The isoelectric pH values of a number of proteins are given in Table 8.9. Since the IpH value varies with the ionic strength of the solution, the values given are only approximate for different ionic strengths. The values of the table are largely for an ionic strength of 0.1 and range all the way from around 1 for pepsin, with many acidic groups, to 11 for lysozyme, with many basic groups. The protamin salmin, containing much basic arginine, has an IpH of around 12. Table 8.9 gives the distribution of a number of groups in several proteins which determine the isoelectric pH values and various chemical properties.

Proteins act as buffers on both sides of the isoelectric pH. The isoelectric pH values of most of the body proteins are below the pH of blood and tissue fluids and cells in which the proteins are found. This means that the body proteins are generally held at a pH alkaline to their isoelectric points and exist to a considerable extent as negative ions or salts with the cations Na^+, K^+, Ca^{++}, and Mg^{++}. In other words, the body proteins exist largely as buffers composed of $protein^-/H \cdot protein$. It is of interest that, in general, the imidazolium groups of histidine and the α-ammonium groups are responsible for the buffer action of proteins at physiologic pH. It will be seen from Table 8.9 that these are the only groups in proteins dissociating appreciably at physiologic pH.

Crystallization of proteins. Many of the proteins have been obtained in crystalline condition. Vegetable proteins in general are easy to crystallize. Among the animal proteins some hemoglobins crystallize very readily, while proteins such as serum albumin and ovalbumin are difficult to crystallize.

Table 8.9. Distribution of Groups in Some Proteins
Values are numbers of groups per 1,000,000 grams of protein.

Protein	Indole	Hydroxyl	Phenoxyl	Amide	—SH	Cysteine/2 cystine—S	Cations	Free anions	Total ionic
Aldolase	11.3	132.4	29.3	64.7	0	9.3	129.0	86.0	215.0
Casein (whole)	5.9	101.1	34.8	114.3	—	2.8	99.7	91.2	190.9
β-Casein	3.2	107.8	17.7	114.3	0	0	84.1	80.5	164.6
Chymotrypsinogen	27.3	193.9	14.9	109.4	10.8	27.5	76.7	23.0	99.7
Collagen	0	158.3	5.5	47.0	0	0	91.7	77.2	168.9
Edestin	7.2	92.4	23.5	126.8	4.2	7.2	128.6	104.2	232.8
Fibrinogen (human)	16.2	118.5	30.4	106.4	3.3	51.7	124.9	90.8	215.7
Gliadin	2.9	64.4	17.7	321.0	—	21	31.95	0	31.95
Insulin	0	67.3	69.0	99.5	0	104	68.4	78.5	146.9
β-Lactoglobulin	9.4	82.1	20.4	76.5	9.1	19.1	104.3	141.5	245.8
Myoglobin (horse)	11.5	71.4	13.3	47.1	0	0	173.6	126.5	300.1
Myosin (rabbit)	3.9	84.1	18.8	85.7	0	11.7	139.2	131.5	270.7
Salmin	0	87.0	0	0	0	0	490	0	490
Serum albumin (human)	0.98	70.6	26.0	63.0	5.8	46.7	142.7	120.2	262.9

Many of the enzyme proteins have been crystallized. Among these are urease, pepsin, trypsin, and catalase.

The crystallization of proteins often may be expedited by the addition of a salt such as ammonium sulfate or sodium chloride and adjustment toward the isoelectric pH. The addition of definite amounts of alcohol or acetone is occasionally advantageous. The added substances and adjustment to the isoelectric pH decrease the solubility of the protein. The protein is also least dissociated at the isoelectric pH and may crystallize best in this condition. However, some proteins crystallize best in the form of protein salt.

The relative ease of crystallization of proteins as compared with poly-saccharides is due to the high polarity of the protein molecules, giving rise to strong directional fields of force which orient the molecules and promote crystal formation.

Viscosity of protein solutions. The viscosity of protein solutions varies widely with the kind of protein and concentration. The viscosity of a protein in solution is closely related to molecular shape, long molecules giving higher viscosity than those more nearly globular in form. Viscosity measurements are of value in calculating the dimensions (axial lengths) of protein molecules. For a given shape large protein molecules give higher viscosities than small ones. Viscosity is least at the isoelectric pH, which means that protein ions orient in solution to increase frictional resistance to flow more than do neutral molecules.

Hydration of proteins. While proteins, as well as many other substances, combine with and hold a certain amount of water through the action of poorly defined adsorptive forces of attraction, the peptide chains constituting protein molecules contain many polar groups ($-NH_2$, $-COOH$, $-OH$, $-CO-$, $-NH-$, etc.) which tend to combine with water and become hydrated. The nitrogen and oxygen containing groups of proteins contain unshared electron pairs, and these unite with the hydrogen of water to form more or less loose complexes of the type:

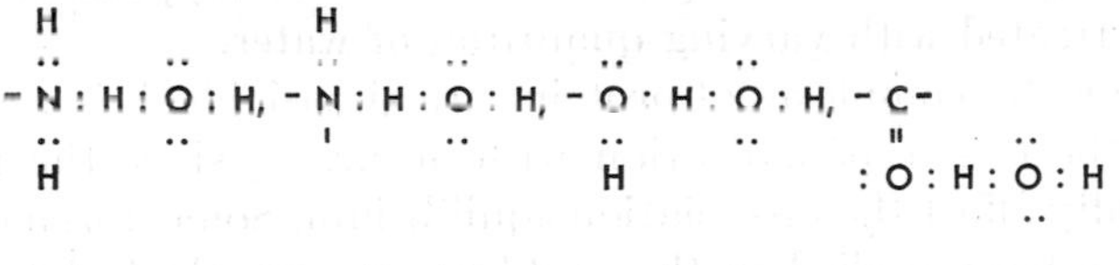

$$
\begin{array}{llll}
H & H & & \\
\ddot{} & \ddot{} & & \\
-N:H:O:H, & -N:H:O:H, & -O\cdot H:O:H, & -C- \\
\ddot{} & | & \ddot{} & \| \\
H & H & & :O:H:O:H
\end{array}
$$

Since the water molecules combined with protein polar groups also possess unshared electron pairs, they may combine with more water to form aggregates attached to the polar groups such as:

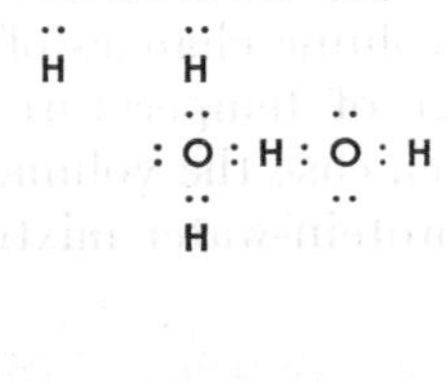

$$
\begin{array}{l}
H \\
\ddot{} \\
-N:H:O:H \quad \text{etc.} \\
\ddot{} \quad \ddot{} \\
H \quad H \\
\quad \ddot{} \\
\quad :O:H:O:H \\
\quad \ddot{} \\
\quad H
\end{array}
$$

Ionized acidic groups of proteins possess more attraction for water than do the nonionized groups because of the attraction of the negative charge for the hydrogen of water:

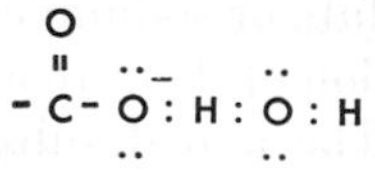

$$-C-O:H:O:H$$

Also, the positively charged ions of proteins coordinate readily with electrons of the oxygen of water:

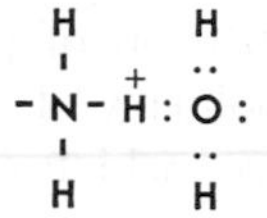

$$-N-H:O:$$

Accordingly, proteins hydrate to a greater extent when in the form of ions (protein salts) than they do as undissociated molecules (in the isoelectric condition).

The water complexes with proteins are dissociable:

$$-N:H:O:H \rightleftharpoons -N: + H:O:H$$

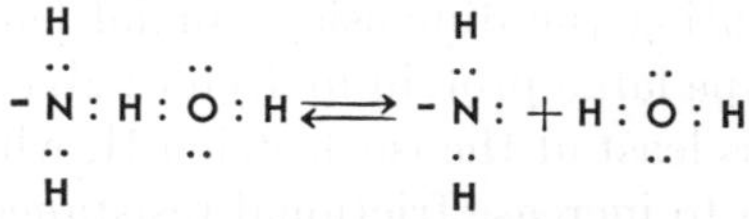

When electrolytes, sugars, alcohols, and other substances which form complexes with water are added to protein solutions, there is competition for the water, and the degree of hydration of the protein is decreased.

In general, the combination of proteins with water is, within limits, dependent upon the concentration of the protein solution, the pH of the solution in relation to the isoelectric pH of the protein, the presence of other dissolved substances which combine with water or form complexes with the protein, and the temperature of the solution.

That proteins do combine with water has been proved by observations showing changes in light absorption, dielectric values, protein density, etc., of proteins treated with varying quantities of water.

Since the water complexes of proteins are dissociable, it is very difficult to determine the degree of hydration with accuracy, since the method used may markedly affect the dissociation equilibrium. Some dozen different procedures have been applied to the problem, among which determination of the freezing-point depression and vapor-pressure effects of crystalloids added to protein solutions may be mentioned. In applying these methods, the assumption is made that the water not bound by protein constitutes the solvent for the crystalloid added, and the lowering of the freezing point or vapor pressure beyond that calculated if all water present acted as solvent is taken as an index of bound water. Another method, the dilatometric method, is based upon the volume changes of protein-water systems when cooled through a wide range of temperature as compared with an equal weight of water alone. In each case the volume progressively decreases, but the effect is greater in the protein-water mixture. The difference is utilized in calculating bound water. The values for bound water obtained by different methods vary over such a wide range that the validity of such determina· tions is extremely doubtful. For example, results on 1 per cent gelatin solutions by different methods indicate from 1 to 7 g of water to be bound per gram of gelatin.

Despite the fact that the combination of proteins with water represents reversible equilibria, some of the water is held with great tenacity, and the removal of the last traces of water from proteins by ordinary drying procedures is very difficult and often incomplete.

The swelling of proteins when placed in aqueous solutions is definitely associated with hydration of the molecules, though a number of additional processes may be involved. The swelling of protein gels is discussed in the chapter dealing with the Donnan membrane equilibrium and is intimately related to osmotic effects within the gel induced by the Donnan membrane phenomenon.

The combination of living tissues with water is largely determined by hydration of the tissue proteins. A certain degree of tissue hydration is essential for normal function. Severe dehydration of tissue proteins such as that caused by water deprivation leads to serious derangements of function.

Solubility and salting out of proteins. The solubility of a protein depends upon the proportions and distribution of polar hydrophilic groups and nonpolar hydrophobic groups in the molecule and the resulting protein dipole moment. The ionic polar groups of protein molecules interact electrostatically both within the same molecule and with surrounding molecules, tending to form aggregates and opposing solubility. This interaction between protein-charged groups is decreased in pure water with a high dielectric constant; that is, the degree of interaction is inversely proportional to the dielectric constant of the solvent. The polar water molecules interact with the polar groups of proteins, tending to increase solubility. In the case of albumins, pseudoglobulins, and other water-soluble proteins the protein-water interactions promoting solubility predominate over the protein-protein interactions opposing solubility, and the proteins are water-soluble.

The addition of an organic solvent, such as acetone or alcohol, to a solution of protein in water decreases the dielectric constant of the solvent and also displaces some of the water molecules associated with the protein and decreases the concentration of water present in the solution. These effects tend to decrease the solubility of the protein, and the addition of such solvents is often utilized in the precipitation of proteins from solution. This is generally done at low temperatures to avoid protein denaturation.

When small amounts of salt are added to a protein dissolved in pure water, the activity coefficient of the protein is decreased and its solubility is increased. Likewise, proteins, such as euglobulins, which are insoluble in pure water become soluble in the presence of small amounts of salts. This phenomenon, often called "salting in," is due to the forces of attraction between the protein ions and the salt ions. At low salt concentrations the increase in the logarithm of protein solubility, S, is proportional to the ionic strength of the solvent.

At high concentrations of very soluble salts such as ammonium sulfate, sodium sulfate, and phosphate buffers, proteins are "salted out" of solution. This salting out is due to a decrease in the activity of water, which diminishes the solubilizing interactions between water and the polar protein groups. The solubility, S, of many proteins at high salt concentrations decreases logarithmically as the salt concentration increases:

$$\log S = \beta - K_s \omega$$

where S = the protein solubility in the salt solution, ω = the ionic strength of the salt solution, β = the solubility of the protein in pure water (generally hypothetical and obtained by extrapolation of the solubility curve to $\omega = 0$), and K_s = the salting-out constant. The values of K_s vary with protein and salt. For example, the K_s values for horse hemoglobin and $MgSO_4$, $(NH_4)_2SO_4$, and Na_2SO_4 are 0.33, 0.71, and 0.76, respectively; while the K_s values for fibrinogen and NaCl and $(NH_4)_2SO_4$ are 1.07 and 1.46.

The relation of solubility of several proteins to ionic strength is shown in Fig. 8.8 taken from Cohn and Edsall (34). It will be observed from this figure that salting out may be used effectively in the separation of proteins from solution.

In general, precipitation of a protein from solution is most complete (its solubility is least) at or near its isoelectric pH, as would be expected, because the protein is least soluble at this pH. However, there are some instances in which the addition of much salt causes the precipitation of a protein salt which separates best at a pH other than the isoelectric pH. For example, Sorenson found that the solubility of horse carboxyhemoglobin shows minimum solubilities in concentrated ammonium sulfate at pH 6.6 (near

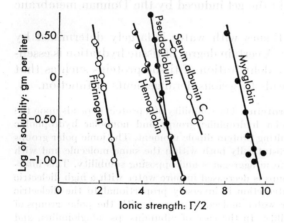

Figure 8.8. The solubility of proteins in ammonium sulfate solutions. (From Cohn, E. J., and Edsall, J. T.: *Proteins, Amino Acids, and Peptides*. Reinhold Publishing Corp., New York, 1943.)

the isoelectric pH) and also at pH 5.4. The precipitate at pH 5.4 was combined with much sulfate and considered to be carboxyhemoglobin sulfate.

The solubility of proteins and the effects of salts are treated extensively by Cohn and Edsall (34) and Taylor (36).

The effect of temperature upon the solubility of proteins in strong salt solutions is highly variable. Horse carboxyhemoglobin is about ten times more soluble at 0° than at 25° C in strong phosphate solution. Vegetable seed globulins are more soluble in salt solutions at higher than at lower temperatures. The solubility of egg albumin in salt solutions shows little variation with temperature.

The precipitation of proteins by salting out is one of the most used and valuable methods for the isolation and purification of proteins.

Precipitation of proteins with positive and negative ions. Combination with dyes.

Proteins may be precipitated from solution by a variety of positive and negative ions. Such precipitations are of importance in the isolation of proteins, in the deproteinization of blood and other biologic fluids and extracts for analysis, and in the preparation of useful protein derivatives.

The positive ions most commonly used for protein precipitation are those of heavy metals, such as Zn^{++}, Cd^{++}, Hg^{++}, Fe^{+++}, Cu^{++}, and Pb^{++}. These ions precipitate proteins from solutions alkaline to the protein isoelectric pH, because at this pH the protein is dissociated as protein⁻ which combines with the positive metal ion to give an insoluble precipitate of metal proteinate. The metal ions may be removed from the metal proteinate by acidification (protein⁻ converted to protein⁺) or by precipitation of the metal by hydrogen sulfide or other agent. Metal protein precipitates are often dissolved by the addition of strong alkali. It is evident from the above facts that the pH of the protein solution (within a certain range) is of primary importance for the most complete precipitation of proteins by heavy metal ions.

The positive ions of organic bases combine with proteins on the alkaline side of the protein isoelectric pH, and some of these combinations are insoluble. Proteins of the protamin class, which are very basic in character, readily form insoluble compounds with various ordinary proteins. A notable example is the combination of protamin with insulin to form protamin insulinate (protamin-insulin), which is widely used in the treatment of diabetes mellitus. The isoelectric pH of insulin is about 5.3, while the isoelectric pH of protamin is high on the alkaline side (9.7–12.4). When insulin and protamin are mixed in solution at pH 7, the insulin is alkaline to its isoelectric pH and exists as insulin⁻, while the protamin is acid to its isoelectric pH and is present as protamin⁺. Accordingly, the positive and negative ions combine to form protamin insulinate. When this material is injected for the treatment of diabetes, it is gradually decomposed to yield insulin slowly to the body, thereby more nearly simulating pancreatic secretion of insulin than when insulin is injected alone.

Negative ions combine with proteins when in the form of protein⁺ (pH of the protein solution is acid to the protein isoelectric pH) to form protein salts. Several of these salts are insoluble and provide valuable methods for the precipitation of proteins from solution. Among the more common protein precipitants involving negative ion precipitation are tungstic acid, phosphotungstic acid, trichloracetic acid, picric acid, tannic acid, ferrocyanic acid, and sulfosalicylic acid. When the above agents are added to protein solutions at the proper pH, precipitates of protein tungstate, phosphotungstate, picrate, tannate, etc., are formed. These precipitates are generally dissolved, and the protein salts are decomposed upon the addition of alkali (forms protein⁻). Tungstic acid, phosphotungstic acid, trichloracetic acid, and picric acid are commonly used for the preparation of protein-free filtrates of blood and other biologic materials preliminary to analysis. Hides are converted to leather by treatment with tannic acid, which reacts with skin proteins to form insoluble protein tannates.

Rawlins and Schmidt (37) have shown that acid dyes (dissociate as acids ⟶ dye⁻), such as Biebrich scarlet and naphthylamine brown, combine in definite proportions with proteins acid to the isoelectric pH (protein⁺), the amount of dye combining being a function of pH and protein⁺ concentration. Similarly, basic dyes (base ⟶ dye⁺), such as methylene blue, induline scarlet, and safranine y, combine with proteins on the alkaline side of the isoelectric pH (protein⁻). Since the protein-dye combinations are often highly insoluble, it is readily possible to determine the amount of dye combined with a given weight of protein. The above workers were able to plot dye-protein titration curves and to calculate the equivalent combining weights of proteins from their results.

The combination of proteins with dyes is of much importance in the staining of tissues and microorganisms for microscopic examination. The bactericidal action of various dyes used in the treatment of infections such as acriflavin is probably related to combination of the dye with cellular proteins of the infecting organism rendering them incapable of normal function.

Precipitation of proteins by specific antibody proteins. The injection of a foreign protein into an animal generally causes the appearance of so-called specific immune bodies or antibodies against the protein injected. For example, if a rabbit is given a series of injections with egg albumin at frequent intervals, its blood serum will develop the property of forming a precipitate with very minute amounts of egg albumin but not with other proteins. The injection of egg albumin causes the production of antibody proteins in the rabbit that specifically precipitate the egg albumin (antigen). The antibody proteins are present in the γ-globulin fraction of blood serum and represent normal serum proteins which have been altered as a result of the presence of the injected protein (antigen).

The precipitation of proteins by their specific immune sera antibody proteins (precipitin reaction) affords a highly sensitive and specific method for the detection of proteins.

Reaction of proteins with nitrous acid. Since proteins generally contain some free amino groups, they react with nitrous acid to liberate nitrogen, with replacement of the amino group by a hydroxyl group, as is the case in the reaction of amino acids with nitrous acid. Treatment of proteins with nitrous acid accordingly destroys the free amino groups, and produces deaminized proteins.

Acylation of proteins. Acid groups R—CO— may be introduced into the free hydroxyl and amino groups of proteins by treatment with acid chlorides and anhydrides. Acetylated, benzoylated, and benzenesulfonated proteins may be readily prepared. Ketene, $CH_2{=}C{=}O$, is a valuable reagent for the acetylation of proteins. It reacts with amino and hydroxyl groups as follows:

$$R-NH_2 + CH_2 = C = O \longrightarrow R-NH-CO-CH_3$$
$$R-OH + CH_2 = C = O \longrightarrow R-O-CO-CH_3$$

By controlling the conditions it is possible to acetylate the amino groups of proteins with ketene without acetylating the hydroxyl groups.

The acylation of proteins is of importance in studies of the influence of free amino and hydroxyl groups upon the physiologic properties of the protein. For example, acetylation of only the amino groups of insulin reduces its physiologic activity by about 20 per cent, while acetylation of both amino and tyrosine hydroxyl groups abolishes its activity, indicating that free phenolic hydroxyl groups are much more important to the function of insulin than are free amino groups.

Sulfhydryl-disulfide exchange reactions of peptides and proteins. Much evidence has accumulated (38) that peptides and proteins containing intramolecular disulfide linkages form aggregates linked by intermolecular disulfide bonds, —S—S—. These aggregates are formed in a chain reaction initiated by a substance containing a free sulfhydryl group, —SH, such as glutathione or another protein or peptide. The process may be illustrated diagrammatically as follows:

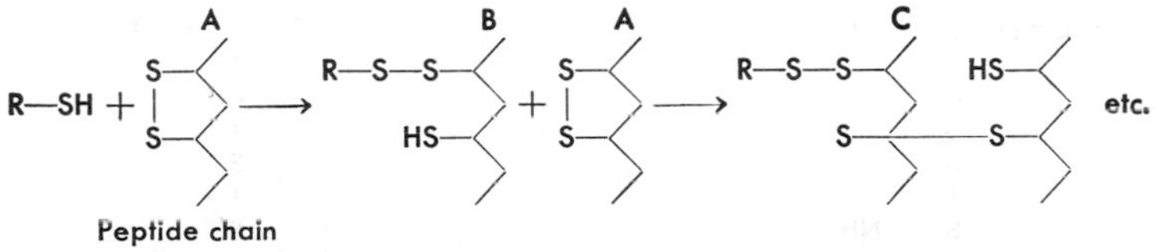

Peptide chain

R—SH reacts with the peptide chain A, containing an intramolecular —S—S— group, to form B, containing a free —SH group. B then reacts with another A to produce C, containing two A groups (also R—S—S—), and since C contains a free —SH group, it in turn may react with A to form an aggregate with three A groups, etc. The denaturation of proteins appears often to involve such aggregations. The process appears to be involved in the formation of cross —S—S— linkages when fibrinogen is aggregated into fibrin, and there is some evidence to indicate its operation in the formation of cross linkages in the mitotic apparatus of cell division.

Cleavage of —S—S— groups of proteins. Since the —SH groups formed by the reduction of —S—S— groups in proteins are unstable and may reoxidize to —S—S— compounds, other methods which give more stable cleavage products are desirable when proteins are to be split into simpler peptides for studies on amino acid sequence and other properties.

As indicated previously, Sanger split the —S—S— linkages of insulin to yield chain peptides by oxidation with performic acid, which breaks the —S—S— bond to form cysteic acid groups. If we designate a protein containing an —S—S— group by R—S—S—R', the reaction may be expressed as follows:

$$R-S-S-R' + 6H \cdot CO_3H \longrightarrow R-SO_3H + R'-SO_3H + 6H \cdot COO^- + 4H^+$$

where R—SO$_3$H and R'—SO$_3$H = peptides with a terminal cysteic acid group. Oxidation by performic acid has the disadvantage especially of disrupting tryptophan groups in the protein.

Swan (39) has found that the —S—S— group in proteins is split by sulfite in the presence of cupric ions to form two thiosulfate groups (S-sulfocysteic acid groups). The reaction appears to take place in stages in which Cu^{++} is reduced to Cu$^+$:

$$3R-S-S-R + 3SO_3^- \longrightarrow 3R-S-SO_3^- + 3RS^-$$
$$3RS^- + 2Cu^{++} + SO_3^- \longrightarrow R-S-SO_3^- + 2R-S-Cu$$
$$2RS-Cu + 4Cu^{++} + 2SO_3^- \longrightarrow 2R-S-SO_3^- + 6Cu^+$$

The over-all reaction is:

$$3R-S-S-R + 6SO_3^- + 6Cu^{++} \longrightarrow 6R-S-SO_3^- + 6Cu^+$$

This method of —S—S— cleavage has been applied to trypsinogen and chymotrypsinogen by Neurath and associates (40) and to wool keratin by Swan.

Cystine may exist in proteins as a component of a single peptide chain or of two peptide chains linked by the —S—S— linkage:

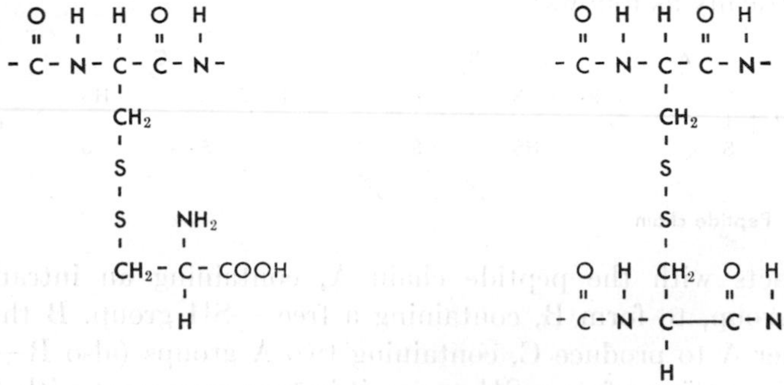

$$
\begin{array}{ccc}
\overset{O}{\underset{\|}{}}\ H\ H\ \overset{O}{\underset{\|}{}}\ H & \qquad & \overset{O}{\underset{\|}{}}\ H\ H\ \overset{O}{\underset{\|}{}}\ H \\
-C-N-C-C-N- & & -C-N-C-C-N- \\
\text{CH}_2 & & \text{CH}_2 \\
S & & S \\
S\ \ \ \text{NH}_2 & & S \\
\text{CH}_2-C-\text{COOH} & & \text{CH}_2 \\
\text{H} & & -C-N-C----C-N- \\
\textbf{A} & & \textbf{B}
\end{array}
$$

The —S—S— linkages of proteins may be reduced to two —SH groups by treatment with reducing agents such as sodium cyanide, cysteine, thioglycolic acid, and glutathione. Reduction of structures such as A forms a molecule of free cysteine and leaves a cysteine molecule in the peptide chain. Reduction of a structure such as B breaks the cross —S—S— linkage between the peptide chains, separating them, and leaving cysteine molecules present in each chain.

The presence of certain —S—S— groups is necessary for the full activity of insulin. Their reduction to —SH groups results in the loss of about 50 per cent of the insulin activity.

Oxidation of —SH groups of proteins. Some proteins contain free —SH groups which may be readily oxidized by agents such as ferricyanide, cystine, tetrathionate, porphyrindin, and iodine. These oxidations apparently consist in the oxidation of two —SH groups to an —S—S— group. Presumably such an oxidation may involve two —SH groups in the same peptide chain, or in different peptide chains which would cause linkage of the chains and formation of a different and more complex protein structure.

The above oxidizing agents may be used for the quantitative estimation of free —SH groups in proteins. The —S—S— linkages of proteins may be determined by reduction of the protein with thioglycolic acid, which reduces —S—S— to —SH groups which are then estimated. The —S—S groups may be obtained from the difference in free —SH groups in the protein before and after reduction.

The determination of free —SH groups in proteins is of importance in studying their relation to properties of the protein (insulin activity, for example) and in studying the denaturation of proteins by heat coagulation and other agencies. In general, the denaturation of a protein causes an increase in the number of free —SH groups.

Halogenation of proteins. When proteins are treated with alkaline iodine solution (NaOI), iodine is incorporated into the protein molecule. Hydrolysis of iodized protein yields diiodotyrosine, indicating that iodine substitutes into the tyrosine ring. More drastic methods of treatment lead to halogenation of the indole and imidazole groups of tryptophan and histidine. When proteins are treated with alkaline bromine solution (NaOBr), the cystine groups are oxidatively destroyed.

Iodine of iodides taken by mouth is utilized by the body in forming the iodized protein thyroglobulin, the precursor of thyroxine, the hormone of the thyroid gland. When thyroglobulin is hydrolyzed, it yields the iodine-containing compounds diiodotyrosine and thyroxin. Harington and Rivers (38) found thyroxin in the hydrolysis products of casein which had been treated with iodine. Practically all iodized proteins have some thyroid activity (increase metabolic rate).

Reaction of proteins with formaldehyde. Formaldehyde combines with proteins to change their properties markedly. Egg albumin becomes incoagulable by heat when treated with formaldehyde. Formaldehyde converts casein, soybean proteins, and other proteins into inert hard horny masses which are produced commercially as plastics (artificial ivories) in large quantities. Formaldehyde reacts with the proteins of tissues and hardens them when they are preserved in its solutions.

The chemical reactions involved in the action of formaldehyde upon proteins are obscure. Undoubtedly one of the reactions is combination of formaldehyde with various amino groups in a manner similar to its reaction with the amino groups of amino acids.

Color reactions of proteins and amino acids. Because of their peptide structure and the presence of different amino acid groups in their molecules, proteins react with a variety of agents to form colored products. Several of these color reactions of proteins are of importance in the qualitative detection and quantitative estimation of proteins and of their constituent amino acids.

a) The ninhydrin reaction. The reaction of ninhydrin with amino acids has been discussed in detail on page 289, which should be consulted for the mechanism of reaction. Ninhydrin reacts with free α-amino acids and with proteins, proteoses, peptones, and peptides to give a blue color. The test is both the most general and one of the most delicate reactions known for the qualitative detection of proteins and their hydrolytic products. It may be used to show the presence of amino acids in urine and in deproteinized body fluids. Apparently all amino acids of protein hydrolysis give the ninhydrin reaction. The colors given by different amino acids vary in shade and depth. The ninhydrin reaction is of value in detecting the end point of protein hydrolysis, at which time the color value is constant.

b) The biuret reaction. When urea is heated to about 180° C, it decomposes to form biuret:

$$
\begin{array}{l}
\underset{\text{Urea}}{
\begin{array}{c}
NH_2 \\
| \\
C = O \\
| \\
NH_2 \\
| \\
NH_2 \\
| \\
C = O \\
| \\
NH_2
\end{array}}
\quad
\longrightarrow
\quad
\underset{\text{Biuret}}{
\begin{array}{c}
NH_2 \\
| \\
C = O \\
| \\
NH \\
| \\
C = O \\
| \\
NH_2
\end{array}}
\;\; + NH_3
\end{array}
$$

If a strongly alkaline solution of biuret is treated with very dilute copper sulfate, a violet color is obtained. This reaction is given by substances containing two —$CONH_2$ groups joined either directly or through a carbon or nitrogen atom. Compounds containing —CH_2NH_2, —$C(NH)NH_2$, and —$CSNH_2$ in place of —$CONH_2$ groups give the test. Peptide structures as found in proteins and their derivatives which contain

$$
\begin{array}{c}
H \\
| \\
- CO - NH - C - CO - NH - \\
| \\
R
\end{array}
$$

linkages also give the biuret test. Of the amino acids, histidine gives a positive test. Dipeptides do not give the test, two or more peptide linkages being required.

When protein solutions are made strongly alkaline with sodium or potassium hydroxide and very dilute copper sulfate is added, a purplish to pinkish violet color is obtained, the color depending upon the complexity of the protein. Proteins give a purplish violet color while proteoses and peptones give a decided pink color, and peptides give a very light pink color. Gelatin gives an almost blue color.

The biuret test apparently is due to coordination of cupric ions with the unshared electron pairs of peptide nitrogen and the oxygen of water to form a colored coordination complex, which may be represented in diagram as follows:

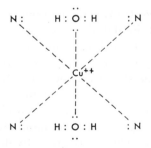

The presence of magnesium sulfate in the solution to be tested interferes with the biuret reaction because of the precipitation of magnesium hydroxide. Large amounts of ammonium salts also interfere with the test, but this may be minimized by the addition of a large excess of alkali.

The biuret reaction is extensively used as a delicate test for the presence of proteins in biologic materials. It has been converted into an excellent method for the quantitative determination of proteins in blood serum and other fluids.

The ninhydrin and biuret reactions are the most general of the color tests for proteins.

c) **Xanthoproteic reaction (yellow protein reaction).** The addition of concentrated nitric acid to protein solutions generally causes the formation of a white precipitate which turns yellow upon heating, the color becoming orange when the solution is made alkaline. Insoluble proteins are turned yellow and orange upon the surface. The yellow stains upon the skin caused by nitric acid are the result of the xanthoproteic reaction. The xanthoproteic reaction is due to nitration of the phenyl rings present in tyrosine, phenylalanine, and tryptophan to give yellow nitro substitution products, which become orange-colored upon the addition of alkali (salt formation). Most proteins give the xanthoproteic reaction.

d) **Millon's test for tyrosine.** Millon's reagent is a solution of mercurous and mercuric nitrates containing nitric acid. When it is added to a protein solution, a white precipitate is generally first formed, which turns red upon heating. Secondary proteoses and peptones give only a red solution. Insoluble proteins turn red when they are suspended in water and heated with the reagent. The reaction is not specific for proteins, since it is given by phenols in general. Since tyrosine is the only phenolic amino acid in proteins, a positive test indicates the presence of tyrosine. Solutions which are alkaline must be neutralized with acid (not HCl) before testing; otherwise, the mercury of the reagent is precipitated. Chlorides interfere with the reaction probably because the nitric acid forms free chlorine from them which destroys the colored compound. The reaction is dependent upon the formation of a colored mercury compound with the hydroxyphenyl group.

e) **The Hopkins-Cole or glyoxylic acid reaction for tryptophan.** The reagent contains glyoxylic acid, which may be prepared by reduction of oxalic acid with sodium amalgam or magnesium powder:

$$CHO$$
$$|$$
$$COOH$$
Glyoxylic acid

When a solution of tryptophan or protein which contains tryptophan is mixed with the reagent and the mixture is layered over concentrated sulfuric acid, a violet ring appears at the interface of the liquids. The reaction is characteristic of the indole ring, and other compounds than tryptophan give the test. However, since tryptophan is the only amino acid in proteins which contains the indole group, a positive test indicates the presence of tryptophan. Gelatin and other proteins which do not contain tryptophan fail to give the test. The nature of the colored products formed in the test is unknown. Chlorates, nitrates, nitrites, and excess chlorides prevent the reaction. A number of aldehydes other than glyoxylic acid give similar color reactions with tryptophan. Formaldehyde used similarly gives a violet color (Acree-Rosenheim reaction). When p-dimethylaminobenzaldehyde (Ehrlich's reagent) and strong HCl are added to solutions of tryptophan and of proteins containing it and the mixture is heated, a dark blue color appears.

f) *The Nitroprusside reaction.* Proteins which contain free —SH groups (cysteine) give a reddish color with sodium nitroprusside, $Na_2Fe(CN)_5NO \cdot 2H_2O$, in ammoniacal solution. Many proteins which give a negative test react positive after heat coagulation or denaturation by other means, indicating the liberation of free —SH groups. The cystine —S—S— groups in a protein may be reduced to —SH groups by reducing agents such as NaCN, after which they give the nitroprusside reaction.

g) *Folin's reaction.* Folin's amino acid reagent is sodium 1,2-naphthoquinone-4-sulfonate. This reagent gives a deep red color with amino acids in the presence of alkali.

h) *The Sullivan reaction for the determination of cysteine and cystine.* Sullivan and associates (41) have developed a remarkably specific colorimetric method for the quantitative determination of cysteine (and cystine after reduction to cysteine) in protein hydrolysates. The method is based upon the red color produced when cysteine is treated with sodium 1,2-naphthoquinone-4-sulfonate in alkaline solution in the presence of the powerful reducing substance, sodium hydrosulfite ($Na_2S_2O_4$). The method has been widely used for the determination of cystine in proteins.

i) *Sakaguchi reaction.* This reaction is a test for arginine, either free or combined, in proteins. The test consists in treating the sample solution with α-naphthol and sodium hypochlorite, with the slow development of an intense red color. Various substances which contain the guanidine group give the reaction, but since arginine is the only amino acid in proteins which contains this group, the test is specific for arginine when applied to proteins. Free arginine is stated to give a positive test in a concentration of 0.0004 mg per ml.

The reaction has been modified and adapted to the quantitative determination of arginine.

j) *Unoxidized sulfur test.* This is a test for the presence of sulfur-containing amino acids. The protein or amino acid is boiled with strong alkali to split out sulfur as Na_2S, detected by the addition of lead acetate, which causes the formation of brown to black lead sulfide.

Denaturation and coagulation of proteins. (*a*) *Heat coagulation.* Coagulation and precipitation of proteins from their solutions by heating is one of the oldest and most commonly used processes of deproteinization of tissue extracts. Although not all proteins are coagulated by heat (gelatin, for example), most of those present in tissues are coagulable. Heat coagulation and precipitation occur best near the isoelectric pH of the protein. Heat-coagulated protein is generally soluble in acids, alkalies, and strong urea and salicylate solutions and is reprecipitated when the acid or alkali is neutralized and the urea or salicylate is removed by dialysis. Generally the original or native protein is soluble in salt solution at its isoelectric pH, whereas the coagulated protein is insoluble at this same pH.

The presence of water is necessary for heat coagulation. Native protein which has been dried and heated to 100° C retains its solubility.

b) Steps in the heat coagulation process. If a coagulable protein is dissolved in dilute acid or alkali and the solution is heated briefly, no visible change occurs. However, when the solution is cooled and neutralized, the protein immediately coagulates and precipitates. While the original protein possessed considerable solubility at its isoelectric pH, the precipitate is no longer soluble at this pH, and it differs from the original protein in various other properties. Heating the protein causes disorganization of the peptide chains as the result of breaking cross linkages and other actions, with resultant unfolding of the chains and marked changes in properties. This process is called "denaturation." When the solution is neutralized, the denatured protein is precipitated at its isoelectric pH, which is generally somewhat higher than that of the original protein.

Proteins possess more or less characteristic coagulation temperatures which may be altered by changing the pH. The coagulation temperature may be studied accurately by heating an isoelectric solution of the protein in the presence of considerable salt. Upon carefully heating such a mixture, a temperature is reached at which the protein is rapidly denatured. The salt facilitates immediate precipitation of the denatured protein. The temperature at which this occurs is the coagulation temperature of the protein. The coagulation temperature is lowered by the addition of small amounts of acid or alkali, and it can be raised by the addition of much salt. Edestin is not coagulated when boiled in saturated sodium chloride solution.

c) Denaturation of proteins by different processes. Protein denaturation involves changes within the molecule that cause the protein to become insoluble in solvents in which it was originally soluble. As indicated above, the heat coagulation of protein involves two steps, the first of which is denaturation and consists of marked alteration of the arrangement of the peptide chains, with associated changes in properties. Proteins may be similarly denatured by numerous agents and processes. Denaturation may be effected by solution in acid or alkali and standing for some time at ordinary temperature, or by briefly heating. Treatment with alcohol, acetone, and other organic solvents leads to denaturation. Solution of proteins in strong urea, salicylate, and guanidine salts causes denaturation. Long-chain alkyl sulfates (wetting agents), such as sodium dodecyl sulfate, $CH_3(CH_2)_{11}$—O—SO_3Na, are extremely efficient agents for the denaturation of proteins, a fraction of a milligram per milliliter of solution often being effective. The initial action of proteolytic enzymes may cause denaturation before any essential peptide hydrolysis occurs. A protein often slowly becomes denatured as the result of standing in solution, even in water, for a protracted period.

The denaturation of proteins is caused by various physical agencies besides heat. Denaturation is caused by exposure to x-rays or ultraviolet light and by visible light in the presence of a photosensitizer. Violent shaking of a protein solution leads to denaturation as a result of surface action. It has been established that protein films adsorbed into surfaces and interfaces may be acted upon by the unbalanced surface forces to cause denaturation of protein in the film. Proteins may also be denatured by subjection to very high pressures.

The processes of denaturation, regardless of character, appear to cause similar types of change in proteins, with the formation of products possessing different properties than the original native protein. The most obvious change is that the denatured protein is insoluble at the isoelectric pH of the original protein and coagulates and precipitates in neutral solution.

  d) *Characteristics of denatured proteins.* X-ray studies of denatured proteins show a more crystalline structure than is found in undenatured proteins, indicating a fibrous keratin type of structure. This means that denaturation of a globular protein such as egg albumin leads to an unfolding and uncoiling of peptide chains, which must occur as the result of the rupture within the chains of the cross linkages that hold them in the coiled state. Denaturation of certain proteins, such as myosin, egg albumin, and horse and ox hemoglobin (not dog or sheep), by strong urea solution causes dissociation into smaller particles.

Further evidence that the peptide chains are uncoiled as a result of denaturation is found in the increased viscosity of denatured proteins in urea solution; the increase is due to change from a globular to a more elongated or fibrous structure.

Denatured proteins, because of their elongated molecules, may be used for the preparation of fibers by passing their solutions through the fine holes of spinnerets into precipitating solutions.

The chemical characteristics of denatured proteins are different from those of the original protein. Denaturation does not involve the hydrolysis of peptide linkages. Denaturation of proteins leads to an increase in the number of reactive —SH and —S—S— groups. Some native proteins possess —SH groups which react with nitroprusside (red color) and —S—S— groups which react after reduction to —SH. Others may show the presence of reactive —SH but not —S—S— groups, or vice versa. In general, all processes of protein denaturation cause an increase in the number of reactive —SH and —S—S— groups. The appearance of —SH groups in denaturation is not the result of reduction of —S—S— groups, but may involve release from a coordinate type of linkage. These reactive groups may also be protected in the folds and coils of the peptide chains from the action of reagents used for their detection. Denaturation uncoils the peptide chains and releases reactive groups. Native egg albumin contains no detectable —SH groups. However, upon denaturation the number of —SH groups detectable is equal to the number after complete hydrolysis with strong acid, indicating that denaturation causes the appearance of all of the —SH groups in this protein. The extent of denaturation of egg albumin may be accurately followed by determining the reactive —SH groups.

Denaturation also leads to an increase in the number of reactive phenolic hydroxyl groups (of tyrosine), and undoubtedly of other groups which have not been investigated adequately.

As previously indicated, denaturation generally changes the isoelectric pH of a protein, causing it to be somewhat higher. Denaturation causes little change in the combination of proteins with acids and alkalies (titration curves).

Denatured proteins have less capacity to combine with water than do native proteins.

Denaturation generally changes not only the solubility of proteins, but also their capacity to crystallize. No denatured protein has been crystallized.

Denaturation of protein enzymes leads to their inactivation.

The digestibility of proteins by proteolytic enzymes may be markedly altered by denaturation. Native hemoglobin is not digested by trypsin, whereas denatured hemoglobin is readily digested. Denaturation increases the digestibility of egg albumin by trypsin without altering the rate of digestion by pepsin.

The capacity of hemoglobin to form a loose combination with oxygen, which is essential for oxygen transport from the lungs to the tissues, is lost upon denaturation.

The specific immune globulins of blood function as antibodies against their specific antigens, and combine with them. This property is destroyed by denaturation. The antigenic properties of proteins, represented by their capacity to stimulate the production of specific antibodies when injected into an animal, are decreased but not destroyed by denaturation.

e) Reversibility of denaturation. The denaturation of egg albumin by acid with subsequent neutralization of the acid does not reverse the denaturation process, but causes the precipitation of denatured albumin. This kind of experiment leads to the general conclusion that denaturation is irreversible. Anson and Mirsky (42) first demonstrated the reversibility of denaturation in their work on hemoglobin. When hemoglobin is denatured in acid solution and then allowed to stand for a very short time before exact neutralization in a solution just sufficiently acid or alkaline to dissolve the hemoglobin, about two-thirds of the hemoglobin does not precipitate upon neutralization. This soluble hemoglobin crystallizes in the same form and has the same absorption spectrum and affinity for oxygen as native hemoglobin. Adjustment of the pH of the denatured hemoglobin permits reorganization (recoiling) of the peptide chains as they are in the native substance; globin and serum albumin behave similarly. Hemoglobin may be denatured by dissolving it in neutral sodium salicylate. It then becomes insoluble in salt solution which dissolves native hemoglobin, shows an altered absorption spectrum, and is digested by trypsin. Upon removal of the salicylate, the denaturation of the hemoglobin is completely reversed. It regains its original solubility and absorption spectrum, and is not digested by trypsin. A mobile equilibrium exists between native and denatured hemoglobin in salicylate solution, the point of equilibrium depending upon the salicylate concentration:

hemoglobin + salicylate $\rightleftharpoons$ hemoglobin
    Native   Denatured

Increasing the salicylate concentration increases the denatured hemoglobin, and vice versa.

When crystalline trypsin is heated for a short time in acid solution at 70–100° C it becomes insoluble in a salt solution which dissolves native trypsin, and at the same time it loses its proteolytic activity. If the hot acid solution of trypsin is cooled properly, the trypsin regains its original solubility and activity completely. Trypsin may also be denatured and inactivated by treatment with alkali and then reactivated by placing in salt free acid at pH 2 for several hours.

Crystalline pepsin is denatured and inactivated by adjusting its solutions to pH 8.5 and is partly renatured and reactivated by adjusting the pH to 5.4 for 24 to 48 hours.

So far it has been possible to reverse entirely or partly the denaturation of only a limited number of proteins.

f) Some general principles of denaturation.

1. The statement is often made that denaturation is an all-or-none phenomenon. This means that if half of the molecules in a protein solution are found to be denatured by one test, then other tests will show the same degree of denaturation. This undoubtedly represents an oversimplified generalization.

2. Protein denaturation is a reaction of the first order. This does not indicate that only one step is involved in denaturation, but shows that one single phase of the process is slower than the others and determines the speed of denaturation.

3. The point of equilibrium in a denaturation process is independent of the protein concentration. This indicates that denaturation does not cause a change in the number of protein molecules, which has been demonstrated also by osmotic pressure measurements. The linkages broken in denaturation are cross linkages within the coiled peptide chain. In a few instances, such as the denaturation of horse and ox hemoglobin by urea, there is also dissociation into smaller particles.

4. The temperature coefficient of denaturation is generally very high. Ordinarily the rate of a chemical reaction is increased only two or three times by an increase in temperature of 10° C. This is known as the "Q_{10} value," or the "temperature coefficient of the reaction." The temperature coefficient, Q_{10}, of protein denaturation has the surprisingly high value of about 600 at the isoelectric pH of the protein but is less in acid solution. No other chemical process is known to have such a high temperature coefficient. It is interesting to note that the heat destruction of bacteria, antibodies, enzymes, and other biologically active materials and that of the fertilization of the ovum all have temperature coefficients around 600. This suggests that protein denaturation is a primary process in all these phenomena.

THE ISOLATION AND PURIFICATION OF PROTEINS

The isolation of proteins from tissues and their purification represents one of the most important problems of biochemistry, and often a very difficult problem. In general, proteins are extracted from ground tissues by aqueous solvents, such as water, dilute salt solutions, dilute acids or alkalies, and occasionally with mixtures of water and organic solvents, such as alcohol or glycerol. After the crude extract is obtained, it may be subjected to a variety of procedures and treatments for the isolation of specific proteins. These separations are based upon procedures which remove the desired protein from solution, leaving the undesired proteins in solution as much as possible, or upon the reverse in which the undesired proteins are precipitated out, leaving the desired more purified protein in solution, from which it then may be removed if necessary.

While the peptide linkages binding amino acids together in chains are relatively stable to ordinary extraction and separation procedures, the organization of the peptide chains into the unique helical and folded structures upon which the biologic properties of proteins often depend is quite labile and easily altered by heat, organic solvents, acids and alkalies, and various other reagents, with the formation of denatured proteins.

The proteins of cells, and particularly of disrupted tissue cells used in protein isolation, are mixed with a variety of other biologic substances, such as nucleic acids, carbohydrates, lipids, etc., with which the proteins may react to form more or less stable combinations from which the protein may be difficult to separate in unaltered form. The formation of protein-lipid complexes, insoluble in aqueous solvents, may prevent the extraction of a protein. Preliminary extraction of a ground tissue with an organic solvent such as butyl alcohol often breaks up such complexes and extracts the lipid, leaving the protein in a form which can be taken up in aqueous solvents. Acetone powder preparations of tissues are frequently employed for the extraction of proteins when the amount of fatty material interferes with direct extraction from the fresh tissue. The cold ground tissue is extracted two or three times with several volumes of cold acetone (0–5° C) and then washed with cold ether, dried in the cold, and powdered. Most proteins suffer little denaturation by this treatment. Proteins are extracted from the acetone powder with the usual solvents. Extraction of a tissue with acetone also inhibits enzyme action which might inactivate the proteins to be extracted. The dry acetone powders often may be kept for a long time without deterioration and used as needed for protein extraction.

In working with protein solutions in the processes of isolation and purification, it is desirable to keep the protein concentration in solution as high as possible, since dilution often favors protein denaturation.

The peptide-chain organizations of many proteins are very easily altered by heat, and even mild temperatures for a relatively short time may cause protein denaturation and loss of characteristic biologic properties such as enzyme or hormonal activities. In general, therefore, in extracting proteins from disrupted tissues, the temperature should be kept as low as possible. Tissue grinding also should be done at low temperature. In some instances a particular protein to be separated is more resistant to heat denaturation than other proteins in solution. In such cases it may be advantageous to subject the crude extract to a mild heat treatment which causes denaturation and precipitation of much of the undesired associated proteins. At times it is advantageous to lyophilize a crude tissue protein extract before further extraction and separation. In this process the extract is quickly frozen at low temperature, generally with solid carbon dioxide (dry ice), and then evaporated to dryness in the frozen state under high vacuum. In many cases such lyophilized protein preparations are relatively stable for long periods at moderate temperatures. These lyophilized preparations may then be used for protein isolation by the usual techniques. After a protein has been isolated and purified, it is often preserved in the lyophilized state.

In general, a protein in solution is likely to be most stable and subject to least denaturation at the pH at which it occurs naturally in cells. This is most often near the neutral point, and, when possible, extraction is most advantageous in this pH region. However, it is frequently the case that proteins are not appreciably extracted from tissues at this pH and must be extracted with acid or alkaline solutions. In such cases it is essential to determine the pH range in which the protein remains unaltered and to stay within this range in the extraction process. There are instances in which the desired protein is more resistant to acid or alkali denaturation than undesired associated proteins, and proper treatment with acid or alkali may precipitate out and remove the undesired proteins. It will be remembered that, in general, proteins are least soluble at the isoelectric pH and that different proteins have appreciably different isoelectric points. Consequently, it is frequently possible to precipitate either the desired protein or the undesired proteins from a mixture in solution by proper adjustment of pH. It may be possible at one pH to precipitate and remove undesired proteins and then by changing the pH to precipitate and obtain the desired protein. The isoelectric precipitation of proteins is extremely valuable in their separation and purification.

As indicated previously, proteins may be salted out of solution by adding large quantities of soluble salts, such as ammonium sulfate, sodium sulfate, and magnesium sulfate. Different proteins show different solubilities at given concentrations of salts (ionic strengths), and it is frequently possible to effect practically complete separation of a given protein from solution by proper adjustment of salt concentration, or to precipitate in sequence several proteins from a solution by progressively increasing the salt concentration. Such salt precipitations are generally carried out at definite pH values of the solution (around the isoelectric pH of the protein to be precipitated) and at low temperatures. The addition of an organic solvent, such as alcohol or acetone, along with salt, pH, and temperature control, is often advantageous. The organic solvent decreases protein solubility. Cohn and associates effected very important separations of plasma proteins based upon differential precipitation at definite ionic strengths, pH values, alcohol concentrations, and low temperatures. This work is given in detail in Chapter 15. Salts and other electrolytes and small molecules are generally removed from solutions of protein preparations by dialysis in the cold through cellophane membranes. Electrodialysis also at times may be used to advantage.

Adsorption techniques have been rather widely used in the separation and purification of proteins. A number of adsorbing agents, such as kaolin (hydrated aluminum silicate), $Ca_3(PO_4)_2$, $Al(OH)_3$, $Fe(OH)_3$, $Mg(OH)_2$, $BaSO_4$, $BaCO_3$, and ion exchange resins, have been used. The adsorbing agent may selectively adsorb and remove undesired proteins from solution, leaving the desired protein, or vice versa. The adsorbed protein may be eluted from the adsorbant by extraction with a solvent at a pH above or below the pH at which adsorption occurred. Fractionation of proteins by pouring protein solutions through columns of adsorbing agents in glass tubes (column chromatography) is also utilized. The different proteins in solution may adsorb to different extents on a given adsorbent under a given set of conditions and appear in successive regions along the tube, the more readily adsorbed proteins being located nearer the top of the tube. The different proteins may then be eluted from the adsorbent in the various column regions. One disadvantage of the adsorption technique is due to protein denaturation which may occur at adsorption interfaces, and this has been a severe handicap to its use.

The process of fractional centrifugation has proved valuable in the separation and purification of proteins with very large molecules, such as the virus proteins. By proper control of the rotor speed, the viruses are sedimented out while the tissue proteins remain in solution.

The electrophoresis apparatus of Tiselius, the operation of which is based upon different migration velocities of charged particles in an electric field (for detailed discussion, see Chapter 15) provides a valuable technique for the separation of proteins in solution. It has been of much importance in the separation and characterization of plasma proteins.

Plain paper chromatography is of little value for protein separation, because the firm adsorption of proteins on the paper prevents their movement and fractionation. However, if a solution containing a mixture of proteins (such as serum) is streaked on paper wet with the proper buffer solution and a strong electric potential applied across the paper, the different protein molecules migrate at different velocities on the paper and fractionate into zones which can be localized by spraying the dried paper with a solution which gives a color reaction with the protein, such as ninhydrin. After the different protein spots have been located, another run can be made under the same conditions, the appropriate regions of the paper cut out, and the different proteins extracted from the paper. This process of paper electrophoresis is widely utilized in determining the kinds and amounts of proteins in pathologic sera. For this purpose the paper chromatogram is treated with a protein stain which localizes and identifies the different kinds of proteins on the chromatogram. The depth of staining in each place on the paper is proportional to the quantity of protein present, which can be obtained by placing the chromatogram in a scanning apparatus that measures the depth of staining in each region of the chromatogram.

Various types of apparatus for the separation of proteins by electrophoresis on a macro scale have been devised and are discussed by Svensson (43). Such apparatus often consists of electrodes separated by several compartments between diaphragms, such as glass filter discs. The protein separation is effected by varying the pH of the solutions relative to the isoelectric points of the proteins present, causing differential migration in the compartments.

In order to separate a protein from tissues and purify it to a high degree, it is frequently necessary to resort to a combination of the procedures and techniques outlined above. The student may consult the book *Amino Acids and Proteins*, by David M. Greenberg, Chapter V, for the detailed laboratory procedures used in the isolation and purification of 20 important proteins, most of which are obtained by methods yielding crystalline products. The very frequent use in these procedures of salting out and pH control emphasizes their great importance in protein chemistry.

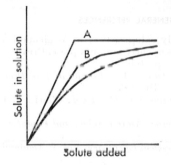

Figure 8.9

It is often important to determine the purity of a protein preparation which is to be used for a rigorous study of its physical and chemical properties and its biologic activity, and this is often a difficult problem. The fact that a protein is obtained in crystalline condition is not an indication of purity to the extent that well-formed crystals may be an index of purity in the case of simple organic compounds. Crystalline proteins originally considered pure have been shown to be mixtures of several components. For example, crystalline β-lactoglobulin from cow's milk has been shown to contain several distinct proteins though for a long time it was thought to be quite homogeneous.

Several methods are utilized in determining the purity of a protein preparation. One method of approach is to determine the solubility of the protein in a given solvent in relation to various excesses of protein added to the solvent. Theoretically the solubility of a pure substance in a solvent at constant temperature is independent of the amount of solid substance in contact with the solvent, which is not true in the case of mixtures. In the case of a pure substance, as more and more substance is added to a given amount of solvent, all of the substance dissolves until a sharp saturation limit is reached, after which no more solution takes place as excess solid is added. The solubility curve is an ascending straight line until saturation is reached, where there is a sharp break, and the remainder of the curve is a straight line parallel to the solute axis. If the solid is a mixture of substances which have different solubilities, there is more than one break in the curve. If the solid represents a solid solution of the components, there is no break in the curve, but a gradual sloping out to a smooth curve as excess solid is added to the solvent. The general shapes of the solubility curves for a pure solid (*A*), of a solid which is a mixture of two substances (B), and of a solid which is a solid solution of two or more substances (C) are illustrated in Fig. 8.9.

While the determination of protein purity from solubility curves is theoretically sound, the actual measurements of protein solubility with sufficient accuracy to establish the true curves are often very difficult, and application of the method is rather limited.

The behavior of a solution of protein in the ultracentrifuge often gives valuable evidence as to its homogeneity. If the protein particles all sediment at the same rate, then the protein may be, but is not necessarily, homogeneous, because by coincidence both the desired protein and its contaminant may sediment at the same rate.

Migration of a protein preparation in the electrophoresis apparatus of Tiselius at a given pH also is very helpful in assaying its purity. If the protein moves as a single sharp boundary, then it may be pure. However, since the migration of proteins in an electric field is determined by size, shape, and charge, two different proteins may have combinations of these characteristics which cause them to migrate together. If, however, it is shown that the protein moves as a single sharp boundary over a wide range of pH values for the solution, then the evidence as to its purity is rather conclusive.

If a protein preparation is homogeneous according to both sedimentation in the ultracentrifuge and migration in the electrophoresis apparatus, it is considered to be essentially pure. The student will find a comprehensive discussion of protein isolation by Taylor in *The Proteins*, edited by Neurath and Bailey, Vol. I, Part A, Chapter I.

GENERAL REFERENCES

Advances in Protein Chemistry, yearly volumes 1944—. Academic Press, New York.
Annual Review of Biochemistry. These yearly volumes present reviews of advances in the chemistry of the proteins.
Block, R. J., and Bolling, D.: *The Amino Acid Composition of Proteins and Foods*, 2nd ed. Charles C Thomas, Springfield, Ill., 1951.
Block, R. J., and Weiss, K. W.: *Amino Acid Handbook*. Charles C Thomas, Springfield, Ill., 1956.
Cohn, E. J., and Edsall, J. T.: *Proteins, Amino Acids, and Peptides as Ions and Dipolar Ions*. Reinhold, New York, 1943.
Edsall, J. T., and Wyman, J.: *Biophysical Chemistry*, Vol. I. Academic Press, New York, 1958.
Fieser, L. F., and Fieser, M.: *Organic Chemistry*, 3rd ed., Chap. 16. Reinhold, New York, 1956.
Greenberg, D. M.: *Amino Acids and Proteins*. Charles C Thomas, Springfield, Ill., 1951.
Haurowitz, F.: *Chemistry and Biology of Proteins*. Academic Press, New York, 1950.
Meister, A.: *Biochemistry of the Amino Acids*. Academic Press, New York, 1957.
Neurath, H., and Bailey, K. (eds.): *The Proteins*, Vols. 1A, IB, IIA, IIB. Academic Press, New York, 1953, 1954.
Schmidt, C. L. A. (ed.): *Chemistry of the Amino Acids and Proteins*, 2nd ed. Charles C Thomas, Springfield, Ill., 1944.
Wolstenholme, G. E. W., and Cameron, M. P. (eds.): *The Chemical Structure of Proteins*. Little, Brown & Co., Boston, 1953.

SPECIAL REFERENCES

1. Whitaker, J. R., and Deatherage, F. E.: *J. Am. Chem. Soc.*, **77**, 3360, 1955.
2. Vickery, H. B., and Schmidt, C. L. A.: *Chem. Revs.*, **9**, 169, 1931.
3. Neurath, H., and Bailey, K. (eds.): *The Proteins*, Vol. I, Part A, p. 99. Academic Press, New York, 1953.
4. Gortner, R. A.: *J. Biol. Chem.*, **36**, 177, 1916. Gortner, R. A., and Holm, G. E.: *J. Am. Chem. Soc.*, **39**, 2477, 1917; **42**, 632, 821, 2378, 1920. Gortner, R. A., and Norris, E. R.: *ibid.*, **45**, 550, 1923.
5. Gortner, R. A., and Blish, M. J.: *J. Am. Chem. Soc.*, **37**, 1630, 1915.
6. Craig, L. C.; Gregory, J. D.; and Barry, G. T.: *Cold Spring Harbor Symposia Quant. Biol.*, **14**, 24, 1950.
7. Martin, A. J. P., and Synge, R. L. M.: *Biochem. J.*, **35**, 294, 1941.

8. Moore, S., and Stein, W. H.: *J. Biol. Chem.*, **192**, 663, 1951. Moore, S., and Stein, W. H.: *Ann Rev. Biochem.*, **21**, 521, 1952. Stein, W. H., and Moore, S.: *Cold Spring Harbor Symposia Quant. Biol.*, **14**, 179, 1950.
9. Hirs, C. H. W.; Stein, W. H.; and Moore, S.: *J. Biol. Chem.*, **211**, 944, 1954.
10. Hirs, C. H. W.; Stein, W. H.; and Moore, S.: *J. Biol. Chem.*, **211**, 941, 1954. Hirs, C. H. W.; Moore, S.; and Stein, W. H.: *ibid.*, **235**, 634, 1960.
11. Stokes, J. L.; Gunness, M.; Dwyer, I. M.; and Caswell, M. C.: *J. Biol. Chem.*, **160**, 35, 1945.
12. Rittenberg, D., and Foster, G. L.: *J. Biol. Chem.*, **133**, 737, 1940.
13. Fruton, J., in *Advances in Protein Chemistry*, **5**, 15, 1949.
14. Van Slyke, D. D.: *J. Biol. Chem.*, **12**, 275, 1912.
15. Moore, S., and Stein, W. H.: *J. Biol. Chem.*, **176**, 367, 1948.
16. Levy, M.: *J. Biol. Chem.*, **99**, 767, 1933.
17. Neurath, H., and Bailey, K. (eds.): *The Proteins*, Vol. I, Part A. Academic Press, New York, 1953.
18. Levy, A. L.: *Nature*, **165**, 152, 1950.
19. Fischer, E., and Otto, E.: *Ber.*, **36**, 2106, 2982, 1903.
20. Bergmann, M., and Zervas, L.: *Ber.*, **65**, 1192, 1932.
21. Bailey, J. L.: *Nature*, **164**, 889, 1949. Bailey, J. L.: *J. Chem. Soc.*, p. 3461, 1950.
22. Goodman, M., and Kenner, G. W.: *Advances in Protein Chem.*, **12**, 465, 1957.
23. Gortner, R. A.; Hoffman, W. F.; and Sinclair, W. B.: *Colloid Symposium Monograph*, **5**, 179, 1928. Hoffman, W. F., and Gortner, R. A.: *Cereal Chem.*, **4**, 221, 1927.
24. Lipmann, F. A., and Levene, P. A.: *J. Biol. Chem.*, **98**, 109, 1932. Lipmann, F. A.: *Biochem. Z.*, **262**, 9, 1933.
25. Sanger, F., and Tuppy, H.: *Biochem. J.*, **49**, 463, 481, 1951. Sanger, F., et al.: *ibid.*, **53**, 366, 1953, **60**, 541, 1955. Harris, J. I.; Sanger, F.; and Naughton, M. A.: *Arch. Biochem. Biophys.*, **65**, 427, 1956.
26. Astbury, W. T.: *Fundamentals of Fiber Structure*, Oxford University Press, 1933. Low, B. W., in Neurath, H., and Bailey, K. (eds.): *The Proteins*, Vol. I, Part A, p. 235. Academic Press, New York, 1953. Kendrew, J. C., and Bailey, K., in Neurath, H., and Bailey, K.: *The Proteins*, Vol. II, Part B, Chaps. 23 and 24. Academic Press, New York, 1954. Edsall, J. T., and Wyman, J.; *Biophysical Chemistry*. Academic Press, New York, 1958.
27. Pauling, L.; Corey, R. B.; and Branson, H. R.: *Proc. Natl. Acad. Sci. U.S.*, **37**, 205, 1951.
28. Pauling, L., and Corey, R. B.: *Proc. Natl. Acad. Sci. U.S.*, **37**, 729, 1951.
29. Rich, A., and Crick, F. H. C., in *Symposium on Gelatin and Glue*, Cambridge, England, July, 1957. Also see Edsall, J. T., and Wyman, J.: *Biophysical Chemistry*, p. 118. Academic Press, New York, 1958.
30. Pauling, L., and Corey, R. B.: *Proc. Natl. Acad. Sci., U.S.* **37**, 282, 1951.
31. Burk, N. F., and Greenberg, D. M.: *J. Biol. Chem.*, **78**, 197, 1930.
32. Benoit, H.: *Ann. Phys.*, **6**, 561, 1951.
33. Von Hippel, P. H., and Waugh, D. F.: *J. Am. Chem. Soc.*, **77**, 4311, 1955.
34. Cohn, E. J., and Edsall, J. T.: *Proteins, Amino Acids, and Peptides*. Reinhold, New York, 1943.
35. Tiselius, A.: *Trans. Faraday Soc.*, **33**, 524, 1937.
36. Taylor, J. F., in Neurath, H., and Bailey, K. (eds.) *The Proteins*, Vol. I, Part A, p. 36. Academic Press, New York, 1953.
37. Rawlins, L. M. C., and Schmidt, C. L. A.: *J. Biol. Chem.*, **82**, 709, 1929.
38. Jensen, E. V.: *Science*, **130**, 1319, 1959.
39. Swan, J. N.: *Nature*, **180**, 643, 1957.
40. Pechere, J. F.; Dixon, G. H.; Maybury, R. H.; and Neurath, H.: *J. Biol. Chem.*, **233**, 1364, 1958.
41. Sullivan, M. X.; Hess, W. C.; and Howard, H. W.: *J. Biol. Chem.*, **145**, 621, 1942.
42. Anson, M. L., and Mirsky, A. E.: *J. Gen. Physiol.*, **9**, 169, 1925; *J. Phys. Chem.*, **35**, 185, 1931.
43. Svensson, H.: *Advances in Protein Chemistry*, **4**, 251, 1948.

9

Nucleic acids and nucleoproteins

The nucleoproteins play an important role, as primary constituents of chromatin, in the processes of cell division and reproduction and in the transmission of hereditary factors. The nucleoproteins consequently constitute one of the most important classes of conjugated proteins. They are formed by combinations of simple proteins, generally of basic character, with nucleic acids, which are complexes of purine and pyrimidine bases, sugar, and phosphoric acid. Nucleoproteins make up a large part of the nuclear material of cells and are also present in the cytoplasm. Nucleoproteins, probably more than any other constituents, are concerned with vital cellular organization and function. So far as has been determined, the disease-producing viruses of both plants and animals are complex nucleoproteins. The staphylococcus bacteriophage seems to be a nucleoprotein.

Nucleic acids. Miescher (1) first separated nucleic acid from pus cells by digesting them for weeks with dilute hydrochloric acid and then shaking the mixture with ether in a separatory funnel. A heavy solid layer separated at the bottom of the funnel and consisted of almost pure nuclear material. Miescher then found that he could obtain this material more conveniently by digesting pus cells with artificial gastric juice, which did not digest the nuclear substance. He considered the product the characteristic constituent of the cell nucleus and called it "nuclein." The properties of nuclein were remarkable. It possessed much stronger acidic properties than proteins. It was soluble in dilute alkalies, but insoluble in dilute acids, water, and organic solvents. It contained a relatively large amount of phosphorus.

Hoppe-Seyler and his students quickly confirmed Miescher's observations and also proved the presence of nuclein (nucleic acid) in yeast and the red cells of birds and reptiles and various other tissues. In his later work Miescher studied the nuclear material of ripe salmon sperm, which was available in

340

large amounts. He found this material to consist of a salt of the acidic nuclein and a basic substance quite different from the known proteins, which
he called "protamin." The elementary composition of Miescher's salmon
sperm nuclein was close to that of nucleic acids prepared in recent times.
Miescher's studies of nuclein convinced him that it was a complex phosphorus-containing polybasic acid of high molecular weight, since it was not
dialyzable. He recognized it to be nonprotein in character, and a new type of
biologic substance.

Altman devised a procedure for the separation of essentially protein-free
nuclein from tissues and first introduced the term "nucleic acid," by which
it since has been designated. Substances of the nucleic acid type have been
prepared from a great variety of tissues, including thymus, fish sperm, spleen,
pancreas, liver, testicle, intestine, placenta, mammary gland, brain, kidney,
nucleated blood cells, thyroid, lung, lymphatic gland, mesenteric and lymphatic ganglia, tumor tissue, yeast, bacteria, viruses, and bacteriophages.

Most of the earlier and much of the later work on the chemistry of the
nucleic acids has been done on yeast and thymus nucleic acids. The earlier
work was done largely by the schools of Albrecht Kossel, P. A. Levene, and
Walter Jones, and is outlined in the monographs on nucleic acids by Levene
and Bass (2) and by Jones (3). Comprehensive recent reviews are those of
Todd (4) and Markham and Smith (5). *The Nucleic Acids, Chemistry and
Biology*, Vols. I, II, and III, edited by Chargaff and Davidson (Academic
Press, New York, 1955 and 1960) gives a comprehensive treatment of all
phases of nucleic acids and nucleoproteins by outstanding authorities in
the field.

Both yeast and thymus nucleic acids are composed of phosphoric acid, a
sugar, and nitrogenous bases. When yeast nucleic acid is treated with dilute
alkali, it is split into components, each of which is made up of one molecule
each of phosphoric acid, sugar, and nitrogenous base. The components are
called "nucleotides" and are differentiated by containing different bases. A
nucleotide may be designated by the word formula nitrogenous base—
sugar—phosphoric acid.

The phosphoric acid component occupies a terminal position and is in
ester combination, as shown by hydrolysis of a nucleotide with the enzyme
nucleotidase (a phosphatase), which removes the phosphoric acid and leaves
a compound called "nucleoside," which is composed of nitrogenous base-
sugar. The nitrogenous base also occupies a terminal position in a nucleotide,
because careful acid hydrolysis removes the base and leaves a sugar phosphate ester.

Enzyme hydrolysis:

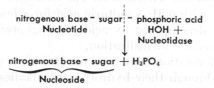

Acid hydrolysis:

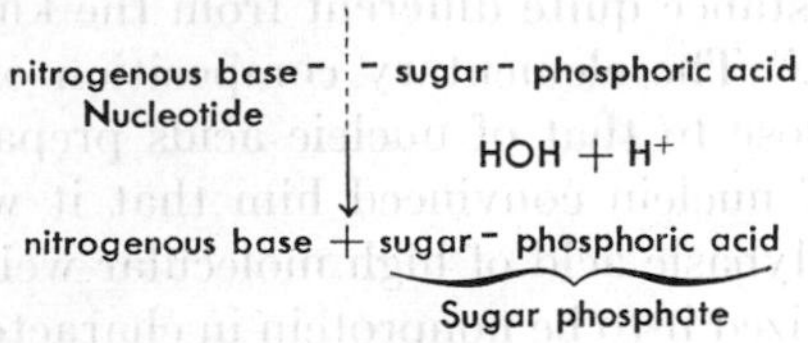

nitrogenous base ⁻ ⁺ sugar ⁻ phosphoric acid
Nucleotide

HOH + H⁺

nitrogenous base + sugar ⁻ phosphoric acid

Sugar phosphate

The nucleic acids isolated from many types of tissues have all been found to yield nucleotides similar to those obtained from yeast and thymus nucleic acids.

The nitrogenous bases present in all nucleic acids are purines and pyrimidines.

The sugar present in yeast nucleic acid has been identified as D-ribose and that in thymus nucleic acid as D-2-deoxyribose. These are the only sugars so far found in the nucleic acids from which the sugars have been isolated and identified, and they are assumed to be the sugars universally present in nucleic acids:

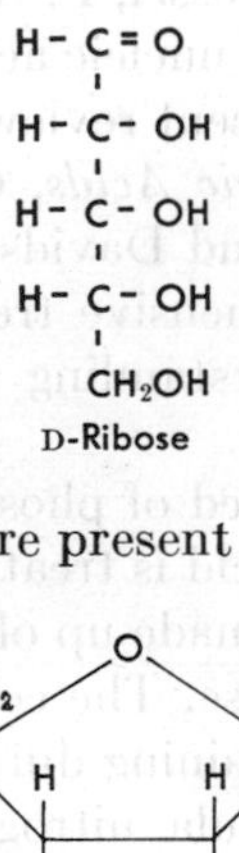

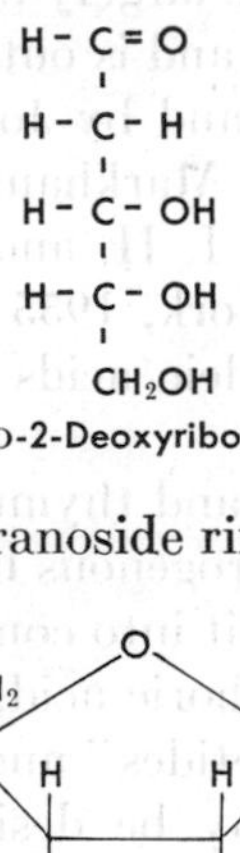

$$
\begin{array}{cc}
H-C=O & H-C=O \\
| & | \\
H-C-OH & H-C-H \\
| & | \\
H-C-OH & H-C-OH \\
| & | \\
H-C-OH & H-C-OH \\
| & | \\
CH_2OH & CH_2OH \\
\text{D-Ribose} & \text{D-2-Deoxyribose}
\end{array}
$$

Both sugars are present in nucleic acids as the β-furanoside ring structures:

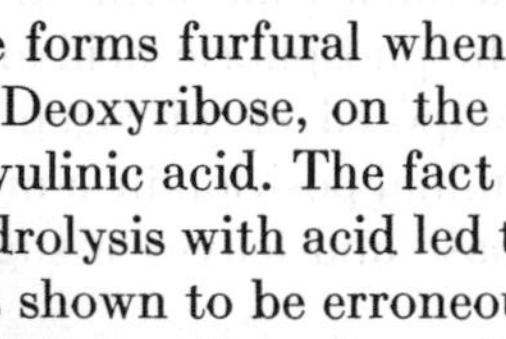

β-D-Ribofuranose 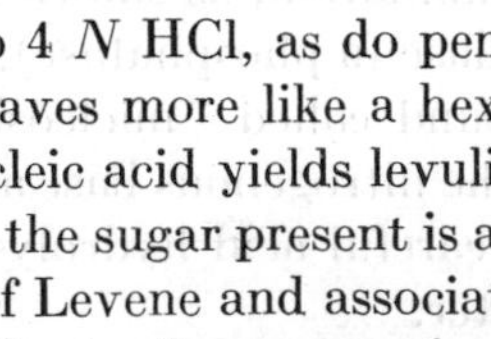   β-D-2-Deoxyribofuranose

Ribose forms furfural when boiled with 3 to 4 N HCl, as do pentoses in general. Deoxyribose, on the other hand, behaves more like a hexose and yields levulinic acid. The fact that thymus nucleic acid yields levulinic acid upon hydrolysis with acid led to the belief that the sugar present is a hexose. This was shown to be erroneous by the work of Levene and associates, who isolated 2-deoxyribose from the hydrolytic products of pure guanine nucleoside prepared from thymus nucleic acid. The nucleoside was completely hydrolyzed by heating with 0.01 N sulfuric acid for a few minutes. 2-Deoxyribose is very easily decomposed by acids, and ignorance of this fact long prevented its isolation and identification.

Recently much information relative to the structural units of nucleic acids has been obtained through their hydrolysis by alkalies, acids, and specific enzymes, and the isolation of hydrolysis products through the application of paper chromatography, column chromatography with ion exchange resins, and countercurrent distribution extraction. The fact that the purines and pyrimidines, both free and combined, show characteristic absorption of light in the ultraviolet spectrum has made their identification and estimation possible by spectrophotometry using very small quantities of material.

The pyrimidine bases found in nucleic acids are uracil, thymine, cytosine, 5-methylcytosine, and 5-hydroxymethylcytosine:

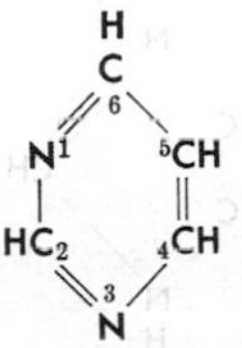

| Pyrimidine | Uracil
2,6-Dihydroxy-pyrimidine | Thymine
5-Methyl uracil |

| Cytosine
2-Hydroxy-6-amino-pyrimidine | 5-Methylcytosine | 5-Hydroxymethylcytosine |

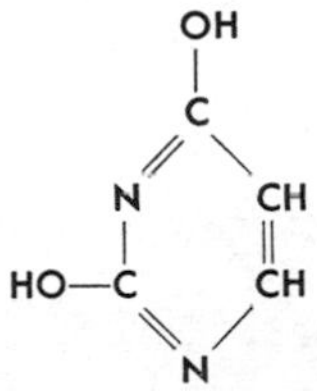

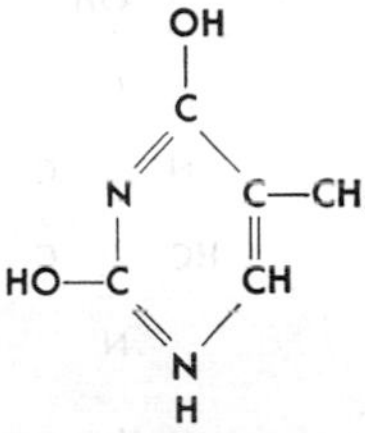

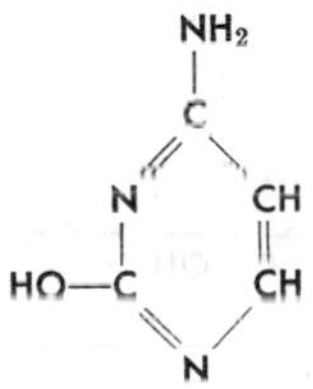

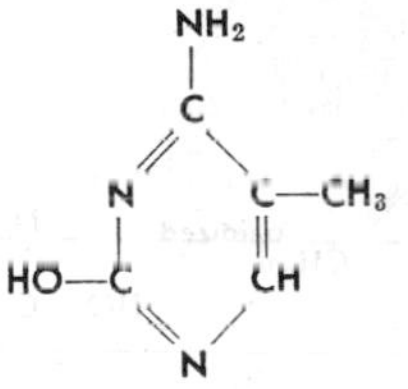

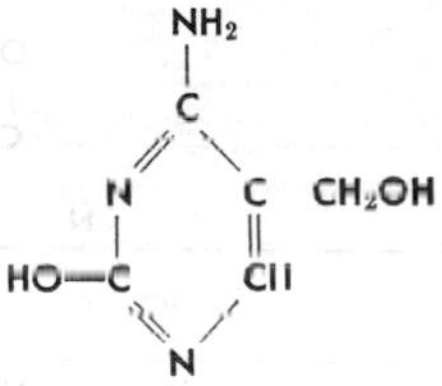

The new numbering system of the pyrimidine ring used by *Chemical Abstracts* differs from that indicated above in that the N atom at the bottom of the ring is numbered 1, and the others to the left around the ring 2, 3, 4, 5, 6 in sequence. However, the older system is used in this book, because it is generally encountered in the literature and because the pyrimidine ring is a part of the purine ring system, where it is numbered according to the older system. According to the *Chemical Abstracts* system of numbering, uracil is 2,4-dihydroxypyrimidine or 2,4-pyrimidinediol, and cytosine is 2-hydroxy-4-aminopyrimidine or 4-amino-2-pyrimidineol.

All of the pyrimidines exist in the tautomeric keto and enol forms, as shown below for uracil:

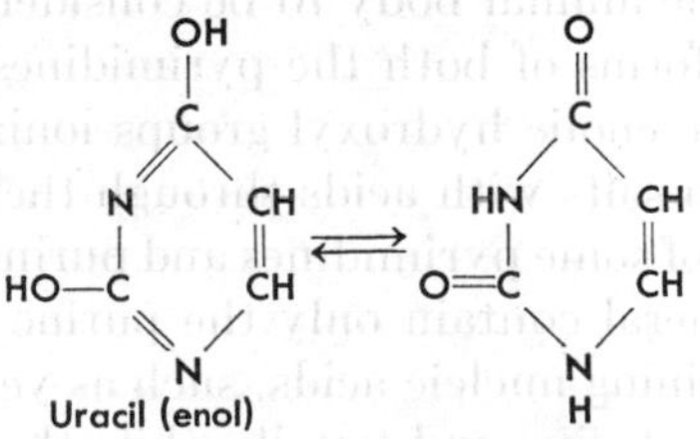

Uracil (enol)   Uracil (keto)

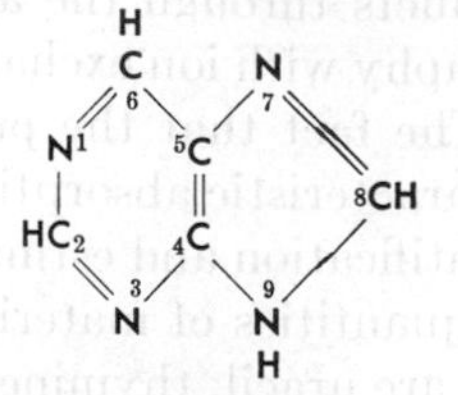

Purine

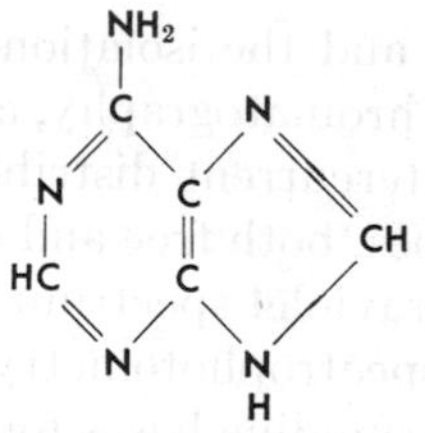

Adenine
6-Aminopurine

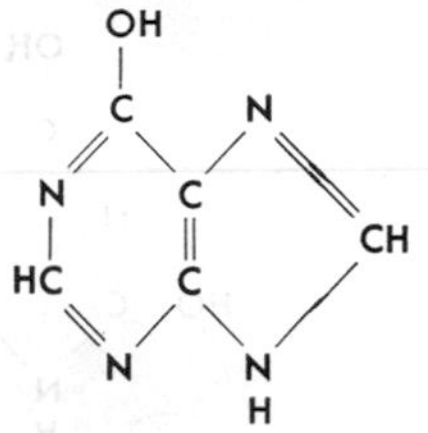

Hypoxanthine
6-Hydroxypurine
Formed by hydrolysis of adenine

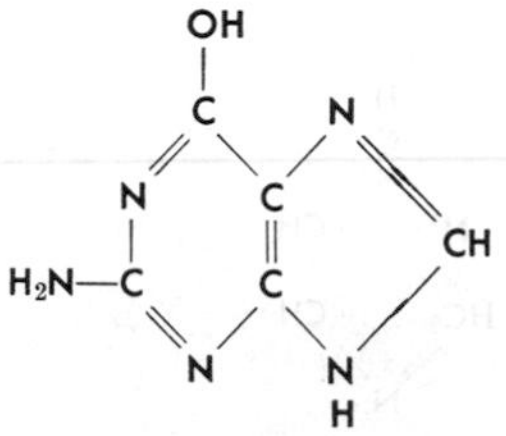

Guanine
2-Amino-6-hydroxypurine

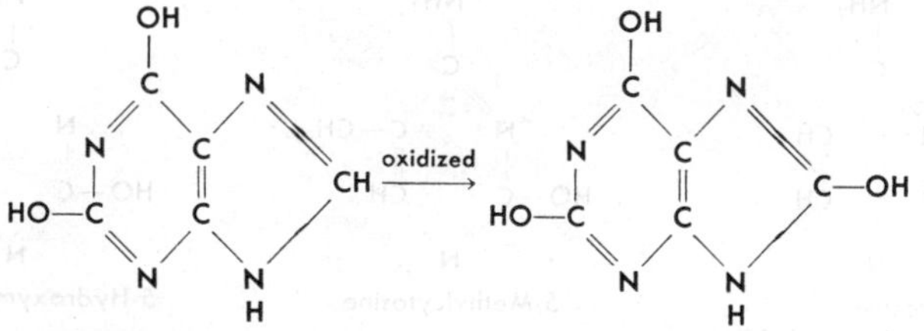

Xanthine
2,6-Dihydroxypurine
Formed by hydrolysis of
guanine and by oxidation
of hypoxanthine

oxidized ⟶

Uric acid
2,6,8-Trihydroxypurine

The hydroxypurines (enol or lactim forms), like the hydroxypyrimidines, exist also in the tautomeric keto forms (lactam forms).

The purine bases found in nucleic acids are amino and hydroxy derivatives of purine, which is made up of two rings, one of which is the pyrimidine ring.

It will be observed that adenine and guanine, constituents of nucleic acids, are converted by hydrolysis to the purine bases hypoxanthine and xanthine, respectively, and that hypoxanthine may be oxidized to xanthine, and xanthine to uric acid. Such conversions are involved in the metabolism of adenine and guanine in the animal body to be considered in Chapter 25.

The enol or lactim forms of both the pyrimidines and purines form salts with bases; that is, the enolic hydroxyl groups ionize as acids. The pyrimidines and purines form salts with acids through their weakly basic nitrogen atoms. The pK values of some pyrimidines and purines are given in Table 9.1.

Nucleic acids in general contain only the purine bases adenine and guanine. The ribose-containing nucleic acids, such as yeast nucleic acid, contain the pyrimidine bases cytosine and uracil; while the deoxyribose-containing nucleic acids, such as thymus nucleic acid, have cytosine, thymine, and a

Table 9.1

Compound	pK₁	pK₂
Pyrimidine	1.30	
Cytosine	4.6	12.16
5-Methylcytosine	4.6	12.4
Thymine	9.5	>13
Uracil	9.5	>13
Purine	2.39	8.93
Adenine	4.15	9.80
Guanine	3.3	9.2
Hypoxanthine	8.8	12.0
Uric acid	5.4	10.6
Xanthine	7.53	11.63

small amount of 5-methylcytosine as their pyrimidines. 5-Hydroxymethyl-cytosine has been found in bacteriophages (6).

Structures of nucleosides. The nucleosides, as previously indicated, generally are composed of a purine or pyrimidine base linked to either D-ribose or D-2-deoxyribose through a β-N-glycoside linkage. This linkage in the purine nucleosides is at position 9 of the purine, and in the pyrimidine nucleosides at position 3 of the pyrimidine (position 1 in the new numbering system). The furanoside ring form of the sugar is present. Representative formulas of nucleosides are given below:

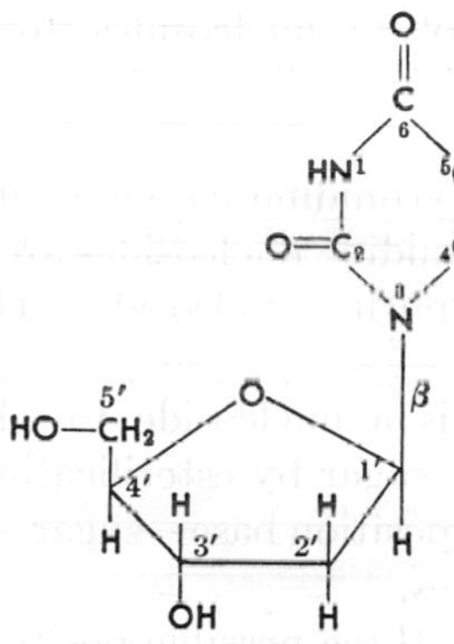

Uridine
Uracil-3-D-ribofuranoside
Uracil-3-riboside

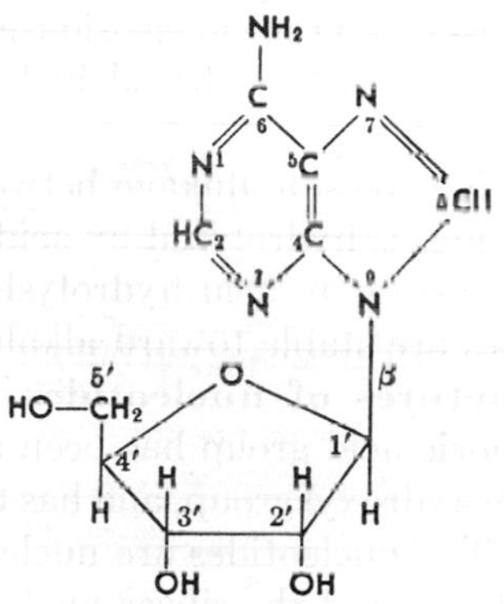

Adenosine
Adenine-9-ribofuranoside
Adenine-9-riboside

Since the sugar always exists as a furanose ring and the linkage to the purine or pyrimidine base is a β-glycosidic linkage, the general formulas of ribose and deoxyribose nucleosides are:

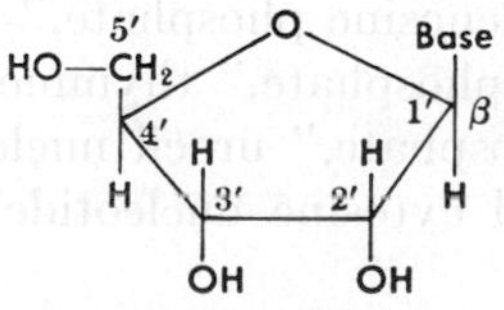

D-ribose nucleoside

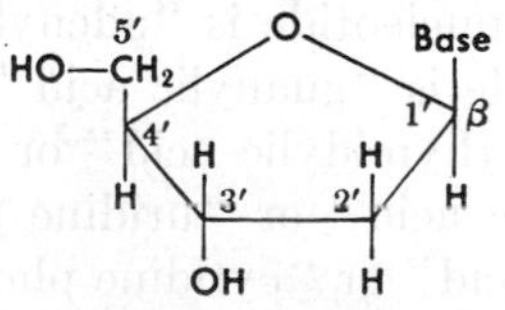

D-2'-Deoxyribose nucleoside

The pyrimidine bases are always attached to the sugar through N at position 3 of the base, and the purine bases are always attached to the sugar through N at position 9 of the base.

The nucleosides are designated as follows when the kind of sugar present is ignored: "uridine," uracil nucleoside; "cytidine," cytosine nucleoside; "thymidine," thymine nucleoside; "adenosine," adenine nucleoside; "guanosine," guanine nucleoside; "inosine," hypoxanthine nucleoside.

When it is necessary to designate the sugar and name the nucleosides more accurately, we have names such as "uracil-3-D-riboside," "uracil-3-D-2'-deoxyriboside," "guanine-9-D-riboside," and "guanine-9-D-2'-deoxyriboside," the furanose ring structure of the sugar being assumed. Since the pyrimidine ring atoms are numbered 1 through 6 and the purine ring atoms are numbered 1 through 9, the positions in the sugar rings are numbered 1 through 5 and primed 1' through 5'. By this system of numbering substituents at the various positions may be clearly indicated.

Enzymes which split the N-glycosidic bond of nucleosides are present in animal tissues, particularly liver. Originally the action was considered to be a hydrolysis and the enzymes were called "nucleosidases." However, Kalckar (7) has shown the reaction to be a reversible phosphorolysis rather than a hydrolysis:

$$\underset{\text{Guanosine}}{\underset{\text{Inorganic}}{\text{Guanine-ribose} + \text{phosphate}}} \rightleftarrows \text{Guanine} + \text{Ribose-1-phosphate}$$

Such enzymes are properly designated "phosphorylases" rather than "nucleosidases." True nucleosidases which hydrolyze nucleosides to sugar and base have been found in bacteria. *Escherichia coli* contains a uridine phosphorylase.

The N-glycoside linkage between purine or pyrimidine base and sugar in nucleosides is hydrolyzed by acids, but the pyrimidine nucleosides are much more resistant to acid hydrolysis than are the purine nucleosides. The nucleosides are stable toward alkalies.

Structures of nucleotides. A nucleotide is a nucleoside to which a phosphoric acid group has been attached to the sugar by esterification at a definite hydroxyl group, and has the general composition base—sugar—phosphate. The nucleotides are nucleoside phosphates.

In the case of the ribose nucleosides there are three possible positions for phosphate esterification—namely, 2', 3', and 5'. Since there are free hydroxyl groups only at the 3' and 5' positions in the deoxyribose nucleosides, phosphate can be attached only at these positions.

The nucleotides are named generally according to the purine or pyrimidine base present, and also as phosphates of the corresponding nucleosides. Thus, adenine nucleotide is "adenylic acid" or "adenosine phosphate," guanine nucleotide is "guanylic acid" or "guanosine phosphate," thymine nucleotide is "thymidylic acid" or "thymidine phosphate," uracil nucleotide is "uridylic acid" or "uridine phosphate," and cytosine nucleotide is "cytidylic acid" or "cytidine phosphate."

As in the case of the nucleosides, the nucleotides may contain either ribose or deoxyribose as the sugar component. This leads to names such as "guanine ribonucleotide," "guanine deoxyribonucleotide," "cytosine ribonucleotide," "uracil ribonucleotide," etc. When the position of the phosphate group in the nucleotide is known, it is customary to name the nucleotide as a phosphate derivative of the corresponding nucleoside. Thus, if a nucleotide contains adenine and ribose and is phosphorylated in the 5′ position it is called "adenine-9-D-riboside-5′-phosphate." Similarly, we have "guanine-9-D-riboside-3′-phosphate," "uracil-3-D-riboside-5′-phosphate," etc. If it is unnecessary to indicate the nature of the sugar present the nucleotides may be designated more simply as "adenosine-5′-phosphate," "guanosine-3′-phosphate" etc. Representative formulas and names of nucleotides are given below:

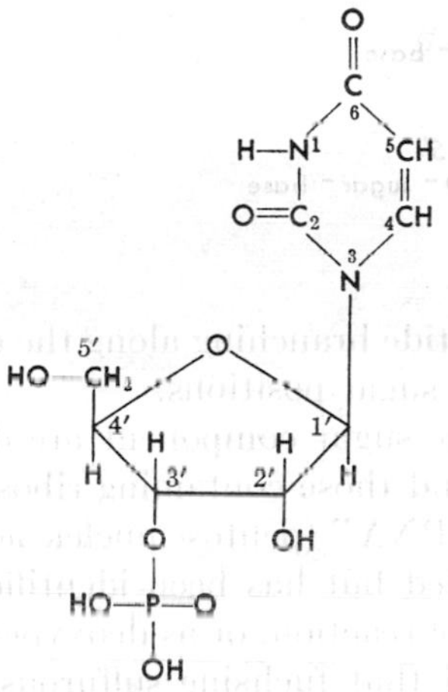

Uracil nucleotide
Uridylic acid
Uridine-3′-phosphate
Uracil-3-D-riboside-3′-phosphate

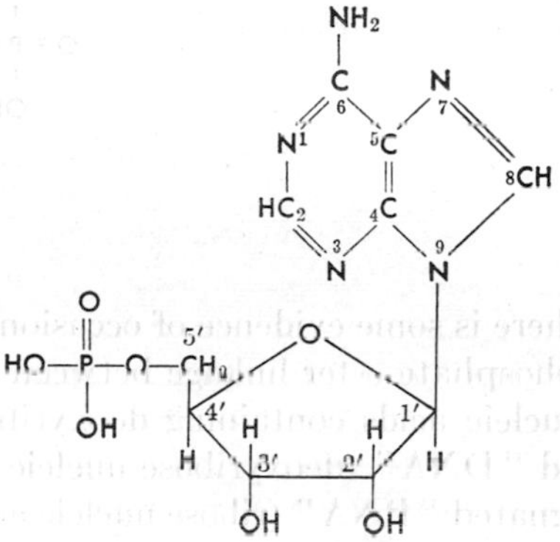

Adenine nucleotide
Adenylic acid
Adenosine-5′-phosphate
Adenine-9-D-riboside-5′-phosphate

The phosphate groups are rapidly hydrolyzed off from nucleotides to form nucleosides by many nonspecific phosphatases, such as intestinal phosphatase, acid prostatic phosphatase, bone phosphomonoesterase, and almond phosphatase. In addition to these nonspecific phosphatases which hydrolyze many other phosphate monoesters, there are some phosphatases which rather specifically hydrolyze nucleotides, and these are designated "nucleotidases." They include 5′-nucleotidases, found widespread in mammalian tissues, especially muscle and nerve, in bull semen, in snake venoms, and in potatoes, which hydrolyze off the phosphate group in the 5′ position of nucleotides. 3′-Nucleotidases, which hydrolyze off the 3′ phosphate group of nucleotides, are found in various vegetable sources, such as germinating barley and germinating rye grass seed, and plant leaves, such as those of corn, soybean, and lawn grass.

Acid hydrolysis of nucleotides splits the N-glycosidic linkage between sugar and base to give the base and sugar phosphate.

Alkaline hydrolysis splits the phosphate group from nucleotides to form the nucleosides.

Structures of the nucleic acids. The evidence accumulated by many workers over a long period of time indicates that both deoxyribonucleic acids (DNA) and ribonucleic acids (PNA) are chain polynucleotides of high molecular weight in which the mononucleotides are joined by phosphodiester linkages at the 3′ and 5′ sugar hydroxyl positions:

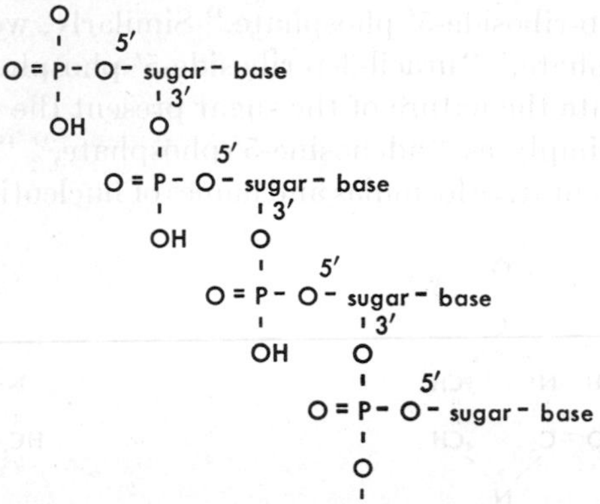

$$
\begin{array}{c}
O \\
\| \\
O = P - O - \overset{5'}{\text{sugar}} - \text{base} \\
| \qquad\;\; {}^{3'} \\
OH \qquad O \\
\quad | \quad\; {}^{5'} \\
O = P - O - \text{sugar} - \text{base} \\
| \qquad\;\;\; {}^{3'} \\
OH \qquad O \\
\quad\quad | \quad\; {}^{5'} \\
O = P - O - \text{sugar} - \text{base} \\
| \qquad\qquad {}^{3'} \\
OH \qquad O \\
\quad\quad\quad | \quad {}^{5'} \\
O = P - O - \text{sugar} - \text{base} \\
| \\
O
\end{array}
$$

There is some evidence of occasional nucleotide branching along the chain by phosphate ester linkage between 2′ and 3′ sugar positions.

Nucleic acids containing deoxyribose as the sugar component are designated "DNA" (deoxyribose nucleic acids), and those containing ribose are designated "RNA" (ribose nucleic acids) or "PNA" (pentose nucleic acids). In many cases the sugar has not been isolated but has been identified as pentose by a color reaction, such as the orcinol reaction, or as deoxypentose by the color reaction of Feulgen, who found that fuchsine sulfurous acid (Schiff's reagent) gives a red color with the deoxyribose of DNA but not with the ribose of RNA. Such color reactions have been widely used in the histochemical localization of DNA and PNA in cells. Most of the material reacting with the Feulgen reagent is localized in the cell nucleus and is DNA, while the pentose-reacting material is largely in the cytoplasm and is RNA.

1. Structure of ribose nucleic acids, RNA. When ribose nucleic acids are treated with mild alkaline reagents, they are rapidly converted into a mixture of their component mononucleotides. The position at which the sugar group of one mononucleotide is linked through an esterified phosphate group to the sugar of the succeeding mononucleotide has been difficult to determine:

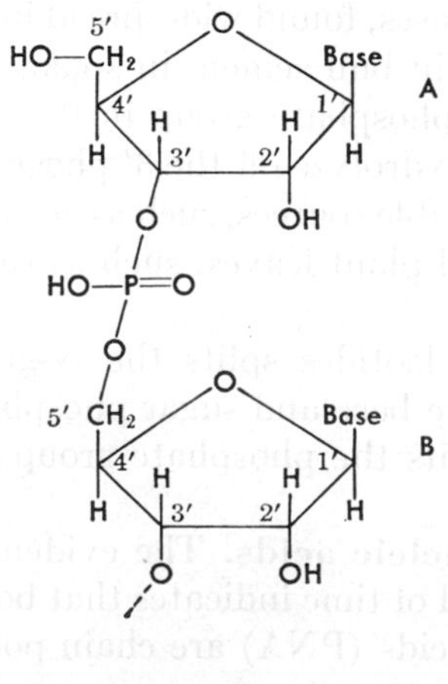

Obviously, nucleoside groups, such as A and B, might be linked through a phosphate diester group involving any pair of hydroxyl groups, such as 5', 2'; 3', 5'; 2', 3'; etc. Evidence for phosphorylation at the 5' hydroxyl was obtained by Cohn and Volkin (8), who treated ribonucleic acid with the enzyme ribonuclease, followed by intestinal phosphatase in the presence of arsenate, which inhibits the phosphomonoesterase present and prevents hydrolysis of the nucleotide phosphate group. In this way the phosphodiester groups between the nucleotides were hydrolyzed by the diesterase action of ribonuclease and intestinal phosphatase to give a mixture of products. From this digest 5'-phosphates of guanosine, adenosine, cytidine, and uridine were isolated. Cohn and Volkin also (9) treated nucleic acids with snake venom diesterase and isolated large amounts of nucleoside-5'-phosphates from the digest.

The above enzymatic hydrolysis of nucleic acids to give nucleoside-5'-phosphates (nucleotides) indicates that the 5' position in the sugar groups is primarily involved in the phosphate linkage of mononucleotides to form polynucleotides, the nucleic acids.

As pointed out previously, mildly alkaline reagents rapidly break ribonucleic acids into mononucleotides. However, in this case the nucleotides represent a mixture of nucleoside-2'-phosphate and nucleoside-3'-phosphate, which originally were designated "nucleotide a" and "nucleotide b" before the phosphate positions were established (10). This evidence, along with that from enzymatic hydrolysis given above, indicated the mononucleotides in ribonucleic acids to be linked by phosphate groups esterified at the 5' position of the sugar group of one mononucleotide and either the 2' or 3' position of the sugar group of another nucleotide, or possibly both types of linkage are present. The situation was clarified by the work of Brown and Todd (11). These workers have shown that cyclic phosphates, in which a phosphate group is esterified to both the 2' and 3' positions of the sugar group, are intermediate products in the hydrolysis of ribonucleic acids. These cyclic phosphates, upon further hydrolysis, yield both the nucleoside-2'-phosphate and the nucleoside-3'-phosphate.

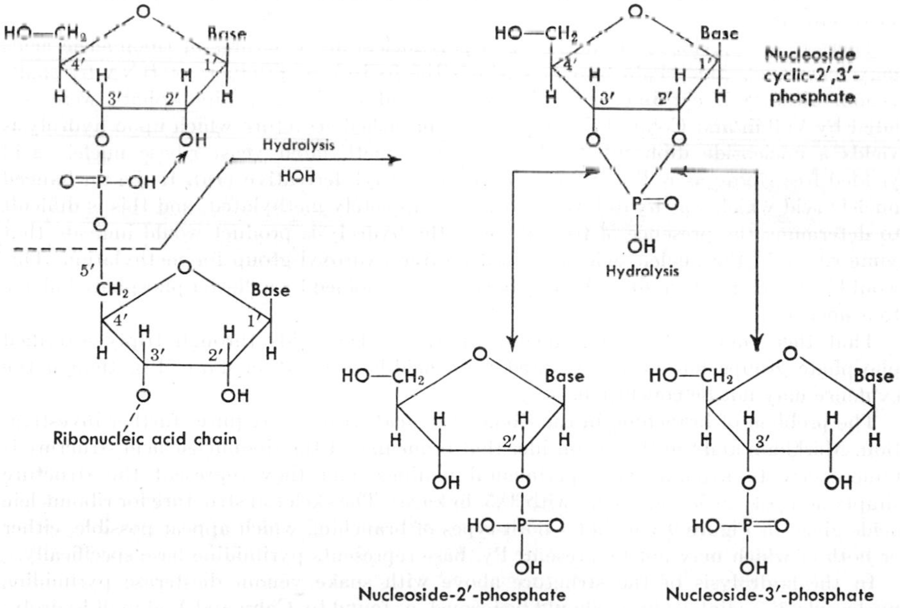

Synthetic adenosine-2'-benzyl phosphate and adenosine-3'-benzyl phosphate, in which the benzyl group replaces a mononucleotide in linkage to the phosphate group, were each found to yield a mixture of adenosine-2'-phosphate and adenosine-3'-phosphate when the benzyl group was hydrolyzed off with either acid or alkali, indicating the intermediate formation of a cyclic phosphate derivative. Synthetic cyclic nucleoside-2′,3′-phosphates were prepared and found to yield mixtures of the nucleoside-2′-phosphate and nucleoside-3′-phosphate upon hydrolysis, just as the ribonucleic acids do. The free nucleoside-2′-phosphates and nucleoside-3′-phosphates are not converted to cyclic nucleoside phosphates in the hydrolysis process. Markham and Smith (12) identified cyclic nucleoside-2′,3′-phosphates in the barium carbonate and the ammonia hydrolysates of ribonucleic acids. These workers also (13) demonstrated the formation of the pyrimidine cyclic phosphate mononucleotides, uridine-2′,3′-phosphate and cytidine-2′,3′-phosphate, in ribonuclease digests of ribonucleic acid, showing that cyclic phosphate esters are formed during enzymatic as well as acid and alkaline hydrolysis of ribonucleic acids.

The above evidence does not indicate whether the internucleotide phosphate bond of the ribonucleic acids is between the 2′ and 5′ or the 3′ and 5′ positions of the sugar groups. It is of interest that ribonuclease has been found to hydrolyze only pyrimidine nucleotide phosphate linkages in ribonucleic acids, leaving the purine nucleotides linked together. That the 3′ hydroxyl sugar group is esterified with phosphate was indicated by Brown and Todd (14), who found that cytidine-3′-benzyl phosphate and uridine-3′-benzyl phosphate are hydrolyzed by ribonuclease to give the nucleotides cytidine-3′-phosphate and uridine-3′-phosphate. The isomeric cytidine-2′-benzyl phosphate and uridine-2′-benzyl phosphate were unaffected by the ribonuclease. None of the corresponding purine esters were acted upon. These results indicate a phosphate diester 3′,5′ linkage between pyrimidine nucleotides of ribonucleic acids. Volkin and Cohn (15) showed that spleen nuclease yields nucleoside-3′-phosphates (nucleotides) of both purines and pyrimidines when acting upon ribonucleic acids. Heppel and associates (16) treated ribonucleic acid with purified spleen nuclease and obtained guanosine-3′-phosphate and adenosine-3′-phosphate, with no indication of the formation of cyclic phosphates.

The evidence presented above provides a high degree of certainty that the ribose nucleic acids (RNA) have as their fundamental structure a chain of mononucleotides linked together through phosphate diester bonds between the 3′ and 5′ positions of the sugar groups.

There is some evidence that the main polynucleotide structures of ribonucleic acids may have nucleotide chain branches. From the hydrolysis products of RNA by snake venom diesterase, cytidine, 2′,5′-diphosphate and uridine-2′,5′-diphosphate were isolated by Volkin and Cohn (17), suggesting a branched structure which upon hydrolysis yields a nucleoside diphosphate. Hydrolysis of methylated yeast ribose nucleic acid yielded free ribose as well as its mono- and dimethyl derivative (18). If the unchanged nucleic acid which was hydrolyzed had been completely methylated, and this is difficult to determine, the presence of free ribose in the hydrolysis product would indicate that some ribose in the nucleic acid possessed no free hydroxyl group for methylation. This would be true if the 2′ hydroxyl group of ribose were joined by a diester phosphate linkage to a nucleotide branch.

That there may be chain branching in ribonucleic acids through triply esterified phosphate groups has been suggested from acid-base titration data (19), though the evidence may not be conclusive.

The problem of branching in the ribonucleic acid structure requires further investigation. Markham and Smith (5) consider that branching of the ribonucleic acid structure is unnecessary to explain the experimental findings, and they represent the structure simply as a polynucleotide chain with 3′,5′ linkages. The skeleton structure for ribonucleic acids given in Figure 9.1 includes both types of branching which appear possible, either or both of which may not be present. Py. base represents pyrimidine base specifically.

In the hydrolysis of the structure above with snake venom diesterase pyrimidine nucleoside-2′,5′-diphosphates should be formed, as found by Cohn and Volkin, if hydrolysis occurs at the dotted lines. This would necessitate the groups at a and b to be pyrimidine nucleotides in order that the structure may conform with the principles of pancreatic ribonuclease action upon ribonucleic acids.

The general principles governing ribonuclease action on ribonucleic acids have been well established (20). Pancreatic ribonuclease, also referred to as "ribonuclease I," catalyzes the cleavage of only certain strictly defined internucleotide bonds, and these are the phosphate bonds linking the 3' position of the sugar in a pyrimidine nucleotide to the 5' position of the sugar in an adjacent pyrimidine or purine nucleotide. The phosphate bonds between adjacent purine nucleotides and the phosphate bonds linking pyrimidine nucleotides at the 5' position with purine nucleotides at the 3' position are not hydrolyzed. These points relative to ribonuclease action are illustrated in the diagrammatic structure of Figure 9.2.

Hydrolysis of ribonucleic acids by ribonuclease leads to the intermediate formation of 2',3'-cyclic pyrimidine nucleoside phosphates, as previously pointed out. The fundamental hydrolysis by ribonuclease may be indicated schematically as follows:

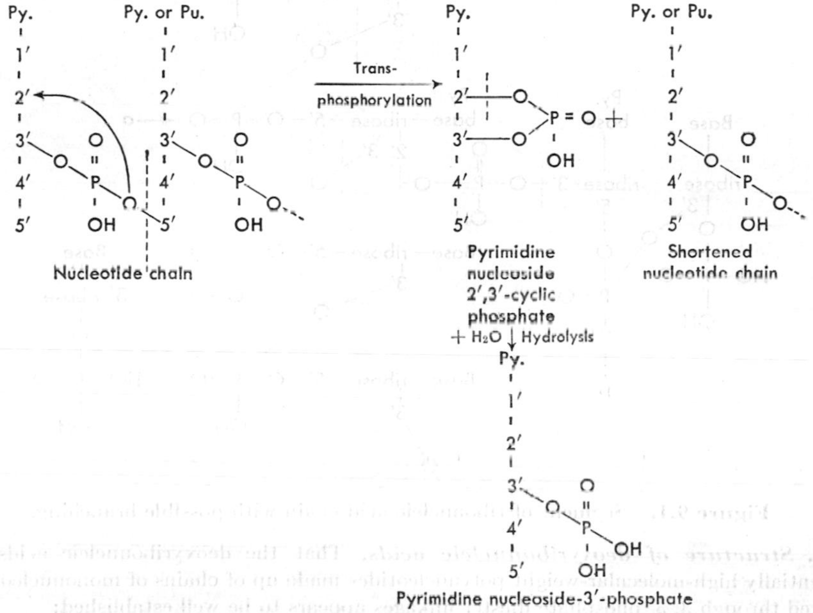

Py.   Py. or Pu.   Py.   Py. or Pu.

1'   1'   1'   1'

2'←   2'   Trans-   2'——O.   2'
                         phosphorylation ————→   >P = O +
3'   O   3'   O   3'——O | 3'   O
       || || OH ||
4'   P   4'   P   4'   4'   P
       | | |
5'   OH   5'   OH   5'   5'   OH

Nucleotide chain   Pyrimidine   Shortened
                                                     nucleoside   nucleotide chain
                                                     2',3'-cyclic
                                                     phosphate
                                                     + H₂O ↓ Hydrolysis
                                                        Py.

                                                        1'

                                                        2'

                                                        3'   O
                                                               ||
                                                        4'   P
                                                               | OH
                                                        5'   OH
                                                     Pyrimidine nucleoside-3'-phosphate

The action of ribonuclease involves two steps. The first is transphosphorylation, in which the phosphate bond to the 5' position of the adjacent pyrimidine or purine nucleotide is broken, and this released phosphate group is united at the 3' position to form the cyclic phosphate as shown. This 2',3'-cyclic phosphate is then hydrolyzed by the enzyme to give the pyrimidine nucleoside 3'-phosphate (nucleotide). Ribonuclease does not act upon 2',5'-linkages between nucleotides (11).

The product of ribonuclease action consists of a mixture of the free pyrimidine nucleotides with phosphate attached in the 3' position, 3'-cytidylic acid and 3'-uridylic acid; unbranched di-, tri-, and tetranucleotides; and unbranched more complex oligonucleotides. A pyrimidine nucleotide is always an end group in the oligonucleotides and has phosphate attached at the 3' position.

Volkin and Cohn (21) separated many of the products of ribonuclease action on yeast and calf liver ribonucleic acids and studied their composition. This study as well as the results of Markham and Smith (22) show ribonucleic acid chains to be made up of pyrimidine-pyrimidine, pyrimidine-purine, and purine-purine groups of nucleotides. However, it is not yet possible to represent the nucleotide sequence in any nucleic acid with certainty, as has been done for the amino acid sequence in insulin and some other proteins.

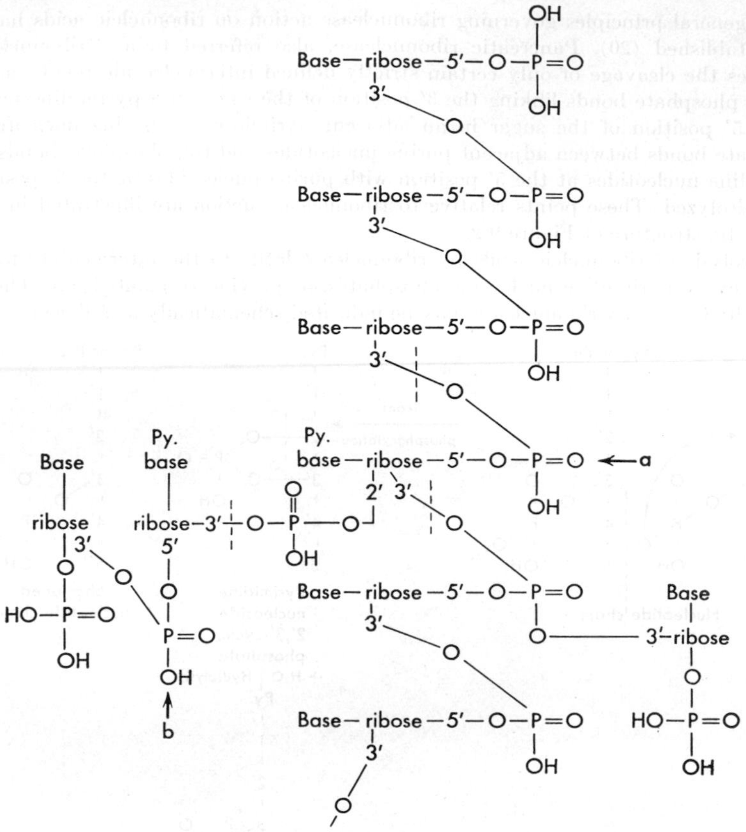

Figure 9.1. Segment of ribonucleic acid chain with possible branching.

2. Structure of deoxyribonucleic acids. That the deoxyribonucleic acids are essentially high-molecular-weight polynucleotides made up of chains of mononucleotides linked through 3,′5′ phosphate diester linkages appears to be well established:

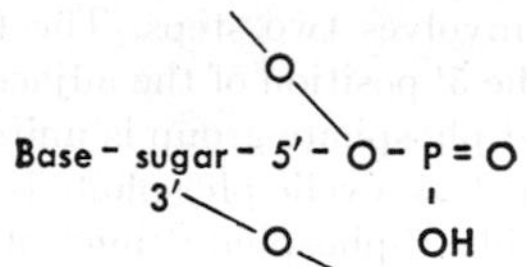

Segment of polynucleotide chain of DNA

This structure is supported by the acid-base titration of deoxyribose nucleic acids (23). Since only the 3′ and 5′ hydroxyl groups of deoxyribose in the nucleotides are available

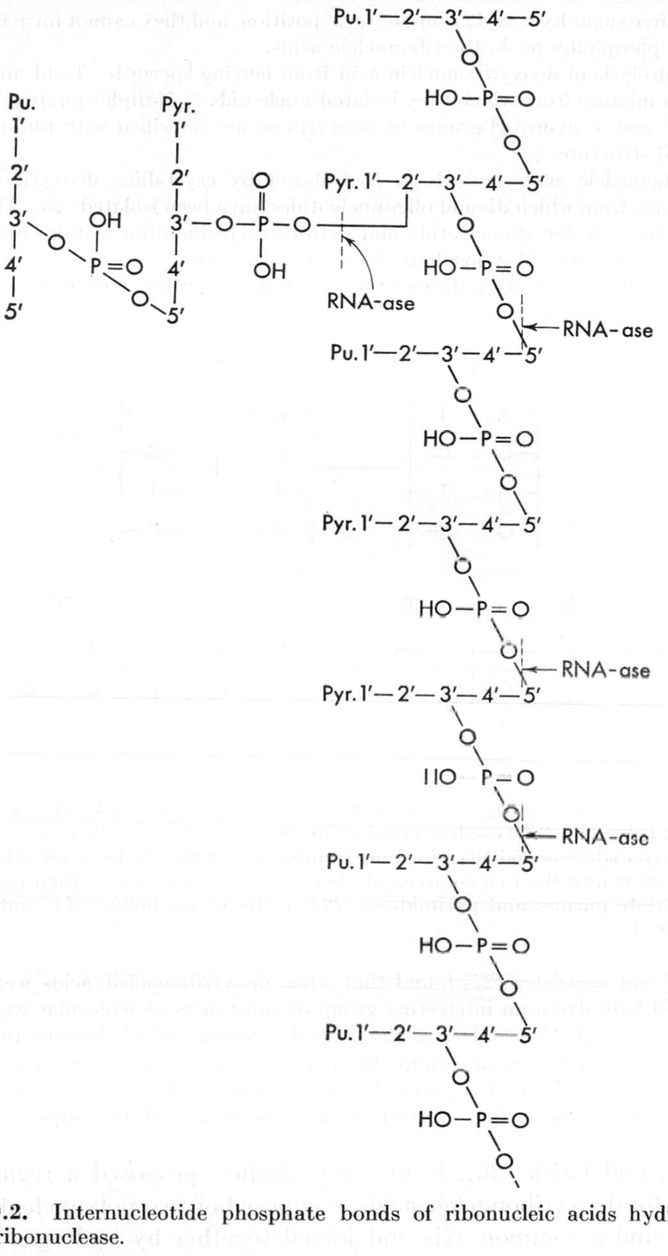

Pu. 1'—2'—3'—4'—5'

Pu.　　　Pyr.
1'　　　1'
|　　　|
2'　　　2'　　O
|　　　|　　‖
3'　OH　3'—O—P—O—
|　O　　4'　　|
4'　\\P=O　　OH
|　/　O　　
5'　　O—5'

HO—P=O
O
Pyr. 1'—2'—3'—4'—5'
O
HO—P=O
O
RNA-ase → (←RNA-ase)

Pu. 1'—2'—3'—4'—5'
O
HO—P=O
O
Pyr. 1'—2'—3'—4'—5'
O
HO—P=O
O ←RNA-ase
Pyr. 1'—2'—3'—4'—5'
O
HO—P=O
O ←RNA-ase
Pu. 1'—2'—3'—4'—5'
O
HO—P=O
O
Pu. 1'—2'—3'—4'—5'
O
HO—P=O
O

Figure 9.2. Internucleotide phosphate bonds of ribonucleic acids hydrolyzed by pancreatic ribonuclease.

for esterification with phosphate, it is reasonable to suppose that the nucleotides are joined by phosphate at these positions in the deoxyribose nucleic acids. Of course, alternate 5',5' and 3',3' linkages are a theoretical possibility in both ribonucleic acids and deoxyribonucleic acids. However, such a linkage is not in keeping with the behavior of deoxyribose nucleic acids to hydrolytic agents.

It is very interesting that while the ribonucleic acids are readily hydrolyzed to mononucleotides by alkali, the deoxyribose nucleic acids are resistant to alkaline hydrolysis. This resistance to alkaline hydrolysis appears to be due to the fact that in these substances there is no free sugar hydroxyl group in the 2′ position, and they cannot form intermediate cyclic 2′,3′ phosphates as do the ribonucleic acids.

Acid hydrolysis of deoxyribonucleic acid from herring sperm by Todd and associates (24) gave a mixture from which they isolated nucleoside-3′,5′-diphosphates showing that both the 3′ and 5′ hydroxyl groups of deoxyribose are esterified with phosphate in the nucleic acid structure.

Deoxyribonucleic acids have been hydrolyzed by crystalline deoxyribonuclease to yield mixtures from which di- and oligonucleotides have been isolated (25). The dinucleotides, adenine-cytosine dinucleotide and cytosine-cytosine dinucleotide, were shown to be joined together by 3′,5′-phosphate diester linkages (26).

All of the above evidence indicates the essential correctness for the deoxyribonucleic acid structure given above.

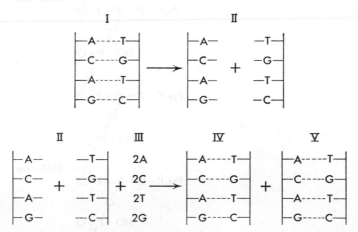

Figure 9.3.   Representing duplication or synthesis of the DNA helix. *I* represents a section of a helix with the two deoxynucleotide strands linked together through hydrogen bonds between adenine and thymine and guanine and cytosine. In duplication the helix, *I*, is dissociated into the two component strands, *II*, each of which then combines with the appropriate purines and pyrimidines, *III*, to form two helices, *IV* and *V*, like the parent helix, *I*.

Chargaff and associates (27) found that when deoxyribonucleic acids were subjected to mild acid hydrolysis, an interesting group of substances of molecular weight around 15,000 was obtained. These substances are called "apurinic acids," because the hydrolysis selectively splits off the purine groups from the mononucleotides along the nucleic acid chain but does not remove the pyrimidine bases. These substances accordingly contain deoxyribose phosphate residues instead of purine mononucleotide groups.

Watson and Crick (28), from x-ray studies, proposed a regular helical structure for deoxyribonucleic acids, composed of two polynucleotide chains coiled around a common axis and joined together by hydrogen bonds between the nucleotide purine and pyrimidine bases. The bases are arranged perpendicular to the fiber axis and are joined together in pairs, always with a purine of one nucleotide chain hydrogen bonded to a pyrimidine in the other nucleotide chain. These linkages appear to be most probable between adenine and thymine and between guanine and cytosine. This structure provides an interesting theory as to how the structure may lead to its own duplication (synthesis of additional DNA), as indicated in Figure 9.3. This

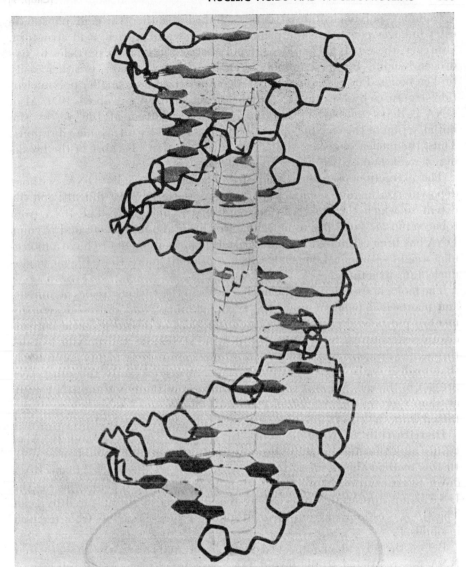

Figure 9.4. A pair of DNA chains wound as a helix about the fiber axis. The ring structures of the sugars are shown, from each of which protrudes a base linked to an opposing base of the other chain at the same level by a hydrogen bond. These hydrogen bonds between the bases serve as horizontal supports holding the chains together. (Taken from Crick, F. H. C., *Scientific American*, **191**, 56, (No. 4), by courtesy of the author and publisher.)

type of structure is in accordance with many of the properties of deoxyribose nucleic acids. Figure 9.4 illustrates the Watson-Crick helix.

Nomenclature of the nucleic acids as polynucleotides is simple. Yeast nucleic acid is " yeast polyribonucleotide," and thymus nucleic acid is "thymus polydeoxyribonucleotide." General terms are "pentose" and "deoxypentose polynucleotides."

Complex polynucleotide structures linked together through phosphate ester linkages constitute the primary aggregates of nucleic acid structure. However, these polynucleotides are polymerized into larger particles by hydrogen bonding between amino and enolic hydroxyl groups, or other easily broken bonds. For example, DNA is depolymerized into smaller polynucleotide structures by lowering the pH below 5.6 or raising it above 10.9. Also, DNA is depolymerized by heating in neutral solution at 100° C, by the initial action of the enzyme deoxyribonuclease, and by ultrasonic vibrations. Thus, the nucleic acids are subject to "denaturation" because of the breaking of weak bonds, just as are the proteins.

The extraction of nucleic acids from tissues, especially DNA, without depolymerization and change of particle size is exceedingly difficult, and the extent to which this has been accomplished is uncertain. The PNA from tobacco mosaic virus has a molecular weight of about 300,000, and thymus DNA has been estimated by light-scattering measurements to have a molecular weight of about 4,000,000, which represents more than 10,000 mononucleotide structures.

The biologic specificity of the nucleic acids in the various tissues of animals and plants is dependent upon the types, numbers, and orders of arrangement of purine and pyrimidine mononucleotides in the nucleic acid polynucleotide structures, as well as the polymerization of the polynucleotides through hydrogen bonding into larger aggregates. It is highly improbable that nucleic acids extracted from tissues represent exactly the substances present in the cells. Also, it is doubtful that any of the DNA and RNA preparations represent homogeneous chemical compounds. The nucleic acids obtained from the crystalline plant viruses probably are the best preparations.

Distribution of nucleic acids in tissues. The DNA and RNA of tissues may be determined by the method of Schmidt and Thannhauser (29). In this method the tissue is treated with warm alkali, which breaks RNA down to its component nucleotides; these are soluble in acid, whereas the DNA is not appreciably affected by the alkali and is precipitated by acid. The RNA is estimated from the acid soluble P and the DNA from the acid insoluble P.

Before the advent of improved methods of analysis it was thought that RNA was restricted to plant and DNA to animal tissues. This idea arose from the fact that yeast nucleic acid is of the RNA and thymus nucleic acid of the DNA type. Both DNA and RNA have been found in practically all cell types examined. However, it has been found that the proportions of DNA and RNA in a cell are dependent upon the relative proportions of nuclear material and cytoplasm present. Cells rich in nuclear material contain a preponderance of DNA, whereas those with much cytoplasm and little nuclear material contain chiefly RNA. Calf thymus, rich in nuclear material, contains about four times as much DNA as RNA, and rat liver contains about four times as much RNA as DNA.

It is highly significant that the nuclei of tissue cells from animals of a given species contain relatively constant quantities of DNA per nucleus.

Thus, determination of DNA in a tissue permits estimation of the number of cells in the tissue. Present evidence indicates that chromosomes are largely composed of deoxyribose nucleoproteins. The hereditary units, the genes, are located in the chromosomes, where only the deoxyribose nucleoproteins are found, which suggests that these nucleoproteins are the major constituents of the genes.

Ribose nucleic acids are particularly abundant in the cytoplasm of embryonic cells and of actively secreting exocrine cells of certain mammalian tissues, such as the pancreas. The associated protein is of the histone type.

The nucleus of embryonic cells is low in nucleic acids of either type, but the nucleolus, like the cytoplasm, is rich in ribose nucleic acids.

Table 9.2 gives the nucleotide composition of ribonucleic acids (RNA) isolated from a number of sources. The values represent molar ratios of guanylic, uridylic, and cytidylic acids relative to adenylic acid with an assigned value of 10 (30).

Table 9.2.   Nucleotide Composition of Ribonucleic Acids

Source	Adenylic acid	Guanylic acid	Cytidylic acid	Uridylic acid	Purine, or Pyrimidine
Beef liver	10	17.0	10.4	7.8	1.49
Calf liver	10	17.9	14.9	8.4	1.20
Chicken liver	10	17.1	13.6	10.6	1.12
Human liver	10	30.6	27.5	11.0	1.26
Pig liver	10	18.8	15.8	9.1	1.23
Rabbit liver	10	16.9	14.6	10.3	1.08
Rat liver	10	17.5	13.9	10.9	1.10
Beef pancreas	10	12	32	10	1.2
Calf thymus	10	23.8	13.9	6.5	1.65
Cat brain	10	14.7	12.0	9.5	1.15
Baker's yeast	10	11.9	7.2	11.4	1.17
Tobacco mosaic virus (TMV)	10	8.5	6.2	8.8	1.24
Rat liver nuclei	10	14.8	14.3	12.9	0.91
Rat liver microsomes	10	16.9	14.7	10.3	1.08
Rat liver mitochondria	10	16.9	15.1	11.0	1.03
Rat liver cell sap	10	17.3	16.5	9.8	1.04

Table 9.3 gives the purine and pyrimidine bases found in various deoxypentose (DNA) nucleic acids. The values represent molar proportions of bases per 100 g atoms of P (31).

As pointed out above, the deoxypentose nucleic acid content of cell nuclei has been determined. From the number of nuclei analyzed and the total DNA found, the mean DNA content per nucleus can be calculated. Table 9.4 gives the nuclear content of deoxyribose nucleic acids calculated per nucleus for a number of tissues (32).

The DNA content per cell nucleus for the somatic tissues of a given organism show a striking constancy. Still more striking is the fact that sperm nuclei contain only half the DNA present in various somatic cell nuclei. Since the sperm nuclei contain only one set of chromosomes, and the somatic nuclei, which contain double the amount of DNA found in the sperm nuclei,

Table 9.3.   Purine and Pyrimidine Bases of Deoxynucleic Acids

Source	Adenine	Guanine	Cytosine	5-Methyl-cytosine	Thymine
Beef thymus	29.0	21.2	21.2		28.5
Beef liver	28.8	21.0	21.1		29.0
Human thymus	30.9	19.9	19.8		29.4
Human liver	30.3	19.5	19.9		30.3
Calf thymus	28.7	21.7	20.7	1.7	27.2
Beef sperm	28.7	22.2	20.7	1.3	27.2
Human sperm	30.9	19.1	18.4		31.6
Horse spleen	29.6	22.9	20.1		27.5
Hen erythrocytes	28.8	20.5	21.5		29.2
Herring sperm	27.8	22.2	20.7	1.9	27.5
Wheat germ	26.5	23.5	17.2	5.8	27.0
Yeast	31.7	18.3	17.4		32.6
Vaccinia virus	29.5	20.6	20.0		29.9
				5-Hydroxy-methyl-cytosine	
E. coli phage T2	32.5	18.2		16.7	32.6
E. coli phage T4	32.3	18.3		16.3	33.1
E. coli phage T6	32.5	17.8		16.3	33.5

Table 9.4.   Average Deoxyribonucleic Acid (DNA) Content per Nucleus in
Various Animal Tissues
Calculated as mg $\times 10^{-9}$

Animal	Sperm	Erythrocyte	Heart	Kidney	Liver	Pancreas	Spleen
Beef	3.42			6.63	7.05	7.15	7.26
Calf				6.25	6.22		
Carp	1.64	3.49					
Chicken	1.26	2.49	2.45	2.20	2.66	2.61	2.55
Dog				5.3	5.5		
Frog		15.0			15.7		
Human	3.25	7.30		8.6	10.36		
Rat			6.50	6.74	9.47	7.38	6.55
Shad	0.91	1.97			2.01		
Toad	3.70	7.33					
Trout, brown	2.67	5.79					

have two sets of chromosomes, the DNA content of the cell nucleus is a measure of the number of chromosome sets present. In agreement with this, Mirsky and Ris (33) found the nuclei of tissues having more than two sets of chromosomes (polyploid cells) to have a correspondingly higher content of DNA. This increase in DNA per nucleus is particularly found in mammalian liver cells, which exhibit polyploidy. Many data have accumulated from various species in support of the above relations (34). For example, diploid conidia of *Aspergillus* have twice the nuclear DNA and twice the number of chromosome sets as haploid *Aspergillus* conidia. A similar parallelism between the number of chromosome sets and nuclear DNA has been found in haploid through tetraploid yeasts.

It is interesting that the amount of DNA per cell nucleus is not only constant for the somatic tissues of a given organism, but remains unchanged when the organism is subjected to such drastic influences as prolonged starvation, changes in diet, and conversion of normal cells to precancerous and cancerous cells by feeding carcinogens. The remarkable constancy in the DNA content per cell nucleus has made it possible to calculate the number of cells in a given tissue sample of an organism from a determination of its DNA content. If one knows the number of cells in a tissue sample, then other constituents of the tissue, such as lipids, ribonucleic acids, proteins, etc., can be calculated as average content per cell.

It is of interest that the haploid sperm nucleus and haploid egg nucleus of *Ascaris megalocephala* have been found to contain the same amounts of DNA (35), which means the chromosome sets in the sperm and egg have the same average amount of DNA.

The evidence cited above appears conclusive that DNA is the constituent of chromosomes primarily concerned with the genetic process and in some manner carries the code of genetic information controlling development of the organism. The genetic function of DNA is strongly supported by the fact that when bacteriophage enters a bacterial cell and causes new phage synthesis and disruption of the bacteria, the process takes place in such a manner that nearly all of the material which enters the cell is DNA. Very little protein associated with the phage DNA is transmitted.

The evidence given above shows that the quantity of DNA per set of chromosomes for a given organism is constant. However, the percentage of DNA per set of chromosomes is variable, due primarily to variation in the quantity of protein present. For example, chromosomes isolated from calf tissues show the following percentages of DNA and protein, respectively: thymus, 39, 8.5; kidney, 20, 99, liver, 26, 39. Carp erythrocyte chromosomes have 41 per cent DNA and 4 per cent protein (34).

Preparation of nucleoproteins and nucleic acids. Nucleoproteins. Nucleoproteins have been extracted from tissues by many different processes. These generally involve extraction with solvents such as water, dilute alkaline solutions, buffer solutions of pH 4–11, and sodium chloride solutions. Acid is then added and causes precipitation of the nucleoproteins in the isoelectric region (pH 3–5). Some of these methods of preparation undoubtedly may produce important changes in the nucleoproteins due to rupture of the nucleic acid-protein bond. This has led to the development of milder procedures designed to obtain the nucleoproteins in as nearly native condition as possible. Extraction of tissues with very mild solvents (neutral salts, weakly alkaline solutions) and precipitation of the nucleoproteins by salting out with ammonium sulfate or calcium chloride appears to give better results. The deoxypentose nucleoproteins show peculiar behavior in sodium chloride solutions, which provides a good method of separation. They are soluble in 1 to 2 M NaCl, forming viscous opalescent solutions, but are insoluble in 0.14 M NaCl, despite the fact that they are soluble in very dilute sodium chloride solutions (0.02 M or less) and in pure water. The minced tissues are first washed with 0.14 M NaCl to remove cytoplasmic substances and then extracted with 1 to 2 M NaCl, which removes nucleoproteins. The solution is clarified and diluted with water to a concentration of 0.14 M NaCl, whereupon the nucleoproteins precipitate in fibrous form.

Differential centrifugation has been applied with success to the isolation of various high molecular nucleoproteins from tissues. The nucleoproteins of large molecular weights centrifuge down at lower speeds than the cytoplasmic proteins do and may be separated from them. This procedure avoids all but the mildest of chemical action and is preferable when it can be applied. The nucleoproteins of chicken embryo, chicken tumor, Rous sarcoma, and of various mammalian cells and tissues have been prepared by this method. It has also been very valuable for the isolation of the virus nucleoproteins.

It should be pointed out that since the nucleic acids are relatively strong acids and combine at tissue pH with basic proteins, the isolation of nucleoprotein from a macerated tissue does not guarantee that the nucleoprotein obtained existed as such within the cell structure. It is very reasonable to expect ribonucleic acids (RNA) to exist in cells in combination with various proteins.

Nucleic acids. As previously indicated, Miescher prepared nucleic acids from pus and salmon sperm by peptic digestion, which removed the protein and left the nucleic acids. Miescher's preparations were generally contaminated with protein. Altman extracted tissues with sodium hydroxide, which decomposed the nucleoproteins into sodium salts of nucleic acids and protein. Protein was removed by mild acidification with acetic acid, and sodium nucleate was then precipitated by the addition of alcohol. Most of the later methods of preparing nucleic acids have been modifications of Altman's procedure, in which the conditions of alkali extraction, protein removal, or nucleic acid separation have been altered. The nucleic acids obtained by such methods are undoubtedly often markedly depolymerized and changed from the native state. Recognition of this fact has recently led to the introduction of mild methods of preparation.

The deoxypentose nucleic acids of thymus and liver may be obtained by first preparing solutions of the corresponding nucleoproteins in water or 1 M NaCl and then saturating the solutions with sodium chloride, which decomposes the nucleoprotein to form sodium nucleate and protein chloride. The sodium nucleate remains in solution, while the protein chloride is precipitated by the salt. After removal of the protein, the sodium nucleate is precipitated by addition of alcohol.

$$\underset{\text{Nucleoprotein}}{\overset{+\ -}{\text{protein nucleate}} + \text{NaCl}} \longrightarrow \overset{+\ -}{\text{protein Cl}} + \overset{+\ -}{\text{Na nucleate}}$$

Sevag, Lackman, and Smolens (36) have described a mild procedure for the separation of nucleic acids from nucleoproteins. The nucleoprotein is decomposed by treatment with 0.5 per cent sodium carbonate at 50°C for an hour or two, after which the pH is adjusted to 7 and the solution is shaken with chloroform containing a little amyl alcohol. The protein separates at the interface as a protein-chloroform gel which may be separated by centrifugation. The remaining solution contains the sodium salt of nucleic acid, which can be precipitated with alcohol.

Mayers and Spizizen (37) have described an improved method for the isolation of nucleic acids from bacteriophages based upon extraction with 1 per cent sodium lauryl sulfate (Duponol C) followed by precipitation with half-saturated sodium acetate.

While nucleic acids are often extracted directly from tissues, the purer preparations are obtained by decomposition of the isolated nucleoproteins.

Since the nucleic acids in most cases may be separated from nucleoproteins by mild treatment with alkali, precipitation by salt, etc., it is obvious that the linkage between the nucleic acid and protein is weak. The nucleoproteins are salts of the nucleic acids with the basic proteins. Other types of weak linkages, such as hydrogen bonding, also may be involved.

Proteins of nucleoproteins. The protein components of nucleoproteins vary from relatively simple polypeptide structures in sperm to complex protein molecules of very high particle weight in the virus nucleoproteins.

The protamins are the simplest protein components of nucleoproteins. They have been isolated only from sperm and ripe testicles of fish. The protamins are of low molecular weight (a few thousand) and are very basic in character. When hydrolyzed they yield a large proportion of basic amino acids, chiefly arginine, and relatively few other amino acids, which are of the monoaminomonocarboxylic type. The protamins, salmin of salmon sperm and clupeine of herring sperm, yield arginine as the sole basic amino acid. The protamins contain arginine and monoaminomonocarboxylic acids in the molecular ratio 2:1. The isoelectric pH values of the protamins lie high in the alkaline range and are around 12 for salmin and clupeine. Accordingly, the protamins exist as positive ions at all physiologic pH values. The protamin nucleoproteins are saltlike combinations of protamin$^+$ and nucleic acid$^-$. Because of their basic character, the protamins combine with some of the acidic proteins to form insoluble salt type complexes, protamin$^+$ protein$^-$. Protamin-insulin is such a combination.

The histones represent a class of simple proteins which enter into nucleoprotein formation. They are more complex than the protamins, although they are still relatively small proteins. When hydrolyzed they yield a greater variety of amino acids than do the protamins. Basic amino acids predominate in the composition of histones, but to a much lesser degree than in the protamins. However, the histones are decidedly basic in character and have alkaline isoelectric points. Nucleoproteins containing them are called "nucleohistones" and are salt combinations of nucleic acid and protein, as are the nucleoprotamins.

Nucleohistones have been isolated from bird erythrocytes, the ripe sperm of certain animals, and the thymus gland. Calf thymus nucleohistone has a molecular weight of about 2,000,000 and is very asymmetric in shape, as indicated by the axial ratio of 36 to 1. Its isoelectric pH is acidic and is near 4.

The protamins of the ripe sperm of spawning salmon are formed from the muscle proteins of the fish. It is interesting to note that histones are present in the unripe testis, and this suggests that they are intermediate products in the formation of the protamins.

Besides the relatively simple protamins and histones, complex proteins enter into the composition of many nucleoproteins. These nucleoproteins represent much firmer combinations than do the nucleoprotamins and nucleohistones. They cannot be separated into protein and nucleic acid by high salt concentrations alone, but must receive more drastic treatment in which the protein component is denatured before separation occurs. This may be accomplished by treatment with alkali. Nucleoproteins of this type have been isolated from liver by salt extraction followed by isoelectric precipitation. These liver nucleoproteins contain 15 to 20 per cent of lipid, of which 30 to 40 per cent is phospholipid. They appear to be complexes of nucleic acid and lipoproteins, and the nucleic acid is of the deoxypentose type. Similar nucleoproteins consisting of nucleic acid-lipoprotein in which the nucleic acid is of the pentose type have been isolated from a number of animal tissues. These nucleoproteins are apparently derived from the cytoplasm. Several viruses have been investigated and found to be nucleolipoprotein complexes. These include vaccinia virus, chicken tumor virus, equine encephalomyelitis virus, and rabbit papilloma virus.

A number of the plant viruses have been isolated as crystalline nucleoproteins, chiefly by differential centrifugation and salting out with ammonium sulfate. Among these are tobacco, cucumber, and tomato viruses. The molecular weights of these nucleoprotein complexes are enormous, the values ranging from two to three million for the simple ones to 40 to 60 million for tobacco mosaic virus. Most of the molecular mass appears to reside in the protein component. Nucleic acid constitutes only 5.8 per cent of tobacco mosaic virus. The protein of this virus has been shown to contain at least 13 amino acids. Tobacco mosaic virus exists in a number of different strains. The nucleic acid of each strain is of the pentose type.

Knight (39) gives the amino acid compositions of a number of strains of tobacco mosaic virus as shown in Table 9.5.

Table 9.5. Amino Acid Content of Highly Purified Preparations of Some Strains of Tobacco Mosaic Virus*

Amino Acid	Strain								
	TMV	M	J14D1	GA	YA	HR	CV3	CV4	M.D.†
Alanine	5.1	5.2	4.8	5.1	5.1	6.4		6.1	0.2
Arginine	9.8	9.9	10.0	1.11	11.2	9.9	9.3	9.3	0.2
Aspartic acid	13.5	13.5	13.4	13.7	13.8	12.6		13.1	0.2
Cysteine	0.69	0.67	0.64	0.60	0.60	0.70	0	0	
Cystine	0		0		0	0		0	
Glutamic acid	11.3	11.5	10.4	11.5	11.3	15.5	6.4	6.5	0.2
Glycine	1.9	1.7	1.9	1.9	1.8	1.3	1.2	1.5	0.1
Histidine	0	0	0	0	0	0.72	0	0	0.01
Isoleucine	6.6	6.7	6.6	5.7	5.7	5.9	5.4	4.6	0.2
Leucine	9.3	9.3	9.4	9.2	9.4	9.0	9.3	9.4	0.2
Lysine	1.47	1.49	**1.95**	1.45	1.47	1.51	**2.55**	**2.43**	0.04
Methionine	0	0	0	0	0	2.2	0	0	0.1
Phenylalanine	8.4	8.4	8.4	8.3	8.4	5.4	9.9	9.8	0.2
Proline	5.8	5.9	5.5	5.8	5.7	5.5		5.7	0.2
Serine	7.2	7.0	6.8	7.0	7.1	5.7	9.3	9.4	0.3
Threonine	9.9	10.1	10.0	10.4	10.1	8.2	6.9	7.0	0.1
Tryptophan	2.1	2.2	2.2	2.1	2.1	1.4	**0.5**	**0.5**	0.1
Tyrosine	3.8	3.8	3.9	3.7	3.7	6.8	3.8	3.7	0.1
Valine	9.2	9.0	8.9	8.8	9.1	6.2	8.8	8.9	0.2

* The values given in the table represent percentages of the indicated amino acids. In order to facilitate comparison, the values which are considered to differ significantly from those of TMV are in boldface type.
† Mean deviation of the values of single determinations from the averages given. Three to five preparations of each strain were analyzed for each amino acid, with the exception of cysteine, and the results were averaged to give the figures presented.

The localization of nucleic acids and nucleoproteins in cells has been accomplished partly through specific dye-staining techniques, such as that of Feulgen for deoxypentose nucleic acids, and partly by the use of the ultraviolet microscope. The latter instrument has a quartz optical system and permits the use of monochromatic ultraviolet light. It provides about twice the resolving power of the ordinary microscope. The nucleic acids strongly absorb ultraviolet light at 2600 Å on account of the presence of the pyrimidine rings and can be localized in cells on this basis. Different types of proteins associated with the nucleic acids can also be distinguished by their ultraviolet absorption. Caspersson and associates (39) have made extensive studies of the distribution of nucleic acids and proteins in cells by using the ultraviolet microscope. These workers found a rapid synthesis of nucleic acid in developing embryonic tissue, most of which was RNA of the cytoplasm. They also found the protein associated with cytoplasmic nucleic acids of embryonic cells to differ from that of adult cells. The embryonic protein was of the basic histone type, whereas the adult protein was of the more complex tryptophan- and tyrosine-containing type.

The synthesis of cellular protein in general appears to be correlated with the presence of RNA. The latter is produced in the heterochromatic regions of the nucleus and apparently represents the basis of nuclear control over protein synthesis (and growth).

The fact that viruses in general seem to be nucleoproteins is of interest in relation to protein synthesis. The virus nucleoproteins increase in quantity at the expense of tissue components of their hosts. In this case the synthesis of only one protein progresses parallel with RNA synthesis, whereas the synthesis of various types of protein within the cell appears to be linked with RNA synthesis.

Avery, MacLeod, and McCarty (40) isolated the sodium salt of deoxypentose nucleic acid (mol. wt. 500,000) from type III pneumococcus and have found minute amounts of it to cause the transformation of unencapsulated R cells of type II pneumococcus into fully encapsulated S cells of type III. It represents the first instance in which specific hereditary transformation has been achieved *in vitro* by a known chemical agent. Its implications for cancer and genetic research are exceedingly important.

Biologic importance of the nucleotide structure. Several nucleotides other than those serving as components of nucleic acids have been found in tissues, and a number of these perform very important functions. These will be considered in detail in later chapters, but the following statements will serve to indicate their importance.

A pentose nucleotide containing adenine occurs in muscle and is called "muscle adenylic acid." This substance combines with two molecules of phosphoric acid to form a pyrophosphate, adenylic pyrophosphate. Adenylic pyrophosphate may also be looked upon as the nucleoside adenosine combined with three molecules of phosphoric acid. It accordingly is called "ATP" (adenosine triphosphate). ATP is an exceedingly important phosphorylating agent in tissues. Apparently the decomposition of ATP directly yields the energy to muscles, which causes their contraction.

The oxidation of foods in tissues involves the removal of hydrogen which is often passed to so-called hydrogen acceptors before being oxidized and converted to water. These hydrogen acceptors constitute catalytic oxidation-reduction systems. Some of these substances are complex nucleotides. For example, coenzyme I is constituted nicotinic acid amide—ribose—phosphoric acid—phosphoric acid—ribose—adenine.

Coenzyme II is similar to coenzyme I except that it has a phosphate attached to ribose. Both coenzymes I and II are the prosthetic groups of specific conjugated proteins and perform their functions when so combined.

The flavoproteins are also hydrogen acceptors and are composed of riboflavin phosphate united to specific protein. Riboflavin phosphate is a nucleotide type of substance:

$$\underbrace{\text{Isoalloxazine}}_{\substack{\text{base}}} - \underbrace{\text{ribityl}}_{\substack{\text{alcohol from}\\ \text{ribose}}} - \text{phosphoric acid}$$

$$\overbrace{\hspace{4cm}}^{\text{Riboflavin}}$$

Nicotinic acid amide (niacin) and riboflavin are classed as vitamins of the B group. Their conversion into nucleotide type structures enables them to perform at least a part of their vitamin functions.

It has been known for a long time that nucleic acids and their hydrolytic products cause increased white cell counts in the blood of animals (leucocytosis). This effect has been demonstrated for the sodium salt of yeast nucleic acid, the yeast purine nucleotides, guanylic and adenylic acids, and even the purine bases adenine and guanine. The specific effect appears to be a stimulation of the bone marrow to produce increased numbers of polymorphonuclear neutrophils. The product commonly used in medical practice to stimulate leucocytosis is called "pentnucleotide" and consists of the sodium salts of yeast nucleotides. It is administered by intramuscular injection.

The nucleotides are very potent stimulators of leucocytosis when leucocyte formation has been specifically depressed. The normal physiologic stimulus to the leucopoietic tissues (leucocyte forming) may be nuclear breakdown products of disintegrating leucocytes and other cells.

SPECIAL REFERENCES

1. Miescher, F.: Hoppe-Seyler's Medicinisch-Chemische Untersuchungen. A. Hirschwald, Berlin, 1871, p. 441.
2. Levene, P. A., and Bass, L. W.: Nucleic Acids. Chemical Catalog Co., New York, 1931.
3. Jones, W.: Nucleic Acids. Longmans, New York, 1920.
4. Todd, A. R.: Harvey Lectures, Series XLVII, 1951–52.
5. Markham, R., and Smith, J. D., in Neurath, H., and Bailey, K. (eds.): The Proteins, Vol. II, Part A. Academic Press, New York, 1954.
6. Wyatt, G. R., and Cohen, S. S.: Nature, 170, 1072, 1952.
7. Kalckar, H. M.: J. Biol. Chem., 158, 723, 1945; 167, 477, 1947.
8. Cohn, W. E., and Volkin, E.: Nature, 167, 483, 1951.
9. Cohn, W. E., and Volkin, E.: Arch. Biochem. Biophys., 35, 465, 1952.
10. Cohn, W. E.: J. Cellular Comp. Physiol., 38, Suppl. 1, 21, 1951. Volkin, E., and Carter, C. E.: J. Am. Chem. Soc., 73, 1516, 1951.
11. Brown, D. M., and Todd, A. R., in Chargaff, E., and Davidson, J. N. (eds.): The Nucleic Acids, Vol. I, Chap. 12. Academic Press, New York, 1955.
12. Markham, R., and Smith, J. D.: Biochem. J., 52, 552, 1952.
13. Markham, R., and Smith, J. D.: Research, 4, 344, 1951; Nature, 168, 406, 1951.
14. Brown, D. M., and Todd, A. R.: J. Chem. Soc., 2040, 1953.
15. Volkin, E., and Cohn, W. E.: Federation Proc., 11, 303, 1952.
16. Heppel, L. A.; Markham, R.; and Hilmol, R. J.: Nature, 171, 1152, 1953.
17. Volkin, E., and Cohn, W. E.: J. Biol. Chem., 203, 319, 1953.
18. Anderson, A. S.; Barker, G. R.; Gulland, J. M.; and Lock, M. V.: J. Chem. Soc., 369, 1952.
19. Gulland, J. M.: Cold Spring Harbor Symposia Quant. Biol., 12, 95, 1947.
20. Schmidt, G., in Chargaff, E., and Davidson, J. N.: The Nucleic Acids, Vol. I, Chap. 12. Academic Press, New York, 1955.

21. Volkin, E., and Cohn, W. E.: *J. Biol. Chem.*, **205**, 767, 1953.
22. Markham, R., and Smith, J. D.: *Biochem. J.*, **52**, 558, 565, 1952.
23. Gulland, J. M.; Jordan, D. O.; and Taylor, H. F. W.: *J. Chem. Soc.*, 1131, 1947. Jordan, D. O., in Chargaff, E., and Davidson, J. N.: *The Nucleic Acids*, Vol. I, Chap. 13. Academic Press, New York, 1955.
24. Dekker, C. A.; Michelson, A. M.; and Todd, A. R.: *J. Chem. Soc.*, 947, 1953.
25. Brown, D. M., and Todd, A. R., in Chargaff, E., and Davidson, J. N.: *The Nucleic Acids*, Vol. I, Chap. 12. Academic Press, New York, 1955.
26. Sinsheimer, R. L., and Koerner, J. F.: *J. Am. Chem. Soc.*, **74**, 283, 1952.
27. Tamm, C.; Hodes, M. E.; and Chargaff, E.: *J. Biol. Chem.*, **195**, 49, 1952.
28. Watson, J. D., and Crick, F. H. C.: *Nature*, **171**, 737, 1953.
29. Schmidt, G., and Thannhauser, S. J.: *J. Biol. Chem.*, **161**, 83, 1945.
30. Magasanik, B., in Chargaff, E., and Davidson, J. N.: *The Nucleic Acids*, Vol. I, Chap. 11. Academic Press, New York, 1955.
31. Chargaff, E., in Chargaff, E., and Davidson, J. N.: *The Nucleic Acids*, Vol. I, Chap. 10. Academic Press, New York, 1955.
32. Mirsky, A. E., and Ris, H.: *J. Gen. Physiol.*, **34**, 451, 1951. Vendrely, R., and Vendrely, C.: *Experientia*, **4,**, 434, 1948; **5**, 327, 1949. Allfrey, V. G.; Mirsky, A. E.; and Stern, H.: *Advances in Enzymology*, **16**, 411, 1955.
33. Mirsky, A. E., and Ris, H.: *Nature*, **163**, 666, 1949.
34. Allfrey, V. G.; Mirsky, A. E.; and Stern, H.: *Advances in Enzymology*, **16**, 411, 1955.
35. Mirsky, A. E., and Ris, H.: *J. Gen. Physiol.*, **34**, 451, 1951.
36. Sevag, M. G.; Lackman, D. B.; and Smolens, J.: *J. Biol. Chem.*, **124**, 425, 1938.
37. Mayers, V. L., and Spizizen, J.: *J. Biol. Chem.*, **210**, 877, 1954.
38. Knight, C. A.: *J. Biol. Chem.*, **171**, 297, 1947.
39. Caspersson, T., and Theorell, B.: *Chromosoma*, 2, 132, 1941. Caspersson, T.: *ibid.*, 1, 562, 1940. Caspersson, T., and Schultz, J.: *Nature*, **143**, 602, 1939.
40. Avery, O. T.; MacLeod, C. M.; and McCarty, M.: *J. Exptl. Med.*, **47**, 403, 1928.

The chemical composition of the body represents all the physical and chemical basis of protoplasm and of the living processes which occur in it. Much discussion relative to it has occurred in the chapters on lipids, carbohydrates, and proteins.

The earlier work on the composition of tissues had to do primarily with the quantities of the various elements and of lipids, proteins, carbohydrates, minerals, water, etc., present. With the development of better techniques of isolation and analysis, it became possible to demonstrate the presence of a large number of different substances in tissues which are important in their functioning or as the products of their metabolism. Because tissues contain enzymes which may alter cell constituents after death, and particularly after mechanical disintegration, often it is necessary to proceed with great care in order to minimize these changes. In some instances, as in the isolation of glycogen, the tissues are excised quickly and heated in order to stop enzyme action. At times a specific enzyme poison may be added to prevent decomposition of a substance to be isolated; an example is the addition of sodium fluoride to muscle hash to prevent the enzymatic decomposition of hexose diphosphate. Another valuable procedure consists in freezing the tissue with liquid air or carbon dioxide snow, followed by powdering the frozen tissue and drying it at low temperature (lyophile process). In this way the cellular enzymes are inhibited by the low temperature; and after the powdered tissue is dry, its various constituents, including some enzymes, may be preserved for a long time. This lyophilized product may be used for the isolation of tissue constituents by extraction with appropriate solvents and other procedures.

The composition of tissues is dynamic, not static. There is continuous synthesis of the larger protoplasmic constituents from smaller molecules and continuous decomposition of these larger structures into smaller molecules. The composition of any given tissue at any given time represents a balance between processes of synthesis and processes of decomposition, and between processes that bring substances to the tissues as foods and those that remove substances from tissues as excretory products.

Numerous important tissue constituents are present in very small amounts at any given time, though the total amounts formed and decomposed during the course of a day may be considerable. When several substances are formed and decomposed in sequence in a process such as:

$$A \longrightarrow B \longrightarrow C \longrightarrow D, \text{ etc.}$$

the rate of the process is controlled by the slowest reaction. The least reactive substance accumulates in the largest amount, while the most reactive substance is present in least amount. Many of the most active and important molecules of tissues accordingly are present in only minute amounts. Their chemical instability and low concentration often cause detection and isolation to be difficult. Without doubt, numerous such tissue constituents await discovery.

The major proportion of the human body is composed of the six elements oxygen, carbon, hydrogen, nitrogen, calcium, and phosphorus. The remainder, about 1 per cent, is composed of potassium, sulfur, sodium, chlorine, magnesium, iron, and traces of elements such as iodine, fluorine, copper, and zinc. A large proportion of the oxygen and hydrogen of the body is present as water. The elementary composition of the body on a dry weight basis is given in Table 10-1.

The elementary composition of the body indicates nothing about the kind of substances which compose it, or about the nature of the chemical processes by which it is produced and maintained. The molecular composition is all-important in these relations.

Table 10.1.   Approximate Elementary Composition of the Body
Dry weight basis

Element	Per Cent
Carbon	50
Oxygen	20
Hydrogen	10
Nitrogen	8.5
Calcium	4
Phosphorus	2.5
Potassium	1
Sulfur	0.8
Sodium	0.4
Chlorine	0.4
Magnesium	0.1
Iron	0.01
Manganese	0.001
Iodine	0.00005

Reprinted by permission from *A Textbook of Biochemistry*, 2nd ed., by R. J. Williams, published by D. Van Nostrand Co., Inc., 1942.

The human body as a whole is composed of about two-thirds water and one-third solids. Proteins and lipids each constitute roughly 15 per cent of the body weight, carbohydrates about 0.5 per cent, mineral matter about 5 per cent, and other substances something less than 1 per cent.

The organic compounds of tissues include not only those substances which are structural components, such as proteins, cholesterol, phospholipids, and glycolipids, but also a great diversity of substances which are foods for tissues, compounds essential for the metabolic processes of tissues, and waste products of tissues. Among the organic constituents which serve primarily as foods for tissues are substances such as glycogen, glucose, fats, all the common amino acids, and the vitamins. Some of the compounds present in tissues which are involved in metabolic processes directly or indirectly are sugar phosphates, creatine, creatine phosphate, adenylic acid, adenosine triphosphate (adenylic pyrophosphate); other nucleotides, coenzymes, flavoproteins, and cytochromes; various hormones; and many enzymes (proteins). Also, many organic acids are involved as intermediate products in the metabolic breakdown of fatty acids, glucose, and amino acids; these include acetoacetic and β-hydroxybutyric acids; pyruvic and lactic acids; citric, isocitric, α-ketoglutaric, oxaloacetic, malic, fumaric, and succinic acids. Waste products of tissues include substances such as carbon dioxide, urea, creatinine, and uric acid.

The inorganic constituents of tissues are represented by the cations Na^+, K^+, Ca^{++}, Mg^{++}, Fe^{++}, and Fe^{+++}, with traces of other ions, such as Zn^{++} and Cu^{++}, and by the anions Cl^-, HCO_3^- (organic), $H_2PO_4^-$, $HPO_4^=$, $PO_4^\equiv$, and $SO_4^=$. Some of the cations are combined with protein anions. It is interesting to note that in the body Na^+ ions are the chief cations of blood plasma and of extracellular fluids in general, while K^+ ions are the chief cations within cells.

The above lists of substances found in tissues are only partial and include those of more or less known function. Many compounds of unknown significance have been discovered in tissues.

COMPOSITION OF INDIVIDUAL TISSUES

Since the body is composed of many different organs and several different types of tissues with different characteristic functions, the composition of the individual tissues is of far more importance than the composition of the body as a whole in understanding body organization and function. Whereas most of the specialized organs and tissues contain more or less of most of the constituents enumerated above, most of these tissues contain relatively large amounts of secondary specialized materials necessitated by the nature and function of the tissue. These materials may or may not represent increased quantities of normal constituents and may be localized within the cells or as intercellular substance. Examples are the large amount of keratin in epidermal tissue; of collagen in cartilage; of mineral matter in bones and teeth; of phospholipids, cholesterol, and glycolipids in brain and nerve tissue; of glycogen in liver; of hemoglobin in red blood cells; of fat in adipose tissue; of hormones in endocrine glands; and of the contractile protein myosin in muscle.

The average distribution of organs and tissues in the human body is given in Table 10.2.

Table 10.2.   Weight of Body Tissues and Organs
70-kg man

Tissue or Organ	Weight in kg	Per Cent of Body Weight
Muscle	29.10	41.5
Fatty tissue	12.6	18
Skeleton	11.1	15.8
Blood	5.6	8.0
Skin	4.8	6.9
Brain	1.7	2.4
Liver	1.6	2.3
Stomach and intestines	1.27	1.8
Lungs	1.0	1.4
Heart	0.33	0.47
Kidneys	0.27	0.38
Spleen	0.13	0.18
Cerebrospinal fluid	0.13	0.18
Pancreas	0.10	0.14
Salivary glands	0.05	0.07
Testicles	0.03	0.04
Thyroid	0.03	0.04
Thymus	0.016	0.02
Adrenals	0.007	0.01
Parathyroids	0.0004	0.0006
Pituitary	0.0003	0.0001

Magnus-Levy, *Biochem. Z.*, 24, 363–380, 1910.

The gross composition of tissues is generally designated by the contents of water, solids, proteins, lipids, carbohydrates, and extractives. The extractives include the water-soluble substances removed from tissues by treatment with hot water. They are composed of inorganic and a large variety of organic substances.

The composition of a definite type of tissue, such as mammalian striated muscle, shows some species variations but on the whole is characteristic. A young rapidly growing tissue generally contains more water and less total lipids and mineral matter than a more adult tissue. Many other variations in composition are also characteristic of tissue age.

The state of nutrition of an animal may markedly influence the composition of tissues. The glycogen content of the liver of a poorly nourished animal may amount to 1 per cent or less, whereas the liver glycogen of this same animal on a high carbohydrate diet may be as high as 15 per cent. The glycogen content of the muscles and other tissues shows similar but less spectacular variations. The very great variation in the fat content of tissues with the nutritive state is well known. The proteins of the blood may become severely reduced as the result of inadequate dietary proteins. The mineral and water contents of tissues also vary with the intake of these materials.

The composition of tissues may be drastically altered by pathologic conditions. Liver and muscle glycogen are very low in uncontrolled severe diabetes mellitus, whereas liver glycogen is very high in glycogenosis or von Gierke's disease. Very large amounts of fat may be deposited in the liver in pathologic conditions such as acute yellow atrophy. In the xanthomatoses or lipoidoses which appear to be congenital diseases of childhood there is accumulation of excess lipid in large cells of the reticuloendothelial system. The type of lipid in the cells varies. It is glycolipid (kerasin) in Gaucher's disease, phospholipid in Nieman-Pick's disease, and cholesterol and its esters in Schüller-Christian syndrome. In cases of progressive muscle dystrophy the muscles may show a marked decrease in creatine, adenosine triphosphate, and other extractives. Abnormal deposition of calcium salts may occur in tissues in cases of pathologic calcification, and the mineral content of bone may be depleted in conditions of hyperparathyroidism. Pathologic variations in the composition of blood are numerous and form the basis of much of our modern clinical diagnosis.

Tables 10.3 and 10.4 give the gross composition of the adult human body.

While the gross composition of tissues may bring out a few points of interest, it is the detailed molecular composition which affords insight into

Table 10.3.   Chemical Composition of Adult Human Body
Values are given in per cent

	Total Body	Water	Ether Extract	Crude Protein (N×6.25)	Ash	Ca	P
Skin	6.33	57.71	14.23	27.33	0.62	0.0034	0.070
Skeleton	17.58	28.17	25.04	19.71	26.62	10.68	4.61
Teeth	0.08	5.00*		23.00*	67.95	25.05	12.09
Striated muscle	39.76	70.09	6.60	21.94	1.01	0.0066	0.156
Brain, spinal cord, nerve trunks	2.99	75.09	12.35	11.50	1.37	0.0147	0.299
Liver	2.34	71.58	3.11	22.24	1.35	0.0133	0.303
Heart	0.52	62.95	16.58	17.48	0.61	0.0058	0.144
Lungs†	3.30	77.28	1.32	19.20	1.03	0.0090	0.132
Spleen*	0.11	78.69	1.19	17.81	1.13	0.0089	0.217
Kidneys	0.51	70.58	7.18	19.28	0.87	0.0057	0.188
Pancreas*	0.14	73.08	13.08	12.69	0.93	0.0143	0.155
Alimentary tract	1.86	77.40	9.17	12.77	0.53	0.0140	0.098
Adipose tissue	11.37	23.02	71.57	5.85	0.20	0.0078	0.031
Remaining tissue, solid	11.43	59.29	22.47	17.28	0.85	0.0257	0.088
Remaining tissue, liquid	0.59	81.45	2.55	13.58	0.82	0.0044	0.104
Bile, content of bladder and alimentary tract	0.99						
Hair and nails	0.10						
Average (weighted) all tissues	98.91	55.74	19.66	18.82	5.49	1.928	0.936
Total composition whole body weighing 53.80 kilos	100.00	55.13	19.44	18.62	5.43	1.907	0.925
Composition fat-free body		69.38		23.43	6.83	2.400	1.164

* Chemical composition assumed.
† Congested with blood.
From Forbes, R. M.; Cooper, A. R.; and Mitchell, H. H.: *J. Biol. Chem.*, **203**, 361, 1953.

Table 10.4. Mineral Composition of Human Tissues
Values represent per cent of fresh tissue unless otherwise stated, and generally
are the average for the analyses on two adult male bodies

Tissue	Ca	P	Mg	B p.p.m.*	Co p.p.m.*	Be p.p.m.*	Sr p.p.m.*
Skin	0.014	0.075	0.0075	0.39	0.019	0	
Skeleton	10.83	5.0	0.18	0.74	0.028	0	55
Teeth	25.46	13.24	0.62				
Striated muscle	0.014	0.13	0.019	0.28	0.007	0	0
Nerve tissue	0.028	0.26	0.01	0.05	0.015		
Liver	0.01	0.17	0.0065	0.09	0.095	0.006	0
Heart	0.017	0.11	0.014	0.39	0.034		
Lungs	0.025	0.17	0.0058	0.15	0.038	0.011	0
Spleen	0.010	0.169	0.0124	0.08			
Kidney	0.039	0.16	0.02	0.031	0.034	0	
Alimentary tract	0.021	0.10	0.017	0.024	0.021	0	0
Adipose tissue	0.006	0.011	0.0061	0.10	0.011		
Remaining tissue (solid)	0.12	0.15	0.012	0.19	0.033		
Remaining tissue (liquid)	0.018	0.11	0.0046		0.015		
Whole body	1.76	0.94	0.04				
Fat free whole body	2.11	1.12	0.048				
Bone ash	38.41	17.75	0.636				

* Parts per million
Data from Forbes, R. M.; Mitchell, H. H.; and Cooper, A. R.: *J. Biol. Chem.*, **223**, 972, 1956.

the finer structures and physiologic functions of tissues. This has not been completely determined for any tissue. Since blood is the easiest of the tissues to obtain and analyze, our knowledge of its composition is more nearly complete than that of any other tissue. The composition of blood will be considered in a separate chapter. Much has been learned of the composition of muscle which is of importance in understanding muscle contraction. The composition of brain and nerve tissue and its relation to function are much less well understood. While the liver and kidneys and other glandular organs are of primary importance, our knowledge of their compositions is very incomplete.

In recent years much progress has been made in the partition of cells into their component structures, such as nuclei, mitochondria, microsomes, lysosomes, and cytoplasm, based upon cellular disintegration and differential centrifugation, generally in sucrose media (1). It has been possible to localize many enzymes in these cellular structures. A table showing the distribution of enzymes in the nuclei, mitochondria, microsomes and soluble fractions of rat liver cells is given by Dixon and Webb (2). Combination of information on the morphology of cells and cellular structures obtained by phase contrast and electron microscopy and of information on the biochemical properties of cellular structures indicates a very high degree of both morphological and biochemical organization within the cell. Results indicate that the localization of enzymes and enzyme systems are such as to permit essentially compartmented biochemical reactions to proceed within cells relatively uninfluenced by other systems present, which would not be possible in homogenous mixtures of the cellular enzymes and reactants. For example, the enzymes of the electron transport system (oxidative chain) are highly organized relative to each other in the mitochondria and represent the site of oxidative phosphorylation and formation of adenosine triphosphate (ATP). The enzyme systems concerned with protein synthesis are localized in the microsomes, and certain hydrolytic enzymes in the lysosomes (3). The enzymes of glycolysis are almost entirely present in the soluble cytoplasm.

While the major localization of groups of enzymes may be in certain cellular structures, there is considerable overlapping so that the same enzyme is frequently found, at least to some extent, in different locations.

Table 10.5 gives the gross composition of the rat liver cell and of its struc-

Table 10.5.   Compositions of Whole Rat Liver Cells and
Their Structural Components
Values represent grams per 100 g except as indicated

Tissue	Substance	Value
Whole cell	Water	71.6
	Total protein, fresh tissue	1.29
	Total lipid, dry tissue	15.2
	Fat, dry tissue	4.1
	Cholesterol, dry tissue	2.4
	Phospholipid, dry tissue	8.3
	DNA, fresh tissue	0.192
	RNA, fresh tissue	0.588
Nuclei	Nucleoprotein, fresh tissue	2.00
	Total lipid, dry tissue	10.5–18.13
	DNA, fresh tissue	0.184
	RNA, fresh tissue	0.064
Mitochondria	Total protein, fresh tissue	3.5–4.0
	Total lipid, dry tissue	25–30
	Phospholipid, dry tissue	16.5–19.8
	DNA, % of total cell nucleic acid	11.7
	RNA, % of total cell nucleic acid	19–46
Microsomes	Total lipid, dry tissue	40
	Total protein, fresh tissue	1.9–2.1
	RNA, % of total cell nucleic acid	50

Data from Spector, W. S. (ed.): *Handbook of Biological Data.* Saunders, Philadelphia, 1956.

tural components. The relatively large amount of lipid present in mitochondria and microsomes is noteworthy, especially the large amount of phospholipid in mitochondria.

The more detailed composition of individual tissues, particularly in relation to function, is interspersed throughout the following chapters and is given special attention in Chapter 27.

SPECIAL REFERENCES

1. Schneider, W. C., and Hogeboom, G. H.: *Ann. Rev. Biochem.*, **25,**, 201, 1956. Ernster, L., and Lindberg, O.: *Ann. Rev. Physiol.*, **20**, 13, 1958.
2. Dixon, M., and Webb, E. C.: *Enzymes.* Academic Press, New York, 1958, p. 630.
3. De Duve, C.: "Lysosomes, A New Group of Cytoplasmic Particles." In Hayashi, T. (ed.): *Subcellular Particles.* Ronald Press, New York, 1959, p. 128.

11

Enzymes

An understanding of other branches of biochemistry depends in no small degree on a thorough grounding in the nature, properties, and actions of the substances primarily responsible for the chemical changes occurring in plants and animals. Thus, digestion and absorption of food are processes necessitating the actions of an array of different enzymes. The myriad of reactions involved in the intermediary metabolism of protein, fat, and carbohydrate are enzymatically controlled. The processes concerned with intracellular oxidation and reduction, carbon dioxide and oxygen transport, calcification, detoxication, muscle contraction, blood clotting, excretion and secretion—all these and many more are mediated by enzymes.

Definition. Definitions in great variety have been offered for enzymes. Probably none of them has met with the approval of a majority of workers in the field. Haldane defines an enzyme as a soluble, colloidal, organic catalyst which is produced by a living organism. This definition excludes such low molecular weight catalysts as glutathione, adenylic acid, and ascorbic acid. More important than a definition is an understanding of the physical and chemical properties, actions, limitations, etc., of enzymes.

Enzymes as catalysts. Whether or not enzymes act in accordance with the strict concept of catalysis is of minor importance; the fact that they act catalytically is important. In their presence certain chemical reactions proceed faster than in their absence. A solution of lactose does not hydrolyze appreciably at body temperature, but on the addition of even a minute quantity of a preparation of the enzyme lactase, the monosaccharides glucose and galactose are rapidly formed. The addition of acid to supply H^+

will accomplish the same end, although the reaction is much slower at body temperature than when the enzyme is employed.

Proteins are hydrolyzed by acid (H^+ as catalyst) only after protracted boiling, whereas in the body this hydrolysis is accomplished at a relatively low temperature and at a faster rate through the action of various enzymes acting catalytically.

Even though in some cases a unit weight of enzyme is capable of transforming a million or more times its weight of substrate (any substance acted upon by an enzyme), there is "exhaustion" or "wearing out" of the enzyme.

Stern (1) feels that the spontaneous breakdown of enzymes induces the decomposition of a great many substrate molecules, and that the inactivation of enzymes is not intrinsically coupled with the mechanism of their action but may result from incidental and irreversible side reactions.

Chemical nature of enzymes. Enzymes are proteins. There has been considerable controversy regarding the protein nature of enzymes. Willstätter and others championed the "carrier theory." They believed that the enzyme was "carried" by some high molecular weight colloid, not necessarily protein in nature. They further felt that the carrier was exchangeable. Enzymatic activity was demonstrated in solutions which did not respond to typical protein tests, such as the biuret and xanthoproteic reactions. It is now known that the concentration of protein present as enzyme was too low in these instances to give positive tests. The other view, that enzymes are proteins or contain proteins, is now generally accepted. The following brings together a few of the chemical and physical similarities of proteins and enzymes.

With the possible exception of some fat-splitting enzymes from plant seeds, the enzymes are soluble to some extent in water, glycerol, and dilute alcohol. They are precipitated from solution by protein-precipitating agents, such as concentrated alcohol, ammonium sulfate, and trichloracetic acid. They are nondialyzable because of their colloidal nature, although certain enzymes contain small dissociable and dialyzable molecules, known as "prosthetic groups" (see below).

Chemical analyses of purified crystalline enzymes give values typical for proteins. Thus, Sumner reported the analysis of his crystalline urease in the following percentages: C, 51.6; H, 7.1; N, 16; and S, 1.2. Isoelectric points of many enzymes are known. Enzymes appear to follow the general principle of protein chemistry in that they are least soluble at this pH. Northrop (2) determined the isoelectric point of pepsin to be at pH 2.7 and pointed out that the minimum solubility is also at this acidity. Further, at this pH precipitation is brought about by the minimum quantity of alcohol.

At a pH of 3 pepsin hydrolyzes and inactivates trypsin at comparable rates; at pH 8 trypsin hydrolyzes and inactivates pepsin. On the other hand, pepsin and papain can be partially degraded by aminopeptidase enzyme without loss of activity, indicating the nonessential nature of some amino acids in the peptide chains for enzyme action.

Enzymes like proteins are more stable in concentrated solutions. They are subject to denaturation by changes in pH or by increasing the temperature of their solutions. These denaturations with inactivation are often reversible processes.

This brief discussion indicates the parallel behavior and properties of proteins and enzymes. Much of our important earlier knowledge of the chemical and physical properties of enzymes together with methods of purification and crystallization is due to Northrop and his coworkers (2). Dixon and Webb have more recently brought together a wealth of information on enzymes in their excellent monograph (3).

The most nearly complete analysis of the amino acid content of an enzyme is found in the work of Velick and Ronzoni (4). Table 11.1 lists the amino acid composition of highly purified aldolase and D-glyceraldehyde phosphate dehydrogenase, along with the estimated number of each amino acid residue per molecular weight of enzyme. Special attention should be given to the remarkable correlation between the amino acid nitrogen calculated from the amounts of amino acids found and the total nitrogen determined by the Kjeldahl method. Also, it should be noted that the majority of calculated residues approach whole numbers. The glutamic acid level of the dehydrogenase is among the lowest reported for a protein and the valine level is one of the highest.

Table 11.1.   Amino Acid Composition of Aldolase and D-glyceraldehyde Phosphate Dehydrogenase

| Amino Acid | Aldolase | | Dehydrogenase | |
	Grams per 100 g protein	No. of residues per 140,000 g	Grams per 100 g protein	No. of residues per 99,100 g
Glycine	5.61	104.7	6.03	79.6
Alanine	8.56	134.6	6.72	74.7
Valine	7.40	88.5	12.0	104.9
Leucine	11.5	122.8	6.78	51.2
Isoleucine	7.87	84.0	9.1	68.7
Half cystine	1.12	13.1	1.09	9.0
Methionine	1.17	11.0	2.70	18.0
Serine	6.57	87.6	6.7	63.2
Threonine	7.1	76.4	6.9	57.4
Arginine	6.33	50.9	5.23	29.8
Histidine	4.21	38.0	5.01	32.0
Lysine	9.54	91.4	9.42	63.9
Proline	5.71	69.4	3.67	31.6
Phenylalanine	3.06	26.0	5.55	33.3
Tyrosine	5.31	41.1	4.57	25.0
Tryptophan	2.31	15.9	2.05	9.9
Aspartic acid	9.7	102.1	12.4	93.2
Glutamic acid	11.4	108.8	6.8	45.8
Amide nitrogen %	0.91	91.0	0.95	67.2
Diphosphopyridine nucleotide nitrogen %			0.20	2.0
Total nitrogen as amino acids, %	16.9		16.9	
Total nitrogen by Kjeldahl, %	16.8		16.4	

From Velick, S., and Ronzoni, E.: *J. Biol. Chem.*, **173**, 627, 1948.

Occasionally reports appear which concern an active enzyme preparation apparently free of protein. Thus, Albers, Schneider, and Pohl (5) reported a preparation having pepsin activity on casein. The material, referred to as "pepsidin," passes through collodion membranes, is not precipitated from solution by sulfosalicyclic acid, is heat and acid stable and soluble in 70 per cent alcohol. The authors suggest that the substance is a polypeptide capable of digesting casein without the protein carrier with which it may normally be combined. Such findings are difficult to reconcile at present.

The enzymes so far elucidated are divided chemically into two groups: (a) the simple protein enzymes, containing, as the name implies, only a simple protein; and (b) the complex protein enzymes. Among the latter a prosthetic group is associated with a specific protein. As an example, the enzyme carboxylase or decarboxylase is composed of the prosthetic group thiamine pyrophosphate intimately associated with a specific protein. Dissociation of these two entities results in inactivation. Neither component alone constitutes an enzyme. The small dialyzable molecule thiamine pyrophosphate is known as "cocarboxylase"; it is an example of a coenzyme and is also the prosthetic group of the enzyme.

The term "apoenzyme" refers to the protein part of a conjugated enzyme. The apoenzyme in combination with its prosthetic group (coenzyme) constitutes a complete enzyme, or holoenzyme.

Coenzymes, prosthetic groups of enzymes. The concept of prosthetic groups, cofactors, coenzymes, and carrier substrates is a useful one. We visualize some enzymes operating only when the proper protein (apoenzyme) and coenzyme are associated to form the active enzyme. Much has been written regarding ways and means of differentiating between prosthetic group, coenzyme, and substrate, but a practical distinction has not evolved to cover all cases. There is little or no problem in such a situation as that where thiamine pyrophosphate + protein forms the enzyme decarboxylase. Here it is clear that an α-keto acid such as pyruvic is the substrate. On the other hand, S-adenosyl methionine, the active form of methionine which participates in a variety of methylation reactions, can be considered the coenzyme in these transmethylation systems. Looked at another way, one could say that active methionine in yielding a methyl group to nicotinic acid amide is acting as one of the substrates to the enzyme mediating the reaction.

Attempts to differentiate coenzyme and substrate on the basis of the tightness of the bond between these molecules and the protein apoenzyme—i.e., dissociation constants—has not helped clarify the situation.

One logical approach to the matter is to consider coenzymes and prosthetic groups as synonymous and to understand that some coenzymes may also act as substrate molecules in a rather strict sense of the term. This may someday prove to be far from ideal, but for the present it allows use of the valuable concept of coenzymes and does not add to the complexity of an already complex situation.

The following compounds constitute many of the known coenzymes or prosthetic groups:

1. Cocarboxylase, or thiamine pyrophosphate, the coenzyme of carboxylase or decarboxylase, was first isolated from yeast. It occurs in animal tissues also. Tauber presented a method for its synthesis from thiamine, sodium pyrophosphate, and dehydrated phosphoric acid. It has the following formula:

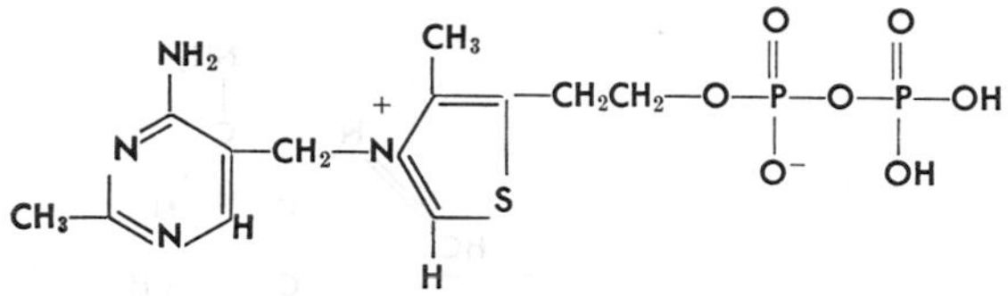

Thiamine Pyrophosphate
Cocarboxylase

The manner in which decarboxylase removes CO_2 from pyruvic acid and other α-keto acids is not completely understood. A proposed mechanism is presented in the discussion of thiamine in Chapter 18.

2. Lipoic acid, also known as "thioctic acid," acts as a coenzyme by itself and possibly in combination with thiamin. This conjugate is known as "lipothiamide." It is not entirely clear at this time whether the conjugate actually is a coenzyme, although it exists in plant and animal tissues. It has been synthesized both chemically and biosynthetically (6). The coenzyme is involved in α-keto acid metabolism as a dehydrogenase and as a decarboxylase. Soper and others (7) proved the structure of lipoic acid to be 6,8-thioctic acid, as indicated:

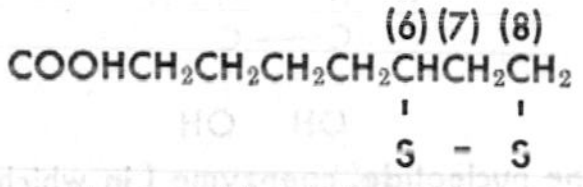

$$\overset{(6)\,(7)\,(8)}{COOHCH_2CH_2CH_2CH_2CHCH_2CH_2}$$
$$S - S$$

Lipoic acid, oxidized form

A discussion on the coenzyme activity can be found in Chapter 18 in the section on thiamin.

Lipothiamide has the following structure:

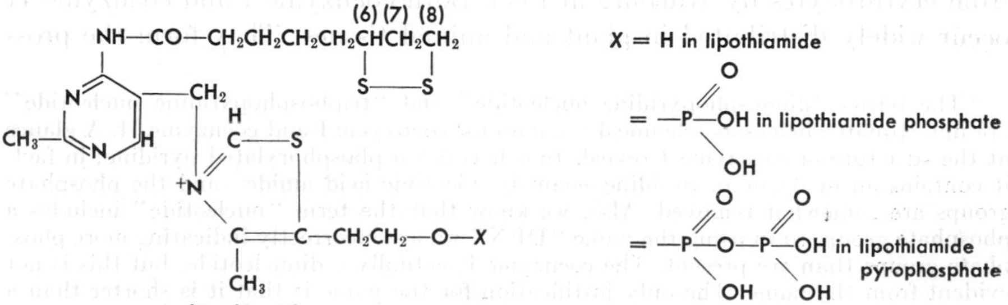

Lipothiamide

X = H in lipothiamide

$= -\overset{O}{\underset{\displaystyle OH}{P}}-OH$ in lipothiamide phosphate

$= -\overset{O}{\underset{\displaystyle OH}{P}}-O-\overset{O}{\underset{\displaystyle OH}{P}}-OH$ in lipothiamide pyrophosphate

Good evidence for the existence of triphosphothiamine in rat liver has been obtained (8), but at present it is not known whether this molecule has coenzyme or other physiologic activity.

3. **Coenzyme I**, or cozymase, the prosthetic group of a number of enzymes, was first noted in yeast juice. It has also the more descriptive name "diphosphopyridine nucleotide"* (DPN), and the following structure is assigned to it:

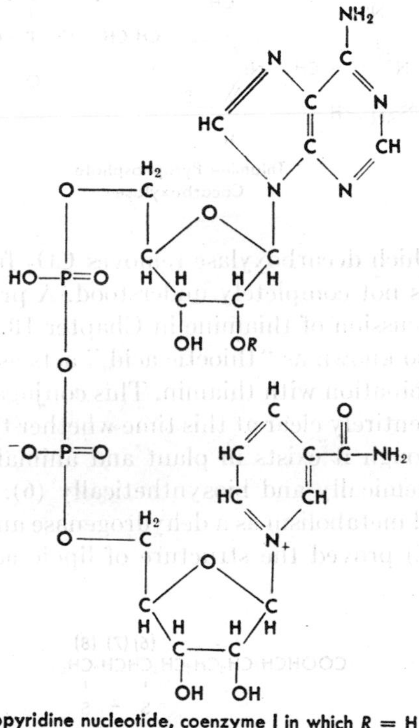

Diphosphopyridine nucleotide, coenzyme I in which R = H
Triphosphopyridine nucleotide, coenzyme II in which R = PO(OH)$_2$

4. **Coenzyme II**, or triphosphopyridine nucleotide, contains, as the name implies, one more phosphate residue than coenzyme I. The third phosphate group is at carbon atom 2 of the ribose attached to adenine. It was isolated from erythrocytes by Warburg in 1935. Both coenzyme I and coenzyme II occur widely distributed in plant and animal tissues. They form the pros-

---

* The terms "diphosphopyridine nucleotide" and "triphosphopyridine nucleotide" are unfortunate choices as (chemical?) names for coenzyme I and coenzyme II. A glance at the structure of coenzyme I reveals that it is not a phosphorylated pyridine; in fact, it contains an analogue of pyridine—namely, nicotinic acid amide—and the phosphate groups are somewhat removed. Also, we know that the term "nucleotide" includes a phosphate group, so in using the name "DPN" we are incorrectly indicating more phosphate groups than are present. The coenzyme is actually a dinucleotide, but this is not evident from the name. The only justification for the name is that it is shorter than a name that gives an accurate chemical description of the compound. The names are so entrenched in scientific writing that it seems most improbable that they will be replaced.

thetic groups of a large number of enzymes, primarily dehydrogenases. The pyridine part of the molecule is easily oxidized and reduced; i.e., it can pick up two hydrogen atoms and transfer them to another hydrogen acceptor.

Some confusion has resulted from applying the terms "coenzyme I" and "coenzyme II" to these entities when the general term "coenzyme" refers to a large number of prosthetic groups. Both coenzymes I and II are prosthetic groups and, of course, coenzymes to which these specific designations have been assigned. Likewise, the terms "cocarboxylase," referring to thiamine pyrophosphate, and "codecarboxylase," referring to pyridoxal phosphate, must not be confused.

5. Riboflavin phosphate was first isolated from bottom yeast. Its association with a specific protein to form Warburg's yellow enzyme was known for a long time before it was found that other specific proteins (apoenzymes) can associate with it to form other enzymes, such as L-amino acid oxidase and cytochrome C reductase. The coenzyme is frequently referred to as "flavin mononucleotide" (FMN). Synthesis was accomplished in 1935 by two groups of German workers (9,10) establishing the constitution of FMN as given. The chemical name is 6,7-dimethyl-9-D-1'-ribityl isoalloxazine-5'-phosphate. Note that the pentose derivative here is a ribitol residue, the sugar alcohol of ribose, and thus contains no oxygen bridge.

Oxidation-reduction in the riboflavin containing coenzymes is accomplished by addition of two hydrogen atoms, one at position 1 and the other at 10, and their subsequent loss to the next link in the oxidation-reduction chain:

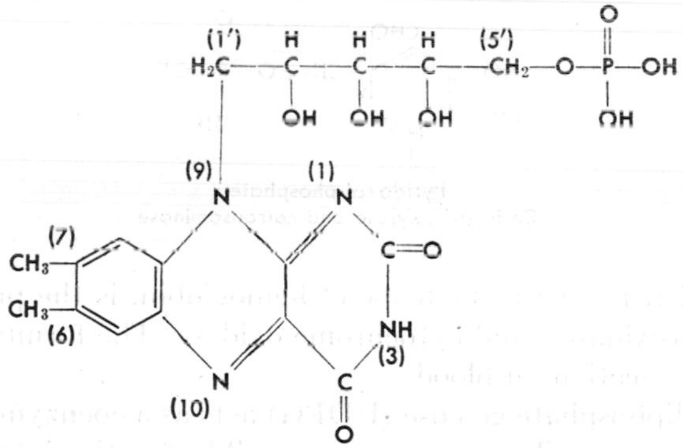

Riboflavin phosphate

6. Alloxazine adenine dinucleotide was synthesized by Christie and co-workers in 1954 (11), confirming the structure proposed some years before. It is composed of riboflavin phosphate together with a molecule of adenine ribose phosphate (adenylic acid) and is thus a dinucleotide structure generally referred to as "flavin adenine dinucleotide" (FAD). It forms the prosthetic group of a variety of the so-called flavoprotein enzymes, such as D-amino acid oxidase, xanthine oxidase, and others:

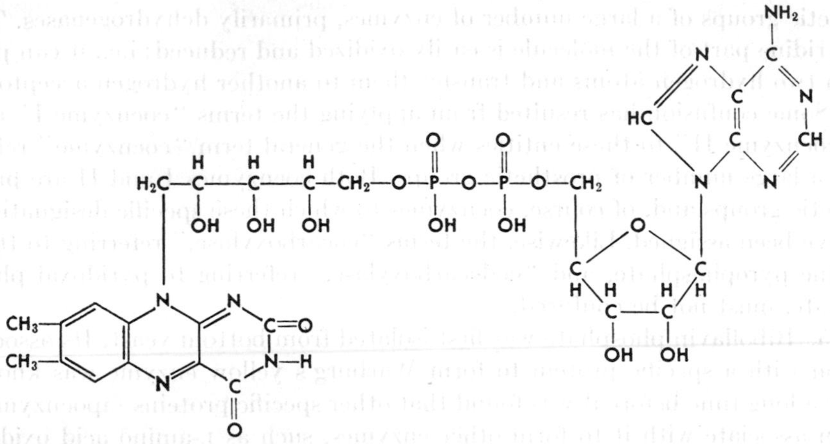

Flavin adenine dinucleotide

7. Pyridoxal phosphate has recently been shown to be involved in the coenzyme of both amino acid decarboxylating enzymes and certain transaminating enzymes. The vitamin pyridoxine is first oxidized to the aldehyde and then phosphorylated. The terms "codecarboxylase" and "cotransaminase" are employed, depending on which type of enzyme the prosthetic group is associated with. It is established now that the compound is the phosphoric acid ester of the hydroxy methyl group on carbon 5 of pyridoxal (12,13):

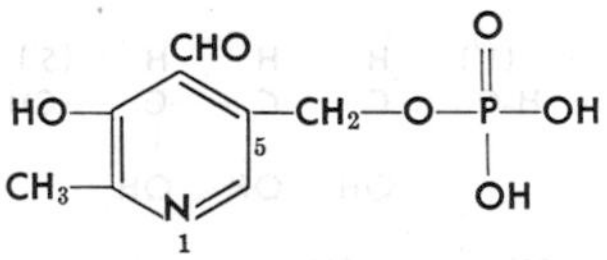

Pyridoxal phosphate
Codecarboxylase and cotransaminase

8. Heme, identical with the heme of hemoglobin, is the prosthetic group of catalase, peroxidases, and cytochrome oxidase. The formula of heme can be found in the section on blood.

9. Uridine diphosphate glucose (UDPG) acts as a coenzyme and as a substrate to an enzyme. The enzyme responsible for the interconversion of glucose and galactose was originally called "galactowaldenase," since the change in position of the hydroxyl about carbon atom 4 of the sugar was thought to be a Walden inversion. Since it now appears that the change in position of the hydroxyl group is not a Walden inversion, but probably involves an oxidation-reduction mechanism, Kalckar (14) proposed the more appropriate name "uridine diphosphogalactose-4-epimerase" for this enzyme. Galactose and glucose are epimers; they differ in the configuration about one carbon only. He has established that this reaction requires DPN as coenzyme.

UDPG has been isolated from animal tissues and from yeast by Caputto and coworkers (15). Uridine is a uracyl-ribose nucleoside. The following structure represents the coenzyme:

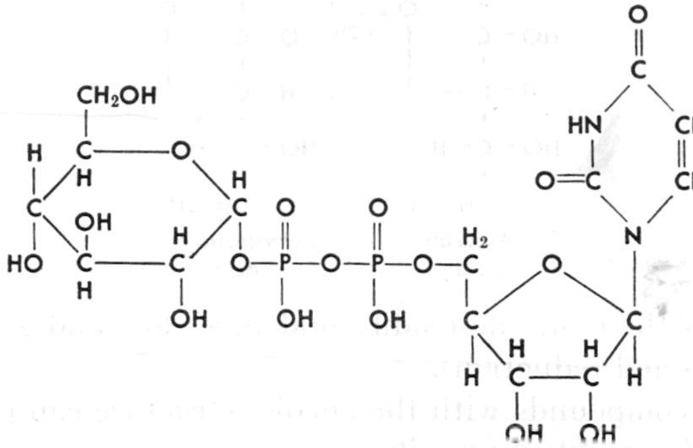

Uridine diphosphate glucose (UDPG)

Note α-glucoside link to carbon 1 of glucose and β-link to carbon 1 of ribose.

The mechanism of action of UDPG has been studied by Leloir (16) and by Kalckar (14). Glucose-1-PO_4 or galactose-1-PO_4 reacts with uridine triphosphate (UTP) to form UDPG or UDPGal plus pyrophosphate:

$$\text{Glucose-1-}PO_4 + \text{UTP} \longrightarrow \text{UDPG} + \text{PP}$$
$$\text{Galactose-1-}PO_4 + \text{UTP} \longrightarrow \text{UDPGal} + \text{PP}$$

The conversion of glucose to galactose can take place reversibly by inversion of the 4 carbon hydroxyl under the influence of uridine diphosphogalactose 4-epimerase in the presence of DPN and UDPG or UDPGal. The same net effect results from the action of another enzyme, uridyl transferase, which "trades" glucose-1-PO_4 of UDPG for galactose-1-PO_4:

$$\text{UDPG} + \text{gal-1-}PO_4 \rightleftharpoons \text{UDPGal} + \text{gluc-1-}PO_4$$

In the latter instance UDPG or UDPGal would be acting as coenzyme.

UDPG can be enzymatically oxidized to uridine diphosphate glucuronic acid (UDPGA) by UDPG dehydrogenase. This molecule acts in various glucuronic acid transfer systems. The enzyme is found in liver and apparently exclusively in the microsome fraction. Bilirubin of blood serum is converted to a glucuronide ester (17). Alcoholic (corticosteroids) and phenolic glucuronides are formed by this transfer mechanism (18). Various amines accept glucuronic acid from UDPGA; for example, aniline-N-glucosiduronic acid was isolated from rabbit urine following the administration of aniline (19).

A review on various aspects of UDPG metabolism is available (20).

10. Ascorbic acid has been proposed as a coenzyme for the system responsible for the conversion of parahydroxy phenylpyruvic acid to 2,5 dihydroxyphenylpyruvic acid (21) in the intermediary metabolism of tyrosine (see tyrosine metabolism). The enzyme (ascorbic acid plus protein) apparently operates as a dehydrogenase involving the enediol structure of the vitamin:

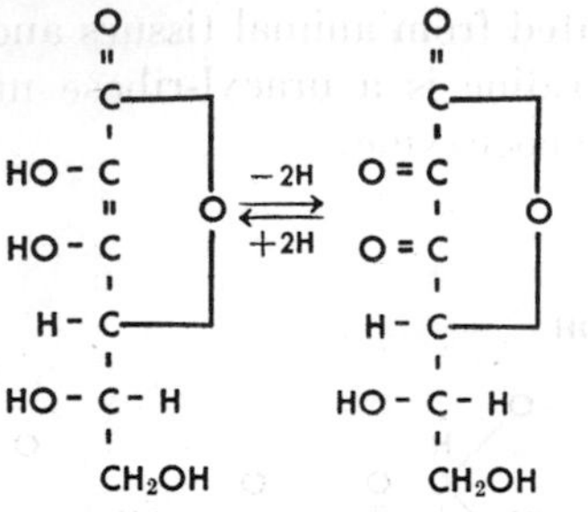

L-Ascorbic acid ⇌ L-Dehydroascorbic acid

This structure of the molecule readily undergoes loss and gain of hydrogen atoms (oxidation and reduction).

Certain other compounds with the enediol structure can replace ascorbic acid under certain conditions *in vitro*.

11. In 1945 Lipmann (22) announced the presence of a coenzyme required in certain acetylation reactions. It was named "coenzyme A" and was shown to contain the vitamin pantothenic acid (23).

Coenzyme A (CoA) has now been characterized as a complex nucleotide. The composition of the molecule in words is adenine-phosphorylated ribose (C-3)-phosphate-phosphate-pantothenic acid-β-mercaptoethylamine. The structure is given below:

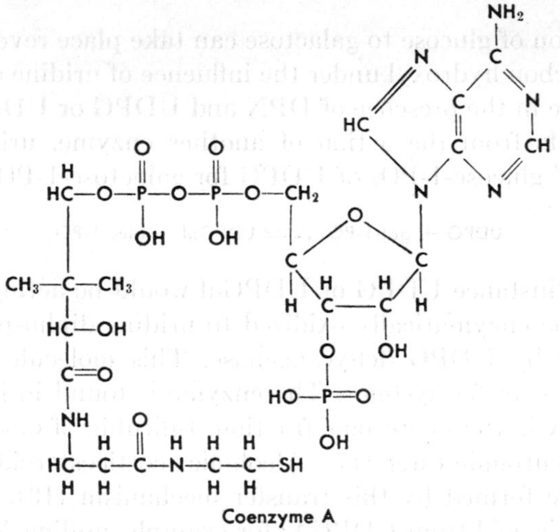

Coenzyme A

The biosynthesis of coenzyme A by extracts of certain microorganisms, rat liver, or rat kidney has been reported (24). Three enzymes were found to be involved, and the following scheme was suggested as the major pathway for CoA biosynthesis: Pantothenic acid ⟶ 4'-phosphopantothenic acid ⟶ 4'-phosphopantothenylcysteine ⟶ 4'-phosphopantetheine ⟶ coenzyme A.

For brevity the coenzyme is often written CoA-SH, which indicates the physiologically active part of the molecule, the sulfhydryl group. This group is readily acetylated to form the high-energy compound acetyl coenzyme,

A (CoAS-COCH$_3$), isolated by Lynen and coworkers (25). The acetylated coenzyme is the donor of acetyl groups in the normal formation of compounds such as citrate, acetylcholine, and acetoacetate.

For years the term "active acetate" has been employed to designate a molecule known to be intimately involved in a number of metabolic processes. Acetylated CoA is this molecule. The various biochemical reactions involving CoA are discussed in detail in the section on intermediary metabolism.

12. Folic acid coenzymes are involved in the metabolism of one carbon units. Active coenzymes include the N^{10}–formyltetrahydrofolic acid and the N^5–formyl derivative. They represent "active" C_1 compounds and function in the interconversion of glycine and serine and in the synthesis of methionine from homocysteine. Carbon atoms 2 and 8 of the purine ring involve one carbon transfer and thus folic acid coenzymes. Histidine synthesis and catabolism also utilize folic acid coenzymes, as does the oxidation of phenylalanine to tyrosine. The appropriate structures and a discussion of these reactions can be found in the section on folic acid in Chapter 18. A discussion of one carbon metabolism is also given in Chapter 25.

13. Glutathione is the tripeptide γ-glutamylcysteinylglycine with a wide distribution in plant and animal tissues. It has been implicated as a coenzyme in several different reactions. Edwards and Knox (26) showed that a liver enzyme required glutathione in the cis-trans isomerization of maleoylacetoacetate to fumarylacetoacetate. Glutathione also is involved in the glyoxylase system in which methyl glyoxal is converted into lactic acid (27). It likewise acts as a coenzyme for formaldehyde dehydrogenase in the conversion of formaldehyde to formate (28). The reduced form of glutathione (GSH) is active in these reactions:

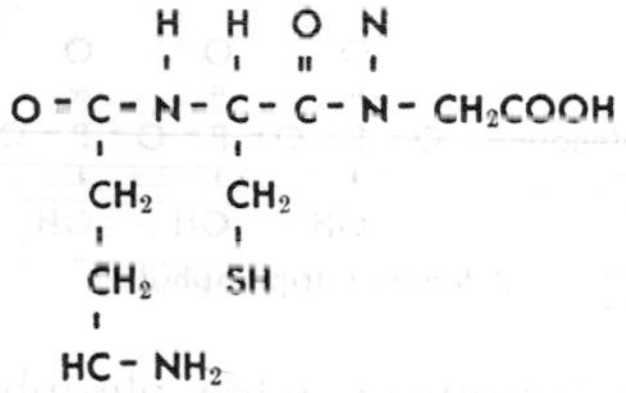

Glutathione, reduced form, γ-glutamylcysteinylglycine

14. Hypoxanthine has been identified as a coenzyme in the oxidation of sulfite to sulfate by an enzyme system (sulfite oxidase) from dog liver (29):

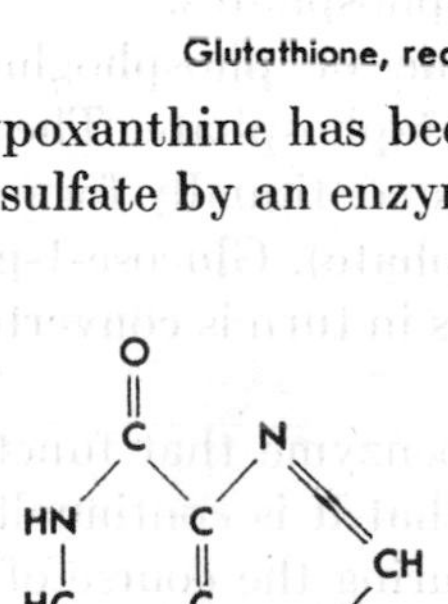

Hypoxanthine

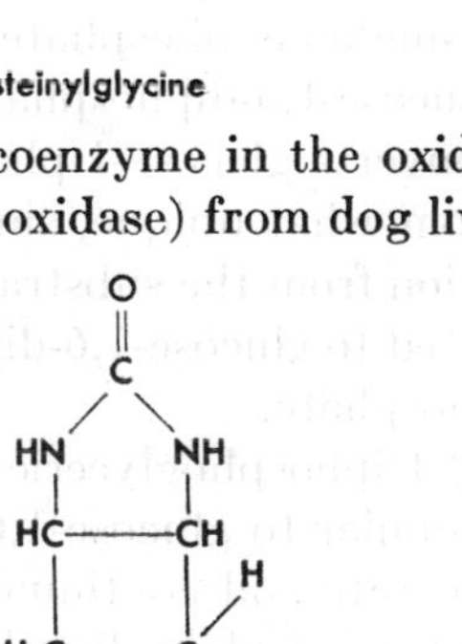

Biotin

15. Some evidence exists for a coenzyme role of the vitamin biotin in oxaloacetic carboxylase, the enzyme which brings about decarboxylation of oxaloacetate (30). Biotin has the structure shown above.

16. S-adenosyl methionine is the "active form" of methionine in transmethylation reactions and thus constitutes the coenzyme of the transmethylating enzymes involving the methionine methyl group. The formation of creatine and of choline are examples of methylation reactions (see Protein Metabolism, page 1037). Cantoni (31) demonstrated the formation of this active methionine through the reaction of the amino acid with ATP:

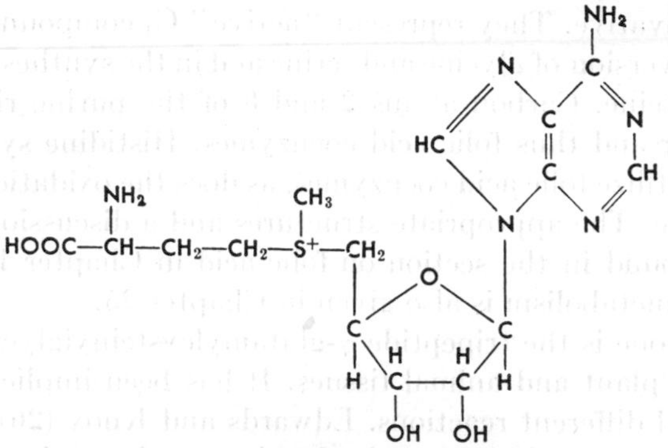

S-Adenosyl methionine, active methionine

17. Adenosine triphosphate (ATP), adenosine diphosphate (ADP), and adenosine monophosphate (AMP) are coenzymes according to the concept expressed earlier. These compounds are active in phosphate transport and/or transphosphorylations in connection with various specific enzyme systems.

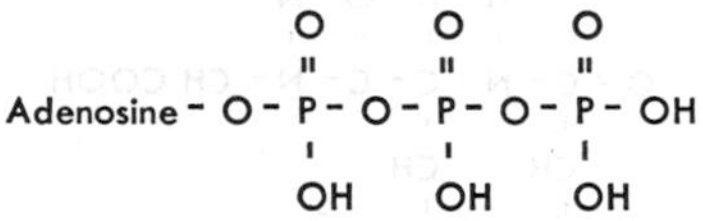

Adenosine triphosphate

Adenosine diphosphate contains one less phosphate.

Adenosine monophosphate contains two less phosphates.

18. Glucose-1,6-diphosphate is the coenzyme of phosphoglucomutase which converts glucose-1-phosphate to glucose-6-phosphate. The situation here is somewhat unique, since the coenzyme is continually formed during the reaction from the substrate (glucose-1-phosphate). Glucose-1-phosphate is converted to glucose-1,6-diphosphate, and this in turn is converted to glucose-6-phosphate.

19. 2,3-Diphosphoglyceric acid is another coenzyme that functions in a manner similar to glucose-1,6-diphosphate, in that it is continually formed from substrate and continually disappearing during the course of reaction. The enzyme is widely distributed in tissues and in red blood cells and has been obtained in crystalline form. It is called "phosphoglyceric acid mutase"

or "phosphoglyceromutase" and mediates the reaction in which 2-phospho-glyceric acid is converted into 3-phosphoglyceric acid.

20. Cytidine diphosphate choline (CDPC) is the coenzyme utilized in the synthesis of lecithins (32). The synthesis involves the reaction of the coenzyme with a 1,2-diglyceride to form a lecithin and cytidine monophosphate (CMP):

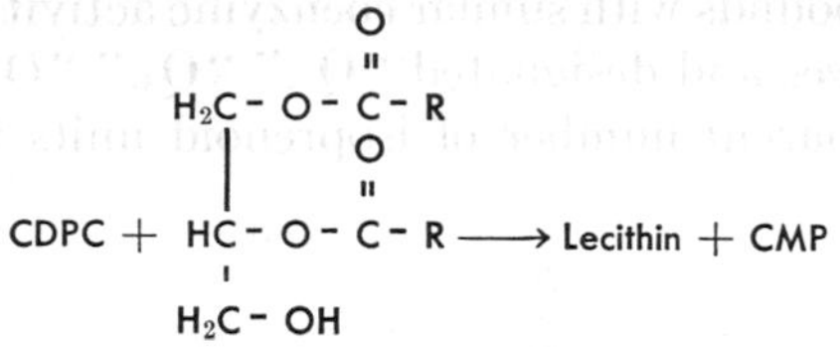

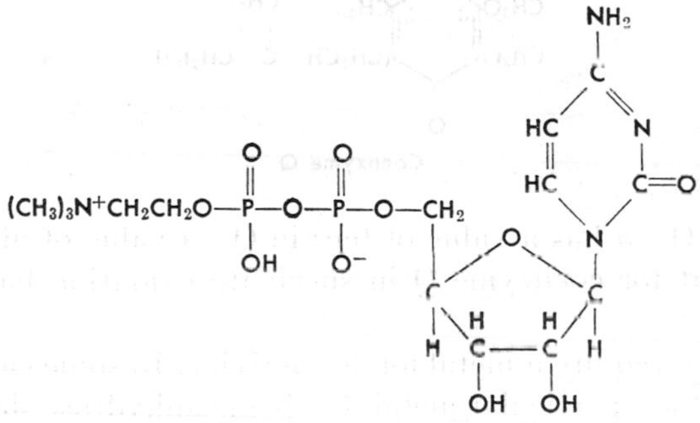

$$
\begin{array}{c}
\quad\quad\quad\quad O \\
\quad\quad\quad\quad \| \\
H_2C-O-C-R \\
\quad\quad\quad\quad O \\
\quad\quad\quad\quad \| \\
CDPC + HC-O-C-R \longrightarrow Lecithin + CMP \\
\quad\quad\quad \| \\
H_2C-OH
\end{array}
$$

Cytidine diphosphate choline

21. "Active sulfate" is the term applied to the coenzyme adenosine-3'-phosphate-5'-phosphosulfate by Lipmann (33). This worker prepared the compound from sulfate and ATP and assigned the following structure to it:

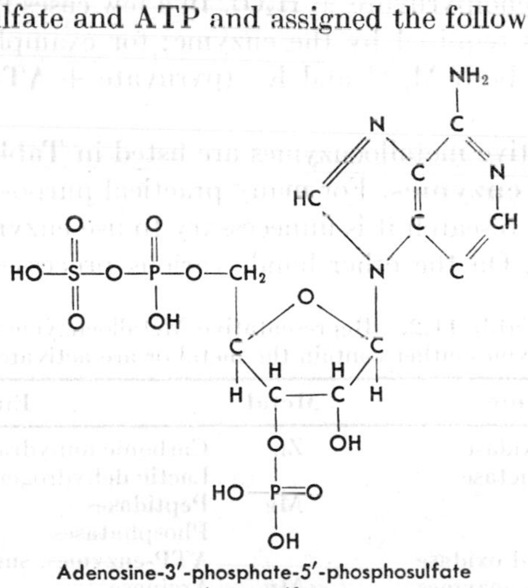

Adenosine-3'-phosphate-5'-phosphosulfate
Active sulfate

It is involved in the enzymatic sulfation of phenols and of hexosamine deriv-atives as in the formation of chondroitin sulfuric acid, and in other sulfate transfer reactions. The enzymes involved are sulfatases.

22. In 1957 Crane and others (34) isolated a crystalline quinone (coenzyme Q) from the lipids of beef heart mitochondria and showed that it is an integral part of the electron transport system of these particles.

Q-275 (maximum absorption at 275 mμ) from heart mitochondria is now referred to as "Q_{10}" and is 2,3-dimethoxy,5-methyl benzoquinone with a ten-unit isoprenoid side chain at position 6 (35).

Four related compounds with similar coenzyme activity have been isolated from microbial sources and designated "Q_9," "Q_8," "Q_7," and "Q_6," corresponding to the apparent number of isoprenoid units in the side chain at position 6 (36):

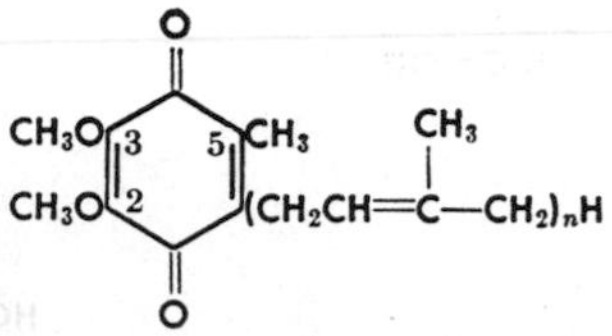

Coenzyme Q

In coenzyme Q_{10} n has a value of ten; in Q_9, a value of nine; etc.

A requirement for coenzyme Q in succinate oxidation has been demonstrated (37).

Many enzymes require a metal ion for activity. In some cases the requirement is specific for a particular metal. Carbonic anhydrase shows no activity upon removal of zinc, and no other metal is known to replace zinc in this enzyme. In other cases more than one metal is able to bring about activation; for example, Mg^{++}, Mn^{++}, or Zn^{++} activates enolase (2-phosphog'ycerate $\longrightarrow$ phosphoenolpyruvate + H_2O). In a few cases it appears that two metal ions may be required by the enzyme; for example, pyruvate phosphokinase requires both Mg^{++} and K^+ (pyruvate + ATP $\longrightarrow$ phosphopyruvate + ADP).

Some representative metalloenzymes are listed in Table 11.2.

Purification of enzymes. For many practical purposes in industry and often in laboratory research it is unnecessary to use enzyme preparations of the highest purity. On the other hand, various processes may require the

Table 11.2.   Representative Metalloenzymes
The enzymes either contain the metal or are activated by it

Metal	Enzyme	Metal	Enzyme
Mo	Xanthine oxidase	Zn	Carbonic anhydrase
	Nitrate reductase		Lactic dehydrogenase
Cu	Tyrosinase	Mg	Peptidases
	Phenolase		Phosphatases
	Ascorbic acid oxidase		ATP-enzymes, such as the hexokinases
Fe	Cytochrome enzymes	Mn	Arginase
	Catalase		Phosphoglucomutase
	Peroxidases		Dipeptidases
	Tryptophan oxidase	Co	Peptidases
	Homogentisicase		
Ca	Lecithinases A and C		
	Lipases		

absence of interfering substances. A great deal of our present knowledge of the properties of enzymes has been developed since workers were able to obtain them in a high state of purity. Obviously, chemical analyses of only the purest preparations give the desired information. The chemist aims at enzyme synthesis, but first he must analyze and characterize. The extreme complexity of the protein molecule, however, places such an accomplishment in the distant future.

Some enzymes occur and function within the cell (intracellular), and others are secreted to function elsewhere (extracellular). Purification of the former is complicated by the necessity of disrupting the cell wall so the enzyme can be taken into solution. Some of the common methods used for this are: (a) maceration of tissue with an abrasive material, such as sand, or by high-speed, specially designed pulverizers; (b) alternate freezing and thawing; (c) thorough dehydration, followed by grinding, leaving the material in an easily extractable form; (d) homogenization followed by high-speed centrifugation to separate various particulate bodies, such as mitochondria, which may contain certain enzymes and be nearly free of others present in the whole cell; and (e) autolysis. The last process involves self-digestion by so-called catheptic enzymes of tissues.

Water, glycerin, or various buffer solutions may be employed to dissolve the enzyme liberated by a method such as one of the above. Many other small and large molecules are taken into solution, and the next step generally involves the separation of the enzyme from contaminating material.

Dialysis eliminates small molecules, both organic and inorganic. Protein impurities are often removed by alcohol, ammonium sulfate, or isoelectric precipitation. Or the enzyme itself may be precipitated, leaving the bulk of the impurities in solution.

Adsorption and elution procedures have played an important role in enzyme purification. Under controlled conditions of pH, temperature, concentration, etc., various adsorbents, such as alumina and kaolin, preferentially adsorb certain molecules. By changing one or more of the conditions, usually the pH, the adsorbed molecules may often be eluted into pure solvent.

Electrophoresis, paper chromotography, and column chromotography have been used to advantage in the purification of enzymes and many other molecules. A comprehensive treatment on techniques of enzyme isolation is available (38).

No set rules are available for one attempting to purify an enzyme. In most instances the processes have been worked out in a more or less trial-and-error fashion, but in general they follow the procedures used in the isolation of proteins. Generally if isoelectric precipitation or adsorption is used, the procedure must be repeated a number of times before highly purified products result. The above methods of approach are some that have been employed successfully.

In the purification of proteins, it is essential to work with concentrated solutions (1–10 per cent). Protein stability is greater in concentrated than in dilute solutions, and proteins are more easily separated from concentrated solutions. It was Northrop (2) who developed this principle and made such excellent use of it in establishing procedures for the purification and subsequent crystallization of a number of enzymes.

Intracellular enzyme distribution. A variety of particulate structures have been identified in the cytoplasm of plant and animal cells. Some of these can be separated from the remainder of the cell in varying degrees of homogeneity. Enzyme determinations of the various fractions of cells then yield information of cellular localization of some enzymes.

A piece of tissue can be homogenized (ground) by special techniques in a medium such as sucrose solution so that the cells are disrupted and with little apparent damage to mitochondria, nuclei, etc. Because of the difference in size and density of the various particles, high-speed centrifugation separates various particulate fractions from the supernatant. Hogeboom has been one of the leading workers in this field and has discussed the techniques for fractionating liver cells (39).

Dixon and Webb (3) list some 50 enzymes in a table showing comparative concentrations in nuclei, mitochondria, microsome, and supernatant fractions from rodent liver cells. As examples, lactate dehydrogenase and nucleoside phosphorylase are found primarily in the supernatant, cholesterol esterase and alkaline phosphatase in the microsome fraction, succinic dehydrogenase and cytochrome oxidase in the mitochondria, and coenzyme I pyrophosphorylase in the nucleus. Some enzymes appear not to be associated mainly with any one fraction.

Crystalline enzymes. In the first edition of this book a partial list of enzymes that had been crystallized was presented. Now the list is so extensive and clouded in some instances by reports of work which cannot be repeated by others that no such listing will be presented here.

Photomicrographs of around 50 or 60 crystalline enzymes are presented by Dixon and Webb (3), and 15 others are listed but not illustrated. Many of the enzymes are pictured in different crystalline forms, and other illustrations show forms of enzymes from various sources. In most cases the magnification is given, and in all cases an original literature reference is supplied, adding to the value of this excellent book on many aspects of enzymes. We will now consider briefly the details of preparing three different crystalline enzymes, primarily to indicate methods of approach.

The following is Northrop's (2) procedure for the purification and crystallization of pepsin from bovine gastric juice. A number of the details are not given here. It will be noted that purification is effected primarily by $MgSO_4$ precipitation and that no adsorption-elution is employed.

Immediately following death of the animal the content of the fourth pouch is filtered in the cold. The filtrate is saturated with ammonium sulfate, decanted, and then filtered with suction. The precipitate is dissolved in very dilute HCl. This solution is cooled to $-10°$ C; and after the addition of cold acetone, it is centrifuged and the supernatant fluid again cooled, whereupon additional cold acetone is added producing a precipitate of impure enzyme. This is dissolved in dilute HCl, and then additional purification is accomplished by fractional precipitation with saturated $MgSO_4$ solution. Five such precipitations followed by re-solution, are carried out. The volume relation of crude enzyme solution and $MgSO_4$ solution used is critical, since this regulates the final electrolyte concentration and thus the type of protein that precipitates.

The final precipitate, containing the enzyme, is dissolved in sodium acetate and the pH of the solution brought to 3 with H_2SO_4. After one more precipitation with $MgSO_4$, the precipitate produced gives a clear yellow solution in $N/10$ sodium acetate. The preparation is now highly purified, and crystallization is induced by acidifying to pH 3 and allowing to stand in the cold. The precipitate formed in this step is dissolved in a minimum quantity of water at 45° C, and on slow cooling to room temperature crystals of pepsin form. They are yellowish in color.

Compare with the foregoing, the following simple procedure used by Sumner (40) to crystallize urease from jack bean meal.

Fat-free jack bean meal is stirred for a few minutes with 31.6 per cent aqueous acetone. The mixture is transferred to a gravity filter and placed in an ice chest at about 2° C. The next day urease crystals can be recovered from the filtrate by centrifugation.

Recrystallization (41) from water can be effected by addition of cold acetone and phosphate buffer of pH 6.3.

Anson (42) used the following procedure to prepare crystalline carboxypeptidase.

To the exudate of frozen pancreas standing overnight at 5° C, 5 N acetic acid is added until the solution is green to brom cresol green. After keeping the solution at 37° C for two hours the suspended matter is filtered off and the filtrate diluted with 10 times its volume of water. The resulting precipitate is obtained by decantation and filtration and suspended in water. To this is added 0.2 M $Ba(OH)_2$ until the mixture is alkaline to phenolphthalein. All the enzyme is dissolved by the $Ba(OH)_2$. The undissolved protein is removed by centrifugation, and N acetic acid is added to the supernatant fluid until it gives an orange color with phenol red. The globulin crystals of carboxypolypeptidase appear slowly on standing. Recrystallization can be induced by dissolving the protein in dilute NaOH and neutralizing.

Figure 11.1 shows some crystalline enzymes.

Mode of action of enzymes. No complete explanation is at hand to account for the mechanism of enzyme action. The most likely postulate is that of Michaelis and Menten (43) and is known as the enzyme-substrate complex theory. This theory, through more recent work, has become quite widely accepted. The following equations set forth the two phases of enzyme action according to this hypothesis: (It is generally assumed that the surface of an enzyme molecule contains "active centers.")

enzyme + substrate $\rightleftarrows$ enzyme-substrate complex
enzyme-substrate complex $\rightleftarrows$ enzyme + products of enzyme action

An early attempt to picture enzyme hydrolysis by such a mechanism is due to Van Slyke and Cullen (44). Figure 11.2, taken from a review by Van Slyke (45), is a graphic representation of the enzyme-substrate complex theory. It is assumed that a substrate molecule, before it is hydrolyzed, first combines with the enzyme and leaves the enzyme surface as its reaction products.

More specifically, Stern (46), proposed an enzyme-substrate complex as an intermediate in the decomposition of ethyl hydrogen peroxide by the enzyme catalase. He made an intensive study of the two phases of this reaction and was able to relate spectroscopic observations and volumetric analysis to the course of reaction. It was observed that an intermediate composed

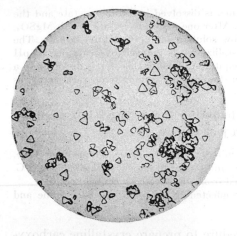

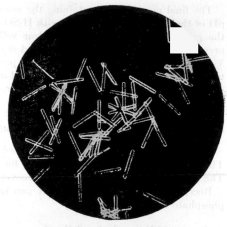

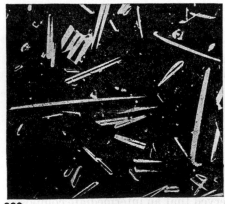

Figure 11.1. (*Top*) Tripsinogen and trypsin crystals. (J. H. Northrop, *Crystalline Enzymes*. Columbia University Press, New York, 1939.) (*Center*) Chymotrypsinogen crystals and chymotrypsin crystals. (J. H. Northrop, *op. cit.*) (*Bottom*) Carboxypeptidase crystals. (M. L. Anson: *J. Gen. Physiol.*, **20**, 663, 1937.)

of the enzyme and substrate forms rapidly and then decomposes into enzyme and product molecules. The latter were not completely identified.

Chance (47) later offered further evidence for such a complex. He showed that when peroxidase enzyme catalyzes the oxidation of a substance such as leucomalachite green by H_2O_2, the enzyme first forms a compound with the peroxide. This was demonstrated by spectrophotometric studies in which changes in the absorption spectrum were found when peroxidase combined with H_2O_2.

Good evidence exists for the formation of an enzyme substrate intermediate in the reaction of sucrose phosphorylase with the substrate glucose-1-phosphate (48).

The acyl derivative of glyceraldehyde-3-phosphate dehydrogenase was identified spectrophotometrically upon the addition of acetyl phosphate to

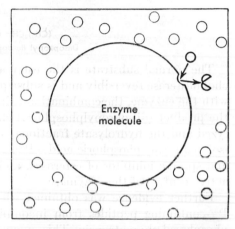

Figure 11.2. Diagram illustrating assumed mode of hydrolysis by an enzyme. The small circles represent substrate molecules. (D. D. Van Slyke, "The Kinetics of Hydrolytic Enzymes and Their Bearing on Methods for Measuring Enzyme Activity," in *Advances in Enzymology*, Vol. II, pp. 33–47. Copyright, 1942, Interscience Publishers, Inc., New York.)

the enzyme (49). Krimsky and Racker (50) reported the isolation of a crystalline acyl derivative of this enzyme. This derivative was taken to be the enzyme-substrate complex. Under certain reaction conditions 1-3,diphosphoglycerate and glyceraldehyde-3-phosphate dehydrogenase formed what appeared to be a thiol ester with the —SH group of the enzyme protein. The properties indicated that this was an intermediate in the enzyme action. The complex is reduced by DPNH to form an aldehyde and the DPN enzyme. Acetyl phosphate reacts similarly with the enzyme, and this intermediate was also isolated. The mechanism of this reaction might be illustrated as follows:

$$
\underset{\text{(acetyl phosphate)}}{R-\overset{\displaystyle O}{\overset{\displaystyle \|}{C}}-OPO_3H_2} \;+\; \underset{\text{(SH enzyme)}}{\underset{|}{\overset{|}{\underset{\text{Protein}}{SH}}}} \;\rightleftharpoons\; \underset{\text{(acetyl enzyme)}}{R-\overset{\displaystyle O}{\overset{\displaystyle \|}{C}}\underset{|}{\underset{\text{Protein}}{\overset{|}{S}}}}
$$

$$
\underset{\text{(DPN enzyme)}}{\text{DPN-S-protein}} \;+\; \underset{\text{(aldehyde)}}{R\overset{H}{\overset{\|}{C}}=O} \;\longleftarrow\; \text{DPNH}
$$

Several different amino acids or functional groups of amino acids have been identified as parts of active centers in enzyme molecules. Certainly the implicated group or amino acid by itself does not constitute the active center. The surrounding amino acid residues in the same or even in proximate peptide chains must be involved. Serine (—OH group), cystine (—SH group), and histidine have been rather well established as essential foci of active centers. The experimental data are frequently not clear-cut, although the industrious pursuit of studies in this difficult field has markedly increased our knowledge of protein structure and of enzyme action.

An example of this type of work is that of Schaffer and coworkers (51), who treated cholinesterase with diisopropyl fluorophosphate (DFP) containing P^{32}:

$$(CH_3)_2CH - O \diagdown \diagup F$$
$$P$$
$$\diagup \diagdown$$
$$(CH_3)_2CH - O \qquad O$$

Diisopropyl fluorophosphate (DFP)

The normal substrate is the ester acetyl choline, which reacts with the cholinesterase reversibly and is subsequently hydrolyzed. When DFP reacts with the enzyme, the combination is irreversible and sufficiently stable that the product (diisopropylphosphoryl cholinesterase) can be partially hydrolyzed and the hydrolysate fractionated. By such means these investigators isolated serine phosphoric acid—P^{32}. DFP is known to be a highly effective and specific inhibitor of esterases, and so it is assumed that it reacts with active centers of the enzyme.

Further evidence was obtained when Schaffer and others (52) isolated P^{32}-containing peptides from incomplete hydrolysates of P^{32}-diisopropylphosphoryl chymotrypsin. This enzyme has some esterase activity. Among the peptides identified was glycylaspartylphosphoserylglycine. This might be more readily visualized written thus:

$$P^*$$
$$|$$
gly-asp-ser-gly

in which P^* = the radioactive phosphate group. P^{32}-containing peptides with this amino acid sequence have been obtained from other enzymes treated similarly. This is one of many examples of an approach to the study of chemical characteristics of the active center. Further details can be found in (3).

From the work of Finkle and Smith (53) it would appear that although crystalline papain (in the reduced state) has several —SH groups, only one thiol group per molecule of papain is enzymatically active.

Some of the hydrolytic enzymes, such as trypsin, chymotrypsin, and acetylcholinesterase, appear to have but one active center on the basis of reactivity with DFP. Acyl derivatives on the serine hydroxyl of chymotrypsin have been prepared by reaction with such compounds as benzoyl chloride, p-nitrophenylacetate, and acetic anhydride. The acyl derivatives appear to be on the serine hydroxyl and are similar but less stable than the DFP reaction products. In these cases the evidence indicates reaction at the active center.

From such facts and other data, Cunningham (54) has proposed a mechanism for the action of hydrolytic enzymes. He proposes that formation of the active center involves hydrogen bond formation between the serine —OH and an adjacent uncharged imidazole nucleus (of histidine). Polarization of the resulting structure—i.e., a partial negative charge (δ^-) on the oxygen and a partial positive charge (δ^+) on the imidazole nitrogen—causes the serine oxygen to become a nucleophilic agent which will attack the carbonyl of the substrate (as in the acyl compounds mentioned above or in normal substrates). A "nucleophilic agent" is one which is electron-donating, and

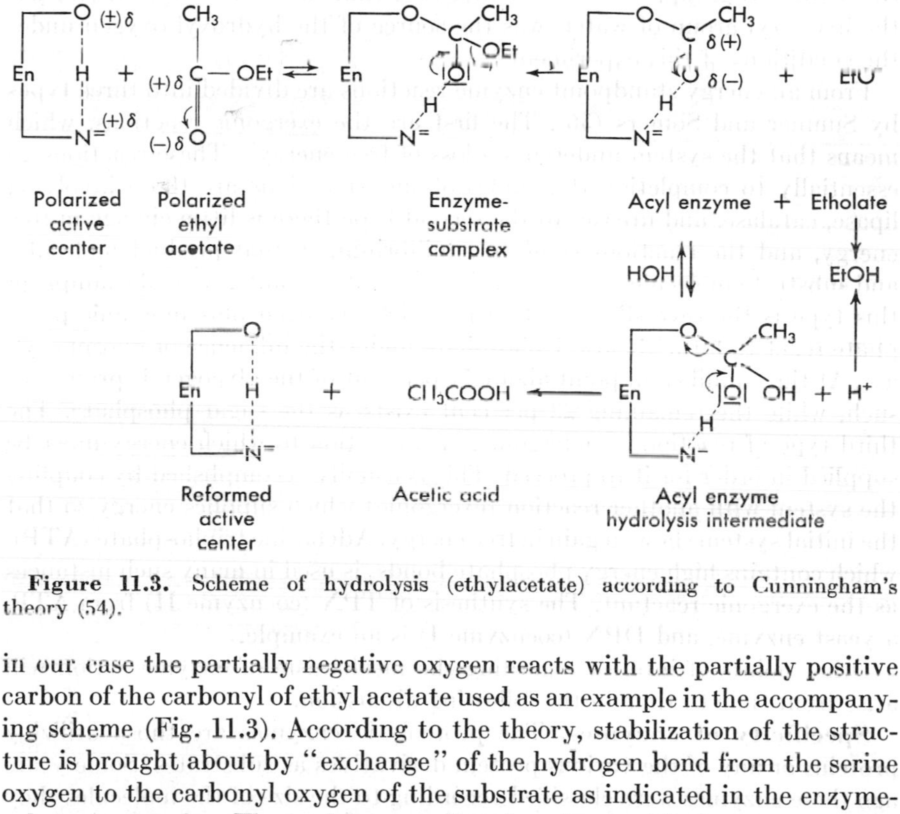

Figure 11.3. Scheme of hydrolysis (ethylacetate) according to Cunningham's theory (54).

in our case the partially negative oxygen reacts with the partially positive carbon of the carbonyl of ethyl acetate used as an example in the accompanying scheme (Fig. 11.3). According to the theory, stabilization of the structure is brought about by "exchange" of the hydrogen bond from the serine oxygen to the carbonyl oxygen of the substrate as indicated in the enzyme-substrate complex. The acyl intermediate is written with the proton on the imidazole nitrogen. As deacylation occurs, this positive charge is lost simultaneously with the attack of the nucleophilic reagent HOH, which completes hydrolysis. Thus ethylate is formed, and as deacylation of enzyme occurs, forming acetic acid, a H^+ is released from water, which reacts with ethylate to form ethanol. The enzyme active center is thus reformed and is available to repeat the process.

Oxygen of mass 18 has been useful in establishing enzymatic pathways in some instances. A number of investigators have studied oxygen uptake in systems containing substrate, enzyme, and $O_2{}^{18}$ or H_2O^{18} to determine the source of oxygen in a reaction such as enzymatic hydroxylation. Mason (55) has studied various enzymes that catalyze reactions of molecular oxygen ("oxidases") by means of tracer oxygen.

The enzyme peroxidase was studied in a system containing salicylic acid (2-hydroxybenzoic acid); dihydroxyfumarate, which increases the enzyme action; and $O_2{}^{18}$ or H_2O^{18}, as isotope source. The compound 2,3 dihydroxy-benzoic, was isolated, and the source of the oxygen in the hydroxyl intro-duced under the influence of the enzyme at position 3 was found to contain the theoretical amount of $O_2{}^{18}$ when the reaction was carried out in the presence of $O_2{}^{18}$—H_2O. When O_2—H_2O^{18} was used, no isotope was found in this hydroxyl group. This clearly indicates that molecular oxygen, and not the hydroxyl group of water, was the source of the hydroxyl oxygen under the conditions of this experiment.

From an energy standpoint enzyme reactions are divided into three types by Sumner and Somers (56). The first are the exergonic reactions, which means that the system undergoes a loss of free energy.* These reactions go essentially to completion. Examples of such reactions are those involving lipase, catalase, and urease. In the second type there is little change in free energy, and the reactions come to equilibrium, so that product molecules and substrate molecules are present in constant amounts. A good example of this type is the reversible reaction in which glycogen plus inorganic phos-phate react to form glucose-1-phosphate under the influence of phosphoryl-ase. At the equilibrium point about 77 per cent of the glycogen is present as such, while the remaining 23 per cent exists as the sugar phosphate. The third type of reaction is endergonic, or a reaction to which energy must be supplied in order for it to proceed. This is usually accomplished by coupling the system with another reaction (exergonic) which supplies energy so that the initial system shows a gain in free energy. Adenosine triphosphate (ATP), which contains high energy phosphate bonds, is used in many such instances as the exergonic reactant. The synthesis of TPN (coenzyme II) from ATP, a yeast enzyme, and DPN (coenzyme I) is an example.

Other points of interest regarding the mechanism of enzyme action will arise from time to time in the following discussion.

Specificity of enzymes. The proteolytic enzymes are those utilizing proteins or any of the various protein derivatives as substrates. Some years ago these enzymes were classified according to the size of the molecules they supposedly cleave. Thus, pepsin and chymotrypsin were classed as proteases, since they were thought to start the hydrolysis of only large protein mole-cules. The low molecular weight peptides were supposedly hydrolyzed by another group of proteolytic enzymes, the peptidases, such as polypeptidase and dipeptidase.

Through the recent work of many investigators, primarily Bergmann and coworkers, our views on the specificity and the classification of proteolytic enzymes have of necessity undergone important changes.

---

* The student is advised to read the section on free energy at this point, pages 787–794.

Bergmann (57) and associates synthesized many small peptides of known constitution and subjected them to the action of various enzymes. Hydrolysis products of these peptides are readily identifiable, and thus the course and rate of enzyme action can be studied precisely. Many of the enzymes, formerly assigned the specific function of starting native protein hydrolysis, are found to hydrolyze synthetic di-, tri-, and tetrapeptides. In many cases the rates of reaction are comparable to the rates determined for the hydrolysis of large protein molecules.

As an example of this outstanding work, consider the synthetic peptide carbobenzoxy-L-glutamyl-L-tyrosylglycine amide:

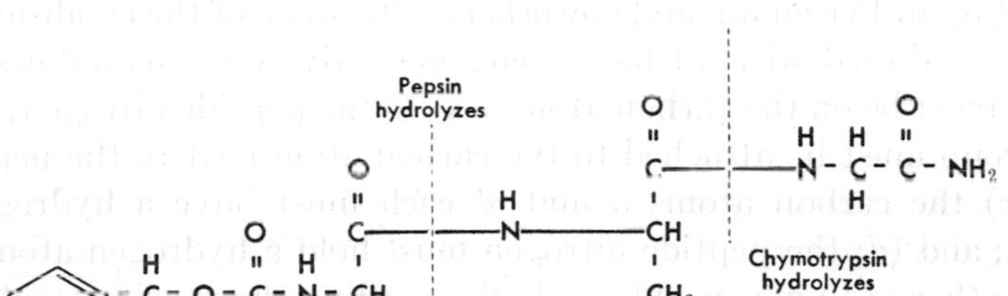

Carbobenzoxy-L-glutamyl-L-tyrosylglycine amide

Pepsin hydrolyzes this peptide at the linkage indicated between the glutamic acid and tyrosine residues. But if the carbobenzoxy group is removed, restoring the basic amino group in glutamic acid, pepsin no longer attacks the peptide. The restoration of the amino group affects the neighboring peptide bond to make it pepsin resistant.

Chymotrypsin hydrolyzes the original molecule as indicated at the peptide bond between tyrosine and glycine amide. This action is not altered by removing the carbobenzoxy group, but if the carboxyl group of glycine amide is regenerated, the resulting compound is resistant to the enzyme. The latter alteration does not affect the action of pepsin, however. It was further found that tyrosine or phenylalanine must be present in the position indicated for either of these enzymes to be active. The amino acids also must be the natural antipodes. Pepsin in general appears to bring about scission at the peptide linkages involving the amino groups of the aromatic amino acids. The enzyme trypsin generally hydrolyzes peptides containing lysine or arginine. It is interesting that neither of these enzymes requires free terminal amino or carboxyl groups in their substrates.

The term "endopeptidases" was suggested by Bergmann (58) for those enzymes, such as pepsin and trypsin, which are capable of attacking both centrally located and terminal peptide bonds. Exopeptidases, such as aminopeptidase (amino polypeptidase) and carboxypeptidase (carboxypolypeptidase) hydrolyze only terminal peptide bonds—the former a peptide bond involving an amino acid containing a free amino group, and the latter a terminal peptide bond of an amino acid containing a free carboxyl group.

A high degree of specificity exists among the exopeptidases, as illustrated by the following example. The compound L-leucylglycine is readily hydrolyzed by a dipeptidase preparation, as indicated below:

$$
\begin{array}{c}
\text{H} \quad \text{H} \quad \text{NH}_2 \quad \text{O} \quad | \quad \text{H} \\
| \quad | \quad | \quad \| \quad | \\
\text{CH}_3\text{-}\ \text{C}\text{---}\text{C}\text{---}\text{C}\text{---}\text{C}\text{-}\ \text{N}\text{-}\ \text{C}\text{-}\ \text{COOH} \\
| \quad | \quad '\,\alpha \quad | \quad '\,\alpha' \\
\text{CH}_3 \quad \text{H} \quad \text{H} \quad \text{H} \quad \text{H}
\end{array}
$$

Dipeptidase hydrolyzes——→
Leucylglycine

According to Bergmann and coworkers (59), some of the conditions which may not be altered without loss of enzyme activity are as follows: (a) the carboxyl must be on the carbon atom next to the peptide nitrogen; (b) a free amino group must be attached to the carbon atom next to the peptide carbonyl; (c) the carbon atoms α and α' each must have a hydrogen atom attached; and (d) the peptide nitrogen must hold a hydrogen atom.

Many other examples could be cited regarding the specificity of the proteolytic enzymes. The above are sufficient, however, to indicate that the spatial configuration and arrangements of individual amino acids in the substrate molecule are the important criteria in determining the specificity of many, and perhaps all of the proteolytic enzymes. The size of the substrate molecule must be of minor importance.

Among other groups of enzymes varying degrees of specificity are found. The fat-hydrolyzing enzyme lipase, for instance, is capable of splitting a great variety of compounds comprising the naturally occurring neutral fats. These are glycerol esters of high molecular weight fatty acids and differ in their composition according to the various fatty acids present. Fatty acid esters of monohydroxy alcohols, on the other hand, require enzymes known as "esterases" for their hydrolysis.

A high degree of specificity is found among the carbohydrases. For instance, maltase hydrolyzes maltose but not sucrose or lactose. Sucrase and lactase split sucrose and lactose but not other disaccharides into their component sugars. Amylase acts upon starch, glycogen, and dextrins exclusively. Hydrogen peroxide and monoethyl hydrogen peroxide are decomposed by catalase, but diethyl hydrogen peroxide is not attacked. The action of tyrosinase is not restricted to the oxidation of tyrosine, although only related compounds are attacked.

The highest degree of specificity may be found in some of the tissue oxidation-reduction enzymes. According to Stern cytochrome oxidase has but the single substrate, reduced cytochrome c.

Since all the enzymes are proteins, it is obvious that various functional groups are more or less available for reaction, depending upon the structure of the individual molecule. Little is known about the essential nature of these groups for enzyme action. Sumner and Somers (60) present a table of some 30 enzymes, indicating, where known, the essential or nonessential nature of such groups as primary amino, tyrosyl, and sulfhydryl. Barron discusses this subject in some detail (61). It must be that the essentiality of certain groups is related in some way to enzyme specificity.

An interesting development is the use of proteolytic enzymes to study the "core" of certain biologically active protein molecules. In some instances the enzymes used do not completely break down the substrate molecules, and it has been suggested that the resistant "core" may be an unaltered portion of the original molecule from which "the clothes have been stripped" (62).

After treating cytochrome c to peptic enzyme digestion, a hydrolysis product was isolated which had a biologic activity of catalyzing the oxidation of ascorbic acid but was no longer active in the cytochrome oxidase system (63).

Insulin has been subjected to chymotrypsin action and some small fragments removed for study. A larger fragment with a molecular weight of about 5000 was found to be slowly attacked by chymotrypsin but rapidly attacked by trypsin. In general trypsin is thought to hydrolyze denatured proteins more readily than native proteins. Here is another example of the "core" of protein molecules (64).

Enzyme kinetics. * According to the law of the mass action, the rate of a chemical change is proportional to the product of the concentrations (activities) of the reacting substances. If only one substance is reacting, the rate of reaction is proportional to the concentration of this substance. This is a first-order reaction. Many hydrolytic reactions appear to be first-order reactions and therefore have velocities proportional to the concentration of material undergoing hydrolysis. During the inversion of sucrose by H^+ a molecule of water reacts for every molecule of sucrose hydrolyzed, but since the concentration of water is great compared to that of sugar, little over-all change in water concentration accompanies a large change in sugar concentration, and the reaction rate is governed by the concentration of sugar present, or:

$$V \propto [a]$$

This equation states that the velocity, V, of the reaction is proportional to the concentration of reacting substance, $[a]$. By introducing a velocity constant, k, the speed of reaction can be equated to k times $[a]$, or:

$$V = k[a]$$

After the reaction has proceeded for time t, the original concentration has changed and there remains $[a - x]$ as the concentration of reacting substance. The velocity of the reaction at time t must then be governed by the amount of material equal to $[a - x]$, and this velocity can be expressed in the differential equation:

$$V = \frac{dx}{dt} = k[a - x]$$

where k = a velocity constant for the specific reaction, x = the amount of substance changed in time t, $a - x$ = the concentration of original material remaining at time t, and V = the reaction velocity at time t.

This equation merely states that the reaction velocity is equal to a factor times the concentration at any time.

* For a more comprehensive discussion, see E. S. West's *Textbook of Biophysical Chemistry*, 2nd ed. The Macmillan Co., New York, 1956.

By integrating the above equation, the following more useful form is obtained:

$$k = \frac{1}{t} \log_e \frac{[a]}{[a - x]}$$

This equation states that the velocity constant, k, is equal to the reciprocal of time t (in seconds, minutes, or hours) times the natural log of the original concentration $[a]$ divided by the remaining concentration $[a - x]$ at time t.

Another form of the equation is:

$$k = \frac{1}{(t_2 - t_1)} \log_e \frac{C_1}{C_2}$$

or, changing to $\log_{10}$,

$$k = \frac{2.303}{(t_2 - t_1)} \log_{10} \frac{C_1}{C_2}$$

where C_1 and C_2 are the concentrations of reacting substance at times t_1 and t_2, respectively.

The value of k can be calculated from this equation by determinations of the concentration of reacting substance at two time intervals. If the values of k for different times of reaction agree well, the chemical change is taken to be a first-order reaction.

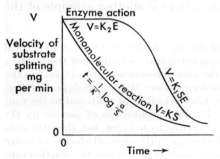

V

Velocity of
substrate
splitting
mg
per min

Enzyme action

$V = K_2 E$

Monomolecular reaction $t = \frac{1}{k} \log \frac{a}{x}$

$V = K_1 SE$

$V = KS$

Time →

Effect of duration of reaction on velocity
as substrate concentration falls

Figure 11.4. Time curve of simple first-order decomposition reaction contrasted with typical curve of substrate decomposition by an enzyme. (D. D. Van Slyke, "The Kinetics of Hydrolytic Enzymes and Their Bearing on Methods for Measuring Enzyme Activity," in *Advances in Enzymology*, Vol. II, pp. 33–47. Copyright, 1942, Interscience Publishers, Inc., New York.)

Under certain conditions many enzyme reactions proceed according to the first-order reaction equation. Van Slyke points out, however, that in many instances the speed of hydrolysis by enzymes follows a two-phase curve, and only when the substrate is in low concentration does the rate follow the monomolecular curve. At higher substrate concentrations the rate of hydrolysis is constant and governed by the concentration of enzyme.

Consider Figure 11.4 from a review by Van Slyke (45). The lower curve of the graph is a typical first-order curve and indicates the progress of inversion of sucrose by H^+. The upper curve represents enzymatic sucrose hydrolysis. It is evident that at the beginning of the experiment the enzymatic hydrolysis is constant for some period of time, and so is not dependent on substrate concentration (10 or 20 per cent sucrose). This, the first phase of the reaction, is followed by a decreasing velocity after the sugar concentration has been lowered to 3 or 4 per cent. Finally the rate parallels the concentration of sucrose remaining and finishes as a "die-away" curve. Van Slyke says that it is only an imitation of a first-order curve.

The expressions $V = K_1 SE$ and $V = KS$ are altogether similar to the equation $V = k[a]$ used at the beginning of this discussion, since E = enzyme concentration, which is constant, while S and $[a]$ both denote substrate concentration. But $V = K_2 E$ states that the reaction velocity is equal to a constant times the enzyme concentration (upper part of curve). This means that the reaction velocity is independent of substrate concentration. When this is true, the reaction is said to be of zero-order, and the differential equation is $dx/dt = k$, which yields $k = [x]/t$ upon integration, where $[x]$ = the amount of S that has undergone change in time t.

The first-order equation holds only in reactions that go essentially to completion and in reactions with constant enzyme concentration.

Another test to determine whether an enzymatic reaction is actually one of the first order is to plot determined values of $\log [a]/[a - x]$ against t from the first-order equation:

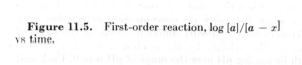

$$k = \frac{2.303}{t} \log \frac{[a]}{[a - x]}$$

A straight line with the slope of $k/2.303$ results if the rate of reaction follows first-order

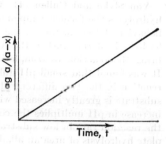

Figure 11.5. First-order reaction, $\log [a]/[a - x]$ vs time.

kinetics. This is illustrated in Figure 11.5 and is more readily visualized by rearranging the integrated equation to yield:

$$\frac{k}{2.303} = \log \frac{[a]/[a - x]}{t}$$

The first-order equation makes it practical to calculate the time required to transform one half of the original substrate. At this time, $t_{1/2}$, in the course of the reaction, $x = a/2$ or $0.5a$. Upon substitution of this value in the first order equation, we have:

$$t_{1/2} = \frac{2.303}{k} \log \frac{a}{a - 0.5a} = \frac{2.303}{k} \log 2$$

or

$$t_{1/2} = \frac{0.693}{k}$$

Likewise, if we know the amount of substrate decomposed in one minute, we can calculate the amount decomposed at other times. Suppose it is found that 30 per cent of the substrate is decomposed in one minute, so that $t = 1$; k can then be found thus:

$$k = 2.303 \log \frac{100}{100 - 30}$$

and

$$k = 2.303 \log 1.428$$

or

$$k = 0.356 \text{ (at one minute)}$$

Then at three minutes, $t = 3$, and x can be found:

$$3 \times 0.356 = 2.303 \log \frac{100}{100 - x}$$

$$\frac{1.068}{2.303} = \log \frac{100}{100 - x}$$

$$2.91 = \frac{100}{100 - x}$$

and

$$x = 65.6$$

At three minutes 65.6 per cent of the original substrate concentration would be decomposed in this reaction.

Applications of our knowledge of enzyme kinetics are many, both in industry and in the research laboratory. From the first-order equation the time required to bring about a desired amount of change in a substrate can be calculated, or the amount of change that can be expected in a desired time interval may be determined. A certain new industrial process involving enzymatic action may be economically feasible only if a sizable fraction of the substrate can be converted into the desired products during a practical time interval. Or a determination in the laboratory by enzyme action might be highly valuable or useless, depending on the time required to bring it about.

The additions to our knowledge on the mechanisms of enzyme action through kinetic studies are important. The following example from Van Slyke's review (45) indicates an excellent practical application of information obtained from studies on enzyme kinetics.

Van Slyke and Cullen (44) wanted to determine urea by the use of urease, which hydrolyzes the former compound into CO_2 and ammonia. It was necessary to know the behavior of the enzyme in the two phases of the velocity curve in order to speed the hydrolysis at the start of the reaction when the substrate concentration is high and to bring the reaction to completion when the substrate concentration approaches zero. It was found that small pH differences have markedly different effects on the speed of reaction in the two different phases. The velocity for the combination of enzyme and substrate is greatly increased with increasing pH over the range of pH 6 to 9. Each unit increase in pH multiplies the combining velocity elevenfold. Since this velocity governs the reaction rate in low substrate concentration, it is obvious that to bring about complete hydrolysis of urea an alkaline medium is desirable at the end of the determination. But the decomposition constant governing the rate of hydrolysis in more concentrated solution of substrate shows an optimum pH of 6.8. So it is best to start the reaction near this acidity. These conditions were met by initiating the reaction in a nearly neutral phosphate buffer of sufficient buffer capacity to maintain this pH during the early stages, but of insufficient capacity to prevent a pH rise as appreciable ammonium carbonate forms during the later stage of hydrolysis. Van Slyke and Cullen used these conditions to develop a rapid and practical method of urea determination over 20 years ago. The method is still in widespread use.

In many enzyme studies, even with dilute substrate concentrations, the data obtained experimentally and those calculated from the first-order equation are in disagreement. This is not at all surprising, in view of the number of variables known to affect the rate of enzyme action. Often at least one of these variable is not, or cannot be, controlled. Slight changes in pH or temperature may alter a reaction rate very considerably. An enzyme may be activated or inactivated by conditions unknown or beyond the control of the investigator. In this respect slight changes in inorganic ion concentration or the formation or destruction of oxidizing or reducing substances are important. Substances toxic to enzymes may be formed; gases may be produced or absorbed which can alter enzyme activity. The accumulation of products of enzyme action often slow down the speed of reaction, possibly through the reverse of the desired reaction—i.e., synthesis by the enzyme—or by attaching themselves to the "active centers" of the enzyme and thus bringing about a degree of inactivation.

Some of the important factors known to affect the rate of enzyme action will now be discussed individually.

FACTORS AFFECTING RATE OF ENZYME ACTION

1. Concentration of substrate. It can safely be said that only in certain instances does the velocity of an enzyme action parallel the substrate concentration. When all variables can be controlled and the substrate concentration is low, such a correlation can often be demonstrated. Figure 11.6, after Meyers and Free (65), demonstrates this relationship. Above a certain substrate concentration, the rate of enzyme action ceases to increase. In fact, data from early work by Michaelis and Menten (43) show, in addition to this, that with sufficiently high substrate concentration the rate of action is actually slowed (invertase acting on sucrose).

It is interesting to reconsider Figure 11.2 and Van Slyke's explanation for the fact that the rate of enzyme action does not increase beyond a certain increase in substrate concentration. It is assumed that the substrate molecule combines in some way with the enzyme and then, after a time interval, the reaction products are freed. Following another time interval, a new substrate molecule attaches at the point of combination on the enzyme. The total reaction time involving one substrate molecule then is the sum of the times required for attachment and for the removal of the products. The more abundant the substrate molecules, the less time may be required for the attachment; and Van Slyke reasoned that this time interval, with sufficient substrate concentration, may become negligible compared with the interval

Figure 11.6. The effect of substrate concentration on enzyme activity. These data were obtained by determining the number of milligrams of reducing sugar formed in reaction mixtures in which the amount of enzyme (pancreatic amylase) was constant. The amount of substrate indicates the number of cubic milliliters of 1 per cent soluble starch present in the reaction mixtures all of which had the same total value. (From Meyers, V. C., and Free, A. H.: *Am. J. Clin. Path.,* **13,** 42, 1943.)

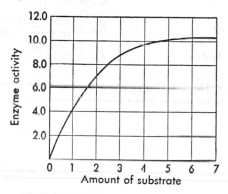

involving decomposition. So that with substrate concentrations at or above this level, the enzyme operates at full speed, because the intervals when it is unused become negligible. On this basis a further increase of substrate concentration does not increase the reaction rate, as indicated in Figure 11.6.

From a practical standpoint such findings are valuable in the clinical or research laboratory determination of an enzyme. By employing sufficient substrate to insure maximum rate of enzyme action, the variable of substrate concentration is removed, and calculations and interpretations are simplified.

The Michaelis-Menton constant. According to the early views of Henri and of Michaelis and Menton, it may be assumed that the substrate, S, combines with the enzyme, E, to form the complex, ES, according to the reversible reaction:

$$E + S \underset{k_2}{\overset{k_1}{\rightleftharpoons}} ES$$

in which k_1 = the velocity constant characteristic for the reaction leading to the formation of ES and k_2 = that characteristic for the dissociation of ES. The next step involves the formation of products, P, of the enzyme action and the reformation of free enzyme, giving the step-by-step reaction:

$$E + S \underset{k_2}{\overset{k_1}{\rightleftharpoons}} ES \overset{k_3}{\longrightarrow} P + E$$

The first satisfactory analysis of the relation of substrate concentration to the velocity of enzyme catalyzed reactions was offered by Michaelis and Menton (43) as early as 1913. The well-known Michaelis constant, K_m, which they derived, is without doubt the most fundamental characteristic of an enzyme. It can be defined as the substrate concentration at half-maximum velocity.

Michaelis and Menton thought of K_m as representing the dissociation constant of ES which would be k_2/k_1. However, Briggs and Haldane (66) pointed out that the Michaelis constant as measured in kinetic studies actually represents $(k_2 + k_3)/k_1$ from the above equation. The value of the final equation and the agreement of theoretical and experimental data are not altered by this difference in concepts.

In the reaction above, let $[E]$ = total concentration of enzyme, free and combined; $[ES]$ = concentration of enzyme-substrate complex; $[E] - [ES]$ = concentration of free enzyme; and $[S]$ = concentration of substrate S, with the condition that $[S]$ is very large compared to $[E]$ (to saturate the enzyme).

The dissociation constant, K_m, for the reversible reaction $E + S \rightleftharpoons ES$ can be written:

$$K_m = \frac{([E] - [ES])[S]}{[ES]} = \frac{[E][S] - [ES][S]}{[ES]}$$

or

$$K_m = \frac{[E][S]}{[ES]} - \frac{[ES][S]}{[ES]} = \frac{[E][S]}{[ES]} - [S]$$

And:

$$K_m + [S] = \frac{[E][S]}{[ES]} \quad \text{or} \quad [ES] = \frac{[E][S]}{K_m + [S]}$$

The velocity constant for ES decomposition into E plus products of enzyme action is k_3. Now if we let v = the determined velocity of the over-all enzymatic process:

$$v = k_3[ES] \text{ and } \frac{v}{k_3} = [ES]$$

so we may write

$$v = \frac{k_3[ES]}{K_m + [S]}$$

The maximal velocity, V, will be attained when all of the enzyme is bound to substrate, so that the rate of $ES \longrightarrow$ products is at a maximum, and under these conditions:

$$[ES] = [E] \text{ and } V = k_3[ES] = k_3[E]$$

Substituting V for $k_3[E]$ gives one form of the Michaelis-Menton equation:

$$v = \frac{V[S]}{K_m + [S]}$$

from which it is seen that

$$(K_m + [S])v = V[S]$$

and

$$K_m + [S] = \frac{V[S]}{v}$$

or

$$K_m = \frac{V[S]}{v} - [S] = [S]\left(\frac{V}{v} - 1\right)$$

Both K_m and V are constants, and so the curve represented by the equation is a rectangular hyperbola, as in Figure 11.7. Note that this is the same shape as the curve represented in Figure 11.6, taken from actual data on enzyme activity in relation to substrate concentration. So the theoretical considerations agree well with experimental findings in many but certainly not in all cases.

Since one definition of K_m is the substrate concentration at which the reaction develops half the maximum velocity V, it is helpful to substitute $\dfrac{V}{2}$ for v in the Michaelis-Menton equation:

$$v = \frac{V[S]}{K_m + [S]}$$

to get

$$\frac{V}{2} = \frac{V[S]}{K_m + [S]}$$

Then:

$$\frac{1}{2} = \frac{1[S]}{K_m + [S]} \quad \text{and} \quad \frac{2}{1} = \frac{K_m + [S]}{[S]}$$

so

$$2[S] = K_m + [S] \quad \text{and} \quad K_m = [S]$$

when the reaction velocity is one-half maximal velocity. This equation tells us that the substrate concentration necessary to develop one-half the maximum (or limiting) velocity is equal to the Michaelis constant K_m.

In the foregoing development of K, the concentration of substrate and enzyme is in moles per liter by convention. The condition set forth that $[S]$ must be large compared to $[E]$ is easily met, since molecular weights of enzymes (proteins) are tremendous compared

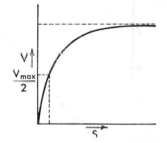

Figure 11.7. Theoretical curve of enzyme velocity, as determined by substrate concentration.

to many substrates, such as sugars or urea, and $[E]$ is generally small compared to $[S]$ It was stated in the early part of the discussion of kinetics that in such a reaction as the hydrolysis of sucrose one molecule of water reacts for each molecule of sugar reacting. But since the water concentration is very high and remains nearly constant, it need not be considered in the development of K_m.

K_m is more than simply the dissociation constant of ES. Consider that many enzyme reactions may involve something approaching the reaction:

$$E + S \rightleftharpoons ES \rightleftharpoons ES' \rightleftharpoons ES'' \rightleftharpoons EP \longrightarrow E + P$$

From this it is clear that K_m is the dissociation constant of a complicated series of equilibria.

In practice it is impractical to obtain data at high enough substrate concentration to reach the maximal velocity, V, so K_m, or substrate concentration at velocity $V/2$, is difficult to determine.

In order to obviate this objection, Lineweaver and Burk (67) proposed that the experimental data be plotted as a straight line and then maximum velocity, V, be found by extrapolation. Taking the reciprocal of each side of the Michaelis equation yields a linear function; i.e., graphs as a straight line. More recent workers (68) have proposed variations of this equation:

$$v = \frac{V[S]}{K_m + [S]}$$

or

$$\frac{1}{v} = \frac{K_m + [S]}{V[S]} = \frac{K_m}{V[S]} + \frac{[S]}{V[S]} = \frac{K_m}{V} \times \frac{1}{[S]} + \frac{1}{V} \quad \text{(linear equation)}$$

Table 11.3.   Data on Reaction Rates of Decarboxylation of Dihydroxyphenylalanine (DOPA) by DOPA Decarboxylase at Different Substrate Concentrations*
Beef adrenal was the enzyme source

$[S]M$	$\dfrac{1}{[S]}$	v, observed velocity, μl CO_2 per mg protein per hr.	$\dfrac{1}{v}$
2×10^{-3}	0.5×10^3	30.4	3.3×10^{-2}
1×10^{-3}	1.0×10^3	25.5	3.9×10^{-2}
7.5×10^{-4}	1.33×10^3	21.9	4.5×10^{-2}
5×10^{-4}	2.0×10^3	19.2	5.2×10^{-2}
4×10^{-4}	2.5×10^3	17.5	5.7×10^{-2}
2.5×10^{-4}	4.0×10^3	13.3	7.6×10^{-2}

* Unpublished data, courtesy of Dr. J. H. Fellman, Departments of Biochemistry and Neurology, University of Oregon Medical School, Portland.

This is the reciprocal equation, and when $1/v$ is plotted on the vertical axis against $1/[S]$ on the horizontal axis, a straight line is obtained. The slope of the line is equal to K_m/V and it intercepts the vertical axis at a point equal to $1/V$.

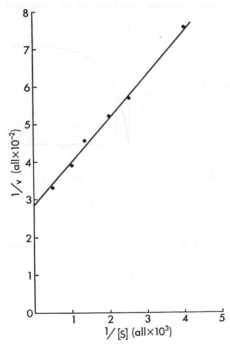

Figure 11.8.   Lineweaver-Burk plot of data from Table 11.3.

From the data in Table 11.3, the Lineweaver-Burk plot shown in Figure 11.8 is obtained. The intercept is at 2.8×10^{-2} which equals $1/V$, and $V = 35.8$. The slope K_m/V is obtained—at $1/[S] = 2.5$, for example—as follows. At this point on the curve $1/v = 5.7$. This value minus $2.8 = 2.9$ and $\dfrac{2.9 \times 10^{-2}}{2.5 \times 10^3} = 1.16 \times 10^{-5}$. K_m then equals $1.16 \times 10^{-5} \times 35.8 = 41.5 \times 10^{-5}$, or 4.15×10^{-4}. This is the substrate molarity at which the reaction velocity is one-half maximal or $V/2$.

Table 11.4 lists the K_m values for a number of enzymes catalyzing specific reactions. The pH optima of a number of enzymes are also given here; this pH effect will be discussed shortly.

Table 11.4. pH Optima and Michaelis Constants for Some Enzymes

Enzyme	Source	Substrate	pH Optimum	K_m
Phosphatase	Mammalian tissue	Monophosphoric esters	9.0–9.2	
Phosphatase	Bone	Glycerophosphate		< 0.003 M
Phosphatase	Aspergillus	Glycerophosphate	5.5	0.09 M
Lipase (esterase)	Pancreas	Ethyl butyrate	7.0	> 0.03 M In phosphate buffer
Maltase	Human intestine	Maltose	6.1	
Saccharase (sucrase)	Mammalian intestine	Sucrose	6.2	0.02 M
Amylase	Saliva and pancreas	Starch	6.0–7.0	0.8–0.25%
Urease	Soybean	Urea	7.2–7.9 ca.	0.025 M
Pepsin	Stomach	Various proteins	1.5–2.5	4.5% for ovalbumin
Dipeptidase	Intestine	Dipeptides	7.3–8.1	0.02–0.07 M for glycylleucine
Carboxylase	Yeast	α-Keto acids	4.8	0.01 M for pyruvic acid
Catalase	Liver	H_2O_2	6.3–9.5	0.025 M

Data taken from a more comprehensive table in Stern's review (1).

2. Concentration of enzyme. Within fairly wide limits the speed of an enzymatic reaction is proportional to the enzyme concentration. This can be shown to hold for many enzyme systems, providing interfering conditions do not develop and the substrate concentration is maintained constant.

Figure 11.9. The effect of enzyme concentration on enzyme activity. These data were obtained by determining the number of milligrams of reducing sugar formed in digestion mixtures containing different amounts of pancreatic amylase. The pancreatic amylase was supplied as duodenal contents and the values of the abscissa indicate the number of cubic milliliters of duodenal contents present in the digestion mixtures. The digestion mixture was buffered at an optimum pH and contained optimum amounts of chloride and substrate. (From Meyers, V. C., and Free, A. H.: *Am. J. Clin. Path.*, **13**, 42, 1943.)

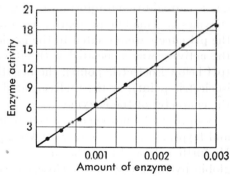

Figure 11.9 taken from a paper by Meyers and Free (65) brings out this point clearly.

Impure pepsin and trypsin show reaction velocities more nearly proportional to the square root of the enzyme concentration. Northrop, however, demonstrated that highly purified pepsin, within limits, does digest protein at a rate about proportional to its concentration. In the presence of increased concentrations of reaction products this linear relationship may not hold.

3. Concentration of reaction products. It has been observed by Northrop that the addition of products of enzyme action to a system containing purified enzyme destroys the linear relationship between enzyme concentration and reaction rate. Thus, if peptic digestion products are added to a system in which purified pepsin is hydrolyzing protein, the rate of reaction is similar to the rate obtained with a crude pepsin preparation.

Nelson and Anderson (69) demonstrated that the addition of either glucose or fructose inhibits the hydrolysis of 2 per cent sucrose by yeast invertase. Many instances of like nature are known. Explanations for this retarding effect of reaction products on enzyme action usually involve the assumption that a more stable complex of enzyme and reaction products than of enzyme and substrate is formed, which ties up the "active centers" of a certain proportion of the enzyme molecules. It is also assumed by some that in the presence of high concentrations of reaction products some resynthesis by enzyme may occur; this would obviously result in an apparent decrease in rate of decomposition.

4. Effect of pH. We have already seen that the activity of an enzyme is determined in large degree by the pH of the system in which it operates. Each enzyme has a pH optimum—i.e., a H^+ concentration at which the enzyme reacts at maximum speed. The pH optimum changes, sometimes radically, with varying conditions of time, temperature, concentration of substrate, or other factors. On the other hand, very slight changes toward either side of the pH optimum may result in profound alterations of reaction rates. It is probable that changes in pH alter the equilibrium point between synthesis and hydrolysis by certain enzymes. Wilcox (70) explains the sensitivity of urease to pH change on this basis.

The effect of hydrogen ion concentration on the speed of enzyme action has led to additional information regarding the mechanics of action. Since enzymes are colloidal proteins or contain proteins, it was early assumed that the pH effects were related to the isoelectric pH values of the enzymes; i.e., the activity was associated with either the positively charged enzyme ion (pH below isoelectric point), the negatively charged enzyme ion (pH above isoelectric point), or the undissociated molecule (isoelectric), depending on the character of the enzyme.

Northrop (2), however, showed that the optimum pH values for pepsin and trypsin vary, depending on what protein the enzymes are hydrolyzing. He further showed that the rate of hydrolysis of casein, gelatin, and hemoglobin by these enzymes is closely correlated to the titration curves of the proteins.

The titration curves indicate the degree of ionization of the substrate molecules as positive or negative ions. He interprets his data as indicating that pepsin attacks the positive substrate ions and that trypsin hydrolyzes the negative ions formed at higher pH. Figure 11.10, from one of Northrop's papers (71), clearly demonstrates this interesting relationship.

In case of fat or carbohydrate substrate molecules similar reasoning is not applicable.

Kunitz and Northrop accounted for the decrease in tryptic action above pH 8, Figure 11.10, by demonstrating an equilibrium mixture of active and

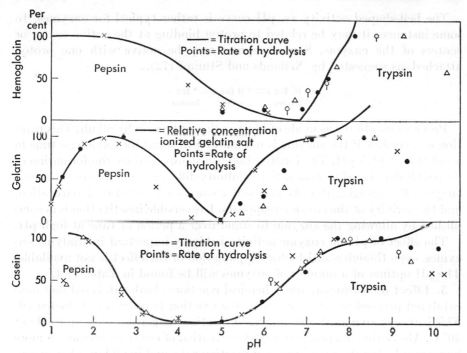

Per
cent

Figure 11.10. Relative rate of hydrolysis of proteins by pepsin or trypsin and per cent of protein present as salt, at various pH levels   (From Northrop, J. H.: *J. Gen. Physiol.*, **5**, 263, 1923.)

inactive trypsin above this pH and a further shift toward the inactive form with increasing alkalinity.

Figure 11.11 shows the relation of pH to the activity of the amylases of wheat flour. The data are for a one-hour incubation at 27° C, with all conditions but the acidity held constant for each experiment. Note the marked

Figure 11.11. The influence of hydrogen ion concentration on the activity of wheat-flour amylase. Ten grams of wheat flour autodigested at 27° for 1 hour. (Data: Rumsey.) (Reproduced by permission from *Outlines of Biochemistry*, 2nd ed., by R. A. Gortner, published by John Wiley & Sons, Inc., New York, 1938, p. 942.)

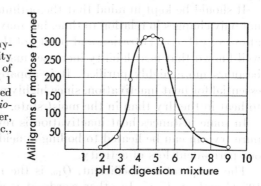

difference in reaction rate at pH 5 and pH 7. Also note the steep slope of the curve near the optimum pH. Such data prompted an earlier statement to the effect that small changes from the optimum pH may result in profound alterations in enzyme reaction rates.

The bell-shaped activity vs. pH curve is rather typical for enzymes. In some instances it may be related to proton binding at the active center or centers of the enzyme. Some enzymes may be active with one proton attached, as suggested by Neilands and Stumpf (72).

$$H_2 \text{ Enz} \rightleftarrows H \text{ Enz} \rightleftarrows \text{Enz}$$

inactive   active   inactive

Previous mention was made of inactivation of trypsin by alkali. This reaction is reversible if the enzyme is not allowed to stand for too long a time in a solution of high pH. The inactivation is accompanied by the formation of reversible denatured protein with a solubility differing from that of the active enzyme. Rearranging the pH to about 2 causes a reversal of denaturation, and the activity of the enzyme reappears. Irreversible inactivation is accomplished by allowing the enzyme to stand over a period of time at high pH.

The effect of pH on enzyme activity is highly important in studying enzymes, even though a satisfactory explanation of the effect is not available. The pH optima of a number of enzymes will be found in Table 11.4.

5. Effect of temperature. Chemical reactions, both catalyzed and noncatalyzed proceed at a faster rate as the reaction temperature is increased. This is true of enzymatically catalyzed reactions in general only up to about 50° C. Above this temperature heat inactivation of enzymes becomes a more important factor than the increased reaction rate, and in all but a few exceptional cases the speed of reaction slows and ceases around 70° to 80° C.

The optimum temperature of an enzyme is that temperature at which the greatest amount of substrate is changed in unit time. As will be pointed out in the next section, assigning an optimum temperature to any enzyme is hazardous unless the time of the reaction is also expressed. In the case of the digestive enzymes of the gastrointestinal tract, which involve relatively long periods of action, the optimum temperature is around 40° C. Certain plant enzymes may have optimum temperatures as high as 60° C.

It should be kept in mind that the optimum temperature for any enzyme not only changes in relation to time, but may also change in relation to alterations of pH, concentration and purity of the enzyme preparation, etc. It is well known that heat lability increases markedly as an enzyme preparation becomes more highly purified. It is apparent, furthermore, that water is essential for heat inactivation, since highly purified enzymes are more stable to heat in the dry than in the moist state.

In some instances heat inactivation is reversible. Northrop showed that pure trypsin can be heated to boiling in acid solution for a short time without permanent loss of activity.

The temperature coefficient, Q_{10}, is the ratio of reaction rates at $T° + 10°$ C and at $T°$ C. In other words, it is an expression of the increase in reaction rate for a 10° C increase in temperature. The Q_{10} values of enzyme reactions vary from about 1.1 to 5.3 as limits. The majority have values of 3 or less.

The Q_{10} values for a few enzymes are found in Table 11.5.

Table 11.5. Q_{10} Values For Some Enzymes

Enzyme	Q_{10} Value	
Catalase	2.3	(0–10°)
	2.19	(10–20°)
Urease	1.81	(20–30°)
	1.90	(30–40°)
Maltase (yeast)	1.90	(10–20°)
	1.44	(20–30°)
	1.28	(30–40°)
Succinic oxidase	2.0	(30–40°)
	2.1	(40–50°)
Invertase	1.76	(15–25°)
	1.62	(25–35°)

It is now assumed that for a molecule to undergo decomposition (first order reaction) or for two molecules to collide and react (second-order reaction) the molecules must possess a certain energy of activation, usually expressed as E, and also called the "critical increment." The value of E, in calories per mol of substrate, differs with different substrates and also for the same reaction under the influence of different catalysts. At 20° C a definite per cent of sucrose molecules in solution—say, in the presence of H+ possess this energy of activation and can therefore be hydrolyzed to hexoses. If the temperature of this solution is raised to 30° C, it is obvious that a greater percentage of sugar molecules is endowed with the necessary energy of activation, E. Thus the speed of reaction is faster at the elevated temperature.

An uncatalyzed reaction has a higher E value than the same reaction in the presence of a catalyst. Enzymes, then, lower the energy of activation or critical increment of reactions they catalyze.

With H+ as catalyst the energy of activation for the inversion of sucrose is 25,560 cal per mol of sugar. But with the enzyme sucrase as catalyst the critical increment is about 9000 cal per mol. It is obvious that at temperatures consistent with enzyme action a great many more sucrose molecules possess energy corresponding to 9000 cal per mol than to 25,560 cal per mol, and, consequently, sucrase greatly increases the rate of sucrose hydrolysis. In other words, the presence of the proper enzyme mediates a chemical reaction at a lower energy level, and thus at a lower temperature.

The Arrhenius equation allows the calculation of the E value of a reaction. One of the usable forms of this equation is:

$$E = \frac{2.303(\log_{10} k_2 - \log_{10} k_1)R}{\dfrac{1}{T_1} - \dfrac{1}{T_2}}$$

where k_2 and k_1 are the velocity constants for the reaction at the absolute temperatures T_2 and T_1, respectively; R = the gas constant, 1.987 cal per degree; and E = the energy of activation or the critical ncrement in calories per mol of substrate within the temperature range studied.

6. Effect of time. Gortner (73) points out that the element of time is generally not given sufficient consideration in discussing factors that affect the rate of enzyme action. He states that there cannot be an optimum hydrogen ion concentration or an optimum temperature independent of time. He indicates further that the optimum temperature of many enzymes from warm-blooded animals is approximately 37° C only if time is measured in hours; if time is measured in days, the optimum temperature may be much lower; if time is measured in minutes, perhaps the optimum temperature will be as high as 70° C or above. Obviously Gortner is correct that the time element is important in defining other conditions which regulate the rate of enzyme action.

An interesting relationship of time and temperature in an enzyme action is cited by Gortner from a paper by Willaman and Davison (74). A sorghum mill experienced difficulty in filtration because of the presence of small amounts of starch which gelatinized at the temperature employed. This material clogged the filter presses and could be avoided only by the impractical expedient of employing large amounts of infusorial earth. The use of starch-splitting enzymes at temperatures above 60° C was attempted, and in the short time that the enzymes remained active at such temperatures sufficient starch was hydrolyzed to obviate the difficulty in filtration of the sorghum juice.

7. State of oxidation of enzyme. A group of enzymes sometimes referred to as the "papainases" or the "sulfhydryl enzymes" are activated by certain reducing agents and inactivated by aeration or other mild oxidizing treatment. Papain, catheptic enzymes, urease, succinic dehydrogenase, and others belong to this class.

Glutathione, cysteine, H_2S, and HCN activate these enzymes. It was felt by some workers that such activation might be accounted for by removal of inactivating heavy metal ions. More recent work indicates that actual reduction of disulfide linkages (—S—S—) in the enzyme molecule to sulfhydryl (—SH) groups may be responsible for the activation.

Hellerman (75) pictured the activation thus:

$$2 \text{ enz} - \text{SH} \underset{\text{red}}{\overset{\text{ox}}{\rightleftharpoons}} \text{enz} - \text{S} - \text{S} - \text{enz} + 2\text{(H)}$$

Active reduced form   Inactive oxidized form

This reaction is freely reversible under the proper experimental conditions.

More recently this same author (76) demonstrated the existence in urease of two types of sulfhydryl groups. He showed that it requires 2 mols of p-chloromercuribenzoate per 21,300 g of urease protein to inactivate the enzyme completely. The addition of the first mol of the mercuribenzoate, although it reacts with —SH groups, causes no inactivation. Complete inactivation accompanies the addition of the second mol of the mercuribenzoate. The reaction is reversed by the addition of cysteine hydrochloride.

Other compounds, such as iodoacetamide, can be used to "remove" the first residue weight of sulfhydryl, and then inactivation, again freely reversible, can be accomplished by the addition of one mol of mercuribenzoate.

Whether the activating agents, such as cysteine, H_2S, HCN, and glutathione, remove metal inhibitors or simply reduce —S—S— to —SH is not apparently settled as yet. At any rate, the state of oxidation of these enzymes is just as important a consideration as temperature, pH, etc. It is likely that in living tissues highly essential roles are played by a number of compounds in maintaining various enzymes in the proper state of oxidation.

8. Activators. Many ions and molecules have the capacity to activate some enzymes. Metal ions are activators of a number of enzymes. Table 11.2 (page 386) shows this relationship. Pepsin (as proenzyme pepsinogen) is activated by H^+ to form the active enzyme. Many reducing agents (cysteine, glutathione) act as enzyme activators of SH enzymes, as indicated previously. Enzymes themselves activate other enzymes or proenzymes; i.e., enterokinase activates trypsinogen to form active trypsin. Trypsinogen, chymotrypsinogen, and pepsinogen are known as "zymogens," and enzymes which activate zymogens are called "kinases." Further discussion appears in Chapter 12.

A detailed kinetic treatment of enzyme activation and other facets of enzymology can be found in the book by Reiner (77).

9. Enzyme inhibition. The pharmacologic action of drugs is based largely on enzyme inhibition. Common examples are found in the action of the sulfonamide drugs and the antibiotics (see Chapter 32). In the great majority of cases the enzyme (or coenzyme) inhibited is not known as yet. However, studies along such lines have led to the development of hundreds of new drugs for use in medicine and veterinary sciences. Other enzyme inhibition studies have been directed specifically toward increasing our understanding of specific reactions or metabolic pathways in plants and animals. The development of "nerve gases," insecticides, and herbicides (weed killers) is based on enzyme inhibition studies, as are some recent developments in antidotes to certain of these inhibitors.

Competitive inhibition, as the term implies, means competition between normal substrate and inhibitor molecules for the enzyme to form enzyme-substrate or enzyme-inhibitor molecules. The over-all rate of inhibition in a given reaction is governed primarily by the affinities of inhibitor molecules and normal substrate molecules for the enzyme and by the concentrations of the reactants. The enzyme is not sufficiently specific, so that molecules chemically similar to normal substrate molecules react and tie up active sites of the enzyme. These sites are then not available to the normal substrate molecules. The complex of inhibitor and enzyme is of such a nature that addition of sufficient substrate will relieve the inhibition.

One classical example of competitive inhibition involves malonic acid as an inhibitor of succinic dehydrogenase. This enzyme forms complexes with both malonic and succinic acids (enzyme-inhibitor and enzyme-substrate complexes), and with the proper concentrations of reactants succinate is not dehydrogenated (oxidized) to fumaric acid. On the other hand, with sufficient succinate present the inhibition by malonate can be completely overcome.

Since the enzyme-inhibitor complex can react only to dissociate into enzyme plus inhibitor, the effective concentration of enzyme is reduced by the presence of an inhibitor, and reaction rate is lowered. Mathematical treatment leads to a Lineweaver-Burk type of equation with the form $y = ax + b$, which is the form of this equation for the uninhibited system. Since b represents the vertical intercept and in both cases $= 1/V$, the vertical intercept is at the same point on the plot in competitive inhibition and with no inhibition. This is indicated in Figure 11.12. The slope is steeper for the inhibited reaction, which denotes lowered velocity (since the vertical axis is the reciprocal of velocity). For details of the mathematical treatment, see (3), (72), and (77).

Noncompetitive inhibition differs from the competitive type primarily in the formation of an irreversible complex between inhibitor and enzyme.

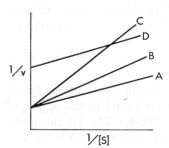

Figure 11.12. Illustration of competitive inhibition and noncompetitive inhibition as Lineweaver-Burk-type plots. A, Normal, uninhibited enzyme; B and C, two concentrations of a competitive inhibitor; D, noncompetitive inhibition.

This combination can be at the site or sites on the enzyme molecule ordinarily occupied by the normal substrate or at a different site removed sufficiently so as to have no influence on the normal substrate binding. In either case the enzyme is in effect removed from participation by an amount depending upon inhibitor concentration. Increasing substrate concentration in this situation does not relieve inhibition. Heavy metal ions, cyanide, and other substances are well-known examples of noncompetitive inhibitors. In many cases the chemical derivatives formed are stable complexes. From the applicable equation and the Lineweaver-Burk plot, the intercept $1/V$ and the slope are increased by a factor involving concentration of inhibitor. This is seen graphically in Figure 11.12. For mathematical treatment and discussion of other types of inhibition, see (3) and (72).

It is significant that in competitive inhibition the intercept is the same as without inhibition and that in noncompetitive inhibition the intercept is higher on the vertical axis and the slope is greater. Such features are useful in distinguishing the two types of inhibition from experimental data on enzyme action.

Urease is irreversibly inactivated by ultraviolet light. Papain, another of the sulfhydryl enzymes, was inactivated to the extent of 90 per cent in 53 sec. by ultraviolet light, while trypsin, not a —SH enzyme, required the same treatment for 12 minutes to attain this degree of inactivation (78). From such data and other reports it is clear that —SH enzymes are far more sensitive to ultraviolet light. Purified acetylcholinesterase was found to be very resistant to ultraviolet radiation. Hargreaves (79) believes that the inactivation after very large doses of ultraviolet light is not due to an effect on —SH groups, and he concluded that —SH groups do not play an important role (active centers) in this enzyme.

Trypsin is markedly inhibited by some naturally occurring peptides and proteins. Pancreatic extracts contain a basic peptide with a molecular weight of around 9000, which combines with and inactivates trypsin. Soybeans contain a protein which acts similarly (80). Shulman (81) isolated a potent inhibitor of several proteolytic enzymes from human urine and plasma. The molecular weight was found to be 16,700. The combination of inhibitor with trypsin was virtually irreversible around neutral pH, although the inhibitor could be recovered from the complex by treatment with 2.5 per cent trichloroacetic acid. Interestingly enough, the inhibitor showed anticoagulant activity similar to that of soybean trypsin inhibitor.

Table 11.6 lists several examples of enzymes and their inhibitors or inactivators.

Table 11.6. Some Examples of Enzyme Inhibitors

Enzyme	Inhibitors
Pyrophosphatase, brain	HCHO, iodoacetate, alloxan, F^-
Arginase	Ornithine, lysine, L-amino acids
Lipase	Benzaldehyde, some metal ions
Carboxylase	HCHO, CH_3CHO, C_6H_5CHO
Phosphatase, alkaline	Chelating compounds, arsenate, F^-
Choline esterase	Physostigmine (eserine), atropine
Urease	Heavy metals, o-quinone
Carbonic anhydrase	CO, sulfanilamide
Cytochrome oxidase	CN^-, H_2S, CO, azide
Succinic dehydrogenase	Malonate, hematin, Se
Carboxypeptidase	Iodoacetate, S^-, CN^-
α-Ketoglutaric oxidase	Parapyruvate

Space does not allow a discussion of the interesting mechanisms involved in some of these inhibitions. The last example in Table 11.6 is interesting, since the data indicate that parapyruvate (dimer of pyruvate) inhibits α-ketoglutaric oxidase through formation of a stable complex with lipoic acid, the coenzyme of this oxidative decarboxylating system (82).

Turnover numbers of enzymes. Turnover numbers are useful in indicating the relative activity of enzymes. The turnover number may be defined for practical purposes as the number of mols of substrate converted to products per mol of enzyme per minute.

In order to determine the turnover number of an enzyme, the enzymatic reaction must proceed at maximal velocity V, and in accordance with the zero-order equation. As pointed out earlier, this is true when [ES] is maximal; i.e., when all of the enzyme is bound by substrate. Under these conditions:

$$V = k_3[ES] = k_3[E] \text{ or } k_3 = \frac{V}{[E]}$$

where, by convention, V = mols of substrate converted per minute and $[E]$ = mols of enzyme taking part in the reaction.

When there is more than one catalytic center on the enzyme molecule, the equation should be:

$$k_3 = \frac{V}{\text{no. of active centers} \times [E]}$$

which gives the mols of substrate converted per mol active center of the enzyme. Unfortunately, the number of active centers per molecule of enzyme is known for only a few enzymes, and the more approximate equation $k_3 = \dfrac{V}{[E]}$ must be used. When the turnover number of catalase acting upon H_2O_2 was calculated according to the latter equation, a value of about 5,000,000 was obtained, the highest known. However, since it is known that each catalase molecule has four active centers, the turnover number more properly should be one-fourth of 5,000,000, or 1,250,000. Turnover numbers for β-amylase, fumarase, and α-amylase of about 250,000, 100,000 and 19,000, respectively, have been calculated, but since the number of active centers per molecule of enzyme is unknown, it is at present impossible to calculate their turnover numbers by the more exact equation. Approximate turnover numbers, such as we have, indicate the extreme rapidity with which the series of reactions:

$$E + S \rightleftarrows ES \longrightarrow products + E$$

takes place.

SYNTHESIS OF ENZYMES AND ENZYME INDUCTION

Surprisingly little information is available on enzyme synthesis. This is a problem constituting a primary hub of all biology, and only in recent years have we started to gain an insight into the many ramifications involved. Most of our information has come from studies with microorganisms through the use of inducers (or inductors). Inducers are substrate molecules or chemically related compounds for the enzyme whose synthesis they bring about.

The enzyme β-galactosidase is synthesized at a rapid rate in *E. coli* under the influence of the inducer galactose (83). The enzyme is almost undetectable in the noninduced microorganism. Other induced enzyme syntheses have been accomplished. Much of this type of work is reviewed in a publication of an international symposium on enzymes (84).

In mammals fewer clear-cut examples of enzyme induction are known. One is the demonstration by Knox and Mehler (85) of a tenfold increase in tryptophan peroxidase, now called "tryptophan pyrrolase" (tryptophan $\longrightarrow$ formyl kynurenine), of rabbit liver after administering tryptophan. Similar increases were found in liver tissue of rats and guinea pigs within a few hours after giving the amino acid orally, subcutaneously, or intraperitoneally. Normal levels were recorded 15 to 20 hours later, indicating a rapid response and decline. The induced response has been shown to be clearly evident within an hour following tryptophan administration, and the data support the contention that the net increase in enzyme activity was the result of enzyme (protein) synthesis (86, 87). The rate of enzyme formation was found by Lee (88) to be independent of the inductor dose, but the maximal level of the enzyme and the time this level was reached were linearly related to the quantity of tryptophan administered.

The alkaline phosphomonoesterase activity of chick embryos was shown to increase markedly following the injection of disodium phenylphosphate (89). The acid phosphomonoesterase activity was not increased under the conditions employed.

Many investigators have turned their attentions to this intriguing field, but at the present time our total knowledge of enzyme production is indeed meager. Neilands and Stumpf (72) discuss the mechanism of induction and suggest that "the inducer might play a catalytic role in enzyme synthesis by becoming incorporated in the enzyme-forming system."

CLASSIFICATION OF ENZYMES

The classification of enzymes is difficult. New developments in enzyme chemistry have altered our views considerably and changed the positions of certain enzymes in a systematic classification. Various authorities have proposed classifications differing in important respects, due primarily to the basis of classification employed. Haldane (90), for example, classed all the C-N linkage hydrolyzing enzymes together, while others separate urease from the enzymes pepsin, trypsin, etc., which also break this linkage.

Dixon and Webb (3) present a table of 659 enzymes (including cofactors where known, source of enzyme, substrates and the reaction, and references). More than 350 of these are classified as transferring enzymes and 221 as hydrolyzing enzymes. The remainder are classed in a group including synthetases, enzymes adding groups to double bonds, stereoisomerases, and a miscellaneous group.

Many authors still prefer to classify enzymes on the basis of substrate attacked, principally because it simplifies somewhat this difficult field for the beginner, since in most cases the name of an enzyme is derived from its substrate with the suffix "-ase" added. A number of the enzymes discovered earlier retain their original names—for example, "pepsin," "rennin," "trypsin," and "amylase."

The outline to follow is presented with the thought in mind of bringing together some of the important information about typical enzymes of the various classes. It is based largely on substrate attacked, is not intended to be at all complete, and is, in the main, simplified by the omission of many synonyms and enzymes of doubtful occurrence. A more detailed classification will be found immediately following.

1. CARBOHYDRATE-HYDROLYZING ENZYMES (GLYCOSIDASES)

Cellulases are found in molds, bacteria, and snails. They hydrolyze cellulose into small carbohydrate fragments without the production of glucose. These enzymes are responsible for the digestion of cellulose by such animals as cows and sheep, in which case the enzymes are produced by bacteria in the digestive tract. Other enzymes with similar distribution, their functions implied by their names, are inulinase, xylanase, and mannanase.

Amylases, such as pancreatic amylase (amylopsin), salivary amylase (ptyalin), and malt amylase from plants, are typical of this group. They are conveniently divided into α- and β-amylases on the basis of different points of attack on such oligosaccharides as starches, glycogens, amylopectins, amyloses, and dextrins.

The α-amylases (animal origin) are now frequently referred to as "endoamylases" and the β-amylases as "exoamylases." This follows the concept put forth by Bergmann regarding the endo- and the exopeptidases (referred to previously). The α- or endo-amylases (pancreatic and salivary amylase) hydrolyze more interior linkages of the branched oligosaccharides (starches, glycogens, etc.), producing fragments larger than maltose, and then more slowly liberate this sugar. The linear amylose molecule after extensive hydrolysis is converted completely to maltose (87 per cent) and glucose (13 per cent) (91). In all cases the attack is at the α-1,4-glucoside linkage.

The β- or exoamylases are of plant origin and hydrolyze oligosaccharides from the nonreducing end of the chain at the second α-1,4-glucosidic linkage, forming a molecule of β-maltose, and then another, etc., until in the case of amylose the molecule is completely converted to β-maltose. In the branched substrates, such as amylopectin or starch, this enzyme again removes β-maltose molecules consecutively from the nonreducing ends until a branch point—i.e., a 1,6-glucoside bond—is reached. Both α- and β-amylases from various sources have been crystallized. Bernfeld (92) has reviewed many aspects of the amylase enzymes.

The α-1,6-glucoside linkages (branch points) are not attacked by the α- or β-amylases but are specifically hydrolyzed by an enzyme in intestinal mucosa named "oligo-1,6-glucosidase" by Larner and McNickle (93).

Sucrase, also called "invertase" and "saccharase," occurs in many plants, in yeast, and also in intestinal juice and perhaps in pancreatic juice. It hydrolyzes sucrose to glucose and fructose. The term "invertase" is derived from the fact that a sucrose solution is dextrorotatory; but because fructose is highly levorotatory, the mixture after enzyme hydrolysis rotates polarized light to the left, and thus the rotation has become inverted. The enzyme is logically referred to as "β-fructosidase," because it hydrolyzes sugars containing a β-fructose residue (fructose with the β configuration).

Maltase is found in yeast and pancreatic and intestinal juice, but has a wide general distribution in plant and animal tissues. It acts on maltose to form glucose only. Certain other α-glucosides are also hydrolyzed by maltase enzyme(s). Another name applied to this enzyme is "α-glucosidase."

Lactase occurs in the intestine of young mammals. It appears that the majority of the enzyme activity is intimately bound to the cells of the intestinal mucosa, since hydrolysis of ingested lactose does occur before it reaches the blood stream, but intestinal juice and aqueous extracts of the mucosa show only slight activity, while finely minced mucosa is quite active. Adult mammalian intestinal tissue does contain the enzyme, contrary to some reports. Lactose (milk sugar) is a β-D-galactoside and is hydrolyzed by lactase to glucose and galactose. The enzyme is also called a β-D-galactosidase.

Emulsin is a system of enzymes found principally in bitter almonds. One of these, β-glucosidase, hydrolyzes β-glucosides, such as amygdalin, found in bitter almonds. The products are glucose, benzaldehyde, and HCN. This enzyme assumes importance in many studies, since any glucoside which it can split is classed as a β-glucoside. Apparently all naturally occurring glucosides are of the β form and β-glucosidase alone is able to hydrolyze them. Both an α- and a β-galactosidase are present also.

β-Glucuronidase, a type of glycosidase, is found in many animal tissues. It hydrolyzes (and may synthesize) glucuronic acid conjugates. Many β-D-glucuronides appear in the urine normally. An enzyme preparation from calf spleen was used to hydrolyze glucuronides of urinary steroids (94). When hyaluronidase hydrolyzes hyaluronic acid, there are produced various chain-length oligosaccharides which are likewise acted upon by β-glucuronidase (95). See (96) and (97) for reviews of this subject.

2. PROTEIN-HYDROLYZING ENZYMES
   (PEPTIDE BONDS)

a) Animal proteinases or endopeptidases.

Pepsin is found in the gastric juice of mammals. It is secreted by the chief cells as a zymogen (precursor) called "pepsinogen." A pepsinogen has been isolated from the gastric mucosa of the shark also. Hydrogen ion activates pepsinogen to pepsin, which starts the hydrolysis of many native proteins. As Bergmann and others have demonstrated, the enzyme is also capable of hydrolyzing a number of small synthetic peptides *in vitro*, and, consequently, it is logical to assume that a similar action may occur *in vivo*, although this action may be of little importance in the process of digestion. The enzyme has slight milk-clotting activity. See also phosphoamidase (miscellaneous enzymes).

Rennin is found in gastric juice. It is the enzyme primarily responsible for coagulation of milk (casein). It is one of the most recently crystallized enzymes and is capable of clotting about 10 million times its weight of milk at 37° C in 10 minutes. The process of clotting involves a change in the casein molecules to give what is called "paracasein," which then forms calcium paracaseinate, the clot. In the absence of Ca^{++} no clot forms. A number of proteolytic enzymes capable of clotting milk have been found to hydrolyze such a compound as N-(p-chlorophenyl)-amidophosphoric acid (phosphoamidases). This involves the scission of a P—N bond, and it was suggested (98) that the breaking of this bond in casein, and not proteolysis, is the first step in milk coagulation. Pepsin, chymotrypsin, and rennin have a fairly constant ratio of phosphoamidase and milk-clotting activity. The process is not well understood.

Trypsin and chymotrypsin are found in pancreatic tissue and in pancreatic juice as the zymogens, trypsinogen, and chymotrypsinogen. Both enzymes are capable of splitting a wide variety of native proteins. The products vary with experimental conditions, but small split products can be obtained in many cases. Small synthetic peptides of the proper constitution are also split by these enzymes. Chymotrypsin, for instance, splits L-tyrosine amide and glycyltyrosine amide at the amide linkage but hydrolyzes benzoyltyrosylglycine amide at the tyrosylglycine linkage. Both enzymes have slight milk-clotting activity. Trypsin is slightly active in the conversion of prothrombin to thrombin in the process of blood coagulation. This action seems to be analogous to the activation of trypsinogen by enterokinase. The following step—thrombin action on fibrinogen—probably involves proteolytic enzymatic activity.

Cathepsins are found intimately associated with various mammalian tissues and organs. At least four different cathepsins can be isolated from beef spleen or kidney. There may be a catheptic enzyme in gastric juice. These enzymes are differentiated primarily by dissimilar degrees of activation afforded by sulfhydryl activators, such as cysteine or glutathione, and also by their activities on synthetic peptides of varying structure. Their *in vivo* function is not too clear but may be related to protein synthesis and hydrolysis within the tissue and organ cells.

b) Plant proteinases or endopeptidases.

Papain is found in the milky juice and fruit of the papaya. It has strong proteolytic action and milk-clotting power. Many authors speak of "papain-like enzymes" or "sulfhydryl enzymes," meaning those enzymes which apparently depend on free —SH groups for their activity. They are activated by H_2S, HCN, cysteine, etc., the sulfhydryl activators.

Chymopapain is similar to papain in distribution and activity.

Ficin is obtained from fig latex. It has proteolytic and milk-clotting activity and hydrolyzes certain synthetic peptides, such as benzoylarginine amide.

Bromelin is found in pineapple fruit and leaves. It hydrolyzes proteins and certain small peptides and clots milk.

It has been suggested (99) that the "-ain" ending be used to form the generic names of newly discovered proteolytic enzymes from plants.

The preparation and properties of several more plant proteinases can be found in a series of articles by Greenberg and Winnick (100). An interesting table compiled by these authors contains many characteristics of 11 plant proteinases.

The foregoing enzymes were formerly classed as proteinases, because they were thought to be involved only in the beginning of the hydrolysis of large protein molecules. It is evident now that such is not the case. There is no satisfactory classification based on size of substrate molecules.

The term "proteinases" or "endopeptidases" is generally retained for these enzymes, however, since the evidence indicates that they hydrolyze the more centrally located peptide bonds and not terminal bonds of the peptide chains in proteins. This distinguishes them from the peptidases or exopeptidases, which do attack the terminal bonds somewhat preferentially. The proteases include both types. Some of the peptidases (exopeptidases) will now be considered.

c) **Exopeptidases.**

Polypeptidases. This is a group of enzymes containing, as examples:

Aminopeptidase or *aminopolypeptidase,* an enzyme occurring primarily in intestinal juice of animals, but also in many organs and in blood. Certain bacteria also have an enzyme with similar properties. It hydrolyzes polypeptides at the end having a free amino group, yielding an amino acid and a smaller peptide. The process may be repeated, since the smaller peptide would also contain a free amino group.

Carboxypeptidase or *carboxypolypeptidase* has a wide distribution but is found especially in pancreatic juice. It functions like aminopeptidase except that the end of the peptide chain having a free carboxyl group is attacked, producing an amino acid and a smaller peptide, which may again be attacked by the enzyme.

Basic carboxypeptidase, isolated from beef pancreas, was so named because it hydrolyzes lysine and arginine from the synthetic substrates benzoylglycyllysine and benzoylglycylarginine (101). These substrates are not attacked by carboxypeptidase.

Dipeptidase is found in intestinal juice and many organs. It is clear that a number of different dipeptidases exist. They hydrolyze dipeptides to amino acids.

Tripeptidase has been isolated from horse erythrocytes and purified 500 to 750 times. It operates as a first-order reaction on all substrates tested (102).

A number of more specific peptidases are known. Only two will be mentioned.

Leucylpeptidase is found in hog intestinal juice, beef muscle, certain plants, and bacteria. It is especially active in hydrolyzing certain peptides containing leucine as a terminal amino acid.

Iminodipeptidase (formerly called "prolinase") is specific for dipeptides which possess the free amino group of proline or hydroxyproline and a free carboxyl group. It does not attack tripeptides. The enzyme has been purified from swine kidney and shows increasing activity with increasing alkalinity up to pH 9 (103).

3. ENZYMES HYDROLYZING NONPEPTIDE C—N LINKAGES (CALLED "AMIDASES" OR "DESAMIDASES")

Urease, from jack beans and other seeds and also liver, spleen, and red blood cells of some species, hydrolyzes urea to CO_2 and NH_3. One of the enzymes crystallized early

(1926), it has received a great amount of study. It is a sulfhydryl enzyme and finds importance in the laboratory determination of urea in blood and in urine. The function of urease in animal tissues is unknown.

Arginase is found especially in the nuclei of liver cells; highly potent preparations have been made from ground liver. A preparation from beef liver upon activation with Mn^{++} liberated 3300 μ moles of urea per minute per mg protein at pH 9.5 (104). It has been found also in intestinal mucosa and in certain molds. Arginase converts arginine into urea and the amino acid ornithine. This important function is further discussed under the Krebs-Henseleit cycle for urea production.

Glutaminase is located primarily in the kidney, although other tissues apparently contain small amounts. Glutamine, the amide of glutamic acid, is hydrolyzed to glutamic acid and ammonia by the enzyme. This apparently constitutes the primary mechanism of ammonia production in the body and further discussion of the matter is found under metabolism. A specific method for the determination of glutamine in biologic fluids is based on the activity of this enzyme (105):

$$COOH - CHNH_2CH_2CH_2CONH_2 \longrightarrow COOHCHNH_2CH_2CH_2COOH + NH_3$$

$$glutamine \xrightarrow[H_2O]{glutaminase} glutamic\ acid + ammonia$$

Asparaginase occurs in liver and other animal tissues, in plants, yeast, and in bacteria. Asparagine is split into ammonia and aspartic acid by this enzyme.

Purine amidases, adenase, and *guanase* are present in liver and other tissues, including blood. Adenase removes an amino group from adenine to form hypoxanthine and ammonia, while guanase does the same to guanine to form xanthine and ammonia.

Aspartase found in a number of bacteria removes NH_3 from aspartic acid yielding fumaric acid:

$$COOHCHNH_2CH_2COOH \longrightarrow COOHCH = CHCOOH + NH_3$$

$$Aspartic\ acid \xrightarrow{aspartase} Fumaric\ acid + ammonia$$

Hippuricase is found in a number of animal tissues and is responsible for the hydrolysis of hippuric acid to benzoic acid and glycine. Certain other amino acids in combination with benzoic acid as well as with taurocholic and glycocholic acids are also attacked.

4. LIPID-HYDROLYZING ENZYMES

Lipases are widespread in plants. The pancreas is the primary animal source. Blood serum and some other tissues have low concentrations of the enzyme. Very small amounts of the enzyme have been reported in gastric juice. Glyceryl esters of fatty acids (neutral fats) are hydrolyzed by the enzyme to fatty acids and glycerol. Simpler esters, such as methyl butyrate, are attacked very slowly by the lipases.

Esterases are found primarily in the liver of animals and are also widespread in plants. The simpler esters, such as amyl acetate, are hydrolyzed by this group of enzymes. The number of such enzymes may be large, though there is no need to postulate a specific enzyme for each different ester. They show little or no activity toward neutral fats.

Cholesterase, in blood and other tissues, hydrolyzes cholesterol esters, yielding cholesterol and fatty acids. This enzyme has received little attention.

Lecithinases (phospholipases). At least four distinct enzymes are known to hydrolyze lecithins. These have been named "phospholipase A," "B," "C," and "D" or "lecithinase A," "B," "C," and "D" (3). Lecithinase A hydrolyzes lecithin at the ester linkage on the number 1 or α' carbon atom. It also acts similarly on cephalins, forming L-α-lysolecithin or L-α-lysocephalin and fatty acid (106). The enzyme is found in some snake venoms and in pancreatic extracts.

Phospholipase B is also found in venoms and in various animal and plant tissues. It removes the remaining fatty acid from lysolecithin or lysocephalin, yielding the corresponding L-α-glycerylphosphorylcholine or the cephalin derivative.

Phospholipase C (the α-toxin of *Cl. welchii*) is found in venoms, bacterial toxin, and brain. The enzyme hydrolyzes lecithin to yield phosphorylcholine and a diglyceride (107). Phospholipase D is found in plants and acts upon various phosphatides, producing phosphatidic acids and choline, ethanolamine, or serine (108).

The accompanying generalized scheme, Figure 11.13, indicates the foregoing reactions. L-α-Lecithin is used as the substrate. It should be kept in mind that many ramifications regarding specificity are not precisely known. The point at which each of the four enzymes hydrolyzes the molecule is indicated.

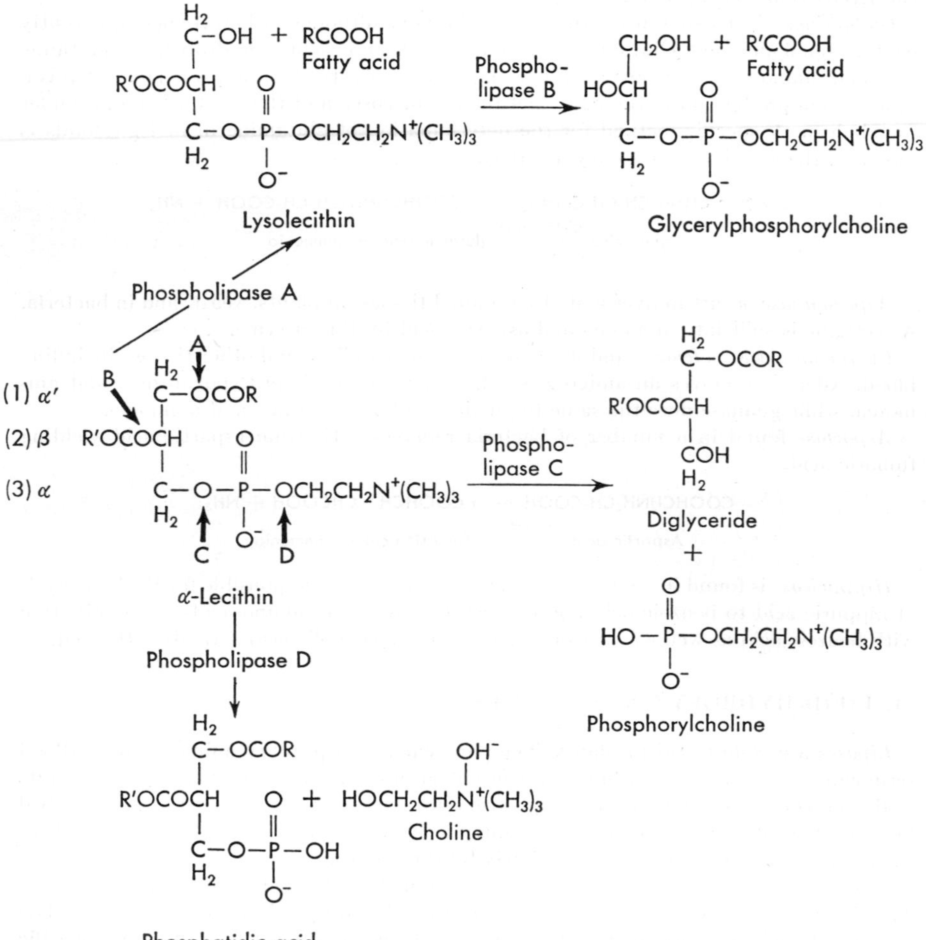

$$
\begin{array}{l}
\text{H}_2 \\
\text{C-OH} \ + \ \text{RCOOH} \\
| \qquad\qquad\quad \text{Fatty acid} \\
\text{R'OCOCH} \quad \text{O} \\
| \qquad\qquad\;\; \| \\
\text{C-O-P-OCH}_2\text{CH}_2\text{N}^+(\text{CH}_3)_3 \\
\text{H}_2 \quad\; | \\
\qquad\quad \text{O}^-
\end{array}
$$

Lysolecithin

$\xrightarrow[\text{lipase B}]{\text{Phospho-}}$

$$
\begin{array}{l}
\text{CH}_2\text{OH} \ + \ \text{R'COOH} \\
| \qquad\qquad\quad \text{Fatty acid} \\
\text{HOCH} \quad \text{O} \\
| \qquad\quad\;\; \| \\
\text{C-O-P-OCH}_2\text{CH}_2\text{N}^+(\text{CH}_3)_3 \\
\text{H}_2 \quad\; | \\
\qquad\quad \text{O}^-
\end{array}
$$

Glycerylphosphorylcholine

Phospholipase A

(1) α'
(2) β
(3) α

$$
\begin{array}{l}
\qquad\;\; \text{A} \\
\text{H}_2 \;\downarrow \\
\text{C-OCOR} \\
| \\
\text{R'OCOCH} \quad \text{O} \\
| \qquad\qquad\;\; \| \\
\text{C-O-P-OCH}_2\text{CH}_2\text{N}^+(\text{CH}_3)_3 \\
\text{H}_2 \;\uparrow \quad | \;\uparrow \\
\qquad\;\; \text{C} \quad \text{O}^- \; \text{D}
\end{array}
$$

α-Lecithin

$\xrightarrow[\text{lipase C}]{\text{Phospho-}}$

$$
\begin{array}{l}
\text{H}_2 \\
\text{C-OCOR} \\
| \\
\text{R'OCOCH} \\
| \\
\text{COH} \\
\text{H}_2
\end{array}
$$

Diglyceride

+

$$
\begin{array}{l}
\quad \text{O} \\
\quad \| \\
\text{HO-P-OCH}_2\text{CH}_2\text{N}^+(\text{CH}_3)_3 \\
\quad | \\
\quad \text{O}^-
\end{array}
$$

Phosphorylcholine

Phospholipase D

$$
\begin{array}{l}
\text{H}_2 \\
\text{C-OCOR} \\
| \\
\text{R'OCOCH} \quad \text{O} \ + \ \text{HOCH}_2\text{CH}_2\text{N}^+(\text{CH}_3)_3 \\
| \qquad\qquad\;\; \| \qquad\qquad\qquad \text{Choline} \\
\text{C-O-P-OH} \\
\text{H}_2 \quad\; | \\
\qquad\quad \text{O}^-
\end{array}
$$

OH$^-$

Phosphatidic acid

Figure 11.13. The action of the phospholipases (lecithinases) on a lecithin molecule. Heavy arrows indicate bonds attacked by each of the four enzymes.

Many other enzymes concerned with hydrolysis of various lipid fractions must exist in plant and animal tissues. A few not mentioned here have been proposed, but obviously many have so far gone unrecognized.

5. OTHER ESTER-HYDROLYZING ENZYMES

a) The phosphatases. A great variety of phosphatases exists in plant and animal tissues. Among the better recognized members of this group are:

Phosphomonoesterases occur in a variety of tissues. The acid and the alkaline phosphatases of serum are so called because of optimum activity at an acid and at an alkaline pH, respectively. The determination of these enzymes is important in a number of clinical conditions. Prostate gland phosphatase has been distinguished from other serum phosphatases. Phosphomonoesterases have also been found in bone, kidney, red blood cells, and intestinal mucosa. Urine contains phosphatases which may or may not be identical with those of serum or with those of prostate gland. Milk contains a distinct phosphomonoesterase enzyme, and a number of others have been observed in various seeds and plant tissues. The differentiation of these enzymes is difficult in many cases; it is usually based on pH optima, varying effects of activators and inactivators, rate of action under specified conditions, and other criteria. They all have a property in common; i.e., they hydrolyze monophosphoric acid esters. Disodium phenyl phosphate, β-glycerol phosphate, and, more recently, sodium phenolphthalein phosphate are used as substrates in the laboratory determination of phosphatase activity. A report (109) describes many properties as well as the optimum conditions for the assay of human red cell phosphomonoesterase.

A group of *phosphodiesterases* is known to occur quite widespread in plant and animal tissues. These enzymes hydrolyze only one ester linkage in a diesterified phosphoric acid. A member of the preceding group would be required to complete the hydrolysis.

Phosphorylase is found in a great variety of plant and animal tissues. Rabbit muscle contains about 40 to 80 mg per 100 g. Yeast and plant tissues also contain the enzyme. Phosphorylase-a has been crystallized as an euglobulin and shows 60 to 70 per cent of maximum activity without addition of the prosthetic group, adenylic acid. Phosphorylase b requires the addition of adenylic acid for activity. The enzyme mediates the following reversible reaction:

$$\text{glycogen (or starch)} + \text{inorganic PO}_4 \rightleftharpoons \text{glucose 1 phosphate}$$

It is seen that the enzyme brings about two reactions, it breaks glycogen into glucose units (or the reverse) and inserts phosphate groups (or removes them). A further discussion of this enzyme can be found under carbohydrate metabolism. The relation of pyridoxal phosphate to the enzyme can be found in Chapter 18, in the discussion of pyridoxine.

Nucleoside phosphorylase, found in bacteria, yeast, and various animal tissues, reacts with nucleosides and phosphate to yield ribose-1-phosphate and free base (hypoxanthine, guanine). The animal enzyme also carries out the reaction with deoxyribose-containing nucleosides.

A *pyrophosphatase* has been demonstrated in red blood cells. Adenosine triphosphatase of muscle is also a pyrophosphatase. The enzyme hydrolyzes adenosine triphosphate (ATP) into adenosine diphosphate (ADP) and inorganic phosphate, with the release of a large amount of free energy used as the immediate source of energy for muscular contraction and probably for other cellular activity.

Another pyrophosphatase is known to remove one phosphate group from thiamine pyrophosphate, forming thiamine phosphate and inorganic phosphate. A review on enzymatic phosphate transfer by Axelrod (110) and another covering the phosphorylases by Kornberg (111) can be consulted for further details.

The accompanying formulas show the general structures for the substrates acted upon by phosphomonoesterases, phosphodiesterases, and pyrophosphatases:

$$
\begin{array}{ccc}
\overset{\text{O}}{\underset{\underset{\text{OH}}{|}}{\overset{\|}{\text{R}-\text{O}-\text{P}-\text{OH}}}}
&
\overset{\text{O}}{\underset{\underset{\text{OH}}{|}}{\overset{\|}{\text{R}-\text{O}-\text{P}-\text{O}-\text{R}'}}}
&
\overset{\text{O}\quad\text{O}}{\underset{\underset{\text{OH}\quad\text{OH}}{|\quad\;|}}{\overset{\|\quad\|}{\text{R}-\text{O}-\text{P}-\text{O}-\text{P}-\text{OH}}}}
\\[2em]
\textbf{Phosphate monoester} & \textbf{Phosphate diester} & \textbf{Pyrophosphate ester}
\end{array}
$$

In a review (97) the term "monophosphoadenosine triphosphatase" was proposed for the specific adenosine triphosphatase which splits only the terminal phosphate group of adenosine triphosphate (ATP).

Nucleinases, or polynucleotidases of intestinal juice and other tissues and of yeast, decompose nucleic acids into nucleotides.

Nucleotidases have a similar distribution and hydrolyze nucleotides to nucleosides and H_3PO_4.

Phytase from plants, especially cereals, hydrolyzes phytic acid into inositol and phosphoric acid.

b) Cholinesterase, chlorophyllase, sulfatases, pectinesterase.

Cholinesterase occurs in the heart, intestinal mucosa, brain, blood, and other tissues. A number of lower animals are good sources. Acetylcholine, a mediator of nerve impulses, is hydrolyzed by this enzyme to give choline and acetic acid. It has been established that two such enzymes exist in animal tissues: (a) a true or specific cholinesterase, which hydrolyzes only acetylcholine, and (b) a pseudo- or nonspecific cholinesterase, which hydrolyzes also some closely related compounds and a number of simpler esters such as methyl butyrate. The two enzymes are distinguished most suitably at present by their specificity. The mechanism of hydrolysis by cholinesterase is discussed in detail by Davies and Green (112). The synthesis of acetylcholine is not mediated by this enzyme but requires choline acetylase (see Transacylases).

Chlorophyllase occurs in all green plants. In water solution the enzyme hydrolyzes chlorophyll to phytol, an alcohol, $C_{20}H_{39}OH$, and the monocarboxylic acid, chlorophyllin, the alcohol and acid present in chlorophyll. In ethyl or methyl alcohol solutions, however, the enzyme catalyzes the exchange of phytyl for ethyl or methyl radicals, forming the corresponding ethyl or methyl chlorophyllide, which compounds crystallize readily. Either of these compounds is generally what is referred to as crystalline chlorophyll.

Sulfatases have been proposed on the basis of substrates attacked. An enzyme which hydrolyzes glucose monosulfate and is called "glucosulfatase" was found in a certain species of snails. Kidney, brain, etc., contain a phenolsulfatase which is capable of hydrolyzing phenolsulfates to phenol and sulfuric acid.

Pectinesterase, or pectase, found in the peel of citrus fruits, de-esterifies pectin by hydrolysis, forming pectic acid and methyl alcohol.

6. OXIDATION-REDUCTION ENZYMES

A detailed discussion of these enzymes can be found in Chapter 21 on biologic oxidations. Important classes of these enzymes are: *dehydrogenases, oxidases, peroxidases, hydrases,* and *mutases.*

7. TRANSAMINASES

The best-known enzymes of this group are *glutamic-aspartic transaminase*, which catalyzes the transfer of the amino group of glutamic acid to oxaloacetic acid, forming aspartic and α-ketoglutaric acids, and *glutamic-alanine transaminase* (amino group to pyruvic acid). For some time before the work of Cammarata and Cohen (113) it was thought that these were probably the only amino acid transaminase enzymes. But these workers have established the presence in pig liver and rabbit liver of 22 distinct amino acid transaminases. Various microorganisms contain similar enzymes. Pyridoxal phosphate is the coenzyme (cotransaminase) in these systems. Further details can be found in recent volumes of *Annual Reviews of Biochemistry* and *Advances in Enzymology.*

8. TRANSMETHYLASES

Guanidoacetic transmethylase from liver (114) is responsible for creatine synthesis. The reaction employs the coenzyme S-adenosylmethionine (active methionine) and guanidoacetic acid to form creatine and adenosylhomocysteine.

Nicotinamide transmethylase, also found in liver (115), converts nicotinamide to N-methyl-nicotinamide. The methyl group is supplied by S-adenosyl methionine, and adenosylhomocysteine remains.

9. TRANSACYLASES

Choline acetylase is presumably a single enzyme which catalyzes the transfer of acetyl groups from acetyl coenzyme A (acetyl CoA) to choline. The synthesis of acetyl choline has been carried out in a cell-free system. The enzyme has been found in brain and other nervous tissue as well as in muscle of a variety of species. A partially purified system from squid head ganglion was shown to catalyze the synthesis of acetylcholine from acetyl CoA and choline with the production of a stoichiometric amount of sulfhydryl (free CoA) (116).

Glucosamine acetylase mediates the reaction between acetyl-CoA and glucosamine to form N-acetylglucosamine and free CoA. The enzyme is found in liver.

10. DECARBOXYLASES

Carboxylase or decarboxylase is widely distributed in plant and animal tissues. Yeast is an excellent source. The enzyme is involved in α-keto acid decarboxylation:

$$RCOCOOH \rightleftharpoons RCHO + CO_2$$

At the present time some confusion exists regarding the two prosthetic groups involved in enzymes acting as α-keto acid decarboxylases—i.e., thiamine pyrophosphate and lipothiamide pyrophosphate (LTPP). It has been proposed that in pyruvic- and α-keto glutaric decarboxylations the active form of the coenzyme is LTPP (117), although lipoic acid has coenzyme activity by itself (see Chapter 18 under Thiamine, page 694). It is probable that distinct enzymes exist using either one or the other of these two coenzymes.

Histidine decarboxylase is found in animal tissues and in bacteria. Histidine is decarboxylated yielding histamine and CO_2. The coenzyme is pyridoxal phosphate.*

Oxaloacetate decarboxylase from bacteria decarboxylates oxaloacetic forming pyruvic acid and CO_2. This enzyme appears to have no requirement for a thiamine-containing or a pyridoxal-containing coenzyme, but does require Mn^{++} or Mg^{++}.

Lysine decarboxylase, found in bacteria forms CO_2 and cadaverine (pentamethylene-diamine) from lysine, employs pyridoxal phosphate as coenzyme.

11. MISCELLANEOUS ENZYMES

Catalase occurs widespread in plant and animal tissues, specifically wherever cytochrome systems are found. Liver tissue offers a good source for preparing the crystalline enzyme. It decomposes hydrogen peroxide into water and molecular oxygen. Ethyl hydrogen peroxide is also decomposed by the enzyme. The coenzyme is heme.

Carbonic anhydrase occurs primarily in red blood cells and in the parietal cells of the gastric mucosa. It catalyzes the following reaction:

$$H_2CO_3 \rightleftharpoons H_2O + CO_2$$

[*Text continued on p. 428.*]

---

* Some authors consider nonoxidative decarboxylations as hydrolysis reactions, based on such a mechanism as:

$$Histidine + H_2O \xrightarrow{enzyme} histamine + H_2CO_3$$

Some reactions appear to follow this mechanism, although Rothberg and others (118) have established that in the decarboxylation of aspartic, glutamic, and malonic acids and tyrosine by their respective pyridoxal phosphate dependent enzymes the CO_2 produced arose exclusively from substrate. This was determined by conducting the decarboxylations in the presence of H_2O^{18} and examining the oxygen of the evolved CO_2. No O^{18} was found. The cleavage in these experiments was therefore nonhydrolytic.

Table 11.7.   Classification of the Enzymes

Part A

Type and Specific Name	Important Sites of Occurrence	Substrate	Reaction Products
I Carbohydrate-hydrolyzing. Glycosidases			
Cellulases	Molds, bacteria, snails	Cellulose	Various carbohydrate fragments
Inulases	Similar	Inulin	Fructose
Xylanases	Similar	Xylans	Xylose
Amylases	Saliva (ptyalin), pancreatic juice, malt products	Starch, glycogen, dextrins	Maltose
Sucrase (invertase)	Intestinal juice, yeast	Sucrose	Glucose + fructose
Lactase	Intestinal mucosa	Lactose	Glucose + galactose
Maltase	Small intestine, yeast, malt	Maltose	Glucose
Emulsin-a group	Bitter almonds, other plants	β-Glucosides	Glucose + other products
II Protein-hydrolyzing			
A Proteinases (endopeptidases)			
Pepsin	Gastric juice and mucosa	Proteins and derivatives	Proteoses, peptones, peptides, amino acids
Rennin	Similar	Casein	Paracasein
Trypsin	Pancreatic juice	Proteins and derivatives	Proteoses, peptones, peptides, amino acids
Chymotrypsin	Similar	Similar	Similar
Cathepsin	Protein-containing tissues	Proteins	Various split products
Papain	Papaya fruit	Proteins and derivatives	Proteoses, peptones, peptides, amino acids
Chymopapain	Similar	Similar	Similar
Bromelin	Pineapple fruit and leaves	Similar	Similar
B Peptidases (exopeptidases)			
Carboxypeptidase	Pancreatic juice, many tissues	Polypeptides	Smaller peptides + amino acids
Aminopeptidase	Intestinal juice, many tissues	Similar	Similar
Dipeptidases, various ones	Similar	Dipeptides	Amino acids
Leucylpeptidase	Hog intestinal juice, beef muscle	Peptides—terminal leucine residue	Smaller peptides + leucine
Iminopeptidase	Pancreatic juice	Peptides—terminal proline residue	Smaller peptides + proline

Table 11.7. Classification of the Enzymes (*Continued*)

Type and Specific Name	Important Sites of Occurrence	Substrate	Reaction Products
III Nonpeptide C-N linkage hydrolyzing			
Urease	Jack, bean, some seeds, liver	Urea	$CO_2 + NH_3$
Arginase	Liver, intestinal mucosa, molds	Arginine	Urea + ornithine
Glutaminase	Kidney, liver	Glutamine	Glutamic acid + NH_3
Aspartase	Bacteria	Aspartic acid	Fumaric acid + NH_3
Adenase	Liver, other tissues	Adenine	Hypoxanthine + NH_3
Guanase	Similar	Guanine	Xanthine + NH_3
IV Ester-hydrolyzing			
A Lipids			
Lipase	Pancreatic juice, many plants	Neutral fats	Fatty acids + glycerol
Esterases-a group	Liver, plants	Monohydroxy alcohol esters	Alcohol + acid
Cholesterase	Blood, other tissues	Cholesterol esters	Cholesterol + fatty acid
Lecithinase	Kidney, brain intestinal mucosa	Lecithin	Diglycerides, choline + phosphate
			Other combinations
B Phosphatases			
Phosphomonesterase	Many plant, animal tissues	Monophosphoric acid esters	Alcohol + phosphate
Phosphodiesterase	Similar	Diphosphoric acid esters	Monoester + alcohol
Phosphorylase	Similar, especially muscle	Glycogen + phosphate	Glucose-1-phosphate
		Starch + phosphate	
Nucleoside phosphorylase	Animal tissues, bacteria	Nucleosides	Sugar phosphate + base
Adenosine triphosphatase	Muscle	Adenosine triphosphate	Adenosine diphosphate + phosphate
Nucleinase (polynucleotidase)	Intestinal juice, yeast	Nucleic acid	Nucleotides
Nucleotidase	Similar	Nucleotides	Nucleosides + phosphate
Phytase	Plants, especially cereals	Phytic acid	Inositol + phosphate
C Others			
Choline esterase	Animal tissues	Acetylcholine	Choline + acetate
Chlorophyllase	Green plants	Chlorophyll	Phytol + chlorophyllide-a
Sulfatase	Animal, plant tissue	Sulfuric acid esters	Alcohol + sulfate

Table 11.7.   Classification of the Enzymes (*Continued*)

Part B

Type and Specific Name	Prosthetic Group	Important Sites of Occurrence	Substrate	Reaction Products
V Oxidation-Reduction				
A Dehydrogenases				
Alcohol dehydrogenase	Coenzyme I	Yeast, animal tissues	Ethyl alcohol	Acetaldehyde
Lactic dehydrogenase	Coenzyme I	Yeast, muscle	Lactic acid	Pyruvic acid
Malic dehydrogenase	Coenzyme I	Muscle, plants	Malic acid	Oxaloacetic acid
Isocitric dehydrogenase	Coenzyme I	Similar	Isocitric acid	Oxalosuccinic acid
Glucose dehydrogenase	Coenzyme I or II	Liver, animal tissue	Glucose	Gluconic acid
Glutamic dehydrogenase	Coenzyme I or II	Muscle, liver, bacteria	Glutamic acid	α-Ketoglutaric acid
Succinic dehydrogenase	Riboflavin phosphate	Muscle, plants	Succinic acid	Fumaric acid
Aldehyde dehydrogenase	Flavinadenine dinucleotide	Liver, plants, milk	Hypoxanthine, certain aldehydes	Xanthine, acids
Uricase	Flavinadenine dinucleotide	Liver of most mammals	Uric acid	Allantoin
Amino acid oxidase	Flavinadenine dinucleotide	Kidney, liver, other tissues	Amino acids	α-Keto acids + NH_3
Xanthine oxidase		Liver, plants, milk	Xanthine	Uric acid
B Oxidases				
Tyrosinase (monophenol oxidase)	Cu	Mushrooms, other plants, animal tissue	Tyrosine, other monophenols	Various oxidation products
Polyphenol oxidase	Cu	Similar	Di- and trihydroxy phenols	Melanin, other oxidation products
Cytochrome oxidase	Heme	Plant, animal tissue containing cytochrome	Reduced cytochrome c	Oxidized cytochrome c
Ascorbic oxidase	Cu	Plant, animal tissue	Ascorbic acid	Dehydroascorbic acid
Tyraminase (amine oxidase)	—	Liver, other tissues	Tyramine, other monoamines	p-Oxyphenylacetic acid + NH_3, other oxidation products
Histaminase (diamine oxidase)	—	Kidney, other tissues	Histamine, other diamines	Oxidation products
C Peroxidases, require H_2O_2				
Horseradish peroxidase	Heme	Horseradish	Aromatic amines and phenols especially	Oxidation products
Milk peroxidase	Heme	Milk	Similar	Oxidation products
Cytochrome c peroxidase	Heme	Yeast, other tissues	Reduced cytochrome c	Oxidized cytochrome c

Table 11.7. Classification of the Enzymes (*Continued*)

Type and Specific Name	Prosthetic Group	Important Sites of Occurrence	Substrate	Reaction Products
VI Carboxylases (decarboxylases)				
Carboxylase	Thiamine pyrophosphate	Yeast, plant, animal tissue	Pyruvic acid	Acetaldehyde + CO_2
Tyrosine carboxylase	Pyridoxal phosphate	Bacteria	Tyrosine	Tyramine + CO_2
Histidine carboxylase	Same	Bacteria, kidney	Histidine	Histamine + CO_2
Lysine carboxylase	Same	Bacteria, yeast	Lysine	Cadaverine + CO_2
Oxaloacetate carboxylase	Mg^{++}	Bacteria	Oxaloacetic acid	Pyruvic acid + CO_2
VII Transaminases				
Glutamic-aspartic transaminase	Pyridoxal phosphate	Bacteria, liver, heart	Glutamic acid + oxalo-acetic acid	α-Ketoglutaric acid + aspartic acid
Glutamic-alanine transaminase	Same	Similar	Glutamic acid + pyruvic acid	α-Ketoglutaric acid + alanine
VIII Transmethylases				
Guanidoacetic transmethylase	S-adenosyl methionine	Liver	Guanidoacetic acid	Creatine
Nicotinamide transmethylase	S-adenosyl methionine	Liver	Nicotinamide	N-methyl nicotinamide
IX Transacylases				
Choline acetylase	Coenzyme A	Nervous tissue, muscle	Choline	Acetylcholine
Glucosamine acetylase	Coenzyme A	Liver	Glucosamine	N-acetyl glucosamine
X Miscellaneous				
Cytochrome reductase	Riboflavin phosphate	Plant, animal tissues	Oxidized cytochrome c	Reduced cytochrome c
Catalase	Heme	Similar	H_2O_2	$H_2O + O_2$
Carbonic anhydrase	Zn^{++}	Red cells, parietal cells	H_2CO_3	$H_2O + CO_2$
Hyaluronidase	——	Bacteria, testes	Hyaluronic acid	Hydrolysis products
Lysozyme	——	Egg white		Lyses certain micro-organisms
Thiamine-destroying enzyme	——	Some fish tissues	Thiamine	Hydrolysis products
Hexokinase*	——	Plant, animal tissues	Glucose + ATP	Glucose-6-phosphate + ADP
Phosphoglucomutase*	——	Similar	Glucose-1-phosphate	Glucose-6-phosphate
Phosphohexoseisomerase*	——	Similar	Glucose-6-phosphate	Fructose-6-phosphate
Phosphoglyceromutase*	——	Similar	3-Phosphoglyceric acid	2-Phosphoglyceric acid
Aldolase (zymohexase)*	——	Similar	Fructose-1, 6-diphosphate	Triose phosphates

* See chapter on metabolism for other enzymes involved in carbohydrate metabolism.

Its importance in carbon dioxide transport and in HCl production in the stomach is considered in detail elsewhere. Zinc is required for enzyme activity.

Thiaminase or thiamine-destroying enzyme is heat-labile and contains a heat-stable and dialyzable fraction. It is found in fish tissues and in bacteria and catalyzes the hydrolysis of thiamine at the methylene bridge between the pyrimidine and the thiazole rings. The products of the scission are 2-methyl-4-amino-5-hydroxymethyl pyrimidine and 4-methyl-5-β-hydroxymethyl thiazole. See structure of thiamine. Further discussion is given in (119).

Hyaluronidase or *mucinase* is found in bacteria and mammalian tissues, especially testis. It is capable of hydrolyzing the mucopolysaccharide hyaluronic acid. Of importance also is the capacity of the enzyme to affect the permeability of tissue membranes. This may be related to fertilization and bacterial invasion. Only recently has this substance taken an important place in enzymology. For further information, consult (120) and (121).

Lysozyme, crystallized from egg white (122), lyses cells of a number of microorganisms. This action may be due to the enzyme's ability to hydrolyze the mucopolysaccharide of the cell. See (123) for other details.

Renin, not to be confused with rennin, originates in the kidneys and acts on a component of the pseudoglobulin fraction of blood plasma. This globulin fraction has many names: "hypertensinogen," "renin activator," "prehypertensin," "preangiotonin," and others. Renin acts on it to form a heat-stable, dialyzable substance with pronounced pressor and vasoconstrictor action, known variously as "angiotonin" or "hypertensin." Recent work indicates that this enzyme is proteolytic in nature.

Phosphoamidase refers to a group of proteolytic enzymes which have the capacity of splitting the P—N bond in such a compound as N-(p-chlorophenyl)-amidophosphoric acid. See the discussion under rennin for the relation of these enzymes to the theory of milk coagulation.

Transpeptidase is a name applied to proteolytic enzymes capable of synthesizing peptide bonds by inserting an amino acid into the peptide chain or by adding one amino acid to another. As an example Waley and Watson (124) showed that in the hydrolysis of lysyltyrosyllysine by trypsin and chymotrypsin, lysyllysine was formed. These authors postulate a carboxyl transpeptidation as follows:

$$\text{lysine} + \text{lysyl/tyrosyllysine} \longrightarrow \text{lysyllysine} + \text{tyrosyllysine}$$

Further details covering a number of instances of such reactions are available (125).

Transketolase is widely distributed in plant and animal tissues. It has been crystallized from yeast. It transfers a ketol group ($CH_2OHCO—$) from xylulose-5-phosphate to one of several aldehydes. When ribose-5-phosphate is the acceptor molecule there is formed sedoheptulose-7-phosphate and glyceraldehyde-3-phosphate (126). Thiamine pyrophosphate is the coenzyme. The reactions are discussed in detail under Pentose Cycle pages 994–997.

Transaldolase has also been found in plant and in animal tissues. The enzyme mediates the transfer of the three end carbons ($CH_2OHCOCHOH—$) of sedoheptulose-7-phosphate to glyceraldehyde-3-phosphate, with the formation of fructose-6-phosphate and erythrose-4-phosphate. The enzyme apparently does not contain a coenzyme (127). Further details are given under Pentose Cycle.

The preceding classification, Table 11.7, lists many of the known enzymes. It is based on substrate and/or linkage attacked. One or more sources of the enzymes, one or more substrates, and the principal reaction products are noted. The prosthetic group is given for many of the complex protein enzymes listed in Part B.

SYNTHESIS BY ENZYMES

The classification and the above outline note only a few of the enzymes known to be important in the metabolism of plants and animals. For the most part, especially in connection with the hydrolytic enzymes, only the actions involving the breaking of various chemical linkages to produce smaller molecules have been mentioned. It is immediately obvious that this is only part of the story. In plants and in animals the building of large molecules from smaller ones is equally important. Our knowledge of the mechanisms of these reactions is indeed meager.

One needs only contemplate the presence of polysaccharides such as starch, glycogen, and cellulose, or proteins or fats in plants and animals to realize the importance of the synthetic enzymatic processes.

Many instances of enzyme synthesis of small molecules in plant and animal tissues are known. If the definition of "synthesis" is restricted to the combination of molecules to produce a new molecule, a large part of these need not be considered here.

Of the many *in vitro* attempts to bring about a synthesis through the catalytic mediation of an enzyme, few have been successful. Hydrolytic enzyme reactions are know to be reversible equilibrium reactions; but in general the proper conditions have not been found to bring about the reverse of the hydrolytic process in the laboratory.

Important in this connection is the removal from the sphere of action of the synthetic product; this would aid, by the mass law effect, the synthetic reaction and lessen the speed of the hydrolytic reaction. It is often difficult to establish such conditions, and this may account, in a large part, for failure in many *in vitro* enzyme synthesis experiments. Also, the possibility of different enzymes mediating reactions in different directions cannot be ruled out entirely at present. A good example of just such a situation is found in the choline esterase and choline acetylase relationship. Here the former enzyme is responsible for the hydrolysis, and the latter for the synthesis of acetylcholine. Other instances in which an enzyme has brought about a synthesis are noted below.

One of the early demonstrations of *in vitro* enzyme synthesis was carried out by adding a crude emulsin preparation to L-arabinose in alcohol. After several months, and with further additions of emulsin, α-ethyl-L-arabinoside was isolated. It was supposed that an enzyme specific for this reaction was contained in the emulsin preparation. The following reaction was made to proceed from right to left in this instance:

$$\text{glucoside} + \text{HOH} \rightleftharpoons \text{sugar} + \text{alcohol}$$

Wasteneys and Borsook (128) in 1930 reported that protein digests treated with pepsin formed a high molecular weight substance. Emulsification of the mixture and increasing the concentrations of the reacting substances led to synthesis of a substance named "plastein" by these workers. This material was digested by pepsin at low pH and, according to Svedberg, has a molecular weight of 1000 or less. Most investigators do not regard plastein as a protein. Kumamoto (129) reported somewhat similar experiments.

Collier (130) also prepared plastein from concentrated digests of egg albumin and papain or crystalline pepsin. He pointed out that the hydrolysis of the egg albumin and the synthesis from the hydrolysis products by these enzymes require the same activators and that both processes have about the same optimum pH. Thus, the direction of the enzyme reaction is largely determined by the concentration of the reacting substances. The matter of plastein formation remains controversial, however.

More carefully controlled experiments involving enzymatic peptide bond synthesis were carried out by Bergmann and various coworkers (131, 132, 133). They arranged their experiments so that as the peptide bonds formed, the products thus synthesized crystallized as insoluble substances and were in effect removed from the sphere of action. The following is an example of this type of peptide bond synthesis. Chymotrypsin was the enzyme used:

benzoyl-L-tyrosine + glycine anilide ⟶ benzoyl-L-tyrosylglycine anilide

This field has been extended recently by a number of investigators. A review (62) should be consulted for those interested in further details.

Tauber (134) reported the formation of protein-like substances with molecular weights as high as 500,000 through the action of chymotrypsin on peptic digests of several proteins.

It is important to consider enzymes other than the proteinases in the overall picture of protein synthesis. Since energy is required, systems involving high-energy phosphate bonds, electron transfers, CoA, etc., must be intimately associated with such processes. Considerable information on protein synthesis can be found in Chapter 25.

Glutamyl-cysteine synthetase brings about the combination:

glutamic acid + cysteine + ATP ⇌ γ-glutamyl-cysteine + ADP + PO₄

This dipeptide then reacts with glycine under the influence of glutathione synthetase as follows:

γ-glutamyl-cysteine + ATP ⇌ glutathione + ADP + PO₄

Both enzymes are found in liver. Note that the reactions are driven to the right by utilizing ATP energy (135).

At least a half-dozen enzymes are known which synthesize different acyl-CoA compounds. As an example, acetyl-CoA synthetase brings about the following reaction:

acetate + CoA + ATP ⇌ acetyl-CoA + AMP + PP

This enzyme is found in animal and plant tissues and uses ATP energy to drive the reaction to the right, but with elimination of pyrophosphate (PP) (136, 137), rather than orthophosphate, as in the case of glutathione synthetase as indicated above.

Certain fatty acid esters have been made in excellent yield by various workers. Sym (138) for instance, reported that bile salts aid materially in ester synthesis by lipases or esterases. Nearly theoretical yields of some esters were obtained by adding a solution of bile salts to fatty acid and alcohol dissolved in carbon tetrachloride and then incubating in the presence of pancreatin (a commercial preparation from pancreas containing a number of enzymes including lipase).

A number of polysaccharides and disaccharides have been synthesized by enzymes. Cori and Cori (139) synthesized glycogen from glucose-1-phosphate and phosphorylase prepared from brain, heart, muscle, or liver. The reaction is as follows:

$$\text{glycogen (or starch) + inorganic phosphate} \rightleftarrows \text{glucose-1-phosphate}$$

Starch and some dextrins have been prepared similarly. Colowick and Sutherland (140) reported that with a purified phosphorylase and glucose-1-phosphate an equilibrium is established with 77 per cent of polysaccharide and 23 per cent of glucose-1-phosphate. This equilibrium point is the same regardless of the end from which it is approached, provided other experimental conditions are maintained constant.

Sucrose, apparently similar in all respects to the naturally occurring product was synthesized from glucose-1-phosphate and fructose by a phosphorylase from *Pseudomonas saccharophila* Doudoroff (141).

A great many of the synthetic enzyme reactions are actually transfer reactions. It was indicated earlier that Dixon and Webb (3) classify a majority of the known enzymes as various types of transferases. The phosphorylases, of course, do mediate transfers, as do the transaminases, transacylases, transmethylases, and many others.

The large number of observations on sugar and polysaccharide synthesis by enzymes has expanded our knowledge of carbohydrate metabolism to an important degree. Further discussion can be found in Chapter 24.

ENZYME UNITS AND DETERMINATION OF ACTIVITY

In order that the determinations of enzyme activity may be uniform and reproducible, it is desirable to carry out the determinations under conditions such that the rate of reaction is maximal, which means that sufficient substrate S should be present to bind all of the enzyme E as ES and the reactions give zero-order kinetics, $V = K[E]$ (where $[E] = [ES]$). It is also desirable to determine the initial rate of reaction in order to minimize the chances of enzyme inactivation with time and also to obviate the effect of the accumulation of reaction products upon the rate of the reaction.

The activity of enzymes is customarily expressed in units which are based usually upon an arbitrary amount of substrate conversion in a definite time interval associated with a definite weight of dry enzyme (as per gram) or of enzyme nitrogen (as per milligram). Standardized techniques are used with controlled pH, temperature, substrate concentration, etc. The application of enzyme units is of importance in industry, since enzyme preparations are generally priced according to activity, and also in the clinical laboratory, where the activity of an enzyme in blood, urine, or other body fluid is ordinarily reported in units.

Willstätter's definition of a saccharase unit is that amount of enzyme which, when added to 25 ml of a 12 per cent sucrose solution in 1 per cent Na_2HPO_4, at 15.5° C, will reduce the optical rotation to zero in one minute.

A unit of urease is that amount of enzyme which will produce 1 mg of ammonia nitrogen from urea at 20° C, pH 7.0 in five minutes. On this basis, the activity of Sumner's crystalline urease is 133,000 units per gram.

The phosphatase activity of blood serum is often measured as Bodansky units. If a serum contains 3 mg per cent of phosphorus as inorganic phosphate and 8 mg per cent after incubating under standard conditions in the presence of a suitable phosphate ester substrate, the serum contains 5 Bodansky units of phosphatase per 100 ml (8 − 3 = 5).

Northrop and coworkers determine proteinase activity by the extent of hydrolysis of specially prepared hemoglobin. The following technique, given in principle only, is the method of Anson (142) for the estimation of pepsin activity.

One milliliter of enzyme solution is added to 5 ml of the specially prepared hemoglobin solution at pH 1.6 (HCl) and mixed. After 10 minutes at 25° C, 10 ml of 0.3 N trichloracetic acid are added, and after thorough mixing the suspension is filtered or centrifuged. To 5 ml of the filtrate are added 10 ml of 0.5 N NaOH and 3 ml of phenol reagent. The color developed is read against a standard containing tyrosine.

The method depends on the fact that a certain quantity of hemoglobin is digested by the enzyme to products which do not precipitate with the concentration of trichloracetic acid used. The tyrosine and tryptophan in the split products of the filtrate react with the phenol reagent and produce color in an amount proportional to their concentration, and this is a measure of the pepsin activity.

For diagnostic purposes enzyme studies are generally restricted to blood amylase, for information regarding pancreatic activity; urine and especially blood acid and alkaline phosphatase, of diagnostic value in a number of diseases; and the transaminase activity of blood, which is a diagnostic aid in connection with certain heart conditions. Other enzyme determinations will probably prove of value to the clinician as further information and techniques develop.

Rossi (143) has summarized much of the work on the diagnostic use of enzyme determinations.

CLINICAL APPLICATIONS OF ENZYMES

Trypsin has proved to be of value in the treatment of several clinical conditions. The purified enzyme has been administered parenterally, orally, and intramuscularly. In the treatment of acute thrombophlebitis (a blood clot and inflammation in a vein) small recurrent intramuscular injections have been beneficial in many patients (144). The effect is not through enzymatic dissolution of the clot but appears to be related to amelioration of the inflammatory process. Some types of ulcers have responded well to trypsin therapy (145), as have some specific traumatic injuries, such as boxers' black-eye and a number of other injuries to athletes and others. The enzyme has been used experimentally in a variety of conditions, including refractory wounds, infections, some specific gastrointestinal disorders, carcinoma, and rheumatic diseases. Varying degrees of benefit have been reported but in some instances were not confirmed by other workers.

Streptokinase is a bacterial enzyme obtained principally from β-hemolytic streptococci. "Plasminogen" is the term given to the inactive form of a blood protease enzyme. In some way streptokinase activates plasminogen to form an active protease, called "plasmin." The mechanism of this activation apparently involves another molecule in blood, a proactivator, found to be a second factor in human plasminogen preparations. The work of Sherry and coworkers (146) indicates that human plasminogen is activated in two steps: (a) the conversion in a stoichiometric manner of the proactivator by streptokinase to a plasminogen activator and (b) the enzymatic reaction of this activator with plasminogen to form the proteolytic enzyme plasmin.

Plasmin has a lytic effect on blood clots through its fibrinolytic action. On this basis, streptokinase has been used therapeutically in attempts to remove clots. It has been administered intravenously, intramuscularly, and orally. Oral administration resulted in anti-inflammatory effects in patients (147), apparently on the basis of activation of salivary plasminogen and oral absorption of the resultant plasmin.

Hyaluronidase and cholinesterase have been employed in some clinical conditions. The results have been controversial.

The clinical use of enzymes is reviewed by Tanyol and others (148).

Some of the significant sources of information on the subject of enzymes are as follows: the recent volumes of *Annual Reviews of Biochemistry* (149) and the annual editions of *Advances in Enzymology* (150); *The Enzymes*, in four volumes (151); *Chemistry and Methods of Enzymes*, by Sumner and Somers (152); *Enzymes*, by Dixon and Webb (3); *Outlines of Enzyme Chemistry*, 2nd edition, by Neilands and Stumpf (72); *Behavior of Enzyme Systems*, by Reiner (77).

SPECIAL REFERENCES

1. Storn, K. G.: *The Chemistry and Technology of Food and Food Products*, 2nd ed., edited by M. B. Jacobs, Interscience Publishers, New York-London, 1951.
2. Northrop, J. H.: *Crystalline Enzymes*. Columbia University Press, New York, 1939.
3. Dixon, M., and Webb, E. C.: *Enzymes*. Academic Press, New York, 1958.
4. Velick, S., and Ronzoni, E.: *J. Biol. Chem.*, **173**, 627, 1948.
5. Albers, H.; Schneider, A.; and Pohl, I.: *Z. physiol. Chem.*, **277**, 205, 1943.
6. Reed, L. J., and De Busk, B. G.: *J. Biol. Chem.*, **199**, 881, 1952.
7. Soper, Q. F.; Buting, W. E.; Cochran, J. E.; and Pohland, A.: *J. Am. Chem. Soc.*, **76**, 4109, 1954.
8. Rossi-Fanelli, A.; Siliprandi, N.; and Fasella, P.: *Science*, **116**, 711, 1952.
9. Kuhn, R.; Reinemand, K.; Weygand, F.; and Ströbele, R.: *Ber.*, **68**, 1765, 1935.

10. Karrer, P.; Becker, B.; Benz, F.; Frie, P.; Salomon, H.; and Schröpp, K.: *Helv. chim. Acta*, 18, 1435, 1935.
11. Christie, S. M. H.; Kenner, G. W.; and Todd, A. R.: *J. Chem. Soc.*, Part I, 1954, p. 46.
12. Gunsalus, I. C., in *Phosphorus Metabolism*, edited by W. D. McElroy, and B. Glass. Johns Hopkins Press, Baltimore, 1951, p. 417.
13. Heyl, D.; Luz, E.; Harris, S. A.; and Folkers, K.: *J. Am. Chem. Soc.*, 73, 3430, 1951.
14. Kalckar, H. M.: *Science*, 125, 105, 1957.
15. Caputto, R.; Leloir, L. F.; Cardini, C. E.; and Paladini, A. C.: *J. Biol. Chem.*, 184, 333, 1950.
16. Leloir, L. F.: *Arch. Biochem. and Biophys.*, 33, 186, 1951.
17. Schmid, R.; Hammaker, L.; and Axelrod, J.: *Arch. Biochem. Biophys.*, 70, 285, 1957.
18. Isselbacher, K. J., and Axelrod, J.: *J. Am. Chem. Soc.*, 77, 1070, 1955.
19. Axelrod, J.; Inscoe, J. K.; and Tompkins, G. M.: *Nature*, 179, 538, 1957.
20. Kalckar, H. M.: *Advances in Enzymol.*, 20, 111, 1958.
21. Sealock, R. R.; Goodland, R. L.; Sumerwell, W. N.; and Brierly, J. M.: *J. Biol. Chem.*, 196, 761, 1952.
22. Lipmann, F.: *J. Biol. Chem.*, 160, 173, 1945.
23. Lipmann, F.; Kaplan, N. O.; Novelli, G. D.; Tuttle, L. C.; and Guirard, B. M.: *J. Biol. Chem.*, 167, 869, 1947.
24. Brown, G. M.: *J. Biol. Chem.*, 234, 370, 1959.
25. Lynen, F.; Riechert, E.; and Rueff, L.: *Ann. Chem.*, 574, 1, 1951.
26. Edwards, S. W., and Knox, W. E.: *J. Biol. Chem.*, 220, 79, 1956.
27. Crook, E. M., and Law, K.: *Biochem. J.*, 52, 492, 1952.
28. Strittmatter, P., and Ball, E. G.: *J. Biol. Chem.*, 213, 445, 1955.
29. Fridovich, I., and Handler, P.: *J. Biol. Chem.*, 221, 323, 1956.
30. Lichstein, H. C.: *Arch. Biochem. Biophys.*, 71, 276, 1957.
31. Cantoni, G. L.: *J. Biol. Chem.*, 189, 745, 1951; *J. Am. Chem Soc.*, 74, 2942, 1952.
32. Kennedy, E. P., and Weiss, S. B.: *J. Biol. Chem.*, 222, 193, 1956.
33. Lipmann, F.: *Science*, 128, 575, 1958.
34. Crane, F. L.; Hatefi, Y.; Lester, R. L.; and Widmer, C.: *Biochem. Biophys. Acta*, 25, 220, 1957.
35. Wolf, D. E.; Hoffman, C. H.; Trenner, N. R.; Arison, B. H.; Shunk, C. H.; Linn, B. O.; McPherson, J. F.; and Folkers, K.: *J. Am. Chem. Soc.*, 80, 4752, 1958.
36. Lester, R. L.; Crane, F. L.; and Hatefi, Y.: *J. Am. Chem. Soc.*, 80, 4751, 1958.
37. Crane, F. L.; Widmer, C. L.; Lester, R. L.; and Hatefi, Y.: *Biochim. Biophys. Acta*, 31, 476, 1959.
38. Schwimmer, S., and Pardee, A.: *Advances in Enzymol.*, 14, 375, 1953. Schneider, W. C.: *Advances in Enzymol.*, 21, 1, 1959.
39. Hogeboom, G. H., in Colowick, S. P., and Kaplan, N. O. (eds.): *Methods in Enzymology*, Vol. 1, p. 16. Academic Press, New York, 1955.
40. Sumner, J. B.: *J. Biol. Chem.*, 69, 435, 1926.
41. Sumner, J. B.: *J. Biol. Chem.*, 70, 97, 1926.
42. Anson, M. L.: *J. Gen. Physiol.*, 20, 663, 1936–37; *Science*, 81, 467, 1935.
43. Michaelis, L., and Menten, M. L.: *Biochem. Z.*, 49, 333, 1913.
44. Van Slyke, D. D., and Cullen, G. E.: *J. Biol. Chem.*, 19, 141, 1914.
45. Van Slyke, D. D.: *Advances in Enzymol.*, 2, 33, 1942.
46. Stern, K. G.: *J. Biol. Chem.*, 114, 473, 1936.
47. Chance, B.: *J. Biol. Chem.*, 151, 553, 1943.
48. Hassid, W. Z., and Dudoroff, M.: *Advances in Carbohydrate Chem.*, 5, 29, 1950.
49. Harting, J., and Chance, B.: *Federation Proc.*, 12, 714, 1953.
50. Krimsky, I., and Racker, E.: *Science*, 122, 319, 1955.
51. Schaffer, N. K.; May, S. C., Jr.; and Summerson, W. H.: *J. Biol. Chem.*, 206, 201, 1954.
52. Schaffer, N. K.; Simet, L.; Harshman, S.; Engle, R.; and Drisco, R. W.: *J. Biol. Chem.*, 225, 197, 1957.
53. Finkle, B. J., and Smith, E. L.: *J. Biol. Chem.*, 230, 669, 1958.
54. Cunningham, L. W.: *Science*, 125, 1145, 1957.
55. Mason, H. S.: *Proceedings of the International Symposium on Enzyme Chemistry*, Tokyo and Kyoto, 1957, p. 220, and *Advances in Enzymol.*, 19, 79, 1957.

56. Sumner, J. B., and Somers, G. F.: *Chemistry and Methods of Enzymes*, 3rd ed. Academic Press, New York, 1953, Chap. 1.
57. Bergmann, M., and Fruton, J. S.: *Advances in Enzymol.*, **1**, 63, 1941.
58. Bergmann, M.: *Advances in Enzymol.*, **2**, 49, 1942.
59. Bergmann, M.; Zervas, L.; Fruton, J. S.; Schneider, F.; and Schleich, H.: *J. Biol. Chem.*, **109**, 325, 1935.
60. Sumner, J. B., and Somers, G. F.: *Chemistry and Methods of Enzymes*, 3rd ed. Academic Press, New York, 1953, p. 9.
61. Barron, E. S. G.: *Advances in Enzymol.*, **11**, 201, 1951.
62. Balls, A. K., and Jansen, E. F.: *Ann. Rev. Biochem.*, **21**, 1, 1952.
63. Tsou, C. L.: *Nature*, **164**, 1134, 1949.
64. Butler, J. A. V.; Phillips, D. M. P.; Stephen, J. M. L.; and Creeth, J. M.: *Biochem. J.*, **46**, 74, 1950.
65. Meyers, V. C., and Free, A. H.: *Am. J. Clin. Path.*, **13**, 42, 1943.
66. Briggs, G. E., and Haldane, J. B. S.: *Biochem. J.*, **19**, 338, 1925.
67. Lineweaver, H., and Burk, D.: *J. Am. Chem. Soc.*, **56**, 658, 1934.
68. Hofstee, B. H. J.: *Science*, **116**, 329, 1952. Eadie, G. S.: *J. Biol. Chem.*, **146**, 85, 1942; *Science*, **116**, 688, 1952.
69. Nelson, J. M., and Anderson, R. S.: *J. Biol. Chem.*, **69**, 443, 1926.
70. Wilcox, J. M.: *Proc. Soc. Exptl. Biol. Med.*, **27**, 228, 1929.
71. Northrop, J. H.: *J. Gen. Physiol.*, **5**, 263, 1923.
72. Neilands, J. B., and Stumpf, P. K.: *Outlines of Enzyme Chemistry*, 2nd ed. John Wiley & Sons, New York, 1958, p. 132.
73. Gortner, R. A.: *Outlines of Biochemistry*, 2nd ed. John Wiley & Sons, New York, 1938, p. 942.
74. Willaman, J. J., and Davison, F. R.: *Ind. Eng. Chem.*, **16**, 609, 1924.
75. Hellerman, L.: *Physiol. Revs.*, **17**, 454, 1937.
76. Hellerman, L.; Chinard, F. P.; and Deitz, U. R.: *J. Biol. Chem.*, **147**, 443, 1943.
77. Reiner, J. M.: *Behavior of Enzyme Systems*. Burgess Publishing Co., Minneapolis, 1959, p. 120.
78. Kauffman, F. L., and Urbain, W. M.: *J. Am. Chem. Soc.*, **66**, 1250, 1944.
79. Hargreaves, A. B.: *Arch. Biochem. Biophys.*, **57**, 41, 1955.
80. Davie, E. W., and Neurath, H.: *J. Biol. Chem.*, **212**, 507, 1955.
81. Shulman, N. R.: *J. Biol. Chem.*, **213**, 655, 1955.
82. Montgomery, C. M.; Fairhurst, A. S.; and Webb, J. L.: *J. Biol. Chem.*, **221**, 369, 1956.
83. Monod, J.; Cohen-Bazire, G.; and Cohn, M.: *Biochem. et Biophys. Acta*, **9**, 648, 1952.
84. Gaebler, O. H. (ed.): *Enzymes: Units of Biological Structure and Function*. Academic Press, New York, 1956.
85. Knox, W. E., and Mehler, A. H.: *Science*, **113**, 237, 1951.
86. Lee, N. D., and Williams, R. H.: *J. Biol. Chem.*, **204**, 477, 1953.
87. Lee, N. D., and Williams, R. H.: *Biochim. et Biophys. Acta*, **9**, 698, 1952.
88. Lee, N. D.: *J. Biol. Chem.*, **219**, 211, 1956.
89. Kato, Y., and Moog, F.: *Science*, **127**, 812, 1958.
90. Haldane, J. B. S.: *Enzymes*. Longmans, London, 1930.
91. Meyer, K. H., and Gonon, W. F.: *Helv. chim. Acta*, **34**, 294, 1951.
92. Bernfeld, P.: *Advances in Enzymol.*, **12**, 379, 1951.
93. Larner, J., and McNickle, C. M.: *J. Biol. Chem.*, **215**, 723, 1955.
94. Cohen, S. L.: *J. Biol. Chem.*, **192**, 147, 1951.
95. Meyer, K.; Linker, A.; and Rapport, M. M.: *J. Biol. Chem.*, **192**, 275, 1951.
96. Fishman, W. H.: *The Enzymes*, Vol. I, Part 1, edited by J. B. Sumner and K. Myrbäck. Academic Press, New York, 1950, p. 635.
97. Altman, K. I., and Dounce, A. L.: *Ann. Rev. Biochem.*, **21**, 29, 1952.
98. Holter, H., and Li, S. O.: *Acta Chem. Scand.*, **4**, 1321, 1950.
99. Greenberg, D. M., and Winnick, T.: *J. Biol. Chem.*, **135**, 761, 1940.
100. Greenberg, D. M., and Winnick, T.: *Ann. Rev. Biochem.*, **14**, 47, 1945.
101. Folk, J. E.: *J. Am. Chem. Soc.*, **78**, 3541, 1956.
102. Adams, E.; Davis, N. C.; and Smith, E. L.: *J. Biol. Chem.*, **199**, 845, 1952.
103. Davis, N. C., and Smith, E. L.: *J. Biol. Chem.*, **200**, 373, 1953.
104. Robbins, K. C., and Shields, J.: *Arch. Biochem. Biophys.*, **62**, 55, 1956.

105. Archibald, R. M.: *J. Biol. Chem.*, **154**, 657, 1944.
106. Hanahan, D. J.: *J. Biol. Chem.*, **207**, 879, 1954.
107. Hanahan, D. J., and Vercamer, R.: *J. Am. Chem. Soc.*, **76**, 1804, 1954.
108. Tookey, H. L., and Balls, A. K.: *J. Biol. Chem.*, **218**, 213, 1956.
109. Tsuboi, K. K., and Hudson, P. B.: *Arch. Biochem. and Biophys.*, **43**, 339, 1953.
110. Axelrod, B.: *Advances in Enzymol.*, **17**, 159, 1955.
111. Kornberg, A.: *Advances in Enzymol.*, **19**, 191, 1957.
112. Davies, D. R., and Green, A. L.: *Advances in Enzymol.*, **20**, 283, 1958.
113. Cammarata, P. S., and Cohen, P. P.: *J. Biol. Chem.*, **187**, 439, 1950.
114. Cantoni, G. L., and Vignos, P. J.: *J. Biol. Chem.*, **209**, 647, 1954.
115. Cantoni, G. L.: *J. Biol. Chem.*, **189**, 203, 1951.
116. Korkes, S.; del Campillo, A.; Korey, S. R.; Stern, J. R.; Nachmansohn, D.; and Ochoa, S.: *J. Biol. Chem.*, **198**, 215, 1952.
117. Reed, L. J., and DeBusk, B. G.: *Federation Proc.*, **13**, 723, 1954.
118. Rothberg, S., and Steinberg, D.: *J. Am. Chem. Soc.*, **79**, 3274, 1957.
119. Fujita, A.: *Advances in Enzymol.*, **15**, 389, 1954.
120. Meyer, K., and Rapport, M.: *Advances in Enzymol.*, **13**, 199, 1952.
121. Hoffman, P.; Meyer, K.; and Linker, A.: *J. Biol. Chem.*, **219**, 653, 1956.
122. Alderton, G.; Ward, W. H.; and Fevold, H. L.: *J. Biol. Chem.*, **157**, 43, 1945.
123. Hestrin, S.: *Ann. Rev. Biochem.*, **22**, 85, 1953. Smith, E. L.; Kimmel, J. R.; Brown, D. M.; and Thompson, E. O. P.: *J. Biol. Chem.*, **215**, 67, 1955.
124. Waley, S. G., and Watson, J.: *Nature*, **167**, 360, 1951.
125. Balls, A. K., and Jansen, E. F.: *Ann. Rev. Biochem.*, **21**, 1, 1952.
126. Horecker, B. L., and Smyrniotis, P. Z.: *J. Biol. Chem.*, **212**, 811, 1955.
127. Horecker, B. L.; Smyrniotis, P. Z; and Hurwitz, J.: *J. Biol. Chem.*, **223**, 1009, 1956.
128. Wasteneys, H., and Borsook, H.: *Physiol. Revs.*, **10**, 110, 1930.
129. Kumamoto, K.: *J. Biochem. (Japan)*, **28,**, 95, 1938.
130. Collier, H. B.: *Can. J. Research*, **18**, 255, 272, 1940.
131. Bergmann, M., and Fraenkel-Conrat, H.: *J. Biol. Chem.*, **124**, 1, 1938.
132. Bergmann, M., and Behrens, O. K.: *J. Biol. Chem.*, **124**, 7, 1938.
133. Bergmann, M., and Fruton, J. S.: *J. Biol. Chem.*, **124**, 321, 1938.
134. Tauber, H.: *J. Am. Chem. Soc.*, **73**, 1288, 1951.
135. Snoke, J. E.; Yanari, S.; and Bloch, K.: *J. Biol. Chem.*, **201**, 573, 1953.
136. Lipman, F.; Jones, M. E.; Black, S.; and Flynn, R.: *J. Am. Chem. Soc.*, **74**, 2384, 1952.
137. Millerd, A., and Bonner, J.: *Arch. Biochem. Biophys.*, **49**, 343, 1954.
138. Sym, E. A.: *Enzymologia*, **1**, 156, 1936.
139. Cori, G. T., and Cori, C. F.: *J. Biol. Chem.*, **135**, 733, 1940.
140. Colowick, S. P., and Sutherland, E. W.: *J. Biol. Chem.*, **144**, 423, 1942.
141. Hassid, W. Z.; Doudoroff, M.; and Barker, H. A.: *J. Am. Chem. Soc.*, **66**, 1416, 1944. Doudoroff, M.; Barker, H. A.; and Hassid, W. Z.: *J. Biol. Chem.*, **168**, 725, 1947. Doudoroff, M.; Hassid, W. Z.; and Barker, H. A.: *ibid.*, **168**, 733, 1947.
142. Anson, M. L.: *J. Gen. Physiol.*, **22**, 79, 1938.
143. Rossi, G. V., in Martin, G. J.: *Clinical Enzymology.* Little, Brown and Co., Boston, 1958, Chap. 5.
144. Innerfield, I.: *Surgery*, **36**, 1090, 1954.
145. Kryle, L. S.; Calvelli, E.; Bonham, D. T.; and Kupperman, H. S.: *Angiology*, **7**, 287, 1956.
146. Troll, W., and Sherry, S.: *J. Biol. Chem.*, **213**, 881, 1955. Alkjaersig, N.; Fletcher, A. P.; and Sherry, S.: *J. Biol. Chem.*, **233**, 81, 1958.
147. Innerfield, I.; Shub, H.; and Boyd, L. J.: *New Eng. J. Med.*, **258**, 1069, 1958.
148. Tanyol, H.; Swain, W. M.; and Beiler, J. M.; in Martin, G. J.: *Clinical Enzymology.* Little, Brown and Co., Boston, 1958, Chap. 4.
149. *Annual Review of Biochemistry.* Annual Reviews, Inc., Palo Alto, California.
150. *Advances in Enzymology.* Interscience Publishers, New York-London.
151. *The Enzymes*, edited by Sumner, J. B., and Myrbäck, K. Academic Press, New York, 1950–52.
152. Sumner, J. B., and Somers, G. F.: *Chemistry and Methods of Enzymes*, 3rd ed. Academic Press, New York, 1953.

12

Digestion of food

Only a small portion of the food we eat is in the proper form for absorption into the blood or the lymph system of the body. Such things as water, uncombined mineral salts, and uncombined vitamins may not need digestive action prior to absorption. But the bulk of our food must undergo profound chemical changes before the resulting molecules can be absorbed. The proteins and protein split products must be hydrolyzed to amino acids, the oligosaccharides and polysaccharides to hexose sugars, and the fats to fatty acids and glycerol, in part at least. Other lipids are also hydrolyzed to smaller product molecules. The many reactions and enzymatic processes involved in these changes constitute digestion.

A number of factors aid the digestive processes. Cooking of foods produces several changes. It softens certain tissues, breaks the cellulose covering around starch granules allowing better access to digestive enzymes, partially hydrolyzes some food components, brings about coagulation of liquid proteins of eggs and other foods, and improves the flavor of some, which may result in increased flow of saliva and gastric juice. The ripening of fruits and vegetables and the aging of many foods produce desirable chemical changes. Mastication greatly increases the surface area of foods for better contact with the digestive juices. Absorption from the intestine by removing digested molecules brings about, by a mass law effect, more nearly complete enzyme action. The high water content of the chyme due to the flow of the several digestive juices and to fluids taken with foods aids the hydrolytic processes. The most important factor is, of course, the action of the enzymes and other specific components of the digestive juices.

The enzymes and other compounds important in digestion are secreted

437

by various glands of the body. The control of these secretions is nervous, hormonal, or both. At least five distinct secretions are known to be involved. The first of these to contact ingested food is the saliva.

SALIVA

Saliva is a mixture of secretions from the submaxillary, the sublingual, the parotid, and also the buccal glands of the mouth. The secretion of one set of glands differs from that of another. The sublingual glands, for example, secrete a watery solution containing primarily mucin, a glyco-protein, while the parotid glands secrete little of this material but a good deal of the amylase enzyme called "ptyalin." Variations in composition occur among species and among members of one species. In man considerable variation may be found in saliva produced at different times or under the influence of different stimuli.

Composition of saliva. Saliva is a colorless, slightly viscid liquid composed on the average of 99.42 per cent water and 0.58 per cent solids. The solids are roughly two-thirds organic matter, primarily ptyalin and mucin. The remaining third is composed of the inorganic ions Ca^{++}, Mg^{++}, Na^+, K^+, $PO_4^=$, Cl^-, HCO_3^-, and $SO_4^=$. The concentration of these ions bears little relation to their concentration in blood serum except in the case of Na^+ and Cl^- ions. The data in Table 12.1, taken from the work of deBeer and Wilson (1), show the relative values of certain inorganic ions in serum and saliva obtained about simultaneously from an anesthetized dog. Pilocarpine was used to stimulate salivary secretion. The saliva values are averages for the

Table 12.1. Inorganic Composition of Serum and of Saliva in Milliequivalents per Liter

	Na$^+$	K$^+$	Ca^{++}	Cl$^-$	HCO$_3^-$
Serum	130.6	4.2	5.2	110.3	26.4
Saliva	128.9	11.4	9.8	101.2	60.1

From E. J. deBeer and D. W. Wilson, *J. Biol. Chem.*, **95**, 671, 1932.

secretions of the left and right parotid glands and are in milliequivalents per liter. For monovalent ions one ion weight in milligrams is one milliequivalent, thus 35.46 mg of Cl^- equals a milliequivalent of chloride ion, and 40 mg of Ca^{++} equals two milliequivalents since calcium has an equivalent weight of 20.

It is of interest that intravenously administered $CaCl_2$ brought about increased levels of the component ions in saliva, while the injection of either NaCl or KCl into the blood did not materially affect the composition of the saliva.

Sodium and potassium were determined in the saliva of 200 normal individuals. With paraffin stimulation a mean sodium concentration of 90 mg per cent (39.2 meq/1) was found in the age group 5 to 19 years and 60 mg per cent (26.1 meq/1) in the age group 50 to 59 years. In unstimulated saliva sodium and potassium increased with age. Stimulated saliva had a higher sodium and a lower potassium content than unstimulated saliva (2).

Becks and associates (3) have made careful studies of the calcium and phosphorus content of resting saliva and saliva obtained by chewing paraffin and other substances. They found differences in the levels of these ions in the two types of saliva. The calcium and inorganic phosphorus in the resting saliva of 650 patients averaged 5.8 and 16.8 mg per cent, respectively.

Krasnow (4) reported about 300 mg per cent total protein, 7.5 mg per cent cholesterol and 0.13 mg per cent lipid phosphorus in saliva from normal persons. The potassium content of human saliva is often found to be higher than the sodium content. Values of from 60 to 80 mg per cent for potassium and of from 30 to over 100 mg per cent for sodium have been reported.

The carbon dioxide tension of saliva is difficult to determine with accuracy, and indeed little data on the subject are available. Rapp (5) states that it is suggested that the CO_2 tension of saliva is about 60 mm Hg. This would make the $CO_2 + H_2CO_3$ content around 8 volumes per cent, considerably higher than the CO_2 content of expired air.

The CO_2 capacity of paraffin-stimulated saliva from 15 caries-free children averaged 31 ml per 100 ml of saliva according to Hubbell (6). Karshan (7) found similar levels for stimulated saliva, although later he (8) reported an average of 13.4 volumes per cent in unstimulated saliva of 21 persons aged 10 to 29 years. He also indicated a correlation between caries activity and CO_2 capacity of saliva. The student should refer to the material on blood plasma CO_2 capacity for a review of the significance of capacity vs tension of CO_2. Briefly the CO_2 capacity indicates the total CO_2 as bicarbonate, carbonic acid, and that in physical solution after equilibrating saliva with an atmosphere containing about 5.5 per cent CO_2 (about 42 mm Hg tension). On the other hand, the CO_2 tension of saliva refers to the amount dissolved and that present as H_2CO_3.

By calculation it can be shown that at a salivary pH of 6.75, the ratio $HCO_3^-: H_2CO_3$ is about 4.5:1.

Many other compounds have been reported to occur in saliva. Among these are lactic and ascorbic acids, choline, phenols, urea, glucose, thiocyanates, iodides, nitrates, and various enzymes, including phosphatase, carbonic anhydrase, lipase, and, of course, the well-known salivary amylase.

The tremendous variations reported for the constituents of saliva are due primarily to individual differences of saliva produced by the subjects studied, to various methods used to stimulate the flow of saliva (which alter its composition) and also to inadequate analytical methods in many cases.

A great amount of literature can be found on the relation of salivary composition to tartar formation on teeth and to dental caries. For the most part definite correlations are lacking. The various journals in the field of dentistry should be consulted for further information on these subjects.

The specific gravity of saliva varies from 1.002 to 1.012.

Schneyer (9) found that in young men average values for resting saliva production were 69 per cent of the total from the submaxillary glands, 26 per cent from the parotid glands, and 5 per cent from the sublingual glands. From his own observations and from those of others he arrived at a value of 0.35 to 0.38 ml per minute as representative of the minute volume of resting saliva in young adult males. Actual salivary production is influenced by many factors, such as the amount of fluid and foods taken, degree of mastication, etc., and probably averages around 1200 to 1500 ml per day for a normal adult.

Acidity of saliva. Rather wide variations in the pH of saliva were found by Starr (10) for a large series of normal humans. His range was from pH 5.75 to 7.05, although 86 per cent of the samples showed values of from pH 6.35 to 6.85. Hanke and coworkers (11) reported values of 6.1 to 6.5 for the pH of saliva from various parts of the mouth of 323 children. An average value of 6.75 was found by Brawley (12) for the pH of resting saliva of 3405 normal individuals aged three weeks to 101 years.

Salivary pH depends primarily on the ratio $HCO_3^-:H_2CO_3$ which in turn is governed to some degree by the ratio of these substances in blood. Saliva produced during or immediately after hyperventilating, which lowers the H_2CO_3 fraction of blood, has an increased pH. The loss of CO_2 from saliva must be prevented if accurate pH determinations are to be made.

Functions of saliva. The saliva acts to maintain the mouth in a moist and clean condition and the pH about constant. It acts as a lubricant aiding both mastication and swallowing. Mucin is a slippery substance. By dissolving many substances of the food, the saliva brings them into contact with the taste buds. Ptyalin of saliva (salivary amylase) starts the digestion of starch, dextrins, and glycogen in the mouth, and, after swallowing, the process may or may not continue, depending on how rapidly the swallowed food becomes mixed with the acid gastric juice which inactivates salivary amylase. In many individuals very little salivary amylase action occurs. This action is of little importance in the over-all process of digestion, and indeed digestion seems to proceed normally in its absence.

Stimulation of salivary secretion. Salivary secretion is not under hormonal control. The following factors govern secretion:

1. Reflex stimulation from the thought, smell, or sight of food. Most individuals have often experienced salivary secretion from talking about some specially liked food.

2. Mechanical stimulation due to presence of substances in the mouth. It is interesting that the type of saliva varies a good deal, depending on the type of food or other substance in the mouth.

3. Chemical stimulation from the action of substances on the taste buds, such as condiments, sugar, and other dissolved chemical substances of foods.

DIGESTION IN THE STOMACH

As the swallowed food enters the stomach physiologic responses and chemical changes ensue. It is these we are concerned with in gastric digestion. The secretion of the various fractions of gastric juice, the digestion, primarily of protein, and the removal of the chyme into the intestine are the primary factors to be considered.

The presence of HCl in gastric juice was first demonstrated by Prout in 1824. The American Army Surgeon Beaumont, in 1822, was provided with an excellent human subject for gastric study in the person of Alexis St. Martin. This individual was accidently shot in the stomach from close range, and though Beaumont wanted to repair the wound, Alexis would have none of it. Nevertheless, the wound healed, and healed in such a way that a permanent gastric fistula remained, through which Beaumont was able to observe visually gastric activity under the influence of many foods and under conditions of anger, fear, etc., of the subject. These observations were carried on, intermittently, for a number of years after Alexis was taken into the employ of Beaumont. Some most interesting reading can be found in the memoirs of Beaumont covering these observations which extended until 1833 (13).* He confirmed the presence of HCl in gastric juice and predicted the presence of some other substance capable of digesting protein foods. It was not until 1036 that Schwann demonstrated the presence of such a substance in gastric juice. He gave it the name pepsin.

Beaumont demonstrated among many other things that food in the stomach causes gastric secretion—this he was able to observe directly. He also showed that such mechanical stimulation as tickling the mucosa with a feather causes secretion, and that fear, anger, and excess alcohol inhibit it.

Experimental procedures were later devised to obtain gastric juice for experimental study. One approach to this was through the surgical preparation of an accessory stomach or pouch. The Heidenhain pouch and the Pavlov pouch are well known in physiologic studies in animals. More recently improvements have been devised by various workers. The purpose is to supply a pouch with the nerve and blood supply intact and so arranged that swallowed food cannot enter it. The uncontaminated secretions are thus available for chemical and enzymatic study. Also, factors governing stimulation and inhibition of secretion can be evaluated.

Another method of obtaining gastric juice is by use of a stomach tube. This is applicable to human beings, since the tube may be inserted into the stomach and allowed to remain over a period of time without a lot of discomfort to the individual. Samples of the secretions produced under the influence of drugs, previously taken food, or other stimuli may be aspirated periodically for study. This procedure has become routine in many clinical studies.

Stimulation of gastric secretion. Many factors are involved in the stimulation of gastric juice. These are generally divided into three phases.

1. Cephalic phase. This name was applied by Ivy, replacing the earlier name "psychic phase." It refers to the stimulation of gastric secretion produced by the taste, smell, or sight of food. Even the thought of palatable food may evoke secretion. It has been shown that the amount of secretion bears a relation to the favor in which a specific food stands with an individual or experimental animal.

2. Gastric phase. This phase refers to the stimulatory effect of food in the stomach, although the purely mechanical effect is secondary to the chemical effect. This chemical effect, especially pronounced in the case of water-soluble products of meat and various peptones and peptides, accounts for most of the stimulation in this phase. The mechanism of the chemical

---

* For contemporary studies on a human being with a gastric fistula, see S. Wolf and H. G. Wolff (14).

secretion is not yet clear, but the leading theory holds that these stimulants, called "secretogogues," bring about the production of a hormone by the pyloric mucosa. This substance then is absorbed into the blood stream and activates the secreting glands of the stomach on reaching them. Many of these stimulants cause a copious secretion when introduced into the stomach, but they have little effect on intravenous injection. Edkins (15) found that certain extracts of ground pyloric mucous membrane evoked a copious flow of gastric juice when administered intravenously. He coined the name "gastrin" for the active material in these extracts and felt that this substance, prepared by him *in vitro*, was normally formed *in vivo* from peptones, meat extractives, and other material contacting the pyloric mucosa. More recently other tissue extracts were found to contain a substance or substances similarly active. Histamine was found to be a powerful stimulant for gastric secretion; it was isolated from gastric mucosa and other tissues, and consequently gastrin and histamine were supposed to be one and the same substance. This view is now held by many, although considerable experimental work tends to invalidate such a theory. Some reports indicate that the active principle is protein in nature, although Edkins demonstrated an increased, rather than a decreased, activity on boiling his preparations. It is impossible at present to be certain whether gastrin is identical with histamine.

3. Intestinal phase. This third phase of gastric secretion is not well understood. Certain foods placed directly in the duodenum of experimental animals cause gastric secretion, and drainage of the duodenal contents decreases gastric secretion. It is thought that the mechanism of stimulation is similar to that concerned in the gastric phase; i.e., hormonal.

The composition of gastric juice. Gastric juice is a watery solution produced by three types of cells of the gastric mucosa; pepsin by the chief cells, HCl by the parietal cells, and mucin by the columnar epithelial cells. Gastric juice, as such, is a mixture containing about 99.4 per cent water. The solids are composed of the organic substances mucin (glycoprotein), pepsin, and possibly small amounts of lipase and other enzymes of little or no importance in digestion. Some organic acids such as lactic are always found in small quantity. The inorganic constituents are H^+, Na^+, K^+, Cl^-, and small amounts of phosphates.

Pepsin is secreted by the chief cells of the gastric glands in an inactive state called "pepsinogen." It is activated by hydrogen ion yielding the enzyme pepsin. At pH 4.6 or below the activation becomes autocatalytic; that is, pepsin activates pepsinogen. This enzyme starts the digestion of many native proteins, splitting them into smaller fragments. Under the proper conditions small peptides and even amino acids may be produced, as indicated in Chapter 11. The extent of pepsin action depends upon the length of time of contact with food in the stomach, the pH, and other factors. The optimum pH of the enzyme is low and varies according to the nature of the substrate molecules from around 1.5 to 2.5; hence it is inactivated shortly after entering the intestine.

It is questionable if rennin is a constituent of human gastric juice. According to Dotti and Kleiner (16), none is present in adult gastric juice. In ruminants rennin is found in the fourth stomach. It has recently been crystallized and is distinct from pepsin. Pepsinogen and pepsin have also been crystallized. Casein of milk is acted on in some way by rennin to form paracasein, which in the presence of calcium ions forms insoluble calcium paracaseinate. Many proteolytic enzymes including pepsin have this milk-clotting power, but to a lesser degree.

"Phosphoamidase" is the name applied to certain proteolytic enzymes capable of clotting milk and also able to hydrolyze such a compound as N—(p-chlorophenyl)amidophosphoric acid. It was found that rennin, chymotrypsin, and pepsin have a fairly constant ratio of milk-clotting and phosphoamidase activity (breaking a P—N bond), and the suggestion was made (17) that the first step in the coagulation of casein is not proteolysis, but the hydrolysis of P—N bonds. It has been reported that pure crystalline rennin shows such activity only upon the addition of a thermostable activator from crude rennin or milk (18). The purpose of clotting milk and other liquid proteins, such as egg white, in the stomach is to prolong the stay of these substances to allow more time for digestive action.

Gastric lipase has been reported as a constituent of gastric juice, but its presence as a secretory product is doubtful. Its action in the stomach could be of little or no importance in digestion.

Buchs (19) reports that pig gastric mucosa contains "enormous" quantities of cathepsin which can be extracted by highly acid solution. Extracts prepared with weakly acid solutions or with glycerin contain only traces of the enzyme. Lysozyme is apparently a normal constituent of gastric juice (20).

The important small mucoprotein intrinsic factor is produced in the stomach. This factor is discussed with vitamin B_{12} in Chapter 18.

Hydrochloric acid of gastric juice. Gastric juice, as stated before, is a mixture of various secretions. Its composition varies considerably, depending on the type of stimuli acting to bring about secretion. Mixed gastric juice has been analyzed by many workers, but pure parietal cell secretion has not been collected. Its composition has been arrived at indirectly, especially by Hollander (21). He plotted total acidity of gastric juice against neutral chloride content and found that the curve was a straight line and that an inverse ratio exists between these two factors. On extrapolating the curve to a point representing zero concentration of neutral chloride, the corresponding value for the acidity was found to be 165 meq per liter. This was taken to be the HCl concentration; this concentration is isotonic with blood. At this point phosphates also showed zero concentration, and thus it was Hollander's belief that pure parietal cell secretion is a solution of isotonic HCl only. Other workers confirmed important parts, but not all, of his work. Gray (22) confirmed the total chloride content, but arrived at a lower value for HCl concentration. His calculations show values of 166 meq of chloride ion, 159 meq of hydrogen ion (HCl), and 7 meq of potassium ion per liter as the composition of parietal cell secretion. Such a solution is also isotonic. It would be about 0.16 N HCl with a pH close to 0.9. According to Hollander, the composition is practically independent of the rate of formation, the strength of the stimulus, and probably the nature of the stimulus.

All evidence points to the blood as the immediate source of the chloride ion used to form HCl. In the gastric circulation the arterial blood has a higher chloride content than venous blood while active secretion is in progress. Even the general circulation shows this effect. As quickly as one to two minutes after the injection of radioactive chloride into the general circulation, it appears in the gastric juice. There is little doubt that the blood supplies the chloride ion and that the lymph and tissues are drawn upon to make up the deficit.

There remains to be established the mechanism of HCl formation. For many years this problem has received philosophical attention, but only recently have theories been postulated on experimental evidence.

Theories of HCl production. The mechanism of HCl production is not known. Many facts are established and various theories have substantial experimental backing. The earlier theory of Davenport (23) though well founded in many respects, is now thought to be incomplete as an explanation for production of all the HCl of gastric juice. Davenport demonstrated a high concentration of carbonic anhydrase in the parietal cells of the gastric mucosa. This enzyme brings about the reversible hydration of CO_2: $H_2O +$ $CO_2 \rightleftharpoons H_2CO_3$. The theory holds that CO_2 is converted into H_2CO_3 in the parietal cells and that the carbonic acid ionizes to form $H^+ + HCO_3^-$. The hydrogen ions in some way are secreted, and since electrical neutrality must be maintained, negative ions accompany them. Chloride ions are taken from the blood to be secreted with the H^+. The bicarbonate ions remaining are used to replace the chloride ions taken from the blood. This theory cannot account for total H^+ production, since Davies and coworkers (24) and others have established that more H^+ is produced than molecules of oxygen used by a secreting gastric mucosa. This indicates that more CO_2 is required than that available from oxidative processes within the parietal cells. The problem is not as simple as might be depicted by the equation: $C_6H_{12}O_6 \longrightarrow$ $6CO_2 + 6H_2O \longrightarrow 6H_2CO_3 \longrightarrow 6H^+ + 6HCO_3^-$.

Davies and coworkers (25, 26) proposed that although glucose may be the source of some of the H^+ (according to the equation above) water is one substance which is capable of supplying equivalent amounts of acid and base in sufficient quantity to account for the rapid production of gastric acid. Theories were proposed to account for breaking water into H^+ and OH^- ions, and mechanisms put forth to account for the required energy for this action and for the transport of the H^+ produced (27). The equations HOH $\longrightarrow$ $H^+ + OH^-$ and $OH^- + CO_2 \longrightarrow HCO_3^-$ depict in general terms part of what may proceed according to this theory.

It is discouraging that as late as 1959 Davenport in a review (28) stated that all that is known of the metabolic aspects of gastric HCl secretion was covered in a symposium held in 1955 (29). Thus, progress in our understanding of this significant field is slow. Davenport summed up his views (29) at the symposium mentioned, as follows: The secretory mechanism consists of at least four parts: (*1*) Aerobic and anaerobic reactions in the parietal cells produce high energy phosphate bonds ($\sim$P). These provide energy to drive the secretory reactions. (*2*) The secretory reactions may be indicated in three steps; (*a*) One $\sim$P combines with a reduced low-energy precursor to form a reduced high-energy precursor. (*b*) This high-energy compound is oxidized yielding a H^+, a low-energy precursor, and an electron. The energy of the parent compound is utilized in transporting the H^+ against a concentration gradient. (*c*) The oxidized low-energy precursor becomes reduced by substrate electrons and is available to undergo reaction (*2(a)*)—that is, combine with $\sim$P. (*3*) The electron liberated in reaction (*2(b)*) is finally accepted by oxygen. One oxygen molecule is reduced for each four H^+ secreted producing four hydroxyl ions (or their equivalent). Four electrons are required to produce $2OH^-$ from O_2. (*4*) The OH^- produced are neutralized by various buffers, including the system $CO_2 + H_2O \longrightarrow H_2CO_3$ and $H_2CO_3 \longrightarrow H^+ + HCO_3^-$, in which case the H^+ reacts with the OH^- to form water.

The high energy phosphate bond may reside in ATP or creatine phosphate. The compounds yielding H^+ for gastric juice are substrate molecules (from metabolism of glucose, for example).

The above attempt to explain HCl secretion is admittedly far from complete. Further details can be found in the publication of the symposium referred to (29).

The electrophysiologic theory of gastric HCl production is reviewed by Rehm and Dennis (30). James (31) has reviewed the entire field also.

Stimulation and inhibition of gastric secretion. Fat in the intestine, according to Ivy and others, causes the production of a substance, apparently hormonal in nature, which inhibits gastric secretion and gastric motility. Active preparations have been obtained from intestinal mucosa by Ivy and associates. On injecting such material, secretion is inhibited over a period of hours. The active principle has been named enterogastrone. Interesting applications of such preparations in allaying ulcer development and in treating certain ulcers have been reported by Ivy (32). The motility inhibition may be due to a separate factor in the preparations. Urogastrone from urine also inhibits gastric secretion.

Small repeated doses of alkali or of dilute alcohol or of bile have a secretogogue effect on the stomach mucosa. Dilute HCl also stimulates secretion, but higher concentrations are inhibitory. Repeated injections of acetyl β-methyl choline chloride (Mecholyl) cause a copious secretion of gastric juice. Pilocarpine also stimulates secretion. According to Hollander (33), and contrary to the previously accepted view, this drug stimulates the production of HCl, pepsin, and water, and not primarily of mucin.

Histamine is one of the most potent gastric secretogogues. It is used in clinical studies to test the response of the gastric secretory mechanism. This will be brought out further under the discussion of gastric analysis.

A number of factors tend to neutralize or dilute the acid of the stomach. The glycoprotein mucin and ingested food proteins buffer the acid. Saliva dilutes the acid, and the alkaline duodenal regurgitations neutralize some of it.

The significance of gastric urease in relation to ammonia formation from urea and the part these play in neutralizing gastric juice in normal human beings and in certain cases of peptic ulcer have been studied in some detail (34).

Functions of HCl in gastric juice. Hydrochloric acid is essential for the activation of pepsinogen in the stomach. It also has an important antiseptic action resulting in less gastric fermentation and also aids in the prevention of body infections. Its direct action on foodstuffs is probably of minor importance. On entering the duodenum with the chyme, it has the important function of activating prosecretin (see intestinal digestion).

In man stomach emptying after a mixed meal is completed in three to five hours. Fatty foods leave the stomach slowly, proteins more rapidly, and carbohydrate foods most rapidly. Liquids begin to leave almost as soon as they enter the stomach.

Many other factors are involved in regulating the rate of emptying of the stomach. The mechanism responsible for opening the pyloric sphincter and closing it after a small amount of chyme has entered the duodenum is not too clear. It is established that the acidity of the chyme is not a specific stimulus for this, since the stomach is capable of emptying an alkaline content. A number of factors, of which the acidity of the chyme is but one, are known to be capable of causing closure of the sphincter. The rhythmic opening of the pyloric sphincter is related to gastric motility.

Gastric analysis. The clinical value of an examination of gastric contents is somewhat restricted. The material is difficult to obtain compared to blood or urine; the methods of analysis are far from perfected, and often the results of analysis are difficult to interpret. Most frequently the free and the combined hydrochloric acid are determined. Since lactic acid may be produced in larger amounts by fermentation when the HCl content is low, the organic acid fraction is sometimes determined. Pepsin activity, blood, and bile are estimated less frequently. Microscopic examination may be used to establish the nature and number of various cells present. The emptying time of the stomach is also often of interest.

A test meal—such as the Ewald meal, consisting of dry toast and tea—is given the subject in the postabsorptive state. Many test meals have been proposed and used by various workers. Recently a 7 per cent alcohol solution has been advocated by some workers.

Histamine as previously pointed out stimulates gastric secretion. It is sometimes used in place of a test meal. It has the advantage that by the use of enough histamine or by a second injection maximal stimulus may be obtained and sustained secretory function studied. It also eliminates many factors concerning the test meal itself, such as dislike for tea and variations in the composition of the toast or the tea. Histamine stimulation has been criticized, however, because it provides no food in the stomach, and since the gastric stimulating hormone and histamine have not been positively identified as the same substance, it is felt by many that it may not be a physiologic stimulus.

One of the above procedures is generally used to evoke a flow of gastric juice, and samples are then aspirated through a stomach tube for study. It was customary some years ago to remove a sample one hour after the test meal, but more adequate information is obtained by the fractional technique of Rehfuss. The stomach is first emptied of the residual gastric content and then the test meal is given. Successive samples are removed at 15-minute intervals for an hour, or longer if it seems advisable.

The samples are strained or filtered, and certain qualitative and quantitative estimations conducted.

Hydrochloric acid. An aliquot of the filtered gastric contents is titrated with standard alkali to a pH of about 3.5. Töpfers reagent (dimethylamino-azobenzene), or other indicators which may yield a sharper end point are used. Standard buffered mixtures may be employed for color reference in the titration. This gives the free hydrochloric acid. Reference to the titration curves of strong acids indicates that HCl is almost completely converted to salt at pH 3.5.

Total acidity may be determined in the same sample by adding phenol-phthalein and continuing the titration to the end point of this indicator. Phenol red is preferred by some because it gives a color change around pH 7 (phenolphthalein changes at about pH 8.5), and titrating to this pH excludes some of the buffer material which is titrated when phenolphthalein is used.

By subtracting the free from the total acidity, the combined acidity is obtained. This value includes the HCl present as protein salts, the organic acids, and the titratable acidity of certain buffers such as phosphates.

It is common practice to express the results in milliliters of 0.1 N NaOH required to titrate 100 ml of gastric juice. These values are called "units." Total acidity of gastric juice removed from the stomach one hour after the test meal varies in normal individuals over the wide range of from 35 to 70 units. It is normally highest at this time, and this level is maintained for about one-half hour and declines to the resting level after another one or two hours. Free acidity normally runs parallel to total acidity and varies from 20 to 50 units.

Like many clinical determinations, the titration of free HCl in gastric juice is not an exact method. In fact, it need not be, since the normal variations are great. Only values outside the normal range are clinically significant, and they can be found with the methods employed.

Achlorhydria refers to the absence of HCl in the gastric juice. It is common in pernicious anemia, but a high percentage of older persons also show this condition.

Pepsin. In one method for the determination of peptic activity, capillary glass tubes are filled with egg albumin. After heat coagulation of the protein, the tubes are placed in containers with known amounts of gastric juice adjusted to a definite pH. The peptic activity is calculated after measuring the length of the albumin column liquefied by the enzyme at the ends of the tubes in a definite time interval. Hemoglobin, gelatin, and other proteins are used as substrates in the various techniques described.

Blood. Blood may be tested for by the very sensitive benzidine reaction. A green or blue color develops in the presence of minute quantities of blood on the addition of an acetic acid solution of benzidine and then the addition of a little hydrogen peroxide.

The significance of abnormal findings in gastric analysis cannot be discussed here. Textbooks on laboratory diagnosis should be consulted for such information.

DIGESTION IN THE INTESTINE

After the chyme enters the intestine, three distinct secretions are involved in the completion of the digestive processes: the pancreatic juice, the intestinal juice or succus entericus, and the bile.

PANCREATIC JUICE

The digestive juice secreted by the pancreas is a clear watery solution containing about 1.5 per cent solids. Approximately two-thirds of the solids are inorganic and one-third organic. The latter consists of proteins, including several enzymes and smaller molecules. The concentration of inorganic salts is about isomolar with that of blood plasma, close to 160 millimolar, and the positive and negative ions are equivalent. Table 12.2 from Gamble and McIver (35) shows the ionic composition of dog pancreatic juice.

Table 12.2.   Ionic Composition of Pancreatic Juice from Dog

Cations, ml 0.1 N per 100		Anions, ml 0.1 N per 100	
Na^+	148	Cl^-	81
K^+	7	HPO_4^-	1
Ca^{++}	6	HCO_3^-	79
Total	161		161

From J. W. Gamble and M. A. McIver, *J. Exptl. Med.*, **48**, 849, 1928.

The pH of pancreatic juice varies from 7 to 8 roughly. The alkalinity is due primarily to HCO_3^-. It has been estimated that an adult secretes about 650 ml of pancreatic juice in 24 hours. The specific gravity averages 1.008.

The blood plasma is the source of the cations, the bicarbonate, and perhaps the other inorganic ions. In cats the alkali reserve of the resting pancreas and of this gland after copious secretion stimulated by secretin is the same. Also, the concentrations of sodium, potassium, and calcium in the cat's pancreas are not changed after profuse secretion (36).

Ball and coworkers (37) administered bicarbonate containing radioactive carbon to dogs by intravenous injection. They found the radioactive bicarbonate in the pancreatic juice in a short time, and at levels four to five times that of blood serum. Since the total CO_2 content of the pancreatic juice was found to be four or five times that of serum, these workers concluded that the blood is the primary source of CO_2 in pancreatic juice.

The enzymes of this digestive juice will be considered presently.

Stimulation of pancreatic secretion. When chyme enters the duodenum, secretin in some way is made available to enter the blood stream and travel to the pancreas, where it exerts its hormonal effect of stimulating this gland to secrete. The above statement is based on good evidence which very briefly is as follows: In 1902 Bayliss and Starling (38) found that a hydrochloric acid extract of mucosa of the duodenum contained something that on injection into an animal's blood brought about pancreatic secretion. They also demonstrated that introduction of HCl into the intestine caused the pancreas to secrete even after denervation of this organ. They concluded that the mechanism of stimulation is a chemical or hormonal one, and they proposed the name "secretin" for the hormone involved.

Later work has established that their general assumptions are correct. Ivy, Farrel, and Leuth (39), for example, transplanted a loop of intestine and also the tail of the pancreas into subcutaneous tissue in dogs. This procedure destroyed the nerve supply of these organs. When acid was placed in the isolated loop, the transplanted pancreas secreted. A number of similar experiments afford proof for the hormonal nature of pancreatic stimulation.

Various workers have proposed that secretin exists in a prosecretin form in the intestinal mucosa and that acid brings about the required change in some way. Potent extracts can be prepared by extracting intestinal mucosa with dilute HCl. But other substances in contact with the mucosa also cause the production or liberation of the hormone. Fatty acids, alcohol, or even water are effective.

The purification of secretin has been reported by various workers.

Agren (40) made careful analyses of highly purified crystalline secretin. He reported that one molecule contains two molecules of arginine and proline, one molecule of histidine, aspartic, and glutamic acids, and three of lysine. A molecular weight of 5000 was found by the ultracentrifuge method of Svedberg. Agren suggested that the polypeptide contains 50 amino acid residues. Niemann (41) calculated from Agren's data that the secretin molecule probably contains 36 amino acids and proposed the following partial empirical formula:

$$L_3Ar_2P_2H_1Gl_1As_1M_1X_{25}$$

where L = lysyl, Ar = arginyl, P = prolyl, H = histidyl, Gl = glutaminyl, As = asparaginyl, M = methionyl, and X = unknown amino acid residues.

Blood serum apparently contains an enzyme termed "secretinase" by Ivy and coworkers (42), since incubation of secretin with serum results in destruction of the hormone.

Harper and Raper (43) have extracted a second hormone from the small intestine which stimulates the secretion of pancreatic enzymes. They named the substance "pancreozymin."

Enzymes of pancreatic juice. Trypsin and chymotrypsin are elaborated in their zymogen or inactive forms called "trypsinogen" and "chymotrypsinogen." These have been crystallized. Enterokinase is an enzyme apparently produced in the small intestine, and it is responsible for converting trypsinogen into active trypsin. A small amount of trypsin can then act autocatalytically to convert more trypsinogen and also chymotrypsinogen into active enzymes.

The mechanism of this reaction has been studied by various investigators. It is now clear that activation of trypsinogen and chymotrypsinogen involves cleavage of a single peptide bond between a basic amino acid and an isoleucyl-valyl sequence. Upon activation of trypsinogen by trypsin, there is released a peptide with the probable structure valyl—(aspartyl)$_4$—lysine, and active trypsin. It appears therefore that the single hydrolytic event leading to active enzyme involves hydrolysis of a lysyl—isoleucine bond (44).

Neurath and coworkers (45) studied various physical and chemical properties of the precursor proteins during the course of activation. Their data indicate that the decrease in specific rotation of chymotrypsinogen and trypsinogen is directly correlated with the appearance of enzyme activity. It was suggested that the observed changes in optical rotation arise from structural rearrangements and that this change is intra- rather than intermolecular. The activation of zymogens is reviewed by Neurath (46).

Trypsin and chymotrypsin are generally classed as proteinases (endopeptidases), since they attack peptide chains not at terminal bonds, but at more centrally located bonds. Thus small peptide chains result from the action of these enzymes. This is not to be construed as meaning that these enzymes cannot hydrolyze terminal groups under the proper conditions. Certainly work with specific polypeptide substrates indicates that the amino acid arrangement on the peptide chain is of great importance in establishing what bonds will be broken by any proteolytic enzyme. It is, however, safe to assume that these two enzymes (proteinases) do produce large protein breakdown products during intestinal digestion. These are called "proteoses," "peptones," and "polypeptides." Some amino acids are undoubtedly produced also. The enzyme specificity determines what type of protein is readily attacked by the enzymes. Thus, trypsin is highly active toward the basic proteins, histones, and protamins, while pepsin of the gastric juice does not attack them appreciably.

Carboxypeptidase is another proteolytic enzyme in pancreatic juice. It splits the peptide bond at the end of the peptide chain having an amino acid with a free carboxyl group. The action can be repeated until an entire peptide chain is reduced to amino acids if the proper arrangement exists. If the amino acid configuration is not one that this enzyme can handle, other enzymes in intestinal juice may finish the hydrolysis.

Steapsin or pancreatic lipase is a potent lipolytic enzyme of pancreatic juice. It appears that the enzyme as elaborated is not very active, but a number of substances, such as soaps, bile salts, certain proteins, and amino acids, can activate it.

It is well established that triglyceride hydrolysis is far from complete in the intestine. Mattson (47) has reviewed this field and reported much of his own work. This investigator studied digestion products of triglycerides with fatty acids in known positions. After feeding 2-oleoyl dipalmitin to rats for instance, lipids were isolated from the intestinal lumen. The monoglycerides were found to be predominantly monoolein, and the free fatty acids were palmitic acid. From such *in vivo* work and various *in vitro* studies with pancreatic lipase (48), Mattson concludes that the hydrolysis of triglycerides is a series of directed step-by-step reactions from triglyceride to 1,2-diglyceride to 2-monoglyceride and that the enzyme is specific for ester groups on the primary hydroxyl groups. Free glycerol could result from enzymatic isomerization of the 2-monoglyceride to the 1-monoglyceride followed by lipolytic hydrolysis.

Amylopsin or pancreatic amylase (an α-amylase) hydrolyzes starches, dextrins and glycogens. The enzyme attacks more interior linkages in the branched oligosaccharides, such as starch and glycogen, producing units larger than maltose and then producing maltose. Amylose (linear molecule) following exhaustive hydrolysis with amylase is converted completely to maltose (87 per cent) and glucose (13 per cent) (49). The $1,4$-α-glucoside linkage is attacked in all cases.

Some differences in enzyme content of pancreatic juice in response to different test meals were demonstrated by Guth and coworkers (50) in dogs.

INTESTINAL JUICE

The intestinal juice or succus entericus is a mixture of the secretions of various glands of the intestinal mucosa. It is concerned with digestion by virtue of its mucin and fluid content which help lubricate and aid in keeping the partly digested food particles in motion along the intestinal tract.

The enzymes of the small intestinal mucosa probably operate intracellularly, and the enzymes present in the gut contents may arise from desquamation rather than from secretion.

The composition of intestinal juice varies from time to time and from one level of the intestine to another. In general, however, the mixed juice may contain from 1 to 2 per cent solids, primarily mucin, enzymes, and inorganic salts. The organic and inorganic matter is distributed about equally. The pH of the juice is generally 7 to 8. Various types of cells are always present.

Comprehensive analyses of the inorganic constituents of succus entericus obtained from isolated loops at different levels of the intestines of dogs are reported by deBeer, Johnston, and Wilson (51).

The secretion of intestinal juice is stimulated by food in the intestine. This acts mechanically through reflex nervous stimulation.

Enzymes of intestinal cells. Aminopolypeptidase hydrolyzes small peptides at the bond involving an amino acid with a free amino group. It can continue to remove amino acids from this end of the chain, provided the proper arrangement of amino acids exists. A dipeptidase breaks dipeptides into two amino acids. A prolinase is apparently a specific enzyme and is responsible for the hydrolysis of small peptides containing proline probably as a terminal group. The enzymes noted above, along with carboxypeptidase from pancreatic juice and probably others not yet well defined, constitute what previously was referred to as "erepsin." They complete protein digestion to the amino acid stage. In general, they are inactive on native protein molecules; other enzymes, such as pepsin and trypsin, must initiate the hydrolytic processes.

Nucleoproteins are hydrolyzed by the digestive enzymes. It is not clear where the various enzymes involved are produced. It is known that intestinal cells contain a polynucleotidase which splits nucleic acids into individual nucleotides. A nucleotide contains ribose or deoxyribose, phosphoric acid, and a purine or pyrimidine base. The nucleotides are further hydrolyzed by an intestinal phosphatase called "nucleotidase," yielding phosphate and a nucleoside. Finally, a part of the nucleoside, in the presence of phosphate, is converted by nucleosidase (a phosphorylase) to base and a sugar phosphate. Intestinal contents also contains enterokinase, the enzyme responsible for the activation of trypsinogen elaborated in the pancreatic juice.

The disaccharide hydrolyzing enzymes lactase, sucrase, (invertase), and maltase are found in mucosal cells.

The general structures of the phospholipids should be reviewed at this point (Chapter 6). Structures and reactions referred to in the following paragraph can be found in Chapter 11.

Although little progress has been made in the purification of intestinal enzymes hydrolyzing the phospholipids, it is probable that lecithins, cephalins, etc., are hydrolyzed by the same enzymes and the name "phospholipase" is better suited than the older term "lecithinase." Different phospholipases capable of splitting different linkages in these molecules occur in the intestine. Hydrolysis at the linkage between the primary alcohol of glycerol and the phosphate (phospholipase C action) yields a diglyceride and phosphorylcholine. The diglyceride would be handled as fat and the phosphorylcholine absorbed or further split by a phosphatase. Original removal of the fatty acid on the primary alcohol group of glycerol yields a lysolecithin (or cephalin), a strong hemolytic substance. Phospholipase A brings about this action; the enzyme is found in animal and plant tissues and in snake venom. Phospholipase B, also found in animal tissues, abolishes the hemolytic action of the lysolecithins by splitting off the secondary hydroxyl fatty acid, forming glycerylphosphorylcholine.

More information on phospholipid hydrolysis in plants and in animal tissues other than the intestine is available than that relating to digestion. For a review, consult Kennedy (52).

THE BILE

The third intestinal secretion important in digestion is bile. It is secreted continuously by the liver cells and is stored in the gall bladder. Though small amounts may enter the intestine regularly, the ingestion of food and other stimulants bring about emptying of the gall bladder, and thus larger quantities of bile enter the intestine at this time. Bile contains, in addition to the liver secretion, constituents added by the mucosa of the gall bladder and the biliary passage. During its stay in the gall bladder, water and certain inorganic salts are absorbed. This important concentration results in bile which may contain ten times the solids found in liver bile. A mucin-containing fluid is secreted by the gall bladder, and this, along with the concentration, results in a more viscous bile as it leaves this organ. Certain excretory products may be added to the bile by the gall bladder.

Composition of bile. The concentrating effect of the gall bladder is brought out well by the data in Table 12.3, which shows averages and ranges for various constituents of bladder bile compared with those of liver bile. Bladder bile is fairly viscous; it is yellow, green, or other colors, depending on the species and on how long after death it is obtained. The amount of bile secreted by man has been estimated at from 500 ml to 1100 ml per 24 hours.

Table 12.3. Composition of Human Bile—Averages and Ranges of Data of Various Reports Since 1900
Parts per 1000

Constituent	Bladder Bile	Fistula Bile
Water	888.6	973.4
Total solids	[111.4 (47–165)	26.6 (10–40)
Bile acids	51.8 (14–92)	10.9 (4.2–18.3)
Mucin and pigment	34.2 (18–43)	6.1 (4.3–9.3)
Total lipid	22.5 (19–26)	3.4 (2.9–4.2)
Neutral fat	3.7 (1.5–5.6)	1.1 (0.4–3.0)
Fatty acids	9.7 (9–10.9)	1.1 (0.8–1.4)
Phospholipids	2.0 (1.8–2.2)	0.6 (0.5–0.6)
Cholesterol	6.3 (3.5–9.3)	1.2 (0.8–1.7)
Inorganic ions	8.5	7.5 (5.8–9.2)

Hepatic duct bile is generally alkaline because of the bicarbonate present. It may have a pH as high as 8.6 or as low as 6.9. An average of a number of reports gives a pH 7.7. In the gall bladder part of the bicarbonate is absorbed; as a result of this and also on account of the Donnan membrane equilibrium, bladder bile may be nearly neutral or in some instances as acid as pH 5.5.

Hepatic bile, intestinal juice, gastric juice, and saliva all have approximately the same total electrolyte content. They are also about isomolar with blood plasma. Bladder bile is the exception and averages around one-third more in electrolyte concentration.

Concentration of hepatic duct bile by the gall bladder can increase the specific gravity from 1.010 to as much as 1.040. Three important constituents of bile, cholesterol, bile salts, and bile pigments, as well as the chemically related porphyrins, will be discussed individually.

Cholesterol. Bile contains considerable cholesterol (Table 12.3). The sterol is synthesized and excreted by the liver. The concentration of cholesterol in bile is usually not related to diet, although in a patient with an excessively high serum cholesterol level it was shown by Hellman and co-workers (53) that the feeding of corn oil lowered serum cholesterol to about the same extent as the increase in fecal sterols. After butter feeding the increased serum level was about the same as the decreased fecal sterols.

Cholesterol is converted into bile acids by the liver (see further under Bile Acids). It was reported that lowering of serum cholesterol by dietary means resulted in an increase in fecal bile acids (54).

Some of the cholesterol excreted into the intestine is converted by bacterial enzymes into various products, including coprostanol in humans (55).

Bile acids and bile salts. The parent bile acids found in human bile are hydroxylated cholanic acids. In all cases the hydroxyl groups have the α orientation (see Chapter 6). The ring system is saturated. Quantitatively, the principal acids are cholic acid (3α, 7α, 12α-trihydroxycholanic acid), chenodeoxycholic acid (3α, 7α-dihydroxycholanic acid), and deoxycholic acid (3α, 12α-dihydroxycholanic acid). A variety of other bile acids are found in various animal species (56). In man and in several animal species it is established that the bile acids are derived from cholesterol (57).

In human and other mammalian bile the acids are conjugated with glycine and taurine in variable ratios. These conjugates are present as sodium salts— the bile salts—due to nearly complete ionization of the acids at physiologic pH. The conjugation involves loss of water from the carboxyl of the bile acid and the $-NH_2$ of the amino acid as in peptide bond formation. Glycocholic acid and taurocholic acid are the conjugation products of cholic acid. Elliot (57) proposed that cholyl CoA is an intermediate in the conjugation and that its formation by guinea pig liver microsomes may be represented thus:

$$\text{Cholic acid} + \text{ATP} + \text{CoA} \rightleftharpoons \text{Cholyl CoA} + \text{AMP} + \text{PP}$$

It is likely that conjugation in all cases involves activated bile acids.

Taurine ($NH_2-CH_2-CH_2-SO_3H$) is derived from cysteine through cysteinsulfinic acid and 2-aminoethanesulfinic acid. This series of reactions is discussed under cystine in Chapter 25.

The concentration of bile salts varies considerably. An average value for human bladder bile is 3 or 4 per cent.

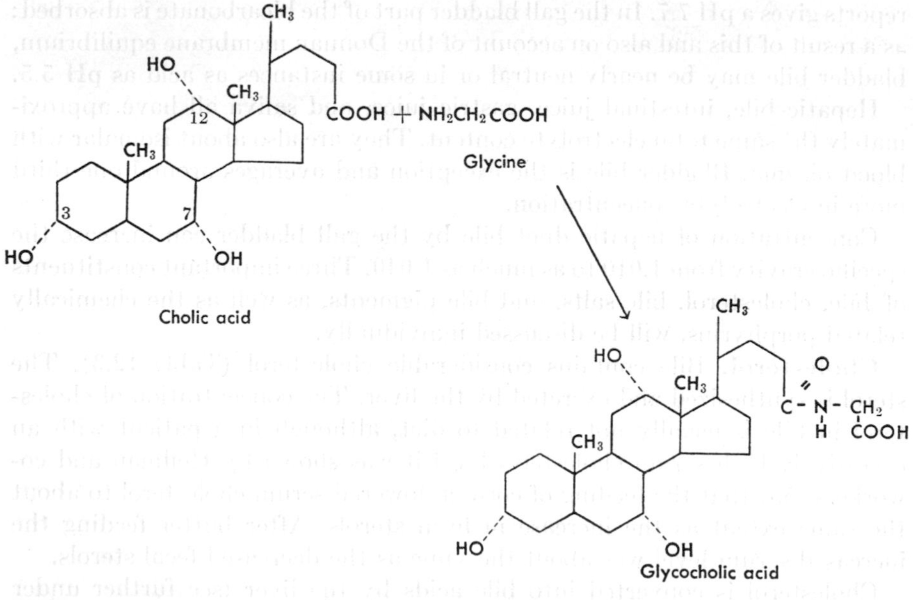

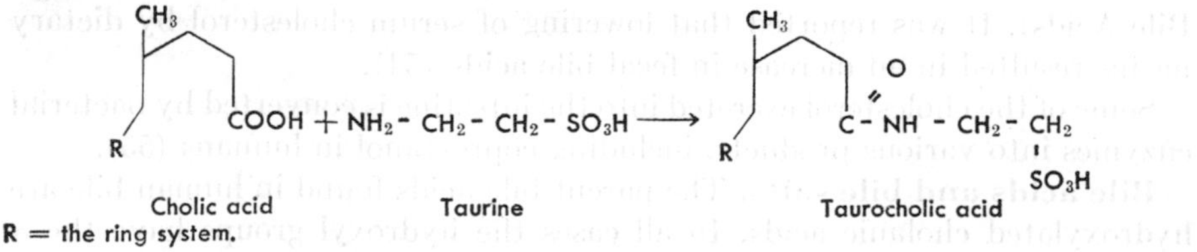

Cholic acid + NH₂CH₂ COOH (Glycine) → Glycocholic acid

Cholic acid + $NH_2-CH_2-CH_2-SO_3H$ (Taurine) → Taurocholic acid

R = the ring system.

Chenodeoxycholic acid is the same as cholic acid except for a H replacing the OH at position 12. Deoxycholic acid differs from cholic acid in that the OH at position 7 is replaced by H.

The steps in the conversion of cholesterol to bile acids are not yet clearly defined. Katzman and others (59) have reviewed this field. It was shown that 3α, 7α-dihydroxycoprostane (60) and 7α-hydroxycholesterol (61) are transformed into taurocholic and taurochenodeoxycholic acids in the rat. These investigators suggested that hydroxylation of cholesterol at carbon 7 is a primary step in bile acid biosynthesis. Other steps have been proposed. Deoxycholic acid is formed from cholesterol and is readily converted into cholic acid in the rat (62).

Circulation of bile salts. Normally small amounts of bile salts occur in the feces. Synthesis of these compounds keeps the total body supply about constant, however. During normal digestion, when the bulk of the bile is delivered to the intestine, the bile salts are largely resorbed by the portal blood and are removed by the liver and re-excreted in the bile. This circulation of bile salts has very important functions. It appears that fatty acids as well as certain fat-soluble vitamins are absorbed from the intestine through mechanisms involving the bile salts. Combinations of fatty acid and bile salts known as "choleic acids" are water-soluble and as such are more readily absorbed. A discussion of this problem can be found under fat absorption in Chapter 13. Vitamin K and cholesterol are poorly absorbed from the intestine in the absence of bile salts.

In his review on bile salt circulation, Josephson (63) gives figures from experimental work on cholecystectomized patients, indicating that the bile salts take part in the circulation about three times. So the absorption of digestion products mediated by a given quantity of bile salts is greatly increased through the circulation mechanism.

Functions of bile and bile salts. Besides the part played in absorption of fats, etc., the bile salts are important because of their capacity to lower surface tension. This property accounts for the emulsification of fats with the concurrent production of a great surface area, which enables lipase and other enzymes to act more efficiently. Also, the lipase is activated by surface tension-lowering substances. Bile salts stimulate peristalsis, and they also have a chologogue effect; that is, they stimulate the further production of bile. Most of the functions of the bile are attributable to the bile salts it contains. However, the alkalinity of the bile is of value in neutralizing part of the acid chyme from the stomach. Also, certain substances are excreted via the bile—that is, cholesterol, bile pigments, and certain drugs.

In bile fistula animals, the feces contain large amounts of fats and fatty acids due to poor absorption in the absence of bile salts. The color of the feces is generally gray because of no bile pigments. Over an extended time such animals show marked decalcification and other abnormalities of bone. Vitamin K deficiency follows a continued loss of bile in many species, including man. Dogs have been kept alive for periods of a year or so in the complete absence of bile.

Gallstones. Gallstones occur not infrequently in the gall bladder and sometimes in the bile ducts. There may be one stone or great numbers of small stones. They contain cholesterol, bile pigments, soaps, $CaCO_3$, and small amounts of other constituents. Stones have been found that are nearly pure cholesterol and others that contain almost all $CaCO_3$. Neither the mechanism nor the cause of their formation is understood, but they are formed by precipitation of these substances from bile. Many stones if cut in cross section are seen to be built up of concentric rings deposited one on top of the other.

The gall bladder. It has been pointed out that the gall bladder has the important function of concentrating the liver bile. Also, certain toxic substances are excreted by the mucosa, and other substances are absorbed and maintained for the body.

The pressure developed in the gall bladder is available to bring about emptying when the proper stimulus is applied—food in the intestine. Fats and meat are especially good stimulants. Secretin also stimulates. Bile salts, as previously indicated, have a profound stimulatory effect.

Extracts of the intestinal mucosa contain a substance which on intravenous injection brings about contraction and emptying of the gall bladder. Ivy and associates have given the name "cholecystokinin" to this hormone.

Bile pigments. The principal bile pigments are biliverdin and bilirubin. The color of bile is due primarily to these and to derivatives of them. They are considered to be excretory products. Oxidations and reductions of these form a great variety of other pigments. Certain of the pigments are found in urine, in feces, in bile, and in certain instances in the skin and other parts of the body.

Especially through the work of Whipple and Mann and their coworkers it has been established that bile pigment is formed by the cells of the reticuloendothelial system in various parts of the body. The bone marrow appears to be the most active site of formation. The ultimate sources of bile pigment are the hemoglobin of broken-down red blood cells and to a lesser degree myohemoglobin (muscle hemoglobin).

Biliverdin is the pigment formed by the reticuloendothelial cells. It is reduced by these cells as well as by the liver to form bilirubin. Little or no biliverdin is found in blood, but bilirubin is present in small amounts normally.

The mechanism and reactions involved in the formation of biliverdin from hemoglobin are not well understood. Also, the terminology here is in an unsatisfactory state, since a great many products have been reported by various workers, and many times new names have been applied to previously named compounds. Some substances previously thought to be entities are now known to be mixtures. This discussion will be limited to a few of the better known compounds involved in these changes.

The first step in biliverdin production involves the hydrolysis of hemoglobin to the protein globin and the iron-containing porphyrin heme. By oxidative scission the iron-prophyrin ring is opened, and a compound or various compounds called "verdohemin" result. The opening of the porphyrin ring in some way labilizes the removal of iron, and this results in the formation of the bile pigment biliverdin. Inspection of the formulas of heme and of biliverdin indicates that the site of this scission is at the α-methene bridge, i.e., between two different pyrrole carbon atoms, one holding a vinyl and the other a methyl group. The iron released is utilized for new hemoglobin formation or is built into ferritin for storage. Some may be excreted.

It also appears that other precursors of biliverdin exist in which the ring opening occurs before the removal of protein. The terms "verdoglobin" and "choleglobin" have been applied to these substances. Choleglobin may be defined as bile pigment-hemoglobin—in other words, combined native protein (globin) and open ring iron-poryphyrin. Further changes yield biliverdin. The actual mechanism of pigment formation is more complicated than indicated here, since some of the reactions have not been followed with certainty.

The above changes are presented schematically in Figure 12.1. It is not to be taken that the scheme represents proved steps of the reactions; it is an attempt to summarize the facts and supply the possible pathways.

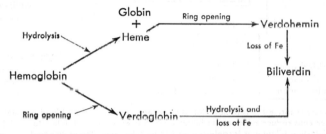

Figure 12.1. Schematic representation of bile pigment formation.

After the excretion of bile pigments into the intestine, further changes occur with the formation of a number of new compounds. Several of these are established as to identity and chemical structure.

It is generally agreed that bilirubin on entering the intestine is reduced (addition of H) by bacterial enzymes to urobilinogen, identical with stercobilinogen. Some of this material is oxidized (removal of H) to urobilin. The addition and removal of H can occur at various atoms in the rings, so that a number of different compounds are possible. The urobilinogen not oxidized is in part absorbed by the portal system, removed by the liver, oxidized there to bilirubin and re-excreted in the bile. Small amounts of urobilinogen may escape removal from the blood by the liver and so be excreted by the kidney. In voided urine this material is oxidized to urobilin. Normally there is very little of this in urine, but in instances of impaired liver function and in obstructive jaundice larger amounts are found.

It is interesting that the small amount of urobilinogen normally present in bile—from incomplete oxidation to bilirubin by the liver—disappears in experimental bile fistula. This is explained by the fact that urobilinogen is produced in the intestine, absorbed, and re-excreted. If no bilirubin is excreted into the intestine, no urobilinogen is formed, and that already present is soon removed with the feces. Consequently, the fistula bile becomes urobilinogen-free.

The urobilin formed normally in the intestine through oxidation of urobilinogen is identical with stercobilin and is primarily responsible for the brown color of the feces. Small amounts of bilirubin and other pigments also occur normally in feces. The terms "stercobilin" and "urobilin" are used for the same pigment, depending on whether it occurs in feces or in urine.

Figure 12.2 is a schematic representation of the circulation and excretion of bile pigments and derivatives.

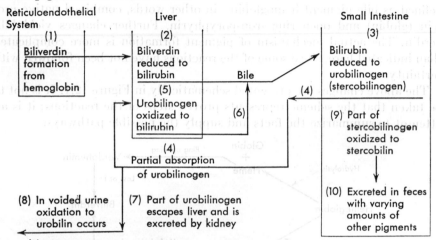

(1) Biliverdin formed in reticuloendothelial system—removed from blood by liver.
(2) Liver cells reduce biliverdin to bilirubin which is excreted with bile into small intestine.
(3) In intestine bilirubin is largely reduced to urobilinogen (stercobilinogen).
(4) But part of urobilinogen is absorbed and returned to liver.
(5) Liver oxidizes this urobilinogen to bilirubin.
(6) This bilirubin is excreted with bile.
(7) But part of blood urobilinogen (4) escapes liver and is excreted by the kidney.
(8) In voided urine urobilinogen may be rapidly oxidized to urobilin (stercobilin).
(9) Back in intestine (3) part of stercobilinogen not absorbed is oxidized to stercobilin.
(10) Stercobilin is excreted in feces with varying amounts of other pigments.

Figure 12.2.   Bile pigments, circulation, and excretion.

Mesobilirubinogen has long been a well-characterized reduction product of bilirubin; it can be readily prepared *in vitro* by sodium amalgam reduction. But on oxidation of this substance *in vitro*, not stercobilin, but urobilin IX, a is formed. The "IX,a" designates a configuration of side chains corresponding to mesoporphyrin IX (see further under porphyrins). Urobilin IX,a is optically inactive, while stercobilin is strongly levorotatory.

Another product, a dextrorotatory pigment, *d*-urobilin, was isolated after incubating mesobilirubinogen with bile (64, 65, 66, 67).

d-Urobilin was also crystallized from an extract of feces of patients whose intestinal flora had been altered by antibiotics (68). It was thought by Watson and Lowry that the compound resulted from hydrogenation and then dehydrogenation of mesobilirubin to form the dextrorotary urobilin. Upon reduction of *d*-urobilin, the compound *d*-urobilinogen was obtained. The latter was crystallized also from feces extracts of patients taking antibiotics (69). Watson and others stated that the *d*-urobilinogen was formed by bacterial activity. The significance of these pigments remains to be established.

The work of Watson and coworkers indicates that mesobilirubinogen is the primary product formed by reduction of bilirubin in the intestine and that *d*-urobilin and *d*-urobilinogen are secondary products requiring bacterial enzymatic action for their formation, and further that stercobilinogen (urobilinogen) is formed from mesobilirubinogen in the intestine and can be oxidized to stercobilin (urobilin). Figure 12.3 summarizes this concept.

A normal adult may excrete 1 or 2 mg of bile pigment in the urine and as much as 250 mg in the feces in one day.

The accompanying structures show a number of the compounds discussed:

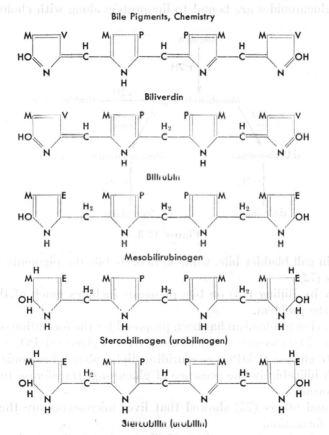

Bile Pigments, Chemistry

Biliverdin

Bilirubin

Mesobilirubinogen

Stercobilinogen (urobilinogen)

Stercobilin (urobilin)

The side groups in the bile pigments are as follows:

$$M = - CH_3 \text{ (methyl)}$$
$$P = - CH_2CH_2COOH \text{ (propionic acid)}$$
$$V = - CH = CH_2 \text{ (vinyl)}$$
$$E = - CH_2CH_3 \text{ (ethyl)}$$

The van den Bergh reaction has been used for many years in the determination of bilirubin in blood plasma. In practice, plasma is treated with diazatized sulfanilic acid in acid solution, producing a colored complex which lends itself to quantitative estimation. Only part of the bilirubin present reacts under these conditions; this is the so-called direct reacting bilirubin. After the addition of alcohol, more plasma bilirubin reacts—so-called indirect reacting bilirubin. Bilirubin glucuronide is now established as the direct acting form, and unconjugated bilirubin, due to its insolubility in aqueous solution, is the indirect bilirubin. A monoglucuronide and a diglucuronide are now established as constituents of direct bilirubin (70). The conjugation involves ester formation with the carboxyl group of the propionic acid residues of bilirubin and the C-l-hydroxyl of glycuronic acid (71).

In bile the diglucuronide is the main pigment with smaller amounts of monoglucuronide. Unconjugated bilirubin appears not to occur normally in bile. The glucuronides are bound to lipoprotein along with cholesterol and

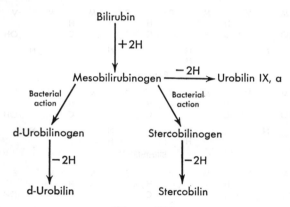

Figure 12.3.

bile acids in gall bladder bile, while in hepatic bile the pigments are bound to proteins (72).

A review by Billing (73) on bile pigments includes much of the clinical aspects of the problem.

The following mechanism has been proposed for the formation of bilirubin glucuronide (74): glucose $\longrightarrow$ glucose-6-PO$_4$ $\longrightarrow$ glucose-1-PO$_4$ $\longrightarrow$ uridine diphosphate glucose (UDPG) $\longrightarrow$ uridine diphosphate glucuronic acid; this reacts with bilirubin in the presence of glucuronyl transferase to give bilirubin glucuronide.

Schmid and others (75) showed that liver microsomes are the principle site of this formation.

The porphyrins. In a variety of disease states abnormal amounts of other pigments may be excreted in the urine and feces. These pigments are closely related to the protoporphyrin in the hemoglobin molecule, but they are chemically distinct from it.

It is now clear that the porphyrins are intermediates in the synthesis of protoporphyrin of heme and are not, as was suspected some years ago, breakdown products of heme.

Fischer synthesized the four possible isomers containing only methyl and ethyl groups on the porphyrin ring. These were named "aetioporphyrin I," "II," "III," and "IV." They do not occur in nature, but naturally occurring porphyrins are classified according to the correspondence of the positions of the side groups with the ethyl and methyl groups of the synthetic aetioporphyrins. Fifteen isomers are possible by substituting four methyl, two propionic acid, and two vinyl groups on the basic porphyrin ring. These are called the "protoporphyrins," and a number of natural porphyrins contain these groups. By mild reduction of the protoporphyrins, hydrogen adds to the double bond of each vinyl group, and the resulting 15 possible isomers containing ethyl in place of vinyl groups are known as the "mesoporphyrins."

At the present time our knowledge of the biosynthesis of the porphyrins— and thus of protoporphyrin, heme, chlorophyll, etc.—is fairly complete. Each carbon atom and each nitrogen atom of the porphyrin structure is identified as to source, largely through the work of Shemin and his coworkers.

It was found as early as 1948 that red blood cells of birds can synthesize heme *in vitro* (76), and soon after cell free extracts of duck erythrocytes were obtained which also accomplished heme synthesis from the proper substrates (77). Through the use of labeled compounds it was shown that the N atom and the α-carbon atom of glycine were incorporated into the pyrrol structure, but that the carboxyl carbon was not used. Acetate, or succinate arising from acetate, is also incorporated into the pyrrol precursor (porphobilinogen). When four porphobilinogen molecules unite in the proper manner, a porphyrin molecule results. In protoporphyrin (see structures) eight of the 34 carbon atoms and the four nitrogen atoms arise from glycine; the other 26 carbon atoms are derived from succinate (78). Although eight glycine molecules are involved in the synthesis of one porphyrin molecule, four of the N atoms and eight carbon atoms (each carboxyl) are lost in the synthetic process. Upon degradation of protoporphyrin synthesized from glycine-2-C^{14} it was found (79) that four of the carbon atoms were in the four methene bridges and the other four were distributed one in each pyrrol ring (next to the nitrogen). The remaining ring carbons and side-chain carbons are thus derived from succinate. Studies with carboxyl labeled and methylene labeled succinate have amply confirmed this (80).

Succinyl CoA (active succinate) reacts with glycine to form α-amino-β-keto-adepic acid. This compound is decarboxylated (the glycine carboxyl) to form δ-aminolevulinic acid, and two molecules of this compound condense with the loss of water to form porphobilinogen. Now four molecules of porphobilinogen condense with the loss of $4NH_3$, and the probable first intermediate formed is uroporphyrinogen, which is decarboxylated (four acetic acid side chains $\xrightarrow{-CO_2}$ four methyl side chains) yielding the intermediate coproporphyrinogen. Oxidative decarboxylation (two propionic acid side chains $\xrightarrow[-H]{-CO_2}$ two vinyl side chains) yields protoporphyrin. Falk and coworkers (81) demonstrated the enzymatic formation of uroporphyrin from porphobilinogen. Uroporphyrin and coproporphyrin are oxidative products (loss of H) of uroporphyrinogen and coproporphyrinogen, by conversion of the four saturated carbon bridges ($—CH_2—$) to the methene ($—CH=$) structures. The enzyme system which converts coproporphyrinogen III to protoporphyrin has been studied by Granick and coworkers (82). Wintrobe and others (83) demonstrated the presence of an enzyme in erythrocytes capable of incorporating iron (Fe^{++}) into protoporphyrin to form heme *in vitro*. Labbe (84) has studied an enzyme system in rat liver mitochondria which brings about heme synthesis from Fe^{++} and protoporphyrin.

In the structures herewith the α-carbon atom of glycine is marked with a asterisk (*), so that the eight positions the α-carbon atoms assume in the protoporphyrin molecule can readily be visualized. Variations in the manner in which the porphobilinogen molecules unite lead to either a I series or a III series porphyrin. The mechanism here is incompletely known, although an enzyme bringing about formation of porphyrin from porphobilinogen has been purified (85). In the structure of uroporphyrin III the side chains on ring D are acetic acid and propionic acid from left to right. Uroporphyrin I is identical to the III series compound save for a reversal of the positions of these two groups on this D ring. Coproporphyrin III has methyl and propionic acids groups on the D ring and coproporphyrin I is the same but has the positions of these two groups reversed. Shemin has reviewed in detail the earlier work covering the biosynthesis of the porphyrins (86).

The enzymatic formation of δ-aminolevulinic acid by particulate free extracts from two microorganisms was shown by Shemin and others (87) to involve conversion of succinate to succinyl-CoA and the condensation of this active form with a pyridoxal phosphate derivative of glycine. δ-Aminolevulinic acid and CO_2 were the reaction products:

$$\text{COOH} - \text{CH}_2 - \text{CH}_2 - \text{CO} - \text{CoA} + \overset{*}{\text{C}}\text{H}_2\text{NH}_2\text{COOH} \longrightarrow$$
$$\underset{\text{Succinyl CoA}}{} \underset{\text{Glycine}}{}$$

$$\text{HOOC} - \overset{*}{\text{C}}\text{HNH}_2 - \text{CO} - \text{CH}_2 - \text{CH}_2 - \text{COOH} \xrightarrow{-CO_2} \overset{*}{\text{C}}\text{H}_2\text{NH}_2 - \text{CO} - \text{CH}_2 - \text{CH}_2 - \text{COOH}$$
$$\underset{\alpha\text{-Amino-}\beta\text{-Keto-adipic acid}}{} \underset{\delta\text{-Aminolevulinic acid}}{}$$

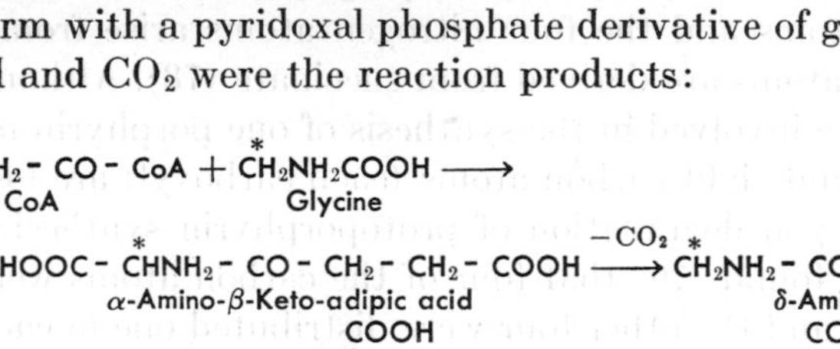

2 δ-Aminolevulinic acid ⟶ Porphobilinogen

4 Porphobilinogen ⟶ uroporphyrinogen + 4NH₃

Uroporphyrinogen $\xrightarrow{-CO_2}$ coproporphyrinogen $\xrightarrow[\text{decarboxylation}]{\text{ox.}}$ protoporphyrin IX $\xrightarrow{+Fe^{++}}$ heme

Uroporphyrinogen $\xrightarrow{-H}$ uroporphyrin

Coproporphyrinogen $\xrightarrow{-H}$ coproporphyrin

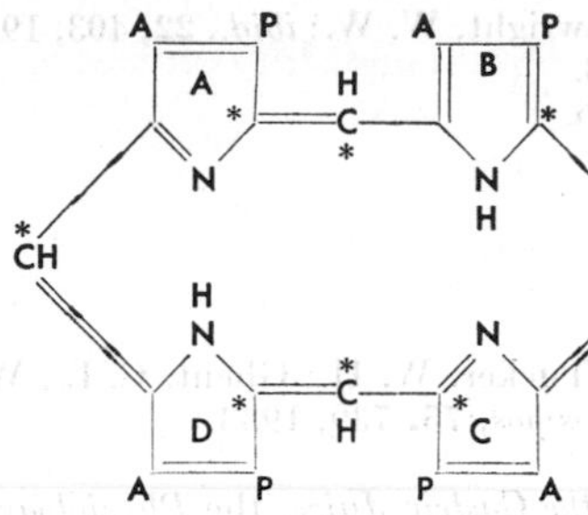

Uroporphyrin III

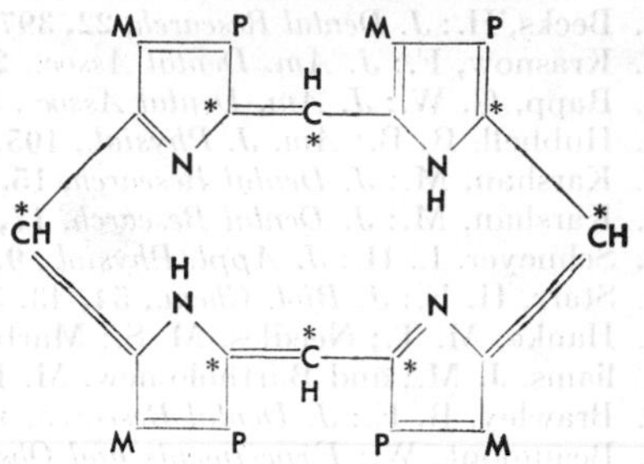

Coproporphyrin III

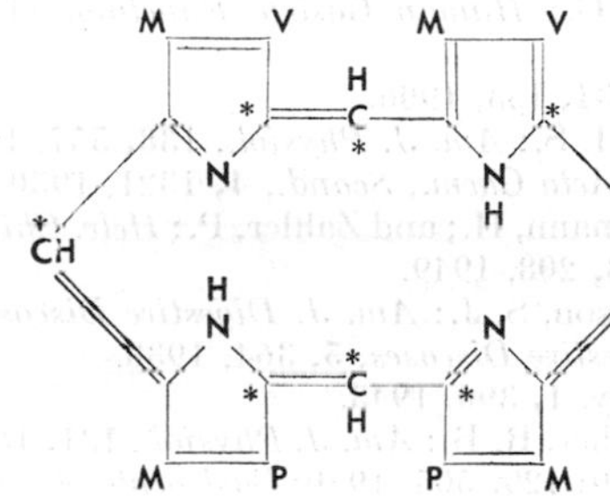

Protoporphyrin IX
(Type III)

Asterisks indicate carbon atoms arising from the α-carbon of glycine. The side chains in the structures are as follows:

$$M = - CH_3 \text{ (Methyl)}$$
$$V = - CH = CH_2 \text{ (vinyl)}$$
$$P = - CH_2 - CH_2 - COOH \text{ (propionic acid)}$$
$$A = - CH_2 - COOH \text{ (acetic acid)}$$

Coproporphyrins I and III occur normally in human urine in minute and about equal amounts. In a variety of diseases the excretion of these porphyrins may be greatly increased, and the ratio of the amounts of the two compounds excreted varies widely in different conditions.

For instance, in lead poisoning and in poliomyelitis the excretion is practically all of the type III isomer, while the type I isomer predominates in the urine of an individual with infectious hepatitis. Colorless precursors are normally present in urine, and these can be converted to coproporphyrin by treatment with a dilute iodine solution.

In acute porphyria the urine contains porphobilinogen which gives a positive Ehrlich reaction (color formation with dimethyl amino benzaldehyde in acid solution). This has been made the basis of a simple test for this compound in urine by Watson and Schwartz (88).

Experimental porphyria has been produced in animals by administering the compound Sedormid (allylisopropylacetylurea). A brief summary of this interesting problem is given by Rimington (89).

SPECIAL REFERENCES

1. deBeer, E. J., and Wilson, D. W.: *J. Biol. Chem.*, **95**, 671, 1932.
2. Niedermeier, W.: *Federation Proc.*, **12**, 251, 1953.

3. Becks, H.: *J. Dental Research*, **22**, 397, 1943. Wainwright, W. W.: *ibid.*, **22**, 403, 1943.
4. Krasnow, F.: *J. Am. Dental Assoc.*, **25**, 216, 1938.
5. Rapp, G. W.: *J. Am. Dental Assoc.*, **33**, 191, 1946.
6. Hubbell, R. B.: *Am. J. Physiol.*, **105**, 436, 1933.
7. Karshan, M.: *J. Dental Research*, **15**, 383, 1935.
8. Karshan, M.: *J. Dental Research*, **17**, 328, 1938.
9. Schneyer, L. H.: *J. Appl. Physiol.*, **9**, 79, 1956.
10. Starr, H. E.: *J. Biol. Chem.*, **54**, 43, 55, 1922.
11. Hanke, M. T.; Needles, M. S.; Marberg, C. M.; Tucker, W. H.; Ghent, C. L.; Williams, J. M.; and Bartholomew, M. D.: *Dental Cosmos*, **75**, 739, 1933.
12. Brawley, R. E.: *J. Dental Research*, **15**, 79, 1935.
13. Beaumont, W.: *Experiments and Observations of the Gastric Juice, the Physiology of Digestion*. Printed by F. P. Allen, Plattsburgh, N. Y., 1933.
14. Wolf, S., and Wolff, H. G.: *Human Gastric Function*. Oxford University Press, London, New York, 1947.
15. Edkins, J. S.: *J. Physiol.*, **34**, 133, 1906.
16. Dotti, L. B., and Kleiner, I. S.: *Am. J. Physiol.*, **138**, 557, 1943.
17. Holter, H., and Li, S. O.: *Acta Chem., Scand.*, **4**, 1321, 1950.
18. Mattenheimer, H.; Nitschmann, H.; and Zahler, P.: *Helv. Chim. Acta*, **35**, 1970, 1952.
19. Buchs, S.: *Enzymologia*, **13**, 208, 1949.
20. Lobstein, O. E., and Fogelson, S. J.: *Am. J. Digestive Diseases*, **18**, 282, 1951.
21. Hollander, F.: *Am. J. Digestive Diseases*, **5**, 364, 1938.
22. Gray, J. S.: *Gastroenterology*, **1**, 390, 1943.
23. Davenport, H. W., and Fisher, R. B.: *Am. J. Physiol.*, **131**, 165, 1940–41. Davenport, H. W.: *ibid.*, **128**, 725, 1939; **129**, 505, 1940; *Gastroenterology*, **1**, 383, 1943.
24. Davies, R. E.; Longmuir, N. M.; and Crane, E. E.: *Nature*, **160**, 506, 1947.
25. Davies, R. E.: *Biol. Revs.*, **26**, 87, 1951.
26. Crane, E. E.; Davies, R. E.; and Longmuir, N. M.: *Biochem. J.*, **43**, 321, 1948.
27. Davies, R. E., and Ogston, A. G.: *Biochem. J.*, **46**, 324, 1950.
28. Davenport, H. W.: *Ann. Rev. Physiol.*, **21**, 183, 1959.
29. Davenport, H. W., in Murphy, O. R. (ed.): *Metabolic Aspects of Transport across Cell Membranes*. University of Wisconsin Press, Madison, 1957, Chap. 13.
30. Rehm, W. S., and Dennis, W. H.: *ibid.*, Chap. 14.
31. James, A. H.: *The Physiology of Gastric Secretion*. Edward Arnold Ltd., London, 1957.
32. Ivy, A. C.: *Gastroenterology*, **3**, 443, 1944.
33. Hollander, F.: *Gastroenterology*, **2**, 201, 1944.
34. FitzGerald, O., and Murphy, P.: *Irish J. Med. Sci.* 6th Series, **97**, 1950.
35. Gamble, J. L., and McIver, M. A.: *J. Exptl. Med.*, **48**, 849, 1928.
36. Oldfelt, C. O.: *J. Physiol. (London)*, **102**, 362, 1943.
37. Ball, E. G.; Tucker, H. F.; Solomon, A. K.; and Vennesland, B.: *J. Biol. Chem.*, **140**, 119, 1941.
38. Bayliss, W. M., and Starling, E. H.: *J. Physiol. (London)*, **28**, 325, 1902.
39. Ivy, A. C.; Farrell, J. I.; and Lueth, H. C.: *Am. J. Physiol.*, **82**, 27, 1927.
40. Agren, G.: *J. Physiol. (London)*, **94**, 553, 1939.
41. Niemann, C.: *Proc. Natl. Acad. Sci. U. S.*, **25**, 267, 1939.
42. Greengard, H.; Stein, I. F.; and Ivy, A. C.: *Proc. Soc. Exptl. Biol. Med.*, **46**, 149, 1941.
43. Harper, A. A., and Raper, H. S.: *J. Physiol. (London)*, **102**, 115, 1943.
44. Davie, E. W., and Neurath, H.: *J. Biol. Chem.*, **212**, 515, 1955.
45. Neurath, H.; Rupley, J. A.; and Dreyer, W. J.: *Arch. Biochem. and Biophys.*, **65**, 243, 1956.
46. Neurath, H.: *Advances in Protein Chem.*, **12**, 319, 1957.
47. Mattson, F. H.: *Food Research*, **21**, 34, 1956.
48. Mattson, F. H., and Beck, L. W.: *J. Biol. Chem.*, **219**, 735, 1956.
49. Meyer, K. H., and Gonon, W. F.: *Helv. Chim. Acta*, **34**, 294, 1951.
50. Guth, P. H.; Komarov, S. A.; Shay, H.; and Style, C. Z.: *Am. J. Physiol.*, **187**, 207, 1956; **192**, 1, 1958.
51. deBeer, E. J.; Johnston, C. G.; and Wilson, D. W.: *J. Biol. Chem.*, **108**, 113, 1935.
52. Kennedy, E. P.: *Ann. Rev. Biochem.*, **26**, 119, 1957.
53. Hellman, L.; Rosenfeld, R. S.; Insull, W., Jr.; and Ahrens, E. H., Jr: *J. Clin. Invest.*, **36**, 898, 1957.
54. Gordon, H.; Lewis, B.; Eales, L.; and Brock, J. F.: *Lancet*, **II**, 1299, 1957.

55. Rosenfeld, R. S.; Fukushima, D. K.; Hellman, L.; and Gallagher, T. F.: *J. Biol. Chem.*, **211**, 301, 1954.
56. Haslewood, G. A. D.: *Physiol. Revs.*, **35**, 178, 1955.
57. Bergström, S., and Bergström, B.: *Ann. Rev. Biochem.*, **25**, 177, 1956.
58. Elliot, W. H.: *Biochem. J.*, **65**, 315, 1957.
59. Katzman, P. A.; Doisy, E. A., Jr.; Matschiner, J. T.; and Doisy, E. A.: *Ann. Rev. Biochem.*, **28**, 257, 1959.
60. Lindstedt, S.: *Acta Physiol. Scand.*, **40**, 1, 1957.
61. Bergström, S., and Lindstedt, S.: *Biochim et Biophys. Acta*, **19**, 556, 1956.
62. Bergström, S., and Gloor, U.: *Acta Chem. Scand.*, **9**, 1545, 1955.
63. Josephson, B.: *Physiol. Revs.*, **21**, 463, 1941.
64. Watson, C. J., and Schwartz, S.: *Proc. Soc. Exptl. Biol. Med.*, **49**, 636, 1942.
65. Schwartz, S., and Watson, C. J.: *Proc. Soc. Exptl. Biol. Med.*, **49**, 641, 1942.
66. Schwartz, S.; Sborov, V.; and Watson, C. J.: *Proc. Soc. Exptl. Biol. Med.*, **49**, 643, 1942.
67. Watson, C. J.; Sborov, V.; and Schwartz, S.: *Proc. Soc. Exptl. Biol. Med.*, **49**, 647, 1942.
68. Watson, C. J., and Lowry, P. T.: *J. Biol. Chem.*, **218**, 633, 1956.
69. Lowry, P. T ; Cardinal, R.; Collins, J.; and Watson, C. J.: *J. Biol. Chem.*, **218**, 641, 1956.
70. Talafant, E.: *Nature*, **180**, 1050, 1957.
71. Schachter, D.: *Science*, **126**, 507, 1957.
72. Verschure, J. C. M.: *Clin. Chim. Acta*, **1**, 30, 1956.
73. Billing, B. H.: *Advances in Clin. Chem.*, **2**, 268, 1959.
74. Billing, B. H., and Lathe, G. H.: *Am. J. Med.*, **24**, 111, 1958.
75. Schmid, R.; Hummaker, L.; and Axelrod, J.: *Arch. Biochem. Biophys.*, **70**, 285, 1957.
76. Shemin, D.; London, I. M.; and Rittenberg, D.: *J. Biol. Chem.*, **173**, 799, 1948.
77. Shemin, D.; Russel, C. S.; and Abromsky, T.: *J. Biol. Chem.*, **215**, 613, 1955.
78. Shemin, D., and Wittenberg, J.: *J. Biol. Chem.*, **192**, 315, 1951.
79. Wittenberg, J., and Shemin, D.: *J. Biol. Chem.*, **185**, 103, 1950.
80. Shemin, D., and Kumin, S.: *J. Biol. Chem.*, **198**, 827, 1952.
81. Falk, J. E.; Dresel, E. I. B.; Benson, A.; and Knight, B. C.: *Biochem. J.*, **63**, 87, 1956.
82. Granick, S., and Mauzerall, D.: *Federation Proc.*, **17**, 248, 1958.
83. Schwartz, H. C.; Cartwright, G. E.; Smith, E. L.; and Wintrobe, M. M.: *Blood*, **14**, 486, 1959.
84. Labbe, R. F.: *Biochim. Biophys. Acta*, **31**, 589, 1959.
85. Lockwood, W. H., and Rimington, C.: *Biochem. J.*, **167**, 8 p, 1957.
86. Shemin, D.: *The Harvey Lectures*. Academic Press, Inc., New York, 1956, p. 258.
87. Kikuchi, G.; Kumar, A.; Talmage, P.; and Shemin, D.: *J. Biol. Chem.*, **23**, 1214, 1958.
88. Watson, C. J., and Schwartz, S.: *Proc. Soc. Exptl. Biol. Med.*, **47**, 393, 1941.
89. Rimington, C.: *Ann. Rev. Biochem.*, **26**, 561, 1957.

13

Absorption from the intestine

The process of absorption refers to the normal passage of substances into the blood and lymph. Primarily, we are concerned with this process as it occurs in the small intestine. It has been pointed out that the primary purpose of digestion is to break down the foodstuffs into small water-soluble or otherwise diffusible particles to facilitate the process of absorption. It should be kept in mind also that digestion and absorption processes have the added function of minimizing the entrance of toxic molecules into the blood. Thus, food proteins and peptides, many of which are highly undesirable in the blood, are hydrolyzed to the harmless and, indeed, valuable and essential amino acids preceding their absorption. Fatty acids from fat hydrolysis are resynthesized into fats before their entrance into the blood stream. The fatty acids—but not the neutral fats, of course—are toxic in high concentration. The polysaccharide carbohydrates and even the disaccharides are of little value in the blood stream, and so they are hydrolyzed to monosaccharides before absorption.

The mechanisms accounting for the absorption of amino acids, sugars, and fatty acids will be discussed in detail in the following pages. The absorption of minerals, vitamins, and other substances are considered in appropriate chapters.

The small intestine is the principal organ of absorption. In the mouth and esophagus absorption is negligible, except in the case of certain drugs. The stomach is also not suited to food absorption, although alcohol and a few other substances are known to pass this mucosa to some degree. In the large intestine water absorption occurs; normally little or no absorbable food remains in the intestinal contents by the time it reaches this organ.

466

The small intestine in man is about 27 ft long. Because of the many folds and the millions of villi, the area offered for absorption is estimated at ten or so square meters. This is an important factor in absorption. Another important factor is the time that the digested material is in contact with the intestine. Ordinarily five to eight hours are required for the remains of a meal to pass into the large intestine. Under various conditions, such as diarrhea, this may be greatly altered.

The villi, some five million in man, are the primary sites of absorption. Each contains lymphatic vessels with the flow of lymph controlled by valves so that it can pass out of the intestine only. This lymphatic system makes up one of the two important routes that absorbed particles travel to enter the blood stream. The second consists of the arterial system. In man one artery enters each villus, and these are collected into the portal vein and hence the blood goes to the liver.

The passage of particles through the mucosa of the small intestine cannot be predicted from a knowledge of known chemical and physical laws. For instance, the prominent plant sterol, ergosterol, is not absorbed from the intestine. But cholesterol, the main animal sterol, is absorbed readily. These two molecules differ only slightly in chemical structure. Sulfates are not absorbed readily, but chlorides, phosphates, etc., are. The common hexose sugars enter the blood at a faster rate than do the pentoses, although the latter are smaller molecules. Glucose, NaCl, and other small molecules do not pass the mucosal lining from the blood into the intestinal lumen, as might be expected if the processes were purely those of diffusion, osmosis, etc. It is readily seen from these few examples that absorption from the intestine depends to a considerable degree on a specificity of this living tissue. It allows the passage of specific molecules and not of others, and it regulates the rate of passage of substances. This is one part of the absorption process that is not well understood.

Fat absorption. Not all fats are absorbed at equal rates or to an equal degree. Lard and other common dietary fats may be almost completely absorbed—that is, 98 or more per cent. Sperm oil is absorbed poorly—only about 15 per cent—and some other fats even less completely. Practically all fat absorption occurs in the small intestine. Emulsification and lipolytic hydrolysis take place rapidly as the chyme enters the duodenum.

Fat absorption may be thought of in terms of preparatory phase (digestive changes), transport phase (molecules entering the mucosal cells), and transportation phase (removal from cells and transport by blood or lymph systems).

Actually the absorption process and the various resyntheses that occur go on in a single layer of epithelial cells. The products of absorption and resynthesis are discharged on the other side of the cells, where they may be picked up by the intestinal lymphatics or the portal blood.

The mechanism of fat absorption is not thoroughly understood today. A number of theories have been presented over the past 50 years, none of which has enjoyed universal acceptance.

In 1896 Munk proposed one of the earliest theories—that fat is absorbed as a fine emulsion. He felt that the minute fat droplets might pass the epithelial wall, since it appears as neutral fat in the lymphatic system. He did not offer a good explanation for the force which could bring this about.

Pflüger in 1900 offered his soap theory of absorption. He felt that the fats are hydrolyzed by lipase, and then the fatty acids react with base of the bile and pancreatic juice to form sodium salts of the fatty acids. These are water-soluble and as such easily transported across the mucosal wall. The glycerol formed in the hydrolysis is also water-soluble and readily diffusible. Somewhere before entering the lymphatics in the villi, the reaction must be reversed and the neutral fat re-formed.

After the disclosure that sodium soaps are not stable at pH values below 8 to 9 and that the small intestine is practically never alkaline, this theory lost credence.

A more intriguing theory of absorption is that of Verzár (1). He also believes that fat in the intestine is hydrolyzed to fatty acids and glycerin. But he feels that the bile salts act as hydrotropic agents to bring the water-insoluble fatty acids into solution. He was able to demonstrate this action *in vitro* and showed that the fatty acids are partly in a diffusible form, even in acid solution. The proportion of bile acids produced to fatty acids generally ingested is small. Verzár presumes that the bile acids combine with fatty acids (these are known as "choleic acids") and convey them through the intestinal wall, whereupon the bile salt fatty acid combination breaks up and the bile salt is set free. Bile salts are supposedly adsorbed to the surface of the epithelial cells, where they can dissolve more fatty acid molecules and convey them into the cells.

Another theory of fat absorption is that of Frazer (2). His views are summarized very briefly as follows. A part of the ingested fat is absorbed as highly emulsified, neutral fat particles. These enter the lacteals and are carried by the lymphatic circulation to the systemic blood. The other fraction of food fat is enzymatically hydrolyzed and the products in the case of long chain triglycerides are fatty acids and mono- and diglycerides, rather than fatty acids and glycerol. The fatty acids through the hydrotropic action (solubilizing action) of bile salts and possibly by other means are transported through the intestinal wall, are resynthesized into neutral fat molecules, and enter the portal blood stream. After arrival at the liver, sufficient metabolic alterations supposedly intervene so that little of this fat finds its way into the systematic circulation.

Most of Frazer's data on blood lipid levels depends on chylomicron counts. Microscopic examination of blood serum with dark ground illumination reveals bright particles in Brownian movement. These are the chylomicrons. They range in size from 35 mμ to 1μ. Supposedly they are covered with a protein layer that helps maintain them in the colloidal state. A correlation has been demonstrated between chylomicron counts and the level of blood fat determined chemically.

Reiser and coworkers (3) prepared synthetic triglycerides in which the glycerol was labeled with C^{14} and the fatty acids with conjugated double bonds. The latter are useful in tracing the paths of fatty acids in the body. Rats with thoracic duct cannulas were given the doubly tagged neutral fat and analyses were made for C^{14} and for the tagged fatty acid in various lipid fractions of the thoracic duct lymph. The authors concluded that about one-half to one-third of the ingested glyceride was hydrolyzed to monoglycerides, and the remainder was completely hydrolyzed during digestion. It was further indicated that the fraction of glycerol that was hydrolyzed in the intestine was not the glycerol used in resynthesis of lymph glycerides. Also, about one-half of the phospholipids of lymph synthesized in part from the administered neutral fat utilized the hydrolyzed fatty acids and endogenous glycerol, while the remaining half arose from absorbed glycerides.

If glycerol of ingested fat is not the glycerol of the triglycerides in the lymph, then what is the source of the glycerol? To answer this question Reiser and coworkers (4) fed the monopalmitic acid ester of dihydroxyacetone to rats. This compound was tagged with C^{14} in both the fatty acid and in the alcohol molecules. Analyses of lymph lipids (thoracic duct) demonstrated that the compound fed was hydrolyzed to the extent of a little more than 70 per cent, but no fatty acid esters of dihydroxyacetone appeared in the lymph. The latter compound was reduced to glycerol and then converted to triglycerides. It was postulated that normally during fatty acid absorption, esterification of dihydroxyacetone with fatty acid and subsequent reduction and further esterification occur, probably in the intestinal mucosa.

With newer techniques for the separation of lipid fractions additional information on fat absorption has been developed. Countercurrent distribution has been used by various workers to separate monoglycerides, diglycerides, etc. Coniglio and Cate (5) used this technique in a study of intestinal absorption of carboxyl-labeled palmitic acid or tripalmitin in rats. At various times following the oral administration of the labeled fat or fatty acid the animals were sacrificed, and various lipid fractions were separated from intestinal contents, intestinal wall, and liver. C^{14} activity was determined in the purified fractions. During absorption C^{14} activity was found in mono-, di-, and triglycerides as well as in free fatty acids of the intestinal contents, with the major part of the activity in the free acids and the triglycerides. At the same time the intestine showed most of the label in triglycerides and the mono- and diglycerides had the least. After feeding free palmitic acid more of the activity was in the free fatty acid fraction of intestinal contents, although considerable activity also resided in di- and triglycerides. These findings indicate that glyceride synthesis as well as hydrolysis occurs in the intestinal contents. Other workers have observed this also.

During the course of absorption the phospholipids of the intestinal wall increased in C^{14} activity, while the activity of the triglycerides decreased. Such findings indicate phospholipid synthesis within the intestinal mucosa and are in accord with results of other investigators. It is clear also that mono- and diglycerides are converted into triglycerides (and phospholipids), since the lymph is known not to contain mono- or diglycerides in man (6) or in the rat (7).

The liver lipids three hours following the ingestion of the labeled compounds showed C^{14} activity in phospholipids and triglycerides, with small but significant activity in mono- and diglycerides. The origin of the last two substances in hepatic tissue is not known.

It is interesting from this standpoint that Mead and Fillerup (8) found considerable mono- and diglycerides in human blood plasma after feeding tagged fatty acid methyl esters. They offered various possible explanations to account for the partial glycerides in blood including the possibility of hydrolysis of triglycerides in transit.

An unusual opportunity for absorption studies was afforded by a human with chyluria. This woman had an anomolous connection between the intestinal lymphatics and the left renal pelvis (9), allowing drainage of the lymph into the urine. Blomstrand and Ahrens (6) administered C^{13}-containing oleic and palmitic acids to this individual either free or in triglycerides. Determination of C^{13} activity in the various separated lipid fractions of urine allowed the investigators to follow incorporation of the compounds into the different types of lipids. It was found that oleic and palmitic acids were incorporated into triglycerides to a large degree and that the triglycerides constituted the main transport form of these acids—about 90 per cent of the total isotope content of lymph. From 3 to 9 per cent of the isotope found its way into phospholipid, and 1 to 7 per cent was found in nonesterified fatty acids. Other measurements showed that about 90 per cent of the triglycerides of the chyle were of dietary origin, while only around 20 per cent of the phospholipids and nonesterified fatty acids represented absorbed fatty acids. This indicated that these two fractions were largely of endogenous origin, but that some phospholipid was synthesized from the fed fats or fatty acids.

About one-fifth of fed phospholipid was absorbed into the lymph in rats without undergoing hydrolysis in the experiments of Chaikoff and others (10).

It is pretty well established that in the absorption process fatty acids (fed either as neutral fat or free fatty acids) longer than 12 carbons in chain length are transported almost exclusively via the lymph (11), while those with less than 12 carbons are transported to a greater extent by the portal blood (12). Resynthesis of absorbed free fatty acids into glycerides occurs in the intestinal wall and to a lesser extent in other tissues.

However, it appears that the short-chain acids absorbed by the portal system may largely be transported to the liver without first undergoing resynthesis into triglycerides. Thus, Borgstrom (13) found that during absorption of C^{14} decanoic acid in rats 63 to 73 per cent of the total C^{14} activity in portal blood was present as free decanoic acid and amounted to 4 or 5 mg per cent. It is likely that free fatty acid absorption (portal system) is an active process. Smyth and Taylor (14) showed that the sodium salts of acetic, propionic, and butyric acids could be transferred from the mucosal to the serosal side of isolated everted intestinal loops against a concentration gradient and that the transfer was oxygen dependent.

It follows that in general the fraction of fat absorption via either route will depend upon the percentage of the longer-chain fatty acids in the lipids of the food eaten. In foods eaten by the United States population on the average, the large majority of fatty acids are longer than 12 carbons, so most of fat absorption goes via the lacteals and into the intestinal lymph.

Cholesterol is absorbed in the small intestine and unsaturated fats and fatty acids enhance absorption (15). Saturated fats in the intestine inhibit cholesterol absorption. Bile salts are required for absorption of cholesterol in the rat (16), and the majority of that absorbed is found in the lymph, where around 70 per cent was esterified regardless of the amount absorbed. Chaikoff and others (17) concluded that esterification may not be involved in cholesterol absorption, as was previously held.

Turner has employed fats tagged with I^{131} in studies of absorption and transport of fat. He reviewed the field of fat absorption and his work using the iodine isotope (18).

It is difficult to summarize a field with so much information lacking. However, the following are some of the facts which seem to be established or have experimental backing:

1. Some neutral fat is absorbed without hydrolysis.

2. Hydrolysis products, di- and monoglycerides, as well as fatty acids, can be absorbed.

3. Bile salts aid absorption of the various fractions.

4. Resynthesis occurs within the single layer of epithelial cells lining the mucosa forming triglycerides.

5. Long-chain fatty acids are transported via the lymphatics, predominantly as triglycerides, and shorter-chain acids by the portal system, mostly as free fatty acids.

6. Phospholipids are partially hydrolyzed but are absorbed without hydrolysis. Phospholipid synthesis occurs in the lining cells from mono- and diglycerides, the phospholipids are transported into the lacteals.

7. Cholesterol is absorbed in the free state. Bile salts are required, and unsaturated fats enhance absorption.

Nonesterified fatty acids (NEFA) in the blood may constitute an important vehicle of fatty acid transport from adipose depots to other tissues. However, these fatty acids are not "free" but are almost entirely bound to serum proteins and principally to the albumin. In normal humans the NEFA concentration is about 0.5 meq per liter and the "free" fatty acid concentration is perhaps less than 0.01 per cent of this value (19, 20). The half-life of the NEFA is extremely short, allowing for a rapid transfer of fatty acids to the tissue cells.

Normally the feces contain small amounts of unabsorbed lipids. Continued excretion of large amounts of fats characterizes the condition known as "steatorrhea" (coeliac disease in children). Diarrhea, upset electrolyte balance, and vitamin deficiencies lead to malnutrition. Impaired fat absorption in one type of the disease may result from insufficient bile due to obstruction or other reasons. French and coworkers (21) reported considerable success in the dietary treatment of adult idiopathic steatorrhea. In the steatorrhea that develops in a high percentage of patients following gastrectomy the disturbance was considered by Shingleton and coworkers (22) to be a deficiency in fat digestion rather than faulty absorption. Vitamin B_{12} absorption may be impaired following gastrectomy (deficient intrinsic factor), and the vitamin along with intrinsic factor has been used in the treatment of steatorrhea and the anemia which sometimes accompanies the disease.

Carbohydrate absorption. In man absorption of carbohydrates from sites other than the small intestine is negligible. Under normal circumstances only monosaccharides are absorbed. The other carbohydrates, such as the disaccharides and polysaccharides, must first be hydrolyzed to the monosaccharide stage. Lactose and sucrose in the blood stream are readily eliminated by the kidneys, although some maltose may be hydrolyzed by the blood maltase and the glucose utilized. The absorption of the monosaccharides is normally quite complete, and most of it enters the portal blood.

The rates of absorption are markedly different for the various monosaccharides, indicating as pointed out previously that the absorption process is more involved than one of simple diffusion. For instance, Cori (23) reported that in rats the absorption coefficients (milligrams sugar absorbed per 100 g of rat in one hour) are in the following order: galactose > glucose > fructose > mannose > xylose > arabinose. It was also found that glucose from a 25, 50, or 80 per cent solution was absorbed at the same rate. This was considered as evidence that the absorption rate is independent of the concentration in the intestine. It should be noted that the two pentose sugars studied were absorbed more slowly than the hexoses.

Cori felt that each sugar has an independent rate of absorption, but other work indicates that by varying certain experimental conditions, this rate can be altered. Thus, McKay and Clark (24) showed that when variable volumes of the same concentration of glucose were given to rats (stomach tube), the absorption coefficient was related to the dose of glucose. Under voluntary feeding conditions they found absorption rates far higher than those previously reported. By maintaining rats in a cold environment, the coefficients were found to be even further elevated, due largely to the increased appetite of the animals.

The mechanism of the absorption of glucose (or other physiologically important sugars) is indeed obscure. Since glucose is absorbed selectively at a high rate, it was early postulated that some metabolic alteration may take place in the molecule to make it chemically distinct from the blood glucose and thus increase the diffusion gradient.

Although the experimental data are not convincing, many workers explained glucose absorption on the basis of phosphorylation and then dephosphorylation. In some of the early experiments enzyme inhibitors, such as iodoacetate or phlorizin, did decrease glucose absorption in animals when given with the sugar (25, 26). Since these compounds were thought to be rather specific phosphorylation reaction inhibitors at that time, the conclusion was easily reached that phosphorylation was a prerequisite to transport of glucose into the blood. Later work has indicated that iodoacetate inhibits many sulfhydryl enzymes and is not specific for phosphorylating enzymes. Furthermore, phlorizin appears to inhibit principally some of the oxidative reactions and not the enzymes involved in the formation of sugar phosphates (27).

The absorption problem has been approached by newer techniques by Landau and Wilson (28). These workers studied the absorption of sugars in sacs of hamster intestine *in vitro* by the use of C^{14}-labeled compounds. They concluded that only a small fraction of the absorbed glucose passed through glucose-6-phosphate as an intermediate. In the hamster, then, phosphorylation of glucose may not be necessary for absorption. These workers also confirmed other investigators' work indicating that glucose is not converted into 2 mols of triose phosphate and recondensed to sugar during absorption. Such a theory had some backing at one time and has been reviewed by Wilson (29).

If phosphorylation of glucose is not involved in absorption, as seems to be the case at this time, we are left with no solid explanation to account for the transport mechanism.

It is established that "active" transport (transport against a concentration gradient) is involved, since it is suppressed under anaerobic conditions (30). Passive transport also accounts for some absorption. Quastel (31) has reviewed the absorption of sugars briefly. He previously demonstrated that K+ ions have a marked effect on absorption rates, and that Na+ and Mg++ are required while Ca++ and phosphate are not essential to active transport (32).

Protein absorption. The absorption of protein digestion products has been considered the result of a simple diffusion process, since the amino acids are in general sufficiently water-soluble to account for their passage across the intestinal mucosa without the intervention of chemical alteration. At present, however, there are indications that the process may be more complex. Matthews and Smyth (33), for instance, showed that when DL-alanine was introduced into the lumen of a segment of small intestine of a cat, the L, or natural isomer, appeared in the blood in a concentration three times that of the D isomer during the absorption process. These workers feel that the data corroborate previous postulates of a steriochemically specific mechanism in the intestinal wall for the absorption of L-amino acids.

It is now believed that amino acids are absorbed both passively (diffusion) and by active transport. In intestinal sacs of the hamster active transport has been demonstrated for proline, threonine, alanine, glycine, serine, valine, histidine, hydroxyproline, phenylalanine, isoleucine, and leucine (34). The active absorption of alanine and of phenylalanine is completely inhibited by an equal concentration of L methionine, while glycine transport is inhibited to the extent of 35 per cent (31). Quastel states that such findings are consistent with the view that these amino acids may have affinities for a common intestinal absorption mechanism but that the rates of active absorption may not be proportional to the affinities. These may be examples of competitive inhibitions of transport.

It is known that the amino acids readily enter the portal blood with small amounts finding their way into the lymph system. The absorption is a rapid process, since only small quantities of amino acids are present in the intestine at any time. In other words, as they are liberated from proteins by the digestive processes, they are quickly transported into the blood, and the over-all time of amino acid absorption must then be governed largely by the rate of hydrolysis of the protein constituents in the intestine.

It is probable that some small peptides are absorbed; various workers have reported an increased polypeptide-nitrogen content of portal blood during the digestion and absorption of protein.

Abel and coworkers (35) established beyond doubt the presence in blood of free amino acids. They employed the "vividiffusion" method. Arterial blood from an animal was led through suitable dialyzing tubes immersed in a saline solution and back into a vein of the animal. Dialysis was allowed to proceed for a number of hours, and the concentration of diffusible molecules was increased in the saline to an extent that a number of amino acids, and other molecules, could be identified in crystalline form after evaporation of the saline.

More recently it has been established that the amino acid nitrogen of blood increases in a rather consistent fashion after the ingestion of a given amount of protein. The intravenous administration of moderate amounts of an amino acid mixture leads to a rapid rise in blood amino acid nitrogen without appreciable loss in the urine. The transitory nature of this increased blood level indicates active participation of tissues in removing the amino acids from the blood.

One important problem, which can only be mentioned here, involves the absorption of undigested protein molecules. That both animals and man do absorb native protein has been amply demonstrated experimentally by many workers. Ratner and Gruehl (36) showed that unsplit proteins are able to pass the intestinal wall under normal conditions not only in experimental animals of various ages but also in humans, both young and old. They believe that small amounts of unaltered protein are absorbed regularly.

As we all know, there are many individuals who are allergic to sea foods, strawberries, or even milk, wheat, or other common foods. Supposedly absorption from the intestine of small amounts of proteins of the foods is largely responsible for the many types of allergic reactions exhibited by such individuals.

FORMATION AND COMPOSITION OF FECES

During the passage of the intestinal contents through the small intestine the products of digestion, along with many other compounds such as vitamins, water, and mineral salts, are absorbed. When the contents reach the large intestine, the absorption process, with the exception of water, is normally completed. Here more water and NaCl are absorbed, and the remaining material leaves the body as feces. The consistency of the feces depends to a large degree on the water content, or stated differently, on the degree to which the process of water absorption has been carried. Certainly other factors, such as gastrointestinal motility and nature of diet, affect the consistency of the feces also.

Small variations in diet have little or no effect on the nature of the feces. However, an exclusively vegetable diet tends to yield a larger bulk and softer consistency feces, while on a meat diet the feces are harder and the quantity is less. Even during starvation feces are produced, though the quantity is markedly diminished.

The water content of the feces is usually from 60 to 70 per cent by weight. The 20 to 30 per cent dry matter is composed primarily of undigested dietary constituents, such as cellulose material, hair, and seeds, fatty material, mineral matter, and bacteria. The undigested food protein, carbohydrate, and fat amount to very little, since the digestion and absorption of these substances is normally 95 to 98 per cent complete. Practically all the nitrogen present is of bacterial origin.

The normal dark brown color of the feces is due to bile pigment derivatives. The primary pigment is stercobilin arising from oxidation of the precursor stercobilinogen. Small amounts of bilirubin and biliverdin are sometimes present.

Indole and skatole arising from bacterial enzymatic action on the amino acid tryptophan are the primary compounds responsible for the disagreeable odor of the feces. Hydrogen sulfide and methyl mercaptan (CH_3SH) likewise have displeasing odors, and these substances may be present in considerable amounts at times.

The large intestine is the site of bacterial multiplication. Many billions of bacteria may be excreted daily in the feces. *Escherichia coli* is ordinarily the predominating organism, although many others frequently are found in the feces.

The excrement is generally slightly alkaline; the pH varies from 7 to 7.5 on a normal diet. The inclusion of considerable milk or lactose in the diet may lead to more favorable conditions for certain acidophilus organisms, and the fecal pH may then be lowered.

SPECIAL REFERENCES

1. Verzár, F.: *Absorption from the Intestine*. Longmans, New York, 1936.
2. Frazer, A. C.: *Biochem. Soc. Symposia*, Cambridge, England, No. 9, 5, 1952.
3. Reiser, R.; Bryson, M. J.; Carr, M. J.; and Kuiken, K. A.: *J. Biol. Chem.*, **194**, 131, 1952.
4. Reiser, R., and Williams, M. C.: *J. Biol. Chem.*, **202**, 815, 1953.
5. Coniglio, J. C., and Cate, D. L.: *Am. J. Clin. Nutrition*, 7, 646, 1959.
6. Blomstrand, R., and Ahrens, E. H., Jr.: *J. Biol. Chem.*, **233**, 321, 1958.
7. Reller, H. H.; Benedict, J. H.; Mattson, F. H.; and Beck, L. W.: *Federation Proc.*, 13, 474, 1954.
8. Mead, J. F., and Fillerup, D. L.: *J. Biol. Chem.*, **227**, 1009, 1957.
9. Blomstrand, R.; Thorn, N. A.; and Ahrens, E. H., Jr.: *Am. J. Med.*, 24, 958, 1958.
10. Bloom, B.; Kiyasu, J. Y.; Rinehardt, W. O.; and Chaikoff, I. L.: *Am. J. Physiol.*, 177, 44, 1954.
11. Bloom, B.; Chaikoff, I. L.; and Reinhardt, W. O.: *Am. J. Physiol.*, **166**, 451, 1951.
12. Kiyasu, J. Y.; Bloom, B.; and Chaikoff, I. L.: *J. Biol. Chem.*, **199**, 415, 1952.
13. Borgstrom, B.: *Acta Physiol. Scand.*, **34**, 71, 1955.
14. Smyth, D. H., and Taylor, C. B.: *J. Physiol.*, **141**, 73, 1950.
15. Lin, T. M.; Karvinen, E.; and Ivy, A. C.: *Am. J. Physiol.*, **183**, 86, 1955.
16. Siperstein, M. D.; Chaikoff, I. L.; and Rinehardt, W. O.: *J. Biol. Chem.*, **198**, 111, 1952.
17. Daskalakis, E. G., and Chaikoff, I. L.: *Arch. Biochem. Biophys.*, **58**, 373, 1955.
18. Turner, D. A.: *Am. J. Diges. Diseases*, **3**, 594, 682, 1958.
19. Goodman, D. S.: *J. Am. Chem. Soc.*, **80**, 3892, 1958.
20. *Nutrition Revs.*, 17, 147, 1959.
21. French, J. M.; Hawkins, C. F.; and Smith, N.: *Quart. J. Med.* (New Series), **26**, 481, 1957.
22. Shingleton, W. W.; Isley, J. K.; Floyd, R. D.; Sanders, A. P.; Baylin, G. J.; Postlethwait, R. W.; and Ruffin, J. M.: *Surgery*, **42**, 12, 1957.
23. Cori, C. F.: *J. Biol. Chem.*, **66**, 691, 1925.
24. McKay, E. M., and Clark, W. G.: *Am. J. Physiol.*, **135**, 187, 1941–42.
25. Verzár, F., and Sullman, H.: *Biochem. Z.*, **289**, 323, 1937.
26. Beck, L. V.: *J. Biol. Chem.*, **143**, 403, 1942.
27. Lotspeich, W. D., and Keller, D. M.: *J. Biol. Chem.*, **222**, 843, 1956.
28. Landau, B. R., and Wilson, T. H.: *J. Biol. Chem.*, **234**, 749, 1959.
29. Wilson, T. H.: *J. Biol. Chem.*, **222**, 751, 1956.
30. Wilson, T. H., and Wiseman, G.: *J. Physiol.*, **123**, 116, 1954.
31. Quastel, J. H.: *Am. J. Clin. Nutrition*, **8**, 137, 1960.
32. Riklis, E., and Quastel, J. H.: *Canad. J. Biochem. Physiol.*, **36**, 347, 1958.
33. Mathews, D. M., and Smyth, D. H.: *J. Physiol.* (London), 116, 20p, 1952.
34. Wiseman, G.: *J. Physiol.*, **127**, 414, 1955; **133**, 626, 1956.
35. Abel, J. J.; Rowntree, L. G.; and Turner, B. B.: *Trans. Assoc. Am. Physicians*, **5**, 275, 611, 1913–14.
36. Ratner, B., and Gruehl, H. L.: *J. Clin. Invest.*, **13**, 517, 1934.

14

Detoxication in the body, the metabolism of foreign compounds

Detoxication mechanisms or detoxication reactions are those biochemical changes proceeding in the body which convert molecules foreign to the body to compounds more readily excretable. Many of the reactions classed under this heading are well established; others are known only partially, and some have not been followed at all. Only the end products are known in many instances, whereas in others the intermediates in the reaction are known. Since in many reactions, the toxicity is not eliminated, but only lessened, or in special cases even increased, the term "detoxication" is rather too inclusive. It is, however, useful in covering a broad field of study with the connotation implied in the first sentence above.

In 1947 the book *Detoxication Mechanism* by Williams (1) was published; there were some 290 pages. In 1959 the second edition of *Detoxication Mechanism* appeared (2), containing some 790 pages. This is a rapidly developing field!

There are marked species variations in not only the qualitative but also the quantitative capacity to detoxify an administered foreign molecule. In one species the detoxified metabolite excreted may be wholly different from that in another species, or a small or large part of the administered compound may be excreted unchanged. The capacity to detoxify may be overtaxed. This can be demonstrated by the administration of a compound requiring a naturally occurring molecule in the body as a part of the process of detoxication. For instance, the amino acid cysteine is used in the synthetic detoxication of bromobenzene. Small amounts of this foreign molecule are detoxified by a number of animal species with no untoward effects; but above a certain intake of bromobenzene over a period of time the body fails to supply sufficient cysteine, and the result is a deficiency of the amino acid for its other metabolic roles, and growth is adversely affected. Another interesting instance involves the changes in detoxifying benzoic acid. In most species studied this compound is largely excreted as hippuric acid (benzoylglycine). As the dose of benzoic acid is increased, the capacity of the animal to furnish endogenous glycine for

476

this process is exceeded, and then a greater part of the benzoic acid is excreted combined with glucuronic acid.

It is convenient in discussing the subject of detoxication mechanisms to include both the detoxication of putrefaction products—i.e., foreign molecules produced in the intestine through bacterial enzymatic action on normal digestion products—and detoxication of medicinals and other foreign compounds taken with foods. No more than a brief survey with typical examples can be presented here.

Production and metabolism of foreign compounds in the large intestine. Bacterial enzyme systems in the large intestine bring about many biochemical alterations of the small amounts of unabsorbed food molecules. In a few instances the substances produced have a degree of toxicity, and after absorption into the body they are metabolized in various ways to aid in their elimination.

From carbohydrates the products formed are innocuous or even beneficial, since such acids as acetic and butyric may be absorbed and utilized. Methane, CO_2, and H_2 may be absorbed to some extent without effect.

Neutral fats are hydrolyzed by bacterial action to products normal to the gut. The choline fraction of phospholipids may yield the abnormal amine neurine, which has a low order of toxicity (3):

$$(CH_3)_3N^+CH_2CH_2OH \longrightarrow (CH_3)_3N^+CH = CH_2$$
$$OH^- \hspace{4.5cm} OH^-$$

Choline   Neurine

The amino acids escaping absorption in the small intestine are subjected to a variety of metabolic changes, including decarboxylation, deamination, oxidation, reduction, and combinations of these.

The diamines cadaverine (pentamethylendiamine) and putrescine (tetramethylenediamine) arise from decarboxylation of lysine and ornithine (from arginine), respectively. These and other amines are also found in putrefying flesh and were once thought to be responsible for ptomaine poisoning. Because of the established low toxicity of these molecules, it is now known that other toxins in such foods are responsible for the ill effects. Animal tissues, including the intestinal mucosa, as well as *E. coli*, an organism normal to the large intestine, contain diamineoxidase which oxidizes these amines, and thus they may not reach the blood stream.

Tyramine from decarboxylation of tyrosine, indole ethylamine from tryptophan, and histamine from histidine are known to be formed also. Histamine is a potent capillary dilator and constrictor of smooth muscle. Its hormonal action in connection with exciting gastric secretion is discussed in Chapter 12. Histaminase of animal and bacterial origin oxidize this amine to β-imidazoleacetaldehyde according to the general reaction:

$$R-CH_2NH_2 + O_2 \longrightarrow R-CHO + NH_3 + H_2O_2$$

Histamine taken by mouth is largely altered before reaching the blood. This is reasonable, since the intestinal wall is known to be a rich source of histaminase. Other means of detoxifying histamine and tyramine are discussed under conjugation mechanisms on the following pages.

The accompanying formulas show some of the molecules resulting from decarboxylation of amino acids:

$$NH_2(CH_2)_4CHNH_2COOH \xrightarrow{-CO_2} NH_2(CH_2)_5NH_2$$

Lysine   Cadaverine

$$Arginine \longrightarrow NH_2(CH_2)_3CHNH_2COOH \xrightarrow{-CO_2} NH_2(CH_2)_4NH_2$$

Ornithine   Putrescine

HO—⟨ ⟩—CH_2CHNH_2COOH $\xrightarrow{-CO_2}$ HO—⟨ ⟩—$CH_2CH_2NH_2$

Tyrosine   Tyramine

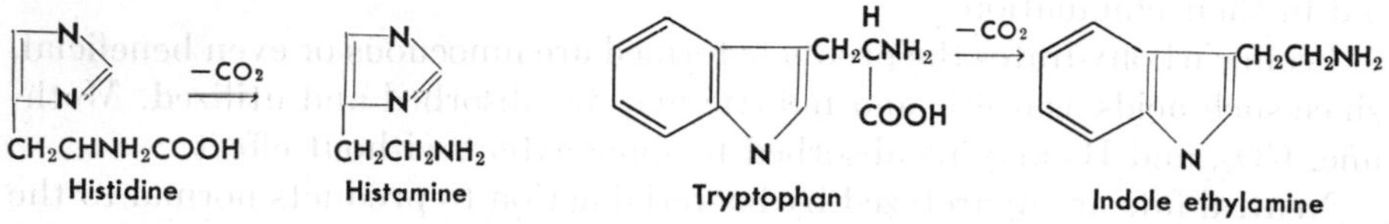

CH_2CHNH_2COOH $CH_2CH_2NH_2$ Tryptophan   Indole ethylamine

Histidine   Histamine

$\xrightarrow{-CO_2}$

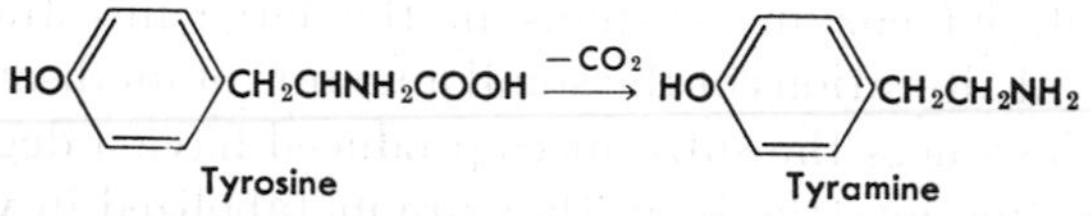

Many products other than amines are produced in the intestine from amino acids by bacterial enzymes. Acids result from deamination. Of these the aromatic amino acids yield various products requiring detoxication in the body following their absorption. The acids produced may be decarboxylated and then oxidized to an acid with one less carbon in the side chain, and this may be repeated a second and a third time. Thus, the deamination of tyrosine yields p-hydroxyphenylpyruvic acid, and decarboxylation followed by oxidation yields p-hydroxyphenylacetic acid. Further reactions yield benzoic acid and finally phenol. The accompanying reactions indicate some of the compounds known to result from similar changes in the aromatic amino acids in the intestine:

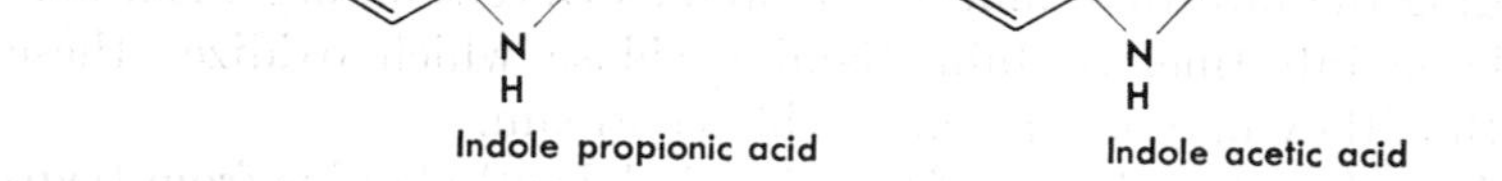

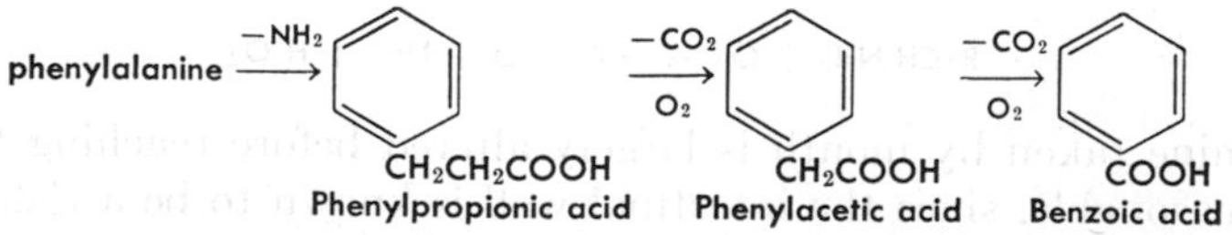

tryptophan $\xrightarrow{-NH_2}$ [indole]CH_2CH_2COOH $\xrightarrow[O_2]{-CO_2}$ [indole]CH_2COOH $\xrightarrow{-CO_2}$

Indole propionic acid   Indole acetic acid

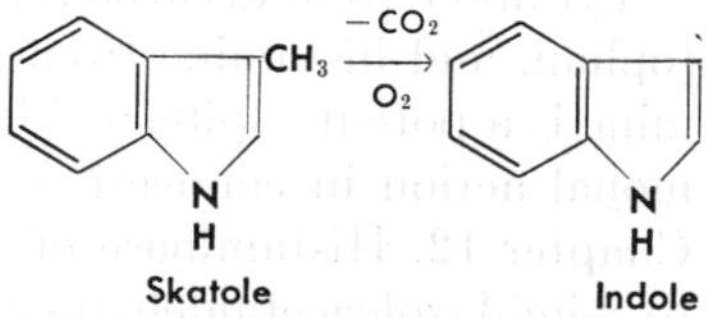

[indole]CH_3 $\xrightarrow[O_2]{-CO_2}$ [indole]

Skatole   Indole

phenylalanine $\xrightarrow{-NH_2}$ ⟨ ⟩CH_2CH_2COOH $\xrightarrow[O_2]{-CO_2}$ ⟨ ⟩CH_2COOH $\xrightarrow[O_2]{-CO_2}$ ⟨ ⟩$COOH$

Phenylpropionic acid   Phenylacetic acid   Benzoic acid

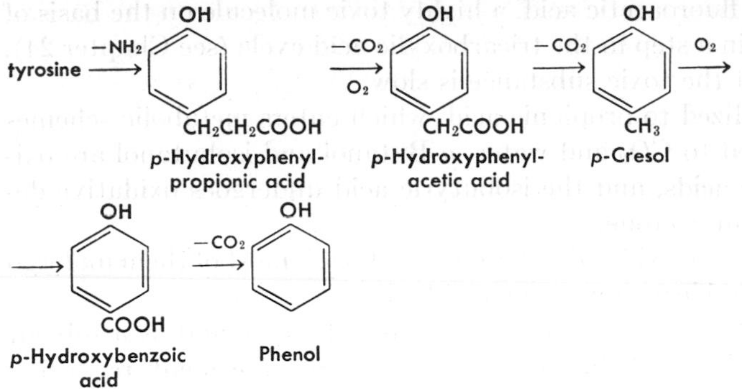

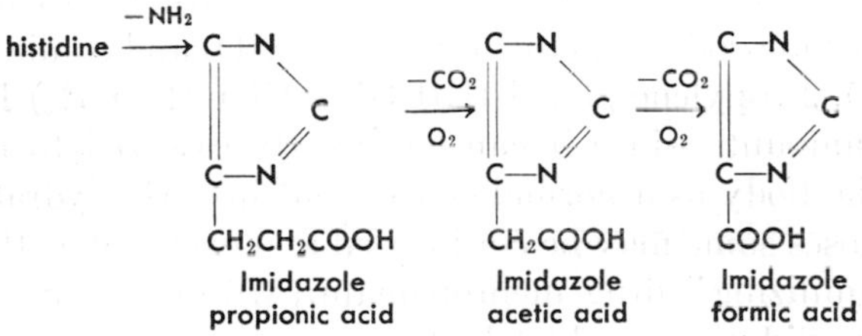

tyrosine $\xrightarrow{-NH_2}$

OH

CH_2CH_2COOH

p-Hydroxyphenyl-
propionic acid

$\xrightarrow[O_2]{-CO_2}$

OH

CH_2COOH

p-Hydroxyphenyl-
acetic acid

$\xrightarrow{-CO_2}$

OH

CH_3

p-Cresol

$\xrightarrow{O_2}$

$\longrightarrow$

OH

COOH

p-Hydroxybenzoic
acid

$\xrightarrow{-CO_2}$

OH

Phenol

histidine $\xrightarrow{-NH_2}$

C—N
‖   \
‖   C
C—N /
|
CH_2CH_2COOH

Imidazole
propionic acid

$\xrightarrow[O_2]{-CO_2}$

C—N
\
C
/
C—N
|
CH_2COOH

Imidazole
acetic acid

$\xrightarrow[O_2]{-CO_2}$

C—N
\
C
/
C—N
|
COOH

Imidazole
formic acid

We will now consider some of the reactions utilized by the body to lessen the toxicity or increase excretability of foreign molecules which make their way into the system either as a result of absorption of some of the compounds referred to or as a result of ingesting them in foods, medicines, or other forms. Such biotransformations can be classed under four main types: oxidation, hydrolysis, reduction, and synthesis or conjugation. In many cases combinations of these processes are used in detoxifying a given compound.

Oxidation. A large variety of foreign compounds are destroyed in the body by oxidation. This process has already been noted in connection with intestinal bacterial metabolic changes in the deaminated aromatic amino acids. Similar oxidative changes do occur in various tissues of the body.

Other types of oxidation include conversion of aldehydes to acids, hydroxylation of ring systems, oxidation of sulfur compounds, oxidative ring scission, and various others.

Primary alcohols either are oxidized through aldehyde, carboxylic acid, and on to CO_2 and water or are conjugated (as glucuronide principally) without previous alteration or following oxidation to acids. Examples of these different approaches are well known.

Methanol is eliminated largely as formate in man, and the slow process of formate elimination adds to the toxicity of this compound. Ethanol is oxidized (in time) to CO_2 and water. Acetaldehyde and acetic acid are intermediates, and the latter may go into various metabolic schemes. A number of enzymes are involved in ethanol metabolism. A discussion of this can be found in Chapter 24. A small portion of ingested alcohol is excreted unchanged in the urine and in the expired air.

Several halogenated alcohols are used as industrial solvents and have been studied in the light of toxicity and detoxication. An example is fluoroethanol, which is oxidized to fluoroacetic acid, a highly toxic molecule on the basis of its inhibitory effect in a step in the tricarboxylic acid cycle (see Chapter 24). Further oxidation of the toxic substance is slow.

n-Propanol is oxidized to propionic acid, which enters metabolic schemes and can be converted to CO_2 and water. n-Butanol and isobutanol are oxidized rapidly to the acids, and the isobutyric acid undergoes oxidative decarboxylation to form acetone.

Secondary alcohols are oxidized to ketones, although most of them undergo conjugation (glucuronides) to an appreciable degree.

Ethylene glycol (CH_2OH—CH_2OH), used as antifreeze and as a solvent for many compounds, is highly toxic. There is disagreement regarding whether this molecule or its metabolic products cause the toxicity. The intermediate oxidation products glyoxal (CHO—CHO) and oxalic acid have been implicated (4). Propylene glycol (CH_2OH—CHOH—CH_3) has no toxicity in moderate amounts, since it can be directly oxidized to lactic acid and handled by the body as a normal constituent in carbohydrate metabolism. With larger doses some may be conjugated and excreted as the glucuronide.

The "tranquilizing" drug meprobamate (Miltown, Equanil) is excreted largely as the oxidation product hydroxymeprobamate, which has none of the activity of the drug (5). Meprobamate is 2-methyl-2-propyl-1,3-propanediol dicarbamate. The oxidation takes place on the methyl group to form the hydroxymethyl derivative of the drug, which is excreted in the urine and accounted for 60 per cent of the dose administered to dogs, according to Walkenstein and coworkers (5). The compound studied by these investigators was tagged with C^{14} in both carbamate groups. No hydrolysis of the carbamate ester groups was observed:

$$H_2C - OCONH_2$$
$$|$$
$$CH_3C - CH_2CH_2CH_3 \quad \text{Meprobamate}$$
$$|$$
$$H_2C - OCONH_2$$

Chloral or chloral hydrate has been used as a hypnotic in man over many years by the medical profession and by others (it is commonly known as knockout drops, etc.). In man chloral, $CCl_3CH(OH)_2$ (sometimes written as trichloroacetaldehyde, CCl_3CHO) is partly oxidized to trichloroacetic acid and excreted as salts of this acid. A larger proportion is excreted as trichloroethanol (reduction product) and the glucuronide of this alcohol (conjugation product; see further) (6):

$$CCl_3CH(OH)_2 \longrightarrow CCl_3COOH$$

Many primary aliphatic amines undergo oxidation to the corresponding acid, and the nitrogen is converted to urea according to the general reaction:

$$R-CH_2NH_2 \longrightarrow R-COOH + NH_2CONH_2$$

Oxidation of benzylamine ($C_6H_5CH_2NH_2$) yields benzoic acid which is excreted in conjugated form (see further).

An example of hydroxylation as a mechanism of oxidative detoxication involves the metabolism of benzene. Aside from phenol there are formed hydroquinone or quinol $(p\text{-}C_6H_4(OH)_2)$, catechol $(o\text{-}C_6H_4(OH)_2)$ and hydroxyquinol $(1,2,4\text{-}C_6H_3(OH)_3)$ also called "hydroxyhydroquinone." These three hydroxy benzene compounds are conjugated with sulfuric acid and with glucuronic acid in various proportions among different species.

Oxidative scission of an aromatic ring is exemplified in the conversion of benzene (through catechol) to muconic acid (COOHCH=CH—CH=CHCOOH). Parke and Williams (7) isolated C^{14} containing muconic acid from rabbit urine after dosing the animals with C^{14} benzene.

The sulfur of a variety of organic sulfur compounds is oxidized to sulfate to varying degrees. The sulfate may be excreted in organic or inorganic form or as neutral (unoxidized) sulfur. Thus, the sulfur of thioglycollic acid (COOHCH$_2$SH) used in many hair-waving preparations is excreted as organic sulfate and neutral sulfur by rabbits, while in rats nearly half the dose is excreted as inorganic sulfate (8).

Hydrolysis. The hydrolytic cleavage of ester, amide, glucoside and other linkages constitutes a significant approach to molecular alteration of foreign molecules (and, of course, normal metabolic compounds) in the body.

The drug procaine, NH_2—$C_6H_4COOCH_2CH_2N(C_2H_5)_2$, is rapidly hydrolyzed (procaine esterase) to p-aminobenzoic acid and diethylamino ethanol. After intravenous injection in man very little procaine appears unchanged in the urine. The glucoside cardiac drugs occurring in digitalis undergo hydrolysis, yielding sugars and the aglucone (remainder of molecule). The alkaloid drug atropine (tropyl tropate, an ester) is hydrolyzed to tropic acid and tropine principally in the liver by atropine esterase. Acetyl salicylic acid (aspirin) is partly hydrolyzed, yielding salicylic and acetic acids by a rather nonspecific liver esterase:

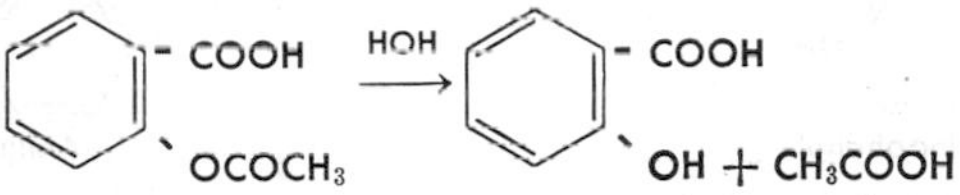

Acetylsalicylic acid   Salicylic acid + acetic acid

Diisopropylfluorophosphate (DFP) is an example of the pharmacologically active alky fluorophosphates (fluorophosphonates). DFP is extremely toxic; in minute doses it is a parasympathomimetic agent (stimulates parasympathetic nerves). It is hydrolyzed in the body to HF and the dialkyl-phosphate, especially by a liver enzyme (9):

$$(C_3H_7O)_2POF \xrightarrow{HOH} (C_3H_7O)_2PO(OH) + HF$$

Reduction. Many nitro compounds are reduced in the body to amino compounds. Picric acid is partly reduced to picramic acid, but both appear in urine after ingestion of the former:

$$C_6H_2OH(NO_2)_3 \longrightarrow C_6H_2OH(NO_2)_2NH_2$$

Picric acid   Picramic acid
2,4,6-trinitrophenol   2-amino-4,6-dinitrophenol

Trinitrotoluene (TNT) undergoes a similar change in that a nitro group is reduced to an amino group. Interest in the fate of nitro compounds in the body has taken on more importance since the discovery of the antibiotic chloromycetin (a p-substituted nitrobenzene). Some naturally occurring glucosides are also nitro compounds. Williams and coworkers (10) have studied the fates of o-, m-, and p-nitrophenols in rabbits. These compounds are eliminated in the urine mainly in the conjugated form as nitrophenylglucuronides and as ethereal sulfates. The nitro groups are reduced only partially (6, 10, and 14 per cent for the o-, m-, and p-compounds, respectively). The p-nitrophenol is quite toxic, but the reduction product p-aminophenol is not very toxic. However, the toxicity of the intermediates p-nitrosophenol and p-hydroxyaminophenol is quite marked. A succeeding article by the same authors (11) describes their work on the toxicity of nitrobenzene in rabbits.

Chloral or chloral hydrate is partly reduced to trichloroethanol, CCl_3-$CH(OH)_2 \longrightarrow CCl_3CH_2OH$. The hydroxyl group so produced is available for glucuronic acid conjugation.

Other types of reduction reactions employed by the body include: (a) conversion of —S—S— linkages to —SH groups thus $RS-S-R' \longrightarrow RSH + R'SH$; (b) conversion of azo compounds to amines as in the case of p-dimethylaminoazobenzene (butter yellow). A number of metabolites of this compound have been observed, including the products of reductive cleavage (splitting the azo linkage) p-aminophenol, N,N-dimethyl-p-phenylenediamine and aniline (12). The compounds are shown herewith:

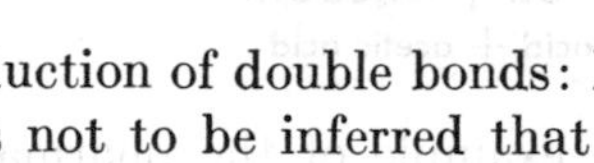

p-Dimethylaminoazobenzene 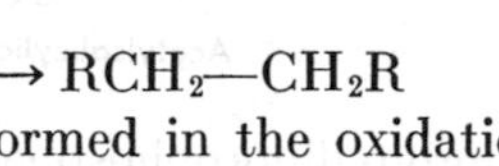   N,N-Dimethyl-p-phenylenediamine

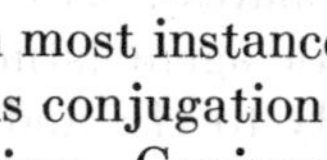

p-Aminophenol 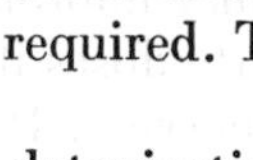   Aniline

(c) reduction of double bonds: $RCH-CHR \longrightarrow RCH_2-CH_2R$

It is not to be inferred that the products formed in the oxidation, the hydrolysis, or the reduction reactions just discussed are in all cases ready for excretion. In most instances further alterations are required. These changes are classed as conjugation or synthesis reactions.

Conjugation. Conjugation for the purpose of detoxication or for increasing excretability usually follows oxidation, reduction, or hydrolysis of foreign molecules, although some compounds are conjugated without previous alteration.

The most common type of conjugation is the formation of an ester or an ether type of linkage with glucuronic acid—e.g., with a carboxyl or with a hydroxyl group of the foreign compound. The body readily produces glucuronic acid from glucose. The mechanism of this synthesis is discussed in Chapter 24. A variety of compounds containing phenolic or alcoholic hydroxyl groups or carboxylic acids are conjugated to form glucuronides:

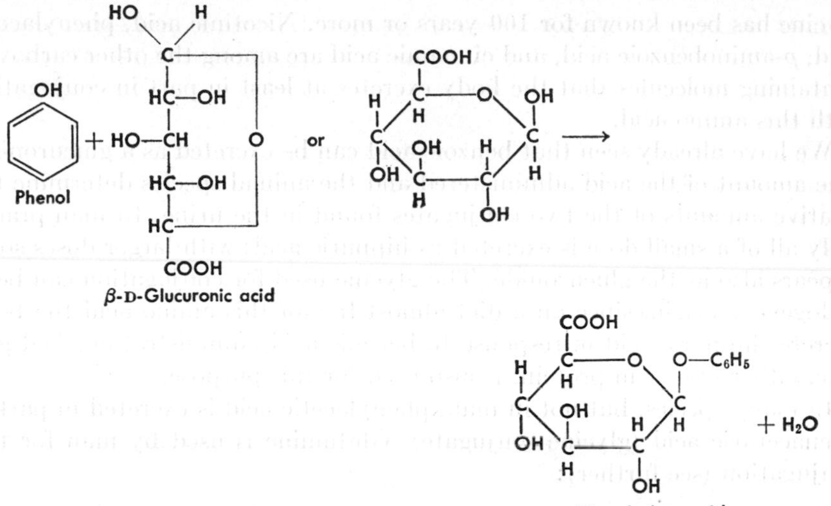

Phenol + β-D-Glucuronic acid or → Phenyl glucuronide (β-glucoside or "ether" type) + H_2O

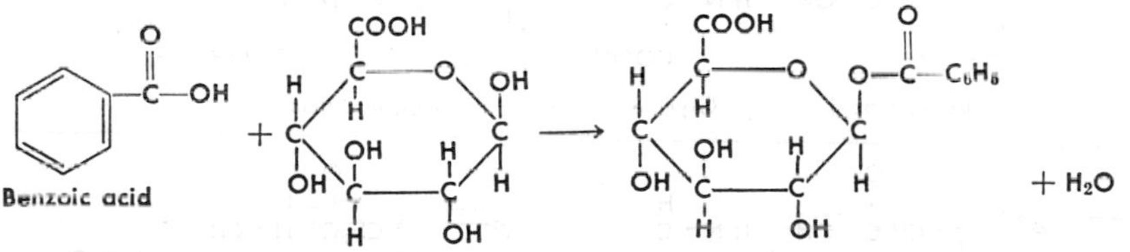

Benzoic acid + β-D-Glucuronic acid → Benzoyl glucuronide (β-acyl or "ester" type) + H_2O

Chloramphenicol or chloromycetin is a broad spectrum antibiotic used clinically with great success. A brief discussion of the drug and its action can be found in Chapter 32. The drug is largely metabolized in man, although the glucuronide and the deacylated drug have been isolated from urine and constitute the major excretion products (13):

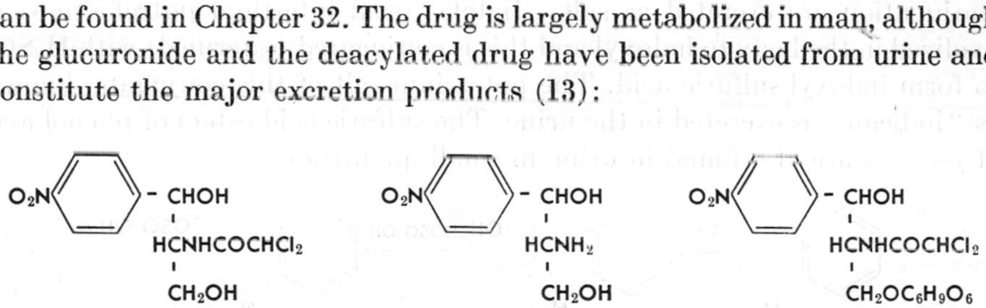

O_2N— — CHOH
        |
    HCNHCOCHCl₂
        |
    CH₂OH
Chloramphenicol

O_2N— — CHOH
        |
      HCNH₂
        |
    CH₂OH
Deacylated drug

O_2N— — CHOH
        |
    HCNHCOCHCl₂
        |
    CH₂OC₆H₉O₆
Chloramphenicol glucuronide

Bilirubin, a bile pigment, is conjugated and excreted in the bile as the glucuronide. The presence of a mono- and a diglucuronide has been established (14). The conjugation involves ester formation with carboxyl groups of the propionic acid residues of bilirubin (15). Further discussion can be found in Chapter 12.

A second and important type of conjugation involves the amino acid glycine. The formation of hippuric acid in the body from benzoic acid and glycine has been known for 100 years or more. Nicotinic acid, phenylacetic acid, *p*-aminobenzoic acid, and cinnamic acid are among the other carboxyl-containing molecules that the body excretes at least in part in conjugation with this amino acid.

We have already seen that benzoic acid can be excreted as a glucuronide. The amount of the acid administered and the animal species determine the relative amounts of the two conjugates found in the urine. In man practically all of a small dose is excreted as hippuric acid; with larger doses some appears also as the glucuronide. The glycine used for conjugation can be of endogenous origin, since on a diet almost free of this amino acid the body excretes hippuric acid in response to benzoic acid administration. Fed glycine, either free or in protein, is also used for this purpose.

In many species, but not in man, phenylacetic acid is excreted in part as phenaceturic acid (glycine conjugate). Glutamine is used by man for this conjugation (see further):

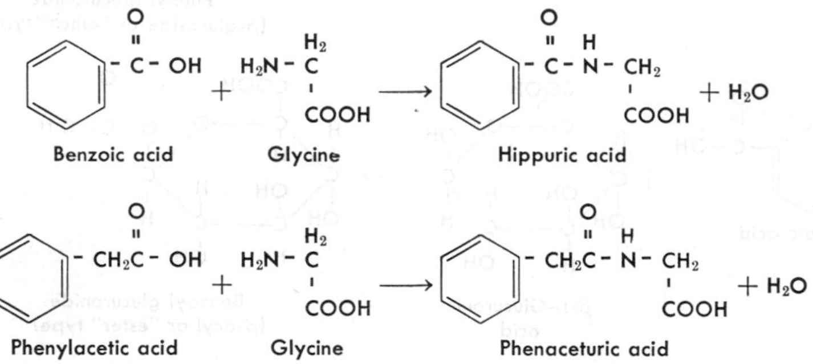

Benzoic acid   Glycine   Hippuric acid

Phenylacetic acid   Glycine   Phenaceturic acid

Sulfuric acid is used by the animal body for detoxication of various compounds with phenolic hydroxyl groups. The ethereal sulfates formed in this conjugation are excreted as salts. Indole (from intestinal putrefaction) is oxidized in the body to indoxyl and this is conjugated (esterified) with H_2SO_4 to form indoxyl sulfuric acid. The potassium salt of this conjugate, known as "indican," is excreted in the urine. The sulfuric acid esters of phenol and of *p*-cresol are also found in urine in small quantities:

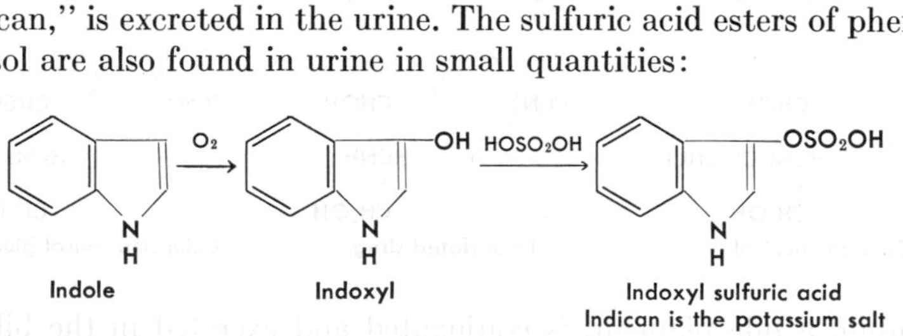

Indole   Indoxyl   Indoxyl sulfuric acid
                        Indican is the potassium salt

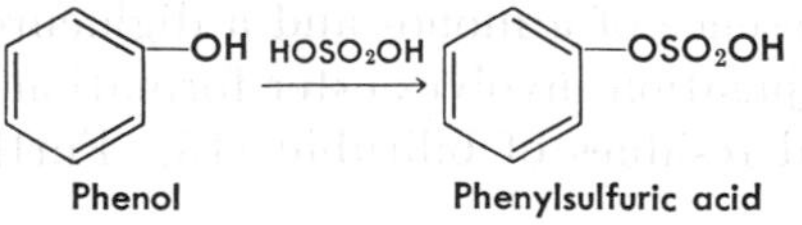

Phenol   Phenylsulfuric acid

An interesting example of species differences in detoxication mechanisms involves phenylacetic acid. Human beings detoxify this substance by conjugation with glutamine (the amide of glutamic acid); chickens employ the amino acid ornithine; and glycine is used by the dog and some other species. The glycine conjugate (phenaceturic acid) has already been discussed:

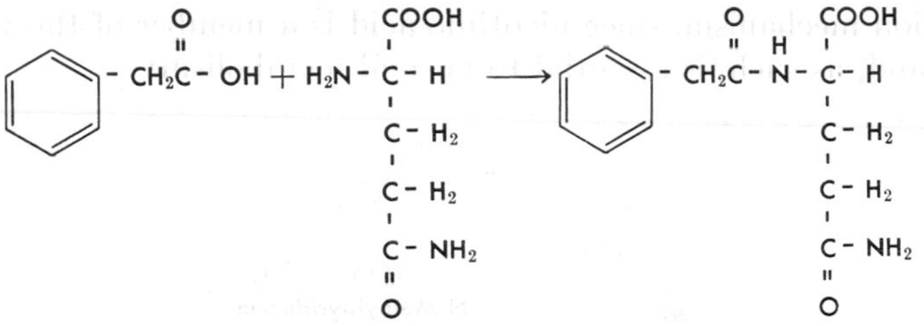

Phenylacetic acid   Glutamine   Phenylacetylglutamine

Although the cyanide radical is extremely poisonous to the body, very small quantities may be harmless. The —CN⁻ radical is converted to the relatively nontoxic thiocyanate radical, —CNS⁻, and excreted as salts of this acid radical.

Lang showed that the following reaction is mediated by an enzyme in animal tissues, and he gave the enzyme the name "rhodanese" (16); "rhodanate" is another name for thiocyanate, CNS⁻:

$$HCN + Na_2S_2O_3 \longrightarrow NaHSO_3 + NaCNS$$

Thiosulfate or colloidal sulfur must be present in order for the enzyme to convert cyanide to thiocyanate. The enzyme may have considerable significance in animals that eat foods containing cyanogenic substances.

Gal and Greenberg (17) have shown that nitriles such as acetonitrile, CH_3CN, are catabolized in the body in part by release of cyanide. Certain enzyme inhibitors were found to increase and others to decrease the urinary thiocyanate resulting from the cyanide formed.

Wood and Cooley (18) indicate that CN⁻ reacts in the body with the —S—S— linkage of cystine to form cysteine and another molecule, which is probably 2-aminothiazoline-4-carboxylic acid. Thiocyanate in urine following cyanide intake is thought to result from the spontaneous breakdown of the thiazoline. The latter compound isolated from rat urine after giving sulfur-labeled cystine just prior to cyanide was found to contain the isotopic sulfur. Such a mechanism represents an independent avenue of cyanide detoxication:

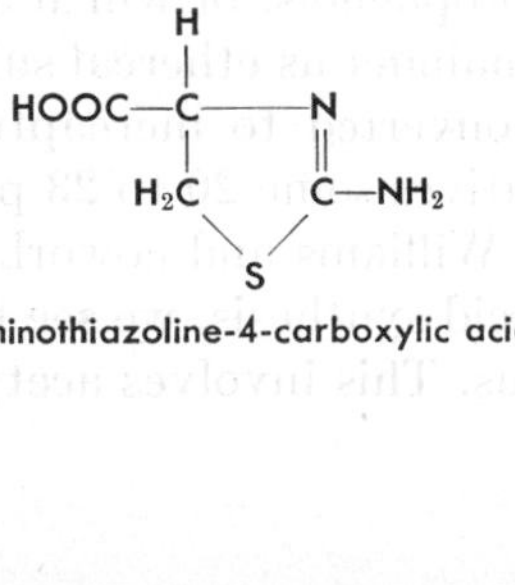

2-Aminothiazoline-4-carboxylic acid

Methylation as a detoxication process is rather limited in the body. The nitrogen atom of pyridine is methylated, and the compound N-methylpyridinium hydroxide is excreted. Nicotinic acid, a pyridine derivative, also appears in the urine to some extent as the methylated conjugate trigonelline, the methylated betaine of nicotinic acid. This can hardly be considered a detoxication mechanism, since nicotinic acid is a member of the vitamin B complex and, as such, is essential to normal metabolism:

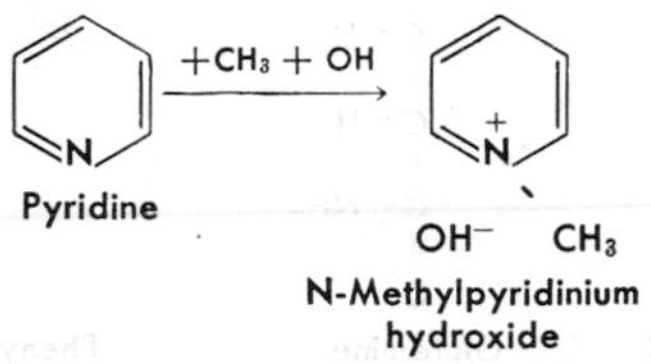

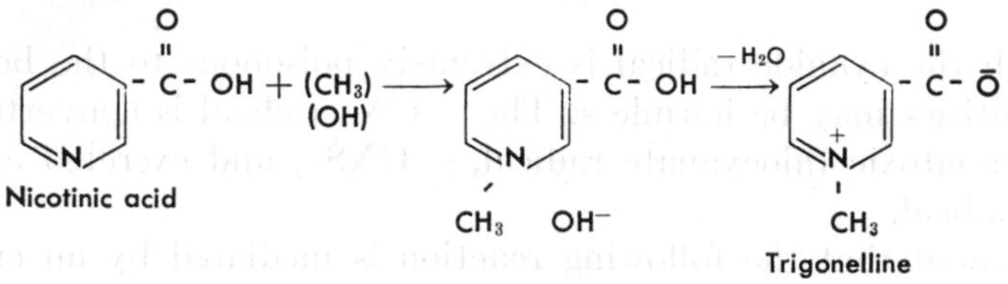

Pyridine

N-Methylpyridinium hydroxide

Nicotinic acid

Trigonelline

Cysteine is used in the so-called mercapturic acid synthesis. Acetylation of cysteine apparently precedes conjugation with the substance to be detoxified. Only a few instances are known in which this type of detoxication is employed. Benzene and halogenated aromatic hydrocarbons are among the substances handled in this way. Bromobenzene when taken into the body is excreted to a considerable degree as *p*-bromophenylmercapturic acid:

Bromobenzene   Acetylated cysteine   p-Bromophenylmercapturic acid

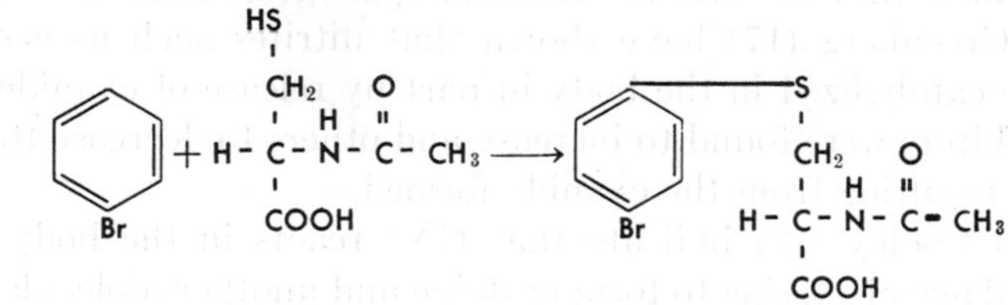

In rabbits 64 per cent of fed fluorobenzene (1 g per kg) can be recovered unchanged in the expired air. Chlorobenzene is expired unchanged to the extent of 25 to 30 per cent. Small amounts of bromo- and iodobenzene are also expired (6 and 3 per cent, respectively). Around one-third of the fluorobenzene is oxidized to fluorophenols, of which about one-third are excreted as glucuronide and the remainder as ethereal sulfate. Only 1 or 2 per cent of the fluoro compound is converted to mercapturic acid, whereas with the other three halogen derivatives some 20 to 23 per cent is found in the urine in this form, according to Williams and coworkers (19).

From the mercapturic acid synthesis, we see that acetylation plays a part in detoxication mechanisms. This involves acetylation of an α-amino group of an amino acid—i.e., cysteine. The body also acetylates aromatic amino groups. The acetylation of *p*-aminobenzene sulfonamide (sulfanilamide) is an example of this type of detoxication. As much as half of the excreted sulfanilamide may be acetylated in man:

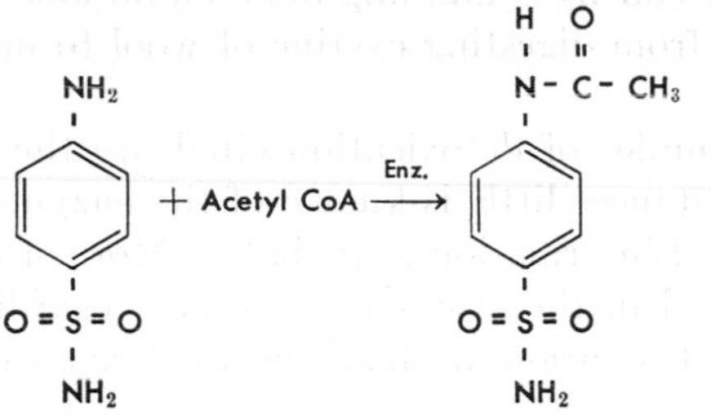

$$NH_2 \quad + \text{ Acetyl CoA} \xrightarrow{\text{Enz.}} \quad N-C-CH_3$$

Sulfanilamide   p-N-Acetyl benzenesulfonamide
(acetylated sulfanilamide)

The following two detoxications are in a category by themselves, since an administered drug, and not a normal body metabolite, is responsible for the detoxication. However, because of the close similarity to other processes, it is felt advisable to give the matter brief mention here.

A most interesting instance of detoxication by the reverse of the mercapturic acid synthesis (discussed previously) is found in selenium poisoning. This element may replace sulfur in cysteine and methionine in body tissues if it is ingested over periods of time in sufficient quantity. In certain areas (parts of South Dakota, for example) the soil is high in selenium, and consequently the vegetation grown there acquires considerable of this element. Not only farm animals but also human beings have developed selenium poisoning as a result of eating the food and drinking the water from such an area. Selenized steers were given *p*-bromobenzene in the hope of removing from their bodies some selenium-containing cysteine as a mercapturic acid. The selenium blood levels dropped markedly, and the urinary excretion of selenium rose on this therapy (20). Lemley (21) reported the use of bromobenzene in treating a human case of selenium poisoning. After the oral administration of small amounts of this compound, the urinary excretion rose markedly, and the selenium was associated with the mercapturic acid fraction of the urine. A marked improvement in the patient's clinical condition was also noted.

The compound dithiopropanol-1 ("BAL" for British Anti-Lewisite), also known as "2,3-mercaptopropanol," was developed during World War II as a detoxicant for certain war poisons. During the years that have followed, it has been found that this compound is valuable for the removal from the body of a number of toxic metals. The excretion of such metals as arsenic, cadmium, mercury, and gold is markedly increased after the administration of BAL. At present the exact mechanism of this detoxication is unknown. It is known, however, that certain toxic metal ions combine with the —SH groups of body enzymes or other important —SH-bearing molecules and thus inactivate them. It is probable that dithiopropanol-1, having a greater affinity for certain metals, "pulls" them from their enzyme combination and forms a similar complex which is rather readily excreted. A recent review by Randall and Seeler (22) covers much of the experimental and clinical work on BAL.

It is of interest that the common clothes moth is capable of accomplishing a somewhat similar end by combining toxic metal ions of poisons with SH⁻ and H_2S produced from digesting cystine of wool to make highly insoluble sulfides (23).

Most of the examples of detoxication cited are the result of enzymatic action. In many instances little is known of the enzymes involved, while in others a great deal of information is available. More or less specific enzymes have been mentioned in the discussion. Details regarding a number of enzymes related to detoxication mechanisms are discussed by Bernheim (24).

SPECIAL REFERENCES

1. Williams, R. T.: *Detoxication Mechanisms*. John Wiley & Sons, Inc., New York, 1947.
2. Williams, R. T.: *Detoxication Mechanisms*, 2nd ed. John Wiley & Sons, Inc., New York, 1959.
3. Miyazaki, M.: *J. Biochem.*, 19, 329, 1934.
4. Fellows, J. K.; Luduena, F. P.; and Hanzlik, P. J.: *J. Pharmacol.*, 89, 210, 1947.
5. Walkenstein, S. S.; Knebel, C. M.; Macmullen, J. A.; and Seifter, J.: *J. Pharmacol. Exptl. Therap.*, 123, 254, 1958.
6. Marshall, E. K., and Owens, A. H.: *Johns Hopkins Hosp. Bull.*, 95, 1, 1954.
7. Parke, D. V., and Williams, R. T.: *Biochem. J.*, 55, 337, 1953.
8. Freeman, M. V.; Draize, J. H.; and Smith, P. K.: *J. Pharmacol.*, 118, 304, 1956.
9. Mounter, L. A.: *Federation Proc.*, 15, 317, 1956.
10. Robinson, D.; Smith, J. N.; and Williams, R. T.: *Biochem. J.*, 50, 221, 1951.
11. Robinson, D.; Smith, J. N.; and Williams, R. T.: *Biochem. J.*, 50, 228, 1951.
12. Mueller, G. C., and Miller, J. A.: *J. Biol. Chem.*, 185, 145, 1950.
13. Glazko, A. J.; Dill, W. A.; and Rebstock, M. C.: *J. Biol. Chem.*, 183, 679, 1950.
14. Talafant, E.: *Nature*, 180, 1050, 1957.
15. Schachter, D.: *Science*, 126, 507, 1957.
16. Lang, K.: *Biochem. Z.*, 259, 243, 1933.
17. Gal, E. M., and Greenberg, D. M.: *Federation Proc.*, 12, 207, 1953.
18. Wood, J. L., and Cooley, S. L.: *Federation Proc.*, 12, 292, 1953.
19. Azouz, W. M.; Parke, D. V.; and Williams, R. T.: *Biochem. J.*, 50, 702, 1952.
20. Moxon, A. L.; Schaefer, A. E.; Lardy, H. A.; Du Bois, K. P.; and Olson, O. E.: *J. Biol. Chem.*, 132, 785, 1940.
21. Lemley, R. E.: *Lancet*, 60, 528, 1940.
22. Randall, R. V., and Seeler, A. O.: *New Engl. J. Med.*, 239, 1004, 1040, 1948.
23. Waterhouse, D. F.: *Nature*, 169, 550, 1952.
24. Bernheim, F., in *The Enzymes*, Vol. II, Part 2, edited by J. B. Sumner and K. Myrbäck. Academic Press, New York, 1952, p. 844.

15

Blood and other body fluids

BLOOD

Unicellular organisms such as the ameba obtain food and dispose of waste products through processes of diffusion with the aqueous media in which the organisms exist. If the surrounding fluid is of the proper composition so that the processes of diffusion can maintain a rather definite composition of the fluids within the cell (homeostasis), then the organism thrives. Changes in the composition of the surrounding fluid due to the accumulation of waste products, the depletion of food substances, or other causes prevent the maintenance of this proper composition of the intracellular fluids, and the organism ceases to function.

With the evolution of larger multicellular and multiorgan forms of animal life the composition of cellular fluids could not be maintained through the processes of simple diffusion alone. To meet this situation the circulating tissue, blood, was evolved.

In the higher animal forms the tissue cells are bathed in interstitial fluid from which essential substances are withdrawn and to which waste products are added by the processes of diffusion. The composition of interstitial fluid in turn is maintained within proper limits by diffusion between it and the circulating blood through the capillary walls. The composition of blood is maintained within physiologic limits by the provision of special mechanisms to add foods to the blood (gastrointestinal system, lungs), to remove waste products from it (kidneys, lungs, intestines, skin), and to produce the characteristic blood cells, proteins, hormones, and other constituents not directly obtainable from the food supply. Thus the higher animal forms are provided

489

with the means for maintaining their cellular environment relatively independent of external influences.

General functions of blood. Blood is the transport tissue of the body, the storehouse from which tissues draw their foodstuffs and other substances necessary for their activities, and the medium into which tissues discharge their waste products for transportation to the organs of excretion, the kidneys, the intestines, the lungs, and the skin. The general functions of blood may be subdivided and itemized into the following statements:

1. Food transport. Blood receives the products of digestion and absorption from the intestine and transports them to the tissues for utilization.

2. Transport of waste products. The waste products of tissue metabolism, such as urea, uric acid, creatinine, and many other substances, pass into the blood, which transports them to the kidneys and other organs of excretion for elimination from the body.

3. Gaseous transport. The hemoglobin of blood forms a loose combination with oxygen (oxyhemoglobin) in the lungs, which is carried to the tissues to provide oxygen for the oxidation of foods and the production of energy. The carbon dioxide formed in these tissue oxidations is picked up by the blood and carried to the lungs, where it is exhaled.

4. Hormone transport. The endocrine glands, such as the pituitary, thyroid, pancreas, ovary, and testes, synthesize specific substances necessary for the activity of various body tissues. These substances, known as "hormones," pass into the blood and are transported to the tissues requiring them.

5. Regulation of body pH. The chemical processes involved in tissue metabolism form carbon dioxide and many other substances which tend to change the pH of body fluids. Various food substances, such as lactic and citric acids, and drugs, such as sodium bicarbonate and ammonium chloride, tend to lower or raise the pH of blood and tissues upon entrance into them. For normal function the pH of blood and of tissue fluids may vary only within relatively narrow limits. Both the blood and tissues contain efficient buffer systems which help maintain the pH within these limits.

6. Regulation of fluid balance between blood and tissues. Because the blood plasma contains much more protein than the lymph bathing the tissues, the osmotic pressure of plasma is a bit higher than that of the lymph. The small noncolloidal particles diffuse freely between blood and lymph and thus do not contribute to an osmotic difference between the fluids. The distribution of fluid between blood and lymph is determined by the balance between blood pressure, which tends to force fluid from the blood into the lymph, and the osmotic pressure of blood plasma, which tends to draw fluid from the lymph into the blood. The blood pressure in the arterial ends of the capillaries is greater than the effective osmotic pressure of the plasma (difference between plasma and lymph), thereby forcing fluid through the capillary walls into the lymph of the tissue spaces. On the other hand, in the venous ends of the capillaries the osmotic pressure is greater than the blood pressure and fluid is drawn from the tissue spaces into the blood. In such a way the blood functions to maintain the circulation and amount of fluid in the tissue spaces. This function is specifically related to the plasma proteins, particularly the albumin fraction.

7. Regulation of body temperature. Owing to the high specific heat of water, the circulating blood is efficient in maintaining a rather uniform temperature within the body by transferring heat from warmer to cooler tissues.

8. Defense against infection. The blood provides two of the most important mechanisms against infective agents.

One of these mechanisms resides in the large ameboid leucocytes, the polymorphonuclear leucocytes, and the monocytes. These cells engulf and digest invading bacteria and cellular debris.

The antibodies or immune bodies of the blood plasma represent a second mechanism of defense. These substances are specific proteins which are formed as the result of the entry of foreign protein, bacterial or otherwise, into the blood and tissues. The protein stimulating the production of antibodies is the antigen, and the immune bodies produced are generally rather specific in their reactions to the antigen which caused their formation. The antibodies include: (a) agglutinins, which specifically cause the clumping together of the kind of cells (bacteria, corpuscles, etc.) that served as antigen; (b) hemolysins or cytolysins, which bring about the hemolysis of red cells or the cytolysis of other tissue cells which served as antigens; (c) precipitins, which specifically precipitate the antigenic protein; and (d) antitoxins, which specifically counteract the toxins produced by certain pathogenic organisms, such as diphtheria toxin.

All the antibodies appear to be specific proteins belonging to the gamma globulin fraction of plasma proteins.

9. Prevention of hemorrhage. While it is vital that blood remain fluid and circulate freely within the vascular system, it also is highly important that large amounts of blood not be lost from the body through hemorrhage resulting from traumatic injury. When blood vessels are broken and blood escapes over the injured tissues, a complex series of chemical reactions takes place in the blood and leads to the formation of blood clots (coagulation) which tend to seal off the leaks in the injured vessels. The blood-clotting mechanism is so organized that it normally does not operate so long as the blood is contained within the blood vessel walls. In fact, the blood contains substances which function as anticlotting agents within the circulatory system.

The processes by which the coagulation of blood is brought about are complicated, and their detailed operation will be considered in a later section. However, the chief points involved may be summarized briefly as follows. The coagulation process takes place in the plasma and consists in the action of the protein thrombin upon the protein fibrinogen to form fibrin. The fibrin separates in long threads which enmesh the blood cells and fluid to form the clot. When thrombin is injected into the circulation of an animal, it may prove fatal quickly because of intravascular coagulation. Consequently, thrombin formation takes place after blood escapes from the blood vessels.

The substance from which thrombin is produced and which is normally present in circulating blood is the protein prothrombin. When blood escapes from the vascular system and comes in contact with injured tissue, reactions occur which activate prothrombin to thrombin. The substances which activate prothrombin to thrombin are the so-called thromboplastic substances (thromboplastins) and calcium ions. Thromboplastic substances are added to the blood by the blood platelets, which disintegrate when the blood escapes from the blood vessels. Thus, the traumatic injury which permits blood to escape from the vessels sets off the processes which coagulate the blood and stop the hemorrhage.

The coagulation of blood takes place in two major consecutive stages as follows:

1. Prothrombin activation:

$$\text{prothrombin} + \text{thromboplastins} + Ca^{++} \longrightarrow \text{thrombin}$$

2. Conversion of fibrinogen to fibrin:

$$\text{fibrinogen} + \text{thrombin} \longrightarrow \text{fibrin}$$
$$\text{Forms clot}$$

General characteristics of blood. The blood mass of healthy adults makes up about 6 to 8 per cent of the body weight, is higher for men than for women, and is subject to considerable individual variation. The normal blood volume for women has been estimated at about 65 ml and for men 79 ml per kilogram of body weight. On this basis the body of a 70-kg man would contain about 5500 ml of blood. The blood volume generally varies from 2000 to 2900 ml per square meter of body surface and is more nearly proportional to surface area than to body weight.

Blood volume may be estimated in a number of ways, but in general the methods depend upon determination of the plasma volume or red-cell volume and then calculation of total blood volume from the plasma-cell ratio as determined by the hematocrit.

Plasma volume is commonly obtained by injecting into a vein a known amount of a harmless dye, such as T-1824, which does not readily enter the erythrocytes or pass through the capillaries. After allowing time for uniform mixing of the dye in the circulation (15 to 30 minutes), the concentration of dye in the plasma is determined, and the dilution factor calculated, from which the plasma volume is obtained. Knowing the plasma-cell ratio from the hematocrit determination permits calculation of the total blood volume. Correction must be made for loss of dye through the capillaries and kidneys.

Albumin labeled with radioactive I^{131} (I^{131}-albumin) is widely used for determining plasma and blood volume according to the dilution principle given above, due to good retention in the vascular system and easy assay through its radioactivity.

The most widely used method of determining red cell volume is based upon labeling the cells with radioactive Cr^{51} by treatment with $Na_2Cr^{51}O_4$, which is readily taken up by the cells without injury. A definite volume of tagged cells of known radioactivity is injected and allowed to mix, and the radioactivity of the cells in a sample of blood is determined. From the decrease in radioactivity the dilution factor and plasma and blood volumes are obtained (1).

Blood is a viscous fluid made up of the cellular components erythrocytes (red cells), leucocytes (white cells), and platelets suspended in a colloidal medium, the plasma. It is opaque on account of the large number of cells in suspension, and red in color on account of the hemoglobin of the erythrocytes.

As previously indicated, when blood coagulates, the fibrinogen present in plasma is converted to fibrin that separates as threads which enmesh the blood cells and fluid to form a clot. Upon standing, the clot retracts due to shortening of the fibrin threads and squeezes out a clear fluid called serum. If blood is prevented from clotting by adding oxalate (to precipitate Ca^{++}) or by other means and is centrifuged, the heavier cells are thrown to the bottom of the containing vessel and the lighter plasma forms a layer on top. The chief quantitative difference between plasma and serum is that plasma contains the protein fibrinogen while serum does not. Ordinarily, blood cells (chiefly erythrocytes) make up 40 to 45 per cent of the total blood volume. By the use of special graduated centrifuge tubes (hematocrit tubes) the relative volumes of cells and plasma may be determined readily.

Some of the general characteristics of human blood are summarized in the diagram below.

Detailed composition of blood. The composition of blood, as of any other tissue, is tremendously complex. The composition of the cellular elements is widely different from that of the plasma in which they are suspended. In turn, the erythrocytes, leucocytes, and platelets differ greatly in composition. Because the erythrocytes represent most of the cellular mass of the blood, they contribute quantitatively most of the cellular constituents.

> →FIBRIN, forms basis of clot.
>
> →PLASMA ─────────────────────────┤
>   50–60 per cent by volume.   └→SERUM, squeezed from clot.
>   Solids, 8–9 per cent.
>   Specific gravity, 1.026.
>   Viscosity, 1.7–2 (water = 1).
>   Freezing point about −0.55° C.
>   Total molal concentration about 0.30.
>   Osmotic pressure at 37° C about 7.6 atm.
>   pH about 7.4 av, range 7.33–7.51.
>
> BLOOD, 6–8 per cent of body wt, 66–78 ml/kg. 2,000–2,900 ml/sq m.
>   Specific gravity, 1.060 av, viscosity, 3.6–5.3, pH about 7.4 av, range 7.33–
>   7.51, freezing point about 0.55° C.
>
> →BLOOD CELLS, 40–45 per cent by volume, made up chiefly of erythrocytes.
> |PLATELETS or THROMBOCYTES, 200,000–400,000 per cu mm,
>   diameter about 2.5 μ.
>   LEUCOCYTES, 5000 to 10,000 per cu mm, composed of granulocytes, lymphocytes, monocytes.
>   ERYTHROCYTES, 4,500,000–6,000,000 per cu mm. Biconcave disks; diameter, 6–9 μ; specific gravity, about 1.090; solids about 35 per cent; hemoglobin, 31–33 per cent; stroma protein, 0.5–1.0 per cent.

In view of these facts, the composition of blood as a whole generally affords a very different picture from the compositions of plasma and cells separately. For example, the solid content of plasma is 8 to 9 per cent, of red cells about 35 per cent, and of whole blood 19 to 23 per cent. Again, the hemoglobin content of whole blood ranges from 11 to 17 g per 100 ml, while that for packed red cells varies from 31 to 37 g per 100 ml.

For most purposes, both research and clinical, the composition of whole blood, or of blood serum or plasma, is determined. This practice is dictated both by matters of convenience of analysis and the significance of the results obtained.

The composition of cells is often calculated from the hematocrit value and analyses of whole blood and plasma or serum.

The amounts of blood constituents vary continually within certain limits, and at any given time depend upon the balance between the processes adding substances to the blood and the processes removing substances from it. The quantity of water in blood can be increased appreciably by drinking large volumes of water and producing hydremia. At the same time the concentrations of other blood constituents are proportionately lowered. Conversely, inadequate water intake may lead to a marked body dehydration and decrease in the water content of blood (anhydremia). This causes a proportional increase in other blood constituents. Increased rates of absorption from the intestine for a period after meals cause increases in the food constituents of blood, whereas fasting causes decreases. Severe exercise rapidly removes food substances from the blood and greatly increases the rate of addition of waste products to it.

The composition of blood may vary widely from the normal as a result of pathologic conditions, and such variations contribute much in the diagnosis of diseased states and in following the efficiency of treatment. For example, the blood glucose level is high in diabetes mellitus, blood urea is high in certain forms of nephritis, and the hemoglobin is low in anemia.

In view of the various factors which may affect the composition of blood, it is necessary, for comparable results, that blood for analysis be drawn under definitely specified conditions. This is generally accomplished by taking samples 12 to 14 hours after the last meal (postabsorptive) and with the subject in the resting state, in order to obviate the effects of intestinal absorption and exercise. Samples taken in the morning before breakfast generally conform with these requirements.

Tables 15.1 and 15.2 give the normal ranges or averages of many of the constituents of human blood with some indications of pathologic variations. Blood contains traces of numerous other substances which have not been estimated. Some determinations of hormones, particularly sex hormones, have been made, but these are not included in the table. The student is referred to the book *Normal Values in Clinical Medicine*, by Sunderman and Boerner, for a comprehensive treatment of the composition of blood.

A glance at Table 15.1 on the composition of blood undoubtedly suffices to impress upon the student the complexity of blood as a tissue and, it is

[*Text continued on p. 499.*]

Table 15.1. Composition of Human Blood
Values are given for whole blood unless otherwise specified

Constituent	Normal Range	Comments
Total Solids, per cent.	19–23.7	High in anhydremia and polycythemia, low in hydremia and anemia.
I. Nitrogen Compounds:		
Total N, per cent.	3.0–3.7	Varies chiefly with variations in blood proteins.
A. *Proteins, per cent.*	18.5–23.0	
Plasma proteins, per cent.	6.5–7.5	
Serum proteins, per cent.	6.0–6.9	High in anhydremia, low in nephrosis.
Albumins (serum), per cent.	4.7–5.7	Low in nephrosis, high in anhydremia.
Globulins (serum), per cent.	1.3–2.5	High in anhydremia, nephrosis, infections.
A/G ratio.	1.2–1.8	
Fibrinogen (plasma), per cent.	0.2–0.4	High in infections, low in cirrhosis of liver.
Hemoglobin, per cent.	11–17	High in polycythemia, low in anemias.
B. *Nonprotein N, mg per cent.*	28–39	High in nephritis, eclampsia.
Amino acids, mg per cent.	30–50	High in leukemia, severe nephritis, acute yellow atrophy of the liver.
Amino acid N, mg per cent.	4.5–7.0	High in leukemia, severe nephritis, acute yellow atrophy of the liver.
Glutathione, mg per cent.	25–41	Localized in red cells.
Urea, mg per cent.	19–33	High in nephritis and kidney failure, low in nephrosis.
Urea N, mg per cent.	9–15	High in nephritis and kidney failure, low in nephrosis.
Ergothioneine, mg per cent.	10–25	Localized in red cells.
Glutamine (plasma), mg per cent.	6–10	Important source of urinary ammonia.
Creatine, mg per cent.	3–5	High in terminal nephritis.
Uric acid, mg per cent.	1–3	High in gout, nephritis, arthritis, eclampsia.
Creatinine, mg per cent.	1.2–1.5	High in nephritis.
Citrulline (plasma), mg per cent.	0.3–1.0	Formed in liver in urea cycle.
Bilirubin (plasma), mg per cent.	0.2–0.8	High in biliary obstruction, hemolytic anemias.
Guanidine, mg per cent.	0.3–0.5	
Indican (plasma), mg per cent.	0.025–0.035	High in constipation.
Urobilin (plasma), mg per cent.	0.2	Formed by reduction of bilirubin in intestine.
Ammonia, mg per cent.	<0.1*	
Adrenaline, mg per cent.	0.1	High during excitement.
Adrenaline-like substance.	4.1–9.6	Micrograms per 100 ml (1 μg = 0.001 mg).

Table 15.1.   Composition of Human Blood (Continued)
Values are given for whole blood unless otherwise specified

Constituent	Normal Range	Comments
II. Nonnitrogenous Organic:		
A. *Carbohydrate*		
Glucose (true sugar), mg per cent	65–90	High in diabetes, low in hyperinsulinism.
Glycogen, mg per cent, av	5.5	All localized in granulocytes. (Wagner, *Arch. Biochem.*, 11, 249, 1946.)
B. *Lipids (plasma)*, mg per cent	360–820	High in diabetes, prolonged starvation.
Fats (serum), mg per cent	150–250	As above.
Cholesterol total (serum), mg per cent	150–250	High in diabetes, nephritis, biliary obstruction, etc.
Free cholesterol (serum), mg per cent	42–70	
Esterified cholesterol (serum), mg per cent	108–180	
Phospholipids (serum), mg per cent (lecithins, cephalins, sphingomyelins)	135–170	High in diabetes, nephritis.
Lipid phosphorus (serum), mg per cent	8–10	
Total fatty acids (serum), mg per cent	200	Normally varies widely.
C. *Miscellaneous substances*		
Acetone bodies (as acetone) mg per cent	0.5–0.8	High in diabetes, starvation.
Citric acid, mg per cent	1.3–2.3	
α-Ketoglutaric acid, mg per cent	8–10	
Lactic acid, mg per cent	6–16	Increased markedly by exercise.
Pyruvic acid, mg per cent	0.8–1.2	Increased by exercise.
III. Vitamins:		
Vitamin A (serum), international units per 100 ml	35–40	Low in deficiency.
α-Tocopherol (serum), mg per cent	0.6–1.6	Vitamin E.
Ascorbic acid (plasma), mg per cent	0.7–1.5	Vitamin C. Low in scurvy.
Biotin, μg per 100 ml	0.07–0.1	
Carotenoids (serum), μg per 100 ml	6–312	Convertible to vitamin A.
Niacin, mg per cent	0.52–0.83	Low in pellagra.
Pantothenic acid, μg per 100 ml	18–35	
Riboflavin, μg per 100 ml	13–85	Vitamin B_2.
Thiamine, μg per 100 ml	5.5–9.5	Vitamin B_1. Low in polyneuritis.

Table 15.1. Composition of Human Blood (*Continued*)

Values are given for whole blood unless otherwise specified

Constituent	Normal Range	Comments
IV. Enzymes:		
Amylase (serum), units.	60–180	Somogyi, *Arch. Internal Med.*, **67**, 665, 1941.
Lipase (serum).	0–1.5	Ml N/20 free acid liberated from olive oil. Comfort and Osterberg, *Arch. Internal Med.*, **66**, 688, 1940.
Acid phosphatase (serum), units.	0.0–1.1	
Alkaline phosphatase (serum), units.	2.2–8.6	Shinowara, Jones, Reinhart, *J. Biol. Chem.*, **142**, 921, 1942.
V. Inorganic and Ionic:		
A. Total cations (serum), meq/l.	142–150	Low in diabetic acidosis, alkali deficit (base deficit).
Calcium (serum), mg per cent.	9–11	Low in infantile tetany, high in hyperparathyroidism.
Calcium (serum), meq/l†.	4.5–5.5	
Magnesium (serum), mg per cent.	2.2–2.7	
Magnesium (serum), meq/l.	1.8–2.2	
Potassium (serum), mg per cent.	14.1–24.5	High in pneumonia, acute infections, in uremia.
Potassium (serum), meq/l.	3.5–6.5	
Sodium (serum), mg per cent.	310–350	Low in diabetic acidosis, alkali deficit (base deficit).
Sodium (serum), meq/l.	135–155	
Iron, mg per cent.	42–55	Nearly all in hemoglobin of red cells.
Iron (serum), mg per cent.	0.06–0.18	
Copper, mg per cent.	0.15–0.20	0.2–0.26 in serum.
B. Total anions (serum), equivalent to 142–150 meq/l of cations		
Chlorides (as Cl^-), mg per cent.	250–320	High in nephritis, congestive heart failure, eclampsia, anemia; low in diabetes, fever, and pneumonia.
Chlorides (as Cl^-), meq/l.	77–93	
Chlorides (as $NaCl$), mg per cent.	450–530	
Chlorides (as $NaCl$), meq/l.	77–93	
Bicarbonate (as HCO_3^-), meq/l in serum.	24.9–26.2	Low in diabetic acidosis, high in alkali excess (base excess). meq/l of cation (equals 17 ml of 1 N NaOH).
Proteinate (serum), binds about.	17	47–114 in cells.
Phosphorus (serum), total, mg per cent.	8–18	High in nephritis, low in rickets, values 1–2 mg per cent higher in children.
Phosphorus, as inorganic phosphate (serum), mg per cent.	3.2–4.3	

Table 15.1. Composition of Human Blood (*Continued*)

Values are given for whole blood unless otherwise specified

Constituent	Normal Range	Comments
Phosphorus, as inorganic phosphate (serum), meq/l	1.6–2.7	1–2 mg per cent higher in children.
Sulfur, total nonprotein, mg per cent	2–4	
Sulfur (as sulfate), mg per cent	0.1–1.1	0.5–1.1 in serum.
Sulfur (as sulfate), meq/l in serum	0.3–0.7	
Sulfur (as ethereal sulfate), mg per cent	0.1–1.0	About same in serum.
Sulfur (as neutral sulfur compounds)	2.2–4.5	1.7–3.5 mg per cent in serum.
Iodine, total, μg per 100 ml	8–15	High in hyperthyroidism, low in cretinism.
Iodine, protein-bound (serum)	6–8.4	Micrograms per 100 ml.

VI. Blood Gases:

CO_2 content (serum), vols per cent	45–65	Milliliters of gas per 100 ml in vols per cent.
CO_2 capacity (serum) at 40 mm CO_2, vols per cent	55–75	The CO_2 contents and capacities are high in alkali excess (base excess),
CO_2 content (venous blood), vols per cent	50–60	respiratory deficiency; tetany; low in diabetic acidosis, nephritis.
CO_2 content (arterial blood), vols per cent	45–55	
O_2 content (arterial blood), vols per cent	15–22	Oxygen contents and capacity increased in polycythemia, anhydremia;
O_2 content (venous blood), vols per cent	11–16	low in respiratory and cardiac diseases and in anemia.
O_2 capacity (exposed to air), vols per cent	16–24	

* E. J. Conway and R. Cooke, *Biochem. J.*, **33**, 457, 1939.

† Milligram equivalent/1 = milligrams of substance per liter/formula weight, and multiplied by the valence in case of ionic substances. For 10 mg per cent of Ca^{++} we have 100 mg/l, and meq/l = (100/40) × 2 = 5; 350 mg per cent of Na^{+} = 3,500 mg/l = (3,500/23) × 1 = 152 meq/l.

hoped, will indicate the importance of knowing considerable about the constituents of blood as they are related to the normal and pathologic metabolic processes of the body. In view of the importance of several blood constituents as indices of common pathologic conditions, the medical student should begin to learn their normal values. In order to facilitate this, an abbreviated tabulation is inserted (Table 15.2).

Most of the constituents of blood which represent food substances or products derived from tissue activities, and which are not specifically characteristic of blood as a tissue, are discussed in their proper relations in other chapters. Such substances include glucose, lipids, amino acids, and various other constituents. The remainder of the discussion of blood will be limited largely to those constituents which are more less specifically related to the composition and function of blood as a tissue. Among these constituents blood proteins are of most importance.

Table 15.2. Normal Values of Blood Constituents Commonly of Clinical Importance
Values are for whole blood unless otherwise stated

Constituent	Normal Range
Hemoglobin, g per 100 ml	
Men	12–17
Women	11–15
Plasma proteins, g per 100 ml	6.5–7.5
Serum proteins, g per 100 ml	6.0–6.9
Albumins (serum), g per 100 ml	4.7–5.7
Globulins (serum), g per 100 ml	1.3–2.5
A/G ratio	1.2–1.8
Fibrinogen (plasma), g per 100 ml	0.2–0.4
Glucose, mg per cent (true sugar)	65–90
Nonprotein N, mg per cent	28–39
Urea, mg per cent	19–33
Urea N, mg per cent	9–15
Creatinine, mg per cent	1.2–1.5
Uric acid, mg per cent	1–3
Cholesterol, total (serum), mg per cent	150–250
Cholesterol, free (serum), mg per cent	42–70
Cholesterol, esterified (serum), mg per cent	108–180
Calcium (serum), mg per cent	9–11; meq/l, 4.5–5.5
Sodium (serum), mg per cent	310–350; meq/l, 135–152
Potassium (serum), mg per cent	14.1–24.2; meq/l, 3.6–6.2
Chlorides (serum) as NaCl, mg per cent	576–612; meq/l, 98.5–104.5
Phosphorus as inorganic phosphate (serum), mg per cent	3.2–4.3; meq/l, 1.6–2.7
CO_2 capacity (serum) at 40 mm CO_2, vols per cent	55–75
O_2 capacity (exposed to air), vols per cent	16–24
Ascorbic acid (plasma), mg per cent	0.7–1.5
Iodine, μg per 100 ml	8–15
Bilirubin (plasma), mg per cent	0.2–0.8
Amylase, Somogyi units	60–180
Lipase (serum), ml N/20 free acid liberated from olive oil,	
upper normal limit	1.5
Acid phosphatase (serum), units	0.0–1.1
Alkaline phosphatase (serum), units	2.2–8.6

FORMED ELEMENTS OF BLOOD

The formed elements of blood—erythrocytes, leucocytes, and platelets—constitute the mobile cells of blood, which are produced by specialized tissues such as the bone marrow and are discharged into the blood for the performance of specialized functions.

ERYTHROCYTES

General characteristics. The erythrocytes or red cells of blood are non-nucleated biconcave disks ranging in diameter from about 6 to 9 μ, with an average value of about 7.5 μ. The thickness of the erythrocytes is about 1 μ in the center and 2 to 2.4 μ at the thickest part toward the periphery. They contain about 35 per cent of solids, of which some 31 to 33 per cent is hemoglobin. The specific gravity of erythrocytes averages about 1.090.

Wintrobe (2) gives the normal range of erythrocytes per cubic millimeter of blood in the United States as 4,600,000 to 6,200,000 for men, and 4,200,000 to 5,400,000 for women. The numbers of erythrocytes may be enormously increased in polycythemia and decreased in some of the anemias. It has been estimated that the adult human body contains around 10^{12} erythrocytes which carry about 950 g of hemoglobin.

The erythrocyte structure is made up essentially of a stroma meshwork composed of proteins and lipids, within which the hemoglobin is distributed and intimately held. Apparently proteins and lipids similar to those making up the stroma mass are concentrated at the surface of the erythrocyte to constitute a delicate cell membrane. This membrane is readily permeable to water, small uncharged organic molecules such as CO_2, urea, glucose and creatinine, and HCO_3^-, Cl^-, and OH^- ions. Most of the cations of red cells are K^+ with a small amount of Na^+, whereas the concentration of Na^+ is high and of K^+ low in plasma. It has been shown that radioactive Na^{+24} and K^{+42} readily pass from plasma into red cells and the reverse, and that the movement of both Na^+ and K^+ across the red cell membrane and maintenance of vastly different concentrations in plasma and erythrocytes is due to active transport (Chapter 5) of both Na^+ and K^+ (3).

The distributions of Na^+ and K^+ between plasma and erythrocytes is something as follows (values = meq per liter):

	Plasma	Erythrocytes
Na^+	135–152	18
K^+	3.6–6.2	80

These values illustrate the very large gradients of Na^+ and K^+ between cells and plasma, which require much metabolic energy for their maintenance by active transport.

Most of the calcium of blood is in the plasma, and most of the magnesium is in the cells.

The erythrocytes contain somewhat less lipid material than plasma, due mainly to a low content of neutral fat. They contain more phospholipid and somewhat less cholesterol than does plasma. While the greater portion (about two-thirds) of plasma cholesterol is esterified with fatty acids, most of the erythrocyte cholesterol is in the free state.

The distribution of smaller uncharged molecules between erythrocytes and plasma shows great variations. Some substances, such as glucose and urea, are distributed between plasma and cells according to water content, whereas other substances, such as glutathione and ergothioneine, appear to be localized entirely within the cells.

Formation. Erythrocytes and other blood cells are formed in the red bone marrow (hematopoietic tissue), which is estimated to range from about 1300 to 4200 ml in human adults. The cavities of all bones are filled with red bone marrow at birth. With development, the red bone marrow of the bones of the extremities in particular is progressively replaced by fat cells (fatty marrow). This process also takes place to a lesser extent in other bones. After the age of 20 years most of the blood-forming red bone marrow is located in flat bones, such as ribs, sternum, vertebrae, clavicles, scapulae, skull, and pelvis. Samples of marrow for examination are usually obtained by sternal puncture. Microscopic study of bone marrow reveals the numbers and proportions of the various types of blood cells being formed and is of much value in the diagnosis and treatment of hematologic diseases.

The formation of erythrocytes in the bone marrow progresses through the stages:

megaloblast ⟶ early erythroblast ⟶ intermediate erythroblast ⟶
or rubriblast   or prorubricyte   or rubricyte

late erythroblast ⟶ reticulocyte ⟶ erythrocyte
or metarubricyte

The cells in all stages up to reticulocytes are nucleated. Reticulocytes, as well as erythrocytes, pass into the blood, the reticulocytes comprising about 0.5 to 3.0 per cent of the red cells. The reticulocytes are differentiated from the erythrocytes in being slightly larger than the adult erythrocyte and in possessing a reticulum or "skein" which may be demonstrated by proper staining. The proportion of reticulocytes serves as an index of the activity of the bone marrow in red cell formation.

The formation of erythrocytes in bone marrow is dependent upon adequate supplies of protein and iron for hemoglobin production (minute amounts of copper are essential for iron utilization) and upon the "maturation" or antipernicious anemia principle, which is essential to the development of erythrocytes through the various stages. It has been isolated as red crystals from liver and is the vitamin B_{12} (cyanocobalimin).

It has been found that the vitamin pteroylglutamic acid (folic acid) provides a powerful stimulus for red cell maturation, and it is used as a therapeutic agent in the treatment of pernicious anemia. However, folic acid does not prevent the central nervous system involvement in the disease, as does the maturation principle, and it appears to be most valuable when used in conjunction with liver extract or B_{12}. Vitamin B_{12} has been shown to be effective in the treatment of pernicious anemia, even when given in microgram quantities, and, unlike folic acid, improves the neurologic symptoms.

The physiologic stimulus for the production of erythrocytes is a lowering of the oxygen content in the blood to the bone marrow. This may arise through hemorrhage, anemia due to deficiency (iron, protein, maturation factor), hemolysis (laking) of the red cells, or impairment of circulation to the bone marrow (probable in polycythemia vera). Exposure to high altitudes subjects the blood to lowered oxygen pressure in the lungs, with a resultant decrease in oxygen content and anoxemia in the tissues, including the bone marrow. Under these conditions the marrow increases its rate of hemoglobin and cell production so that the increased quantities of these in the blood can transport sufficient oxygen to the tissues under the reduced oxygen pressure. This response of the bone marrow constitutes one of the most important aspects of acclimatization to life at higher altitudes. At high altitudes the erythrocyte count may rise to 8,000,000 or higher.

The administration of small amounts of cobalt to animals and man stimulates erythropoiesis (red cell formation), and continued administration will eventually produce and maintain a polycythemia (4). This cobalt effect appears to be related to an increase in the hormone erythropoietin in blood which stimulates red cell formation (5).

Human erythrocytes have been shown to contain erythrocuprein, a copper-containing protein (0.32–0.36 per cent Cu) to the extent of 30–36 mg per 100 ml of packed cells (6).

Destruction. The number of erythrocytes in the circulation normally is fairly constant, and since new cells are being produced constantly, the destruction of erythrocytes must be a continual process. Most erythrocyte destruction takes place in the spleen, but to some extent in bone marrow and other reticuloendothelial tissues. The breakdown of hemoglobin liberated in erythrocyte destruction leads to the separation of iron and the formation of bile pigments. A considerable proportion of the iron liberated is reused for the formation of hemoglobin.

Shemin and Rittenberg (7) gave glycine containing N^{15} to a human being. Some of the N^{15} was incorporated into the heme of hemoglobin. By following the rate of decrease of this N^{15} in heme, these workers calculated the average life span of the red cell to be about 125 days. This means that 0.8 per cent of the red cells are destroyed and produced each day.

Hemolysis. The process of hemolysis or laking consists in the release of hemoglobin from the stroma into the surrounding solution. Hemolysis does not appear to result simply from rupture of the cell membrane, since fragmentation of the cells alone is often insufficient to release the hemoglobin. The osmotic pressure of plasma and within the erythrocytes is about that of 0.9 per cent sodium chloride solution (isotonic or physiologic saline). When erythrocytes are placed in such an isosmotic solution, the fluid volume of the cell remains unchanged as shown by cell size. When placed in hypotonic solution, however, water passes from the solution into the cells and causes them to swell. If the hypotonicity is sufficiently great, causing the swelling to exceed a certain limit, the hemoglobin escapes from the cells to form a clear dark red solution. The stroma or "ghosts" remain as spheroidal, feebly refractile bodies which may be centrifuged off. It appears that a certain concentration of salts and possibly other substances is necessary within the erythrocyte in order for stroma to bind and hold the hemoglobin. When this concentration is lowered by the entrance of excess water into the cell, the hemoglobin is released.

Normally, hemolysis of more susceptible cells begins at salt concentrations of 0.45 to 0.39 per cent and is complete at concentrations of 0.33 to 0.30 per cent. The fragility test is based upon determination of the resistance of the cells to hemolysis as the salt concentration of the suspending fluid is lowered. Hemolysis in pure water proceeds rather rapidly. It is greatly increased by fat solvents, such as ether and chloroform, which dissolve stroma lipids, and by saponin, bile salts, soaps, and other wetting agents, which probably tend to break up the lipid-protein complexes of stroma. Acids and alkalies also promote hemolysis. The venoms of certain poisonous snakes contain powerful hemolysins. Various bacteria also form very active hemolytic agents.

The blood of an animal sensitized to the erythrocytes of another animal contains the immune bodies, hemolysins, which hemolyze the antigenic red cells.

The hemolysis of erythrocytes in relation to the Rh factor is highly important in medicine. The Rh substance, so-called because it was first detected in the antibodies formed in guinea pigs by injection of the red cells of the rhesus monkey, is present in the erythrocytes of about 85 per cent of the white population. This Rh factor or principle acts as an antigen. The erythrocytes of an Rh+ individual may contain one of several Rh antigens more or less like the Rh substance found in monkey cells. Human serum normally does not contain the antibody to the Rh factor, and the latter must be detected by the use of specially prepared animal serum or serum from an Rh− individual who has been exposed to Rh antigen. If an Rh− person receives a transfusion from an Rh+ donor, the Rh− individual develops antibodies against the Rh+ red cells. A subsequent transfusion of Rh+ blood into such a sensitized person may cause hemolysis of the Rh+ red cells with severe consequences. Also, since the Rh factor may be inherited, an Rh− mother may have an Rh+ child through paternal inheritance. During pregnancy in such a case, Rh antigen from the fetus may cause the production of antibodies in the mother, which passing to the fetus may cause destruction of the erythrocytes with disastrous results. In turn, such a mother may suffer severe reactions if given a transfusion of Rh+ blood. In view of these facts, the determination of the Rh characteristics of blood has become of much importance.

When red cells are suspended in hypertonic (hyperosmotic) solutions, water passes from the cells, and they shrink in volume. This shrinkage may be sufficient to cause the cells to appear wrinkled under the microscope. Such cells are said to be "crenated."

LEUCOCYTES

The leucocytes or white cells are of several varieties and generally are larger than the erythrocytes. Unlike erythrocytes, the leucocytes are nucleated and contain proteins, lipids, and other constituents characteristic of tissue cells in general. The leucocytes are a bit lighter than the erythrocytes and appear as a white "buffy" coat on top of the layer when blood is centrifuged. The normal range of leucocytes in the blood of adults (both sexes) is generally considered 5000 to 10,000 per cubic millimeter.

The distribution of the types of leucocytes normally present in human blood is about as follows:

Type	Cells per cu mm of Blood
Neutrophils, 10–15 μ, polymorphonuclear	3,000–7,000 (54–62 per cent)
Eosinophils, 10–15 μ, polymorphonuclear	50–500 (1–3 per cent)
Basophils, 10–15 μ, polymorphonuclear	0–50 (0–0.75 per cent)
Monocytes, 12–20 μ, single large nuclear mass	100–600 (3–7 per cent)
Lymphocytes, 10–20 μ, single large nucleus	1,000–3,000 (25–33 per cent)

All leucocytes except lymphocytes contain cytoplasmic granules and collectively are called "granulocytes." The lymphocytes are globular in shape, possess relatively clear cytoplasm, and exhibit less ameboid motion than most of the granulocytes.

In pathologic states the leucocyte count may be abnormally low (leucopenia) or high (leucocytosis). Infections are generally accompanied by leucocytosis, which represents one of the mechanisms of defense. This defense is accomplished through phagocytosis and digestion of invading bacteria and cell debris by neutrophils, eosinophils, and monocytes (granulocytes).

The phagocytic leucocytes move from the blood into injured or infected tissue by diapedesis. This consists of "crawling" through the interstices between the thin mosaic cells of capillary walls. The movement of leucocytes appears to be directed by chemotaxis —that is, the effect of concentration gradients of certain chemical agents. They tend to move from a less acid to a more acid region, and this probably is partly responsible for their movement into infected tissue, where a local acidosis develops. Injured tissues are said to liberate a substance called "leucotaxin" which is chemotactic to the leucocytes. Some amino acids, nucleic acids, and foreign proteins also appear to have a chemotactic effect.

The presence of proteolytic enzymes in leucocytes correlates with their phagocytosis and digestion of bacteria and cellular debris, which contain a large proportion of protein.

Although it appears established that lymphocytes contain immune bodies, presumably as γ-globulin, it is uncertain as to whether the lymphocytes form these substances or simply store them.

The granulocytic leucocytes, sometimes called the "true leucocytes," are formed chiefly in the hematopoietic tissues of bone marrow, whereas the lymphocytes are formed largely in the spleen and lymph nodes, and only to a limited extent in the bone marrow.

Leucocytes are destroyed through phagocytosis by the macrophage cells of the spleen, and bone marrow, and Kupffer cells of the liver. It appears, therefore, that the reticuloendothelial system plays the leading role in the destruction of both leucocytes and erythrocytes.

BLOOD PLATELETS

The blood platelets or thrombocytes are colorless oval disks, and their number normally ranges from 200,000 to 400,000 per cubic millimeter of venous blood. The number in arterial is about 12 per cent higher than in venous blood, and the number in cutaneous blood is some 15 per cent lower than in venous. The number of platelets increases after hemorrhage and may decrease in some types of purpura, a condition in which there is subcutaneous extravasation of blood.

The volume of the blood platelets ranges from 0.35 to 0.56 ml per 100 ml of blood. The greatest diameter of platelets varies from 1.8 to 3.6 μ or larger, and their volume averages about 5 cu μ.

Not a great deal is known about the chemical composition of platelets other than that they contain protein and a considerable amount of phospholipid, much of which appears to be cephalin.

As previously indicated, platelets disintegrate when blood is shed and contribute thromboplastic substances necessary for the activation of prothrombin to thrombin in the coagulation process.

The platelets originate in the fragmentation of the cytoplasm of megakaryocytes (histocytic giant cells) of bone marrow, spleen, lungs, etc. Their life span is uncertainly given as three to five days.

BLOOD PROTEINS

The total protein content of whole blood amounts on the average to some 22 per cent and represents a bit more than 3 per cent of protein nitrogen, as

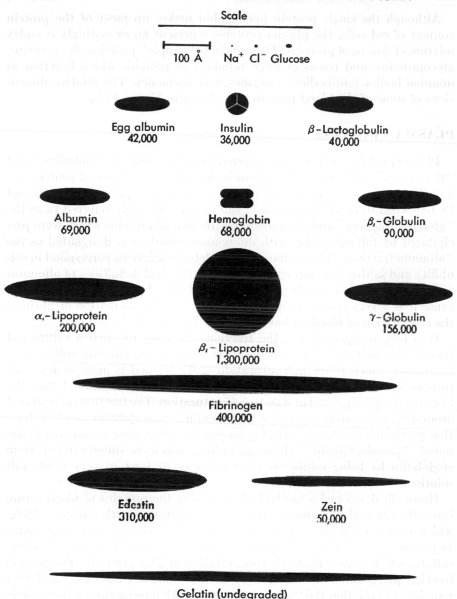

Figure 15.1. Relative dimensions of various proteins. (Personal communication and courtesy of Dr. J. L. Oncley.)

contrasted with an average of only about 32 mg per cent of nonprotein nitrogen in blood.

The hemoglobin of the red cells represents about two-thirds of the mass of blood proteins, and the plasma proteins about one-third. The proteins of stroma, leucocytes, and platelets represent insignificant quantities of the total blood proteins.

Although the single protein hemoglobin makes up most of the protein content of red cells, the plasma proteins represent an exceedingly complex mixture of dozens of proteins. These include "simple" proteins, lipoproteins, glycoproteins, and traces of large numbers of proteins which function as immune bodies (antibodies), enzymes, and hormones. The relative dimensions of some of the blood proteins are shown in Figure 15.1.

PLASMA PROTEINS

Plasma proteins are generally referred to as "albumins," "globulins," and "fibrinogen," and these designations include the complexity of proteins referred to above. The fraction of plasma proteins precipitated or salted out by half-saturation with ammonium sulfate was originally referred to as the "globulin fraction," and the remaining fraction of proteins which were precipitated by full saturation with ammonium sulfate was designated as the "albumin fraction." These albumin and globulin fractions correspond in solubility and salting-out characteristics to the classical definitions of albumins and globulins. Fibrinogen is precipitated with the globulin fraction, but, because it is a very special protein concerned with the formation of fibrin in the coagulation of blood, it has received a separate designation.

It is now recognized that the fractions obtained by such a salting-out process are mixtures, since precipitation begins at ammonium sulfate concentrations much below half-saturation (2.05 M) and is more or less continuous up to full saturation (4.1 M). The older workers noted that the fibrinogen is precipitated at 0.20 to 0.25 saturation. The fraction precipitated around 0.33 saturation was called "euglobulin" (true globulin), and the fraction precipitated subsequently by raising the saturation to 0.5 was designated "pseudoglobulin" (false globulin), which is differentiated from euglobulin by being soluble in pure water or at least in very dilute salt solution.

Howe (8) developed a method of separating the proteins of blood serum into albumin and globulin fractions by precipitation with sodium sulfate, which permitted their estimation from Kjeldahl nitrogen determinations. In this procedure he treated 1 ml of serum with 30 ml of 22.2 per cent sodium sulfate, which gave a final salt concentration of 21.5 per cent. The protein fraction precipitated was designated as the "globulin fraction," and that remaining in solution the "albumin fraction." Determination of the protein nitrogen remaining in solution permitted calculation of total albumin. Subtraction of the albumin nitrogen from the total protein nitrogen of serum gave the globulin nitrogen, from which total globulin could be calculated. By precipitating serum at sodium sulfate concentrations of 13.5, 17.4, and 21.5 per cent Howe obtained what he designated as "euglobulin," "pseudoglobulin," and "total globulin" values. While it is now recognized that the fractions given by the Howe method are mixtures, up until recent years most of the clinical data on serum proteins (albumins and globulins) have been obtained by it. In fact, this method, or some modification of it is still rather generally used in clinical laboratories and has yielded results of much value in diagnosis and treatment.

Study of plasma proteins by electrophoresis. Tiselius (9) developed the electrophoretic method of protein analysis and applied it to a study of plasma proteins. The theoretical basis of the method was worked out particularly by Svensson (10) and by Dole (11), and the factors involved in the application of the method to the study of plasma proteins were worked out by Armstrong and associates (12).

The electrophoretic method of analysis is based upon the principle that proteins in solution at pH values above and below their isoelectric points migrate in an electric field toward the pole bearing a charge opposite to that of the protein. Protein molecules of the same kind move at the same rate and form sharp boundaries in the solution.

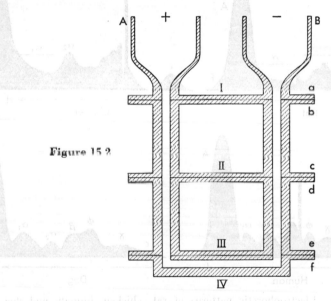

Figure 15.2

The Tiselius electrophoresis cell for use in studying the migration of proteins in an electric field consists of a specially designed glass U tube composed of four separable compartments and in principle may be represented by the cross-section diagram of Figure 15.2.

Compartments I, II, III, and IV fit closely together along the faces of the plates *a*, *b*; *c*, *d*; and *e*, *f*; which may be pushed into alignment to form a U-shaped channel, or out of alignment to permit the addition and removal of solution to and from a compartment. In operation, the apparatus is filled with a solution of protein in a buffer at the proper pH and ionic strength to a level slightly above the *c*, *d* plane. Section III is then slipped to one side, and excess solution is rinsed from section II with buffer. Section II and the remainder of the cell are filled with the buffer and aligned. Positive and negative electrodes are connected through the buffer solution of *A* and *B*. In working with plasma the proteins generally are placed in sodium diethylbarbiturate buffer (Veronal) at a pH of 8.6, and this same buffer is used above the protein solution to make contact with the electrodes. Upon application of an electric field the smaller, more highly charged albumin molecules move faster than the globulin molecules, and after a time the different types of proteins become separated into zones marked by more or less distinct boundaries. The refractive index within a zone and boundary varies from point to point in the tube with variations in protein concentration. By the use of appropriate optical equipment it is possible to make photographic records of these refractive index variations and to determine the relative rates of migration of the various protein components present. From such

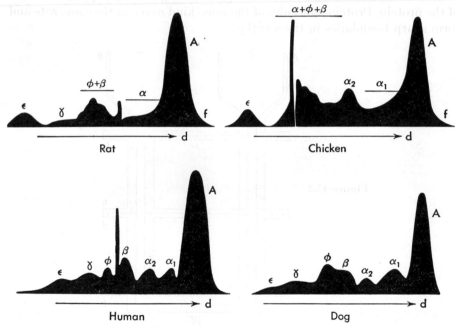

Figure 15.3. Electrophoretic patterns of rat, chicken, human, and dog. (From Deutsch, H. F.: *J. Biol. Chem.*, **161**, 5, 9, 13, 1945.)

photographic records, designated "electrophoretic patterns," it is possible to determine the nature and quantities of the protein components of plasma. Typical electrophoretic patterns of normal plasma proteins are shown in Figure 15.3.

It will be observed that the patterns consist of a series of peaks in a definite sequence of sizes and shapes. A represents the albumin, α the α-globulin, β the β-globulin, ϕ the fibrinogen, and γ the γ-globulin fractions of plasma proteins. The amounts of the different protein components present are calculated from the areas under the peaks of the electrophoretic patterns.

The electrophoretic patterns of the plasmas of different animal species are different and characteristic and represent species variations in the various plasma proteins. Also, it has been found that the electrophoretic patterns of human plasma may vary widely from the normal in pathologic states; in fact, analysis by electrophoresis is contributing much to our understanding of the plasma proteins in disease.

The chief limitation of electrophoretic analysis is due to the fact that the separation of the protein components of a solution depends solely upon their mobility in an electric field. This mobility is a function primarily of particle size, shape, and electric charge, the latter varying with pH. With a given pH, at which the charges of proteins with different isoelectric points may vary widely, the other factors affecting mobility may compensate so that different proteins migrate together and appear as a homogeneous peak in the electrophoretic pattern. Also, some of the proteins may form loose associations with each other, or with other plasma constituents, such as lipids, to yield aggregates that migrate quite differently from the proteins alone. As a matter of fact, a γ-globulin fraction which appeared almost homogeneous by electrophoresis was shown to consist of two or more components by ultracentrifugal analysis.

By the use of the ultracentrifuge in conjunction with electrophoresis and by varying the pH of the protein solution during electrophoretic analysis so as differently to vary the charge of different proteins, it has been possible to improve the separation and characterization of the proteins of plasma.

Luetscher (13) has shown that while human plasma albumin appears homogeneous at pH values above 7 by electrophoresis, at pH 4 two definite peaks appear. The α-globulin component of plasma has been shown to contain two proteins, α_1- and α_2-globulins; the β-globulin fraction has been shown to contain β_1- and β_2-globulins; and the β_1-globulins in turn consist of at least four proteins. It appears that each of the β_1-, β_2-, α_1-, and α_2-globulin components is a mixture of lipoproteins and essentially lipid-free proteins. The γ-globulin fraction likewise is a mixture, and two components of widely different particle sizes have been found. As previously indicated, the immune bodies or antibodies of blood belong to the γ-globulin fraction. By immunologic analysis distinct antibodies against measles, influenza, diphtheria, mumps, pertussis, poliomyelitis, scarlet fever, typhoid, vaccinia, infectious hepatitis, and lymphocytic choriomeningitis, all presumably γ-globulins, have been demonstrated. It is apparent, therefore, that plasma contains an extremely complex mixture of proteins, and that only a beginning has been made in the characterization of the proteins present.

Armstrong, Budka, and Morrison determined the protein distribution in normal pooled human plasma by electrophoresis. Their results are summarized in Table 15.3, along with isoelectric pH values.

Table 15.4, modified after Oncley, Scatchard, and Brown (14), lists the various protein components of normal human plasma which have been obtained in relatively homogeneous condition, with their approximate molecular weights and concentrations in plasma.

The β_1-globulin of molecular weight 1,300,000 is also called X-protein and contains about three times as much lipid material as protein.

Pillemer and Hutchinson (15) have devised a method for the fractionation of serum proteins (albumins and globulins) based upon low-temperature precipitation with methanol. These workers found that at a methanol concentration of 42.5 per cent, pH 6.7 to 6.9, ionic strength about 0.03, and temperature 0° C, the globulins are almost quantitatively precipitated while nearly all the albumin fraction remains in solution. Results by this procedure gave albumin values for normal sera within 5 per cent and of pathologic sera within 10 per cent of electrophoretic values. This procedure has the limitation of requiring a cold room.

Table 15.3. Relative Distribution of Normal Human Plasma Proteins by Electrophoresis

Protein Component	Per Cent of Total Protein	I. pH
Albumins	55.2	
Globulins, total	44.9	
A/G Ratio	1.23	
α-Globulins, total	14.0	5.1
α_1-Globulins	5.3	
α_2-Globulins	8.7	
β-Globulins	13.4	5.6
γ-Globulins	11.0	6.0
Fibrinogen	6.5	5.4

Table 15.4. Proteins of Normal Human Plasma

Protein	Approx. Mol. Wt.	Approx. Conc. g/100 ml
Albumins	69,000	3.2
Globulins		1.8
α_1-Globulin	200,000	0.2
α_2-Globulin	300,000	0.1
β_1-Globulin	90,000	0.2
β_1-Globulin	150,000	0.2
β_1-Globulin	500,000–1,000,000	0.1
β_1-Globulin	1,300,000	0.2
β_2-Globulin	150,000	0.2
γ-Globulin	156,000	0.5
γ-Globulin	300,000	0.1
Fibrinogen	400,000	0.2

From Oncley, J. L.; Scatchard, G.; and Brown, A.: *J. Physiol. & Colloid Chem.*, **51**, 194, 1947.

Milne (16) has proposed a method of serum protein fractionation and analysis which is a modification of the Howe sodium sulfate method. The euglobulins are precipitated by 19.6 per cent and the total globulins by 26.8 per cent sodium sulfate. The filtrate from the total globulin precipitation contains the albumin fraction. The fractions are calculated as follows:

Protein of filtrate 26.8 per cent precipitation = albumin.
Total serum protein — albumin = total globulin.
Protein in filtrate from 19.6 per cent precipitation — albumin = pseudoglobulin, chiefly α_1- and α_2-globulins.
Total globulin — pseudoglobulin = euglobulin, chiefly β- and γ-globulins.

The above fractions were checked by electrophoretic analysis.

Association complexes of plasma proteins. Large proportions of the lipids (cholesterol, phospholipids, and fatty acids), bile salts, and fat-soluble vitamins of plasma, such as the carotenoids, are present as water-soluble complexes with the globulins. In this way the water-insoluble lipids are held in stable aqueous solution at relatively high concentrations. The lipids are combined especially with α_1- and β_1-globulins into lipoprotein complexes, the so-called α_1- and β_1-lipoproteins. These aggregates have molecular weights of about 200,000 and 1,300,000, respectively.

The lipoproteins of plasma generally contain much cholesterol, some as much as 20 per cent. Large amounts of phospholipids and some fatty acids also usually are present. Most of the lipids associated with plasma proteins may be separated by extraction with fat solvents.

The albumins are characterized by forming reversible complexes with a great variety of substances. These include the anions and cations of many acid and basic dyes; the anions of alkyl sulfonic acids, fatty acids, many aromatic carboxylic acids, amino acids, and acetylated amino acids; many types of naphthoquinone and sulfonamide derivatives; and other substances. It is through the formation of such complexes that plasma albumin plays a highly significant role in the transportation of substances in the blood stream. It is also of interest to note that many of these complexes, particularly those with the anions of fatty acids and acetylated amino acids, greatly increase the stability of albumin solutions and their resistance to denaturation by heat and other agents.

It is of interest and importance that a β_1-globulin with a molecular weight of about 90,000 combines with two atoms of iron per molecule to form a complex, siderophilin or transferrin, which serves to transport iron in the blood. Copper also is transported as an α-globulin complex, ceruloplasmin, which has a molecular weight of about 150,000 and contains eight atoms of copper in the molecule. Ceruloplasmin constitutes about 0.3 per cent of the total plasma protein and accounts for practically all of the plasma copper. In Wilson disease, which is rare and inherited, the plasma ceruloplasmin falls to very low levels, and there is a marked increase in the copper of brain and liver. Since the copper of ceruloplasmin is dissociable, the substance may function to regulate copper distribution by releasing and binding it at various locations in the body.

In view of the above evidence it becomes obvious that the formation of molecular associations in plasma gives to it an additional complexity of composition and has much to do with its physical characteristics and, also, with its biologic functioning.

Fractionation of plasma proteins by ethanol at low temperatures and low salt concentrations. During World War II Cohn and associates at Harvard University developed methods for the large-scale separation of blood plasma into protein fractions valuable to the medical services of the Armed Forces (17). The method consists in the precipitation of plasma proteins by different concentrations of ethyl alcohol at low temperature, pH, and ionic strength (salt concentration). The plasma is separated into six major fractions by alcohol precipitation, which are designated as fractions "I," "II +

III," "IV-1," "IV-4," "V," and "VI." These fractions are subfractionated into their components by various procedures involving further alcohol precipitation under controlled conditions, salting out, etc. A brief outline of the procedure of separating plasma proteins into the major fractions by what is known as "method 6," which was evolved from earlier methods, is given below.

The starting material, normal plasma, has a pH of about 7.4 and a salt concentration which gives it an ionic strength of about 0.16.

Fraction I. Obtained by precipitating plasma with 8 to 10 volumes per cent of alcohol at $-3°$ C, ionic strength 0.14, and pH 7.2, fraction I contains most of the fibrinogen of plasma and small amounts of albumin, and α-, β-, and γ-globulins. This fraction serves for the preparation of fibrin films and fibrin foam for use in surgery, especially neurosurgery. Fraction I also serves as starting material for the preparation of purified fibrinogen. From it fibrinogen has been obtained which is clottable to fibrin to the extent of 98 per cent or better.

Fraction II + III. Obtained from the spernatant liquid from fraction I by raising the alcohol concentration to 25 per cent by volume at $-5°$ C, pH 6.8, and ionic strength 0.09, the fraction II + III precipitate contains essentially all the γ-globulins (antibodies), most of the β-globulin, including the β_1-lipoprotein (X-protein), and small amounts of albumin, α-globulin and fibrinogen. In addition, prothrombin, isoagglutinins, and plasminogen are present in fraction II + III. Plasminogen is the proenzyme of plasma which upon activation becomes the proteolytic enzyme, plasmin (fibrinolysin).

By appropriate subfractionation of fraction II + III it is possible to separate and obtain the γ-globulins, β_1-lipoprotein, prothrombin, isoagglutinins, and plasminogen in more or less purified and concentrated conditions.

The γ-globulins may be obtained in a purity of 98 per cent or better and are used especially in measles prophylaxis. It is probable that they will be found of value in developing immunity to various other diseases.

The prothrombin is activated to thrombin, which is used in surgery to stop bleeding (hemostatic agent).

The isoagglutinins of fraction II + III represent the anti-A and anti-B isoagglutinins, which react with the specific A and B substances of red cells, and the anti-Rh isoagglutinins. These isoagglutinins may be separated for use in blood typing.

Fraction IV-1. This fraction is precipitated from the supernatant of fraction II + III by reducing the alcohol concentration to 18 per cent by volume at $-5°$ C, ionic strength 0.09, and pH 5.2.

Fraction IV-1 contains a large proportion of the α-globulin, much of which is a lipoprotein containing 35 per cent lipid (phospholipid, cholesterol, and fatty acid). Small amounts of β- and γ-globulins are also present, as is a blue-green pigment.

Fraction IV-4. This fraction is obtained from the supernatant of fraction IV-1 by raising the alcohol concentration to 40 volumes per cent at $-5°$ C, ionic strength 0.11, and pH 5.8.

This fraction contains chiefly α- and β-globulins and some albumin. The enzyme, serum esterase, and also a specific iron-binding globulin are present in the globulin fraction. The iron-binding globulin is of importance in the transport of iron in the blood. The α- and β-globulins of fraction IV-4 are virtually lipid-free.

Fraction V. The protein in the supernatant from fraction IV-4 is almost entirely albumin, which is precipitated as fraction V by an alcohol concentration of 40 volumes per cent at $-5°$C, ionic strength 0.11, pH 4.8. The precipitated albumin of fraction V contains about 4 per cent of α- and 1 per cent of β-globulin, which can be largely removed by dissolving the precipitate in water and adding alcohol to 10 per cent by volume at $-3°$ C, ionic strength 0.01, and pH 4.6. The precipitate is filtered off, and the filtrate contains albumin of 97 to 99 per cent purity. By crystallization the globulin impurities can be reduced to a few tenths of 1 per cent.

The albumin solution may be evaporated to dryness at a low temperature and the dry albumin powder may be kept indefinitely. A 25 per cent solution of albumin has proved of much value for intravenous administration in the treatment of shock. A small amount (0.04 M) of the sodium salt of acetyltryptophan is generally added to the albumin in order to stabilize it in solution and prevent denaturation.

Fraction VI. The supernatant from fraction V is evaporated at low temperature to give fraction VI, which contains very small quantities of albumin and α-globulin, large amounts of salts, and many nonprotein substances of low molecular weight.

The great advantages of the above procedure of fractionation of plasma proteins reside in the facts that the method yields the proteins in their natural undenatured biologically active states, and the procedure is easily applied to large-scale operations.

Cohn and associates determined the distribution of plasma proteins in the various fractions separated by the alcohol low-temperature process. Their results are summarized in Table 15.5.

Table 15.5.   Distribution of Proteins in Fractions Separated from
Normal Human Plasma

	Grams Protein per 100 ml of Plasma					
Fraction	Total Protein	Albumin	α-Globulin	β-Globulin	γ-Globulin	Fibrinogen
Whole plasma	6.03	3.32	0.84	0.78	0.66	0.43*
Fraction I	0.43	0.02	0.02	0.08	0.05	0.26
Fraction II + III	1.63	0.07	0.18	0.62	0.60	0.16
Fraction IV	0.97	0.10	0.54	0.31	0.02	
Fraction V	2.96	2.90	0.06			
Fraction VI	0.06	0.03	0.03			

* Estimated by electrophoresis and probably too high as compared with estimation by conversion of fibrin.
From Cohn, E. J.; Oncley, J. L.; Strong, L. E.; Hughes, W. L. Jr.; and Armstrong, S. H., Jr.: *J. Clin. Invest.* **23**, 427, 1944.

Table 15.6 summarizes the chief protein components of the fractions and subfractions of plasma, together with their chief functions and established clinical uses.

Lipoproteins. About three fourths of the total lipids of blood plasma are present in combination as β_1-lipoproteins, and it appears that essentially all of the lipids in fasting plasma are present as globulin-lipoprotein complexes. The bonds joining lipids and proteins in the lipoproteins are relatively weak, since most of the lipid can be removed by extraction with fat solvents.

The ultracentrifugal technique of separating the lipoproteins of plasma is based upon their low densities (hydrated densities 0.93–1.145 g per milliliter) relative to other proteins because of the lipid present (18). The serum samples are first mixed with a salt solution to give a density (1.063 g per milliliter at 20° C) at which only the lipoproteins will rise to the surface under centrifugation in a preparative centrifuge for 13 to 16 hours at 80,000 times gravity. The top lipoprotein fraction is removed, mixed with salt solution to give a solution density of 1.063 g per milliliter, run in the analytical supercentrifuge at 215,000 times gravity, the rate of flotation of the lipoprotein fractions toward the surface of the solution determined photographically, and the S_f constants calculated (see Chapter 5). In this case, since the particles rise toward the top of the tube instead of moving toward the bottom, the constants, instead of being sedimentation constants, are flotation constants, S_f.

Table 15.6. Protein Components of Plasma Fractions (Whole Blood)

	Principal Function	Principal Protein Related to Function	Concentrated in Plasma Fraction	Plasma Protein in Fraction Per cent	Concentration of Active Function Times That of Plasma: Per g protein	Concentration of Active Function Times That of Plasma: Per *ml* product	Established Clinical Use
RED CELLS (45% of blood containing 30% hemoglobin)	Respiratory	Hemoglobin					Whole blood or red cell transfusion.
PLASMA (55% of blood containing 7% proteins)	Osmotic regulation of blood volume	Albumin	V	48	1.3	5.4	Shock, burns, edema, hypoproteinemia.
	Blood coagulation	Fibrinogen	I	6	21		Fibrin films as dural substitutes.
		Prothrombin, thrombin	III-2	3	20		Fibrin foam and thrombin as hemostatic agent.
	Immunological	Blood grouping globulins	III-1	3	24	36	Blood grouping.
		Complement C'1	III-2		15		
		Complement C'2	IV		8		
		γ-globulins	II	6	8	25	Measles prophylaxis
	Carbohydrate and lipid solution and transport	β globulins	III, IV				
		α-globulins	IV				
	Regulatory	Fibrinolytic enzyme	I, III-2	10			
		Phosphatase and other enzymes	III, IV				
		Hypertensinogen	IV-3, 4				
		Thyrotropic hormone	IV-3, 4				
		Gonadotropic hormones	III, VI				

From Cohn, E. J.: *Science in Progress*, Series IV. Yale University Press, New Haven, 1945, p. 286.

The higher the S_f values, the lower the density of the lipoproteins. For example, the hydrated density of S_f 100 lipoproteins is 0.95 g per milliliter, and that of S_f 4 lipoproteins is 1.041 g per milliliter. By centrifuging serum at other solution densities, such as 1.125, and 1.20, further separation of the lipoproteins may be achieved.

Determination of the lipoprotein distribution according to S_f values is being utilized clinically, since certain of these substances appear to be related to atherosclerosis. Gofman gives the following classification: S_f 70 and greater includes the chylomicrons and some smaller aggregates which increase greatly after fat-containing meals (alimentary lipemia). S_f 30–70 includes the major lipoprotein fraction of alimentary lipemia and varies according to fat ingestion. Little is known as to the significance of the S_f 20–30 fraction. S_f 10–20 includes the lipoproteins which appear to be related to atherosclerosis, and is consequently of special clinical interest. S_f 2–8 lipoproteins contain much cholesterol and phospholipid and appears to correspond to the β-lipoproteins. This fraction varies from individual to individual but is relatively constant for a given person.

Chaikoff and associates (19) analyzed four serum lipoprotein fractions obtained by the ultracentrifugal flotation technique from a number of animal sera. The average compositions of these fractions for human sera are shown in Table 15.7, compiled from their data.

It will be noted from the table that the β_1-lipoproteins (fraction A) carry much the largest proportion of serum lipids, with the α_1- and α_2-lipoproteins (Fractions C and B) following in order. The transport of triglycerides, cholesterol, and phospholipids as lipoproteins appears to be in the same quantitative order as transport of total lipids.

Table 15.7.   Composition of Four Fractions of Lipoproteins
from Human Serum*
Values represent milligrams per fraction per 100 ml of serum

Lipoprotein fraction†	Lipo-protein	Pro-tein	Total lipid	Per cent lipid	Phospho-lipid	Cholesterol, free	Cholesterol, esters	Tri-glycerides
A (5 sera) d < 1.063	435	72	363	83	89	35	128	111
B (5 sera) d 1.063–1.107	90	31	59	65	26	5.8	21	6.8
C (5 sera) d 1.107–1.220	399	237	162	40	79	8.8	51	23
D (5 sera) d > 1.220	‡	‡	34		29	5.3§	‖	‖

* Sera of male adults 14 hours after the last meal.
† Fraction A had the properties of a mixture of β-lipoproteins, and fractions B and C of α_2- and α_1-lipoproteins respectively. Fraction D was a mixture of lipoproteins and serum albumin and globulin.
‡ Mixture of lipoproteins and proteins.
§ Total cholesterol.
‖ Concentrations too low to measure.

Formation of plasma proteins. Madden and Whipple (20) have reviewed the older evidence for the production and utilization of plasma proteins.

There is excellent evidence to the effect that the liver is the sole source of fibrinogen formation. In experiments in which the liver is poisoned with agents such as chloroform and phosphorus (hepatic poisons), the blood fibrinogen falls rapidly and somewhat in proportion to the liver injury. Upon regeneration and repair of the liver, the plasma fibrinogen returns to normal. Similarly, plasma fibrinogen values fall rapidly after hepatectomy. Drury and McMaster (21) removed the blood from rabbits and defibrinated and reinjected it. By repetition of the process as much as 90 per cent of the fibrinogen was removed. These animals regenerated their plasma fibrinogen with large excesses in five to six hours. However, if the animals were first hepatectomized, the fibrinogen was not regenerated but continued to fall rapidly. This work shows that both the utilization and formation of fibrinogen must proceed rapidly.

Various kinds of evidence show that the liver is also the site of formation of at least most of the blood albumin and globulin. Whipple and associates utilized dogs depleted of their plasma proteins by plasmapheresis in studying plasma protein formation. In depletion of plasma proteins by plasmapheresis the dogs are bled about one-fourth of their blood volume daily and sufficient corpuscles suspended in physiologic saline are reinjected to prevent anemia. Upon daily repetition of the process the plasma protein level may be brought down to a definite concentration such as 4 g per 100 ml, and later maintained at this value by the removal of appropriate amounts of plasma. The minimum amount of plasma protein in grams removed from the dog per week in order to maintain the given plasma protein level is called the "basal output." This basal output will remain constant for a given dog on a given basal diet for an indefinite period. By varying the diet and determining the amount of plasma protein which must be discarded to maintain the basal level, it is possible to estimate the efficiencies of various diets for the formation of plasma proteins. The amount of plasma protein which must be removed to maintain the constant plasma level represents the amount of plasma protein synthesis on a given diet.

Whipple and associates prepared a plasmapheresed dog with an Eck fistula, in which the portal vein is surgically connected to the vena cava, thereby shunting blood from the intestines around the liver and markedly interfering with liver function. They found that such an animal was only about one-tenth as efficient in the formation of plasma proteins as control dogs subjected to plasmapheresis but without Eck fistulas.

The low plasma protein levels (hypoproteinemia) seen in cases of cirrhosis of the liver provide clinical evidence of the importance of this organ in plasma protein formation, most of which is represented by albumins and globulins.

The formation of antibodies and γ-globulins in general appears to be well established as a function of plasma cells (22).

Tarver and Reinhardt (23) have made a study of the formation of plasma and other tissue proteins by the use of methionine containing radioactive S^{35}. Since methionine is a general constituent of tissue proteins, the rate and extent of its incorporation into these proteins may be used to shed light upon their synthesis. The above workers injected the radioactive methionine into normal and hepatectomized dogs and determined the rate of its incorporation into the proteins of tissues and into the globulin, albumin, and fibrinogen fractions of plasma. Their results were as follows:

1. The hepatectomized and normal dogs incorporated methionine into body tissue proteins at the same rates, showing that the various extrahepatic tissues synthesize their own proteins.

2. The radioactive methionine did not appear in the fibrinogen of the plasma of the hepatectomized animals, showing that the liver is solely responsible for fibrinogen formation.

3. As judged by the rates of methionine incorporation into plasma albumin and globulin, the normal animal formed albumin 20 times and globulin 7 times faster than the hepatectomized animal. Synthesis of any albumin by the hepatectomized animal appeared problematical, since the albumin fraction as separated undoubtedly contained some globulin.

In view of the above evidence, it appears justified to conclude that the liver forms all the fibrinogen, essentially all the albumin, and the larger proportion of the globulin fraction of plasma.

Whipple and coworkers studied the basal output of plasma proteins by plasmapheresed dogs (see above) when fed various proteins alone or when incorporated in an adequate basal diet. The weight of plasma protein formed per 100 g of dietary protein was calculated. Some of their results are summarized in Table 15.8.

Table 15.8. Biologic Values of Some Food Proteins in the Formation of Plasma Proteins of Dogs

Values represent grams of plasma protein formed per 100 g of food protein as supplement to a basal adequate diet

Food Protein	Plasma Protein Formation, g
Serum, beef	38
Yeast, fresh, autoclaved	28
Kidney, pork, cooked	22
Rice, polished	19*
Lactalbumin	18
Skeletal muscle, beef	18
Egg white	17
Irish potato, powdered	16
Liver, pork, raw or cooked	15
Soybean	14
Heart, beef	13
Casein	12
Red blood cells, dog	10
Brain, pork	8
Stomach, beef	7
Zein (of corn)	0

* Potency when fed as basal protein.

While the values determined for the potencies of different proteins in forming plasma proteins are necessarily only approximate, they differentiate strikingly between those proteins which are good and those which are poor sources of amino acids for plasma protein synthesis. As might be expected, serum proteins are outstanding in potency for plasma protein synthesis. In some instances certain proteins, such as those of rice and potato, appear to be more effective for globulin than for albumin synthesis. Another vegetable protein, that of the soybean, gives high albumin-globulin ratios, as do standard animal proteins, such as those of muscle, liver, and kidney.

Whipple and associates as well as other workers have shown that the animal body contains protein reserves which can be utilized for the formation of plasma proteins. Whipple's procedure for determining this reserve store of plasma protein-building material in the dog is as follows. The plasma proteins of a normal dog are depleted by daily plasmapheresis while the dog is fed a constant basal diet which is low in protein but adequate. It is found that more plasma protein must be removed in the first weeks of plasmapheresis than in subsequent weeks in order to maintain a steady low plasma protein level. This excess plasma protein removed in the first weeks of a prolonged period of plasmapheresis under such conditions represents the reserve store of body protein convertible to plasma protein. It has been estimated that normal dogs possess sufficient body protein reserves convertible to plasma protein to form one to two times as much plasma protein as is normally present in circulating blood.

Not only is it true that tissue protein reserves are used for the formation of plasma proteins, but also, conversely, as will be shown later, plasma proteins serve for the formation and maintenance of tissue proteins. Thus a dynamic state exists between tissue and plasma proteins so that each may be used for conversion into the other as occasion demands.

Variations in plasma proteins. The variations of plasma proteins in pathologic states represents a very large and important subject, which cannot be considered adequately here.

Total plasma proteins tend to be increased in dehydration (hemoconcentration), and in various diseases such as lymphogranuloma venereum, granuloma inguinale, sarcoid, leprosy, and multiple myeloma. The latter disease, which represents a tumor of the bone marrow, is characterized by the presence of so-called Bence-Jones protein in the plasma which may appear in the urine. Bence-Jones protein represents a group of proteins, some of which have been obtained in crystalline form with a molecular weight of about 37,000. Otherwise, they are characterized by their peculiarity of precipitating from neutral or slightly acid solution at 45° to 58° C upon slow heating, dissolving completely or partially upon boiling, and reprecipitating when the solution is cooled.

Bence-Jones proteins probably are present exclusively in the urine of all multiple-myeloma patients (24). Putnam (25) has shown that the Bence-Jones proteins differ from normal serum proteins in amino acid sequence and end groups, which suggests that they are not derivatives of normal serum proteins but represent abnormal proteins synthesized by the multiple-myeloma tumor cell.

In a rare congenital condition there is lack of ability to form γ-globulins (agammaglobulinemia), which means that persons so afflicted are lacking in antibodies and are particularly susceptible to infections (26). Absence of two β-globulins from the serum in the disease has also been observed.

A case of analbuminemia in a 31-year-old woman has been reported (27) in which no serum albumin could be detected by electrophoresis or by immunochemical procedures.

A number of conditions have been recognized in which abnormal proteins are present in serum. These include macroglobulinemia in which serum γ-globulins of very high molecular weight and rich in carbohydrate are present (28). In some cases the macroglobulins precipitate in the cold (between 10 and 20° C) and redissolve on warming, and are called "cryoglobulins" (cold globulins).

An interesting γ-globulin of high molecular weight (S = 24–27), properdin, has been found to be a normal serum constituent (29), and to have the property of lysing many gram-negative bacteria.

Plasma proteins may be decreased as the result of dietary deficiencies, hemorrhage, nephrosis due to the large reduction in albumin, liver diseases which interfere with plasma protein formation, and malaria.

Many diseases are characterized by alterations in plasma albumin, globulin, and fibrinogen values with little or no abnormality in the quantity of total plasma proteins.

In general a decrease in the albumin is accompanied by an increase in the globulin fraction, and vice versa. Infections often cause marked increases in γ-globulins due to antibody formation.

Plasma fibrinogen is increased especially in acute infections, nephrosis, cirrhosis, and pregnancy, and after x-radiation. It falls sharply in some liver diseases, presumably due to interference with its formation.

Enzymes in blood. Quite a few enzymes have been found in blood plasma, such as amylase, lipase, catalase, arginase, aldolase, adenosine polyphosphatases, β-glucuronidase, histaminase, peptidases, glutamic-aspartic transaminase, lactic dehydrogenase, and acid and alkaline phosphatases. Little is known relative to most of them. They apparently originate from disintegration of tissue and blood cells. Blood levels of some of these enzymes often provide useful clinical information.

Serum amylase apparently originates in the pancreas and salivary glands. It is markedly elevated in the early stages of certain types of acute pancreatitis, in patients with obstruction of the pancreatic duct, and when there is inflammation of the parotid gland (mumps). Serum lipase also originates in the pancreas and shows the same clinical variations as amylase in conditions involving the pancreas.

Serum alkaline phosphatase (optimum pH about 9) is formed chiefly by osteoblasts of bone and is high in Paget's disease and osteomalacia. It is also increased in certain cases of hepatic diseases and in obstructive jaundice. It seems probable that the enzyme in the latter cases originates in the liver.

Normal serum acid phosphatase (optimum pH 4.9) appears to originate mainly in the liver and spleen. Acid phosphatase activity is present in several tissues, but the adult prostate gland forms and contains enormously more than any other tissue. In metastasizing prostatic carcinoma the enzyme is released to the blood and its acid phosphatase activity markedly increases. Prostatic acid phosphatase is inhibited by L-tartrate, which differentiates it from nonprostatic acid phosphatase.

The peptidases of serum increase in conditions causing excessive tissue breakdown, such as shock, fever, and traumatic injury, and in hemolytic anemia due to the disruption of red cells.

Glutamic-aspartic transaminase activity markedly increases in the serum of patients with liver cell damage (as in hepatitis) and to a lesser degree and transiently in patients with myocardial infarction (coronary thrombosis). The increase in the enzyme appears to be due to release from damaged tissues, both liver and heart cells being especially rich in transaminases.

It is probable that the levels of various serum enzymes will assume increasing clinical importance in the future as better methods of estimation are developed and more is known about the relation of the enzymes to pathologic states.

FUNCTIONS OF PLASMA PROTEINS

The chief functions of plasma proteins may be summarized in the following statements:

1. By contributing to the viscosity of plasma they help provide the resistance to blood flow in the vascular system, which is essential for efficient heart action.

2. They serve as a source of nutrition for the tissues of the body.

3. Through their osmotic effect they aid in regulating the distribution of fluid between the blood and tissues.

4. They provide for the control of hemorrhage through mechanisms for blood coagulation.

5. They contribute to the solution and transport of lipids, fat-soluble vitamins, bile salts, hormones, and various drugs in the blood through the formation of complexes.

6. In the γ-globulin fraction they provide antibodies for defense against infection.

While most of these functions have been discussed in more or less detail, it is desirable to consider especially the nutritive, fluid-regulating, and coagulation functions of the plasma proteins.

Nutritive functions of plasma proteins. Whipple and associates (20) showed that the fasting dog can be maintained in nitrogen equilibrium and also in weight equilibrium for many days by the intravenous administration of whole dog plasma. The animal uses up the injected plasma proteins to supply the protein needs of all his tissues. The albumin-globulin ratio of the blood remains unchanged, showing that the body draws upon the albumin and globulin fractions at about the same rate for the maintenance of its tissues.

It has been demonstrated that injected plasma proteins are broken down by tissue cells to simpler products (probably amino acids) and then utilized for the formation of tissue proteins (30).

Benditt and associates (31) have shown that protein-depleted rats fed a protein-free basal ration and given rat serum intravenously build up their plasma and tissue proteins better than when they are given an equivalent amount of nitrogen as hydrolyzed casein either orally or intravenously.

Role of plasma proteins in the regulation of fluid balance. Starling (32) first pointed out the importance of the plasma proteins in helping regulate the distribution of fluid between the blood and tissues.

The small molecules of plasma and tissue fluid (lymph), such as glucose, amino acids, urea, and salts, freely diffuse back and forth through the blood capillaries and exert about the same total osmotic pressure in both fluids. However, plasma and lymph proteins do not freely diffuse through the capillary walls, and since the protein concentration of plasma is much higher than of lymph, the osmotic pressure of plasma exceeds the osmotic pressure of lymph by the difference in the protein osmotic pressures of the two fluids. This difference in the osmotic pressures of lymph and plasma is estimated to average about 22 mm of mercury and represents the "effective osmotic" pressure or oncotic pressure of plasma. The distribution of fluid between the blood and tissues is regulated by the balance between the blood pressure tending to force fluid into the tissue spaces and the effective protein osmotic pressure of plasma tending to draw fluid from the tissue spaces into the blood. The blood pressure at the arterial end of the capillary is estimated to be about 34 mm and at the venous end about 12 mm of mercury. If the effective plasma osmotic pressure remains essentially constant at 22 mm throughout the capillary (it increases slightly), the movement of fluid from the blood to the tissues and from the tissues to the blood along the capillary may be represented by the diagram of Figure 15.4.

At the arterial end of the capillary the blood pressure exceeds the opposing protein osmotic pressure by 12 mm and tends to drive fluid into the tissue spaces under this pressure. As the blood flows along the capillary, the blood pressure falls and with it the force driving fluid into the tissue spaces. At

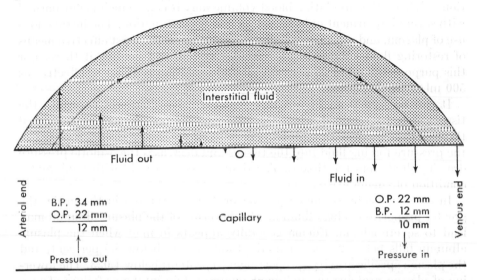

Figure 15.4

some point along the capillary, such as O, the blood pressure and protein osmotic pressure are equal, and no fluid flows in either direction. Beyond O the protein osmotic pressure progressively exceeds the blood pressure and draws fluid from the tissue spaces into the blood. This movement of fluid increases to a maximum at the venous end of the capillary, where the difference between protein osmotic pressure and blood pressure is maximum. Because there is less difference between osmotic and blood pressures in the venous than in the arterial part of the capillary, a greater proportion of the capillary is involved in the return of fluid to the blood (venous) than in the flow of fluid to the tissues (arterial).

The albumin fraction of plasma is responsible for most of the effective osmotic pressure of plasma because it is present in the largest quantity, its molecular weight is much the smaller (69,000 against an average of about 170,000 for other proteins), and, having the lowest isoelectric pH, it binds more cations at the pH of plasma (7.4) than do the other plasma proteins. These bound ions are restrained from passing through the capillary walls by the nondiffusible negative protein ions (Donnan effect). Since the concentration of nondiffusible protein ions in plasma is higher than in lymph, the concentration of diffusible ions is also higher. This unequal distribution of diffusible ions due to the Donnan effect has been estimated to account for about 20 per cent of the osmotic pressure of plasma proteins.

The albumin fraction of plasma normally contributes about 80 per cent of the effective osmotic pressure of plasma. It has been shown that each gram of albumin holds about 18 ml of fluid in the blood stream through its osmotic effect. This greater osmotic pressure and fluid holding capacity of plasma albumin is the basis for the special value of purified albumin solution, such as prepared by the procedure of Cohn, in the treatment of shock. In conditions of shock the circulating blood volume may become much below normal with severe impairment of heart action and tissue function. The intravenous use of plasma, and especially of albumin solution, is the most effective means of restoring fluid volume to the vascular system and holding it there. For this purpose 100 ml of 25 per cent albumin solution is about as effective as 500 ml of whole plasma.

It can be seen from Figure 15.4 that excessive fluid will pass into the tissues and be retained when the plasma osmotic pressure is decreased through decreased plasma protein concentration. Such a decrease increases the pressure forcing fluid into the tissues and decreases the osmotic pressure drawing fluid from the tissues. The tissues become turgid with fluid, and a condition of edema exists.

In cases of nephrosis much plasma protein is excreted in the urine, the greater proportion being albumin. This lowering of the plasma albumin may lead to severe edema. Edema generally appears in man when the plasma albumin falls below 2.5 per cent, the total protein below 5.5 per cent, and the plasma specific gravity (proportional to protein) below 1.023. The lowering of plasma proteins through inadequate protein intake or failure of protein synthesis because of disease may also lead to edema.

Burns and the toxins of certain bacteria may increase capillary permeability and permit escape of plasma proteins into the tissues, with resulting severe edema. In such cases the protein osmotic pressure (effective) is increased in the tissue fluids at the same time it is decreased in the blood.

Reference to Figure 15.4 shows that excessive fluid may pass into the tissues as the result of disturbances in capillary blood pressure. In cases of right heart failure and obstruction of large veins, the flow of blood is obstructed from the venous end of the capillary and the blood pressure within the capillary rises. This increases the flow of fluid to the tissues and reduces the return of fluid to the blood, resulting in edema.

COAGULATION OF BLOOD

The problem of blood coagulation is enormously complex, and despite the work of many investigators over a long period, many phases still remain obscure. It is possible here to give only a brief discussion of the principles relating to blood coagulation and some of the factors involved as known at the present time. Further information may be obtained in books and review articles (33).

MECHANISMS OF COAGULATION

The major processes involved in the coagulation of blood have been shown to be the conversion of the proenzyme prothrombin to the enzyme thrombin and the action of thrombin upon fibrinogen to form fibrin, which separates as long fibers or threads in a three-dimensional network or mesh that holds the formed elements of blood. Fibrin threads are made up of needlelike micelles packed lengthwise into bundles. These fibrin threads, when freshly formed, are extremely adhesive, and stick to each other, blood cells, tissues, and foreign substances. This adhesiveness of the fibrin threads causes the clotted blood to hold together and to stick firmly to injured tissues, thereby effectively stopping hemorrhage. Upon standing, the fibrin threads shorten or retract and squeeze serum from the clot.

Since blood normally does not clot within the vascular system (the injection of thrombin solutions into the blood stream produces disastrous clotting), thrombin is present in the circulating blood in an inactive form, prothrombin, which becomes activated to thrombin when blood escapes due to injury or is withdrawn from the blood vessels.

When blood is shed over tissues or drawn into ordinary glass or other vessels, it clots within a reasonably short time. Preliminary to this process the platelets stick together (agglutinate) on the surface of the injured tissues or the walls of the containing vessel and are disrupted. If, however the surfaces of the needles and vessels used in drawing blood are coated with a nonwettable material, such as silicone, the platelets are not broken up and may be centrifuged off at high speed. The resulting deplateletized plasma may be kept without coagulation. When disrupted platelets or small amounts of extracts of lung, brain, or other tissues are added to the deplateletized plasma, coagulation takes place, showing that these materials contain substances which activate prothrombin to thrombin. These activating substances are called "thromboplastins" or "thromboplastic substances."

When freshly drawn blood is treated with a small amount of sodium oxalate (2 mg per milliliter), the calcium is removed as insoluble oxalate and the blood does not coagulate, showing that Ca^{++} ions are necessary for coagulation. The cells may be centrifuged off to give oxalated plasma. Disrupted platelets or tissue extracts do not coagulate oxalated plasma, showing that Ca^{++} ions are required to act with thromboplastins in converting prothrombin to thrombin. Also, purified prothrombin solutions may be prepared, and these are activated to thrombin by the combined actions of thromboplastins and Ca^{++} ions.

Purified thrombin solutions promptly coagulate oxalated plasma or purified fibrinogen solutions, showing that Ca^{++} ions are not necessary for the final stage of coagulation.

Methods of estimating prothrombin have been devised by Quick and associates (34), and Warner and associates (35). The Quick one-stage technique involves the addition of thromboplastin to recalcified plasma and noting the coagulation time. Since with an excess of thromboplastin the limiting factor in the plasma is generally prothrombin, the amount of prothrombin present is inversely related to the time required for coagulation. This time is called the "prothrombin time." It has been found in this test that the thrombin content of the mixture rises gradually in the test interval and that coagulation occurs when 10 to 20 per cent of the prothrombin has been converted to thrombin. Thus, the test is a measure of the speed with which

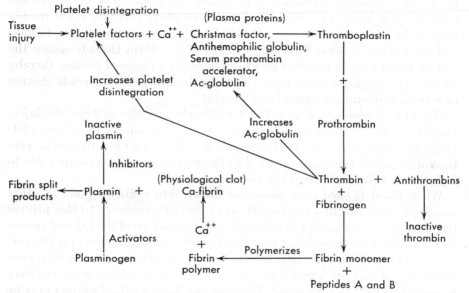

Figure 15.5. Diagrammatic representation of substances and processes involved in blood coagulation.

the thrombin can be built up to the clotting level. In the Warner two-stage procedure thromboplastin and Ca^{++} ions are allowed to react with the plasma prothrombin until conversion to thrombin is complete. The amount of thrombin formed is then determined by its action upon purified fibrinogen solution.

Quick (36) has shown in stage I, the conversion of prothrombin to thrombin, that the amount of prothrombin converted to thrombin depends directly upon the concentrations of calcium and thromboplastin, and, thus, is not enzymatic. Also, Quick and Stefanini (37) have shown that Ca^{++} ions are associated with prothrombin as a complex in the activation to thrombin. This is indicated by the fact that the inhibition of coagulation by sodium oxalate is a relatively slow process, whereas the precipitation of free Ca^{++} ions by oxalate is a very rapid process. The delayed action of oxalate in inhibiting coagulation presumably is due to the time required for the oxalate to decalcify the Ca^{++}-prothrombin complex. In agreement with this view is the fact that about three times as much oxalate as is equivalent to the calcium of blood must be added to prevent coagulation. In the process of prothrombin activation it seems probable, as suggested by Ferguson (38), that prothrombin, Ca^{++} ions, and thromboplastin form a complex which then decomposes to give thrombin. Purified thrombin does not contain calcium.

That the conversion of fibrinogen to fibrin by thrombin is enzymatic is indicated by the fact that thrombin can convert several million times its own weight of fibrinogen to fibrin.

Evidence such as that given above shows that blood coagulation proceeds in two major stages, the activation of prothrombin to thrombin and the conversion of fibrinogen to fibrin:

1. Activation stage:

Prothrombin + thromboplastin + $Ca^{++} \longrightarrow$ thrombin

2. Conversion stage:

Fibrinogen + thrombin $\longrightarrow$ fibrin

Each of these stages represents a complex of reactions involving various components or factors. Figure 15.5 represents the over-all coagulation process.

SUBSTANCES INVOLVED IN BLOOD COAGULATION

In order to understand better the over-all coagulation process, it is desirable first to consider the substances known to be involved in it. These include not only the major reactants, such as prothrombin, thrombin, thromboplastins, fibrinogen and Ca^{++}, but also a number of important less-well-understood substances or factors which serve as accelerators or inhibitors of the coagulation process.

Fibrinogen and fibrin. Fibrinogen occurs in human plasma to the extent of about 0.3 per cent and represents about 4 per cent of the total plasma protein. It has the solubility characteristics of a globulin, is isoelectric at about pH 5.3, and has a molecular weight of 300,000 to 350,000. The fibrinogen molecules are very elongated ellipsoids with axial dimensions of 700×38 Å. Purified fibrinogen solutions are quickly coagulated by purified thrombin solutions in the absence of Ca^{++}.

Fibrinogen is precipitated from plasma by 0.25 saturation with $(NH_4)_2SO_4$, by 0.5 saturation with NaCl, or by making plasma 0.75 M with Na_2SO_4. Fraction I of Cohn, obtained by precipitating plasma with 8 to 10 volumes per cent ethanol at $-3°$ C, pH 7.2, and ionic strength 0.14, contains 60–65 per cent fibrinogen. This preparation has been further purified by Edsall and associates, so that it contains 98 per cent or better of clottable protein (39). Seegers and coworkers (40) obtain purified fibrinogen by allowing fresh frozen plasma to thaw slowly until all ice is just gone; other proteins are redissolved, and only part of the fibrinogen has redissolved. The undissolved fibrinogen fraction is centrifuged off, washed, and dissolved. Fractionation of this preparation with $(NH_4)_2SO_4$ yields an excellent product.

When purified thrombin (proteolytic enzyme) acts upon purified fibrinogen solutions, the fibrinogen is hydrolyzed to yield fibrin monomer or profibrin and cofibrin (fibrinopeptide) composed of two peptides A and B (41). The molecular weight of peptide A is 2000 and of peptide B 2400. Peptide A contains 10 amino acid residues and peptide B 12 residues. Glutamic acid is the N-terminal and arginine the C-terminal amino acid in peptide A, while in peptide B arginine is the C-terminal group. The N-terminal group is yet to be identified. The two peptides are highly acidic, due to the presence of much glutamic and aspartic acids. Since in the action of thrombin on fibrinogen arginine is the C-terminal group in both peptides formed, and N-terminal glycine residues appear in the resultant fibrin, thrombin appears to split the bonds between glycine and arginine in the N-terminal region of the arginine molecule. Some 3 per cent of the fibrinogen molecule is split off by the action of thrombin (9000 mass units), and four bonds appear to be broken, which would correspond to the release of two molecules each of peptides A and B. This removal of highly acidic peptides from fibrinogen by the action of thrombin leaves the profibrin with a much reduced negative charge compared to fibrinogen and may represent the essential change preliminary to the polymerization of fibrin monomer to fibrin as found in clotted blood. The fibrin monomer molecules polymerize by end-to-end and side-to-side aggregation into bundles or fibers which form a gel meshwork. Fibrin formed in the absence of Ca^{++} has a less dense structure than when Ca^{++} is present, and it appears that Ca^{++} is necessary to yield firm physiologic clots.

The bonds first formed in the polymerization of fibrin monomer and not involving Ca^{++} are weak bonds corresponding to hydrogen bonds, since they are readily broken by moderately strong urea solutions. The interaction of Ca^{++} in the polymerization of the fibrin monomer to fibrin is associated with the appearance of much stronger bonding concerning which little is known.

The action of thrombin on fibrinogen as outlined above may be represented as follows:

1. Fibrinogen + thrombin ⟶ fibrin monomer + 2 peptide A + 2 peptide B
2. x fibrin monomer ⟶ (fibrin monomer)$_x$
                      Fibrin

Fibrinolytic enzyme system of plasma. All mammalian sera contain the precursor (plasminogen or profibrinolysin) of an enzyme (plasmin or fibrinolysin) which is capable of rapidly hydrolyzing fibrin (42). Plasminogen is activated to the enzyme plasmin by activators present in serum, tissues, urine, and bacteria. Plasmin has great affinity for fibrinogen, and the purest fibrinogen preparations are still contaminated with plasminogen.

Plasmin is a proteolytic enzyme which acts at neutral pH to hydrolyze not only fibrin but also a number of other proteins into several large and some smaller peptides. It appears that plasmin splits arginine-lysine linkages.

Plasmin, unlike thrombin, does not convert fibrinogen to fibrin, though it digests both fibrinogen and fibrin.

The molecular weight of plasmin appears to be around 100,000.

The physiologic role of plasmin is digestion and resolution of fibrin clots. According to present concepts, plasminogen activator is produced in blood vessel walls and released upon injury. The plasminogen is associated with fibrinogen and is present within the clot. Activator released by the injured blood vessels permeates into the clot and converts plasminogen to plasmin, which then slowly breaks down the fibrin and resolves the clot. The plasmin formed in the circulation and not involved in clot dissolution is inactivated by plasmin inhibitors or antiplasmins, which appear to be α_2- and α_1-globulins.

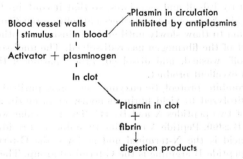

Presumably the plasminogen in the clot is not accompanied by significant amounts of antiplasmins.

There is a very rare clinical condition, afibrinogenemia, in which there are very low levels of plasma fibrinogen. A few cases with congenital absence of fibrinogen from the blood have been reported. In these cases it was impossible to detect any fibrinogen by the usual salting-out and heat-coagulation tests. The blood of such individuals upon being drawn is incoagulable, yet the bleeding time from a small puncture wound may be normal or nearly so, indicating that such slight hemorrhage can be controlled by mechanisms other than blood coagulation. Transfusions restore normal coagulability.

Cases of congenital afibrinogenemia show bleeding tendencies very similar to those of hemophilia, though generally less severe. They may be free from hemorrhage for relatively long periods of time, but death due to hemorrhage generally occurs at a relatively early age.

Several cases have been reported with fibrinogen values slightly below 0.02 per cent. These individuals showed some but not severe bleeding tendencies. It appears that a fibrinogen level of 0.02 per cent is sufficient for effective coagulation.

While only a few cases of congenital afibrinogenemia have been studied, it appears that the condition may be hereditary.

Low plasma fibrinogen levels have been observed in certain cases of carcinoma, myelogenous leukemia, subacute appendicitis, tuberculosis, Bang's disease, pneumonia, and scurvy. It is important to remember that infection generally causes an increase in fibrinogen.

Prothrombin and thrombin. Prothrombin, the precursor of thrombin, is strongly adsorbed by $Mg(OH)_2$, $Ca_3(PO_4)_2$, $Al(OH)_3$, and $BaSO_4$. Seegers and associates (43) prepared purified prothrombin by first obtaining a concentrate from beef plasma by isoelectric precipitation, redissolving the precipitate, adsorbing the prothrombin on $Mg(OH)_2$, and decomposing the adsorption complex with CO_2. The eluted prothrombin in solution was then fractionated with $(NH_4)_2SO_4$ and finally separated by isoelectric precipitation.

The purified prothrombin contained 14.49 per cent nitrogen, 10 per cent tyrosine, and 4.3 per cent carbohydrate. Glucosamine, sulfur, and tryptophan were present.

Prothrombin is isoelectric at about pH 4.2 and has the electrophoretic mobility of an α_1-globulin and a molecular weight around 63,000 (44).

When prothrombin is dissolved in 30 per cent sodium citrate, the molecule is slowly split (several hours) into three smaller molecules (with molecular weights of 5000 and about 15,000 and 45,000), and a larger heterogenous aggregated molecule is formed. The molecule whose molecular weight is around 45,000 and the aggregated molecule both have thrombin activity (45).

Thrombin obtained by the action of citrate upon prothrombin is called "citratethrombin."

When purified prothrombin is treated with Ca^{++} alone, no thrombin is formed, but when it is acted upon by thromboplastin accelerator globulin, other factors, and Ca^{++}, it is converted to thrombin, which is designated "biothrombin" to differentiate it from thrombin formed by the action of citrate.

The molecular weight of thrombin appears to be not very different from that of prothrombin, but somewhat less.

A substance, dicoumarin, 3,3'-methylene-bis(-4-hydroxycoumarin) was discovered by Link and associates (46) in spoiled sweet clover which causes a hemorrhagic disease in cattle:

Dicoumarin

The failure of blood to clot in sweet clover disease is due to the low level of prothrombin. Dicoumarin appears to interfere specifically with the formation of prothrombin by the liver. The mechanism of this interference is obscure.

The oral administration of a single dose of dicoumarin to humans causes a slow decrease in blood prothrombin, which reaches its lowest level in 48 to 96 hours, and again becomes normal in about a week. Dicoumarin is used clinically in cases of threatened thrombosis to reduce the probability of intravascular clot formation.

Hypoprothrombinemia with serious bleeding tendencies may be encountered in liver diseases, such as cirrhosis due to obstructive jaundice, toxic hepatitis and atrophic cirrhosis. Also, any condition which prevents absorption of vitamin K leads to hypoprothrombinemia. Since bile salts are necessary for the absorption of the vitamin, hypoprothrombinemia may occur as the result of diversion of bile from the intestine in surgical procedures or as a result of obstruction in the common bile duct.

The administration of vitamin K orally or by injection has proved remarkably effective in treating cases of hypoprothrombinemia.

Thromboplastins. When blood is collected without tissue contamination and kept in contact with neutral surfaces (silicone-coated), it fails to clot. The addition of a small amount of watery extract of almost any tissue, however, causes rapid coagulation.

Purified prothrombin in the presence of Ca^{++} ions is inactive, but the addition of such tissue extracts causes rapid conversion to thrombin. This coagulation factor is especially abundant in lung, brain, thymus, testes, and platelets.

The coagulation factor of tissues and platelets has been designated by several terms including "cytozyme," "zymoplastic substance," "thrombokinase," "thromboplastic substance," "thromboplastin," or simply "kinase," although at present the terms "thromboplastin" and "thromboplastic substance" are used most commonly. The evidence indicates that there are a number of thromboplastic substances.

Howell (47) showed that extraction of tissues with either water or lipid solvents yields active thromboplastins. The ether-soluble lipids contain cephalin, which alone was found to be active, but much less so than when combined with some unknown protein factor. The cephalin was heat stable as a thromboplastic agent but the cephalin-protein complex was heat labile. Various workers have shown cephalin to be a thromboplastin component.

Chargaff (48) separated from beef lung a thromboplastic lipoprotein containing some pentose nucleic acid, with a molecular weight of about 170,000,000, which powerfully activated prothrombin. He considered this material represented practically all the thromboplastic activity of the lung tissue.

The venoms of certain snakes, particularly of Russell's viper, contain a powerful coagulating factor. Trevan and MacFarlane (49) found the venom did not coagulate oxalated or citrated blood and had no effect on fibrinogen. They showed the coagulating effect of venom to be greatly increased by the addition of tissue lipids or lecithin, suggesting that these substances act as cofactor with the venom thromboplastic agent. It was found that the venom alone would not coagulate plasma from which the lipids had been extracted with petroleum ether. Addition of the extracted lipids or lecithin to the venom before addition to the plasma, however, caused rapid coagulation.

Zak (50) showed that oxalated plasma extracted with petroleum ether will not coagulate upon recalcification. Clotting occurs upon the addition of the extracted lipids.

The above evidence seems to show that thromboplastins are complex lipoproteins in which cephalin or other phospholipids are components.

While thromboplastic activity is shown immediately by tissue extracts, it is not normally present in blood, but arises only in cases of injury and hemorrhage after platelets disintegrate and release what has been called "platelet factor 3," which in combination with certain plasma proteins and Ca^{++} forms a thromboplastin complex capable of activating prothrombin to thrombin.

A number of plasma and platelet factors interact to yield the thromboplastic complex which activates prothrombin to thrombin. Various substances also are of importance as inhibitors and regulators of the coagulation process. Such substances are considered in the following discussion.

Calcium. Ionized calcium is necessary for coagulation. The removal of Ca^{++} ions by precipitation as oxalate or fluoride, or their suppression by citrate, which forms slightly dissociated calcium citrate, prevents coagulation indefinitely.

The chelating agents, such as ethylenediaminetetraacetate, form very slightly dissociated complexes with Ca^{++} and are effective anticoagulants:

$$\text{HOOC-H}_2\text{C} \quad \quad \text{H} \quad \text{H} \quad \quad \text{CH}_2\text{-COOH}$$
$$\text{N-C-C-N}$$
$$\text{HOOC-H}_2\text{C} \quad \quad \text{H} \quad \text{H} \quad \quad \text{CH}_2\text{-COOH}$$

Ethylenediaminetetraacetic acid

The tervalent ions of scandium, yttrium, and lanthanum, and Mg^{++} ions have been found to inhibit coagulation strongly, presumably through displacement of Ca^{++} ions from the prothrombin complex.

The quantity of Ca^{++} ions required for coagulation has wide optimum, ranging from 0.025 to 0.0025 M. Above and below this range coagulation is depressed and finally inhibited.

Accelerator globulin (Ac-globulin, proaccelerin, labile factor, factor V). Accelerator globulin, present in plasma, is involved in the processes by which prothrombin is converted to thrombin. It was discovered in 1944 by Owren while studying a patient with a hemorrhagic disease (congenital parahemophilia) whose blood was deficient only in this factor. Ac-globulin is very labile and rapidly disappears from stored plasma. It may be deficient in the plasma of persons with liver disease. Before plasma Ac-globulin (proaccelerin) becomes functional in the coagulation process, it is converted to serum Ac-globulin (accelerin) by the action of thrombin. While some conversion of prothrombin to thrombin occurs in shed blood without the action of Ac-globulin, the process is slow. As soon as some thrombin is formed, it acts to form serum Ac-globulin, which enormously increases the rate of conversion of prothrombin to thrombin:

Plasma Ac-globulin + thrombin ⟶ serum Ac-globulin

Antihemophilic globulin, AHG (antihemophilic factor [AHF], factor VIII, thromboplastinogen, platelet cofactor 1). Antihemophilic globulin is a plasma protein essential for the conversion of prothrombin to thrombin, and it is deficient in the blood of persons with hemophilia.

Hemophilia (bleeder's disease) is congenital and is inherited as a sex-linked Mendelian recessive which occurs frequently in males but is transmitted through females. The blood of hemophiliacs generally clots very slowly, and the clots are not normally firm and do not hold well. The blood of hemophiliacs appears normal relative to the coagulation mechanism except for the deficiency in antihemophilic globulin.

The clinical control of hemophilic bleeding during surgery and after traumatic injury presents a major problem. Transfusions of normal plasma or blood, and intravenous administration of antihemophilic globulin found in Cohn's fraction I of plasma appear to be the most effective treatments, all of which, however, afford only temporary protection.

Serum prothrombin accelerator, SPCA (autoprothrombin I, factor VII, proconvertin, stable factor). Serum prothrombin accelerator is characterized by correcting the "delayed prothrombin time" of the blood of patients treated with dicoumarin and with vitamin K deficiency. The active material is present in both plasma and serum, and in Cohn's plasma fraction III, and has the electrophoretic mobility of a β-globulin. SPCA is stable on storage.

Christmas factor, CF (plasma thromboplastin component, PTC; factor IX, antihemophilic factor B, platelet cofactor II, autoprothrombin II). Christmas factor is characterized by its ability to correct the coagulation defect in Christmas disease or hemophilia B and to promote the conversion of prothrombin to thrombin. Christmas factor was named after the first patient in whom the deficiency of the factor was discovered. It is associated with the β_2-globulin fraction of plasma, is present in both serum and plasma, and in fractions III and IV-I of Cohn, and is relatively stable on storage.

Platelets. During coagulation the platelets clump, put out pseudopodia, and partially disintegrate, undergoing what has been called "viscous metamorphosis." During the process many microscopically visible granules are released from the platelets which can be separated by high-speed centrifugation. These particles together with serum Ac-globulin rapidly convert prothrombin to thrombin and apparently represent a component of active blood thromboplastin. The particles may be identical with or related to platelet factor 3, the substance from disintegrated platelets which combines with plasma factors to form thromboplastin. Platelet factor 3 can be thrown down by high-speed centrifugation. It contains much phospholipid, which appears essential for the coagulation process.

During platelet disruption histamine, norepinephrine, and serotonin (5-hydroxytryptamine) are liberated, and since these substances have vasoconstrictor activity, they probably play a role in the control of bleeding. The agglutination or clumping of platelets at the site of vascular injury also aids in hemostasis.

Platelet dissolution in blood may be prevented by coating needles, syringes, tubing, and other vessels used in drawing the blood with silicone or other water-repellent substances. When such blood is centrifuged to remove the platelets (and other cells), the resultant deplateletized plasma may be kept for long periods of time without coagulation. However, the addition of lysed platelets or platelet extracts to it causes prompt coagulation.

In the condition known as "thrombocytopenia" there is a prolonged bleeding time due to a deficiency of blood platelets, which decreases thromboplastin formation and thrombin production.

Some cases of thrombocytopenia (primary thrombocytopenia) are idiopathic, the cause being unknown. Secondary thrombocytopenia may be associated with certain leukemias and anemias and a number of infections, or may be caused by certain drugs or chemicals and by ionizing radiation (x-rays, γ-rays, etc.).

Heparin. Heparin is an anticoagulant factor which was first obtained from liver by Howell and Holt in 1918 (51). Heparin is a polymer of D-glucuronic acid and D-glucosamine in which both the amino and some of the hydroxyl groups are combined with sulfuric acid, which causes it to be a strongly acidic substance (see Chapter 7). Thus heparin is an acidic mucopolysaccharide. It has a molecular weight of about 17,000.

Heparin is formed in the metachromatic granules of the mast cells of Ehrlich, which are chiefly found along blood vessel walls. Heparin has been isolated as a crystalline barium salt from both liver and lung.

Heparin alone has no effect upon the coagulation process. It has no inhibitory effect upon the conversion of purified prothrombin to thrombin. However, when heparin is combined with a serum albumin cofactor it becomes a powerful anticoagulant. This heparin-albumin complex strongly inhibits the conversion of prothrombin to thrombin, and also it inactivates thrombin. Thus it functions as both an antiprothrombin and an antithrombin.

Thrombin formed in the coagulation process acts upon platelets to cause viscous metamorphosis and release of a thromboplastic factor. Heparin is antagonistic to this process and thereby aids in the prevention of thrombus formation. The extent to which the very small amount of heparin in normal blood functions to prevent intravascular clotting is uncertain, though its effect would appear to be small, since plasma contains other coagulation inhibitors capable of preventing intravascular coagulation.

The injection of heparin into an animal causes the liberation of lipoprotein lipase (clearing factor) into the blood (52). Lipoprotein lipase, or clearing factor, is responsible for digestion of triglycerides associated with chylomicrons and lipoproteins, thereby clearing up the turbidity of lipemic plasma.

It is of interest that both anaphylactic shock and shock due to peptone injection cause an outpouring of heparin from the mast cells which appears to be responsible for the incoagulability of the blood under these conditions (53).

The chief uses of commercial heparin are as anticoagulant in blood analysis and administration to patients to prevent thrombosis.

Antithrombins. Seegers and associates (54) consider that there are four antithrombins which function as inhibitors of coagulation to protect against intravascular coagulation. Antithrombin I is considered to be fibrin which strongly adsorbs thrombin. Antithrombin II refers to the plasma protein which combines with heparin to give the complex with antiprothrombin and antithrombin properties discussed above. Antithrombin III appears to be a plasma protein which inactivates thrombin, the activity of both the antithrombin and thrombin disappearing in the process, with the result that serum contains much less antithrombin III than does plasma. Extraction of plasma with ether removes antithrombin III activity, presumably by breaking up a lipoprotein complex. However, such ether extracted plasma still exhibits much antithrombin activity, and the substance(s) responsible for this activity are referred to as "antithrombin IV."

It is of interest that the antithrombins of plasma can inactivate more than twice the potential yield of thrombin from the prothrombin of blood.

Hirudin is the anticoagulant present in the cervical glands of the common medicinal leech (Hirudo) and is the oldest known specific anticoagulant. While little recent work has been done upon hirudin, the older observations suggested it to be an albumose. Mellanby (55) considered it to act as an antithrombin.

Various other inhibitors of coagulation have been reported in blood and tissues (56). A powerful inhibitor has been found in the ether extract of brain tissue. Such preparations also have been obtained from plasma, serum, and other tissues. These substances have antithromboplastic activity.

SUMMARY OF BLOOD COAGULATION

As a result of considerations involving the various processes and factors involved in blood coagulation, it appears that the over-all process may be outlined as follows:

I. Prothrombin activation stage. As blood flows from broken blood vessels over injured tissues, platelets undergo viscous metamorphosis, partially disintegrate, and liberate phospholipid (phosphatidyl ethanolamine or cephalin) rich granules (platelet factor 3) which, in conjunction with plasma protein factors and Ca^{++}, form thromboplastin. The thromboplastin acts with prothrombin to form some thrombin:

$$\text{Prothrombin} + \text{thromboplastin} \xrightarrow[Ca^{++}]{} \text{thrombin}$$

This thrombin then acts upon plasma Ac-globulin to form serum Ac-globulin:

$$\text{Plasma Ac-globulin} + \text{thrombin} \longrightarrow \text{serum Ac-globulin}$$

The serum Ac-globulin then enormously increases the rate of thrombin formation from prothrombin by thromboplastin and Ca^{++}:

$$\text{Prothrombin} + \text{thromboplastin} \xrightarrow[\substack{Ca^{++} \\ \text{serum Ac-globulin}}]{} \text{thrombin}$$

Thrombin produced initially also increases the rate of viscous metamorphosis of the platelets to afford more thromboplastin for the coagulation process:

$$\text{Platelets} + \text{thrombin} \xrightarrow[\text{surface contacts}]{} \text{platelet factors}$$

When 10–20 per cent of the plasma prothrombin has been converted to thrombin, coagulation, involving the transformation of fibrinogen to fibrin, takes place.

II. Conversion of fibrinogen to fibrin. The proteolytic enzyme thrombin acts upon fibrinogen to form fibrin monomer, or cofibrin, and peptides A and B:

$$\text{Fibrinogen} + \text{thrombin} \longrightarrow \text{fibrin monomer} + 2 \text{ peptide A} + 2 \text{ peptide B}$$

The fibrin monomer then polymerizes to form fibrin:

$$x \text{ fibrin monomer} \longrightarrow (\text{fibrin monomer})_x$$
$$\text{fibrin polymer}$$
$$\text{or fibrin}$$

The fibrin polymer then interacts with Ca^{++} to form the more solidified physiologic fibrin of the clot:

$$\text{Fibrin} + Ca^{++} \longrightarrow Ca^{++}\text{-fibrin}$$
$$\text{physiologic fibrin}$$

The over-all coagulation process then is:

1. Prothrombin + Ca^{++} $\longrightarrow$ thrombin
        Christmas factor
        Ac-globulin
        Antihemophilic globulin
        Serum prothrombin accelerator
        Platelet factors
        (thromboplastin formed)
2. Fibrinogen + thrombin $\longrightarrow$ fibrin

After coagulation occurs, thrombin is rapidly inactivated by antithrombins:

$$\text{Thrombin} + \text{antithrombins} \longrightarrow \text{inactive thrombin}$$

The fibrin clot is slowly broken down by plasmin, as outlined in the above discussion of fibrin and fibrinogen:

$$\text{Fibrin} + \text{plasmin} \longrightarrow \text{fibrin split products}$$

MacFarlane (57) considers that the formation of active thromboplastin in plasma proceeds by a sequence of reactions as follows:

$$\text{Christmas factor} + \text{antihemophilic globulin} + Ca^{++} \longrightarrow \text{intermediate product I}$$
$$\text{Intermediate product I} + \text{platelet factor} \longrightarrow \text{intermediate product II}$$
$$\text{Intermediate product II} + \text{Ac-globulin} \longrightarrow \text{active thromboplastin}$$
$$\text{or prothrombin activator}$$

Seegers also considers that thromboplastin formation involves a sequence of reactions (56).

USES OF PLASMA PROTEINS IN MEDICINE

Serum albumin preparations (Cohn's fraction V) are used to restore blood volume in combating shock, and γ-globulins (Cohn fraction II) are used for measles prophylaxis and in other clinical conditions. Crude preparations of antihemophilic globulin have been used for hemophiliacs, but as yet such preparations are difficult to make. Prothrombin and thrombin are used topically for the control of bleeding. Such application is frequently made internally by the use of these substances on fibrin foam, which is readily absorbed and causes no undesirable reactions. Fibrin foam, film, and tubing are prepared from fibrin clots and used for various purposes. Fibrin film has been found very useful as a substitute for the dura mater in brain surgery.

HEMOGLOBIN AND RELATED SUBSTANCES

The heme proteins, to which hemoglobin belongs, constitute one of the most important classes of biologic substances. They are almost universally present in aerobic organisms, but apparently do not occur in anaerobic forms. Representatives are found in both plants and animals. Among the heme proteins are found the respiratory proteins of animals, such as the hemoglobins, myoglobins, erythrocruorins, and chlorocruorins; cellular oxidation catalysts of both animals and plants, such as the cytochromes, cytochrome oxidase, and peroxidase; and catalase, which catalyzes the decomposition of hydrogen peroxide in both plants and animals.

As a class, the heme proteins are formed by conjugation of proteins with heme, an iron-porphyrin compound, which serves as the prosthetic group.

The porphyrins represent a class of highly important substances to which both heme and the chlorophylls belong. The porphyrins are derivatives of a parent compound, porphin, of the following structure:

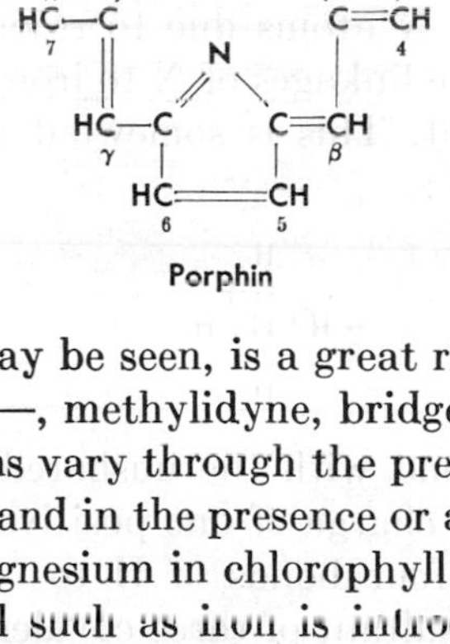

Porphin

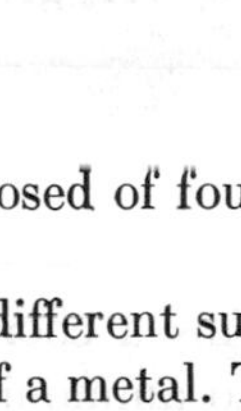

Porphin, as may be seen, is a great ring composed of four pyrrole groups linked by —CH—, methylidyne, bridges.

The porphyrins vary through the presence of different substituent groups in positions 1-8, and in the presence or absence of a metal. The metal is iron in heme and magnesium in chlorophyll.

When a metal such as iron is introduced into porphyrin, it enters the center of the great ring and forms bonds with the four nitrogen atoms, at the same time displacing two H^+ (protons) with which two of the nitrogen atoms are combined. This leaves two net negative charges distributed among the nitrogen atoms, which are balanced by positive charges of the metal. In the case of ferrous iron the compound formed possesses no net charge. However, if the iron is in the ferric state, the resulting compound has one net positive charge which holds a hydroxyl group or the anion of an acid.

Fischer and associates (58) synthesized the porphyrin of heme, protoporphyrin, and then introduced iron into it with the formation of heme. Since they introduced ferric iron, the substance produced was ferriheme or ferriprotoporphyrin. This was obtained as the chloride which is called "hemin," the formula of which is as follows:

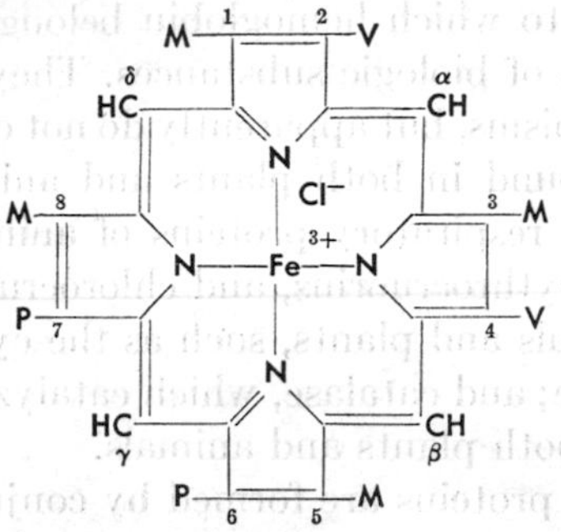

$$M = -CH_3$$
$$V = -CH{=}CH_2$$
$$P = -CH_2-CH_2-COOH$$

Hemin

Ferriheme chloride, ferriprotoporphyrin

When the iron is in the ferrous state, the compound is ferroheme or ferroprotoporphyrin, and the metal holds no additional group.

It will be noted that protoporphyrin and heme contain methyl groups in positions 1, 3, 5, and 8; vinyl groups in positions 2 and 4; and propionic acid groups in positions 6 and 7. While the iron atom displaces two protons from two —NH groups when it enters the ring, producing the equivalent of two negative charges on the two N atoms, it appears that these negative charges become distributed between all the N atoms due to resonance within the structure. Accordingly, all four of the linkages of N to iron in the porphyrin ring are considered to be equivalent. This is somewhat analogous to the addition of H^+ to NH_3 giving $NH_4{}^+$:

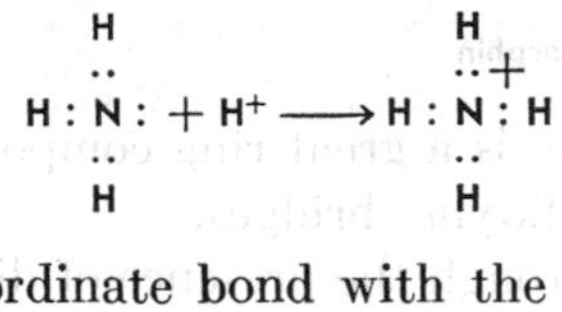

$$H:N:\ + H^+ \longrightarrow H:N:H$$

in which H^+ forms a coordinate bond with the unshared electron pair of NH_3 and gives to ammonium a net charge of one positive which is shared among all four H atoms. Here all four bonds of H to N are equivalent, despite the fact that they are the resultant of three covalent bonds and one coordinate bond.

Solutions of the heme proteins and other heme derivatives exhibit absorption spectra in the spectrophotometer which are generally characteristic for the individual substances, and frequently are of value for qualitative detection and quantitative estimation. Table 15.9 lists the chief wavelengths of light in millimicrons absorbed in the visible spectrum by hemoglobin and related substances.

By use of isotopic tracers it has been shown that duck erythrocytes synthesize heme completely from glycine and succinate, glycine supplying eight carbon atoms and nitrogen, and succinate supplying 26 carbon atoms (59). The synthesis of porphyrins and heme is given in Chapter 12.

Table 15.9

Compound	Wavelength Maxima Absorption, mμ
Acid hematin	662
Hemoglobin	565
Oxyhemoglobin	514, 544.8, 576.9, 640.2
Carboxyhemoglobin	535, 570.9
Methemoglobin	500, 540, 578, 634
Cyanmethemoglobin	414, 540
Oxymyoglobin	418, 542
Carboxymyoglobin	428, 540
Sulfhemoglobin	540, 578, 618
Verdohemoglobin	624
Oxyverdohemoglobin	590, 610
Carboxyverdohemoglobin	620
Protoporphyrin*	557.2, 582.2, 602.4
Hematoporphyrin*	508.7, 524.8, 548.7, 572.4, 593.1
Deuteroporphyrin*	549.3, 572.6, 592.4
Uroporphyrin I, III*	511.3, 526.6, 553.6, 577.6, 597.9
Coproporphyrin I, III*	550.9, 574.6, 593.9
Mesoporphyrin*	508.7, 524.8, 548.7, 572.4, 593.1

* In 25 per cent HCl.

Hemoglobins. Hemoglobins, the respiratory proteins of vertebrate erythrocytes, are formed by conjugation of basic histone proteins, globins, with ferroheme (ferroprotoporphyrin).

The hemoglobins of different species are different as shown by differences in crystal form. These differences are related to differences in the globin part of the molecule, since the heme component is the same in all hemoglobins. These chemical differences are reflected in differences in physical properties, such as solubility, affinity for oxygen, and other characteristics.

Human hemoglobin contains about 0.34 per cent iron, and, assuming one atom of iron per molecule of hemoglobin, the minimal molecular weight may be calculated to be 16,400 ($0.34 : 100 : : 55.84 : x$). Osmotic pressure and ultracentrifugal measurements indicate an actual molecular weight of 63,000 to 67,000 for human hemoglobin, a value four times that of the minimal molecular weight ($4 \times 16,400 = 65,600$). This means that four iron atoms and four heme groups are present in the hemoglobin molecule. Vickery (60), from iron and amino acid determinations, calculated the molecular weight of horse hemoglobin as about 66,700. Hemoglobin molecules in general appear to consist of four ferroheme groups combined with one globin molecule, the small differences in molecular weight being due to globin differences.

Hemoglobin is characterized by having a very large proportion of histidine residues, about 35 per molecule, which have pK values near 7, making hemoglobin an excellent protein buffer in the physiologic pH range.

Hemoglobin contains at least four sulfhydryl groups (—SH) (61). These

—SH groups appear to be important in relation to the affinity of hemoglobin for oxygen, since blocking them (with mercurials) markedly changes the oxygenation curve (62).

The hemoglobin molecule contains about 36 negatively and 36 positively charged groups which are not titratable in the native molecule but become titratable when hemoglobin is denatured by acid (63).

The heme groups appear to be attached to the globin surface at three places. Granick (64) considered that the two propionic acid groups of heme are united to two strongly basic groups of globin, and Wyman (65) presented evidence that the iron of heme is linked to a histidine imidazole nitrogen atom in globin. According to these views, the linkages of heme and globin in hemoglobin may be diagrammatically represented:

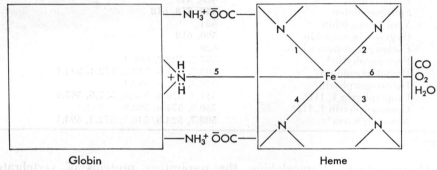

Globin   Heme

Figure 15.6A

In hemoglobin solutions in the absence of O_2 valence 6 is attached to H_2O, and the oxygenation of hemoglobin involves displacement of this H_2O by O_2:

$$HHb \cdot H_2O + O_2 \rightleftharpoons HHbO_2 + H_2O$$

The six linkages of the iron atom in hemoglobin appear to be quite analogous to the linkages in the ferrocyanide ion:

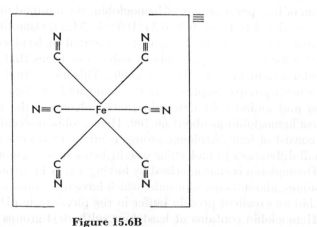

Figure 15.6B

In ferrocyanide all the bonds are equivalent on account of resonance, and the group as a whole has a net negative charge of four. In the above ferrocyanide formula four of the cyanide groups may be pictured as lying in the plane of the paper, and one as lying above and the other below this plane.

In the hemoglobin formula the four N atoms of the protoporphyrin ring may be considered to be connected to iron by linkages 1, 2, 3, and 4 in the plane of the paper, while linkage 5 to the imidazole N is below this plane, and linkage 6, which in ferrohemoglobin unites with O_2 and CO, is above this plane. In ferrohemoglobin the heme complex possesses no net charge, but in ferrihemoglobin there is a net positive charge of one, which holds a negative group such as hydroxyl. In passing from ferro- to ferrihemoglobin, the molecule loses its capacity to combine with O_2 and CO.

Granick considers that the linkage of iron to the imidazole N in hemoglobin may be responsible for maintaining the iron in the ferrous state and giving to the sixth linkage the property of reversibly combining with O_2 and CO. In this connection it is of interest to note that when heme is split from globin by the action of acids or alkalies in the presence of oxygen, the iron quickly autooxidizes to the ferric state.

Pauling and Coryell (66) showed that ferrohemoglobin is strongly paramagnetic and possesses four unpaired electrons. The oxygen molecule, O_2, contains two unpaired electrons. When O_2 adds to ferrohemoglobin to form oxyferrohemoglobin (oxyhemoglobin), the unpaired electrons of both the iron and oxygen become paired, and oxyhemoglobin is diamagnetic. The manner in which the O_2 molecule is held in oxyhemoglobin is probably related to its failure to convert the hemoglobin to the ferric state.

The best approximate model of the hemoglobin molecule appears to be a spheroidal or egg shape structure 54 Å wide, 52 Å thick, and 71 Å long. There is a relatively deep groove around the center of the molecule along the greater axis.

The globin molecule (molecular weight 66,000) of normal human hemoglobin (hemoglobin A) is made up of four polypeptide chains, two α- and two β-chains, both types having valine as the N-terminal amino acids. The N-terminal amino acid sequence of the α-chains is valine-leucine, and that of the β-chains is valine-histidine-leucine (67).

Normal human hemoglobin, or hemoglobin A, is represented by $\alpha_2^A \beta_2^A$, indicating the presence of two α- and two β-chains of the A hemoglobin type in the molecule.

Fetal hemoglobin, or hemoglobin F, usually makes up 70 to 80 per cent of the hemoglobin of a full-term infant, the rest of the hemoglobin being of the adult or A type. Fetal hemoglobin of the infant is generally entirely replaced by adult hemoglobin, A, by the end of the first year of life.

Fetal hemoglobin differs from normal adult hemoglobin in crystal form, electrophoretic mobility, IpH, solubility, resistance to alkali, absorption spectrum, chromatographic behavior, amino acid composition, N-terminal amino acids, and immunologic properties. These differences are all due to differences in the compositions of the globin molecules of normal and fetal hemoglobins, the heme groups of all types of hemoglobin being alike.

It is inferred that the four heme groups of the hemoglobins are arranged symmetrically on the four globin peptide chains, since all four hemes appear to possess the same chemical properties.

Abnormal hemoglobins. In recent years a total of ten abnormal forms of hemoglobin have been found in human blood (68), all of which are differentiated because of differences in composition and properties of the globin molecule, such as those indicated above for normal hemoglobins A and F.

While an abnormal hemoglobin was discovered in human placental blood by Körber in 1866, it was the discovery of an electrophoretically abnormal hemoglobin, hemoglobin S, in the erythrocytes of persons with sickle-cell anemia by Pauling and associates in 1949 (69) that marked the beginning of systematic searches for abnormal types of hemoglobin.

The erythrocytes of persons with sickle-cell anemia contain a mixture of normal hemoglobin (A) and sickle-cell hemoglobin (S), and the sickling process is due to deoxygenation of sickle-cell hemoglobin, which causes a reversible change in red cell shape from a biconcave disc to a sickle-shaped form. The rapidity and degree of sickling is proportional to the amount of hemoglobin S in the cells. Ordinarily sickling does not occur unless hemoglobin S represents at least 50 per cent of the total cell hemoglobin.

In addition to sickle-cell hemoglobin S, abnormal hemoglobins X, C, D, E, G, H, I, J, and M have been found in human bloods, often associated with well-recognized pathologic states. The types of hemoglobin present in the blood are determined by genetic factors and are transmitted according to Mendelian principles. Normal hemoglobin A may be present with abnormal hemoglobin (sickle-cell anemia), or only abnormal hemoglobin may be present, as in sickle-cell hemoglobin D disease, in which hemoglobins S, D, and F are present but normal A is absent.

Jones and associates (70) have studied the gross structure of hemoglobin H (71) and found it to be composed of four β-peptide chains, according to which it may be represented as $\beta_4{}^H$. This work suggests that hemoglobin H disease represents an abnormal production of β-chains only and that other abnormal hemoglobins may represent combinations of peptide chains, such as $\alpha\beta_3$, α_4, $\alpha_3\beta$, $\beta_2\gamma_2$, etc. These workers have obtained evidence that the α-chains of hemoglobins A and F are identical. This work also suggests that biologic synthesis of α- and β-chains is genetically controlled.

Figure 15.7 shows different electrophoretic rates of different hemoglobins (72).

Myoglobins. The myoglobins are intracellular tissue pigments present in both invertebrates and vertebrates, occurring in the red muscle of the vertebrates. They combine with molecular oxygen to form complexes, oxymyoglobins, which serve as oxygen reservoirs within the cells.

Theorell (73) crystallized the myoglobin of horse heart and found that it contains 0.345 per cent iron, which indicates a minimal molecular weight of about 16,000. The molecular weight of both horse heart and skeletal myoglobins has been found to be about 17,000, as determined by diffusion and osmotic measurements. The myoglobins, in distinction from the hemoglobins, possess only one iron atom and one heme group per molecule. The isoelectric pH of horse heart myoglobin is 6.78 and is the same for both the oxygenated and deoxygenated forms. The myoglobins are much more soluble than the hemoglobins. This, combined with their smaller particle size, causes them to pass through the kidney glomerular membrane more easily than the hemoglobins and accounts for their occasional appearance in the urine after severe muscle trauma.

The myoglobins of different species, just as the hemoglobins, appear to be differentiated from each other by differences in the globin component as shown by variations in amino acid contents.

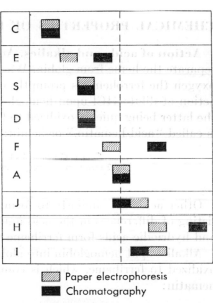

Figure 15.7. Comparison of the relative mobilities of different types of human hemoglobin in paper electrophoresis (hatched blocks) and chromatography (filled blocks). (From *Conference on Hemoglobin*, National Academy of Sciences, National Research Council, Publication 557, 1958.)

▨ Paper electrophoresis
■ Chromatography

Erythrocruorins. The erythrocruorins, containing ferroheme, serve widely as respiratory pigments among the invertebrates from protozoans up, though they are present without apparent regularity. Although they are found in the larval stages of certain insects, they do not occur in the adult forms. The erythrocruorins are characterized by rather low isoelectric pH values (4.5–6.0) as compared with the hemoglobins and myoglobins, and most of them have molecular weights of a million or more. In most cases they are present in simple solution in the blood. Little is known about the proportions of heme present in these pigments and of their other chemical properties.

Chlorocruorins. Like the erythrocruorins, the chlorocruorins are invertebrate respiratory pigments. They occur in various marine worms, in simple solution and not in blood cells. Their molecular weights are of the order of several million, and the molecules contain many iron atoms and heme groups. Spirographis chlorocruorin, the most completely studied of the group, has a molecular weight of about three million, contains 1.2 per cent iron and appears to contain about 190 ferroheme groups per molecule.

Hemochromogens. Heme combines reversibly with a large variety of organic nitrogenous substances, such as amines, cyanides, pyridine, nicotine, and proteins, to form hemochromogens. Accordingly, the hemoglobins and related substances represent a class of hemochromogens. Ferroheme forms complexes with cyanide and pyridine of the following types:

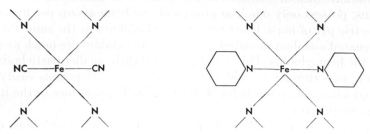

in which two cyanide and two pyridine groups are attached to the iron. Amines other than pyridine probably are attached to heme in a similar manner.

CHEMICAL PROPERTIES OF HEMOGLOBINS

Action of acids and alkalies. Acids and alkalies act upon hemoglobin to separate the heme from globin. When the reactions occur in the presence of oxygen the ferroheme is promptly oxidized to ferriheme. For example, the action of dilute HCl upon hemoglobin splits it into globin and ferroheme, the latter being quickly oxidized to ferriheme which holds a chlorine ion and is called "acid hematin," or hemin:

$$\text{hemoglobin} + \text{HCl} \longrightarrow \text{globin} + \text{ferroheme}$$
$$2 \text{ ferroheme} + \tfrac{1}{2}\text{O}_2 + 2\text{HCl} \longrightarrow 2 \text{ ferriheme chloride}$$
$$\text{Hemin}$$

Other acids act similarly to form acid hematin, the only variations consisting of differences in the acid anion held by the ferriheme. Thus sulfuric and hydriodic acids form ferriheme sulfate and iodide, respectively.

Alkalies split hemoglobin into globin and ferroheme, the latter then being oxidized to ferriheme, which is combined with hydroxyl ion to give alkali hematin:

$$\text{hemoglobin} + \text{alkali} \longrightarrow \text{globin} + \text{ferroheme}$$
$$2 \text{ ferroheme} + \tfrac{1}{2}\text{O}_2 + \text{HOH} \longrightarrow 2 \text{ ferriheme hydroxide}$$
$$\text{Alkali hematin}$$

If this reaction is carried out in the presence of a strong reducing agent, such as sodium hydrosulfite, $Na_2S_2O_4$, the ferroheme is retained in the ferrous state. Globin may be coupled with heme to form hemoglobin (ferrohemoglobin) by carrying out the reaction at the proper pH and in the presence of hydrosulfite to keep the heme in the reduced state. Ferriheme also may be combined with globin to form methemoglobin (ferrihemoglobin).

Methemoglobin is directly split by acids and alkalies into globin and acid and alkali hematin, respectively. In this case the heme already is in the ferriheme state.

Oxyhemoglobin. The primary function of hemoglobin in blood is to transport O_2 from the lungs, where the oxygen pressure is high, to the tissues, for utilization where the oxygen pressure is low. As previously indicated, this is accomplished through the formation of a dissociable hemoglobin-oxygen complex, oxyhemoglobin (ferrooxyhemoglobin):

$$\text{hemoglobin} + O_2 \rightleftarrows \text{oxyhemoglobin}$$

According to the mass law, the reaction is shifted to the right by an increase in oxygen pressure (lungs) and to the left by a decrease in oxygen pressure (tissues). The hemoglobin in blood is 95 to 96 per cent converted to oxyhemoglobin at an oxygen tension of 100 mm (pressure in lung alveoli), and the hemoglobin is said to be 95 to 96 per cent saturated with oxygen. Below this pressure the degree of saturation varies with the oxygen tension.

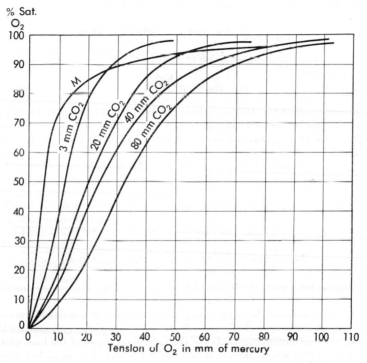

Figure 15.8. Plot of per cent of saturation against tension of O_2 in millimeters of mercury. (From Bock, A. V.: *J. Biol. Chem.*, 59, **366**, 383, 1924.)

Thus it is possible to plot curves showing the per cent oxygen saturation of hemoglobin at various oxygen tensions. Such curves may be considered either as saturation or dissociation curves of hemoglobin. These curves simply show the points of equilibrium in the above equation at different oxygen pressures. Thus, if the per cent saturation of hemoglobin is 90 at 60 mm O_2 tension, this means in terms of the equation that 90 per cent of the total hemoglobin is oxyhemoglobin and 10 per cent is unchanged.

Figure 15.8 shows oxygen saturation curves (or dissociation curves) of hemoglobin in blood drawn from data of Bock and associates (74). The four curves represent the oxygenation of hemoglobin at different O_2 tensions when the CO_2 tension is at 3, 20, 40, and 80 mm respectively and the temperature is 37.5° C. The curve for 40 mm CO_2 tension is the curve for hemoglobin in normal blood. M is the oxygenation curve of myoglobin.

The oxygenation curves of hemoglobin in blood are generally different from the rectangular hyperbolic curves expected as a result of mass action, and are approximately sigmoid in shape. They are represented by the equation:

$$\frac{[HBO_2]}{[Hb]} = K(pO_2)^n$$

where K is a constant and the value of n determines the degree to which the hyperbolic curve (when $n = 1$) approaches a true sigmoid shape. If $[HBO_2]$ is represented by per cent oxygen saturation of the total hemoglobin, y, then $[Hb]$ as per cent of total hemoglobin is $100 - y$. If O_2 tension (pO_2) is represented by x, we have:

$$\frac{y}{100 - y} = Kx^n \text{ and } y = 100Kx^n - yKx^n$$

then
$$y + yKx^n = 100Kx^n$$

and
$$\frac{y}{100} = \frac{Kx^n}{1 + Kx^n}$$

which is generally called the Hill equation. For the sigmoid curve at 40 mm pCO_2 of blood (normal blood curve) shown in Figure 15.8, $n = 2.5$. If all four hemes of hemoglobin reacted with O_2 in the same way, the curve should be hyperbolic and n would equal 1. The fact that n is larger than 1 indicates that, whereas each heme group before oxygenation may have the same affinity for O_2, as soon as one heme happens to combine with O_2, the affinities of the other heme groups toward O_2 change and the oxygenation of hemoglobin proceeds in stages, with the affinity for O_2 changing as oxygenation proceeds. This phenomenon is referred to as "interaction of heme groups." Roughton and associates (75) demonstrated by measurement of the rates of oxygenation and deoxygenation of hemoglobin that the processes do take place in stages, which may be represented by:

$$Hb_4 \underset{-O_2}{\overset{+O_2}{\rightleftarrows}} Hb_4O_2 \underset{-O_2}{\overset{+O_2}{\rightleftarrows}} Hb_4O_4 \underset{-O_2}{\overset{+O_2}{\rightleftarrows}} Hb_4O_6 \underset{-O_2}{\overset{+O_2}{\rightleftarrows}} Hb_4O_8$$

In these formulas Hb represents an equivalent of hemoglobin containing one iron atom (16,400 g).

The complex relations of the oxygenation-deoxygenation of hemoglobin according to the above stages have been worked out by Pauling and associates (76) and are shown in Figure 15.9. The equilibrium constants for the individual stages of the hemoglobin reaction with O_2 show that deoxygenation is favored in the first three steps but oxygenation is favored in the last stage. This means that loading the iron atoms of three heme groups with O_2 increases the affinity of the iron atom of the fourth heme group for O_2.

The ratios of the four equilibrium constants K_1, K_2, K_3, and K_4 in the step oxygenation of sheep hemoglobin were found by Roughton and associates (80) to be $1:1.76:1.31:17.7$, indicating the variability in the affinity of the four heme iron atoms for O_2. According to these ratios, the first iron atom oxygenated has the least and the fourth iron atom oxygenated has the most affinity for O_2.

The rate of combination of O_2 with hemoglobin is exceedingly rapid (77). At an O_2 pressure of 75 mm the hemoglobin in the intact red cell (sheep) is 50 per cent converted to oxyhemoglobin in 0.05 second (half-time).

It is of interest that the myoglobins of muscle and the hemoglobin of the lamprey eel both of which contain only one heme group per molecule, give oxygenation curves which are rectangular hyperbolas as expected from the mass law (Figure 15.8). The myoglobins have more affinity for O_2 than do the hemoglobins, which facilitates their function of serving as O_2 reservoirs in cells. It is also interesting that when human hemoglobin solutions are highly diluted, the oygxenation curves also become rectangular hyperbolas due to dissociation into four apparently equivalent molecules (molecular weight about 17,000), each containing one heme group. In the red cell and in concentrated solutions the hemoglobin molecule thus shows entirely different oxygenation curves because it is a polymer and contains four heme groups.

From the curves it can be seen that for a given oxygen tension the per cent saturation of hemoglobin with oxygen decreases with increase in the CO_2 tension and vice versa. Barcroft (78) showed the effect of the CO_2 to be due to its acidity, and since similar effects could be produced with other acids, this indicates that the CO_2 effect is a pH effect. The curve at 40 mm CO_2 tension represents the oxygenation of hemoglobin at normal plasma pH (7.44), that at 80 mm CO_2 the oxygenation at a plasma pH of 7.24, that at 20 mm CO_2 the oxygenation at a plasma pH of 7.64. The pH values within the red cells containing the hemoglobin are a bit lower (possibly 0.1–0.2 pH) than in the plasma but proportional to the plasma pH values. The isoelectric pH of hemoglobin is commonly taken to be about

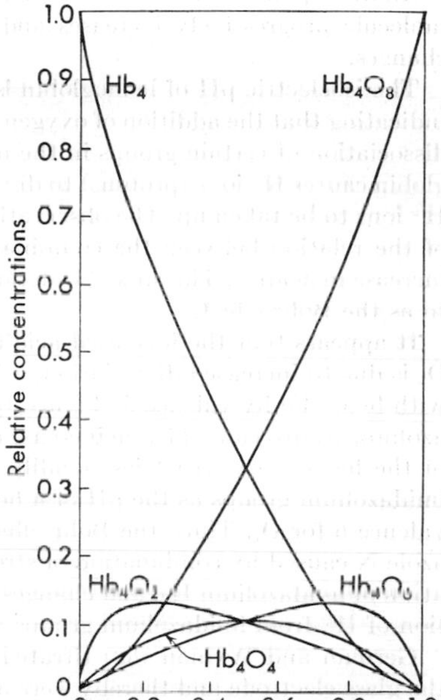

Figure 15.9. Curves representing stages in the oxygenation of hemoglobin. (From Coryell, C. D.; Pauling, L.; and Dodson, R. W.: *J. Phys. Chem.*, **43**, 829, 1939.)

6.8 and of oxyhemoglobin about 6.6. At pH values within the normal blood range both hemoglobin and oxyhemoglobin act as weak acids and exist partly as anions and partly as undissociated molecules (less dissociated). As the pH is increased by decreasing CO_2 tension or other means, the H^+ ion concentration decreases and hemoglobin molecules dissociate H^+:

$$\text{hemoglobin} \rightleftharpoons H^+ + \text{hemoglobin}$$

As the pH is decreased by increasing CO_2 tension or other means, the H^+ ion concentration increases, and H^+ ions are combined with the hemoglobin anions to form undissociated hemoglobin molecules. Accordingly, we can conclude that hemoglobin anions have more affinity for O_2 than do undissociated hemoglobin molecules. Thus an increase in pH increases hemoglobin anions and affinity for O_2, whereas a decrease in pH has the reverse effect.

As to be expected, the oxygenation of hemoglobin at a given O_2 tension decreases with an increase in temperature, and vice versa. In other words, a rise in temperature facilitates the dissociation of oxyhemoglobin. The combination of hemoglobin with oxygen is also affected by the presence of electrolytes. At lower oxygen tensions hemoglobin holds less oxygen in the presence of electrolytes than in pure solution, whereas at higher oxygen tensions it holds more oxygen in the presence of electrolytes.

As pointed out above, the hemoglobin molecule contains four atoms of iron and four heme groups. The iron atom of each heme can hold one O_2 molecule. Bernhart and Skeggs (79) have estimated that each gram of human hemoglobin can hold 1.36 ml of oxygen as a maximum. If we take the molecular weight of hemoglobin as 65,600, then a formula weight should bind $65,600 \times 1.36 = 89,216$ ml of O_2. If each iron atom of hemoglobin binds a gram molecule of O_2 (22,400 ml), then the volume of O_2 bound by a formula weight of hemoglobin should be $4 \times 22,400 = 89,600$ ml, which is in good agreement with the above calculation of 89,216 ml. Also, the molal ratio of $Fe:O_2 = 1:1$, and this corresponds to grams $Fe:$ milliliters $O_2 = 55.84:22,400$, which means that 55.84 g of hemoglobin iron combines with 22,400 ml of O_2. This represents a combining capacity of 401 ml of O_2 per gram of hemoglobin iron (22,400/55.84).

Another point of interest is that as oxygen is added, the acidity of the hemoglobin molecule progressively increases and that as the pH changes, the affinity for oxygen changes.

The isoelectric pH of hemoglobin is at about 6.8 and that of oxyhemoglobin is at 6.6, indicating that the addition of oxygen to the iron atoms of hemoglobin increases the acidic dissociation of certain groups in the molecule. In other words, the oxygenation of hemoglobin causes H^+ ions (protons) to dissociate, and deoxygenation of oxyhemoglobin causes H^+ ions to be taken up. The observations of Bohr and associates (81) led to the discovery of the relation between the combination of hemoglobin with oxygen and the resulting increase in acidity. This linked function of oxygenation and acidity accordingly is referred to as the Bohr effect.

It appears that the increased acidity when the Fe atom of hemoglobin combines with O_2 is due to increased dissociation of H^+ from the imidazolium group of globin combined with heme Fe by valence 5 (Figure 15.6A). A decrease in H^+ dissociation from the imidazolium groups caused by an increase in the $[H^+]$ of a hemoglobin solution causes valence 6 of the heme Fe to react less readily with O_2, while increased H^+ dissociation from the imidazolium groups as the pH of a hemoglobin solution is raised increases the affinity of valence 6 for O_2. Thus, the Bohr effect results from electron shifts around Fe and imidazole N caused by combination of strongly electronegative O_2 with Fe (increased dissociation of imidazolium H), and changes in affinity of valence 6 for O_2 as a result of dissociation of H^+ from imidazolium groups as the pH is changed.

German and Wyman (82) titrated hemoglobin and oxyhemoglobin with alkali using the glass electrode and thereby were able to calculate the pK values of the oxygen linked acidic group of hemoglobin, which operates in the physiologic pH range, before and after oxygenation. The pK value of this group in hemoglobin was found to be 7.93, and that in oxyhemoglobin, 6.68. In other words, the addition of oxygen to the heme iron changes the pK of an acid group from 7.93 to 6.68, which represents a large increase in acidity.

An equivalent of oxyhemoglobin (16,400 g, equivalent to 1 heme) at physiologic pH dissociates 0.7 equivalent more H^+ ions than does hemoglobin. At the tissues when oxyhemoglobin anions (HbO_2^-) lose O_2 and become hemoglobin anions (Hb^-), the latter combine with 0.7 equivalent of H^+ ions from H_2CO_3 to form bicarbonate ions, $H\bar{C}O_3$:

$$HbO_2^- \rightleftharpoons Hb^- + O_2$$

$$Hb^- + \overset{+}{H} \cdot H\bar{C}O_3 \rightleftharpoons HHb + HCO_3^-$$

At the lungs oxygenation of hemoglobin to oxyhemoglobin increases the acidic dissociation, so that one equivalent of oxyhemoglobin yields 0.7 equivalent of H^+ ions, which combine with $H\bar{C}O_3$ ions to form H_2CO_3 and liberate CO_2, which is exhaled:

$$HHbO_2 \rightleftharpoons Hb\bar{O}_2 + H^+$$
$$H^+ + H\bar{C}O_3 \rightleftharpoons H_2CO_3 \rightleftharpoons H_2O + CO_2$$

Thus we see that the difference in acidity of hemoglobin and oxyhemoglobin provides a mechanism for the transport of 0.7 equivalent of CO_2 as $H\bar{C}O_3$ ions per equivalent of hemoglobin without change in pH. Much of the CO_2 is transported from tissues to lungs by this mechanism.

Wyman (83) presented evidence to show that the increase in acidity of hemoglobin upon oxygenation is due to increased dissociation of H^+ ions from the histidine imidazole groups of hemoglobin. It is logical to assume that these imidazole groups are the ones attached by a nitrogen linkage to the heme iron atoms.

Carbon monoxide hemoglobin or carboxyhemoglobin. The poisonous action of carbon monoxide is due chiefly to combination with hemoglobin and myoglobin to form carboxyhemoglobin and carboxymyoglobin and thereby to interfere with the oxygenation of these substances. Carbon monoxide also combines with ferrous cytochrome oxidase, one of the respiratory enzymes of tissues, and prevents its action, particularly at higher concentrations of the gas.

Carbon monoxide adds on to the heme iron atoms exactly as does oxygen but with much more affinity. The over-all reactions of O_2 and CO with hemoglobin (Hb):

$$O_2 + Hb \rightleftharpoons HbO_2$$
$$CO + Hb \rightleftharpoons HbCO$$

take place when hemoglobin is exposed to either gas. When hemoglobin is exposed to a mixture of the gases, there is competition for the hemoglobin according to the equation:

$$HbO_2 + CO \rightleftharpoons HbCO + O_2$$

It is interesting to note that light promotes the dissociation of carboxyhemoglobin, which necessitates equilibrating blood or hemoglobin solutions with CO in the dark when studying reaction of the gas with hemoglobin.

It has been shown that the relative proportions of hemoglobin combining with O_2 and CO when hemoglobin solutions are saturated with a mixture of the two gases are proportional to the partial pressures of the gases in the mixture. This relationship is arrived at as follows:

$$\frac{[HbCO][O_2]}{[HbO_2][CO]} = K \quad \text{or} \quad \frac{[HbCO]pO_2}{[HbO_2]pCO} = K \quad \text{or} \quad \frac{[HbCO]}{[HbO_2]} = \frac{KpCO}{pO_2}$$

in which pCO and pO_2 represent the partial pressures of CO and O_2, and K is the affinity constant of the reaction. The value of K for human blood at 38° C is about 210, which means that under these conditions the affinity of human hemoglobin for CO is 210 times greater than its affinity for O_2. From the above equation the following expressions for the fractions of hemoglobin converted to HbCO and HbO_2 by a mixture of the gases may be derived:

$$\frac{[HbCO]}{[HbCO] + [HbO_2]} = \frac{KpCO}{pO_2 + KpCO}$$

and

$$\frac{[HbO_2]}{[HbCO] + [HbO_2]} = \frac{pO_2}{pO_2 + KpCO}$$

These equations hold only when all the hemoglobin is converted to carboxy- and oxyhemoglobin.

Table 15.10

| CO Per Cent | Per Cent HbCO | |
	Air 760 mm	Oxygen 760 mm
0.04	52	13
0.08	68	22
0.12	77	30
0.16	81	36
0.20	84	42
0.24	86	46
0.28	88	50

Table 15.10 gives the approximate percentages of carboxyhemoglobin formed in human blood when it is equilibrated in the dark with air plus CO and with oxygen plus CO at 760 mm and 38° C. The figures of the table show that when very small amounts of CO are present in air, a relatively large proportion of the hemoglobin is converted to carboxyhemoglobin. This explains the exceedingly poisonous action of the gas when such mixtures are breathed. The figures also show that if a person poisoned by breathing air containing CO is given pure oxygen, the conversion of carboxyhemoglobin to oxyhemoglobin will be promoted. In such a case the high oxygen concentration in the blood tends to displace CO from carboxyhemoglobin by mass action, and the CO is irreversibly exhaled by the lungs:

$$HbCO + O_2 \longrightarrow HbO_2 + CO$$

High concentration   Exhaled by lungs

Haldane (84) pointed out that the anoxic symptoms caused by CO poisoning greatly surpass in severity those of anemia when the blood oxygen content is the same in the two conditions. In such cases of CO poisoning some of the iron atoms of the hemoglobin molecule hold CO and some hold O_2 molecules. At the low oxygen tensions present in the tissues and capillaries these mixed molecules give up their oxygen much less readily than do hemoglobin molecules holding the same quantity of oxygen alone. Consequently, the presence of CO with oxygen in the hemoglobin molecule may cause severe tissue hypoxia, whereas the same oxygen content in the absence of CO may prove adequate. Carbon monoxide thus exerts a double action. It prevents the uptake of normal quantities of oxygen in the lungs and interferes with the unloading of oxygen in the tissues.

Carboxyhemoglobin is strikingly distinguished from hemoglobin and oxyhemoglobin by its cherry red color. The skin and tissues of victims of CO poisoning are tinged with this color. The absorption spectrum of carboxyhemoglobin shows bands with centers at 570 and 535 mμ, respectively, which are close to the bands of oxyhemoglobin. Various chemical tests for carboxyhemoglobin in blood have been devised. A simple test is to treat the suspected blood with a little NaOH, dilute it greatly, and then compare it with normal blood similarly treated. The normal blood shows a greenish hue, while the CO blood remains pink. Simple dilution without adding alkali also shows the CO blood to be pink, as compared with the more brownish red of normal blood.

Methemoglobin or ferrihemoglobin. The oxidation of the ferrous iron of hemoglobin to the ferric state results in the formation of methemoglobin or ferrihemoglobin. Methemoglobin is dark brown in color, in contrast to the purple of hemoglobin, the dark red of oxyhemoglobin, and the cherry red of carboxyhemoglobin. It is readily reduced back to hemoglobin by strong reducing agents, such as hydrosulfite.

The iron of methemoglobin carries an extra positive charge and holds a hydroxyl or other negative group. Since the hemoglobin molecule contains four heme groups with their ferrous iron atoms, the oxidation of hemoglobin to methemoglobin proceeds in stages, so that intermediate molecules containing both ferrous and ferric iron atoms must be formed in the oxidation process:

$$Hb_4(Fe^{++})_3(Fe^{+++}-OH), \; Hb_4(Fe^{++})_2(Fe^{+++}-OH)_2, \; etc.$$

Conversion of ferrous to ferric iron in hemoglobin destroys its capacity to combine with O_2 and CO, and methemoglobin consequently is useless in the transport of O_2. It appears that the intermediate compounds of hemoglobin oxidation, in which some ferrous iron is present, combine with O_2 and in proportion serve to transport it.

Various oxidizing agents convert hemoglobin to methemoglobin, ferricyanide and nitrite being most commonly employed in the laboratory. Molecular O_2 rather slowly converts hemoglobin of blood to methemoglobin upon standing.

Neill and Hastings (85) showed that fully oxygenated hemoglobin is resistant to oxidation, and that conversion of hemoglobin to methemoglobin proceeds through oxidation of the deoxygenated form. The oxidation of hemoglobin to methemoglobin in blood or in hemoglobin solutions may be represented as follows, where Hb indicates the amount of hemoglobin corresponding to one iron atom:

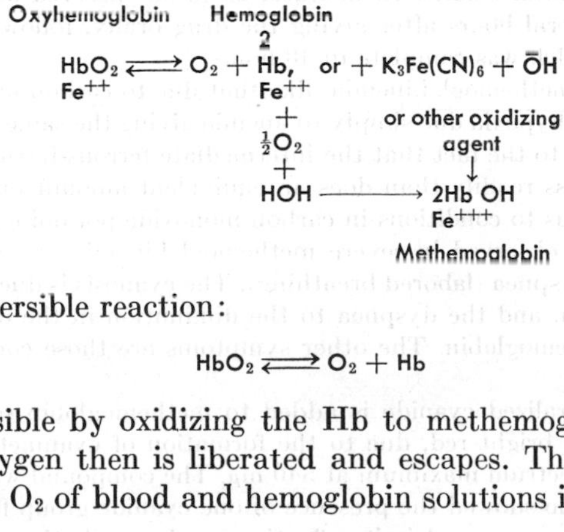

$$\begin{array}{ccc}
Oxyhemoglobin & Hemoglobin & \\
& 2 & \\
HbO_2 \rightleftharpoons & O_2 + Hb, & \text{or} + K_3Fe(CN)_6 + \bar{O}H \\
Fe^{++} & Fe^{++} & \\
& + & \text{or other oxidizing} \\
& \tfrac{1}{2}O_2 & \text{agent} \\
& + & \downarrow \\
& HOH \longrightarrow & 2Hb \; OH \\
& & Fe^{+++} \\
& & Methemoglobin
\end{array}$$

When the reversible reaction:

$$HbO_2 \rightleftharpoons O_2 + Hb$$

is made irreversible by oxidizing the Hb to methemoglobin which cannot hold O_2, the oxygen then is liberated and escapes. This fact is utilized in determining the O_2 of blood and hemoglobin solutions in the gas apparatus of Van Slyke.

Normally, the conversion of hemoglobin to methemoglobin takes place in the circulating blood, but the reducing systems present in red cells tend to prevent the accumulation of any appreciable quantity of methemoglobin. The amount present in human blood has been estimated to range from 1.1 to 2.4 per cent of the total hemoglobin, with an average value of 1.7. It is interesting to note that glutathione, which is present in high concentration in the erythrocytes, reduces methemoglobin to hemoglobin, which may represent an important function of the compound. Cox and Wendel (86) found that high concentrations of methemoglobin in dog erythrocytes are reduced at a rate of about 10 to 12 per cent per hour, which decreases with decreasing methemoglobin concentrations.

Many different chemical agents have been found to convert hemoglobin to methemoglobin. These include oxidizing agents, such as chlorates, nitrites (both inorganic and organic), ferricyanides, quinones, peroxides, and various oxidizing dyes; reducing agents, such as hydroquinone, pyrogallol, hydroxylamine, and hydrazobenzene; and compounds which are neither pronounced oxidizing nor reducing agents, such as aminophenol, azoxybenzene, nitrobenzene, aniline, acetanilide, and the sulfonamide drugs. It appears that agents which are not capable directly of oxidizing hemoglobin to methemoglobin are first converted in the blood to such agents or to substances which catalyze the oxidation of hemoglobin to methemoglobin. Thus it seems that the action of aromatic amino and nitro compounds may be the result of their conversion to aminophenols and then into corresponding quinones which are oxidizing agents. Another mechanism by which some of these agents may promote methemoglobin accumulation in blood is by inhibition of the systems which reduce the methemoglobin normally formed in blood.

Although most of the agents listed above presumably may cause methemoglobinemia in circulating blood, this is not true in all cases. For example, ferricyanide does not penetrate the red cell and consequently may be absorbed and excreted without forming methemoglobin. Nitrite, on the other hand, rapidly penetrates the erythrocytes and produces methemoglobinemia.

Clinically, methemoglobinemia is most often observed in factory workers who have absorbed through the skin or lungs aromatic nitro and amino compounds, such as nitrobenzene, nitrophenols, and aniline, and in patients taking large amounts of drugs such as acetanilide and sulfonamides. Dennig (87), from experiments on dogs poisoned with acetanilide, concluded that the conversion of about two-thirds of the hemoglobin to methemoglobin causes fatal results. In nonfatal cases he observed an increase in blood methemoglobin for several hours after giving the drug orally, followed by reversion to normal hemoglobin, which was complete in 48 hours.

The hypoxia due to methemoglobinemia, like that due to carbon monoxide poisoning, is more severe than the hypoxia due simply to anemia giving the same total blood oxygen content. This is related to the fact that the intermediate ferrous-ferrihemoglobin oxygen complexes release O_2 less readily than does an equivalent amount of oxyhemoglobin, a situation quite analogous to conditions in carbon monoxide poisoning.

The chief symptoms observed in severe methemoglobinemia are cyanosis (blue skin and membranes) and dyspnea (labored breathing). The cyanosis is due to the dark brown color of methemoglobin, and the dyspnea to the diminution in the oxygen transported to the tissues by the hemoglobin. The other symptoms are those commonly associated with tissue anoxia.

When carefully neutralized cyanide is added to methemoglobin solutions, the color changes from brown to bright red, due to the formation of cyanmethemoglobin which shows an absorption spectrum maximum at 540 mμ. The compound was first crystallized by von Zeynek (88), who showed the presence of one cyanide group for each iron atom. The importance of this compound is its effectiveness in combating cyanide poisoning. Cyanide poisons primarily by combining with the cytochrome oxidase enzyme of tissues, thereby blocking intracellular oxidations. The conversion of a part of the hemoglobin of blood to methemoglobin permits the latter to withdraw the cyanide from tissue cytochrome oxidase, which then allows cellular oxidations to proceed. The cyanide is then detoxified by conversion to thiocyanate. Sodium nitrite is generally given intravenously in order to provide the requisite methemoglobin.

Methemoglobin also forms complexes with many other substances. These include nitric oxide, azide, hydrogen sulfide, hydrogen peroxide, cyanate, thiocyanate, and fluoride.

Sulfhemoglobin. Hoppe-Seyler (89) observed the production of a greenish hemoglobin derivative in the reaction of hydrogen sulfide on oxyhemoglobin which has been shown to be sulfhemoglobin. This substance appears to be formed from hemoglobin only in the presence of oxygen, indicating that oxyhemoglobin reacts with H_2S. Sulfhemoglobin contains one more sulfur atom than does hemoglobin. Lemberg (90) has suggested that the most probable mechanism of reaction between oxyhemoglobin and H_2S is as follows:

$$Hb(XH_2)O_2 + H_2S \longrightarrow Hb(X)S + 2H_2O$$

Oxyhemoglobin   Sulfhemoglobin
X = group attached
to 2H, probably in
globin molecule

The exact linkage of the sulfur atom in the molecule is uncertain.

Complete conversion of hemoglobin to sulfhemoglobin has never been accomplished. *In vitro* preparations are generally mixed with a green pigment, choleglobin.

Sulfhemoglobin does not combine reversibly with O_2 but may be oxidized to sulfmethemoglobin. However, it does combine with carbon monoxide to form carboxysulfhemoglobin.

The presence of sulfhemoglobin in blood has been reported in a number of conditions. These include therapy with sulfonamides and aromatic amine drugs such as phenacetin and acetanilide, dosage with sulfur, severe constipation, and cases of severe bacteremia due to *Clostridium welchii*. The H_2S for sulfhemoglobin production arises in the intestine from bacterial action upon sulfur compounds. Normally, it is rapidly oxidized to sulfate after absorption into the body, but when produced in excessive quantities and when certain catalytic agents are present, it may lead to the formation of sulfhemoglobin. However, blood seldom contains more than 10 per cent sulfhemoglobin. It is of interest to note that sulfhemoglobin, unlike methemoglobin, is not converted back to functional hemoglobin in blood but persists in the corpuscles throughout their life span of several months.

The detection and determination of hemoglobin and related substances. Hemoglobin and most of its derivatives may be identified by their characteristic absorption bands observed with a spectroscope or a spectrophotometer.

The hemoglobins of different species are differentiated by variations in the globin component, and the oxyhemoglobin of each species crystallizes in a characteristic form. All hemoglobins give the same hemin (acid hematin) crystals when treated with acids, since heme is common to all of them.

Color tests based upon reaction of guaiac, o-tolidine, and benzidine with acid hematin in the presence of hydrogen peroxide afford sensitive tests for the presence of small amounts of hemoglobin or blood. Such tests are of importance in the clinical and medicolegal detection of blood.

The quantitative determinations of hemoglobin, carboxyhemoglobin, and methemoglobin in blood are most accurately accomplished by the gasometric methods of Van Slyke and associates (91).

Clinical estimations of blood hemoglobin most commonly are carried out by colorimetric or spectrophotometric examination of solutions containing acid or alkali hematin, or alkali hemoglobin, or carboxyhemoglobin. Since practically all the blood iron is present in the hemoglobin, its determination (colorimetric or spectrophotometric) may also be used for the estimation of blood hemoglobin. When appreciable quantities of methemoglobin or carboxyhemoglobin are present in blood, the oxygen capacity as measured by the gasometric method is the only procedure which gives values for functional hemoglobin. The gasometric method generally serves as a standard against which other procedures are checked.

Verdohemoglobin or green hemoglobin. Verdohemoglobin appears to be the substance formed in the first stage of the conversion of hemoglobin to bile pigments. According to Watson (92), verdohemoglobin is formed by removing the α-methylidyne bridge

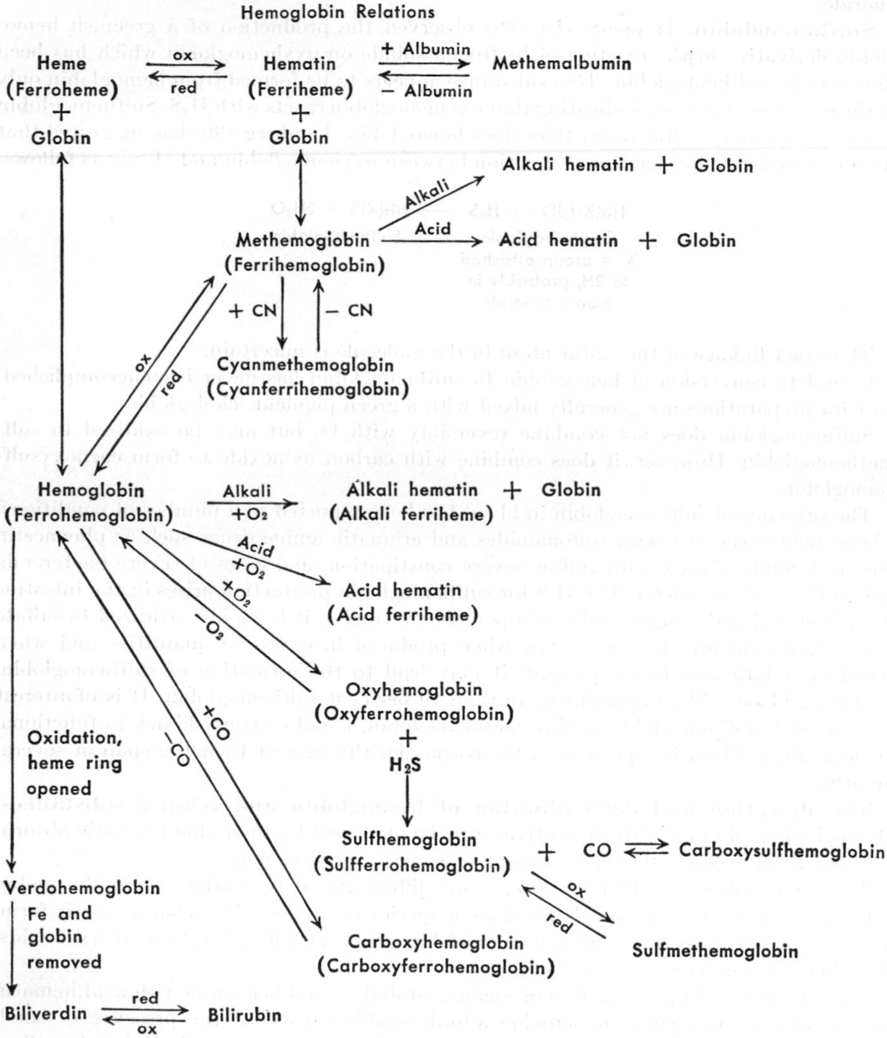

Figure 15.10

and opening the heme ring of hemoglobin, with the iron remaining attached. The exact structure of the resulting iron-containing group is unknown. Barkan and Walker (93) state that the iron of verdohemoglobin is more easily split off than is the iron of hemoglobin. These workers found the blood pigment of normal persons to contain about 5 per cent of this type of easily split-off iron. Havemann (94), by the use of a direct method, estimated that as much as 8 per cent of the total hemoglobin of normal persons is in the form of verdohemoglobin.

The details of the conversion of the heme of hemoglobin to bile pigments have been considered in the discussion of bile pigments in Chapter 12.

Methemalbumin. Methemalbumin is formed through the combination of free hematin (ferriheme) with albumin. When hematin is present in the circulating blood, it is always in combination with albumin as methemalbumin. Normally, methemalbumin is present in blood only at birth, when it appears to be present in umbilical cord blood.

Relations of blood pigments. The diagram, Figure 15.10, shows the chemical relations of hemoglobin and many of its derivatives.

CEREBROSPINAL FLUID

The cerebrospinal fluid is formed by the choroid plexus and appears first in the lateral ventricles. From the latter it passes to the third and fourth ventricles and finally to the subarachnoid space. The amount of cerebrospinal fluid present in the ventriculosubarachnoid space of adults as determined by the amount which can be removed by lumbar puncture is 100 to 150 ml. The quantity in the newborn varies from a few drops to 5 ml, and then increases with age to the adult value. The cerebrospinal fluid is renewed several times per day.

Cerebrospinal fluid is differentiated in composition from plasma to a much greater degree than is lymph. It is a clear, colorless fluid of low viscosity and, unlike lymph and plasma, does not coagulate. The protein content is exceedingly low and ranges from 15 to 55 mg per 100 ml. About 80 per cent of the protein is albumin and 20 per cent globulin. The amount of protein varies with the region from which the fluid is drawn. Ventricle fluid contains less protein than fluid from the cisterna magna, and the latter contains less than lumbar fluid. Fibrinogen is absent. The glucose content of cerebrospinal fluid uniformly is less than that of plasma, though it varies in proportion to the plasma level. At a plasma glucose level of 75 to 100 the fluid level is 47 to 78, while at a plasma level of 150 to 200 the fluid level is 73 to 112. The amount of Ca^{++} present in the fluid is only about half that found in serum (4.1 to 5.9 mg per 100 ml), while the Na^+ is considerably higher and the K^+ a little lower than in serum. The chlorides of cerebrospinal fluid are considerably higher than in plasma, while the P is much lower. The bicarbonate content of the fluid is about the same as for plasma and is equivalent to 40 to 60 volumes per cent CO_2. The pH values of the fluid and plasma are about the same.

Cerebrospinal fluid contains 0 to 5 cells per cubic millimeter, and in a high percentage of cases no cells are present.

Because of the ease of obtaining cerebrospinal fluid and the clinical interest associated with it, much information relative to its properties and composition has been obtained.

SYNOVIAL FLUID

Synovial fluid is a clear, light yellow, viscous fluid which serves to lubricate the articular surfaces of joints. Fluid from the knee joint of man contains an average of 3.4 per cent solids, of which about 2.8 per cent is protein made up of about two-thirds albumin and one-third globulin. Close to 1 per cent mucin and a highly variable quantity of hyaluronic acid (4–295 mg per 100 g) are present, these substances contributing largely to the lubricating qualities of the fluid. It contains a number of enzymes, such as hyaluronidase (spreading factor), amylase, protease, and lipase. The electrolyte and diffusible nonelectrolyte (glucose, urea, uric acid, etc.) content of synovial fluid indicates that it is essentially a dialysate of plasma to which various substances have been added by joint tissues.

AQUEOUS AND VITREOUS HUMORS

The anterior chamber of the eye is filled with a clear, limpid fluid, the aqueous humor, which maintains the necessary intraocular pressure and provides nutrients to the lens and cornea, which have no blood supply. The aqueous humor contains about 25 mg per cent protein and diffusible substances rather similar to those of a blood transudate. The aqueous humor originates by flow of fluid from the posterior into the anterior chamber, secretion by the ciliary body, and diffusion from blood vessels of the iris. Aqueous humor passes from the anterior chamber through the canal of Schlemm, which means that the fluid is constantly being renewed. In fact, it has been shown that the water exchange in the aqueous is at the fantastic rate of about 20 per cent of the aqueous volume per minute. The rate of electrolyte turnover in the aqueous is much slower, being only about 1 per cent per minute; it involves largely sodium, which is secreted into the aqueous by the ciliary body against a concentration gradient, and represents a case of active transport or a "sodium pump," requiring metabolic energy.

Increased secretion of aqueous may raise the intraocular pressure sufficiently to cause the disease known as glaucoma. Since administration of the drug acetazolamide (Diamox) (2-acetylamino-1,3,4-thiadiazole-5-sulfonamide), which is an inhibitor of carbonic anhydrase, often reduces the elevated pressure, it appears that carbonic anhydrase may be involved in the active transport mechanism.

The posterior chamber of the eye is filled with vitreous humor, which consists essentially of a hyaluronic acid-protein gel permeated by a fluid similar to aqueous humor. The protein of the vitreous is called "vitrein."

Table 15.11. Composition of Prostatic Fluid of Man

pH	6.3–6.45
Specific gravity	1.022
Water, per cent	92.7–93.6
Sodium, mg per cent	343–363; = 149–158 meq per liter
Potassium, mg per cent	109–238; = 29–61 meq per liter
Calcium, mg per cent	116–132; = 29–33 meq per liter
Chloride, mg per cent	124–163; = 35–46 meq per liter
Phosphorus, acid sol., mg per cent	20–55; = 0.65–1.77 meq per liter
Carbon dioxide, vols. per cent	69–120; = 3.1–5.4 mM per liter
Total nitrogen, mg per cent	295–511
Nonprotein nitrogen, mg per cent	30–90
Total protein, g per cent	2.46–2.64
Citric acid, g per cent	0.48–2.68
Glucose, mg per cent	Trace—16.4
Fructose, mg per cent	28–73, rabbit semen
Spermine, mg per cent	90–200, human semen
Total lipids, mg per cent	286
Cholesterol, mg per cent	62–105
Acid phosphatase	Present
Alkaline phosphatase	Present
Fibrinolysin	Present
Fibrinogenase	Present
Hyaluronidase	Present in sperm

SEMEN

The seminal fluid, or semen, is a suspension of spermatozoa in seminal plasma, which is a mixture of secretions from the prostate, seminal vesicles, epididymis, urethral glands, Cowper's glands, and vasa deferentia. Semen is very viscous and clots readily due to the presence of fibrinogen, but the clot is rapidly broken down by fibrinolysin of prostatic fluid. The pH of human semen varies from 7.1 to 7.5. An outstanding characteristic of semen is its high concentration of fructose (90–520 mg per cent). Much citrate also may be present, averaging about 480 mg per cent. The content of acid phosphatase is enormous (54,000–420,000 units per 100 ml) and is contributed by prostatic fluid. Other enzymes present are amylase, cholinesterase, β-glucuronidase, hyaluronidase, 5′-nucleotidase, diamine oxidase, alkaline phosphatase, and proteases. Semen contains the basic polyamino compounds spermine, $H_2N—(CH_2)_3—NH—(CH_2)_4—NH—(CH_2)_3 \cdot NH_2$, and spermidine, $H_2N—(CH_2)_3—NH—(CH_2)_4 \cdot NH_2$, which are derived from the prostate. The characteristic odor of semen appears to be due to such compounds.

The composition of prostatic fluid is given in Table 15.11.

The major proportion of seminal plasma is prostatic fluid. The chemistry of prostatic fluid has been reviewed by Huggins (95) and of semen by Mann (96).

INTERSTITIAL FLUID

Interstitial fluid is essentially an ultrafiltrate of plasma in which the greater proportion of the protein has been removed and to which the tissue cells have added various substances. Interstitial fluid represents the transport medium between the blood and tissue cells. It carries food materials to the cells and removes their waste products. Interstitial fluid enters the tissue spaces at the arterial ends of capillaries, where blood pressure exceeds the opposing colloidal osmotic pressure of plasma, and passes from the tissue spaces back into the blood at the venous ends of the capillaries, where the plasma colloid osmotic pressure exceeds the blood pressure. Also, interstitial fluid passes into the lymph capillaries and through lymph channels is circulated back into the venous blood.

The passage of fluid through the blood capillaries is opposed both by the plasma colloid osmotic pressure and the tissue tension, which varies greatly with different tissues, being low in loose areolar tissues, such as the eyelids, and high in dense tissues, such as muscles.

When inulin is injected intravenously, it passes through the capillary walls and is distributed throughout both plasma and interstitial fluid, and the inulin space (determined by dilution of the injected sample) thus represents both plasma and interstitial space. However, injected radioactive I^{131} albumin is retained within the vascular system, and the I^{131} albumin space represents plasma space. Thus inulin space minus I^{131} albumin space equals interstitial fluid space. According to such determinations, plasma equals about 5 per cent and interstitial fluid about 15 per cent of the body weight.

Despite the relatively large volume of interstitial fluid, its rather uniform distribution throughout the enormous organ tissue networks without local pooling makes it impossible to obtain directly a sample for analysis. However, various transudates of blood plasma of low protein content (0.4–1.3 g per 100 ml) have been analyzed, and the values obtained undoubtedly represent close approximations to the composition of interstitial fluid under various conditions. The diffusible nonelectrolytes, such as urea and glucose, tend to be uniformly distributed between plasma and interstitial fluid. Because of the higher nondiffusible negative protein ion concentration of plasma, interstitial fluid has a slightly higher concentration of diffusible negative ions (Cl^-, HCO_3^-, etc.) and a slightly lower concentration of diffusible positive ions (Na^+, K^+, etc.) than does plasma (Donnan effect). Since different tissue cells differ markedly in the kinds and quantities of substances added to the surrounding fluid, variations in the composition of interstitial fluid from different regions of the body are to be expected.

The parenchymal cells of organs are bound together by intercellular cement of gel consistency containing hyaluronic acid through which interstitial fluid permeates. This cement acts as a barrier to the passage of large molecules, such as proteins, and to bacteria, viruses, and particulate matter, while permitting ready passage of small electrolyte ions, small organic molecules, and water.

The enzyme hyaluronidase, secreted by various microorganisms, breaks down the cement barrier by depolymerizing hyaluronic acid. This permits spread of infection through the tissues, and hyaluronidase is referred to as the "spreading factor."

LYMPH

As indicated above in the discussion of interstitial fluid, some of this fluid enters the lymph capillaries and is passed on into the larger lymphatic vessels, which finally converge to form the thoracic and right lymphatic ducts that join the left and right subclavian veins, respectively. The total lymph flow into the blood through the lymph ducts appears to be 1 to 2 liters per day in an average human adult.

Lymphocytes from lymph nodes and intestinal lymphatic tissue are passed into the lymph stream and thereby enter the blood.

Since lymph represents interstitial fluid collected in the lymphatic system from many different kinds of tissues, which modify its composition to different degrees, it is not surprising that the composition of lymph shows marked variations according to where it is sampled for analysis. The concentrations per unit of water of readily diffusible nonelectrolytes, such as urea and glucose, are about the same in plasma, interstitial fluid, and lymph, while the concentrations of diffusible ions such as K^+, Na^+, Cl^-, and HCO_3^- vary according to protein content, which determines the Donnan distribution. Cervical and thoracic lymph contain around 3 per cent, subcutaneous lymph about 0.25 per cent, and liver lymph as much as 6 per cent protein, with the albumin to globulin ratio higher than in plasma (3:1 to 5:1), as might be expected. The lymph transports plasma proteins synthesized in the liver to the blood stream.

Stead and Warren (97) found that raising the venous pressure within subcutaneous tissue to 30 mm raised the protein concentration of subcutaneous lymph from 0.24 per cent to 1.3 per cent, indicating increased filtration of plasma proteins into the interstitial spaces.

The lymphatic capillaries are much more permeable than blood vascular capillaries, permitting India ink, Evans Blue, and other very small particles to be picked up when subcutaneously injected. The lacteal lymphatics take up the fine fat globules from fat absorption at the intestine and transport them in the thoracic duct to the left subclavian vein. Thus, after a fatty meal the thoracic duct lymph becomes milky from fat globules and is termed "chyle." Such lymph generally contains 5 to 15 per cent fat.

Lymph contains fibrinogen, prothrombin, and other components of the coagulation mechanism and slowly coagulates to form softer and less bulky clots than those produced by plasma.

SWEAT

Sweat is the secretion of the sweat glands and is produced to cool the body. That sweat is a secretion and not simply a filtrate of plasma is indicated by the fact that it is put out at a pressure of 250 mm of mercury or more. The sweat glands are controlled by the autonomic nervous system and also by adrenal cortical steroids which affect the quantity of electrolytes present. The so-called insensible perspiration (no fluid visible on the skin) generally amounts to 800 to 1200 ml per day, while the volume of sweat produced per day during muscular exercise at elevated temperatures may be as much as 14 liters. The water content of sweat generally varies between 99.2 and 99.7 per cent and the pH ranges from 4.7 to 7.5. Small amounts of many nitrogenous and other organic compounds, such as lactic acid, are present in sweat. The total nonprotein nitrogen (mainly urea) varies from about 0.07 g. per day to as much as 1.0 g. per hour during copious sweating. The quantity

Table 15.12. Approximate Amounts and Ranges of a Number of Substances in Various Body Fluids

Values represent mg/100 ml unless otherwise indicated. Cervical lymph values are for the dog and other values are for man except as indicated. Single values represent averages. Values from many sources, obtained by various analytical methods, for gross comparative purposes only.

	Blood plasma	Cervical lymph- dog	Thoracic lymph	Cerebro- spinal fluid	Aqueous humor	Synovial fluid	Sweat	Tears	Sebum (g per 100 g)
Protein (g per 100 ml)	6.5–7.5	3.6	2.8–3.6	0.028	0.025	2.8	0	0.67	Free fatty acids 22–32
Albumin (g per 100 ml)	4.7–5.7	2.4	1.6–2.4	0.015		1.9		0.39	Combined fatty acids 27–41
Globulin (g per 100 ml)	1.3–2.5	1.3	1.2	0.013		0.9		0.28	
Fibrinogen (g per 100 ml)	0.2–0.4	+	+	0		0			
Amino acids	30–50	4.3		7.5			11–32 0		Unsapon. matter 25–36
Total lipid	360–820	300	dog 200–7300	very low			0		
Cholesterol	150–250	55	75	trace					Squalene 3.3–11.2
Fatty acids	295–340	240		1–3					
Creatinine	1.0	1.4	1.0	1.2			0.1–1.3	0.03	Hydrocarbons 5–20
Urea	25	23	23, dog	10–15			12–57		Aliphatic alcohols 5–20
Glucose	65–90	132	65–90	47–78	55–110	65–90	reducing sub. 2.8–40	2 5	Cholesterol 4.7–6.9
Sodium	310–350	360	310–350	345	400–415	310	29–294	334	Cholesterol 2.7–6.9
Potassium	19	19	18.3	11–16	13–24.5	16	21–126	12–23	
Calcium	9–11	9.8	7.7	4.5–5.2	14		1–8		
Chloride	335	430	335	420–450	410–435	328	30–300	118–138	
Phosphorus inorg.	3.2–4.3	5.9	3.9	1.2–2.1			0–2		
CO₂ content (vols. %)	55–75	59		40–60	63			60	
pH	7.35–7.45	7.4	variable with lipid content	7.35–7.40		7.29–7.45	3.8–6.5	7.3–7.7	
Water (g per 100 ml)	94	96	variable with lipid content	98.3–99.2	99+	96.5	99.2–99.7	98.2	

of electrolytes in sweat varies enormously, (Na$^+$, 12.6–127 meq per liter; K$^+$, 5–32 meq per liter; and Cl$^-$, 8.5–85 meq per liter) being composed chiefly of Na$^+$ and Cl$^-$, though considerable K$^+$ also may be present. Muscular exercise increases the salt concentration as well as the volume of sweat. Persons acclimated to hot humid climates secrete less sweat of lower electrolyte content than do unacclimated individuals.

The loss of large volumes of sweat with accompanying electrolytes may result in hypertonic decrease in blood and other body fluids and cause severe cramps (miner's cramps), which are prevented and relieved by small amounts of salt in the drinking water.

TEARS

Tears are produced by the lachrymal glands as a clear, limpid fluid, which as secreted is isotonic, but which becomes hypertonic due to evaporation as the fluid passes over the cornea. When the flow is copious, the fluid is isotonic. The function of tears is to lubricate the surface of the cornea, to fill in irregularities of the corneal surface to improve optical properties, and to protect the eye from injury. The lachrymal glands are innervated by parasympathetic fibers which are carried in the lachrymal nerve, a branch of the ophthalmic nerve. The lachrymal nerve fibers end in the cornea and conjunctiva. Excessive lachrymation is caused by abnormal stimuli to the cornea or conjunctiva, and also by sneezing, coughing, and psychic stimuli.

Tears contain quantities of small organic molecules and electrolytes comparable to those in blood when the samples are collected to minimize evaporation (copious flow). The pH of tears generally is around 7.4 as found in plasma, though exceptionally it may range from 5.2 to 8.3. The protein content of tears is around 0.7 g per 100 ml, with an albumin-globulin ratio of about 1.5. Small amounts of mucin derived from the conjunctiva are present, which contribute to the lubricating property of tears, as do the other proteins present.

Tears contain the enzyme lysozyme, which lyses the cells of a number of microorganisms by breaking down the mucopolysaccharide component of their outer layers. Lysozyme therefore serves to protect the eye from infectious agents.

The partial compositions of a number of body fluids are given in Table 15.12.

GENERAL REFERENCES

Albritton, E. C. (ed.): *Standard Values in Blood.* W. B. Saunders Co., Philadelphia, 1952. Wyman, J., Jr.: "Heme Proteins," *Advances in Protein Chem.,* **4**, 407, 1948.

Biggs, R., and MacFarlane, R. G.: *Human Blood Coagulation and Its Disorders,* 2nd ed. Blackwell's Scientific Publications, Oxford, 1957. Seegers, W. H.: "Coagulation of the Blood," *Advances in Enzymol.,* **16**, 23, 1955.

Conference on Hemoglobin. Natl. Acad. Sciences-Natl. Res. Council, Publication 557, Washington, D. C., 1958.

Edsall, J. T.: "The Plasma Proteins and Their Fractionation," *Advances in Protein Chem.,* **3**, 383, 1947.

Lemberg, R., and Legge, J. W.: *Hematin Compounds and Bile Pigments.* Interscience Publishers, New York, 1949.

Link, K. P.: "The Anticoagulant from Spoiled Sweet Clover Hay," *Harvey Lectures,* **39**, 162, 1943–1944.

Quick, A. J.: "The Anticoagulants Effective in Vivo with Special Reference to Heparin and Dicoumarol," *Physiol. Revs.,* **24**, 297, 1944.

Scheraga, H. A., and Laskowski, M., Jr: "The Fibrinogen-Fibrin Conversion," *Advances in Protein Chem.,* **12**, 1, 1957.

Spector, W. S., (ed.): *Handbook of Biological Data.* W. B. Saunders Co., Philadelphia, 1956.

Sunderman, F. W., and Boerner, F.: *Normal Values in Clinical Medicine.* W. B. Saunders Co., Philadelphia, 1949.

Tullis, J. L. (ed.): *Blood Cells and Plasma Proteins.* Academic Press, New York, 1953.

SPECIAL REFERENCES

1. Gregersen, M. I., and Rawson, R. A.: *Physiol. Revs.*, **39**, 307, 1959.
2. Wintrobe, M. M.: *Clinical Hematology*, 4th ed. Lea & Febiger, Philadelphia, 1956.
3. Lefevre, P. G.: *Active Transport Through Animal Cell Membranes*, Protoplasmologia Handbuch der Protoplasmaforschung VIII. Springer-Verlag, Wien, 1955. Solomon, A. K.: *J. Gen. Physiol.*, **36**, 57, 1952.
4. Waltner, K., and Waltner, K.: *Klin. Wochschr.*, **8**, 313, 1929.
5. Goldwasser, E.; Jacobson, L. O.; Fried, W.; and Plzak, L.: *Science*, **125**, 1085, 1957.
6. Markowitz, H.; Cartright, G. E.; and Wintrobe, M. M.: *J. Biol. Chem.*, **234**, 40, 1959.
7. Shemin, D., and Rittenberg, D.: *Federation Proc.*, **5**, 153, 1946.
8. Howe, P. E.: *J. Biol. Chem.*, **49**, 93, 109, 1921.
9. Tiselius, A.: *Trans. Faraday Soc.*, **33**, 524, 1937.
10. Svensson, H.: *Arkiv. Kemi, Mineral. Geol.*, **17A**, No. 14, 1943; **22A**, No. 10, 1946.
11. Dole, V. P.: *J. Am. Chem. Soc.*, **67**, 1119, 1945.
12. Armstrong, S. H., Jr.; Budka, M. J. E.; and Morrison, K. C.: *J. Am. Chem. Soc.*, **69**, 416, 1947.
13. Luetscher, J. A., Jr.: *J. Am. Chem. Soc.*, **61**, 2888, 1939.
14. Oncley, J. L.; Scatchard, G.; and Brown, A.: *J. Phys. and Colloid Chem.*, **51**, 184, 1947.
15. Pillemer, L., and Hutchinson, M. C.: *J. Biol. Chem.*, **158**, 299, 1945.
16. Milne, J.: *J. Biol. Chem.*, **169**, 595, 1947.
17. Edsall, J. T.: "The Plasma Proteins and Their Fractionation," *Advances in Protein Chem.*, **3**, 383, 1947.
18. Lindgren, F. T.; Elliott, H. A.; and Gofman, J. W.; De Lalla, O. F., and Gofman, J. W., in Glick, D. (ed.): *Methods of Biochemical Analysis*, Vol. I, p. 459. Interscience, New York, 1954. Havel, R. J.; Eder, H. A.; and Bragdon, J. H.: *J. Clin. Invest.*, **35**, 641, 1955.
19. Hillyard, L. A.; Entenman, C.; Feinberg, H.; and Chaikoff, I. L.: *J. Biol. Chem.*, **214**, 79, 1955.
20. Madden, S. C., and Whipple, G. H.: *Physiol. Revs.*, **20**, 194, 1940.
21. Drury, D. R., and McMaster, P. D.: *J. Exptl. Med.*, **50**, 569, 1929.
22. Bing, J., and Plum, P.: *Acta Med. Scand.*, **92**, 415, 1937. Bjørneboe, M.; Gormsen, H.; and Lundquist, F.: *J. Immunol.*, **55**, 121, 1947. Ehrich, W. E., in Tullis, J. L. (ed.): *Blood Cells and Plasma Proteins*, p. 187. Academic Press, New York, 1953.
23. Tarver, H., and Reinhardt, W. O.: *J. Biol. Chem.*, **167**, 395, 1947.
24. Collier, F. C., and Jackson, P.: *New England J. Med.*, **248**, 409, 1953.
25. Putnam, F. W.: *J. Biol. Chem.*, **233**, 1448, 1958. Fried, M., and Putnam, F. W.: *Federation Proc.*, **18**, 230, 1959.
26. Good, R. A., and Mazzitello, W. R.: *Diseases of the Chest*, **29**, 9, 1956. Gitlin, D.; Hitzig, W. H.; and Janeway, C. A.: *J. Clin. Invest.*, **35**, 1199, 1956.
27. Bennhold, H.; Peters, H.; and Roth, E.: *Verhandl. deut. Ges. inn. Med.*, **60**, 630, 1954.
28. Putnam, F. W.: *J. Biol. Chem.*, **233**, 1448, 1958.
29. Pillemer, L.; Blum, L.; Lepow, I. H.; Ross, O. A.; Todd, E. W.; and Wardlaw, A. C.: *Science*, **120**, 279, 1954. Pillemer, L.; Schoenberg, M. D.; Blum, L., and Wurz, L.; *Science*, **122**, 545, 1955.
30. Walter, H.; Haurowitz, F.; Fleischer, S.; Lietze, A.; Cheng, H. F.; Turner, J. E.; and Friedberg, W.: *J. Biol. Chem.*, **224**, 107, 1957.
31. Fuller, J.; Humphreys, E. M.; Steffee, C. H.; Wissler, R. W.; and Benditt, E. P.: *Federation Proc.*, **8**, 356, 1949.
32. Starling, E. H.: *J. Physiol. (London)*, **19**, 312, 1895–1896.
33. Biggs, R., and MacFarlane, R. G.: *Human Blood Coagulation and Its Disorders*, 2nd ed. Blackwell's Scientific Publications, Oxford, 1957. MacFarlane, R. G.: *Physiol. Revs.*, **36**, 479, 1956. Seegers, W. H.: *Advances in Enzymol.*, **16**, 23, 1955. Several articles in Tullis, J. L. (ed.): *Blood Cells and Plasma Proteins*. Academic Press, New York, 1953.
34. Quick, A. J.; Stanley-Brown, M.; and Bancroft, F. W.: *Am. J. Med. Sci.*, **190**, 501, 1935.
35. Warner, E. D.; Brinkhous, K. M.; and Smith, H. P.: *Arch. Pathol.*, **18**, 587, 1934. *Am. J. Physiol.*, **114**, 667, 1936. *J. Exptl. Med.*, **66**, 801, 1937.
36. Quick, A. J.: *Marquette Med. Rev.*, **13**, 89, 1948.
37. Quick, A. J., and Stefanini, M.: *J. Gen. Physiol.*, **32**, 191, 1948.

38. Ferguson, J. H.: *Am. J. Physiol.*, **119**, 755, 1937.
39. Edsall, J. T.: *Advances in Protein Chem.*, **3**, 446, 1947.
40. Ware, A. G.; Guest, M. M.; and Seegers, W. H.: *Arch. Biochem.*, **13**, 231, 1947.
41. Gladner, J. A.; Folk, J. E.; Laki, K.; and Carroll, W. R.: *J. Biol. Chem.*, **234**, 62, 1959. Folk, J. E.; Gladner, J. A.; and Laki, K.: *ibid.*, **234**, 67, 1959.
42. Sherry, S.; Fletcher, A. P.; and Alkjaersig, N.: *Physiol. Revs.*, **39**, 343, 1959.
43. Seegers, W. H.; Loomis, E. C.; and Vandenbelt, J. M.: *Arch. Biochem.*, **6**, 85, 1945.
44. Lamy, F., and Waugh, D. F.: *J. Biol. Chem.*, **203**, 489, 1953.
45. Seegers, W. H.: *Advances in Enzymol.*, **16**, 23, 1955.
46. Campbell, H. A.; Smith, W. K.; Roberts, W. L.; and Link, K. P.: *J. Biol. Chem.*, **138**, 1, 1941.
47. Howell, W. H.: *Am. J. Physiol.*, **31**, 1, 1912.
48. Chargaff, E.: *J. Biol. Chem.*, **160**, 351, 1945.
49. Trevan, J. W., and MacFarlane, R. G.: *Med. Research Council Ann. Rept.*, p. 143, 1936.
50. Zak, E.: *Arch. exptl. Pathol. Pharmakol.*, **70**, 27, 1912.
51. Howell, W. H., and Holt, E.: *Am. J. Physiol.*, **47**, 328, 1918.
52. Hahn, P. F.: *Science*, **98**, 19, 1943. Engelberg, H.: *J. Biol. Chem.*, **222**, 601, 1956.
53. Jacques, L. B., and Waters, E. T.: *J. Physiol.*, **99**, 454, 1941. Best, C. H.: *Harvey Lectures*, 1940–41, Series 36, p. 66.
54. Seegers, W. H.; Johnson, J. F.; and Fell, C.: *Am. J. Physiol.*, **176**, 97, 1954.
55. Mellanby, J.: *J. Physiol. (London)*, **38**, 28, 1909.
56. Seegers, W. H.: *Advances in Enzymol.*, **16**, 23, 1955.
57. MacFarlane, R. G.: *Physiol. Revs.*, **36**, 494, 1956.
58. Fischer, H., and Zeile, K.: *Ann.*, **468**, 98, 1929. Fischer, H.; Treibs, A.; and Zeile, K.: *Z. physiol. Chem.*, **193**, 138, 1930.
59. Shemin, D., and Kumin, S.: *J. Biol. Chem.*, **198**, 827, 1952.
60. Vickery, H. B.: *Ann. N. Y. Acad. Sci.*, **51**, 87, 1941.
61. Benesch, R. E.; Lardy, H. A.; and Benesch, R.: *J. Biol. Chem.*, **216**, 663, 1955.
62. Riggs, A. F.: *J. Gen. Physiol.*, **36**, 1, 1952.
63. Steinhart, J., and Zaiser, E. M.: *Advances in Protein Chem.*, **10**, 151, 1955.
64. Granick, S.: *Ann. N. Y. Acad. Sci.*, **48**, 659, 1947.
65. Wyman, J., Jr.: *Advances in Protein Chem.*, **4**, 407, 1948.
66. Pauling, L., and Coryell, C. D.: *Proc. Natl. Acad. Sci. U. S.*, **22**, 210, 1936.
67. Rhinesmith, H. S.; Schroeder, W. A.; and Pauling, L.: *J. Am. Chem. Soc.*, **79**, 4682, 1957. Rhinesmith, H. S.; Schroeder, W. A.; and Martin, N.: *ibid.*, **80**, 3358, 1958.
68. Itano, H. A.: *Advances in Protein Chem.*, **12**, 215, 1957. Conference on Hemoglobin, Natl. Acad. Sci.-Natl. Research Council, Publ. 557, 1958, several articles.
69. Pauling, L.; Itano, H. A.; Singer, S. J.; and Wells, I. C.: *Science*, **110**, 543, 1949.
70. Jones, R. T.; Schroeder, W. A.; Balog, J. E.; and Vinograd, J. R.: *J. Am. Chem.Soc.*, **81**, 3161, 1959.
71. Rigas, D. A.; Koler, R. D.; and Osgood, E. E.: *J. Lab. Clin. Med.*, **47**, 51, 1956.
72. Conference on Hemoglobin, Natl. Acad. Sci.-Natl. Research Council, Publ. 557, p. 166, 1958.
73. Theorell, H.: *Biochem. Z.*, **252**, 1, 1932; **268**, 46, 1934.
74. Bock, A. V.; Field, H., Jr.; and Adair, G. S.: *J. Biol. Chem.*, **59**, 353, 1924.
75. Roughton, F. J. W.: *Proc. Roy. Soc. (London)*, **144B**, 29, 1955.
76. Coryell, C. D.; Pauling, L.; and Dodson, R. W.: *J. Phys. Chem.*, **43**, 825, 1939.
77. Hartridge, H., and Roughton, F. J. W.: *J. Physiol.*, **62**, 232, 1927.
78. Barcroft, J.: *The Respiratory Function of the Blood.* Cambridge University Press, England, 1914. Barcroft, J.: *The Respiratory Function of the Blood*, II. Hemoglobin. Cambridge University Press, England, 1928.
79. Bernhart, F. W., and Skeggs, L. J.: *J. Biol. Chem.*, **147**, 19, 1943.
80. Roughton, F. J. W.; Otis, A. B.; and Lyster, R. L. J.: *Proc. Roy. Soc. (London)*, Series B, **144**, 29, 1955.
81. Bohr, C.; Hasselbalch, K.; and Krogh, A.: *Skand Arch. Physiol.*, **16**, 402, 1904.
82. German, B., and Wyman, J., Jr.: *J. Biol. Chem.*, **117**, 533, 1937.
83. Wyman, J., Jr.: *Advances in Protein Chem.*, **4**, 407, 1948.
84. Haldane, J. S.: *J. Physiol. (London)*, **18**, 430, 1895. Douglas, C. G.; Haldane, J. S.; and Haldane, J. B. S.: *ibid.*, **44**, 275, 1912.
85. Neill, J. M., and Hastings, A. B.: *J. Biol. Chem.*, **63**, 479, 1925.

86. Cox, W. W., and Wendel, W. B.: *J. Biol. Chem.*, **143**, 331, 1942.
87. Dennig, A. D.: *Arch. klin. Med.*, **65**, 524, 1900.
88. Von Zeynek, R. V.: *Z. physiol. Chem.*, **33**, 426, 1901.
89. Hoppe-Seyler, F.: *Centr. med. Wiss.*, 436, 1866.
90. Lemberg, R., and Legge, J. W.: *Hematin Compounds and Bile Pigments*, p. 494. Interscience, New York, 1949.
91. Van Slyke, D. D., and Neill, J. M.: *J. Biol. Chem.*, **61**, 523, 1924. Van Slyke, D. D.: *ibid.*, **73**, 121, 1927.
92. Watson, C. J.: *Downey's Handbook of Hematology*, Vol. 4, Paul B. Hoeber, Inc., New York, 1938. Watson, C. J.: *Blood*, **1**, 99, 1946.
93. Barkan, G., and Walker, B. S.: *J. Biol. Chem.*, **131**, 447, 1939.
94. Havemann, R.: *Klin. Wochschr.*, **20**, No. 21, 543, 1941.
95. Huggins, C.: *Physiol. Revs.*, **25**, 281, 1945.
96. Mann, T.: *The Biochemistry of Semen.* John Wiley & Sons, New York, 1954.
97. Stead, E. A., and Warren, J. V.: *J. Clin. Invest.*, **23**, 283, 1944.

16

Chemistry of respiration

GENERAL CONSIDERATIONS

The average adult man at rest absorbs and utilizes some 250 ml of O_2 and produces and eliminates about 200 ml of CO_2 per minute. During severe exercise these quantities may be increased by ten times or more. The volumes per cent differences in the gaseous contents of arterial and venous blood

Table 16.1. Gaseous Content of Arterial and Venous Blood of Man, in Volumes Per Cent
Averages and Ranges

Blood	O_2	CO_2	N_2*
Arterial	19.6 (17.3–22.3)	48.2 (44.6–50.4)	0.9
Venous	12.6 (11.0–16.1)	54.8 (51.0–57.7)	0.9
Difference	7.0	6.6	0.0

* Calculated from partial N_2 pressure and solubility coefficient.

represent the gaseous transport of blood. Thus, if the oxygen content of arterial blood is 20 volumes per cent and of venous blood 13 volumes per cent, this means that each 100 ml of arterial blood transports 7 ml of O_2 to the tissues where it is utilized for tissue oxidations. This represents 70 ml of oxygen transport per liter of blood. If the body is using 250 ml of O_2 per minute at rest, then about 3.5 l of blood per minute must pass through the lungs. During severe exercise the quantity of blood passing through the lungs is enormously increased, though not in direct proportion, because the transport per unit volume of blood is increased under these conditions.

Table 16.1 gives representative values, in volumes per cent, for O_2, CO_2, and N_2 in arterial and venous blood of man. The difference between arterial and venous contents represents gaseous transport per 100 ml of blood.

The quantities of O_2 and CO_2 transported in blood are far greater than the amounts in physical solution. This means that these gases are present largely in chemical combinations which are both readily formed and readily broken down in the blood. The quantities of physically dissolved gases in blood may be calculated from the partial pressures of the gases and their solubility coefficients. The so-called Bunsen solubility coefficient of a gas is defined as the volume of gas (measured at 0° C and 760 mm Hg pressure) dissolved by a unit volume of liquid when the liquid is equilibrated with the gas under 1 atm of pressure (760 mm) at a specified temperature. Thus, at 38° C 1 ml of blood plasma dissolves 0.024 ml of O_2, 0.51 ml of CO_2, and 0.012 ml of N_2 when equilibrated with the respective gases at 760 mm pressure. Accordingly, at 38° C the absorption coefficients in plasma of O_2, CO_2, and N_2 are 0.024, 0.51, and 0.012, respectively.

Alveolar air is saturated with water vapor at body temperature, and this water vapor exerts a pressure of about 48 mm under these conditions. If the total pressure of alveolar air is 760 mm, the pressure due to dry O_2 + CO_2 + N_2 is $760 - 48 = 712$ mm. If the quantities of O_2, CO_2, and N_2 present in dry alveolar air are 14, 5.6, and 80 per cent, respectively, we may calculate the partial pressures exerted by each of these gases as follows:

Partial pressure of O_2 = $0.14 \times (760 - 48) = 0.14 \times 712 = 100$ mm
Partial pressure of CO_2 = $0.056 \times (760 - 48) = 0.056 \times 712 = 40$ mm
Partial pressure of N_2 = $0.80 \times (760 - 48) = 0.80 \times 712 - 570$ mm

From these partial pressures of O_2, CO_2, and N_2 and the solubility coefficients of the gases in plasma, we may calculate the volumes per cent of the gases physically dissolved in plasma. For example, 1 ml of plasma at 38° C dissolves 0.024 ml of O_2 under 760 mm of O_2 pressure. However, under 100 mm of O_2 pressure, as in alveolar air, 1 ml of plasma will dissolve only $100/760 \times 0.024 = 0.0031$ ml of O_2, and 100 ml of plasma then will dissolve $0.0031 \times 100 = 0.31$ ml of O_2. Thus, blood plasma contains 0.31 volume per cent of physically dissolved O_2. The calculations for the volumes per cent of physically dissolved gases in plasma at 38° C may be summarized as follows:

$$O_2 = 0.024 \times \frac{100}{760} \times 100 = 0.31 \text{ volume per cent}$$

$$CO_2 = 0.51 \times \frac{40}{760} \times 100 = 2.68 \text{ volumes per cent}$$

$$N_2 = 0.012 \times \frac{570}{760} \times 100 = 0.90 \text{ volume per cent}$$

While a considerable amount (around 40 per cent) of the CO_2 and all of the N_2 are transported in physical solution, most of the O_2 is carried in chemical combination.

The composition of air inspired into the lungs, calculated on a dry basis, is remarkably uniform. The respiratory movements are so controlled with respect to depth and frequency that normally the composition of the alveolar air in contact with the lung capillaries also is maintained within narrow limits. The composition of the expired air varies considerably with variations in the respiratory movements. Stated differently, under normal conditions the rates at which O_2 is taken into the lung alveoli and CO_2 is removed from them are such as to maintain relatively constant the composition of alveolar air.

Table 16.2 gives representative values, in volumes per cent, for the compositions of inspired, expired, and alveolar air of man calculated on a dry basis.

Table 16.2.   Composition of Inspired, Expired, and Alveolar Air in Man at Rest in Volumes Per Cent

Gas	Inspired Air	Expired Air	Alveolar Air
O_2	20.95	16.1	14.0
CO_2	0.04	4.5	5.6
N_2	79.0	79.2	80.0

The differences in N_2 content of inspired, expired, and alveolar air are not related to the production of N_2 in the body but are due simply to inequalities in the volumes of O_2 used and of CO_2 produced. The N_2 contents of arterial and venous blood are the same.

In the lungs the alveolar air is separated from the blood only by a thin layer, 1 to 2 μ thick, of capillary and alveolar endothelium. Across this membrane O_2 diffuses from the alveolar air into the blood and CO_2 diffuses from the blood into the alveolar air. The surface of contact between the air and the alveolar membranes is enormous, amounting to an estimated 50 to 100 sq m, and 25 to 50 times the total surface area of the body. The ratio of this alveolar surface to the volume of blood in the lungs at any time is so great that during the fraction of a second (about 0.7 sec) that the blood remains in the alveolar capillaries the gases of the blood practically come to equilibrium with those of the alveolar air.

The rates at which gaseous exchange between the blood and alveolar air take place are determined by several factors among which are: (a) the partial pressures of the gases in the alveolar air and in the blood of the lung capillaries, (b) the rates of passage of the gases across the membranes, (c) the area of the absorbing surface, (d) the time spent by the blood in the lung capillaries, (e) the volume of blood in the lung capillaries at any one time, and (f) the rates of the chemical reactions in blood by which O_2 is taken up and CO_2 is liberated.

Chemical control of breathing. The respiratory movements are so regulated as to control the rates at which O_2 is added to and CO_2 removed from the alveolar air of the lungs. At rest, breathing normally is rather slow and shallow, because the rates of removal of O_2 from the alveolar air and of addition of CO_2 to it are relatively slow. During exercise, however, the rate and depth of breathing must be stepped up in order to supply the increased demand for O_2 and to excrete the increased quantity of CO_2 formed in tissue oxidations. At high altitudes, where the partial pressure of O_2 in the inspired air is decreased, the rate of pulmonary ventilation is increased in compensation. The rate of excretion of CO_2 from the lungs is of importance in regulating the acid-base balance and pH of the blood and tissues. Thus, when the pH of the blood falls below normal, as in diabetic acidosis, respiratory movements are increased to blow off more CO_2, thereby decreasing the dissolved CO_2 and H_2CO_3 and H^+ ion concentration of blood and tissue fluids. In conditions of alkalosis, in which the pH of the blood and tissue fluids rises above normal, respiration is depressed and the rate of removing CO_2 is decreased. This causes the partial pressure of CO_2 in the tissues and blood to build up, thereby increasing the H_2CO_3 and lowering the pH. As will be pointed out in more detail later, the rate at which CO_2 is excreted by the lungs is of primary importance in regulating the acid-base balance of the body, and it is through automatic control of the respiratory movements that this is accomplished.

The rate and depth of breathing are regulated by a nervous mechanism activated by both chemical and physical stimuli, detailed discussions of which may be found in texts on physiology. At this point we are particularly interested in the mechanisms of chemical control, which are of primary importance, and which operate involuntarily to regulate pulmonary ventilation as necessary to supply O_2, remove CO_2, and help regulate the acid-base balance of the body.

The chemical control of respiration is mediated directly or indirectly through the respiratory center located in the medulla oblongata, which sends impulses to the respiratory apparatus. The neurons of the respiratory center are stimulated directly by increases in CO_2 pressure and H^+ ion concentration (decreases in pH). Conversely, the center is depressed by decreases in CO_2 pressure and H^+ ion concentration (increases in pH).

Chemoreceptors located in the carotid and aortic bodies situated at the bifurcations of the carotid arteries and the arch of the aorta, respectively, also play a role in the chemical regulation of respiration. These chemoreceptors are stimulated by a decrease in the O_2 pressure and by increases in the CO_2 pressure and H^+ ion concentration of arterial blood. These effects upon the chemoreceptors are transmitted reflexly along nerve fibers to the respiratory center, from which impulses pass to the respiratory apparatus. It appears that the chief effect upon the chemoreceptors is exerted by decreased O_2 pressure and that effects produced by changes in CO_2 and H^+ ion concentration are of little physiologic significance. Small decreases in O_2 tension in the blood do not affect the respiration appreciably. Only when the O_2 content of inspired air is decreased to about one-half that of normal air (10–11 per cent) is the stimulatory effect upon breathing observed in a subject at rest. The effect generally becomes marked only when definite signs of hypoxia appear (cyanosis) and when the O_2 content of the inspired air has been reduced to some 7 to 8 per cent. With exercising subjects the effects are pronounced at a higher O_2 content of the inspired air.

As a result of the effect of O_2, CO_2, and blood pH upon respiration through the respiratory center (and the chemoreceptors), we have an automatic mechanism which tends to control lung ventilation so as to meet best the physiologic requirements of the body. Upon exposure to high altitudes, where the O_2 pressure is decreased, there follows a decrease in the partial pressure of O_2 in the blood and a decrease in the O_2 present in the chemoreceptors. This causes stimuli to pass to the respiratory center and then to the respiratory apparatus, thereby increasing the rate and depth of breathing and the supply of O_2 to the lung alveoli. Also, in conditions of acidosis, in which the pH of the blood and tissues drop, the respiratory center is stimulated and causes increased blowing off of CO_2, which tends to raise the pH. Conversely, in alkalosis, respiration is depressed and CO_2 is retained to lower the pH.

The breathing of increased concentrations of CO_2 powerfully stimulates respiration. A mixture of 95 per cent O_2 and 5 per cent CO_2 is at times used to resuscitate persons suffering from CO poisoning. The CO_2 present stimulates respiration, and the high concentration of O_2 aids in displacing CO from its combination with hemoglobin. The breathing of very high concentrations of CO_2 may quickly cause convulsions. Such treatments have been used for certain mental cases in place of insulin and electric shock.

Gray (1) demonstrated that each of the chemical and physical factors which regulate breathing exerts a stimulating or depressing effect independent of all the others, and that the character of the breathing at any given time is the resultant of the arithmetical sum of all these partial effects. With an individual at rest the pulmonary ventilation is controlled largely by the action of CO_2 and H^+ ions upon the respiratory center. Gray has developed an equation by which the combined effects of CO_2 tension and H^+ ion concentration upon respiration may be calculated. This equation is as follows:

$$VR = 0.22H^+ + 0.262pCO_2 - 18.0$$

in which VR = number of times alveolar ventilation is increased over the resting value due to H^+ ion and CO_2 changes, H^+ = H^+ ion concentration of arterial blood in billionths of a mol per liter, and pCO_2 = the alveolar pressure of CO_2 in millimeters of mercury.

In the normal individual at rest with an arterial blood pH of 7.44 (H^+ = 36.3 billionths of a mol per liter) and an alveolar pCO_2 of 38.2 mm, the respiratory response is zero:

$$VR = 0.22 \times 36.3 + 0.262 \times 38.2 - 18 = 0$$

If such an individual breathes 5 per cent CO_2, so that the arterial pH drops to 7.336 (H^+ = 46.1) and the alveolar pCO_2 rises to 46.7 mm, the rate of pulmonary ventilation becomes:

$$VR = 0.22 \times 46.1 + 0.262 \times 46.7 - 18 = 4.4$$

Thus, under the stimulus of 5 per cent CO_2 in the inspired air, the respiratory center increases the alveolar ventilation to 4.4 times the normal rate.

From the above calculations it can be seen that both H^+ ion concentration and pCO_2 in the blood exert marked effects upon pulmonary ventilation rate.

OXYGEN TRANSPORT

In the processes of O_2 transport from inspired air to the tissues the O_2 diffuses across the alveolar and lung capillary endothelium into the blood plasma, where it is physically dissolved according to its absorption coefficient and partial pressure. Most of it diffuses across the red cell membranes into the cells and is combined with hemoglobin to form oxyhemoglobin.

$$Hb + O_2 \rightleftharpoons HbO_2$$

The partial pressure of the dissolved O_2 of venous blood coming to the lungs is about 40 mm on the average for a person at rest, and roughly 70 per cent of the hemoglobin is present as oxyhemoglobin. The O_2 partial pressure in alveolar air is about 100 mm, and the partial pressure of the O_2 of the blood leaving the lungs (arterial blood) is about 90 mm. At this partial pressure of dissolved O_2, the hemoglobin in the cells is about 97 per cent converted to oxyhemoglobin. This arterial blood, containing physically dissolved O_2 at 90 mm pressure in equilibrium with oxyhemoglobin and carrying about 20 volumes per cent of total O_2, passes to the capillary beds with little loss of oxygen. The O_2 partial pressure in the fluid surrounding the tissue cells is low, 30 mm or less. Consequently, when the arterial blood arrives at the tissues, the O_2 partial pressure of the blood initially exceeds that of the fluid bathing the capillaries by some 60 mm. The physically dissolved O_2 of the plasma passes through the tissue capillaries into the interstitial fluid and then across the tissue cell membranes into the cells where the O_2 pressure is only 10 mm or lower. As the physically dissolved O_2 of plasma diffuses into the tissues, the partial pressure of O_2 in the plasma drops, and O_2 diffuses from the red cells, where the pressure is higher, into the plasma; oxyhemoglobin in the red cells then dissociates because of the lowered O_2 pressure, and keeps up the supply of O_2 to the plasma and tissues so long as the blood remains in the capillaries. Normally in these processes in resting man only about one-third to one-fourth of the oxyhemoglobin is deoxygenated, and the partial pressure of O_2 drops from around 90 mm in arterial blood to 40 mm in venous blood.

During exercise the demand for O_2 in the tissues is increased. This demand is met through an increased rate of the circulation through the lungs and tissues, through increased respiration to provide more O_2 to the lungs, and, because of lowered O_2 tension in the interstitial fluid and tissue cells, through a greater degree of deoxygenation of oxyhemoglobin in the capillaries. In vigorous exercise the rate of blood flow may be three or more times faster than at rest, and most of the oxyhemoglobin of arterial blood may lose its oxygen to the tissues in the capillary beds. Under these conditions O_2 may be supplied to the tissues at a rate ten times faster than in the resting state.

The flow of O_2 in the respiratory circuit with the partial pressures of O_2 at various positions in the circuit are summarized below. The partial pressures vary with the atmospheric pressure and the rate of utilization of O_2 by the tissues:

Inspired air $\longrightarrow$ alveolar air $\longrightarrow$ arterial blood in lungs and capillaries $\longrightarrow$
O_2 158 mm O_2 100 mm O_2 90 mm
                                      $Hb + O_2 \longrightarrow HbO_2$

                   capillary beds $\longrightarrow$ interstitial fluid $\longrightarrow$ inside tissue cells
                     O_2 40 mm O_2 30 mm or less O_2 10 mm or less
             $HbO_2 \longrightarrow Hb + O_2$

Thus it is seen that the movement of O_2 in the respiratory circuit to the tissues is effected under a continual O_2 pressure gradient and that hemoglobin serves as a reservoir which is charged with O_2 in the lungs and unloaded in the tissues. This charging and unloading of hemoglobin is controlled through the partial pressure of the physically dissolved O_2 in the plasma, which in turn is dependent upon the pressure of O_2 in the alveolar air and in the tissue fluids.

The role of hemoglobin in O_2 transport. The combination of O_2 with hemoglobin and the various factors which affect this combination have been considered at some length in Chapter 15. At this time the student should review this discussion and study the oxygen dissociation curves of hemoglobin given there. By way of summary from that discussion, it has been found that the oxygenation of hemoglobin is affected chiefly by the degree to which the hemoglobin dissociates as an acid and exists as hemoglobin anions, and this is determined by the pH, which in turn varies with the CO_2 tension of the blood. Decreasing the CO_2 tension raises the pH and increases the acidic dissociation of hemoglobin to form more hemoglobin anions, which have more affinity for O_2. Increasing the CO_2 tension and lowering the pH decreases the concentration of hemoglobin anions and decreases the combination with O_2.

The effect of CO_2 upon the oxygenation of hemoglobin is a bit more than just a pH and hemoglobin dissociation effect. CO_2 reacts with hemoglobin to form carbaminohemoglobin, which has much less affinity for O_2 than does hemoglobin. Consequently, when the CO_2 tension of blood is increased, the affinity of hemoglobin for O_2 is decreased and vice versa.

Increase in temperature causes a decrease in the oxygenation of hemoglobin and vice versa. The electrolyte concentration (ionic strength) of blood also affects oxygenation probably through changes in activities. Ordinarily the variations in electrolyte concentration of blood are insufficient to have an appreciable effect.

The marked effect of pH upon the combination of O_2 with purified human hemoglobin is shown in Table 16.3.

Table 16.3.   Relation of pH to Oxygenation of Purified Hemoglobin

	O_2 Tension, mm Hg	Per Cent Oxygenation
pH 6	5.6	3.7
	26.8	22.0
	56.7	60.0
	86.1	78.3
pH 6.6	33.0	50.0
	46.9	68.7
	51.9	73.7
pH 8.3	5.0	50.0
	8.4	76.9
	18.1	93.5

From G. S. Adair, *J. Biol. Chem.*, **63**, 530, 1925.

It will be noted from the table that as the pH is increased, the per cent oxygenation of the hemoglobin for a given O_2 tension increases. The affinity of hemoglobin for O_2 shown at pH 8.3 is striking. In this case even at 5 mm O_2 tension the hemoglobin is 50 per cent oxygenated, while at 18 mm O_2 tension it is 93 per cent oxygenated.

Table 16.4, compiled from data of Henderson and associates illustrates the variation of the oxygenation of hemoglobin in human blood with variations in CO_2 tension.

Table 16.4.   Variation of Hemoglobin Oxygenation with Variation in pCO_2

pO_2 mm	Per Cent Hemoglobin Oxygenated			
	pCO_2 3mm	pCO_2 20 mm	pCO_2 40 mm	pCO_2 80 mm
5	13.5	6.8	5.5	3.0
10	38.0	19.5	15.0	8.0
20	77.6	50.0	39.0	26.0
40	96.7	87.0	76.0	63.5
60	100.0	96.3	90.5	85.0
80	100.0	99+	96.0	93.7
100	100.0	100.0	98.6	97.1
760	100.0	100.0	100.0	100.0

From L. J. Henderson, A. V. Bock, H. Field, Jr., and J. L. Stoddard, *J. Biol. Chem.*, **59**, 383, 1924.

The values in the table for the oxygenation of hemoglobin at a pCO_2 of 40 mm represent the normal behavior of hemoglobin in blood. At lower and higher pCO_2 tensions the oxygenation of hemoglobin is relatively increased and decreased, respectively. As previously mentioned, these CO_2 effects are largely pH effects and represent different affinities of hemoglobin anions and hemoglobin molecules for O_2.

The figures of the table also show that, if the CO_2 tension in a sample of blood oxygenated at a given O_2 tension is increased, the blood will lose O_2 as a result of dissociation of oxyhemoglobin. For example, consider blood at a pCO_2 of 40 mm and a pO_2 of 20 mm. Under these conditions 39 per cent of the hemoglobin is oxygenated. Now suppose pCO_2 is raised to 80 mm and pO_2 maintained constant at 20 mm. The table shows that under these conditions only 26 per cent of the hemoglobin is oxygenated. Raising pCO_2 by 40 mm has caused one-third of the oxyhemoglobin to dissociate. This effect is due chiefly to lowering the pH, thereby adding H^+ ions to the oxyhemoglobin and decreasing its affinity for O_2. When oxygenated blood reaches the capillary beds, CO_2 from the tissues enters the blood to increase pCO_2, which in turn promotes the dissociation of oxyhemoglobin and the liberation of O_2 to the tissues. Conversely, loss of CO_2 from the blood in the lungs promotes oxygenation of hemoglobin.

Figure 16.1, constructed from data of Barcroft (2) on purified hemoglobin and of Henderson and associates (3) on blood, shows the remarkable contrast in the oxygenation of purified hemoglobin solutions and of hemoglobin as it exists in blood at 40 mm CO_2 tension and normal pH. The sigmoid shapes of the curves are the result of the combined effects of pH (more sigmoid as pH drops), electrolyte concentration, and hemoglobin concentration. As pointed out in Chapter 15, the sigmoid shape of the curve for oxygenation of concentrated hemoglobin solutions is chiefly due to combination of O_2 with the four heme iron atoms in steps. In very dilute solutions the oxygenation curve becomes a rectangular hyperbola due to depolymerization into units containing only one heme group. In normal whole blood the shape of the oxygenation curve of hemoglobin in the red cells is determined by a pH of about 7.25 (inside the cells), an ionic strength of about 0.16, and a very high concentration of hemoglobin (about 30 per cent in the cells).

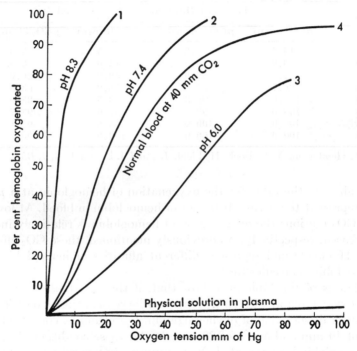

Figure 16.1.   Plot showing per cent of hemoglobin oxygenated against oxygen tension millimeters of mercury. Curves 1, 2, and 3 represent oxygenation of dialyzed hemoglobin solutions at specified pH levels. Curve 4 represents oxygenation of hemoglobin in normal blood. (From Barcroft, J.: *The Respiratory Function of the Blood*, Part II, *Hemoglobin.* Cambridge University Press, London, 1928.)

If the situation represented by curve 2 for purified hemoglobin existed in the circulating blood, the hemoglobin would take up O_2 readily in the lungs but would not release it efficiently to the tissues. The oxygen dissociation curve 4 of hemoglobin in normal blood shows that oxygenation and deoxygenation are nicely adapted to the needs of the body. At 100 mm of alveolar tension the hemoglobin is practically completely oxygenated; this insures full utilization of the O_2-carrying capacity of the hemoglobin under normal conditions. The gradual slope of the curve above 60 mm O_2 tension guarantees that most of the hemoglobin (90 per cent or better) will be oxygenated even when there is a very considerable decrease in the O_2 content of the inspired air. The rather sharp slope of the lower part of the curve insures that O_2 will be given up efficiently to the tissues when the blood arrives at the tissues where the O_2 tension is relatively low. Normally, when at rest, and when the demand for O_2 by the tissues is low, only one-third or one-fourth of the O_2 carried by hemoglobin in arterial blood is given up to the tissues, and the O_2 tension in the blood falls to 30 to 40 mm. In severe exercise, however, most of the hemoglobin is deoxygenated, and the O_2 tension in the blood may fall to 10 mm or less. Stated more precisely, when the hemoglobin of blood is fully oxygenated, a drop of O_2 tension from 90 to 40 mm, a drop of 50 mm, would release only about one-fourth of the combined O_2, while a further drop to 0 mm O_2 pressure, a drop of 40 mm, would release the remaining three-fourths of the combined O_2. Thus the curve shows that the hemoglobin system in blood gives up O_2 about three times as efficiently in the lower ranges of O_2 tension as it does in the higher ranges.

An increase in temperature facilitates the dissociation of oxyhemoglobin, and the fact that the temperature of actively metabolizing cells is a bit higher than in resting tissues promotes the release of O_2 to them. In patients with high fevers the general body temperature is sufficiently elevated to cause hemoglobin to release its O_2 more readily to the tissues. In animals whose body temperature varies with the environment (poikilothermic animals) the capacity of their hemoglobin to supply O_2 to the tissues progressively decreases as the body temperature falls.

Toxicity of oxygen. While the N_2 of air is inert chemically, it plays a very important role as a diluent of oxygen. Paul Bert (4) first observed that warm-blooded animals show toxicity when exposed to high O_2 tensions. Exposure to O_2 at 3 atm or more causes symptoms indicating profound effects upon the central nervous system, and the animals may collapse and die in violent convulsions. It appears that such toxicity is related to oxidation of —SH groups in brain enzymes and inactivation of the enzymes (5). The breathing of O_2 at 1 atm for prolonged periods irritates the lungs and may cause fatal lung edema, a situation in which the animal dies of hypoxia even though breathing much O_2. The explanation of course resides in the fact that because of fluid in the alveolar spaces the inspired O_2 cannot diffuse into the blood in sufficient amounts. Another effect of breathing O_2 at high partial pressures is concerned with its effects upon CO_2 transport, which will become more apparent after CO_2 transport has been discussed. In brief, the effect is as follows.

As previously pointed out in Chapter 15, oxyhemoglobin is a stronger acid than hemoglobin, and at the erythrocyte pH (about 7.25) oxyhemoglobin is dissociated into H^+ and anions to a greater extent than hemoglobin is:

$$HHbO_2 \rightleftharpoons H^+ + HbO_2^-$$
$$HHb \rightleftharpoons H^+ + Hb^-$$

This means that at the red cell pH Hb^- combines with more H^+ than does HbO_2^-. Therefore, when a given quantity of oxyhemoglobin is deoxygenated at the tissues, a certain increased amount of H^+ becomes combined as undissociated HHb, and this H^+ is largely taken from H_2CO_3 with the formation of an increased quantity of HCO_3^-:

$$H_2CO_3 + Hb^- \rightleftharpoons HHb + HCO_3^-$$

At the lungs oxygenation of hemoglobin forms oxyhemoglobin, a stronger acid, which dissociates an increment of H^+ to combine with HCO_3^- to form H_2CO_3, the latter decomposing to water and CO_2, which is exhaled:

$$HCO_3^- + HHbO_2 \rightleftharpoons HbO_2^- + H_2CO_3 \rightleftharpoons H_2O + CO_2 \text{ exhaled}$$

Thus the deoxygenation of oxyhemoglobin in the tissues and the oxygenation of hemoglobin in the lungs represent an important mechanism for CO_2 transport. When O_2 at high partial pressure is breathed, so much O_2 is physically dissolved in the blood that the O_2 requirements of the tissues may be met with little or no deoxygenation of oxyhemoglobin. This decreases the conversion of the acidic H_2CO_3 to the basic HCO_3^- with an accompanying fall in pH to values below normal. Thus a condition of CO_2 (or H_2CO_3) excess exists in the extracellular and intracellular fluids of the body. At 38° C plasma dissolves only about 0.31 volume per cent of O_2 at an alveolar O_2 tension of 100 mm. If the alveolar O_2 tension is raised to 3 atm (2280 mm), the physically dissolved O_2 in plasma becomes 7 volumes per cent, which is about the total quantity of O_2 transported by blood under normal conditions. Such a situation would seriously interfere with HCO_3^- formation and lead to H_2CO_3 excess and seriously lowered pH. In the therapeutic use of O_2 in hospitals it is common practice to place the patient in an oxygen tent at a partial O_2 pressure of 300 to 400 mm, which represents air to which O_2 has been added to raise the O_2 content to around 50 per cent.

By breathing O_2 at a controlled safe partial pressure, aviators may increase their ceiling of operations from about 15,000 to 40,000 ft. This ceiling cannot be increased indefinitely by breathing O_2, however, because, as the total alveolar pressure in the lungs decreases, the vapor pressure of the lung water tends to sweep out the O_2. This, of course, may be circumvented by pressurizing the aircraft so that both the total atmospheric pressure and the O_2 content are maintained.

It has been found that breathing O_2 at an elevated tension is the cause of retrolental fibroplasia in the immature infant.

CARBON DIOXIDE TRANSPORT

General considerations. As indicated above, the transport of CO_2 is related to the transport of O_2, and neither can be fully understood without knowledge of both.

Normally the oxidations in the tissues of the adult human at rest produce some 200 ml of CO_2 per minute, which must be eliminated through the lungs. During severe exercise the amount is increased enormously. Since CO_2 reacts with water to form carbonic acid:

$$CO_2 + H_2O \rightleftharpoons H_2CO_3$$

its transport in the blood to the lungs for excretion must be effected by mechanisms which prevent pH changes beyond physiologic limits. As a matter of fact, the pH of venous blood ordinarily is only 0.01 to 0.03 lower than the pH of arterial blood.

The flow of CO_2 from the tissues through the respiratory circuit to the atmosphere is effected under a pressure gradient somewhat as follows:

tissues 50 mm or more pCO_2 } $\longrightarrow$ venous blood 46 mm pCO_2 } $\longrightarrow$ alveolar air 40 mm pCO_2 } $\longrightarrow$ expired air 32 mm pCO_2 } $\longrightarrow$ atmospheric air 0.3 mm pCO_2 }

The quantity of CO_2 transported is represented by the difference in the CO_2 contents of arterial and venous bloods. This varies considerably between individuals and for a given individual under different conditions. Ordinarily, the normal transport of CO_2 by an individual at rest is considered to average about 5 ml per 100 ml of blood, or 50 ml per liter of blood. This is accomplished in such a manner that the CO_2 tension of venous blood (46 mm) is only about 6 mm higher than that of arterial blood (40 mm).

The transport of CO_2 in blood is accomplished by physical solutions in plasma and red cell fluid, as bicarbonate formed by reaction of H_2CO_3 with the bases of blood buffer systems, and as carbaminohemoglobin (hemoglobin carbamate), which is formed by direct reaction of CO_2 with an amino group of hemoglobin.

Calculations relating to carbon dioxide transport. The transport of CO_2 involves a complex physicochemical system containing CO_2, H_2CO_3, HCO_3^-, HPO_4^-, H_2PO_4, plasma protein buffer systems, hemoglobin buffer systems, and many other substances. The chief buffer systems concerned with CO_2 transport in blood are as follows:

Plasma	Cells
$\dfrac{HCO_3^-}{H_2CO_3}$, $\dfrac{proteinate^-}{H.protein}$	$\dfrac{HCO_3^-}{H_2CO_3}$, $\dfrac{Hb^-}{HHb}$, $\dfrac{HbO_2^-}{HHbO_2}$

In the above buffer systems plasma proteins and the hemoglobins function as polybasic acids at physiologic pH. Although the symbols used, HHb, Hb^-, $HHbO_2$, HbO_2^-, proteinate$^-$, and H.protein, indicate only one acidic H on the acids and one negative charge on the anions (salt forms), it must be kept in mind that generally more than one of each is involved. The acid forms, H.protein, HHb, and $HHbO_2$, still are anions and bind cations (salts), though to a lesser extent than the anions, proteinate$^-$, Hb^-, and HbO_2^-. The situation is analogous to that of the phosphate buffer systems, PO_4^-/HPO_4^-, HPO_4^-/H_2PO_4, $H_2PO_4^-/H_3PO_4$, in which the salt form (anion) may also be the acid form.

The charges on the anions of all types in the body are balanced electrically by cations such as Na^+, K^+, Mg^{++}, Ca^{++}. The chief cation in plasma is sodium, and that in the cells potassium. In the following discussion it is to be understood that anion symbols represent salt forms balanced electrically by cations, which in general are designated by B.

Since the transport of most of the CO_2 is effected through chemical reactions involving definite molecular or equivalent proportions of CO_2, H_2CO_3, HCO_3^-, and hemoglobin, it is desirable to be able to express the quantities of these substances so as to show such relations. It is customary to do this in terms of millimols per liter or as milligram equivalents per liter. The method of arriving at such expressions and some of their applications to calculations involved in CO_2 transport are given below.

Calculations involving CO_2, H_2CO_3, and HCO_3^-. CO_2 hydrates in solution to form H_2CO_3:

$$CO_2 + H_2O \rightleftharpoons H_2CO_3$$

The quantity of CO_2 dissolved is proportional to the partial pressure of the gas; this means that the above reaction is freely reversible. Consequently, the dissolved CO_2 actually is present as both CO_2 and H_2CO_3. As pCO_2 increases and decreases, H_2CO_3 increases and decreases in proportion. Ordinarily in biochemical calculations all the dissolved CO_2 is considered to be present as H_2CO_3.

If pK_1 of carbonic acid is calculated upon the assumption that all the CO_2 dissolved in plasma is present as H_2CO_3, the value of 6.1, which is ordinarily used, is obtained. However, Stadie and O'Brien (6) point out that actually the value of pK_1 for H_2CO_3 is about 3.7, indicating that it is a rather strong organic acid. This means that when CO_2 is dissolved in water, only a small fraction is hydrated to H_2CO_3. Since the amount of H_2CO_3 present is not equal to but is proportional to the amount of CO_2 dissolved, the pK_1 of 6.1 is really only an apparent constant. However, it is perfectly valid for calculations when we go on the assumption that all the CO_2 dissolved in body fluids is present as H_2CO_3. The total dissolved CO_2 is readily available for reaction as H_2CO_3, because, as H_2CO_3 is used up, more is quickly formed.

As pointed out in the first part of this chapter, the quantity of a gas dissolved in a liquid is directly proportional to the partial pressure of the gas in the liquid and to its solubility coefficient, which represents the volume of gas dissolved by a unit volume of liquid under 760 mm pressure of the gas and at a specified temperature. The solubility coefficient of CO_2 in plasma at 38° C is 0.51; this means that each milliliter of plasma dissolves 0.51 ml of CO_2 when the plasma is equilibrated with CO_2 at 760 mm and 38° C. At 40 mm CO_2 pressure in arterial blood we would have:

$$\frac{40}{760} \times 0.51 = 0.0268 \text{ ml of dissolved } CO_2$$

per milliliter of plasma. Also, we would have $0.0268 \times 100 = 2.68$ ml per 100 ml of plasma (volumes per cent), and $2.68 \times 10 = 26.8$ ml per liter of plasma. Since the molecular volume of CO_2 is 22,260 ml, 1 mM of CO_2 is 22.26 ml. Consequently, at 40 mm CO_2 pressure, plasma dissolves $26.8/22.26 = 1.2$ mM of CO_2. As previously indicated, this is taken to represent H_2CO_3, so under 40 mm CO_2 tension plasma contains 1.2 mM of H_2CO_3.

General expressions for calculating millimols of H_2CO_3 in plasma for any CO_2 pressure are arrived at as follows. For each millimeter of CO_2 pressure the following amount of CO_2 is dissolved:

$$\frac{1}{760} \times 0.51 = 0.000671 \text{ ml per ml of plasma}$$

$$\frac{1}{760} \times 0.51 \times 100 = 0.0671 \text{ ml per 100 ml of plasma (volumes per cent)}$$

$$\frac{1}{760} \times 0.51 \times 1000 = 0.671 \text{ ml per 1000 ml of plasma}$$

$$= \frac{0.671}{22.26} = 0.03 \text{ mM}$$

Thus we see that for each millimeter of CO_2 pressure in plasma at 38° C we have 0.03 mM of H_2CO_3 (dissolved CO_2). At 40 mm CO_2 pressure in arterial blood we have $40 \times 0.03 = 1.2$ mM of H_2CO_3, while at 46 mm CO_2 pressure in venous blood we have $46 \times 0.03 = 1.38$ mM of H_2CO_3. Consequently, the amount of CO_2 transported physically dissolved per liter of plasma and calculated as millimols of $H_2CO_3 = 1.38 - 1.2 = 0.18$ mM. The values in terms of volumes per cent are calculated by multiplying pCO_2 by the constant 0.067. At 40 mm the amount physically dissolved in plasma $= 0.067 \times 40 = 2.68$ volumes per cent. At 46 mm CO_2 we have $0.067 \times 46 = 3.08$ volumes per cent. The transport in volumes per cent then would be $3.08 - 2.68 = 0.4$. To summarize, mM $H_2CO_3 = 0.03 \times pCO_2$, and volumes per cent CO_2 as $H_2CO_3 = 0.067 \times pCO_2$.

Another way of interconverting millimols and volumes per cent is as follows. Since each millimol of CO_2 represents 22.26 ml of CO_2, each millimol of CO_2 per liter of plasma represents 2.226 ml per 100 ml of plasma, or 2.226 volumes per cent of CO_2. Thus, when plasma contains 25.2 mM of CO_2 per liter, it contains $25.2 \times 2.226 = 56.1$ volumes per cent CO_2. Vice versa, if plasma contains 56.1 volumes per cent CO_2, it contains $56.1/2.226 = 25.2$ mM of CO_2.

Since blood contains the bicarbonate buffer system, we may apply the Henderson-Hasselbalch equation, $pH = pK_1 + \log [HCO_3^-]/[H_2CO_3] = 6.1 + \log [HCO_3^-]/[H_2CO_3] = 6.1 + \log [HCO_3^-] - \log [H_2CO_3]$, for the calculation of any one of the variables pH, $[HCO_3^-]$, and $[H_2CO_3]$ if the other two are known.

Calculation of $[HCO_3^-]$:

$$\log [HCO_3^-] = \log [H_2CO_3] + pH - 6.1$$

Suppose a sample of plasma contains 1.2 mM of H_2CO_3 at pH 7.4; then $\log [HCO_3^-] = \log 1.2 + 7.4 - 6.1 = 0.0792 + 7.4 - 6.1 = 1.38$, and $[HCO_3^-]$ = antilog of $1.38 = 24$ mM.

Similarly, $[H_2CO_3]$ may be calculated if $[HCO_3^-]$ and pH are known:

$$\log [H_2CO_3] = \log [HCO_3^-] + 6.1 - pH$$

Total CO_2 present in plasma or any other bicarbonate buffer system may be calculated for any pCO_2 at any given pH. Since each mol of HCO_3^- and of H_2CO_3 is equivalent to a mol of CO_2:

$$\text{total } CO_2 = [HCO_3^-] + [H_2CO_3]$$

also $\quad pH = 6.1 + \log \dfrac{[HCO_3^-]}{[H_2CO_3]} = 6.1 + \log \dfrac{[HCO_3^-] + [H_2CO_3] - [H_2CO_3]}{[H_2CO_3]}$

and $\quad pH = 6.1 + \log \dfrac{[\text{total } CO_2] - [H_2CO_3]}{[H_2CO_3]}$

Since $[H_2CO_3]$ in millimols in plasma may be calculated by multiplying pCO_2 by the constant 0.03, this equation becomes:

$$pH = 6.1 + \log \frac{[\text{total } CO_2] - (0.03 \times pCO_2)}{(0.03 \times pCO_2)}$$

Suppose we wish to calculate [total CO_2] at pH 7.4 and 40 mm pCO_2. We have:

$$7.4 = 6.1 + \log \frac{[\text{total } CO_2] - (0.03 \times 40)}{(0.03 \times 40)}$$

and $\quad \log \dfrac{[\text{total } CO_2] - (0.03 \times 40)}{(0.03 \times 40)} = 7.4 - 6.1 = 1.3$

then $\quad 1.3 = \log \dfrac{[\text{total } CO_2] - 1.2}{1.2}$

Taking the antilog of both sides of the equation, we have:

$$\text{antilog } 1.3 = \frac{[\text{total } CO_2] - 1.2}{1.2}$$

and $\quad 20 = \dfrac{[\text{total } CO_2] - 1.2}{1.2}$

and $\quad 1.2 \times 20 = [\text{total } CO_2] - 1.2$
or $\quad [\text{total } CO_2] = 1.2 \times 20 + 1.2 = 25.2$ mM per liter of plasma

A very much simpler method of calculating [total CO_2] is as follows:

$$[\text{total } CO_2] = [HCO_3^-] + [H_2CO_3] = \left(\frac{[HCO_3^-]}{[H_2CO_3]} + 1 \right) [H_2CO_3]$$

Since: $\quad R = \dfrac{[HCO_3^-]}{[H_2CO_3]}$

then $\quad [\text{total } CO_2] = (R + 1)[H_2CO_3]$

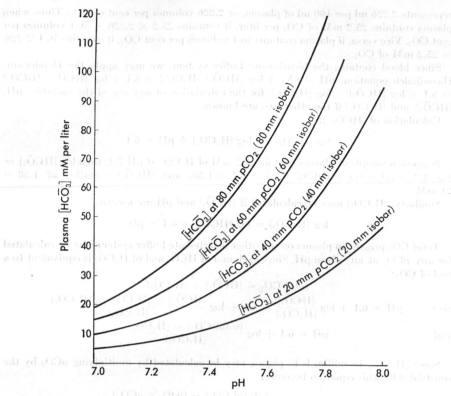

Figure 16.2.   Variations in plasma $[H\overline{C}O_3]$ with pH at different CO_2 tensions.

Since $[H_2CO_3]$ in millimols $= 0.03 \times pCO_2$, we have:

$$[\text{total } CO_2] = (R + 1) \times 0.03 \times pCO_2$$

The value of R is obtained for any pH from:

$$pH = 6.1 + \log [H\overline{C}O_3]/[H_2CO_3] = 6.1 + \log R$$
and $$\log R = pH - 6.1, \quad R = \text{antilog } (pH - 6.1).$$

If total CO_2 is calculated by the above equation at a given pH and pCO_2 we may easily calculate $[HCO_3^-]$, since

$$[\text{total } CO_2] = [HCO_3^-] + [H_2CO_3] = [HCO_3^-] + 0.03 \times pCO_2$$
and $$[HCO_3^-] = [\text{total } CO_2] - 0.03 \times pCO_2$$

If $[\text{total } CO_2] = 25.2$ mM and pCO_2 is 40 mm,

then $$[HCO_3^-] = 25.2 - 0.03 \times 40 = 25.2 - 1.2 = 24 \text{ mM}$$

By use of the equation

$$pH = pK_1 + \log \frac{[\text{total } CO_2] - 0.03pCO_2}{0.03pCO_2}$$

it is possible to calculate pCO_2 if pH and $[\text{total } CO_2]$ are known. Suppose we wish to calculate pCO_2 of plasma at pH 7.4 when $[\text{total } CO_2]$ is 25.2 mM. Substituting in the above equation, we have:

$$7.4 = 6.1 + \log \frac{25.2 - 0.03p\text{CO}_2}{0.03p\text{CO}_2}$$

and

$$1.3 = \log \frac{25.2 - 0.03p\text{CO}_2}{0.03p\text{CO}_2}$$

$$\text{antilog } 1.3 = \frac{25.2 - 0.03p\text{CO}_2}{0.03p\text{CO}_2}$$

and

$$20 = \frac{25.2 - 0.03p\text{CO}_2}{0.03p\text{CO}_2}$$

$20 \times 0.03p\text{CO}_2 = 25.2 - 0.03p\text{CO}_2, 0.6p\text{CO}_2 = 25.2 - 0.03p\text{CO}_2, 0.6p\text{CO}_2 + 0.03p\text{CO}_2$
$= 25.2, 0.63p\text{CO}_2 = 25.2,$ then $p\text{CO}_2 = 25.2/0.63 = 40$ mm.

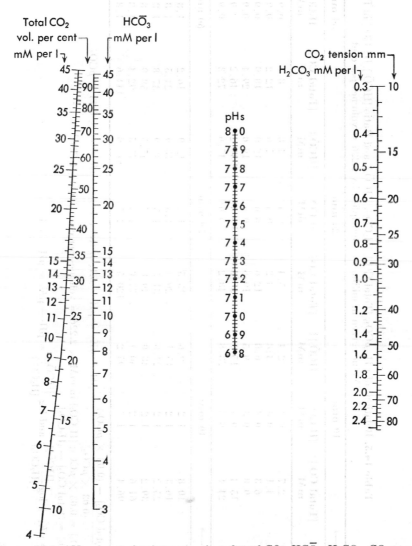

Figure 16.3.   Nomogram for determination of total CO_2, HCO_3^-, H_2CO_3, CO_2 tension, and pH of plasma. (From Van Slyke, D. D., and Sendroy, J., Jr.: *J. Biol. Chem.*, **79,** 783, 1928.)

Table 16.5. Relations of pH, pCO_2, [Total CO_2], [H_2CO_3], [HCO_3^-], and Ratio [HCO_3^-]/[H_2CO_3] in Plasma at 38° C
Values given in millimols—multiplied by 2.226 = volumes per cent

$pCO_2 \rightarrow$	10 mm			20 mm			30 mm			
pH	[Total CO_2]* mM	[H_2CO_3]† mM	[HCO_3^-]‡ mM	[Total CO_2] mM	[H_2CO_3] mM	[HCO_3^-] mM	[Total CO_2] mM	[H_2CO_3] mM	[HCO_3^-] mM	$\dfrac{[HCO_3^-]§}{[H_2CO_3]} = R$
7.0	2.7	0.3	2.4	5.4	0.6	4.8	8.1	0.9	7.2	8.0
7.2	4.1	0.3	3.8	8.2	0.6	7.6	12.2	0.9	11.3	12.6
7.4	6.3	0.3	6.0	12.6	0.6	12.0	18.9	0.9	18.0	20.0
7.6	9.8	0.3	9.5	19.6	0.6	19.0	29.4	0.9	28.5	31.7
7.8	15.4	0.3	15.1	30.8	0.6	30.2	46.2	0.9	45.3	50.2
8.0	24.1	0.3	23.8	48.2	0.6	47.6	72.3	0.9	71.4	79.5

$pCO_2 \rightarrow$	40 mm			50 mm			60 mm			
pH	[Total CO_2]* mM	[H_2CO_3]† mM	[HCO_3^-]‡ mM	[Total CO_2] mM	[H_2CO_3] mM	[HCO_3^-] mM	[Total CO_2] mM	[H_2CO_3] mM	[HCO_3^-] mM	$\dfrac{[HCO_3^-]§}{[H_2CO_3]} = R$
7.0	10.8	1.2	9.6	13.5	1.5	12.0	16.2	1.8	14.4	8.0
7.2	16.3	1.2	15.1	20.4	1.5	18.9	24.5	1.8	22.7	12.6
7.4	25.2	1.2	24.0	31.5	1.5	30.0	37.8	1.8	36.0	20.0
7.6	39.2	1.2	38.0	49.0	1.5	47.5	58.9	1.8	57.1	31.7
7.8	61.6	1.2	60.4	77.0	1.5	75.5	92.4	1.8	90.6	50.2
8.0	96.4	1.2	95.2	120.5	1.5	119.0	144.6	1.8	142.8	79.5

* $\log \dfrac{[\text{total } CO_2] - (0.03 \times pCO_2)}{(0.03 \times pCO_2)} = \text{pH} - pK_1 = \text{pH} - 6.1$, or [total CO_2] = $(R + 1) \times 0.03 \times pCO_2$.

† [H_2CO_3] = $0.03 \times pCO_2$; [H_2CO_3] in mM × 2.226 = volumes per cent CO_2 as H_2CO_3.

‡ [HCO_3^-] = [total CO_2] − [H_2CO_3].

§ pH = $pK_1 + \log \dfrac{[HCO_3^-]}{[H_2CO_3]}$, and $\log \dfrac{[HCO_3^-]}{[H_2CO_3]}$ = pH − pK_1 = pH − 6.1.

An alternate procedure is to calculate R for the given pH from the equation pH = 6.1 + log R, and then to calculate pCO_2 from the expression [total CO_2] = $(R + 1) \times 0.03pCO_2$. At pH 7.4 the value of R is 20, and if [total CO_2] is 25.2 mM, we have: 25.2 = $(20 + 1) \times 0.03pCO_2$, or 25.2 = $21 \times 0.03pCO_2$, or 25.2 = $0.63pCO_2$, and pCO_2 = 25.2/0.63 = 40 mm.

Table 16.5 summarizes relations of pH, pCO_2, [total CO_2], [$HC\bar{O}_3$], [H_2CO_3], and [$HC\bar{O}_3$]/[H_2CO_3] or R for blood plasma.

It will be observed from the figures of Table 16.5 that both total CO_2 and $HC\bar{O}_3$ vary directly with pCO_2 at any given pH; that is, they are straight-line functions. At any given value of pCO_2 both total CO_2 and $HC\bar{O}_3$ increase with increases in pH, the rate of increase accelerating as the pH rises. The curves of Figure 16.2 show the variations in plasma [$HC\bar{O}_3$] with variations in pH at fixed CO_2 pressures.

Van Slyke and Sendroy (7) prepared a nomogram from which pCO_2, [total CO_2], [H_2CO_3], [$HC\bar{O}_3$], and pH may be obtained if values for any two of the four scales are known. It is only necessary to draw a line through these two values, and it will pass through points on the other scales representing the other values. This nomogram is given in Figure 16.3, and the student should check it against values given in Table 16.5.

Calculations involving hemoglobin in carbon dioxide transport. Hemoglobin not only transports O_2 in blood but also provides the means for the transport of most of the CO_2. It does this by taking up H^+ ions to form bicarbonate and by reacting directly with CO_2 to form carbaminohemoglobin.

The equivalent weight of hemoglobin for the purposes of calculation is generally taken as 16,700 g, the quantity combining with 1 mol of O_2 and representing one heme group. This equivalent weight of hemoglobin often is referred to as 1 mol. If a sample of blood contains 15 g of hemoglobin per 100 ml, it contains 150 g per liter. Since an equivalent weight of hemoglobin is 16,700 g, the blood contains 150/16,700 = 0.00898 equivalent of hemoglobin per liter. In terms of milliequivalents per liter this represents 0.00898 $\times$ 1000 = 8.98. This is also referred to as millimols per liter. Since CO_2 transport is usually expressed as millimols per liter or milliequivalents per liter, hemoglobin concentration also is generally expressed correspondingly in its relations to CO_2 transport.

In order to derive an expression by which grams of hemoglobin per 100 ml of blood may be converted easily to millimols per liter, we may proceed as follows. Each gram of hemoglobin per 100 ml of blood represents 10 g per liter of blood. This represents 10/16,700 = 0.0005988 mol, and 0.0005988 $\times$ 1000 = 0.5988 millimol per liter. For practical use we may consider that each gram of hemoglobin per 100 ml of blood represents 0.6 millimol or milliequivalent per liter. Thus, for blood with 15 g of hemoglobin per 100 ml, there are 15 $\times$ 0.6 = 9 mM per liter. Conversely, if there are 9 mM of hemoglobin per liter of blood, there are 9/0.6 = 15 g of hemoglobin per 100 ml of blood.

DETAILED MECHANISMS OF
CARBON DIOXIDE TRANSPORT IN BLOOD

1. Physically dissolved as CO_2 calculated as H_2CO_3. Carbon dioxide is transported physically dissolved in both plasma and cells. The pCO_2 is the same in plasma and cells. However, the solubility factor per liter for CO_2 in plasma is 0.03, whereas in cells it is 0.025. Suppose we wish to calculate the total CO_2 transported by physical solution (calculated as H_2CO_3) per liter of blood. Suppose the pCO_2 of arterial blood is 40 mm, and that of venous blood 46 mm. Also, suppose the hematocrit determination shows a value of 46 per cent, meaning that the blood is 46 per cent cells and 54 per cent plasma by volume. We must, therefore, calculate the H_2CO_3 of 540 ml of arterial and venous plasma and of 460 ml of arterial and venous cells in order to arrive at the correct value for CO_2 transported as H_2CO_3 in 1 l of whole blood.

$[H_2CO_3]$ per liter of venous plasma $= 46 \times 0.03 = 1.38$ mM, and in a liter of venous cells $= 46 \times 0.025 = 1.15$ mM.

In 540 ml of venous plasma there are $1.38 \times 0.54 = 0.75$ mM of H_2CO_3, and in 460 ml of venous cells there are $1.15 \times 0.46 = 0.53$ mM of H_2CO_3.

$[H_2CO_3]$ per liter of arterial plasma $= 40 \times 0.03 = 1.2$ mM, and in a liter of arterial cells $= 40 \times 0.025 = 1.0$ mM.

In 540 ml of arterial plasma there are $1.2 \times 0.54 = 0.65$ mM of H_2CO_3, and in 460 ml of arterial cells there are $1.0 \times 0.46 = 0.46$ mM of H_2CO_3. Summarizing:

Plasma transport $=$ venous plasma transport $-$ arterial plasma transport $= 0.75$ mM $- 0.65$ mM $= 0.10$ mM.

Cell transport $=$ venous cell transport $-$ arterial cell transport $= 0.53$ mM $- 0.46$ mM $= 0.07$ mM.

Total H_2CO_3 transport $= 0.1 + 0.07 = 0.17$ mM.

It will be seen from these calculations that H_2CO_3 accounts for only a relatively small proportion of the CO_2 transported. For example, if in the case cited the total CO_2 transport were 2.25 mM, then the CO_2 transported as H_2CO_3 would be $0.17/2.25 \times 100 = 7.5$ per cent. Of the dissolved CO_2 transported the plasma generally accounts for the larger proportion.

2. Transported in chemical combination. By far the greater proportion of CO_2 is transported in blood in chemical combination as $H\bar{C}O_3$. This $H\bar{C}O_3$ is formed through the reactions of the base components of plasma and cell buffers with H_2CO_3. The reaction of an amino group of hemoglobin with CO_2 to form carbaminohemoglobin also accounts for a considerable proportion of CO_2 transport.

Formation of $H\bar{C}O_3$ in plasma. The chief buffers of plasma are the bicarbonate-carbonic acid system, $H\bar{C}O_3/H_2CO_3$, and the proteinate-protein system, proteinate$^-$/H.protein. On the average the $H\bar{C}O_3$ in plasma is around 25 mM or meq per liter, and the proteinate$^-$ represents about 15 meq of base per liter. Practically all the transport for CO_2 as $H\bar{C}O_3$ provided by the plasma is due to reaction with proteinate$^-$ according to the equations:

$$\underset{\underset{\text{tissues}}{\uparrow}}{\overset{\overset{\text{lungs}}{\uparrow}}{CO_2 + H_2O}} \rightleftarrows H_2CO_3 + \text{proteinate}^- \rightleftarrows H\bar{C}O_3 + \text{H·protein}$$

The pCO_2 in the tissues is higher than in the arterial blood coming to the capillaries, so CO_2 diffuses into the blood and forces the above reversible reactions to the right, causing an increase in the quantity of $H\bar{C}O_3$. This increase in $H\bar{C}O_3$ represents transport due to plasma proteins. It is true that the phosphate buffer system, $HPO_4^=/H_2PO_4^-$, and organic acid buffer systems form some HCO_3^-, but quantitatively this is insignificant:

$$HPO_4^- + H_2CO_3 \rightleftarrows HCO_3^- + H_2PO_4^-$$

When the venous blood reaches the lungs, CO_2 diffuses into the alveolar air and is exhaled into the atmosphere. This causes the reactions above to shift to the left with decomposition of the transport increment of HCO_3^-.

The pH of average normal arterial plasma decreases about 0.025 unit in passing through the capillaries and becoming venous plasma. With this change in pH, the plasma proteinate⁻ takes up H^+ ions sufficient to form 0.09 mM of HCO_3^-. This represents the transport of 0.09 mM of CO_2 by the plasma proteins. If the total transport of CO_2 is 2.25 mM, this represents $0.09/2.25 \times 100 = 4$ per cent of the total transport. While this transport of CO_2 varies, in general it represents only a few per cent of the total transport.

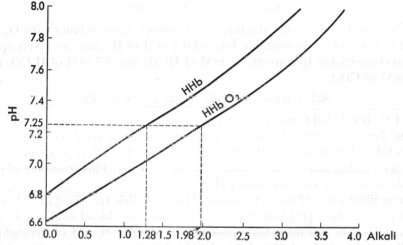

Figure 16.4. Equivalents of alkali per equivalent of HHb and HHbO₂. An equivalent of hemoglobin is the quantity corresponding to 1 mol of O_2 or one heme group. At pH 7.25, the pH within the red cell, oxyhemoglobin reacts with 0.7 equivalent more alkali than does hemoglobin. (Modified from *Quantitative Clinical Chemistry*, Vol. 1, *Interpretations* by J. P. Peters and D. D. Van Slyke. Williams & Wilkins Co., Baltimore, 1931.)

Formation of HCO_3^- by hemoglobin. Isohydric transport of CO_2.

As previously pointed out, oxyhemoglobin is a stronger acid than hemoglobin, the isoelectric pH of oxyhemoglobin being about 6.6 and that of hemoglobin about 6.8. Consequently, at the red cell pH of about 7.25, oxyhemoglobin dissociates to form more anions than does hemoglobin. Figure 16.4, adapted from Peters and Van Slyke, shows the alkali titration curves of oxyhemoglobin and hemoglobin within the physiologic pH range.

These titration curves are almost straight lines, indicating that oxyhemoglobin and hemoglobin are polyvalent acids. From the figure it can be seen that each mol of hemoglobin (amount equivalent to one O_2) requires about 2.7 equivalents of alkali to cause 1 unit of pH change (buffer capacity of 2.7), while oxyhemoglobin requires about 2.9 equivalents of alkali per unit pH change (buffer capacity of 2.9). Since a monovalent acid, such as acetic, at the pH of its greatest buffer capacity (pH = pK_1), has a buffer capacity of only 0.57, it is obvious that oxyhemoglobin and hemoglobin must contain five or more acid groups which dissociate within the physiologic pH range.

The fact that oxyhemoglobin is a considerably stronger acid than hemoglobin is of paramount importance to CO_2 transport. From the figure it will be seen that, at a red cell pH of 7.25, an equivalent of oxyhemoglobin dissociates 1.98 equivalents of H^+ ions, while hemoglobin yields only 1.28 equivalents. This means that at pH 7.25 1 mM or milliequivalent of oxyhemoglobin dissociates 0.7 mM more H^+ ions than does 1 mM of hemoglobin. In other words, when oxyhemoglobin of arterial blood reaches the capillary beds and gives up O_2 to the tissues and becomes less acidic hemoglobin, for each millimol of O_2 (22.4 ml) released the hemoglobin formed takes up 0.7 mM of H^+ ions from H_2CO_3 to form 0.7 mM of $HC\bar{O}_3$:

$$Hb^- + H_2CO_3 \rightleftharpoons HC\bar{O}_3 + HHb$$

When the blood reaches the lungs and hemoglobin combines with O_2, for each millimol of oxyhemoglobin formed 0.7 mM of H^+ ions are given up by the oxyhemoglobin to convert 0.7 mM of $HC\bar{O}_3$ into 0.7 mM of H_2CO_3 and 0.7 mM of CO_2:

$$HC\bar{O}_3 + HHbO_2 \rightleftharpoons Hb\bar{O}_2 + H_2CO_3 \rightleftharpoons H_2O + CO_2$$

The CO_2 is exhaled from the lungs.

The formation of this $HC\bar{O}_3$ at the tissues and its conversion to CO_2 at the lungs take place because of the difference in acid strength of oxyhemoglobin and hemoglobin and can take place at a constant pH. This transport of CO_2 is called the isohydric (constant pH) transport.

As an illustration of the importance of the isohydric transport of CO_2, consider the following problem. Suppose the circulating blood contains 15 g of hemoglobin per 100 ml. This represents $15 \times 0.6 = 9$ mM of hemoglobin per liter. If the hemoglobin of arterial blood is 96 per cent oxygenated, the blood contains $9 \times 0.96 = 8.64$ mM of oxyhemoglobin per liter. Now suppose in the venous blood 70 per cent of the hemoglobin is present as oxyhemoglobin. This represents $9 \times 0.70 = 6.30$ mM of oxyhemoglobin. In other words, in passing through the capillary beds $8.64 - 6.30 = 2.34$ mM of oxyhemoglobin lose O_2 and are converted to 2.34 mM of hemoglobin, which form $2.34 \times 0.7 = 1.64$ mM of $HC\bar{O}_3$. In the lungs the 2.34 mM of hemoglobin form 2.34 mM of oxyhemoglobin, which react with $2.34 \times 0.7 = 1.64$ mM of $HC\bar{O}_3$ to liberate 1.64 mM of CO_2, which is exhaled. Thus the process of deoxygenating oxyhemoglobin at the tissues and oxygenating hemoglobin in the lungs provides isohydric transport for 1.64 mM of CO_2 per liter of blood. If the total CO_2 transport in the above example were 2.25 mM per liter of blood, the isohydric transport would amount to $1.64/2.25 \times 100 = 73$ per cent of the total CO_2 transported.

In earlier discussion it has been pointed out that dissolved CO_2 exists in body fluids in the following dynamic equilibrium:

$$CO_2 + H_2O \rightleftharpoons H_2CO_3$$

in which the amount of H_2CO_3 present is proportional to pCO_2. Now in the capillary beds large amounts of CO_2 must be taken up quickly from the tissues by the blood, passed into the red cells, and there converted first to

H_2CO_3 and then into HCO_3^- by the hemoglobin system. Also in the lungs, when HCO_3^- is decomposed to form H_2CO_3, large amounts of this H_2CO_3 must be quickly changed to CO_2 for exhalation. The uncatalyzed reaction:

$$CO_2 + H_2O \rightleftharpoons H_2CO_3$$

proceeds too slowly to meet these requirements. It has been found, however, that the red cells contain the enzyme carbonic anhydrase, which powerfully catalyzes the reaction in both directions, thereby causing both the formation and the breakdown of H_2CO_3 in the cells to proceed at rates sufficiently fast to meet the requirements for CO_2 transport.

Each mol of oxyhemoglobin at a cell pH of 7.25 dissociates about 2 H^+ ions, and each mol of hemoglobin dissociates about 1.3 H^+ ions, and, since the anions formed are balanced by equivalent cations, we may represent the formulas of oxyhemoglobin and hemoglobin at pH 7.25 by the formulas K_2HbO_2 and $K_{1.3}H_{0.7}Hb$, respectively. The reactions involved in the iso-hydric transport of CO_2 at pH 7.25 in the cells by the hemoglobin system may be shown as follows:

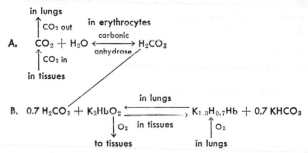

In the tissues where pCO_2 is high (50 mm or more), CO_2 diffuses into the plasma and then into the red cell. This causes reaction A to shift to the right by mass action and increases the concentration of H_2CO_3 in the cell. This increased concentration of H_2CO_3, along with the simultaneous loss of O_2 to the tissues, shifts reaction B to the right with the formation of an increment of HCO_3^- [0.7 mM of HCO_3^- for each millimol of O_2 (22.4 ml) given up to the tissues]. In the lungs, where pO_2 is high, O_2 diffuses into the plasma and cells and oxygenates hemoglobin. This, along with the simultaneous blowing off of CO_2 from the lungs, causes reaction B to shift to the left with the simultaneous decomposition of an increment of HCO_3^- and the formation of an equivalent amount of H_2CO_3 [0.7 mM of HCO_3^- decomposed and 0.7 mM of H_2CO_3 formed for each millimol of O_2 (22.4 ml) taken up]. As H_2CO_3 increases in the cell, reaction A shifts to the left, liberating CO_2, which is exhaled.

At a respiratory quotient (CO_2/O_2) of 0.7, found in the severely fasted subject, 0.7 mM of CO_2 is exhaled for each millimol of O_2 utilized. Under these conditions the hemoglobin buffer system could transport all the CO_2 isohydrically. Ordinarily the respiratory quotient varies from 0.7 to 1.0. If the quotient is 1.0, then 0.3 mM of CO_2 (per millimol of O_2 used) beyond the isohydric transport must be carried with pH change. This means that in the equation above reaction B would be shifted farther to the right in the tissues and farther to the left in the lungs, somewhat exceeding the isohydric transport and causing some pH change. Under these conditions the reactions for the formation of $HC\bar{O}_3$ in the plasma would undergo wider excursions with the transport of more CO_2. The maximum pH change in the cells under severe exercise, with the transport of a maximum amount of CO_2 and O_2 and at a respiratory quotient of 1.0, would not exceed 0.12. Since the plasma buffers have about one-third the buffer capacity of the hemoglobin system against CO_2, the maximum pH change would be reduced to 0.08.

Under ordinary conditions in the resting subject, when minimal amounts of CO_2 and O_2 are being transported, even at an RQ of 1.0, the pH difference between arterial and venous cells would be only about 0.03. However, the RQ of the resting subject is generally around 0.8, and under these conditions the pH change from arterial to venous cells is only about 0.01, and from arterial to venous plasma only 0.02 to 0.03. Thus it is evident that the mechanisms of CO_2 transport and the buffer systems of the cells and plasma are so adjusted that large quantities of CO_2 may be carried in the blood with insignificant changes in blood pH.

The over-all reactions for the formation of $HC\bar{O}_3$ from hemoglobin buffers in the cells, and without indicating isohydric transport or any quantitative aspects, may be represented by the equations:

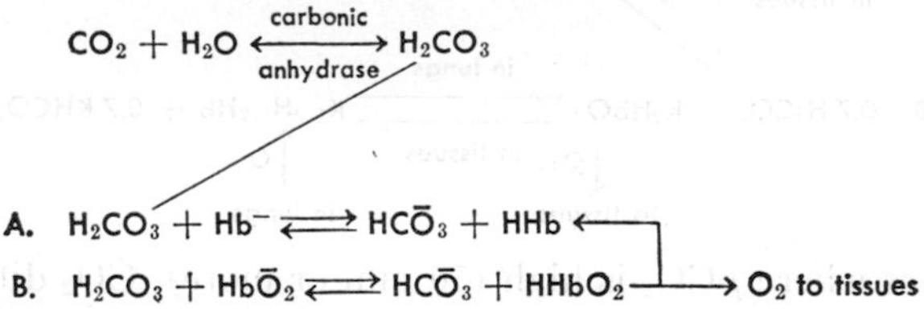

$$CO_2 + H_2O \underset{\text{anhydrase}}{\overset{\text{carbonic}}{\longleftrightarrow}} H_2CO_3$$

A. $H_2C\bar{O}_3 + Hb^- \rightleftharpoons HC\bar{O}_3 + HHb \longleftarrow$

B. $H_2CO_3 + Hb\bar{O}_2 \rightleftharpoons HC\bar{O}_3 + HHbO_2 \longrightarrow O_2$ to tissues

Ordinarily the entrance of CO_2 into the cells at the tissues causes a slight drop in pH. This means that the concentration of oxyhemoglobin anions, $Hb\bar{O}_2$, is decreased, and that of oxyhemoglobin molecules, $HHbO_2$, is increased. Since $HHbO_2$ releases O_2 more readily than $Hb\bar{O}_2$ does, the addition of CO_2 to blood in the capillary beds promotes the delivery of O_2 to the tissues by oxyhemoglobin. On the other hand, loss of CO_2 from the blood in the lungs slightly raises the pH within the cells and converts some of the hemoglobin molecules, HHb, to hemoglobin anions, Hb^-, which have more affinity for O_2 than HHb molecules do. Thus the loss of CO_2 in the lungs promotes oxygenation of hemoglobin.

3. Transport as carbaminohemoglobin. Roughton (8) has reviewed the role played by hemoglobin in the transport of CO_2 through the formation of carbaminohemoglobin.

It is well established that many substances containing the amino group reversibly react with CO_2 to form unstable carbamino compounds according to the equations:

$$\underset{H}{R-N-H} + CO_2 \rightleftharpoons \underset{H}{R-N-COOH} \rightleftharpoons \underset{H}{R-N-COO^-} + H^+$$

Among substances giving such a reaction are NH_3, aliphatic amines, and amino acids. The acid salts of NH_3, amines, and amino acids containing NH_4^+ and $-NH_3^+$ groups do not react. Also, H_2CO_3, HCO_3^-, and $CO_3^=$ do not form carbamino compounds.

Since the reaction is reversible, an increase in pCO_2 increases carbamino formation and vice versa. Also, because a carboxyl group is introduced, the carbamino compounds are more acidic than the substances from which formed. From the equations it can be seen that the addition of alkali to remove the H^+ ions dissociated from the carbamino compounds will shift the reactions to the right and promote carbamino formation. Also, the addition of alkali assures the presence of free $-NH_2$ groups which are necessary for the reaction. As to be expected, an increase in temperature promotes dissociation of carbamino compounds. In other words, they are best formed and kept at low temperatures.

An amino group of hemoglobin appears to be particularly suited for reacting reversibly with CO_2 to form carbaminohemoglobin. This reaction is oxygen linked in that hemoglobin reacts much more readily than oxyhemoglobin does. The anions of hemoglobin and oxyhemoglobin are the active substances. Apparently there is a shift in the location of the charge on the anion in the process of carbaminohemoglobin formation, since the total charge remains the same. The reactions may be represented:

$$Hb^- \cdot \overset{\overset{\displaystyle H}{|}}{N} - H + CO_2 \rightleftarrows Hb \cdot \overset{\overset{\displaystyle H}{|}}{N} - COO^-$$

$$Hb\bar{O}_2 \cdot \overset{\overset{\displaystyle H}{|}}{N} - H + CO_2 \rightleftarrows HbO_2 \cdot \overset{\overset{\displaystyle H}{|}}{N} - COO^-$$

Roughton and associates found that hemoglobin reversibly forms more than three times as much carbaminohemoglobin as oxyhemoglobin does at a given pCO_2. Thus 10 mM of hemoglobin per liter at a pCO_2 of 35 mm formed 1.12 mM of carbaminohemoglobin, while this amount of oxyhemoglobin at the same pCO_2 formed only 0.31 mM. Since the carbamino reactions are freely reversible, this means that oxygenation of blood containing carbaminohemoglobin causes the carbaminohemoglobin to decompose and release CO_2, and also the loss of O_2 from blood promotes the formation of carbaminohemoglobin.

The general relations of carbaminohemoglobin to CO_2 transport may be summarized in the diagram:

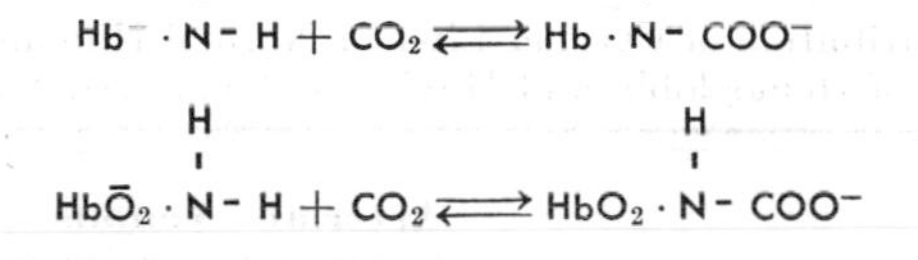

In the tissues as O_2 is given up, CO_2 reacts with hemoglobin according to the pCO_2 to form carbaminohemoglobin, and in the lungs as O_2 is taken up, the carbaminohemoglobin decomposes to release CO_2, which is exhaled. Thus, deoxygenation of the blood in the tissues promotes the formation of carbaminohemoglobin as well as the formation of $HC\bar{O}_3$, and oxygenation of blood in the lungs facilitates the loss of CO_2 from carbaminohemoglobin as well as from $HC\bar{O}_3$.

Since carbaminohemoglobin is quickly decomposed upon acidification and yields CO_2, just as does $HC\bar{O}_3$, a special method of analysis must be used for its detection and estimation. In the method of Ferguson and Roughton (9) blood is made alkaline and treated at once with an excess of $BaCl_2$. This precipitates H_2CO_3 and $HC\bar{O}_3$ as $BaCO_3$ and leaves the barium salts of carbaminohemoglobin in solution. The $BaCO_3$ is centrifuged off, and the carbamino CO_2 is determined in the supernatant solution by acidifying in Van Slyke's gasometric apparatus. The alkaline pH used tends to stabilize the carbamino compounds. While such determinations appear to be approximate, it is believed that probably some 20 per cent more or less of the total CO_2 is transported by the carbamino reactions.

Distribution of carbon dioxide transport in blood. As already pointed out, the CO_2 transported in blood as dissolved CO_2 amounts only to a few per cent, and the plasma buffers provide transport for only a small fraction as $HC\bar{O}_3$. Most of the transport of CO_2 is due to the hemoglobin buffer systems, which provide the mechanisms for the transport of some 90 per cent as $HC\bar{O}_3$ and carbamino compounds.

Table 16.6. Distribution of CO_2 per Liter of Normal Human Blood Containing 8.93 mM per liter of Hemoglobin and Having a Hematocrit Value of 40 Per Cent

	Arterial	Venous	Difference = (Transport)	Per Cent
Total CO_2 in 1 Liter of Blood	**21.53 mM**	**23.21 mM**	**1.68 mM**	**100**
Total CO_2 in plasma of 1 l of blood (600 ml)	15.94	16.99	1.05	62.5
As dissolved CO_2	0.71	0.80	0.09	5.4
As HCO_3	15.23	16.19	0.96	57.0
Total CO_2 in erythrocytes of 1 l of blood (400 ml)	5.59	6.22	0.63	37.5
As dissolved CO_2	0.34	0.39	0.05	2.9
As carbamino CO_2	0.97	1.42	0.45	26.8
As $HC\bar{O}_3$	4.28	4.41	0.13	7.7

From H. W. Davenport, *The ABC of Acid-Base Chemistry*, 3rd ed. University of Chicago Press, Chicago, 1950. From data in *Blood; A Study in General Physiology* by L. J. Henderson. Yale University Press, New Haven, 1928.

Table 16.6, taken from *The ABC of Acid-Base Chemistry* by Davenport (10), shows the distribution of CO_2 transport in the blood of a normal man at rest. The table shows two rather peculiar things. In the first place, while the red cells are known to provide base for the transport of most of the CO_2 as $HC\bar{O}_3$ and carbaminohemoglobin, the table shows that 62 per cent of the total CO_2 is transported in the plasma. What is more striking is that, while most of the $HC\bar{O}_3$ is formed from base in the cells, the plasma contains

0.96 mM of transport $HC\bar{O}_3$ (57 per cent of transport), while the cells contain only 0.13 mM (7.7 per cent of transport).

Two facts permit explanation of the situation. In the first place, plasma generally represents more than half the volume of blood and also contains a higher percentage of water. Each milliliter of plasma, on the average, contains about 0.94 ml of water, and each of cells about 0.64 ml. Suppose we calculate the millimols of $HC\bar{O}_3$ transported per liter of water in the plasma and cells, making use of the values given in the above table. Since 600 ml of venous plasma contain 0.96 mM of transport $HC\bar{O}_3$, 1,000 ml contain $0.96/0.6 = 1.6$ mM. Now, since 1 l of plasma contains 0.94 l of water, 1 l of plasma water contains $1.6/0.94 = 1.7$ mM of transport $HC\bar{O}_3$. In the case of venous cells, since 400 ml of cells contain 0.13 mM of transport $HC\bar{O}_3$, 1 l contains $0.13/0.4 = 0.325$ mM. Since 1 l of cells contains only 640 ml of water, then 1 liter of cell water contains $0.325/0.64 = 0.51$ mM of transport $HC\bar{O}_3$. Summarizing:

Total transport $HC\bar{O}_3$ in plasma per liter of blood $= 0.96$ mM
Concentration of transport $HC\bar{O}_3$ per liter of plasma water $= 1.7$ mM
Total transport $HC\bar{O}_3$ in cells per liter of blood $= 0.13$ mM
Concentration of transport $HC\bar{O}_3$ per liter of cell water $= 0.51$ mM

Thus we see that, while the amount of transport $HC\bar{O}_3$ present in the plasma of a liter of venous blood is 7.3 times that in the cells (0.96/0.13), the concentration of transport $HC\bar{O}_3$ per liter of plasma water is only 3.3 times that in a liter of cell water (1.7/0.31).

The chloride-bicarbonate shift. The chief reason why most of the transport $HC\bar{O}_3$, though formed in the cells, is present in the plasma is that as the HCO_3^- ions increase in the cells, many of them pass through the cell membrane into the plasma, and an equivalent number of Cl ions passes from the plasma into the cells. The reason for this chloride-bicarbonate shift is found in Donnan's principle of membrane equilibrium, which the student should review at this time. The chief ions in the plasma are HCO_3^-, Cl^-, OH^-, H^+, protein$^-$, and Na^+, and in the cells HCO_3^-, Cl^-, OH^-, H^+, hemoglobin$^-$, oxyhemoglobin$^-$, and K^+. Of these the red cell membrane is freely permeable only to Cl^-, HCO_3^-, and OH^- ions. Owing to the very high concentration of negative protein ions (HbO_2^- and Hb^-) within the cell, a net Donnan effect exists across the cell membrane as a result of nondiffusible negative ions on the inside of the cell and diffusible HCO_3^-, Cl^-, and OH^- ions both within the cell and in the plasma. Under such conditions the concentrations of diffusible negative ions in the plasma will be greater than their concentrations in the cell. In other words, $[HCO_3^-]_p > [HCO_3^-]_c$, $[Cl^-]_p > [Cl^-]_c$, and $[OH^-]_p > [OH^-]_c$. Also, according to the Donnan principle, the following relation should apply relative to the ratios of diffusible ion concentrations in cells and plasma:

$$r = \frac{[HCO_3^-]_c}{[HCO_3^-]_p} = \frac{[Cl^-]_c}{[Cl^-]_p} = \frac{[OH^-]_c}{[OH^-]_p}$$

Although the cell membrane is not freely permeable to H^+, it is to OH^-, and this assures proportionality of pH values in cells and plasma. Since the following is true for the relations between H^+ and OH^- ions in cells and plasma:

$$[H^+]_c[OH^-]_c = [H^+]_p[OH^-]_p = K_w$$

and

$$\frac{[OH^-]_c}{[OH^-]_p} = \frac{[H^+]_p}{[H^+]_c}$$

We may write:

$$r = \frac{[HCO_3^-]_c}{[HCO_3^-]_p} = \frac{[Cl^-]_c}{[Cl^-]_p} = \frac{[OH^-]_c}{[OH^-]_p} = \frac{[H^+]_p}{[H^+]_c}$$

Now suppose we consider these facts in relation to the transport of CO_2 in blood. As arterial blood reaches the capillary beds, we have a well-balanced Donnan relation between the ratios:

$$\frac{[HCO_3^-]_c}{[HCO_3^-]_p} = \frac{[Cl^-]_c}{[Cl^-]_p} = \frac{[OH^-]_c}{[OH^-]_p}$$

When CO_2 enters the blood for transport, much of it quickly reacts with Hb^- in the cells to increase greatly the $HC\bar{O}_3$ present:

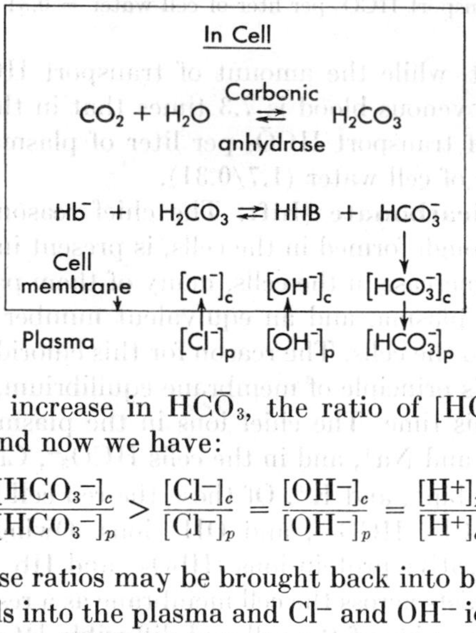

In Cell

$$CO_2 + H_2O \underset{\text{anhydrase}}{\overset{\text{Carbonic}}{\rightleftarrows}} H_2CO_3$$

$$Hb^- + H_2CO_3 \rightleftarrows HHB + HCO_3^-$$

Cell membrane

$$[Cl^-]_c \quad [OH^-]_c \quad [HCO_3^-]_c$$

Plasma

$$[Cl^-]_p \quad [OH^-]_p \quad [HCO_3^-]_p$$

As a result of this increase in $HC\bar{O}_3$, the ratio of $[HCO_3^-]_c$ to $[HCO_3^-]_p$ greatly increases, and now we have:

$$\frac{[HCO_3^-]_c}{[HCO_3^-]_p} > \frac{[Cl^-]_c}{[Cl^-]_p} = \frac{[OH^-]_c}{[OH^-]_p} = \frac{[H^+]_p}{[H^+]_c}$$

In order that these ratios may be brought back into balance, HCO_3^- ions diffuse from the cells into the plasma and Cl^- and OH^- ions diffuse from the plasma into the cells until again:

$$\frac{[HCO_3^-]_c}{[HCO_3^-]_p} = \frac{[Cl^-]_c}{[Cl^-]_p} = \frac{[OH^-]_c}{[OH^-]_p} = \frac{[H^+]_p}{[H^+]_c}$$

The number of negative ions passing from cells to plasma must equal the number passing from plasma to cells in order to maintain electrical neutrality of the plasma and cell fluids.

In the lungs the chloride-bicarbonate shift is exactly reversed. As the oxygenated hemoglobin reacts with $HC\bar{O}_3$ to form H_2CO_3 and liberate CO_2, which is blown off, $[HCO_3^-]_c$ goes down, again upsetting the ionic ratios, but in the reverse direction. Under these conditions:

$$\frac{[HCO_3^-]_c}{[HCO_3^-]_p} < \frac{[Cl^-]_c}{[Cl^-]_p} = \frac{[OH^-]_c}{[OH^-]_p} = \frac{[H^+]_p}{[H^+]_c}$$

Consequently, HCO_3^- ions pass from plasma into cells and Cl^- and OH^- ions from cells to plasma until the ratios are restored. Thus we see that, owing to the Donnan effect, most of the transport $H\bar{C}O_3$ may be formed in the cells, transported in the plasma, and finally decomposed to liberate CO_2 in the cells at the lungs where the CO_2 is blown off.

It will be observed that the Donnan effect accounts for a difference in pH between the cells and plasma and that OH^- ions move into the cells as HCO_3^- ions move out, and vice versa. The plasma is very poorly buffered against CO_2, whereas the cells are heavily buffered against it. The HCO_3^- shift from cells to plasma and reverse as CO_2 is taken up and given off is highly important in minimizing pH changes in plasma during CO_2 transport.

The total number of osmotically active particles in the cells increases upon the uptake of CO_2 and decreases when CO_2 is given off. This is compensated for by a flow of water into the cells as CO_2 is taken up and a flow from the cells as CO_2 is given off at the lungs. This results in venous erythrocytes being a bit larger than arterial erythrocytes.

Because of the chloride-bicarbonate shift between cells and plasma, great care should be exercised in drawing blood for carbon dioxide and chloride analysis where the contents of these are to be determined on separated plasma or serum. If CO_2 is permitted to escape from the blood, the bicarbonate of the plasma will decrease, and the chlorides will increase. For analytical purposes the blood is drawn into a centrifuge tube, covered with a thick layer of mineral oil, and capped until the plasma or serum can be separated in the centrifuge, which should be done as rapidly as possible.

Table 16.7, taken from Davenport's *ABC of Acid-Base Chemistry*, illus-

Table 16.7. Distribution of Carbon Dioxide and Chloride in 1 l of Normal Human Blood Containing 8.93 mM of Hemoglobin per Liter and Having a Hematocrit of 40 Per Cent

	Arterial	Venous	Difference
Plasma (600 ml)			
pH	7.455	7.429	−0.026
Net negative charges on plasma proteins	7.89 mM	7.80 mM	−0.09 mM
Bicarbonate ions	15.23 mM	16.19 mM	+0.96 mM
Chloride ions	59.59 mM	58.72 mM	−0.87 mM
Erythrocytes (400 ml)			
Net negative charges on hemoglobin	22.60 mM	21.15 mM	−1.45 mM
Bicarbonate ions	4.28 mM	4.41 mM	+0.13 mM
Carbamino CO_2 ions	0.97 mM	1.42 mM	+0.45 mM
Chloride ions	18.11 mM	18.98 mM	+0.87 mM

From Davenport, H. W.: *The ABC of Acid-Base Chemistry*, 3rd ed. University of Chicago Press, Chicago, 1950. From data in *Blood; A Study in General Physiology* by L. J. Henderson, Yale University Press, New Haven, 1928.

trates the magnitude of the chloride-bicarbonate shift in the transport of CO_2.

In the table it can be seen that the pH of arterial plasma was 0.026 higher than that of venous plasma. The net negative protein charges of arterial plasma exceeded those of venous plasma by 0.09 mM, equivalent to the formation of 0.09 mM of $HC\bar{O}_3$, through reaction with H_2CO_3 at the tissues. The negative hemoglobin charges of arterial blood exceeded those of venous blood by 1.45 mM, equivalent to the formation of 1.45 mM of $HC\bar{O}_3$ + carbaminohemoglobin upon deoxygenation at the tissues. The negative protein charges in the cells of arterial blood exceeded those in the plasma by $22.60 - 7.89 = 14.71$ mM, and in venous blood these ions in the cells exceeded those in the plasma by $21.15 - 7.80 = 13.35$ mM. These differences indicate approximately the driving force of the Donnan effect across the red cell membrane.

The table shows that the plasma of venous blood contained $0.96 - 0.09 = 0.87$ mM more HCO_3^- ions than could be formed in the plasma (0.09 mM), and the plasma of venous blood contained 0.87 mM less Cl^- ions than the plasma of arterial blood. Also, the cells of venous blood contained 0.87 mM more Cl^- ions than the cells of arterial blood. This means that as HCO_3^- ions were formed within the cells upon entry of CO_2 from the tissues, 0.87 mM of HCO_3^- ions passed from the cells into the plasma and 0.87 mM of Cl^- ions passed from the plasma into the cells. The reverse shift occurred in the lungs.

Davenport (10) calculated the $[HCO_3^-]_c$ and $[HCO_3^-]_p$ per kilogram of water for normal arterial and venous blood and obtained ratios as follows:

$$\text{arterial, } 0.70 = [HC\bar{O}_3]_c/[HC\bar{O}_3]_p = 0.76, \text{ venous}$$

Carbon dioxide absorption curves of blood. Figure 16.5, constructed from data of Henderson (curves 4, 5, 6, 7) and with data from Peters and Van Slyke (curves 2,3), shows the total CO_2 contents at different CO_2 tensions of oxygenated and deoxygenated whole blood (curves 4,5), and of plasma of oxygenated and deoxygenated whole blood (curves 6,7). Curves 2 and 3 show the behavior of sera first separated from blood (at 30 and 60 mm pCO_2) and then exposed to different CO_2 tensions. Curve 1 shows the behavior of a pure solution of 25 mM $HC\bar{O}_3$ for comparison.

Curve 1 for $HC\bar{O}_3$ solution shows that above 20 mm pCO_2 the total CO_2 increases very little with increasing pCO_2, the increase being solely due to dissolved CO_2. Below 20 mm pCO_2 the $HC\bar{O}_3$ begins to decompose into CO_3^- and H_2CO_3:

$$2HC\bar{O}_3 \rightleftarrows CO_3^- + H_2CO_3 \rightleftarrows H_2O + CO_2$$

and, at 0 mm pCO_2 all the $HC\bar{O}_3$ has been converted to CO_3^-.

Curve 2 shows the behavior of serum separated from blood at 30 mm pCO_2 and then exposed to different tensions of CO_2. Curve 3 represents the same thing, except that in this case the serum was separated from blood at 60 mm pCO_2. It will be noted that these sera act very much like the $HC\bar{O}_3$ solution, except that they have more capacity to take up CO_2 with increases in pCO_2. This is due to the presence of protein anions which react with H_2CO_3 to form a small amount of $HC\bar{O}_3$:

$$CO_2 + H_2O \rightleftarrows H_2CO_3 + \text{protein}^- \rightleftarrows H \cdot \text{protein} + HCO_3^-$$

At 0 mm pCO_2 these curves show that much of the serum CO_2 is still retained as CO_3^-, just as in the case of $HC\bar{O}_3$ solution (curve 1).

Curve 3 shows a higher CO_2 content for serum separated from blood at 60 mm pCO_2 than does curve 2 for serum separated at 30 mm. This is due to the higher HCO_3 content of the serum separated from cells at 60 mm, since there is more bicarbonate-chloride shift between cells and plasma at the higher CO_2 tension.

Curves 4 and 5 show the CO_2 contents of oxygenated and deoxygenated whole blood, respectively, at different CO_2 tensions. It will be noted that deoxygenated blood has more capacity to take up CO_2 at a given pCO_2 than oxygenated blood does. This is due to the fact that hemoglobin forms more bicarbonate from H_2CO_3 than does oxyhemoglobin owing to the greater affinity of Hb^- than of HbO_2 for H^+ ions.

Curves 6 and 7 show that the CO_2 contents of the sera of whole oxygenated and deoxygenated bloods are higher than for the whole bloods at a given CO_2 tension (curves

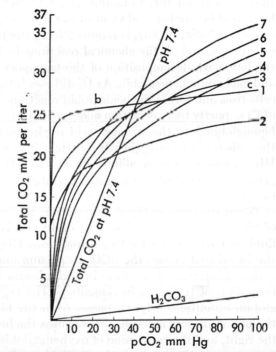

CO_2 absorption curves:
1. 25 mM $HC\overline{O}_3$; b to $c = HC\overline{O}_3 +$ H_2CO_3; a to b = chiefly $HC\overline{O}_3 +$ $C\overline{O}_3$; a = all $C\overline{O}_3$
2. Serum separated from blood at $pCO_2 = 30$ mm
3. Serum separated from blood at $pCO_2 = 60$ mm
4. Oxygenated blood
5. Deoxygenated blood
6. Plasma of oxygenated blood
7. Plasma of deoxygenated blood

Figure 16.5. Curves 4, 5, 6, and 7 plotted from data in *Blood, A Study in General Physiology* by L. J. Henderson, Yale University Press, New Haven, 1928. Curves 2 and 3 from *Quantitative Clinical Chemistry*, Vol. 1, *Interpretations* by J. P. Peters and D. D. Van Slyke, Williams & Wilkins Co., Baltimore, 1931.

4 and 5). This is due to the fact that, while most of the HCO_3 is formed in the cells, most of it is found in the plasma (or serum) owing to the bicarbonate-chloride shift.

It is interesting to observe from curves 4,5,6, and 7 that all the CO_2 may be removed from whole blood by reducing pCO_2 to 0 mm in striking contrast to separated serum (curves 2 and 3) and $HC\overline{O}_3$ solutions (curve 1). This is due to the fact that as CO_2 is removed the hemoglobin and oxyhemoglobin react with all the HCO_3 ions present:

$$\left.\begin{array}{l} HHb + HC\overline{O}_3 \rightleftharpoons Hb^- + H_2CO_3 \rightleftharpoons H_2O + CO_2 \\ HHbO_2 + HC\overline{O}_3 \rightleftharpoons Hb\overline{O}_2 + H_2CO_3 \rightleftharpoons H_2O + CO_2 \end{array}\right\}\text{off}$$

These reactions go to completion to the right as pCO_2 is reduced to zero. As indicated above, plasma or serum proteins decompose a small amount of $HC\overline{O}_3$ under these conditions.

A thorough study of the CO_2 absorption curves in the figure and of the above discussion will do much to help the student understand why whole blood is peculiarly adapted for the transport of CO_2.

Integration of carbon dioxide and oxygen transport. In Figure 16.6 an attempt has been made to show the principal chemical reactions involved in the transport of both CO_2 and O_2 and to show how these reactions are interrelated. The figure shows the flow of O_2 into, and of CO_2 from, the blood in the lungs, and the flow of O_2 from, and of CO_2 into, the blood in the tissues.

As the venous blood reaches the lungs, its pCO_2 is higher and its pO_2 lower than in alveolar air. Consequently, CO_2 diffuses from the blood into the lungs and is exhaled, and O_2 diffuses from the lungs into the blood and forms oxyhemoglobin. As CO_2 is removed from the blood, the pCO_2 in plasma and cells drops, and all the chemical reactions in both cells and plasma shift to the left, with decomposition of the transport increments of H_2CO_3, $HC\bar{O}_3$, and carbaminohemoglobin. As O_2 diffuses into blood, the pO_2 in plasma and cells rises and forces the hemoglobin reactions to the left, promoting the loss of CO_2, partly by mass action and particularly by converting the weaker acid hemoglobin into the stronger acid oxyhemoglobin. Also, loss of CO_2 from the cells tends to raise the pH a little, causing the hemoglobin to form more Hb^- anions with more affinity for O_2 than HHb. The loss of CO_2 and oxygenation of hemoglobin go on simultaneously, and each process facilitates the other.

When the arterial blood passes from the lungs to the capillaries, its pO_2 of 90 mm is higher and its pCO_2 of 40 mm is lower than in the interstitial fluid and tissues. Under these conditions CO_2 passes from the tissues into the blood and causes the pCO_2 in plasma and cells to rise. Through mass action this forces all reactions in both plasma and cells to the right, with the formation of transport increments of H_2CO_3, $HC\bar{O}_3$, and carbaminohemoglobin. Simultaneously, O_2 passes from the blood to the tissues and lowers the pO_2 in plasma and cells. This causes the hemoglobin reactions to shift to the right, and the conversion of oxyhemoglobin to hemoglobin facilitates the formation of $HC\bar{O}_3$ and carbaminohemoglobin. Also, the CO_2 entering the cells causes a slight drop in pH, and this results in the oxyhemoglobin giving up its O_2 a bit more readily. Thus, in the capillary beds the loss of O_2 from the blood facilitates the taking up of CO_2, and the taking up of CO_2 promotes the release of O_2.

The functioning of the O_2 and CO_2 transport mechanism of blood may be likened to a chemical piston which in the lungs is moved to the left by the mass action push of O_2 on one side and the mass action pull of CO_2 on the other. In the tissues the piston moves to the right with CO_2 pushing and O_2 pulling.

Significance of nitrogen in respiration. The N_2 present in blood, tissue fluids, and tissues is in physical solution only, and its quantity depends upon the alveolar N_2 partial pressure and the solubility coefficient of nitrogen. Ordinarily pN_2 in the alveolar air is about 570 mm, and the solubility

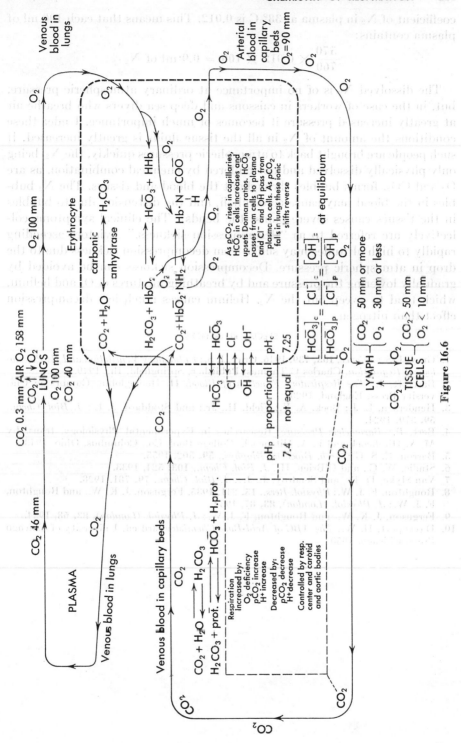

Figure 16.6

coefficient of N_2 in plasma at 38° C is 0.012. This means that each 100 ml of plasma contains:

$$\frac{570}{760} \times 0.012 \times 100 = 0.9 \text{ ml of } N_2$$

The dissolved N_2 is of no importance at ordinary atmospheric pressure, but, in the case of workers in caissons and deep sea divers who breathe air at greatly increased pressure it becomes of much importance. Under these conditions the amount of N_2 in all the tissue fluids is greatly increased. If such people are brought back to atmospheric pressures quickly, the N_2, being only physically dissolved and not buffered by chemical combination, as are O_2 and CO_2, forms bubbles throughout the blood and tissues. The N_2 bubbles in the blood may cause aeroemboli, and the distension due to bubbles in the tissues causes severe pains (the bends). The clinical symptoms collectively are referred to as "decompression sickness." Aviators ascending rapidly to high altitudes may suffer from decompression sickness due to the drop in atmospheric pressure. Decompression sickness can be avoided by gradually lowering the pressure and by breathing mixtures of O_2 and helium, which tend to sweep out the N_2. Helium causes much less decompression effect than nitrogen.

SPECIAL REFERENCES

1. Gray, J. S.: *Science*, **103**, 739, 1946. Gray, J. S.: *Pulmonary Ventilation and Its Physiological Regulation*. Charles C Thomas, Publisher, Springfield, Ill., 1949.
2. Barcroft, J.: *The Respiratory Function of Blood*. II. Hemoglobin. Cambridge University Press, England, 1928.
3. Henderson, L. J.; Bock, A. V.; Field, H., Jr.; and Stoddard, J. L.: *J. Biol. Chem.*, **59**, 379, 1924.
4. Bert, P.: *Barometric Pressure*. Researches in Experimental Physiology, trans. by M. A. Hitchcock and F. A. Hitchcock. College Book Co., Columbus, Ohio, 1943.
5. Barron, E. S. G.: *Arch. Biochem. Biophys.*, **59**, 502, 1955.
6. Stadie, W. C., and O'Brien, H.: *J. Biol. Chem.*, **103**, 524, 1933.
7. Van Slyke, D. D., and Sendroy, J., Jr.: *J. Biol. Chem.*, **79**, 781, 1928.
8. Roughton, F. J. W.: *Physiol. Revs.*, **15**, 241, 1935. Ferguson, J. K. W., and Roughton, F. J. W.: *J. Physiol. (London)*, **83**, 87, 1934.
9. Ferguson, J. K. W., and Roughton, F. J. W.: *J. Physiol. (London)*, **83**, 68, 1934.
10. Davenport, H. W.: *The ABC of Acid-Base Chemistry*, 3rd ed. University of Chicago Press, Chicago, 1950.

17

Renal function, acid-base balance, electrolyte and water balance

GENERAL CONSIDERATIONS

Water is the most abundant constituent of the body. It is a necessary component of cell structures, though it may be only loosely held by hydrogen bonds. It provides the fluid medium within which the chemical reactions of the body take place and substances are transported. Because of its high specific heat, it absorbs or gives off much heat with relatively small changes in temperature, thereby serving as a sort of temperature buffer system for the body. Since the rate of turnover of water in the body is high, the supply must be continually renewed, and among supplies to the body water ranks next to oxygen as a vital substance.

Electrolytes are distributed in solution throughout all the body fluids, blood, lymph, intracellular fluids, digestive juices, and urine. The cations of these electrolytes are Na^+, K^+, Ca^{++}, and Mg^{++}, with Na^+ and K^+ predominating. Quantitatively, the chief cation of plasma and other extracellular fluids is Na^+, and of intracellular fluids K^+. Among the anions of the body are Cl^-, HCO_3^-, $H_2PO_4^-$, $HPO_4^=$, $SO_4^=$, protein$^-$, and the anions of many organic acids, usually in small amounts. Quantitatively, the chief anions of plasma and other extracellular fluids are Cl^- and HCO_3^-, while in intracellular fluids they are, in decreasing amounts, inorganic and organic phosphates, protein$^-$, $SO_4^=$, and HCO_3^-. The intracellular fluids of most tissues contain very little Cl^-.

Since generally the proteins of tissue fluids and structural tissue proteins exist in the body at pH values above their isoelectric points, they ionize as acids.

593

The electrolytes of body fluids have various functions, the chief of which is to contribute most of the osmotically active particles, to provide buffer systems and mechanisms for the regulation of pH (acid-base balance), and to give the proper ionic balance for normal neuromuscular irritability and tissue function. A rough general expression of the relation between irritability and the ions of body fluids is as follows:

$$\text{Irritability} \propto \frac{[Na^+] + [K^+]}{[Ca^{++}] + [Mg^{++}] + [H^+]}$$

which indicates that irritability is directly proportional to the concentrations of Na^+ and K^+ ions and inversely proportional to the concentrations of Ca^{++}, Mg^{++}, and H^+ ions. The relations, however, are not entirely as simple as depicted by this relation. K^+ ions in low concentrations are excitatory, and in higher concentrations are inhibitory, particularly in relation to nerve synapses and myoneural junctions. In addition, the ratio Na^+/K^+ is important in this connection. The relation of K^+ to heart action is of particular interest. At high concentrations K^+ ions cause widespread intracardiac block, first in the auricle, then at the A-V node, and finally in the ventricle. The heart stops in diastole. Low concentrations of K^+ ions impair the contractility of heart muscle.

Under normal conditions fluids constitute about 70 per cent of the body mass. These fluids contain dissolved substances, chiefly electrolytes, which produce an osmotic pressure of about 7.5 atm. (equivalent to 0.9 per cent NaCl) and provide buffer systems which help maintain the pH within physiologic limits. In maintaining normal conditions in the body it is necessary to have the proper distribution of total fluids between blood, tissue spaces, and tissue cells, and to have the proper composition of these fluids. If too much fluid moves from plasma to the tissue spaces, edema results, while the movement of excessive fluid from the tissue spaces to the plasma causes dehydration. The relation of plasma proteins and blood pressure to the distribution of fluid between plasma and tissues has been considered in Chapter 15, which the student should review.

The two chief tasks in maintaining the proper composition of plasma and extracellular fluids and thus, indirectly, the composition of intracellular fluid are: (1) maintenance of the total electrolyte concentration, osmotic pressure, and volume, and (2) maintenance of the proper acid-base balance and pH. These tasks are the functions of the kidneys primarily and the lungs secondarily, which will be considered in detail later.

The membranes of the tissue cells generally are permeable to water, either OH^- or H^+ or both, and HCO_3^- ions. Chloride ions pass readily into and out of certain cells, such as erythrocytes and cells of the gastric mucosa, yet muscle cells contain exceedingly small quantities of Cl^- ions. Cell membranes exhibit restricted permeability to phosphate ions.

In some peculiar manner the quantity of sodium salts (Na^+ ions) in the plasma and lymph determines the volumes of these fluids. Thus, if the intake of salt is greatly increased or if excessive amounts are given intravenously or subcutaneously, the volumes of these fluids may be increased to the production of tissue edema. Conversely, the loss of large quantities of sodium, as in profuse sweating and severe diarrhea and vomiting, decreases the volumes of plasma and other extracellular fluids which can be maintained. The administration of pure water without salt after such experiences does not correct the dehydration because of the sodium deficiency; in fact, the dehydration is increased, because the water carries more electrolytes into the urine and further increases the deficiency. Here we have the anomalous situation of dehydrating the body by drinking water. This situation is often summed up by the statement that the tissues will not hold water without salt. The administration of NaCl along with water in such cases restores both the electrolyte and the water balance. Conversely, the administration of potassium salts has a diuretic effect and tends to decrease fluid volumes.

As previously indicated, Na^+ ions predominate in extracellular fluids and K^+ ions in intracellular fluids. Also, intracellular fluids contain more Mg^{++} and much less Ca^{++} than extracellular fluids do. As pointed out in the discussion of membrane permeability in Chapter 5 (which the student should review at this time), the maintenance of widely different concentrations of ions such as Na^+ and K^+ in intracellular and extracellular fluids against concentration gradients is accomplished by the expenditure of cellular energy in the active transport of ions across cell membranes. The work done by the kidneys in this active transport is discussed in Chapter 33.

Conditions which stop or reduce cellular metabolism, such as hypoxia, the presence of enzyme poisons, and low temperature, tend to equalize the distribution of ions between extracellular and intracellular fluids.

Maintenance of relatively constant volumes and compositions of extracellular fluids (plasma plus interstitial fluid plus specialized fluids) is essential to maintenance of normal cellular function, and many of the pathologic conditions with which the physician has to deal have their origins in disturbances of extracellular fluid volume and composition.

RENAL FUNCTION

Because the kidneys play a dominant role in regulating the volume and composition of body fluids, some knowledge as to how the kidneys function is mandatory for the proper understanding of acid-base balance and electrolyte and water balance.

The tissue cells of the body take food materials from the surrounding interstitial fluid and pass their waste products into this fluid. In turn, food substances at a higher concentration in blood plasma pass into the interstitial fluid, and waste products at a higher concentration in interstitial fluid pass into blood plasma. Thus there are concentration gradients which move food materials from plasma to interstitial fluid to cells and waste products from cells to interstitial fluids to the plasma. The waste products are removed from the plasma by the excretory organs, the lungs, the intestine, the skin, and primarily the kidneys.

The chief waste products of the body are carbon dioxide derived from the oxidation of all organic foods; various nitrogenous substances, such as urea, creatinine, and uric acid, from protein metabolism; sulfur and phosphorus compounds, also largely from protein metabolism; and excess quantities of water, sodium, potassium, calcium, and chloride. Many other substances in small amounts are eliminated from the body as waste products.

Carbon dioxide is largely eliminated through the lungs. The intestine excretes most of the calcium, magnesium, and iron, and some other substances. The skin normally eliminates considerable amounts of water by insensible evaporation. During active perspiration the skin may eliminate massive quantities of water containing large amounts of sodium chloride, considerable urea, and smaller amounts of other substances. However, it is the kidneys upon which falls the burden of excreting most of the solid waste products (55–70 g per 24 hours) and excess water of the body.

Aside from the gross excretion of solid waste products in urine, the kidneys help regulate the electrolyte and acid-base balance and osmotic pressure of blood by the controlled excretion of Na^+, K^+, Cl^-, HCO_3^-, and $HPO_4^=$. In addition, the kidneys form ammonia to be used for the neutralization of urinary acids, thereby saving fixed cations to the blood and tissues.

The kidneys apparently play an important role, through formation of the enzyme renin, in the maintenance of blood pressure.

The chief function of the kidneys is the regulated excretion of substances from the blood so as to keep the composition of blood and tissue fluids within the limits compatible with normal tissue metabolism. This is accomplished through operation of the unit mechanisms called "nephrons," of which it is estimated that each kidney possesses something over one million. Figure 17.1 indicates gross nephron structure with the blood supply.

The nephron proper consists of a glomerulus which serves as a filter and a subjoined tubule which regulates the composition of urine by selective absorption of substances from the glomerular filtrate and the excretion of substances into it. The tubule is composed of three segments. Directly attached to the glomerulus is the proximal segment, or proximal convoluted tubule, which has the greatest diameter and is composed of irregular epithelial cells having brushlike striations at their internal borders. The proximal convoluted tubule passes to the thin intermediate segment, or the loop of Henle, which is made up of very flat or squamous cells. The loop of Henle leads into the distal segment, or distal convoluted tubule, containing rather regular epithelial cells without the brushlike striations characteristic of the proximal tubule. The distal tubule passes to the arborized system of collecting tubules leading to the kidney pelvis from which urine flows through the ureter to the bladder. Figure 17.2, taken from Homer Smith, diagrammatically represents the structure of a human nephron.

The blood supply to the nephron is through an afferent arteriole which breaks up within the glomerulus to form a complex tuft of parallel capillaries which converge into the efferent arteriole. The efferent arteriole in turn divides into a plexus of capillaries closely applied to the basement membrane of the tubule cells.

Glomerular function. Cushny proposed the theory that urine formation begins with filtration of plasma in the glomerulus to produce protein-free glomerular fluid. Richards and associates (1) have analyzed the glomerular fluid of frogs and other cold-blooded animals for various constituents

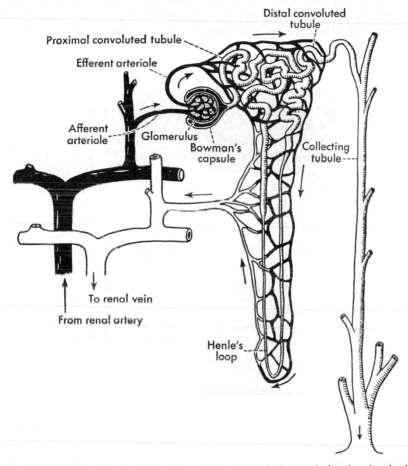

Figure 17.1. The microscopic anatomy of a single kidney tubule, showing its blood supply. (From Hunter, F. R., and Hunter, G. W.: *College Zoology*. W. B. Saunders Co., Philadelphia, 1949.)

and found the concentrations to be the same as in plasma with the exception of proteins and lipids or substances combined with these large aggregates. It was definitely proved, as Cushny had postulated, that glomerular fluid is an ultrafiltrate of plasma in these animals. Conclusive indirect evidence has shown such to be the case for the human and other warm-blooded animals.

The mechanisms of renal function are treated comprehensively in the books of Smith, Lewis and Wolstenholme, and Wolf given in the general references. Manery has written a comprehensive review of water and electrolyte metabolism (2).

The glomerular membrane is freely permeable to all the small molecules of the plasma. Also, it permits ready passage of the polysaccharide inulin with a molecular weight of about 5100. Purified egg albumin (molecular weight 40,000) also gets through, but serum albumin (molecular weight 68,000) normally does not. Most of the mesh surface of the glomerular membrane is sufficiently coarse to permit the passage of particles around 20 Å in diameter, and about half of this surface allows particles of about 50 Å to

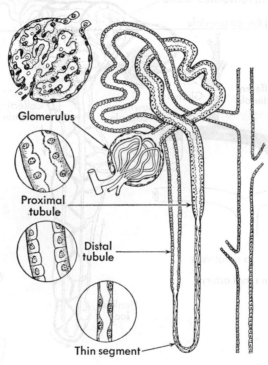

Figure 17.2. Diagrammatic representation of a human nephron. (From Smith, H. W.: *Lectures on the Kidney.* University Extension Division, University of Kansas, 1943.)

pass through. The nature of the particle also has some influence upon its ability to permeate the membrane.

The filtration rate in the glomerulus is determined primarily by the blood flow and pressure. The blood hydrostatic pressure within the glomerulus, which averages about 60 mm Hg, forces fluid through the membrane. This is opposed by the plasma osmotic pressure, which is about 25 mm higher than the osmotic pressure of the capsular fluid, and by the tension within Bowman's capsule, or the capsular pressure, which averages about 15 mm. Thus the average effective filtration pressure is about $60 - (25 + 15) = 20$ mm Hg. Ordinarily obstruction of a ureter causes cessation of urine production when the pressure in the ureter is about 20 mm.

The blood hydrostatic pressure within the glomerulus varies from about 50 to 70 per cent of the mean aortic arterial pressure of 90 mm. Other factors remaining constant, the glomerular filtration rate (GFR) varies with changes in glomerular hydrostatic pressure. This hydrostatic pressure varies directly with pressure changes in the renal artery, when there are no changes in tonus of the renal arterioles. Constriction of the afferent arterioles decreases glomerular hydrostatic pressure, while constriction of the efferent arterioles increases this pressure, with corresponding changes in glomerular filtration rate. Generally, moderate decreases in pressure in the renal artery are compensated for by increased tonus and constriction of the efferent arterioles, thereby decreasing renal blood flow but increasing glomerular hydrostatic pressure and the fraction of plasma filtered. The afferent arterioles may show increased tonus, but to an extent insufficient to prevent an increased glomerular plasma filtration fraction. When the mean arterial pressure decreases to 60–70 mm Hg, urine formation ceases, since the glomerular hydrostatic pressure becomes too low to maintain filtration.

Various nonphysiologic factors may alter the filtration rate. It may be decreased by occlusion of afferent arterioles by emboli (clots), by increased intracapsular pressure due to obstruction in the tubules and larger urinary channels, and by decreased permeability of the glomerular membrane because of infection. Increased filtration is caused by increased blood pressure, decreased plasma protein osmotic pressure, and increased glomerular permeability. Changes in glomerular permeability cause alterations in the sizes of molecules passed through as well as the amount of filtration.

It is estimated that the filter surface area of the glomeruli of the kidneys is normally about 1.56 sq m, and that about 700 ml of plasma or 1200 ml of blood per minute flow over this area. Under normal conditions this produces about 125 ml of glomerular filtrate per minute, for a 70-kg adult.

Tubular function. The quantity of glomerular fluid formed in the kidneys is enormously greater than the amount of urine excreted due to reabsorption of most of the water as the fluid passes through the tubules. This reabsorption of water is indicated by the much greater concentration of dissolved substances in urine than in plasma and glomerular filtrate. The solute concentration in plasma and glomerular fluid is normally around 0.3 osmolar per liter, while in urine the solute concentration may rise to 1.4 osmolar, representing a concentration of nearly fivefold.

The pH of glomerular filtrate is about the same as that of plasma, 7.4, and the filtrate is nearly isosmotic with plasma. As the glomerular filtrate passes through the proximal tubules 80–85 per cent of the electrolytes (Na^+, K^+, Cl^-, HCO_3^-, $HPO_4^=$, and $SO_4^=$) and of the water and practically all of the glucose, amino acids, and ascorbic acid are reabsorbed. Thus of 125 ml glomerular filtrate passing through the proximal tubules only some 20–25 ml reaches the loop of Henle and the distal tubules. This fluid is now essentially devoid of glucose and amino acids (very small amounts of each), is isosmotic, and has a pH of 7.4, since water and electrolytes have been absorbed in the proportions present in glomerular fluid. The reabsorption which takes place in the proximal tubules is referred to as "obligatory absorption," since it is relatively independent of the composition and volume of body fluids and so far as known is not under hormonal control.

As indicated above, normally about 80 per cent of the water of the glomerular fluid is reabsorbed into the plasma by the proximal tubules, and the remaining 20 per cent passes to the distal tubules. When the plasma volume increases because of water intake, the cardiac output and glomerular filtration rate increase so that a smaller proportion than normal of the water is absorbed by the proximal tubules and more passes on to the distal tubules. Conversely, in cases of dehydration and excessive concentration of plasma (and other body fluids) the opposite conditions exist, and less water comes to the distal tubules. Thus, the proximal tubules permit more water to pass when the plasma is too dilute and less to pass when the plasma is too concentrated.

Urine formation is completed as the fluid from the proximal tubules flows through the loops of Henle and distal tubules where the cells, through special mechanisms, reabsorb most of the water, various nonelectrolytes, and especially sodium salts from the fluid, and add such substances as K^+, H^+, NH_4^+, and creatinine (at higher plasma levels only) to it. Of the 20–25 ml of fluid reaching the loops of Henle per minute only 0.5 to 2.0 ml enters the collecting tubules.

The reabsorption of electrolytes, chiefly sodium salts, by the distal tubular cells is under the control of adrenal cortical hormones, aldosterone, and deoxycorticosterone. When the electrolyte concentration and osmotic pressure of plasma fall below a certain level, the adrenal cortex secretes more of these hormones, which increase absorption of sodium salts, thereby restoring a larger proportion of electrolyte to the plasma and relieving the lowered electrolyte concentration and osmotic pressure. When the plasma electrolytes and osmotic pressure rise above normal, the adrenals secrete less hormones, permitting the excretion of more sodium salts and lowering the electrolyte concentration and osmotic pressure of plasma.

In Addison's disease of the adrenals the secretion of cortical hormones may be greatly decreased, causing failure to reabsorb sodium salts in the distal tubules and their loss in the urine with profound disturbance of body fluid volume and composition.

The reabsorption of water by the distal tubules is under the control of the antidiuretic hormone vasopressin, which is released into the blood by the neurohypophysis. When the electrolyte concentration and osmotic pressure of plasma rise above normal, the neurohypophysis is stimulated to release more vasopressin, which causes more reabsorption of water back into the plasma by the distal tubules, with less water excretion in the urine, to aid in relieving the condition. Conversely, when the electrolyte concentration and osmotic pressure fall below normal, less vasopressin is released into the blood, decreasing water reabsorption by the distal tubules and increasing excretion in the urine, to relieve the condition.

In the clinical condition diabetes insipidus, frequently associated with lesions of the hypophysis or hypothalamus, there is a deficiency in the secretion of vasopressin and a decrease in the distal tubular reabsorption of water. Many liters of urine with exceedingly low specific gravity (1.002 to 1.006) may be excreted, which is associated with great thirst and water intake. The condition is controlled by administration of vasopressin preparations.

Experimental diabetes insipidus may be caused by section of the hypophyseal stalk or destruction of the supraoptic nuclei, which causes atrophy of the neurohypophysis.

The net over-all concentration of urine relative to glomerular filtrate is determined by the degree to which reabsorption of water exceeds reabsorption of total solutes in the glomerular filtrate.

About 180 liters of glomerular filtrate on the average are formed per 24 hours, of which some 178.8 liters (99.4 per cent) are reabsorbed. Table 17.1, taken from Gamble (3), shows the average total quantities of various ions present in glomerular fluid and urine per day and the amounts reabsorbed by tubular action. For example, it will be seen that 25,560 mM of Na^+ are filtered by the glomeruli and 25,449 mM are reabsorbed by the tubules (99.6 per cent).

Table 17.1

	A Plasma Conc (mM/l)	B Filtered A × 180 (mM)	C Found in Urine (mM)	D Reabsorbed B − C (mM)	Per Cent Reabsorbed (D/B × 100)
Na	142	25,560	111	25,449	99.6
Cl	103	18,540	119	18,421	99.4
K	5	900	60	840	93.4
HPO₄	1	180	30	150	83.4
SO₄	0.5	90	23	67	74.4

From Gamble, J. L.: *Chemical Anatomy, Physiology and Pathology of Extracellular Fluid.* Harvard University Press, Cambridge, Mass., 1954.

Figure 17.3, taken from Gamble, shows the chief differences in the compositions of normal blood plasma and urine.

Kidney clearance. As the blood containing waste products passes through the kidneys, a certain proportion of these substances is removed per unit time, and the amount of any one substance excreted in the urine during this time is equivalent to the amount of the substance in a definite volume of blood or plasma. Specifically the kidney clearance of a substance represents the minimum volume of blood required to furnish the amount of substance excreted in the urine in one minute. Plasma rather than whole-blood clearances are determined because of the unequal distributions of substances between plasma and cells and the wide variations in the proportions of plasma and cells in blood.

The clearance, C, of a substance may be represented by the equation:

$$C = \frac{UV}{P}$$

where U = the concentration of substance per milliliter of urine, V = the

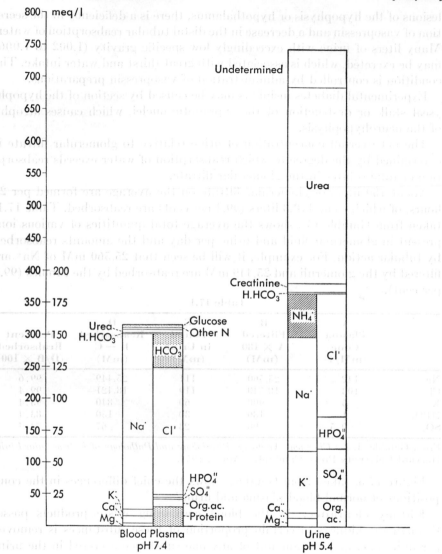

Figure 17.3
(Reprinted by permission of the author and publisher from Gamble, J. L.: *Chemical Anatomy, Physiology, and Pathology of Extracellular Fluid.* Harvard University Press, Cambridge, 1954.)

milliliters of urine secreted per minute, and P = the concentration of substance per milliliter of plasma. Suppose a subject puts out 120 ml of urine in an hour containing 900 mg of urea, and that the plasma urea concentration is 22 mg per 100 ml. The urinary excretion of urea per minute is $900/60 = 15$ mg $= 0.125 \times 120 = UV$, and the concentration of urea in the plasma, P, is $22/100$ or 0.22 mg. The urea clearance, C, is:

$$C = \frac{UV}{P} = \frac{0.125 \times 120}{0.22} = \frac{15}{0.22} = 68 \text{ ml}$$

This means that the amount of urea excreted per minute by the kidneys equals the amount of urea present in 68 ml of plasma, and does not mean that all of the urea is extracted from 68 ml of plasma as it flows through the kidney. Now if the glomerular filtrate volume per minute in the subject were the normal 125 ml per minute with a plasma clearance of 68 ml, then $68/125 = 0.54$ of the urea was removed from the 125 ml of glomerular filtrate. The fraction of a substance removed from the glomerular filtrate is called the "extraction ratio," and for the example given it is 0.54.

When the rate of urine flow is 2 ml or more per minute in the adult, the clearance for a substance is called "clearance maximum," C_m. At reduced urine flows the clearance does not represent the full capacity of the kidneys.

When the concentrations of a substance in plasma and glomerular filtrate are equal, and the substance is not absorbed or excreted by the tubules, its clearance represents the rate of glomerular filtration. The glomerular filtration rate, as determined by clearance, amounts to around 125 ml per minute per 1.73 sq m surface area for men and a bit less for women.

The polysaccharide inulin (molecular weight about 5000) is most commonly used for determination of glomerular filtration rates, though other substances, such as creatinine, thiosulphate, and mannitol, may be used. When creatinine is ingested, the clearance is about 175 ml per minute, indicating that 50 ml of plasma have been cleared by tubular excretion ($175 - 125 = 50$). Without the ingestion of creatinine the clearance approaches that of inulin. This does not mean the ingested (exogenous) creatinine is handled differently from endogenous creatinine by the tubules, but rather that as plasma creatinine values rise above a certain level due to creatinine ingestion, the tubules begin to excrete creatinine. Consequently, glomerular filtration rates are determined from creatinine clearances at normal plasma levels of creatinine.

Any substance which is not combined with plasma protein and which shows lower clearance than inulin must be reabsorbed by the tubules. For example, urea C_m normally ranges from about 64 to 99 ml and averages about 75 ml. This is 50 ml less than the glomerular filtration rate, indicating tubular reabsorption. The average proportion of urea absorbed is given by the expression:

$$\frac{\text{Inulin clearance (125)} - \text{urea clearance (75)}}{\text{Inulin clearance (125)}} = \frac{50}{125} = 0.4$$

which means that an average of 40 per cent of the urea present in glomerular filtrate is reabsorbed by the tubules. This tubular reabsorption of urea represents passive diffusion with the water being reabsorbed. The urea clearance is frequently used as a test for kidney function.

The clearances of many substances, such as Na^+, K^+, HCO_3^-, Cl^-, $SO_4^=$, $HPO_4^=$, amino acids, glucose, uric acid, and ascorbic acid, show clearances less than inulin and are reabsorbed by the tubules.

There are a number of substances which have clearances greater than the inulin clearance, which means that these substances are secreted into tubular fluid by the tubular cells. Such substances include H^+, NH_4^+, phenolphthalein, N'-methylnicotinamide, penicillin, phenol red, p-aminohippurate, and iodopyracet (Diodrast), which is a compound of 3,5-diiodo-4-pyridone-N-acetic acid and ethanolamine:

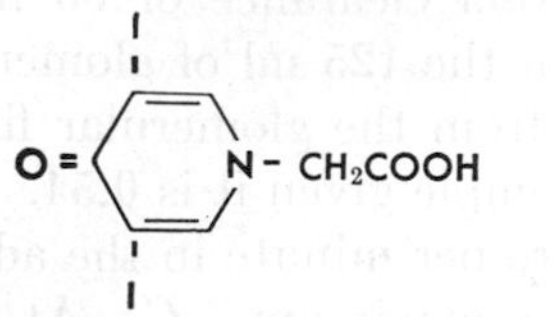

O=⟨ ⟩N-CH₂COOH   H₂N-⟨ ⟩-CO-NH-CH₂COOH

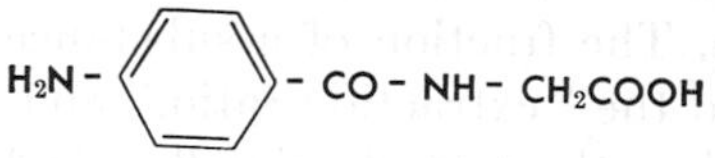

                                          p-Aminohippuric acid

3,5-Diiodo-4-pyridone-N-acetic acid

The tubular secretion of iodopyracet and of p-aminohippurate (PAH) is so effective that at low plasma levels of these substances they do not appear in the renal venous blood, indicating complete removal by one passage of blood through the kidney. Their clearances accordingly are a measure of the renal plasma flow per minute and amount to about 700 ml for the average adult, which represents a renal blood flow of about 1200 ml per minute (about one-fourth of the total cardiac output!).

Since p-aminohippurate is less bound to plasma proteins than iodopyracet, does not enter red cells, and is more easily determined than iodopyracet, it is replacing iodopyracet in the determination of renal blood flow.

When the C_m values for p-aminohippurate and iodopyracet are 700, this means that $700 - 125 = 575$ ml of plasma are cleared of these substances by tubular secretion into tubular fluid.

When the glomerular filtration rate is divided by the renal plasma flow, the fraction of plasma filtered through the glomeruli is obtained:

$$\frac{125}{700} = 0.178$$

which means that about one-fifth of the plasma brought to the glomeruli becomes glomerular filtrate.

Transport maximum, T_m, and renal threshold. Transport maximum, T_m, represents the maximum rate at which the tubules can reabsorb or excrete a substance. At normal blood sugar levels (for example, 100 mg per 100 ml of plasma) urine contains essentially no glucose, which means that the tubules are reabsorbing 125 mg of glucose per minute from the glomerular fluid. Suppose the plasma glucose level is raised to 500 mg per 100 ml; then the glomerular filtrate will contain $5 \times 125 = 625$ mg of glucose per minute. Suppose under these conditions the kidney excretion of glucose is 300 mg per minute. This means that the tubules can reabsorb as a maximum 325 mg of glucose per minute, or that the T_m for glucose is 325.

In the case of substances excreted by the tubules, such as PAH, the amount appearing in the urine per minute when the plasma level exceeds the excretory capacity represents the excretory T_m.

In the operation of both tubular reabsorption and excretion there are substances which compete with each other for the cellular mechanisms involved, indicating that the same entire mechanism or a part of it may function with different substances. For example, substances actively excreted by the tubules such as PAH, iodopyracet, penicillin, etc., may mutually depress their individual urinary excretions when given together in high dosage. Similarly, competition for mechanisms with decreased tubular reabsorption and increased urinary excretion are shown by sugars such as xylose and glucose, by various amino acids, and by sodium chloride and ascorbic acid. It is very interesting that the tubular reabsorption of ascorbic acid is decreased by the simultaneous tubular excretion of PAH.

Renal threshold. Various substances in plasma, such as glucose, ascorbic acid, Na^+, and Cl^-, do not appear in urine appreciably until their plasma concentrations rise to certain values, and such substances are referred to as "threshold substances." These substances are reabsorbed from glomerular filtrate by the tubules.

Specifically the renal threshold for a substance is the plasma concentration of the substance above which it appears in the urine, a constant glomerular filtration rate being assumed since the efficiency of tubular reabsorption decreases with increased rate of flow in the tubules. The renal threshold generally lies at a much lower plasma level of a substance than the plasma level at which the tubules show T_m.

The glucose renal threshold in the adult shows wide variations, most generally being between 140 and 170 mg per 100 ml of plasma.

The plasma concentration above which a substance appears in the urine is referred to as the "threshold of appearance." Another useful concept is the "threshold of retention" at which the urine and plasma concentrations of a substance are equal. When the plasma level of a substance exceeds the threshold of retention, the concentration of the substance in the urine will be higher than in plasma, while if the plasma concentration of the substance is less than the threshold of retention, the urine concentration will be less than the plasma concentration.

The thresholds of appearance and retention for K^+ in man average about 11 and 11.7 mg per 100 ml of plasma, respectively. Generally the threshold of retention is a bit greater than the threshold of appearance.

Various principles and facts relative to renal operation are brought out in Figures 17.4 and 17.5.

Figure 17.4, taken from Homer Smith, diagrammatically shows the relations of the tubules to the excretion of inulin, glucose, urea, and iodopyracet, with clearance values for these substances.

Figure 17.5, taken from Smith (4), shows the relations of clearances to plasma concentration for a number of substances. The clearance values given represent averages. It has been found that these clearances are proportional to body surface area, just as is energy metabolism, the average surface area being 1.73 sq m. Consequently, the above clearances represent values per 1.73 sq m of body area. The normal clearance for any given individual will be proportionately more or less, depending upon his surface area.

Relation of the kidneys to hypertension. Goldblatt (5) showed that when the blood flow to a kidney of the dog is considerably reduced (ischemic kidney) by a clamp on the renal artery, hypertension ensues which persists for several weeks and slowly subsides. The condition is relieved by removal

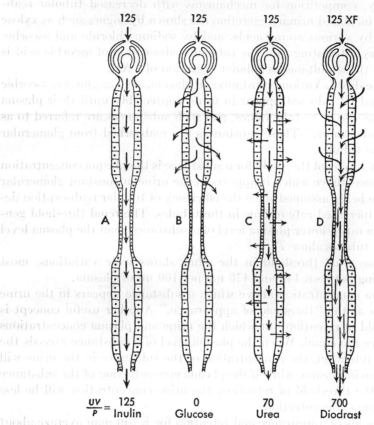

Figure 17.4. Scheme to illustrate the excretion of (*A*) inulin, which is excreted solely by filtration with no tubular reabsorption; (*B*) glucose, which is filtered but at normal plasma level and rate of filtration, is completely reabsorbed by the tubule; (*C*) urea, which is filtered, but in part escapes from the tubular urine by diffusion; (*D*) Diodrast, which is excreted both by filtration and tubular excretion. UV/P is the clearance in each instance, e.g., the virtual volume of blood cleared per minute. (*U* and *P* are the concentrations per unit volume of urine and plasma, and *V* is urine flow per minute.) The inulin clearance is taken as equal to the rate of filtration of plasma. *F* is the fraction of Diodrast filterable from the plasma, 1.00—*F* being the fraction bound to plasma proteins. (From Smith, H. W.: *Lectures on the Kidney.* University Extension Division, University of Kansas, 1943.)

of the clamp or of the ischemic kidney. The condition is made more severe when both kidneys are made ischemic, or one is made ischemic and the other removed. That the pressor effect is not of nervous origin has been demonstrated by transplanting the kidney to be made ischemic to the neck or groin, where the same hypertensive effects are observed.

Experimental renal hypertension appears to involve the following mechanisms (6). The ischemic kidney liberates into the blood an enzyme, renin, which splits hypertensin I, a polypeptide, from hypertensinogen, an α_2-globulin formed by the liver. Hypertensin I has no pressor activity; however, an enzyme present in plasma, "hypertensin-converting enzyme," acts upon hypertensin I to form hypertensin II, which is a powerful pressor agent. Tissues in general and kidney and intestine in particular contain a dipeptidase enzyme which destroys hypertensin II.

Different hypertensins have been obtained, depending upon the animal source of renin and of the α_2-globulin (hypertensinogen) upon which it acts.

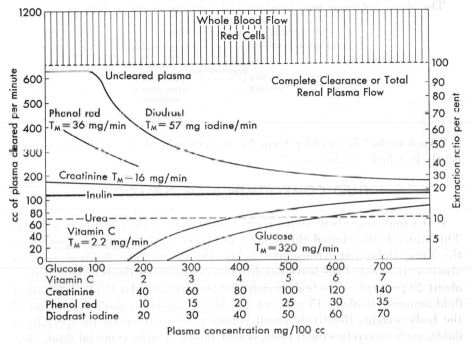

Figure 17.5. Diagrammatic summary of excretion of various types of compounds by the human kidney. Average normal Tm values are used in the calculation of the clearances at various plasma levels. (From Smith, H. W.: *The Kidney*. Oxford University Press, New York, 1956.)

Skeggs and associates (7) obtained hypertensin I from horse plasma, which was converted to active hypertensin II by the action of "hypertensin-converting enzyme" from horse plasma.

Hypertensin II of the horse is an octapeptide:

Asp - Arg - Val - Tyr - Ileu - His - Pro - Phe
 1   2   3   4   5   6   7   8

In the formation of horse hypertensin II from hypertensin I, the dipeptide His—Leu is split off, and if it is split from the C-terminus of hypertensin I, then hypertensin I is the decapeptide:

Asp - Arg - Val - Tyr - Ileu - His - Pro - Phe - His - Leu
 1   2   3   4   5   6   7   8   9   10

Elliott and Peart (8) produced a pressor decapeptide by the action of rabbit renin on ox serum which had the composition:

$$\underset{1}{Asp} - \underset{2}{Arg} - \underset{3}{Val} - \underset{4}{Tyr} - \underset{5}{Val} - \underset{6}{His} - \underset{7}{Pro} - \underset{8}{Phe} - \underset{9}{His} - \underset{10}{Leu}$$

This hypertensin appears to differ from horse hypertensin I only in having valine instead of isoleucine at position 5.

The plasma of normal persons appears not to contain hypertensin II (the active hypertensin), but Skeggs found sufficient present in the plasma of individuals with essential hypertension to maintain elevated blood pressure.

The above relations may be shown diagrammatically as follows:

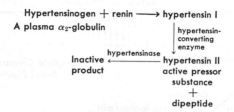

"Angiotonin" is an older term for hypertensin II. Angiotonin more recently is called "angiotensin."

FLUID COMPARTMENTS OF THE BODY

Water makes up about 70 per cent of the weight of the adult human body. This water is distributed throughout the body as the major component of the intracellular and extracellular fluids. The intracellular fluids amount to about 50 per cent of the body weight. The extracellular fluids represent then about 20 per cent of the body weight. Of the extracellular fluids, interstitial fluid amounts to about 15 per cent and blood plasma to about 5 per cent of the body weight. Relatively small volumes are represented by specialized fluids, such as cerebrospinal fluid, ocular fluids, lymph, synovial fluid, etc., which to a greater or lesser degree are included in determinations of the other fluid compartments. Figure 17.6, from Gamble (3), shows the relations between the various fluid compartments.

Measurement of fluid compartments. The measurement of fluid compartments is based upon the intravenous injection of a known amount of a substance which distributes throughout a given compartment or compartments and, after time for mixing, determination of its concentration in plasma, and correction for the amount excreted or destroyed in the body, so that the quantity of substance in the fluid compartment is known when the sample for analysis is taken (9). The fluid compartment is obtained by dividing the grams of substance present in the fluid compartment by the grams of substance per liter of plasma.

As an example of the calculations involved in determining fluid compartments, consider the following illustration. The sugar alcohol mannitol is excreted entirely by the kidneys. Suppose a subject receives 21 g of mannitol intravenously, and after a time for equilibration, 11 g have been excreted in the urine and the serum contains 0.7 g per liter. The quantity of mannitol in the body at the time of sampling, Q, is 10 g ($Q = 21 - 11 = 10$ g), and the concentration of mannitol per liter of fluid, C, is 0.7 g. Then the fluid volume or space occupied by the mannitol, V, is:

$$V = \frac{Q}{C} = \frac{10}{0.7} = 14.3 \text{ l}$$

When the concentrations, C, are expressed as grams per liter of water, then the volumes obtained represent liters of water.

The ideal characteristics of a substance for the measurement of a fluid compartment are: (a) the substance is evenly distributed throughout the fluid compartment being measured without passage into another fluid phase;

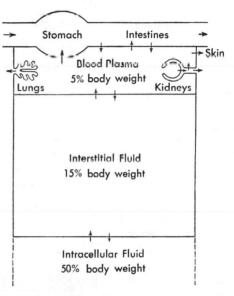

Figure 17.6. Distribution of fluids between body compartments. (This figure reprinted by permission of the author and publisher from Gamble, J. L.: *Chemical Anatomy, Physiology and Pathology of Extracellular Fluid.* Harvard University Press, Cambridge, 1954.)

(b) a representative sample of the diluted substance can be obtained for analysis, generally from plasma or serum; (c) the amount of substance retained in the body at the time of sampling can be determined from the amount injected and correction for the quantity destroyed in the body or excreted by any route. No substance in practice meets all of these ideal requirements completely, but a number of compounds give very useful approximate values. Figure 17.7 from Elkinton and Danowski (9) shows the distributions of various substances in the fluid compartments of the body.

It is customary in the literature to refer to substance space. Deuterium oxide, D_2O, and radioactive tritium oxide, or THO, distribute throughout all body fluids, so that total body fluid volume is obtained by determining D_2O and THO spaces. Some error arises from the fact that deuterium and tritium from D_2O and THO slowly exchange with hydrogen atoms of various body substances. However, this generally amounts to no more than 5 per cent and does not seriously affect their usefulness. Antipyrine space also represents approximate total fluid volume. From the dilution of known amounts of these substances in the body the total body water is obtained. The values for total body water determined with D_2O, T_2O, and antipyrine

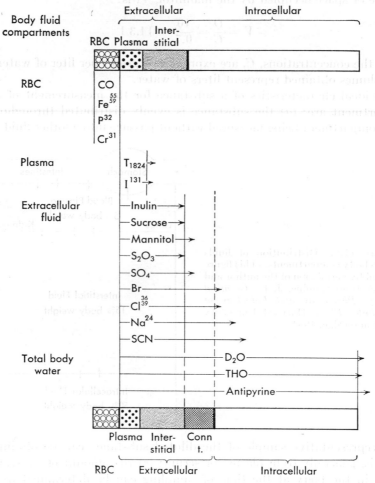

Figure 17.7. Substances used to measure compartments of the body fluids. It is obvious that many of the reference substances diffuse beyond the particular fluid phases, yielding volumes of distribution greater than the actual plasma, extracellular fluid, or total body water. D_2O, THO, and antipyrine penetrate red blood cells as they do other cells. (From Elkinton, J. R., and Danowki, T. S.: *The Body Fluids.* Williams & Wilkins Co., Baltimore, 1955.)

agree rather well with each other and with total body water determined by desiccation.

Extracellular fluid volume appears to be most nearly represented by the inulin space, though the slowness of inulin diffusion into extracellular fluids represents a disadvantage. The thiosulphate space appears to represent the extracellular fluid volume rather well.

As indicated in Chapter (15), plasma volume is generally determined by use of I^{131}-albumin or the dye Evans blue (T-1824).

The intracellular fluid volume is equal to the total fluid volume minus the extracellular volume, or it is represented by the D_2O space minus the inulin space.

The interstitial fluid volume is equal to the extracellular fluid volume minus the plasma volume (inulin space minus I^{131}-albumin space).

The interstitial fluid represents a fluid buffer between plasma and intracellular fluid. Since plasma is subject to rather sudden variations in composition through absorption from the intestine, the interposition of interstitial fluid between plasma and intracellular fluid aids in maintaining the composition of intracellular fluid more constant than otherwise would be the case. With this arrangement the kidneys have the opportunity to compensate for changes in plasma before they are seriously reflected upon the intracellular fluid.

WATER METABOLISM

In a lean 70-kg human adult the total free water is about 49 l (70 per cent of body weight). The extracellular water amounts to about 14 l, of which some 3 l are in plasma and 11 l in interstitial fluid and lymph. The intracellular water amounts to about 35 l (49 − 14).

The quantity of water required by the body is determined by the amount needed to give the proper volume and osmotic concentration to the body fluids, and to compensate for water lost by excretion through the kidneys, skin, lungs, and intestines.

Body water is derived from drinking water and beverages, the water content of foods eaten, and the water formed in the oxidation of foods which amounts to 0.6 g, 0.4 g and 1.07 g per gram of carbohydrate, protein, and fat oxidized, respectively. This oxidative or metabolic water is roughly proportional to the calorific value of foods, amounts to 100–140 g per 1000 calories, and varies with the proportions of the different foods utilized.

The amount of water required depends upon the water lost from the body, which fluctuates widely under different conditions.

1. **Urinary excretion.** The urine volume of a normal adult varies greatly, but generally it ranges from 1000 to 2000 ml and averages about 1200 ml.

The urine volume decreases with increased loss of water through the skin, lungs, and intestines, and vice versa. The volume also varies with diet. A very high protein diet produces large quantities of urea and other substances requiring much water for kidney elimination, while this is not the case with diets high in carbohydrate and fat. The amount of water required for the elimination of waste products in the urine varies with the concentrating capacity of the kidneys. The kidneys normally can concentrate urine to a specific gravity of 1.035 as a maximum, and have an obligatory requirement of about 600 ml of water per day to excrete the average load of waste products. In cases of severe kidney disease the concentrating capacity of the kidneys may fall so low that urine of a specific gravity of only 1.005 is formed, and in such conditions the obligatory water requirement is enormously increased.

Urinary excretion of water beyond the water obligatorily required for the elimination of waste products is referred to as "facultative water excretion" or "loss."

2. Pulmonary excretion. The quantity of water exhaled by the lungs per day normally averages about 400 ml, but it may be greatly increased in fevers with hyperventilation. This water loss from the lungs is all obligatory.

3. Fecal excretion. Ordinarily the quantity of water lost in the feces averages about 200 ml per day, but it may be greatly increased in cases of diarrhea and lead to severe dehydration. At the same time, large quantities of electrolytes containing an excess of $BHCO_3$ over BCl may be lost, leading to total electrolyte deficiency and acidosis. This water loss is obligatory.

4. Loss from the skin. The loss of water from the skin by insensible cutaneous evaporation, when there is no visible sweating, averages about 400 ml per day. This is an obligatory loss. Loss by sweating varies from 0 to as much as 14 liters per day during severe exercise in a hot, humid environment. The concentrations of electrolytes in sweat vary greatly; $[Na^+]$ from 12 to 120, $[Cl^-]$ from 8 to 80, and $[K^+]$ from 5 to 30 meq per liter. Thus it is seen that prolonged copious sweating may lead to both severe dehydration and electrolyte deficiencies, especially Na^+ and Cl^- deficiencies. The loss of Na^+, in particular, reduces the volume of plasma and other extracellular fluids which can be maintained, and thus tends to accentuate the dehydration and stabilize it until the deficiency is corrected by taking both salt and water. In severe dehydration the tissue cells lose K^+ and gain Na^+, which upsets the normal ionic balance and function.

Men doing hard labor at elevated temperatures and sweating profusely long have been known to suffer severe muscle cramps and nausea. This condition is aggravated by drinking pure water, because the diuresis increases the electrolyte deficit, but it is relieved by saline solution.

The loss of water through the skin (and lungs) in patients with fever may be large, though there is no obvious sweating. The loss of water by the body increases about 13 per cent for each degree C increase in temperature.

Water balance. The water balance of an average adult in a temperate environment is outlined in Table 17.2, as modified from Wolf (10).

From the table it will be seen that for water balance an average obligatory intake of 1600 ml is required to meet the obligatory loss of 1600 ml. The facultative loss, all through the kidneys, balances the facultative intake. The water requirement is roughly equal to 1 ml per metabolic calorie. The values in the table are for an adult at light work. A greatly decreased water intake is required during starvation because of reduced kidney excretion. During starvation appreciable water is provided by the oxidation of tissue components.

Water balance is achieved in the body through control of intake by the stimulus of thirst, and control of renal excretion by the antidiuretic hormone (vasopressin). A "thirst center," which is medially located in the vicinity

Table 17.2. Water Balance for a Normal Human Adult
Values represent milliliters per 24 hours

Water Source	Intake Obligatory	Intake Facultative	Organ of Excretion	Output Obligatory	Output Facultative
Drinking water and beverages	600	600	Kidneys	600	600
Food water	700	0	Skin	400	0
Oxidative			Intestines	200 (fecal)	0
water	300	0	Lungs	400	0
Subtotal	1600	600		1600	600
Total		2200			2200

of the third ventricle, causes the sensation of thirst when the extracellular fluids become hypertonic or are decreased in volume.

The hormone vasopressin of the posterior pituitary regulates absorption of water in the distal tubules of the kidney. Vasopressin secretion is stimulated by increased osmolarity of the extracellular fluids, causing more reabsorption of water in the tubules and less excretion in the urine.

In the case of water deprivation and body dehydration, water deficiency first appears in the plasma, which is directly connected with the channels of excretion. As the plasma becomes more concentrated and its osmotic pressure increases, water passes to the plasma from the interstitial fluid. Then, as the interstitial fluid becomes more concentrated, water passes into it from the intracellular fluid. Thus, since water passes all membranes freely, in water deprivation all compartments lose water, with maintenance of equal osmotic pressures in them. However, since the intracellular compartment contains the most water, it loses the most. As the tissue cells become dehydrated, they also lose potassium to the extracellular fluid, and this potassium is then excreted in the urine. At least some of this cellular potassium is replaced by sodium, which upsets the normal cellular ionic balance and functions of the cells. The loss of cellular water induces thirst, which is the main symptom in the first two days of water deprivation. Continued dehydration of muscle and nerve cells causes functional abnormalities leading to weakness and confusion. Death usually occurs when about 20 per cent of the total body water has been lost. It seems probable that much of the effect of water deficiency upon the body is related to dehydration of cellular proteins with changes in their physiologic functioning.

Although a certain concentration of sodium salts in body fluids is necessary for the maintenance of normal fluid volumes, excessive amounts lead to dehydration. The upper limit of salt excretion by the kidneys is about 300 meq per liter (1.75 per cent NaCl), and when salt solutions stronger than this are taken, the excess salt is excreted along with the water necessary for its excretion, leading to dehydration. The harmful effects of drinking sea water are related to this dehydrating effect.

The intravenous injection of large volumes of glucose solution without salt is equivalent to the injection of pure water so far as effects upon body fluids are concerned. The glucose is metabolized, leaving the water, which dilutes the body fluids and causes diuresis with salt loss. The salt deficiency leads to excess water excretion and dehydration.

When the water content of body fluids is appreciably increased without proportionate increase in electrolytes, a condition of water intoxication with nausea and muscle cramps occurs. This is often seen in persons drinking large volumes of water after severe sweating during which the body fluid and electrolytes have been depleted. Normally the kidneys are very efficient in the excretion of excess water and maintenance of body fluid concentrations.

The maintenance of water equilibrium in the infant is less efficient than in the adult. The body of the infant contains about 80 per cent water, as compared with 70 per cent in the adult. An infant weighing 7 kg will contain about 5.6 l of body water, of which some 4.2 l are intracellular and 1.4 l extracellular fluid. His daily output and input of water at equilibrium is about 0.7 l, which is 50 per cent of his extracellular fluid. On the other hand, the normal adult at water equilibrium has a turnover equivalent to only about 18 per cent of his extracellular fluid. Thus, it is obvious that failure to take in or retain water, and excess loss of body fluids through diarrhea, vomiting, and sweating more quickly cause dehydration in the infant than in the adult. The loss of body fluids by the infant also causes a proportionately greater loss of body electrolytes than in the adult, with more acute deficiencies and derangements of ionic balances.

ELECTROLYTES OF BODY FLUIDS

While the electrolyte contents of extracellular fluids can generally be obtained by direct analysis, the electrolytes of intracellular fluids must be determined indirectly and are subject to many errors, with the result that our knowledge of the composition of intracellular fluid is incomplete. As an example of the approach to the problem, suppose the electrolyte content of the heart muscle of an animal is to be determined. A known amount of a substance which distributes throughout extracellular fluid, such as thiosulfate, is injected intravenously. After a short time to permit equilibration, samples of plasma and heart muscle are taken and analyzed for thiosulfate and other electrolytes. The thiosulfate and electrolyte concentrations in plasma and interstitial fluid are assumed to be essentially the same. From the dilution factor of thiosulfate in plasma and the plasma electrolyte concentrations, the volume of extracellular fluid in the tissue and the electrolytes present in this amount of extracellular fluid can be calculated. When these electrolyte values are subtracted from the electrolyte values obtained on the whole wet muscle tissue, the values for intracellular electrolytes are obtained. The total water of the tissue sample is obtained by desiccation, and this minus the extracellular water of the tissue represents the tissue intracellular water. Then the concentrations of electrolytes in the intracellular water may be calculated.

The total electrolyte equivalent of a body fluid may be readily obtained by determining the total cation equivalent present and doubling this value, since electrical neutrality must be maintained. For example, if the total cation equivalent of plasma is found to be 155 meq per liter, then the total electrolyte equivalent is 310.

The electrolyte composition of plasma, exclusive of protein salts, is very similar to that of interstitial fluid, while the composition of intracellular fluid is quite different. Table 17.3 shows the detailed electrolyte composition of normal plasma, and Table 17.4 the approximate composition of muscle intracellular fluid.

Table 17.3. Electrolyte Composition of Normal Human Plasma per Liter of Water

	Mg/100 ml	Mg/l		mM/l	meq/l	Milliosmols* per Liter
Cations						
Na$^+$	327	3,270, ÷ 23 =	142		142	142
K$^+$	19	190, ÷ 39 =	5		5	5
Ca^{++}	10	100, ÷ 40 =	2.5, × 2 =		5	2.5
Mg^{++}	3.6	36, ÷ 24 =	1.5, × 2 =		3	1.5
Total cations				151	155	151
Anions						
Cl$^-$	365	3,650, ÷ 35.5 =	103		103	103
HCO$_3$$^-$	165	1,650, ÷ 61 =	27		27	27
HPO$_4$$^=$	9.6	96, ÷ 96 =	1, × 2 =		2	1
SO$_4$$^=$	4.8	48, ÷ 96 =	0.5, × 2 =		1	0.5
Organic acids$^-$				6	6	6
Protein$^-$				2	16	2
Total anions				139.5	155	139.5

* Milliosmols = millimols. In case of electrolytes such as NaCl and CaCl$_2$, 1 millimol = 2 and 3 milliosmols, respectively, because of dissociation.

Table 17.4. Approximate Composition of Muscle Intracellular Fluid
Values are milliequivalents per liter of cell water

Cations	meq/l	Anions	meq/l
Na$^+$	10	HCO$_3$$^-$	8
K$^+$	148	Phosphates plus other	
Ca^{++}	2	nonprotein ions	136
Mg^{++}	40	Protein$^-$	56
Total	200		200

While the values for K$^+$, Mg^{++}, and Na$^+$ of intracellular muscle fluid can be determined with considerable accuracy, the value for Ca^{++} is uncertain because of difficulty in determining the very small amount present. Potassium ions make up by far the greater proportion of cations in intracellular fluid, followed by Mg^{++} and Na$^+$. The Mg^{++} concentration of intracellular fluid is many times greater than in interstitial and other extracellular fluids. It is very probable that the distribution of ions, particularly cations, is not uniform throughout living cell protoplasm, due to combination with proteins, nucleoproteins, and other anionic substances concentrated in specific cell regions and structures.

The anions of intracellular fluid are predominantly those of organic phosphates (ATP, creatine phosphate, sugar phosphates, etc.), inorganic phosphate, various organic acids, and protein. The concentration of HCO_3^- in intracellular fluid is low, between one-third and one-fourth of the concentration in plasma. While there is some evidence (2) for the presence of Cl^- in the intracellular fluid of muscle, the quantity must be extremely small. Manery (2) gives a comprehensive discussion of the electrolytes of various tissues and fluids.

The differences in the distribution of diffusible electrolytes between plasma and interstitial fluid and between extracellular fluid compartments in general

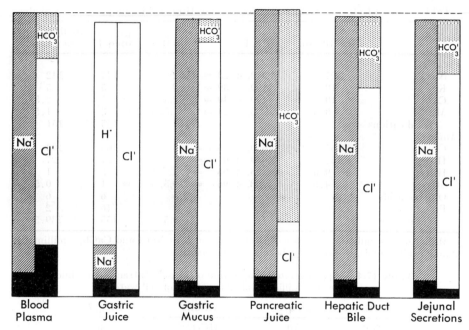

Figure 17.8. Electrolyte composition of gastrointestinal secretions. (From Gamble, J. L.: *Chemical Anatomy, Physiology and Pathology of Extracellular Fluids.* Harvard University Press, Cambridge, Mass., 1954.)

are related to the differences in protein content of the fluids and the resultant Donnan distributions.

While the Donnan principles certainly must apply in the distribution of diffusible ions between interstitial and intracellular fluids, the operation of active ionic transport across the membranes separating these fluids obscures the Donnan effects. The fact that various ions, such as Ca^{++} and Mg^{++}, form nondiffusible complexes with the proteins of extracellular and intracellular fluids also may make uncertain calculations of the ionic distribution ratios, since the proportion of the substance in the freely diffusible ionic form is unknown.

The various fluids of the body—plasma, interstitial fluid, and intracellular fluid—tend to maintain osmotic equilibrium despite variations in electrolyte distribution. It will be noted that the concentration of cations in intracellular fluid is appreciably higher than in interstitial fluid, yet these fluids are in osmotic balance. Much of the anion equivalence of intracellular fluid is supplied by protein, each protein molecule bearing about eight negative charges or equivalents. Then $8K^+$ associated with nondiffusible protein, if completely ionized, would yield only nine osmotically active particles:

$$K_8 \text{ protein} \rightleftharpoons \text{protein}^{8-} + 8K^+$$

However, in the interstitial fluid, where Na^+ is the chief cation, the concentration of protein is relatively low and most of the cation is associated with univalent anion (Cl^- and HCO_3^-). In this case $8Na^+$ associated with these ions would yield 16 osmotically active particles:

$$8NaCl \longrightarrow 8Na^+ + 8Cl^-$$

Thus it is evident that intracellular fluid must contain more cations (and total electrolyte equivalence) than interstitial fluid for the fluids to be in osmotic balance.

Figure 17.8, from Gamble, shows the electrolyte compositions of gastrointestinal secretions as compared to plasma. It will be noted that while the total electrolyte concentrations are very similar, there are wide variations in the distribution of ions in the fluids, which give to them their individual characteristics. These fluids are isosmotic.

CONTROL OF THE OSMOTIC PRESSURE, VOLUME AND COMPOSITION OF EXTRACELLULAR FLUID

The control of the quantity and composition of extracellular fluid is essential to control of the intracellular fluids upon which normal cellular and organ function depend. Most of the clinically observed disturbances involving electrolyte and fluid balance originate in the extracellular fluid, and therapeutic measures are formulated upon the basis of correcting these disturbances in the extracellular fluid. This concern with the extracellular fluid is a matter of practical necessity because of the difficulties in obtaining and analyzing intracellular fluids.

Control of total electrolytes and osmotic pressure. The central nervous system is especially sensitive to appreciable changes in the osmotic pressure of its intracellular fluid, which is in balance with and regulated by the osmotic pressure of the surrounding extracellular fluid. Death may result from either water intoxication or deprivation due to hypotonicity and hypertonicity of brain intracellular fluids, respectively.

The electrolyte concentration and osmotic pressure of extracellular fluid are regulated by the kidneys, which excrete more electrolyte and less water or more water and less electrolyte, as required, to maintain the composition of plasma and other extracellular fluids. The major proportion of extracellular fluid electrolytes is composed of Na^+ and Cl^- ions, and regulation of the composition of extracellular fluid by the kidneys is chiefly effected through variation in the excretion of these ions.

The amount of water excreted by the kidneys is determined by the amount of antidiuretic hormone (ADH) or vasopressin coming to them from the neurohypophysis. When the plasma osmotic pressure increases above normal, the neurohypophysis is stimulated to release more hormone, which increases water reabsorption in the distal kidney tubules, with less excretion in the urine. When the plasma osmotic pressure falls below normal, less hormone is released, and more water is excreted, to increase plasma osmotic pressure.

The amount of sodium salts excreted by the kidneys is controlled by adrenal cortical hormones aldosterone and deoxycorticosterone. At lowered plasma osmotic pressures the adrenals are stimulated to release more hormones, which increase the reabsorption of sodium salts in the distal kidney tubules, with less being excreted in the urine. Conversely, at elevated plasma osmotic pressures less hormones are secreted, and more electrolytes pass out in the urine.

Thus, by excreting more water and less sodium salts when the plasma becomes too dilute and less water and more sodium salts when the plasma is too concentrated, the kidneys function to regulate the total electrolyte concentration and osmotic pressure of plasma. Since plasma is in osmotic and electrolyte equilibrium with interstitial and other extracellular fluids, control of the composition of plasma by the kidneys is in effect control of the composition of the other extracellular fluids. This control of extracellular fluid composition is reflected in control of intracellular fluid composition.

In addition to regulation of the electrolyte concentration and osmotic pressure by the kidneys, the thirst mechanism also plays an important role. At elevated plasma osmotic pressures osmoreceptors in the hypothalamus are stimulated to cause the "thirst sensation," which causes an increased water intake that dilutes the extracellular fluids back toward normal.

Extracellular fluid volume control. While the electrolyte concentration and osmotic pressure of extracellular fluid are of paramount importance, the total quantity of extracellular fluid present in the body is also very important. A normal plasma volume is essential to normal heart action and blood circulation. When greatly decreased due to hemorrhage or other causes, tissue hypoxia and other manifestations of shock appear. In congestive heart failure the kidney excretion of sodium is decreased, which leads to sodium retention and an increase in plasma volume and extracellular fluid volume in general. This tends to overload the failing heart and cause tissue edema. The expansion of extracellular fluid volume is associated also with an increase in intracellular fluid volume, so that the volumes of all body fluid compartments are increased.

Plasma volume is primarily dependent upon the concentration of plasma proteins, particularly the albumin fraction, which determines the effective osmotic pressure of plasma and the capacity to maintain the proper fluid volume distribution between the vascular system and interstitial fluid spaces (see Chapter 15). Marked plasma protein depletion, especially of the albumin fraction, results in decreased plasma volume. When the plasma volume is reduced by hemorrhage, interstitial fluid moves into the vascular system to help maintain plasma volume and circulatory efficiency. However, this represents an emergency compensation only, since the protein content of the plasma is low. Such situations are best corrected by intravenous administration of whole blood, or plasma or concentrated albumin solution, to restore the normal osmotic balance and volume.

The total extracellular fluid volume of the body in some unknown manner is a function of the total sodium content of the body and fluctuates directly as the sodium content. While the kidney mechanisms rather closely regulate the electrolyte concentration and osmotic pressure of extracellular fluids, these mechanisms are relatively insensitive to changes in extracellular fluid volume.

When hypertonic salt solutions, such as sea water, are ingested, water passes from the intracellular fluid to expand the extracellular fluid volume until osmotic balance is attained. Unless compensated for by the intake of water, severe intracellular dehydration and concentration may occur, with damage to the central nervous system in particular, and with fatal results. If isotonic NaCl solution is administered, there is a proportionate increase in extracellular fluid volume without the diuresis following the administration of water alone. Excess salt is excreted in the urine for several days, and the extracellular fluid volume gradually returns to normal. When a person is on a salt-free diet, the excretion of Na^+ and Cl^- by the kidneys gradually decreases until these ions are practically absent from the urine. Under such conditions the kidneys retain the proper amounts of sodium and water to maintain the electrolyte concentration and osmotic pressure of extracellular fluids within the normal range, but since the total body sodium is depleted, the volume of the extracellular fluids is proportionately decreased. This decrease in extracellular fluid volume is the reason for the clinical use of low-sodium diets in patients with congestive heart failure and hypertension.

The direct relation of the sodium content and the tonicity of extracellular fluid to the volume and tonicity of intracellular fluid is the result of the osmotic balance between these fluids, which is maintained primarily by the transfer of water from the intracellular to the extracellular fluid when the osmotic concentration of extracellular fluid is increased and the reverse transfer of water from extracellular to intracellular fluid when the osmotic pressure of extracellular fluid is decreased.

As pointed out by Welt (11), in clinical conditions with low extracellular sodium (hyponatremia) the amount of sodium necessary to be given to correct the deficit must be calculated on the basis of total body water and not upon only the extracellular fluid volume, despite the fact that the sodium does not enter the cells appreciably. When salt is added to the extracellular compartment to increase its tonicity, a definite volume of water is transferred from intracellular to extracellular fluids to establish osmotic equilibrium, and sufficient salt must be given to bring the concentration in this water to normal as well as to correct the deficit in the extracellular fluid.

Suppose analysis of a patient's serum shows a deficit of 10 mM of sodium per liter (also 10 mM of associated anion, considered as Cl$^-$, per liter), and assume that from the weight of the patient, 80 kg, a volume of 48 l total body water is estimated (0.60 × 80). Then the serum sodium and the extracellular fluid sodium can be increased 10 mM by giving the patient 480 mM of NaCl.

The above situation may be better understood if the processes taking place are analyzed. A sodium and chloride deficit each of 10 mM per liter represent a deficit of 20 milliosmols (mOsm) per liter. Assuming a normal mOsm concentration of 310 per liter, the initial concentration in the extracellular fluid of the patient was 290 mOsm per liter. When NaCl is added to the extracellular fluid, its osmotic pressure increases and fluid passes from the intracellular compartment.

The initial extracellular fluid volume of the patient was 16 l (0.20 × 80), and the milliosmol deficit 20 per liter, or a total of 20 × 16 = 320. The intracellular fluid volume was 32 l (48 − 16) and represented 32 × 290 = 9280 total milliosmols. In order to increase the concentration of the intracellular fluid to normal 310 mOsm per liter, the volume must be reduced to 29.935 l (9280/310 = 29.935 l). This is equivalent to the transfer of 32 − 29.935 = 2.065 l of water from the intracellular to the extracellular compartment. The NaCl required to provide the normal concentration to this volume of water is 310 × 2.065 = 640 mOsm.

Thus, it is evident that to raise the concentration in the 16 l of extracellular water from 290 to 310 mOsm per liter (16 × 20 = 320), and that of the 2.065 l of water transferred from intracellular to extracellular fluid from 0 to 310 mOsm per liter (2.065 × 310 = 640), 960 mOsm of NaCl (320 + 640) must be administered to the patient. Since each millimol of NaCl equals 2 mOsm, this represents 480 mM of NaCl, the quantity calculated as necessary to correct the deficit on the basis of total body water.

Another approach here is as follows: The volume of extracellular water theoretically would become 18.065 l, and the concentration 4640/18.065 = 256.85 mOsm per liter, leaving a deficit of 310 − 253.85 = 53.15 mOsm per liter, or a total deficit of 18.065 × 53.15 = 960 mOsm = 480 mM of NaCl, which should be given to the patient.

Figure 17.9 illustrates diagrammatically the fluid and electrolyte relations in a case such as discussed above.

In cases of dehydration where there is a deficit of water with increased sodium, the water deficit may be calculated (11) from the ratio of the elevated serum sodium concentration to the normal serum sodium concentration. The increase in serum sodium concentration is inversely proportional to the total body water volume.

$$\frac{\text{Normal serum [Na}^+\text{]}}{\text{Elevated serum [Na}^+\text{]}} = \frac{\text{Body water volume}}{\text{Normal body water volume}}$$

or

$$\text{Body water volume} = \frac{\text{Normal serum [Na}^+]}{\text{Elevated serum [Na}^+]} \times \text{Normal body water volume}$$

Then the water deficit is:

Normal body water volume − Body water volume

For example, suppose the 80-kg subject above with a normal total body water of 48 l has a serum sodium value of 160 meq per liter as compared with a normal value of 138 meq per liter. Then his body water is given by:

$$\text{Body water volume} = \frac{138}{160} \times 48 = 41.37 \text{ l}$$

$$\text{Body water deficit} = 48 - 41.37 = 6.63 \text{ l}$$

Variations in extracellular fluid volume and electrolytes. If one considers only the volume and electrolyte concentrations of extracellular fluids, there are six possible alterations of volume and/or concentration (11).

	Intracellular	Extracellular
I	Water = 32 liters Electrolytes = 290 mOsm/l Electrolyte deficit = 20 mOsm = 10 mM NaCl/l Total oloctrolytes = 32×290 − 9280 mOsm Total electrolyte (NaCl) deficit = 32×20 = 640 mOsm	Water = 16 liters Electrolytes = 290 mOsm/l Electrolyte deficit = 20 mOsm/l Total electrolytes = 16×290 = 4640 mOsm Electrolyte deficit = 16×20 − 320 mOsm
II	Water = 29.935 liters Total electrolytes = 9280 mOsm = $\frac{9280}{29.935}$ = 310 mOsm per liter, which is normal	Water = 18.065 liters Electrolytes = 4640 mOsm = $\frac{4640}{18.065}$ = 256.85 mOsm/l Total electrolyte deficit = (310−256.8)×18.065 = 53.15×18.065 = 960 mOsm = 480 mM NaCl required

Figure 17.9. Diagram I shows the initial distribution of water and electrolytes in intracellular and extracellular compartments in a hypothetical patient weighing 80 kg with an extracellular deficit of 10 mM sodium chloride (20 mOsm) per liter of water. Diagram II shows the shift of water from intracellular to extracellular compartments when NaCl is given to the patient and the amount required to bring the mOsm concentration up to the normal value of 310.

Changes in extracellular fluid volume are indicated by changes in the hematocrit value of blood and of the concentrations of hemoglobin and plasma proteins. An expansion of volume decreases hematocrit and the concentrations of hemoglobin and plasma proteins, while a contraction of volume has the opposite effect.

Isotonic expansion of extracellular fluid, in which both water and salt are in normal proportions but the volume is above normal, is observed after parenteral administrations of saline solution in excess, which may lead to edema of the lungs and extremities. The hematocrit, hemoglobin, and plasma protein values are low. Intracellular fluid volume is unchanged, since there is osmotic balance between extracellular and intracellular fluids. Kidney excretion of both sodium salts and water is increased in compensation if function is normal. Serum sodium concentration is normal in isotonic expansion.

Hypertonic expansion results from the accumulation or retention of sodium without a proportionate increase in water, but with an over-all expansion of extracellular fluid volume. Since the extracellular fluid is hypertonic, water passes from the intracellular fluid until osmotic balance is attained, resulting in the expanded extracellular volume and cellular dehydration. This condition may be observed as the result of drinking hypertonic salt solution, such as sea water, which contains nearly four times as much sodium as extracellular fluid. The hematocrit, hemoglobin, and plasma protein values are low. Kidney excretion of both sodium salts and water is increased in compensation if function is normal. Serum sodium concentration is high.

Hypotonic expansion of extracellular fluid, in which there is an accumulation of water without a proportionate increase in salt, is observed occasionally when large volumes of salt-free fluids, such as 5 per cent glucose solution, are given to patients with decreased renal function. Since the extracellular fluid is hypotonic, water passes into the intracellular fluid and increases its volume until osmotic balance is reached. The hematocrit, hemoglobin, and plasma protein values are low. Insofar as kidney function permits, compensation is effected by increased excretion of water and decreased excretion of salt. Plasma sodium concentration is low.

Isotonic contraction, in which there are proportional decreases in both extracellular salt and water, occurs as the result of loss of isotonic fluids from the body (gastrointestinal secretions) in conditions such as diarrheal disease and pernicious vomiting. Since the volume of these secretions per day is large (saliva 1500 ml, gastric juice 2500 ml, pancreatic juice 700 ml, bile 500 ml, intestinal mucosal secretions 3000 ml, total 8200 ml) as compared to the total extracellular volume (14,000 ml), the continued loss of a considerable proportion of these secretions results in severe extracellular dehydration and total electrolyte depletion (chiefly Na^+ and Cl^-). Figure 17.8 (page 616), from Gamble, shows the compositions of various gastrointestinal secretions relative to the composition of plasma.

In isotonic contraction cardiovascular disturbances arise because of decreased plasma volume, and the kidneys fail to excrete normal quantities of nitrogenous waste products, as evidenced by increased blood nonprotein nitrogen. The volume of urine decreases, and unless plasma volume, blood pressure, and kidney function are restored by administration of salt and water, kidney function may cease and the patient become comatose and die of circulatory collapse.

In isotonic contraction intracellular fluid volume remains normal, because extracellular fluid is isotonic. Hematocrit, hemoglobin, and plasma protein values are high. The kidneys tend to compensate by excreting both less salt and less water. Plasma sodium concentration is normal.

Hypertonic contraction occurs when there is excessive loss of water relative to the loss of sodium salts, such as is found in persons deprived of water or who because of illness or inattention fail to take water, in persons subjected to copious sweating without adequate intake of water (and salt), and in persons with diabetes mellitus or insipidus when the large loss of water in the urine is not balanced by water intake.

In hypertonic contraction water passes from intracellular to extracellular fluid to establish osmotic equilibrium at a higher tonicity than normal for both fluids; that is, both intracellular and extracellular dehydration exist. Since the volume of intracellular is more than twice that of extracellular fluid, in hypertonic contraction the major proportion of the water is lost from the intracellular compartment. The chief clinical manifestations are due to the effects of cellular dehydration in the central nervous system.

In hypertonic contraction the hematocrit, hemoglobin, and plasma protein values are high. The kidney excretion of salt is increased and that of water decreased if function is normal. Serum sodium concentration is high.

Hypotonic contraction results when excessive salt relative to water is lost from the body. This happens in the adrenal cortical hormone deficiency of Addison's disease (deficient sodium reabsorption in distal kidney tubules) and may be observed after traumatic brain injury (cerebral salt-wasting syndrome). In some patients with chronic renal disease the capacity of the kidneys to reabsorb sodium salts is markedly decreased, which leads to excessive salt loss relative to water, and hypotonic contraction ensues.

In hypotonic contraction water passes from the extracellular to the intracellular fluid to establish osmotic equilibrium, which further contracts the extracellular volume. The chief clinical manifestations are due to the decreased plasma volume and its effects upon cardiac function and circulation.

In hypotonic contraction the hematocrit, hemoglobin, and plasma protein values are high, the kidney excretion of sodium salts is decreased, and that of water increased. The plasma sodium concentration is low.

From the above discussion it will be seen that the extracellular fluid volume cannot be judged from the concentration of serum sodium but is indicated by values for the hematocrit, hemoglobin, and plasma proteins.

ACID-BASE BALANCE

General considerations. The acid-base balance of the body is concerned with the metabolism of H^+ ions or protons, the mechanisms of their origin in the body, and the ways in which they are handled and excreted so as to maintain the pH of the body fluids relatively constant.

While the pH of extracellular fluids generally is maintained around 7.4, values for intracellular fluids obtained largely by staining with intravital dyes—which also serve as pH indicators, and which are subject to error—show more variation and generally average lower than the pH of extracellular fluids. For example the following intracellular pH ranges have been found for rat tissues: stomach parietal cells 6.4–6.6, duodenal cells 6.8–7.0, peripheral liver cells 7.1–7.5, central liver cells 6.7–7.0, Kupffer cells 6.4–6.5, bone 6.5–7.3.

The chief acids of the body are H_2CO_3, HHb, $HHbO_2$, and other proteins; various organic acids, such as lactic, pyruvic, and citric acids; organic phosphates; and phosphoric and sulfuric acids. These are the substances which are the H^+ ion or proton donors.

The chief bases of the body, which are the H^+ ion or proton acceptors, are the anions of the weak acids, such as HCO_3^-, Hb^-, and HbO_2^-; protein$^-$ in general; $HPO_4^=$; and the anions of organic acids and organic phosphates.

The buffer systems of the body accordingly are made up of the weak acids and their salts (anions):

$$\text{Proton acceptors} \longrightarrow \frac{\overset{B^+}{HCO_3^-}}{H_2CO_3}, \frac{\overset{B^+}{Hb^-}}{HHb}, \frac{\overset{B^+}{HbO_2^-}}{HHbO_2}, \frac{\overset{B^+}{Protein^-}}{H \cdot Protein} \text{ etc.}$$
$$\text{Proton donors} \longrightarrow$$

where B^+ = a cation such as Na^+ or K^+.

When the pH of body fluids is below normal, the ratio of proton acceptors (bases) to proton donors (acids) is below normal; and when the pH of body fluids is above normal, the ratio of proton acceptors to proton donors is above normal.

When protons are added to body fluids, they are taken up by the buffer bases (anions) to form the buffer acids; and when there is a deficit of protons, they are given to the body fluids by the buffer acids, the process tending always to regulate and minimize the change in $[H^+]$ or pH:

$$H^+ + \text{buffer bases} \underset{H^+ \text{ decrease}}{\overset{H^+ \text{ increase}}{\rightleftharpoons}} \text{buffer acids}$$

The ratios of the buffer salts to buffer acids change in proportion to the change in $[H^+]$ or pH, and the pH change within a fluid is represented by the Henderson-Hasselbalch equation for any one of the buffer systems present, such as the $BHCO_3/H_2CO_3$ buffer system:

$$pH = pK_a + \log \frac{B^+HCO_3^-}{H_2CO_3}$$

While the buffer systems of body fluids represent the first mechanism involved in the regulation of pH, the major role in this regulation is played by the kidneys, which excrete more or less H^+ ions (acid) in the urine as the $[H^+]$ of the plasma increases and decreases. This action of the kidneys is importantly supplemented by the respiratory mechanism, which operates to decrease respiration and retain more $CO_2(H_2CO_3)$ in the body fluids when the $[H^+]$ is below normal (pH elevated, alkalosis) and to increase respiration and decrease the $CO_2(H_2CO_3)$ in body fluids when the $[H^+]$ is above normal (pH lowered, acidosis).

It should be pointed out that according to older concepts, the cations

Na^+, K^+, Ca^{++}, and Mg^{++} are considered to be the bases of the body; the older and much of the recent literature use this concept. This older view considers that the Na^+ ion of a buffer salt, such as $NaHCO_3$, neutralizes a strong acid HA:

$$NaHCO_3 + HA \longrightarrow NaA + H_2CO_3$$

which, of course, is not true. The reaction is as follows:

$$Na^+HCO_3^- + H^+A^- \longrightarrow H_2CO_3 + Na^+ + Cl^-$$

in which HCO_3^- combines with H^+ from the acid HA to form the weakly dissociated acid H_2CO_3, which breaks up into H_2O and CO_2, and the CO_2 is eliminated; that is, the anion of the weak acid (HCO_3^-) is the proton acceptor or base which neutralizes the H^+ ions. A cation such as Na^+, of course, must be associated with the HCO_3^- to maintain electrical neutrality, but it does not neutralize acids.

The total equivalence of all the cations present in a tissue or body fluid must equal the total equivalence of all the anions present. Then twice the cation equivalence equals the total electrolyte equivalence.

The total cation equivalence may be readily determined, and in the older literature it is considered to be the total base equivalence, while the anion equivalence is considered to represent the acids. According to the modern (Brönsted) concept, the total base of a body fluid or tissue is represented by all of the anions of the weak acids present which combine with H^+ (HCO_3^-, protein$^-$, Hb$^-$, $HPO_4^=$, etc.). Since considerable of the cation equivalence is balanced by Cl^- and other anions which do not neutralize H^+, the base equivalence is less than the cation equivalence to this extent. The total cation equivalence of an extracellular fluid minus the Cl^- equivalence closely approximates the total base equivalence, because this difference essentially represents the equivalence due to HCO_3^-, protein$^-$ Hb$^-$, $HPO_4^=$, etc., associated with the cations not balanced by Cl^-.

The metabolic processes of the body continually form acidic substances which without operation of the buffer systems, kidneys, and lungs would rapidly lower the pH to a fatal level.

The oxidation of the carbon of foods in the human adult with average exercise (2500 calories) forms about 400 l of CO_2 per day, which represents about 90 equivalents of acid (H_2CO_3). This CO_2 is largely eliminated through the lungs, but it is buffered and transported in extracellular fluids with exceedingly little change in pH.

The nucleoproteins, phosphoproteins, and phosphatides of foods and tissues, when broken down, liberate phosphoric acid. The oxidation of sulfur-containing amino acids, such as cystine and methionine, in cells yields sulfuric acid. Lactic and pyruvic acids in considerable quantities escape from muscles during strenuous exercise.

Certain foods, such as the juices of fruits and vegetables, contain citric and other organic acids and the potassium and sodium salts of these acids. When metabolized in the body, the organic acid components are oxidized to CO_2 and water, and the cations K^+ and Na^+ are released as $BHCO_3$, which increases body base. Thus the metabolism of a mol of monosodium citrate forms a mol of $NaHCO_3$.

In general, the acid load formed by metabolic processes in the body greatly exceeds the base load, and it is the handling of this large amount of acid which is of primary concern in the normal regulation of the acid-base balance.

Certain substances used as drugs have decided effects upon the acid-base balance of the body. For example, NH_4Cl is taken to the liver, where the ammonia component is converted to neutral urea and HCl is released, which must be neutralized. Of course, the ingestion of $NaHCO_3$ leads directly to an increase in body base (HCO_3^-) and may cause alkalosis.

Various pathologic states tend to upset the acid-base balance by increasing the acid components.

In severe diabetes mellitus the liver forms the relatively strong organic acids β-hydroxybutyric and acetoacetic in large amounts, which escape into the extracellular fluids. As much as 50–100 g of these acids and their salts may be excreted in the urine per day.

In nephritis the kidneys may be unable to excrete much of the acid load formed in the body, which accumulates and leads to severe acidosis.

In pernicious vomiting, as observed in duodenal and pyloric obstruction, and in gastric lavage, HCl in large amounts may be lost from the stomach. Since this is formed from Cl^- of plasma and H_2CO_3 in the gastric cells by a reaction such as the following:

$$B^+Cl^- + H_2CO_3 \longrightarrow \underset{\text{to plasma}}{B^+HCO_3^-} + \underset{\text{into stomach}}{HCl}$$

the loss of a mol of HCl from the stomach leaves a mol of $BHCO_3$ to increase the base of plasma and extracellular fluid and leads to base excess and alkalosis. Normally the HCl formed in the stomach passes into the intestine, where it is neutralized by $BHCO_3$ secreted from plasma in pancreatic and intestinal juices to re-form BCl, which is absorbed back into the blood stream to re-establish the original acid-base balance.

In severe cases of diarrhea the loss of pancreatic and intestinal secretions containing $BHCO_3$ is large, and since this $BHCO_3$ comes from plasma and other extracellular fluid, the acid-base balance is upset, to cause acid excess or acidosis.

Both Na^+ and K^+ (mainly Na^+) and small amounts of Ca^{++} and Mg^{++} are present in gastric juice, pancreatic juice, and intestinal secretions. Prolonged severe vomiting leads not only to alkalosis, but to total electrolyte deficiency (mainly Na^+) and decreased extracellular fluid volume (isotonic contraction). Also, severe diarrheal disease causes not only acidosis but, in addition, total electrolyte deficiency (mainly Na^+) and decreased extracellular fluid volume (isotonic contraction).

Thus it is evident that the body must be provided with mechanisms for regulating the acids and bases of the blood and other body fluids with respect to both the total quantities present and also the ratios of bases to acids which determine the pH. These control processes, as previously indicated, are supplied by the buffer systems of the body and renal and respiratory mechanisms.

Respiratory regulation of acid-base balance. The ventilation of the lungs or the minute volume of air passing into and out of the lungs determines the CO_2 tension in the alveolar air, and this tends to regulate the amount of dissolved CO_2 (H_2CO_3) in the blood and other body fluids. An increase in ventilation due to either an increased rate or depth of breathing or both (hyperpnea) lowers the CO_2 tension of alveolar air and causes equilibrium with dissolved CO_2 in the blood and other body fluids to be established at a lower concentration than normal, thus tending to raise the pH. Conversely, decreased lung ventilation due to slow and shallow breathing raises the CO_2 tension of alveolar air and causes equilibrium with dissolved CO_2 in the blood and other body fluids to be established at a higher concentration than normal and thus tends to lower the pH of these fluids.

Since the respiratory apparatus is stimulated by increased H^+ ion concentration (lowered pH) and increased pCO_2 and is depressed by decreased H^+ ion concentration (increased pH) and decreased pCO_2, the rates of pulmonary ventilation and alveolar pCO_2 are automatically controlled in the direction of maintaining normal pH relations in the blood and other body fluids. Thus, in an alkalosis, in which the pH is above normal and the ratio HCO_3^-/H_2CO_3 is high, the respiratory apparatus is depressed, lung ventilation is decreased, the pCO_2 of alveolar air is increased, and the H_2CO_3 in blood and other fluids is increased, tending to lower the ratio HCO_3^-/H_2CO_3 and the pH toward normal. In an acidosis, with lowered pH and a lowered HCO_3^-/H_2CO_3 ratio, the respiratory apparatus is stimulated, lung ventilation is increased, alveolar pCO_2 is decreased, and body fluid H_2CO_3 is decreased, tending to increase the ratio HCO_3^-/H_2CO_3 and pH of blood and other fluids toward normal.

Renal regulation of the acid-base balance. The pH of the urine is determined by the substances which the kidneys must remove from the blood in order to help keep blood pH within physiological limits. Urine normally is a strongly buffered solution, particularly because of the large amounts of phosphates excreted, though it contains smaller quantities of many buffer systems. The pH of urine normally varies between 4.8 and 7.4. It appears that the kidneys are unable to excrete urine more acid than pH about 4.5 and more alkaline than pH 8.2. On ordinary diets the pH of urine is generally a bit on the acid side, and the quantity of acid titratable to a plasma pH of 7.4 is appreciable. This titratable acidity between the pH of urine and of plasma represents the amount of acid removed from the blood by the kidneys in helping maintain a normal plasma pH. In severe alkalosis the pH of urine may exceed that of blood, and the concentration of urinary $H\overline{C}O_3$ may be three or four times that of normal plasma. In such conditions the urine shows a titratable alkalinity rather than acidity.

Ordinarily urine acidity is titrated to phenolphthalein after the addition of sodium oxalate to precipitate calcium. Normally a 24-hour sample of urine shows the equivalent of 20 to 40 ml of 1 N acid. In severe acidosis such as found in diabetes, the value may rise to 150 ml of 1 N acid.

Gamble (12) has shown that the pCO_2 of urine is generally that of arterial blood, about 40 mm. This represents about $0.03 \times 40 = 1.2$ mM of dissolved CO_2 per liter.

At a constant pCO_2 of 40 mm it is possible to calculate the quantities of $\overline{HCO}_3$ contained in urine at different pH values. At the lower range of urinary pH (4.5) practically no $\overline{HCO}_3$ is present (0.03 mM/l), while at the upper range of pH (8.2) much is present (151 mM/l). Thus we see that practically no base as $\overline{HCO}_3$ is excreted in the $\overline{HCO}_3/H_2CO_3$ buffer system at the lowest urinary pH, while a great deal is excreted at the higher pH values. At urinary pH values of 7.5, 7.0, and 6.5 there are 30, 9.6, and 3 mM of $\overline{HCO}_3$ per liter of urine, respectively. The quantities represent 2.5, 0.8, and 0.25 g of $BHCO_3$ figured as $NaHCO_3$ per liter, respectively.

The phosphates constitute the most important buffer of normal urine quantitatively. This buffer system is composed of $HPO_4^=/H_2PO_4^-$. While the blood contains relatively little phosphate buffer because of kidney efficiency in excreting phosphate, much phosphate buffer passes through the blood into the urine as a result of the metabolism of phosphorus compounds.

At a plasma pH of 7.4 the ratio of $B_2^+HPO_4^=$ to $B^+H_2PO_4^-$ is 5, which represents about 83 per cent $B_2^+HPO_4^=$ and 17 per cent $B^+H_2PO_4^-$. The excretion of $B^+H_2PO_4^-$ in the urine represents the removal of acid from the plasma and tends to raise plasma pH, while the excretion of $B_2^+HPO_4^=$ tends to lower plasma pH. When urine of pH 4.8 is formed, around 99 per cent of the phosphate excreted is $B^+H_2PO_4^-$, while at a urine pH of 8.2 about 97 per cent $B_2^+HPO_4^=$ is excreted.

The proportions of acid and salt (base) of an acid excreted in the urine at a given pH may be calculated from the pK values using the Henderson-Hasselbalch equation. While the values obtained at extreme salt-acid ratios are not accurate, they show the approximate relations. Table 17.5 gives such calculations for important urinary acids. It is obvious that when the kidneys excrete a very acid urine, much HCO_3^- (base) and Na^+ of the plasma is conserved to help prevent a drop in plasma pH and maintain the

Table 17.5. Relation of Urinary pH to Per Cent of Salt and Acid Buffer Components Excreted in Urine

Urine	Buffer Systems in Urine							
pH	$B^+HCO_3^-/H_2CO_3$		$B_2^+HPO_4^=/B^+H_2PO_4^-$		B^+HB^-/HHB^*		B^+Ac^-/HAc^*	
4.5	2.4	97.6	0.63	99.37	9.1	90.9	83.4	16.6
6.0	44.2	55.8	16.6	83.4	97.6	2.4	99.4	0.6
7.0	88.8	11.2	66.6	33.4	99.8	0.2	100	0
7.4	95.2	4.8	83.3	16.7	100	0	100	0
8.0	98.8	1.2	95.2	4.8	100	0	100	0
8.2	99.2	0.8	97	3	100	0	100	0

* HB^- and HHB = β-hydroxybutyrate ion and β-hydroxybutyric acid, respectively; Ac^- and HAc = acetoacetate ion and acetoacetic acid, respectively. In diabetes mellitus about 75 per cent of these acids in urine is β-hydroxybutyric acid.

electrolyte concentration. The amount of $B^+HCO_3^-$ conserved is equal to the equivalents of urinary acid obtained by titrating the urine with alkali to the pH of plasma. When the kidneys excrete urine at a high pH $B^+HCO_3^-$ is removed from the plasma to compensate a rise in plasma pH.

This conservation of plasma HCO_3^- by the excretion of an acid urine is exceedingly important in cases of severe diabetes when large quantities of β-hydroxybutyric and acetoacetic acids are formed and accumulate in the tissues and blood. These are strong organic acids which are neutralized by reaction with HCO_3^- and other buffer bases, thereby lowering the pH. At plasma pH these acids exist 100 per cent as anions (salts). However, if they are excreted by the kidneys in urine at a pH of 4.5 to 4.8, more than half is present as free acid. This means a proportionate removal of H^+ ions from plasma and an increase in HCO_3^- and other plasma bases.

From the above discussion we may conclude that the excretion of acid and base by the kidneys is adjusted to help maintain normal plasma pH. As the plasma pH rises above normal owing to excess HCO_3^- and other bases, the kidneys excrete more of these bases in the urine to lower plasma pH. Conversely, when the plasma pH is below normal, the kidneys increase the excretion of plasma acids to raise the plasma pH.

Another very important way in which the kidneys conserve Na^+ and HCO_3^- is formation of ammonia and substitution of NH_4^+ for Na^+ in the urine. In severe diabetic acidosis the equivalent of 500 ml of $1 N NH_3$ may be excreted per day, so that as much or more Na^+ and HCO_3^- are conserved to the body through ammonia formation in the kidney as by acid excretion by the kidney.

The mechanisms of sodium reabsorption and bicarbonate and acid formation in the kidney. The H^+-Na^+ and K^+H^+-Na^+ exchanges. The student will find excellent discussions of these very important phases of electrolyte and acid-base balance in the articles of Pitts (13) and Gilman and Brazeau (14), and in the books by Welt (11) and Elkinton and Danowski (9).

As indicated above, the kidneys play the dominant role in regulating both the electrolyte concentration and acid-base balance of extracellular fluids. The processes involved have been studied by many investigators over a long period of time, but Pitts and associates worked out the modern concept explaining the detailed mechanisms by which the kidneys operate in performing these functions.

The glomerular filtrate contains the electrolytes and acids and bases present in plasma. The chief cation present is Na^+, and the chief anions are Cl^-, HCO_3^-, and $HPO_4^=$; that is, the chief electrolytes in glomerular fluid may be represented as Na^+Cl^-, $Na^+HCO_3^-$, and $Na_2^+HPO_4^=$. The main buffers are the $Na^+HCO_3^-/H_2CO_3$ and $Na_2^+HPO_4^=/Na^+H_2PO_4^-$ systems. At a pH of 7.4 about 95 per cent of the CO_2 is present as $Na^+HCO_3^-$, and about 83 per cent of the phosphate is present as $Na_2^+HPO_4^=$.

Normally, as the glomerular filtrate passes into the tubules most of the water is reabsorbed, and the greater proportion of the Na^+ is taken up by the tubular cells in exchange for H^+ formed in the tubular cells (from

H_2CO_3); this Na^+ is returned to the plasma in association with HCO_3^- formed from H_2CO_3 in the tubular cells. The formation of H^+ and HCO_3^- from H_2CO_3 in the tubular cells (both proximal and distal) is catalyzed by the enzyme carbonic anhydrase. The principles involved are shown in the diagram of Figure 17.10.

While the anions of buffer salts other than phosphate ($HPO_4^=$) may accept H^+ in the H^+-Na^+ exchange and secretion of acid into the tubular

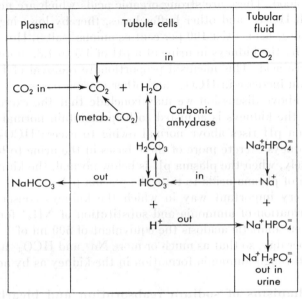

Figure 17.10

fluid, normally it is $HPO_4^=$ which is the chief H^+ acceptor. This exchange amounts to the over-all reaction:

$$H_2CO_3 + Na_2^+HPO_4^- \longrightarrow Na^+HCO_3^- + Na^+H_2PO_4^-$$

Tubule   Tubular   Into plasma   Out in urine
cells   fluid

by which half the sodium of the basic salt $Na_2^+HPO_4^=$ is converted to plasma $Na^+HCO_3^-$, and the other half is excreted in the urine as the acid salt $Na^+H_2PO_4^-$. Thus, Na^+ and HCO_3^- are returned to the plasma and H^+ is excreted in the urine to help maintain normal acid-base balance and electrolyte concentration.

Pitts and associates (15) showed that a subject made acidotic with NH_4Cl excreted much more acid in the urine when also given phosphate. This was due to increased amounts of $HPO_4^=$ in the tubular fluid to accept H^+ from the tubular cells and promote the H^+-Na^+ exchange.

In severe diabetic acidosis, in which large amounts of the relatively strong ketone acids, β-hydroxybutyric and acetoacetic, are formed, their sodium salts in high concentration are present in the glomerular filtrate and pass to the tubules. In such a condition the H^+-Na^+ exchange mechanism operates with sodium β-hydroxybutyrate and sodium acetoacetate so that much of the Na^+ is returned to the plasma as $Na^+HCO_3^-$ and proportionate amounts of free β-hydroxybutyric and acetoacetic acids are excreted in the urine.

As shown in Figure 17.10, the CO_2 for the formation of H^+ and HCO_3^- in the tubular cells is supplied by the general CO_2 pool (plasma), by CO_2 entering from the tubular fluid, and by CO_2 derived from the metabolism of tubular cells.

While the diagram of Figure 17.10 indicates only H^+ exchanging with Na^+ in the H^+-Na^+ exchange mechanism, the evidence shows that K^+ competes with H^+ in the exchange for Na^+ in the distal tubules (11). Administration of K^+ causes increased exchange of K^+ and less exchange of H^+ for Na^+ in the tubules, which leads to acidosis. In K^+ depletion of extracellular fluid the reverse occurs, with more H^+ and less K^+ exchange for Na^+, which causes alkalosis. The H^+-Na^+ exchange mechanism in reality is the H^+K^+-Na^+ exchange mechanism in the distal tubules where K^+ excretion takes place.

Not all of the Na^+ which is reabsorbed in the kidney tubules is reabsorbed through the H^+-Na^+ exchange mechanism. A part of the glomerular filtrate load of Na^+ is taken up, along with Cl^- and other anions, such as HPO_4^- and SO_4^-, by the proximal tubular cells and returned to the plasma by an active Na^+ transport mechanism (sodium pump, see Chapter 5). The anions appear to be absorbed passively. They are carried along by the attraction of the Na^+ ions and maintain electrical neutrality. Most of the water also is reabsorbed along with the electrolytes in the proximal tubules.

The $Na^+HCO_3^-$ of glomerular fluid normally disappears as the fluid passes through the tubules, and in effect it is reabsorbed into the plasma. Until recently it was believed that this $Na^+HCO_3^-$ is taken up directly by the tubular cells and passed back into the plasma. However, Pitts and associates (16) and Brazeau and Gilman (17) showed that by altering the alveolar pCO_2 (and extracellular CO_2) the amount of $Na^+HCO_3^-$ reabsorbed by the renal tubules can be changed markedly. When respiratory alkalosis was produced (by hyperventilation), with low extracellular pCO_2 and low pCO_2 in renal tubular cells, less $Na^+HCO_3^-$ was reabsorbed by the tubules and more excreted in the urine. Conversely, in respiratory acidosis, with high extracellular and tubular cell pCO_2, the tubular reabsorption of $Na^+HCO_3^-$ was greatly increased with a proportionate decrease in urinary excretion. The sulfonamide drug acetazoleamide (Diamox):

$$CH_3-CO-N-C \overset{S}{\underset{N--N}{\bigwedge}} C-S-NH_2$$

Acetazoleamide (Diamox)

inhibits the action of the enzyme carbonic anhydrase. When given to an animal, it accordingly inhibits the conversion of CO_2 to H_2CO_3 in the kidney tubules and limits the supply of H^+ and HCO_3^- for the H^+-Na^+ exchange. Berliner and associates (18) found that experimental animals given acetazoleamide ceased excreting titratable acid in the urine and excreted as much as 50 per cent of the $Na^+HCO_3^-$ of the glomerular filtrate in the urine, indicating the operation of the H^+-Na^+ exchange mechanism in the absorption of $Na^+HCO_3^-$ from the glomerular fluid by the tubules. When respiratory acidosis is produced in an animal which has been given acetazoleamide, the elevated pCO_2 of the tubular cells forms sufficient H_2CO_3 to supply the necessary amounts of H^+ and HCO_3^- to offset the decreased carbonic anhydrase activity and permit normal H^+-Na^+ exchange.

The above evidence shows then that $Na^+HCO_3^-$ absorption from the glomerular filtrate by the tubular cells is dependent upon the H^+-Na^+ exchange mechanism. The process is diagrammed in Figure 17.11. From this illustration it is seen that when $Na^+HCO_3^-$ of glomerular fluid enters the tubules, Na^+ enters the tubule cells and, with HCO_3^- formed in the

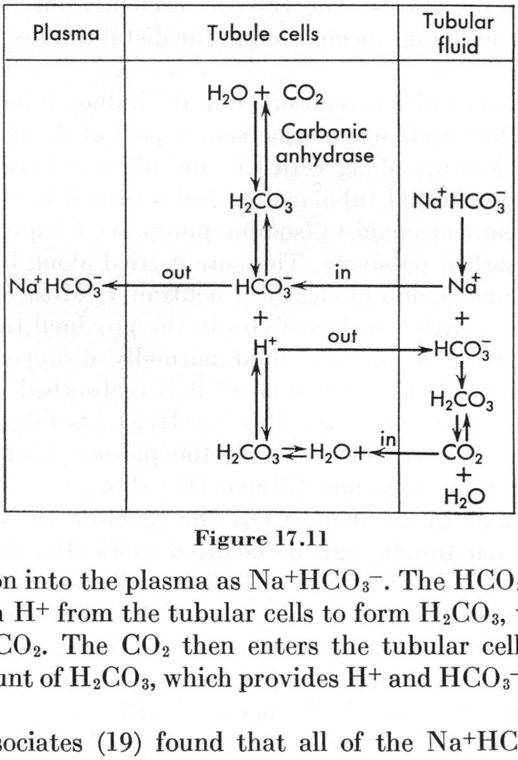

Plasma	Tubule cells	Tubular fluid
	$H_2O + CO_2$ ↕ Carbonic anhydrase	
	H_2CO_3	$Na^+HCO_3^-$
$Na^+HCO_3^-$ ← out —	HCO_3^- ← in —	Na^+
	+	+
	H^+ — out →	HCO_3^-
		↓
		H_2CO_3
		⇕
	$H_2CO_3 \rightleftharpoons H_2O +$ ← in —	CO_2 + H_2O

Figure 17.11

cells, is passed on into the plasma as $Na^+HCO_3^-$. The HCO_3^- in the tubular fluid reacts with H^+ from the tubular cells to form H_2CO_3, which breaks up into H_2O and CO_2. The CO_2 then enters the tubular cells and forms an equivalent amount of H_2CO_3, which provides H^+ and HCO_3^- for the H^+-Na^+ exchange.

Pitts and associates (19) found that all of the $Na^+HCO_3^-$ normally is reabsorbed in the tubules from glomerular fluid at plasma bicarbonate concentrations from 13 to 24 meq per liter. At plasma concentrations above 28 meq per liter absorption is incomplete, a maximum of 2.8 meq per 100 ml of glomerular filtrate being absorbed, and all in excess being excreted in the urine. The renal plasma threshold for bicarbonate excretion normally lies between 25 and 27 meq per liter. This means that the plasma bicarbonate concentration tends to be balanced around 25 to 27 meq per liter. When plasma bicarbonate is normal or reduced, all of it in glomerular filtrate is absorbed in the tubules. When the bicarbonate of plasma is elevated by ingestion of bicarbonate, that in excess of the normal amount is excreted.

This apparently fixed bicarbonate threshold varies under certain conditions. It is reduced in hyperventilation (respiratory alkalosis), and bicarbonate is excreted in the urine as compensation. The threshold is raised when the plasma Na^+Cl^- concentration is low, which retains more $Na^+HCO_3^-$ in the plasma (and other extracellular fluids) to help maintain the total electrolyte concentration and osmotic pressure.

The H^+-Na^+ exchange mechanism is controlled by the steroid hormones of the adrenal cortex (such as aldosterone and deoxycorticosterone). In Addison's disease the secretion of these hormones is deficient, and the H^+-Na^+ exchange may be greatly decreased, causing both decreased H^+ excretion and Na^+ and HCO_3^- reabsorption in the tubules. As a result, plasma HCO_3^- and pH fall, producing an acidosis, and plasma Na^+ and also Cl^- are depleted.

While large amounts of sodium are lost in the urine in adrenal cortical hypofunction (Addison's disease), the excretion of potassium is decreased and the concentration of potassium in the plasma accordingly increases (hyperkalemia). Also, in Addison's disease there is hypotonic contraction of extracellular fluids, and water passes into the intracellular compartment, causing hypotonic expansion of intracellular fluid.

Loeb (20) found that giving large amounts of NaCl to patients with Addison's disease causes plasma electrolytes to gradually return toward normal, with striking clinical improvement.

In hyperfunction of the adrenal cortex the H^+-Na^+ exchange mechanism is stimulated to increased activity, leading to increased tubular excretion of acid and reabsorption of Na^+ and HCO_3^-, which causes a rise in plasma pH and alkalosis. Excessive K^+ and Cl^- losses also occur in adrenal cortical hyperfunction.

Acid-base balance control by ammonia formation in the kidneys. Nash and Benedict (21) first demonstrated that renal tubular cells form ammonia from a precursor in renal arterial blood and secrete it into tubular fluid. This ammonia formation takes place in the distal tubules (22). It has been found that about two-thirds of the ammonia formed in the kidney is produced by deamidation of glutamine and one-third by oxidative deamination of amino acids (23):

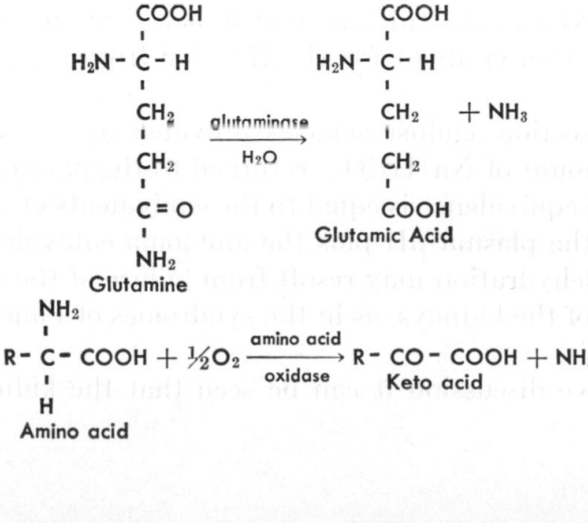

$$
\begin{array}{ll}
\underset{\text{Glutamine}}{\begin{array}{l}
\text{COOH} \\
| \\
H_2N-C-H \\
| \\
CH_2 \\
| \\
CH_2 \\
| \\
C=O \\
| \\
NH_2
\end{array}}
\xrightarrow[H_2O]{\text{glutaminase}}
&
\underset{\text{Glutamic Acid}}{\begin{array}{l}
\text{COOH} \\
| \\
H_2N-C-H \\
| \\
CH_2 \\
| \\
CH_2 \\
| \\
\text{COOH}
\end{array}}
+ NH_3
\end{array}
$$

$$
\underset{\text{Amino acid}}{\begin{array}{l}
NH_2 \\
| \\
R-C-COOH \\
| \\
H
\end{array}}
+ \tfrac{1}{2}O_2
\xrightarrow[\text{oxidase}]{\text{amino acid}}
\underset{\text{Keto acid}}{R-CO-COOH} + NH_3
$$

The NH$_3$ formed in the distal tubular cells enters the tubular fluid, where it combines with H$^+$ from the tubular cells to form NH$_4$$^+$. This NH$_4$$^+$ then replaces Na$^+$ in a sodium salt of the tubular fluid, such as Na$^+$Cl$^-$. The Na$^+$ is reabsorbed by the H$^+$-Na$^+$ exchange mechanism and re-enters the plasma as Na$^+$HCO$_3$$^-$. The NH$_4$$^+$ is excreted in the urine as NH$_4$Cl. The diagram of Figure 17.12 shows the mechanisms involved.

That the H$^+$-Na$^+$ exchange mechanism is involved in the conservation of Na$^+$HCO$_3$$^-$ by NH$_3$ formation in the kidney is shown by giving acetazoleamide to a severely acidotic animal excreting much acid and NH$_4$$^+$ in the urine (14). The administration of acetazoleamide causes the urine to become

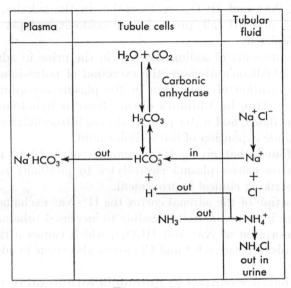

Figure 17.12

alkaline, showing that the H$^+$-Na$^+$ exchange mechanism has been inactivated, and the NH$_4$$^+$ excretion in the urine drops markedly. In such a condition NH$_3$ continues to be produced in the kidney, but very little can pass into the tubular fluid and be retained unless at the same time H$^+$ is added to the fluid to form NH$_4$$^+$ and thus maintain a concentration gradient for continued diffusion of NH$_3$ from the tubular cells to the fluid. Vice versa, the presence of NH$_3$ in the tubular fluid to act as an acceptor for H$^+$ provides a concentration gradient for H$^+$ diffusion from the tubular cells into the fluid.

The total protection against acidosis provided by the kidneys is determined by the amount of Na$^+$HCO$_3$$^-$ returned to the plasma by the tubules. This bicarbonate equivalence is equal to the equivalents of alkali required to titrate urine to the plasma pH plus the ammonia equivalents in the urine.

Acidosis and dehydration may result from failure of the ammonia-secreting mechanisms of the kidneys, as in the syndromes of Fanconi and of lower nephron nephrosis.

From the above discussion it can be seen that the kidneys provide the major control of the electrolyte and acid-base balance of the body, and this is achieved principally through the H^+-Na^+ exchange mechanism, NH_3 formation, and the kidney threshold for bicarbonate. While the chief cation concerned in regulation of electrolyte concentration and acid-base balance is Na^+, in severe acidosis the K^+, Ca^{++}, and Mg^{++} concentrations in plasma are elevated, which leads to excessive excretion in the urine.

The operation of the H^+-Na^+ exchange mechanism and the absorption of water from the more concentrated tubular fluid in the kidneys require the expenditure of energy, which must be provided by metabolism of the tubular cells. A minimum of about 850 calories must be expended by the kidneys in the formation of a liter of normal urine. Conditions which limit the supply of O_2 and food materials to the kidneys, such as shock and impaired heart function, result in decreased energy production and kidney function.

Control of the acid-base balance by buffer systems. The buffer systems of the various body fluid compartments qualitatively are as follows:

Plasma:

$$\frac{B^+HCO_3^-}{H_2CO_3},\ \frac{B^+protein^-}{H \cdot protein},\ \frac{B_2^+HPO_4^-}{B^+H_2PO_4^-},\ \frac{B^+org.\ acid^-}{H \cdot org.\ acid}$$

The balancing cation B^+ is chiefly Na^+.

Erythrocytes:

$$\frac{B^+HCO_3^-}{H_2CO_3},\ \frac{B^+Hb^-}{HHb},\ \frac{B^+HbO_2^-}{HHbO_2},\ \frac{B_2^+HPO_4^-}{B^+H_2PO_4^-},\ \frac{B^+org.\ acid^-}{H \cdot org.\ acid}$$

The balancing cation B^+ is chiefly K^+.

Interstitial fluid. As in plasma, except less protein buffers.

Intracellular. Very much as in plasma, except the protein buffer system and the buffer systems composed of various organic phosphates predominate. There is very little $BHCO_3/H_2CO_3$ buffer within tissue cells. Also, the balancing cation B^+ is chiefly K^+.

From the quantitative viewpoint the important buffers in plasma are the bicarbonate-carbonic acid and proteinate-protein buffers. In the erythrocytes the hemoglobin buffer systems dominate, with much less bicarbonate-carbonic acid buffer. While the quantitative buffer relations within cells are much less well known than they are in extracellular fluids, protein and phosphate buffer systems appear to represent most of the buffer capacity. The approximate quantities of the chief buffer components of plasma and erythrocytes are shown in Table 17.6.

Table 17.6. Approximate Quantities of Chief Buffer Components in Plasma and Erythrocytes

Values represent milliequivalents per liter of plasma or cells

	$B^+HCO_3^-$	H_2CO_3	Protein-*
Plasma	25	1.25	13
Erythrocytes	11	1.0	55

* The B^+ protein$^-$/$H \cdot$ protein buffer systems are complex, and only the total protein-milliequivalents can be given.

The pH values of different body compartments vary. On the average they are somewhat as follows: intracellular fluid 7 or a bit below, erythrocytes 7.25, plasma 7.4, interstitial fluid 7.4, cerebrospinal fluid 7.4.

All the values vary within certain ranges under different physiologic and pathologic conditions. Since tissue membranes generally are freely permeable to OH^- or H^+ ions or both, the pH values of different fluids are proportional if not equal. Disturbances in the pH of one fluid thus are reflected in pH disturbances in other fluids, and the buffering capacities of plasma, erythrocytes, interstitial fluid, and intracellular fluid are mutually supportive.

Since blood represents a large mass of rapidly circulating fluid carrying a very efficient system of buffers, it is ideally suited to help regulate the pH of interstitial and intracellular fluids and to prevent extreme local variations in pH. Also, since the condition of the blood buffers is indicative of the situation relative to the buffer systems of the body in general, determination of the condition of blood buffers is used clinically to assay the general state of body buffers.

1. Buffer action against CO_2. Since very great quantities of CO_2 (H_2CO_3) are being continually formed by the tissues, its buffering is of much importance and is effected chiefly by the extracellular fluids, particularly by the hemoglobin buffer systems of the erythrocytes.

In plasma the following reversible reactions occur:

(a) $CO_2 + H_2O \rightleftharpoons H_2CO_3 \rightleftharpoons HCO_3^- + H^+$

(b) $H^+ + protein^- \rightleftharpoons H \cdot protein$

Reaction (a), uncatalyzed by carbonic anhydrase, is slow, and the amount of protein$^-$ to react with H^+ is relatively small, with the result that only a small amount of CO_2 entering the blood is converted to HCO_3^- in the plasma. Interstitial fluid has less capacity (less protein$^-$) to buffer CO_2 than does plasma.

Most of the buffering action against CO_2 is provided by the hemoglobin buffer systems of the erythrocytes, where the following reactions take place:

(c) $CO_2 + H_2O \xrightleftharpoons[\text{anhydrase}]{\text{carbonic}} H_2CO_3 \rightleftharpoons HCO_3^- + H^+$

(d) $H^+ + Hb^- \rightleftharpoons HHb$
(e) $H^+ + HbO_2^- \rightleftharpoons HHbO_2$

Reaction (c) is very fast due to the presence of the enzyme carbonic anhydrase, and there is a very high concentration of hemoglobin$^-$ ions (Hb^- and HbO_2^-) to combine with the H^+ ions from H_2CO_3 and form HCO_3^-. Consequently, the buffering capacity of the blood against CO_2 is, for practical purposes, determined by the amount of hemoglobin in blood. In reactions (d) and (e) Hb^- is more effective than HbO_2^- in buffering against increased CO_2, because HHb dissociates less readily than does $HHbO_2$, causing reaction (d) to shift further to the right than reaction (e). Conversely, reaction (e) is more effective than reaction (d) in buffering against decreased CO_2.

As pCO_2 increases, all of the above reactions shift to the right with the formation of more HCO_3^- as Hb^- and HbO_2^- combine with the H^+ from H_2CO_3. The ratios of the buffer systems change:

$$\frac{HCO_3^- \text{ incr.}}{H_2CO_3 \text{ incr. a bit more,}} \qquad \frac{Hb^- \text{ decr.}}{HHb \text{ incr.,}} \qquad \frac{HbO_2^- \text{ decr.}}{HHbO_2 \text{ incr.}}$$

corresponding to a slightly lower pH.

As pCO_2 decreases, all of the above reactions shift to the left, and the hemoglobin acids donate H^+ ions to HCO_3^- to form H_2CO_3, which in turn produces H_2O and CO_2. This is associated with changes in the ratios of the buffer systems opposite to those taking place when pCO_2 increases, with a proportionate small rise in pH (few hundredths of a pH unit). Thus, because of the operations of and large capacity of the hemoglobin buffer systems, much CO_2 can be taken up by blood as HCO_3^-, or can be given up by blood through decomposition of HCO_3^-, with very little change in pH. In fact, the buffer capacity of the hemoglobin buffers is so great that when the pCO_2 of blood is reduced to zero, the hemoglobin buffer acids decompose all of the HCO_3^- and all of the CO_2 is removed from blood. If the pCO_2 of plasma is reduced to zero, a part of the HCO_3^- is decomposed by the protein acid (reactions (a) and (b)), and the remaining HCO_3^- is converted to CO_3^{--} with loss of half of its CO_2:

$$2B^+HCO_3^- \longrightarrow B_2^+CO_3^{--} + H_2O + CO_2$$

The diagram below shows the relations of the buffer systems of the erythrocytes to changing CO_2 tensions:

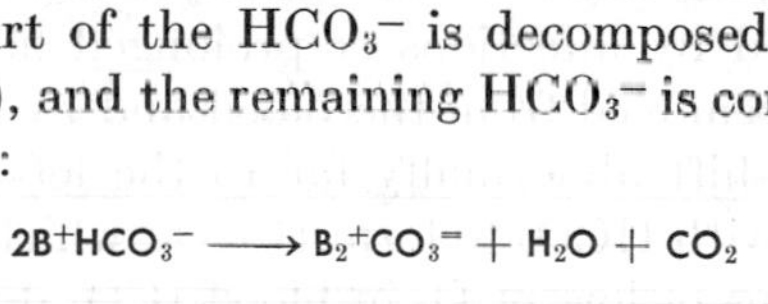

$$H_2O + CO_2$$
Increasing pCO_2

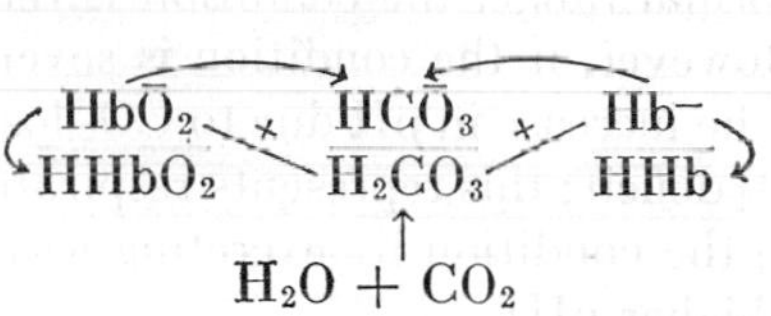

$$H_2O + CO_2$$
Decreasing pCO_2

As HCO_3 ions are formed in the cells, many of them diffuse into the plasma and Cl^- ions diffuse from the plasma into the cells (chloride-bicarbonate shift). Thus, while the HCO_3 is formed from the hemoglobin buffer systems in the cells, it is distributed between cells and plasma. While plasma buffers form little HCO_3, the supply of HCO_3 in the plasma is maintained indirectly by the hemoglobin buffers.

The effect of varying pCO_2 upon the erythrocyte reactions:

$$CO_2 + H_2O \rightleftharpoons H_2CO_3 + Hb^- \rightleftharpoons HCO_3^- + HHb$$
$$CO_2 + H_2O \rightleftharpoons H_2CO_3 + HbO_2^- \rightleftharpoons HCO_3^- + HHbO_2$$

is of much importance. In conditions in which respiratory exchange is deficient, such as lobar pneumonia, respiratory paralysis, and morphine narcosis, CO_2 continues to be poured into the blood by tissue metabolism, but lung ventilation is below normal. This means that the CO_2 and H_2CO_3 contents of tissue fluids and blood rise above normal. In the blood the chief compensatory mechanism is the mass action shift of the above reactions to the right, causing an increase in $HC\bar{O}_3$ so that the total $HC\bar{O}_3$ contents of the cells and the plasma increase. Under these conditions both $HC\bar{O}_3$ and H_2CO_3 are above normal, and we have a condition which is called "CO_2 excess." If the pH of the blood remains in the normal range, the condition is compensated CO_2 excess; if the pH is below normal, it is uncompensated CO_2 excess. At times a condition of severe respiratory CO_2 acidosis may develop. The kidneys help compensate the condition by excreting more acid and ammonia in the urine.

Under certain conditions the respiration may be increased above normal with the blowing off of abnormally large quantities of CO_2. This occurs at high altitudes as a result of the stimulating effect of hypoxia upon the respiratory mechanism, at times in cases of hysteria, and may be observed in high fevers induced by infections or prolonged hot baths. As excessive amounts of CO_2 are removed from the blood and pCO_2 falls below normal, the above reactions shift abnormally far to the left with the hemoglobin buffer acids reacting with $HC\bar{O}_3$ to form H_2CO_3, which is eliminated as CO_2. Under these conditions of low pCO_2 in blood (CO_2 deficit) the $HC\bar{O}_3$ is decreased. If the $HC\bar{O}_3$ and H_2CO_3 are decreased in proportion so that the pH remains within the normal range, the condition is referred to as "compensated CO_2 deficit." However, if the condition is severe and the decrease in $HC\bar{O}_3$ does not offset the increase in pH due to CO_2 loss, we have a condition of uncompensated CO_2 deficit; this represents respiratory alkalosis. The kidneys help compensate the condition by excreting less acid and ammonia in the urine (urine at a higher pH).

A condition of CO_2 excess and respiratory acidosis may be readily induced by breathing air or O_2 containing CO_2 (5 to 7 per cent). Such a condition is difficult to cause by holding the breath because of the stimulating effect of CO_2 upon the respiratory center. However, severe CO_2 deficit and respiratory alkalosis may result from prolonged forced breathing.

Since the components of the hemoglobin and oxyhemoglobin buffer systems interact with the components of the bicarbonate-carbonic acid buffer system as shown above, when other variables are constant, the total CO_2 and $HC\bar{O}_3$ of whole blood vary inversely as the hemoglobin content.

Erythrocytes per unit volume normally contain about 60 per cent as much $HC\bar{O}_3$ as plasma does. In polycythemic blood, in which the cell volume may be very large compared to plasma volume, the whole blood $HC\bar{O}_3$ and CO_2 are low even though the concentrations in cells and plasma are normal. Conversely, $HC\bar{O}_3$ and total CO_2 may be above normal in anemic blood simply because of the relatively large plasma volume.

It should be kept in mind that deoxygenated blood is much more efficient than oxygenated in buffering against CO_2, because Hb^- combines with H^+ more firmly than does HbO_2, and consequently Hb^- reacts with H_2CO_3 to form more HCO_3 than does HbO_2 at a given physiologic pH.

Carbon dioxide titration curves of blood. If blood is equilibrated with increasing CO_2 tensions and the total CO_2 and pH of the true plasma determined, the quantities of HCO_3 present for each pH may be calculated by procedures outlined previously. This constitutes a titration of blood with CO_2 and indicates the capacity of the blood to form HCO_3 with variations in pCO_2 and pH. As is to be expected, true plasma of deoxygenated blood forms more HCO_3 per increment of pH and pCO_2 change than does the true plasma of oxygenated blood. Henderson (24) carried out such experiments

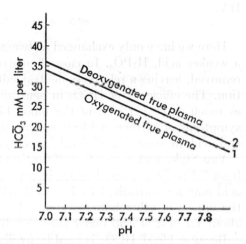

Figure 17.13. CO_2 titration curves of blood; pH changed by changing pCO_2. (1) True plasma of oxygenated blood, and (2) true plasma of deoxygenated blood. True plasma is plasma separated after whole blood has been equilibrated with CO_2 at 10, 20, 40, 60, 80 mm.

on oxygenated and deoxygenated normal blood. Table 17.7 gives his values for pCO_2, pH, and total CO_2 in the true plasmas of oxygenated and deoxygenated blood. The values for $[HCO_3]$ per liter were calculated from his data.

Table 17.7. Showing Variations of Total CO_2 and HCO_3 in True Plasma of Blood with Variations in pCO_2 and pH

| | | Oxygenated | | | Deoxygenated | |
| | | Total CO_2 | HCO_3 | | Total CO_2 | HCO_3 |
pCO_2	pH	mM/l	mM/l	pH	mM/l	mM/l
10	7.819	15.5	15.2	7.847	16.6	16.3
20	7.621	20.1	19.5	7.652	21.6	21.0
40	7.413	25.4	24.2	7.445	27.2	26.0
60	7.307	29.8	27.0	7.318	30.8	29.0
80	7.192	31.5	29.1	7.224	33.6	31.2

From data in *Blood; A Study in General Physiology* by L. J. Henderson. Yale University Press, New Haven, 1928.

Using data from the table, we may plot millimols of HCO_3 per liter against pH for the true plasma of oxygenated and deoxygenated blood. Such a plot is shown in Figure 17.13. It will be noted that straight lines are obtained. These represent the normal buffer lines against CO_2.

2. Buffer action against nonvolatile acids. When nonvolatile acids enter the blood, they react with the anions of the buffer systems and are neutralized. However, it is the $HC\bar{O}_3$ of the $HC\bar{O}_3/H_2CO_3$ buffer system which is primarily concerned with such neutralization. This is true for two reasons. In the first place, the concentration of $HC\bar{O}_3$ is highest of any of the buffer anions. In the second place, $HC\bar{O}_3$ is peculiarly efficient in neutralizing acids because in the process H_2CO_3 is formed which breaks up into CO_2, and this being exhaled makes the reaction irreversible:

$$HC\bar{O}_3 + HA \rightleftharpoons A^- + H_2CO_3 \longrightarrow \underset{\text{exhaled}}{CO_2}$$

A reaction such as the following would be much less efficient in neutralizing HA:

$$HPO_4^- + HA \rightleftharpoons A^- + H_2P\bar{O}_4$$

Here we have only exchanged a stronger acid, HA, for a mixture of it and a weaker acid, $H_2P\bar{O}_4$. In case of neutralization with $HC\bar{O}_3$ the H_2CO_3 is removed, leaving a relatively neutral salt and a decreased $HC\bar{O}_3$ concentration. The efficiency of $HC\bar{O}_3$ in neutralizing nonvolatile acids is such that as much as 80 per cent of the blood bicarbonate may be used up before symptoms of extreme acidosis appear (increased respiration or hyperpnea, and acidotic coma if sufficiently severe).

Van Slyke and associates (25) estimate that when the pH of blood falls from 7.4 to 7.0, as may happen in severe diabetic acidosis, about 18 mM of acid may be neutralized by $HC\bar{O}_3$, 8 mM by Hb^- and $Hb\bar{O}_2$, and 2 mM by the anions of other buffer systems. Plasma protein anions neutralize only about 1.7 mM of acid under these conditions.

Because blood $HC\bar{O}_3$ is readily available for the neutralization of acids and quantitatively is by far the most important, the blood $HC\bar{O}_3$ is referred to as the "alkali reserve." Since the quantity of $HC\bar{O}_3$ present in blood reflects the condition of the blood buffers in general, and, since it may be determined readily, estimation of blood $HC\bar{O}_3$ or alkali reserve is a routine clinical procedure.

Excessive amounts of $HC\bar{O}_3$ in the body are buffered by the hemoglobin and other buffer systems to some extent. However, as the pH of the blood rises, the respiration is depressed, and this permits the accumulation of excessive amounts of $CO_2(H_2CO_3)$, which tends to bring the ratio $HC\bar{O}_3/H_2CO_3$ and the pH back to normal. At the same time the kidneys excrete a more alkaline urine. When kidney excretion has lowered $HC\bar{O}_3$ to normal, the lungs have blown off the excess CO_2 and normal conditions are re-established.

Alkalies introduced into the blood react quickly with H_2CO_3 to form HCO_3^-:

$$OH^- + H_2CO_3 \longrightarrow HCO_3^- + H_2O$$

In previous discussion it has been pointed out that respiratory acidosis and alkalosis may be produced by CO_2 retention (CO_2 excess) and excessive CO_2 excretion (CO_2 deficit), respectively. The so-called metabolic types of acidosis and alkalosis are referable to decreases or increases in total buffer anions, chiefly $HC\bar{O}_3$, not related to respiratory changes in blood CO_2. Examples of metabolic acidosis are observed in diabetic and nephritic acidosis when the quantities of nonvolatile acids to be neutralized react with abnormal quantities of buffer anions, particularly $HC\bar{O}_3$. A similar condition may be caused by the ingestion or injection of HCl, NH_4Cl, or other acids. The ingestion of alkaline earth chlorides, such as $CaCl_2$ and $MgCl_2$, produces an effect about equal to that produced by an equivalent amount of HCl. This is due to the fact that very little of the metal ion is absorbed, while most or all of the Cl^- passes into the blood. While the exact mechanism is unknown, the effect is equivalent to membrane hydrolysis of the metal chloride with absorption of HCl, which, of course, is quickly neutralized by blood buffers.

In cases of metabolic acidosis the chief effects noted are a decrease in the alkali reserve HCO_3 and total CO_2 of the blood and lowered blood pH. The lowered pH stimulates respiration to blow off CO_2 in an attempt to bring the ratio $HC\bar{O}_3/H_2CO_3$ and the pH to normal. Also, the kidneys excrete a more acid urine and more ammonia to conserve HCO_3. If the condition is mild and the pH is within normal range, it is referred to as "compensated metabolic acidosis" ("compensated base or alkali deficit"). If the pH is below the normal range, the condition is "uncompensated metabolic acidosis" ("uncompensated base or alkali deficit").

Metabolic alkalosis may be caused by the ingestion or injection of $NaHCO_3$ or other basic substances, or of substances, such as sodium lactate and sodium citrate, which give $NaHCO_3$ when metabolized. As the pH rises, the respiration is depressed to retain CO_2 and lower the pH, and the kidneys excrete urine at a higher pH to remove excess $HC\bar{O}_3$ from the blood. The blood $HC\bar{O}_3$, H_2CO_3, and total CO_2 are high. If the condition is mild and the pH within normal ranges due to a normal HCO_3^-/H_2CO_3 ratio, the condition is "compensated metabolic alkalosis" ("compensated base or alkali excess"). If the pH is above normal, the condition is "uncompensated metabolic alkalosis."

The role of tissue buffers in the regulation of acid-base balance of extracellular fluids. Van Slyke and Cullen (26) and Shaw (27) have estimated the total buffer capacity of the adult human body available for neutralization of acid before a fatal pH is reached as about six times that of blood, equivalent to the neutralization of about 900 ml of 1 N acid (9000 meq). This means that the tissue buffers (including bone) must be capable of neutralizing about 750 ml of this 1 N acid.

The tissue cells aid in regulating the acid-base balance of the body through exchanging H^+, K^+, and Na^+ between the extracellular and intracellular fluids (9).

Figures 17.14 and 17.15 show the exchanges taking place between extracellular and intracellular fluids in conditions of metabolic alkalosis and acidosis.

In metabolic alkalosis H^+ and K^+ shift from intracellular to extracellular fluid in exchange for Na^+, which enters the cells. The H^+ reacts with extracellular HCO_3^- to form H_2CO_3. The kidneys excrete K^+ and Na^+ with

HCO_3^-, and respiration is decreased to retain CO_2 (H_2CO_3). Each of these processes helps compensate the alkalosis.

In metabolic acidosis the ionic shifts between extracellular and intracellular fluids are reversed. The movement of H^+ (and K^+) from extracellular fluid into the cells in exchange for Na^+ leaves HCO_3^- in the extracellular fluid:

$$H_2CO_3 \rightleftarrows HCO_3^- + H^+$$
$$\text{into cells}$$

to help raise the pH. The H^+ entering the cells is taken up by the intracellular buffer systems. The kidneys increase excretion of H^+ and decrease excretion of Na^+, K^+, and $H\bar{C}O_3$. Respiration is stimulated to increase excretion of CO_2. Each of these processes helps compensate the acidosis.

In respiratory alkalosis due to hyperventilation H^+ and K^+ pass from intracellular to extracellular fluid in exchange for Na^+, which enters the cells.

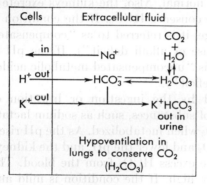

Figure 17.14. Alkalosis. pH of E.C.F. decreased by ionic shifts.

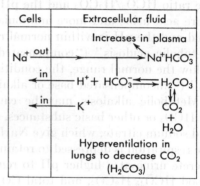

Figure 17.15. Acidosis. pH of E.C.F. increased by ionic shifts.

The H^+ reacts with HCO_3^- to form H_2CO_3 to compensate the alkalosis. The kidneys excrete less H^+ and more HCO_3^-, along with K^+ and Na^+.

In respiratory acidosis the ionic shifts between extracellular and intracellular compartments are reversed to those in respiratory alkalosis, with H^+ and K^+ entering the cells and Na^+ passing from the cells into extracellular fluid. The shift of H^+ into the cells leaves HCO_3^- in the extracellular fluid to raise the pH:

$$H_2CO_3 \rightleftarrows HCO_3^- + H^+$$
$$\text{into cells}$$

and the H^+ is taken up by intracellular buffers. The kidneys compensate by increased excretion of H^+ and of NH_4^+ with anions such as Cl^-, and by decreased excretion of Na^+ and K^+ (NH_4^+ is substituted for these).

In prolonged severe metabolic acidosis the $Ca_3(PO_4)_2$ of bone may be drawn upon to neutralize acid:

$$Ca_3(PO_4)_2 + 4HA \longrightarrow 3Ca^{++} + 2H_2PO_4^- + 4A^-$$

The Ca^{++}, $H_2PO_4^-$, and A^- ions are excreted in the urine. This process may result in serious demineralization of the skeleton.

Effect of digestion upon the acid–base balance. The alkaline tide.
It has been found that shortly after a meal the alveolar CO_2 is increased,
the urine pH rises, the plasma bicarbonate rises, and the chloride falls. This
so-called alkaline tide after a meal is due to formation of gastric HCl from
Cl^- ions and H^+ ions in plasma, leaving HCO_3^- and OH^- ions to increase pH.
The condition is very mild and disappears after the gastric HCl is neutralized
in the intestine to form NaCl, which is absorbed into the blood and re-estab-
lishes the status quo. The alkaline tide is most pronounced after meals which
stimulate much gastric secretion, such as heavy protein meals. It may be
greatly diminished or disappear in conditions of achlorhydria, in which little
gastric HCl is secreted. This may be true after meals consisting chiefly of
fat and carbohydrate.

**The bicarbonate-carbonic acid buffer system of blood as an index
of the acid-base balance of the body.** Since the various changes in the
acid-base balance of the body are reflected in the buffer systems of the blood,
and since the state of the blood buffers is mirrored in the bicarbonate-carbonic acid buffer system, and finally because the bicarbonate buffer system
is easily assayed in the laboratory, practically all estimations of body acid-
base balance are based upon analysis of the bicarbonate buffer system. In
practice it is customary to use plasma for such analyses, since its buffer
composition reflects the condition of the blood buffers, and because it represents a more constant material than whole blood where the volume of cells
relative to the volume of plasma may vary considerably. Heparin is used as
anticoagulant instead of oxalate or other salts which may affect the buffer
systems of the blood.

The variables relating to a bicarbonate-carbonic acid buffer system are
pCO_2, total CO_2, HCO_3^-, H_2CO_3, and pH. If two of these are known, the
others may be calculated.

Total CO_2 may be obtained readily by acidification in the Van Slyke gas
apparatus, and pH may be determined with the glass electrode. In order
that results obtained from determinations of total CO_2 and pH may be compared and properly interpreted, it is necessary to use oxygenated (arterial)
blood, since the total CO_2, HCO_3^-, H_2CO_3, and pH all change from arterial to
venous blood. The equivalent of arterial blood may be obtained by soaking
the arm in hot water (46°–47° C) for ten minutes or longer and withdrawing
the sample from the antecubital vein or a vein on the back of the hand.
Special equipment and techniques are required in drawing the samples and
separating and analyzing the plasma.

Blood may be equilibrated at 38° C and at a definite pCO_2, generally
40 mm in the presence of excess O_2, and the total CO_2 determined on plasma
separated from the equilibrated blood (so-called true plasma). Under these
conditions the plasma total CO_2 essentially represents the alkali reserve of
arterial blood at the normal pCO_2 of 40 mm. If the pCO_2 of the arterial blood
is higher than 40 mm in the subject, the values at 40 mm CO_2 are too low,
and if the pCO_2 of the subject's blood is lower than 40 mm, the values obtained are too high. However, the results at 40 mm indicate the capacity of

the blood to take up CO_2 under normal conditions. Since nearly all the CO_2 taken up represents $HC\bar{O}_3$, the CO_2 capacity at 40 mm pCO_2 is defined specifically as the alkali reserve.

Since the $[H_2CO_3]$ varies directly as pCO_2, the total quantity of H_2CO_3 at any pCO_2 is readily calculated ($0.03 \times pCO_2$), and under all physiologic and pathologic conditions is small relative to $[HC\bar{O}_3]$. When total CO_2 is high, $HC\bar{O}_3$ is high and vice versa. When $HC\bar{O}_3$ or total CO_2 is high and pH is below normal, pCO_2 is high. If pCO_2 is normal and pH above normal, $HC\bar{O}_3$ and total CO_2 are high. When the ratio $HC\bar{O}_3/H_2CO_3$ is high (above 20:1), the pH is above normal; and when it is low, the pH is below normal.

The true plasma of oxygenated normal blood may be considered to be characterized by the following relations:

pH	pCO_2 mmHg	[total CO_2] vols %	[total CO_2] mM/l	$[HC\bar{O}_3]$ vols %	$[HC\bar{O}_3]$ mM/l	$[H_2CO_3]$ vols %	$[H_2CO_3]$ mM/l	$\dfrac{[HC\bar{O}_3]}{[H_2CO_3]}$
7.4	40	56	25.2	53.4	24	2.57	1.2	20

The various conditions of the $HC\bar{O}_3/H_2CO_3$ buffer system of plasma which are possible, and which are observed, may be summarized as follows:

1. Normal condition. [total CO_2], $[HC\bar{O}_3]$, $[H_2CO_3]$, $[HC\bar{O}_3]/[H_2CO_3]$, pH, pCO_2 normal as given above.

2. Uncompensated base (alkali) excess. $[HCO_3^-]$ high without proportionate increase in $[H_2CO_3]$; $[HCO_3^-]/[H_2CO_3]$ and pH above normal; [total CO_2] high.
May be caused by:
Overdosage with $NaHCO_3$; excessive vomiting or loss of stomach HCl by gastric washing (lavage).
Symptoms:
Tetany if pH rises markedly.
Compensation:
Diminished respiration; excessive urine excretion (diuresis); and excretion of urine at a high pH.

3. Uncompensated base (alkali) deficit. $[HCO_3^-]$ decreased without proportionate decrease in $[H_2CO_3]$; $[HCO_3^-]/[H_2CO_3]$ and pH below normal; [total CO_2], below normal.
May be caused by:
Severe diabetic and nephritic acidosis; deep ether anesthesia with hypoxia causing much lactic acid to accumulate; cardiac failure causing hypoxia and lactic acid accumulation; ingestion or injection of acids or NH_4Cl.
Symptoms:
Labored breathing (dyspnea); diuresis; coma if severe.
Compensation:
Increased respiration; increased excretion of acid and ammonia in urine. Ammonia excretion may be deficient in nephritis.

4. Uncompensated CO_2 deficit. $[H_2CO_3]$ decreased without a proportionate decrease in $[HC\bar{O}_3]$; $[HC\bar{O}_3]/[H_2CO_3]$ and pH above normal; [total CO_2] below normal.
May be caused by:
Excessive pulmonary ventilation (hyperpnea) due to hypoxia, fever, hot baths, hysteria.
Symptoms:
Tetany if pH rises markedly.
Compensation:
Excretion of urine at a high pH; decreased respiration as soon as cause is removed.

5. *Uncompensated* CO_2 *excess.* [H_2CO_3] increased without proportionate increase in [$HC\bar{O}_3$]; [HCO_3]/[H_2CO_3] and pH below normal; [total CO_2] above normal.

May be caused by:

Lobar pneumonia with physical obstruction of respiration; respiratory paralysis; morphine narcosis.

Symptoms:

Labored or difficult breathing (dyspnea).

Compensation:

Increased excretion of acid and ammonia in the urine; increased respiration if cause is removed.

6. *Compensated base (alkali) or* CO_2 *excess.* [HCO_3^-] and [H_2CO_3] both proportionately high; [HCO_3^-]/[H_2CO_3] and pH normal; [total CO_2] high.

Cause of compensated base excess:

Dosage with $NaHCO_3$ in repeated small doses gradually to increase plasma $HC\bar{O}_3$, or slow absorption of $NaHCO_3$. (This is the intermediate compensation stage for uncompensated base excess.)

Symptoms:

None evident.

Compensation:

Excretion of urine at a pH higher than normal to reduce blood $HC\bar{O}_3$; decreased respiration; retention of CO_2.

Cause of compensated CO_2 excess:

Respiration chronically retarded so that pCO_2 is elevated moderately for a considerable period of time. (This is the intermediate compensation stage for an uncompensated CO_2 excess.)

Symptoms:

May have cyanosis due to hypoxia if respiration is sufficiently reduced.

Compensation:

Increased respiration if cause is removed; excretion of more acid in the urine (urine at a lower pH).

7. *Compensated base (alkali) or* CO_2 *deficit.* [HCO_3^-] and [H_2CO_3] both proportionately low; [HCO_3^-]/[H_2CO_3] and pH normal; [total CO_2] below normal.

Cause of compensated base deficit:

Moderate acidosis due to diabetes or nephritis with acids being added to the blood at a rate for which the body can compensate; diarrheal acidosis; ingestion or injection of moderate amounts of acids at a slow rate. (These represent the compensation stage for uncompensated base deficit.)

Symptoms:

Hyperpnea.

Compensation:

Increased respiration; excretion of more acid and ammonia in the urine.

Cause of compensated CO_2 deficit:

Moderate overventilation with lowered [H_2CO_3] for which the body can compensate; intermediate stage in compensation of an uncompensated CO_2 deficit.

Symptoms:

Hyperpnea.

Compensation:

Decreased respiration to build up H_2CO_3 when the exciting cause is removed; excretion of less acid and ammonia in the urine (urine at a higher pH).

According to older terminology the term "base" of the above conditions is replaced by "alkali."

The best indication as to the condition of the acid-base balance in a patient is afforded by the level of plasma HCO_3^- and the plasma pH. Ordinarily in the laboratory total CO_2 and pH are determined, from which

$[HCO_3^-]$ may be calculated. Suppose the total plasma CO_2 is 15 mM per liter and the plasma pH is 7.2. Then from the Henderson-Hasselbalch equation:

$$7.2 = 6.1 + \log \frac{[HCO_3^-]}{[H_2CO_3]}$$

and

$$\log \frac{[HCO_3^-]}{[H_2CO_3]} = 7.2 - 6.1 = 1.1, \text{ and } \frac{[HCO_3^-]}{[H_2CO_3]} = \frac{12.6}{1}$$

which means that the total CO_2 present as HCO_3^- is:

$$\frac{12.6}{13.6} \times 100 = 92.6 \text{ per cent} = 15 \times 0.926 = 13.89 \text{ mM per liter}$$

Representation of the acid-base balance of blood on charts. As has been explained previously, if either pCO_2 and total CO_2, or pH and total CO_2 are determined on blood plasma, then all the other variables of the bicarbonate-carbonic acid buffer system may be calculated. In order to visualize better the whole picture of the buffer system, it is customary to prepare charts upon which a number of these variables are shown and from which the others may be calculated. One of the best systems is based upon plotting pH against millimols of HCO_3^- per liter in true plasma of oxygenated blood. Another system is to plot pCO_2 against total CO_2.

Figure 17.16 shows a chart for plotting pH against millimols of $H\bar{C}O_3$. On this chart we have line LM, which is the normal CO_2 buffer line of true plasma of oxygenated blood. The broken curves show the variation in $H\bar{C}O_3$ with pH at constant values of pCO_2 (pCO_2 isobars). These curves were plotted from values in Table 16.5 (page 576). Line OP on the chart represents the normal pH line at 7.4. The normal point on the chart is at J, where the pH is 7.4, pCO_2 is 40 mm, and $[H\bar{C}O_3]$ is 24 mM per liter. The normal buffer line, LM, the normal pCO_2 isobar, and the normal pH line, OP, pass through this point. Area W (LJP) is the region of CO_2 excess and respiratory acidosis. Area X (PJM) is the region of base excess and metabolic alkalosis. Area Y (MJO) represents CO_2 deficit and is the region of respiratory alkalosis. Area Z (LJO) is the region of base deficit and metabolic acidosis.

The nature of the $H\bar{C}O_3/H_2CO_3$ buffer system of any blood may be quickly seen by plotting the pH and $[H\bar{C}O_3]$ of its true plasma separated from an oxygenated sample on the chart.

Table 17.8 shows the values calculated for pCO_2, $[H_2CO_3]$, and $[H\bar{C}O_3]$ when the pH and [total CO_2] values indicated are found by analysis of the true plasma of oxygenated blood.

The points A, B, C, etc., corresponding to the pH and HCO_3^- values of Table 16.5 are plotted on the chart. It will be noted that B represents uncompensated CO_2 excess or respiratory acidosis, D and E represent uncompensated base excess or metabolic alkalosis, G represents uncompensated CO_2 deficit or respiratory alkalosis, and K and I represent uncompensated base deficit or metabolic acidosis. Point C may represent either compensated

CO_2 excess or base excess—that is, either compensated respiratory acidosis or metabolic alkalosis—while H may represent either compensated CO_2 deficit or base deficit—that is, either compensated respiratory alkalosis or metabolic acidosis. Point A, lying on the normal buffer line, represents uncompensated CO_2 excess or respiratory acidosis; while point F, also lying on the buffer line, represents uncompensated CO_2 deficit or respiratory alkalosis.

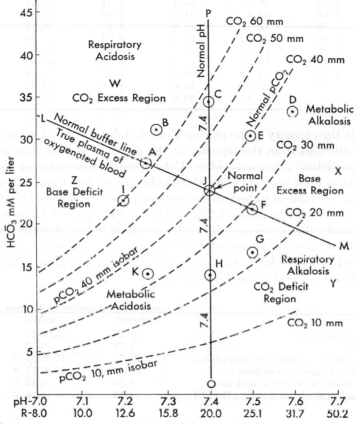

Calculations:

$\dfrac{[HCO_3^-]}{[H_2CO_3]} = R;\ \log R = pH - 6.1;\ R = \text{antilog } (pH - 6.1)$

$[\text{total } CO_2] = (R + 1) \times 0.03 \times pCO_2$

$pCO_2 = \dfrac{[\text{total } CO_2]}{(R + 1) \times 0.03}$

$[H_2CO_3] = 0.03 \times pCO_2$

$[HCO_3] = [\text{total } CO_2] - [H_2CO_3]$

pH and [total CO_2] are determined on plasma of oxygenated whole blood and [HCO_3] is calculated by the above equations.

Figure 17.16

The analysis of plasma buffer systems as outlined above obviously is too complicated and time-consuming to be used routinely in clinical laboratories. For clinical purposes it is rather generally customary to separate the plasma from venous blood, equilibrate it with CO_2 at 40 mm, and determine the total CO_2 content. This is expressed as the alkali reserve of the plasma. It

Table 17.8.   If Total CO_2 and pH Values of True Plasma of Oxygenated Blood Shown in Columns 1 and 2 are Obtained by Analysis, the Other Values Are Obtained by Calculation

	pH	Total CO_2 mM/l	pCO_2 mm	H_2CO_3 mM/l	HCO_3^- mM/l	R
A	7.25	28.05	61.5	1.85	26.2	14.2
B	7.30	33.0	65.3	1.96	31.04	15.8
C	7.40	36.0	57.1	1.71	34.29	20.0
D	7.60	34.0	34.7	1.04	32.96	31.7
E	7.50	31.32	40.0	1.2	30.12	25.1
F	7.50	22.46	28.7	0.86	21.60	25.1
G	7.50	17.23	22.0	0.66	16.57	25.1
H	7.40	15.75	25.0	0.75	15.0	20.1
I	7.20	24.48	60.0	1.80	22.68	12.6
J	7.40	25.2	40.0	1.20	24.0	20.0
K	7.25	15.0	32.9	0.99	14.01	14.2

represents the capacity of the plasma alone to take up CO_2 at normal pCO_2, which is different from the capacity in the presence of cells (true plasma). Such a procedure gives some idea of the quantitative value of the blood buffer systems but does not show the whole picture and cause of the condition. Since the clinical history of the patient generally suggests the cause of plasma alkali reserve abnormalities, this enables the clinician to assess approximately the significance of results obtained in this simplified manner.

The CO_2 capacity of plasma at 40 mm pCO_2 (alkali reserve) as commonly determined in clinical laboratories correlates roughly as follows with unspecified conditions of acidosis and alkalosis.

	Plasma CO_2 Capacity at 40 mm pCO_2	
	Volumes %	mM/l
Normal extremes	53–78	23.8–35
Alkalosis	>78	>35
Mild acidosis (no apparent symptoms)	40–53	17.9–23.8
Moderate acidosis (symptoms)	30–40	13.5–17.9
Severe acidosis (severe symptoms)	<30	<13.5
Terminal acidosis (diabetic), pH <7.1	<15	<6.7

The nature of the urine excreted in extreme conditions of acidosis and alkalosis is of considerable interest. The chief relevant characteristics are as follows:

Extreme Acidosis	Extreme Alkalosis
1. pH around 4.5	1. pH around 7.8
2. No HCO_3^-	2. Much HCO_3^-
3. Increased chloride	3. Decreased chloride
4. Increased acid, up to 150 ml of 1 N	4. Urine becomes alkaline, alkali titratable
5. Increased NH_3, up to 600 ml of 1 N	5. No ammonia
6. Decreased cations (Na^+, K^+, etc.)	6. Increased cations
7. Large volume (diuresis)	7. Some diuresis

Table 17.9 shows the variations of plasma electrolytes in several pathological states. The cation variations chiefly involve Na^+.

Table 17.9.   Cations and Anions of Plasma in Pathologic States Compared to
Those of Normal Plasma
Values are milliequivalents per liter of water

Condition of Subject	Cations, Total	Anions			
		HCO$_3^-$	Cl$^-$	Keto-acids	Other anions
Normal	155	27	103		25
Diabetic ketosis (acidosis)	142	5	80	24	33
Fasting ketosis (acidosis)	155	15	101	13	26
Diarrhea	148	11	100		37
Addison's disease	126	22	73		31
NH$_4$Cl acidosis	155	12	117		26
Nephrosis	150	20	113		17
Chronic nephritis	157	21	101		35
Chronic nephritis (terminal)	146	6	87		53
Pyloric obstruction (vomiting)	146	59	42		45
Duodenal obstruction (vomiting)	150	43	48	32	27
Habitual vomiting	155	33	96		27

Data from the charts of Gamble (3).

POTASSIUM METABOLISM

Maintenance of the proper K$^+$ concentration of extracellular fluids is essential, particularly for proper function of the heart. High concentrations of K$^+$ cause widespread intracardiac block, while low concentrations impair the contractility of heart muscle.

Maintenance of proper intracellular K$^+$ concentrations is essential for various enzymatic reactions, for the normal contractility of muscle, and for impulse transmission and other functions of the nervous system.

The widespread distribution of potassium in foods normally precludes the development of potassium deficiency. Experimental potassium deficiency in rats causes diminished growth, kidney hypertrophy, necrosis of heart muscle, loss of hair, and finally death.

Excretion of potassium by the kidneys. Control of the K$^+$ balance of the body by the kidneys is not as efficient as the control of Na$^+$ balance. Whereas an animal on a Na$^+$-deficient diet may show practically no Na$^+$ excretion in the urine, there is always an obligatory excretion of potassium, regardless of the potassium intake which continues even during prolonged starvation, the K$^+$ arising from cellular breakdown. This obligatory excretion (30–60 meq per day) is apparently related to the K$^+$H$^+$-Na$^+$ exchange in the distal tubules, where the reabsorption of Na$^+$ is dependent upon exchange for H$^+$ and K$^+$. However, it has been found that in both animals and humans deprived of potassium but maintained without stress to minimize adrenal cortical activity K$^+$ is conserved by the kidneys.

The mechanisms by which the kidneys excrete K$^+$ differ from those for the excretion of Na$^+$. It appears that normally most or all of the K$^+$ of glomerular filtrate is reabsorbed along with anions such as Cl$^-$ in the proximal tubules, and the K$^+$ which appears in the urine is secreted by the distal tubular cells in the H$^+$K$^+$-Na$^+$ exchange mechanism (28). The operation of the H^+K^+-Na^+ exchange mechanism in the distal tubules is shown in Figure 17.17. Anions other than $HPO_4^=$ may serve as acceptors of K^+ as well as of H^+.

Since K^+ and H^+ are competitive with each other in the H^+K^+-Na^+ exchange mechanism, conditions which increase H^+ excretion decrease K^+ excretion and vice versa. However, H^+ has much greater affinity for the exchange mechanism than does K^+.

When extracellular K^+ is elevated (also tubular cell K^+) by administration of potassium salts, tubular H^+ excretion is decreased, K^+ and HCO_3^- excretions are increased, and acidosis results. Conversely, when extracellular K^+ is depleted, H^+ excretion is increased, and K^+ and HCO_3^- excretions are decreased, causing alkalosis.

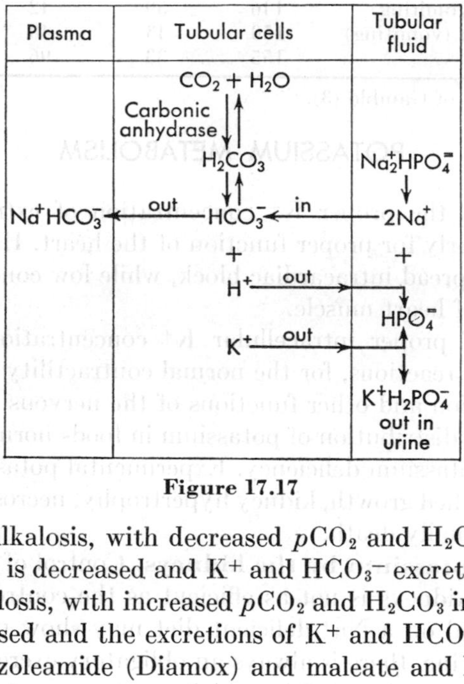

Plasma	Tubular cells	Tubular fluid
	$CO_2 + H_2O$ Carbonic anhydrase H_2CO_3	$Na_2^+HPO_4^=$
$Na^+HCO_3^-$ ← out — HCO_3^- ← in		↓ $2Na^+$
+		+
H^+ — out →		$HPO_4^=$
K^+ — out →		$K^+H_2PO_4^-$ out in urine

Figure 17.17

In respiratory alkalosis, with decreased pCO_2 and H_2CO_3 in the tubular cells, H^+ excretion is decreased and K^+ and HCO_3^- excretions are increased. In respiratory acidosis, with increased pCO_2 and H_2CO_3 in tubular cells, H^+ excretion is increased and the excretions of K^+ and HCO_3^- are decreased.

The drug acetazoleamide (Diamox) and maleate and Li^+, which inhibit the carbonic anhydrase enzyme, decrease H^+ excretion and increase Na^+, K^+, and HCO_3^- excretion.

The operation of the H^+K^+-Na^+ exchange is under the control of adrenal corticosteroid hormones (aldosterone, deoxycorticosterone).

Administration or increased production of these steroids (in hyperadrenocorticism), increases the exchange, with the retention of Na^+ and excretion of increased amounts of H^+, K^+, and NH_4^+ in the urine. An alkalosis and K^+ depletion result.

In a deficiency of adrenal corticosteroids, as seen in Addison's disease, the exchange is decreased, with decreased urinary excretion of both H^+ and K^+, and increased Na^+ and HCO_3^- excretion, leading to an acidosis and K^+ elevation in extracellular and intracellular fluids.

Distribution of potassium in the body. The potassium intake of the adult generally is between 4 and 8 g (100 to 200 meq) per day. Total body potassium of the normal male adult determined by K^{42} dilution appears to be about 47 milliequivalents per kilogram of body weight (29). In females the average value found was about 41 meq per kilogram. Elkinton and Danowski (9) estimate the following amounts of K^+ to be present in the major depots of the body of a healthy 60 kg adult.

Muscle (intracellular)	2600 meq
Erythrocytes (intracellular)	200 meq
Liver (intracellular)	160 meq
Extracellular fluid	54 meq

About 100 meq of K^+ are secreted in the gastrointestinal fluids and 100 meq excreted in the urine per day.

While most of the K^+ excretion is through the kidneys, more K^+ than Na^+ is excreted in the feces.

The unequal distribution of K^+ between extracellular and intracellular fluid exists only in the living organism and entirely disappears when the animal dies.

The maintenance of high concentrations of K^+ in intracellular and low concentrations in extracellular fluid, and of high concentrations of Na^+ in extracellular and low concentrations in intracellular fluid, is the result of active transport of Na^+ from intracellular to extracellular fluid (sodium pump, see Chapter 5). The concept is that K^+, Na^+, and H^+ pass across the cell membrane rather freely, as occurs when the cell dies. However, the sodium pump mechanism, which requires metabolic energy, in the living cell continually moves Na^+ from the intracellular to the extracellular fluid at a rate which maintains a high $[Na^+]$ in extracellular fluid and low $[Na^+]$ in intracellular fluid. Electrical neutrality in the cell is maintained by the diffusion of sufficient K^+ and H^+ into the cell to balance the deficit of cations caused by the sodium pump mechanism. Most of this balancing is done by K^+, accounting for the high concentration of K^+ in intracellular fluid. Thus, we see that the K^+H^+-Na^+ exchange mechanism appears to operate not only in the renal tubules, but probably also in tissues generally.

Alterations in the potassium contents of extracellular and intracellular fluids. There are a number of conditions which lead to changes in the K^+ concentrations of extracellular and intracellular fluids and the distributions of K^+ between these fluids.

The administration and retention of excessive amounts of water or glucose solution (as in parenteral therapy) dilutes both the extracellular and intracellular fluids, with an attendant drop in $[K^+]$ in both fluids, though the total body K^+ is unchanged. This situation occurs in patients unable to excrete their water loads, as in cases of kidney disease with acute tubular damage.

There are a number of processes which lead to increased cellular K^+. Since

K+ is an obligatory component of cellular structure, cellular K+ increases during growth and tissue repair processes. Testosterone, a hormone of the testis, increases cellular protein synthesis and also cellular K+.

The processes of carbohydrate metabolism are importantly related to movement of K+ between extracellular and intracellular compartments. When glucose is taken from extracellular fluid into tissue cells and converted to glycogen, K+ also moves into the cells. Conversely, when glycogen breaks down in cells and the glycogen content is depleted, the cells lose K+. These changes in K+ within cells appear to be related to the formation and breakdown of sugar phosphates.

Since insulin promotes glycogen formation, the administration of insulin, particularly with glucose, greatly increases the movement of K+ into cells.

Progressive dehydration causes loss of cellular K+, and rehydration causes K+ to shift back into the cells.

As previously indicated, alkalosis causes K+ (and H+) to shift from intracellular to extracellular fluid, and acidosis causes the reverse. These shifts of K+ and H+ into and out of cells are associated with opposite shifts of Na+.

In the peculiar disease familial periodic paralysis there are seizure episodes in which extracellular K+ decreases because of increased shift into tissue cells.

The loss of K+ through external routes may upset the body balance.

The continual, and at times excessive, urinary excretion of K+ by patients not receiving adequate amounts for maintenance leads to depletion.

As previously pointed out, the administration of adrenal corticosteroids causes increased K+ excretion, as also does the administration of pituitary adrenocorticotropic hormone (ACTH), which stimulates cortical activity.

Conditions leading to K+ depletion in extracellular fluid (and in tubular cells) cause increased renal excretion of H+ by the H+K+-Na+ exchange mechanism and alkalosis.

Excessive renal losses occur in various diseases in which the secretion of adrenal cortical hormones is increased (conditions of stress).

The excessive breakdown of body tissues in high fever and in wasting diseases generally leads to increased renal loss of K+.

Severe and prolonged vomiting, generally associated with pyloric or duodenal obstruction, causes the loss of gastric juice and its electrolyte content, with depletion of body K+ and alkalosis. With [K+] depletion of extracellular fluid due to initial increased excretion of K+ and Na+ with HCO₃⁻, and if there is repletion of water without potassium, K+ moves out of cells and Na+ and H+ move into cells, increasing extracellular HCO₃⁻, and leading to more alkalosis. Also, with low extracellular K+ and low renal tubular cell K+, the excretion of H+ ions is increased, to raise extracellular HCO₃⁻ and produce alkalosis. In such conditions there may be the paradoxical situation of alkalosis associated with an acid urine. The alkalosis is repaired only after the K+ deficiency is corrected.

The ionic shifts between extracellular and intracellular compartments in cases of K+ depletion are different from those of the customary H+K+-Na+ exchange in that instead of H+ and K+ moving in opposite directions to

Na$^+$, the movement of K$^+$ from the cells is balanced by the movement of Na$^+$ and H$^+$ into the cells.

Severe diarrhea, particularly as seen in infants, causes acidosis because of excessive loss of HCO$_3$$^-$ over Cl$^-$ and depletion of total electrolytes and dehydration. The K$^+$ stores are depleted, but because of the dehydration the extracellular [K$^+$] may be elevated.

The factors causing the exchange of K$^+$ between extracellular and intracellular fluids are shown in Figure 17.18.

While extracellular [K$^+$] is increased in a number of clinical conditions, generally excess K$^+$ is readily disposed of by the kidneys. Persistent increase in extracellular K$^+$ generally indicates impaired excretion, as seen in oliguric

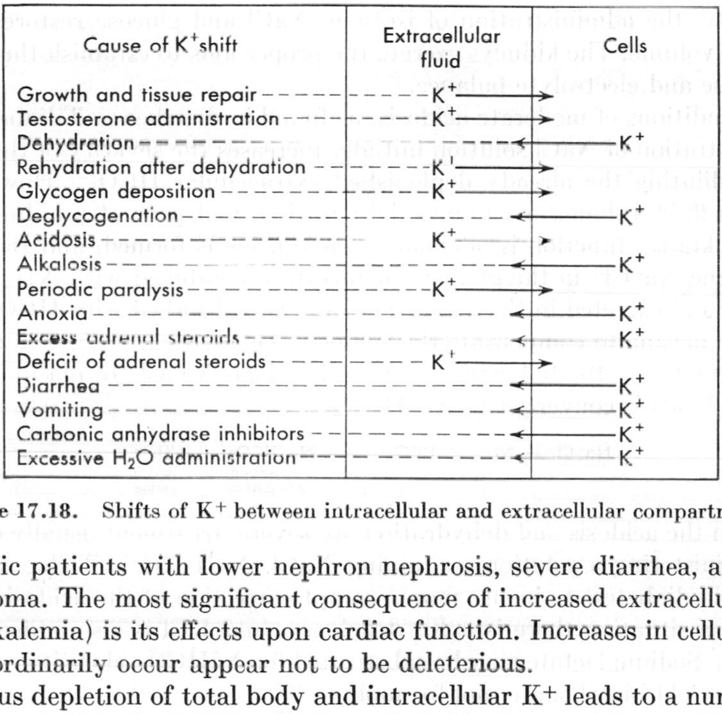

Cause of K$^+$ shift	Extracellular fluid	Cells
Growth and tissue repair	K$^+$ →	
Testosterone administration	K$^+$ →	
Dehydration		← K$^+$
Rehydration after dehydration	K$^+$ →	
Glycogen deposition	K$^+$ →	
Deglycogenation		← K$^+$
Acidosis	K$^+$ →	
Alkalosis		← K$^+$
Periodic paralysis	K$^+$ →	
Anoxia		← K$^+$
Excess adrenal steroids		← K$^+$
Deficit of adrenal steroids	K$^+$ →	
Diarrhea		← K$^+$
Vomiting		← K$^+$
Carbonic anhydrase inhibitors		← K$^+$
Excessive H$_2$O administration		← K$^+$

Figure 17.18. Shifts of K$^+$ between intracellular and extracellular compartments.

or anuric patients with lower nephron nephrosis, severe diarrhea, and diabetic coma. The most significant consequence of increased extracellular K$^+$ (hyperkalemia) is its effects upon cardiac function. Increases in cellular K$^+$ which ordinarily occur appear not to be deleterious.

Serious depletion of total body and intracellular K$^+$ leads to a number of disturbances: histologic kidney lesions, diminished growth, impaired glucose metabolism (tolerance), alterations in gastric secretion, impaired neuromuscular function, alterations in the electrocardiogram, cardiac arrest, and death.

Parenteral fluid therapy. The clinical correction of disturbances in fluid, electrolyte, and acid-base balances is based upon the application of principles discussed above and constitutes a major problem in medical practice. Generally extracellular fluid and electrolyte deficits are repaired by oral administration of water, sodium chloride, and potassium compounds, or potassium-rich foods when this is possible. Otherwise, isotonic NaCl solution, isotonic NaCl solution plus KCl, or such electrolyte solutions containing glucose (for energy) are given intravenously. Generally, if kidney function is adequate, fluid volume and electrolyte repair may be achieved with isotonic NaCl solution, and by this solution with KCl and glucose if there is potassium deficiency. The metabolism of glucose provides energy to the tissues, and its deposition as glycogen in cells increases the transfer of K^+ from extracellular fluid into the cells.

In the correction of hypertonic fluid contraction with electrolyte excess where there is a water deficit, isotonic (5 per cent) glucose solution may be used to advantage. The provision of water is generally accomplished by giving isotonic glucose, since the glucose is taken up by the cells and metabolized.

In isotonic fluid contraction where there is proportionate loss of water and electrolytes, as in severe vomiting and diarrhea, if kidney function is adequate, the administration of isotonic NaCl and glucose restores extracellular volume. The kidneys excrete the proper ions to establish the correct acid-base and electrolyte balance.

In conditions of moderate acidosis, as found in diarrhea and diabetes, the administration of NaCl solution initially increases the severity of the acidosis by diluting the already depleted extracellular HCO_3^-. However, it restores fluid volume, overcomes dehydration, and promotes kidney function. If kidney function is adequate, acidic urine is formed, and the excess Cl^- of the Na^+Cl^- in the glomerular filtrate is combined with NH_4^+ in the tubules and excreted in the urine. The Na^+ is reabsorbed with HCO_3^- back into the plasma to compensate the acidosis. The over-all process in the kidneys amounts to the following reaction, in which Na^+Cl^- of plasma (extracellular fluid) is converted to $Na^+HCO_3^-$:

$$Na^+Cl^- + NH_4^+ + HCO_3^- \longrightarrow \underset{\substack{\text{Absorbed} \\ \text{into plasma}}}{Na^+HCO_3^-} + \underset{\substack{\text{Out in} \\ \text{urine}}}{NH_4^+Cl^-}$$

When the acidosis and dehydration are severe, treatment usually consists in administering a solution containing NaCl, $NaHCO_3$, and glucose (with insulin in diabetes) to insure more prompt correction of the acidosis. Often in such a situation there is a K^+ deficiency, and KCl is also added to the solution. Sodium lactate may be substituted for $NaHCO_3$, since it is metabolized to yield bicarbonate mol for mol.

Conditions of alkalosis are seldom treated by the administration of acids, though occasionally NH_4Cl solutions are used, the ammonia being converted to neutral urea in the liver with the release of HCl, which reacts with body buffers. The administration of isotonic NaCl solution dilutes the extracellular HCO_3^-, to ameliorate the alkalosis somewhat, and expands the extracellular fluid volume, which may be desirable. Often in such cases as the alkalosis of vomiting there is K^+ depletion, and this deficit must be corrected by administering potassium before the kidneys can compensate the alkalosis by excreting bicarbonate and retaining Cl^-.

Each patient with fluid and electrolyte disturbances presents an individual problem to the physician, who, to apply the proper corrective measures, must take many facts into consideration. Books such as those of Welt, and

Elkinton and Danowski, given in the references, consider the treatment of such disturbances in detail. The book by Pickering and Fisher (30) gives an excellent treatment of the fundamental disturbances in fluid and electrolyte balance and their therapeutic correction. Figure 17.19, taken from this book, summarizes the water and electrolyte requirements of the average adult hospital patient based upon caloric expenditure.

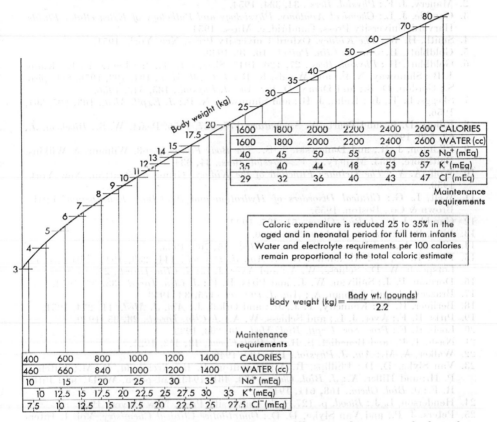

Maintenance requirements

1600	1800	2000	2200	2400	2600	CALORIES
1600	1800	2000	2200	2400	2600	WATER (cc)
40	45	50	55	60	65	Na$^+$ (mEq)
35	40	44	48	53	57	K$^+$ (mEq)
29	32	36	40	43	47	Cl$^-$ (mEq)

Caloric expenditure is reduced 25 to 35% in the aged and in neonatal period for full term infants Water and electrolyte requirements per 100 calories remain proportional to the total caloric estimate

$$\text{Body weight (kg)} = \frac{\text{Body wt. (pounds)}}{2.2}$$

Maintenance requirements

400	600	800	1000	1200	1400	CALORIES
460	660	840	1000	1200	1400	WATER (cc)
10	15	20	25	30	35	Na$^+$ (mEq)
10	12.5	15	17.5	20	22.5	25	27.5	30	33	K$^+$ (mEq)
7.5	10	12.5	15	17.5	20	22.5	25	27.5	Cl$^-$ (mEq)

Figure 17.19. Twenty-four-hour caloric expenditure and water and electrolyte requirements in the average hospitalized patient. (From Pickering, D. E., and Fisher, D. A.: *Fluid and Electrolyte Therapy. A Unified Approach.* Medical Research Foundation of Oregon, Portland, 1959.)

GENERAL REFERENCES

Elkinton, J. R., and Danowski, T. S.: *The Body Fluids.* Williams & Wilkins Co., Baltimore, 1955.

Gamble, J. L.: *Chemical Anatomy, Physiology and Pathology of Extracellular Fluids.* Harvard University Press, Cambridge, Mass., 1954.

Lewis, A. A. G., and Wolstenholme, G. E. W. (eds.): *The Kidney.* Little, Brown & Co., Boston, 1954.

Pickering, D. E., and Fisher, D. A.: *Fluid and Electrolyte Therapy. A Unified Approach.* Medical Research Foundation of Oregon, University of Oregon Medical School, Portland, 1959.

Smith, H. W.: *The Kidney.* Oxford University Press, New York, 1951.

Smith, H. W.: *Principles of Renal Physiology.* Oxford University Press, New York, 1956

Welt, L. G.: *Clinical Disorders of Hydration and Acid-Base Equilibrium*, 2nd ed. Little, Brown & Co., Boston, 1959.

Wolf, A. V.: *The Urinary Function of the Kidney*. Grune & Stratton, New York, 1950.

SPECIAL REFERENCES

1. Richards, A. N.: *Harvey Lectures*, 1934–1935; *Proc. Roy. Soc. (London)*, **B126**, 398, 1938; *Bull. N. Y. Acad. Med.*, **14**, 2nd series, 1938.
2. Manery, J. F.: *Physiol. Revs.*, **34**, 334, 1954.
3. Gamble, J. L.: *Chemical Anatomy, Physiology and Pathology of Extracellular Fluids*. Harvard University Press, Cambridge, Mass., 1954.
4. Smith, H. W.: *The Kidney*. Oxford University Press, New York, 1951.
5. Goldblatt, H.: *Am. J. Clin. Pathol.*, **10**, 40, 1940.
6. Goldblatt, H.: *Physiol. Revs.*, **27**, 120, 1947. Skeggs, L. T., Jr.; Lentz, K. E.; Kahn, J. R.; Shumway, N. P.; and Woods, K. R.: *J. Exptl. Med.*, **104**, 193, 1956. Schapiro, S.; Gordon, D. B.; and Drury, D. R.: *Am. J. Physiol.*, **185**, 543, 1956.
7. Skeggs, L. T., Jr.; Kahn, J. R.; and Shumway, N. P.: *J. Exptl. Med.*, **103**, 295, 301, 1956.
8. Elliott, D. F., and Peart, W. S.: *Nature*, **177**, 527, 1956. Peart, W. S.: *Biochem. J.*, **62**, 520, 1956.
9. Elkinton, J. R., and Danowski, T. S.: *The Body Fluids*, p. 68. Williams & Wilkins, Baltimore, 1955. Manery, J. F.: *Physiol. Revs.*, **34**, 334, 1954.
10. Wolf, A. V.: *The Urinary Function of the Kidney*. Grune & Stratton, New York, 1950.
11. Welt, L. G.: *Clinical Disorders of Hydration and Acid-Base Equilibrium*. Little, Brown & Co., Boston, 1955.
12. Gamble, J. L.: *J. Biol. Chem.*, **51**, 295, 1922.
13. Pitts, R. F.: *Am. J. Med.*, **9**, 356, 1950.
14. Gilman, A., and Brazeau, P.: *Am. J. Med.*, **15**, 765, 1953.
15. Pitts, R. F., and Alexander, R. S.: *Am. J. Physiol.*, **144**, 239, 1945. Pitts, R. F.; Lotspeich, W. D.; Schiess, W. A.; and Ayer, J. L.: *J. Clin. Invest.*, **27**, 48, 1948.
16. Dorman, P. J.; Sullivan, W. J.; and Pitts, R. F.: *J. Clin. Invest.*, **33**, 82, 1954.
17. Brazeau, P., and Gilman, A.: *Am. J. Physiol.*, **175**, 33, 1953.
18. Berliner, R. W.; Kennedy, T. J., Jr.; and Orloff, J.: *Am. J. Med.*, **11**, 274, 1951.
19. Pitts, R. F.; Ayer, J. L.; and Schiess, W. A.: *J. Clin. Invest.*, **28**, 35, 1949.
20. Loeb, R. F.: *Proc. Soc. Exptl. Biol. Med.*, **30**, 808, 1933.
21. Nash, T. P., and Benedict, S. R.: *J. Biol. Chem.*, **48**, 463, 1921.
22. Walker, A. M.: *Am. J. Physiol.*, **131**, 187, 1940.
23. Van Slyke, D. D.; Phillips, R. A.; Hamilton, P. B.; Archibald, R. M.; Futcher, P. H.; and Hiller, A.: *J. Biol. Chem.*, **150**, 481, 1943. Lotspeich, W. D., and Pitts, R. F.: *J. Biol. Chem.*, **168**, 611, 1947.
24. Henderson, L. J.: *Blood*, p. 127. Yale University Press, New Haven, 1928.
25. Peters, J. P., and Van Slyke, D. D.: *Quantitative Clinical Chemistry*, Vol. I, Interpretations, p. 894. Williams & Wilkins Co., Baltimore, 1931.
26. Van Slyke, D. D., and Cullen, G. E.: *J. Biol. Chem.*, **30**, 289, 1917.
27. Shaw, L. A.: *Am. J. Physiol.*, **79**, 91, 1926.
28. Smith, H. W.: *Principles of Renal Physiology*. Oxford University Press, New York, 1956.
29. Edelman, I. S.; Olney, J. M.; James, A. H.; Brooks, L.; and Moore, F. D.: *Science*, **115**, 447, 1952.
30. Pickering, D. E., and Fisher, D. A.: *Fluid and Electrolyte Therapy. A Unified Approach*. Medical Research Foundation of Oregon, University of Oregon Medical School, Portland, 1959.

18

The vitamins

INTRODUCTION

The historical development of the discovery of the vitamins is an interesting one. Space does not allow for more than a cursory review here. One of the primary questions we can answer, however, is: Why did investigators start searching in foods and elsewhere for the substances we now call vitamins?

A great many feeding experiments with animals and some with human beings pointed to the fact that substances other than minerals, water, carbohydrate, protein, and fat were required for good nutrition.

In the Japanese Navy a high proportion of the sailors suffered for many years from beriberi, a condition now known to be a vitamin deficiency disease. Takaki, after many attempts finally was able in the 1880's to arrange certain reforms in the diet of the Japanese Navy. Meat and vegetable allowances were increased, and evaporated milk was added to the dietary. The effects on the health of the men were so dramatic that extension of the reforms were undertaken, and few cases of beriberi appeared among the Japanese Navy men thereafter.

Scurvy, another deficiency disease, was so widespread among various of the early sailing crews that long voyages were usually attended by a high incidence of sickness and loss of life. It was the English who early introduced limes or lemons into the diet of their sailing men to help protect against scurvy. The English sailors are still called "limies"; the term supposedly originated from the fact that they carried crates of limes aboard the vessels.

There are many early recorded instances of practical applications of nutrition among human beings. The basis for many of these applications was a chance observation, or the result of lore too remote to find recorded.

Several animal experiments stand out among those which caused leading investigators to inquire further into the "accessory factors," as the then unknown vitamins were later called by Hopkins. In 1881 Lunin attempted to grow mice on diets consisting of partially purified protein (casein), fat (milk fat), and sugar. He added various inorganic salts to the diets but was unable to maintain life in his animals for more than short periods.

Natural foods, such as milk, allowed long-continued growth. At this early date the question was raised as to the possibility of milk containing unknown and essential nutrients.

In many parts of the world where polished rice constitutes an appreciable share of man's diet, the condition of beriberi has long been known. The Dutch physician Eijkman in Java as early as 1897 showed that the addition of rice polishings to the diet would ameliorate the beriberi. He produced polyneuritis, a primary symptom of beriberi, in chickens by raising them on polished rice. Other chickens given unpolished rice showed no symptoms. Extracts of rice polishings were found to cure the deficiency symptoms, sometimes dramatically.

Funk (1) attempted to isolate the active principle in rice polishings that was responsible for relieving beriberi in pigeons and other animals. After various extractions and fractionations, he obtained a crystalline substance that in very small quantities was highly curative for pigeon beriberi. It was also active prophylactically when given with a diet known to bring on the deficiency symptoms. A similar material was soon isolated from yeast, and Funk found that it contained basic nitrogen. Since the substance was apparently essential to life and seemed to be an amine, he coined the term "vitamine." The term, without the final "e" is, of course, used now for a great variety of "accessory food substances." This work did much to stimulate further investigation and thought in the field of nutrition, as did Funk's suggestion that not only beriberi, but also rickets, scurvy, and pellagra are diseases due to deficiencies in the diet.

Early in this century a comprehensive and pertinent experiment was initiated at the University of Wisconsin. This work ultimately demonstrated that great differences with respect to growth and reproduction in animals exist in different rations comprised essentially of the same amounts of the digestible nutrients. Sixteen heifer calves were divided into four groups, and each group was fed one of the following rations: (a) nutrients of the corn plant only, (b) nutrients of the wheat plant only, (c) nutrients of the oat plant only, and (d) a mixture of equal parts of the first three rations. The rations were so compounded that they contained almost the same quantity of protein, fat, and carbohydrate.

Growth and reproduction on such rations were studied over a period of several years. Marked differences in response were noted. The animals on the all-corn ration thrived, produced vigorous young, and milked well. The wheat-fed animals were unable to perform these physiologic functions in a satisfactory manner. On the other two rations intermediate performances were found. Wheat-fed animals changed to the corn ration showed marked improvement in a year with respect to milk secretion and in size of offspring. The converse was found after changing corn-fed animals to the wheat ration.

It is obvious that chemical analyses of rations for protein, fat, and carbohydrate are inadequate to allow an appraisal of their physiologic value. In these experiments the wheat-fed animals suffered multiple deficiencies, including one of vitamin A. Other deficiencies in this ration and in others of the rations used are now understood.

It is important here to point out that this experiment was of great value in demonstrating that other substances than the three major foodstuffs are essential to good nutrition. Certainly the influence of this work on future experimentation has been tremendous. These and further experiments of a similar nature are described by Hart and coworkers (2,3).

By 1912 or so the experimental approach to nutritional problems was assuming an ever increasing importance. The course of events from that time on can well be given consideration under the discussion of the individual vitamins. There is little to be gained by considering the vitamins in the chronological order of their discovery; a preferable approach is to group them as fat-soluble or water-soluble vitamins and to discuss them under these two large headings.

What are vitamins? A strict definition of a vitamin would be cumbersome and perhaps of little value. We know that they are chemical entities; a large number of them have been isolated, characterized, and then synthesized. Certainly they are essential in maintaining the metabolic processes at a normal level in animals, and some have important roles in plant metabolism also. With some exceptions, all animal species require the major vitamins preformed in the diet for the obvious reason that they are unable to synthesize them from other food constituents. But certain precursors suffice in some instances because the animal can convert these to the vitamins. Plants and various microorganisms synthesize vitamins, animals eat the plants and store certain vitamins, and the animal tissues also serve as vitamin sources for other species. Although rather exact roles for some of the vitamins in the chain of metabolic events are understood, it is safe to say that the complete function of any one of the vitamins in the body is unknown.

A. THE FAT-SOLUBLE VITAMINS

The terms vitamers or isotels have been recommended to indicate different chemical compounds with similar physiologic actions. Thus the various chemical forms of vitamin D are isotels, or the vitamers D. Beside vitamin D, vitamins A, E, and K are fat-soluble. Various isotels of each are now well known.

VITAMIN A

The discovery of vitamin A resulted from feeding experiments with rats and mice using purified rations.* Although McCollum is generally credited with the discovery of this vitamin, the investigations of several groups of workers led up to it. Hopkins (1) in 1912 reported that young rats grew poorly on a purified ration but that the addition of a small amount of whole milk (4 per cent of the total solids eaten) induced normal and continued growth. Osborne and Mendel (2) at about the same time were studying rat growth on purified rations and among other things varied the source of fat. With lard or with almond oil as the fat source, growth was unsuccessful. Butter fat or egg yolk fat added to the diet brought about good growth. Also, small amounts of cod liver oil brought about growth in animals that had stopped growing on diets containing lard. These workers described inflamed eyes in their rats progressing after a time to a purulent state. Butter fat or cod liver oil quickly cured this condition also. Here we see one of the very early instances of the experimental production of xerophthalmia in animals (vitamin A deficiency). McCollum and Davis (3) were also active along these lines at this time and in 1915 announced that ether extracts of butter or of egg yolk contain some organic complex essential for continued growth of rats on the diets employed. This substance was termed "fat-soluble A" by McCollum and now, of course, is known as vitamin A. Xerophthalmia in rats was shown to be due to a deficiency of "fat-soluble A" by McCollum and Simmonds (4) in 1917.

Vitamin A occurs in animal tissues only, but many plant tissues contain substances which, when fed to rats suffering from xerophthalmia, for instance, will relieve the condition. Thus one must distinguish between vitamin A content and vitamin A activity. A number of the carotenoid pigments of plants act as precursors of vitamin A. In other words, the

* The terms "purified rations or synthetic rations" will of necessity be used throughout the following discussion. Some insight into their meaning is important. In contradistinction to natural foods—i.e., milk, meat, and vegetables—a purified ration contains "purified" protein, such as casein or zein; fat, such as lard or butter fat washed with hot water, or extracted with various solvents; carbohydrate in the form of various sugars, dextrins, or starches which can be obtained quite free from contaminating substances; and a mixture of purified minerals plus distilled water. The term purified is used here in anything but an exact sense, since most any degree of purity can be obtained in a ration. At the present time highly purified vitamins may be added to the rations if this is desired.

animal can consume these pigments and bring about chemical alterations in them to produce vitamin A. Carrots and yellow corn contain no vitamin A, but since carotenes are present, they afford vitamin A activity to animals that eat them.

This situation, now quite clear to us, was a baffling one during the early stages of its clarification. Steenbock (5) early postulated that the vitamin A activity of foods was due to the yellow pigments they contained. He demonstrated vitamin A activity in the hydrocarbon carotene, $C_{40}H_{56}$, isolated from carrots and other vegetables. A closely related pigment, xanthophyll $C_{40}H_{54}(OH)_2$, possessed no activity. But various animal sources of vitamin A were known to be colorless or nearly so, and it was only after many years work by various investigators that carotene and certain other chemically related pigments were found to be precursors of vitamin A but not the vitamin itself. If the animal were able to synthesize one of the precursors in sufficient quantity and then convert it to the vitamin, there would be no need for either in the diet. Obviously this is not the case.

The relationship of the pigment precursors to the vitamin will be made clearer in the following section.

The chemistry of vitamin A. A number of naturally occurring pigments can be converted into vitamin A by animal tissues. These pigments, known as the "carotenoid pigments," are found primarily in green leafy plants and yellow vegetables. They are important sources of vitamin A for man and some animals.

Kuhn and Karrer showed that β-carotene is a symmetrical molecule containing two β-ionone rings connected by a carbon chain. It has the following structure:

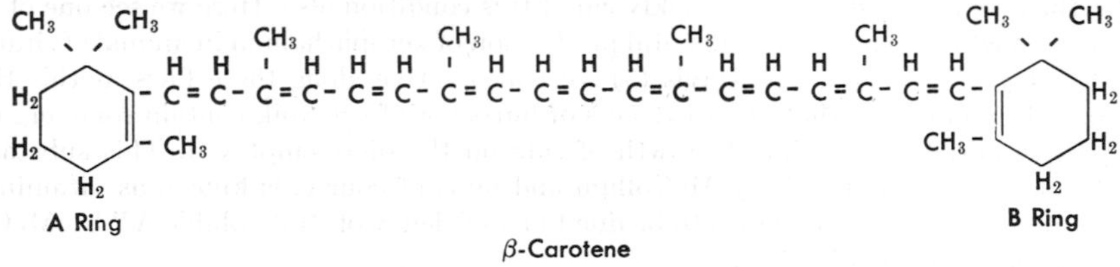

β-Carotene

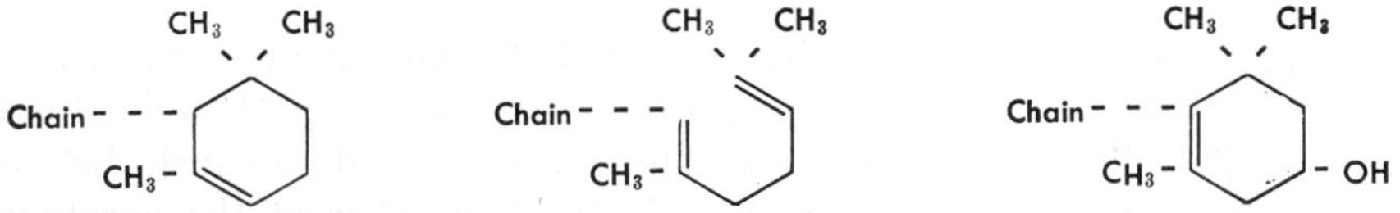

B ring in α-carotene
shift in double bond

B ring in γ-carotene
open ring

B ring in cryptoxanthin
hydroxyl group

Because of the marked chemical similarity of the carotenoid pigments, it is practical to show their differences without setting down the entire formulas. The two rings in β-carotene are marked A and B. The formula of α-carotene, for instance, can be indicated by showing the difference in the B ring of this pigment compared to the B ring of β-carotene. The remainder of the molecules are identical.

Since the A ring in these pigments is a β-ionone ring these compounds

are vitamin A precursors. In xanthophyll (found in nature with the carotenes) each ring contains an hydroxyl group, and thus this pigment does
not yield vitamin A. Licopene has two open rings (as the B ring in γ-carotene) and hence no activity.

Table 18.1. Relative Vitamin A Activity of Some Naturally Occurring Pigments

Pigment	Formula	β-Ionone rings	Relative Vitamin Activity
β-Carotene	$C_{40}H_{56}$	2	55–100*
α-Carotene	$C_{40}H_{56}$	1	53
γ-Carotene	$C_{40}H_{56}$	1	30
Neo-β-carotene B	$C_{40}H_{56}$	2	50
Cryptoxanthine	$C_{40}H_{55}OH$	1	55
Xanthophyll	$C_{40}H_{54}(OH)_2$	0	0
Lycopene	$C_{40}H_{56}$	0	0

* Varies in different species. Also, the problem of whether one or two molecules of
vitamin A can be obtained from a molecule of β-carotene is not unequivocally settled.

Table 18.1 summarizes some of the above facts in regard to a few of the
naturally occurring pigments. The naturally occurring carotenoid pigments
exist as mixtures of sterioisomers due to cis-trans isomerism about the conjugated double bonds of the carbon chain. Neo-β-carotene U, neo-β-carotene
B, and others have been isolated and studied. Kemmerer and Fraps (6)
showed that the rat digestive tract is capable of bringing about a steric rearrangement of some neo-β-carotene U into β-carotene and that this accounts
for the vitamin A activity of this neo compound. A few other isomers with
varying degrees of vitamin activity have been isolated in pure enough form
for study (7).

A comprehensive review on the biosynthesis and function of carotinoid
pigments is available (8).

The central double bond of β-carotene can be oxidized, and after scission
at that point it is theoretically possible that two molecules of vitamin A
result. An aldehyde, subsequently reduced to the alcohol, or vitamin A, may
be an intermediate. Other carotenes, such as α- and γ-carotenes, cannot
yield more than one molecule of the vitamin on oxidative scission. This is
because a β-ionone ring is an essential part of the vitamin A molecule
(vitamin A_1), and while β-carotene contains two such rings, α- and γ-carotene each have but one β-ionone ring. The second ring in these two pigments
varies in structure, and there is no vitamin A activity associated with this
part of the molecule after oxidation at the central double bond.

The manner in which animals convert the various precursor pigments
into vitamin A is not understood. Presumably it is an enzymatic process.
Until recently it was thought that the liver was the main site of this transformation. Sexton, Mehl, and Deuel (9) injected carotene intravenously into
rats. Carotene but not vitamin A was deposited in the liver. When carotene
was given orally, vitamin A was found in the liver. In some of their experiments rats died of a vitamin A deficiency while their livers contained sufficient carotene to maintain them for a year had the carotene been given orally
in small doses over that period of time. These workers pointed out that the

conversion of carotene to vitamin A is an extrahepatic function in the rat and suggested the wall of the intestine as a possible site for this transformation. This view has been supported by further work.

Although Koehn (10) reported that one molecule of β-carotene is converted into two molecules of vitamin A in the rat, other investigators have not confirmed this finding and, in fact, the weight of evidence now indicates that only one molecule of vitamin A is obtained (11). Glover and Redfearn (12) propose an attractive scheme of carotene conversion into vitamin A. They suggest that in the intestine the initial attack on β-carotene occurs at one end of the molecule and proceeds through progressive β-oxidation to the formation of retinene, which is reduced to the vitamin and absorbed. Experimental data and theoretical considerations increase the plausibility of this scheme. It is possible also that a small amount of β-carotene may undergo symmetrical scission and produce two molecules of vitamin A.

A number of observations led to the belief that the hypothyroid animal is unable to convert carotene into vitamin A in a normal manner. The thyroid gland is known to be involved in carotene and vitamin A metabolism but various aspects of the manner in which the thyroid hormone is involved are not yet clear.

The administration of thiourea or thiouracil to animals depresses thyroid activity, whereas desiccated thyroid or thyroxine produces hyperfunction.

Baumann and coworkers (13) administered carotene to both hypothyroid and hyperthyroid rats, depleted of body stores of vitamin A, in order to study the role of the thyroid gland in the conversion of this pigment into the vitamin. Determinations of vitamin A in the livers revealed a decreased storage in the hypothyroid animals and a greater than normal storage in the hyperthyroid rats. Animals given thiourea and thyroxine together stored normal amounts. The data were interpreted as indicative of a physiologic role of the thyroid in the conversion of carotene into vitamin A.

Later workers (14) reported that the thyroid hormone stimulates intestinal absorption of carotene in rats and that thiouracil inhibits the absorption. Given together, the thyroid hormone counteracts the inhibition of absorption by the drug. These workers suggest that the findings of Baumann and others (13) can be interpreted on the basis of absorption effects.

This problem, however, remains unresolved. Arnrich and Morgan (15) recovered more vitamin A from livers of hypothyroid rats than from the normal controls after small amounts of carotene were administered. This difference disappeared when the dose of carotene was increased twentyfold. They concluded that absorption, transformation, and utilization of carotene are not affected by thyroid activity.

The relationship of insulin to vitamin A metabolism is unclear. It has been felt by various workers that diabetic individuals have impaired efficiency of carotene conversion into vitamin A. Sobel and others (16) showed definitely that the conversion was markedly lowered in alloxan diabetic rats. In isolated intestinal loops from such rats Rosenberg and Sobel (17) demonstrated a marked diminution in the conversion process.

Vitamin A_1, $C_{20}H_{29}OH$, and vitamin A_2, $C_{20}H_{27}OH$, are alcohols with the accompanying structures:

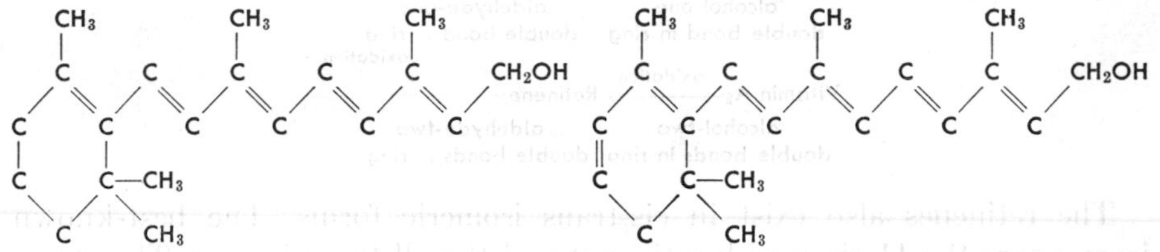

All trans vitamin A_1 All trans vitamin A_2

Vitamin A_2 contains one more double bond in the ring (18,19). It is a dehydro vitamin A_1 formed by the loss of two H atoms in the body. Animals fed β-carotene or A_1 show the presence of both A_1 and A_2 in their tissues. No carotinoids are known from which the animal body can form A_2 directly.

Vitamin A exists naturally in several isomeric forms. This is a cis-trans isomerism resulting from configurational differences about the double bonds in the side chain. To obviate repetition the various isomeric structures of vitamin A are not presented. This point is brought out in the next section on the chemistry of the retinenes.

The major naturally occurring form of vitamin A is the all trans isomer. Neo-vitamin A (13-cis) has about 85 per cent of the potency of the all trans form and occurs in various fish liver oils. As much as one-third of the total potency of some fish oils may be due to this isomer. The 11-cis isomer (neo-b) was found to comprise the bulk of the vitamin in certain crustacea (20). It has around three-fourths the biologic activity of the trans isomer. Vitamin A_2 is found in many animal tissues but is more abundant in freshwater fishes. It has only about half the activity of A_1. Presumably the A_2 molecule is also found naturally in various isomeric forms. A large part of the vitamin in livers of fishes and mammals is present in ester form. A short review on the occurrence of vitamin A isomers is available (21).

For a better understanding of these relationships it is advisable to consider the retinenes. From the retina of the dark-adapted eye two closely related compounds have been isolated. They were named retinene$_1$ and retinene$_2$, and it was established by Morton, Salah, and Stubbs (18) that these compounds are the aldehydes (oxidation products) corresponding to vitamin A_1 and vitamin A_2. The relationship of the retinenes to vision will be considered later.

Morton and coworkers oxidized vitamin A_1 and isolated what appeared to be retinene$_2$, the aldehyde corresponding to vitamin A_2. Derivatives of this aldehyde and of retinene$_2$ prepared by oxidation of vitamin A_2, were identical. They were also able to oxidize retinene$_1$ to retinene$_2$. It appears that the alcohol group of vitamin A_1 is first oxidized to the aldehyde yielding retinene$_1$, and then further oxidation, by removal of two hydrogen atoms from the ring, yields retinene$_2$. Thus vitamin A_2 and retinene$_2$ differ from their sub-one relatives by an additional double bond in the ring.

These changes are presented in graphic form below:

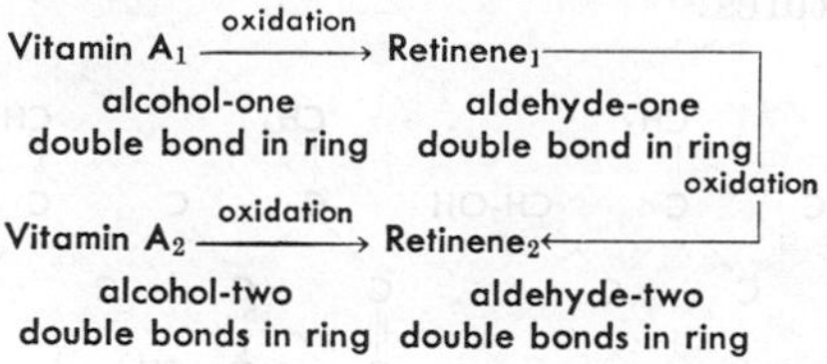

$$\text{Vitamin A}_1 \xrightarrow{\text{oxidation}} \text{Retinene}_1$$

alcohol-one   aldehyde-one
double bond in ring   double bond in ring

oxidation

$$\text{Vitamin A}_2 \xrightarrow{\text{oxidation}} \text{Retinene}_2$$

alcohol-two   aldehyde-two
double bonds in ring double bonds in ring

The retinenes also exist in cis-trans isomeric forms. The best-known isomers are the 11-cis (neo-b retinene) and the all trans isomer. The structures of these two retinenes are shown with most of the H atoms omitted to simplify the formulas. It is apparent that similar isomers exist in both the retinene$_1$ and the retinene$_2$ series.

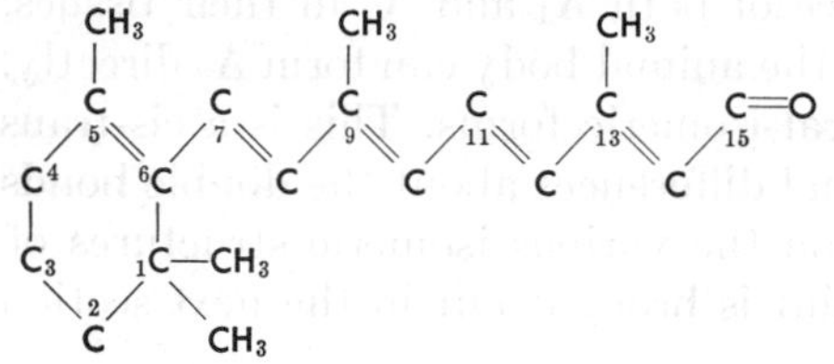

All trans retinine$_1$

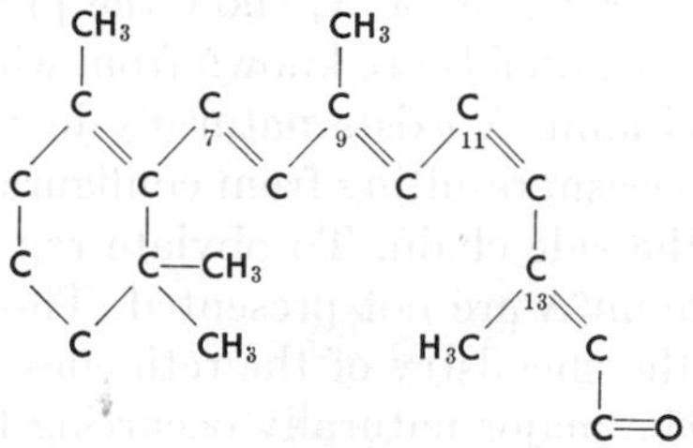

Neo-b retinene$_1$, 11-cis

Vitamin A has been synthesized by many different workers. Cawley and others (22) reported the synthesis of vitamin A and showed that their purified product contained vitamin A$_1$ and neo-vitamin A in the ratio of 1.5 or 2 to 1. This is similar to the ratios found in fish liver oils, and these authors propose that physiologic vitamin A is a mixture of these two geometric forms. Crystalline vitamin A from their synthetic concentrates was reported to be identical with natural vitamin A crystals in biologic potency and certain physical properties. A synthesis of the vitamin from cyclohexanone was reported (23). Another synthesis by Wendler and others (24) is of interest.

The determination of vitamin A. The determination of vitamin A may be carried out by use of a photoelectric colorimeter or preferably with a spectrophotometer. Vitamin A forms a blue color with antimony trichloride in chloroform, and this reaction is made the basis of a colorimetric and also of a spectrophotometric method (Carr-Price reaction).

Vitamin A in solution shows a maximum absorption in the ultraviolet region of the spectrum of light at a wavelength 325 to 328 mμ. With a spectrophotometer it is practical to determine vitamin A quantitatively by comparing the amount of light of 325 mμ wavelength transmitted by the vitamin A solution (in isopropyl alcohol for instance) and that transmitted by the pure solvent. If the Beckman type of spectrophotometer is used, the transmittance is set to 100 per cent for the pure solvent and the light transmitted by the vitamin in the same solvent is estimated. This value will be less than 100 per cent, and by proper calculations the extinction coefficient can be found.

In order to calculate vitamin A units from such a determination, a further factor relating vitamin potency and extinction coefficient is necessary. This factor has been estimated by a great many workers and is obtained by determining biologically the vitamin

A content of a sample (rat assay) and examining the same sample spectrophotometrically. Since the rat assay method generally gives somewhat different results from laboratory to laboratory, this factor, known as the "*E* value," or conversion factor, ranges in practical applications from 1600 to 1700 to as much as 2200. The value to accept as correct is a matter of considerable controversy. Many workers use a factor of 2000 for natural vitamin A fish oils in which the vitamin is present as a mixture of free alcohol and vitamin A esters. Pure vitamin A alcohol has an *E* value of around 1750.

The extinction coefficient, $E_{1cm}^{1\%}$ multiplied by the appropriate conversion factor gives the units of vitamin A per gram of the oil tested. Since a unit of vitamin A is very nearly equivalent to 0.3 μg, the weight of vitamin A can be calculated also.

Obviously, this method is applicable to many substances other than vitamin A-containing oils. Usually because of low vitamin content in other substances, such as liver or other tissues, it is necessary to carry out purification and concentration of the vitamin before the determination can be made. This generally involves saponification and extraction procedures.

The various forms of vitamin A occurring in nature have, as far as we know at the present, similar qualitative physiologic effects in the animal body. They differ chemically as we have seen, and there are marked differences in certain physical characteristics. The biologic potencies differ markedly also. These statements hold also for the active pigment precursors. A brief résumé of certain properties of the more important vitamin A sources is of interest. Table 18.2 contains certain pertinent data in these respects.

Table 18.2. Physical Characteristics and Biological Potency of Outstanding Vitamin A Sources

Source	Crystal Form	MP	Absorption Maximum mμ	Conversion Factor	Biological Potency IU/μg
Vitamin A$_1$	Yellow prisms	62–64°	325–328	1,900	3.3
Vitamin A$_2$	Not crystallized	——	351	1,125	1.3
Neo-vitamin A	Yellow needles	59–60°	328	1,675	ca. 3.3
β-Carotene	Red	183°	—	—	1.66

Under highly standardized experimental conditions the biologic assay assumes a good deal of significance. These conditions are outlined in the sixteenth edition of the *United States Pharmacopoeia* and elsewhere. The method employed is the "rat curative" assay. Either the U.S.P. Reference Cod Liver Oil or one of the stable crystalline vitamin A esters is administered to a group of animals as a primary control of rate of growth of the partially vitamin A-depleted rats. This growth rate is compared to that of other groups given the material under test. Various levels of the unknown material and of the standard material can be given to different groups of rats. The larger the number of animals and the more varied the levels of test materials employed, the more successful is the assay likely to be.

Absorption of vitamin A. In the small intestine the vitamin A esters of foods are hydrolyzed to fatty acids and the free vitamin. The vitamin is absorbed here mainly by the lymphatic system and appears in blood plasma as the ester indicating reesterification in the intestinal wall. Carotene is absorbed in the small intestine, and that which is not converted here into vitamin A proceeds via the portal system to the blood. Bile salts aid in carotene but not in vitamin A absorption.

Physiologic functions of vitamin A. At this time we cannot make a qualitative distinction in the physiologic effects of the various vitamin A active substances, except in the case of neo-b vitamin A, which is the only isomer capable of oxidation to neo-b retinene used to combine with a protein to form a visual pigment (see further under Eyes).

Growth. In the absence of a vitamin A source, animals fail to grow and may die before body stores are completely exhausted, and often before typical deficiency symptoms develop. The mechanism of the cooperation of vitamin A in the growth processes is not understood. Perhaps it involves the well-established relation of vitamin A to normal development of various epithelial tissues. In the presence of subminimum amounts of dietary vitamin A life is prolonged, with or without growth, and a variety of deficiency symptoms develop. It is to be understood that symptoms may appear even in the presence of "normal" growth.

Epithelial tissue. The epithelium of a wide variety of organs in the body undergoes changes in vitamin A deficiency. Changes have been demonstrated in the salivary glands, tongue and pharynx in the mouth, in the respiratory tract, the genitourinary tract, in the eyes, and in certain glands of internal secretion. The primary change according to Wolbach and Bessey (25) involves atrophy of the epithelium and the formation of a stratified keratinizing epithelium. This replacement epithelium is similar in all tissues involved and is comparable in structure with epidermis. Detailed descriptions of these changes can be found in the review by the authors just mentioned and in a recent book by Follis (26).

The chemical and physiologic functions of these lining tissues are thus altered. The degree of alteration depends upon the degree and length of time of the deficiency. This must be the ultimate cause of many of the distresses accompanying a deficiency of the vitamin.

Eyes. There are various eye conditions resulting from vitamin A deficiency. Early symptoms in rats (and other species) are enlargement of the eye lids and inflammation of the conjunctiva. This is followed by corneal changes leading to blindness. In man night blindness, or nyctalopia, is one of the early symptoms of deficiency (see further). If the deficiency is slight, further changes may not be seen, but with a more severe deficiency, especially in children, xerosis and keratomalacia develop. The eyelids stick together as a result of a purulent discharge. Small ulcers may appear on the cornea, and blindness may ensue. Metaplasia of the corneal epithelium and vascularization of the substantia propria are typical findings and generally lead to infection and obstruction of the ducts of the ocular glands.

During World War I Denmark exported a great deal of butter, and, as a result, many children were without this source of vitamin A. Xerophthalmia with resulting blindness was becoming common among the children of the poorer people. Bloch (27) studied the condition, and after he demonstrated that butter or cod liver oil in the diet cured the xerophthalmia (unless it was advanced to an irreversible stage), the government stopped the export of butter and the people again consumed it. As a result, this eye condition was largely eliminated. Moore (28) in 1940 reported that of the children attending hospitals in the Philippines, one-half had xerophthalmia, and that in the

Dutch East Indies, some 4000 children in 500,000 were blind chiefly because of this condition.

Night blindness is a common condition in man during famine and is prevalent in certain parts of the world continuously as a result of low vitamin A intake. In this country some workers feel that a degree of night blindness occurs especially among children. This condition is studied by measuring one's ability to adapt to dim illumination after looking at a bright light. The biophotometer is an instrument for determining dark adaptation. An individual looks at a bright light source for a given time and then the interval required for the person to see a dim light is measured. If the dark adaptation time is prolonged or the intensity of the dim light required for perception after a certain time interval is greater than normal, a vitamin A deficiency is indicated. The administration of extra vitamin A to an individual exhibiting a prolonged dark adaptation time brings about the return of this value toward normal. Although some controversy exists as to the value of the test in determining a person's vitamin A status, some investigators feel that the instrument has considerable merit.

In a review on nutritional night blindness Dowling and Wald (29) discuss biochemical, physiologic, and histologic findings in the rat retina during depletion of, and repletion with, vitamin A. Liver and blood vitamin A as well as retinal opsin and rhodopsin were determined in rats on a diet deficient in vitamin A. Liver vitamin A fell to low levels in the first three weeks; then the blood level dropped to about zero during the next week, and the rhodopsin content declined, marking the onset of night blindness. Later the opsin level fell, and this was accompanied by histologic deterioration of the retina.

If vitamin A was administered to depleted, night blind animals before histologic changes occurred, the recovery was rapid (30 to 60 hours depending upon the degree of deficiency). Recovery took far longer if the vitamin was withheld until histologic alterations had developed.

The basis for the relationship of the dark adaptation test to vitamin A status lies in the work of Hecht (30) and of Wald (31). The latter investigator pointed out a functional role of vitamin A in vision. As early as 1935 (32) he indicated a mechanism involving vitamin A in vision. In the retina the cones are concerned with acute perception and the rods are involved with vision in dim light. A pigment in the retinal rods called "rhodopsin" is a protein complex with retinene. Under the influence of light the retinene is isomerized, which is likely responsible for visual excitation, and then the pigment is hydrolyzed by water to the protein opsin and retinene (33). Some of the details of this mechanism are discussed on the following pages. Resynthesis of rhodopsin from a specific retinene isomer and opsin must keep pace with its photochemical alteration under the influence of light (and then water hydrolysis) in order to maintain normal vision. Bright light markedly depletes the stores of rhodopsin in the rods. This accounts for the well-known fact that an individual has difficulty in seeing after entering a dark or dimly lit room from a well-lit place. After several minutes, during which time rhodopsin is synthesized, vision improves to the point that one may marvel at his inability to see a short time before. So rhodopsin synthesis is associated with vision in dim light or darkness. It is customary for the physician to wear red glasses for ten or more minutes before examining a patient in the fluoroscope room. The purpose of this is to dilate the pupils and to assure sufficient retinal rhodopsin for optimal vision in the dim light associated with fluoroscopic examinations.

Through unknown mechanisms there is a loss of vitamin A in the photochemical reactions involving rhodopsin. If the blood is not well supplied with vitamin A, the time required for rhodopsin synthesis is lengthened or the total synthesis may not reach optimum quantities. Under such circumstances dark adaptation is subnormal.

The original hypothesis of Wald has gone essentially unchallenged, although more details of the mechanisms involved are now known.

Wald (34) described the in vitro synthesis of rhodopsin in a system containing (a) vitamin A, the precursor of retinine; (b) opsin, the protein of rhodopsin; and (c) liver alcohol dehydrogenase (apoenzyme plus DPN or cozymase), which brings about oxidation of vitamin A to retinene. The vitamin A used in the system was purified from fish liver oil. When crystalline vitamin A was employed, rhodopsin was not synthesized. Vitamin A as well as the retinenes exist in various cis-trans isomeric forms due to the conjugated double bonds. Only one isomer, the neo-b or 11-cis retinene, unites with opsin to form rhodopsin. Neo-b vitamin A was synthesized and converted into neo-b retinine by Oroshnik (35). Wald showed that the aldehyde condenses with opsin to form rhodopsin, thereby establishing the physiologic activity of the 11-cis isomer.

Thermal denaturation of rhodopsin releases the appropriate cis retinene, but bleaching by light yields a mixture of all-trans isomers. This is a somewhat unique example of photo stereoisomerization (33).*

Light bleaching (associated with vision) of rhodopsin produces opsin plus trans retinene. These cannot condense efficiently to form the visual pigment rhodopsin.

Light, especially of short wavelengths, isomerizes trans retinene to the cis form. This reaction is slow, and mixtures are produced. An enzyme in the retina specifically and rapidly (especially in dim light) catalyzes the conversion of all-trans retinine to neo-b retinene (neoretinene b) (36,37). The enzyme is called "retinene isomerase." The liver may likewise contain the enzyme.

Several isomers are available in the blood stream, and for rapid, efficient reformation of rhodopsin, the trans form of retinine produced upon light bleaching must be converted into the 11-cis form. Since the vitamin A isomers and the retinene isomers are readily interconverted by oxidation-reduction mechanisms (alcohol dehydrogenase or retinene reductase), trans

* Vol. 74, Art. 2, of the Annals of the New York Academy of Sciences consists of a series of some 20 papers presented at a conference on Photoreception in New York early in 1958.

vitamin A is likewise enzymatically isomerized to the cis form and can then be oxidized to cis retinene. It is clear that the isomerizations are requisite components of the rhodopsin cycle.

Figure 18.1 presents these interrelations.

In the cones, used primarily in color perception, the visual pigment, called "iodopsin," is composed of the same retinene isomer but a protein different from that found in rhodopsin (38).

In permanently fresh-water fishes the retinal rods contain vitamin A_2, and oxidation yields retinene$_2$. Wald named the conjugated protein composed of retinene$_2$ and opsin "porphyropsin." In the cones of such fish retinene$_2$ combines with a different protein, cone opsin, to form the visual pigment cyanopsin. Actually both rods and cones contain small amounts of visual pigments other than the primary ones indicated above.

The four photoreceptor pigments mentioned are best identified by determining their ability to absorb various wavelengths of light. Thus the maximum absorption of rhodopsin is found to be at 500 mμ, that of iodopsin at 562 mμ, that of porphyropsin at 522 mμ, and that of cyanopsin at 620 mμ.

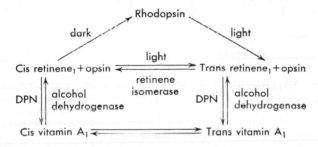

Figure 18.1.   The rhodopsin cycle.

The structures of all trans retinene and of neo-b or 11-cis retinene were shown previously.

Although many details of the actual processes involved in vision are totally unknown, an interesting hypothetical scheme was advanced by Kropf and Hubbard (33). It was established that interconversion of cis and trans retinene could be accomplished while the isomers were attached as chromophores to opsin (38). Rhodopsin at low temperatures is converted by light into metarhodopsin in which retinene is in the all-trans form. This reaction is reversible under the influence of light, indicating that metarhodopsin is also photosensitive. The isomerization of 11-cis to trans retinene, while attached to opsin, is thought to be responsible for visual excitation. The next step, the hydrolysis of metarhodopsin (bleaching), produces opsin and trans retinene. These steps are indicated schematically in Figure 18.2.

The trans retinene may be isomerized in the eye by retinene isomerase and conjugated with opsin to participate again in the visual process.

Another view as to the types of reactions responsible for nerve impulse associated with vision is due to Abrahamson (39). This investigator and his coworkers believe that stimulus may result from configurational changes in the opsin of rhodopsin. The light-induced changes in rhodopsin take place in several steps according to these workers: (a) isomerization of retinene in less than a microsecond; (b) loss of a hydrogen ion from retinene (chemical change); and, at the same time, (c) a configurational change in opsin occurring in milliseconds, the exact nature of which is unknown and (d) hydrolysis of the isomerized chromophore from the protein opsin.

Reproduction. In rats reproduction fails in a vitamin A deficiency. Males develop rather rapidly an atrophy of the germinal epithelium; this is reversed after administration of the vitamin. In females the normal estrous cycle is not maintained. In slight deficiencies fairly normal reproduction is possible, although with a severe deficiency few if any live young are born. Alterations in the lining of the reproductive tract appear to interfere with the nutrition of the embryo (40). Cattle are known to show poor reproduction

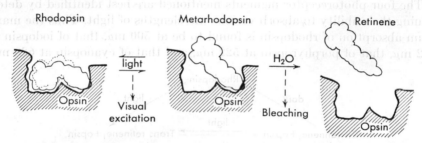

Figure 18.2. Hypothetical scheme showing the effect of light on vertebrate rhodopsins. In rhodopsin, the neo-b (11-*cis*) chromophore fits into the chromophoric site on opsin. This site is fitted also, although less well, by the iso-a (9-*cis*) chromophore of isorhodopsin, which is shown by the dotted line. Light isomerizes the *cis* chromophore to the all-*trans* configuration, thus decreasing the interaction between the chromophore and opsin. This is all-*trans* metarhodopsin, which hydrolyzes readily to retinene and opsin. The isomerization of rhodopsin to metarhodopsin is probably responsible for visual excitation, but bleaching is due to the hydrolysis of metarhodopsin. (From Kropf, A., and Hubbard, R.: *Ann. N. Y. Acad. Sci.,* 74, 266, 1958.)

in A deficiency also. Practically no data are available regarding human reproduction in relation to vitamin A deficiency.

Skin. Only comparatively recently has a vitamin A deficiency been associated with specific lesions of the skin in man. Perhaps the earliest description of this condition was reported in 1931 by Frazier and Hu (41) in China. In this country the first report appeared in 1938 by Youmans and Corlette (42).

The lesions vary considerably in different individuals. The general features of the deficiency involve dryness and roughness of the skin. This appears early in the deficiency and is due to a suppression of the sweat glands. A keratosis, especially of the hair follicles, is a prominent feature. Papules, masses of keratinized epithelium, develop, and these are readily felt by rubbing a finger over the involved area. The sides and backs of the thighs and the lateral parts of the forearm are most frequently involved, although the condition is often more extensive. Such lesions are considered by many workers to be one of the earliest symptoms of A deficiency in humans. Some reports concern the presence of the skin condition without perceptible abnormalities of the eyes, indicating that the former condition may precede the latter.

High vitamin A intake has been used successfully by Straumfjord (43) in treating a human skin condition resembling acne vulgaris.

Certain unsaturated dimers used in the neoprene rubber industry were found to produce a reversible alopecia in mice at the site of topical application (44). These investigations also showed that the compounds inactivated free sulfhydryl compounds and sulfhydryl enzymes. One theory of keratin formation includes the assumption that cysteine sulfhydryl groups (—SH) in adjacent polypeptide chains are oxidized to cystine disulfide bonds (—S—S—) which helps account for the rigidity of keratin molecules.

Vitamin A in a corn oil and alcohol solution also produced an alopecia when applied to the animals, and this was reversible, although there was no *in vitro* inactivation of sulfhydryl compounds due to the vitamin. Alopecia is common in humans taking excess vitamin A (see Hypervitaminosis A). On the other hand, certain dermatoses characterized by hyperkeratosis are frequently treated with high vitamin A intake. Such apparently contradictory findings are difficult to reconcile. The problem of hyperkeratosis and vitamin A has been critically reviewed by Lowe and Morton (11).

Bones and Teeth. Bone growth is markedly impaired in vitamin A deficiency. Cessation of growth in parts of the body as well as abnormal growths are encountered. The situation is not well understood at present.

Teeth are derived from epithelial tissue, and so it is logical to expect a correlation between dietary vitamin A and tooth development. In a deficiency one finds, among other things, poor development of the ameloblasts and odontoblasts, with a consequent lack of dentin or abnormal formation of it (45). Both abnormal bone and tooth formation are reversed by vitamin A administration.

Urolithiasis. A condition in which urinary calculi are present is known as "urolithiasis." In a long-standing vitamin A deficiency in rats Higgins (46) found that a high percentage of his animals developed this condition. The calculi were composed primarily of calcium phosphate. According to this worker, the deficiency allows keratinization of the genitourinary tract epithelium followed by bacterial invasion and alkalinuria. These factors predispose to calcium phosphate precipitation. Vitamin A therapy and an acid ash diet are rather effective in alleviating the condition. In a number of humans this regime was also effective in bringing about dissolution of urinary calculi. Other factors than a vitamin deficiency can be and often are involved, in which cases vitamin therapy may be of no value.

Infections. Vitamin A has been called the "antiinfective vitamin." This is poor terminology, since it is far too inclusive a term and is, therefore, misleading. The vitamin does help to establish and maintain a resistance to infection in the body, especially in tissues which undergo keratinization in a deficiency of it, since in such tissues bacterial invasion is not countered as it is in healthy tissue. It has not been proved of any value in a variety of specific infectious diseases, nor has it been shown to affect general immunity to disease.

Carbohydrate metabolism. A more specific function of vitamin A in metabolism involves its role in glucose synthesis from triose molecules. Wolf and coworkers (47) showed that in rats the incorporation of acetate, lactate, or glycerol into liver glycogen was drastically reduced in vitamin A deficiency. These workers postulated that vitamin A is involved directly or indirectly in the conversion of trioses into glucose, since the administration of glucose to the deficient animals led to normal liver glycogen deposition. In a second paper (48) it was demonstrated that in vitamin A deficiency the rat adrenal cortex cells responsible for glucocorticoid hormone production undergo degeneration and that, because of this hormone deficiency, gluconeogenesis is depressed. This accounts very nicely for the over-all presence, but not the details, of the biochemical lesion in vitamin A deficiency resulting in depressed glucose synthesis. These authors did not speculate further, but it is tempting to picture vitamin A or a closely related molecule acting as a coenzyme in one or more enzyme systems involved in some step in the synthesis of one or more cortical hormones controlling a triose $\longrightarrow$ glucose reaction.

Blood levels of vitamin A. In man the blood levels of vitamin A show great variations even among institutionalized patients. Van Bruggen and coworkers, (49) studied, among other things, the blood levels of vitamin A in patients on the hospital diet and of those on the same diet supplemented daily with 100,000 International Units (I.U.) of vitamin A. In 36 unsupplemented patients the vitamin A averaged 149 I U., and in 35 who had taken the vitamin supplement for 18 months, 256 I.U. per 100 ml of plasma. From 40 or less to 200 or 300 I.U. per 100 ml of plasma is the usually reported range. This is equivalent to around 15 to 60 or 90 μg, since one unit is approximately 0.3 μg of vitamin A.

In rats it appears that the plasma vitamin A level is proportional to the level of free vitamin A in the liver but not to the total store including vitamin A esters. Such a situation may hold in man also and possibly explains the marked normal plasma level variations.

Hypervitaminosis A. Excess vitamin A intake in humans leads to a number of untoward symptoms, including, in the acute phase, headache, nausea and vomiting, and drowsiness, supposedly related to increased spinal fluid pressure. A single dose of 1 million or more units may bring on such symptoms in a matter of hours. In the chronic disease, resulting from the long-time daily ingestion of 100,000 units more or less, the findings include anorexia, dry itchy skin, alopecia, cracking of the lips, and painful areas over various bones. Often the serum alkaline phosphatase is elevated. In a 1958 review of the subject (50) it is indicated that hypervitaminosis A occurs more frequently than is generally realized. The removal of excess vitamin A from the diet generally results in rapid recovery.

Hillman (51) reported the experimental production of hypervitaminosis A in a man on two different occasions. During a 14-day period, and later during a 25-day period, this individual ingested around 1 million units of A per day as a water-emulsified preparation. The clinical picture resembled accidental vitamin A poisoning. Plasma vitamin A reached the fantastic level of over 1800 μg per 100 ml toward the end of the longer period of excessive ingestion. The normal level for this individual was around 50 μg per 100 ml of plasma. Prominent among the symptoms was a type of dermatitis. Also noted were headache, cheilosis with chapping and splitting of the lips, gastrointestinal disturbances, some visual disturbances, generalized weakness, and pain with tenderness over the long bones.

Sources of vitamin A. Many marine fish oils, especially the liver oils, have high concentrations of the vitamin. Samples of oil containing as much as 1 million units per gram have been obtained. Soupfin shark, lingcod, halibut, and swordfish are among the species whose liver oils contain very high concentrations at certain seasons. The average values are much lower in these and other commercially employed species. Table 18.3 shows the vita-

Table 18.3. Vitamin A and Vitamin D Content of Several Fish Liver Oils*

Common Name	Vitamin A U.S.P. units/g Range	Vitamin A U.S.P. units/g Average	Vitamin D I.U./g Range or Average
Soupfin shark (male)	45,000–200,000	120,000	5–25
Halibut	40,000–160,000	87,000	1,000–5,000
Sablefish	50,000–190,000	90,000	600–1,000
Lingcod	40,000–550,000	175,000	1,000–6,000
Albacore tuna	10,000–60,000	25,000	25,000–250,000
Bonito	15,000–60,000	35,000	50,000
Swordfish	20,000–400,000	250,000	2,000–25,000
Black sea bass	100,000–1,000,000	300,000	5,000
Cod	1,000–6,000	2,000	85–500
Herring†	50–300	90	25–160

* Adapted from C. Butler, *Com. Fisheries Rev.*, **8**, 13, 1946.
† Figures for oil from entire body.

min A and the vitamin D contents of a number of fish liver oils (52). Synthetic vitamin A preparations, such as vitamin A palmitate, are now used in great quantity. Such products have no fishy taste and are preferred by many to natural concentrates. Eggs, milk, cheese, and the green leafy vegetables are good sources, and many of the yellow crops, such as corn and carrots, are fair vitamin A sources for man and some animals.

Kitol. Whale liver oil contains considerable quantities of a provitamin A named "kitol" by Embree and Shantz (53). These workers give a provisional formula of $C_{40}H_{58}(OH)_2$ (twice vitamin A) for the material which in a purified state was stated to be a yellow glassy solid at room temperature. It has little or no biologic activity. Heating to above 200° C produces vitamin A from this material mol for mol. Small amounts of kitol were found in shark liver oil and in the oil obtained from the liver of a lamb.

It has been suggested that in the case of the whale and certain other animals the deposition of biologically inactive kitol is a defense mechanism to obviate excessive vitamin A concentration in the body.

Units and requirements of vitamin A. The U.S.P. (*United States Pharmacopoeia*) unit and the International Unit (I.U.) of vitamin A are identical. The international standard is a specially prepared vitamin A acetate, and one unit of vitamin A is equal to the activity of 0.344 μg of this ester. This is equivalent to 0.3 μg of vitamin A and to 0.6 μg of β-carotene.

A comprehensive treatise by Moore (54) on most aspects of vitamin A was published in 1957.

Vitamin A requirements of various animal species are fairly well established. In the case of humans the picture is so complicated by individual variations, differences in diets—and, consequently, by the intake of other vitamins, differences in activity, growth rates, etc.—that actual data on requirements are lacking. The Food and Nutrition Board, National Research Council, with the cooperation of many nutrition workers has prepared tables of Recommended Daily Allowances (Table 18.5, page 697) for a number of nutrients. The recommended vitamin A intake for a 65-kg man is given in this table as 5000 I.U. per day. This figure represents an estimate and may not be an optimum intake. In a deficiency of vitamin A, either frank or suspected, as much as 100,000 U.S.P. units per day are frequently administered to adults over extended periods.

VITAMIN D

The disease rachitis, now commonly called "rickets," has apparently plagued mankind since ancient times. In 1650 infant rickets was described by Glisson in England. The disease was rampant especially among the children of the lower classes of people in England (and other sections of the world) for centuries. Infection was early postulated as a cause of the disease. Around London the abundance of fog was held by some to be a contributing factor. It is now known that the latter assumption was correct, although at that time it may have been predicated on erroneous beliefs. In other words, the lack of sunshine due to the fog was a predisposing factor.

The curative value of liver, especially cod liver oil, was known centuries ago. Late in the eighteenth century it was used in parts of England as a therapeutic agent, although its specific value in preventing or curing rickets was apparently unknown until many years later. As late as 1920 Hess and Unger (1) indicated that rickets was a very common disorder of infants living in the temperate zone. After World War I infant rickets in various parts of Europe was widespread.

Our present-day knowledge of rickets and the chemical nature of the vitamers D is based primarily on a series of seemingly unrelated findings. Important among these are the following:

1. In 1918 Mellanby (2) produced the first clear-cut experimental rickets in animals. Dogs were fed various diets of milk and porridge or bread and milk. Rickets developed regularly on such diets. He was able to demonstrate the presence of the antirachitic factor in cod liver oil and showed that this substance was far superior to butter fat and peanut, olive, or linseed oils in curing or protecting against rickets in his dogs.

2. Huldschinsky in 1919 (3) demonstrated marked clinical improvement in severely rachitic children by playing ultraviolet light on their bodies. This finding was important not only from the clinical standpoint but also afforded impetus to the theory, doubted by many, that sunlight is beneficial in the treatment of rickets.

3. In 1922 McCollum and coworkers (4) demonstrated that cod liver oil contains a specific substance (vitamin) concerned with calcium deposition in rachitic rats. The presence of "fat-soluble A" in cod liver oil had been known for some time. By running

air through the oil at 100° C he destroyed the xerophthalmia-curing principle, but the oil maintained a high activity in respect to calcium metabolism. Thus the dual vitamin nature of cod liver oil was established.

4. Two groups of investigators reported in 1924 that the irradiation of certain foods with ultraviolet light endowed them with antirachitic (vitamin D) activity. Steenbock and coworkers (5) and Hess (6) reported this remarkable finding at about the same time. Shortly after this it was demonstrated that the sterol fraction of foods actually contained the material that became antirachitic on irradiation and specifically that ergosterol was capable of a high degree of activation.

5. Angus and coworkers (7) isolated crystalline vitamin D in 1931. They accomplished this by high vacuum distillation of the products obtained upon ultraviolet irradiation of ergosterol. This was named "calciferol" and is referred to as vitamin D_2.

6. Vitamin D_3, activated 7-dehydrocholesterol, was isolated by Windaus and coworkers (8) in 1936. They irradiated this sterol in benzene and were able to separate crystalline derivatives of the vitamin. The name vitamin D_3 was proposed for the substance at that time. It is established now that small amounts of 7-dehydrocholesterol accompany animal cholesterol. The skin contains this precursor, and thus ultraviolet light, from the sun or from artificial sources, is able to activate and yield vitamin D_3 to the body.

As a result of the preceding findings and, of course, many other outstanding observations, the value of sunlight and many artificially produced vitamin D products in the treatment of rickets was realized. In the early 1930's vitamin D milk (ultraviolet irradiated) was widely available in the larger centers of population, and a number of highly concentrated vitamin D preparations were marketed previous to that time. Likewise, the elucidation of the chemistry of the various vitamers D and the photochemical changes proceeding during the ultraviolet irradiation of the precursors were markedly hastened. It became evident that two forms of vitamin D are of importance in human nutrition; calciferol (vitamin D_2), produced from irradiation of the plant sterol ergosterol, and vitamin D_3, the activation product of the animal sterol 7-dehydrocholesterol. Many other vitamers are known, but they are at present of academic interest only. Dihydrotachysterol, or AT 10, is a reduction product of tachysterol; the latter is one of the products of irradiation of ergosterol (see further). The parent substances which can be activated are also known as provitamins.

Chemistry of vitamin D. The compounds with vitamin D activity are closely related to the perhydrophenanthrencyclopentane ring system, and thus to the naturally occurring sterols. Only the two antirachitic substances calciferol or vitamin D_2 and vitamin D_3 will be discussed in any detail.

When ergosterol dissolved in alcohol, benzene, ether, etc., is irradiated with ultraviolet light, a series of photochemical reactions takes place:

ergosterol $\longrightarrow$ lumisterol $\longrightarrow$ tachysterol $\longrightarrow$ calciferol
(vitamin D_2) $\longrightarrow$ toxisterol $\longrightarrow$ suprasterol I and suprasterol II

Ergosterol does not absorb visible light but does absorb various wavelengths in the ultraviolet spectrum. The absorption maxima are at 260, 270, 282, and 293.5 mμ. The absorption of ultraviolet light supplies energy for the transformations noted above. The reactions are photochemical. Nothing is added to or removed from the molecules during these rearrangements; all the compounds are isomeric, and their structures are known. It should not be inferred that all the ergosterol is converted to lumisterol and that this compound is then converted to the next in the series. Various rearrangements proceed simultaneously so that mixtures of the various products are present at any one time. Ergosterol and lumisterol are not antirachitic. Tachysterol, after reduction to dihydrotachysterol, is used especially in the treatment of some types of human tetany. Calciferol is the most important product obtained and under carefully regulated conditions over 50 per cent of the ergosterol originally present can be recovered in this form. Toxisterol, or substance 248, is toxic to animals and man and is not antirachitic. It has very marked absorption at wavelength 248 mμ. Suprasterols I and II, the end products of irradiation, are likewise not antirachitic and possess low toxicity.

The products formed during the activation of 7-dehydrocholesterol have not been studied intensively. It is generally believed that the molecular rearrangements are similar to those established in the case of ergosterol irradiation. The formulas opposite show the similarity between the change from 7-dehydrocholesterol to vitamin D_3 and from ergosterol to vitamin D_2.

There is no vitamin D_1; the original proposal for such a vitamin was later shown to be in error, since the material was found to be a mixture of calciferol and lumisterol. Vitamin D_2 and vitamin D_3 are of importance in nutrition and medicine. The value of other vitamers D cannot be accurately assessed at present, since small amounts may occur in natural sources and their value, if any, is not established. Vitamin D_4 is activated 22-dehydroergosterol. Vitamin D_5 is activated 7-dehydrositosterol. A number of other products also have some degree of antirachitic activity.

The chemistry of vitamin D has been reviewed by Deuel (9) and also by Dam (10). See also recent issues of *Annual Reviews of Biochemistry*.

Sources of vitamin D. It is practical to consider the natural and "synthetic" sources of the antirachitic vitamins at this time, since interesting differences in regard to "animal vitamin D" (activated 7-dehydrocholesterol) and "plant vitamin D" (calciferol) content of the different substances arise.

At present many commercial vitamin D products are available in concentrated form. Calciferol dissolved in vegetable oil or in propylene glycol is marketed for use primarily in infant and child feeding. High-potency capsules (100,000 units for instance) are also available. These preparations contain vitamin D_2.

Vitamin D milk is widely distributed in the United States. Practically all the evaporated milk is fortified with concentrates to increase the vitamin D content. Either D_2 or D_3 may be used. Fluid milk is now generally fortified with concentrates (D_3 primarily), although some years ago direct irradiation was employed (D_3). Irradiated yeast (D_2) is a high-potency product. It is used as such to some extent in human and more in animal nutrition. When it is fed to cows, a part of the vitamin D is transferred to the milk. Cod liver oil is a popular source of vitamin D (D_3) for infant and child feeding. Many

Scheme of Rearrangements in Ultraviolet Irradiation of Ergosterol
and of 7-Dehydrocholesterol Producing Vitamins D_2 and D_3

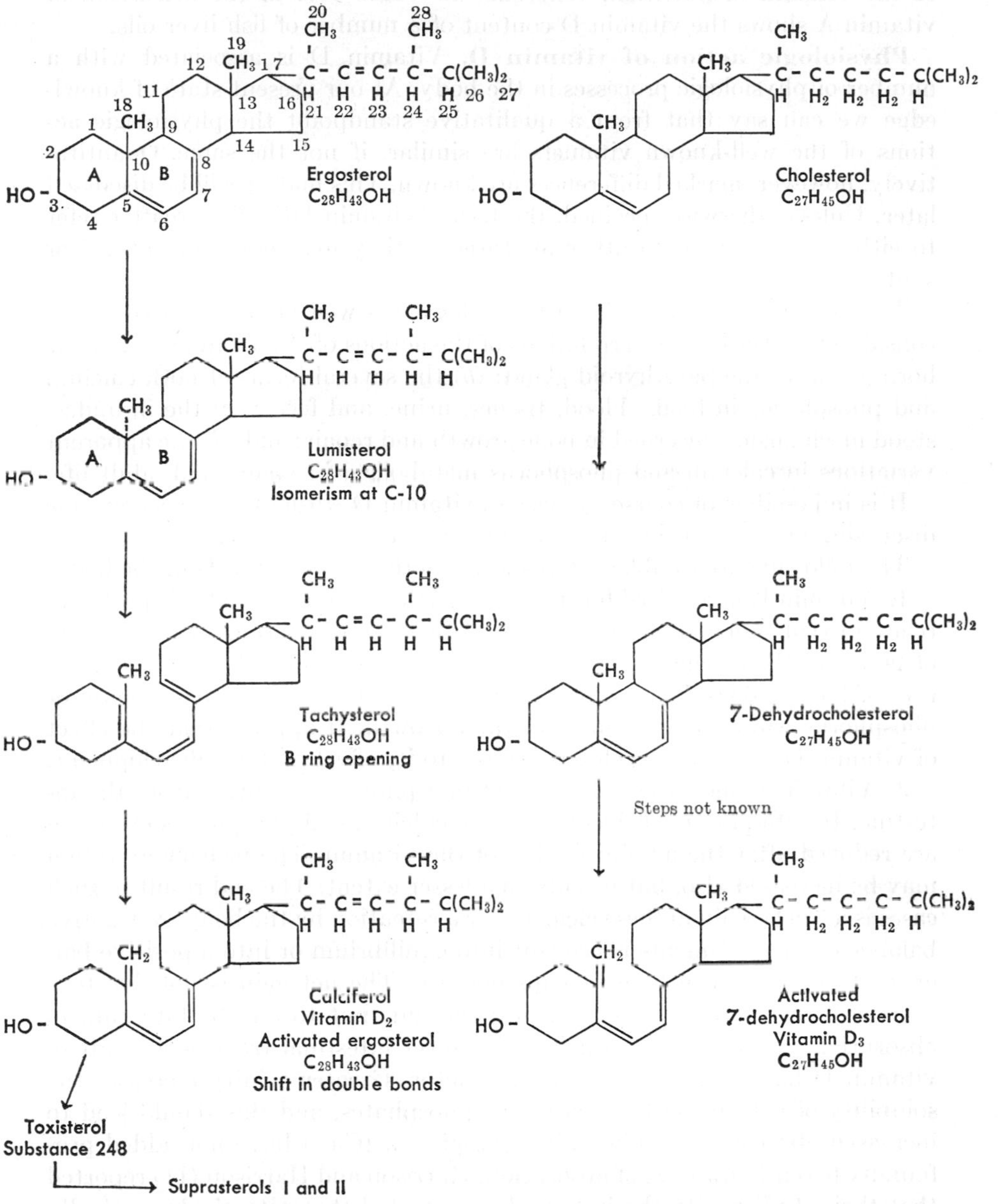

$$\begin{array}{cc} 20 & 28 \\ CH_3 & CH_3 \end{array}$$

19
CH_3 17 —C– C= C– C– $C(CH_3)_2$
11   12   H   H   H   H   H   26   27
18   13   16   21   22   23   24   25
CH_3 9
1
2
A   10   B   8
HO– 3   7
4   5   6
14   15

Ergosterol
$C_{28}H_{43}OH$

CH_3 —C– C– C– C– $C(CH_3)_2$
H H_2 H_2 H_2 H
CH_3
CH_3
HO –

Cholesterol
$C_{27}H_{45}OH$

CH_3 CH_3
CH_3 —C– C= C– C– $C(CH_3)_2$
H   H   H   H   H
CH_3
CH_3
A   B
HO –

Lumisterol
$C_{28}H_{43}OH$
Isomerism at C-10

CH_3 CH_3
CH_3 —C– C= C– C– $C(CH_3)_2$
H   H   H   H   H
CH_3
HO –

Tachysterol
$C_{28}H_{43}OH$
B ring opening

CH_3 CH_3
CH_3 —C– C– C– C– $C(CH_3)_2$
H H_2 H_2 H_2 H
CH_3
HO –

7-Dehydrocholesterol
$C_{27}H_{45}OH$

Steps not known

CH_3 CH_3
CH_3 —C– C= C– C– $C(CH_3)_2$
H   H   H   H   H
CH_3
CH_2
HO –

Calciferol
Vitamin D_2
Activated ergosterol
$C_{28}H_{43}OH$
Shift in double bonds

CH_3 CH_3
CH_3 —C– C– C– C– $C(CH_3)_2$
H H_2 H_2 H_2 H
CH_3
CH_2
HO –

Activated
7-dehydrocholesterol
Vitamin D_3
$C_{27}H_{45}OH$

Toxisterol
Substance 248

⟶ Suprasterols I and II

other types of preparations, some containing D_2 and some D_3, are also
marketed. (See Table 18.3, page 673.)

Naturally occurring foods have practically no vitamin D activity. Milk
contains insignificant amounts as far as infant and child nutrition is concerned unless vitamin D is added. Grains and vegetables in general have
still less. Butter and liver have small quantities. It is interesting that, in con-

trast to many fish livers, this organ in mammals is not considered a source of the vitamin in nutrition. Reference to Table 18.3 in the discussion of vitamin A shows the vitamin D content of a number of fish liver oils.

Physiologic action of vitamin D. Vitamin D is associated with a number of physiologic processes in the body. At our present state of knowledge we can say that from a qualitative standpoint the physiologic actions of the well-known vitamers are similar, if not the same. Quantitatively, however, marked differences are known. This matter will be discussed later. Unless otherwise specified, the term "vitamin D" will hereafter refer to either D_2 or D_3 or to other mixtures as they may occur in natural or synthetic preparations.

The complexity of vitamin D physiology can well be appreciated if one considers: (a) the close interrelations of the actions of the vitamin and of the hormone(s) of the parathyroid gland; (b) the several forms of both calcium and phosphorus in foods, blood, tissues, urine, and feces; (c) the ill-understood mechanism concerned in bone growth and repair; and (d) the apparent variations in calcium and phosphorus metabolism in young and adult life.

It is impossible, of course, to discuss vitamin D without at the same time discussing various aspects of the points, a, b, c, and d above.

The following are established as specific actions of vitamin D in the body:

1. Vitamin D is required for normal growth in mammals. This is probably related to calcium and phosphorus absorption and utilization. When the rate of bone growth is below normal, as is the case in vitamin D deficiency, the rate of body growth is likewise retarded. A deficiency of dietary calcium or phosphorus will also result in subnormal growth. It appears that the effect of vitamin D on growth is closely related to its effect on bone development.

2. Vitamin D increases calcium and phosphorus absorption from the intestine. In vitamin D deficiency the fecal calcium and phosphorus excretion are reduced after the administration of the vitamin. The urinary excretion may be increased also, but usually to a lesser extent. The end result in such cases is a "net" gain in these elements or a retention by the body. A negative balance of these elements is brought into equilibrium or into a positive balance. The mechanism here remains obscure. The net gain is not due to a decreased reexcretion of calcium into the gut, but to an absolute gain in absorption. A change in the pH of the lower intestinal tract as a result of vitamin D has been suggested as one factor. Greater acidity increases the solubility of calcium salts, such as the phosphates, and this should lead to increased absorption. Studies with isotopic Ca (Ca^{45}) have not added profoundly to our knowledge of absorption. Harrison and Harrison (11) reported that their studies with the isotope demonstrated that vitamin D markedly increases Ca absorption from the large intestine and from the distal end of the small intestine in rats but has little effect on absorption in the proximal end of the small intestine, where Ca absorption normally is greatest. It was also suggested that vitamin D increases the efficiency of Ca absorption only under conditions in which the intestinal Ca is poorly soluble. Increased absorption as soon as one hour after Ca^{45} by stomach tube in the rat has been

observed. Maximal absorption of Ca^{45} resulted from 10 I.U. of vitamin D in the rat, although a hundredfold increase in vitamin intake resulted in further elevation of blood Ca^{45}. This increase was apparently due to the action of vitamin D on bone salts (12).

Bile salts are concerned in some way with calcium absorption, and vitamin D is thought by some workers to increase the activity of these molecules in enhancing calcium absorption. Certainly other mechanisms, more subtle than these, must be in operation.

3. Vitamin D is antirachitic. Rickets is a disease of the young. The disease may involve a low blood calcium level or a low blood phosphorus level. In humans the latter type is generally seen. Either can be produced in animals by dietary means. In infancy the inorganic phosphorus level (primarily as $HPO_4^=$ and $H_2PO_4^-$) of blood is normally 4 to 6 mg per cent. In rickets this may be decreased to 1 or 2 mg per cent.

At the ends of bones during normal growth the osteoblasts, or boneforming cells, appear as the cartilage cells degenerate and disappear. After capillaries grow into this site, the osteoblasts deposit bony matrix. The process is a continuous one in that new osteoblasts are always under formation.

In a vitamin D deficiency the cartilage cells do not degenerate but continue to grow; consequently, capillaries and osteoblasts are not formed. The cartilage tissue increases in size and remains uncalcified. In more severe deficiency bone mineral may be resorbed, leaving a greater area of osteoid tissue. The time and the degree of the deficiency obviously determine the extent of the abnormality. In infants and children clinical symptoms of severe deficiency are readily seen on gross examination. Enlargements of the ankle, knee, and wrist joints are noted. Other prominent features are bowed legs, delayed closure of the fontanelle, beading of the ribs at the costochondral junction ("rachitic rosary"), and delayed tooth eruption. The mineral content of bone decreases as the severity of the rickets progresses. The ash on a dry, fat-free basis may reach one-half to one-third or less of the normal value.

The administration of vitamin D to rachitic animals brings about the degeneration of cartilage cells, the growth of capillaries in this area, and ossification.

For further details, see the classical description of the histologic changes in rachitic and healing bone by Shohl and Wolbach (13).

How does the presence of vitamin D bring about such remarkable and rapid effects? Here again our information on actual mechanisms is almost nil. The increased absorption of calcium and phosphorus from the gut due to vitamin D is not the answer, since healing of rachitic bones in animals can take place without food or with food devoid of these minerals. Also, the intravenous administration of calcium and phosphorus salts to raise blood levels is not effective in initiating healing. The administration of parathyroid hormone or of AT 10, both of which increase blood calcium, likewise produces little or no antirachitic effect.

It was demonstrated in 1928 by Hess (14) that when rachitic bone is placed in blood serum from rachitic animals no change takes place, but if serum from a normal animal is used, calcification is initiated. Robison (15) demonstrated the presence of an enzyme capable of splitting inorganic phosphate from organic combination (phosphatase). Various phosphatase enzymes are now known to be in the body. In bone cartilage and especially in rachitic osteoid tissue the concentration is high. This incidentally increases the blood content of the enzyme. The level is of value in diagnosing early rickets and some other bone abnormalities. Many investigators have found rather good agreement between vitamin D deficiency and increased blood alkaline phosphatase. In a study of a large number of children, aged six months to 2.5 years, a mean value for the serum phosphatase of 9.4 Bodansky units was reported (16) for the normals, whereas the rachitic children had in general over twice this phosphatase activity. It was also indicated that the increased enzyme activity correlated well with severity of the clinical symptoms of rickets. Apparently the enzyme is responsible, under normal conditions, for liberating inorganic phosphate from organic combination and thus increasing at the site of ossification the ion product $Ca^{++} \times PO_4^{=}$. It has been suggested that bone is deposited in the matrix only when the solubility product of $Ca^{++} \times PO_4^{=}$ in plasma is exceeded, and perhaps that the calcium and phosphate ions must be present in a special form.

At any rate the process of ossification requires phosphatase enzymes, and it now appears that a number of other enzymes are likewise intimately involved in the process. The glycolytic process with the many enzymes involved may not only provide some as yet unidentified organic phosphate ester as the substrate for phosphatase, but may also supply the energy requirements.

Rachitic bone contains glycogen and the enzymes required for the glycogenolysis process. When such bone slices are placed in the proper medium containing inorganic phosphate, calcification takes place. However, if phlorizin is also added, calcification does not proceed. This substance is known to inhibit phosphorylase, the enzyme responsible for the conversion of glycogen plus inorganic phosphate into glucose-1-phosphate. The inference is that this block precludes the further steps leading to the required phosphate ester which might act as phosphatase enzyme substrate. Upon the addition of glucose-1-phosphate, the compound which the system is unable to produce, calcification proceeds in the presence of the inhibitor. By studying inhibitors of other enzymes in the system, the conclusion has been reached (17) that phosphorylative glycolysis plays an important role in the calcification process. It is likely that normal bone calcification *in vivo* likewise involves such complicated mechanisms to supply a special type of phosphate ester in order that phosphatase may liberate phosphate ions at the active calcifying site.

For the normal bone formation or for calcification of rachitic bone, vitamin D is required. What part it plays is still questionable. Its activity may involve some effect on the phosphatase enzyme system, or the state of serum calcium or phosphorus or both, or the various cells concerned with laying down bone. Phosphorylated vitamin D, but not the unaltered molecule, was shown to have a marked initial activating effect on kidney alkaline phosphatase (18). What part, if any, this might play in bone formation is not now apparent.

The rat differs from other species in vitamin D requirement. A rachitic condition is easily induced in this animal by keeping him on a diet with an upset calcium-phosphorus balance (4 or 5 to 1 for instance), and bone healing will proceed in the absence of vitamin D if the animal fails to grow or loses weight. This will be discussed further under the section on vitamin D assay.

4. Harrison and Harrison (19) demonstrated a specific function of vitamin D on kidney tubular reabsorption of phosphate. They developed rickets in dogs and then by phosphate clearance studies showed that the administration of large doses of vitamin D definitely increased phosphate reabsorption. At equilibrium the plasma phosphate was thus elevated, and these workers postulated that such an effect is probably part of the antirachitic action of vitamin D. Such an action is definitely antirachitic since it tends to conserve phosphate and to increase the $Ca^{++} \times PO_4^=$ product of the plasma. It has been pointed out that the increased tubular reabsorption may be a secondary effect to the primary increase in circulating calcium (20).

5. Citric acid is a normal constituent of many body tissues, including bone. Rachitic rats given vitamin D show increased urinary excretion of citric acid and increased levels in blood, bone, kidney, heart, and small intestine, with no elevation in liver (21, 22). Such findings indicate a rather general effect of the vitamin on citric acid metabolism. Steenbock and co-workers (23, 24) have continued with *in vitro* enzyme studies and demonstrated that addition of vitamin D to either a rachitogenic or a nonrachitogenic diet resulted in a depression of *in vitro* citric acid oxidation by kidney homogenates or mitochondria. In further experiments the addition of the vitamin to an *in vitro* system of kidney mitochondria reduced citrate oxidation (25). These findings help explain the increased tissue citrate levels in a deficiency of the vitamin.

6. It has been suggested that vitamin D increased the activity of the enzyme phytase in the rat intestine. This enzyme hydrolyzed food phytic acid (grains primarily), yielding inorganic phosphate. More phytic acid is excreted in the feces of rats and dogs in a deficiency state than when the vitamin is given. The rat intestine produces phytase and in rachitic rats phytic acid of a high cereal diet is completely hydrolyzed only when vitamin D is given. However, the increased enzyme activity does not liberate sufficient inorganic phosphate to account for the antirachitic action of the vitamin (26).

It is necessary at this point to digress and bring the parathyroid glands into the discussion. One of the primary actions of the parathyroid hormone is to increase the urinary excretion of phosphate and concomitantly reduce the plasma phosphate level. It is known too that an increased plasma calcium level tends to lessen the activity of the parathyroid glands and that a low level results in increased activity.* On the basis of these two facts and on an imposing accumulation of data of their own on the action of vitamin D, the parathyroids, etc., on calcium and phosphorus metabolism, Albright and Reifenstein (28) interpreted the results of Harrison and Harrison on the basis that the increased kidney reabsorption of phosphate resulted from decreased parathyroid activity (from increased blood calcium level). Albright and coworkers showed that in a patient with idiopathic hypoparathyroidism the administration of large doses of vitamin D increased urinary calcium and phosphorus excretion more than the decrease in fecal calcium and phosphorus excretion. The extra mineral obviously came from bone, and negative balances of these two elements developed. Albright feels that a primary action of vitamin D is to increase the urinary excretion of phosphate, but that the action is quantitatively far less than that of the parathyroid hormone. In the case of an individual with a normal parathyroid, he feels that this action is masked by the ability of the vitamin to increase the absorption of calcium from the intestine, leading to an increased serum calcium level, which inhibits parathyroid hormone production, resulting in lessened urinary phosphate excretion. Under these conditions the serum phosphate increases, whereas in the individual with a parathyroid hormone deficiency the end result on plasma phosphate is opposite after the administration of vitamin D. Increased blood calcium cannot have an effect on a nonfunctional parathyroid gland.

The other primary action of the parathyroid hormone (besides increasing urinary phosphate excretion) is to increase a low blood calcium level or maintain a normal one by removal of calcium from bone. Excess hormone causes hypercalcemia.

As a result of the two established actions of the hormone, two schools of thought on its primary action have developed. One group holds that parathyroid hormone brings about increased phosphate excretion by the kidney and that changes in blood calcium and phosphate levels are secondary to this. A variety of experiments indicates increased phosphate excretion, followed by elevation of the blood calcium, upon administration of the hormone.

The other school claims that parathyroid hormone brings about dissolution of bone calcium and that the renal effects are secondary. Evidence in favor of this theory is found in the various experiments in which nephrectomized animals, unable to excrete phosphate, respond to the hormone with an increase in blood calcium.

In one such experiment, nephrectomy (rats) appeared to nullify the effects of the hormone upon blood phosphate levels while the action as regards blood calcium was maintained. These workers (29) were led to postulate that

---

* Patt and Luckhardt (27) decalcified dog blood and perfused this through an intact thyroid-parathyroid preparation in another dog. On transfusing this blood, the recipients showed increases in blood calcium of 1.3 to 4.9 mg per cent in 1.5 to 3 hours and an increase in phosphate. Normal blood perfused and then transfused brought about no significant change in the blood calcium level of the recipient. The evidence seems to indicate, as pointed out by the authors, that a low blood calcium level is a direct stimulus for the parathyroid glands to increase the hormone output.

normally the hormone has a direct and independent effect on both calcium and phosphorus metabolism.

Other workers (30), using nephrectomized dogs, claimed that the calcium mobilizing action of the hormone is not dependent upon kidney function and went so far as to state that the increased phosphate excretion resulting from administration of the hormone was an artifact.

It is advisable at present to keep in mind the two well-established actions of the hormone without regard to which one is primary—they are both obviously important.

Unlike vitamin D, the hormone has little effect on the absorption of either calcium or phosphorus in the gut. Overdosage with parathyroid hormone brings about bone demineralization and hypercalcemia. Hypercalcification, on the other hand, may result from massive doses of vitamin D. The hormone has no effect on the healing of rachitic bones, but in a hormone deficiency tetany, vitamin D is effective in regulating the blood calcium and phosphorus levels. Usually large doses, 50,000 to 200,000 I. U. of vitamin D per day, are required for this in humans.

Another important drug in this respect is dihydrotachysterol (AT 10). This product has been used in human parathyroid hormone deficiency with considerable success. It is administered orally in oil solution, a distinct advantage over parathyroid hormone, which must be given parenterally. AT 10 is very slightly antirachitic; it increases calcium absorption from the intestine, brings about resorption of calcium from bone to increase the blood level, and increases urinary excretion of phosphate. The last two actions are those of the parathyroid hormone; the first two are those of vitamin D. Quantitatively the actions of AT 10 are less than those of either the vitamin or the hormone. Albright and coworkers have studied the effects of the three substances, parathyroid hormone, AT 10, and vitamin D, important in the physiologic regulation of deranged calcium and phosphorus metabolism in a variety of clinical conditions. The book by Albright and Reifenstein (28) has the best bibliography available and an excellent discussion of this and closely related subjects. These authors give the following table to depict the intermediate activity of AT 10 between the actions of vitamin D and parathyroid hormone with respect to the criteria listed.

Table 18.4. Relative Effect of Vitamin D, Dihydrotachysterol, and Parathyroid Hormone on Intestinal Calcium Absorption and Urinary Phosphorus Excretion

	Calcium Absorption	Urinary Phosphorus Excretion
Vitamin D	++++	++
Dihydrotachysterol	++	+++
Parathyroid hormone	+	++++

From Albright, F., and Reifenstein, E. C.: *Parathyroid Glands and Metabolic Bone Disease.* Williams & Wilkins Co., Baltimore, 1948, p. 134.

Vitamin D, especially in large doses, is somewhat effective in bringing about calcium resorption from bone; AT 10 is far more effective; and the parathyroid hormone has still greater activity. The hormone has a very short action, a matter of hours, and may bring about its maximum effect very rapidly (four to ten hours). AT 10 has a longer period of action, up to several days, and requires a day or two to act. The vitamin may be effective for long periods of time and is slow to exert its effect.

Multiple C^{14}-labeled calciferol was prepared by Kodicek (31). One mg of the compound in oil was given to a rachitic rat by mouth. After 24 hours, analyses showed that only 30 per cent of the C^{14} activity remained as vitamin D, although all the C^{14} activity was recovered. The bulk of the breakdown products were not identified. The liver contained 5.7 per cent of the dose, the bones 1.4 per cent, the intestines 0.6 per cent, the kidney 0.2 per cent, and the blood 1.2 per cent. It was of interest that tissues concerned with phosphate turnover, such as kidney, bone and intestine, contained significant amounts of the labeled vitamin D (32).

Vitamin D assay. Vitamin D is determined most successfully at the present by animal assay. Rats or chicks are employed, and the standardized procedures yield excellent and reproducible results. The rat assay method is used for vitamin products intended for human consumption. Chicks do not respond to vitamin D_2 as they do to D_3 on a rat unit basis. In the assay of vitamin D products for the poultry industry it is necessary to use chicks as the test animal. In this procedure the vitamin product is fed to groups of chicks at various levels with a standardized diet, and the level of bone ash after a certain number of days is the criterion used to establish the vitamin level in the test material.

The rat, as indicated elsewhere, is unique as regards the development of rickets. No extreme caution is required to deprive a ration of vitamin D for the production of rickets in this species. It is only necessary to arrange the calcium-phosphorus ratio of the diet to about 4 or 5 to 1. Of the various rachitic rations developed, the Steenbock 2965 ration is employed most generally. This is composed of wheat gluten, yellow corn, calcium carbonate, and salt. Weanling rats restricted to water and this diet for 18 to 21 days develop a rather reproducible rachitic condition. Small additions of test material are given daily for the following five days (in one procedure) or eight days to groups of the standard rachitic rats. One group receives a known amount of vitamin daily (U.S.P. Reference cod liver oil). After a further day or two without supplement, the animals are sacrificed. The rachitic metaphysis of the distal ends of the longitudinally sectioned radius and ulna are examined for new bone growth brought about by the vitamin administered. This is readily seen on gross examination after treating the bones with $AgNO_3$ solution and then reducing the silver phosphate by light. Black areas develop wherever bone mineral exists. At the provisional zone of calcification a rather straight continuous line of new bone is seen when the proper amount of vitamin D was administered, which led to the name "line test" for such an assay. The extent of new calcification compared with that found in the animals receiving the known amount of vitamin D is an index of the vitamin intake, and thus the content of the test material. Details of the method may be found in recent volumes of the *U.S. Pharmacopoeia*.

Chemical methods of vitamin D determination are undergoing constant improvement. The method of Mulder and coworkers (33) compared favorably with results from rat or duck bioassay, although interference due to vitamin A was not eliminated. A method applicable to complex irradiation mixtures of the vitamin was developed by Shaw and others (34).

Species differences to vitamin D_2 and D_3. It was early established that vitamin D_2 and D_3 showed about 40,000 U.S.P. units of vitamin D activity per milligram by the rat assay procedure. It was also found that the chick did not respond to a certain number of rat units of D_2 as it did to the same number of units of D_3. In fact, about 100 times the number of units of D_2 as of D_3 were found to be necessary to produce equal bone ash in assay chicks.

Human beings do not show such a variation in response to the two forms of vitamin D. Different response is questioned by many. Jeans (35) and other workers, however, felt that D_3 by oral administration is about 1.5 times as active as D_2 in human beings. Other forms of the vitamin have not been studied in man. The action of AT 10 has been discussed briefly.

Hypervitaminosis D. Vitamin D toxicity brings about increased absorption of Ca and P from the intestine and thus increased blood levels of these minerals. Calcification of a variety of tissues in different species have been observed. Gilman and Gilbert (36) reported arterial lesions and kidney injury in rats. Calcification of the vascular system was prominent in D_3 toxicity in calves (37). In dogs toxic symptoms included a reduction of glomerular filtration and renal flow which may be secondary to renal calcification (38). Obviously, human toxicity has not been studied experimentally, although Jeans and Stearns (39) showed growth retardation in infants on elevated intakes.

Standards and requirements. One U.S.P. unit of vitamin D is taken as the activity of 0.025 μg of pure crystalline vitamin D_3. This is equal to the I.U. Other units have largely been dropped.

The human requirements have not been established with accuracy. This is not surprising, since the requirements are subject to so many variables. However, a number of clinical studies with infants and children have led to a fair understanding of the intake required to obviate symptoms and signs of suboptimal growth and bone development. The Food and Nutrition Board, National Research Council, sets the recommended intake at 400 I.U. per day for infants and at 400 I.U. daily during childhood. The allowance is set at 400 I.U. during pregnancy and lactation also (see Table 18.5, page 696). Adults apparently have little or no need for the vitamin. Under certain dietary conditions a vitamin requirement may be demonstrated. In many diseases of calcium and phosphorus metabolism the vitamin is beneficial. But under ordinary dietary conditions normal adults appear to maintain normal calcium and phosphorus metabolism without benefit of extra vitamin D.

A publication covering a symposium of bone structure and metabolism (40) contains a great deal of information on these and related subjects.

VITAMIN K

In 1929 Dam (1) reported that chicks developed a hemorrhagic condition and prolonged blood clotting time when raised on specific synthetic rations. In 1935 he (2) proposed the term vitamin K (Koagulations-vitamin) for a factor in certain foods which protected chicks against this hemorrhagic syndrome. Primarily the affected chicks exhibited internal hemorrhage and prolonged blood-clotting time (up to several hours in some cases). Many foods were tested for vitamin K activity by Dam, and he reported that hog liver was very high, cod liver oil practically devoid of activity, and egg yolks low in activity. Among the vegetable material tested, hemp seed was found to be an excellent source. The factor was found to be fat soluble; even large amounts of the other fat-soluble vitamins had no beneficial effect on the course of the syndrome. Thus vitamin K was differentiated from the other fat-soluble vitamins A, D, and E.

Another group of investigators had been working along similar lines and reported similar findings. In 1935 Almquist and Stokstad (3) reviewed the earlier work done in their laboratory and showed that fish meal was an excellent source of the antihemorrhagic factor, or vitamin K. It was especially interesting that during slight putrefaction the fish meal improved as a source of this factor. They also showed that in alfalfa the factor was localized in the unsaponifiable fraction of the ether extract.

It was logical that workers in this field initiated attempts at isolation of the active principle or principles in the products found to be the best sources.

Dam, Karrer, and their coworkers isolated the vitamin from alfalfa in 1939 (4). In the same year Doisy (5) and associates isolated the principle from both alfalfa and from fish meal. It was evident that the vitamin from alfalfa was chemically different from the product obtained from fish meal. Vitamin K_1 was used to designate the former and vitamin K_2 the latter. Synthesis of vitamin K was accomplished by various workers in 1939.

Chemistry of vitamin K. Phthiocol was the first pure chemical shown to have vitamin K activity. It is not, however, a naturally occurring vitamin, but its structure was known and thus this helped in the elucidation of the quinoid structure of the vitamin. Vitamin K_1 is 2-methyl-3-phytyl-1,4-naphthoquinone, and K_2 differs only in that it contains a longer side chain at position 3 (5). The structures of these compounds are given below:

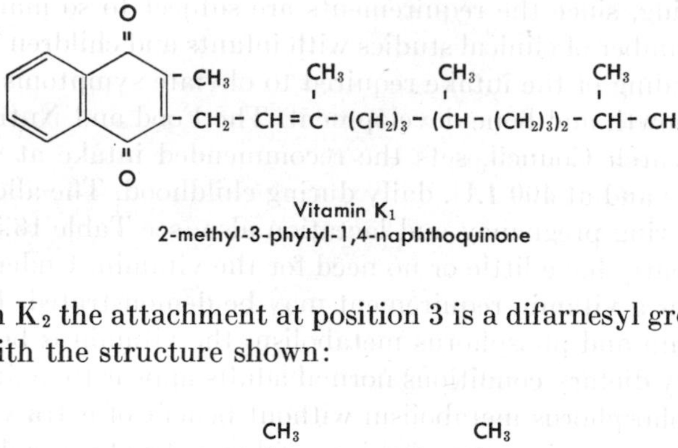

$$\text{— CH}_2\text{— CH = C — (CH}_2)_3\text{— (CH — (CH}_2)_3)_2\text{— CH — CH}_3$$

Vitamin K_1
2-methyl-3-phytyl-1,4-naphthoquinone

In vitamin K_2 the attachment at position 3 is a difarnesyl group, a 30-carbon chain with the structure shown:

$$\text{— CH}_2(\text{CH = C — CH}_2\text{CH}_2)_5\text{— CH = C — CH}_3$$

Synthesis of many derivatives of naphthoquinone with vitamin K activity followed the elucidation of structure. One of the simplest proved to be as effective as the naturally occurring vitamin, on a mol basis. This compound, now called "menadione" or K_3, is 2-methyl-1,4-naphthoquinone. It is readily obtainable in the pure crystalline state.

Some of the water-soluble derivatives are of importance. Since the natural products as well as the synthetic menadione are fairly insoluble in water, their parenteral administration is impractical. Diphosphates, diacetates, disulfates, and a bisulfite addition compound (as salts) of menadione have been used for parenteral and oral therapy. Most, but not all, synthetic compounds appear to owe their vitamin K activity to conversion *in vivo* to 2-methyl-1,4-naphthoquinone:

O O O – PO$_3$Na$_2$

– CH$_3$ – CH$_3$ – CH$_3$
– OH

O O O – PO$_3$Na$_2$

Phthiocol	Menadione	Synkavite
2-Methyl-3-	(vitamin K$_3$)	Tetra sodium
hydroxy-1,4-	2-Methyl-1,4-	salt of 2-methyl-
naphthoquinone	naphthoquinone	1,4-naphtho-
		hydroquinone-1,4-
		diphosphate

In some instances the water-soluble derivatives of K$_3$ are relatively ineffective. They also show some toxic symptoms in humans (6). For this reason
investigators have studied the properties of water soluble derivatives of the
naturally occurring K$_1$, such as disodium 2-methyl-3-phytyl-1,4-naphtho-
hydroquinone-1,4-diphosphate. This compound was shown to be highly
effective (7).

A review of the chemistry and biochemistry of vitamin K by Isler and
Wiss is available (8).

Physiologic aspects of vitamin K. In a nutritional deficiency of vitamin K chicks show a hemorrhagic syndrome characterized by internal bleeding and long blood-clotting time. A severely affected bird may bleed to death
as a result of pulling out a pin feather. In rats and some other species it is
difficult to produce the deficiency by feeding rations devoid of the vitamin.
Such species are supplied with the vitamin from intestinal bacteria which
synthesize it. The microorganisms are decomposed in part, and the vitamin
thus becomes available for absorption. This also occurs normally in the
human being.

If the growth of intestinal flora is minimized by drug administration (certain sulfonamide drugs, for example), a vitamin K deficiency can be developed in rats and other species by feeding rations low in this factor. Since the
vitamin requires bile salts for its absorption, any means that eliminate the
flow of bile into the intestine (bile fistula, for example) can, under the proper
conditions, result in lessened absorption and a vitamin K deficiency.

Regardless of the way in which a deficiency is produced, the end result is
a lowering of the blood plasma prothrombin. If this becomes severe, blood-
clotting time is lengthened and various manifestations of the hemorrhagic
syndrome may ensue. The liver requires the vitamin for the synthesis of
prothrombin. An attractive early theory postulated a specific role of the
vitamin as a prosthetic group of the enzyme thrombin, required in blood
clotting and formed from prothrombin of the plasma. It has been well established that this is not the case. That the vitamin must interact with tissue
cells seems clear, since no amount of it has been demonstrated to affect the
coagulation of normal or of K-deficient blood *in vitro.*

Quick and Collentine (9) produced vitamin K deficiency in dogs by means
of surgical procedures which allowed the bile to drain through the ureters
into the urinary bladder (cholecystnephrostomy). When the prothrombin

level had reached very low levels, either vitamin K_1 or menadione (2-methyl-1,4-naphthoquinone) was administered. It was found that as little as 9 μg per kilogram of body weight of K_1 restored the prothrombin time to normal in 4 hours, whereas the synthetic material, even in enormous doses was capable of bringing about only a 40 per cent regeneration of the prothrombin level. These workers postulated from these and other observations that vitamin K serves as the prosthetic group for the apoenzyme required for the mechanism involved in prothrombin synthesis, and that menadione forms a much less efficient system to serve this function. In dogs with low levels of prothrombin resulting from lack of intestinal bile, the administration of K_1, K_2, menadione, or Synkavite (see formula) corrected the condition. Orally K_1 was the least active on a molar basis, whereas intravenously all four showed about the same activity (10).

The newborn infant is subject to an alimentary vitamin K deficiency, since the vitamin is not readily passed from mother to fetus. The disease is characterized by low prothrombin levels and, consequently, a tendency to hemorrhage. Often a spontaneous abatement of this tendency ensues, as a result probably of establishment of intestinal flora in the infant. As pointed out previously, many common intestinal flora synthesize the vitamin, and a part of it becomes available to the host. The administration of vitamin K to women just previous to delivery or to the newborn infant is now common practice. Such therapy has markedly reduced the incidence of this hemorrhagic disease of infancy.

Purification of 2-C^{14}-methyl-3-phytyl-1,4 naphthoquinone (vitamin K_1-C^{14}) and 2-C^{14}-methyl-1,4 naphthoquinone (menadione-C^{14} or K_3-C^{14}) was described by Woods and Taylor (11). The methyl group carries the label in these compounds. After administering K_1-C^{14} to rats, the largest amount of radioactivity was present in the liver and the other tissues examined showed levels proportional to the amount of the compound given. There was no evidence of metabolism of the C^{14}-containing methyl group to CO_2 (12). In pregnant rats both K_1-C^{14} and menadione-C^{14} were found in fetal tissue indicating the passage of both compounds through the placental barrier. Again K_1-C^{14} was concentrated in the liver of the adults, while menadione-C^{14} was not (13).

The mechanism by which vitamin K controls prothrombin synthesis is unknown. The vitamin has been implicated in electron transport, but the data are not clear-cut (14). A role of K_1 in oxidative phosphorylation was proposed by Martius (15). In K deficiency or following bishydroxycoumarin (Dicumarol) administration in chicks "uncoupling" of oxidative phosphorylation (see Chapter 24) was observed in vitro in liver cell mitochondria preparations.

In some forms of liver damage the synthesis of prothrombin is curtailed. This may become a dangerous situation, since vitamin K treatment often is of no avail.

Dicumarol. Because of the closely interrelated physiologic actions of vitamin K and the drug bishydroxycoumarin in blood coagulation, it is advisable to consider the latter compound briefly at this time. As early as 1921 it was known that cattle and hogs eating spoiled sweet clover hay were likely to develop a serious syndrome known as "sweet clover disease." This disease was fatal in many instances and was characterized primarily by prolonged blood-clotting time followed by hemorrhage. Although Roderick (16) had studied the disease from the standpoint of the veterinarian, it was not until the late 1930's that a concerted effort on the part of biochemists was initiated to study the active hemorrhagic principle of spoiled sweet clover hay. Link and associates (17, 18, 19, 20) during a brilliant series of researches isolated, characterized, and finally synthesized the active principle. It proved to be 3,3′-methylene-bis(4-hydroxycoumarin) and was given the name "Dicumarol." The oral administration of the drug to animals or to man brings about a marked lowering of the blood plasma prothrombin level and a consequent lengthening of clotting time, following a latent period of one to several days, depending on the dose. The mechanism by which the drug brings this about is obscure. It is likely, however, that it is due to a decrease in prothrombin production and not to an increased utilization. Although it was assumed for many years that the situation exemplified the well-known phenomenon of metabolite-antimetabolite competition, it appears now that this is not the case (21). However, vitamin K is essential in the liver for the production of prothrombin, and Dicumarol in some way prevents the normal function of the vitamin in this process.

Medical men were supplied with the drug for experimental purposes soon after its synthesis. Many of the early experiences were discouraging, but during the course of time, as better control of its use developed, it has taken an important place among the many newly discovered medicinals. The primary value of the drug lies in its ability to lower the blood prothrombin level within controllable limits. As a result, the incidence of thrombophlebitis after certain types of surgery has been markedly lowered.

Warfarin, used as a rat poison throughout the world (see Chapter 32), has been used with considerable success in humans as an anticoagulant (22). It possesses five or possibly ten times the activity of Dicumarol and appears to lack most of the drawbacks of the latter drug. An overdose, as in the case of Dicumarol, can be counteracted by vitamin K (23).

The use of anticoagulants such as Dicumarol, Warfarin, and other closely related compounds is rather routine in selected types of surgery and in some heart conditions.

A classic review of the Dicumarol story by its discoverer, K. P. Link, is available (23).

The structures of Dicumarol and of Warfarin sodium are given below:

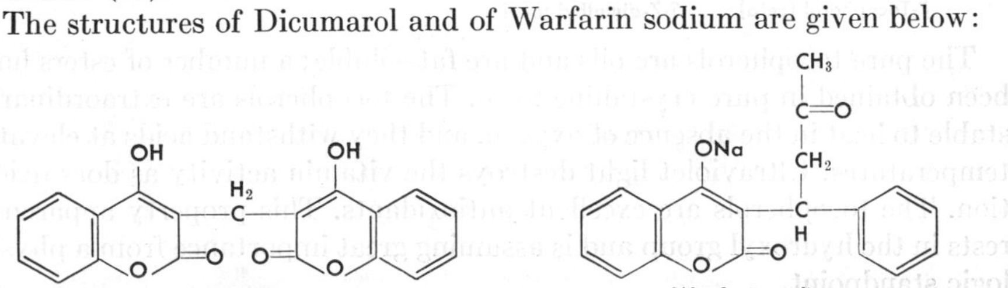

Dicumarol
3,3′-Methylene-bis(4-hydroxycoumarin)

Warfarin sodium
3-(α-acetonylbenzyl)-4-hydroxycoumarin, sodium

Determination of vitamin K. The biologic method of Almquist (24) for the determination of vitamin K is sensitive and accurate. It depends upon the degree of regeneration of prothrombin as a result of administered K active substances in chicks depleted of prothrombin. Details can be found in the original work or in Johnson's compilation (25) of methods of vitamin determination.

Chemical methods for menadione include the spectrophotometric method for the 2,4-dinitrophenylhydrazone derivative (26, 27) and a polarographic method (28).

VITAMIN E

The earliest indication that natural foods contain material specifically concerned with reproduction is found in a report by Mattill and Conklin (1). They indicated that rats fed on a milk diet supplemented with yeast (B vitamins) and iron were unable to bear young. In 1922 Bishop and Evans (2) announced the existence of a factor X in certain foods and indicated the necessity of the substance in the diet for normal rat reproduction. The known vitamins were supplied, and growth on their diet was quite normal, but reproduction failed. The active substance was later termed "vitamin E," and now at least seven compounds with E activity are known to occur in a variety of plant and animal tissues. These are called the "tocopherols." The terms "antisterility vitamin" and "fertility vitamin" have also been widely applied to the vitamers E.

Chemistry of the tocopherols. As early as 1927 it was recognized that vitamin E remained in the nonsaponifiable fraction of the lipids of foods containing it. It was not until 1936 that crystalline derivatives of the material with vitamin activity were isolated. Evans and coworkers (3) prepared three crystalline allophanates of compounds from the nonsaponifiable fraction of wheat germ oil and showed that the original alcohol obtained by hydrolysis of one of them had high vitamin E activity. These workers gave the active alcohol the name "α-tocopherol" (*tokos*, childbirth; *phero*, to bear; and *-ol*, designating an alcohol). Fernholz (4) worked out the structure of α-tocopherol in 1938, and it was synthesized by Karrer and coworkers (5) in the same year.

There are seven known naturally occurring tocopherols, all derivatives of tocol, 2 methyl-2-[trimethyl-tridecyl]-6-hydroxychromane (6). The "-tridecyl" indicates a 13 carbon chain:

Tocol
2 Methyl-2-[trimethyl-tridecyl]-6-hydroxychromane

α-Tocopherol (alpha)	5-7-8-trimethyl tocol	ε-Tocopherol (epsilon) 5-methyl tocol
β-Tocopherol (beta)	5-8-dimethyl tocol	η-Tocopherol (eta) 7-methyl tocol
γ-Tocopherol (gamma)	7-8-dimethyl tocol	δ-Tocopherol (delta) 8-methyl tocol
ζ-Tocopherol (zeta)	5-7-dimethyl tocol	

The pure tocopherols are oils and are fat-soluble; a number of esters have been obtained in pure crystalline form. The tocopherols are extraordinarily stable to heat in the absence of oxygen, and they withstand acids at elevated temperatures. Ultraviolet light destroys the vitamin activity as does oxidation. The tocopherols are excellent antioxidants. This property apparently rests in the hydroxyl group and is assuming great importance from a physiologic standpoint.

Many synthetic compounds also have E activity. Esters such as the phosphate and acetate are active. The 5,7-dimethly-8-ethyl homolog is also active.

Vitamin E deficiency. In man deficiency symptoms are not well established, primarily because known cases of deficiency are rare. It is agreed that man requires vitamin E, but any relations to muscle dystrophies, habitual abortions, and creatinuria are not well established. A study of a case by Woodruff (7) is enlightening. This patient showed impaired absorption of vitamin E (also fat and vitamin A). No tocopherol could be detected in blood serum after a test dose of 600 mg of α-tocopherol administered with bile salts or with Tween 80 (a surface active agent). After three months on high daily intake of vitamin E, the blood level was still too low to be determined, although the creatinuria disappeared. During the deficiency state a muscle biopsy showed marked muscular atrophy and the level of tocopherol was extremely low. In further periods of high vitamin intake there appeared to be a correlation between severity of creatinuria and the serum tocopherol level.

More concrete information is available on the relation of vitamin E to disease in the case of other animal species. In the female rat a mild deficiency of vitamin E may or may not disturb the estrous cycle or the reproduction process. A further deficiency is usually attended by resorption of the fetuses starting some eight or ten days after a normal conception. After resorption, conception may again follow, but the fetuses die from lack of blood supply and are resorbed as before. The administration of vitamin E during the first days of gestation generally is followed by the birth of normal young. This indicates that the abnormal state developed in the female rat as a result of E deficiency is a reversible one.

In the male rat irreversible changes occur during a prolonged deficiency. The testes of such animals are smaller than in normal animals of comparable age. Various stages of degeneration can be found on histologic examination. The end result is a degeneration of the germinal epithelium (irreversible change) with complete sterility. It should be kept in mind that varying degrees and lengths of deficiency are accompanied by marked differences in the physiologic picture. For details of the pathologic changes see Follis (8).

A common finding in rats on E-deficient diets is a rather typical muscle dystrophy. Both sexes and all age groups are susceptible. The young born to E-depleted mothers often show a spasticity of the hind limbs as early as the twenty-fifth day of life (9). Older animals require a longer depletion period.

A hyaline degeneration and disappearance of striations are typical of the syndrome. Leucocyte infiltration, proliferation of the sarcolemma nuclei, and an increase in fat globules may also be seen.

In the rat vitamin E therapy is often of no value, although the rabbit and the guinea pig, which are subject to the same type of muscle degeneration, respond to administered tocopherols with regeneration of damaged fibers and a return to normal appearance of the tissue.

Hepatic necrosis in the rat is a dietary disease involving vitamin E, cystine, and selenium (Factor 3) (10). Salts such as selenites or selenates can replace Factor 3 or vitamin E in the special diets employed and protect against symptoms. Further discussion can be found under selenium in the chapter on mineral metabolism, Chapter XXX.

Striated muscle in animals has a low creatine content during vitamin E deficiency. On the other hand, the urinary creatine increases, and may reach 15 times the normal level in rabbits when symptoms of muscle dystrophy appear. Creatinine excretion remains normal. The administration of vitamin E to deficient animals brings about a decreased excretion of creatine and an increased concentration in striated muscle.

Dining and Fitch (11) injected glycine-2-C^{14} into rabbits. In E-deficient animals high liver and low muscle creatine were found. The data showed that vitamin E deficiency in the rabbit leads to an increased rate of creatine synthesis and an increased turnover of muscle creatine. In man certain neuromuscular diseases have features in common with the muscle dystrophy produced in rabbits as a result of E deficiency. Tocopherol had no effect on the creatine excretion in humans suffering from progressive muscle dystrophy in the experiments of Fleischmann (12). This suggests fundamental differences in such neuromuscular disturbances in these two species.

Red blood cells from vitamin E-deficient rats are readily hemolyzed by dialuric acid *in vitro* or *in vivo*, while the cells are completely resistant if the animals have received adequate amounts of tocopherol (13). Bioassay procedures for vitamin E active compounds have developed on the basis of the degree of hemolysis *in vitro* in relation to the amount of tocopherol administered.

Kaunitz and Pappenheimer (14) showed an increased oxygen consumption in skeletal muscle of E-deficient rats and chickens *in vitro*. This biochemical change even precedes the histologic alterations. Houchin (15) reported a 40 per cent decrease in the elevated oxygen consumption of dystrophic rabbit and hamster muscle slices after the addition of α-tocopherol phosphate to the medium.

Monkeys develop muscular dystrophy, anemia, leucocytosis, an elevated excretion of creatine and allantoin, and a reduced excretion of creatinine in vitamin E deficiency (16). An elevated concentration of skeletal muscle desoxyribonucleic acid (DNA) and an increase in DNA and ribonucleic acid (RNA) in bone marrow as well as an increased bone marrow RNA/DNA ratio was found in E-deficient monkeys by Dinning and Day (17).

Much of the physiologic action of vitamin E appears to be related to its antioxidant capacity. The tocopherols exert a marked protective action (antioxidant) toward dietary vitamin A. On minimal vitamin A intake, rat growth is improved by inclusion of tocopherol in the diet and the incidence of gastric ulcers as a result of vitamin A deficiency is markedly reduced (18). Certain antioxidants are able to replace vitamin E in some of its physiologic functions, at least over short periods. Thus, Draper and coworkers (19) showed that vitamin E-deficient diets supplemented with methylene blue or N,N-diphenyl paraphenylenediamine sustained reproductivity in 60 female rats through two reproduction cycles. The latter compound was found to prevent degeneration of testes and lability of red cells to hemolysis in rats fed E-deficient diets (20), and it delayed the onset of dystrophy symptoms in guinea pigs (21).

The belief that tocopherol may participate in cellular electron transport systems (22) has apparently been resolved. No evidence has been found that α-tocopherol can undergo reversible oxidation-reduction to tocopheryl quinone. The isolation of a quinone (Q_{275} or coenzyme Q) from heart mitochondria by Crane and coworkers (23) and the demonstration of its part in electron transport has resolved the problem and led to the conclusion that tocopherol is not physiologically active in this respect. (See coenzyme Q in Chapter 11.)

Assay, biopotency, and units of vitamin E. Biologic methods for vitamin E assay have been improved and shortened, and important strides in chemical analyses have been made. The prevention of fetal resorption in depleted rats by the test material remains a standard procedure. Bunyan and coworkers (24), using the rat antisterility bioassay, reported that ʒ-tocopheryl acetate was about half as active as dl-α-tocopheryl acetate. Thus, the α, β, and ʒ forms have significant biologic activity, while γ tocopherol has only slight activity and the monomethyl tocopherols are probably without significant activity.

Various other techniques are used, such as the liver storage bioassay in the chick and the bioassay involving prevention of hemolysis of rat red blood cells *in vitro*. In a critical study of this method by Friedman and others the authors describe a single dose procedure (25).

A partial chemical separation and determination of the seven naturally occurring tocopherols has been described (26). Paper chromatographic separation of tocopherols was reviewed by Blaxter (6). Colorimetric determination of pure products is practical. A variety of methods are available (27).

The I.U. of dl-α-tocopherol is defined as the activity of 1.1 mg, and 1.49 I.U. equal 1 mg of the d form (28).

Occurrence of tocopherols. The most potent natural source of tocopherols is found in the vegetable oils; of these, wheat germ oil has the highest concentration. Corn oil and cottonseed oil contain far less. Fish oils are poor sources. Lettuce and alfalfa are good sources of the vitamin. Other foods have little activity. Of the animal tissues, liver is usually the highest in vitamin E, although the level is generally low in all animal material. Synthetic tocopherol is now rather generally employed in clinical work, as a standard in either biologic or physico-chemical assay, and as a source of the vitamin in experimental animal work. The advantages of such material are obvious.

Requirements of vitamin E. Although animal requirements for vitamin E are fairly well established, there are no acceptable experimental data on human requirements. Attempts have been made, however, to estimate human needs. Hickman and Harris (29) predicted that the human requirements for mixed natural tocopherols is about 30 mg per day.

B. THE WATER-SOLUBLE VITAMINS

Included in the group of water-soluble vitamins are the well-established members of the B complex. Many writers include choline, inositol, and p-aminobenzoic acid with the B vitamins. Ascorbic acid (vitamin C) and compounds with related activity, such as citrin (vitamin P), are also water-soluble vitamins.

THE VITAMIN B COMPLEX

It is general practice to include in the so-called B complex any water-soluble vitamin found in yeast, liver, or other good source of the well-established members of this group, such as thiamine, riboflavin, and niacin. Though such a practice has justification, it has made the B complex truly complex. The terminology is at present somewhat improved, though the literature of a few years ago and more is often baffling to the uninitiated. As an example, some 15 different names have been applied to the vitamin now known as "thiamine." This factor is also called "vitamin B_1" by many, although the former term is preferable since it has been adopted by the Council on Pharmacy and Chemistry of the American Medical Association, the American Association of Biological Chemists, and the American Institute of Nutrition. "Riboflavin," the presently accepted name for another member of this group, was previously referred to as "vitamin B_2," "vitamin G," and the "P-P factor" (pellagra preventive). A third factor, "niacin" (accepted name) was only a few years ago almost universally referred to as "nicotinic acid."

The various scientific groups, including those referred to above, have done a great deal to unify the terminology of the vitamins. After these organizations officially adopt a name, other synonyms slowly disappear from the literature, and a certain degree of clarification results. The present trend is to adopt a name that implies in some degree at least the chemical nature of the compound in question. For example, the name "pteroylglutamic acid" has replaced the name "folic aid" (another member of the B complex). As a result of the official adoption of vitamin names and discriminating editorial service on the part of the proper authorities, the situation regarding vitamin terminology is much improved, and there is a continued gain in unification.

THIAMINE

A thiamine deficiency in man leads to the condition known as beriberi; in animals the syndrome is referred to as polyneuritis. Reference has been made to the studies by Takaki, who demonstrated that through the proper dietary reforms the incidence of beriberi in the Japanese Navy could be practically eliminated. Also, the important discovery of Eijkman that chickens develop symptoms resembling beriberi when fed a diet of polished rice and that the symptoms disappear on adding rice polishings to the diet has been discussed in the introductory remarks of the preceding section. The work of Funk was also mentioned. He attempted to isolate the active principle of rice polishings responsible for preventing or curing the symptoms in fowl which develop when these animals are fed diets of polished rice. It was this work that led him to propose the term "vitamine" (now vitamin) for the basic material he isolated that was effective prophylactically or curatively in very small amounts.

At about this time progress in the field was markedly aided by the studies of McCollum and coworkers. In 1915 McCollum and Davis (1) reported that growth of young rats on purified diets was poor when dextrin constituted the carbohydrate of the ration, but if lactose was used, growth was fairly good. They also showed that heating the lactose destroyed the growth-promoting principle and that the active substance was water and alcohol soluble. The term "water-soluble B" was employed by McCollum to differentiate the factor from his earlier designated growth factor, "fat-soluble A."

Yeast was found to be an excellent source of the water-soluble B, and in 1920 Emmett and Luros (2) reported that autoclaved yeast no longer contained the antiberberi principle of Funk but did contain a substance that promoted growth of rats on certain synthetic diets. This was the first clear-cut demonstration of the dual nature of water-soluble B in yeast. We now know that these workers were dealing with thiamine (water-soluble B_1 or antiberiberi principle of Funk) which was destroyed in the yeast by autoclaving, and riboflavin which promoted rat growth with the rations employed and is not destroyed in yeast by the heat treatment used.

In 1926 the antiberiberi vitamin (thiamine) was isolated from rice polishings by Jansen and Donath (3). The synthesis of thiamine was accomplished in 1936 by Williams and coworkers (4).

Chemistry of thiamine. Soon after the purification and crystallization of thiamine, it was evident that a pyrimidine nucleus was a part of the molecule and that there also was present a substituted thiazole ring. In the synthesis of Williams and coworkers, the substituted pyrimidine (2 methyl-5-bromomethyl-6-aminopyrimidine hydrobromide) was reacted with 4 methyl-5-β-hydroxyethylthiazole to yield the bromide-hydrobromide of the vitamin. The naturally occuring thiamine is a chloride-hydrochloride.

After Williams converted the bromide derivative to the chloride-hydrochloride, it was identical with thiamine isolated from natural sources. The work required for the synthesis of this molecule is, of course, not depicted by the reaction. Years of investigation by many scientists all over the world culminated in success.

One gram of thiamine can be dissolved in 1 ml of water; this gives an acid solution due to the hydrochloride on the amino group. It is soluble to about 1 per cent in alcohol but rather insoluble in other common organic solvents.

Thiamine exhibits absorption bands in the ultraviolet spectrum. At pH 7 (aqueous solution) the maxima are at 235 and 267 mμ (5). At lower pH values the absorption spectrum changes. This influence of hydrogen ion on absorption is characteristic of many basic nitrogen compounds.

The molecule reacts with platinum chloride to form microcrystalline rosettes. It also forms insoluble compounds with phosphotungstic and tannic acids. Thiamine picrate was one of the early derivates to be crystallized. Sulfates, nitrates, etc., have also been prepared. Many of these derivatives have vitamin activity.

The melting point is between 248 and 250° C. This is for the hemihydrate, which crystallizes as white monoclinic needles. The odor of thiamine is highly characteristic and very like that of yeast. The characteristic odor of yeast is due in large part to the contained thiamine.

Thiamine is destroyed at elevated temperatures unless the pH is low. In alkaline solution complete destruction results from boiling for short periods. At a pH of 3.5 boiling results in little destruction. In yeast autoclaving at 120° C for short periods does not destroy the vitamin, but after two or three hours nearly complete destruction is accomplished.

Thiamine is readily oxidized; under controlled conditions thiochrome is formed, and this is the basis for a quantitative determination of the vitamin. On reduction hydrogen is added to the thiamine molecule, and vitamin activity disappears.

Schultz (6) prepared a series of 39 compounds chemically related to thiamine; 16 of these showed some vitamin activity.

The structure of thiamine as the free base is shown below. The naturally occuring molecule and the synthetic vitamin contain a hydrochloride on the

Table 18.5.   Food and Nutrition Board,
Recommended Daily Dietary
Designed for the Maintenance of Good
(Allowances are intended for persons

	Age Years	Weight kg. (lb.)	Height cm. (in.)	Calories	Protein gm.
Men..................	25	70 (154)	175 (69)	3200[3]	70
	45	70 (154)	175 (69)	3000	70
	65	70 (154)	175 (69)	2550	70
Women...............	25	58 (128)	163 (64)	2300	58
	45	58 (128)	163 (64)	2200	58
	65	58 (128)	163 (64)	1800	58
	Pregnant (second half)			+300	+20
	Lactating (850 ml. daily)			+1000	+40
Infants[4]	0–1/12[4]				See
	2/12–6/12 6 (13)		60 (24)	kg. × 120	Footnote
	7/12–12/12 9 (20)		70 (28)	kg. × 100	4
Children...............	1–3	12 (27)	87 (34)	1300	40
	4–6	18 (40)	109 (43)	1700	50
	7–9	27 (60)	129 (51)	2100	60
	10–12	36 (79)	144 (57)	2500	70
Boys..................	13–15	49 (108)	163 (64)	3100	85
	16–19	63 (139)	175 (69)	3600	100
Girls..................	13–15	49 (108)	160 (63)	2600	80
	16–19	54 (120)	162 (64)	2400	75

About the Recommended Daily Allowances:

In 1940 the Food and Nutrition Board of the National Research Council undertook the development of a dietary standard for the United States. The nutrient allowances were formulated, as far as possible and practical, to be "suitable for the maintenance of good nutrition in essentially the total population rather than those allowances which would fulfill minimal needs for the average person." This philosophy has been retained through the revisions of 1945, 1948, 1953, and 1958.

The board has relied on published data, and the combined judgment of a large group of nutrition authorities.

Implicit in the chosen term "recommended allowances" is the feeling of the board that the set standards are neither final nor minimal nor optimal requirements. The values given in the table represent "levels of nutrient intake appearing desirable for use in planning diets and food supplies." In general they are higher than the average requirements but lower than the amounts needed in deficiency states.

It is pointed out by the board that if these allowances are used in dietary evaluations, it should be appreciated that most persons whose consumption equals or exceeds the standards are presumably adequately nourished but not all who fail to reach these goals are malnourished. Involved in such a situation are the individual variations in needs among people, differences in degree of intestinal synthesis and intestinal absorption, variations in metabolic patterns or degree of utilization of certain nutrients, and other factors.

With the exception of vitamin D, it is safe to assume that a good mixed diet of common foods will supply the recommended allowances, and this would hold with many combinations of foods.

amino group and a chloride ion neutralizing the positive charge on the nitrogen atom of the thiazole ring.

Coenzyme activity of thiamine. An important derivative of thiamine is the pyrophosphate. This molecule is known as cocarboxylase and is the coenzyme or prosthetic group of the enzyme decarboxylase, which is involved in the decarboxylation of α-keto acids in the body. The structure of thiamine

National Research Council
Allowances,[1] Revised 1958
Nutrition of Healthy Persons in the U.S.A.
normally active in a temperate climate.)

Calcium gm.	Iron mg.	Vitamin A I.U.	Thiam. mg.	Ribo. mg.	Niacin[2] mg. equiv.	Asc. Acid mg.	Vitamin D I.U.
0.8	10	5000	1.6	1.8	21	75	
0.8	10	5000	1.5	1.8	20	75	
0.8	10	5000	1.3	1.8	18	75	
0.8	12	5000	1.2	1.5	17	70	
0.8	12	5000	1.1	1.5	17	70	
0.8	12	5000	1.0	1.5	17	70	
1.5	15	6000	1.3	2.0	+3	100	400
2.0	15	8000	1.7	2.5	+2	150	400
0.6	5	1500	0.4	0.5	6	30	400
0.8	7	1500	0.5	0.8	7	30	400
1.0	7	2000	0 7	1.0	8	35	400
1.0	8	2500	0 9	1.3	11	50	400
1.0	10	3500	1.1	1.5	14	60	400
1.2	12	4500	1.3	1.8	17	75	400
1.4	15	5000	1.6	2.1	21	90	400
1.4	15	5000	1.8	2.5	25	100	400
1.3	15	5000	1.3	2.0	17	80	400
1.3	15	5000	1.2	1.9	16	80	400

[1] The allowance levels are intended to cover individual variations among most normal persons as they live in the United States under usual environmental stresses. The recommended allowances can be attained with a variety of common foods, providing other nutrients for which human requirements have been less well defined. See text for more detailed discussion of allowances and of nutrients not tabulated.

[2] Niacin equivalents include dietary sources of the preformed vitamin and the precursor, tryptophan. 60 milligrams tryptophan equals 1 milligram niacin.

[3] Calorie allowances apply to individuals usually engaged in moderate physical activity. For office workers or others in sedentary occupations they are excessive. Adjustments must be made for variations in body size, age, physical activity, and environmental temperature.

[4] The Board recognizes that human milk is the natural food for infants and feels that breast feeding is the best and desired procedure for meeting nutrient requirements in the first months of life. No allowances are stated for the first month of life. Breast feeding is particularly indicated during the first month when infants show handicaps in homeostasis due to different rates of maturation of digestive, excretory, and endocrine functions. Recommendations as listed pertain to nutrient intake as afforded by cow's milk formulas and supplementary foods given the infant when breast feeding is terminated. Allowances are not given for protein during infancy.

pyrophosphate is shown in the section on coenzymes in Chapter 11 (see page 373).

Thiaminokinase has been prepared from rat liver and from yeast. This enzyme in the presence of ATP and Mg^{++} synthesizes cocarboxylase from thiamine by transfer of pyrophosphate from ATP to thiamine.

$$R-CH_2-CH_2OH + ATP \xrightarrow[\text{Enz.}]{Mg^{++}} R-CH_2-CH_2-O-\overset{\overset{O}{\|}}{P}-O-\overset{\overset{O}{\|}}{\underset{OH}{P}}-OH + AMP$$

Thiamine   Thiamine pyrophosphate (cocarboxylase)

Westenbrink has reviewed the phosphorylation, cellular distribution, biosynthesis, and metabolism of thiamine (7).

Barron and associates (8) demonstrated that the utilization of α-ketoglutarate is increased by tissues of thiamine-deficient rats after the addition to the tissue of phosphorylated thiamine. Green and others (9) showed that various animal tissues including rabbit muscle and pig heart contain a thiamine-containing enzyme capable of catalyzing the decarboxylation not only of pyruvate, but also of α-ketoglutarate and α-ketobutyrate.

The nonoxidative decarboxylation of pyruvic acid (plants, microorganisms) by the thiamine pyrophosphate (TPP) enzyme from yeast produces acetaldehyde. A proposed mechanism for this reaction (10) is shown:

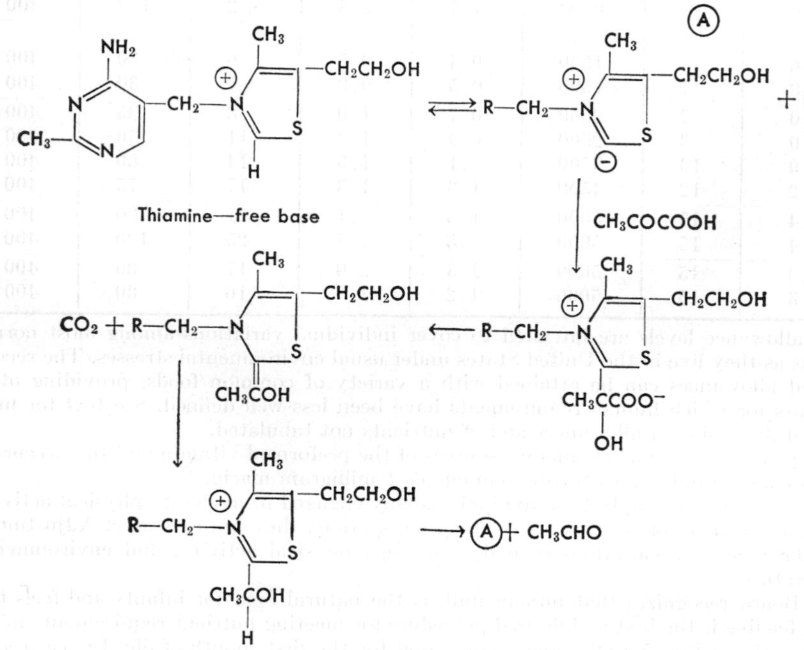

Proposed mechanism for nonoxidative decarboxylation of pyruvic acid (10)

The enzymatic formation of acetoin in both plants and animals involves TPP as coenzyme. Two molecules of acetaldehyde or a molecule of pyruvic acid and a molecule of acetaldehyde form acetoin as follows:

$$CH_3-CHO + OHC-CH_3 \longrightarrow CH_3-CHOH-CO-CH_3$$
$$CH_3-CO-COOH + CH_3-CHO \longrightarrow CH_3-CHOH-CO-CH_3 + CO_2$$

The significance of these reactions is obscure, since no role of acetoin is known.

Transketolase is an enzyme found in plant and animal tissues. TPP is the coenzyme. The reactions involving this enzyme are detailed in Chapter 24. An example of a transketolase reaction involves the transfer of a 2-carbon unit from the 2-keto compound xylulose-5-phosphate to the aldehyde ribose-

5-phosphate forming sedoheptulose-7-phosphate and glyceraldehyde-3-phosphate.

Lipothiamide is a conjugate of lipoic acid and thiamine. The structure can be found under coenzymes in Chapter 11. It has been proposed as an active coenzyme in certain decarboxylations. At present, however, it is not clearly established that this molecule acts as a coenzyme. Specific roles of thiamine pyrophosphate and of lipoic acid in decarboxylations are well established.

Lipoic acid (6,8-dithiooctanoic acid, or 6,8-thioctic acid) functions as a coenzyme in α-keto acid decarboxylation by itself or possibly as the conjugate lipothiamide. Lipoic acid, also called "pyruvate oxidation factor," "protogen," and "acetate replacement factor," is a growth substance for certain protozoa; hence the name "protogen." It also can replace acetate for growth in L. casei, and so the name "acetate replacement factor." The factor is required for normal oxidation of pyruvate by S. faecalis. The term "lipoic" acid was used because the substance is fat-soluble, and the term "thioctic acid" has more recently been applied because it is an 8-carbon acid containing sulfur groups.

In the oxidative decarboxylation of pyruvate and in the presence of pyruvate dehydrogenase in animal tissues, the oxidized, or —S—S—, form of lipoic acid is reduced by pyruvate to form the —SH,—SH molecule. At the same time the acetyl group of pyruvate is transferred to the —SH group on the number 6 carbon of lipoic acid, (11) and CO_2 is split out. Following removal of the acetyl group (to CoA yielding acetyl CoA), the reduced lipoic acid is reoxidized to the —S—S— form and is available for further reaction. A similar mechanism operates in the oxidative decarboxylation of α-ketoglutaric acid with the production of CO_2 and succinyl-CoA:

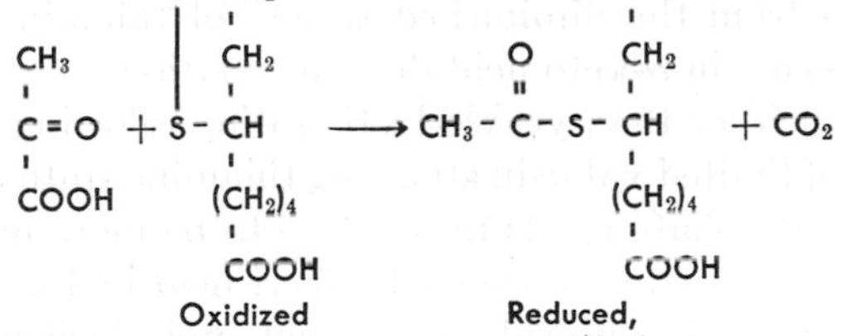

Proposed mechanism for oxidative decarboxylation of pyruvate (11)

Lipoic acid is found in a variety of animal α-keto acid decarboxylases. It is likely that the over-all oxidative decarboxylation of α-keto acids, employing the protein bound form of lipoic acid, can be expressed as follows (12):

$$RCOCOOH + HS-CoA + DPN^+ \xrightarrow{TPP} RCO-S-CoA + CO_2 + DPNH + H^+$$

Reviews by Reed (13) and by Gunsalus (14) are available.

Thiamine deficiency, physiologic function. A number of experimental human thiamine deficiency studies have been reported. A series of experiments by Williams and coworkers (15, 16) is of interest not only from the standpoint of the biochemical and clinical findings, but also because of the advancement in our knowledge of some of the essential features in the design of such experimentation.

In 1957 Brožek (17) reported the results of a comprehensive study from Keys' laboratory. Psychologic changes and biochemical data are presented in human thiamine deprivation. The study consisted of four experimental periods: (a) a month for standardization and collection of control values; (b) partial restriction of the vitamin for 168 days, with daily intakes in three groups of men of 0.61, 1.01, or 1.81 mgs, and energy expenditure of about 3300 Cal; (c) an acute thiamine deprivation period of 15 to 27 days on "thiamine free" diet; and (d) a thiamine supplementation period, 5 mgs daily for nine to 21 days.

Oral administration of thiamine was started for each man when the investigators considered that the deficiency had progressed as far as was safe. At this time nausea and vomiting were present, general weakness was pronounced, anorexia was extreme, and blood pyruvic acid levels were elevated. Thiamine supplementation restored appetites and resulted in a dramatic change in attitude of the subjects.

Performance tests on intelligence were not affected adversely within limits of the experimental conditions. Neurasthenia (nervous exhaustion with many symptoms), emotional deterioration, impaired coordination, and lowering of the pressure-pain threshold all responded dramatically to thiamine administration.

During the period of partial restriction, with the other B vitamins supplied in adequate amounts, the intake of 0.2 mg thiamine per 1000 Cal was at the borderline of deficiency.

Elevated blood pyruvic acid, especially after glucose ingestion, has been observed in advanced thiamine deficiency by various workers (20). This undoubtedly results from the diminished supply of thiamine pyrophosphate, required as coenzyme in α-keto acid decarboxylation.

Blood pyruvic acid or the pyruvic-lactic ratio, following glucose administration has been of limited value in studying thiamine status. Blood thiamine or thiamine pyrophosphate levels may prove to be more informative.

The proceedings of a conference on beriberi held in 1958 contain a great deal of information on the clinical, nutritional, and biochemical problems in this disease (18).

Since the advent of synthetic diets capable of supporting good growth and reproduction in laboratory animals, the development of a thiamine deficiency has been followed closely from both the biochemical and the neurologic standpoint in a number of species.

In pigeons on a severe thiamine deficiency early symptoms are loss of appetite, lassitude, and weight loss. Paralysis and head retraction (opisthotonus) are followed by death in a matter of a few weeks. If the deficiency is less severe, the birds survive for long periods and develop many of the symptoms seen in humans.

Rats lose their appetite after a short period on a deficient diet. If the diet contains small amounts of the vitamin, rather typical symptoms may ensue. A spasticity and stiffness of the hind legs is seen, and later the limbs may become paralyzed.

It is obvious that a large part of the symptomatology of thiamine deficiency is related to pathologic changes in specific parts of the nervous system. It is impractical to discuss here detailed findings of experimental workers in this specialized field. Rinehart, Greenberg, and Friedman (19) made careful studies recently of the lesions of the nervous system of rhesus monkeys subjected to one or more periods of thiamine depletion. Outstanding were the lesions in the nuclear structures of the central nervous system. In the animals depleted two or more times the lesions were more severe and extensive. Certain myocardial changes were observed, and according to some investigators, they are similar to those of the human heart in beriberi.

North and Sinclair (20), on the other hand, subjected rats to three to six successive periods of acute thiamine deficiency over an average survival period of 127 days. Other rats were subjected to a combined thiamine and pantothenic acid deficiency. In both studies there was no evidence of degenerative changes in the distal segments of the sciatic and posterior tibial nerves, in the lumbar dorsal-root ganglia, or in the lumbar cord.

An interesting development is the production of vitamin deficiencies in animals by feeding substances that might be referred to as "antivitamins," or vitamin inhibitors. Pyrithiamine is a synthetic pyridine analog of thiamine. In this compound a —C=C— takes the place of the —S— in the thiazole group of thiamine. Woolley and White (21) showed that mice develop a thiamine deficiency when pyrithiamine is administered. The process is reversible when sufficient extra thiamine is included in the diet. The symptoms are similar to those produced by a thiamine deficiency in other species. Pyrithiamine, also called "neopyrithiamine," was shown to inhibit the biosynthesis of cocarboxylase by chicken blood but not to lessen the combination of cocarboxylase with the apoenzyme to produce the decarboxylating enzyme (22). It was also suggested by Woolley and others (23) that pyrithiamine may affect other thiamine systems than cocarboxylase, since animals dying of typical thiamine deficiency symptoms as a result of administration of the antagonist showed normal levels of liver cocarboxylase. The administration of the antagonist oxythiamine (—OH for —NH$_2$ in thiamine), however, produced low levels of cocarboxylase. Also, De Caro and workers (24) have demonstrated that the normal increases in heat production and in basal metabolic rate (BMR) in the rat following glucose administration are inhibited by pyrithiamine but not by oxythiamine. It seems clear that distinct differences exist in the mechanisms of thiamine inhibition by these two antagonists.

The 2-n-butyl homolog of thiamine (n-butyl group replacing the methyl group on the pyrimidine ring) is a vitamin inhibitor for rats. Emerson and Southwick (25) demonstrated decreased growth rate and certain polyneuritic symptoms in rats fed this compound. The adverse effects were largely obviated by adding thiamine to the diet.

These instances are probably examples of the so-called competition reactions. It is thought that the inhibitor molecule may replace the natural vitamin molecule in an enzyme system, or in some other essential metabolic component, and that such a component is not physiologically active. On the addition of extra vitamin, the normal system, by mass law action perhaps, may again be formed.

It was generally held some years ago that the metabolism of alcohol required thiamine-containing enzymes. Westerfeld and coworkers (26) were especially active in this field. More recent evidence indicates that alcohol ingestion may actually decrease the thiamine requirement. In thiamine deficiency pyruvic acid accumulates in the body as a result of impaired carbohydrate metabolism (pyruvic acid decarboxylation). If thiamine were required for alcohol metabolism, one would expect a decreased rate of removal of this molecule from the body in a deficiency of the vitamin. Westerfeld and coworkers (27) found no decreased rate of alcohol metabolism in pigeons during acute thiamine deficiency. Further work by Westerfeld and Doisy (28) demonstrated that in the pigeon alcohol exerts a sparing action on thiamine. When alcohol was substituted isocalorically for part of the carbohydrate of the diet, the thiamine requirement was lessened. The possibility was pointed out that the metabolism of alcohol and carbohydrate together requires less thiamine than the metabolism of carbohydrate alone. Fat and protein likewise exert a thiamine-sparing action (29). The neurologic findings in alcoholism, it would appear, cannot be explained on the basis of thiamine deficiency resulting from increased demand, but rather as a deficiency resulting simply in lowered intake on the generally inadequate diet of the alcoholic. The specific role of thiamine in relation to neurologic findings in thiamine deficiency in animals or in man cannot be stated.

Metabolism of thiamine. McCarthy and others (30) injected thiamine-S^{35} into normal rats and recovered about 65 per cent of the injected activity in the urine collected during ten days following administration. Thiamine-deficient rats excreted 52 per cent of the original radioactive sulfur in the time period. In each case most of the radioactive sulfur appeared in the neutral sulfur fraction and a small amount as sulfate.

Thiamine requirement. One U.S.P. unit of thiamine is equal to 3 μg of thiamine hydrochloride. This is identical to the I.U. Because of the well-established relationship of thiamine to carbohydrate metabolism, the requirement of this vitamin for man is most accurately predicted on the basis of the caloric intake and primarily the carbohydrate intake. This, however, is not the most practical approach from a nutritional standpoint. Since individual diets vary to such a great extent and because of other individual variations, exact figures for human thiamine requirement are not highly significant. The general trend in the past few years has been to revise downward the estimated daily thiamine need. Thus the recommended dietary allowance adopted by the Food and Nutrition Board of the National Research Council was revised from 0.6 mg to 0.5 mg per 1000 Cal in 1953 and remains essentially the same in the 1958 revision. For a 3000-Cal diet the daily thiamine requirement would be approximately 1.5 mg. (See Table 18.5, page 696.) Such allowances are not to be confused with requirements. The allowances were designed to allow a fair margin above actual requirements. For further discussion of human requirements, see (31).

The use of massive doses of thiamine for various clinical entities, such as nausea of pregnancy and "nervousness," seems to be successful only in isolated cases.

Distribution of thiamine. The vitamin is widely distributed in both plant and animal tissues. In plants the seeds generally contain the highest concentration. Dry peas, beans, and soybeans are excellent sources. The vitamin is concentrated in the outer layers of the grain kernels. Bran and rice polishings are thus rich sources. Whole wheat bread and white bread made from enriched flour contain a good supply of thiamine. Yeast is an outstanding source of thiamine and of certain other members of the B complex. Many nuts have a high concentration of the vitamin. Peanuts contain a good supply, and pecans and brazil nuts have still more.

Milk contains only one tenth the amount of thiamine that is found in peanuts, but because of the comparative quantities consumed, milk is by far a more important dietary source. Many cheeses contain thiamine in amounts comparable to that of milk.

Avocados, gooseberries, and dried prunes contain the highest thiamine content among the fruits. Oranges have around half the quantity found in figs or prunes.

Many animal tissues are excellent sources of the vitamin. Pork chops and fat ham have exceptionally high contents. Many beef cuts are also excellent sources.

Table 18.6 lists the approximate thiamine content of a number of common foods.

It is of interest that though live yeast contains a high concentration of thiamine, the vitamin is not only unavailable to humans, but the yeast also appears to compete with the body in the gastrointestinal tract for other dietary thiamine. Parsons and coworkers (32) fed live yeast to individuals and noted a marked drop in urinary thiamine excretion to less than the basal level (without yeast). On removal of the yeast from the diet urinary excretion rose. The thiamine of killed yeast, on the other hand, is almost completely available. Various workers have demonstrated that the ingestion of viable yeast leads to increased loss of free thiamine in the feces, primarily in the cells of yeast and other organisms, and lessened urinary excretion, which is a good indication of decreased absorption from the intestine.

Some bacteria synthesize thiamine. There has been considerable controversy over the question of availability to the body of the vitamin from this source. Alexander and Landwehr (33) presented evidence which indicates that neither free nor bound (diphosphate) thiamine of the feces is of nutritional value to the individual. They found that most of the vitamin exists in the bacterial cells and that the greatest part was present as bound thiamine, which is not absorbed until it is dephosphorylated. They pointed out that probably no enzyme capable of bringing about this hydrolysis exists in the large intestine. They administered both forms of thiamine by retention enema to an individual and found that the urinary thiamine excretion was not increased and that all the thiamine and cocarboxylase administered were recovered in the next 24-hour stool.

Table 18.6. Approximate Thiamine and Riboflavin Content of Some Common Foods

Food	Thiamine (μg) per 100 g	Riboflavin (μg) per 100 g
Milk, cow	40	150
Cheese, American	40	500
Orange juice	60	55
Peanuts	400	400
Ham	1,200	300
Veal chop	290	220
Beefsteak	200	300
Beef liver	250	2,000
Eggs	170	300
Cornmeal, yellow	400	200
Soybean flour	500	400
Rolled oats	800	150
Whole wheat flour	500	100
White bread	80	100
White bread, enriched	400	300
Wheat germ	3,000	600
White rice	50	20
Brown rice	300	50
Dry peas	800	300
Potato	150	40
Green beans	90	120
Dry beans	500	300
Beets	40	70
Celery	30	30
Yeast, fresh	3,000	1,500
Yeast, dried brewers'	10,000	3,000

By the use of C^{14}-labeled thiamine it was shown that rats did not absorb thiamine from sources other than that supplied in the diet (34). This would indicate that under the conditions employed in these experiments intestinal microorganisms did not add to the total vitamin supply available to the host.

Mickelson (35) has reviewed the subject of intestinal synthesis of vitamins.

Determination of thiamine. Biologic methods for thiamine determination have largely been replaced by physicochemical techniques. Of the former, the rat curative procedure has been widely used. The test material is administered to acutely polyneuritic rats. The duration of cure of rats given various levels of the unknown is compared to the duration after giving known amounts of thiamine. From such data the approximate vitamin content can be calculated.

Yeast fermentation methods and microbiologic methods have been developed and widely used.

The chemical procedures are increasing in popularity because of ease and rapidity compared to animal assays. The most widely employed method involves the isolation of thiamine from the test material, the oxidation of the vitamin to thiochrome, and the comparison of the fluorescence of this compound and the fluorescence produced by oxidizing a known amount of pure thiamine.

Alkaline ferricyanide is used to oxidize thiamine. The blue fluorescing thiochrome can be separated from many interfering substances by isobutyl alcohol extraction. Special equipment is required to make a quantitative comparison of the fluorescence in the sample and in a standard solution. Fluorescence attachments are available for various types of spectrophotometers:

Thiamine $\xrightarrow{\text{oxidation}}$ [chemical structure]

Thiochrome

New developments in colorimetric, polarographic, and chromatographic techniques for thiamine, as well as separation procedures for mono-, di-, and triphosphoric esters are summarized by Horwitt (36).

Mickelsen and Yamamoto (37) have reviewed analytic methods including animal, physicochemical, enzymatic, and microbiologic techniques developed by many investigators over the years.

RIBOFLAVIN

The suggestion that water-soluble B contained more than one active principle was given impetus by the work of Emmett and McKim (1). These workers indicated the presence of two water-soluble vitamins in rice polishings, one that cured rat polyneuritis and another that produced weight gain in rats on specific rations. We now know that the second factor contained riboflavin, and at that time this principle was called "vitamin B₂" or "vitamin G."

Various investigators had studied naturally occurring pigments in foods. Bleyer and Kallmann (2) isolated a crude yellow pigment from whey, and Blooher (3) presented evidence pointing to the probable identity of vitamin G (B₂) and the water-soluble yellow, green fluorescent pigment of whey. In 1932 Warburg and Christian (4) isolated a yellow respiratory ferment (Warburg's yellow enzyme) from bottom yeast. This was later separated into a protein fraction and a small pigment molecule (riboflavin), neither of which alone possessed enzyme activity. Pure riboflavin was isolated from milk and other foods in 1933 by Kuhn and coworkers (5). In the early phases of this work 100 mg of flavin were obtained from a quantity of egg white corresponding to 33,000 eggs. This represents a yield of about 7 per cent based on the content of this pigment now known to be present. Lactoflavin (milk), hepatoflavin (liver), ovoflavin (eggs), and verdoflavin (grass) proved to be chemically identical with riboflavin, and it was recognized that riboflavin is actually what had been called vitamin B₂.

The synthesis of riboflavin was accomplished by two groups of German workers in 1935 (6, 7).

In nature the vitamin is synthesized by all green plants and by most microorganisms, although some bacteria are without this capacity. A review by Stadtman (8) summarizes developments on the biosynthesis and degradation of riboflavin.

Chemistry of riboflavin. The flavins are widely distributed in nature. Many derivatives have been studied. After the elucidation of the structure of lumiflavin (photolysis product of riboflavin), the relation of this compound to the known alloxazines was established. Shortly after this it was predicted that riboflavin differed from lumiflavin in that a D-ribityl group was present in riboflavin, replacing the methyl group at position 9 in lumiflavin. Total synthesis confirmed this prediction.

$$1'\ H\ \ H\ \ H\ \ 5'$$
$$H_2C{-}C{-}C{-}C{-}CH_2OH$$
$$OH\ OH\ OH$$

Riboflavin
6,7-dimethyl-9-(D-1'-ribityl)-isoalloxazine
Riboflavin phosphate has ortho phosphate
ester on primary alcohol group.

The D in the chemical name of riboflavin indicates that the ribityl group is related to the D series of sugars. The one prime (1') indicates attachment of the ribityl group at the first carbon atom, and the 9 that this attachment is to position 9 of the isoalloxazine ring system. A number of syntheses are available for the dimethyl compound (9). See also (10).

The vitamin is not soluble in ordinary fat solvents but is soluble to a limited degree in water. More soluble derivatives, such as the acetate and the phosphate, have been used medicinally. Riboflavin is reversibly reduced by thiosulfate, H_2S, and H_2 to form the colorless leucoriboflavin. Strong oxidizing agents decompose it, but bromine water and H_2O_2 have only a slight effect. The molecule is in general acid-stable and alkali-labile. Either visible or ultraviolet light irreversibly decompose riboflavin. The molecule exhibits absorption maxima at wavelengths of 220, 267, 336, and 446 mμ, and a water solution is yellow and has an intense green fluorescence. The orange-yellow needles of the pure compound melt at 282° C.

A number of analogs and other derivatives have vitamin activity. The 6-ethyl, 7-methyl compound and arabinoflavin (L-arabityl in place of D-ribityl) are active.

Riboflavin deficiency. The early studies of human vitamin deficiencies were complicated by the presence in the subjects of multiple deficiencies. Only recently have the symptoms of a frank ariboflavinosis in man been noted, and it must be said that considerable controversy exists regarding the relation of certain of the symptoms to riboflavin deficiency.

In general, however, the deficiency is associated in man with abnormal ectodermal tissue maintenance. The usual signs of this are: (a) inflammation of the tongue (glossitis)—the tongue assumes a magenta color, and there is flattening of the papillae; (b) cheilosis, or fissuring at the corners of the mouth and of the lips; and (c) a seborrheic dermatitis, often manifested by a sharklike appearance of the skin in the nasolabial folds and elsewhere (11). One of the early experimental studies on human riboflavin deficiency was reported in 1938 (12). The diet was deficient in niacin as well as riboflavin. The cheilosis and seborrheic lesions which developed did not respond to niacin treatment, but disappeared following riboflavin therapy.

Another manifestation of deficiency according to some workers is corneal vascularization. It is known that a similar clinical picture can be produced by a variety of deficiencies and even by certain toxic substances. The value of such findings in diagnosing ariboflavinosis is indeed limited.

Attempts have been made to establish criteria for differentiating between

ocular disturbances of ariboflavinosis and other types of corneal vascularization (12), and between glossitis of riboflavin deficiency and that found in
other diseases (13). The situation is still complicated, however, and many
reports indicate that observers have difficulty in attaching a specific symptom to a specific avitaminosis. In many instances one of these symptoms in
humans has responded to some other member of the B complex but not to
riboflavin. For instance, Cayer and others (14) made a rather intensive biochemical study of a number of patients with glossitis and cheilosis. Excretion
and load tests of various B complex vitamins were studied in these patients
and in normal individuals. Interesting among their findings are: (a) similar
riboflavin levels in some patients with and some without cheilosis, indicating
the possibility that riboflavin deficiency may not have been responsible for
the cheilosis; (b) frequent failure in response to riboflavin; and (c) frequent
response in patients with cheilosis to niacin (nicotinic acid, another member
of the B complex). Some patients responded only after the administration
of yeast or liver extract, sources of many B complex vitamins.

In man on controlled low intake of riboflavin over extended periods,
Horwitt and coworkers (15) observed erythema of the tongue, angular
stomatitis, and scrotal dermatitis as prevalent symptoms.

Bessey and coworkers (16) studied the riboflavin content (and the
coenzymes containing the vitamin; see further) in blood of men on restricted
intakes and of men on liberal intakes of the vitamin. The content in red
blood cells was found to be a reasonably sensitive and practical index for
the evaluation of nutritional status with respect to riboflavin. A critical
review of pathologic changes in riboflavin deficiency can be found in the
book by Follis (17). An informative history of pellagra covering the
recognition of the nutritional aspect and the conquest of the disease was
published by Sydenstricker (18).

With animals long-continued and well-controlled deficiency experiments
are practical. Rats exhibit decreased growth rate; eye changes, including a
keratitis and rather typical cataracts; dermatitis; possibly a type of anemia;
some nerve degeneration; and poor reproduction. Congenital malformation
(19) and a cessation of the estrous cycle (20) have been reported. Definite
symptoms of ariboflavinosis in calves have been reported (21).

Wertman and various coworkers have studied a number of vitamins in
relation to deficiency and factors in resistance to infection in rats. Paper
No. IV of the series (22) concerns a riboflavin deficiency.

Coenzyme activity. The enzymes containing riboflavin are called
"flavoproteins." Two coenzymes are known—riboflavin phosphate, or
flavin mononucleotide (FMN), and flavin adenine dinucleotide (FAD).
The first flavoprotein isolated was Warburg's yellow enzyme; it is composed
of FMN and apoenzyme (specific protein). The enzyme can be separated
into protein and FMN by dialyzing against dilute HCl. No enzyme activity
resides in the individual constituents, but upon recombining them activity
reappears. Highly purified yellow enzyme was found to contain two FMN
molecules per molecular weight of 104,000, which amounts to 0.877 per cent

of the nucleotide in the enzyme (23). Flavin adenine dinucleotide has been isolated from yeast and animal tissues (24) and various plants. Both FAD and FMN have been synthesized (25).

FAD and FMN combine with different apoenzymes to form a large number of oxidation-reduction enzymes. FAD, for example, is found in xanthine oxidase, D-amino acid oxidase, aldehyde oxidase, and fumaric dehydrogenase. FMN is associated with Warburg's yellow enzyme, cytochrome C reductase, L-amino acid oxidase, and others. These enzymes operate in electron transport systems. Details can be found in Chapter 21.

The structures of FAD and FMN are given in the coenzyme section in Chapter 11.

The mononucleotide (riboflavin-5'-phosphate) is synthesized from the vitamin and ATP under the influence of a flavokinase enzyme (26):

$$\text{Riboflavin} + \text{ATP} \xrightarrow{\text{Mg}^{++}} \text{FMN} + \text{ADP}$$

ATP reacts with the mononucleotide to form FAD. The enzyme mediating this reaction has been called "flavin nucleotide pyrophosphorylase" or "FAD synthetase" (27):

$$\text{FMN} + \text{ATP} \xrightarrow{\text{Mg}^{++}} \text{FAD} + \text{PP}$$

It was shown by Tong and others (28) that FMN has a stimulating action in the conversion of iodide into iodoprotein by mitochondrial-microsomal preparations of sheep thyroid glands. The evidence indicated that the increased conversion is enzymatic and is inhibited by thiouracil and some other goitrogenic molecules.

With the accumulation of knowledge regarding riboflavin, one might expect that a deficiency of some specific enzyme system in the body might be correlated with a specific deficiency symptom. No such correlation is known at present, although specific enzyme deficiencies are said to be demonstrable in animals on low riboflavin intakes.

In moderate riboflavin deficiency rat tissues showed no decrease in DPNH dehydrogenase activity (flavoenzyme) according to Burch and coworkers (29). In severe deficiency the activity dropped off somewhat. In the liver of the deficient rats xanthine oxidase activity paralleled the decrease in FAD, while the decrease in D-amino acid oxidase activity followed the decrease in FMN.

Riboflavin antagonists. Galactoflavin is a potent riboflavin antagonist. Emerson and coworkers (30) reported marked growth inhibition in rats on diets containing this compound and reversal of the effect upon addition of sufficient riboflavin to the food. The diethyl derivative acts as a riboflavin antagonist in rats but can replace the vitamin for growth of *L. casei* (31). Egami and others (32) showed that flavin monosulfate inhibits D-amino acid oxidase and acts as a competitive inhibitor of the vitamin in growth of *L. casei*. Fall and Petering (33) synthesized a number of analogs of riboflavin in which the ribityl group is replaced by other groups. The formylmethyl analog was found to be a reversible riboflavin antagonist in the rat. The hydroxyethyl analogue proved to be a potent competitive antagonist of the vitamin in rats and with *L. casei*. The compound also exhibits antifungal and antibacterial activity.

Distribution of riboflavin. Riboflavin is one of the most widely distributed B vitamins, but there are very few common sources that contain high concentrations. All cells of both plants and animals presumably contain the vitamin. Plant seeds synthesize the vitamin during germination. A few bacteria and the yeasts are rich sources. Muscle tissue is low in riboflavin, but certain internal organs, such as the liver and kidney, may contain appreciable amounts. Table 18.6 (page 704) lists the approximate riboflavin content of some common foods. Note the high concentration in liver, wheat germ, and yeast, and the very low content in celery, polished rice, and potatoes. It should be kept in mind that even though potatoes are low in the vitamin, the continued intake at one or even two meals a day by the majority of many races makes the potato an important contributor to the total dietary intake. It was pointed out previously that the thiamine of live yeast is not available to the body. A similar situation exists with riboflavin. Parsons and coworkers (34) showed that the riboflavin in live bakers' yeast is only slightly available to humans but that the vitamin is completely available from samples of the same yeast after it has been specially dried (dead cells). Other workers have reported similar findings. The methods used involve determining the urinary and fecal riboflavin excretions after the oral administration of a known amount of pure riboflavin and comparing these with excretions after known amounts of the vitamin in yeast before and after special drying and heating treatments. See (35) also.

Other foods do not yield their total riboflavin content to the body. For instance, it was reported (36) that in normal women the availability of riboflavin in ice cream was 90 per cent, whereas in green peas and almonds only 41 and 39 per cent, respectively, were available.

The vitamin exists within many plant and animal cells, primarily in combination as one of the two coenzyme forms. The retina and urine and milk contain principally the free vitamin. The nucleotides may in part be combined with specific proteins to form enzymes. In serum of 13 normal adults the sum of the free riboflavin and riboflavin phosphate was found to average $0.8\ \mu g$ per cent, and the riboflavin dinucleotide, $2.4\ \mu g$ per cent. The white cells plus platelets contained $252\ \mu g$ per cent of total riboflavin (both derivatives plus the free vitamin) and the red cells only 22 (37). In a later study Bessey and others (16) found somewhat similar values in plasma and cells, although the levels were lower in individuals on restricted vitamin intake.

Determination of riboflavin. Rats and chicks have served as test animals in the biologic methods. In the rat growth method, young animals are fed a special riboflavin-deficient diet for two or three weeks, after which time growth ceases. Then groups of the depleted rats are given supplements of known amounts of the vitamin, and other groups are supplemented with graded quantities of the test material. Comparisons of growth response over four weeks or more allow the calculation of approximate vitamin content of the substance under examination.

Such methods have largely been replaced by shorter and less expensive procedures. The original microbiologic method of Strong and Snell (38) using *L. casei* has been modified many times and is the basis of the official U.S.P. method (39).

This organism requires riboflavin for growth and lactic acid production. The culture medium can be prepared so that riboflavin is the limiting factor. With such a culture medium the organism responds to the addition of graded doses of the vitamin by producing corresponding increments of acid. In the test the acid production in response to supplements of known amounts of pure vitamin is compared to the acid production produced by adding graded amounts of extracts of tissues or other substance under examination. From such data an estimate of the riboflavin content of the unknown can be made.

Marked variations in technique are required for the preparation of different types of materials for assay. This is especially true in the fluorometric methods, since substances other than riboflavin present in plant and animal tissues are known to fluoresce under the conditions of the test. The intensity of fluorescence of a solution of riboflavin (under specific conditions) is proportional to the concentration of the vitamin. Light of wavelengths in the region 400 to 500 mμ induce the fluorescence, and the intensity of this fluorescence can be measured by one of the various fluorophotometers on the market. In practice riboflavin is determined in an extract of the test substance in terms of the intensity of fluorescence before and after destruction of the vitamin. This is compared with the fluorescence of a known sample of riboflavin or with a solution of a substance such as fluorescein that has been standardized against the vitamin.

Yagi described separation procedures for the various forms of riboflavin employing paper chromatography and paper electrophoresis, and a simplified technique for their determination (40). Murphy and others (41) described procedures for liberating riboflavin from natural sources. An enzymatic method for FAD was developed by DeLuca and coworkers (42).

Riboflavin requirement. There is no U.S.P. unit or I.U. for riboflavin. It is becoming common, and logically so, to refer to quantities of all vitamins of known structure on a weight basis. As is the case with most of the vitamins, the human requirement of riboflavin is not known with any certainty. There are too many complicating factors, and the experimental clinical approach is impractical. Various estimates have been made for average requirements of a large group of people, but these figures cannot be translated to represent the required intake of any one individual. Horwitt and coworkers (43) set the need of an adult on 2200 Cal at between 1.1 and 1.6 mg per day. A riboflavin-depleted individual was able to assimilate at least 6 mg of the vitamin at one time. The Food and Nutrition Board, National Research Council, 1958 Revision, gives as the Recommended Allowance, from 0.5 to 2.5 mg of riboflavin daily depending upon body weight. During pregnancy and lactation, the values given are 2.0 and 2.5 mg per day; see Table 18.5 (page 696).

Bro-Rasmussen has published a comprehensive treatment of available work on riboflavin requirements of man and animals (44). See also the 1958 revision of Recommended Dietary Allowances (45).

In animals more exact data concerning requirements are known. The practical value in agriculture of such information is at once obvious. The establishment of required intakes for optimum growth rate, etc., in various species has been of great value in animal industry.

NIACIN—NICOTINIC ACID

The terms "niacin" and "niacinamide" have replaced the older terms "nicotinic acid" and "nicotinic acid amide" (nicotinamide). The latter names were found to be undesirable because of confusion and the unwarranted belief by many that they were physiologically related to nicotine.

Niacin deficiency in humans leads to serious consequences. It is perhaps the most deleterious of the vitamin deficiencies in North America. Although such a deficiency is involved in pellagra (from the Italian *pelle agra*, rough skin), the disease is perhaps never, except experimentally, uncomplicated by other dietary deficiencies.

Early in this century the incidence of pellagra, especially in many of our southern states, grew at an alarming rate. As late as 1941 there were nearly 2000 reported deaths in the United States from this disease. How many more unrecognized pellagra deaths occurred can scarcely be estimated.

Funk had isolated nicotinic acid from rice polishings as early as 1914, but he did not realize that it was a vitamin. He was studying polyneuritis primarily at this time, and nicotinic acid did not cure this disease, although he noticed a beneficial response when it was given with antineuritic substances. The earliest demonstration that pellagra results from nutritional deficiency was given by Goldberger and others (1) in 1915. It is difficult to overemphasize the significance of this report. It was the forerunner of the clinical experimental approach to the study of pellagra control. These workers studied the effect of a marked change in diet at two orphanages, one in Mississippi and one in Georgia, on the incidence of pellagra among the inmates. The change of diet to one with marked increase in "animal and leguminous protein foods" almost completely eliminated a reoccurrence of pellagra in the high percentage of individuals who had demonstrated the typical syndrome the previous year.

Canine blacktongue, a deficiency syndrome in dogs described by Chittendon and Underhill (2) in 1917, has much in common with human pellagra. It is readily produced by maintaining young dogs on the Goldberger diet.

It was observed shortly after this that many of the foods and preparations effective in curing blacktongue were likewise curative for pellagra, and that, whatever the active substances might be, they always occurred together in natural foods.

In 1935 Warburg and Christian (3) showed that nicotinic acid amide (niacinamide) is an essential constituent of a coenzyme concerned in hydrogen transport (oxidation-reduction system). Now two enzyme prosthetic groups containing niacinamide, coenzyme I and coenzyme II are known. Niacinamide was isolated from a liver concentrate by Elvehjem and co-workers (4), and they demonstrated that the amide or the free acid were effective cures for blacktongue in dogs and also that dogs could be maintained in a normal condition on the basal blacktongue-producing diet by the addition to the diet of small amounts of either compound.

Very soon after publication of the initial paper on this subject by Elvehjem and coworkers the first report concerning the use of niacin in pellagrins appeared (5). The success of the treatment heralded a new era in the clinical approach to the treatment of pellagra.

Nicotinic acid had been known to chemists since 1867, and many laboratories had supplies of the product during the many years that thousands and thousands of individuals were suffering from a lack of it. It is an ironical situation. By no logical reasoning, however, can one cast aspersions for the finding not having been made earlier.

Chemistry of niacin. Niacin or nicotinic acid is pyridine 3-carboxylic acid. Niacinamide or nicotinic acid amide is the acid amide. The structures of these and some related compounds referred to in the following pages are given herewith:

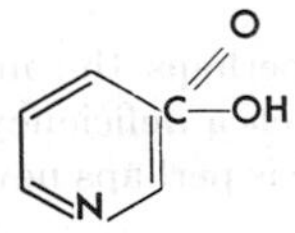

Niacin
(Nicotinic acid)

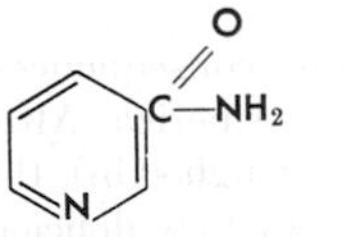

Niacinamide
(Nicotinic acid amide)

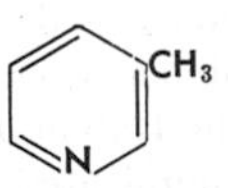

3-Methylpyridine
(β-Picoline)

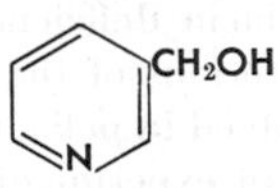

3-Hydroxy-
methylpyridine

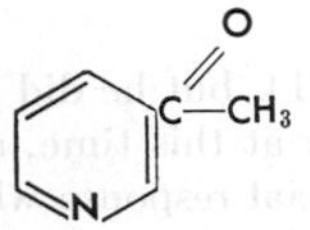

3-Acetylpyridine

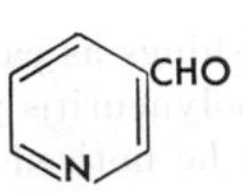

Pyridyl-3-aldehyde

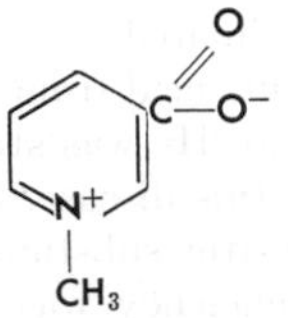

Trigonelline
(N^1-Methylnicotinic acid
betaine)

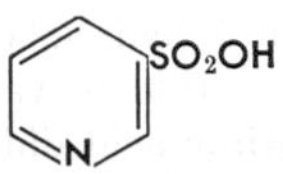

Pyridine-3-sulfonic
acid

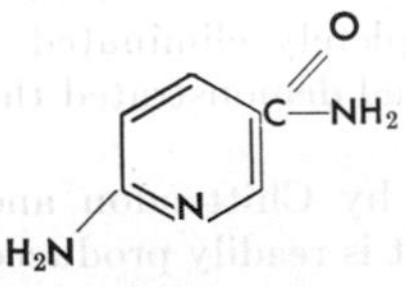

6-Aminonicotinamide

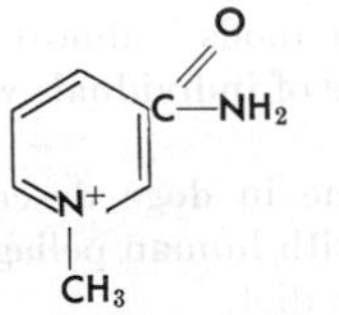

N^1-Methyl-
nicotinamide

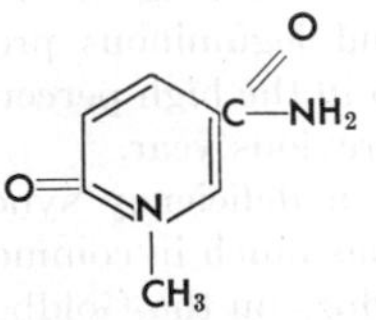

N^1-Methyl-6-
pyridone-3-
carboxamide

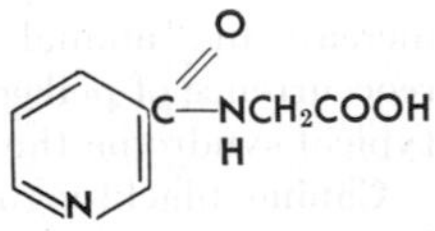

Nicotinuric acid
(Nicotinylglycine)

Niacin and Structurally Related Compounds

Niacin is readily prepared by oxidation of nicotine with strong oxidizing agents, such as permanganate or fuming nitric acid. Many other compounds, such as 3-ethylpyridine, can be oxidized to nicotinic acid. A synthesis from pyridine involves sulfonation of pyridine, distillation of the sodium salt of the 3-pyridine sulfonic acid with KCN to give the nitrile, and saponification of nicotinonitrile to yield nicotinic acid. Bromination of pyridine previous to sulfonation markedly increases the yield (6). The amide is prepared by forcing NH_3 through a solution of the acid at elevated temperature.

Niacin crystallizes as white needles. It is soluble in water to the extent of only about 1 per cent, but quite soluble in alkali (salt formation), alcohol, and glycerin. It forms such salts as the hydrochloride with the basic nitrogen, as well as metallic salts with the carboxyl group. The pure compound melts at about 236° C.

In the human body niacin undergoes various changes. Some of the vitamin is excreted unchanged in the urine, and a substantial portion (depending somewhat on intake) is methylated to N^1-methylnicotinamide. Part of the latter is oxidized to the corresponding 6-pyridone (N^1-methyl-6-pyridone-3-carboxamide). Dogs excrete mainly N^1-methyl nicotinic acid and the betaine.

Using C^{14} carboxy-labeled nicotinamide, Chang and Johnson (7) identified the following metabolites in chickens: β-nicotinylglucuronic acid, nicotinuric acid (nicotinylglycine), both the 2- and the 5-nicotinyl ornithine, 2,5-dinicotinylornithine, and nicotinic acid and the amide. Some decarboxylation of niacin occurs in animals also.

Coenzyme activity. Nicotinamide is the form in which the vitamin is found in its physiologically active combinations. Two well-defined coenzymes contain nicotinamide. These act with a large group of hydrogen-transport enzymes.

Diphosphopyridine nucleotide (DPN) or coenzyme I (CoI) contains nicotinamide—ribose—phosphate—phosphate—ribose—adenine. Preiss and Handler (8) consider the following reactions involved in the biosynthesis of DPN by enzymes in yeast, erythrocytes, or liver.

1. Nicotinic acid + 5-phosphoribosylpyrophosphate $\longrightarrow$ nicotinic acid nucleotide + PP
2. Nicotinic acid nucleotide + ATP $\rightleftharpoons$ desamido—DPN + PP
3. Desamide—DPN + glutamine + ATP + H_2O $\longrightarrow$ DPN + glutamate + AMP + PP

It should be noticed that amide formation ($-NH_2$ from glutamine) occurs following the completion of the dinucleotide structure. No enzyme capable of direct conversion of nicotinic acid to the amide has been found.

The other coenzyme containing niacin is triphosphopyridine nucleotide (TPN), also called "coenzyme II" (CoII). This is composed of nicotinamide—ribose—phosphate—phosphate—ribose-2'-phosphate—adenine. It differs from DPN only in the presence of a third phosphate group on carbon 2' of the ribose attached to adenine. It is synthesized from DPN and ATP. The DPN kinase enzyme mediating the reaction was isolated from pigeon liver by Wang and others (9):

$$DPN + ATP \xrightarrow{Mg^{++}} TPN + ADP$$

To avoid unnecessary repetition, the structures of these coenzymes are not given here. They can be found under coenzymes in Chapter 11 and in Chapter 21, where a discussion of their actions can also be found.

Niacin deficiency. In human pellagra the deficiency is generally not one of niacin alone. The response of pellagrins to niacin treatment is a partial one. The cheilosis, if present, may not be altered, and neurologic symptoms may remain. The term "pellagra" can scarcely be thought of as indicating a specific set of symptoms. In other words, the symptoms in one individual case may be very different from those of another, and the response to various members of the B complex may show little resemblance in the two cases. Variations in the pellagrous syndrome seen in different parts of the world are well known. Other B vitamins and general inanition are certainly involved.

The symptoms generally associated with the condition are: (a) dermatitis, accompanied by pigmentation (exaggerated by sunlight), and erythema of the tongue, which often becomes smooth and atrophic; (b) nervous lesions, especially in late stages, which involve varying regions of the cerebrum and spinal cord fibers (myelin degeneration); (c) gastrointestinal lesions characterized by cyst formation in the colon and atrophy in the later stages; and (d) mottled liver with fatty degeneration.

The nervous symptoms especially are thought to arise from a deficiency other than that of niacin. They are similar, except in distribution, to the findings in thiamine deficiency.

Studies of various tongue lesions in man have led to the conclusion that other members of the B complex are often deficient and that niacin frequently has little or no beneficial effect (10).

Goldsmith and others (11), however, produced clinical pellagra symptoms in humans and reported that all the lesions responded to nicotinamide or to tryptophan.

Horwitt and others (12) studied a group of men on low niacin and tryptophan intake over long periods of time. Other men received the same diet with supplements of the vitamin and tryptophan. Physical changes other than those attributed to the accompanying riboflavin deficiency were not found in either group. No cutaneous lesions such as found in pellagra were noted. It was found from the studies on urinary excretion of niacin metabolites that the amount of N^1-methylnicotinamide in the urine correlated best with the niacin and tryptophan content of the diet.

The "flushing syndrome" is well known in human beings taking nicotinic acid either by mouth or parenterally. The amide does not produce these symptoms. It is the latter compound that is found in natural sources of the vitamin. Some individuals flush with only a few milligrams of niacin, while others are able to take 100 mg without untoward effects. Many people flush on the intravenous administration of 5 or 10 mg of niacin.

In animals experimental niacin deficiency is readily produced. Blacktongue in the dog has been studied intensively, and this syndrome has a close resemblance to that seen in humans, especially with regard to the oral cavity.

Special dietary precautions are required in rats, for example, to show disorders which respond to niacin administration. Diets high in corn or otherwise low in tryptophan predispose to this condition. Corn is low in tryptophan, and it has been suggested that this amino acid is required in the gastrointestinal tract for bacterial synthesis of niacin—an important source of the vitamin in this species. The addition of tryptophan-containing protein, or the amino acid, to the diet of rats cures or prevents the symptoms. It is now established that in some species tryptophan can substitute in the diet for niacin. The conversion of the amino acid to the vitamin has been studied in great detail. A number of compounds arising in the body from tryptophan metabolism have been isolated. Several of these have niacin activity in rats and support growth in neurospora.

At the present time the following scheme best accounts for the experimental findings in studies of the conversion of tryptophan to nicotinic acid in the animal body (13):

Tryptophan $\longrightarrow$ kynurenine $\longrightarrow$ 3-hydroxykynurenine $\longrightarrow$ 3-hydroxyanthranilic acid $\longrightarrow$ 1-amino-4-formyl-1,3-butadiene-1,2-dicarboxylic acid $\longrightarrow$ quinolinic acid $\longrightarrow$ nicotinic acid.

The structures of these compounds can be found under tryptophan metabolism in Chapter 25.

In the rat the site of this transformation was thought to be the gastrointestinal tract. However, it is obvious now that other tissues participate in catalyzing this reaction. Henderson and Hanks (14) removed the gastrointestinal tracts of rats from the duodenum to the anus and then gave them sterile mixtures of amino acids, carbohydrate, salts, etc., by subcutaneous injection. Some of the animals (and unoperated controls) were given tryptophan in the food mixture. Analyses demonstrated the presence of increased amounts of N^1-methylnicotinamide, "free," and total niacin in the urine of both control and enterectomized rats given the amino acid. The N-methyl derivative is known to be formed from niacin in the body. Handley and Bond (15) offered a clear-cut demonstration of this by feeding rats niacin containing C^{13} in the carboxyl group. Results of examination of the isolated and purified N^1-methylnicotinamide from the urine indicated that over 95 per cent of this compound had arisen from the administered niacin. These results establish the activity of body tissues other than the gastrointestinal tract in the conversion of this amino acid to the vitamin.

Serum cholesterol is lowered in humans after the ingestion of large doses of nicotinic acid; the amide is without effect. In young adults the basal metabolism is increased also (16). The mechanism by which blood cholesterol is lowered has not been resolved. In rats the blood levels of cholesterol are also decreased by massive intakes (up to 4 per cent of the diet). This effect was attributed to the great demand for methyl groups used in nicotinic acid detoxication, with a resulting decreased cholesterol synthesis (17).

Goldsmith (18) has reviewed various relationships of niacin in human and animal nutrition. She pointed out that adults are able to convert about 3 per cent of administered tryptophan to niacin compounds. The rat is able to convert to the extent of 10 to 20 per cent, while cats apparently are unable to bring about the transformation (19).

Niacin analogues. Ethyl nicotinate, nicotinic acid N-methylamide, β-picoline (3-methyl pyridine), 3-hydroxymethylpyridine, and 3-acetylpyridine have vitamin activity. The evidence indicates that these compounds are active on the basis of their conversion into nicotinic acid (20). Pyridyl-3-aldehyde added to the diet was effective in niacin-deficient ducks, but pyridyl-3-carbinol and β-picoline were inactive when fed with the diet. They were active given per os, and all three were active upon injection (21).

Niacin antagonists. A number of compounds structurally related to niacin act as antagonists in animals and/or in microorganisms. Pyridine-3-sulfonic acid and 3-acetylpyridine are examples. It is probable that such antagonists are used in the synthesis of DPN or TPN analogs and that these combinations are not physiologically active. Thus the organism is deprived of its normal complement of these coenzymes. In most cases additional niacin overcomes the antagonism. The compound 6-aminonicotinamide produces niacin deficiency symptoms in rats at a level of 15 to 30 mg per kg of diet. The symptoms are prevented by the further addition of 150 to 300 mg of niacinamide per kg of ration. The 6-amino analog is quite active against some tumors in rats, and this tumor inhibition is reversed by niacinamide (22).

Occurrence of niacin. In natural sources the vitamin occurs as the amide, either free or combined as one of the two coenzymes. The various forms are readily absorbed from the gastrointestinal tract. It is not established whether the coenzymes must be hydrolyzed before absorption.

The vitamin is rather widely distributed in both plant and animal tissues. Certain animal organs, including liver, kidney, and heart, as well as lean meat and some fish flesh are outstanding sources. Yeast, peanuts, wheat germ, and dried legumes are in the same category. Fresh legumes and a few green vegetables are good sources, whereas milk, eggs, and most fruits are generally classed as poor sources. The niacin content of 160 Indian foodstuffs, many of which are common constituents of the American diet, has been reported (23). According to the data of this report, dried yeast may contain from 20 to 62, rice polishings around 28, wheat germ 7, sheep liver 15, and pork muscle 2.8, all in milligrams per cent. Milk and eggs contain only 0.1 mg per cent. Elvehjem and coworkers (24) also gave an extensive list of foods and their niacin content. Niacin, like other B vitamins, resides in wheat primarily in the bran and middling fraction. These workers list the niacin content of patent flour 0.80, fancy first clear flour 1.68, second clear flour 5.55, clean shorts 5.44, and wheat feed and screenings 19.2 mg per cent.

Niacin requirement. It should be noted that in the table of recommended dietary allowances (Table 18.5, page 696), the niacin allowance is stated in milligram equivalents. It has been established that in man about 60 mg of food tryptophan are equivalent to 1 mg niacin (due to conversion), so that the required niacin intake varies with the tryptophan content of the diet (12). A diet providing 60 g of mixed protein contains around 600 mg of tryptophan or 10 niacin equivalents from the amino acid. On the basis of other studies and allowing for a liberal safety factor, the recommended daily allowance (1958 revision) has been set at 17 mg niacin equivalents for a 58-kg adult and up to 25 for boys 16 to 19 years old (63 kg).

In a controlled study in four women the mean urinary excretion of N^1-methylnicotinamide and its 6-pyrone were 5.8 and 7.3 mgs per day, respectively (25). With a diet providing 8.7 mg nicotinamide and 770 mg of tryptophan from 60 g of protein daily, these excretions indicate the adequacy of the 21 niacin equivalents ingested.

Exact information on requirements is not available; there are too many complicating factors, such as intestinal synthesis of niacin and the altered requirements resulting from the presence of varying amounts of other nutrients in the diet.

Determination of niacin and related compounds. Dogs and chickens have been used for the biologic assay of the vitamin. In these procedures total vitamin activity is determined. Microbiologic methods are far more practical from the standpoint of time and expense. The present U.S.P. procedure employs *Lactobacillus arabinosus* as the test organism. The culture medium contains all essentials for growth except niacin-active compounds. By graded addition of test material, the amounts added can be estimated by determining acid production and comparing this to acid produced upon addition of niacin (26).

Chemical methods are principally refinements of the original cyanogen bromide procedure adapted to niacin. After extraction of niacin-active substances, hydrolysis converts to niacin, which is reacted with CNBr and a reducing agent to yield a color. The color density is compared to that produced from a known amount of niacin (27).

Methods for a number of niacin metabolites can be found in the paper by Chang *et al.* (7).

A sensitive spectrophotometric method for DPN and TPN in the oxidized and reduced forms was described by Glock and McLean (28).

PANTOTHENIC ACID

In 1933 Williams and coworkers (1) demonstrated the widespread distribution of a substance that acted as a growth factor for a yeast and other microorganisms. At that time these workers applied the name "pantothenic acid" (Greek, from everywhere) to the active principle. Later Williams' group (2) obtained 3 g of a crude pantothenic acid concentrate (40 per cent pure) from 250 kg of liver. Further purification yielded an amorphous product with over 11,000 times the activity (yeast growth) of a standard rice bran extract. The presence of the vitamin was detectable in concentration of 5 parts in 10 billion parts of culture medium.

Other investigators were studying concentrates of plant and animal tissues which showed various physiologic activity. After some years the so-called chick antidermatitis factor from liver, also called the "filtrate factor," was shown to be identical with Williams' pantothenic acid by Woolley, Waisman, and Elvehjem (3) and also by Jukes (4). The former investigators showed that the antidermatitis factor, like pantothenic acid, is alkali and heat labile and is an hydroxy acid derivative of β alanine. They were able to split β-alanine from the active compound and reactivate by coupling the remaining part of the molecule with synthetic β-alanine.

In 1940 pantothenic acid was crystallized in pure form, its structure determined, and its synthesis accomplished by investigators of the Merck Laboratories (5).

Chemistry of pantothenic acid. Chemically, pantothenic acid is α,-γ-dihydroxy-β,β-dimethylbutyryl-β'-alanide. The molecule is perhaps more easily comprehended if it is thought of as a dihydroxydimethylbutyric acid in peptide bond formation with β-alanine. The β' indicates that the amino group is on the β carbon atom rather than on the α carbon, as found in ordinary alanine.

Many syntheses have been developed for this molecule. The direct condensation of β-alanine with the lactone of the substituted butyric acid gives excellent yields and the desired product is obtained directly (6).

Kagan and coworkers (7) reported the synthesis of calcium pantothenate in high yield and in a high state of purity:

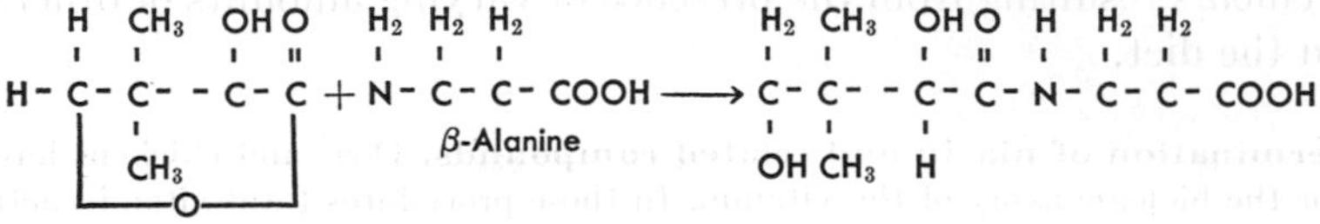

$$
\begin{array}{c}
\text{H CH}_3\ \text{OH O}\quad \text{H}_2\ \text{H}_2\ \text{H}_2 \\
\text{H}-\text{C}-\text{C}-\ -\text{C}-\text{C}\ +\text{N}-\text{C}-\text{C}-\text{COOH} \\
\text{CH}_3 \\
\text{O} \\
\text{Lactone}
\end{array}
\qquad \xrightarrow{\beta\text{-Alanine}} \qquad
\begin{array}{c}
\text{H}_2\ \text{CH}_3\ \text{OH O}\ \text{H}\ \text{H}_2\ \text{H}_2 \\
\text{C}-\text{C}-\ -\ \text{C}-\text{C}-\text{N}-\text{C}-\text{C}-\text{COOH} \\
\text{OH CH}_3\ \ \text{H} \\
\text{Pantothenic acid}
\end{array}
$$

$(CH_2OHC(CH_3)_2CHOHCONHCH_2CH_2CONHCH_2CH_2S)_2$
Pantethine

$CH_3CHOHC(CH_3)_2CHOHCONHCH_2CH_2COOH$
ω-Methylpantothenic acid, N-(α,γ-dihydroxy-β, β-dimethylvaleryl)-β-alanine

$(CH_2OHC(CH_3)_2CHOHCONHCH_2CH_2S)_2$
Bis (β-pantoylaminoethyl) disulfide
Pantothenic acid and related structures

The free acid is a viscous yellow oil, soluble in water and ethyl acetate, but insoluble in $CHCl_3$. It is acid, alkali, and heat-labile. It is readily available as either the sodium or calcium salt. The latter salt is crystalline material fairly soluble in water (7 g per 100 ml) and insoluble in alcohol. It is quite stable, although autoclaving destroys the activity. $[\alpha]_D^{26}$ for the free acid is $+37.5°$ and for the calcium salt, $+24.3°$.

Coenzyme activity. Pantothenic acid is a part of coenzyme A of Lipmann (8), characterized in 1951 by Lynen and coworkers (9). The CoA molecule is a nucleotide of the following composition: adenine—phosphorylated ribose(C-3)—phosphate—phosphate—pantothenic acid—β-mercaptoethylamine.

The structure can be found under coenzymes in Chapter 11. The sulfhydryl group (—SH) is the active part of the molecule; it is readily acylated to yield such molecules as acetyl CoA, succinyl CoA, citryl CoA, etc. The coenzyme is involved in acetylation reactions, such as the detoxication of primary amines (sulfanilamide ⟶ N⁴-acetylsulfanilamide), and in the production of acetyl choline, essential to the transmission of nerve impulses. It is required in the synthesis of acetoacetate and citrate, components of the tricarboxylic acid cycle. These and many other reactions of CoA are discussed in detail in Chapter 21.

The biosynthesis of CoA is reviewed by Novelli (10). Brain tissue homogenates synthesize the coenzyme from pantothenate, ATP, and cysteine. Homogenates of liver, kidney, and muscle show no net synthesis under the conditions used, presumably due to rapid enzymatic destruction. The synthetic pathway in bacteria proposed by Novelli (11) has been confirmed by the use of labeled compounds (12).

The over-all synthesis of CoA in mammalian tissues is pictured as follows (13):

Pantothenate + cysteine + ATP ⟶ N-pantothenylcysteine
N-Pantothenylcysteine ⟶ pantetheine + CO₂
Pantetheine + ATP ⟶ 4'-phosphopantetheine + ADP
4'-Phosphopantetheine + ATP ⟶ dephospho CoA + PP
Dephospho CoA + ATP ⟶ CoA + ADP

The dephospho CoA lacks a phosphate group on carbon 3 of the ribose residue.

Pantetheine is the part of the coenzyme A molecule composed of pantothenic acid in combination with β-mercaptoethylamine. This structure is also called "*Lactobacillus bulgaricus* factor" (LBF) because of its relation to growth of this organism. Pantethine is the disulfide compound and bears the same relation to pantetheine that cystine does to cysteine. The structure and synthesis were reported in 1950 (14).

LBF is a growth factor for various microorganisms and can replace pantothenic acid in the diet of various animals. It is widely distributed in nature and constitutes a second bound form of the vitamin.

Pantothenic acid deficiency. All species of animals investigated require pantothenic acid. The fox, mouse, monkey, rat, pig, dog, chick, and other species have been studied in this respect. Microorganisms also need the vitamin, although some are able to synthesize it and thus do not need an external supply.

In the rat certain fairly well-defined symptoms of deficiency are observed. Retarded growth in young animals is seen. Reproduction is seriously affected. It was demonstrated that institution of a pantothenic acid deficiency as late as the day of mating resulted in failure of implantation, resorption, or defective litters (15). Achromotrichia, or graying of hair, in black rats (and foxes) is related to but not due solely to a pantothenic acid deficiency. Other deficiencies, perhaps including inositol, are involved. The condition has not been produced in rats after adrenalectomy. Adrenal cortical necrosis results from continued deprivation of the vitamin. Rats suffering such a pathologic condition exhibit serious abnormalities in salt and water metabolism.

The cholesterol content of the adrenals is markedly lowered (16), indicating decreased ability on the part of the rat to synthesize this compound under the stress of pantothenic acid deficiency. Cholesterol is the likely precursor of adrenal cortical hormones, and coenzyme A is known to participate in the utilization of acetate in cholesterol formation. Adrenal cortical secretion is decreased in pantothenic acid deficiency (17), and Langwell and co-workers (18) demonstrated a reduced production of corticosterone in rat adrenals during deficiency.

The porphyrin-caked or "bloody" whiskers in rats is another deficiency symptom, although a similar condition can be produced by restricting the water intake. There seems to be an important interrelation of the adrenals, pantothenic acid, and water and porphyrin metabolism.

In chickens growth and appetite are retarded on a pantothenic acid-deficient diet. Also, a dermatitis and a fatty liver condition develop. Egg hatchability is greatly reduced even before the hens demonstrate any visible symptoms (19).

In dogs a pantothenic acid deficiency causes a loss of conditional reflex performance. Gantt and coworkers (20) reported that this loss appears within four to ten days prior to other neurologic symptoms, and without observable behavior changes. Upon addition of the vitamin to the diet, the conditioned reflex function returns to normal. In rats a pantothenic acid deficiency lessened the ability to form conditional reflexes. The authors state that pyridoxine is essential not only for physical health but apparently for normal conditional reflex performance which is the basis of mental health.

A reduction of 30 to 40 per cent in coenzyme A content was found in tissues of pantothenic acid-deficient rats. The utilization of pyruvate by liver tissue was also decreased. In deficient ducks the injection of pantothenate markedly increased the coenzyme A content of liver and the ability of liver slices to utilize pyruvate (21). Deficient rats also show a decreased ability to acetylate administered p-aminobenzoic acid (22).

However, it was reported that in such animals the ability to acetylate a test dose of an aromatic amine was restored in as short a time as three hours after injection of pantothenate (23).

Pantothenyl alcohol (alcohol analog) is growth promoting and prevents achromotrichia in rats. In man it is just as efficient as the vitamin in increasing pantothenic acid excretion in urine after a test dose (24). These facts indicate that the alcohol is converted to the acid (vitamin) in the body. The alcohol, however, does not support growth of *Lactobacillus arabinosus*, and so it seems that this organism cannot carry out the conversion. Deficient rats respond to pantetheine, pantethine, pantothenylcysteine, and pantothenylcystine (25).

Novelli (26) has summarized in detail the characteristic deficiency symptoms in various animal species, and more recently Zucker (27) has reviewed the effects of deficiency on the integrity of the rat intestine.

Pantothenic acid deficiency in man is known only in the cases in which it has been produced experimentally. This undoubtedly results from the wide distribution of the vitamin in plant and animal foods, and to the fact that some microorganisms, such as *E. coli*, synthesize quantities of the vitamin and excrete the excess above their needs. In man this organism is normally found in the gastrointestinal tract. This is an important contributing factor in the absence of human pantothenic acid deficiency.

The extravagant claims for pantothenic acid as an anti-gray hair factor for humans have been adequately disproved in carefully controlled experiments (28).

Hodges and others (29) restricted the pantothenic acid intake of two young men. Two others consumed the same deficient diet plus 1000 mgs daily of the antagonist, ω-methylpantothenic acid. A third group of two men received the diet plus 20 mgs of pantothenic acid daily. After a few weeks the "antagonist" group developed serious personality changes, including irritability and restlessness. Alternate periods of somnolence and insomnia and excessive fatigue after mild exercise were experienced. A little later the men in the "deficient" group noted similar complaints, and soon the symptoms were indistinguishable in the two groups. They developed a staggering gait and gastrointestinal symptoms became common.

Biochemical changes reflected by laboratory tests were not prominent.

The loss of eosinopenic response to adrenocorticotropic hormone (ACTH) was the most consistent.

The men in the "control" group showed none of the above symptoms.

Massive doses of pantothenic acid to the four men who were deficient corrected the faulty eosinopenic response and alleviated most of the clinical symptoms.

Pantothenic acid antagonists. Pantoyltaurine has been studied extensively as an antimetabolite of pantothenic acid. Inclusion of this compound in the diet of animals leads to deficiency symptoms. Twenty-five derivatives of this compound were prepared and studied for inhibitory activity (30). Another antagonist that has been studied in various species is ω-methylpantothenic acid. This compound interferes with the formation of CoA and produces typical deficiency symptoms in animals. This compound was used to produce human pantothenic acid deficiency discussed above. Antagonists of pantothenic acid probably all act by inhibiting normal functions of CoA. It is reasonable to suppose that of the many functions of this coenzyme, some would be affected to a greater extent than others, due to different degrees of coenzyme-apoenzyme and enzyme-substrate affinity, etc. Dietrich and Shapiro (31) showed that ω-methylpantathine markedly inhibited sulfanilamide acetylation at concentrations which were ineffective against citrate formation in pigeon liver homogenates. On the other hand, bis(β-pantoylaminoethyl) disulfide was found to inhibit citrate formation at concentrations which did not affect sulfanilamide acetylation.

The action of 6-mercaptopurine in blocking nuclear mitosis in animals can be reversed by administration of pantothenic acid or coenzyme A.

Occurrence of pantothenic acid. The distribution of this vitamin is so widespread in nature that little comment is required. It is important, however, to understand that in large degree pantothenic acid is found in natural products in bound forms. Yeast, liver, and eggs are outstanding sources. Some meats, skim milk, and sweet potatoes contain moderate amounts of the vitamin, while most other vegetables and fruits have considerably less.

Zook and associates (32) reported the pantothenic acid content of a large number of foods using newer methods which release bound forms of the vitamin.

Requirements of pantothenic acid. Chicks require a dietary source of pantothenic acid, although laying hens get along and continue to lay eggs on diets containing very little of the vitamin. The eggs produced under these conditions are poor in hatchability and in fact reach a level of zero in this respect. A careful study of the pantothenic acid requirement for laying hens (33) indicates that about 650 μg per 100 g of ration is sufficient for the production of eggs of high hatchability. It is interesting that for considerable periods of observation only about 150 μg per 100 g of ration is sufficient for maintenance of the adult chicken. The requirements for various other species are more or less established.

The human requirement is largely unknown. Estimates of 10 to 15 mg per day seem to be met easily even with diets classed below optimum. The estimates lack significance because of the many unknown factors, such as the degree of release of the bound vitamin in the intestinal tract and the amount of intestinal bacterial synthesis of the vitamin as well as the availability of this source.

Assay of pantothenic acid. The growth rate of chicks has been used to determine the pantothenic acid content of various products (34). It is a time-consuming procedure, and although still in use, it has largely been replaced by microbiologic methods, especially since the development of more nearly optimal methods for releasing the bound vitamin from its firm combination (such as in coenzyme A) in plant and animal materials. Certain organisms show a growth response (vitamin effect) to the β-alanine part of the molecule and others to the pantoic acid moiety. Such organisms synthesize pantothenic acid if supplied with a part of the molecule.

An improved technique using *L. casei* was described by Clarke (35). A method for estimating CoA in tissues, involving enzymatic liberation of pantetheine and microbiologic assay of this substance and free pantothenic acid, was reported by Wolff and others (36).

Brown (37) has devised methods for the estimation of pantothenic acid, phosphopantothenic acid, pantetheine, phosphopantotheine, and coenzyme A in a single sample. The major pantothenic acid-containing compound found in animal tissues and in microorganisms was CoA, although phosphopantetheine amounted to from 10 to 25 per cent that of CoA in some tissues and was actually higher in rat kidney.

PYRIDOXINE, PYRIDOXAL, PYRIDOXAMINE, VITAMIN B₆

The complex nature of the B vitamins was further unraveled through the discovery of pyridoxine. Other names applied to the principle included "rat acrodynia factor," "rat antidermatitis factor," and "vitamin H." The term "adermin" was used some in the European literature.

György (1) showed that an eluate of a charcoal adsorbate of yeast extract was able to cure a type of dermatitis in rats that developed on synthetic rations containing B_1 (thiamine) and B_2 (lactoflavin). This condition differed from that found in the absence of the pellagra preventive factor (then thought to be B_2) and was characterized by denuding around the paws, nose, and mouth. Thus at least two antidermatitis factors for the rat became known and the dual nature of so-called B_2 preparations was established.

Various groups of workers isolated the compound from natural sources in 1938. Keresztesy and Stevens (2), for instance, isolated the pure substance from rice polishings and studied certain properties of the material. Its structure was elucidated by Stiller and others (3) and by Harris and coworkers (4) in this country. Details of one method of synthesis were described by Harris and Folkers in 1939 (5). The synthesis was also accomplished at about the same time by a group of German workers headed by Kuhn. The name "pyridoxine" was given to the compound at this time.

There are three compounds, interconvertible in the animal body, which possess vitamin B_6 activity. In general, "pyridoxine" is a general term indicating vitamin B_6 active material. Specifically this is not correct, since pyridoxine is a definite compound, as are pyridoxal and pyridoxamine, and all three have B_6 activity. The phosphorylated compounds likewise have vitamin activity in animals.

Chemistry of pyridoxine. Pyridoxine is a basic substance. The colorless crystals melt at 160° C. The compound is soluble in alcohol and water, but only slightly soluble in ether or chloroform. The vitamin is generally used as the hydrochloride salt which melts at 206° to 208° C with some decomposition. This salt is highly soluble in water (pH about 3), less soluble in alcohol, and insoluble in ether. The vitamin shows marked absorption in the ultraviolet range. Such studies were of value in determining the structure of the molecule (3).

The total synthesis is complicated and involves many steps (5). Syntheses from somewhat related and more readily available pyridine derivatives are numerous (6).

The structures of pyridoxine and some related compounds are shown herewith:

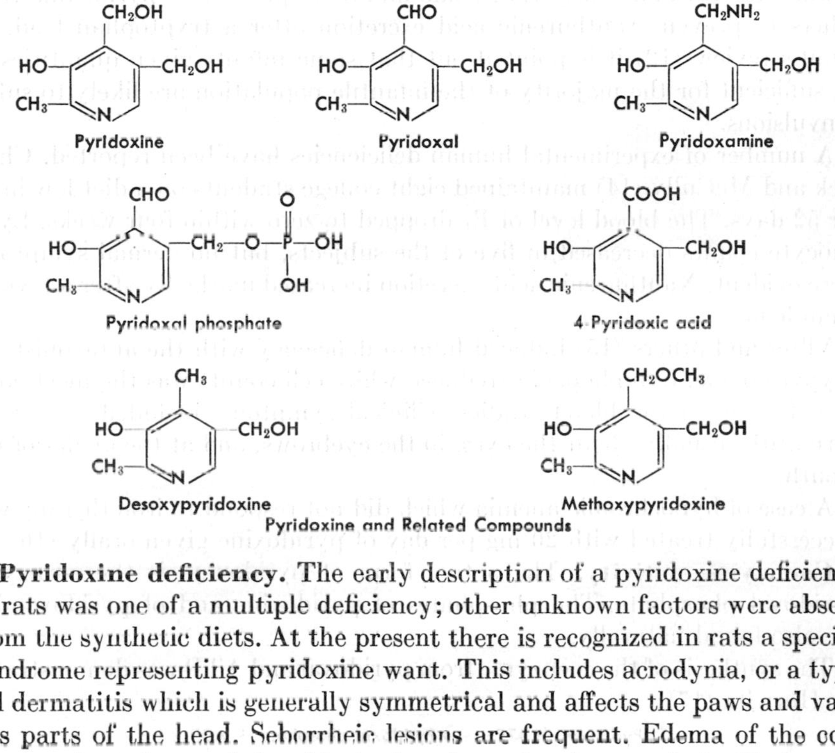

Pyridoxine   Pyridoxal   Pyridoxamine

Pyridoxal phosphate   4-Pyridoxic acid

Desoxypyridoxine   Methoxypyridoxine

Pyridoxine and Related Compounds

Pyridoxine deficiency. The early description of a pyridoxine deficiency in rats was one of a multiple deficiency; other unknown factors were absent from the synthetic diets. At the present there is recognized in rats a specific syndrome representing pyridoxine want. This includes acrodynia, or a typical dermatitis which is generally symmetrical and affects the paws and various parts of the head. Seborrheic lesions are frequent. Edema of the connective tissue layer of the skin is thought to be characteristic (7). Loss of muscle tonus was observed after long-continued deprivation in rats (8), and convulsive seizures have been observed (9). Growth is subnormal on pyridoxine-deficient diets.

All animal species studied show deficiency symptoms, but these vary considerably from one type of animal to another. Mice, for instance, develop fatty livers on a B_6 deficiency (10), while in pigs a microcytic, hypochromic anemia is a characteristic part of the syndrome (11).

Human B_6 deficiency may be more prevalent than was generally recognized. Hunt (12) reviewed a number of cases of apparent B_6 deficiency. In 1951 an outbreak of deficiency in infants was observed in various parts of the country (13). The cardinal symptom in these infants was convulsions, although only a small per cent of the infants developed the deficiency to such an extent. It was soon determined that the deficiency resulted from the use of a commercial liquid, infant-feeding mixture, which during processing had had the B_6 content reduced to very low levels. A change in diet or administration of pyridoxine promptly relieved the symptoms.

In normal tryptophan metabolism very small amounts of xanthurenic acid are formed and excreted in the urine. In B_6 deficiency larger amounts are excreted. The determination of urinary xanthurenic acid after administering tryptophan to a human or animal (load test) gives an indication of the nutritional status with respect to vitamin B_6. It has been found by Bessey and coworkers (13) and others that some infants require more pyridoxine than others to prevent xanthurenic acid excretion after a tryptophan load. In Hunt's review (12) it is pointed out that some infants given quantities of B_6 sufficient for the majority of the infantile population are likely to suffer convulsions.

A number of experimental human deficiencies have been reported. Cheslock and McCully (14) maintained eight college students on a diet low in B_6 for 52 days. The blood level of B_6 dropped to zero within four weeks. Lymphocyte counts decreased in five of the subjects, but no dermal symptoms were evident. Xanthurenic acid excretion increased markedly after a tryptophan load.

Vilter and others (15) induced human deficiency with the antagonist deoxypyridoxine. Lymphopenia (reduced white cell count) was the most common finding in the blood studies. Clinical symptoms included seborrheic dermatitis, usually about the eyes, in the eyebrows, and at the angles of the mouth.

A case of hypochromic anemia which did not respond to iron therapy was successfully treated with 20 mg per day of pyridoxine given orally (16).

Coenzyme activity. The active form of pyridoxine is the coenzyme pyridoxal phosphate. The phosphates of pyridoxine and of pyridoxamine are also found naturally.

The synthesis of the coenzyme from pyridoxal and ATP was demonstrated by Hurwitz (17):

$$\text{Pyridoxal} + \text{ATP} \longrightarrow \text{Pyridoxal phosphate} + \text{ADP}$$

The ever increasing number of molecular interconversions mediated by pyridoxal phosphate-dependent enzymes attests to the significant metabolic role of this vitamin.

The coenzyme is required in the decarboxylation of amino acids. In this function it is referred to as "codecarboxylase" to distinguish it from cocarboxylase which is thiamine pyrophosphate, involved in α-keto acid decarboxylations. Some of the amino acid decarboxylases have been studied in detail. Histidine decarboxylase, for example, produces histamine and CO_2 from histidine. The general reaction is:

$$\text{RCHNH}_2\text{COOH} \longrightarrow \text{RCH}_2\text{NH}_2 + \text{CO}_2$$

A number of amino acid derivatives not found in proteins are also decarboxylated by enzymes requiring pyridoxal phosphate. An example of this is the demonstration by Weissbach and coworkers (18) of the functional role of the coenzyme in the decarboxylation of 5-hydroxytryptophan with the production of 5-hydroxytryptamine (serotonin) plus CO_2.

Another step in tryptophan metabolism involves the pyridoxal phosphate-dependent enzyme kinureninase, which catalyzes the conversion of kynurenine to anthranilic acid.

The significance of these reactions is discussed under tryptophan metabolism in Chapter 25 on protein metabolism. Cysteinesulfinic acid decarboxylase is another example of a decarboxylase using a nonprotein amino acid as substrate. In general the amino acid decarboxylases are highly specific and can be used in the determination of various amino acids by following CO_2 production in purified systems.

The wide scope of amino acid transamination reactions was established by Cammarata and Cohen (19), who studied 22 transaminase reactions in animal tissues and suggested that each involved a distinct enzyme with pyridoxal phosphate as coenzyme. Typical of these enzymes is glutamic-oxalacetic transaminase (glutamic-aspartic transaminase) which mediates the reaction:

$$\text{Glutamate} + \text{Oxalacetate} \rightleftharpoons \alpha \text{ Ketoglutarate} + \text{Aspartate}$$

Diamine oxidase brings about oxidative deamination of certain diamines, such as cadaverine. Pig kidney histaminase and diamine oxidase appear to be identical, with pyridoxal phosphate as coenzyme in both cases (20).

Cysteine desulfhydrase is another pyridoxal phosphate enzyme. It converts cysteine to pyruvate and $H_2S + NH_3$. A number of dehydrases found in animal tissues require pyridoxal phosphate and remove water from hydroxy amino acids. Examples are serine dehydrase (yields pyruvate and $NH_3 + H_2O$) and threonine dehydrase (yields α-ketobutyric acid and $NH_3 + H_2O$).

The coenzyme is required, among other cofactors, in the synthesis of δ-amino levulinic acid, a requisite intermediate in porphyrin synthesis (21).

An interesting role of the coenzyme is found in bacterial enzymes responsible for racemization of certain amino acids. For instance, S. faecalis requires D-alanine for cell wall construction. The organism can convert L-alanine to the D-form, providing pyridoxal phosphate is supplied, since this is the coenzyme of alanine racemase (22).

The presence of 4 mols of pyridoxal phosphate per mol of phosphorylase-a and 2 mols per mol of phosphorylase-b was reported by Cori and Illingsworth (23). The significance of the presence of the coenzyme in this system is not clear.

From the foregoing it is clear that the pyridoxine-active compounds are associated with most of the nonoxidative metabolic changes of amino acids, and with some pathways not involving amino acids. Further details and proposed mechanisms of action of pyridoxal phosphate enzymes can be found in Chapter 25.

Pyridoxine and pyridoxamine can be converted in the body to pyridoxal.

An enzyme system in rat liver catalyzes the oxidation of pyridoxamine or its phosphate to pyridoxal or the phosphate (24).

Biochemical deficiency symptoms in man and animals can in some cases be related to functional roles of the coenzyme form of the vitamin. For instance, severe B_6 deficiency in rats leads to hypochromic anemia with increased erythrocyte count, and decreased hemoglobin, mean cell volume, and mean cell hemoglobin (25). Glycine reacts with succinyl CoA to form α-amino-β-ketoadipic acid, and this is decarboxylated to yield δ-aminolevulinic acid. Since it has been demonstrated that pyridoxal phosphate is required in the synthesis of δ-aminolevulinic acid (in a decarboxylase system), and, further, since this molecule is utilized in the synthesis of protoporphyrin, from which heme is derived, we see the rationale of decreased hemoglobin synthesis in pyridoxine deficiency.

Another example involves the decreased production of taurocholic acid in the bile of B_6 deficient rats. Doisy and coworkers demonstrated that dietary correction brought about increased taurocholic acid production (26). Pyridoxal phosphate is required in the enzyme system catalyzing the decarboxylation of cysteinesulfinic acid which is a source of taurine. The latter compound reacts with cholic acid to form the bile salt, taurocholic acid.

A decreased activity of specific transaminase enzymes in a B_6 deficiency would be expected. This has been demonstrated in various species. Glutamic-aspartic transaminase was decreased in deficient rats (27).

In a deficiency state the decreased transaminase activity of tissues shunts greater amounts of amino acids into other metabolic pathways, such as deamination, accounting for the increased urea production under these conditions.

Vitamin B_6 antagonists. Desoxypyridoxine (2,4-dimethyl-3-hydroxy-5-hydroxymethylpyridine) has a potent B_6 antagonistic action. Its use in animal diets is of value in accentuating B_6 deficiency symptoms and decreasing the time required to develop them. The compound is a strong tyrosine decarboxylase inhibitor, for example, but only in the phosphorylated form (28). Methoxypyridoxine is another antagonist that has been studied in detail. Toxopyrimidine (2-methyl-4-amino-5-hydroxymethyl pyrimidine) administration lowers the B_6 levels of rat tissues and produces liver damage (29). Glutamic acid decarboxylase is inhibited by toxopyrimidine, and the product of the reaction of this enzyme, γ-aminobutyric acid, is lowered in brain tissue of rats just prior to convulsions. Injection of β-hydroxy-γ-aminobutyric acid, but not of γ-aminobutyric acid, suppressed the convulsions resulting from toxopyrimidine (30).

The compound isonicotinic acid hydrazide (INH) has been used successfully in the treatment of tuberculosis. Daily doses of 300 to 900 mg caused increased excretion of kynurenine and xanthurenic acid in tryptophan load tests, according to Price and coworkers (31). The structure of this drug is given with those of B_6 and related compounds. It is chemically related to pyridoxine and acts as a B_6 antagonist. Although it has been assumed that INH is tuberculostatic on the basis of inhibiting one or more pyridoxal phosphate-dependent enzyme systems in sensitive organisms, Youatt (32) considers that this is improbable. She showed that a derivative of INH was tuberculostatic and that the compound did not inhibit transaminase activity in the microorganisms studied.

Fate of vitamin B_6. In man the B_6 active compounds are largely converted to pyridoxic acid and excreted as such in the urine. In women 75 to 85 per cent of an average daily intake of 0.86 mg (range 0.52 to 1.2 mg) of B_6 was excreted as pyridoxic acid (33).

Pyridoxine requirements. All animal species so far studied require B_6. The dietary requirement of mice is increased by feeding rations high in protein (34). After depletion, mice respond better to pyridoxine than to the aldehyde or the amine (35). This is puzzling, since only the latter two have been found in the coenzymes. Many microorganisms required a source of B_6, although in some instances the presence of a specific amino acid in the culture medium may abolish this requirement.

The human requirement is not firmly established. Infants apparently require in the neighborhood of 0.3 mg per day (13). In adults 0.5 mg daily was found to be insufficient (14). A figure of around 2 mg per day is a reasonable estimate for adults and readily obtainable from most diets. It is still questionable whether man makes use of B_6 compounds synthesized by intestinal microorganisms. Reports of excretion of B_6 and metabolites in greater quantity than the intake are numerous (33).

Occurrence of pyridoxine. The best natural sources of pyridoxine are those foods containing other members of the B complex. Yeast, rice polishings, the germ of various grains and seeds and egg yolk are outstanding sources. The vitamin is widely distributed in other foods of both plant and animal nature. In many of its sources pyridoxine is chemically bound to protein and is present in liver, for example, mainly as pyridoxal and pyridoxamine protein complexes.

Determination of pyridoxine. Both rats and chicks have been used in the biologic methods. The rat growth method is used more than other biologic methods. It consists of a depletion period on a specific ration and then a comparison of weight gain of groups fed this ration, supplemented with various levels of pure pyridoxine, and other groups fed the basal ration, plus at least two levels of material under test.

Microbiologic methods are rapid and accurate. Cheslock (36) reported 100 per cent recovery of pyridoxine added to blood filtrates in her modification of the method of Parrish and coworkers (37). Some microorganisms do not respond equally to the different forms of B_6, and in some cases they show no response to one or two of the forms; thus methods for the different molecules are available.

An enzymatic procedure for pyridoxal phosphate capable of estimating as little as 0.03 μg was developed by Wada and others (38). Pyridoxal, pyridoxamine, and pyridoxine are not active in the test.

BIOTIN

Biotin, one of the members of the group of B vitamins, has been known by a variety of names including "bios," "vitamin H," and "coenzyme R."

As early as 1916 the toxicity of diets high in egg white was observed (1). Some years later Boas (2) described "egg white injury" in rats fed diets containing raw egg white as the source of protein. She described muscle incoordination, dermatitis, loss of hair, and nervous manifestations as symptoms of this syndrome. She observed that cooked egg white was not toxic and that liver, yeast, and certain other foods apparently contained a substance that protected rats against the toxicity of the raw egg protein. The protective substance was called "vitamin H" by György. Lease and Parsons (3) showed that chicks were subject to "egg white injury." Williams and coworkers (4) some six years later demonstrated that "egg white injury" in rats and in chicks was actually due to an antivitamin in egg white. This substance, known as "avidin," is a basic protein, and its ability to inactivate biotin was confirmed in 1941 (5).

Previous to this time a potent growth stimulant for yeast had been isolated from dried egg yolk by Kögl and Tonnis (6) and named "biotin." "Coenzyme R" was the name given another growth factor isolated in 1933 (7). It was in 1940 that György, du Vigneaud, and their coworkers (8) announced the identity of vitamin H (antiegg white injury factor), coenzyme R, and biotin.

Du Vigneaud and coworkers characterized biotin and published its structure in 1942 (9). Harris and others announced the synthesis of d-biotin in 1943 (10). Improvements in the synthesis have been numerous (11), and at present biotin is readily available to the research worker.

The elucidation of the nature of biotin is unique among vitamin studies. Real progress developed after the demonstration of the "toxic" effect of egg white, and then it was shown that foods contained a protective substance, vitamin-like in nature. Later it was demonstrated that avidin of egg white combines with and inactivates biotin of foods and perhaps that produced by bacteria in the intestine leading to a dietary deficiency.

Chemistry of biotin. Biotin (d, or natural isomer) is a monocarboxylic acid, only slightly soluble in water (0.03 to 0.04 g per 100 ml at 25° C and 1 g per 100 ml at 100° C) and alcohol (0.06 g per 100 ml at 25° C). Salts of the acid are quite soluble; the sodium salt can be prepared in 20 per cent aqueous solution. The free acid is practically insoluble in acetone and ether. The colorless crystalline needles melt at 231 to 232° C. Water solutions (pH 4–9) are stable at 100° C, and the dry material is also thermo- and photostable. The vitamin is destroyed by acids and alkalies only on rigorous treatment and by oxidizing agents such as peroxide and permanganate.

The specific rotation, $[\alpha]_D^{26}$, is 91.0° in 0.1 N NaOH, and it shows maximum absorption in the ultraviolet at a wavelength of 234 mμ.

The structures of biotin and some related compounds are shown herewith:

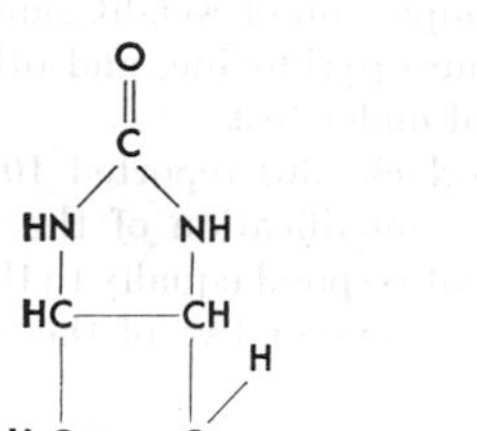

Biotin

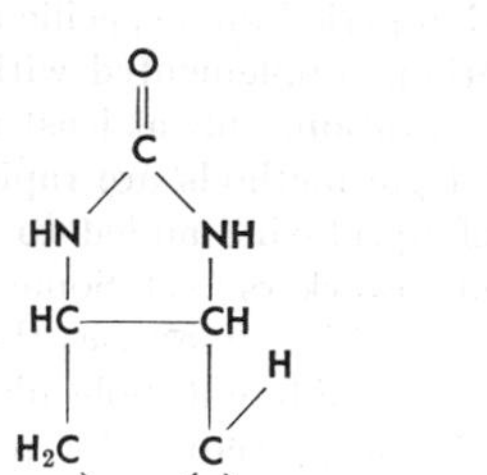

Oxybiotin

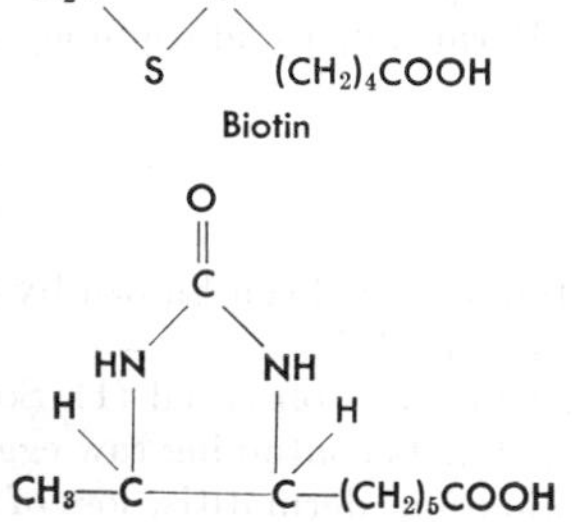

Desthiobiotin

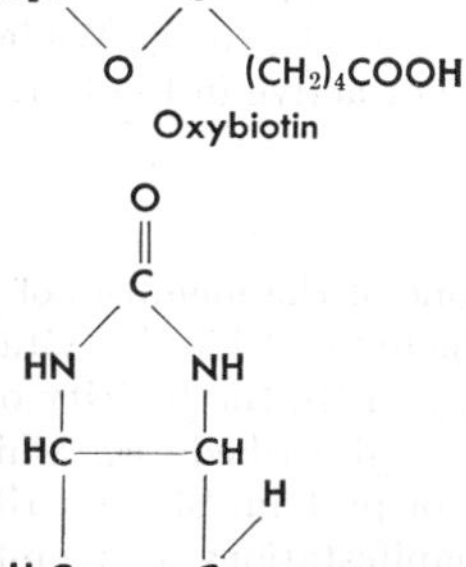

Oxybiotin sulfonic acid

"Biocytin" is a term designating a bound form of biotin first isolated from yeast by Wright and coworkers (12). It was identified as ε-N-biotinyl-lysine (13) and later synthesized (14). It occurs in plant and animal tissues also. The synthetic material reacts in the same way as naturally occurring biocytin with respect to microbiologic activity, combination with avidin, hydrolysis rates, infra-red absorption and other criteria (15). In biocytin the ε-amino group of lysine and the carboxyl of biotin are combined in a manner similar to that in a peptide bond. Another bound form of the vitamin—soluble bound biotin—contained in peptic digests of hog liver and other tissues was found to be convertible to free biotin by an enzyme from liver named "biotinidase" (16).

Biotin deficiency. Various microorganisms, including bacteria, yeasts, and molds, require biotin; it is a vitamin for these organisms. It is also a required dietary vitamin for man, monkey, dog, rat, rabbit, turkeys, chickens, and some other species.

It was early postulated (17) that egg white in the intestinal tract combined with and held in an unabsorbable form the protective factor of the diet. This was based on various observations, including the fact that feces from rats showing egg white injury were protective only after heating. Other workers (18) concluded somewhat the same thing in studies on chicks, and later (19) they showed that a constituent of raw egg white rendered biotin unavailable for yeast growth. Woolley and Langsworth (20) prepared an amorphous fraction from egg white that was 15,000 times as active as egg white. Avidin occurs combined with nucleic acid and carbohydrate. The free protein is highly basic and has a molecular weight of 60,000 to 70,000. One molecule combines with two molecules of biotin (21).

In animals biotin deficiency cannot always be produced by maintaining them on diets deficient in this factor, presumably on account of bacterial synthesis in the intestinal tract. Many experiments have indicated a greater excretion than dietary intake of biotin. This has also been demonstrated in human beings. Besides feeding egg white diets, the symptoms have been produced by incorporating a sulfonamide drug in the diet (to minimize intestinal bacterial growth) or by supplementing the diet with one of the various biotin antagonists (see further).

Hamsters fed a diet containing 40 per cent egg white supplemented with sulfaguanidine showed extreme deficiency in six weeks. Weight gain was far below normal and the animals were irritable and nervous. They showed jerky movements and dragged their hind legs. The eyes were sealed shut with incrustations, and the mouth and nose were swollen. They became nearly hairless. Symptoms disappeared rapidly following daily injections of 4 μg of biotin (22).

Boas (2) fed rats on diets high in raw egg white and observed a dermatitis, loss of hair, and loss of muscular control. Specific studies on nervous tissue and muscle of deficient animals were reported by Sullivan and others (23).

Experimental studies on human biotin deficiency have been reported. Sydenstricker and associates (24) fed egg white-containing diets to adult volunteers. After three to four weeks a transient dermatitis was seen, and shortly thereafter lassitude, anorexia, muscle pains, and hyperesthesia were observed. The administration of 150 to 300 μg daily of a biotin concentrate relieved these symptoms in a few days. During the course of the experiment the urinary excretion of biotin decreased and rose abruptly upon therapy with the vitamin.

Other investigators have not confirmed the production of human biotin deficiency symptoms by feeding egg white or avidin concentrates (25,26). Follis has reviewed the symptomatology of deficiency in animals and in man (27).

Coenzyme activity. The action of biotin as a required component in some specific carboxylations and decarboxylations is well known (28). The coenzyme function is not well defined, however, and no clear-cut knowledge of the mode of action is available. Oxalacetate stimulates the growth of *L. arabinosus* in a medium deficient in both aspartic acid and biotin (29). This probably results from the failure of the deficient organism to condense pyruvic acid with CO_2 to form oxalacetate, which could then be transaminated, forming aspartic acid. It has been demonstrated that $C^{14}O_2$ from $NaHC^{14}O_3$ was incorporated into aspartic acid to a much smaller extent by livers from biotin-deficient chicks than by livers from normal chicks (30). Lichstein (31) presented data demonstrating the presence of bound biotin in purified oxalacetic carboxylase from chick liver. Another example of the involvement of biotin in CO_2 fixation is found in the report of Fisher (32), who showed that certain β-methyl acids are used in the formation of acetoacetate in the presence of CO_2. Rat liver mitochondria from biotin-deficient rats did not form acetoacetate, but this capacity was restored by injecting biotin for three days prior to sacrificing the animals.

In the production of urea in the body, one step involves the reaction of carbamyl phosphate and ornithine to yield citrulline. MacCleod and others (33) showed that livers from biotin-deficient rats were capable of carrying out this conversion at a rate of only 50 per cent that of normal livers.

In microorganisms the role of biotin in purine synthesis is well established (34). One step in the synthesis involves CO_2 fixation (5-aminoimidazole ribotide (AI) + $CO_2 \longrightarrow$ 5-amino-4-imidazolecarboxylic acid ribotide (AICA)). It is at this point that biotin is involved, since AI accumulates in *Saccharomyces cerevisiae* under conditions of biotin deficiency and is utilized in the formation of AICA upon supplying the vitamin (35). Interestingly enough, biotin also appears to be involved in a subsequent step, the formation of the carboxamide derivative (34). The details of these and other reactions concerned with purine synthesis can be found in Chapter 25.

Biotin functions in the synthesis of long-chain fatty acids in animals (36), plants (37), and microorganisms (38). A short review on biotin in fatty acid synthesis is available (39).

Some interesting relations of biotin to enzyme and other protein synthesis in animals has been reviewed (40).

Another specific role of biotin was advanced by Lichstein and Umbreit,

(41) involving the vitamin in enzymatic deamination of various amino acids, including aspartic acid, threonine, and serine. Certain of the conflicting evidence in this field has been resolved (42), and it appears that some organisms do indeed employ biotin in deamination reactions, perhaps as part of a coenzyme (43).

Earlier indications of a functional role of biotin in lipid synthesis (44) have been amply confirmed in later work. Gram and Okey (45) indicated that in a biotin deficiency the rate of fatty acid synthesis in rats is decreased. In a cell-free, fatty acid-synthesizing system from avian liver Wakil and coworkers (46) demonstrated a requirement for both biotin and bicarbonate, although the bicarbonate was not incorporated into the synthesized fatty acids. The latter finding may be explained on the basis of the proposed mechanism of Brady (47) for fatty acid synthesis. He has prepared enzyme systems from liver and shown that acetyl coenzyme A (acetyl CoA) is carboxylated to form malonyl CoA. The CO_2 here may come from $HC^{14}O_3^-$. Malonyl CoA condenses with acetaldehyde (or higher aldehyde), and the condensation product is decarboxylated. Further changes result in fatty acid synthesis; see Chapter 23 for details. The point of interest here is that other workers have established that the carboxylation reaction is mediated by a biotin-requiring enzyme.

The relation of these specific functions of biotin to deficiency symptoms in higher animals is unknown.

Oxybiotin (see formulas) can be utilized by various microorganisms, and it has been demonstrated that higher animals (chicken) can also utilize this molecule without conversion into biotin (48). Biocytin, soluble bound biotin (protein bound), and desthiobiotin are all used in place of biotin by various microorganisms. Pimelic acid ($HOOC(CH_2)_5COOH$) stimulates biotin synthesis in some microorganisms and is growth-promoting in others.

Two biotin molecules, with different chemical structures, known as α- and β-biotin, have been postulated. The question of the identity of these is not definitely settled, although microbiologic assay data (49) support the view that α- and β-biotin are the same compound.

Biotin antimetabolites. Many compounds more or less chemically related to biotin are known to inhibit the growth-promoting effect of biotin on various microorganisms. Each of a series of biotin homologs (various lengths of the side chain) was found to be capable of inhibiting the growth of *Lactobacillus casei* and *Saccharomyces cerevisiae* in the presence of biotin (50). It was pointed out that in this series of compounds the antibiotin activity was similar to the avidin-combining power.

The mode of action of antimetabolites in general is not clear. However, important observations in this field have been reported (51). It is well established that the fermentation rate of biotin-deficient yeast is markedly increased on the addition of biotin to the medium. These authors showed that if certain biotin analogs (oxybiotinsulfonic acid and others) were added prior to the addition of biotin, the stimulatory effect of biotin was lost. However, if biotin had established the increased rate of fermentation, then the addition of the antimetabolites did not directly inhibit fermentation. From this it appears that the inhibitors act by preventing biotin from incorporating into a required coenzyme and not by inhibiting the action of the coenzyme in fermentation processes.

Fate of biotin. The fate of biotin in the body has been studied by Mistry and coworkers (52). Rats and chicks were sacrificed one, two, or three hours following an injection of carboxyl-C^{14}-biotin. A maximum of 14 per cent of the dose was found in the liver. After fractionation of liver homogenates, 39 to 53 per cent of the activity there was found in the supernatant, 18 to 29 per cent in the mitochondria, 15 to 23 per cent in nuclear material, and only 2 per cent in the microsomes. It was established that about 90 per cent of the biotin in the cellular fractions of normal rat liver exists in bound forms, except in microsomes, where 80 per cent is free or as biocytin.

Distribution of biotin. This vitamin enjoys an ubiquitous distribution in plant and animal tissue. Foods rich in biotin include liver, kidney, molasses, yeast, milk, and egg yolk. The high content of biotin in egg yolk and of avidin in egg white is an interesting point for speculation. Vegetables, nuts, and grains also contain biotin in both the free and the combined form. For man and for some other animals the biotin produced by the bacteria of the large intestine may be a more important source (quantitatively) than that of the diet.

Requirement of biotin. The biotin requirement of microorganisms is well established. In animals there is no practical method now of establishing the quantitative need for this vitamin, since large amounts of it are supplied through intestinal bacterial synthesis. In some of the earlier balance studies in man (53) it was found that the urinary excretion of biotin often exceeded the dietary intake, and the fecal excretion was greater than the intake in every case. It would appear from this that a dietary source in man may not be of much importance in meeting the requirements.

Determination of biotin. The assay of biotin is complicated by the presence in natural materials of biotin analogs, some of which may have varying degrees of biotin activity or even antibiotin activity for some of the test organisms used. Animal assays have largely been replaced by microbiologic procedures.

Some materials, such as urine and milk, may be assayed without previous hydrolysis, but in many substances the combined biotin must be released by acid hydrolysis.

Glick and others (54) presented an extremely sensitive method for biotin using *L. arabinosus.*

FOLIC ACID (PTEROYLGLUTAMIC ACID) AND RELATED SUBSTANCES

The development of our present knowledge of folic acid, called "pteroylglutamic acid" (PGA), resulted from many studies of the nutritional needs of animals on the one hand and of bacterial requirements on the other. It is no wonder that this compound (and closely related molecules) has been assigned a wide variety of designations, since so many test animals and different bacteria have been employed under diverse experimental conditions in the elucidation of its nature. Also, a variety of symptoms were used as deficiency criteria in animals. Further complications surely resulted from the fact that the vitamin occurs in several chemical forms. A few of the names previously applied to this vitamin include "vitamin M" (a hematopoietic factor for monkeys), "vitamin B_c" (chick growth factor), "factor R" (bacterial growth), "norite eluate factor" (*Lactobacillus casei*), "*L. casei* factor," "vitamin B_{10}," and "vitamin B_{11}." In 1941 the name folic acid (Latin *folium*, leaf) was assigned to a principle required by *Streptococcus lactis* R by Mitchell, Snell, and Williams (1). The term "folacin" is commonly used now as a synonym for folic acid.

In no other instance has the correlation of the work of the bacteriologist and the nutritionist been so important and productive in the success of elucidating our knowledge of a vitamin. An important link between the two fields of investigation was formed in 1941, when investigators at the University of Wisconsin pointed out certain similarities between a bacterial growth factor and a substance required for chick growth (2). Activity for *L. casei* and for the chick and loss of activity on storage for both were shown to be similar in a preparation from liver. Mitchell, Snell, and Williams (3) developed a method for concentrating the vitamin from spinach to 137,000 times the activity of their standard liver preparation. A crystalline product was obtained by several groups of investigators in 1944 from liver, yeast, and other natural sources.

About this time investigators recognized a difference between fermentation *L. casei* factor and liver *L. casei* factor, although the products of chemical degradation were the same. It developed that the fermentation factor contains three molecules of glutamic acid, one molecule of *p*-aminobenzoic acid, and a substituted pteridine, while the liver factor is chemically similar save for the fact that only one molecule of glutamic acid is present per molecule of vitamin. In 1946 the isolation, proof of structure, and synthesis of folic acid was described by a group of workers at the Lederle Laboratories (4).

Chemistry of folic acid. Folic acid is a yellow crystalline material soluble in water to an extent of only about 0.1 per cent. It is soluble in dilute alcohol and can be precipitated from solution as the barium or lead salts or with basic precipitants, such as phosphotungstic acid. It shows characteristic absorption bands in the ultraviolet and in the infrared portions of the spectrum.

In one of two methods of synthesis used by Angier and others (4) equimolecular amounts of 2,4,5-triamino-6-hydroxypyrimidine, *p*-aminobenzoylglutamic acid and 2,3-dibromopropionaldehyde were allowed to react together in the presence of an acetate buffer. The reaction mixture contained about 15 per cent of active material (microbiologic assay). Purification procedures and final recrystallization from hot water yielded pteroylglutamic acid.

At present the identity of vitamin M, factor U, factors R and S, vitamin B_c, norite eluate factor, and liver *Lactobacillus casei* factor with pteroylglutamic acid (synthetic folic acid) is assured. The fermentation *L. casei* factor differs in that three glutamic acid residues are present per molecule, and vitamin B_c conjugate contains seven glutamic acid residues. Other related molecules known to be active for one or more species of microorganisms include xanthopterin, thymine, and pyracin.

A naturally occurring enzyme, vitamin B_c conjugase, hydrolyzes folic acid-like compounds with several glutamic acid residues to pteroylglutamic acid

(5) and glutamic acid. This enzyme is widely distributed in animal tissues and may be of importance in converting pteroylglutamates to PGA, although pteroylglutamic acid, pteroyltriglutamic acid, and pteroylheptaglutamic acid are active as hematopoietic agents for man.

Two diglutamic acid derivatives have been synthesized. Pteroyl-α-glutamylglutamic acid (Diopterin) is inactive for *L. casei* and *Streptococcus faecalis* R but active in the types of human blood discrasias in which it has been studied. Pteroyl-γ-glutamylglutamic acid is active in certain types of human anemias. There are five triglutamic acid derivatives. The γ,γ-derivative is identical with naturally occurring fermentation *L. casei* factor. The α in these designations indicates that the carboxyl of glutamic acid adjacent to the carbon holding the amino group is involved in the peptide bond, while the γ indicates that the other carboxyl (γ from the carbon holding the amino group) is thus involved:

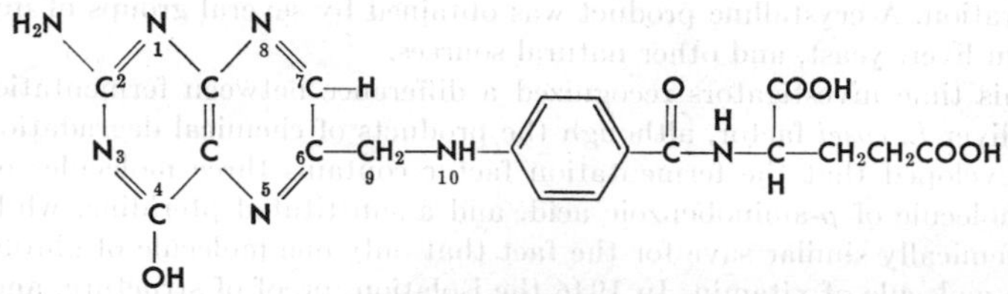

Pteroylglutamic acid (PGA)
Folic Acid

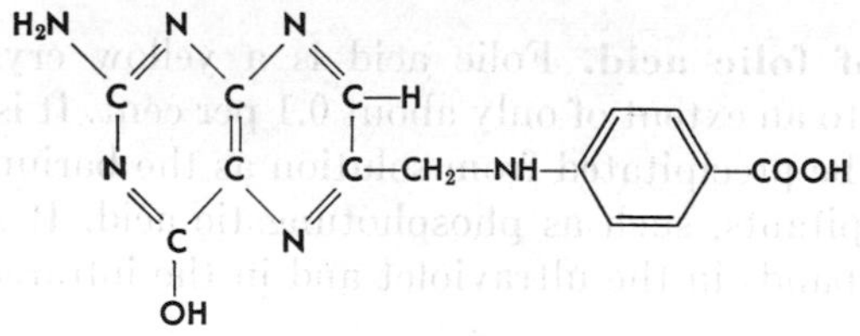

Pteroic acid

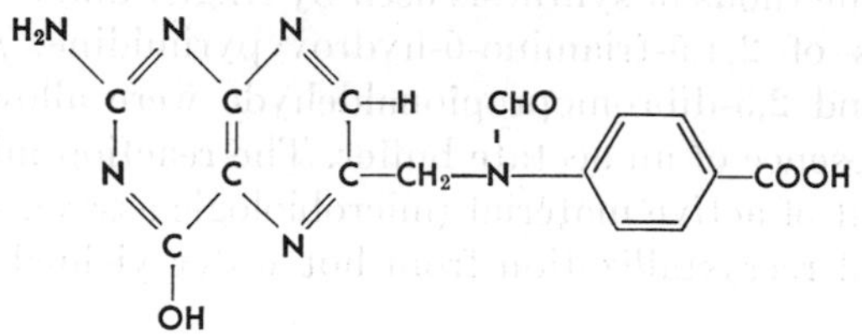

Rhizopterin (N^{10}-formylpteroic acid)

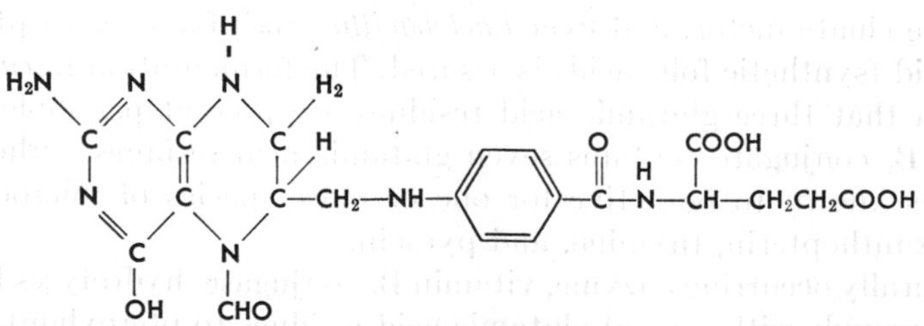

Folinic acid (citrovorum factor)
N^5-Formyl-5,6,7,8-tetrahydropteroylgutamic acid

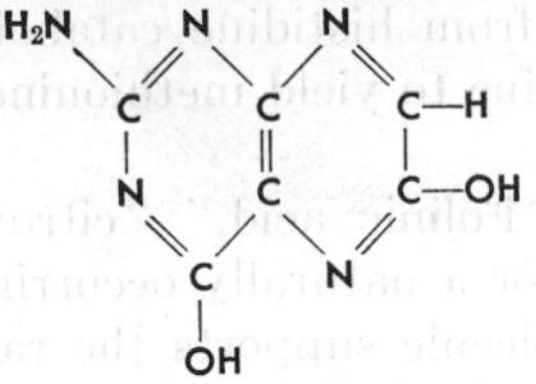

Xanthopterin

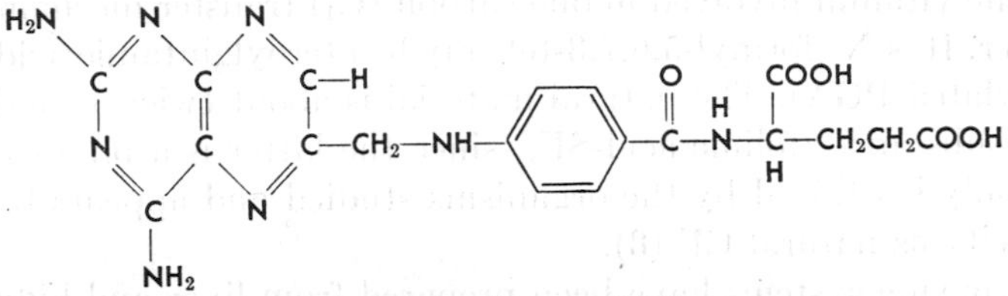

Aminopterin (4-amino PGA)

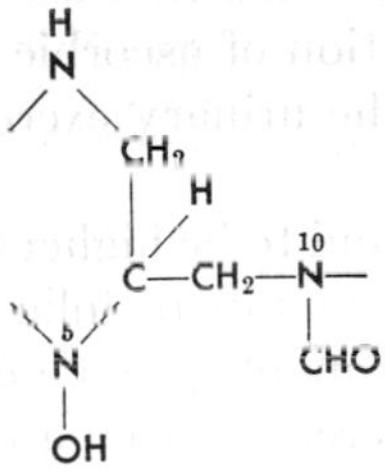

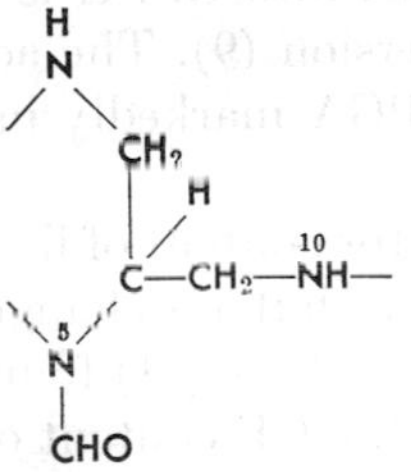

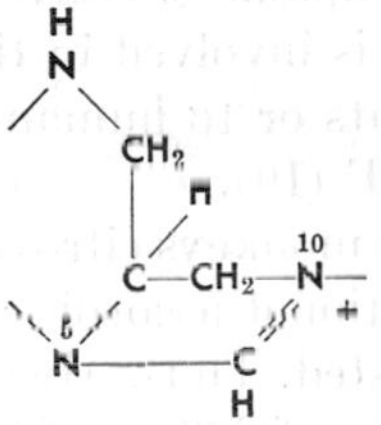

N¹⁰-Formyltetrahydro PGA
Partial structure

N⁵-Formyltetrahydro PGA
Partial structure

N⁵,¹⁰-Methenyltetrahydro PGA
Partial structure

Folic Acid and Some Related Structures

Folic acid deficiency. A deficiency of folic acid is difficult to produce in most animals unless intestinal bacterial growth is inhibited (by feeding a sulfonamide drug, for example). The use of folic acid antagonists has also been widely used to produce deficiency symptoms.

In monkeys a folic acid deficiency leads to a characteristic type of anemia. Rats develop anemia and leukopenia which disappear following the administration of a folic acid active substance. Formic acid and formiminoglutamic acid excretion are increased in a deficiency state in this species (6). In man there results a macrocytic anemia which resembles pernicious anemia except that the nervous involvement of the latter condition is absent. Diarrhea, gastrointestinal lesions, and other symptoms are present. Folic acid is highly effective in the treatment. The vitamin is also effective in treating the anemia of pernicious anemia, although it is without effect on the nervous symptoms, which respond to vitamin B_{12}. The sprue syndrome and some other types of anemia in humans respond to folic acid therapy.

We have seen the requirement for folic acid coenzymes in the synthesis of purines and pyrimidines. In a deficiency of these molecules the production of nucleoproteins is inadequate and the maturation of young red blood cells does not continue.

What part of the symptomatology of deficiency may be related to abnormal interconversion of glycine and serine, or to the impaired handling of formiminoglutamic acid (from histidine catabolism), or to the decreased methylation of homocysteine to yield methionine cannot be defined at this time.

Coenzyme activity. "Folinic acid," "citrovorum factor (CF)," and "leucovorin" are names for a naturally occurring derivative of folic acid. Unlike folic acid, this molecule supports the rapid growth of *Leuconostoc citrovorum*. It has been synthesized (7) and is one of the active coenzyme forms of the vitamin involved in one carbon (C_1) transfer mechanisms mentioned later. It is N^5-formyl-5,6,7,8-tetrahydropteroylglutamic acid (reduced and formylated PGA). The natural material is about twice as active as the synthetic substance (folinic acid-SF), since the latter is a D,L mixture. The L-isomer only is utilized by the organisms studied and appears to have the same activity as natural CF (8).

Active enzyme systems have been prepared from liver and kidney which are capable of converting PGA into CF. It is well established that ascorbic acid is involved in this conversion (9). The administration of ascorbic acid to rats or to humans given PGA markedly increases the urinary excretion of CF (10).

In monkeys citrovorum factor content of liver was found to be higher with additional ascorbic acid intake but no change in the amount of folic acid ingested. Thus, Misra and coworkers (11) found that in monkeys on a daily intake of 200 μg of folic acid the CF content of liver increased from around 568 to 2375 mμg per gram of tissue as the ascorbic acid intake was increased from 0 to 50 mg daily.

Another coenzyme form of the vitamin active in C_1 metabolism is N^{10}-formyltetrahydrofolic acid ($f^{10}FH_4$). Huennekens and coworkers (12) studied the enzymatic formation of this "active" formate molecule and showed that ATP is required. Two steps were observed, the first involving phosphorylation of FH_4 thus:

$$ATP + FH_4 \longrightarrow FH_4\text{-}P + ADP$$

and

$$FH_4\text{-}P + HCOOH \longrightarrow f^{10}FH_4 + P_i$$

This molecule also exists in the form shown in the structures in which the C_1 unit is bridged between N^5 and N^{10} to give $N^{5,10}$-methenyltetrahydrofolic acid ($f^{5,10}FH_4$). This compound is also known as "anhydroleucovorin" and is converted into the more stable N^5 derivative (13), and also into the N^{10} derivative (14) which transfers C_1 units in a number of reactions.

5-Formiminotetrahydrofolic acid has been proposed as another coenzyme by various workers. Miller and Waelsch (15) considered the synthesis of the molecule to involve a reversible formimino transfer with formiminoglutamic acid (FIGLU) thus:

$$FIGLU + THFA \rightleftharpoons formimino\text{-}THFA + glutamic\ acid$$

These authors proposed that the formimino compound undergoes a loss of ammonia and rearrangement to 5,10-methenyl-THFA and subsequent hydrolysis to N^{10}-formyl THFA.

The folic acid coenzymes are involved in a variety of C_1 transfer reactions. Details will not be presented here, since they are discussed in Chapter 25. Some of the better-known reactions are indicated briefly herewith.

1. Interconversion of glycine and serine. Huennekens and coworkers (16) studied the various requirements for serine hydroxymethylase enzyme system of beef liver:

$$\text{Serine} + H_2O + \text{THFA} \rightleftharpoons \text{Glycine} + CH_2OH\text{-}\text{THFA}$$

The hydroxymethyl-THFA capable of reacting with glycine to form serine is visualized as arising from reduction of N^{10}-formyl THFA by TPNH (17).

2. Methionine-homocysteine relationship. Methionine synthesis from homocysteine involves a C_1 transfer and thus a folic acid coenzyme. Some details of this reaction have been studied by Greenberg and others (18) and by Doctor and coworkers (19).

3. Purine and pyrimidine synthesis. Carbon atoms 2 and 8 of the purine ring are supplied by C_1 transfer involving folic acid coenzymes. This subject is reviewed in detail by Hartman and Buchanan (20). The methyl group of the pyrimidine thymine is supplied by folic acid coenzyme (21), although the ring carbons do not involve this type of C_1 transfer.

4. Histidine synthesis. Histidine is not synthesized in quantity in most mammals (man may be an exception). The requirement for folic acid coenzymes in histidine synthesis in microorganisms has been demonstrated (22).

In most of the known reactions involving "active formyl" the N^{10} coenzyme or the $N^{5,10}$ appears to be involved. Folinic acid (the N^5 formyl derivative) is involved in the formylation of glutamate to yield N-formylglutamate and THFA (23) by a hog liver enzyme. These and many other aspects of folic acid coenzymes are reviewed by Huennekens and coauthors (24).

5. Phenylalanine oxidation to tyrosine. Apparently two enzymes are involved in the hydroxylation of phenylalanine, one of which employs reduced folic acid (THFA) as a coenzyme. In this reaction the coenzyme appears to operate as an electron donor rather than in C_1 unit transfer. Kaufman (25) proposes that the reduced folic acid is directly involved in the hydroxylation reaction, in conjunction with an enzyme system from rat liver, and that in the reversible oxidation-reduction of the folic acid a second enzyme requiring TPNH operates to re-form the active, reduced THFA. The conversion of phenylalanine to tyrosine is impaired in humans treated with the folic acid antagonist amethopterin (for carcinoma). The effects were evident in as short a time as 12 hours following injection of the antagonist (26).

Folic acid antagonists. Much has been learned regarding pathways and coenzyme activity through the use of antagonists in animals and in microorganisms.

One of the most potent inhibitors is aminopterin (4-amino PGA). The marked potency of the inhibitor aminopterin is attested to by the fact that when the compound was fed at a level of only 1 mg per kilogram of diet, mice died in a few days (27). It produces anemia and leucopenia in guinea pigs (28) and in rats (29). This antagonist has been used successfully to bring about remissions (not a cure) of acute leukemia in children. Amethopterin (4-amino-N[10]-methyl PGA) has also been used to produce experimental deficiency and in the treatment of leukemia. Goldin and coauthors (30) have reviewed the clinical use of such antagonists.

Amethopterin markedly inhibited nucleic acid synthesis in rats following partial hepatectomy to induce mitosis (31). This is probably explained on the basis that the 4-amino antagonist suppresses formyl-coenzyme synthesis, resulting in inadequate purines and/or pyrimidine production, with the consequent inability of the organism to fabricate nucleic acids.

Timmis (32) has reviewed many antifolic acid compounds with real or potential value in cancer chemotherapy.

Occurrence of folic acid compounds. Green leafy vegetables and yeast are good sources. Many microorganisms contain appreciable quantities and may supply man and other animals, through intestinal synthesis, with significant amounts. Liver contains more folic acid activity than other materials studied (around 300 μg per 100 g). Grains and green leafy vegetables vary from 20 or 30 up to 100 μg per 100 g. Some of the activity may be free in natural products but a larger portion is in a bound form.

Assay of folic acid activity. The microbiologic methods of assay are preferred, since they are more practical than rat or chick assay procedures from the standpoint of time and cost. Even at this time the assay methods are not adequate, especially for differentiating the various active molecules (33). *Lactobacillus casei* (acid production) and *Streptococcus faecalis* (growth) have been employed for total activity toward these organisms. The Association of Official Agricultural Chemists adopted revised procedures in 1958 (34). One of the problems involves hydrolysis of the bound forms of the vitamin in foods. Newer enzymatic procedures for hydrolysis offer promise.

Chemical methods are developing around the fluorescence character of folic acid compounds. Duggan and coworkers (35) surveyed the potential applicability of such methods for the determination of many biologic compounds and list the wavelength of maximum activation and of maximum fluorescence for a variety of molecules including folic acid and folinic acid (CF).

Requirements of folic acid. The quantitative need of folic acid-like compounds under normal conditions of nutrition and health are almost unknown for man and animals. Clinical data are readily available as to the quantities found to be effective in various human anemic states. Also, curative doses for experimentally produced deficiency states in animals have been reported, but these tell us little about requirements under normal conditions. Similarly, the calculated dietary intake of man offers no solution, since so many factors concerning bacterial production in the intestine, variations in absorption, and the relation of other vitamins remain obscure. It has been speculated (36) that 0.5 to 1.0 mg daily will maintain health in humans. A figure considerably lower than this was arrived at by Sheehy and others (37) through studies of individuals with tropical sprue.

VITAMIN B_{12}, COBALAMINS

After many years of intensive work the antipernicious anemia factor of liver extract (used in clinical treatment) was isolated in 1948 by Rickes and coworkers (1) and by Smith (2). Various workers had been studying the same or a similar substance found in other material. The "animal protein factor," which promotes the growth of animals on diets containing vegetable proteins and is found in such materials as fish solubles and cow manure, is similar to the factor isolated from liver extract. The name B_{12} was given to the vitamin.

Rapid progress in isolation of B_{12} followed the finding that the active principle could be separated chromatographically. Activity during purification was followed by microbiologic assay. A pink color seemed to be associated with activity. Red crystals of the pure material were finally isolated (1, 2). The crystals decompose without melting at 300° C.

Chemistry of vitamin B_{12}. Cyanocobalamin crystals are tasteless and odorless. One gram dissolves in about 80 ml of water at room temperature, forming a neutral solution. The pure material is quite soluble in alcohol and insoluble in ether and acetone. In aqueous solution crystalline cyanocobalamin has three absorption maxima at 278, 361, and 550 mμ, with extinction coefficients ($A_{1cm}^{1\%}$) of 115, 107, and 64, respectively. It is remarkable that cobalamin contains about 4.35 per cent cobalt. The molecular weight is 1355 figured on the structure shown below.

Cyanocobalamin has no net charge. The cobalt here has a coordination number of six. One position is satisfied by the CN^- group, and four are satisfied by the nitrogen atoms of the four pyrrole groups. The sixth coordination valence is balanced by the substituted, charged imidazole-ribose-phosphate group. Other B_{12} active compounds are known in which the cyanide radical is replaced by various groups forming other cobalamins, such as hydroxycobalamin, chlorocobalamin, nitrocobalamin, and thiocyanatocobalamin (3). Treatment with cyanide converts these molecules into cyanocobalamin. Ford and coworkers (4) have studied a number of molecules related to cobalamin especially from the standpoint of bacterial synthesis. Pseudocobalamins differ from cyanocobalamin in that the base in the nucleotide is adenine, 2-methyl adenine, or others.

The similarity of the cyanocobalamin molecule and the porphyrins is of interest. In B_{12} two pyrrole rings are joined directly rather than through the methene ($-CH=$) bridge, as in other porphyrins (Chapter 13):

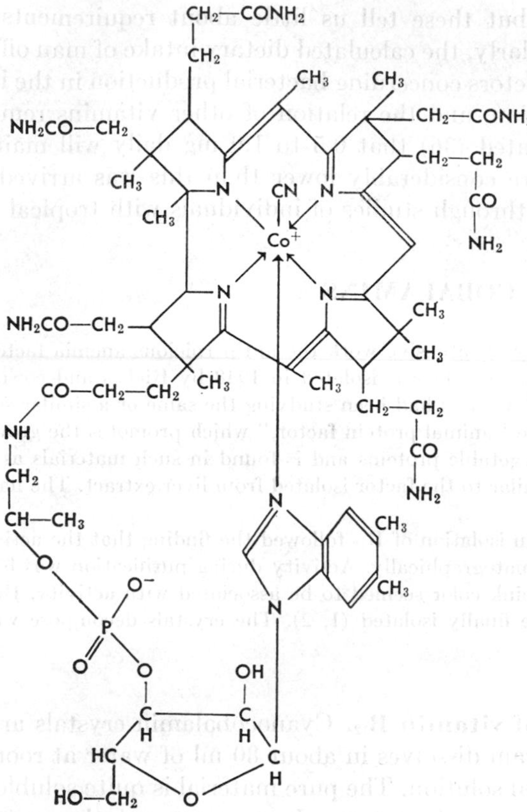

CH₂—CONH₂ ... **Cyanocobalamin**

(structural formula of Cyanocobalamin shown)

Coenzyme activity, physiologic action of vitamin B_{12}. Many microorganisms require B_{12} for growth. Lactic acid bacteria are highly sensitive to deficiency. The B_{12} requirement of some bacteria is met by methionine, or one of the pseudocobalamins. Other microorganisms synthesize quantities of B_{12} above their requirements.

Animal protein factor (APF) was known to be an essential nutrient for growth in experimental animals, and after the discovery of B_{12}, it was established that the vitamin possessed high APF activity in the chick (5). The vitamin is known to be essential for the growth of other laboratory animals and nonruminant farm animals. It is likewise essential in human nutrition.

More specifically, B_{12} has been implicated in several metabolic reactions. The evidence is not clear-cut in all cases, and considerable controversy exists with respect to certain of the proposed functions.

1. In 1957 Johnson and coworkers (6) suggested that B_{12} is concerned in protein biosynthesis. These workers presented evidence indicating that the incorporation of amino acids into protein by microsomal preparations from B_{12}-deficient rat liver and spleen was much less than in the case of such preparations from normal animals. Incorporation of labeled amino acids

was increased when crystalline B_{12} was added to the incubation mixture from deficient animals. It was further shown *in vivo* that serine-3-C^{14} was incorporated into liver proteins of pigs and rats in decreased amount in the deficiency state (7). In Chapter 25 the relation of "pH 5 enzyme" to amino acid activation (a proposed step in protein synthesis) is discussed. Johnson's group (8) injected B_{12}-Co^{60} into rats and found that most of the label of the subsequently isolated cell supernatant was in the pH 5 enzyme fraction. This crude enzyme preparation from deficient rats had little effect on the incorporation of amino acids by microsomes prepared from corresponding normal animals, while enzyme prepared from normal rats brought about a threefold increase in incorporation by microsomes from deficient animals. These and other findings, including enzymatic P^{32} exchange studies, led the authors to postulate that B_{12} enzymes are involved in activating amino acids preparatory to their incorporation into proteins—that is, protein synthesis (9).

Various workers have been unable to confirm important parts of the work of Johnson's group. Arnstein and Simkin (10) found no increased incorporation of labeled phenylalanine into microsomal or cell sap protein as a result of adding B_{12}, although less incorporation was observed in deficient animals. They postulate that the effect of B_{12} may be secondary to some other function. Fraser and Holdsworth (11) did not find the major part of administered B_{12}-Co^{60} in the pH 5 enzyme, but rather in the supernatant of their preparations from chick livers. Since no direct role of B_{12} in amino acid activation or upon incorporation into microsomes was found, these authors also postulate an indirect role of B_{12} in protein biosynthesis. Either a direct or indirect role of B_{12} in protein synthesis is of the utmost biologic consequence, and the unraveling of the discrepancies is awaited with interest.

2. It is fairly well established that cobalamin compounds function in the synthesis of labile methyl groups from one carbon units. Arnstein (12) proposed an oxidation-reduction action of B_{12} in formate metabolism on the basis of studies including the finding that the incorporation of formate-C^{14} into choline was three times as great in B_{12}-depleted animals given the vitamin as in others not supplied with B_{12}. Dinning and Young (13) showed that the reduced conversion of formate to the methyl of thymine by marrow cell suspensions of B_{12}-deficient chicks was restored to normal *in vitro* upon addition of the vitamin. The incorporation of amino acids into protein in these preparations was not affected. In a later paper these authors (14) found that formaldehyde conversion to thymine-methyl was not influenced by B_{12} (it was increased by folic acid). These and other data prompted the authors to suggest that B_{12} functions in the reduction of one-carbon compounds between the formate and formaldehyde levels of oxidation. This reaction is mediated by the enzyme hydroxymethyl tetrahydrofolic dehydrogenase. Dinning and Hogan (15) demonstrated a reduction in the activity of this enzyme in bone marrow from B_{12}-deficient chicks. The addition of B_{12} to *in vitro* systems stimulated the enzyme in marrow (not

in liver) and led to the speculation that B_{12} or a derivative acts as coenzyme for this dehydrogenase.

3. Another area in which B_{12} has been implicated involves the metabolism of deoxyribosides. Wacker and coworkers (16) demonstrated a positive effect of the vitamin on DNA synthesis in *L. leichmannii*. In animals the purported relation of B_{12} to nucleic acid synthesis has not been substantiated by the work of Johnson and coworkers (17).

Other metabolic reactions in which B_{12} has been implicated involve the relation to sulfhydryl groups (18,19) and more recently the effect on acetyl coenzyme A carboxylation, with the production of malonyl CoA (20).

Barker and coworkers (20a) have proposed that in the coenzyme structure the cyanide group is replaced by an extra adenine nucleoside (adenine-sugar) unit. The coenzyme releases the nucleoside upon exposure to light. So far the nature of the sugar in this unit is not established, although it apparently is not ribose but is an aldose. The data indicate that the nucleoside is attached to cobalt in the coenzyme and that the sugar is substituted in the 9 position of adenine.

Coenzyme B_{12} was isolated from sheep, rabbit, chicken and human liver. Quantitative data indicated that at least 48 to 72 per cent of the B_{12} activity of these livers was in the form of coenzyme B_{12}. Cyanocobalamin and hydroxycobalamin, previously isolated from liver, appear to be mainly artifacts, produced during the purification procedure from coenzyme B_{12} (20b).

Deficiency of B_{12}. Johnson (21) has reviewed the methods used to produce deficiency of B_{12} in pigs, chicks, and rats. On a "soy-protein synthetic milk" ration pigs develop B_{12} deficiency. Growth is poor and death ensues unless B_{12} is administered. Development of formed elements of blood is abnormal. The ease with which uncomplicated B_{12} deficiency can be produced in the young pig has made this animal a valuable tool in studying metabolic pathways involving the vitamin. Rats and chicks are susceptible to lack of dietary B_{12}. Growth is poor, and rats also develop porphyrin whiskers and scaly feet (22). Biochemical findings in the deficiency state in animals are discussed under coenzyme activity.

In humans a dietary B_{12} deficiency is rare. In a review (23) B_{12} deficiency symptoms of humans subsisting on diets devoid of animal products are discussed.

Of more interest is the relation of the vitamin to human pernicious anemia and other diseases. Castle and others (24) some years ago suggested that in pernicious anemia there is a deficiency of an intrinsic factor (stomach factor) and an extrinsic factor (food factor). The two factors were thought to react to form something required for the maturation of red blood cells. The extrinsic factor of Castle is now established to be vitamin B_{12}. The intrinsic factor, a low molecular weight mucoprotein, normally occurs in gastric juice; and pernicious anemia is due to a lack of this substance, since B_{12} is not absorbed in its absence. The mechanism by which intrinsic factor brings about absorption is still not clear. The stools of pernicious anemia patients contain large amounts of the vitamin after oral administration if no intrinsic factor is given. Intrinsic factor may combine with B_{12} and in this way bring about absorption across the intestinal mucosa. Parenteral B_{12} alone in minute quantities (a few μg) is highly active as a hematopoietic substance in pernicious anemia patients.

A highly potent intrinsic factor preparation from hog pyloric mucosa was clinically active at a level of 0.3 mg; that is, it increased B_{12} absorption in pernicious anemia patients at this level (25). The molecular weight was found to be about 5000; the material contained 10 per cent nitrogen and less than 3 per cent glucosamine. The binding capacity *in vitro* was found to be 3 μg of B_{12} per mg.

Another role of intrinsic factor appears to involve retention of B_{12} by tissues. Active preparations increased B_{12} uptake of liver slices (26). In liver perfusion experiments B_{12}-Co^{60} was taken up to a slight extent, and the uptake was tremendously enhanced in the presence of intrinsic factor (27).

Sorbitol (sugar alcohol analogue of glucose) enhances B_{12} absorption in man (28). In rats this compound, mannitol, sorbose, and xylose also increased absorption (29).

Vitamin B_{12} is used clinically in diseases other than pernicious anemia. It is effective in various megaloblastic anemias and in neurologic disturbances accompanying various other conditions. Much of the information in this connection has been brought together and summarized (30).

Assay of B_{12}. The most sensitive methods depend upon growth stimulation in microorganisms. Special procedures are required to liberate the vitamin from bound forms as it is extracted from crude samples (31). *Lactobacillus leichmannii* has been used for cobalamins with either growth or acid production as end points. *E. coli* and other organisms have been employed in special instances. The organism *Ochromonas malhamensis* is said to be almost specific for cyanocobalamin (32).

Spectrophotometric methods are sensitive and applicable to pure substances. The U.S.P. method involves the determination of absorbance of a solution of the vitamin at 361 mμ (33).

Details of a radioisotope assay technique for cobalamins and a study of the adaptability of the method to crude samples was reported by Bruening and others (34).

Sources of B_{12}. Plants do not contain vitamin B_{12}. Microorganisms synthesize cobalamins, especially those normally present in the rumen of herbivorous animals. Some bacterial synthesis may occur in humans, but not in sufficient quantity to meet the needs, since man is dependent upon dietary sources. Liver and kidney are excellent sources; animal and fish muscle contain moderate quantities; while vegetables and grains contain little or none of the vitamin.

Requirement of B_{12}. The human requirement of B_{12} is not established but probably is not over 1 μg per day and very likely is less than this. In the absence of intrinsic factor (following gastrectomy) patients may show no signs of pernicious anemia for several years. This is in agreement with the observations of Schloesser and others (35), who estimated the half-life of cobalamin to be over a year in humans. Thus the rate of destruction and/or excretion of the vitamin is exceedingly slow.

INOSITOL

The compound inositol (muscle sugar) was discovered in 1850, and some years later it was shown to be a hexahydroxycyclohexane. It was not until 1928 that Eastcott (1) recognized the nutritional significance of the compound. She isolated a substance from tea, showed that it was essential for the growth of certain yeasts, and identified it with the long-known "Bios I," a concentrate with growth-promoting properties for various microorganisms. In 1940 Woolley (2) produced a type of alopecia in mice by dietary means and showed that inositol prevented the condition. In the course of these studies some of the animals showed spontaneous cures. It was demonstrated that bacteria from the intestinal tract of such animals were able to synthesize much more inositol than were organisms isolated from the tract of animals that retained the symptoms of deficiency. Under specified dietary conditions it was shown that inositol was beneficial in the treatment of the so-called spectacled-eye condition, or denuding about the eyes, in rats (3).

From the following formula the possibility of cis-trans isomerism in the molecule is evident. Seven optically inactive forms and a pair of active isomers can exist. Only one of the optically inactive forms, myo-inositol or meso-inositol, has biologic activity:

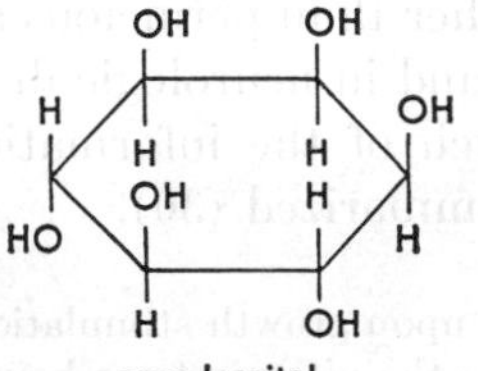

myo-Inositol 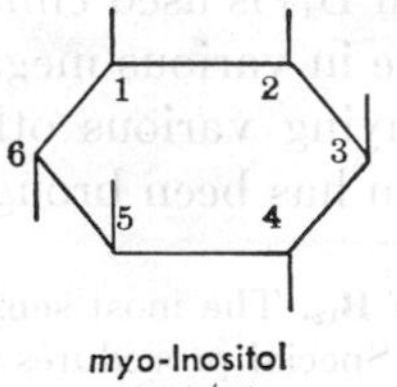   myo-Inositol
                        1235/46

The designation 1235/46 devised by Hornstein (4) indicates that the hydroxyl groups on carbons 1, 2, 3, and 5 are projected in the same direction in space, while those on carbons 4 and 6 are oriented in the opposing plane. Such a system simplifies the nomenclature of the various inositol isomers.

myo-Inositol is a white crystalline material, soluble in water to the extent of about 12.5 per cent at 20° C. It is insoluble in alcohol and ether. The crystals melt at 225° C. It is an alcohol with the same empirical formula as glucose, $C_6H_{12}O_6$.

Synthesis of myo-inositol is not practical as a source of the material, primarily because of the relative ease of isolation from natural sources, many of which contain an abundance of it either in the free or in various combined forms. From the standpoint of proving the structure, the synthesis is highly significant. This was accomplished by various workers (5).

The primary symptoms of deficiency in mice are alopecia and subnormal growth rate. In rats a retarded growth and swelling and loss of hair about the eyes are typical symptoms. The appearance of the animals led to the designation "spectacled-eye condition." Other animals reported to require inositol include the guinea pig, hamster, pig, chicken, and turkey.

Under specified dietary conditions rats develop fatty livers (6) which contain large amounts of cholesterol. Choline, a well-established lipotropic agent, does not prevent the disease, since the diet and supplements used contained liberal amounts. The administration of inositol prevented the accumulation of fat and cholesterol in the livers. This lipotropic action of inositol in rats has been amply confirmed. Best and coworkers (7) reviewed previous work in this field and presented results of their carefully controlled experiments. They concluded that inositol exerts a limited lipotropic effect in rats on a diet very low in fat but that on diets containing fat this effect is abolished. Abels and coworkers (8) reported that in their cases the livers of patients with gastrointestinal cancer invariably were infiltrated with fat. After the administration of inositol postoperatively, the livers of a number of such patients, with one exception, were found to have normal levels of fat.

It is generally agreed that inositol is a lipotropic substance under special conditions and that it may act synergistically with choline or other active molecules giving it more general lipotropic properties.

Ordinarily the cholesterol and phospholipid levels of the blood serum of rabbits rise markedly when diets high in cholesterol are fed. Dotti and others (9), however, reported that 0.5 g of inositol daily added to the high cholesterol diet eliminated the expected rise in blood cholesterol and phospholipid in these animals.

Inositol is in a unique position as far as its status as a vitamin is concerned. Under highly specific dietary conditions a need in several species has been demonstrated. On the other hand, the synthesis of inositol from glucose in the immature rat and in the chick embryo has been demonstrated by Daughaday and others (10). This synthesis has been confirmed by Halliday and Anderson (11) who isolated myo-inositol-C^{14} from rats that had been injected with glucose-1-C^{14}. Of interest in this connection are the findings of Eagle and coworkers (12), who demonstrated that inositol is a required growth factor for each of 18 human cell lines tested in tissue culture.

It appears that inositol can be metabolized as carbohydrate by the rat, since it acts antiketogenically (13). Of a 250-mg dose administered less than 1 mg was recovered in the urine. Deuterium-labeled inositol fed to a phlorizinized rat led to the excretion of deuterium-labeled glucose in the urine (14). Following intraperitoneal injection of C^{14} labeled myo-inositol in fasting rats, about 25 per cent of the dose was recovered in the respired CO_2 in 12 hours. Tissue phospholipids and liver glycogen were labeled to a much smaller extent (15).

Inisitol occurs in nature in the free form and in many combined forms. Methyl and also phosphoric acid derivatives have been isolated from a variety of materials. Mono-, di-, and triphosphoric acid esters are known to occur naturally. The hexaphosphoric acid ester in the form of mixed calcium and magnesium salts is known as "phytin" and constitutes one of the abundant sources in nature. Inositol is readily obtained by $Ca(OH)_2$ hydrolysis of this and other phosphate combinations. The high concentration of phytin in many grains, especially in corn, is an important factor in the supply of dietary phosphate from these sources.

The occurrence of inositol in phospholipids of animal and plant tissues is discussed in Chapter 6.

The very high concentrations of free inositol in seminal plasma of various species is of interest, although no explanation for its presence there is available at present. Thus, Hartree (16) found that boar seminal plasma contained 600–700 mg per 100 ml and that in the bull, human, rabbit, ram, and stallion the levels were less than 100 mg. These levels are far higher than are found in other body fluids.

The most satisfactory assay method for inositol is one of the microbiologic procedures. In these the growth response of *Saccharomyces cerevisiae* (17) or of *Sacch. carlsbergensis* (18) to additions of inositol-containing material to a culture medium devoid of the vitamin is compared to growth with additions of known increments of pure *meso*-inositol. LeBaron and others (19) described a microspectrophotometric method for the determination of inositol in tissues and lipid hydrolysates.

The animal requirements for inositol have not been studied intensively. In rats a 20-mg daily dose was sufficient (probably an excess) to cure inositol deficiency symptoms. Nothing is available on human requirements.

CHOLINE

Choline is often discussed along with the B vitamins. It is not a vitamin in the true sense. The molecule can be synthesized in the animal body providing a source of methyl groups is available. Ethanolamine is readily methylated to form choline, so that a choline deficiency can be produced only on a diet deficient in methyl donors. The subject of methyl donors is discussed in detail in Chapter 25.

p-AMINOBENZOIC ACID

p-Aminobenzoic acid has been known to the chemist for many years. It was not until 1940 that a physiologic role was proposed for this compound. Woods (1) reported the interesting observation that p-aminobenzoic acid (PAB, PABA, or p-AB) counteracts the bacteriostatic action of sulfanilamide *in vitro*. It was subsequently demonstrated that other bacteria would grow normally in the presence of sulfanilamide (and a variety of other sulfonamide drugs) if sufficient p-aminobenzoic acid were present in the culture medium. This antisulfonamide action of PAB was also demonstrated *in vivo*. Mice infected with various pathogenic organisms were protected against disease by the administration of sulfanilamide, but when PAB was given also, the sulfonamide protection was absent.

It was these observations that led to the development of our knowledge in the field of metabolic inhibitors or antagonists—a field which is now a science in itself.

It should be pointed out that PAB is used rather routinely in culturing an organism from patients on sulfonamide therapy. The purpose of culturing an organism in such cases is to identify it, and obviously the bacteriostatic action of the sulfonamide must be counteracted if growth of the organism is to be attained.

The vitamin status of PAB (COOH—C_6H_4—NH_2) is probably restricted to microorganisms where it is utilized in the synthesis of folic acid compounds, and possibly for other functions in growth. Further discussion of the relation of sulfonamide inhibition of PGA synthesis in microorganisms can be found in Chapter 32.

ASCORBIC ACID (VITAMIN C)

Scurvy in man has been known for centuries. The use of fresh vegetables and especially of the juice of lemons and of limes was established as specific cures for the condition centuries ago. The earliest accurate description of the disease and its control was published by Lind in 1757 in his "Treatise on Scurvy." Years later limes became a required article in the diet of the English Navy. The terms "limey" for English sailors and Limehouse for the wharf area in London stem from this fact. Vitamin C deficiency was prevalent not only on long sea voyages because fresh foods were unavailable, but also it was epidemic over parts of the world during times of famine and war. During the war or wars of our own times outbreaks of scurvy in parts of the world have not been uncommon.

Progress in the development of specific knowledge concerning vitamin C was initiated by Holst and Frölich (1) in 1907. These investigators showed that a scorbutic state could be produced in guinea pigs by restricting the diet of these animals to oats and bran. This development paved the way for intensive research into the properties of a protective substance in certain foods as well as into the biochemical defects associated with the scorbutic state.

Zilva and associates (2) provided important information on the concentration of active antiscorbutic material from lemon juice and on certain important chemical properties of the active substance. He showed, for instance, that following oxidative destruction of the principle, the activity could be restored by reduction and proposed a relation between antiscorbutic activity and reducing power of his preparations. In 1928 Szent-Györgyi (3) isolated a strong reducing substance from adrenal glands of rats and from citrus juices. The name "hexuronic acid" was given to this material.

It was only a matter of a few years before "hexuronic acid," and the reducing substance of Zilva were shown to be vitamin C, the antiscorbutic vitamin. Waugh and King (4) reported in 1932 that the vitamin C isolated by them from lemon juice and the reducing hexuronic acid studied by others were identical because of the similarity in many chemical and physical properties as well as in biologic potency in protecting guinea pigs against scurvy.

It was well agreed at this time by workers in the field that vitamin C was an acid with the general formula $C_nH_xO_n$. Several proposed structures were offered, but the true configuration of the molecule was established in 1933 in Haworth's laboratory in England (5). In the same year the synthesis of ascorbic acid was achieved by Reichstein and coworkers (6) and also by Haworth's group (7).

Chemistry of ascorbic acid. Pure vitamin C is a white crystalline odorless substance with a sour (acid) taste. It melts at 190–192° C, and in the crystalline form it is stable for years. It is insoluble in most organic solvents, although a 2 per cent solution can be made in alcohol. In water the vitamin is soluble to the extent of 1 g in 3 ml. The strong reducing property of vitamin C depends on the loss of hydrogen atoms from the hydroxyls on the double-bonded (endiol) carbons. At pH 4 and at 35° C the $E'_0 = +0.166$ volt. A dilute solution of vitamin C has a pH of about 3. The acidity is due to ionization of the enol group on carbon atom 3. The first pK_a is 4.17; this indicates that ascorbic acid is considerably more dissociated than acetic, for instance. The second pK_a is 11.57. Vitamin C, or L-ascorbic acid, in water has a specific rotation $[\alpha]_D^{20} = +23°$. The ultraviolet absorption maximum of ascorbic acid is at a wavelength of 265 mμ.

Ascorbic acid readily forms salts of several metals. It takes up iodine at the double bond and can be reduced here by hydrogenation. Oxidation of ascorbic acid yields dehydroascorbic acid. This is a freely reversible reaction. H_2S, among other things, may be used to reduce the oxidized form in the laboratory. The dehydro form, except in rather acid solution, undergoes hydrolysis at the lactone ring with the formation of diketogulonic acid. The reverse of this reaction does not proceed in the body but can be brought about in the laboratory.

The greater stability of ascorbic acid in acid solution depends on the decreased tendency toward hydrolysis of the lactone ring with decreasing pH. In alkaline solution the hydrolysis is fairly rapid, and such solutions lose vitamin activity in a short period of time. The oxidation of ascorbic acid *in vitro* is catalyzed by various substances. The copper ion is quite active and, of course, the plant ascorbic acid oxidase (a copper-protein enzyme) is highly active. The rate of destructive oxidation is greater with increasing pH. This type of oxidation involves molecular oxygen, and, consequently, in processing vitamin C-containing foods, such as orange juice, the removal of oxygen by nitrogen or CO_2 results in decreased losses of the vitamin during canning or other processing. Low-temperature storage of vegetables before processing, though usually impractical, and a quick preheating (blanching) just previous to canning or freezing also aid in decreasing ascorbic acid destruction.

Unfortunately, the vitamin C loss during blanching of many foods may be considerable owing in part to oxidation at the elevated temperature, and perhaps to a greater extent through solubility of the vitamin in the blanching water:

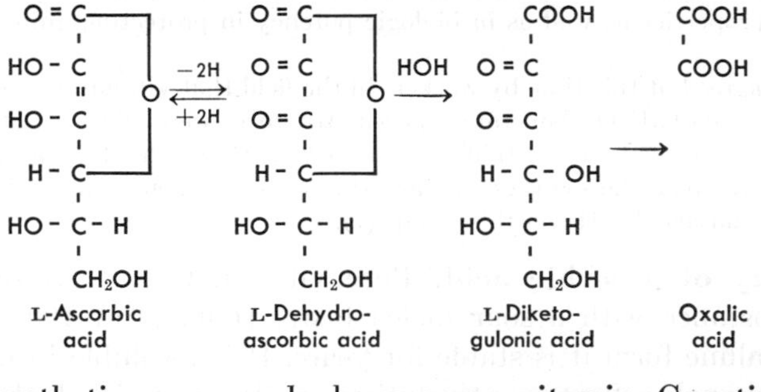

L-Ascorbic acid   L-Dehydroascorbic acid   L-Diketogulonic acid   Oxalic acid

Several synthetic compounds have some vitamin C activity. Thus, 6-desoxy-L-ascorbic acid has about one-third, L-rhamnoascorbic about one-fifth, D-araboascorbic about one-twentieth, and L-glucoascorbic around one-fortieth the activity of L-ascorbic acid. The activity of D-ascorbic acid is nil.

Ascorbic acid deficiency. The primates, including man, and the guinea pig are the only animal species that require a dietary source of vitamin C.

All other animal species studied need the vitamin for normal metabolic functions, to be sure, but they are able to synthesize all their requirement of this factor.

The guinea pig has been the animal of choice in the bulk of the experimental work on the pathologic and biochemical defects associated with ascorbic acid deficiency. This animal is highly susceptible to a lack of vitamin C, and the alterations are known to be similar to those found in human scurvy.

Vitamin C deficiency varies in degree from a mild condition scarcely recognizable to a profound state resulting in death. In human beings the latter condition is not now seen except under extreme stress.

Outstanding among the pathologic defects found in ascorbic acid deficiency is the failure to deposit intercellular cement substance. The presence of an abnormal collagen leads to a tendency to hemorrhage and to slow wound healing. A correlation has been demonstrated between the vitamin C content and the tensile strength of healing wound tissue in guinea pigs (8). Some degree of correlation was also shown in human beings (9). In the teeth of guinea pigs the poor dentine formation which may stop entirely in prolonged and severe deficiency leads to abnormal tooth development. A great deal of our information on vitamin C intake and tooth development has come from the experimental work on guinea pigs reported by Wolbach and coworkers over a number of years (10,11). Correlation between vitamin C intake and human caries is lacking. In human beings little alteration of tooth structure occurs in a deficiency state except in the very young.

In the bones a deficiency results in the failure of the osteoblasts to form the intercellular substance osteoid. Without osteoid, deposition of bone salts is arrested. The resulting scorbutic bone is weak and fractures easily. A detailed description of bone changes in guinea pigs and in man during ascorbic acid deficiency is available (12).

The advanced stage of scurvy in man is easily recognized. In infants the symptoms include irritability and fretfulness, tenderness and swelling of joints, some degree of apathy and pallor, and a desire to remain quite motionless. In adults the advanced stage is attended by loosening or even loss of teeth, accompanied by sore, spongy gums, internal hemorrhage, subcutaneous hemorrhage upon mild injury, painful joints, dyspnea, edema, and anemia. A loss of weight and a marked pallor are also noted.

It is doubtful if all these symptoms are attributable to ascorbic acid deficiency alone; more likely they represent the effects of a multiple deficiency. In support of this view the important contribution of Crandon and others (13) on experimental human deprivation of vitamin C is cited. Crandon remained on a diet totally deficient in vitamin C but supplemented with the other known vitamins for a period of six months.

Some of the pertinent findings are listed herewith. After 41 days the blood plasma ascorbic acid level reached zero. Since it was many weeks later before the first clinical signs were observed, the authors consider the plasma level of vitamin C as a poor index of the vitamin C status of an individual. They consider the ascorbic acid level in the white-cell-platelet layer of blood a good index, since this remained elevated during most of the experimental period and fell to zero only shortly before the onset of clinical signs. The earliest symptoms noted were hyperkeratotic papules over the buttocks and calves. These began to develop after 132 days on the deficient diet. According to these workers, this may be the earliest sign of deficiency. Perifollicular hemorrhages appeared after 161 days. Wound healing failed after the subject had remained on the diet for six months, although it was adequate at about the halfway mark in the experiment. At this time the plasma level of vitamin C had been zero for 44 days and the white-cell-platelet level was 4 mg per 100 ml (normal is 25 to 30 mg per 100 ml).

No gross changes were seen in the gums or teeth although x-ray pictures showed interruptions in the lamina dura in the early acute phase of scurvy. This was considered likely to be a good diagnostic criteria in early scurvy.

Correlation between capillary fragility and vitamin C deficiency was not good, and the authors doubt if the tests are as valuable as they were once thought to be, especially in a subclinical deficiency. No anemia was found at any time during the experiment, nor was there any evidence of decreased resistance to infection.

During the scorbutic state both the glucose and the insulin tolerance tests were found to be normal. Blood lactate disappeared abnormally slowly after exercise.

Following the intravenous administration of ascorbic acid all the signs and symptoms of scurvy disappeared rapidly. The tissue deficiency of this individual is shown by the fact that after the injection of 1 g of the vitamin the plasma level returned to zero after five hours. Even after 3 or 4 g of vitamin C the urinary excretion was subnormal, again demonstrating that the tissues were actively removing the vitamin from the blood stream.

Another interesting experiment on experimental human ascorbic acid deprivation employing several volunteers was conducted in England (14). The findings were somewhat similar to those reported by Crandall and coworkers, although the English workers were attempting to establish requirements as well as to study the pathologic and biochemical aspects of severe and moderate deficiency.

Physiologic functions of ascorbic acid. Ascorbic acid is intimately concerned, in an unknown manner, in the normal production of supporting tissues of mesenchymal origin, such as osteoid, dentin, and collagen.

The outstanding chemical property of the vitamin is its reversible oxidation-reduction between ascorbic and dehydroascorbic acids. This has led to postulates of physiologic action of vitamin C based on the reducing properties of the molecule.

Guinea pigs lose the ability to maintain normal levels of collagen as they become depleted in ascorbic acid, and the administration of the vitamin promptly restores this defect (15). It was felt by Gould some years ago that ascorbic acid promotes collagen formation, in part at least through its action in bringing about hydroxyproline synthesis from proline (16). Collagen contains large amounts of hydroxyproline. Mitoma and Smith (17) showed that hydroxylation of proline was not affected by ascorbic acid and they feel that collagen synthesis and not the amino acid synthesis is at fault in the deficiency state. Gross (18) has suggested that synthesis and breakdown of collagen may be progressing at somewhat the same rate in scorbutic guinea pigs. It may be that the vitamin protects against the breakdown and thus results in a net increase in the amount of collagen present.*

In the scorbutic state tyrosine metabolism is abnormal. The administration of tyrosine or phenylalanine to man or to guinea pigs in the deficiency state results in the urinary excretion of p-hydroxyphenylpyruvic acid, and ascorbic acid medication abolishes the defect (19). Normally the enzyme p-hydroxyphenylpyruvic acid oxidase mediates the oxidation of p-hydroxyphenylpyruvic acid to homogentisic acid. At one time ascorbic acid was considered to be a specific cofactor for this enzyme, but a number of other compounds—some entirely unrelated chemically, such as hydroquinone—were found to replace ascorbic acid in tyrosine oxidation in vitro (20). It was later established that ascorbic acid and compounds which can replace the vitamin in vitro do so by protecting p-hydroxyphenylpyruvic oxidase from inhibition by its substrate (21), and Zannoni and LaDu (22) have now demonstrated that ascorbic acid operates in vivo through this protection of the liver enzyme in guinea pigs.

Ascorbic acid enhances iron absorption from the intestine in humans and animals. The mechanism probably involves the reducing property of ascorbic acid, since iron in the ferrous state is preferentially absorbed.

Ascorbic acid has been implicated in the enzymatic oxidation of DPNH. Kersten and coworkers (23) isolated the enzyme from adrenal microsomes. The system also required sulfhydryl groups to bring about oxidation in the presence of molecular oxygen. These workers suggested that monodehydroascorbic acid acts as an intermediary electron acceptor.

A relationship between ascorbic acid and folic acid has been noted by various investigators. Ascorbic acid administration alleviates symptoms of folic acid deficiency in rats (24). The mechanism of action is indeed obscure. It has been postulated that the effect may be a secondary one mediated through changes in the intestinal microflora by ascorbic acid (25).

Biosynthesis of ascorbic acid. The rat supplies his own ascorbic acid requirement through synthesis, as do most species of animals. Plants also synthesize vitamin C. The rat has been studied extensively to establish the synthetic pathway. Glucose or other hexoses convertible to glucose serve as the starting material. The work of King and associates (26,27) first established through isotope work that carbon 1 of D-glucose becomes carbon 6 of L-ascorbic acid, while carbon 6 of glucose turns up in the 1 position of ascorbic acid. This work indicated that during the biosynthesis the glucose carbon chain underwent inversion of configuration and that the intact glucose chain was converted into ascorbic acid (28).

* Private communication from Dr. D. S. Jackson, Departments of Biochemistry and Surgery, University of Oregon Medical School.

Specific enzymes mediating each step in the scheme of synthesis have been demonstrated in rat liver. Much of the work was done with labeled compounds. A review by Burns (29) gives details of the various studies involved in the development of the pathway. Preliminary to the inversion of the glucose chain the following reactions apparently occur: glucose ⟶ glucose-6-PO₄ ⟶ glucose-1-PO₄ ⟶ UDP-glucose (uridine diphosphate glucose) ⟶ UDP-glucuronic acid ⟶ D-glucuronic acid-1-PO₄ ⟶ D-glucuronic acid. The next step yields L-gulonic acid and then L-gulonolactone, which is converted to L-ascorbic acid, probably through 2-keto L-gulonolactone as an intermediate (30). The structures involved in the biosynthesis are not presented here, since they are given in Chapter 24.

Galactose is converted to ascorbic acid by rats through the following sequence of reactions: galactose ⟶ galactose-1-PO₄ ⟶ UDP galactose ⟶ UDP glucose ⟶ as above for glucose (29).

It is further established that in man, monkeys, and guinea pigs there is a deficiency in the enzyme or enzymes responsible for the conversion of gulonolactone to ascorbic acid. Thus, Burns (31) found no detectable conversion of L-gulonolactone-1-C¹⁴ into labeled L-ascorbic acid in homogenates of human, guinea pig, or monkey liver, while rat liver showed about 8 per cent conversion under similar conditions.

It is interesting that enzymes are present in man, monkey, and guinea pig liver to carry out all the steps previous to the conversion of gulonolactone into the vitamin, and Snyder (32) proposed that the missing reaction results from a gene-controlled enzyme deficiency.

Metabolism of ascorbic acid. In man ascorbic acid is partly excreted unchanged and partly as diketo-L-gulonic acid and oxalic acid. Hellman and Burns (33) using labeled ascorbic acid, found 12 to 24 per cent of the urinary C¹⁴ activity in L-ascorbic acid, 12 to 18 per cent in diketogulonic acid, and 24 to 63 per cent as oxalic acid in several experiments with three subjects. No C¹⁴ was detected in respiratory CO₂. The vitamin exists in the body in an equilibrium between the reduced and the oxidized (dehydro) states, with only a small fraction in the latter form. The oxidized form can be either reduced to ascorbic acid reversibly, or metabolized to diketo-gulonic acid irreversibly. Both the oxidized and reduced forms have vitamin activity, while the diketogulonic acid has none.

Rats and guinea pigs metabolize the carbon chain of ascorbic acid, producing principally CO₂ and oxalic acid, although pathway differences in these species are established (34). Chan and others (35) found that guinea pig liver preparations formed dehydroascorbic acid which was degraded to oxalate, CO₂ and L-xylose. No xylose was found from the catabolism of ascorbic acid by rat kidney in studies by Burns and coworkers (34).

The half-life of ascorbic acid in the guinea pig is only a few days, while in man it has been estimated to be about 16 days (33). This may account for the long period required to produce a deficiency state in man compared to the time involved to produce symptoms in the guinea pig.

Determination of ascorbic acid. Two principles have been employed in the important chemical methods for vitamin C determination. In the first the strong and fairly rapid reducing property of the vitamin is determined by titration against a standard oxidizing solution. At present the dye 2,6-dichlorobenzenoneindophenol (2,6-dichlorophenolindophenol) is the oxidant of choice. Rather than titrate ascorbic acid, an excess of the dye solution may be added to the ascorbic acid solution, and the loss of color due to reduction of the dye, determined by use of a photoelectric colorimeter. Many modifications of each of these approaches have been used. The vitamin is generally extracted from animal or vegetable tissues with metaphosphoric acid (HPO$_3$) or trichloroacetic acid. In the case of vegetable tissue high in ascorbic acid oxidase the enzyme can be destroyed by extracting with hot HPO$_3$. Dehydroascorbic acid does not reduce the 2,6 dye, and, in plant tissue especially, appreciable amounts of the vitamin may exist in this form. Treatment of the acid extract with H$_2$S converts the vitamin C to the reduced form. This is an important consideration, since both forms have vitamin activity. The direct titration methods, the photoelectric method and the xylene extraction method each have certain advantages. The latter is especially adapted to turbid or highly colored ascorbic acid-containing solutions.

Another chemical principle employed in ascorbic acid determination involves the conversion of the vitamin into a soluble colored complex by treatment with 2,4-dinitrophenylhydrazine. The color intensity can be determined in any of the various instruments for this purpose. A critical review of various methods is available (36).

In the various biologic methods the guinea pig is the animal of choice. Practical methods have been developed employing growth, tooth structure, and growth of odontoblasts of incisors as the criterion of the ascorbic acid content of the test material. Details can be found in the sixteenth revision of the *United States Pharmacopoeia* (37).

Ascorbic acid status. Most of the approaches to the study of an individual's nutritional status with respect to ascorbic acid involve an attempt to study the degree of tissue saturation. There is little difficulty in the estimation of blood or urine levels, but such data alone often do not truly reflect the condition in the tissues. It has been pointed out that the level in the white cells may be more significant than that of the plasma for diagnostic purposes. The so-called saturation tests give additional information. The blood and urine levels may well be affected by the intake during the day previous to the time the samples are tested, but the degree of tissue saturation would not be markedly altered unless the intake were very high.

The tissue saturation tests involve a study of urinary ascorbic acid excretion in response to a test dose. In the individual with low reserves the vitamin is held in the tissues, and the total excretion is below normal. In one of the tests 5 mg of ascorbic acid per pound is given orally, and if 50 per cent is excreted during the ensuing 24 hours, the patient is said to have been saturated. Excretion of less than this amount indicates unsaturation. In a severely deficient patient the excretion may be from almost none up to 20 per cent of the test dose.

Human blood plasma ascorbic acid levels of 0.7 to 1.2 mg per 100 ml are considered to be within the normal range. Many investigators consider that levels of 0.4 to 0.7 mg per cent indicate a mild deficiency, and those below 0.4 mg a severe deficiency. On high dietary intakes the plasma level may rise to 2.0 mg per cent.

In older people the blood level may decline. Thus, Berlina (38) found the low average level of 0.13 mg per 100 ml in 20 healthy aged men and women on intakes of 30 to 35 mgs of ascorbic acid per day. Urinary excretion ranged from two-thirds to nearly all of the vitamin C intake.

Distribution of ascorbic acid. Vitamin C is distributed rather widely in nature. Important dietary sources for man include many vegetables and fruits. Canning, cooking, and other processing result in various degrees of vitamin C loss. Fresh vegetables such as broccoli, kale, parsley, and turnip greens have a high content of the vitamin, but these foods are generally not eaten in the raw state. The citrus fruits are also excellent sources and are consumed largely without processing, although for economic reasons they are not an important vitamin C source for the over-all population.

Certain vegetables constitute important sources by virtue of the amount eaten rather than due to a high level of the vitamin. In this class are potatoes, beans, and peas.

Most animal products contain only small amounts of the vitamin. Because the vitamin of milk is largely destroyed in pasteurization or in the evaporation process, another source of vitamin C is regularly supplied to infants.

By definition 1 I.U. or 1 U.S.P. unit is equivalent to 0.05 mg of L-ascorbic acid. This makes 1 mg equal to 20 U.S.P. units.

Table 18.7 gives the ascorbic acid content of a number of foods. The values given are, of course, subject to considerable variation due to climatic and soil conditions, etc.

Table 18.7.   Ascorbic Acid Content of Some Foods

Food	Ascorbic Acid, mg per 100 g
Strawberries	40–80
Watermelon	5–8
Orange juice	40–70
Lemon juice	40–60
Apple	3–10
Pineapple, fresh	20–30
Pineapple, canned	2–10
Potato, white	20–30
Potato, winter stored	5–10
Cabbage, fresh	40–70
Cabbage, cooked	15–20
Sauerkraut	10–20
Lettuce, head	5–10
Turnip greens	100–150
Beans, green (canned)	2–5
Tomato, fresh	20–30
Tomato, juice	10–20
English walnuts (green, unripe)	500–2000

Ascorbic acid requirement. The optimum human requirement for vitamin C remains a controversial matter. The recommended intakes set by the Food and Nutrition Board of the National Research Council (Table 18.5, page 696) are not necessarily based on sound experimental data, since such data are largely lacking. This Board recommends daily ascorbic acid intakes of 75 mg for adults, 100 to 150 mg during pregnancy and lactation, and 30 to 75 mg for children up to 12 years of age. Our present state of knowledge does not indicate whether optimum requirements are higher or lower than these figures. It is certain that a large proportion of our population has an intake considerably lower than the recommended allowances.

A study of ascorbic acid intakes by Olympic athletes in London is of interest. The seven subjects studied in this connection ate duplicate meals, cafeteria style, for a four-day period, and these were assayed for vitamin C as well as for other nutritional constituents. The average intakes were found to be 41, 43, 45, 71, 80, 81, and 98 mg of ascorbic acid per day for these subjects. This interesting paper and a symposium on the nutrition of athletes is reviewed in *Nutrition Reviews* (39).

"VITAMIN P"

After pure ascorbic acid became available, it was noticed that in guinea pigs on scorbutic diets this material, in certain instances, was not as effective in alleviating the tendency to hemorrhage as was one of the natural food sources of ascorbic acid, such as citrus fruits. In 1936 Szent-Györgyi and coworkers (1,2) reported the presence of material in red peppers and in citrus fruits which they claimed was beneficial in the control of hemorrhage in man and in guinea pigs and was chemically different from ascorbic acid. Since the material was thought to be involved in capillary permeability and was first found in paprika, the name "vitamin P" was given the newly discovered factor.

It is difficult to demonstrate a vitamin P deficiency state in animals or in man. It was claimed, however, that guinea pigs on a flavone-free diet supplemented with ascorbic acid developed capillary weakness which responded specifically to vitamin P (3,4).

Many workers feel that the active substances do not warrant the status of a vitamin, since it is possible to produce symptoms only in the scorbutic guinea pig treated with ascorbic acid.

Of the several compounds with "vitamin P" activity the most effective are rutin from buckwheat and esculin from chestnuts. Rutin is 3,5,7,3',4'-pentahydroxyflavone-3-rutinoside. Rutinose is a disaccharide containing glucose and rhamnose. Esculin is 6,7-dihydroxycoumarin-6-glucoside.

The active substances are all of plant origin. In citrus fruits the concentration is higher in the rind than in the juice.

It is not established that the "vitamin" is required in man. No figures can be given for a requirement that may not exist:

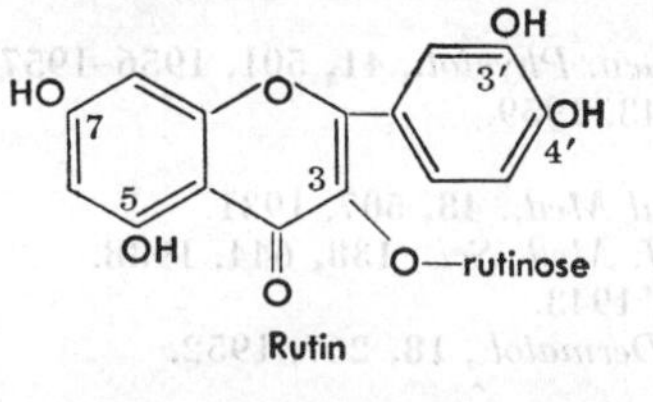

Rutin

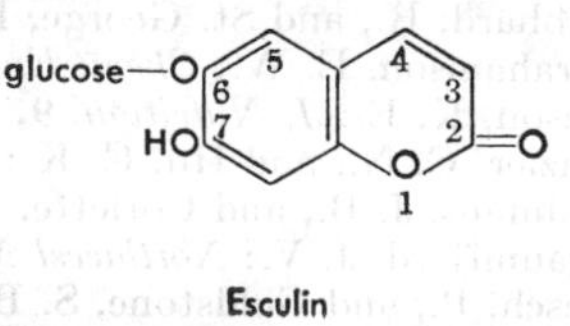

Esculin

SPECIAL REFERENCES

INTRODUCTION

1. Funk, C.: *J. Physiol.*, **45**, 489, 1912–13; **46**, 173, 1913.
2. Hart, E. B.; McCollum, E. V.; Steenbock, H.; and Humphrey, G. C.: *Research Bull.*, No. 17, University Wisconsin Agricultural Experiment Station, June, 1911.
3. Hart, E. B.; McCollum, E. V.; and Steenbock, H.: *J. Agr. Research*, **10**, 175, 1917.

VITAMIN A

1. Hopkins, F. G.: *J. Physiol. (London)*, **44**, 425, 1912.
2. Osborne, T. B., and Mendel, L. B.: *J. Biol. Chem.*, **17**, 401, 1914.
3. McCollum, E. V., and Davis, M.: *J. Biol. Chem.*, **15**, 167, 1913.
4. McCollum, E. V., and Simmonds, N.: *J. Biol. Chem.*, **32**, 181, 1917.
5. Steenbock, H.: *Science*, **50**, 352, 1919.
6. Kemmerer, A. R., and Fraps, G. S.: *J. Biol. Chem.*, **161**, 305, 1945.
7. Morton, R. A.; Salah, M. K.; and Stubbs, A. L.: *Biochem. J.*, **40**, LIX, 1946.
8. Goodwin, T. W.: *Advances in Enzymol.*, **21**, 295, 1959.
9. Sexton, E. L.; Mehl, J. W.; and Deuel, H. J., Jr.: *J. Nutrition*, **31**, 299, 1946.
10. Koehn, C. J.: *Arch. Biochem.*, **17**, 337, 1948.
11. Lowe, J. S., and Morton, R. A.: *Vitamins and Hormones*, **14**, 97, 1956.
12. Glover, J., and Redfearn, E. R.: *Biochem. J.*, **58**, XV, 1954.
13. Johnson, R. M., and Baumann, C. A.: *J. Biol. Chem.*, **171**, 513, 1947.
14. Cama, H. R., and Goodwin, T. W.: *Biochem. J.*, **45**, 236, 1949.
15. Arnrich, L., and Morgan, A. F.: *J. Nutrition*, **54**, 107, 1954.
16. Sobel, A. E.; Rosenberg, A.; and Adelson, H.: *Arch. Biochem. Biophys.*, **44**, 176, 1953.
17. Rosenberg, A., and Sobel, A. E.: *Arch. Biochem. Biophys.*, **44**, 326, 1953.
18. Morton, R. A.; Salah, M. K.; and Stubbs, A. L.: *Nature*, **159**, 744, 1947.
19. Farrar, K. R.; Hamlet, J. C.; Henbest, H. B.; and Jones, E. R. H.: *J. Chem. Soc.*, 2657, 1952.
20. Plack, P. A.; Fisher, L. R.; Henry, K. M.; and Kon, S. K.: *Biochem. J.*, **64**, 17 P., 1956.
21. *Nutrition Revs.*, **15**, 60, 1957.
22. Cawley, J. D.; Robeson, C. D.; Weisler, L.; Shantz, E. M.; Embree, N. D.; and Baxter, J. G.: *Science*, **107**, 346, 1948.
23. Attenburrow, J.; Cameron, A. F. B.; Chapman, J. H.; Evans, R. M.; Hens, B. A.; Jensen, A. B. A.; and Walker, T.: *J. Chem. Soc.*, 1094, 1952.
24. Wendler, N. L.; Slates, H. L.; Trenner, N. R.; and Tishler, M.: *J. Am. Chem. Soc.*, **73**, 719, 1951.
25. Wolbach, S. B., and Bessey, O. A.: *Physiol. Revs.*, **22**, 233, 1942.
26. Follis, R. H., Jr.: *Deficiency Disease*. Charles C Thomas, Publisher, Springfield, Ill., 1958.
27. Bloch, C. E.: *J. Hyg.*, **19**, 283, 1921.
28. Moore, D. F.: *J. Trop. Med. Hyg.*, **43**, 257, 1940.
29. Dowling, J. E., and Wald, G.: *Ann. N. Y. Acad. Sci.*, **74**, 256, 1958.
30. Hecht, S., and Mandelbaum, J.: *J. Am. Med. Assoc.*, **112**, 1910, 1939. Hecht, S.: *Physiol. Revs.*, **17**, 239, 1937.
31. Wald, G.; Jeghers, H.; and Arminio, J.: *Am. J. Physiol.*, **123**, 732, 1938.
32. Wald, G.: *J. Gen. Physiol.*, **19**, 351, 781, 1935–1936; **20**, 45, 1936–1937.
33. Kropf, A., and Hubbard, R.: *Ann. N. Y. Acad. Sci.*, **74**, 266, 1958.
34. Wald, G.: *Science*, **113**, 287, 1951.
35. Oroshnik, W.: *J. Am. Chem. Soc.*, **78**, 2651, 1956.
36. Hubbard, R.: *Federation Proc.*, **14**, 229, 1955.
37. Wald, G.: *Nature*, **175**, 390, 1955.
38. Hubbard, R., and St. George, R. C. C.: *J. Gen. Physiol.*, **41**, 501, 1956–1957.
39. Abrahamson, E. W.: *Chem. Eng. News*, **37**, 43, 1959.
40. Mason, K. E.: *J. Nutrition*, **9**, 735, 1935.
41. Frazier, C. N., and Hu, C. K.: *Arch. Internal Med.*, **48**, 507, 1931.
42. Youmans, J. B., and Corlette, M. B.: *Am. J. Med. Sci.*, **138**, 644, 1938.
43. Straumfjord, J. V.: *Northwest Med.*, **42**, 219, 1943.
44. Flesch, P., and Goldstone, S. B.: *J. Invest. Dermatol.*, **18**, 267, 1952.

45. Wolbach, S. B., and Howe, P. R.: *Am. J. Path.*, **9**, 275, 1933.
46. Higgins, C. C.: *J. Am. Med. Assoc.*, **104**, 1296, 1935.
47. Wolf, G.; Lane, M. D.; and Johnson, B. C.: *J. Biol. Chem.*, **225**, 995, 1957.
48. Wolf, G.; Wagle, S. R.; Van Dyke, R. A.; and Johnson, B. C.: *J. Biol. Chem.*, **230**, 979, 1958.
49. Van Bruggen, J. T., and Straumfjord, J. V.: *J. Lab. Clin. Med.*, **33**, 67, 1948.
50. Jeghers, H., and Marvaro, H.: *Am. J. Clin. Nutrition*, **6**, 335, 1958.
51. Hillman, R. W.: *Am. J. Clin. Nutrition*, **4**, 603, 1956.
52. Butler, C.: *Com. Fisheries Rev.*, **8**, 13, 1946.
53. Embree, N. D., and Shantz, E. M.: *J. Am. Chem. Soc.*, **65**, 910, 1943.
54. Moore, T.: *Vitamin A*. D. Van Nostrand Co., Inc., Princeton, New Jersey, 1957.

VITAMIN D

1. Hess, A. F., and Unger, L. J.: *J. Am. Med. Assoc.*, **74**, 217, 1920.
2. Mellanby, E.: *Lancet*, **196**, 407, 1919.
3. Huldschinsky, K.: *Deut. med. Wochschr.*, **45**, 712, 1919.
4. McCollum, E. V.; Simmonds, N.; and Becker, J. E.: *J. Biol. Chem.*, **53**, 293, 1922.
5. Steenbock, H.: *Science*, **60**, 224, 1924. Steenbock, H., and Black, A.: *J. Biol. Chem.*, **61**, 405, 1924. Steenbock, H., and Nelson, M. T.: *ibid.*, **62**, 209, 1924.
6. Hess, A. F.: *Am. J. Diseases Children*, **28**, 517, 1924.
7. Angus, T. C.; Askew, F. A.; Bourdillon, R. B.; Bruce, H. M.; Callow, R. K.; Fishmann, C.; Philpot, J. St. L.; and Webster, T. A.: *Proc. Roy. Soc. (London)*, **B108**, 340, 1931.
8. Windaus, A.; Schenck, F.; and Verder, F.: *Z. physiol. Chem.*, **241**, 100, 1936.
9. Deuel, H. J., Jr.: *The Lipids*. Interscience Publishers, New York, 1951.
10. Dam, H.: *Progr. in Chem. Fats Lipids*, **3**, 155, 1955.
11. Harrison, H. E., and Harrison, H. C.: *J. Biol. Chem.*, **185**, 857, 1950; **188**, 83, 1951.
12. Carlsson, A., and Lindquist, A.: *Acta Physiol. Scand.*, **33**, 55, 1955.
13. Shohl, A. T., and Wolbach, S. B.: *J. Nutrition*, **11**, 275, 1936.
14. Hess, A. F.: *Proc. Soc. Exptl. Biol. Med.*, **26**, 199, 1928.
15. Robison, R.: *The Significance of Phosphoric Esters in Metabolism*. New York University Press, New York, 1932.
16. Klasmer, R.: *Am. J. Diseases Children*, **67**, 348, 1944.
17. Gutman, A. B., and Yu, T. F.: *Transactions Macy Conference on Metabolic Interrelations*, **1**, 11, 1949.
18. Zetterström, R.: *Nature*, **167**, 409, 1951.
19. Harrison, H. E., and Harrison, H. C.: *J. Clin. Invest.*, **20**, 47, 1941.
20. Nicoloysen, R., and Eeg-Larsen, N.: *Vitamins and Hormones*, **11**, 29, 1953.
21. Bellin, S. A., and Steenbock, H.: *J. Biol. Chem.*, **194**, 311, 1952.
22. Steenbock, H., and Bellin, S. A.: *J. Biol. Chem.*, **205**, 985, 1953.
23. De Luca, H. F.; Gran, F. C.; and Steenbock, H.: *J. Biol. Chem.*, **224**, 201, 1957.
24. De Luca, H. F.; Gran, F. C.; Steenbock, H.; and Reiser, S.: *J. Biol. Chem.*, **228**, 469, 1957.
25. De Luca, H. F., and Steenbock, H.: *Science*, **126**, 258, 1957.
26. Pilleggi, V. J.; De Luca, H. F.; and Steenbock, H.: *Arch. Biochem. Biophys.*, **58**, 194, 1955.
27. Patt, H. M., and Luckhardt, A. B.: *Endocrinology*, **31**, 384, 1942.
28. Albright, F., and Reifenstein, E. C.: *The Parathyroid Glands and Metabolic Bone Disease*. Williams & Wilkins Co., Baltimore, 1948, p. 134.
29. Talmage, R. V.; Kraintz, F. W.; Frost, R. C.; and Kraintz, L.: *Endocrinology*, **52**, 318, 1953.
30. Stewart, G. S., and Bowen, H. F.: *Endocrinology*, **51**, 80, 1952.
31. Kodicek, E.: *Biochem. J.*, **60**, XXV, 1955.
30. Kodicek, E.: *Biochem. J.*, **64**, 25P, 1956.
33. Mulder, F. J.; Roborgh, J. R.; DeMan, T. J.; Keunign, K. J.; and Hanewald, K. H.: *Rec. trav. chim.*, **76**, 733, 1957.
34. Shaw, W. H. C.; Jefferies, J. P.; and Holt, T. E.: *Analyst*, **82**, 2, 8, 1957.
35. Jeans, P. C.: *J. Am. Med. Assoc.*, **106**, 2066, 2150, 1936.
36. Gillman, J., and Gilbert, C.: *Exptl. Med. Surg.*, **14**, 136, 1956.
37. Blackburn, P. S.; Blaxter, K. L.; and Castle, E. J.: *Proc. Nutrition Soc.*, **16**, XVI, 1957.

38. Herzfeld, E.; Loudon, M.; and Zweymuller, E.: *Z. ges. exp. Med.*, **127**, 272, 1956.
39. Jeans, P. C., and Stearns, G.: *J. Pediat.*, **13**, 730, 1938.
40. Wolstenholme, G. E. W., and O'Connor, C. M.: *Ciba Foundation Symposium, Bone Structure and Metabolism*. Little, Brown & Co., Boston, 1956.

VITAMIN K

1. Dam, H.: *Biochem. Z.*, **215**, 475, 1929; **220**, 158, 1930.
2. Dam, H.: *Biochem. J.*, **29**, 1273, 1935.
3. Almquist, H. J., and Stokstad, E. L. R.: *J. Biol. Chem.*, **111**, 105, 1935.
4. Dam, H.; Geiger, A.; Glavind, J.; Karrer, P.; Karrer, W.; Rothschild, E. E.; and Salomon, H.: *Helv. Chim. Acta*, **22**, 310, 1939.
5. McKee, R. W.; Binkley, S. B.; MacCorquadale, D. W.; Thayer, S. A.; and Doisy, E. A.: *J. Am. Chem. Soc.*, **61**, 1295, 1939.
6. *Nutrition Revs.*, **15**, 331, 1957.
7. Mushett, C. W.; Kelley, K. L.; and Hirschmann, R.: *Blood*, **14**, 37, 1959.
8. Isler, O., and Wiss, O.: *Vitamins and Hormones*, **17**, 54, 1959.
9. Quick, A. J., and Collentine, G. E.: *Am. J. Physiol.*, **164**, 716, 1951.
10. Fisher, L. M.; Millar, G. J.; and Jaques, L. B.: *Can. J. Biochem. and Physiol.*, **34**, 1039, 1956.
11. Woods, R. J., and Taylor, J. D.: *Can. J. Chem.*, **35**, 941, 1957.
12. Taylor, J. D.; Millar, G. J.; Jaques, L. B.; and Spinks, J. W. T.: *Can. J. Biochem. and Physiol.*, **34**, 1143, 1956.
13. Taylor, J. D.; Millar, G. J.; and Wood, R. J.: *ibid.*, **35**, 691, 1957.
14. Ames, S. R.: *Ann. Rev. Biochem.*, **27**, 371, 1958.
15. Martius, V. C.: *Proc. Intern. Congr. Biochem.*, 3rd Congr. Brussels, 1955 (Pub. 1956), p. 1.
16. Roderick, L. M.: *Am. J. Physiol.*, **96**, 413, 1931.
17. Campbell, H. A.; Roberts, W. L.; Smith, W. K.; and Link, K. P.: *J. Biol. Chem.*, **136**, 47, 1940.
18. Campbell, H. A.; Smith, W. K.; Roberts, W. L.; and Link, K. P.: *J. Biol. Chem.*, **138**, 1, 1941.
19. Campbell, H. A., and Link, K. P.: *J. Biol. Chem.*, **138**, 21, 1941.
20. Stahmann, M. A.; Huebner, C. F.; and Link, K. P.: *J. Biol. Chem.*, **138**, 513, 1941.
21. Babson, A. L.; Malament, S.; Mangun, G. H.; and Phillips, G. E.: *Clin. Chem.*, **2**, 243, 1956.
22. Shapiro, S., and Ciferri, F. E.: *J. Am. Med. Assoc.*, **165**, 1377, 1957.
23. Link, K. P.: *Circulation*, **19**, 97, 1959.
24. Almquist, H. J.: *J. Assoc. Offic. Agr. Chemists*, **24**, 405, 1941.
25. Johnson, B. C.: *Methods of Vitamin Determination*. Burgess Publishing Co., Minneapolis, Minn., 1948.
26. Sathe, V.; Dave, J. B.; and Ramarkrishnan, C. V.: *Anal. Chem.*, **29**, 155, 1957.
27. Canady, W. J., and Roe, J. H.: *J. Biol. Chem.*, **220**, 563, 1956.
28. Jongkind, J. C.; Buzza, E.; and Fox, S. H.: *J. Am. Pharm. Assoc., Sci. Ed.*, **46**, 214, 1957.

VITAMIN E

1. Mattill, H. A., and Conklin, R. E.: *J. Biol. Chem.*, **44**, 137, 1920.
2. Evans, H. M., and Bishop, K. S.: *Science*, **55**, 650, 1922.
3. Evans, H. M.; Emerson, O. H.; and Emerson, G. A.: *J. Biol. Chem.*, **113**, 319, 1936.
4. Fernholz, E.: *J. Am. Chem. Soc.*, **60**, 700, 1938.
5. Karrer, P.; Fritzsche, H.; Ringier, B. H.; and Salomon, H.: *Helv. Chim. Acta*, **21**, 520, 820, 1938.
6. Blaxter, K. L.: *Ann. Rev. Biochem.*, **26**, 275, 1957.
7. Woodruff, C. W.: *Am. J. Clin. Nutrition*, **4**, 497, 1956.
8. Follis, R. H., Jr.: *Deficiency Disease*. Charles C Thomas, Publisher, Springfield, Ill., 1958, p. 159.
9. Evans, H. M., and Burr, G. O.: *J. Biol. Chem.*, **76**, 273, 1928.
10. Schwarz, K., and Foltz, C. M.: *J. Am. Chem. Soc.*, **79**, 3292, 1957.
11. Dinning, J. S., and Fitch, C. D.: *Federation Proc.*, **16**, 384, 1957.
12. Fleischmann, W.: *Proc. Soc. Exptl. Biol. Med.*, **46**, 94, 1941.
13. Rose, C. S., and György, P.: *Am. J. Physiol.*, **168**, 414, 1952.

14. Kaunitz, H., and Pappenheimer, A. M.: *Am. J. Physiol.*, **138**, 328, 1943.
15. Houchin, O. B.: *J. Biol. Chem.*, **146**, 309, 1942.
16. Dinning, J. S., and Day, P. L.: *J. Exptl. Med.*, **105**, 395, 1957.
17. Dinning, J. S., and Day, P. L.: *J. Nutrition*, **63**, 393, 1957.
18. Jenson, J. L.: *Science*, **103**, 586, 1946.
19. Draper, H. H.; Goodyear, S.; Barbee, K. D.; and Johnson, B. C.: *Brit. J. Nutrition*, **12**, 89, 1958.
20. Sharman, I. M., and Moore, T.: *Biochem. J.*, **69**, 61P, 1958.
21. Shull, R. L.; Ershoff, B. H.; and Alfin-Slater, R. B.: *Proc. Soc. Exptl. Biol. Med.*, **98**, 364, 1958.
22. Donaldson, K. O.; Nason, A.; and Garrett, R. H.: *J. Biol. Chem.*, **233**, 572, 1958.
23. Crane, F. L.; Hatefi, Y.; Lester, R. L.; and Widmer, C.: *Biochim. et Biophys. Acta*, **25**, 220, 1957.
24. Bunyan, J.; Green, J.; Mamalis, P.; and Marcinkiewicz, S.: *Nature*, **179**, 418, 1957.
25. Friedman, L.; Weiss, W.; Wherry, F.; and Kline, O. L.: *J. Nutrition*, **65**, 143, 1958.
26. Bro-Rasmussen, F., and Hjarde, W.: *Acta Chem. Scand.*, **11**, 34, 44, 1957.
27. Rosenkrantz, H.: *J. Biol. Chem.*, **224**, 165, 1957.
28. *National Formulary XI*, 1960, Washington, D. C.
29. Hickman, K. C. D., and Harris, P. L.: *Advances in Enzymol.*, **6**, 469, 1946.

THIAMINE

1. McCollum, E. V., and Davis, M.: *J. Biol. Chem.*, **20**, 641, 1915; **23**, 231, 1915.
2. Emmett, A. D., and Luros, G. O.: *J. Biol. Chem.*, **43**, 265, 1920.
3. Jansen, B. C. P., and Donath, W. F.: *Mededeel. Diesnst Volksgezondheid Nederland Indië*, Pt. 1, 186, 1926; 21, 2150, 1927.
4. Williams, R. R., and Cline, J. K.: *J. Am. Chem. Soc.*, **58**, 1504, 1936. Cline, J. K.; Williams, R. R.; Ruehle, A. E.; and Waterman, R. E.: *ibid.*, **59**, 530, 1937.
5. Wintersteiner, O.; Williams, R. R.; and Ruehle, A. E.: *J. Am. Chem. Soc.*, **57**, 517, 1935.
6. Schultz, F.: *Z. physiol. Chem.*, **272**, 29, 1941.
7. Westenbrink, H. G. K.: *Intern. Congr. Biochem.*, 4th Meeting, Symposium 11, Preprint No. 2, 1 (Vienna, Austria, September 1958).
8. Barron, E. S. G.; Goldinger, J. M.; Lipton, M. A., and Lyman, C. M., *J. Biol. Chem.*, **141**, 975, 1941.
9. Green, D. E.; Westerfeld, W. W.; Vennesland, B.; and Knox, W. E.: *J. Biol. Chem.*, **145**, 69, 1942.
10. DeTar, D. F., and Westheimer, F. H.: *J. Am. Chem. Soc.*, **81**, 175, 1959.
11. Gunsalus, I. C.; Barton, L. S.; and Gruber, W.: *J. Am. Chem. Soc.*, **78**, 1763, 1956.
12. Reed, L. J.; Leach, F. R.; and Koike, M.: *J. Biol. Chem.*, **232**, 123, 1958.
13. Reed, L. J.: *Abstr. Am. Chem. Soc.*, 133rd Meeting, 4c (San Francisco, Calif., April 1958).
14. Gunsalus, I. C.: *Abstr. Am. Chem. Soc.*, 133rd Meeting, 3c (San Francisco, Calif., April 1958).
15. Williams, R. D.; Mason, H. L.; and Smith, B. F.: *Proc. Staff Meetings, Mayo Clinic*, **14**, 787, 1939.
16. Williams, R. D.; Mason, H. L.; Power, M. H.; and Wilder, R. M.: *Arch. Internal Med.*, **71**, 38, 1943.
17. Brožek, J.: *Am. J. Clin. Nutrition*, **5**, 109, 1957.
18. *Nutritional Disease*, edited by Kinney, T. D., and Follis, R. H., Jr. *Federation Proc.*, **17**, No. 3, Supplement No. 2, September 1958.
19. Rinehart, J. F.; Greenberg, L. D.; Friedman, M.: *Am. J. Path.*, **23**, 879, 1947.
20. North, J. D. K., and Sinclair, H. M.: *J. Nutrition*, **61**, 219, 1957.
21. Woolley, D. W., and White, A. G. C.: *J. Biol. Chem.*, **149**, 285, 1943.
22. Woolley, D. W.: *J. Biol. Chem.*, **191**, 43, 1951.
23. Woolley, D. W., and Merrifield, R. B.: *Federation Proc.*, **11**, 458, 1952.
24. De Caro, L.; Perri, V.; and Capelli, V.: *Intern. Z. Vitaminforsch.*, **27**, 475, 1957.
25. Emerson, G. A., and Southwick, P. L.: *J. Biol. Chem.*, **160**, 169, 1945.
26. Westerfeld, W. W.; Stotz, E. W.; and Berg, R. L.: *J. Biol. Chem.*, **149**, 237, 1943; **152**, 41, 1944.
27. Berg, R. L.; Stotz, E. W.; and Westerfeld, W. W.: *J. Biol. Chem.*, **152**, 51, 1944.
28. Westerfeld, W. W., and Doisy, E. A.: *J. Nutrition*, **30**, 127, 1945.

29. Dann, W. J.: *Federation Proc.*, **4**, 153, 1945.
30. McCarthy, P. T.; Cerecedo, L. R.; and Brown, E. V.: *J. Biol. Chem.*, **209**, 611, 1954.
31. Young, C. M., and Lafortune, T. D.: *J. Am. Dietet. Assoc.*, **33**, 98, 1957. Hart, M., and Reynolds, M. S.: *J. Home Econ.*, **49**, 35, 1957.
32. Kingsley, H. N., and Parsons, H. T.: *J. Nutrition*, **34**, 321, 1947.
33. Alexander, B., and Landwehr, G.: *Science*, **101**, 229, 1945.
34. Mameesh, M. S., and Johnson, B. C.: *J. Nutrition*, **65**, 161, 1958.
35. Mickelson, O.: *Vitamins and Hormones*, **14**, 1, 1956.
36. Horwitt, M. K.: *Ann. Rev. Biochem.*, **28**, 411, 1959.
37. Mickelsen, O., and Yamamoto, R. S.: *Methods of Biochem. Anal.*, **6**, 191, 1958.

RIBOFLAVIN

1. Emmett, A. D., and McKim, L. H.: *J. Biol. Chem.*, **32**, 409, 1917.
2. Bleyer, B., and Kallmann, O.: *Biochem. Z.*, **155**, 54, 1925.
3. Blooher, L. E.: *J. Biol. Chem.*, **102**, 39, 1933.
4. Warburg, O., and Christian, W.: *Naturwissenschaften*, **20**, 688, 980, 1932; *Biochem. Z.*, **266**, 377, 1933.
5. Kuhn, R.; György, P.; and Wagner-Jauregg, T.: *Ber.*, **66**, 1034, 1577, 1933.
6. Kuhn, R.; Reinemand, K.; Weygand, F.; and Ströbele, R.: *Ber.*, **68**, 1765, 1935.
7. Karrer, P.; Becker, B.; Benz, F.; Frie, P.; Salomon, H.; and Schöpp, K.: *Helv. Chim. Acta*, **18**, 1435, 1935.
8. Stadtman, E. R.: *Intern. Congr. Biochem.*, 4th Meeting, Symposium 11, Preprint No. 15, 1 (Vienna, Austria, September, 1958).
9. Rosenberg, H. R.: *Chemistry and Physiology of the Vitamins*. Revised photo-offset reprint of first edition. Interscience, New York-London, 1942.
10. Robinson, F. A.: *The Vitamin B Complex*. John Wiley & Sons, New York, 1951, p. 140.
11. Sydenstricker, V. P.: *Ann. Internal Med.*, **14**, 1499, 1941.
12. Sebrell, W. H., and Butler, R. E.: *U. S. Pub. Health Repts.*, **53**, 2282, 1938.
13. Mann, I.: *Am. J. Ophthalmology*, **28**, 243, 1945.
14. Cayer, D.; Ruffin, J. M.; and Perlzweig, W. A.: *Southern Med. J.*, **38**, 111, 1945.
15. Horwitt, M. K.; Harvey, C. C.; Rothwell, W. S.; Cutler, J. L.; and Haffron, D.: *J. Nutrition*, **60**, Supp. No. 1, 1, 1956.
16. Bessey, O. A.; Horwitt, M. K.; and Love, R. H.: *J. Nutrition*, **58**, 367, 1956.
17. Follis, R. H., Jr.: *Deficiency Disease*. Charles C Thomas, Publisher, Springfield, Ill., 1958.
18. Sydenstricker, V. P.: *Am. J. Clin. Nutrition*, **6**, 409, 1958.
19. Warkany, J., and Schraffenberger, E.: *J. Nutrition*, **27**, 477, 1944.
20. Coward, K. H., and Morgan, B. G. E.: *Biochem. J.*, **35**, 974, 1941.
21. Wiese, A. C.; Johnson, B. C.; Mitchell, H. H.; and Nevens, W. B.: *J. Nutrition*, **33**, 263, 1947.
22. Wertman, K. F.; Lynn, R. J.; and Disque, D. T.: *J. Nutrition*, **63**, 311, 1957.
23. Theorell, H., and Åkeson, Å.: *Arch. Biochem. Biophys.*, **65**, 439, 1956.
24. Dimant, E.; Sanadi, D. R.; and Huennekens, F. M.: *J. Am. Chem. Soc.*, **74**, 5440, 1952.
25. Christie, S. M. H.; Kenner, G. W.; and Todd, A. R.: *Nature*, **170**, 924, 1952.
26. Kearny, E. B., and England, S.: *J. Biol. Chem.*, **193**, 821, 1951.
27. Schrecker, A., and Kornberg, A.: *J. Biol. Chem.*, **182**, 795, 1950.
28. Tong, W.; Taurog, A.; and Chaikoff, I. L.: *J. Biol. Chem.*, **227**, 773, 1957.
29. Burch, H. B.; Lowry, O. H.; Padilla, A. M.; and Combs, A. M.: *J. Biol. Chem.*, **223**, 29, 1956.
30. Robinson, F. A.: *The Vitamin B Complex*. John Wiley & Sons, New York, 1951, p. 140.
31. Sydenstricker, V. P.: *Ann. Internal Med.*, **14**, 1499, 1941.
32. Egami, F.; Naoi, M.; Tada, M.; and Yagi, K.: *J. Biochem. (Japan)*, **43**, 669, 1956.
33. Fall, H. H., and Petering, H. G.: *J. Am. Chem. Soc.*, **78**, 377, 1956.
34. Price, E. L.; Marquette, M. M.; and Parsons, H. T.: *J. Nutrition*, **34**, 311, 1947.
35. *Nutrition Revs.*, **6**, 2, 1948.
36. Everson, G.; Wheeler, E.; Walker, H.; and Caulfield, W. J.: *J. Nutrition*, **35**, 209, 1948.
37. Burch, H. B.; Bessey, O. A.; and Lowry, O. H.: *J. Biol. Chem.*, **175**, 457, 1948.
38. Strong, F. M., and Snell, E. E.: *J. Am. Chem. Soc.*, *Anal. Ed.*, **6**, 346, 1939.

39. *The Pharmacopoeia of the United States of America*, 16th revision, December 15, 1960, Mack Publishing Co., Easton, Pa.
40. Yagi, K.: *J. Biochem. (Japan)*, **43**, 635, 1956.
41. Murphy, V. M. R.; Burroughs, R. N.; Reid, B. L.; and Couch, J. R.: *J. Agr. Food Chem.*, **6**, 129, 1958.
42. De Luca, C.; Weber, M. M.; and Kaplan, N. O.: *J. Biol. Chem.*, **223**, 559, 1956.
43. Horwitt, M. K.; Harvey, C. C.; Hills, O. W.; and Liebert, E.: *J. Nutrition*, **41**, 247, 1950.
44. Bro-Rasmussen, F.: *Nutrition Abstr. and Revs.*, **28**, 1, 369, 1958.
45. *Recommended Dietary Allowances, National Academy of Sciences*. National Research Council, Publication 589, Washington, D.C., 1958.

NIACIN—NICOTINIC ACID

1. Goldberger, J.; Waring, C. H.; and Willets, D. G.: *U. S. Pub. Health Repts.*, **30**, 3117, 1915.
2. Chittendon, R. H., and Underhill, F. P.: *Am. J. Physiol.*, **44**, 13, 1917.
3. Warburg, O., and Christian, W.: *Biochem. Z.*, **275**, 464, 1935.
4. Elvehjem, C. A.; Madden, R. J.; Woolley, D. W.; and Strong, F. M.: *J. Am. Chem. Soc.*, **59**, 1767, 1937. Elvehjem, C. A.; Madden, R. J.; Strong, F. M.; and Woolley, D. W.: *J. Biol. Chem.*, **123**, 137, 1938.
5. Fouts, P. F.; Helmer, O. M.; Lepkovsky, S.; and Jukes, T. H.: *Proc. Soc. Exptl. Biol. Med.*, **37**, 405, 1937.
6. McElvain, S. M., and Goese, M. A.: *J. Am. Chem. Soc.*, **63**, 2283, 1941.
7. Chang, M. L. W., and Johnson, B. C.: *J. Biol. Chem.*, **226**, 799, 1957.
8. Preiss, J., and Handler, P.: *J. Biol. Chem.*, **233**, 493, 1958.
9. Wang, T. P.; Kaplan, N. O.; and Stolzenbach, F. E.: *J. Biol. Chem.*, **211**, 465, 1958.
10. *Nutrition Revs.*, **6**, 189, 1946.
11. Goldsmith, G. A.; Sarett, H. P.; Register, U. D.; and Gibbens, J.: *J. Clin. Invest.*, **31**, 533, 1952.
12. Horwitt, M. K.; Harvey, C. C.; Rothwell, W. S.; Cutler, J. L.; and Haffron, D.: *J. Nutrition*, **60**, Supp. No. 1, 1, 1956.
13. Lushbough, C. H., and Schweigert, B. S.: *Ann. Rev. Biochem.*, **27**, 313, 1957.
14. Henderson, L. M., and Hanks, I. V.: *Proc. Soc. Exptl. Biol. Med.*, **70**, 26, 1949.
15. Handley, J. M., and Bond, H. W.: *J. Biol. Chem.*, **173**, 513, 1948.
16. Altschul, R., and Hoffer, A.: *Arch. Biochem. Biophys.*, **73**, 420, 1958.
17. Schön, H.: *Nature*, **182**, 534, 1958.
18. Goldsmith, G. A.: *Am. J. Clin. Nutrition*, **6**, 479, 1958.
19. Bessey, O. A.; Lowe, H. J.; and Salomon, L. L.: *Ann. Rev. Biochem.*, **22**, 545, 1953.
20. Ellinger, P.; Fraenkel, G.; and Kadar, M. M. A.: *Biochem. J.*, **41**, 559, 1947.
21. Van Reen, R., and Stolzenbach, F. E.: *J. Biol. Chem.*, **226**, 373, 1957.
22. Halliday, S. L.; Sloboda, A.; Will, L. W.; and Oleson, J. J.: *Federation Proc.*, **16**, 190, 1957.
23. Swaminathan, M.: *Indian J. Med. Research*, **32**, 39, 1944—reviewed in *Nutrition Revs.*, **4**, 233, 1946.
24. Teply, L. J.; Strong, F. M.; and Elvehjem, C. A.: *J. Nutrition*, **23**, 417, 1942.
25. Morley, N. H., and Storvick, C. A.: *J. Nutrition*, **63**, 539, 1957.
26. *The Pharmacopoeia of the United States of America*, 16th revision, December 15, 1960. Mack Publishing Co., Easton, Pennsylvania.
27. Reddi, K. K., and Kodicek, E.: *Biochem. J.*, **53**, 286, 1953.
28. Glock, G. E., and McLean, P.: *Biochem. J.*, **61**, 381, 1955.

PANTOTHENIC ACID

1. Williams, R. J.; Lyman, C. M.; Goodyear, G. H.; Truesdail, J. H.; and Holoday, D.: *J. Am. Chem. Soc.*, **55**, 2912, 1933.
2. Williams, R. J.; Truesdail, J. H.; Weinstock, H. H., Jr.; Rohrman, E.; Lyman, C. M.; and McBurney, C. H.: *J. Am. Chem. Soc.*, **60**, 2719, 1938.
3. Woolley, D. W.; Waisman, H. A.; and Elvehjem, C. A.: *J. Am. Chem. Soc.*, **61**, 977, 1939.
4. Jukes, T. H.: *J. Am. Chem. Soc.*, **61**, 975, 1939.
5. Stiller, E. T.; Harris, S. A.; Finkelstein, J.; Keresztesy, J. C.; and Folkers, K.: *J. Am. Chem. Soc.*, **62**, 1785, 1940.

6. Williams, R. J.; Mitchell, H. K.; Weinstock, H. H.; and Snell, E. E.: *J. Am. Chem. Soc.*, **62**, 1784, 1940.
7. Kagan, F.; Heinzelman, R. V.; Weisblat, D. I.; and Greiner, W.: *J. Am. Chem. Soc.*, **79**, 3545, 1957.
8. Lipmann, F.; Kaplan, N. O.; Novelli, G. D.; Tuttle, L. C.; and Guirard, B. M.: *J. Biol. Chem.*, **167**, 869, 1947.
9. Lynen, F.; Reichert, E.; and Rueff, L.: *Ann. Chem.*, **574**, 1, 1951.
10. Novelli, G. D.: *Ann. Rev. Biochem.*, **26**, 243, 1957.
11. Novelli, G. D.: *Federation Proc.*, **12**, 675, 1953.
12. Wieland, T.; Maul, W.; and Möller, E. F.: *Biochem. Z.*, **327**, 85, 1955.
13. Hoagland, M. B., and Novelli, G. D.: *J. Biol. Chem.*, **207**, 767, 1954.
14. Snell, E. E.; Brown, G. M.; Peters, U. J.; Craig, J. A.; Wittle, E. L.; Moore, J. A.; McGlohon, V. M.; and Bird, O. D.: *J. Am. Chem. Soc.*, **72**, 5349, 1950.
15. Nelson, M. M., and Evans, H. M.: *J. Nutrition*, **31**, 497, 1946.
16. Winters, R. W.; Schultz, R. B.; and Krehl, W. A.: *Proc. Soc. Exptl. Biol. Med.*, **79**, 695, 1952.
17. Eisenstein, A. B.: *Endocrinology*, **60**, 298, 1957.
18. Langwell, B. B.; Reif, A. E.; and Hansbury, E.: *Endocrinology*, **62**, 565, 1958.
19. Bauernfeind, J. C., and Norris, L. C.: *Science*, **89**, 416, 1939.
20. Gantt, W. H.; Chow, B. F.; and Simonson, M.: *Am. J. Clin. Nutrition*, **7**, 411, 1959.
21. Olson, R. E., and Kaplan, N. O.: *J. Biol. Chem.*, **175**, 515, 1948.
22. Riggs, T. R., and Hegsted, D. M.: *Federation Proc.*, **7**, 297, 1948.
23. Shils, M. E.; Chester, S. A.; and Sass, M.: *Arch. Biochem. Biophys.*, **32**, 359, 1951.
24. Rubin, S. H.; Cooperman, J. M.; Moore, M. E.; and Scheiner, J.: *J. Nutrition*, **35**, 499, 1948.
25. Yang, C. S.; Stewart, B.; and Olson, R. E.: *Federation Proc.*, **15**, 578, 1956.
26. Novelli, G. D.: *Physiol. Revs.*, **33**, 525, 1953.
27. Zucker, T.: *Am. J. Clin. Nutrition*, **6**, 65, 1958.
28. Kerlan, I., and Herwick, R. P.: *J. Am. Med. Assoc.*, **123**, 391, 1943.
29. Hodges, R. E.; Ohlson, M. A.; and Bean, W. B.: *J. Clin. Invest.*, **37**, 1642, 1958.
30. Winterbottom, R.; Clapp, J. W.; Miller, W. H.; English, J. P.; and Roblin, R. O.: *J. Am. Chem. Soc.*, **69**, 1393, 1947.
31. Dietrich, L. S., and Shapiro, D. M.: *Proc. Soc. Exptl. Biol. Med.*, **93**, 191, 1956.
32. Zook, E. G.; MacArthur, M. J.; and Toepfer, E. W.: *U. S. Dept. Agr., Agr. Handbook No. 97*, Sept. 1956.
33. Gillis, M. B.; Heuser, G. F.; and Norris, L. C.: *J. Nutrition*, **35**, 351, 1948.
34. Jukes, T. H.: *J. Nutrition*, **21**, 193, 1941.
35. Clarke, M. F.: *Anal. Chem.*, **29**, 135, 1957.
36. Wolff, R. L.; Dubost, S.; and Brignon, J. J.: *Proc. Soc. Exptl. Biol. Med.*, **95**, 270, 1957.
37. Brown, G. M.: *J. Biol. Chem.*, **234**, 379, 1959.

PYRIDOXINE, PYRIDOXAL, PYRIDOXAMINE, VITAMIN B₆

1. György, P.: *Nature*, **133**, 498, 1934.
2. Keresztesy, J. C., and Stevens, J. R.: *Proc. Soc. Exptl. Biol. Med.*, **38**, 64, 1938.
3. Stiller, E. T.; Keresztesy, J. C.; and Stevens, J. R.: *J. Am. Chem. Soc.*, **61**, 1237,1939.
4. Harris, S. A.; Stiller, E. T.; and Folkers, K.: *J. Am. Chem. Soc.*, **61**, 1242, 1939.
5. Harris, S. A., and Folkers, K.: *J. Am. Chem. Soc.*, **61**, 1245, 1939.
6. Oser, B. L.: *Ann. Rev. Biochem.*, **17**, 381, 1948.
7. Antopol, W., and Unna, K.: *Arch. Path.*, **33**, 241, 1942.
8. Miller, E. C., and Bauman, C. A.: *J. Nutrition*, **27**, 319, 1944.
9. Lepkovsky, S.; Krause, M. E.; and Dimick, M. K.: *Science*, **95**, 331, 1942.
10. Schweigert, B. S.; Sauberlich, H. E.; Elvehjem, C. A.; and Baumann, C. A.: *J. Biol. Chem.*, **165**, 187, 1946.
11. Cartwright, G. E.; Wintrobe, M. M.; and Humphreys, S.: *J. Biol. Chem.*, **153**, 171, 1944.
12. Hunt, A. D., Jr.: *Am. J. Clin. Nutrition*, **5**, 561, 1957.
13. Bessey, O. A.; Adam, D. J.; and Hansen, A. E.: *Pediatrics*, **20**, 33, 1957.
14. Cheslock, K. E., and McCully, M. T.: *J. Nutrition*, **70**, 507, 1960.
15. Vilter, R. W.; Mueller, J. F.; Glazer, H. S.; Jerrold, T.; Abraham, J.; Thompson, C.; and Hawkins, V. R.: *J. Lab. Clin. Med.*, **42**, 335, 1953.
16. Fox, H., and Kondi, A.: *Blood*, **13**, 1054, 1958.

17. Hurwitz, J.: *J. Biol. Chem.*, **205**, 935, 1953.
18. Weissbach, H.; Bogdanski, D. F.; Redfield, B. G.; and Udenfriend, S.: *J. Biol. Chem.*, **227**, 617, 1957.
19. Cammarata, P. S., and Cohen, P. P.: *J. Biol. Chem.*, **187**, 439, 1950.
20. Davidson, A. N.: *Biochem. J.* (*London*), **64**, 546, 1956.
21. Granick, S.: *J. Biol. Chem.*, **232**, 1101, 1958.
22. Olivard, J., and Snell, E. E.: *J. Biol. Chem.*, **213**, 203, 1955.
23. Cori, C. F., and Illingsworth, B.: *Proc. Natl. Acad. Sci.*, *U. S.*, **43**, 547, 1957.
24. Pogell, M. B.: *J. Biol. Chem.*, **232**, 761, 1958.
25. Dinning, J. S., and Day, P. L.: *Proc. Soc. Exptl. Biol. Med.*, **92**, 115, 1956.
26. Doisy, E. A., Jr.; Daniels, M.; and Zimmerman, M. A.: *Federation Proc.*, **15**, 243, 1956.
27. Baldridge, R. C., and Tourtelotte, C. D.: *J. Biol. Chem.*, **227**, 441, 1957.
28. Beiler, J. M., and Martin, G. J.: *J. Biol. Chem.*, **169**, 345, 1947.
29. Nishizawa, Y.; Kodama, T.; and Kooka, T.: *J. Vitaminol.* (*Osaka*), **3**, 309, 1957.
30. Nishizawa, Y.: *J. Vitaminol.* (*Osaka*), **4**, 63, 1958.
31. Price, J. M.; Brown, R. R.; and Larson, F. C.: *J. Clin. Invest.*, **36**, 1600, 1957.
32. Youatt, J.: *Biochem. J.*, **68**, 193, 1958.
33. Marquez, L. R., and Reynolds, M. S.: *J. Am. Dietet. Assoc.*, **31**, 1116, 1955.
34. Miller, E. C., and Baumann, C. A.: *J. Biol. Chem.*, **157**, 551, 1945.
35. Boyd, M. J.; Logan, M. A.; and Tytell, A. A.: *J. Biol. Chem.*, **174**, 1013, 1948.
36. Cheslock, K. E.: *J. Nutrition*, **65**, 53, 1958.
37. Parrish, W. P.; Loy, H. W., Jr.; and Kline, O. L.: *J. Assoc. Off. Agr. Chem.*, **39**, 157, 1956.
38. Wada, H.; Morisue, T.; Sakamoto, Y.; and Ichihara, K.: *J. Vitaminol.* (*Osaka*), **3**, 183, 1957.

BIOTIN

1. Bateman, W. G.: *J. Biol. Chem.*, **26**, 263, 1916.
2. Boas, M.: *Biochem. J.*, **21**, 712, 1927.
3. Lease, J. G., and Parsons, H. T.: *Biochem. J.*, **28**, 2109, 1934.
4. Eakin, R. E.; Snell, E. E.; and Williams, R. J.: *J. Biol. Chem.*, **136**, 801, 1940.
5. György, P.; Rose, C.; Eakin, R. E.; Snell, E. E.; and Williams, R. J.: *Science*, **93**, 477, 1941.
6. Kögl, F., and Tonnis, B.: *Z. physiol. Chem.*, **242**, 43, 1936.
7. Allison, F. E.; Hoover, S. R.; and Burk, D.: *Science*, **78**, 217, 1933.
8. György, P.; Rose, C. E.; Hofmann, K.; Melville, D. B.; and du Vigneaud, V.: *Science*, **92**, 609, 1940.
9. Du Vigneaud, V.: *Science*, **96**, 455, 1942.
10. Harris, S. A.; Wolf, D. E.; Mozingo, R.; and Folkers, K.: *Science*, **97**, 447, 1943. Harris, S. A.; Wolf, D. E.; Mozingo, R.; Anderson, C.; Arth, G. E.; Easton, V. R.; Heyl, D.; Wilson, A. N.; and Folkers, K.: *J. Am. Chem. Soc.*, **66**, 1756, 1944.
11. Baker, B. R.; Querry, M. V.; McEwen, W. L.; Bernstein, S.; Safir, S. R.; Dorfman, L.; and Subbarow, Y.: *J. Org. Chem.*, **12**, 186, 1947.
12. Wright, L. D.; Cresson, E. L.; Skeggs, H. R.; Wood, T. R.; Peck, R. L.; Wolf, D. E.; and Folkers, K.: *J. Am. Chem. Soc.*, **74**, 1996, 1952.
13. Wright, L. D.; Cresson, E. L.; Skeggs, H. R.; Peck, R. L.; Wolf, D. E.; Wood, T. R.; Valiant, J.; and Folkers, K.: *Science*, **114**, 635, 1951.
14. Wolf, D. E.; Valiant, J.; Peck, R. L.; and Folkers, K.: *J. Am. Chem. Soc.*, **74**, 2002, 1952.
15. Wright, L. D.; Cresson, E. L.; Liebert, K. V.; and Skeggs, H. R.: *J. Am. Chem. Soc.*, **74**, 2004, 1952.
16. Thoma, R. W., and Peterson, W. H.: *J. Biol. Chem.*, **210**, 569, 1954.
17. Parsons, H. T.; Gardner, J.; and Walliker, C. T.: *J. Nutrition*, **19**, Supp. 19, 1940.
18. Eakin, R. E.; McKinley, W. A.; and Williams, R. J.: *Science*, **92**, 224, 1940.
19. Eakin, R. E.; Snell, E. E.; and Williams, R. J.: *J. Biol. Chem.*, **136**, 801, 1940.
20. Woolley, D. W., and Langsworth, L. G.: *J. Biol. Chem.*, **142**, 285, 1942.
21. Fraenkel-Conrat, H.; Snell, N. S.; and Ducay, E. D.: *Arch. Biochem. and Biophys.*, **39**, 80, 1952.
22. Ranch, H., and Nutting, W. B.: *Experientia*, **14**, 382, 1958.
23. Sullivan, M.; Kolb, L.; and Nicholls, J.: *Bull. Johns Hopkins Hosp.*, **70**, 177, 1942.

24. Sydenstricker, V. P.; Singal, S. A.; Briggs, A. P.; DeVaughn, N. M.; and Isbel, H.: *Science*, **95**, 176, 1942.
25. Rhoads, C. P., and Abels, J. C.: *J. Am. Med. Assoc.*, **121**, 1261, 1943.
26. Kaplan, I. I.: *Am. J. Med. Sci.*, **207**, 733, 1944.
27. Follis, R. H., Jr.: *Deficiency Disease*. Charles C Thomas, Publisher, Springfield, Ill., 1958, p. 263.
28. Lardy, H. A., and Peanasky, R.: *Physiol. Revs.*, **33**, 560, 1953.
29. Lardy, H. A.; Potter, R. L.; and Elvehjem, C. A.: *J. Biol. Chem.*, **169**, 451, 1947.
30. Bettex-Galland, M.: *Helv. Physiol. et Pharmacol. Acta*, **15**, C54, 1957.
31. Lichstein, H. C.: *Arch. Biochem. Biophys.*, **71**, 276, 1957.
32. Fisher, J. E.: *Proc. Soc. Exptl. Biol. Med.*, **88**, 227, 1955.
33. MacCleod, P. R.; Grisolia, S.; Cohen, P. P.; and Lardy, H. A.: *J. Biol. Chem.*, **180**, 1003, 1949.
34. Moat, A. G.; Wilkins, C. N.; and Friedman, H.: *J. Biol. Chem.*, **223**, 985, 1956.
35. Moat, A. G., and Nasati, F.: *Federation Proc.*, **19**, 313, 1960.
36. Gibson, D. M.; Titchener, E. B.; and Wakil, S. J.: *J. Am. Chem. Soc.*, **80**, 2908, 1958.
37. Kurtz, E. B., Jr., and Miramon, A.: *Arch. Biochem. Biophys.*, **77**, 514, 1958.
38. O'Leary, W. M.: *J. Bacteriol.*, **77**, 367, 1959.
39. *Nutrition Revs.*, **17**, 240, 1959.
40. *Nutrition Revs.*, **17**, 21, 183, 1959.
41. Lichstein, H. C., and Umbreit, W. W.: *J. Biol. Chem.*, **170**, 329, 423, 1947.
42. Lichstein, H. C.: *J. Biol. Chem.*, **177**, 487, 1949.
43. Lichstein, H. C.: *J. Biol. Chem.*, **177**, 125, 1949.
44. Okey, R.; Pencharz, R.; Lepkovsky, S.; and Vernon, E. R.: *J. Nutrition*, **44**, 83, 1951.
45. Gram, M. R., and Okey, R.: *J. Nutrition*, **64**, 217, 1958.
46. Wakil, S. J.; Tichener, E. B.; and Gibson, D. M.: *Biochim. et Biophys. Acta*, **29**, 225, 1958.
47. Brady, R. O.: *Proc. Natl. Acad. Sci., U.S.*, **44**, 993, 1958.
48. McCoy, R. H.; McKibben, J. N.; Axelrod, A. E.; and Hofmann, K.: *J. Biol. Chem.*, **176**, 1319, 1327, 1948.
49. Kreuger, K. K., and Peterson, W. H.: *J. Biol. Chem.*, **173**, 497, 1948.
50. Dittmer, K., and du Vigneaud, V.: *J. Biol. Chem.*, **169**, 63, 1947.
51. Axelrod, A. E.; Purvis, S. E.; and Hofman, K.: *J. Biol. Chem.*, **176**, 695, 1948.
52. Mistry, S. P., and Dakshinamurti, K.: *Federation Proc.*, **19**, 414, 1960.
53. Oppel, T. W.: *Am. J. Med. Sci.*, **204**, 856, 1942.
54. Glick, D.; Lichstein, H. C.; Ferguson, R. B.; and Twedt, R. M.: *Proc. Soc. Exptl. Biol. Med.*, **99**, 660, 1958.

FOLIC ACID (PTEROYLGLUTAMIC ACID) AND RELATED SUBSTANCES

1. Mitchell, H. K.; Snell, E. E.; and Williams, R. J.: *J. Am. Chem. Soc.*, **63**, 2284, 1941.
2. Hutchings, B. L.; Bohonos, N.; and Peterson, W. H.: *J. Biol. Chem.*, **141**, 521, 1941.
3. Mitchell, H. K.; Snell, E. E.; and Williams, R. J.: *J. Am. Chem. Soc.*, **66**, 267, 1944.
4. Angier, R. B.; Boothe, J. H.; Hutchings, B. L.; Mowat, J. H.; Semb, J.; Stokstad, E. L. R.; SubbaRow, Y.; Waller, C. W.; Cosulich, D. B.; Fahrenbach, M. J.; Hultquist, M. E.; Kuh, E.; Northey, E. H.; Seeger, D. R.; Sickels, J. P.; and Smith, J. M., Jr.: *Science*, **103**, 667, 1946.
5. Pfiffner, J. J.; Calkins, D. G.; Bloom, E. S.; and O'Dell, B. L.: *J. Am. Chem. Soc.*, **68**, 1392, 1946.
6. Rabinowitz, J. C., and Tabor, H.: *J. Biol. Chem.*, **233**, 252, 1958.
7. Roth, B.; Hultquist, M. E.; Fahrenbach, M. J.; Cosulich, D. B.; Broquist, H. P.; Brockman, J. A., Jr.; Smith, J. M., Jr.; Parker, R. P.; Stokstad, E. L. R.; and Jukes, T. H.: *J. Am. Chem. Soc.*, **74**, 3247, 1952.
8. Cosulich, D. B.; Smith, J. M., Jr.; and Broquist, H. P.: *J. Am. Chem. Soc.*, **74**, 4215, 1952.
9. Nichol, C. A.: *Federation Proc.*, **11**, 452, 1952.
10. Welch, A. D.; Nichol, C. A.; Anker, R. M.; and Boehne, J. W.: *J. Pharmacol. Exptl. Therap.*, **103**, 403, 1951.
11. Misra, K. P.; Woodruff, C. W.; and Darby, J.: *Federation Proc.*, **16**, 393, 1957.
12. Whiteley, H. R.; Osborn, M. J.; and Huennekens, F. M.: *J. Am. Chem. Soc.*, **80**, 757, 1958.

13. Nichol, C. A.; Anton, A. H.; and Zakrzewski, S. F.: *Science*, 121, 275, 1955.
14. Rabinowitz, J. C., and Pricer, W. E., Jr.: *Federation Proc.*, 16, 236, 1957.
15. Miller, A., and Waelsch, H.: *J. Biol. Chem.*, 228, 397, 1957.
16. Huennekens, F. M.; Hatefi, Y.; and Kay, L. D.: *J. Biol. Chem.*, 224, 435, 1957.
17. Peters, J. M., and Greenberg, D. M.: *J. Biol. Chem.*, 226, 329, 1957.
18. Nakao, A., and Greenberg, D. M.: *J. Biol. Chem.*, 230, 603, 1958.
19. Doctor, V. M.; Patton, T. L.; and Awapara, J.: *Arch. Biochem. Biophys.*, 67, 404, 1957.
20. Hartman, S. H., and Buchanan, J. M.: *Ann. Rev. Biochem.*, 28, 365, 1959.
21. Greenberg, D. M., and Humphreys, G. K.: *Federation Proc.*, 17, 234, 1958.
22. Broquist, H. P.: *Arch. Biochem. Biophys.*, 70, 210, 1957.
23. Silverman, M.; Keresztesy, J. C.; Koval, G. J.; and Gardner, R. C.: *J. Biol. Chem.*, 226, 83, 1957.
24. Huennekens, F. M.; Osborn, M. J.; and Whitely, H. R.: *Science*, 128, 120, 1958.
25. Kaufman, S.: *J. Biol. Chem.*, 234, 2677, 1959.
26. Goodfriend, T. L.: *Federation Proc.*, 19, 6, 1960.
27. Franklin, A. L.; Stokstad, E. L. R.; and Jukes, T. H.: *Proc. Soc. Exptl. Biol. Med.*, 67, 398, 1948.
28. Minnich, V., and Moore, C. V.: *Federation Proc.*, 7, 276, 1948.
29. Swenseid, M. E.; Wittle, E. L.; Moersch, G. W.; Bird, O. D.; and Broun, R. A.: *Federation Proc.*, 7, 299, 1948.
30. Goldin, A., and Mantel, N.: *Cancer Research*, 17, 635, 1957.
31. Barton, A. D., and Laird, A. K.: *J. Biol. Chem.*, 227, 795, 1957.
32. Timmis, G. M.: *J. Pharm. and Pharmacol.*, 9, 80, 1957.
33. Roy, H. W., Jr.: *J. Assoc. Offic. Agr. Chemists*, 40, 855, 1957.
34. Official Methods, *J. Assoc. Offic. Agr. Chemists*, 41, 61, 1958.
35. Duggan, D. E.; Bowman, R. L.; Brodie, B. B.; and Udenfriend, S.: *Arch. Biochem. Biophys.*, 68, 1, 1957.
36. Burton, B. T. (exec. ed.): *The Heinz Handbook of Nutrition*. McGraw-Hill Book Co., Inc., New York, 1959, p. 99.
37. Sheehy, T. W.; Rubini, M. E.; Sigler, M. H.; Perez-Santiago, E.; Baco-Dapena, R.; and Santini, R.: *Federation Proc.*, 19, 56, 1960.

VITAMIN B₁₂, COBALAMINS

1. Rickes, E. L.; Brink, N. G.; Koniuszy, F. R.; Wood, T. R.; and Folkers, K.: *Science*, 107, 396, 1948.
2. Smith, E. L.: *Nature*, 162, 144, 1948.
3. Kaczka, E. A.; Wolf, D. E.; Kuehl, F. A.; and Folkers, K.: *J. Am. Chem. Soc.*, 73, 3569, 1951.
4. Ford, J. E.; Holdsworth, B. S.; and Kon, S. K.: *Biochem. J.*, 59, 86, 1955.
5. Ott, W. H.; Rickes, E. L.; and Wood, T. R.: *J. Biol. Chem.*, 174, 1047, 1948.
6. Wagle, S. R.; Mehta, R.; and Johnson, B. C.: *J. Am. Chem. Soc.*, 79, 4249, 1957.
7. Wagle, S. R.; Mehta, R.; and Johnson, B. C.: *J. Biol. Chem.*, 230, 137, 1958.
8. Wagle, S. R.; Mehta, R.; and Johnson, B. C.: *Arch. Biochem. Biophys.*, 72, 241, 1957.
9. Wagle, S. R.; Mehta, R.; and Johnson, B. C.: *J. Biol. Chem.*, 233, 619, 1958.
10. Arnstein, H. R. V., and Simkin, J. L.: *Nature*, 183, 523, 1959.
11. Fraser, M. J., and Holdsworth, E. S.: *Nature*, 183, 519, 1959.
12. Arnstein, H. R. V.: *Biochim. et Biophys. Acta*, 29, 652, 1958.
13. Dinning, J. S., and Young, R. S.: *J. Biol. Chem.*, 234, 1199, 1959.
14. Dinning, J. S., and Young, R. S.: *J. Biol. Chem.*, 234, 3241, 1959.
15. Dinning, J. S., and Hogan, R.: *Federation Proc.*, 19, 418, 1960.
16. Wacker, A.; Pfahl, D.; and Schröder, I.: *Z. Naturforsch.*, 12b, 510, 1957.
17. Wagle, S. R.; Vaughan, D. A.; Mistry, S. P.; and Johnson, B. C.: *J. Biol. Chem.*, 230, 917, 1958.
18. Ferguson, T. M.; Trunnell, J. B.; Dennis, B.; Wade, P.; and Couch, J. R.: *J. Endocrinol.*, 60, 28, 1957.
19. Jaffe, W. G.: *Proc. Soc. Exptl. Biol. Med.*, 97, 665, 1958.
20. Brady, R. O., and Formica, J. V.: *Federation Proc.*, 19, 227, 1960.
    a. Ladd, J. N.; Hogenkamp, H. P. C.; and Barker, H. A.: *Biochem. & Biophys. Research Communications*, 2, 143 (1960).

b. Personal communication from Dr. H. A. Barker, Dept. Biochemistry, University of California, Berkeley.
21. Johnson, B. C.: *Am. J. Clin. Nutrition*, **6**, 34, 1958.
22. Wong, W. T., and Schweigert, B. S.: *J. Nutrition*, **58**, 23, 1956.
23. *Nutrition Revs.*, **14**, 73, 1956.
24. Castle, W. B.; Ross, J. B.; Davidson, C. S.; Burchenal, J. H.; Fox, H. J.; and Ham, T. H.: *Science*, **100**, 81, 1944.
25. Ellenbogen, L.: *Federation Proc.*, **19**, 332, 1960.
26. Hebert, V.: *Federation Proc.*, **17**, 440, 1958.
27. Toporek, M.: *Federation Proc.*, **19**, 418, 1960.
28. Chow, B. F.; Meier, P.; and Free, S. M.: *J. Am. Clin. Nutrition*, **6**, 30, 1958.
29. Greenberg, S. M.; Herndon, J. F.; Rice, E. G.; Parmalee, E. T.; Gulesich, J. J.; and Van Loon, E. J.: *Nature*, **180**, 1401, 1957.
30. *Vitamin B₁₂* (Merck Service Bulletin). Merck & Co., Inc., Rahway, N. J., 1958, p. 37.
31. Hoff-Jorgensen, E.: *Methods of Biochemical Analysis*. Interscience Publishers, Inc., New York, 1954, p. 81.
32. Ford, J. E.: *Brit. J. Nutrition*, **7**, 299, 1953.
33. *The Pharmacopoeia of the United States of America*, 16th revision, December 15, 1960. Mack Publishing Co., Easton, Pa., p. 186.
34. Bruening, C. F.; Neuss, J. D.; Numerof, P.; and Kline, O. L.: *J. Am. Pharm. Assoc.*, **46**, 66, 1957.
35. Schloesser, L. L.; Deshpande, P.; and Schilling, R. F.: *A.M.A. Arch. Internal Med.*, **101**, 306, 1958.

INOSITOL

1. Eastcott, E. V.: *J. Phys. Chem.*, **32**, 1094, 1928.
2. Woolley, D. W.: *Science*, **92**, 384, 1940; *J. Biol. Chem.*, **139**, 29, 1941.
3. Pavcek, P. L., and Baum, H. M.: *Science*, **93**, 502, 1941.
4. Hornstein, I.: *Science*, **121**, 206, 1955.
5. Anderson, R. C., and Wallis, E. S.: *J. Am. Chem. Soc.*, **70**, 2931, 1948.
6. Gavin, G., and McHenry, E. W.: *J. Biol. Chem.*, **139**, 485, 1941.
7. Best, C. H.; Ridout, J. H.; Patterson, J. M.; and Lucas, C. C.: *Biochem. J.*, **48**, 448, 1951.
8. Abels, J. C.; Kopel, C. W.; Pack, G. T.; and Rhoads, C. P.: *Proc. Soc. Exptl. Biol. Med.*, **54**, 157, 1943.
9. Dotti, L. B.; Felch, W. C.; and Ilka, S. J.: *Proc. Soc. Exptl. Biol. Med.*, **78**, 165, 1951.
10. Daughaday, W. H.; Larner, J.; and Harnett, C.: *J. Biol. Chem.*, **212**, 869, 1955.
11. Halliday, J. W., and Anderson, L.: *J. Biol. Chem.*, **217**, 797, 1955.
12. Eagle, H.; Oyama, V. I.; Levy, M.; and Freeman, A.: *Science*, **123**, 845, 1956.
13. Wiebelhaus, V. D.; Betheil, J. J.; and Lardy, H. A.: *Arch. Biochem.*, **13**, 379, 1947.
14. Stetten, M. R., and Stetten, DeW., Jr.: *J. Biol. Chem.*, **164**, 85, 1946.
15. Moscatelli, E. A., and Larner, J.: *Federation Proc.*, **16**, 223, 1957.
16. Hartree, E. F.: *Biochem. J.*, **66**, 131, 1957.
17. Woolley, D. W.: *J. Biol. Chem.*, **140**, 453, 1941.
18. Sonne, S., and Sobotka, H.: *Arch. Biochem.*, **14**, 93, 1947.
19. LeBaron, F. N.; Folch, J.; and Rothleder, E. E.: *Federation Proc.*, **16**, 209, 1957.

p-AMINOBENZOIC ACID

1. Woods, D. D.: *Brit. J. Exptl. Path.*, **21**, 74, 1940.

ASCORBIC ACID (VITAMIN C)

1. Holst, A., and Fröhlich, T.: *J. Hyg.*, **7**, 634, 1907.
2. Zilva, S. S.: *Biochem. J.*, **22**, 779, 1928.
3. Szent-Györgyi, A.: *Biochem. J.*, **22**, 1387, 1928.
4. Waugh, W. A., and King, C. G.: *J. Biol. Chem.*, **97**, 325, 1932.
5. Herbert, R. W.; Percival, E. G. V.; Reynolds, R. J. W.; Smith, F.; and Hirst, E. L.: *J. Soc. Chem. Ind.*, **52**, 481, 1933.
6. Reichstein, T.; Grussner, A.; and Oppenauer, R.: *Nature*, **132**, 280, 1933.
7. Ault, R. G.; Baird, D. K.; Carrington, H. C.; Haworth, W. N.; Herbert, R.; Hirst, E. L.; Percival, E. G. V.; Smith, F.; and Stacey, M.: *J. Chem. Soc.*, 1419, 1933.
8. Bartlett, M. K.; Jones, C. M.; and Ryan, A. E.: *New Engl. J. Med.*, **226**, 469, 1942.

9. Bartlett, M. K.; Jones, C. M.; and Ryan, A. E.: *New Engl. J. Med.*, **226**, 474, 1942.
10. Boyle, P. E.; Wolbach, S. B.; and Bessey, O. A.: *J. Dental Research*, **15**, 331, 1936.
11. Boyle, P. E.; Bessey, O. A.; and Howe, P. R.: *Arch. Path.*, **30**, 90, 1940.
12. Follis, R. H., Jr.: *Deficiency Disease*. Charles C Thomas, Publisher, Springfield, Ill., 1958, p. 175.
13. Crandon, J. H.; Lund, C. C.; and Dill, D. B.: *New Engl. J. Med.*, **223**, 353, 1940.
14. British Research Council, Accessory Food Factors Subcommittee: *Lancet*, **1**, 853, 1948.
15. Gould, B. S., and Woessner, J. F.: *J. Biol. Chem.*, **226**, 289, 1957.
16. Gould, B. S.: *J. Biol. Chem.*, **232**, 637, 1958.
17. Mitoma, C., and Smith, T. E.: *J. Biol. Chem.*, **235**, 426, 1960.
18. Gross, J.: *J. Exptl. Med.*, **109**, 557, 1959.
19. Morris, J. E.; Harpur, R. T.; and Goldbloom, A.: *J. Clin. Invest.*, **29**, 325, 1950.
20. LaDu, B. N., Jr., and Greenberg, D. M.: *Science*, **117**, 111, 1953.
21. Zannoni, V. G., and LaDu, B. N., Jr.: *J. Biol. Chem.*, **234**, 2925, 1959.
22. Zannoni, V. G., and LaDu, B. N., Jr.: *J. Biol. Chem.*, **235**, 165, 1960.
23. Kersten, H.; Kersten, W.; and Staudinger, H.: *Biochim. et Biophys. Acta*, **27**, 598, 1958.
24. Everson, G. L.; Northrop, L.; Chung, N. Y.; and Getty, R.: *J. Nutrition*, **54**, 305, 1954.
25. Barboriak, J. J., and Krehl, W. A.: *J. Nutrition*, **63**, 601, 1957.
26. Jackel, S. S.; Mosbach, E. H.; Burns, J. J.; and King, C. G.: *J. Biol. Chem.*, **186**, 569, 1950.
27. Horowitz, H. H., and King, C. G.: *J. Biol. Chem.*, **200**, 125, 1953.
28. Burns, J. J., and Mosbach, E. H.: *J. Biol. Chem.*, **221**, 107, 1956.
29. Burns, J. J.: *Am. J. Medicine*, **26**, 740, 1959.
30. Kanfer, J.; Burns, J. J.; and Ashwell, G.: *Biochim. et Biophys. Acta*, **31**, 556, 1959.
31. Burns, J. J.: *Nature*, **180**, 553, 1957.
32. Snyder, L. H.: *Science*, **129**, 7, 1959.
33. Hellman, L., and Burns, J. J.: *J. Biol. Chem.*, **230**, 923, 1958.
34. Burns, J. J.; Kanfer, J.; and Dayton, P. G.: *J. Biol. Chem.*, **232**, 107, 1958.
35. Chan, P. C.; Becker, R. R.; and King, C. G.: *J. Biol. Chem.*, **231**, 231, 1958.
36. Roe, J. H., in Glick, D. (ed.): *Methods of Biochemical Analysis*. Interscience Publishers Inc., New York, Vol. 1, 1954, p. 115.
37. *The Pharmacopoeia of the United States of America*, 16th revision. Mack Publishing Co., Easton, Pa. 1960.
38. Berlina, A.: *Acta Gerontol.*, **6**, 71, 1956.
39. *Nutrition Revs.*, **7**, 315, 1949.

"VITAMIN P"

1. Szent-Györgyi, A., and Rusznyák, I.: *Nature*, **138**, 27, 1936.
2. Bentsath, A.; Rusznyák, I.; and Szent-Györgyi, A.: *Nature*, **138**, 798, 1936.
3. Zacho, C. E.: *Acta Path. Microbiol. Scand.*, **16**, 144, 1939.
4. Bourne, G. H.: *Nature*, **152**, 659, 1943.

19

Introduction to intermediary metabolism

GENERAL CONSIDERATIONS

In studying and teaching metabolism it is customary and convenient to differentiate between "energy metabolism," which deals with the over-all energy production and requirements of the organism, and so-called intermediary metabolism, which is concerned with the specific chemical reactions within the organism. Obviously no such differentiation exists, because energy represents an obligatory component of all chemical reactions, and energy as it appears in metabolism is but an expression of a product of the reactions taking place. Many of these reactions, especially those concerned with the breakdown of substances, yield energy, whereas others, particularly those involving synthesis, absorb energy. The over-all energy flow in the organism produces a net increase in energy which is finally dissipated as heat. Gross energy metabolism, thus, is primarily concerned with heat production in the organism and has been previously considered. It is now our task to study primarily the chemical reactions within cells and tissues that constitute intermediary metabolism. However, upon numerous occasions it will be necessary to discuss energy changes accompanying these reactions. The term "metabolism" is generally interpreted to mean intermediary metabolism unless otherwise specified, and we shall adopt this usage.

The word "metabolism" is very broad in its meaning. It includes all chemical processes within cells and tissues which are concerned with their building up and breaking down and in their functional operation.

The processes of new tissue formation and the maintenance of the structures already formed constitute tissue building up, or synthesis, and in

768

general represent the union of smaller into larger molecules. The reverse process of tissue breakdown obviously is primarily concerned with the splitting of the larger protoplasmic molecules into smaller ones. The metabolism of tissue formation is commonly referred to as "anabolism," and the metabolism of tissue breakdown is called "catabolism." Generally speaking, anabolism and catabolism are but the opposing processes of reversible chemical reactions which may be represented as follows:

$$\text{small molecules} \underset{\text{catabolism}}{\overset{\text{anabolism}}{\rightleftharpoons}} \text{large molecules}$$

When the processes of tissue synthesis (anabolism) exceed those of tissue breakdown (catabolism), growth of the organism occurs, as in the period of immaturity. If these processes balance, there is no change in tissue mass. This represents normal maturity. In the old age of an organism a period is generally reached in which the rate of tissue catabolism exceeds the rate of anabolism and the mass of tissues declines. This is observed in exaggerated form during periods of starvation when the molecules for synthesis are not available, and in certain pathologic states, when the breakdown of tissues may be greatly accelerated.

The building up and breaking down of protoplasm are primarily concerned with protein metabolism, since proteins generally are the chief organic constituents of protoplasm. However, various substances of lipid, carbohydrate, and inorganic nature are also involved.

The functional operations of tissues—such as muscular contraction, the propagation of nerve impulses, the secretory work of various glands, the selective absorption processes of the intestine, and the excretory processes of the kidney and other organs—require a multitude of chemical reactions to provide necessary energy and specific chemical substances.

In muscle contraction the chemical processes primarily concerned are those designed to yield energy in a form which can be transferred to the contractile elements and operate them. These chemical processes involve chiefly the oxidative breakdown of sugars and fatty acids, with the formation of energy-rich adenosine triphosphate (ATP). This last substance transmits its phosphate bond energy to the muscle fibrils and causes contraction.

The energy for the transmission of impulses in the central nervous system and nerves is largely obtained from the breakdown and oxidation of glucose by the same pathways as found in muscle metabolism. Here, too, ATP is formed, which supplies the free energy necessary for the synthesis of acetylcholine and for other processes involved in the generation and transmission of action currents.

The secretions of the endocrine glands—such as the pituitary, thyroid, parathyroid, sex glands, and pancreas—contain substances (hormones) which perform more or less specific roles in regulating tissue metabolism. These hormones are definite chemical substances, each of which is formed from specific substances by specific chemical reactions in a particular kind of tissue. For example, the cells of the thyroid gland combine iodine with the amino acid tyrosine to form diiodotyrosine, which is then converted to the hormone thyroxine. The reactions within the endocrine glands provide both the necessary chemical precursors and the energy necessary for the synthetic reactions. The glands which provide substances for digestion and other purposes also carry out specialized chemical processes for synthesis and energy production.

The cells of the intestinal mucosa are the site of numerous chemical reactions. Energy is provided by these reactions for the active transport of certain sugars and other substances from the lumen into the blood. Fatty acids are combined into glycerides and phospholipids, which then pass into the lymph and blood stream. Sucrose and other substances are split by enzymes of the intestinal cells as they pass through during absorption.

The epithelial cells of the kidney tubules effect reabsorption of glucose, Na^+, and many other substances from glomerular fluid by active transport based upon energy-yielding chemical reactions. In fact, a considerable proportion of the energy production of the body is utilized in active transport mechanisms operating across membranes throughout the body to maintain the proper distribution of ions and diffusible molecules between extracellular and intracellular fluids.

Thus it is seen that the study of metabolism embraces not only the chemistry of tissue formation and breakdown but also the chemistry of the processes in tissues necessary for the formation of various specific compounds required for the operation and regulation of the metabolic machine. In addition, there is included a great complexity of chemical reactions primarily designed to provide energy. These groups of reactions for different primary purposes are not closely compartmented, but generally overlap and integrate. For example, substances formed in the energy-producing reactions may be utilized in synthesis, and the intermediate stages in the production of compounds for synthesis yield energy.

One of the most surprising things about metabolic reactions is that they occur rapidly under very mild conditions of pH and temperature and with few useless side reactions. Also, many of these reactions are difficult or impossible to duplicate in the laboratory, even under drastic conditions. Of course, the reason for this is that most metabolic reactions are catalyzed by specific enzymes, and the study of metabolism is largely interrelated with the study of the mode of action of these enzymes.

It is not amiss to state that the chemistry of metabolism is the chemistry of life itself, and this applies to all living forms. In fact, the general metabolic processes of all organisms, plant and animal, large and small, follow many common pathways. The chemical processes by which yeast metabolizes glucose differ only in a few details from the processes occurring in the tissues of higher animals. Many reactions which have first been observed in microorganisms have later been found to occur as essential processes in animal metabolism. Numerous reactions occurring in plants have their counterparts in animals. One who studies the metabolism of any type of protoplasm is to a large degree studying the metabolism of all types of protoplasm.

A thorough understanding of human metabolism is a necessary part of the training of a physician. Derangements of certain phases of metabolism are frequently associated with pathologic states in either cause or effect relations. As a simple example, the failure of the pancreas to form insulin results in diabetes, which is attended with a marked decrease in the metabolic reactions breaking down glucose and an acceleration in those breaking down fats and tissue proteins. Failure of the thyroid gland to produce thyroxine results in a generalized decrease in the oxidation of foodstuffs in all the tissues of the body and simultaneously a failure adequately to synthesize tissue structures. Failure of the parathyroid glands to form their hormone leads to marked derangements of calcium and phosphorus metabolism. A deficiency of thiamine in the diet causes a deficiency of carboxylase and other enzymes necessary to oxidize pyruvic acid formed in glucose metabolism. This leads to an accumulation of pyruvic acid in tissues and blood, and to the other symptoms making up the syndrome of beriberi. Riboflavin deficiency prevents synthesis of the flavoproteins required for many biologic oxidations. A deficiency of niacin similarly prevents the adequate formation of coenzymes I and II which are also necessary components of biologic oxidation chains. Failure to provide sufficient oxygen to tissues, regardless of cause, prevents adequate tissue synthesis through failure of the energy supply; the result is that the rate of tissue breakdown exceeds the rate of its formation. Acute oxygen deprivation quickly causes death through interruption of the chemical processes supplying energy to the brain.

Much of the science of pharmacology depends upon the use of drugs, vitamins, and hormones which alter one or more metabolic processes of animal tissues or of invading organisms. These effects are frequently exerted upon enzyme systems of the cells. For example, narcotics such as the barbiturates apparently slow down the metabolic reactions of the nervous system by inhibiting the dehydrogenase enzyme systems. The sulfa drugs are effective against invading organisms because they inhibit certain enzymes of the organisms and thereby interfere with their metabolic reactions. The toxicity of poisons is often related to interference with metabolic processes. For example, cyanide is a deadly poison because it combines with cytochrome oxidase, inactivates it, and thereby quickly stops a large proportion of cellular oxidations. The toxicity of mercuric ions is largely due to their combination with the sulfhydryl groups ($-SH$) of enzymes with resulting inactivation. Thus it is seen that the physician is constantly confronted with abnormal states which are the result of, or attended by, changes in the chemical reactions within tissues. The greater his understanding of metabolism, the greater will be his ability to appreciate and practice good medicine.

METHODS OF STUDYING METABOLISM

Our knowledge of metabolism has been gradually accumulated, largely during the last 50 years, through the work of many investigators. The study of the chemical processes of tissues, and the integration of the results obtained into clear over-all pictures of metabolism, is one of the most exacting tasks faced by the scientist. Because of the lability of living tissues and many of their components, the methods of study must be carefully chosen and executed. The structural proteins of tissues, and particularly the dozens of enzyme proteins present, are especially susceptible to denaturation by heat and other agencies. Consequently, it is frequently necessary to work at low temperatures and with careful control of pH and other factors. Many of the highly important constituents of tissues are very reactive and exist in such small quantities at any given time that special methods for their isolation, identification, and estimation are necessary.

Progress made in the study of metabolism has been in proportion to the development of laboratory methods and instruments.

The isolation and purification of many biologic substances from small amounts of tissues and fluids is accomplished by procedures such as paper, column, and gas chromatography; countercurrent extraction; and supercentrifugation.

The purity and physicochemical characteristics of enzymes and other proteins are established by procedures such as electrophoresis and ultracentrifugation.

Many highly sensitive and accurate methods for the qualitative detection and quantitative determination of minute amounts of biologic substances have been developed which are based upon characteristic light absorption in the ultraviolet, visible, and infrared regions of the spectrum by the substances or their derivatives, measured by appropriate colorimeters and spectrophotometers. Some biologic substances, such as porphyrins, exhibit strong fluorescence under light of appropriate wavelength, which may be measured in fluorimeters, affording excellent qualitative and quantitative estimations.

The characteristic behavior of free radicals in powerful magnetic fields (electron spin resonance) appears to offer a powerful tool in the investigation of biologic reaction mechanisms.

Great strides in our acquisition of knowledge are being made through the use of artificially produced radioactive isotopes and of naturally occurring stable isotopes as tracers in metabolic reactions.

The study of tissues, cells, and cell components, with ultraviolet, phase and electron microscopy in conjunction with histochemical techniques, has yielded much valuable information as to both the localization and quantitative relations of enzymes and other substances.

From the above discussion it can be seen that the biochemist, physical chemist, and physicist are meeting on common grounds to provide the methods and instruments for biochemical research which promise rich rewards.

A brief discussion of some of the techniques employed in metabolic studies is given below. For a given problem one of these methods may be adequate, while in others a combination of procedures is necessary.

1. Blood and tissue analysis. It is often possible to obtain information relative to the metabolic activity of an organ by determining the quantities of a substance in the arterial blood to the organ and the venous blood from it (AV difference).

Catheterization through the antecubital vein via the innominate vein and superior vena cava into the right atrium, right ventricle, coronary sinus, or a pulmonary, renal, or hepatic vein may be accomplished under fluoroscopic control. This permits withdrawal of blood samples from various levels of the vascular system and determination of metabolic changes due to the function of different organs when the quantities of substances in the venous samples are compared with the values from samples of arterial blood. Utilization of oxygen, glucose, and other substances by normal and failing hearts, the synthesis of hormones by the adrenal glands, and other metabolic processes have been studied by the catheterization procedure.

A great proportion of metabolic studies necessitates the quantitative estimation of tissue constituents. For example, one may wish to determine whether or not a given substance forms glycogen in the rat. One way of doing this is to fast two groups of rats for a period of time in order to deplete their carbohydrate stores and then to administer the substance in question to one of the groups. After a suitable period the animals of both groups are killed and liver and muscle glycogen are quantitatively determined. Increased glycogen in the tissues of the fed group indicate glycogen formation from the substance in question.

2. Analysis of excretions. The metabolism of various substances in the body produces characteristic end products which appear in the urine, and at times in the feces, and analysis of these excretions often provides useful information. For example, if one feeds an animal a diet containing 12 g of nitrogen as protein and finds only 10 g in the excretions, the animal has retained 2 g of this nitrogen in the form of 12.5 g of tissue protein (2×6.25). Or, if the ingestion of methionine is followed by a prompt increase in urinary sulfate, it is concluded that the body has broken down some of the methionine and oxidized the sulfur to sulfuric acid. The appearance of much glucose in the urine of a diabetic after taking lactic acid indicates the conversion of this acid to sugar in the body.

3. Respiratory exchange. The oxidation of foodstuffs in the body consumes oxygen and produces carbon dioxide. The volume relations of these gases is characteristic for the oxidation of carbohydrate (glucose), of protein (amino acids) and of fats (fatty acids plus glycerol). The respiratory quotients (CO_2/O_2) are 1.00 for carbohydrate, 0.80 for protein, and 0.707 for fats. As is pointed out in Chapter 22, if the protein metabolized in a given time by an animal is determined from urinary nitrogen excretion, and the oxygen consumption and carbon dioxide production are also measured, it is possible to calculate the quantities of carbohydrate, fat, and protein oxidized, and the energy from each. It must be remembered that the respiratory quotients of different organs and tissues may differ considerably at any given time, and the respiratory metabolism of the animal represents the additive effects of the metabolisms of the component tissues. For example, when the animal body shows a respiratory quotient of 0.74, representing an over-all preponderance of fat oxidation, the brain is oxidizing glucose almost exclusively, with an RQ close to 1.00. The respiratory exchange of isolated tissues, tissue slices, and homogenates is often determined and may yield valuable information in metabolic studies.

4. Removal of endocrine glands and other organs. This approach to the study of metabolism has yielded much information. It was early recognized that diabetic patients and animals made diabetic by pancreatectomy exhibit marked alterations of metabolic processes including hyperglycemia (high blood sugar), glucosuria (sugar in the urine), ketonemia (increased blood ketone bodies: acetone, acetoacetic, and β-hydroxybutyric acids), ketonuria, increased urinary nitrogen, low liver and muscle glycogen, and low respiratory quotients. These symptoms are the result of the failure properly to metabolize glucose, with a compensatory increase in the metabolism of fat and protein. When completely diabetic animals are fasted, the blood sugar remains elevated, and glucose and nitrogen continue to be excreted in the urine, and at a relatively constant rate for a considerable period of time. The excretion of ketone bodies also persists. These animals have been rather widely used to determine whether or not a substance forms glucose or acetoacetic acid in the body. For example, if alanine is given to such an animal, a prompt increase in urinary glucose (also nitrogen) is observed, and alanine is thereby shown to be metabolized through the pathway of glucose. On the other hand, the administration of tyrosine causes an increase in urinary ketones, showing that its metabolism proceeds through the formation of acetoacetic acid. Dozens of compounds have been tested in this way. The method can be relied upon for gross results only.

It is possible to produce diabetic animals by administering alloxan and related substances that specifically destroy the islet cells of the pancreas which form insulin, and such diabetic animals may be used for metabolic studies.

Animals with phlorizin diabetes have been used extensively in metabolism studies. When animals subcutaneously are given daily doses of the glucoside phlorizin suspended in oil, the capacity of the renal tubules to reabsorb glucose is destroyed. This permits glucose to pass rapidly through the kidneys into the urine with resulting hypoglycemia and glucosuria. Under these conditions the tissues can use little sugar, so there is a greatly increased rate of protein and fat metabolism, with ketosis. Aside from the hypoglycemia, these animals show a metabolic picture similar to that of depancreatized animals and may be used to determine whether or not an administered substance is metabolized through glucose or acetoacetic acid.

The removal of the pituitary and adrenal glands, as in the case of the pancreas, produces marked changes in metabolism and is frequently resorted to in various types of studies. These effects will be considered later in some detail.

In this connection it should be pointed out that the reverse of glandular removal—that is, the injection of hormones into normal and operated animals—is widely used in metabolic studies. For example, the injection of adrenal cortical hormones into a fasted normal rat causes increased blood glucose and liver glycogen and increased urinary nitrogen. This is interpreted to mean that these hormones increase the rate of glucose and glycogen formation from the amino acids of tissue proteins.

In addition to the removal of endocrine glands, the removal of other organs, such as kidney and liver, is utilized in metabolic studies, particularly when gross over-all effects are to be observed. In addition, various organs may be injured by poisons which act more or less specifically upon certain cells, permitting study of the function of these cells by comparison of the poisoned and normal animal. An example is the destruction of the β-cells of the pancreas by alloxan, which causes diabetes mellitus and thus shows insulin to be formed by the β-cells.

5. Perfusion of living organs. This technique of studying metabolism consists in perfusing living organs *in situ*, or after removal from the body, with blood or other fluids, and studying the changes in composition of the fluids after passage through the organs. Various substances may be added to the perfusing fluids and their chemical changes noted. For example, when liver is perfused with alanine, the pyruvic acid of the perfusate is increased, showing that the liver cells deaminize alanine and form pyruvic acid.

6. Warburg's tissue slice technique. Fresh surviving tissues may be cut into thin slices; placed in appropriate media, such as Ringer's solution; and used to study the chemical changes produced when certain substances are added. These preparations may also be placed in the Barcroft-Warburg manometric apparatus, and their respiratory exchange may be studied. For example, it can be shown that liver slices act upon amino acids to deaminize them and form urea from the ammonia produced. It may also be possible to follow the metabolism of the keto acids formed in the deamination process. The tissue slice technique provides one of our most valuable methods for metabolism studies.

Finely macerated suspensions of tissues (homogenates), instead of slices, occasionally are used for *in vitro* studies. Here the cellular structures are broken down to liberate the enzyme systems. Such preparations do not so nearly simulate the metabolic processes of intact tissues as do tissues slices in which most of the cells are intact.

7. Studies with purified enzyme systems. A large proportion of modern biochemical research is based upon the use of isolated enzymes, in many cases highly purified. The use of a purified enzyme permits kinetic and energetic characterization of the reaction it catalyzes through determination of rate and equilibrium constants. Also, the cofactors required as part of the enzyme system, the inhibitory action of various substances, the effects of pH and temperature, and the presence or absence of certain essential groups, such as —SH, in the enzyme may be determined.

While the *in vitro* study of a reaction catalyzed by a purified enzyme yields important information about the isolated reaction in glass vessels, such a study does not give an accurate picture as to how the reaction proceeds, is controlled, and is related to other metabolic processes in the complex integrated environment of the living cell.

8. Inhibition of enzyme systems with poisons. When one is working with a tissue or extract containing a number of enzymes, it is frequently possible to add a substance which selectively inactivates one or more of the enzymes, thereby permitting a better study of the action of those not inhibited. This is particularly important when the metabolism of a substance proceeds through a succession of reactions catalyzed by different enzymes. Suppose a substance A is metabolized through changes such as:

$$A \longrightarrow B \longrightarrow C \longrightarrow D$$

each catalyzed by a specific enzyme. Suppose we wish to study the formation of C, but that C is very rapidly converted to D and does not accumulate in quantities which can be accurately determined. If a substance can be added which poisons the enzyme catalyzing the conversion of C to D without inhibiting the other enzymes, then C will accumulate. For example, muscle poisoned with iodoacetic acid converts glycogen to hexose phosphates but cannot carry the breakdown farther because essential enzymes have been inhibited.

9. Inborn errors of metabolism. There are a number of metabolic abnormalities which are congenital, present throughout life, and hereditary; Garrod has termed these "inborn errors of metabolism." Such abnormalities are represented by alkaptonuria, pentosuria, cystinuria, congenital porphyria and steatorrhea, albinism, and galactosemia. In some of these conditions failure of a metabolic step leads to the excretion of intermediate products which cannot be carried further along the metabolic path because of specific enzyme deficiency but which the normal animal readily metabolizes. The identification of these intermediate metabolic products in the urine has to a limited extent aided in establishing the steps involved in the metabolism of a substance. The classical example is the information relative to the metabolism of tyrosine and phenylalanine provided by individuals with alkaptonuria and phenylketonuria who excrete intermediate metabolic products of these amino acids in the urine.

10. Competitive analog-metabolite inhibition. This method is based upon the use of substances of different, but similar, structure from that of substances required by the organism, or analogs of required metabolites. These substances act by combining with and inactivating the enzyme system or systems for which the metabolite is a normal cofactor, thus creating a situation equivalent to a deficiency of the metabolite, with the resultant physiologic changes. The bacteriostatic action of sulfanilamide upon microorganisms is due to the fact that it is a structural analog of p-aminobenzoic acid, which is a necessary cofactor for bacterial enzyme systems. The sulfanilamide, because its structure is similar to that of p-aminobenzoic acid, takes its place as cofactor in the enzyme systems, which are thereby inhibited. The action of the sulfanilamide may be reversed by *p*-aminobenzoic acid. The sulfanilamide is termed a "competitive inhibitor."

$$H_2N - \langle \text{benzene ring} \rangle - SO_2NH_2$$
Sulfanilamide

$$H_2N - \langle \text{benzene ring} \rangle - COOH$$
p-Aminobenzoic acid

The substance pyrithiamine is an analog of the vitamin thiamine and when it is given to mice causes typical symptoms of thiamine deficiency because it displaces thiamine in essential enzyme systems. Many analogs of vitamins have been prepared and found to cause deficiency symptoms when given to animals. The effects may be reversed by giving the corresponding vitamins.

When an analog of a metabolite produces metabolite deficiency symptoms that are reversed by giving the metabolite, it is logical to conclude that the metabolite probably functions as a cofactor in one or more enzyme systems.

The field of competitive analog-metabolite inhibition appears to offer considerable promise in the search for agents for the inhibition and possible control of neoplasms and antidotes for toxic drugs. An example in the latter relation is the action of allylnormorphine in abolishing the analgesia of morphine. In such a case morphine may be an analog of some metabolite of unknown structure for which allynormorphine can substitute. The validity of such an explanation has not been demonstrated.

Shive and Roberts (1) have developed a system called "inhibition analysis" based upon the study of natural compounds which noncompetitively antagonize the harmful effects of a structural analog of a given metabolite. The antibacterial action of sulfanilamide may be overcome not only by *p*-aminobenzoic acid but also by the natural products methionine, purines, and sometimes by pteroylglutamic acid. *p*-Aminobenzoic acid is the only one of these substances that inhibits competitively and that can reverse the effects of large doses of sulfanilamide. It appears that *p*-aminobenzoic acid is the cofactor for a number of enzyme systems, which in turn form methionine, purines, etc., necessary for the organism. Accordingly, the addition of sulfanilamide blocks a number of enzyme systems and prevents synthesis of these necessary compounds. The addition of one of these substances, such as methionine, relieves the inhibition in so far as the requirement for methionine is concerned; that is, a part of the sulfanilamide inhibition is removed. The addition of the purine xanthine removes another fraction of the inhibition, etc. The order of addition of these natural substances is important. In the absence of methionine the addition of purines produces no, or less, effect.

When a natural substance decreases the inhibition of an analog metabolite, it is assumed that the enzyme system blocked by the analog forms the natural substance which relieves the inhibition. This procedure of inhibition analysis has been productive in studying the metabolism of microorganisms in particular. The student should consult Woolley's book cited in the references for fuller details.

11. Use of radioactive and stable isotopes as tracer atoms. This method of studying the chemical processes of living things has been used for only a few years, but in that time it has provided a great store of information, much of which could not have been obtained in any other way.

When a molecule of fatty acid, amino acid, sugar, phosphate, or other food substance is taken into the body, it becomes mixed with large numbers of other like molecules in the "metabolic pool," and it is impossible by ordinary methods to trace the chemical pathway of its metabolism. Knoop (2) in 1904 introduced phenyl groups, which are not readily oxidized, into fatty acid chains on the terminal carbon atom and studied the oxidation of these phenyl-substituted fatty acids in the animal body. From the results he developed his theory of β-oxidation in fatty acid metabolism. This was the first successful use of tracers in metabolic studies. There was the serious objection, however, that the introduction of the phenyl group may change the chemical properties of the acids so that they are not oxidized as are the natural unsubstituted acids. This objection, in general, limits the use of molecules tagged with resistant groups.

The ideal way of tagging a molecule for metabolic studies would be to substitute into it an atom having the same chemical properties as the atom replaced and possessing properties by which it can be easily detected in the various compounds formed in metabolic reactions. With the development of the new science of nuclear chemistry, it is now possible to obtain isotopic atoms of practically all the elements essential to living organisms. These isotopes possess the same atomic numbers as the natural atoms and consequently the same chemical properties, except for small differences in the isotopes of light atoms, such as hydrogen. The radioactive isotopes may be easily determined by instruments such as the Geiger-Müller radiation counter and proportional and scintillation counters. Heavy and light isotopes which are not radioactive are determined with the mass spectrometer. Thus we have in these isotopic atoms the kinds of substances ideally suited for the tagging of molecules and studying their pathways of chemical change. This tracer method, supplemented by other techniques, represents the most important procedure yet devised for the study of metabolism. Isotopic tracer compounds permit not only the study of chemical pathways in metabolism but also of the rates of change or turnover of a substance in the body.

In recent years large numbers of radioactive and heavy and light isotopes of the elements have been produced artificially through bombardment of atomic nuclei with protons ($_1H^1$), deuterons ($_1H^2$), α-particles ($_2He^4$), and neutrons ($_0n^1$).

Protons and deuterons carry a single positive charge, α-particles two positive charges, while neutrons are uncharged. Neutrons enter the nuclei of bombarded atoms most readily because, being electrically neutral, they are not repelled by the positively charged nuclei, as are protons, deuterons, and α-particles. Various types of apparatus have been devised to provide the bombarding particles with the required energy. Earlier work utilized α-particles from natural radioactive substances, and neutrons were obtained by the action of radium upon beryllium. A great advance in the production of artificial atoms began with the development of the cyclotron, which may be used to provide any of the bombarding particles in quantities for practical use. The reacting uranium pile, such as is used for the production of material for atomic bombs, is by far the best source of neutrons for isotope production.

The preparation of isotopic atoms and their synthesis into compounds for metabolic and other studies is a complex field of physics and chemistry. The student is referred to the books given in the general references at the end of this chapter for authoritative discussions. The nuclear reaction for the preparation of isotopic C^{14} by neutron bombardment of N^{14} may be represented:

$$_7N^{14} + _0n^1 = _6C^{14} + _1H^1 \quad \text{or} \quad _7N^{14}(n,p)_6C^{14}$$

This equation states that a neutron of atomic number 0 and mass 1, reacts with a nitrogen atom of atomic number 7 and mass 14, to form a carbon atom of atomic number 6 and mass 14, and a proton of atomic number 1 and mass 1.

Table 19.1 lists a number of isotopes used as tracers for metabolic and other studies.

Table 19.1. Some Isotopes of Importance as Tracers

Isotope	Relative abundance, per cent	Preparation	Radiation	Maximum radiation energy, mev	Half-life
$_1H^2$	0.0154				∞
$_1H^3$		$_3Li^6(n,\alpha)_1H^3$	β^-	0.0185	12.1 y*
$_6C^{13}$	1.1				∞
$_6C^{14}$		$_7N^{14}(n,p)_6C^{14}$	β^-	0.156	5,600 y
$_7N^{15}$	0.365				∞
$_8O^{18}$	0.204				∞
$_{11}Na^{24}$		$_{11}Na^{23}(n,\gamma)_{11}Na^{24}$	β^-,γ	1.39, 2.89	15 h
$_{15}P^{32}$		$_{16}S^{32}(n,p)_{15}P^{32}$	β^-	1.712	14.3 d
$_{16}S^{35}$		$_{17}Cl^{35}(n,p)_{16}S^{35}$	β^-	0.169	87.1 d
$_{17}Cl^{36}$		$_{17}Cl^{35}(n,\gamma)_{17}Cl^{36}$	β^-	0.714	3.1×10^5 y
$_{19}K^{42}$		$_{19}K^{41}(n,\gamma)_{19}K^{42}$	β^-	3.58	12.5 h
$_{20}Ca^{45}$		$_{21}Sc^{45}(n,p)_{20}Ca^{45}$	β^-	0.260	152 d
$_{26}Fe^{59}$		$_{27}Co^{59}(n,p)_{26}Fe^{59}$	β^-,γ	0.46, 1.30	45 d
$_{27}Co^{60}$		$_{27}Co^{59}(n,\gamma)_{27}Co^{60}$	β^-,γ	0.31, 1.33	5.3 y
$_{53}I^{131}$		$_{52}Fe^{130}(d,n)_{53}I^{131}$	β^-,γ	0.687, 0.72	8 d

* y = years, d = days, h = hours.

The stable isotopes $_1H^2$, $_8O^{18}$, and $_7N^{15}$ are important tracers, obtained by concentration from natural hydrogen, oxygen, and nitrogen compounds.

Deuterium, present to the extent of about 0.02 per cent in ordinary hydrogen, is generally prepared as deuterium enriched water (heavy water) by electrolysis of water. The gas evolved at the cathode is enriched in protium while the residual water in the cell is enriched in deuterium.

O^{18} is obtained by the fractional distillation or electrolysis of heavy water residues.

N^{15} is obtained by passing NH_3 gas through a solution of ammonium salt in which there is isotopic exchange and enrichment of the NH_4^+ with the heavier isotope:

$$N^{15}H_3 + N^{14}H_4^+ \longrightarrow N^{14}H_3 + N^{15}H_4^+$$

Gas   Solution   Gas   Solution

The ammonium salt in solution becomes enriched with N^{15}. Similarly, C^{13} is concentrated in HCN by passing the gas through cyanide solution:

$$HC^{12}N + C^{13}N^- \longrightarrow HC^{13}N + C^{12}N^-$$

Gas   Solution   Gas   Solution

The compounds enriched with stable isotopes are used as sources of the isotopes for synthesis of compounds for tracer studies. The concentration of stable isotope in an enriched compound is usually expressed as "atoms per cent excess," indicating the number of isotopic atoms in 100 atoms of the element in excess of the natural abundance of the isotope.

The rate at which a radioactive element undergoes change to another element with the emission of radiation represents the rate of radioactive decay of the element. Radioactive decay is expressed in terms of the half-life of the substance, which represents the time required for the initial number of radioactive atoms to be reduced to one-half. The total life of a radioactive element is of no practical value, since in many cases it may approach infinity, but the half-life is readily determined and is very useful in comparing radioactive elements and in calculations.

From the standpoint of kinetics radioactive decay is a true first-order reaction. The probability that a given atom of a radioactive element will decay within a specified time is an intrinsic property of that particular atom and is independent of other atoms of the element present, temperature, pressure, etc. However, in the case of a homogeneous statistically large sample of the atoms a constant fraction will decay in each succeeding unit of time.

The fundamental law of radioactive decay may be calculated as follows. Let N = the number of atoms. The radioactive disintegrations or change, ΔN, in unit time Δt is related to the number of atoms N as follows:

$$\frac{\Delta N}{\Delta t} = -kN \text{ (the } - \text{ sign represents decrease)}$$

where k = the disintegration or decay constant and represents the fraction of all atoms undergoing decay per unit time. With very small intervals of time, dt, we may write the differential equation:

$$\frac{dN}{dt} = -kN \quad \text{or} \quad \frac{dN}{N} = -kdt$$

At time $t = 0$, N_0 atoms are present. At any time t after $t = 0$, the number of atoms present, N, may be obtained by integrating the above equation between the limits $t = 0$ and $t =$ time t, and N_0 and N for the number of atoms:

$$\int_{N_0}^{N} \frac{dN}{N} = -k \int_0^t dt$$

which gives

$$\ln \frac{N}{N_0} = -kt \quad \text{or} \quad \frac{N}{N_0} = e^{-kt}$$

and

$$N = N_0 e^{-kt}$$

The expression:

$$N = N_0 e^{-kt}$$

represents the exponential law for the radioactive decay of a single isotope. The half-life of an isotope is obtained as follows:

$$\ln \frac{N}{N_0} = -kt$$

and

$$\log \frac{N}{N_0} = -\frac{kt}{2.303}$$

and

$$\log \frac{N_0}{N} = \frac{kt}{2.303}$$

At half-life $t_{\frac{1}{2}}$, N has dropped to $N_0/2$ and

$$\log \frac{N_0}{\frac{N_0}{2}} = \frac{kt_{\frac{1}{2}}}{2.303} \quad \text{or} \quad \log 2 = \frac{kt_{\frac{1}{2}}}{2.303}$$

and

$$t_{\frac{1}{2}} = \frac{2.303 \log 2}{k} = \frac{0.693}{k}$$

The half-life of I^{131} is eight days; accordingly its decay constant, k, is calculated as follows:

$$8 = \frac{0.693}{k}$$

and

$$k = \frac{0.693}{8} = 0.0866/\text{day} = 0.0036/\text{hr} = 0.00006/\text{min} = 0.000001/\text{sec}$$

Thus, from the decay constant it is possible to calculate the fraction of radioactive atoms undergoing decay in any unit of time. In the case of I^{131} 0.0866 of the atoms present decay per day and 0.000001 of the atoms decay per second.

The curie is the primary unit of radioactivity and represents 3.7×10^{10} radioactive disintegrations per second. The millicurie accordingly represents 3.7×10^7 and the microcurie 3.7×10^4 disintegrations per second. If the value of the decay constant, k, of a radioactive substance is known, the weight of the substance represented by a curie, etc., may be calculated. In the case of I^{131} this may be done as follows. As shown above, the value of k is

$0.000001 = 10^{-6}$ per sec. Since one mol of I^{131} contains 6×10^{23} atoms (Avogadro number), the number of disintegrations per second per mol is:

$$10^{-6} \times 6 \times 10^{23} = 6 \times 10^{17}$$

One curie of I^{131} represents 3.7×10^{10} disintegrations per second; consequently, the number of mols per curie is:

$$\text{Mols } I^{131} \text{ per curie} = \frac{3.7 \times 10^{10}}{6 \times 10^{17}} = 0.6 \times 10^{-7} = 6 \times 10^{-8} = 0.0000078 \text{ g}$$
$$= 0.0078 \text{ mg.}$$

In the case of C^{14}, with a half-life of 5600 years, one curie is represented by 1.6×10^{-2} mols or 220 mg as compared with 6×10^{-8} mols or 0.0078 mg for I^{131}. Obviously the shorter the half-life, the greater is the intensity of radiation per mol.

In the biologic application of isotopes a number of purposes are served, several of which are outlined below.

An isotope, A, containing C^{14} may be administered to an animal and then compound B isolated, purified, and its radioactivity determined. Also, B may be degraded and the C^{14} activity associated with various carbon atoms determined. From such information it is often possible to establish whether A is a metabolic precursor of B, and the way in which A is converted to B. For example suppose methyl labeled C^{14}-acetate is given to a rat and palmitic acid of high activity is isolated, and that little activity is found in the —COOH group and in succeeding alternate carbon groups, but much activity is present in the α, γ, etc., groups. We may conclude that acetate is a precursor of palmitic acid and that palmitic acid is in effect formed by the successive condensation of acetate, adding two carbon atoms at a time to the chain, with reduction of the —CO— groups to —CH₂— groups:

$$\overset{*}{C}H_3 - COOH + \overset{*}{C}H_3 - COOH \longrightarrow \overset{*}{C}H_3CO - \overset{*}{C}H_2 - COOH \xrightarrow{\text{red.}}$$

$$\overset{*}{C}H_3 - CH_2 - \overset{*}{C}H_2 - COOH + \overset{*}{C}H_3 - COOH \longrightarrow \overset{*}{C}H_3 - CO - \overset{*}{C}H_2 - CH_2 - \overset{*}{C}H_2 - COOH \xrightarrow{\text{red.}}$$

$$\overset{*}{C}H_3 - CH_2 - \overset{*}{C}H_2 - CH_2 - \overset{*}{C}H_2 - COOH, \text{etc.}$$

Another application of isotopes as tracers is in determining the rate of breakdown and synthesis or turnover of a substance in the body. The level of a compound in tissues may remain practically constant due to the rates of synthesis and breakdown balancing each other. If, however, the body store of the compound is labeled by administering the isotopically labeled substance, the rate of breakdown of the compound may be arrived at by following the disappearance of isotope from it. The rate of synthesis of the compound may be ascertained by administering a labeled precursor of the compound and following the rate of appearance of the isotope in the compound. Such studies of turnover rates, initiated particularly by Schoenheimer and associates (3), have shown the levels of body constituents to represent continuous dynamic balances between rates of synthesis and rates of breakdown. Only the use of labeled compounds has made the acquisition of this knowledge possible.

Most metabolic disturbances, whether caused by disease, poisons, drugs, or abnormal diets, are related to changes in the rate of synthesis or breakdown (turnover rate) of a substance or substances of the body. For example, Stetten (4), by determining the turnover rate of uric acid in patients with so-called primary gout, obtained evidence that the elevated level of uric acid in such cases is due to increased rate of synthesis rather than decreased rate of excretion.

Isotopes are utilized in the biologic preparation of labeled compounds for experimental use. For example, uniformly labeled C^{14}-glucose is obtained by hydrolysis of starch produced by plant photosynthesis in an atmosphere containing $C^{14}O_2$, and labeled cholesterol may be obtained from the tissues of rats given large doses of C^{14}-acetate.

12. Studies with microorganisms. Knowledge relative to the metabolic chemical pathways and catalyzing enzymes of microorganisms has accumulated rapidly in recent years. Microorganisms represent very useful tools for the biochemist; since their nutritive requirements are relatively simple, they can be grown rapidly in pure cultures and in large quantities, and the analysis of their metabolic products is more convenient than in case of higher forms.

Mutant strains of microorganisms can be produced experimentally with specific enzymic and metabolic changes associated with specific hereditary (gene) alterations. Study of such mutants has contributed much to our understanding of the mechanism of hereditary processes in general

It has been found in a number of instances that enzymes and metabolic processes first observed in microorganisms are operative in animal cells, and of course the reverse is also true. Thus, at times it is much more convenient and profitable to study the details of a metabolic sequence in microorganisms than in higher animals where it is known to take place.

Microorganisms have been very useful in the study of mechanisms of metabolic inhibition by antimetabolites and antibiotics, and of enzyme adaptation to changes in the constituents of the nutrient medium.

As pointed out in Chapter 8, microorganisms may be used as an analytical tool in the quantitative determination of amino acids. Due to selective fermentation of different sugars by different organisms or strains of organisms, yeasts and bacteria have been used in the estimation of individual sugars in mixtures of sugars.

GENERAL REFERENCES

Calvin, M.; Heidelberger, C.; Reid, J. C.; Tolbert, B. M.; and Yankwich, P. E.: *Isotopic Carbon*, John Wiley & Sons, New York, 1949.

Chase, G. D.: *Principles of Radioisotope Methodology*. Burgess Publishing Co., Minneapolis, 1959.

Dixon, M.: *Manometric Methods*. Cambridge University Press, London, 1951.

Extermann, R. C. (ed.): *Radioisotopes in Scientific Research*. Vol. III: "Research with Isotopes in Human and Animal Biology and Medicine." Pergamon Press, New York, 1958.

Garrod, A. E.: *Inborn Errors of Metabolism*, 2nd ed. Henry Frowde & Hodder & Stoughton, London, 1923.

Hsia, D. Y.: *Inborn Errors of Metabolism*. Year Book Publishers, Chicago, 1959.

Kamen, M. D.: *Isotopic Tracers in Biology*, 3rd ed. Academic Press, New York, 1957.

Umbreit, W. W.; Burris, R. H.; and Stauffer, J. F.: *Manometric Techniques, a Manual Describing Methods Applicable to the Study of Tissue Metabolism*, rev. ed. Burgess Publishing Co., Minneapolis, 1957.

Wolstenholme, G. E. W. (ed.): *Isotopes in Biochemistry*. Blakiston, New York, 1952.

Woolley, D. W.: *A Study of Antimetabolites*. John Wiley & Sons., New York, 1952.

SPECIAL REFERENCES

1. Shive, W., and Roberts, E. C.: *J. Biol. Chem.*, **162**, 463, 1946. Shive, W.: *Ann. N.Y. Acad. Sci.*, **52**, 1212, 1950.
2. Knoop, F.: *Beitr. chem. Physiol. Path.*, **6**, 150, 1905.
3. Schoenheimer, R.: *The Dynamic State of Body Constituents*. Harvard University Press, Cambridge, Mass., 1942.
4. Stetten, D., Jr.: *Bull. N.Y. Acad. Med.*, **28**, 664, 1952.

20

Bioenergetics

GENERAL CONSIDERATIONS

The development, growth, and maintenance of a living organism involves the synthesis from food materials of many specialized substances and the organization of these substances into the types of protoplasm characteristic of the different kinds of cells and tissues making up the organism. The protoplasmic syntheses require the expenditure of energy, as do all of the processes involved in operating the organism, such as maintenance of temperature, movement (mechanical work of muscles), the generation of electrical potentials and current (brain and nerve impulses), the secretion and excretion of fluids, and the transport of substances against concentration gradients (active transport). The energy for these various purposes is generated by the oxidation of foods and is supplied to the tissues in the form of chemical energy contained in specific compounds, and generally associated with certain groups in the compounds. These compounds, through reactions catalyzed and controlled by specific enzyme systems, provide energy for the synthesis of protoplasm and for its operation in all respects.

In order to understand the energy producing and utilizing processes of the body, it is essential to understand certain principles relating to energy in general and chemical energy in particular.

CHEMICAL ENERGY

Different organic compounds yield different amounts of energy when completely oxidized. This heat of combustion is determined by the elementary

785

composition and structure of the substance and also the energy content of the products of combustion. We may state that the total energy liberated is represented by the difference in energy contents of the substance oxidized and of the products of its oxidation. The total amount of energy given off is independent of the pathway of oxidation so long as the products are identical. Table 20.1 gives the calories liberated per mol by the oxidation of several compounds to carbon dioxide and water.

Table 20.1.   Heats of Combustion to Carbon Dioxide and Water

Substance	Calories Liberated per Mol
Ethane, gas	368,400
Ethyl alcohol, liquid	327,600
Acetaldehyde, liquid	279,000
Acetic acid, liquid	209,400
Pyruvic acid, liquid	279,000
Acetone, liquid	426,800
n-Hexane, liquid	989,800
Glucose, solid	673,000
Sucrose	1,349,600

It will be noted that the heat liberated in the combustion of ethane is higher than that liberated in the combustion of its derivatives, alcohol, aldehyde, and acetic acid, each of which is derived from the preceding compound by one stage of oxidation. In other words, each stage of oxidation liberates a definite amount of heat energy which can be calculated by subtraction. We can readily see that 1 mol of liquid acetic acid contains less energy by 158,600 cal (368,000 − 209,400) than 1 mol of gaseous ethane, and less energy by 69,600 cal than acetaldehyde.

Heats of combustion represent the maximum energy obtainable from substances by drastically breaking them down and oxidizing their elements. The heat of combustion of a substance such as glucose, which is oxidized completely to carbon dioxide and water in the body, represents the energy obtainable from it by the body. This oxidation, however, proceeds in many separate stages, and the energy is accordingly liberated in increments corresponding to these stages.

Chemical reactions are always associated with energy changes which finally appear as heat changes and are measured as such. Some reactions proceed with heat evolution, and these are said to be exothermic. Other reactions absorb heat from the surroundings and are endothermic. In general, only those reactions liberating energy are capable of taking place spontaneously (energy flows from a higher to a lower level), though catalysts may be necessary to make them go in actual practice. Reactions which absorb energy proceed only when energy, generally as heat, is supplied. Most of the processes concerned with the breakdown of foods in the body are exothermic, and the catalysts to make them go are enzyme systems present in the tissues.

FREE ENERGY

In order that we may be more precise in our discussion of energy, it is necessary to introduce the concept of free energy, or the energy capable of doing work. From a chemical viewpoint, free energy is also the chemical energy capable of causing chemical reactions.

In order to obtain some idea of the meaning of free energy, let us consider a frictionless heat engine into which we place a certain amount of gas kinetic energy, Q, at the temperature T_1 (on the absolute scale), which passes through the engine to the lower temperature T_2 of the exhaust. If the exhaust temperature, T_2, could be made absolute 0, at which all kinetic energy has been lost, and if the engine could be operated without friction, all Q would be converted to work and would represent free energy. However, in practice the exhaust temperature, T_2, must be much above absolute 0, and only a fraction of the total energy can be converted to work, or appear as free energy. It can be shown theoretically that the maximum work, w, obtainable in a frictionless heat engine from energy, Q, working between temperatures T_1 and T_2, is represented by the equation:

$$W = Q \frac{T_1 - T_2}{T_1}$$

In words, the maximum work is equal to the total energy, Q, multiplied by the ratio of the drop in temperature in passing through the engine to the initial temperature at which Q begins to operate. The above equation may be changed as follows:

$$W = Q \frac{T_1 - T_2}{T_1}$$
$$WT_1 = QT_1 - QT_2$$
$$W = \frac{QT_1}{T_1} - \frac{QT_2}{T_1}$$
$$W = Q - \left(\frac{Q}{T_1}\right) T_2$$

The equation $W = Q - (Q/T_1) T_2$ shows that all Q can appear as work or free energy, $W = Q$, only when $(Q/T_1) T_2 = 0$. This can occur only when the engine exhaust is at absolute 0, and $T_2 = 0$. At all other exhaust temperatures a part of the energy is unavailable and is represented by the exhaust temperature T_2 multiplied by the factor Q/T_1. This factor (Q/T_1) is known as the "entropy" of the system per degree and is generally represented by S.

We may summarize the above for a heat engine by the statement:

$$\text{work} = \text{free energy} = H - T \cdot S$$

where T = the exhaust temperature, H = total energy as heat, and S = the entropy of the process.

All self-operating systems, mechanical or chemical, function energetically according to the equation:

$$F = H - T \cdot S$$

where F = free energy or the energy for work, H = the total heat energy of the system, and S = the entropy per degree.

Since energy for operating physiologic processes is derived from chemical changes, the biochemist is especially interested in the application of the above free energy equation to chemical reactions, for it is only the free energy of these reactions which is useful. The theory of such applications is complex and represents the science of chemical thermodynamics. However, we may be able to obtain some understanding of these applications from what follows. In general, reactions take place in the body at approximately constant temperature, due to a balance between energy production and heat loss. In a reaction such as:

$$A + B \longrightarrow C + D + \text{energy}$$

the energy represented by $A + B$ is greater than that of $C + D$ by the amount of energy given off in the reaction. The system considered as a whole energetically passes, isothermally (T constant), from the condition of $A + B$ to that of $C + D$. The energies and entropies of $A + B$ are different from those of $C + D$.

We are not particularly interested in the energy values of $A + B$ or $C + D$, but we are interested in the energy change in going from $A + B$ to $C + D$, and especially are we interested in the free energy change. Suppose we represent the energy state before reaction by:

$$F_1 = H_1 - T \cdot S_1 \tag{1}$$

and after reaction by:

$$F_2 = H_2 - T \cdot S_2 \tag{2}$$

If we subtract (1) from (2) we have the change in free energy in the reaction:

$$F_2 - F_1 = (H_2 - H_1) - T(S_2 - S_1)$$

Since $F_2 - F_1$, $H_2 - H_1$, and $S_2 - S_1$ represent increments of energy change, these values are designated by the symbols ΔF, ΔH, and ΔS. We now may write the equation:

$$\Delta F = \Delta H - T\,\Delta S$$

which states that the free energy, ΔF, given off in a reaction is equal to the heat energy or enthalpy change minus the entropy change.

Entropy energy, as pointed out above, is the energy of a system (mechanical or chemical) unavailable to do work. For an isothermal reversible process taking place at constant pressure the entropy change can be calculated from calorimetric measurement of the heat of the process and the temperature by the equation:

$$\Delta S = \frac{Q_r}{T}$$

where $Q_r = $ the heat of the reversible process and $T = $ the absolute temperature ($0°$ C $= 273.16°$ absolute). For example, the melting of ice to water at $0°$ C is a reversible process, and the heat of melting or fusion is $1,436$ cal $= Q_r$. The entropy change is:

$$\Delta S = \frac{Q_r}{T} = \frac{1,436}{273.16} = 5.257 \text{ cal per mol per degree}$$

The entire entropy change is given by $T \Delta S = 5.257 \times 273.16 = 1,436$ cal. That is, the heat absorbed in converting 18 g of ice to 18 g of water at $0°$ C, 1436 cal, represents the total entropy change per mol. Since entropy energy is going into the ice in forming water, the entropy of the 18 g of water formed from the ice is 1436 cal greater than the entropy of the ice. In this case the entropy increases and is given a positive sign, $+1436$ cal.

In reversing the above process—that is, converting 18 g of water to 18 g of ice at $0°$ C—1436 cal are given off, and $T \Delta S = -1436$ cal, which means that the entropy of the ice per mol is 1436 cal less than the entropy of the water.

It is obvious that the entropy energy associated with the reversible conversion of water to ice is not available to do work. It is the change in energy accompanying the change in state from crystallized water molecules to liquid water molecules and the reverse at $0°$ C. The difference in energy between the water as ice and water as liquid at $0°$ C is the entropy energy.

The entropy change of a reversible chemical process taking place at constant temperature and pressure may be obtained similarly, as outlined above, from the calorimetric heat of reaction per mol, ΔH. Here the relation is.

$$\Delta H = T \Delta S$$

For irreversible processes entropy changes cannot be obtained as outlined above, but may be obtained from measurement of the heat capacities of substances as outlined in texts on thermodynamics.

Entropy may be considered as a measure of the degree of disorder of a system; the greater the degree of disorder, the greater the entropy of the system. For example, if a solution of I_2 in carbon tetrachloride is overlaid with water (with temperature constant), initially all of the I_2 is in the CCl_4 layer, but as time passes I_2 diffuses into the water layer and back into the CCl_4 layer, but at a faster rate from CCl_4 to water, until the activity of I_2 in the water equals the activity of I_2 in CCl_4, and the system is at equilibrium. The degree of organization of the system is greatest before any I_2 has diffused from CCl_4 to water, and the entropy is least under these conditions. As more and more I_2 diffuses into the water, the degree of organization decreases, and the entropy progressively increases, becoming maximum at equilibrium. This principle applies to chemical reactions as well as all other systems. The entropy of a chemical reaction is maximum at the equilibrium point. In the case of I_2 distributed between CCl_4 and water at equilibrium, the work energy required to remove all of the I_2 from the water and replace it in the CCl_4 would be equivalent to the entropy increase when the system, with all of the I_2 in CCl_4, changes to the state with the I_2 distributed between CCl_4 and water at equilibrium.

Another way of looking at entropy is from the viewpoint of probability. The entropy of a system, mechanical or chemical, increases with increase in the probability of the system. In the above case of I_2 in CCl_4 overlaid with water the most probable state of the system (time neglected) is the equilibrium state at which entropy is maximum.

All forms of energy are the product of two factors, an intensity factor and a capacity factor. For example, the energy involved in the expansion of a gas in the cylinder of an engine is the product of pressure (intensity factor) and volume change (capacity factor), PV; the energy of an electric current is equal to volts (intensity) times coulombs (capacity); and chemical energy is equal to the product of chemical potential (intensity) and moles transformed (capacity). Similarly, the entropy energy of a change in a system, $T \Delta S$, is the product of absolute temperature T (intensity) and ΔS (entropy per degree). That is, the entropy expression, ΔS, is the capacity factor of the entropy energy change of a system.

As pointed out, all energy expressions consist of an intensity factor multiplied by a capacity factor. The intensity factor determines the driving force and direction of energy flow, while the capacity factor determines the extent of the process. For example, suppose a cube, A, of iron weighing 10 g is in contact with a cube, B, of iron weighing 100 g, so that heat may flow freely from one cube to the other. If both cubes are at 25° C, no net heat will flow between the cubes, but the total heat energy of B is ten times that of A (100:10). Now if the temperature of A is raised to 30° C, heat will pass from A to B regardless of the fact that B contains many times the total energy of A, due to its large capacity factor. However, if the mass of B were only 50 g instead of 100 g, the amount of heat flowing from A to B until equilibrium is reached would be decreased in proportion to the decrease in the capacity factor of B (its mass).

The chemical potential is the intensity factor of a chemical reaction which represents the driving force of the reaction and determines the direction in which the net reaction proceeds (reversible reaction). In theory, all reactions are reversible, though for many of them infinite time would be required to reach the equilibrium state.

Only the free energy, ΔF, obtained when a system undergoes change is available to do work. In the case of chemical reactions only those reactions can take place spontaneously in which free energy is given off in the reaction. When a system (mechanical or chemical) loses free energy in a change or reaction, the free energy of the system decreases by a definite amount and is given a negative sign. If the free energy of a system increases in a change, this increase is given a positive sign. For example, in a reaction:

$$A + B \rightleftharpoons C + D$$

if 5000 calories of free energy is given off, meaning that the system $C + D$ represents 5000 calories of free energy less than the system $A + B$, then we say that the free energy change in the reaction, ΔF, is -5000 cal. If it is necessary to heat A and B and to increase the free energy of A + B by 5000 cal in order to make the reaction go, the free energy change, ΔF, is $+5000$ cal. Thus, for a chemical reaction to take place spontaneously, there must be a decrease in free energy; that is, the change in free energy must have a negative sign represented by $-\Delta F$. Also, the extent to which a chemical reaction takes place is determined by the magnitude of $-\Delta F$, the free energy decrease. In other words, we may say that the free energy decrease in a reaction is a measure of the driving force or potential for the reaction.

While there must be a decrease in free energy, $-\Delta F$, for a reaction to occur spontaneously, the fact that a decrease in free energy takes place does not necessarily mean that the reaction will automatically occur. Many substances do not spontaneously react despite the fact that a large decrease in free energy would take place upon reaction. This is due to the fact that a certain amount of "energy of activation" for the reacting molecules is necessary to cause them to react. The action of catalysts such as enzymes in causing biologic reactions to take place is related to the fact that the combination of the enzyme with reacting molecules decreases the activation energy necessary for the reaction (see Chapter 10).

The effect of temperature upon reaction velocity. Energy of activation. The velocity of a reaction is generally increased from two to four times by a temperature rise of $10°$ C.

Arrhenius demonstrated a mathematical relation between the velocity constant of a reaction and the absolute temperature, T. The equation for this relation is:

$$\frac{d \log_e k}{dT} = \frac{E}{R} \cdot \frac{1}{T^2}$$

in which $k =$ the velocity constant, $T =$ the absolute temperature, $E =$ a constant, and $R =$ the gas constant. This equation states that the variation in the natural logarithm of the velocity constant with the absolute temperature is equal to a constant, E, divided by the constant R, multiplied by the reciprocal of the square of the absolute temperature.

When the velocity constants are determined for two different temperatures, they may be designated as k_1 and k_2, and the corresponding temperatures as T_1 and T_2. If the above equation be integrated between the limits of T_2 and T_1, we have:

$$\log_e \frac{k_2}{k_1} = \frac{E}{R}\left(\frac{1}{T_1} - \frac{1}{T_2}\right)$$

and upon changing to common logarithms:

$$2.303 \log \frac{k_2}{k_1} = \frac{E}{R}\left(\frac{1}{T_1} - \frac{1}{T_2}\right)$$

This equation shows the relation of the velocity constants of a reaction at any two temperatures, T_2 and T_1. The constant E is very important and represents the so-called energy of activation of the molecules. E may be readily calculated by determining the values of k_1 and k_2 at temperatures T_1 and T_2 and making the proper rearrangements and substitutions in the equation.

The equation may be written:

$$2.303(\log k_2 - \log k_1) = \frac{E}{R}\left(\frac{1}{T_1} - \frac{1}{T_2}\right)$$

and upon solving for E, we have:

$$E = \frac{2.303(\log k_2 - \log k_1)R}{\dfrac{1}{T_1} - \dfrac{1}{T_2}}$$

The application of this equation to the calculation of the energy of activation, E, for the decomposition of N_2O_5 may be used for illustration. Suppose at 25° C (298° A) the value of the velocity constant k_1 is 0.0000346 and at 35° C (308° A) the value of the velocity constant k_2 becomes 0.000135. Accordingly:

$$\frac{1}{T_1} = \frac{1}{298} = 0.003357$$

$$\frac{1}{T_2} = \frac{1}{308} = 0.003247$$

$$\log k_1 = -4.471$$

and $$\log k_2 = -3.871$$

R is the gas constant and equals 1.987 cal per degree. Upon substituting in the equation, we have:

$$E = \frac{2.303(-3.871 - (-4.471))1.987}{0.003357 - 0.003247}$$

$$= \frac{2.303(-3.871 + 4.471)1.987}{0.00011}$$

$$= \frac{2.303 \times 0.600 \times 1.987}{0.00011} = \frac{2.7359}{0.00011}$$

$$= 24{,}872 \text{ cal/mol}$$

Molecules must possess a certain energy, E, before they are capable of reacting. This is the energy of activation. Suppose we consider the decomposition of N_2O_5 molecules. In any appreciable mass of the substance an enormous number of molecules is present. For a given temperature each molecule possesses a certain average energy (kinetic energy or energy due to structure within the molecule), but not all of the molecules have the same energy. Some possess much more than the average energy of the mass and others less. Only those molecules possessing an energy equal to or greater than E (24,872 cal per mol for N_2O_5) can react. The effect of a temperature rise is to increase the number of molecules possessing an energy equal to or greater than E at any given instant.

In the case of reactions of the second and third order, which depend upon collisions for reaction, only those molecules possessing an energy as great as E are capable of reacting upon collision. The energy of molecules is affected by collision and depends upon the manner in which they collide. Two molecules may collide in such a way that the energy of one molecule is increased and that of the other decreased. Since an increase in temperature increases kinetic energy, it is not surprising that more molecules possess energy as great as E at the higher temperature than at the lower and more molecules can react at the higher than at the lower temperature.

The velocity of many reactions is increased by the presence of small amounts of substances called "catalysts." It has been shown that this is largely accomplished by the catalyst lowering the energy of activation required for reaction. For example, the energy of activation for the decomposition of hydrogen peroxide in aqueous solution is 18,000 cal per mol; but if colloidal platinum be added as catalyst, the energy of activation necessary falls to 11,700 cal per mol. At a given temperature many more molecules of peroxide will possess an energy of 11,700 cal than will possess one of 18,000 cal. Consequently, the number of molecules capable of reacting is much greater in the presence of the catalyst than when it is absent.

It is well known that enzymes, which are protein catalytic agents, are of vital importance in controlling the reactions occurring in the body. It is interesting that they generally have a marked effect in decreasing the energy of activation (also called the "critical increment") necessary for reaction. For example, when the hydrolysis of sucrose is catalyzed by hydrogen ions, the energy of activation for reaction is 25,560 calories; but when the reaction is effected by the specific enzyme, invertase, the energy of activation falls to around 9000 calories.

Much evidence has accumulated to show that catalysts and enzymes function by the formation of some kind of combination with the substrate, which then decomposes into the products of reaction and the catalyst:

$$\text{catalyst} + \text{substrate} \rightleftharpoons \begin{array}{c}\text{catalyst}\\ \text{I}\\ \text{substrate}\end{array} \rightleftharpoons \text{catalyst} + \text{products}$$

Many catalytic actions are reversible, and combination with the catalyst may be considered to be an intermediate stage of reaction in both directions.

The energy given off or absorbed in a chemical reaction is dependent only upon the initial and final states of the reactants and products concerned and is independent of the pathway. Suppose we consider the diagram of Figure 20.1.

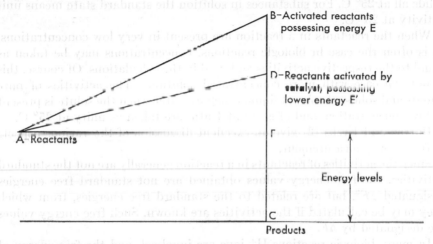

Figure 20.1. Diagram illustrating energy of activation.

The reacting molecules at energy level A are converted into products at energy level C with a total decrease in energy of FC. However, before reaction can occur, the energy of the molecules at A must be raised to a level of B by absorbing energy so that their energy content is as great as the required energy of activation, E. The amount of energy absorbed for activation is FB. The molecules now react to form products at energy level C and give off energy equal to BC. Since energy BF is absorbed for activation and given off in the reaction, the net energy change is FC. Now in the presence of a catalyst, or enzyme, a combination with the reactants is formed at D which represents an energy of activation, $E' = FD$, which is much less than E of the uncatalyzed reaction ($E = FB$). The catalyst-activated molecules at D then decompose into the products at C with the liberation of energy equal to DC. Since energy DF is absorbed for activation, the net energy decrease is FC, as in the uncatalyzed reaction. If the reaction is reversible, energy equal to CB must be absorbed for the uncatalyzed reaction and an amount of energy equal to only CD for the catalyzed action. The activated products at B and D then change into the reactants at A, with the liberation of energy equal to BF and DF, respectively. The net energy increase in reversing the action is equal to FC.

The catalysts in the above process do not change the initial or final products or the net energy involved, but they permit the action to go on at a lower energy of activation.

MEASUREMENT OF FREE ENERGY AND THE RELATION OF FREE ENERGY TO CHEMICAL REACTION

There are a number of ways by which the free energies of chemical reactions may be determined or calculated, the method employed in a given case being dependent upon the availability of the necessary data or of procedures by which these data may be obtained.

Since the free energies of reactions vary with concentrations (activities) of the reactants, temperature, etc., for comparison it is essential to determine free energies under standard conditions. The standard free energy of a reaction is indicated by the symbol ΔF° and represents the free energy of the reaction when the reactants are in their standard states. For pure substances the standard state means gases at 1 atm pressure, and liquids and crystalline solids all at 25° C. For substances in solution the standard state means unit activity at 25° C.

When the reactants in a reaction are present in very low concentrations, as is often the case in biologic reactions, concentrations may be taken as equal to the respective activities and used in the calculations. Of course, this is not the case with more concentrated solutions. The activities of pure liquids and solids, of solvent liquids such as water when the solute is present in low concentration, and of gases at 1 atm are taken as unity at 25° C.

Burton and Krebs (2) give an excellent discussion of the various aspects of free energy measurement.

Since the activities of reactants in a reaction generally are not the standard activities, the free energy values obtained are not standard free energies designated ΔF°, but are related to the standard free energies, from which they may be calculated if the activities are known. Such free energy values are designated by ΔF.

In many biologic reactions H^+ ions are involved, and the free energy of reaction may vary widely with variations in pH. Consequently, the pH at which the free energy is determined must be specified if H^+ ions are involved.

METHODS OF CALCULATING FREE ENERGY CHANGES IN CHEMICAL REACTIONS

A. From equilibrium constants. The most useful method for estimating both the standard free energies, ΔF°, and other free energies of biochemical reactions is based upon the relation between standard free energy and equilibrium constants. The equilibrium constant for a general reversible equilibrium reaction such as:

$$A + B \rightleftharpoons C + D$$

is
$$K = \frac{[C][D]}{[A][B]}$$

where the letters in [ ] represent the activities of the products C and D and the reactants A and B.

The standard free energy, $\Delta F°$, of a reversible reaction is very simply related to the equilibrium constant of the reaction by the equation:

$$\Delta F° = -RT \ln K = \text{calories per mol}$$

where R = the gas constant, 1.987 cal per mol per degree; T = the absolute temperature, and $\ln K$ = the natural logarithm of the equilibrium constant (2.303 log K). Thus it is seen that if the equilibrium constant of a reversible reaction can be determined, the standard free energy of the reaction can be easily calculated. Conversely, if the standard free energy of a reaction, $\Delta F°$, is known, the equilibrium constant, K, of the reaction may be calculated.

Generally the activities of the reactants and products in a biochemical reaction are not standard state activities, and it may be desirable to calculate the free energy change, ΔF, when the reaction takes place at the concentrations (activities) present in a tissue. For a reaction such as:

$$A + B \rightleftharpoons C + D$$

in which the activities of A, B, C, and D are not activities of the standard state (unity), the free energy change, ΔF, is related to the standard free energy change by the equation:

$$\Delta F = \Delta F° + RT \ln \frac{[C][D]}{[A][B]} = \text{calories per mol}$$

Consequently, when the standard free energy change, $\Delta F°$, can be calculated from the equilibrium constant of a reaction, the free energy changes, ΔF, for any concentrations (activities) of reactants and products may be calculated by the above equation.

When a reaction reaches equilibrium, no further change in concentrations of reactants and products takes place, and there is no change in free energy in the reaction at equilibrium ($\Delta F = 0$). Consequently, no work can be obtained from a reaction at equilibrium. The greatest free energy change in a reaction takes place when the activities of reactants and products are farthest from the equilibrium state, and the most work is obtainable under these conditions if there is a decrease in free energy ($-\Delta F$).

Since the entropy of a system is maximum at equilibrium and decreases the farther the system is from equilibrium, a decrease in free energy in a reaction is always associated with an increase in entropy, and the amount of work obtained from a reaction (process) is proportional both to the free energy decrease and the entropy increase.

The relations of free energy and entropy changes to spontaneous and nonspontaneous reactions and reactions at equilibrium are as follows:

	Reaction		
	Spontaneous	Equilibrium	Not spontaneous
Entropy change	+	0	−
Free energy change	−	0	+

Thus it is seen that for a spontaneous reaction $dS > 0$ and $dF < 0$, at equilibrium $dS = 0$ and $dF = 0$, while for a nonspontaneous reaction (requires addition of heat to make it go) $dS < 0$ and $dF > 0$.

Reactions in which there is a free energy decrease $(-\Delta F)$ of the system are called "exergonic reactions"; that is, free energy flows from the system. Conversely, reactions in which there is a free energy increase $(+\Delta F)$ of the system are called "endergonic reactions."

One of the chief functions of living organisms is to maintain biochemical reactions in a state removed from equilibrium so free energy $(-\Delta F)$ may be provided by the reactions to support the living processes. This is accomplished by the intake and oxidation of food and the excretion of waste products. When the reactions within an organism are at equilibrium, the organism is dead!

Another way of looking at metabolic reactions which maintain living processes is from the standpoint of entropy. The metabolic reactions in which foods are oxidized in the body provide energy to maintain vital reactions in states removed from equilibrium so they may take place spontaneously and supply energy. The further these reactions are from equilibrium, the smaller the entropy associated with them. Consequently, living organisms operate to decrease their entropy, and it has been stated that "organisms live on negative entropy," meaning that energy generated in the organisms is used to control the activities of reactants and products of essential reactions so that the entropies represented by the systems as a whole are low (far removed from equilibrium). This enables the reactions to proceed with a decrease in free energy $(-\Delta F)$ and an increase in entropy with the performance of work. In general, the energy to decrease the entropy (negative entropy) of all living things is provided as chemical energy stored up in compounds by photosynthetic processes due to the radiant energy of the sun.

Most biochemical reactions are reversible, at least to some extent, but in order for them to proceed and to reach equilibrium within reasonable time, they must be catalyzed by their specific enzymes. Consequently, the equilibrium constants are generally obtained from reactions catalyzed and brought to equilibrium by the addition of the appropriate enzymes.

An accurate value for the equilibrium constant of a reaction may be unobtainable because the point of equilibrium lies so far to one or the other side of the reversible reaction that some of the concentrations cannot be measured, with the result that free energy changes cannot be obtained by this method.

As an illustration of the calculation of the standard free energy change, $\Delta F°$, in a biochemical reaction we may consider the conversion of glucose-1-phosphate (glucose-1-P) to glucose-6-phosphate (glucose-6-P) by the enzyme phosphoglucomutase, a very important reaction in the metabolism of glucose in the body.

$$\text{Glucose-1-P} \underset{}{\overset{\text{enzyme}}{\rightleftharpoons}} \text{Glucose-6-P}$$

$$5\%\text{———at equilibrium———}95\%$$

The equilibrium constant at 38° C is given by:

$$K = \frac{[\text{glucose-6-P}]}{[\text{glucose-1-P}]} = \frac{95}{5} = 19$$

The standard free energy change, $\Delta F°$, is:

$$\Delta F° = -RT \ln K = -RT(2.303) \log K = -RT(2.303) \log 19$$
$$= -(1.987)(311)(2.303)(1.2788)$$
$$= -1800 \text{ cal or } -1.8 \text{ kcal (kilogram calories) per mol}$$

Suppose, however, that [glucose-1-P] is 0.01 M and [glucose-6-P] is 0.001 M, which are not equilibrium values. Then the free energy change, ΔF, becomes:

$$\Delta F = \Delta F° + RT \ln \frac{[\text{glucose-6-P}]}{[\text{glucose-1-P}]}$$
$$\Delta F = -1800 + (1.987)(311)(2.303) \log \frac{0.001}{0.01}$$
$$= -1800 + (1420)(-1) = -3220 \text{ cal per mol}$$

Now suppose [glucose-1-P] is 0.0001 M and [glucose-6-P] 0.01 M:

$$\Delta F = -1800 + (1.987)(311)(2.303) \log \frac{0.01}{0.0001}$$
$$= -1800 + (1420)(2) = -1800 + 2840 = +1040 \text{ cal per mol}$$

Thus, the reaction would proceed in the reverse direction with glucose-6-P being converted into glucose-1-P by a driving force of 1040 cal per mol; that is, the free energy change, ΔF, from glucose-6-P to glucose-1-P is now -1040 cal per mol, which would spontaneously reverse the net flow of the reaction. Just by changing concentrations the free energy change may be altered so that the net reaction is reversed.

This discussion shows the very great differences in free energy changes associated with chemical reactions proceeding at different concentrations of reactants and products. In the above example, $\Delta F°$ represents the free energy change when the activities of glucose-1-PO$_4$ and glucose-6-PO$_4$ are unity, while ΔF shows how the free energy change varies from $\Delta F°$ when the activities are not unity (in the standard state).

The constant $\Delta F°$ in the equation:

$$\Delta F = \Delta F° + RT \ln \frac{[A][B]}{[C][D]}$$

bears a relation to ΔF similar to that of pK to pH in the Henderson-Hasselbalch equation of buffers:

$$\text{pH} = \text{p}K_a + \log \frac{[\text{salt}]}{[\text{acid}]}$$

When the activities of reactants and products are unity (standard state), the logarithmic term in the equation:

$$\Delta F = \Delta F^\circ + RT \ln \frac{[A][B]}{[C][D]}$$

becomes 0, and $\Delta F = \Delta F^\circ$, just as the logarithmic term of the Henderson-Hasselbalch equation becomes 0 when [salt]/[acid] $= 1$ and pH $=$ pK.

The pK indicates the relative strength of an acid, and the ΔF° the relative free energy change or driving force of a chemical reaction.

In calculating the free energy changes taking place in tissues, it is necessary to assume that the concentrations of reactants and products remain constant (steady state) for the finite time under consideration. This implies that the reactant molecules are replaced by some other process (system) as fast as they are used up in the reaction, and that the products are removed by some other process (system) as fast as they are produced in the reaction. Such an arrangement by which the system (reaction under consideration) is maintained by other systems of the environment is referred to thermodynamically as an "open system." It appears that biochemical reactions in general represent open systems and often proceed for a considerable time in the steady state, which, however, changes to different levels, depending upon physiologic demands.

B. From electromotive force. By definition, the free energy change in a reversible process is equal to the maximum work, W_{max}, possible in the process exclusive of pressure-volume work:

$$\Delta F = W_{max}$$

A chemical reaction which can be arranged as a battery performs maximum work when the current is drawn off in infinitesimal quantities (reversibly). The potential, E, can be measured accurately without drawing appreciable current (running the battery down). Each mol of electrons ($6.02 \times 10^{23} = 1$ faraday $= 96,500$ coulombs) flowing represents the work given by:

$$W_E = \underset{\text{Potential}}{E} \times \underset{\text{Coulombs}}{96,500} = \text{joules}$$

$$\text{Joules}/4.18 = \text{calories}$$

Since this is maximum work, it also represents free energy change. The general expression is:

$$\Delta F = -EnF$$

where E is potential in volts, n is the number of faradays, and F is the faraday (96,500 coulombs). The sign is negative, representing a free energy decrease.

Cytochrome c is a heme protein containing iron, and the iron readily changes reversibly from Fe^{++} to Fe^{+++}. Cytochrome c serves as an important oxidizing agent in tissues and, in turn, is reoxidized by O_2 through cytochrome oxidase. The over-all process for the oxidation of reduced cyto-chrome c to the oxidized form may be represented:

$$\tfrac{1}{2}O_2 + 2Cyt.\ c\ Fe^{++} + 2H^+ \longrightarrow 2Cyt.\ c\ Fe^{+++} + H_2O$$

The potential of the cytochrome c oxidation-reduction system is given by the equation:

$$E = E'_0 + \frac{RT}{nF} \ln \frac{[Cyt.\ c\ Fe^{+++}]}{[Cyt.\ c\ Fe^{++}]}$$

which is the special case of the general equation for an oxidation-reduction system:

$$E = E'_0 + \frac{RT}{nF} \ln \frac{[Oxidant]}{[Reductant]}$$

applying to the cytochrome c system.

At pH 7, and when the concentrations of both cyt. c Fe^{+++} and cyt. c Fe^{++} are equal and unity (standard states), $E = E'_0$. Under these condi-tions $E'_0 = +0.55$ v.

Since in passing from cyt. c Fe^{++} to cyt. c Fe^{+++}, according to the above equation, two mols of electrons are involved, the change in standard free energy, $\Delta F°$, is given by:

$$\Delta F° = -E'_0 nF = -E'_0 2F$$
$$= -(0.55 \times 2 \times 96,500) = -106,172 \text{ joules}$$
$$= -106,172/4.18 = -25,400 \text{ cal}$$

When the concentrations of oxidant and reductant are not standard con-centrations, the free energy change, ΔF, is related to the standard free energy change, $\Delta F°$, by the equation:

$$\Delta F = \Delta F° + RT \ln \frac{[Oxidant]}{[Reductant]}$$

C. From thermodynamic data. 1. Such calculations of free energy may be based upon the relation:

$$\Delta F = \Delta H - T \Delta S$$

where ΔH represents the change in enthalpy (change in heat at constant pressure), and $T \Delta S$ is the change in entropy.

When the substances involved in a chemical process are in their standard states, the free energy change obtained from the above relation is the standard free energy change, $\Delta F°$.

The oxidative conversion of glyceraldehyde-3-phosphate to 3-phosphoglyceric acid is an important process in tissues. For the oxidation reaction involving the undissociated molecules in their standard states we may write the equation:

Glyceraldehyde-3-phosphate + H_2O $\longrightarrow$ 3-Phosphoglyceric acid + H_2
GP   PGA

$$\Delta H = +4000 \text{ cal}$$

The entropy change, $T \Delta S$, is equal to T (entropy of products $-$ entropy of reactants). In this case the difference, ΔS, in passing from GP to PGA is 0.9 cal per degree, and the entropies, S, of H_2 and H_2O are 31.12 and 16.45 cal per degree, respectively. Thus the entropy change at 20° C is:

$$T \Delta S = 293(S_{PGA} - S_{GP} + S_{H_2} - S_{H_2O})$$
$$= 293(0.9 + 31.12 - 16.45) = 4560 \text{ cal}$$
$$\Delta F° = \Delta H - T \Delta S = +4000 - 4560 = -560 \text{ cal}$$

2. The free energy change in a chemical reaction may be obtained from the free energies of formation of the products and reactants when these are available:

ΔF = Free energies of formation of products − free energies of formation of reactants

This method of calculating free energy change may be illustrated for the over-all biologic process:

Glucose + O_2 ⟶ 2 Pyruvate + 2H⁺ + 2H₂O

The standard free energy of formation, $\Delta F°f$, of glucose is $-219,380$ cal, that of 2 pyruvate s $-226,640$ cal, and that of 2 H_2O is $-113,380$ cal. The value for H⁺ is 0.
Thus we have:

$$\Delta F° = (-226,640 - 113,380) - (-219,380)$$
$$= -120,640 \text{ cal}$$

Table 20.2. Free Energies of Formation from Their Elements ($\Delta F°f$) of Some Biologically Important Compounds
Values represent kilocalories per mol of substance in aqueous solution at unit activity and 25° C

Compound	$\Delta F°f$
NH_4^+	19
Acetaldehyde	33.71
Acetone	38.52
Ethyl alcohol	43.39
Water	56.69
Butyrate⁻	84.6
L-Alanine	88.75
Acetate⁻	88.99
Carbon dioxide	92.26
Pyruvate⁻	113.32
Acetoacetate⁻	115
Glycerol	116.76
β-Hydroxybutyrate⁻	121
Lactate⁻	123.64
HCO_3^-	140.29
Fumarate²⁻	144.41
Succinate²⁻	164.97
L-Glutamate⁺²⁻	166.11
L-Aspartate⁺²⁻	167.11
Oxaloacetate²⁻	190.53
α-Ketoglutarate²⁻	190.74
Malate²⁻	201.98
α-D-Glucose	219.38
cis-Aconitate³⁻	220.63
Oxalosuccinate²⁻	268.57
Isocitrate³⁻	277.77
Citrate³⁻	279.36

CALCULATION OF THE FREE ENERGY OF DISSOCIATION OF ACIDS

Often a biochemical reaction involves an acid which is more or less dissociated at the experimental pH, and the free energy change, ΔF_i, varies according to the degree of dissociation.

The free energy of ionization, ΔF_i, of any one acid forming an equilibrium mixture at any given pH is obtained from the general equation:

$$\Delta F_i = 2.3RT \sum (pK_i - pH) - 2.3RT \log \left(1 + \frac{[H^+]}{K}\right)$$

where $\Sigma(pK_i - pH) =$ the sum for all the stages involved in the dissociation (one for each pK), $pH =$ the fixed experimental pH, and the K of the last term in the equation $=$ the constant for the dissociation which is incomplete (highest pK). If at the pH under consideration all stages of dissociation are complete, then the equation simplifies to

$$\Delta F_i = 2.3RT(pK - pH)$$

For example, consider the free energy of ionization of lactic acid at pH 7, where it is completely ionized to lactate⁻. The pK of lactic acid is 3.86. The value of ΔF_i in this case at 25° C (298° A) is:

$$\Delta F_i = 2.3(1.987)(298)(3.86 - 7)$$
$$= 1362(-3.14) = -4,277 \text{ cal/mol}$$

Now consider the free energy of ionization of H_3PO_4 at pH 11, where the first two stages of ionization are complete but the third stage is incomplete. For H_3PO_4 $pK_1 = 1.96$, $pK_2 = 6.7$, and $pK_3 = 12.4$. In this case from the general equation:

$$\Delta F_i = 2.3RT \sum (pK_i - pH) - 2.3RT \log \left(1 + \frac{[H^+]}{K}\right)$$

we have:

$$\Delta F_i = 2.3RT[(1.96 - 11) + (6.7 - 11) + (12.4 - 11)] - 2.3RT \log \left(1 + \frac{10^{-11}}{10^{-12.4}}\right)$$
$$= 1362[(-9.04) + (-4.3) + (1.41)] - 1362[\log 1 + \log 10^{-11} - \log 10^{-12.4}]$$
$$\Delta F_i = 1362(-11.94) - 1362[0 - 11 + 12.4]$$
$$= -16,262 - 0 + 14,982 - 16,889$$
$$= -18,169 \text{ cal/mol}$$

The difference in free energy of ionization at different pH values is easily obtained by calculating the free energy of ionization at each pH and taking the difference between them. For example, we may calculate the difference in free energy of ionization of α-glycerol phosphate ($pK_1 = 2.1$ and $pK_2 = 6.75$) at pH 6 and at pH 7 and 25° C, where the first dissociation is complete and the second dissociation is not complete.

At pH 6:

$$\Delta F_i = 2.3RT[(2.1 - 6) + (6.75 - 6)] - 2.3RT \log \left[1 + \frac{10^{-6}}{10^{-6.75}}\right]$$
$$= 1362[(-3.9) + (+0.75)] - 1362[0 - 6 + 6.75]$$
$$= 1362(-3.15) - 1362(0.75)$$
$$= -4290 - 1021 = -5311 \text{ cal/mol}$$

At pH 7:

$$\Delta F_i = 2.3RT[(2.1 - 7) + (6.75 - 7)] - 2.3RT \log \left[1 + \frac{10^{-7}}{10^{-6.75}}\right]$$
$$= 1362(-5.15) - 1362(-0.25)$$
$$= -7014 + 340 = -6674 \text{ cal/mol}$$

Thus the difference in free energy of ionization at pH 7 and pH 6 is 1363 cal per mol, the greater free energy decrease occurring at pH 7, where the degree of dissociation is greatest.

When a substance such as ATP in the process of hydrolysis gives rise to a new ionizing group, a part of the free energy of hydrolysis is represented by the free energy of ionization. The hydrolysis of ATP may be represented:

$$ATP^{4-} + H_2O \rightleftharpoons ADP^{3-} + P_i^{2-} + H^+$$

In addition to the fact that the reaction of anions with H^+ ions is associated with free energy change, the complexing of substances with metal ions such as Mg^{++} ions involves changes in the free energy relations. Various acidic substances in the body (for example, ATP) are present as anions which are combined to some extent with Mg^{++} ions, and the free energy of hydrolysis is different in the presence and absence of these ions.

CALCULATION OF THE FREE ENERGY OF DILUTION AND CONCENTRATION

Energy changes are associated with changes in the concentration of a solute in solution. In very dilute solutions such as those encountered in biologic systems, where activity may be taken as equal to concentration, the free energy change when a solution, C_1, is diluted to a weaker solution, C_2, is given by the equation:

$$\Delta F = RT \ln \frac{C_2}{C_1}$$

For example, to calculate the free energy change when H^+ ions at 0.01 M, C_1, are diluted to 0.001 M, C_2, at 25° C:

$$\Delta F = RT \ln \frac{0.001}{0.01} = RT(2.303) \log 0.1$$
$$= (1.987)(298)(2.303)(-1) = -1364 \text{ cal/mol}$$

If the 0.001 M solution were concentrated to 0.01 M, work would be done upon the solution and would be given by:

$$\Delta F = RT \ln \frac{C_1}{C_2} = +1364 \text{ cal/mol}$$

INDIRECT CALCULATION OF THE FREE ENERGY OF REACTIONS

Since the free energy change in a process is dependent only upon the initial and final states of the system undergoing change, and is independent of the pathway, it is frequently possible to calculate the free energy change in a reaction indirectly. This is generally accomplished by combining reactions for which the free energy values are known. For example, in the hydrolysis of ATP:

$$ATP + H_2O \rightleftharpoons ADP + P_i$$

the equilibrium lies so far to the right that accurate determination of the equilibrium constant is not possible. However, the free energy of hydrolysis of ATP has been obtained by adding the following reactions:

Glucose-6-P + H_2O $\rightleftharpoons$ Glucose + P_i ($\Delta F' = -2.6$ kcal/mol)
Glucose + ATP $\rightleftharpoons$ Glucose-6-P + ADP   ($\Delta F' = -4.4$ kcal/mol)

When these reactions and their free energy changes are summed up, we have:

$$ATP + H_2O \rightleftharpoons ADP + P_i \qquad (\Delta F' = -7.0 \text{ kcal/mol})$$

The standard free energy change, $\Delta F°$, applied to reactions involving H^+ ions, as is the case in many biologic reactions, implies unit activity of H^+ ions, which is far from reality. For biologic reactions taking place at specified pH a free energy change designated by $\Delta F'$ (3) is used. $\Delta F°$ may be calculated from $\Delta F'$ for a given pH when H^+ ions are involved in the reaction, and vice versa. If H^+ ions are not involved, $\Delta F' = \Delta F°$.

$\Delta F'$ values are often given not only for a specified pH but for the reaction in the presence of approximate physiologic Mg^{++} ion concentrations, of the order of 0.01 M.

Present evidence indicates that the free energy of hydrolysis, $\Delta F'$, of ATP at pH 7 and 25° C, and in the presence of physiologic concentrations of Mg^{++} is 6.9 ± 0.2 kcal per mol. The value -7 kcal per mol is used (3).

Energetically coupled reactions. Foods represented by carbohydrates, fats, and proteins are metabolized in the body to their end products of CO_2, H_2O, urea, etc., in stages, by series of interrelated reactions, with an over-all decrease in free energy which is utilized for synthetic processes and work of various kinds. While many of the individual reactions are exergonic and take place with a decrease in free energy and can proceed spontaneously (when catalyzed by enzymes), others, particularly synthetic reactions, are endergonic and show an increase in free energy; that is, their ΔF values are positive. In order to make the endergonic reactions go, they are coupled with exergonic reactions, so that in the over-all process there is a net decrease in free energy. Thus the free energy derived from one reaction may be utilized to drive another reaction. Processes in which endergonic reactions are coupled with exergonic reactions may be illustrated by the reactions involved in glycogen synthesis:

$$ATP + Glucose \rightleftharpoons Glucose\text{-}6\text{-}P + ADP \qquad (\Delta F = -4.4 \text{ kcal/mol})$$
$$Glucose\text{-}6\text{-}PO_4 \rightleftharpoons Glucose\text{-}1\text{-}P \qquad (\Delta F = +1.7 \text{ kcal/mol})$$
$$(Hexose)_n + Glucose\text{-}1\text{-}P \rightleftharpoons (Hexose)_{n+1} + P_i \qquad (\Delta F = -0.6 \text{ kcal/mol})$$

The over-all reaction is as follows:

$$(Hexose)_n + Glucose + ATP \rightleftharpoons (Hexose)_{n+1} + ADP + P_i \qquad (\Delta F = -3.3 \text{ kcal/mol})$$

ATP in the above reactions = the phosphorylating agent adenosine triphosphate, P_i = inorganic phosphate, $(Hexose)_n$ = a branched glycogen molecule, and $(Hexose)_{n+1}$ = the glycogen molecule to which a glucose group has been added.

PHOSPHATES IN METABOLISM

Phosphorus occurs universally in plant and animal tissues as both inorganic and organic phosphates. Phospholipids, nucleic acids, and phosphoproteins contain organically bound phosphate, and thus phosphorus enters into the essential composition of protoplasm. Aside from being an integral part of protoplasmic structure, organic phosphates of various kinds play vital roles in the chemical processes by which foods are metabolized and energy is produced in a utilizable form. Energy in immediately utilizable form is represented by the phosphorus compound, adenosine triphosphate (ATP), and this substance is essential, not only to supply the energy directly for muscle contraction, but also to serve as a necessary "sparking" or initiating compound for both the synthesis and breakdown of many biologic substances.

The importance of organic phosphates in metabolism was first indicated by the work of Harden and Young (4), who found that the fermentation of glucose by cell-free yeast juice falls off rapidly unless inorganic phosphate is added to the mixture. After phosphate addition there was a rapid increase in fermentation with disappearance of inorganic phosphate and appearance of organically bound phosphate. This organically bound phosphate was found to be present as hexosediphosphoric acid, and this same substance was formed regardless of whether glucose, fructose, or mannose was fermented. It was later shown that the fermenting mixtures contain three sugar phosphates: glucose-6-phosphate, fructose-6-phosphate, and fructose-1,6-diphosphate.

It has been shown that in the metabolism of sugars by yeast all the above sugar phosphates, as well as a number of others, are intermediate products preliminary to the formation of alcohol and carbon dioxide. Of more importance for our purpose is the fact that as a result of the work of Embden, Meyerhof, Parnas, Cori, and their associates (5) it has been shown that organic phosphates concerned with the metabolism of glucose by yeast are also intermediates in the metabolism of glycogen and glucose in muscle and other tissues. One sugar phosphate, glucose-1-phosphate, known as the Cori ester (6), is characteristic of carbohydrate metabolism in animal tissue but apparently is not an intermediate in the metabolism of carbohydrate by yeast.

Fiske and SubbaRow (7) and Eggleton and Eggleton (8) discovered creatine phosphate in vertebrate muscle and found that during muscle contraction it is rapidly broken down to creatine and inorganic phosphate, while during recovery from exercise creatine phosphate is resynthesized. Meyerhof and Suranyi (9) found that the enzymatic breakdown of creatine phosphate liberates much energy. This energy is stored in the N—P bond of the compound.

Ordinarily, when a muscle contracts, glycogen breaks down to give lactic acid, and it was long considered that this process is necessary to yield the direct energy for muscle contraction. However, Lundsgaard (10) poisoned muscles with iodoacetic acid ($CH_2I \cdot COOH$) and found they would still contract for a time without lactic acid formation. He also found that this "a-lactacid" contraction is accompanied by the breakdown of creatine phosphate and that muscle exhaustion occurs when all the creatine phosphate has disappeared. Lundsgaard also showed that the heat produced in muscle contraction is approximately equivalent to the energy liberated in the breakdown of creatine phosphate. This led to the conception that the energy stored in the N—P bond of creatine phosphate serves directly to cause contraction of the muscle fibrils.

Meyerhof and Lohmann (11) discovered arginine phosphate in invertebrate muscle as the functional counterpart of creatine phosphate in vertebrate muscle.

Just as in the case of creatine phosphate, much energy is liberated when the N—P bond of arginine phosphate is broken.

Lohmann (12) isolated adenosine triphosphate (ATP), originally called "adenylpyrophosphate," from muscle.

The phosphate groups may be removed consecutively from adenosine triphosphate to form adenosine diphosphate and monophosphate, respectively. In order to conserve space all these compounds commonly are referred to by their abbreviations: ATP, ADP, and AMP. This will be done in future discussions.

ATP was found to yield much energy when the two end, or pyrophosphate, groups are hydrolyzed off. Meyerhof (13) prepared extracts of muscle in ice-cold isotonic KCl which contained all the enzyme systems required to break glycogen rapidly to lactic acid and also to bring about the decomposition of creatine phosphate and ATP. Lohmann (14) studied the breakdown of creatine phosphate and ATP in these extracts. He found that the decomposition of ATP precedes that of creatine phosphate and that the breakdown of creatine phosphate is due not to hydrolysis but to reaction with ADP formed from ATP decomposition. This sequence of changes may be represented:

$$\text{ATP} + \text{HOH} \longrightarrow \text{ADP} + \text{phosphate} \quad (\Delta F' = -7 \text{ kcal/mol})$$
$$\text{creatine phosphate} + \text{ADP} \rightleftharpoons \text{ATP} + \text{creatine} \quad (\Delta F' = -2.8 \text{ kcal/mol})$$

This reaction is reversible and is known as the Lohmann reaction.

In view of the fact that much energy is liberated with the breakdown of ATP to ADP, that this is the first energy-producing reaction known to occur in muscle contraction, and that the reaction occurs to a great extent in the muscle fibrils, the conclusion was reached that ATP instead of creatine phosphate provides directly the energy for muscle contraction. This opinion is accepted generally at the present time. According to this view, creatine phosphate serves as a reservoir of active phosphate groups to help maintain the concentration of ATP.

The above discussion is sufficient to indicate the importance of organic phosphates in metabolic processes. While the sugar phosphates are not what we call "high-energy compounds," they are obligatory intermediates in the metabolism of carbohydrate in the body. Their formation involves phosphorylation by the high-energy compound ATP.

While the high-energy phosphates, such as ATP and creatine phosphate, are of primary importance in supplying the free energy to drive biologic reactions, several other high-energy compounds, formed directly or indirectly as the result of an ATP reaction, are essential biologic substances.

The following group of formulas represents most of the kinds of high-energy compounds which have been identified as playing roles in metabolic reactions to be considered in later chapters dealing systematically with metabolism. By convention the symbol $\sim$ joining the atoms in a compound represents a high-energy bond—that is, a bond which when involved and broken in a reaction leads to a release of free energy $(-\Delta F)$ which drives the reaction. Most of the high-energy formulas represent acidic substances which at physiologic pH are in the ionized state. The formulas show the preponderant ions present under physiologic conditions.

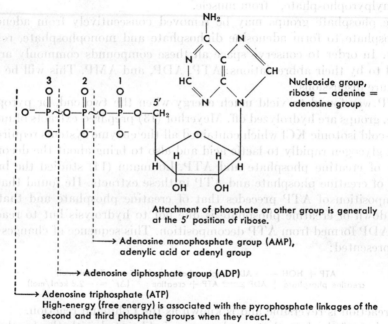

Nucleoside group,
ribose — adenine =
adenosine group

Attachment of phosphate or other group is generally at the 5′ position of ribose.

⟶ Adenosine monophosphate group (AMP), adenylic acid or adenyl group

⟶ Adenosine diphosphate group (ADP)

⟶ Adenosine triphosphate (ATP)
High-energy (free energy) is associated with the pyrophosphate linkages of the second and third phosphate groups when they react.

High-energy phosphates corresponding to ATP and ADP in which the phosphate groups are linked to nucleosides such as inosine, uridine, cytidine, and guanosine are of biologic importance. They are called "inosine triphosphate" and "diphosphate" (ITP and IDP), "uridine triphosphate" and "diphosphate" (UTP and UDP), etc.

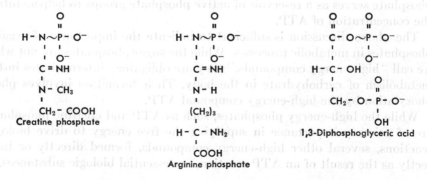

Creatine phosphate

Arginine phosphate

1,3-Diphosphoglyceric acid

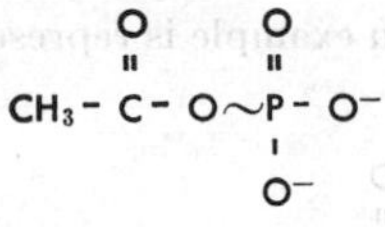

BIOENERGETICS

$$
\underset{\text{Acetyl phosphate}}{CH_3-\overset{\overset{O}{\|}}{C}-O\sim\overset{\overset{}{|}}{\underset{\underset{O^-}{|}}{P}}-O^-}
\qquad
\underset{\text{Inorganic pyrophosphate}}{{}^-O-\overset{\overset{O}{\|}}{\underset{\underset{O^-}{|}}{P}}\sim O-\overset{\overset{O}{\|}}{\underset{\underset{OH}{|}}{P}}-O^-}
\qquad
\underset{\substack{\text{Carbamyl phosphate}\\ \text{Carbamylating agent}}}{H_2N-\overset{\overset{O}{\|}}{C}-O\sim\overset{\overset{}{|}}{\underset{\underset{O^-}{|}}{P}}-O^-}
$$

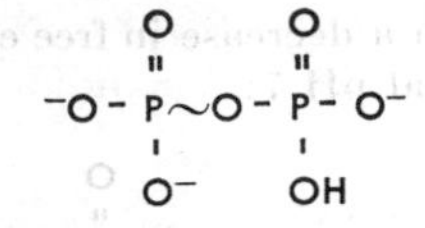

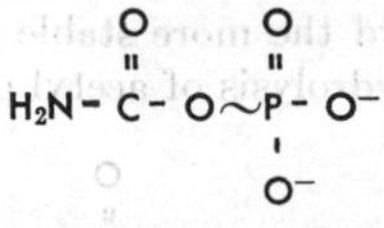

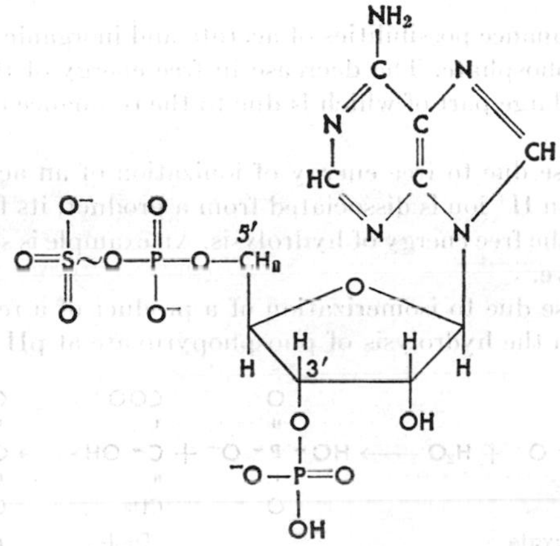

3'-Phosphoadenosine-5'-phosphosulfate
"Active sulfate"
Sulfating agent

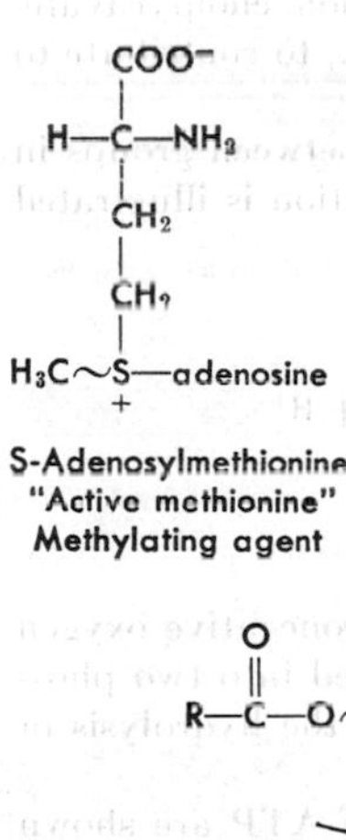

S-Adenosylmethionine
"Active methionine"
Methylating agent

$$
\underset{\text{S-Adenosylmethionine}}{\overset{\overset{\overset{COO^-}{|}}{\underset{\underset{\underset{\underset{CH_3\sim S\text{—adenosine}}{\overset{+}{}}}{|}}{\underset{CH_2}{|}}}{\underset{\underset{}{|}}{H-C-NH_2}}}{}}
$$

The —CH_2— group at the 5'
position of ribose in adenosine
is attached directly to the sulfur atom, $\sim\overset{+}{S}$—CH_2—

$$
\underset{\substack{\text{Acyl coenzyme A compounds. See Chapter 11}\\ \text{for the formula of coenzyme A}}}{R-\overset{\overset{O}{\|}}{C}\sim S\text{—coenzyme A}}
$$

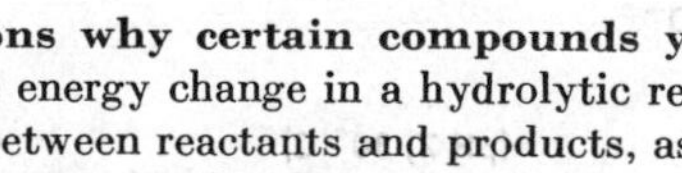

$$
\underset{\substack{\text{Adenyl group}\\ \text{Acyl adenylates, such as fatty acyl adenylates}}}{R-\overset{\overset{O}{\|}}{C}-O\sim\overset{\overset{O}{\|}}{\underset{\underset{O^-}{|}}{P}}-O\text{—adenosine}}
\qquad
\underset{\substack{\text{Adenyl group}\\ \text{Amino acid adenylate}}}{R-\overset{\overset{H}{|}}{\underset{\underset{NH_3^+}{|}}{C}}-\overset{\overset{O}{\|}}{C}-O\sim\overset{\overset{O}{\|}}{\underset{\underset{O^-}{|}}{P}}-O\text{—adenosine}}
$$

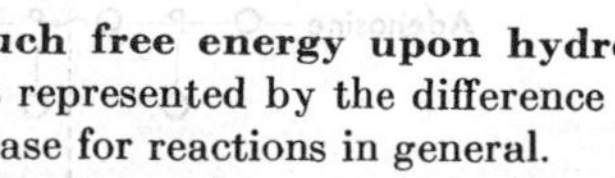

Reasons why certain compounds yield much free energy upon hydrolysis.
The free energy change in a hydrolytic reaction is represented by the difference in free
energy between reactants and products, as is the case for reactions in general.

There are several rather general causes for a free energy decrease $(-\Delta F)$ in the hydrolysis of a high-energy compound. Some of these may be summarized as follows:

1. Free energy decrease due to increase in resonance. The most stable state is represented by the condition in which resonance is at a maximum, and if hydrolysis converts
a substance to products with increased resonance possibilities, this will promote reaction

toward the more stable state, with a decrease in free energy. An example is represented by hydrolysis of acetyl phosphate at pH 7:

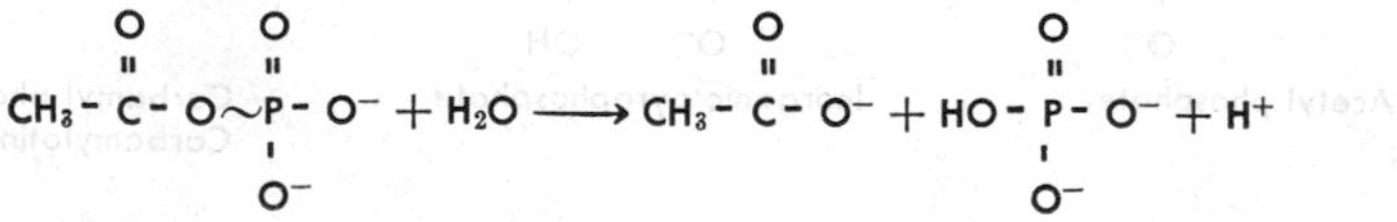

$$CH_3 - \overset{\overset{O}{\|}}{C} - O \sim \overset{\overset{O}{\|}}{\underset{\underset{O^-}{|}}{P}} - O^- + H_2O \longrightarrow CH_3 - \overset{\overset{O}{\|}}{C} - O^- + HO - \overset{\overset{O}{\|}}{\underset{\underset{O^-}{|}}{P}} - O^- + H^+$$

In this case the total resonance possibilities of acetate and inorganic phosphate are much greater than for acetyl phosphate. The decrease in free energy of the reaction at 29° C is −10.1 kcal per mol, a large part of which is due to the resonance relations of reactants and products.

2. Free energy decrease due to free energy of ionization of an acid. When in the hydrolysis of a compound an H⁺ ion is dissociated from a product, its free energy of ionization represents a part of the free energy of hydrolysis. An example is seen in the hydrolysis of acetyl phosphate above.

3. Free energy decrease due to isomerization of a product of a reaction. An excellent example of this is seen in the hydrolysis of phosphopyruvate at pH 7.4 and 30° C:

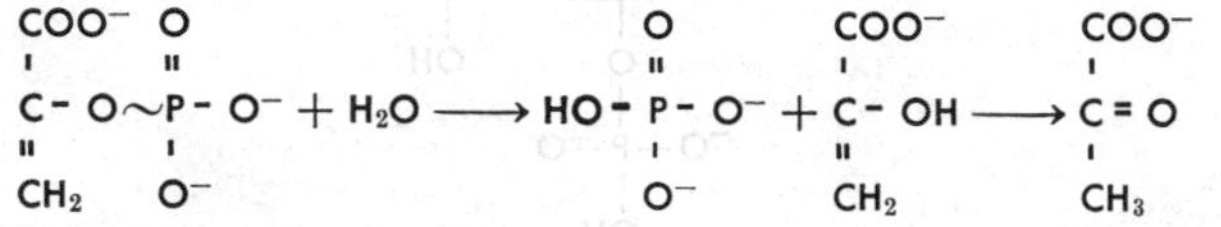

$$\underset{\text{Phosphopyruvate}}{\overset{\overset{\displaystyle COO^-}{|}}{\underset{\underset{\underset{O^-}{|}}{CH_2}}{\overset{\|}{C}}} - O \sim \overset{\overset{O}{\|}}{P} - O^-} + H_2O \longrightarrow HO - \overset{\overset{O}{\|}}{\underset{\underset{O^-}{|}}{P}} - O^- + \underset{\underset{\text{pyruvate}}{\text{Enol-}}}{\overset{\overset{\displaystyle COO^-}{|}}{\underset{\underset{CH_2}{\|}}{C} - OH}} \longrightarrow \underset{\underset{\text{pyruvate}}{\text{Keto-}}}{\overset{\overset{\displaystyle COO^-}{|}}{\underset{\underset{CH_3}{|}}{C} = O}}$$

$\Delta F'$ of hydrolysis for this reaction is −12.7 kcal per mol, and much of this free energy decrease is due to the free energy given off when the product of the reaction, enolpyruvate, isomerizes to ketopyruvate. Also, there is an increase in resonance, etc., to contribute to the free energy decrease.

4. Free energy decrease due to decrease in electrostatic repulsion between groups in a compound. This factor contributing to free energy release in a reaction is illustrated by the hydrolysis of pyrophosphate at pH 7 and 25° C:

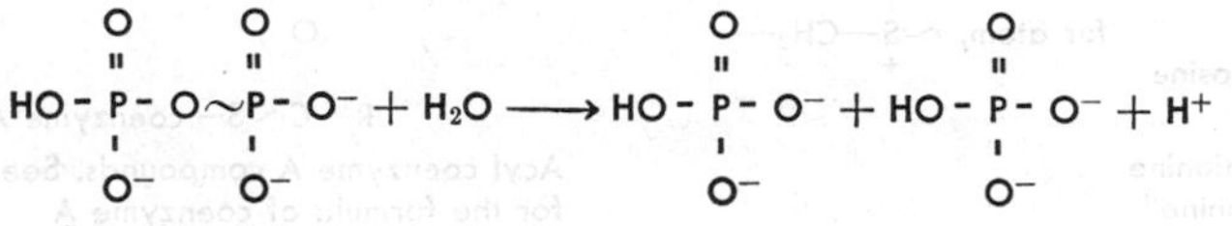

$$\underset{\text{Pyrophosphate}}{HO - \overset{\overset{O}{\|}}{\underset{\underset{O^-}{|}}{P}} - O \sim \overset{\overset{O}{\|}}{\underset{\underset{O^-}{|}}{P}} - O^-} + H_2O \longrightarrow \underset{\text{Phosphate}}{HO - \overset{\overset{O}{\|}}{\underset{\underset{O^-}{|}}{P}} - O^- + HO - \overset{\overset{O}{\|}}{\underset{\underset{O^-}{|}}{P}} - O^-} + H^+$$

The strong forces of electrostatic repulsion existing between the electronegative oxygen atoms of pyrophosphate are relieved when the compound is hydrolyzed into two phosphate ions ($\Delta F' = -8$ kcal per mol). A similar relation is found in the hydrolysis of ATP to ADP and P_i, and of ADP to AMP and P_i.

The free energy decreases occurring in two hydrolytic reactions of ATP are shown below:

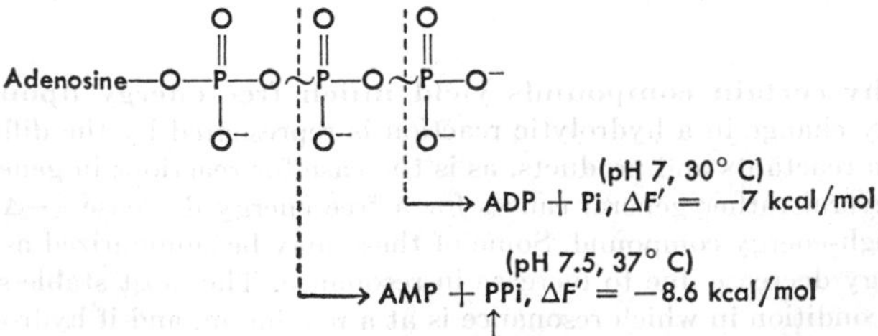

$$Adenosine - O - \overset{\overset{O}{\|}}{\underset{\underset{O^-}{|}}{P}} - O - \overset{\overset{O}{\|}}{\underset{\underset{O^-}{|}}{P}} - O - \overset{\overset{O}{\|}}{\underset{\underset{O^-}{|}}{P}} - O^-$$

(pH 7, 30° C)
⟶ ADP + Pi, $\Delta F' = -7$ kcal/mol

(pH 7.5, 37° C)
⟶ AMP + PPi, $\Delta F' = -8.6$ kcal/mol
↑
(Pyrophosphate)

Hydrolysis of the terminal phosphoryl group of ADP at pH 7.4 and 25° C:

$$\text{ADP} + \text{H}_2\text{O} \longrightarrow \text{AMP} + \text{P}_i \qquad (\Delta F' = -6.9)$$

shows a free energy decrease of 6.9 kcal per mol while hydrolysis of AMP to adenosine and P_i is associated with much less free energy decrease ($\Delta F'$ of the order of -3–4 kcal per mol).

Many high-energy compounds represent acid anhydrides. This is true of the high-energy phosphates, such as ATP, and high-energy compounds formed from ATP by transfer of a group from ATP to another compound. It is of interest that while ordinary acid anhydrides, such as acetic anhydride, which are high-energy compounds, are quickly hydrolyzed by water, the high-energy compounds involved in metabolism, such as ATP, are relatively stable to hydrolysis at physiologic pH. Lipmann (15) points out that the lifetime in water of acetic anhydride is only a few seconds before complete hydrolysis to acetic acid, while the lifetime of acetyl phosphate is several hours and that of pyrophosphate is infinite. The hydrolysis of all these substances liberates much free energy, yet their different structures confer upon them entirely different orders of ease of hydrolysis in solution. Thus the biologically important high-energy compounds are relatively stable to hydrolysis, and may exist in physiologic fluids until their stored free energy is released to drive essential reactions through operation of specific enzyme systems.

GROUP TRANSFER POTENTIALS

General considerations. Most biochemical reactions in the final analysis represent the transfer of a group from one substance to another, and the free energy change associated with the transfer of a group is the "free energy of group transfer" or the "group transfer potential" (3).

As pointed out previously, high-energy compounds, such as ATP, contain certain groups in their structures with which the free energy to drive chemical reactions is associated, and it is the free energy change (decrease) accompanying reactions involving these groups which represents their "group transfer potentials."

In the processes of oxidation of foods in the body more than half of the total energy released is converted into the free energy of ATP. The ATP then, through transfer reactions, may synthesize other high-energy compounds necessary for specific biologic reactions, or the free energy of ATP may be used for the work of muscle contraction, etc. Eventually all of the free energy of such substances is degraded to heat, which aids in maintaining body temperature. The general process may be shown as follows:

Foods + O_2 + Inorganic phosphate $\longrightarrow$ ATP
ATP $\longrightarrow$ Work of muscles, etc.

By transfer reactions:

ATP + Specific compounds $\longrightarrow$ Specific high-energy compounds

These specific high-energy compounds provide the free energy to drive essential biochemical reactions which are catalyzed and controlled by specific enzyme systems.

The hydrolysis of a compound represents the transfer of a group of the compound to a component of water, and thus represents a transfer reaction.

The decrease in free energy in the reaction represents the group transfer potential. For example:

$$\text{ATP}^{4-} + \text{H} \cdot \text{OH} \rightleftharpoons \text{ADP}^{3-} + \text{P}_i{}^{2-} + \text{H}^+$$
$$(\Delta F' \text{ at pH 7 and } 30°\text{ C} = -7 \text{ kcal/mol})$$

and

$$\text{Glucose-6-P}^{--} + \text{H} \cdot \text{OH} \rightleftharpoons \text{Glucose} + \text{P}_i{}^{--}$$
$$(\Delta F' \text{at pH 8.5 and } 38°\text{ C} = -2.9 \text{ kcal/mol})$$

Thus the free energy of group transfer or group transfer potential for the phosphate group from ATP in the first reaction is -7.0 kcal per mol, while for the glucose group in the second reaction it is only -2.9 kcal per mol. The hydrolysis of ATP is essentially irreversible and goes to completion for all practical purposes. However, the hydrolysis of glucose-6-phosphate thermodynamically is appreciably reversible.

Examples of other transfer reactions of biochemical importance with their group transfer potentials are as follows:

1. Phosphorylation of glucose by ATP catalyzed by the enzyme glucokinase to form glucose-6-phosphate, the compound by which glucose enters metabolic pathways:

$$\text{Glucose} + \text{ATP} \rightleftharpoons \text{Glucose-6-P} + \text{ADP}$$
$$(\Delta F' \text{ at } 30°\text{ C and pH 7} = -4.7 \text{ kcal/mol})$$

Thus, the transfer of a phosphate group from ATP to glucose takes place under a driving force (group transfer potential) of -4.7 kcal per mol. The reaction goes essentially to completion and is practically irreversible.

2. Transfer of a phosphate group from creatine phosphate to ADP to form ATP and creatine, the reaction being catalyzed by the enzyme creatine phosphokinase.

$$\text{Creatine-P}^{2-} + \text{ADP}^{3-} + \text{H}^+ \rightleftharpoons \text{ATP}^{4-} + \text{Creatine}$$
$$(\Delta F' \text{ at pH 7.4, } 30°\text{ C, and 0.01 M Mg}^{++} = -2.8 \text{ kcal/mol})$$

Here the group transfer potential is -2.8 kcal per mol. The reaction is reversible. The reversibility of this reaction is biologically very important. The concentration of creatine phosphate in resting muscle is relatively high, while the concentration of ATP is relatively low. When there is a demand for energy, as in muscle contraction, ATP supplies this energy and is converted to ADP. However, the ADP is quickly converted to ATP by reaction with creatine phosphate, which thus serves as a reservoir of free energy to be utilized through ATP. Oxidation of foods reconverts the ADP to ATP, which then reacts with creatine to re-form creatine phosphate and refill the free energy reservoir.

The free energy of hydrolysis of creatine phosphate is higher than that of ATP, and the equilibrium constant of hydrolysis cannot be determined for free energy calculation because the equilibrium lies too far to the right. Consequently, the free energy of hydrolysis of creatine phosphate is obtained by combining the equations (pH 7.4, 30° C, and 0.01 M Mg^{++}):

$$\text{ATP}^{4-} + \text{HOH} \rightleftharpoons \text{ADP}^{3-} + \text{P}_i{}^{2-} + \text{H}^+ \quad (\Delta F' = -7.4 \text{ kcal/mol})$$
$$\text{Creatine-P}^{2-} + \text{ADP}^{3-} + \text{H}^+ \rightleftharpoons \text{ATP}^{4-} + \text{Creatine} \quad (\Delta F' = -2.8 \text{ kcal/mol})$$

Upon summing the equations we have:

$$\text{Creatine-P}^{2-} + \text{HOH} \rightleftharpoons \text{Creatine} + \text{P}_i^{2-} \qquad (\Delta F' = -10.2 \text{ kcal/mol})$$

Thus, hydrolysis of creatine phosphate releases 10.2 kcal per mol of free energy, and its group transfer potential is −10.2 kcal per mol.

In a similar manner the free energies of hydrolysis of other high-energy compounds—such as arginine phosphate, phosphopyruvate, 1,3-diphosphoglycerate, acetyl phosphate, acyl—S—coenzyme A compounds, etc.—are obtained by combining their reactions with ADP to form ATP with the reaction of ATP and H_2O to form ADP. Thus, it can be seen that the accuracy of determining the free energies of hydrolysis of these high-energy compounds depends upon the accuracy of the value for the hydrolysis of ATP. The equilibrium constants of the reactions of the high-energy compounds with ADP to form ATP can usually be determined satisfactorily, from which relatively accurate values for the free energy changes of these reactions can be calculated. Whenever the accepted value for the free energy of hydrolysis of ATP is changed, the other values dependent upon it must be changed accordingly. For example, in the second edition of this book the free energy of hydrolysis of ATP was given as about −12 kcal per mol and that of phosphopyruvic acid as −15.9 kcal per mol. The results of recent improved methods indicate the free energy of hydrolysis of ATP to be about −7 kcal per mol and the free energy of hydrolysis of phosphopyruvate about −12.7 kcal per mol.

3. Transfer of a phosphate group from ATP to H—S—coenzyme A to form phosphoryl—S—coenzyme A and ADP. The reaction is catalyzed by a thiokinase enzyme.

$$\text{ATP} + \text{H - S - CoA} \rightleftharpoons \text{O}^- - \overset{\overset{\text{O}}{\|}}{\underset{\underset{\text{O}^-}{|}}{\text{P}}} \sim \text{S - CoA} + \text{ADP}$$

$$(\Delta F' \text{ at pH } 7.4 \text{ and } 37° \text{ C} = -0.2 \text{ kcal per mol})$$

The reaction is thermodynamically highly reversible.

4. Transfer of a phosphate group to an enzyme. Phosphate-enzyme combinations appear to represent essential intermediates in some biochemical reactions. The free energy change involved in phosphorylating the enzyme phosphoglucomutase has been measured (16) by reaction of the enzyme with glucose-1,6-diphosphate (pH 7.5 and 30° C):

$$\text{Glucose-1,6-P} + \text{Phosphoglucomutase} \rightleftharpoons \text{Phosphoglucomutase-P} + \text{Glucose-6-P}$$
$$(\Delta F' = -0.8 \text{ kcal/mol})$$

The reaction is quite reversible.

The above group of reactions is designed to introduce the student to a few of the kinds of reactions important in cellular metabolism and the relations of free energy changes or group transfer potentials to these reactions. As previously intimated, the free energy stored in ATP directly or indirectly is utilized to make possible the processes involved in the growth, maintenance, and function of protoplasm.

The relative group transfer potentials of compounds are represented by the free energies of hydrolysis of the compounds, since the hydrolytic products represent the physiologic ground states of the substances. Table 20.3 gives a number of phosphate transfer potentials of biologically important phosphoryl donors estimated from their free energies of hydrolysis. The

Table 20.3.   Phosphate Transfer Potentials

Phosphoryl Donor	Potential $\Delta F'$
Enolpyruvate phosphate	-12.8
1,3-Diphosphoglycerate	-11.8*
β-L-Aspartyl phosphate	-11.5
Creatine phosphate	-10.5
Acetyl phosphate	-10.1
Arginine phosphate	-9.0
ATP (α-phosphoanhydride)	-8.0†
ATP (β-phosphoanhydride)	-6.9 ± 0.2
ITP (β-phosphoanhydride)	-6.9
Inorganic pyrophosphate	-6.6
ADP	-6.4
Galactose-1-phosphate	-5.0
Glucose-1-phosphate	-5.0
2-Phosphoglycerate	-4.2
Phosphoglucomutase-phosphate	-4.2
Fructose-6-phosphate	-3.8
Glucose-6-phosphate	-3.3
3-Phosphoglycerate	-3.1
Fructose-1-phosphate	-3.1
Glycerol-1-phosphate	-2.3

* Transfer potential of acyl phosphate only.
† Transfer potential of pyrophosphoryl group.
From Atkinson, M. R., and Morton, R. K., in Mason, H. S., and Florkin, M. (eds.): *Comparative Biochemistry*, Vol. II, Chapter I. Academic Press, New York, 1960.

Table 20.4.   Inorganic Phosphate, Creatine Phosphate and ATP of Muscle

	Inorganic Phosphate		Creatine Phosphate		ATP	
	mg/100 g as P	mg/100 g as H_3PO_4	mg/100 g as P	mg/100 g as creatine-PO_4	mg/100 g as P	mg/100 g as ATP
Rat skeletal muscle†	19	59	79	535	44	360 (1)
Rat diaphragm*	27	85	43	291	35	286 (2)
Rat heart	16	51	13	91	32	266 (3)
Human skeletal muscle	19	60	59	404	34	275 (4)

* All values corrected on the basis of the average dry wt. of control diaphragms.
† Control fat content 2.42% included.
(1) Beatty, C. H.; Peterson, R. D.; Bocek, R. M.; and West, E. S.: *Am. J. Physiol.*, **196**, 1246, 1959.
(2) To be published.
(3) Peterson, R. D.; Beatty, C. H.; Bocek, R. M.; Dixon, H. H.; and West, E. S.: *Arch. Biochem. Biophys.*, **80**, 134, 1959.
(4) Aldes, J. H.; Peterson, R. D.; and West, E. S.: *2nd Intern. Congr. Phys. Med.*, Copenhagen, 98, 1956.

values, $\Delta F'$, represent kcal/mol at pH 7 and 25° C and in the presence of about 0.01 M Mg^{++}.

It is obvious from the table that there is no sharp line of distinction between high-energy compounds and low-energy compounds, but a continual gradation from phosphopyruvate, which shows a very high free energy of hydrolysis and phosphate transfer potential, to glycerol-1-phosphate, with a very low free energy of hydrolysis and phosphate transfer potential. However, in thinking of the distinction between high-energy and low-energy compounds it is customary for biochemists to consider substances with free energies of hydrolysis of -6.5 kcal per mol and greater as belonging to the high-energy group.

Table 20.4 gives some values for high-energy phosphates in rat and human muscle. Ennor and Morrison (17) give the values for creatine phosphate in a number of mammalian tissues, as well as a discussion of the biochemistry and distribution of high-energy phosphates in the animal kingdom.

GENERAL REFERENCES

Atkinson, M. R., and Morton, R. K., in Mason H. S., and Florkin, M. (eds.): *Comparative Biochemistry*, Vol. II, Chap. 1. Academic Press, New York, 1960.
Bray, H. G., and White, K.: *Kinetics and Thermodynamics in Biochemistry*. Academic Press, New York, 1957.
Clark, W. M.: *Topics in Physical Chemistry*, 2nd ed. Williams & Wilkins Co., Baltimore, 1952.
Edsall, J. T., and Wyman, J.: *Biophysical Chemistry*, Vol. I, Chap. 4. Academic Press, New York, 1958.
Ennor, A. H., and Morrison, J. F.: *Physiol. Revs.*, 38, 631, 1958.
Haurowitz, F.: *Progress in Biochemistry Since 1949*, Chap. 1. S. Karger, Basel, Switzerland; Interscience, New York, 1959.
Klotz, I. M.: *Chemical Thermodynamics*. Prentice-Hall, New York, 1950.
Klotz, I. M.: *Energetics in Biochemical Reactions*. Academic Press, New York, 1957.
Krebs, H. A.; Kornberg, H. L., and Burton, K.: *Energy Transformations in Living Matter*. Springer-Verlag, Berlin, 1957. This is a reprint from *Ergebnisse der Physiologie, biologische Chemie, und experimentellen Pharmakologie*, 49, 212, 1957.
Lewis, G. N., and Randall, M.: *Thermodynamics and the Free Energy of Chemical Substances*. McGraw-Hill Book Co., Inc., New York, 1923.
Lipmann, F.: *Advances in Enzymol.*, I, 99, 1941.
Oesper, P., in McElroy, W. D., and Glass, B. (eds.): *Phosphorus Metabolism*, Vol. 1, Chap. IX. Johns Hopkins Press, Baltimore, 1951.
Pardee, A. B., in Greenberg, D. M. (ed.): *Chemical Pathways of Metabolism*, Vol. I, Chap. I. Academic Press, New York, 1954.

SPECIAL REFERENCES

1. Haurowitz, F.: *Progress in Biochemistry Since 1949*. S. Karger, Basel, Switzerland; Interscience, New York, 1959.
2. Burton, K., and Krebs, H. A.: *Biochem. J.*, 54, 94, 1953.
3. Atkinson, M. R., and Morton, R. K., in Mason, H. S., and Florkin, M., (eds.): *Comparative Biochemistry*, Vol. II, Chap. I. Academic Press, New York, 1960.
4. Robison, R.: *The Significance of Phosphoric Esters in Metabolism*. New York University Press, New York, 1932.
5. Barron, E. S. G.: *Advances in Enzymol.*, 3, 151, 1943.
6. Cori, C. F., and Cori, G. T.: *Proc. Soc. Exptl. Biol. Med.*, 34, 702, 1936.
7. Fiske, C. H., and SubbaRow, Y.: *J. Biol. Chem.*, 81, 629, 1929.
8. Eggleton, P., and Eggleton, G. P.: *Biochem. J.*, 21, 190, 1927.
9. Meyerhof, O., and Suranyi, J.: *Biochem. Z.*, 191, 106, 1927.

10. Lundsgaard, E.: *Biochem. Z.*, **217**, 162, 1930; **227**, 51, 1930; **233**,, 322, 1931.
11. Meyerhof, O., and Lohmann, K.: *Biochem. Z.*, **196**, 49, 1928.
12. Lohmann, K.: *Biochem. Z.*, **233**, 460, 1931.
13. Meyerhof, O.: *Naturwissenschaften*, **14**, 1175, 1926; *Biochem. Z.*, **183**, 176, 1927; *J. Gen. Physiol.*, **8**, 531, 1927; *Lancet*, **2**, 1415, 1930; *Chemistry of Muscular Contraction* (lectures delivered at University College, London), 1930.
14. Lohmann, K.: *Biochem. Z.*, **282**, 120, 1935.
15. Lipmann, F., in McElroy, W. D., and Glass, B. (eds.): *Phosphorus Metabolism*, Vol. I, p. 521. Johns Hopkins Press, Baltimore, 1951.
16. Sidbury, J. B., and Najjar, V. A.: *J. Biol. Chem.*, **227**, 517, 1957.
17. Ennor, A. H., and Morrison, J. F.: *Physiol. Revs.*, **38**, 631, 1958.

The atomic hydrogen leaves with a greater possession than it did in the covalent water molecule, and therefore it emerges relatively less positive, or reduced. The oxygen, on the other hand, is oxidized.

21

Biological oxidation and reduction

Oxidation, in the broad sense of the term, occurs when an atom loses electrons, and reduction takes place when an atom gains electrons. For example, consider the following reactions:

$$Zn : \ + Cu^{++} \longrightarrow Zn^{++} + Cu :$$

$$2H \cdot + O : \longrightarrow H : O : H$$

In the first reaction a neutral zinc atom loses two electrons to the dipositive copper ion, forming a dipositive zinc ion and a neutral copper atom. The oxidizing agent, Cu^{++}, oxidizes the reducing agent, Zn:, by taking two electrons from it, and at the same time is reduced to neutral copper atoms, Cu:.

In the second reaction two hydrogen atoms, each bearing an electron, add to the unfilled valence shell of the oxygen atom to produce the covalent water molecule. In the first reaction there is no question about the oxidation-reduction involving the loss and gain of electrons. The oxidation-reduction of the second reaction may be interpreted electronically as follows. The hydrogen atom is in full possession of a valence electron before the reaction takes place. After the reaction occurs, the electron is covalently held by both oxygen and hydrogen atoms. The oxygen atom, attracting the electron more powerfully, possesses it to a greater extent than does the hydrogen atom. This causes the water molecule to be highly polarized, with the oxygen relatively negative and the hydrogen positive. In this reaction the hydrogen atom emerges with less electron possession than before the action. Consequently, it may, in the broad sense, be considered as having been oxidized. On the other hand, the oxygen atom has gained more than half possession of two electrons and has been reduced. The reverse of this action is seen when water is decomposed by passing an electric current through it:

$$H : \overset{..}{O} : H \longrightarrow 2H \cdot + \overset{..}{\underset{..}{O}} :$$

The atomic hydrogen produced has more electron possession than it did in the water molecule and has been reduced. The atomic oxygen certainly has less electron possession than it did in water and has been oxidized.

The oxidation-reduction process between halogens and hydrogen is quite similar to that between oxygen and hydrogen:

$$H \cdot + \cdot \overset{..}{\underset{..}{Cl}} : \longrightarrow H : \overset{..}{\underset{..}{Cl}} :$$

The over-all oxidation of methane to methyl alcohol by oxygen may be represented:

$$\begin{array}{ccc} H & & H \\ \overset{..}{\underset{..}{H : C : H}} + \overset{..}{\underset{..}{O}} : & \longrightarrow & H : \overset{..}{\underset{..}{C}} : \overset{..}{\underset{..}{O}} : H \\ H & & H \end{array}$$

The mechanism of the reaction is not so simple as this, but, judging upon the basis of the electronic formulas of the reactants and the product, the reaction conforms to the definition of oxidation-reduction. The strongly electron-attracting oxygen atom certainly has more electron possession in the methyl alcohol molecule than it did as atomic oxygen, and the electron possession of both carbon and hydrogen is less with the oxygen between them in methyl alcohol than it was when they were directly united in methane. We may state then that the oxygen has been reduced, and the carbon and one hydrogen in methane have been oxidized in the reaction.

The oxidation of hydroquinone to quinone involves not only the loss of electrons but also of H^+ ions:

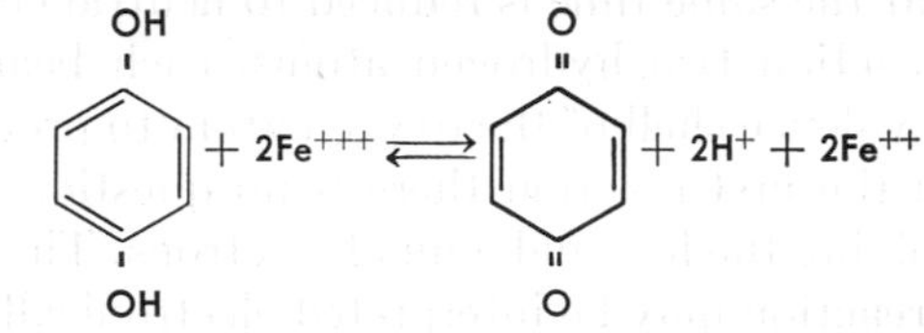

$$\text{Hydroquinone} + 2Fe^{+++} \rightleftharpoons \text{Quinone} + 2H^+ + 2Fe^{++}$$

The oxidation of hydroquinone to quinone represents the loss of two H atoms. It is a dehydrogenation of hydroquinone. The biologic oxidation of organic compounds also generally represents the loss of two H atoms from the molecule for each stage of oxidation and is a dehydrogenation. Conversely, the biologic reduction of compounds represents the reverse process, or hydrogenation.

The over-all oxidation of hydroquinone to quinone by Fe^{+++} is depicted above as if two electrons are accepted simultaneously from hydroquinone by two Fe^{+++} with the simultaneous loss of two H^+. However, the probability of simultaneous ternary collisions between two Fe^{+++} and a hydroquinone molecule is small indeed. The oxidation actually involves two stages, with one Fe^{+++} accepting one electron at each stage and one proton being given off at each stage. Semiquinone is the product of the first stage of oxidation and quinone the product of the second stage:

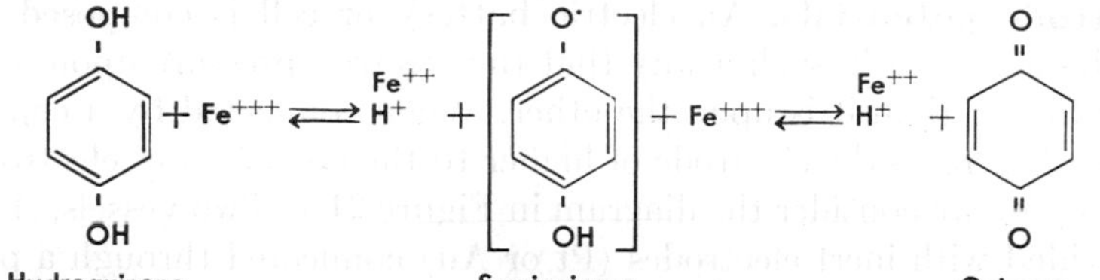

| Hydroquinone | Semiquinone | Quinone |

The semiquinone has an unpaired electron and is called a "free radical." The spins of the two electrons composing the normal covalent bond are in opposite directions and neutralize each other. In semiquinones and other free radicals, which have unpaired electrons, the spin of the lone electron gives to the substance a magnetic moment equal to one Bohr magneton, and the substance is paramagnetic. Such free radical molecules are generally colored and are extremely reactive both with each other and with other substances. For example, two molecules of semiquinone undergo intermolecular oxidation-reduction (a dismutation) with the formation of a molecule of quinone and a molecule of hydroquinone:

$$2 \text{ Semiquinone} \rightleftharpoons \text{Quinone} + \text{Hydroquinone}$$

Free radicals are readily oxidized by electron acceptors, as in the oxidation of semiquinone by Fe^{+++} given above.

Free radicals may be detected, because of their magnetic moments, by electron paramagnetic resonance absorption. When a substance with an unpaired electron is placed in a magnetic field of the proper strength, it absorbs in the microwave region of electromagnetic radiation, from which its presence and concentration may be obtained.

Many organic reactions have been shown to involve free radicals as intermediates, including some enzymatic reactions.

It appears very probable that many biologic oxidations proceed in two stages, involving the loss of one electron and one H^+ at each stage and the formation of a free radical as an intermediate product.

Various oxidation-reduction reactions involve the participation of H^+ ions, and some require OH^- ions. Further examples are:

$$H_3AsO_4 + 2H^+ + 2\epsilon \rightleftharpoons H_3AsO_3 + H_2O$$
$$MnO_4^- + 2H_2O + 3\epsilon \rightleftharpoons MnO_2 + 4OH^-$$
$$MnO_4^{--} + 2H_2O + 2\epsilon \rightleftharpoons MnO_2 + 4OH^-$$
$$MnO_2 + 4H^+ + 2\epsilon \rightleftharpoons Mn^{++} + 2H_2O$$
$$Cr_2O_7^{--} + 14H^+ + 6\epsilon \rightleftharpoons 2Cr^{+++} + 7H_2O$$

The ϵ is used to represent electron in the above expressions. The electrons for the various reactions are provided by suitable reducing agents and, at times, by the negative electrode of an electrolytic cell.

"Oxidation" has been defined, according to older usage, as the addition of oxygen to a substance, or the removal of hydrogen, or an increase in the positive valence. Conversely, the removal of oxygen, or the addition of hydrogen, or a decrease in the positive valence has been referred to as "reduction." All these definitions may be summed up in the statement that oxidation decreases and reduction increases the electron possession of a substance.

Electrode potentials. An electric battery or cell is composed of two electrodes arranged in such a way that the electron pressure upon one electrode is higher than it is upon the other. When connected by a conductor, electrons flow from the electrode of higher to the one of lower electron pressure. Suppose we consider the diagram in Figure 21.1. Two vessels, A and B, are provided with inert electrodes (Pt or Au) connected through a potentiometer for measuring potentials. Ionic conductance between the solutions

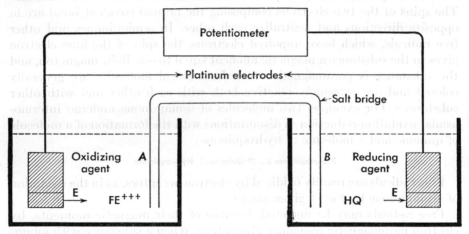

Figure 21.1. Fe^{+++} hydroquinone oxidation-reduction cell. (From West, E. S.: *Textbook of Biophysical Chemistry*, 2nd ed. The Macmillan Co., New York, 1957.)

in the vessels is provided by a salt bridge. Now suppose an oxidizing agent such as Fe^{+++} ions (as ferric salt) is placed in vessel A and a reducing agent capable of being oxidized by Fe^{+++} ions, such as hydroquinone, HQ, is placed in vessel B. The HQ molecules in B give electrons to the electrode in B, release H^+ ions into the solution, and are converted to quinone molecules. In vessel A the Fe^{+++} ions take electrons from the electrode in A, and through the metallic circuit from the electrode in B, and thus from the HQ molecules in B. The Fe^{+++} ions are reduced to Fe^{++} ions in A. The equation for the reaction is:

$$HQ + 2Fe^{+++} \rightleftharpoons Quinone + 2H^+ + 2Fe^{++}$$
$$B \quad\quad A \quad\quad\quad\quad B \quad\quad\quad B \quad\quad A$$

It is seen that the oxidation-reduction reaction occurring through the electrodes is identical with the reaction when the solutions of A and B are mixed. The reaction is reversible and, after a time, comes to equilibrium when the electron pressure on the electrode in B equals that on the electrode in A. By use of a potentiometer in the circuit one may measure the voltage or electron pressure difference between the electrodes in A and B throughout the process until equilibrium is reached, when the potential difference disappears.

In general any oxidizing and reducing agents which react when mixed in solution may be separated into components of an electric cell, as given above, with the oxidation-reduction proceeding through the electrodes. This applies to organic, inorganic, and mixed organic-inorganic oxidation-reduction systems. For any given combination there is an electron pressure or voltage difference established between the electrodes. To be sure, it is often impossible to measure the potential difference accurately because the oxidation reduction process concerned is not freely reversible, and this leads to fluctuations in electron pressure upon the electrodes and uncertain measurements.

The power of a substance as an oxidizing agent depends upon its ability to take up and hold electrons, and, conversely, the power of a substance as a reducing agent depends upon the readiness with which it releases electrons to other substances. Evidently, oxidation-reduction is a relative process. A substance may easily remove electrons from another which releases them readily and entirely fail to remove them from a substance which is a poor reducing agent. In order that the relative oxidizing and reducing powers of various substances may be compared and used intelligently, it is necessary to determine their ability to take up and give off electrons. In many cases this can be done by measuring the voltage of the oxidizing-reducing system against that of a standard electrode which has a constant electron pressure.

Suppose two zinc electrodes are arranged as above so that the voltage difference between them may be measured with a potentiometer. The following process occurs at the surface of each:

$$\text{Zn} \rightleftharpoons \text{Zn}^{++} + 2\epsilon$$

| on metal surface | in solution | on metal surface |

If one electrode, A, is immersed in a solution containing 0.1 M Zn^{++} and the other, B, in a solution containing 0.01 M Zn^{++}, according to the mass law A will be positive to B; and when the electrodes are connected in a circuit, electrons will flow from B to A, Zn atoms will go into solution as Zn^{++} at B, due to loss of electrons (oxidation), and Zn^{++} will deposit as Zn atoms at A, due to combination with electrons (reduction). The electrodes represent an oxidation-reduction system, and the potential between them may be calculated from the equation:

$$E = \frac{RT}{nF} \ln \frac{c_1}{c_2}$$

where R = the gas constant (8.315 joules per degree), T = the absolute temperature, n = the valence change at the electrode, F = the Faraday

(96,500 coulombs), and $\ln$ = the natural logarithm. At 25° C the potential between the electrodes is:

$$E = \frac{8.315 \times 298}{2 \times 96,500} \times 2.3 \log_{10} \frac{0.1}{0.01} = 0.029 \text{ v}$$

Normal electrode potentials. In the reaction for the development of an electric double layer at the interface of a metal, M, and a solution in which it is immersed:

$$M \rightleftharpoons \text{positive ions} + \text{electrons (on metal)}$$

it is not surprising that the electron pressure on the metal varies with the nature of the metal as well as with the concentration of metal ions in the solution. For example, the alkali metals have much higher solution tensions than do metals such as zinc and copper; this means the above reaction proceeds much farther to the right in case of the alkali metals than with zinc and copper. The alkali metals possess much higher electron pressures in contact with a given ionic concentration than the less active metals do. The electromotive series of the metals is simply an arrangement of the metals in the order of decreasing solution tension. Those at the top of the series develop the highest, and those at the bottom the lowest, electron pressures or potentials when compared against equivalent ionic solutions. This brings up the question of how the potential of a zinc electrode, immersed in a given concentration of zinc ions, is compared with the potential of a sodium electrode (as sodium amalgam) in an equivalent concentration of sodium ions. It is impossible to measure the potential of a single electrode against a solution. It is possible, however, to select some electrode as a standard of reference, assign to it an arbitrary value, and measure the potentials of all other electrodes against it. In practice this is done. The standard reference electrode is the so-called normal hydrogen electrode and consists of a platinized platinum electrode under 1 atm of hydrogen pressure immersed in a solution containing H^+ ions at an effective concentration (activity) of 1. This electrode is assigned a potential of 0 under all conditions. Since the potential of an electrode varies with the concentration of its ions in the solution in which it is immersed, the ion concentration must be fixed at a definite value for comparison against the normal hydrogen electrode. Arbitrarily, the ion concentration is taken as unity on the molal basis, which means one symbol weight of effective ions (activity) per 1000 g of solvent. The potential of a metal electrode, immersed in unit concentration of its ions, when connected with a normal hydrogen electrode, is called the "standard" or "normal" electrode potential of the metal. Since variations in temperature affect solution tension and the equilibrium at an electrode, the potential varies with temperature. In making measurements the temperature must be specified. Table 21.1 gives the normal electrode potentials, designated E_0, for a number of metallic electrodes.

Electrodes possessing higher electron pressures than the normal hydrogen electrode are negative, and those possessing lower electron pressures are positive. It will be noted that the more negative the electrode, the greater is the reducing power of the metal. For example, lithium will replace K^+ from its salts:

$$Li + K^+ \longrightarrow Li^+ + K$$

Li loses an electron to K^+, reducing it to K and itself being oxidized to Li^+. Similarly, Li will replace the ions of all metals below it in the potential series in proportion to the difference between the electrode potentials.

Na^+ ions are reduced by all metals above sodium in the table, and Na atoms are oxidized by the ions of all metals below sodium. Similar principles apply to all the metals and their ions.

Table 21.1.   Normal Electrode Potentials at 25° C

Electrode	Electrode Reaction	Normal Electrode Potential (Normal Hydrogen Electrode = 0) E_0 (Volts)
Li^+, Li	$Li = Li^+ + \epsilon$	-2.9595
Rb^+, Rb	$Rb = Rb^+ + \epsilon$	-2.9259
K^+, K	$K = K^+ + \epsilon$	-2.9241
Ca^{++}, Ca	$Ca = Ca^{++} + 2\epsilon$	-2.763
Na^+, Na	$Na = Na^+ + \epsilon$	-2.7146
Mg^{++}, Mg (18°)	$Mg = Mg^{++} + 2\epsilon$	-1.866
Zn^{++}, Zn	$Zn = Zn^{++} + 2\epsilon$	-0.7618
Fe^{++}, Fe	$Fe = Fe^{++} + 2\epsilon$	-0.441
Sn^{++}, Sn	$Sn = Sn^{++} + 2\epsilon$	-0.136
Pb^{++}, Pb	$Pb = Pb^{++} + 2\epsilon$	-0.122
H^+, H_2 (1 atm), Pt.	$\frac{1}{2}H_2 = H^+ + \epsilon$	0.0000 (standard electrode)
Cu^{++}, Cu	$Cu = Cu^{++} + 2\epsilon$	$+0.3441$
Ag^+, Ag	$Ag = Ag^+ + \epsilon$	$+0.7978$
Hg_2^{++}, Hg	$2Hg = Hg_2^{++} + 2\epsilon$	$+0.7986$
Au^{+++}, Au	$Au = Au^{+++} + 3\epsilon$	$+1.36$

Suppose a normal zinc electrode is connected with a normal iron electrode and the potential is measured. The iron electrode is less negative (has less electron pressure) than the zinc electrode and consequently is relatively positive to it. The potential difference between the electrodes is 0.3208 v. If now the iron electrode is connected with a normal lead electrode, the iron becomes the negative and the lead the positive electrode, with a potential difference of 0.319 v. In a like manner, the normal copper electrode is negative to the normal silver electrode with a potential difference of 0.4537 v.

It must be remembered that the potentials for all the electrodes in the table are for the electrodes immersed in ions of unit effective concentration (activity). The normal lithium electrode is negative to the normal potassium electrode, but a potassium electrode in 0.001 M K^+ ion solution is negative to the normal lithium electrode. This illustrates the necessity of considering the concentration of active substances around the electrodes in relation to the values of electrode potentials.

Oxidation-reduction or redox potentials. Certain metals, such as platinum and gold, have very low solution tensions and in themselves are essentially inert when placed in solutions. They are of much value as electrodes for indicating potentials superimposed upon them by oxidation-reduction systems present in the solutions around the electrodes. This type of potential, in which the electrode itself takes no chemical part, is referred to as an "oxidation-reduction potential," though it must be remembered that the potentials of reactive electrodes also involve oxidation-reduction. Earlier in this chapter an electric cell composed of two platinum electrodes immersed in ferric ion and hydroquinone solutions, respectively, was described. There it was pointed out that Fe^{+++} ions around one electrode remove electrons from it and are reduced to Fe^{++} ions, while the hydroquinone at the other electrode adds electrons to it and is oxidized to quinone. In this way the Fe^{+++} ions, the oxidizing agent, remove electrons through the electrodes and metallic circuit from hydroquinone, the reducing agent, and effect its oxidation at a distance. A certain potential difference exists between the electrodes, and its value depends upon the relative electron pressures on the electrodes.

Suppose that a platinum electrode is immersed in a solution containing both Fe^{+++} and Fe^{++} ions. The Fe^{+++} ions, the oxidizing agent, tend to take electrons from the electrode and form Fe^{++} ions, while the Fe^{++} ions, the reducing agent, tend to give electrons to the electrode and form Fe^{+++} ions. The reaction taking place reversibly in the solution at the electrode is:

$$Fe^{++} \rightleftharpoons Fe^{+++} + \epsilon$$

Neither process can take place appreciably unless the electrode is connected with another electrode to which electrons may be given or from which they may be taken. However, a mixture of Fe^{+++} and Fe^{++} ions around the surface of an electrode sets up an oxidation-reduction potential which varies with the ratio of Fe^{+++} to Fe^{++} concentrations. It has been shown by Peters that the potential of the above electrode relative to the normal hydrogen electrode may be calculated if the concentrations of Fe^{+++} and Fe^{++} ions in the solution are known. The equation is as follows:

$$E = E_0 + \frac{RT}{nF} \log_e \frac{[Fe^{+++}]}{[Fe^{++}]}$$

in which E = the potential referred to the normal hydrogen electrode, R, T, n, F, and $\log_e$ have their usual significance, and E_0 = a constant and represents the electrode potential when the ratio of $[Fe^{+++}]$ to $[Fe^{++}]$ is 1. E_0 is obtained by measuring the potential when the ratio $[Fe^{+++}]/[Fe^{++}]$ is 1. When this is done, the equation becomes:

$$E = E_0 + \frac{RT}{nF} \log_e 1$$

Since $\log_e 1$ equals 0, we have:

$$E = E_0 + \left(\frac{RT}{nF} \times 0 \right)$$

and

$$E = E_0$$

Suppose one wishes to calculate the oxidation-reduction potential for a platinum electrode immersed in a solution in which $[Fe^{+++}] = 0.01$ and $[Fe^{++}] = 0.001$. The value of E_0 for this electrode system is $+0.7477$ v at $25°$ C. The calculation is:

$$E = 0.7477 + \frac{8.315 \times 298}{1 \times 96{,}500} \times 2.30259 \log \frac{0.01}{0.001}$$
$$= 0.7477 + (0.05915 \times \log 10)$$
$$= 0.7477 + (0.05915 \times 1)$$
$$= 0.8068 \text{ v}$$

The result, 0.8068 v, represents the oxidation-reduction potential when the electrode is measured against the normal hydrogen electrode.

In actual practice it is customary to measure potentials against a reference electrode, such as the calomel electrode, and then calculate the values to the normal hydrogen electrode. Since there is a constant potential difference between the calomel electrode and the normal hydrogen electrode for a given set of conditions, this is easily done. This practice is followed because the normal hydrogen electrode is difficult and the calomel electrode easy to prepare and operate.

The above equation for the calculation of an oxidation-reduction potential, when only the oxidizing and reducing agents are concerned, may be stated in the general expression:

$$E = E_0 + \frac{RT}{nF} \log_e \frac{[\text{oxidant}]}{[\text{reductant}]}$$

"Oxidant" and "reductant" are commonly substituted for "oxidizing agent" and "reducing agent," respectively, in such equations.

In numerous instances hydrogen ions enter into the oxidation-reduction reactions at electrodes, and in such cases they must be taken into consideration. For example, consider the case of a platinum electrode placed in a solution containing a mixture of quinone (oxidizing agent) and hydroquinone (reducing agent) at a pH below 8, above which the electrode does not function well. The reversible reaction in the solution around the electrode is:

HQ	$\rightleftharpoons$	Q	$+ 2H^+ +$	2ϵ
reductant in solution		oxidant in solution		on electrode

in which HQ and Q represent hydroquinone and quinone, respectively. It can be shown that the oxidation-reduction potential of this electrode is given by the equation:

$$E = E_0 + \frac{RT}{2F} \log_e \frac{[\text{oxidant}]}{[\text{reductant}]} + \frac{RT}{F} \log_e [H^+]$$

According to the mass law, increasing $[H^+]$ decreases the electron concentration on the electrode and the potential. A decrease in $[H^+]$ has the reverse effect. The value of the constant, E_0, is obtained by observing the potential of the electrode when [oxidant] = [reductant] and $[H^+] = 1$. In this case all terms on the right except E_0 become 0, and we have:

$$E = E_0$$

Of course, the value of E_0 may be calculated by measuring the potential at any given hydrogen ion concentration and ratio of oxidant to reductant and substituting the values in the above equation so as to obtain the value of E_0. In some cases the value of E_0 changes with $[H^+]$ as a result of changes in the oxidant or reductant with pH. Often in such cases E_0 remains constant above a certain pH value. For example, the value of E_0 for methylene blue is 0.431 v at any pH above 6. In most organic oxidation-reduction systems, the valence change, n, is 2. This is true for the methylene blue and quinone systems and means that two electrons are lost or gained in passing from one form to the other. At a given temperature—30° C, for example—the above equation may be written:

$$E = E_0 + 0.03 \log_{10} \frac{[\text{oxidant}]}{[\text{reductant}]} - 0.06 \text{ pH}$$

where
$$0.03 \log_{10} = \frac{RT}{2F} \log_e$$

and
$$-0.06 \text{ pH} = \frac{RT}{F} \log_e [H^+] \quad \text{at 30° C}$$

The yellow enzyme system of Warburg functions according to the above equations, as does also the pyruvate-lactate system in the presence of lactate dehydrogenase.

The cytochrome system involves only one valence change, as do the ferri-cyanide-ferrocyanide and $Fe^{+++} - Fe^{++}$ systems. In these cases the equation:

$$E = E_0 + \frac{RT}{F} \log_e \frac{[\text{oxidant}]}{[\text{reductant}]}$$

reduces, at 30° C, to:

$$E = E_0 + 0.06 \log \frac{[\text{oxidant}]}{[\text{reductant}]}$$

In the case of oxidation-reduction systems in which H^+ ions are involved, an oxidation-reduction potential expression, E'_0, is often used. E'_0 includes the value of E_0 plus the factor involving hydrogen ions. For example, in the equation:

$$E = E_0 + \frac{RT}{2F} \log_e \frac{[\text{oxidant}]}{[\text{reductant}]} + \frac{RT}{F} \log_e [H^+]$$

the value assigned E'_0 is:

$$E'_0 = E_0 + \frac{RT}{F} \log_e [H^+]$$

When this is substituted in the previous equation we have:

$$E = E'_0 + \frac{RT}{2F} \log_e \frac{[\text{oxidant}]}{[\text{reductant}]}$$

Table 21.2. pH Relations of Oxidation-Reduction Systems

n Valence Change or H Atoms Involved	k Cations Created by Dehydrogenation	Examples	Equation	Increase in E'_0 per Unit Increase in pH (30°) (Volts)	Increase in E per Unit Increase in $\log \dfrac{[\text{ox}]}{[\text{red}]}$ (Volts)
1	1	Cytochrome $Fe^{++} - Fe^{+++}$	$E = E_0 + \dfrac{RT}{F} \ln^* \dfrac{[\text{ox}]}{[\text{red}]}$	0.0	0.06
2	0	Quinone-hydroquinone (below pH 8)	$E = E_0 + \dfrac{RT}{2F} \ln \dfrac{[\text{ox}]}{[\text{red}]} + \dfrac{RT}{F} \ln [\text{H}^-]$	-0.06	0.03
2	1	Lactate-pyruvate (above pH 7) Yellow enzyme MB–MBH$_2$ (above pH 6) TPN; DPN† (below pH 9)	$E = E_0 + \dfrac{RT}{2F} \ln \dfrac{[\text{ox}]}{[\text{red}]} + \dfrac{RT}{2F} \ln [\text{H}^-]$	-0.03	0.03
2	-1	Acetaldehyde-acetate (above pH 7) MB–MBH$_2$ (below pH 5)	$E = E_0 + \dfrac{RT}{2F} \ln \dfrac{[\text{ox}]}{[\text{red}]} + \dfrac{3RT}{2F} \ln [\text{H}^+]$	-0.09	0.03
2	2	$Sn^{++} - Sn^{++++}$	$E = E_0 + \dfrac{RT}{2F} \ln \dfrac{[\text{ox}]}{[\text{red}]}$	0.0	0.03
n	k	—	$E = E_0 + \dfrac{RT}{nF} \ln \dfrac{[\text{ox}]}{[\text{red}]} + [n - k]\dfrac{RT}{nF} \ln [\text{H}^-]$	$\dfrac{0.06[k - n]}{n}$	$\dfrac{0.06}{n}$

* $\ln = \log$.

† TPN = triphosphopyridine nucleotide = coenzyme II.

DPN = diphosphopyridine nucleotide = coenzyme I.

From *Respiratory Enzymes*, 2nd ed., 1950, by University of Wisconsin Biochemists. Courtesy of Professor C. A. Elvehjem.

and the value of E'_0 is obtained by measuring the potential of the system against the normal hydrogen electrode when the concentrations of oxidant and reductant are equal (ratio = 1). E'_0 values may be determined and utilized when the pH relations of the oxidation-reduction system are unknown. Since E'_0 is dependent upon pH, it is necessary to specify the pH corresponding to each E'_0 value.

Table 21.2 shows the pH relations of various types of oxidation-reduction systems.

While E_0 and E'_0 values often have certain limitations, their use, with proper recognition of these limitations, greatly aids in understanding the functioning of oxidation-reduction systems.

Table 21.3.   Normal Oxidation-Reduction Potentials of Ionic Systems at 25° C

Oxidation-Reduction System	Electrode Reaction	Normal Potential E_0 (Volts)
$Co^{+++} - Co^{++}$	$Co^{++} \rightleftarrows Co^{+++} + \epsilon$	$+1.817$
$Ce^{++++} - Ce^{+++}$	$Ce^{+++} \rightleftarrows Ce^{++++} + \epsilon$	$+1.55$
$Cl_2 - Cl^-$	$Cl^- \rightleftarrows \frac{1}{2}Cl_2 + \epsilon$	$+1.3583$
$Sn^{++++} - Sn^{++}$	$Sn^{++} \rightleftarrows Sn^{++++} + 2\epsilon$	-0.13
$Tl^{+++} - Tl^+$	$Tl^+ \rightleftarrows Tl^{+++} + 2\epsilon$	$+1.211$
$Br_2 - Br^-$	$Br^- \rightleftarrows \frac{1}{2}Br_2 + \epsilon$	$+1.0648$
$Hg_2^{++} - Hg^+$	$\frac{1}{2}Hg_2^{++} \rightleftarrows Hg^+ + \epsilon$	$+0.9011$
O_2 (1 atm) $- OH^-$ (pH7)	$OH^- \rightleftarrows \frac{1}{2}H_2O + \frac{1}{4}O_2 + \epsilon$	$+0.810$
$Fe^{+++} - Fe^{++}$	$Fe^{++} \rightleftarrows Fe^{+++} + \epsilon$	$+0.7477$
$MnO_4^- - MnO_4^-$	$MnO_4^- \rightleftarrows MnO_4^- + \epsilon$	$+0.664$
$I_2 - I^-$	$I^- \rightleftarrows \frac{1}{2}I_2 + \epsilon$	$+0.5345$
$Fe(CN)_6^{4-} - Fe(CN)_6^{3-}$	$Fe(CN)_6^{4-} \rightleftarrows Fe(CN)_6^{3-} + \epsilon$	$+0.4866$
$Cu^{++} - Cu^+$	$Cu^+ \rightleftarrows Cu^{++} + \epsilon$	$+0.455$
$Ti^{+++} - Ti^{++}$	$Ti^{++} \rightleftarrows Ti^{+++} + \epsilon$	$+0.37$
H_2 (1 atm) $- H^+$	$\frac{1}{2}H_2 \rightleftarrows H^+ + \epsilon$	0.0000 (reference electrode)

Table 21.3 gives the E_0 values for a number of ionic reversible oxidation-reduction systems, and Table 21.4 gives E'_0 values at specified pH for several organic reversible systems, most of which are of biologic importance. Some of the latter are approximate but sufficiently accurate to be of significance. The values of E_0 and E'_0 represent the potentials of the systems when the ratio of oxidant to reductant is unity, measured against the normal hydrogen electrode, the potential of which is taken as 0 under all conditions.

The oxidizing component of each system in Tables 21.3 and 21.4 has greater power for taking up and holding electrons than do the oxidizing components of all systems below it, and, conversely, less power than all above it. Also, the reducing component of each system has more power to give up electrons than does the reducing component of any system above it, and less power than any system below it. This means that the $Co^{+++} - Co^{++}$ system oxidizes all systems below it, while all systems below the $Co^{+++} - Co^{++}$ system reduce it. The oxidizing and reducing powers become relatively greater as the differences between the E_0 values of the systems increase.

The curves of Figure 21.2 show the relation of pH to the E_0 values of several oxidation-reduction systems. It will be noted that E_0 is independent of pH in some cases.

Table 21.4. Normal Electrode Potentials of Some Oxidation-Reduction Systems of
Biological Importance
Values for pH 7

System	Potential E'_0 (Volts) E_h*
½O₂/H₂O	$+0.82$, $E_h = +0.80$
NO₃⁻/NO₂⁻	$+0.42$
Dopaquinone/dihydroxyphenylalanine	$+0.37$
Ferricyanide/ferrocyanide	$+0.36$
½O₂/H₂O₂	$+0.30$
Cytochrome a Fe⁺⁺⁺/cytochrome a Fe⁺⁺	$+0.29$, $E_h = +0.37$
Cytochrome c Fe⁺⁺⁺/cytochrome c Fe⁺⁺	$+0.26$, $E_h = +0.33$
2,6-Dichlorophenolindophenol ox./red. †	$+0.22$
Crotonyl-S-CoA/butyryl-S-CoA‡	$+0.19$
Methemoglobin/hemoglobin	$+0.17$
Dehydroascorbic acid/ascorbic acid	$+0.08$
Fumaric acid/succinic acid	$+0.03$
Methylene blue ox./red.	$+0.01$
Cytochrome b Fe⁺⁺⁺/cytochrome b Fe⁺⁺	0.00, $E_h = +0.04$
Hemin Fe⁺⁺⁺/heme Fe⁺⁺	-0.114
Flavoprotein (old yellow enzyme), ox./red.	-0.12
Pyruvic acid + NH₄⁺/alanine	-0.13
Oxaloacetic acid/malic acid	-0.17
Pyruvic acid/lactic acid	-0.19
Acetaldehyde/alcohol	-0.20
Riboflavin, ox./red.	-0.208
1,3-Diphosphoglyceric acid/3-phosphoglyceraldehyde + Pi§	-0.29
DPN⁺/DPN · H + H⁺	-0.32, $E_h = -0.32$
Pyruvic acid + CO₂/malic acid	-0.33
Glutathione, G—S—SG/GSH‖	-0.34
Acetoacetic acid/β-hydroxybutyric acid	-0.35
Uric acid/xanthine	-0.36
Acetyl—S—CoA/acetaldehyde + HS—CoA	-0.41
H⁺/½H₂	-0.42
Acetate + H⁺/acetaldehyde	-0.60
Succinic acid + CO₂/α-ketoglutaric acid	-0.67
Acetic acid + CO₂/pyruvic acid	-0.70

* E_h values represent potentials corrected for the ratio of oxidized to reduced form present
in intact mitochondria, and more accurately represent the potentials operating in cells.
† Ox./red. represents oxidized form/reduced form.
‡ H—S—CoA represents coenzyme A. Crotonyl—S—CoA and butyryl—S—CoA, etc.,
represent the acyl derivatives of coenzyme A.
§ Pi represents inorganic phosphate, a mixture composed of H₂PO₄⁻ and HPO₄⁻.
‖ G—S—S—G and GSH represent the oxidized and reduced forms, respectively.

Potential relations of oxidation-reduction systems. The potential of a reversible
oxidation-reduction system (redox system) varies in proportion to the logarithm of the
ratio of oxidant to reductant, just as the pH of a buffer system varies in proportion to the
logarithm of the ratio of salt to acid. The equations for the two systems are strikingly
similar:

$$pH = pK + \log_{10} \frac{[salt]}{[acid]}$$

$$E = E'_0 + \frac{RT}{nF} \log_e \frac{[oxidant]}{[reductant]}$$

where E'_0 is specified at a given pH for systems in which it varies with pH.

In the buffer equation each ratio of salt to acid represents a definite pH value, and if
one titrates the acid of the buffer with alkali and plots pH against added alkali, a titration

curve is obtained. When the acid is half titrated, the ratio of salt to acid is unity and

$$pH = pK$$

In a similar manner a curve may be plotted for an oxidation-reduction reaction. If one starts with the reduced form of a system and adds to it an oxidizing agent of sufficient

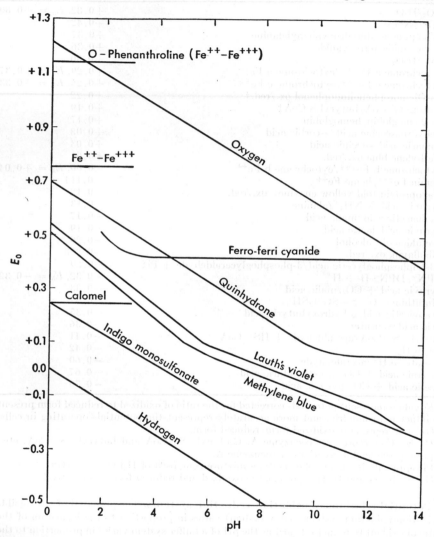

Figure 21.2. E_0 values as a function of pH for various oxidation-reduction systems. (Reprinted by permission from *Outlines of Biochemistry* by R. A. Gortner, 2nd ed. John Wiley & Sons, New York, 1938.)

oxidation potential, the reduced form is progressively converted into the corresponding oxidized form until all the system exists in the oxidized form and the titration is complete. After the addition of each increment of oxidizing agent the ratio of oxidant to reductant in the system is fixed and definite, and the potential shows a definite value in agreement with the equation. If the potentials are plotted against oxidizing agent added, an oxidation-reduction curve is obtained which is similar in form to the curve for a buffer system.

When the system is half oxidized and the ratio of oxidant to reductant is unity, the value of the potential is:

$$E = E'_0$$

E'_0 for an oxidation-reduction system thus corresponds to pK for a buffer system.

Often potentials are plotted against the per cent of the system in the reduced condition. Figure 21.3 shows such a plot of curves for systems with different E'_0 values. The potential represented by a curve at 50 per cent reduction (ratio of oxidant to reductant = 1)

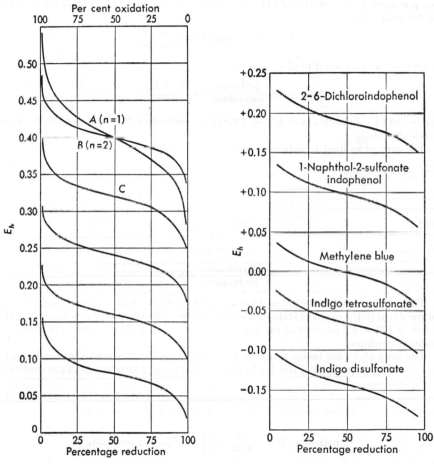

Figure 21.3. Relation between percentage reduction and E_h in systems having different E_0 values. (From *Studies on Oxidation-Reduction I-X* by the staff of the Division of Chemistry, Hygienic Laboratory, U.S. Public Health Service.)

Figure 21.4. Relation of potential to percentage reduction for certain indicators at pH 7.4. (From *Studies on Oxidation-Reduction I-X* by the staff of the Division of Chemistry, Hygienic Laboratory, U.S. Public Health Service.)

is the E'_0 value of the system. It will be observed that the slope of the curves when n (valence change) equals 1 is much steeper than when n is 2. For a given value of n the shape of all the curves is the same, the only difference being in the position on the potential scale, which is determined by the value of E'_0. This is analogous to the plot of different buffer titration curves on the pH scale.

Each complete oxidation-reduction curve extends over a potential range of about 0.15 v when $n = 2$, and 0.30 v when $n = 1$. In cases in which two oxidation-reduction systems react reversibly, the oxidized form of one system will completely oxidize the reduced form of another system which possesses an E'_0 value about 0.15 (or 0.30) v below it. When systems having E'_0 values close together are mixed, the oxidized and reduced forms of both systems coexist in a reversible equilibrium, the ratio of oxidant to reductant for each system depending upon the potential of the mixture and vice versa. Figure 21.4 shows the potential curves of several specific oxidation-reduction systems. Suppose the methylene blue system is mixed with the indigo tetrasulfonate system so that the resulting potential, E_h, is -0.03 v at pH 7 and 30° C. The equations for both of these systems at 30° reduce to:

$$E_h = E'_0 + 0.03 \log \frac{[\text{oxidant}]}{[\text{reductant}]}$$

This may be rearranged to give:

$$\log \frac{[\text{oxidant}]}{[\text{reductant}]} = \frac{E_h - E'_0}{0.03}$$

$E_h = -0.03$ v in both cases; $E'_0 = +0.011$ for methylene blue and -0.046 for indigo tetrasulfonate.

The ratio of oxidant to reductant under these conditions is:

For methylene blue:

$$\log \frac{[\text{oxidant}]}{[\text{reductant}]} = \frac{-0.03 - 0.011}{0.03} = -1.36$$

and
$$\frac{[\text{oxidant}]}{[\text{reductant}]} = 10^{-1.36} = 10^{-2} \times 10^{0.64} = 0.044$$

For indigo tetrasulfonate, calculated similarly, but substituting -0.046 for E'_0:

$$\frac{[\text{oxidant}]}{[\text{reductant}]} = 3.4$$

The ratio, 0.044, for methylene blue at a potential of -0.03 v means that 0.044 mol of the dye is in the oxidized state for each mol in the reduced state. Accordingly, $0.044 \div 1.044 \times 100 = 4.2$ per cent of the dye in the oxidized state, leaving 95.8 per cent in the reduced condition.

The ratio of 3.4 for indigo tetrasulfonate at a potential of -0.03 v represents $3.4 \div 4.4 \times 100 = 77$ per cent of the dye in the oxidized form, which leaves 23 per cent in the reduced state.

From the above it is seen that the ratios of percentage oxidant to reductant for the two systems in equilibrium at pH 7, 30° C, and a potential of -0.03 v are:

$$\text{methylene blue} \quad \frac{4.2}{95.8} = \frac{77}{23} \quad \text{indigo tetrasulfonate}$$

Obviously, if the ratio of methylene blue, 4.2/95.8, is mixed with a 95/5 ratio of sulfonate, the sulfonate system will oxidize the methylene blue system and set up a different equilibrium between different ratios at a different potential. From this it follows that one should know the ratio of oxidant to reductant in each system, as well as the E'_0 values, in order to predict which system will be oxidized when mixed. Since many analytical procedures are based upon oxidative titrations and potential measurements, these points are of considerable importance.

The ascorbic acid, glutathione, cystine, and many other systems are electromotively sluggish because of complex and irreversible reactions taking place at the electrodes, and their potentials cannot be measured directly with accuracy. The E'_0 values of these systems have been obtained indirectly by their action with other reversible oxidation-reduction systems of known E'_0 values.

The systems such as succinate-fumarate, lactate-pyruvate, and alcohol-acetaldehyde are reversible only in the presence of their specific dehydrogenases and carriers. These systems, even then, do not give stable potentials to an electrode, though they are reversible toward other oxidation-reduction systems. If to a sluggish system a reversible system such as methylene blue is added in an amount which is too small to shift the equilibrium appreciably, the mixture then gives significant, steady potentials to an electrode. The reversible dye system is partly reduced by the sluggish system; and, since a relatively very small amount of dye is used, the ratio of oxidant to reductant of the sluggish system is not significantly altered in reducing the dye. The potential of the sluggish system is thus converted into the same value in the reversible dye system, and this can be measured on an electrode. When reversible dye systems are used in this way to measure the potentials of sluggish systems, they are referred to as "mediators."

The relation of oxidation-reduction potentials to energy changes in reactions. Energy for the operation of biologic processes is derived from oxidation-reduction systems. If the E'_0 values of the systems involved are known, it is possible to calculate the free energy change when one system reacts with another.

The potential change, $\Delta E'_0$, when two oxidation-reduction systems of different E'_0 values are mixed may be calculated. Let A and B and AH_2 and BH_2 represent the oxidized and reduced forms of the two systems, respectively. The potentials of these A/AH_2 and B/BH_2 systems are given by the expressions:

$$E_A = E'_{0(A)} + \frac{RT}{nF} \ln \frac{[A]}{[AH_2]} \text{ and } E_B = E'_{0(B)} + \frac{RT}{nF} \ln \frac{[B]}{[BH_2]}$$

When the systems are mixed, reaction proceeds to an equilibrium representing the same potential, E, for both. Then at equilibrium:

$$E'_{0(A)} + \frac{RT}{nF} \ln \frac{[A]}{[AH_2]} = E'_{0(B)} + \frac{RT}{nF} \ln \frac{[B]}{[BH_2]}$$

and

$$E'_{0(A)} - E'_{0(B)} = \frac{RT}{nF} \ln \frac{[B]}{[BH_2]} - \frac{RT}{nF} \ln \frac{[A]}{[AH_2]}$$

and

$$\Delta E'_0 = E'_{0(A)} - E'_{0(B)} = \frac{RT}{nF} \ln ([B] - [BH_2]) - \frac{RT}{nF} \ln ([A] - [AH_2])$$

or

$$\Delta E'_0 = \frac{RT}{nF} \ln \frac{[B][AH_2]}{[BH_2][A]}$$

If $E'_{0(A)}$ is more positive than $E'_{0(B)}$, then A oxidizes BH_2 according to the reversible reaction:

$$A + BH_2 \rightleftharpoons AH_2 + B$$

for which the equilibrium constant, K, is:

$$K = \frac{[B][AH_2]}{[BH_2][A]}$$

Then substituting in the above equation for $\Delta E'_0$ we have:

$$\Delta E'_0 = \frac{RT}{nF} \ln K \text{ or } \Delta E'_0 nF = RT \ln K$$

Since $\Delta F^\circ = -RT \ln K$ (see Chapter 20), $\Delta F^\circ = -\Delta E'_0 nF$, where $\Delta F^\circ =$ the standard free energy change of the reaction, $n =$ the number of electrons (or H atoms) involved, and $F =$ the faraday (96,500 coulombs). The value of $-\Delta E'_0 nF$ is in volt-coulombs or joules; it may be converted to calories by dividing by 4.18, since 1 g cal = 4.18 joules.

Suppose we consider the oxidation of 1 mol of malic acid to oxaloacetic acid by cytochrome c Fe^{+++} (several stages invoved) under conditions such that equimolar concentrations of cytochrome c Fe^{+++} and cytochrome c Fe^{++} and equimolar concentrations of malic acid and oxaloacetic acid are always present throughout the reaction. In other words, each system is maintained at a ratio of oxidant to reductant (1:1) which corresponds to its E'_0 value. The E'_0 value for the cytochrome c system is $+0.26$ v, while for the malic acid/oxaloacetic acid system it is -0.17 v (all at pH 7). The total voltage difference between the systems, $\Delta E'_0$, is $+0.26 - (-0.17) = 0.43$ v. That is the potential driving force, $\Delta E'_0$, for the cytochrome system to oxidize the malic acid/oxaloacetic acid system is 0.43 v. Since the number of electrons involved in the oxidation is two and $n = 2$, we may substitute in the equation:

$$\Delta F^\circ = -\Delta E'_0 nF = -0.43 \times 2 \times 96,500 = -82,990 \text{ joules}$$

or

$$\Delta F^\circ = -82,990/4.18 = -19,854 \text{ cal}$$

Thus the oxidation of 1 mol of malic acid to oxaloacetic acid as outlined yields energy equivalent to 19,854 cal. Similar oxidation of malic acid by the oxygen system $\frac{1}{2}O_2/H_2O$ would yield 45,710 cal:

$$\Delta F^\circ = \frac{-0.99 \times 2 \times 96,500}{4.18} = -45,710 \text{ cal}$$

It is obvious that a difference of 1 v between the E'_0 values of the oxidizing and reducing systems when $n = 2$ represents an energy change per mol of $\Delta F^\circ = \dfrac{-1 \times 2 \times 96,500}{4.18}$ $= -46,172$ cal. Any fractional part of a volt difference represents a proportionate free energy change.

THEORIES OF BIOLOGICAL OXIDATION-REDUCTION

The oxidation of foodstuffs such as sugar, amino acids, and fatty acids in animal tissues proceeds smoothly and rapidly according to the energy needs of the animal. These biologic oxidations occur in water solution, at nearly neutral reaction, and at relatively low temperatures. The mildness of the conditions of biologic oxidations leads one to suspect that they are controlled by the functioning of enzymes, which are organic catalytic systems. As the result of a great deal of investigation by many workers, it has been shown that the oxidative processes in tissues are often complex chain phenomena. The subject of the mechanism of biologic oxidations and reductions is long and complex, and only an outline treatment will be attempted. More details may be obtained from sources such as those referred to at the end of the chapter.

Warburg prepared charcoal in various ways and found that certain preparations of it actively promote the oxidation of amino acids and other organic substances in aqueous solutions of mild reaction and at ordinary temperature. He found charcoal made from blood to be an active catalyst, while that from pure sugar was relatively inert. Upon further investigation he found iron to be present as impurity in the active, and absent from the inactive, preparations. Warburg considered that the iron in his charcoal preparations acts as an oxidation catalyst. He later found a complex iron-containing substance in tissues which functions in oxidative processes and which he referred to as the "*Atmungsferment*," meaning respiratory enzyme.

Accordingly, he put forth his theory of "oxygen activation" in explanation of biologic oxidations.

According to Warburg, the iron complex, $X \cdot Fe$, functions in cellular oxidations as follows:

$$X \cdot Fe + O_2 \longrightarrow X \cdot FeO_2$$

Respiratory
enzyme

$$X \cdot FeO_2 + 2A \longrightarrow 2AO + X \cdot Fe$$

Activated oxygen complex	Metabolite molecules	Oxidized metabolite	

It is now known that while an iron-containing enzyme system (the cytochrome system) is present in tissues, which enables molecular oxygen to serve as an oxidizing agent, the mechanism of its action is not as originally postulated by Warburg. Warburg's *Atmungsferment* is apparently identical with cytochrome oxidase, which will be discussed later.

It was soon found that oxygen activation alone is incapable of accounting for cellular oxidations. The oxygen activation theory was followed by the Wieland theory of "hydrogen activation," according to which certain hydrogen atoms of the metabolite (substance oxidized) are "activated" by an enzyme (dehydrogenase) so that they may be removed by a "hydrogen acceptor," which can be molecular oxygen or other oxidizing agent. The oxidation of lactic to pyruvic acid thus would proceed as follows according to Wieland's theory:

$$CH_3-CHOH-COOH + A \longrightarrow CH_3-CO-COOH + AH_2$$

Lactic acid	Acceptor	Pyruvic acid	Reduced acceptor

As a result of the work of Thunberg in particular, Wieland's theory of the hydrogen activation of metabolites by dehydrogenases and removal of the active hydrogen by acceptors has been well established. Thunberg and others have found a whole series of intracellular enzymes, or dehydrogenases which activate and render labile certain hydrogen atoms in organic molecules so that they may be removed by hydrogen acceptors. These enzymes are specific. Different organic metabolites are activated by different dehydrogenases. When a metabolite is combined with its specific dehydrogenase, it becomes readily oxidizable by various oxidizing agents, such as reversible dyes (methylene blue, for example), and in a few cases by molecular oxygen.

When acetaldehyde is treated with its dehydrogenase in the presence of oxygen, it is oxidized, the oxygen serving as hydrogen acceptor. The fact that most metabolites, even when activated by their specific dehydrogenases, fail to be oxidized by molecular oxygen led to the view, first clearly stated by A. Szent-Györgyi, that both oxygen activation and hydrogen activation are necessary in biologic oxidations.

As work upon the subject progressed, it became increasingly clear that oxygen-activating systems acting with hydrogen-activating systems are generally incapable of bringing about cellular oxidations and that certain so-called carriers, or oxidation-reduction go-betweens, are necessary. In 1921 F. G. Hopkins, of Cambridge University, isolated the peptide glutathione from tissues. He showed that this substance can exist in the reduced sulfhydryl form, designated G—SH, and in the oxidized disulfide form, G—S—S—G. He found that G—SH is readily oxidized to G—S—S—G by oxygen and that G—S—S—G is rapidly reduced back to G—SH by some system in tissues. Hopkins postulated that glutathione functions as a respiratory or oxidation-reduction carrier in tissues. Although it is probable that glutathione functions to a slight extent as a carrier in the oxidations of animal tissues, other carriers have been discovered which are known to be of much greater importance.

A carrier may be defined as a reversible oxidation-reduction system, the oxidized form of which can "accept" hydrogen or electrons and be reduced, and the reduced form can be oxidized by giving hydrogen or electrons to another carrier or to oxygen. The functioning of a simple carrier in which oxygen is the ultimate hydrogen acceptor may be represented as follows:

$$MH_2 \quad + \quad C \quad \longrightarrow \quad M \quad + \quad CH_2$$

| Metabolite activated by dehydrogenase | Oxidized form of carrier | Oxidized metabolite | Reduced form of carrier |

$$CH_2 + O_2 \longrightarrow C + H_2O_2$$
$$H_2O_2 \longrightarrow H_2O + \tfrac{1}{2}O_2$$

Hydrogen peroxide is quickly destroyed by its specific enzyme, catalase.

The fundamental principles of biologic oxidation may be summarized in the following statements:

1. The first process consists in the activation of certain specific hydrogen atoms of the metabolite by a specific dehydrogenase enzyme.

2. The second process involves the transfer of these activated hydrogen atoms from the metabolite to a hydrogen acceptor (carrier) or a series of hydrogen acceptors. The stripping off or loss of the hydrogen atoms (H^+ with an electron) from the metabolite represents oxidation of the metabolite.

3. The final stage of the oxidation process involves the combination of the hydrogen atoms from a carrier with oxygen, by direct or indirect means, to form water. In a few instances molecular oxygen, O_2, may serve directly as the acceptor of activated hydrogen from the metabolite, but in most cases various carrier systems are intermediate agents between the activated metabolite and molecular oxygen.

4. The processes of decarboxylation and hydration are often important supplementary stages in biologic oxidations.

Although it is customary to speak of biologic oxidation, one must never forget that for each oxidation process there is an equivalent reduction process.

A relatively simple illustration of some of the processes of biologic oxidation and reduction is afforded in the conversion of lactic acid to ethanol by yeast.

The first process consists in the action of lactic dehydrogenase upon lactic acid to activate two H atoms which are transferred to the oxidized form of an acceptor, DPN^+ (diphosphopyridine nucleotide):

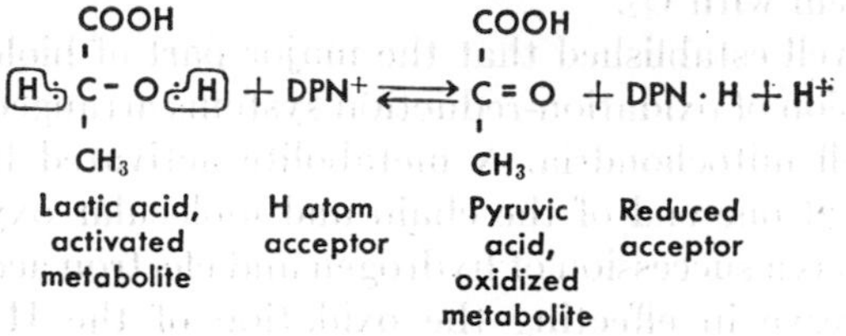

$$\underset{\substack{\text{Lactic acid,}\\\text{activated}\\\text{metabolite}}}{\boxed{H}_3\text{C}-\text{O}\underline{c/H}} + \underset{\substack{\text{H atom}\\\text{acceptor}}}{DPN^+} \rightleftarrows \underset{\substack{\text{Pyruvic}\\\text{acid,}\\\text{oxidized}\\\text{metabolite}}}{\overset{\text{COOH}}{\underset{\text{CH}_3}{C=O}}} + \underset{\substack{\text{Reduced}\\\text{acceptor}}}{DPN \cdot H} + H^+$$

It appears that both the substrate (lactic acid) and the acceptor (DPN^+) become attached to the lactic dehydrogenase protein, the H atoms of lactic acid are activated and then passed to the DPN^+, with formation of pyruvic acid and reduced acceptor. The DPN^+ takes up both electrons of the two H atoms but only one proton (H^+), the other being ionized into the solution The reaction is reversible, meaning that $DPN \cdot H + H^+$ from the medium reduces pyruvic acid back to lactic acid. The oxidized form of the acceptor, DPN^+, runs the reaction to the right, while the reduced acceptor, $DPN \cdot H + H^+$, runs it to the left. The acceptor represents an oxidation-reduction system, $DPN^+/DPN \cdot H + H^+$. Lactic acid, pyruvic acid, DPN^+, and $DPN \cdot H$ are continuously combining with and dissociating from the lactic dehydrogenase.

The second process consists in the decarboxylation of pyruvic acid by the enzyme carboxylase in the presence of its coenzyme, cocarboxylase (thiamine pyrophosphate), and Mg^{++}:

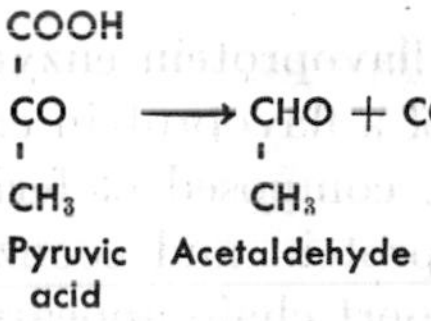

$$\underset{\substack{\text{Pyruvic}\\\text{acid}}}{\overset{\text{COOH}}{\underset{\text{CH}_3}{CO}}} \longrightarrow \underset{\text{Acetaldehyde}}{\overset{\text{CHO}}{\underset{\text{CH}_3}{}}} + CO_2$$

The third process consists in the reduction of acetaldehyde to ethanol by $DPN \cdot H + H^+$, catalyzed by the enzyme alcohol dehydrogenase:

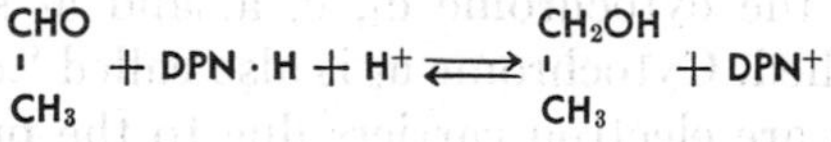

$$\overset{\text{CHO}}{\underset{\text{CH}_3}{}} + DPN \cdot H + H^+ \rightleftarrows \overset{\text{CH}_2\text{OH}}{\underset{\text{CH}_3}{}} + DPN^+$$

The CO_2 formed in the oxidation of foods in the body generally arises through decarboxylation of keto acids produced by the successive stripping off of hydrogen atoms from metabolites formed from carbohydrates, fatty acids, amino acids, etc.

THE ELECTRON TRANSPORT CHAIN OF MITOCHONDRIA

Most biologic oxidations are effected by removal of H atoms from metabolite molecules through the combined actions of specific dehydrogenases and hydrogen acceptors, as previously indicated. This process oxidizes the metabolite and forms a reduced acceptor. There are still the problems of reoxidizing the reduced acceptor so it can continue to function and of eventually converting the hydrogen atoms of the reduced acceptor to water by oxidizing them with O_2.

It has been well established that the major part of biologic oxidation involves a succession of oxidation-reduction systems arranged as an integrated chain in the cell mitochondria. A metabolite activated by its specific dehydrogenase is at one end of the chain and molecular oxygen at the other end. In between is a succession of hydrogen and electron acceptors or carriers which finally serve in effecting the oxidation of the H atoms from the metabolite to H_2O. This chain of carriers or acceptors, including the terminal oxygen system ($\frac{1}{2}O_2/H_2O$), is known as the "electron transport chain." Many investigators over a long period of time have devoted their efforts to establishing its components and their modes of operation. Pertinent discussions of the electron transport chain are to be found in the articles by Conn (1); Green (2), Chance and Williams (3), Neilands (4), and Slater (5).

While there are some details relative to the electron transport chain which await clarification, most of the components of the chain and their functions appear to be rather well established, as shown in Figure 21.5.

In this diagram $M \cdot H_2$ represents the reduced form of the metabolite system with 2H atoms activated by a specific dehydrogenase.

$DPN^+/DPN \cdot H$ represents the diphosphopyridine nucleotide carrier system, which acts as coenzyme with specific dehydrogenases. A chemically closely related system, the triphosphopyridine nucleotide system, $TPN^+/TPN \cdot H$, acts with some dehydrogenases but apparently not in the mitochondria.

$FP/FP \cdot H$ represents the flavoprotein enzyme system, composed of the oxidized and reduced forms of a flavoprotein enzyme.

The cytochrome b system, composed of ferric- and ferroheme forms, is indicated between the flavoprotein and coenzyme Q systems, though its relation to the electron transport chain appears a bit uncertain.

Green and associates appear to have definitely established the position of the coenzyme Q system as next to the cytochrome c_1 system (6).

The positions of the cytochrome c_1, c, a, and a_3 systems in the chain appear well established. Cytochrome a_3 is also called "cytochrome oxidase."

The cytochromes are electron carriers due to the presence of Fe^{+++} and Fe^{++} in the molecules. They do not carry H atoms. Protons, H^+, are liberated when a system carrying H atoms is oxidized by a cytochrome system such as:

$$Q \cdot H_2 + 2 \text{ Cyt. } c_1^{+++} \longrightarrow Q + 2 \text{ Cyt. } c_1^{++} + 2H^+$$

Also, when a cytochrome system is oxidized by a system carrying H atoms, protons are taken up:

$$2 \text{ Cyt. } b^{++} + Q + 2H^+ \longrightarrow 2 \text{ Cyt. } b^{+++} + Q \cdot H_2$$

It should be kept clearly in mind that the flavoprotein dehydrogenases and the cytochrome electron carriers are specific proteins that contain

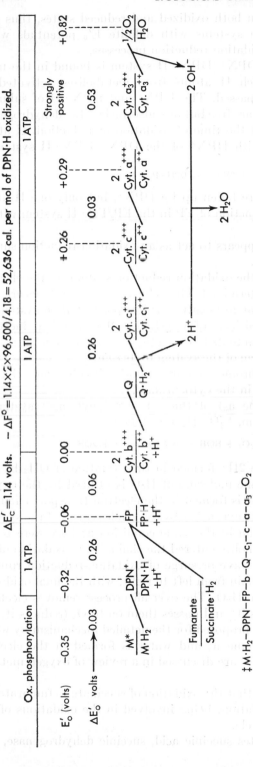

$\Delta E_c' = 1.14$ volts. $-\Delta F^0 = 1.14 \times 2 \times 96,500/4.18 = 52,636$ cal. per mol of DPN·H oxidized.

Ox. phosphorylation	1 ATP			1 ATP		1 ATP		
E_o' (volts)	-0.35	-0.32	-0.06	0.00	$+0.26$	$+0.29$	Strongly positive	$+0.82$
$\Delta E_o'$ volts	0.03	0.26	0.06	0.26	0.03		0.53	

‡M·H$_2$–DPN–FP–b–Q–c$_1$–c–a–a$_3$–O$_2$

Figure 21.5. Diagram of the mitochondrial electron transport chain. *The metabolite system, M´/M·H₂, indicated with an E'ₒ of −0.35 volts, is oxaloacetate/malate. Q/Q·H₂ represents the coenzyme Q system. Cyt.b⁺⁺⁺ represents ferricytochrome b and cyt.b⁺⁺ ferrocytochrome b. Representations for the other cytochromes are similar. The ferricytochromes are the oxidants of the systems and the ferrocytochromes the reductants. Two functional cytochrome groups are involved for each cytochrome system since the oxidation of Fe⁺⁺ to Fe⁺⁺⁺ in the cytochromes is a one electron oxidation-reduction. †The oxidation of succinate to fumarate in the chain is catalyzed by the succinic dehydrogenase, a flavoprotein, which also contains a protoheme group that appears to function as a part of the cytochrome b system. The electrons from succinate are accepted into the chain through the flavoprotein succinic dehydrogenase enzyme, which, thus, in its oxidized, FP, and reduced, FP·H₂, forms constitutes an oxidation-reduction system. See discussion in the text. One molecule of ATP is formed in the oxidation of DPN·H by FP, another in the oxidation of ferrocytochrome b by ferricytochrome c, and a third in the oxidation of ferrocytochrome c by either ferricytochrome a₃ or oxygen (uncertain). The oxidation of succinate in the chain forms only 2 molecules of ATP. The voltage difference between the oxygen and DPN systems (1.14 volts) represents 52,636 calories. ‡Simplified representation of the electron transport chain. Various flavoprotein systems are involved in electron transport chain oxidations.

specific groups which exist in both oxidized and reduced states, thus constituting oxidation-reduction systems with definite E'_0 potentials which carry out in sequence the oxidation-reduction processes.

In the mitochondria the $DPN^+/DPN \cdot H$ system is bound in the mitochondrial structure, to which H atoms from metabolites activated by specific dehydrogenases are passed. The DPN^+ and $DPN \cdot H$ of submitochondrial particles of the cell are free but are adsorbed on the dehydrogenase along with the metabolite at the time of oxidation or reduction. H atoms from the metabolite react with DPN^+ of the $DPN^+/DPN \cdot H$ system as follows:

$$DPN^+ + 2H \cdot \longrightarrow DPN \cdot H + H^+$$

Both electrons of the $2H \cdot$ are taken up by DPN^+, but only one H atom, and one H^+, is released. The action of FP in the $FP/FP \cdot H$ system with H atoms is similar.

The coenzyme Q system appears to act as an oxidation-reduction shuttle between the protein systems.

The E'_0 values of some of the oxidation-reduction systems of the electron transport chain have been determined. The values of all the systems are such that systems to the left are more negative or less positive than systems to the right, so that the oxidized form of a system in the chain is reduced by the reduced form of the system to its left, and the reduced form of the system is oxidized by the oxidized form of the system to its right.

The oxidation of one cytochrome system by another involves only electron transfer from Fe^{++} to Fe^{+++} in the cytochromes.

Cyt. a_3^{++} (ferrocytochrome a_3) of the cyt. $a_3^{+++}/$cyt. a_3^{++} system is oxidized by the oxygen system, $\frac{1}{2}O_2/H_2O$, as follows:

$$2 \text{ Cyt. } a_3^{++} + \tfrac{1}{2}O_2 + HOH \longrightarrow 2 \text{ Cyt. } a_3^{+++} + 2OH^-$$

The $2OH^-$ combine with the $2H^+$ formed in the oxidation of QH_2 by cyt. c_1^{+++} to form $2H_2O$. Since one molecule of H_2O is utilized by the oxygen system, only one net molecule is formed in the electron transport chain.

The oxidation of cyt. a_3^{++} to cyt. a_3^{+++} by oxygen leaves all of the systems of the electron transport chain in the same condition as they were before the two H atoms of the metabolite entered the chain. Thus oxidation of the metabolite is the result of a wave or surge of oxidation-reduction running through the systems of the chain from left to right, with the final oxidation of the metabolite H atoms to H_2O. The over-all process removes electrons from the metabolite (oxidizes it) and passes them on to O_2 (reduces it).

Various theories have been proposed for the detailed mechanism by which O_2 oxidizes reduced cytochrome a_3 and water is formed in the electron transport chain. These theories are discussed in a review of oxygen metabolism by Mason (7).

It will be pointed out later that the oxidation of succinate to fumarate is a very important biologic oxidation, being involved in the oxidations of the tricarboxylic or citric acid cycle.

The enzyme which activates succinic acid, succinic dehydrogenase, is a flavoprotein, which in its oxidized, FP, and reduced, FP · H, forms makes up a flavoprotein system in the electron transport chain. In the oxidative process succinate is adsorbed on the enzyme, two of its H atoms are activated and reduce the oxidized enzyme, FP, to the reduced enzyme, FP · H. The FP · H is then oxidized by cyt. b^{+++} of the cytochrome b system. Thus, two H atoms of succinate enter the electron transport chain through the flavoprotein system and not through the DPN^+ system. Because the $DPN^+/DPN \cdot H$ system is by-passed, only two molecules of ATP are formed.

OXIDATIVE PHOSPHORYLATION

At certain stages in the electron transport chain some of the energy produced by the oxidation is stored up as high-energy phosphate (ATP) for use in metabolic processes. As shown in Figure 21.5, one molecule of ATP is formed when FP oxidizes DPN · H. The voltage difference, $\Delta E'_0$, between these systems is 0.26, and the free energy production $(-\Delta F)$ per mol of DPN · H oxidized is:

$$-\Delta F = \frac{\Delta E'_0 \times n \times F}{4.18} = \frac{0.26 \times 2 \times 96,500}{4.18} = 12,000 \text{ cal}$$

Since the formation of a mol of ATP from ADP and inorganic phosphate requires about 7,000 calories, the free energy made available by this oxidation is adequate. A second molecule of ATP is formed in the oxidations of the chain represented by the segment cytochrome b^{++}—cytochrome c^{+++}— that is, when cytochrome c^{+++} oxidizes cytochrome b^{++} through the intermediate carriers. Here the over-all voltage difference again is 0.26, and represents 12,000 calories for the formation of ATP. A third molecule of ATP is formed in the oxidation of cytochrome c^{++}. Since the potential difference between the cytochrome c system and the cytochrome a system (0.03 v) cannot provide the free energy for the formation of ATP, the energy must arise by the oxidation of cytochrome c^{++} by cytochrome a_3^{+++} or by oxygen. While the E'_0 value of the cytochrome a_3 system is not definitely established, it is strongly positive and would probably provide sufficient free energy for the formation of ATP in the oxidation of cytochrome c^{++}.

Since the voltage difference, $\Delta E'_0$, from the $DPN^+/DPN \cdot H$ system to the oxygen system in the electron transport chain is 1.14, the total free energy production by oxidation of 2 mols of H atoms through the chain is:

$$-\Delta F = 1.14 \times 2 \times 96,500/4.18 = 52,636 \text{ cal}$$

The formation of 3 mols of ATP in the chain represents the production of $3 \times 7,000 = 21,000$ calories of utilizable energy. The efficiency of the over-all process then is:

$$21,000/52,636 \times 100 = 40 \text{ per cent}$$

Various workers (8) have shown that the oxidation of $DPN \cdot H$ through the mitochondrial electron transport chain yields three molecules of ATP per atom of oxygen, or, as commonly stated, the P to O ratio, P/O, is 3. This means that 3 mols of inorganic phosphate, Pi, are converted to 3 mols of ATP in the over-all oxidation of two metabolite H atoms in the chain between the $DPN^+/DPN \cdot H$ and oxygen systems. The process by which ADP is phosphorylated by Pi to ATP in the electron transport chain is called "oxidative phosphorylation," and is limited to the mitochondria. Various oxidations occur in other parts of the cell and liberate heat, but they do not form ATP.

It has been found that carefully prepared mitochondria show large variations in respiration rate and in the oxidation-reduction levels of the systems in the electron transport chain in the presence and absence of inorganic phosphate and phosphate acceptor, such as ADP. This means that the flow of electrons through the systems along the chain is coupled with reactions involving phosphates.

Because the DPN, flavoprotein, and cytochrome systems show characteristically different light absorption in their oxidized and reduced states, Chance and Williams (8) have been able to study the amounts of oxidation and reduction of these systems under various conditions. For example, if to the chain of systems in a steady state of oxidation-reduction an inhibitor, antimycin A, is added, it appears to combine with cyt. b^{++} and prevent its function. This stops the flow of electrons at cyt. b^{++} and it cannot be oxidized by cyt. c_1^{+++}. Spectroscopic observation shows that the cytochrome b, DPN, and flavoprotein systems are completely in the reduced states due to electrons from the activated metabolite, while the cytochrome c, a, and a_3 systems are in the oxidized states due to removal of electrons from them by the oxygen system. Chance and Williams found that the absence of phosphate acceptor, ADP, in the mitochondria blocked electron transport at reduced cytochrome c, cyt. c^{++}. By such spectroscopic evidence it was possible to locate three inhibition points along the electron transport chain and to show that these points represent the regions in which oxidative phosphorylation $(ADP + Pi \longrightarrow ATP)$ takes place.

Various mechanisms have been proposed for the oxidative phosphorylation process. Chance and Williams have proposed the following mechanism in which I and X are intermediates of unknown nature, but evidence indicates their existence; B is the oxidized form of a carrier in the chain; and AH_2 is the reduced carrier which reduces B:

$$B + I \rightleftharpoons BI$$
$$BI + AH_2 \rightleftharpoons BH_2 {\sim} I + A$$
$$BH_2 {\sim} I + X \rightleftharpoons X {\sim} I + BH_2$$
$$X {\sim} I + Pi \rightleftharpoons X {\sim} P + I$$
$$X {\sim} P + ADP \rightleftharpoons ATP + X$$

Other mechanisms for oxidative phosphorylation are discussed by Chance and Williams (8).

Uncoupling agents. A large number of substances "uncouple" oxidative phosphorylation in the electron transport chain; that is, they prevent the formation of ATP but permit oxidation to proceed, even at an accelerated rate, with the generation of heat. This energy, however, is not utilizable for physiologic processes. One of the most studied and potent uncoupling agents is 2,4-dinitrophenol (DNP).

The mitochondria exhibit ATPase activity, that is, ATP added to mitochondria is hydrolyzed to ADP and Pi. DNP might uncouple phosphorylation by causing hydrolysis of $X \sim I$ or $X \sim P$ according to some theories. This would in effect be equivalent to hydrolysis of ATP in that it would block its formation and permit oxidation to proceed without phosphorylation. DNP has been considered to increase the ATPase activity of mitochondria.

Chance and Williams consider that DNP reacts with $X \sim I$ as follows in the uncoupling process:

$$X \sim I + DNP \rightleftharpoons X + DNP \cdot I$$

Other uncoupling agents include methylene blue, brilliant cresyl blue, pentachlorophenol, azide, arsenite, dicoumarol, and the antibiotics chlortetracycline (Aureomycin), bacitracin, and gramicidin. Some of these agents appear to act similarly to DNP while others act differently. Thyroxine is an uncoupling agent and apparently acts by causing swelling of the mitochondria. This appears to be similar to the uncoupling caused by treating mitochondria with water, which also causes uncoupling and swelling. The uncoupling process is discussed by Lehninger, Wadkins, and Remmert (9).

Oxidation of DPN · H and TPN · H. DPN · H formed in the cell outside of the mitochondria can be oxidized by the mitochondria, but at a slower rate and with decreased phosphorylative efficiency.

It is uncertain as to the capacity of mitochondria to oxidize TPN · H directly, though Cheldelin and associates (10) have observed direct phosphorylation coupled to TPN · H oxidation by heart mitochondria supplemented with a heart extract. Lang and Nason (11) have found a TPN · H-cytochrome c reductase in heart muscle, which is a flavoprotein that catalyzes the oxidation of TPN · H through cytochrome c.

Humphrey (12) has found a transhydrogenase in mitochondria which catalyzes the oxidation of TPN · H by DPN+:

$$TPN \cdot H + DPN^+ \rightleftharpoons DPN \cdot H + TPN^+$$

The DPN · H formed then may undergo mitochondrial oxidation.

Transhydrogenase enzymes and their function in biologic oxidation-reduction have been studied especially by Kaplan and associates (13).

Since a great deal of the DPN · H and TPN · H arising in cells outside of the mitochondria is used in the reduction of metabolites, it appears probable that there may be little need for oxidation through the mitochondria.

ORGANIZATION OF THE ELECTRON TRANSPORT CHAIN

It has been found possible to fragment mitochondria into simpler component units by a number of procedures such as sonic vibration, dissolution with cholate and deoxycholate, treatment with digitonin, and extraction with organic solvents. The fragments are concentrated by supercentrifugation. Lehninger and Associates (14) have obtained fragments of mitochondria which carry out oxidation of substrates such as β-hydroxybutyrate (to acetoacetate) with phosphorylation. Green (15) has obtained what he calls miniature mitochondria, or electron transport particles, which he considers to represent subunits of mitochondria. They are about 0.01 as large as the mitochondria. These particles qualitatively carry out all the reactions of the intact mitochondria, but less efficiently, partly due to loss of bound DPN. Green and associates have shown that the systems of the electron transport chain are associated with a small amount of neutral lipid (cholesterol, triglycerides, carotenoids, etc.) and much phospholipid. The lipid is present largely as lipoprotein complexes. Green considers the mitochondrial electron transport chain to consist of an integrated chain of oxidation-reduction systems bound together in a lipoprotein core or matrix.

VARIATION IN THE ELECTRON TRANSPORT CHAIN

Several oxidation-reduction systems other than those discussed above have been proposed as units in the electron transport chain. These include some carotenoids, α-tocopherol, and vitamin K type compounds which are naphthoquinones. Brodie and coworkers (16) have found a vitamin K_1 derivative to be a component of the electron transport chain of *Mycobacterium phlei* involved in the oxidation of succinate by O_2 and the associated formation of ATP (oxidative phosphorylation). This compound cannot be replaced by the coenzyme Q of mammalian tissue in the oxidation of succinate by *M. phlei*, and neither can the vitamin K_1 derivative replace coenzyme Q in the mammalian oxidation of succinate. The exact position of vitamin K_1 derivatives in the electron transport chain of *M. phlei* is unknown, though the oxidation-reduction potential of vitamin K_1 lies between the potentials of the $DPN^+/DPN \cdot H$ and cytochrome b systems.

It appears that ascorbic acid is oxidized to dehydroascorbic acid through a cytochrome segment of the electron transport chain (17) as follows:

$$\text{Ascorbic acid} - c - a - a_3 - O_2$$

There is a chain in cellular microsomes which oxidizes substrate through the DPN system and cytochrome b_5 of the microsomes, which Slater (18) considers very likely to contain the following systems:

$$M \cdot H_2 - DPN - FP - b_5 - c - a - a_3 - O_2$$

However, for this chain to operate it would be necessary to have sufficient cytochrome c in the soluble fraction of cytoplasm, which is questionable, but if true, the oxidation would have to be coupled with the cytochromes a, and a_3 of the mitochondria, which is uncertain. If the chain operates without soluble cytoplasmic cytochrome c, then it would have to be coupled to the mitochondrial chain at cytochrome c.

The tissues of some plants appear to utilize a respiratory chain containing glutathione and ascorbic acid systems:

$$M \cdot H_2 - \frac{TPN^+}{TPN \cdot H} - \frac{G—S—S—G}{2 \ G—SH} - \frac{Dehydroascorbate}{ascorbate} - O_2$$

RATE OF OXIDATION IN THE ELECTRON TRANSPORT CHAIN

The over-all rate of oxygen utilization and utilizable energy (ATP) production in the body is chiefly controlled by the rate of oxidative phosphorylation in the mitochondrial electron transport chain.

Since oxidation in the chain is coupled with substrate or metabolite, all of the transport systems in the chain and oxygen, and with the phosphorylation of ADP by Pi to ATP, the concentration or availability of any of these may become factors in controlling the rate of oxidation or respiration (19). Chance has pointed out that under normal conditions of O₂ level and respiratory chain capacity the rate of oxidation and production of ATP is determined by the concentration of intracellular ADP. In other words, as the quantity of ADP decreases, due to conversion to ATP, oxidation in the mitochondrial chain decreases in proportion, while as the concentration of ADP increases, due to utilization and breakdown of ATP, oxidation in the chain increases to phosphorylate more ADP to ATP. Thus, the concentration of ADP available to the mitochondria automatically controls the rate of oxidation to meet the needs of tissues. Of course, other factors, such as oxygen, substrate, and the electron transport chain, may become controlling factors under certain conditions.

COMPONENTS OF ELECTRON TRANSPORT CHAINS

1. Pyridine nucleotides. Diphosphopyridine nucleotide (DPN) was discovered as a coenzyme in yeast juice by Harden and Young in 1904 (20), and later named "cozymase" by Euler and Myrbach, since it is a coenzyme to the zymase enzyme system of yeast. Meyerhof (21) later found that the enzyme system which converts glycogen to lactic acid in muscle also requires this same coenzyme. It has been found in practically all living tissues, though generally in small amounts. Yeast is a rich source and is used in its preparation.

DPN was isolated in pure form by Euler and associates and its structure determined in 1936 (22).

Triphosphopyridine nucleotide (TPN) was discovered in horse erythrocytes by Warburg and Christian in 1932 (23), and found to serve as a coenzyme to the dehydrogenase which oxidizes glucose-6-phosphate to 6-phosphogluconic acid. Its structure was determined in 1935 (24).

The structures of DPN and TPN were found to be very similar, differing only in that DPN contains two and TPN three phosphate groups. Both substances are dinucleotides composed of nicotinamide, ribose, phosphate, and adenine:

$$\text{Nicotinamide}^+ - \text{D-ribose} - O - \overset{\overset{\textstyle O}{\|}}{\underset{\underset{\textstyle O_-}{|}}{P}} - O - \overset{\overset{\textstyle O}{\|}}{\underset{\underset{\textstyle OH}{|}}{P}} - O - \text{D-ribose} - \text{adenine}$$

In TPN a phosphate group is esterified at the C'_2 position of the ribose group joined to adenine.

The detailed structures are shown below:

Diphosphopyridine and Triphosphopyridine Nucleotide (DPN and TPN) Structures

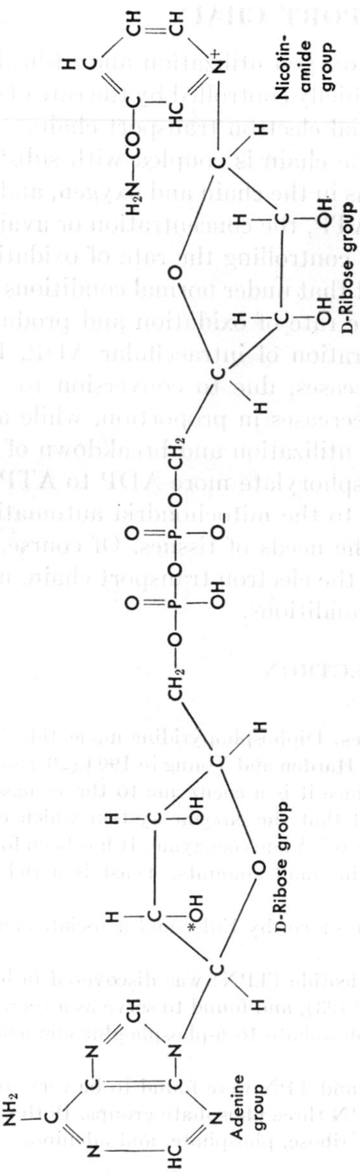

* TPN has a phosphate group esterified at this position. These structures represent the oxidized forms. DPN (NAD) and TPN (NADP) also are known as coenzyme I (CoI) and coenzyme II (CoII) respectively.

The nicotinamide groups of DPN and TPN function in oxidized and reduced forms with specific dehydrogenases to constitute systems in electron transport chains. This oxidation-reduction may be shown as follows, where R represents the structure attached to the nicotinamide group:

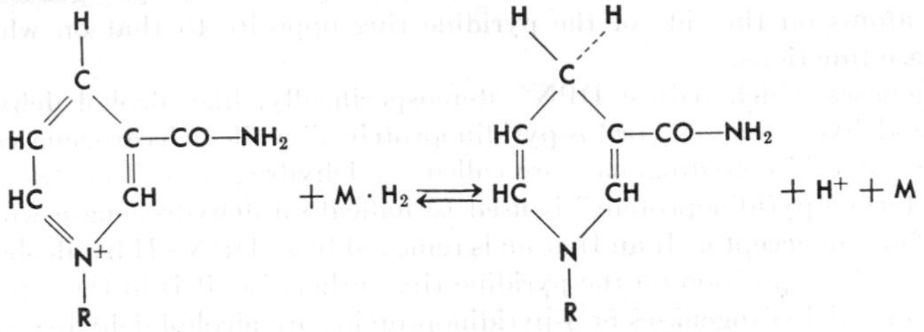

DPN$^+$
Oxidized form   DPN · H
Reduced form

M · H$_2$ represents a metabolite such as malate activated by a specific dehydrogenase. The DPN$^+$ is adsorbed to the dehydrogenase and takes up the two H atoms of the metabolite. One H atom and an electron (equals two electrons) are added to the DPN$^+$ reducing it to DPN · H and an H$^+$ is released to the medium. The reverse reaction represents oxidation of DPN · H by the metabolite, in which H$^+$ is taken up from the medium. The TPN system functions similarly.

Since the pyridine ring is planar, the two H atoms on the nicotinamide group of DPN · H (and TPN · H) project on either side of the plane. It has been shown (25) by the use of substrates labeled with deuterium (D) and DPN$^+$ reduced with deuterium that certain dehydrogenases catalyze the addition and removal of H on one side of the pyridine ring of DPN while other dehydrogenases use the opposite side of the ring.

When DPN$^+$ is reduced with deuterium-labeled alcohol, CH$_3$—CD$_2$—OH, in the presence of yeast alcohol dehydrogenase DPN · D is obtained containing one D atom, and one H atom, and the acetaldehyde formed contains one D atom:

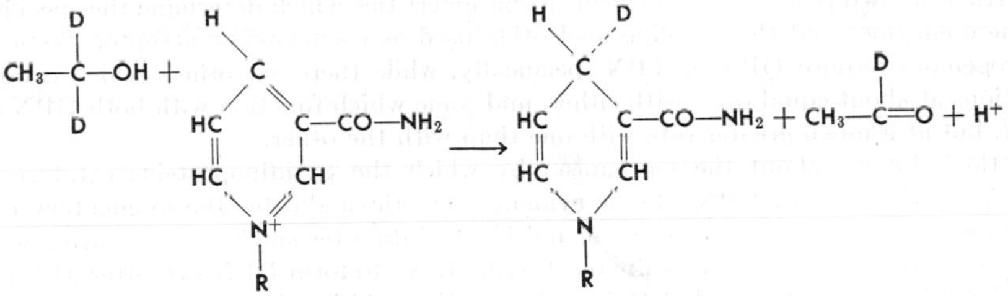

DPN$^+$ DPN · D

The DPN · D, containing H and D on opposite sides of the ring, when oxidized by acetaldehyde and alcohol dehydrogenase (reversal of above reaction), loses all of the D. When the DPN · D is oxidized by pyruvate and lactic dehydrogenase, all of the D is lost and the lactate formed contains an atom of D per molecule:

$$\text{DPN} \cdot \text{D(H)} + \text{CH}_3 - \text{CO} - \text{COOH} \longrightarrow \text{DPN}^+ + \text{CH}_3 - \overset{\overset{\displaystyle \text{OH}}{|}}{\underset{\underset{\displaystyle \text{D}}{|}}{\text{C}}} - \text{COOH}$$

These experiments show that alcohol dehydrogenase acts stereospecifically—that is, adds and removes H atoms to only one side of the pyridine ring. Lactic dehydrogenase also acts upon the same side of the ring as alcohol dehydrogenase, and D or H atoms added through one enzyme can be removed by the other. Now when DPN · D prepared by the alcohol dehydrogenase system was reoxidized to DPN⁺ by a steroid (androstenedione) and β-Hydroxysteroid dehydrogenase, no D was transferred to the testosterone formed, but it remained in the DPN⁺. This means that H instead of D was transferred to form testosterone and that β-hydroxysteroid dehydrogenase adds and removes H atoms on the side of the pyridine ring opposite to that on which alcohol dehydrogenase functions.

Dehydrogenases which reduce DPN⁺ stereospecifically, like alcohol dehydrogenase, are called "α-dehydrogenases" or "α-pyridinoproteins," while dehydrogenases which act like β-hydroxysteroid dehydrogenase are called "β-dehydrogenases" or "β-pyridinoproteins." The term "pyridinoprotein" is used to indicate a dehydrogenase which utilizes DPN or TPN as an acceptor. If an H atom is removed from DPN · H by alcohol dehydrogenase, it is in the α-position on the pyridine ring; otherwise, it is in the β-position.

Examples of α-dehydrogenases or α-pyridinoproteins are alcohol dehydrogenase, lactic dehydrogenase, and malic dehydrogenase; while examples of β-dehydrogenases or β-pyridinoproteins are β-hydroxysteroid dehydrogenase, liver glucose dehydrogenase, phosphoglyceraldehyde dehydrogenase of yeast and muscle, pig heart DPN · H-cytochrome c reductase, and yeast triose dehydrogenase.

Presumably the dehydrogenases which act with the TPN system as coenzyme function stereospecifically relative to H on the different sides of the pyridine ring just as do the dehydrogenases acting with the DPN system.

Both DPN · H and TPN · H have strong light absorption maxima at 340 mμ, and this is used to follow the course of reactions involving them.

2. Dehydrogenases which act with pyridine nucleotides as coenzymes or acceptors. Pyridinoproteins. A very large number of dehydrogenases activate metabolite H atoms and pass them to DPN⁺ or TPN⁺ as acceptors. Several substrates acted upon by dehydrogenases requiring pyridine nucleotides as coenzymes are given in Table 21.5, and comprehensive tables are to be found in *Enzymes* by Dixon and Webb (25). These dehydrogenases are generally named according to the substrates upon which they act, such as lactic dehydrogenase, glucose-6-phosphate dehydrogenase, glutamic dehydrogenase, etc.

Little is known relative to the chemical characteristics which determine the specificity of these enzymes and the pyridine nucleotide used as coenzyme or acceptor. Some dehydrogenases require DPN or TPN specifically, while there are others which catalyze reactions at about equal rates with either, and some which function with both DPN and TPN, but at a much greater rate with one than with the other.

Little is known about the mechanism by which the pyridinoproteins catalyze the transfer of H atoms to DPN⁺. Some evidence (kinetic) indicates the momentary combination of metabolite, dehydrogenase, and DPN⁺ into a ternary complex, during which H atoms of the activated metabolite react with DPN⁺ to form DPN · H, after which the complex dissociates. Removal of H from DPN · H would involve a reverse process.

Spectroscopic evidence suggests that —SH groups may be involved in the union of some of the pyridine nucleotides with dehydrogenases, and the zinc atoms present in a few may function in binding the nucleotide and/or metabolite to the active center of the enzyme.

The pyridine nucleotides are weakly bound by the dehydrogenases and readily dissociate from them, so they may function in consecutive reactions with different dehydrogenases. An example is the coupling of two reactions which take place in the process of anaerobic glycolysis in carbohydrate metabolism:

(a)   3-Phosphoglyceraldehyde + DPN⁺ + Pi ⟶ 1,3-Diphosphoglycerate + H⁺ + DPN · H
(b)   Pyruvate + DPN · H + H⁺ ⟶ Lactate + DPN⁺
(Sum) 3-Phosphoglyceraldehyde + Pi + Pyruvate ⟶ 1,3-Diphosphoglycerate + Lactate

3. Flavoprotein enzymes. A large number of dehydrogenases are flavoproteins composed of specific proteins combined with a flavin group.

Table 21.5. Some Substrates Acted Upon by Dehydrogenases Requiring Pyridine Nucleotides

Substrate	Pyridine Nucleotide	Products	Source of Enzyme
Alcohol	DPN	Acetaldehyde	Yeast, liver, kidney
Lactate	DPN	Pyruvate	Animal tissues
Malate	DPN	Oxaloacetate	Animal tissues
Isocitrate	TPN	α-Ketoglutarate + CO_2	Animal tissues, yeast
Glucose-6-phosphate	TPN	6-Phosphogluconate	Yeast, liver, erythrocytes
β-Hydroxybutyrate	DPN	Acetoacetate	Liver
3-β-Hydroxysteroids	DPN	3-Ketosteroids	Pseudomonas
3-β-Hydroxysteroids	DPN or TPN	3-Ketosteroids	Liver
Betaine aldehyde	DPN	Betaine	Rat liver
Glutamate	DPN or TPN	α-Ketoglutarate + NH_4^+	Yeast, muscle, liver
α-Glycerophosphate	DPN	Phosphodihydroxyacetone	Yeast, muscle, liver
Uridine diphosphoglucose	DPN	Uridinediphosphoglucuronate	Liver
Dihydroorotate	DPN	Orotate	Bacteria
Reduced glutathione (G—SH)	TPN	Ox. glutathione (G—S—S—G)	Liver, yeast

Warburg and Christian (26) in 1932 obtained from brewer's yeast a "yellow enzyme" that catalyzes the oxidation of TPN·H, which they called "the yellow oxidation enzyme," and which is now called the "yellow enzyme of Warburg and Christian," the "yellow enzyme of Warburg," or the "old yellow enzyme." It was found that the yellow component of the enzyme is riboflavin (27) and that the prosthetic group in the flavoprotein enzyme is the nucleotide riboflavin-5'-phosphate, also called "flavin mononucleotide" (FMN).

Warburg and Christian in 1938 (28) found a second riboflavin prosthetic group in renal D amino acid oxidase, flavin adenine dinucleotide (FAD). Since then many riboflavin-containing enzymes have been discovered, most of which contain FAD as the prosthetic group.

Many of the flavoproteins are also metalloproteins, containing metals such as iron, molybdenum, copper, and manganese. While the manner in which the metal is bound is unknown, it often appears to be essential for enzyme action, and is thought to be reversibly reduced during enzymatic reaction.

The formulas of the prosthetic groups of the flavoprotein enzymes riboflavin-5'-phosphate, or FMN, and flavin adenine dinucleotide, FAD, are given below:

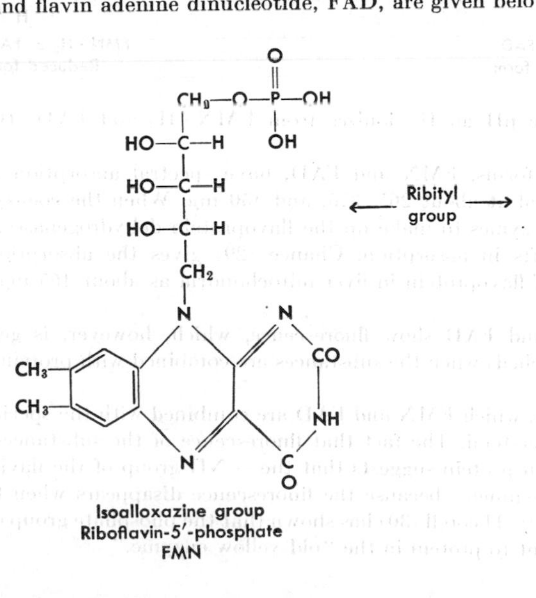

Isoalloxazine group
Riboflavin-5'-phosphate
FMN

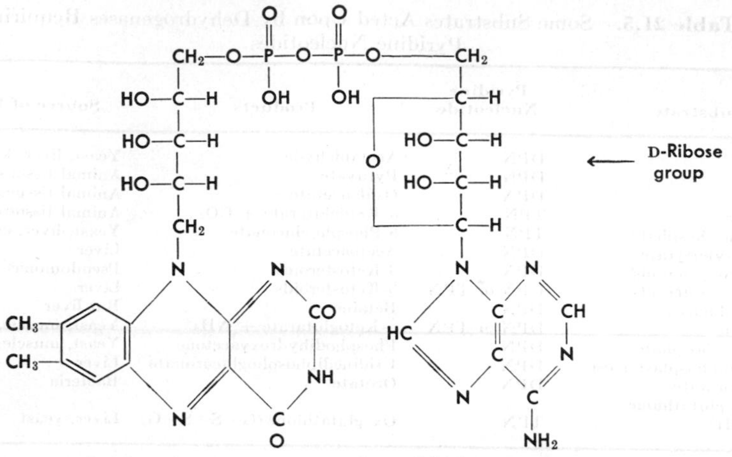

Isoalloxazine group   Adenine group
Flavin adenine dinucleotide
FAD

It will be noted that the group corresponding to the sugar alcohol, ribitol, is present in the isoalloxazine nucleotide of both FMN and FAD. The adenine nucleotide part of FAD contains the usual ribose group.

The functional oxidation-reduction group of both FMN and FAD is the isoalloxazine group, which reacts with H atoms from metabolites or DPN · H as follows:

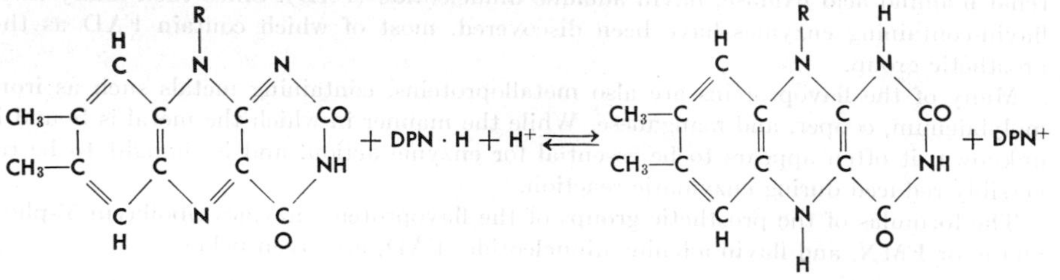

FMN or FAD   FMN · H₂ or FAD · H₂
Oxidized form   Reduced form

At physiologic pH an H⁺ ionizes from FMN · H₂ and FAD · H₂, as it does from DPN · H₂.

The oxidized forms, FMN and FAD, have spectral absorption maxima which are virtually identical at about 265, 375, and 450 mμ. When the coenzymes are combined with their apoenzymes to make up the flavoprotein dehydrogenases, there are variable but definite shifts in absorption. Chance (29) gives the absorption maxima for the oxidized form of flavoprotein in liver mitochondria as about 465 mμ, and for DPN · H as 340 mμ.

Both FMN and FAD show fluorescence, which, however, is generally completely abolished (quenched) when the substances are combined with protein in the flavoprotein enzymes.

The manner in which FMN and FAD are combined with the specific enzyme proteins is not fully understood. The fact that fluorescence of the substances is abolished upon combination with protein suggests that the —NH group of the flavin ring system may be a site of attachment, because the fluorescence disappears when the —NH group is titrated (pK 10.2). Theorell (30) has shown that the phosphate group of FMN is involved in the attachment to protein in the "old yellow enzyme."

Generally the prosthetic group, FMN or FAD, is rather tightly bound to the apoenzyme. In some cases it can be removed by treatment with acid salt solutions, while in others the prosthetic group is held so firmly that it cannot be removed without causing denaturation of the apoenzyme. However, the flavoproteins, glycine oxidase of pig kidney, and D-aspartic acid oxidase of rabbit liver are exceptions, their FAD being relatively easily dissociable from the apoenzyme.

Theorell (31) has found the dissociation constant of FMN with apoenzyme of alcohol dehydrogenase to be around 1.5×10^{-9}:

$$\text{Protein} \cdot \text{FMN} \rightleftharpoons \text{Protein} + \text{FMN}$$

$$K = \frac{[\text{Protein}][\text{FMN}]}{[\text{Protein} \cdot \text{FMN}]} = 1.45 \times 10^{-9}$$

which means that for practical purposes all of the FMN is bound in the flavoprotein.

Mode of action of the flavoprotein enzymes. Based upon mode of action, there are two groups of flavoprotein dehydrogenases.

One group, the so-called aerobic dehydrogenases, accepts H atoms directly from metabolites, and may in turn be oxidized by O_2 without going through the cytochrome systems:

$$M \cdot H_2 + FP \longrightarrow FP \cdot H + H^+ + M$$
$$FP \cdot H + H^+ + O_2 \longrightarrow FP + H_2O_2$$

The oxidation of $FP \cdot H$ by O_2 is the source of H_2O_2 in biologic systems. The H_2O_2 is decomposed by the enzyme catalase and does not accumulate:

$$2H_2O_2 \longrightarrow 2H_2O + O_2$$

The reduced aerobic dehydrogenases may also be oxidized by dyes such as methylene blue, 2,6-dichlorophenolindophenol, and phenazine methosulfate. The aerobic dehydrogenases are concentrated not in the mitochondria but in the cellular cytoplasm.

Among the aerobic flavoprotein dehydrogenases are enzymes such as D- and L-amino acid oxidases, glycine oxidase, sarcosine oxidase, glucose oxidase of *Penicillium notatum*, and mono- and diamine oxidases.

A peculiar group of aerobic or metabolite-oxidizing dehydrogenases contains iron and molybdenum as well as FAD. The best-known of these enzymes is xanthine oxidase, which contains iron, molybdenum and FAD in the ratio 8:2:2. Crystalline xanthine oxidase from milk peculiarly oxidizes both a large number of purines and an even greater number of aldehydes. Unlike the simple flavoprotein enzymes, it is irreversibly inhibited by cyanide, which is probably due to combination of cyanide with essential metal in the enzyme. The crystalline enzyme from liver contains both iron and molybdenum but, unlike milk xanthine oxidase, is not readily autooxidizable. Xanthine oxidases from different sources show variable capacity to oxidize $DPN \cdot H$. Aldehyde oxidase from liver contains iron, molybdenum, and FAD in the ratio 1:1:2. Unlike xanthine oxidase, it does not oxidize purines.

The second group of flavoprotein dehydrogenases, the anaerobic dehydrogenases accept H not from metabolites but from $DPN \cdot H$:

$$DPN \cdot H + FP \rightleftharpoons DPN^+ + FP \cdot H$$

$FP \cdot H$ is not oxidized by O_2 or dyes but through the electron transport chain.

The anaerobic dehydrogenases are located in the mitochondria. These flavoprotein dehydrogenases of the mitochondria include enzymes such as succinic dehydrogenase, butyryl coenzyme A dehydrogenase, and dehydrogenases specific for the longer-chain fatty acid derivatives of coenzyme A. These enzymes catalyze the removal of H atoms from adjacent carbon atoms of the saturated fatty acid chain to form double bonds.

Some of the flavoprotein dehydrogenases of mitochondria cannot be oxidized directly by the electron transport chain but are connected to the chain by a specific enzyme, an "electron-transferring flavoprotein." This enzyme oxidizes FP · H and in turn is oxidized by oxidized cytochrome b.

A group of rather poorly characterized flavoprotein dehydrogenases are the so-called cytochrome-linked dehydrogenases, which appear to contain in their structures an insoluble cytochrome component, such as cytochrome b. Lactic dehydrogenase of yeast (not animal) has been obtained as this kind of complex. Examples of other such enzymes are mitochondrial α-glycerophosphate dehydrogenase and choline dehydrogenase.

An important class of flavoprotein dehydrogenases of mitochondria are the so-called cytochrome reductases. These enzymes catalyze the oxidation of DPN · H and TPN · H and in turn are oxidized by the cytochrome systems:

$$DPN \cdot H + FP \rightleftharpoons DPN^+ + FP \cdot H$$
$$FP \cdot H + 2 \text{ Cyt. } b^{+++} \longrightarrow FP + 2 \text{ Cyt. } b^{++} + H^+$$

Such enzymes are frequently called DPN · H or TPN · H "cytochrome c reductases" because they mediate the oxidation of DPN · H or TPN · H by cytochrome c (but presumably through cytochrome b).

The cytochrome reductases contain iron, which apparently functions in the Fe^{+++} and Fe^{++} states as in the cytochromes, serving to pass electrons from DPN · H or TPN · H to Fe^{+++} of cytochrome b^{+++} by one-electron stages. The cytochrome reductases reduce dyes such as methylene blue. After removal of the iron from the cytochrome reductases, they can no longer oxidize DPN · H or TPN · H but do reduce dyes. The exact relation of the iron in cytochrome reductases to their function awaits clarification.

A flavoprotein enzyme known as "diaphorase," discovered by Straub and associates (32), has the property of transferring H from DPN · H to dyes and reducing them but is not reoxidized by the cytochromes. The relation of diaphorase to the electron transport chain and biologic oxidations is uncertain. Green and associates (33) have shown that Straub's diaphorase appears to be derived from a lipoflavoprotein of heart muscle mitochondria:

$$DPN \cdot H + (Diaphorase)FP \longrightarrow (Diaphorase)FP \cdot H$$
$$(Diaphorase)FP \cdot H + H^+ + \text{Methylene blue} \longrightarrow (Diaphorase)FP + \text{Leucomethylene blue}$$

Table 21.6 gives several flavoprotein enzymes. As shown, it is customary to call the aerobic flavoprotein dehydrogenases "oxidases," as glucose oxidase, D-amino acid oxidase, etc.

4. Coenzymes Q. Crane and associates (34) in 1957 discovered a water insoluble quinone in beef heart mitochondria now known as "coenzyme Q_{10}" with an absorption maximum at 275 mμ. Its structure (35) has been shown to be:

Coenzyme Q_{10}

The compound contains ten isoprenoid groups, $-CH_2-CH=C(CH_3)-CH_2-$, and is called "coenzyme Q_{10}" because of this. Homologs of coenzyme Q_{10} have been found in yeast and bacteria which contain nine, eight, seven, and six isoprenoid units. *Torula utilis* contains Q_9 and Q_7, *Azotobacter* contains Q_8, and *Saccharomyces cereveseiae* contains Q_6.

Coenzyme Q is extracted from mitochondria or mitochondrial particles with isooctane. The extracted particles no longer catalyze the oxidation of succinate or DPN · H unless coenzyme Q along with other extracted lipid components are added. Coenzyme Q

Table 21.6. Some Flavoprotein Dehydrogenase Enzymes

	Reaction Catalyzed	Source
I. Aerobic		
Aldehyde oxidase	Aldehydes + $O_2 \rightarrow$ Organic acids + H_2O_2	Liver
D-Amino acid oxidase	D-Amino acids + O_2 + $H_2O \rightarrow \alpha$-Keto acids + NH_4^+ + H_2O_2	Liver, kidney
L-Amino acid oxidase	L-Amino acids + O_2 + $H_2O \rightarrow \alpha$-Keto acids + NH_4^+ + H_2O_2	Liver, kidney, snake venom
Glucose oxidase	β-D-Glucopyranose + $O_2 \rightarrow \delta$-D-gluconolactone + H_2C_2	Penicillium notatum
Old yellow enzyme	$TPN \cdot H + H^+ + O_2 \rightarrow TPN^- + H_2O_2$	Yeast
Xanthine oxidase	Purines + $O_2 \rightarrow$ Uric acid + H_2O_2	Milk
Xanthine oxidase	Aldehydes + $O_2 \rightarrow$ Organic acids + H_2O_2	Milk
II. Anaerobic		
TPN-Cytochrome c reductase	$TPN \cdot H + 2\ Cyt.c^{+++} \rightarrow TPN^+ + 2\ Cyt.c^{++} + H^+$	Mitochondria
DPN-Cytochrome c reductase	$DPN \cdot H + 2\ Cyt.c^{+++} \rightarrow DPN^+ + 2\ Cyt.c^{++} + H^+$	Mitochondria
Butyryl-CoA dehydrogenase	Butyryl—S—CoA $\rightarrow$ Crotonyl—S—CoA	Mitochondria
Fatty acyl-CoA dehydrogenases	R—CH_2—CH_2—CO—S—CoA $\rightarrow R$—CH=CH—CO—S—CoA	Mitochondria
Succinic dehydrogenase	Succinic acid $\rightarrow$ Fumaric acid	Mitochondria
III. Diaphorase type		
Straub's diaphorase	$DPN \cdot H + H^+$ + Methylene blue $\rightarrow$ Leucomethylene blue + DPN	Pig heart
New yellow enzyme	$TPN \cdot H + H^+$ + Methylene blue $\rightarrow$ Leucomethylene blue + TPN	Yeast

has been found to be associated largely, if not entirely, with lipoprotein$_1$ in heart mitochondria (15). This lipoprotein$_1$ added to isooctane extracted mitochondrial particles along with Q_{10} restores their oxidative capacity. Particle-bound Q_{10} undergoes a cycle of oxidation-reduction. In the presence of DPN $\cdot$ H or succinate it is rapidly oxidized by O_2 through the cytochrome systems, first by the cytochrome c_1 system:

$$DPN \cdot H + H^+ + Q \longrightarrow Q \cdot H_2 + DPN^+$$
$$Q \cdot H_2 + 2 \text{ Cyt. } c_1{}^{+++} \longrightarrow Q + 2 \text{ Cyt. } c_1{}^{++} + 2H^+$$

Reagents which inhibit the electron transport chain at any locus have a corresponding effect on particle-bound Q. Thus, antimycin A, which combines with cyt. b^{++} inhibits reduction of Q by cyt. b^{++}:

$$Q + 2H^+ + 2 \text{ Cyt. } b^{++} \longrightarrow Q \cdot H_2 + 2 \text{ Cyt. } b^{+++}$$

and cyanide, which combines with cyt. $a_3{}^{+++}$ (oxidized cytochrome oxidase) prevents oxidation of coenzyme Q.

The evidence thus indicates that the coenzyme Q system in heart mitochondria probably functions between the cytochrome b and cytochrome c_1 systems.

5. Cytochromes. MacMunn in 1886 (36) observed the four-banded visible absorption spectrum of the typical cytochrome systems (cytochromes a, b, and c) in a wide variety of animal tissues. He called the pigments with these absorption spectra "myohematins" or "histohematins." Because of criticism by Hoppe-Seyler, this early work of MacMunn was generally discredited. However, in 1925 Keilin confirmed and extended the findings of MacMunn and showed that the pigments are widely distributed not only in the tissues of higher animals and plants but also in yeast and bacteria (37). Keilin named these pigments the "cytochromes," meaning cellular pigments.

By spectroscopic means Keilin identified cytochromes, which he called a, b, and c; showed that they exist in oxidized and reduced states; and established their fundamental role in cellular respiration. He extracted cytochrome c, and demonstrated the presence in yeast cells of a heat-labile, autoxidizable enzyme which, in the presence of oxygen, rapidly oxidized the reduced form of cytochrome c. A similar enzyme was soon found in heart muscle and other animal tissues. This enzyme was named "cytochrome oxidase" by Keilin, and we now know it also as "cytochrome a_3."

The reduced forms of the cytochromes give sharp absorption bands which fade out upon oxidation. This property provides a means of following the oxidation and reduction of the cytochromes spectroscopically.

At the time of Keilin's work Warburg had put forward his theory of oxygen activation in biologic oxidation and observed that carbon monoxide inhibits cellular respiration. Haldane had found that light dissociates the combination between CO and hemoglobin, so Warburg then studied the effect of light of various wavelengths upon cellular respiration and found that the CO inhibition of respiration could be relieved by specific wavelengths. He concluded that cells contain a respiratory enzyme, the *Atmungsferment*, which is an iron porphyrin compound and which forms a combination with CO that has absorption maxima at the wavelengths which dissociate the compound and remove the CO inhibition of respiration (600 and 445 mμ). Warburg found the *Atmungsferment* to be inhibited by cyanide and sulfide. Since Keilin found cyanide and sulfide to inhibit the enzymatic oxidation of the reduced cytochromes, he concluded that Warburg's *Atmungsferment* is cytochrome oxidase (cytochrome a_3), which has been thoroughly established.

In addition to the three cytochromes originally discovered by Keilin, he and other workers have found many others, so that at present some 20 are known. As each new cytochrome has been found, it has been designated according to the original cytochrome which it most closely resembles such as a_1, a_2, a_3, a_4; c_1, c_2, c_3, c_4, c_5; b_2, b_3, b_4, b_5; etc.

Cytochromes which spectroscopically are identical but from different species may not cross function in these species, indicating different chemical and biologic properties.

In general the prosthetic groups of the cytochromes are iron porphyrins, but these porphyrins are not all heme porphyrins. The b cytochromes contain iron protoporphyrin (heme) as the prosthetic group; except a_2 the a cytochromes contain "heme a" in which the protoporphyrin contains aldehyde, formyl, higher ethylenic and higher fatty acid groups. Cytochrome a_2 contains a chlorin (a dihydroporphyrin). The c cytochromes contain a mesoporphyrin group linked to the enzyme protein by two thio ether linkages.

Table 21.7 gives several cytochromes, their sources, and some of their properties.

Table 21.7.   Cytochrome Enzymes

| Cyto-chrome | Occurrence | Absorption bands, mμ | | | | | Porph. groups/ mol | E'_0, pH 7 Volts |
| | | Reduced | | | Ox. | M.W. | | |
		α	β	γ	γ			
a_3	Animal tissues, yeast	600		445				
a	Widely distributed	604		450	407			+0.29
c	Widely distributed	550	521	416	407	ca. 13,000	1	+0.26
c_1	Animal mitochondria	553	523	418	410			
b	Widely distributed	563	530	430				0.0
b_5	Animal microsomes	556	526	423	413	16,900	1	+0.02
a_1	Bacteria, yeast	590						
b_1	Bacteria	560						
b_2	Baker's yeast	557	528	424	413	ca. 100,000	1	
b_3	Plant microsomes	559	529	425				+0.04
b_6	Plant chloroplasts	563						−0.06
c_2	Photosynthetic bacteria	550	521	415				
c_3	Sulfate-reducing bacteria	553	525	419		ca. 13,000	2	−0.205
c_5	*Azotobacter vinelandii*	555	526	420	415			+0.32
f	Plant chloroplasts	555	525	423	413	110,000	2	+0.36
h	Helix pomatia hepato pancreas	556	527	422	408	18,500	1	

The differences in absorption maxima of the different cytochromes are related to differences in the iron porphyrin groups present. The α and β absorption bands of the ferrocytochromes disappear upon oxidation, but the γ band remains, though it is shifted to a shorter wavelength.

The mammalian cytochromes are a_3, a, c, c_1, b, and b_5.

Of the animal cytochromes only cytochrome c has been separated from particulate cell structures and obtained in purified form. It is a small protein, molecular weight of 13,000, and contains 0.43 per cent iron, which represents one atom per molecule. The iron-porphyrin group is attached to the protein much more firmly than in the hemoglobins. It is relatively quite stable to heat and acids. The reduced form of cytochrome c is not auto-oxidizable. The standard potential, E'_0, of the cytochrome c system at pH 7 is +0.26 v. Cytochrome c_1 is present with cytochrome c in animal mitochondria, and in intact systems the reduction of c_1 precedes that of c, so that the E'_0 value of c_1 appears to be between the values for cytochromes b and c.

The structure of the porphyrin group of cytochrome c (39) and its mode of attachment to protein (40) are shown below. It will be noted that the porphyrin group is the same as the heme group of hemoglobin with the exception that —SH groups from the protein cysteine groups have added to the vinyl groups of heme to saturate them, and join the porphyrin to the protein by thio ether linkages. A peptide chain of the protein, to which the porphyrin is attached, has been found to consist of the sequence of amino acids indicated in the formula.

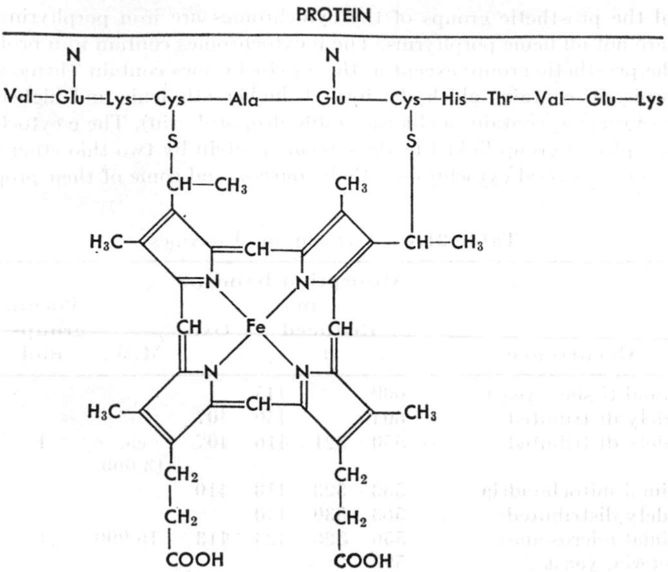

PROTEIN

Linkage of Porphyrin to Protein in Cytochrome c

It appears probable that two histidine residues of the protein also are attached to the iron atom as in hemoglobin.

At physiologic pH ferrocytochrome c does not combine with O_2 or CO, as does hemoglobin, and ferricytochrome c combines only slowly with cyanide (and azide) at high concentration, in contrast with the ready combination of ferrihemoglobin (methemoglobin). This low affinity of ferricytochrome c for cyanide indicates that the reaction is probably of little importance in the inhibition of respiration by cyanide.

Cytochromes a_3, a, b, and c_1, located in animal mitochondria, and b_5, in the microsomes, are tightly bound to particulate cellular material and have not been obtained in pure condition. They can be "solubilized" by treatment with surface active agents such as cholate and deoxycholate, sometimes assisted by hydrolytic enzymes. Cholate and deoxycholate extraction, combined with salt precipitation, have been used extensively in the fractionation of these cytochromes (38). By such procedures it has been possible to separate the a from the b cytochromes, though the solutions obtained may not represent true solutions, since precipitation occurs when the solubilizing agent is removed.

Cytochromes a_3 and a are closely associated in the mitochondrial structure and difficult to separate. Because their absorption bands are very similar, it has been difficult to distinguish between them. Green reports the isolation in his laboratory of cytochrome a in water-soluble, lipid-free form which appears homogeneous in the ultracentrifuge and which contains copper (15). Thus, it appears that copper is associated with the cytochrome oxidase (a + a_3) segment of the electron transport chain, though its function is unknown. Cytochrome oxidase is the molecular oxygen-activating enzyme of the chain. Oxidases which catalyze the oxidation of phenols by O_2 contain copper, which appears to function in the activation of the O_2. Possibly the copper of cytochrome oxidase performs a similar function.

It has been found that cytochrome a does not combine with CO or cyanide, and it is not oxidized by O_2 (autoxidizable). In contrast, ferricytochrome a_3 combines with CO, ferricytochrome a_3 combines with cyanide, and ferrocytochrome a_3 is autoxidizable.

The combination of oxidized cytochrome oxidase with cyanide is the chief reason for the high toxicity of cyanide, since the cyanide complex can no longer function as an electron acceptor in the chain. Most of the respiration of mammalian tissues appears to go through the chain, since cyanide blocks most of the O_2 consumption of the tissues. Ball considers that the cyanide-cytochrome oxidase complex may cease to function because the system has a much lower E'_0 than the normal enzyme.

The cytochrome a_3 system is the terminal cytochrome system in the electron transport chain which, in the reduced form, is oxidized by O_2 to complete mitochondrial oxidation. Cytochrome a_3 is Keilin's cytochrome oxidase and Warburg's *Atmungsferment*. Preparations of cytochrome a_3 so far obtained have generally contained cytochrome a also.

Work with cytochrome b has been particularly difficult and controversial, as pointed out by Wainio and Cooperstein (38), and little reliable information relative to its properties and function is available, though, as indicated in earlier discussion, it appears to play an important role in electron transport. The reduced form of cytochrome b does not auto-oxidize, and the oxidized form does not combine with azide or cyanide.

Cytochrome b_5 (also known as m) has been studied especially by Strittmatter and Ball (41) and is concentrated and tightly bound in the ultramicrosomes. Oxidized cytochrome b_5 is reduced by both DPN · H and TPN · H, but it is uncertain whether reduced cytochrome b_5 is oxidized by cytochrome c. It is considered that cytochrome b_5 may be a component of the DPN · H-cytochrome c reductase system of mammary gland and intestinal ultramicrosomes, since their reductase activities and cytochrome b_5 contents showed constant ratios (42). Since cytochrome b_5 has an E'_0 of $+0.12$ v, Strittmatter and Ball consider that it may play a role as an electron carrier in reductive synthetic reactions of the microsomes.

That the cytochromes are fundamentally important catalysts in tissues has been thoroughly established. However, their isolation in pure form and characterization, both chemically and functionally, in large part remain for the future.

OXIDASES

A great number of oxidations in plants, animals, and microorganisms are effected by molecular oxygen without involving the electron transport chain. These oxidations are catalyzed by oxidase enzymes, or enzyme systems which activate the O_2 and oxidize the substrate. They do not activate H atoms of the substrate, as do the dehydrogenases. The oxidases are very often metallo-proteins, containing metals such as iron, copper, and molybdenum. Iron, if present, is generally in an iron-porphyrin group such as heme. Various oxidases are flavoproteins: for example, xanthine oxidase, aldehyde oxidase, amino acid oxidases, etc., which have been discussed previously.

Since the true oxidases catalyze oxidation of substrates by molecular oxygen, they are also called "oxygenases."

Mason has written a comprehensive review of the oxidases (7) and has differentiated them into three types: oxygen transferases, mixed function oxidases, and electron transfer oxidases.

It has been demonstrated by carrying out oxidase reactions in the presence of $O_2{}^{18}$ and H_2O, or H_2O^{18} and O_2, that different kinds of oxidases cause the labeled oxygen to appear entirely in the oxidized substrate (oxygen transferases), or one atom of the $O_2{}^{18}$ appears in the oxidized substrate and one atom is reduced to O^{--} (mixed function oxidases), or the substrate is oxidized and both atoms of the $O_2{}^{18}$ appear in the H_2O_2 or H_2O formed (electron transfer oxidases).

The intermediary mechanisms postulated to explain the action of the different types of oxidases are too complex to be discussed here, but may be found in Mason's review.

1. Oxygen transferases. Several well-known oxidases are oxygen transferases, particularly enzymes which oxidize various ring structures. Among these are pyrocatechase, homogentisate oxidase, tryptophan oxidase, and indole oxidase. Oxidases of this type which oxidize chain compounds are lipoxidase, which oxidizes unsaturated fatty acids to hydroperoxides, and dihydroxyfumaric acid oxidase, which oxidizes dihydroxyfumaric acid to diketosuccinic acid.

Homogentisate oxidase is involved in the oxidation of homogentisic acid, an intermediate in the metabolism of phenylalanine and of tyrosine. The enzyme occurs in microorganisms and in the kidneys and livers of higher animals, but not in other organs. It catalyzes the oxidation of homogentisic acid as follows:

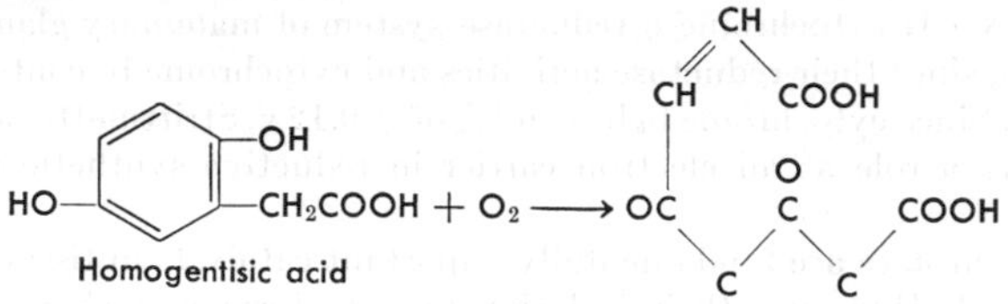

Homogentisic acid   4-Maleylacetoacetic acid

The enzyme contains weakly bound iron, which is necessary for enzymatic activity and which functions in the ferrous state.

Lipoxidase occurs widely distributed in plants and appears to be present in animal tissues also. It oxidizes methylene-interrupted, multiply unsaturated fatty acids in which the double bonds have the cis configuration:

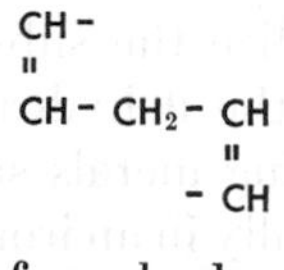

$$CH -$$
$$\parallel$$
$$CH - CH_2 - CH$$
$$\parallel$$
$$- CH$$

In the oxidation O_2 is added to form hydroperoxide groups. There is a concomitant double-bond shift. The over-all reaction may be illustrated as follows, in which linoleic acid is used as an example:

$$\overset{14}{CH_3} - (CH_2)_3 - \overset{13}{CH_2} - \overset{12}{CH} = \overset{11}{CH} - \overset{10}{CH_2} - \overset{9}{CH} = \overset{8}{CH} - CH_2 - (CH_2)_6 - COOH + O_2 \longrightarrow$$

$$CH_3 - (CH_3)_3 - CH_2 - \overset{13}{\underset{OOH}{CH}} - CH = CH - CH = CH - CH_2 - (CH_2)_6 - COOH$$

and

$$CH_3 - (CH_2)_3 - CH_2 - CH = CH - CH = CH - \overset{9}{\underset{OOH}{CH}} - CH_2 - (CH_2)_6 - COOH$$

The hydroperoxide groups are formed on C-13, and also, in a different molecule, on C-9, yielding two products. The double bonds have now become conjugated systems in both products.

Crystalline lipoxidase has been prepared from soybeans and found to have a molecular weight of about 102,000. Some iron was present (less than one atom per three molecules of oxidase); but since inhibitors which combine with iron, such as cyanide and azide, had little effect on the activity of the enzyme, it appears that the iron is not essential. The enzyme activity was destroyed by oxidizing agents such as permanganate, iodine, and quinone, suggesting that it contains a reducing group which may form a peroxide with O_2 and thus represent a catalytic center.

2. Mixed function oxidases. These oxidases cause reduction of one atom of O_2 and utilization of the other atom for specific oxygenation or hydroxylation of the substrate. Two catalytic functions are performed by these enzymes—one the reduction of an atom of oxygen to O^{--}, and the other the transfer of oxygen to the substrate. The operation of these oxidases thus requires not only O_2 but also a source of electrons (reducing agent) to reduce an atom of O_2 to O^{--}. Electron donors for reactions catalyzed by mixed function oxidases are DPN II, TPN · II, o-diphenols, and dihydroxy-fumarate. The mixed function oxidases are metalloproteins with prosthetic groups containing iron, copper, or possibly manganese. Their activities are inhibited by metal-binding agents such as cyanide and azide.

Examples of mixed function oxidases are the phenolase complex, imidazole-acetic acid oxidase, phenylalanine hydroxylase, p-hydroxyphenylpyruvate oxidase, steroid 11 β-hydroxylase, the nonspecific aromatic hydroxylase of liver, and the peroxidase hydroxylating system.

The phenolase complex represents two enzymatic activities which act together, phenol o-hydroxylase (cresolase) and o-diphenol dehydrogenase (catecholase):

$$\text{Monophenol} + 2E + O_2 \longrightarrow \text{o-Diphenol} + O^{--} \text{ (Cresolase)}$$
$$2 \text{ o-Diphenol} + O_2 \longrightarrow 2 \text{ o-Quinone} + 2H_2O \text{ (Catecholase)}$$

The over-all action of the complex appears to be as follows, in which one molecule of o-diphenol provides electrons for the reaction:

$$\text{Monophenol} \mid O_2 \mid \text{o-Diphenol} \longrightarrow \text{o-Diphenol} + \text{o-Quinone} + H_2O$$

The phenolase complex is involved in the formation of melanins (from tyrosine), plant flavonoids and lignins, humus, and some alkaloids.

The complex contains copper, and in the presence of one molecule of o-diphenol two Cu^{++} are reduced to two Cu^{+}, which indicates that the copper is probably essential as the electron acceptor for the cresolase hydroxylation of the monophenol.

The animal enzyme complex is relatively specific in acting upon L-tyrosine and dihydroxyphenyl-L-alanine, while the plant complex acts upon a large variety of mono- and diphenols.

Because both cresolase and catecholase activities appear to be associated with the same protein, as shown by ultracentrifugation and electrophoresis, and both are inhibited to the same degree by metal-binding agents and competitive substrates, it appears that one enzyme protein carries two catalytic centers, one showing cresolase activity and the other catecholase activity.

The enzyme called "tyrosinase," which is widespread in plants, and particularly abundant in potatoes, mushrooms, and dahlia bulbs, oxidizes tyrosine and leads to the formation of black pigments. Tyrosinase is a phenolase complex oxidase.

Imidazoleacetic acid oxidase is involved in the metabolism of histidine and utilizes DPN · H as a source of electrons:

$$\text{Imidazole acetic acid} + O_2 + \text{DPN} \cdot \text{H} + \text{H}^+ \longrightarrow \text{DPN}^+$$
$$+ \; H_2O^* + \text{Hydroxyimidazole acetic acid}^*$$
$$+$$
$$H_2O$$
$$\downarrow$$
$$\text{Formiminoaspartic acid}^*$$

The substances marked with an asterisk contain an O atom from O_2.

A large variety of substances which are "foreign" to organisms and the animal body undergo hydroxylation in the detoxication process. While different mechanisms undoubtedly are involved, liver microsomes contain a mixed-function oxidase, a nonspecific aromatic hydroxylase, which hydroxylates many aromatic compounds. The enzyme requires TPN · H as a source of electrons.

3. Electron transfer oxidases. These oxidases catalyze the reduction of O_2 to H_2O_2 (two electron transfer) or to H_2O (four electron transfer). They are oxygen-obligative if they reduce oxygen only (uricase), but are oxygen-facultative if they can also reduce other electron acceptors. These enzymes act through a variety of prosthetic groups or cofactors, such as Fe, FAD, FMN, DPN, TPN, Mo, and Cu. Xanthine oxidase has a prosthetic group composed of Fe—FAD—Mo.

There are many electron transfer oxidases, among which are uricase, xanthine oxidase, glucose oxidase, monamine oxidase, diamine oxidase, sarcosine oxidase, DPN · H oxidase, ascorbic oxidase, and cytochrome oxidase.

An example of an oxygen-facultative electron transfer oxidase which transfers two electrons with the formation of H_2O_2 is glucose oxidase. It catalyzes the oxidation of d-glucose as follows:

$$\beta\text{-D-Glucopyranose} + O_2 \longrightarrow \delta\text{-D-Gluconolactone} + H_2O_2$$

When the reaction is carried out with $H_2O + O_2{}^{18}$, the isotope is present only in the H_2O_2; if the reaction is carried out with $H_2O^{18} + O_2$, none of the isotope is in H_2O_2.

The enzyme DPN · H oxidase, also an example of a two electron oxygen-facultative oxidase, is an FAD flavoprotein which catalyzes the oxidation of DPN · H to DPN$^+$ by O_2, with the formation of H_2O_2:

$$\text{DPN} \cdot \text{H} + \text{H}^+ + O_2 \longrightarrow \text{DPN}^+ + H_2O_2$$

The oxidation of reduced cytochrome oxidase by O_2 in the electron transport chain is an example of an oxygen-facultative, four-electron-transfer oxidase reaction in which O_2 is reduced to $\bar{O}H$ (the water stage). Various theories as to the mechanism of the reaction have been proposed (7), though none is established. The net over-all result of the oxidation of cytochrome oxidase by O_2 appears to be:

$$4 \text{ Cyt. } a_3^{++} + O_2 + 2H_2O \longrightarrow 4 \text{ Cyt. } a_3^{+++} + 4OH^-$$

Ascorbic oxidase is an oxygen-facultative, four-electron-transfer oxidase containing copper as the prosthetic group:

$$2 \text{ Ascorbic acid} + O_2 \longrightarrow 2 \text{ Dehydroascorbic acid} + 2H_2O$$

The reaction proceeds in a sequence of stages (7).

THE PEROXIDASES OR HYDROPEROXIDASES

The peroxidases all contain ferriprotoporphyrin IX (hemin) as the prosthetic group and are widely distributed in plants and microorganisms. Their occurrence in animal tissues and products is rather limited. As iron-porphyrin compounds, they exhibit characteristic absorption spectra and are inhibited by iron-binding agents.

The peroxidases catalyze the transfer of electrons from donors (substrates) to H_2O_2, reducing it to water. The peroxidases are specific in requiring H_2O_2 as the electron acceptor (oxidizing agent), but various substances may act as substrates or electron donors.

Crystalline peroxidases have been obtained from horseradish root and milk (lactoperoxidase), and highly purified preparations from leucocytes (verdoperoxidase or myeloperoxidase), yeast, and fig sap.

One of the best-known peroxidases is horseradish peroxidase. It has a molecular weight of about 44,000, and contains one hematin prosthetic group per molecule, which can be easily split from the protein with acid-acetone. The protein can be reconverted to the enzyme by addition of hematin. The iron-porphyrin groups of other peroxidases cannot be removed by acid-acetone.

The peroxidases vary in molecular size, but all appear to contain only one atom of iron per molecule.

Peroxidases oxidize many substances, including mono- and polyphenols, leuco dyes, aromatic amines, cytochrome c, nitrite, iodide, DPN · H, and TPN · H.

An example of peroxidase action is the oxidation of hydroquinone by lactoperoxidase of milk:

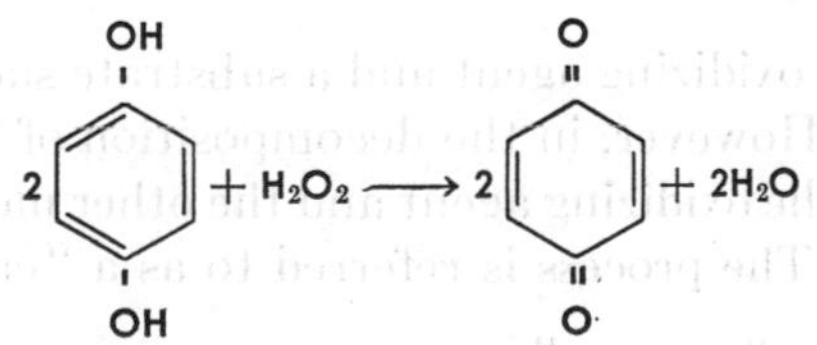

Hydroquinone   Quinone

Yeast contains an unusual peroxidase in that it catalyzes only the oxidation of reduced cytochrome c.

The oxidation of tincture of guaiac by peroxidase to give a blue color is a very sensitive test for peroxidase. The reaction is complex and involves oxidation of pyrogallol with the formation of the blue compound purpurogallin:

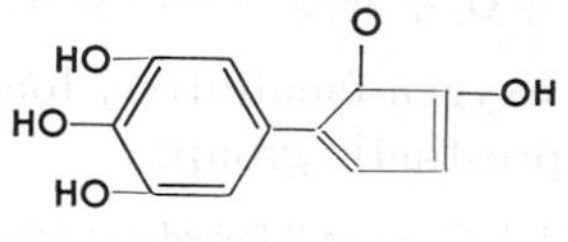

Purpurogallin

Hemoproteins in general show peroxidase activity and catalyze the oxidation of guaiac, benzidine, etc., by H_2O_2 to give colored products, affording sensitive tests for traces of blood in feces, urine, and other materials.

It has been shown (43) that peroxidase forms a green compound with H_2O_2, called "complex I." Complex I is reduced by one electron to form red complex II. Complex II then is reduced by one electron to reform the peroxidase. Detailed mechanisms proposed for peroxidase action are discussed by Mason (7).

CATALASES

Catalases represent a specific type of hemin-containing hydroperoxidases which have the specific property of very rapidly catalyzing the decomposition of H_2O_2:

$$2H_2O_2 \longrightarrow 2H_2O + O_2$$

It may be considered that one molecule of H_2O_2 acts as substrate and electron donor and the other molecule of H_2O_2 serves as electron acceptor or oxidizing agent:

$$H_2O_2 + H_2O_2 \longrightarrow 2H_2O + O_2$$

In effect, one H_2O_2 is reduced to $2HO^-$ and the other is oxidized to $O_2 + 2H^+$, giving a net product of $2H_2O + O_2$.

The oxidation of a substrate by a peroxidase and H_2O_2 is referred to as a peroxidatic reaction:

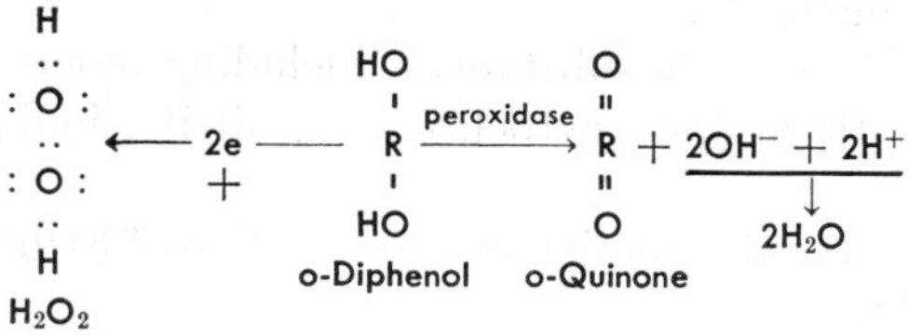

in which H_2O_2 is the oxidizing agent and a substrate such as an o-diphenol is the reducing agent. However, in the decomposition of H_2O_2 by catalase one molecule of H_2O_2 is the oxidizing agent and the other molecule is the reducing agent, or substrate. The process is referred to as a "catalatic reaction":

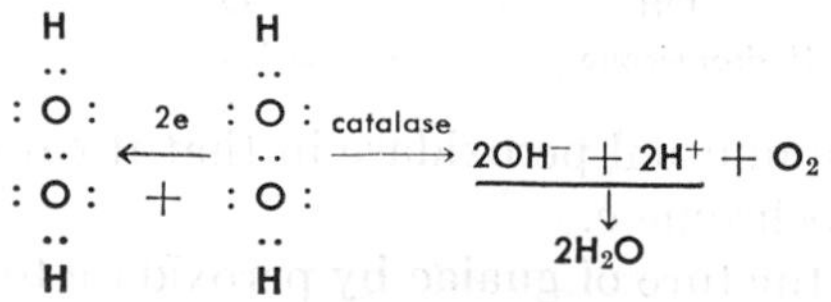

The decomposition of H_2O_2 by catalase (catalatic action) is thus a special case of a peroxidatic reaction, the H_2O_2 serving as both oxidizing agent and substrate.

That catalase enzymes are simply a special type of peroxidase enzymes possessing very high activity toward H_2O_2 as a substrate (catalatic action) but also capable of catalyzing regular peroxidatic reactions has been shown conclusively by Tauber (44). He found that crystalline catalase and very dilute H_2O_2 solutions oxidize various phenols and aromatic amines as do other peroxidases. In the presence of excess H_2O_2 (more than enough to form complex I) the catalase acts upon H_2O_2 much more readily than upon the phenol, etc., as substrate, and the catalatic reaction greatly predominates over the peroxidatic reacton. Since in tissues the concentration of H_2O_2 is apparently very low and that of other catalase substrates relatively high, it is very likely that catalase functions physiologically chiefly as a peroxidase, though also preventing the undue accumulation of H_2O_2 through its catalatic action.

Catalases are among the most widely distributed of the enzymes, occurring in all living things, plant and animal, with the exception of certain microorganisms, the obligate anaerobes.

Crystalline catalases have been obtained from a variety of sources, including liver of man, rat, pig, beef, horse, and sheep, horse erythrocytes and kidney, and *Micrococcus lysodeikticus*. Bonnischen (45) found no difference between crystalline catalases of beef liver and erythrocytes relative to amino acid composition, activity, and immunochemical properties.

Beef liver catalase has a molecular weight around 250,000 and contains four hemin groups per molecule.

Catalases have turnover rates higher than those found for any other enzymes. One molecule of catalase is capable of decomposing more than 2,000,000 molecules of H_2O_2 per minute.

The catalases in the process of decomposing H_2O_2 form intermediate complexes, as do other peroxidases. Research by Chance, Theorell, and Keilin supports the following general mechanism for catalase action. It appears that catalase containing an OH^- attached to the ferric iron of the hemin group reacts first with H_2O_2 to form a catalase peroxide which then acts with a second molecule of H_2O_2:

$$\text{Cat. Fe}^{+++}-\text{OH} + \text{HOOH} \longrightarrow \text{Cat. Fe}^{+++}-\text{OOH} + H_2O$$
$$\text{Cat. Fe}^{+++}-\text{OOH} + \text{HOOH} \longrightarrow \text{Cat. Fe}^{+++}-\text{OH} + H_2O + O_2$$

Catalase also forms complexes with organic hydroperoxides such as ethyl hydrogen peroxide, C_2H_5—OOH, and decomposes them.

BIOLOGICAL REDUCTION

We have seen that biologic oxidations of metabolites for the production of utilizable energy (ATP) and various specific compounds take place through many processes. Of course, all such oxidations are associated with concomitant reductions. However, there are many instances in biochemical phenomena in which reduction of a substance rather than oxidation is the primary functional objective. Such reductions are generally brought about by a metabolite or metabolites first reducing DPN+ or TPN+ to DPN · H and TPN · H, the latter compounds then reducing the substance concerned through the catalytic action of a specific dehydrogenase. In effect, it represents drawing off electrons or/and H atoms from the pyridine nucleotide system of the electron transport chain and passing them on for reduction of the substance; for example:

$$\text{M} \cdot \text{H}_2 \longrightarrow \text{DPN}^+ \searrow \text{FP} \quad \text{etc.}$$
$$\text{H}^+ + \overline{\text{DPN} \cdot \text{H}} \nearrow \overline{\text{FP} \cdot \text{H}}$$

$$
\begin{array}{ccc}
\text{O} + & & \text{OH} \\
\parallel & \xleftarrow{\text{Lactic}} & \mid \\
\text{CH}_3 - \text{C} - \text{COOH} & \xrightarrow{\hspace{1cm}} & \text{CH}_3 - \text{C} - \text{COOH} + \text{DPN}^+ \\
\text{Pyruvic acid} & \text{dehydrogenase} & \mid \\
& & \text{H} \\
& & \text{Lactic acid}
\end{array}
$$

In such a case the metabolite M · H₂ reduces pyruvic acid through the DPN+/DPN · H + H+ system. As previously pointed out, some dehydrogenases specifically require the DPN or TPN system, while others act with either, though generally better with one system than with the other.

THE CITRIC ACID OR TRICARBOXYLIC ACID CYCLE (TCA)

GENERAL CONSIDERATIONS

The activated metabolites, which are oxidized by the mitochondrial electron transport chain to produce most of the utilizable energy (ATP) for biologic purposes, are relatively few in number, and are, of course, derived from the various foods: carbohydrates, fats, and proteins (as amino acids).

These metabolites are the coenzyme A derivatives of fatty acids (acyl—S—CoA), acetyl coenzyme A (CH₃CO—S—CoA), oxaloacetic acid, fumaric acid, and α-ketoglutaric acid. The detailed mechanisms by which these substances are formed will be outlined in the chapters on metabolism to follow. However, their general production is indicated in the following over-all processes:

$$\text{Fatty acids} \longrightarrow \text{Acyl} - \text{S} - \text{CoA} \xrightarrow{\beta \text{ ox.}} \text{CH}_3 - \text{CO} - \text{S} - \text{CoA}$$

$$\text{Carbohydrate (hexoses)} \longrightarrow \text{Pyruvic acid} \longrightarrow \text{CH}_3 - \text{CO} - \text{S} - \text{CoA}$$

$$
\text{Amino acids} \xrightarrow{\text{deam.}} \text{Intermediates}
\begin{cases}
\text{Acetyl—S—CoA} \\
\alpha\text{-Ketoglutaric acid} \\
\text{Oxaloacetic acid} \\
\text{Fumaric acid}
\end{cases}
$$

Several amino acids when metabolized yield acetyl—S—CoA, others yield α-ketoglutaric acid, two (tyrosine and phenylalanine) form fumaric acid, and aspartic acid gives oxaloacetic acid.

The oxidation of acetyl coenzyme A, α-ketoglutaric acid, fumaric acid, and oxaloacetic acid all take place through what is called the "citric acid cycle," while the β oxidation of the fatty acyl coenzyme A derivatives, which forms acetyl coenzyme A, takes place outside of the cycle.

Oxidations in the citric acid cycle, effected through the mitochondrial electron transport chain, normally represent the greater proportion of all oxidations in animal tissues which yield utilizable energy (ATP). In fact, it appears that the citric acid cycle constitutes the major terminal pathway of biologic oxidation in most animal, plant, and bacterial cells.

As the name implies, the citric acid cycle is a cyclic process. The cycle involves a sequence of compounds interrelated by oxidation-reduction and other reactions which finally produce CO_2 and H_2O and store up energy as ATP. Since Krebs discovered the cycle and the presence of citric acid in it, it is also called the "Krebs citric acid cycle." Some components of the cycle contain three carboxyl groups, so another name is the "tricarboxylic acid cycle," or simply the "TCA cycle."

Thunberg (46) found that only a few organic acids, including succinic, fumaric, malic, and citric, are rapidly oxidized by tissue homogenates. Krebs and associates (47), using homogenates of pigeon breast muscle, showed that these acids, added in catalytic amounts, stimulated oxygen consumption. Krebs explained the catalytic effect upon respiration by considering the acids to constitute a cycle by which metabolites such as pyruvate are oxidized. When the homogenates were incubated under anaerobic conditions with pyruvate and oxalo-acetate citrate was found to accumulate. Malonate specifically inhibits succinic dehydrogenase, which catalyzes the oxidation of succinate to fumarate. Malonate added to the homogenate mixtures caused succinate and also citrate and α-ketoglutarate to accumulate. These and other observations enabled Krebs to support his theory. Subsequent work by many investigators has only provided detailed information without altering the basic concept of the citric acid cycle as proposed by Krebs. We now know that pyruvate enters the cycle by first being converted to acetyl coenzyme A.

The citric acid cycle represents one of the most important biochemical mechanisms, and the student should learn it thoroughly. Comprehensive reviews dealing with the cycle are those of Martius and Lynen (48), Krebs (49), and Ochoa (50).

The components of the citric acid cycle, the reactions involved, and the enzymes catalyzing these reactions are shown in Figure 21.6.

The H atoms removed from components of the cycle are oxidized by the electron transport chain as shown.

At physiologic pH the acids of the citric acid cycle are present as anions, citrate, oxaloacetate, etc.

It will be observed from Figure 21.6 that the net effect of the oxidation of citrate and return to oxaloacetate in one turn of the cycle is the production of two CO_2 and two H_2O, which is equivalent to the oxidation of a molecule of acetic acid:

$$CH_3COOH + 2O_2 \longrightarrow 2H_2O + 2CO_2$$

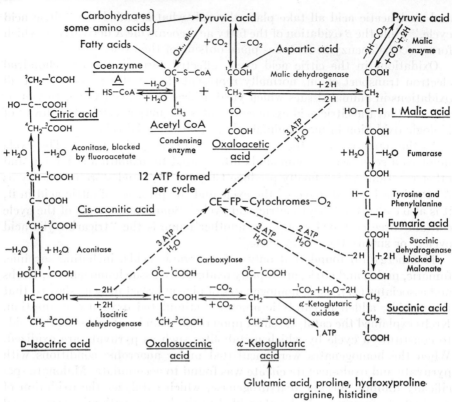

Figure 21.6. Oxidation in the citric acid cycle. CE in the electron transport chain represents the DPN and TPN (coenzyme) systems.

Each turn of the cycle produces 12 molecules of ATP. This is accomplished by the oxidation of eight H atoms from components of the cycle. The oxidation of α-ketoglutarate produces four ATP, three by oxidation of two H atoms through the chain and one by a mechanism to be given later. The oxidation of succinate produces only two molecules of ATP per two H atoms oxidized, because the oxidation begins in the chain at the flavoprotein stage.

INDIVIDUAL REACTIONS OF
THE CITRIC ACID CYCLE

1. Acetyl coenzyme A or acetyl CoA. "Active acetate." As previously indicated, acetyl coenzyme A is formed in the metabolism of carbohydrates, fatty acids, and a number of amino acids. The formula of coenzyme A has been given in the discussion of enzymes (Chapter 11). It is a complex compound made up of β-mercaptoethylamine, pantothenic acid, and 3'-phosphoadenosine diphosphate. The β-mercaptoethylamine group contains a free HS— group, which is the functional group in forming the acetyl and other acyl derivatives. For convenience the formula of coenzyme A is written as HS—CoA, and the acyl derivatives have acyl groups, R—CO—, substituted for H in the HS— group. Accordingly, we write the formula of acetyl coenzyme A or acetyl CoA as CH_3—CO—S—CoA.

Acetyl CoA is not only of primary importance as a component of the critic acid cycle, but, as will be shown later, it is also involved in the synthesis of fatty acids and cholesterol, and in various acetylation reactions, including the acetylation of choline to acetylcholine, an important substance in regulating the activity of nervous tissue.

For a number of years research workers possessed evidence that acetate participates in biologic reactions, and also that for it to function it must be converted into some active derivative or "active acetate." Lynen and associates in 1951 (51) isolated acetyl CoA from baker's yeast and established it as the long-sought "active acetate."

While most of the acetyl CoA involved in the citric acid cycle and other processes is formed in the metabolism of carbohydrates, fats, and proteins (amino acids), it may be formed directly from acetate in animal tissues by the acetate activating enzyme according to the following reactions:

$$AT^? + Acetate \rightleftharpoons AMP\text{-}acetate + PPi$$
$$AMP\text{-}acetate + HS\text{-}CoA \rightleftharpoons CH_3\text{-}CO\text{-}S\text{-}CoA + AMP$$
$$Sum:\quad ATP + Acetate + HS\text{-}CoA \rightleftharpoons CH_3\text{-}CO\text{-}S\text{-}CoA + AMP + PPi$$

In bacterial systems acetyl CoA may be formed from acetyl phosphate and HS—CoA by transacetylation:

$$CH_3\text{-}CO\text{-}O\text{-}PO_3H_2 + HS\text{-}CoA \xrightarrow{\text{phosphotrans-acetylase}} CH_3\text{-}CO\text{-}S\text{-}CoA + Pi$$

Acetyl phosphate   CoA   Acetyl CoA

2. Formation of citric acid from acetyl CoA and oxaloacetic acid. Ochoa and associates (50) established that citric acid is formed by the reaction of acetyl CoA and oxaloacetic acid through action of the "condensing enzyme." These workers isolated the condensing enzyme from pig heart in crystalline condition:

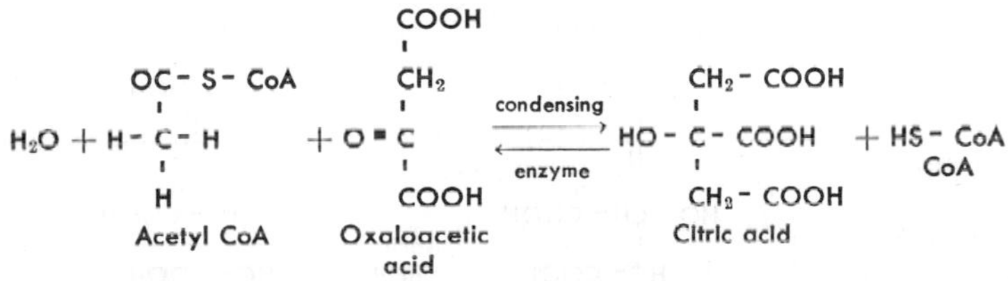

While the reaction is reversible, equilibrium lies far to the right. It was found that condensing enzyme catalyzed the conversion of C^{14}-citrate to C^{14}-oxaloacetate in the presence of HS—CoA. Because of the reversibility of the reaction and the formation of acetyl CoA, citric acid may serve as a potential source of "active acetyl" for biologic acetylations.

In the above reaction the CH_3— of acetyl CoA reacts with the —CO—group of oxaloacetate as shown, presumably forming citryl—S—CoA, which is then hydrolyzed to citric acid and HS—CoA. It appears that the —S—CoA group of CH_3—CO—S—CoA activates the CH_3— group so the addition reaction may proceed. In acetylation reactions, such as the acetylation of choline to acetylcholine acetyl CoA is activated at the carbonyl group:

$$CH_3\text{-}CO\text{-}S\text{-}CoA + Choline \longrightarrow Acetylcholine + HS\text{-}CoA$$

3. Formation of cis-aconitic and isocitric acids from citric acid. The formation of cis-aconitic acid from citric acid is the result of an asymmetric dehydration, and the formation of isocitric acid from cis-aconitic acid is the result of a stereo-specific hydration, both processes apparently being catalyzed by a single enzyme, aconitase:

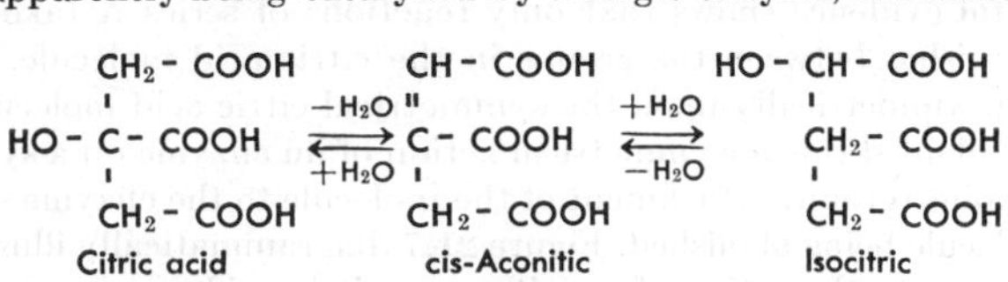

The equilibrium mixture contains about 6 per cent isocitric acid, 4 per cent cis-aconitic acid, and 90 per cent citric acid. Equilibrium thus favors the accumulation of citric acid, but in tissues the reaction readily proceeds to the right because of the conversion of iso-citric acid to oxalosuccinic acid by isocitric dehydrogenase.

The action of aconitase upon both citric and isocitric acid is blocked by fluoroacetic acid, $CH_2F \cdot COOH$, and citric acid accumulates in tissues poisoned by fluoroacetate. It has been found that fluoroacetic acid condenses with oxaloacetic acid to form a fluoro-analogue of citric acid, which competitively inhibits the action of aconitase upon citric acid. The constitution of the fluorotricarboxylic acid formed has not been established.

Asymmetric action of aconitase on citric acid. Citric acid contains no asymmetric carbon atom and is a symmetrical molecule. In the conversion of citric to isocitric acid by aconitase it would be expected that both of the following series of changes (A and B) would occur:

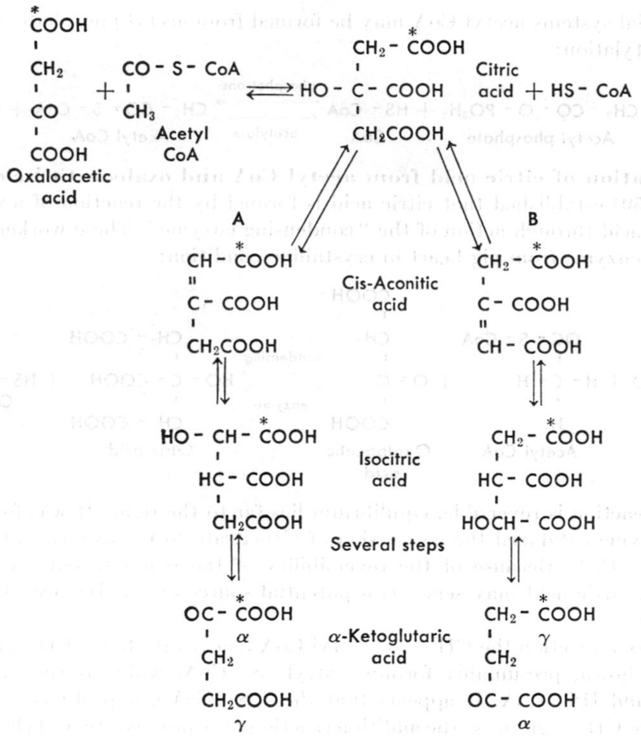

Wood and associates (52) labeled the α-carbon of oxaloacetate with C^{13} (as shown by

—$\overset{*}{C}OOH$ in the above equations) and found the isotope only in the α-carboxyl of the glutaric acid formed. Potter and associates (53) labeled citric acid in the carboxyl of a —CH_2—COOH group by reaction of $NaC^{14}N$ with L-γ-chloro-β-carboxy-β-hydroxy bu-tyric acid and hydrolysis of the nitrile. Liver homogenate (aconitase) acting upon this citric acid yielded α-ketoglutaric acid containing C^{14} entirely in the γ-carboxyl group. Such experimental evidence shows that only reactions of series A take place, and that aconitase distinguishes between the groups in the citric acid molecule. In other words, aconitase acts unsymmetrically upon the symmetrical citric acid molecule.

Ogston (54) explained this unsymmetrical action of an enzyme on a symmetrical mole-cule by a three-point (group) attachment of the molecule to the enzyme surface, the sym-metry of the molecule being abolished. Figure 21.7 diagrammatically illustrates the appli-cation of this theory to the action of aconitase on citric acid.

Not only does aconitase act unsymmetrically upon citric acid, but the condensing enzyme must act unsymmetrically upon oxaloacetate and acetyl CoA in the formation of citric acid, distinguishing between the valences of the oxaloacetate carbonyl double bond in the addition of the CH_3— group of acetyl CoA to it. In this case possibly the oxaloacetate is combined with condensing enzyme at two specific active centers and acetyl CoA at one specific active center, giving the proper orientation of the molecules on the enzyme for asymmetric reaction.

The asymmetric action of enzymes upon various symmetrical substrates is well established.

4. Formation of oxalosuccinic and α-ketoglutaric acids from isocitric acid. Two pyridine nucleotide-linked dehydrogenases in animal tissues catalyze these reactions, one enzyme acting through TPN and the other through DPN. The DPN-linked dehydrogenase is located in the mitochondria and requires AMP (adenylic acid) for maximum

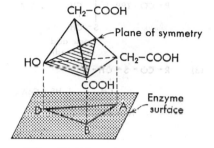

Figure 21.7. The upper part of the figure shows the tetrahedral structure of citric acid, a symmetrical molecule. One carbon is at the center of the tetrahedron and is not shown. In the free citric acid the two —CH_2—COOH groups are equivalent. The surface of the enzyme, aconitase, has three active combining centers, A, B, D, for three specific groups of citric acid, each center specific for a given group so that when the enzyme combines with the acid these three groups are definitely oriented relative to each other. If, for example, the combination of enzyme with citric acid at A, B, D, involves the —CH_2—COOH, —COOH, and —OH groups, respectively, oriented on the enzyme as shown in the figure, then the —CH_2COOH group attached to the enzyme at A is no longer equivalent to the other —CH_2COOH group, and the enzyme acts unsymmetrically upon the acid in forming cis-aconitic and isocitric acids. The combination of acid and enzyme is asymmetric, and only one kind of asymmetry (for a given enzyme and substrate) can be produced.

activity. The dehydrogenases catalyze first an oxidation and then a decarboxylation, Mn^{++} being required for the decarboxylation reaction:

$$
\begin{array}{ccc}
\text{HO} - \text{CH} - \text{COOH} & \text{O} = \text{C} - \text{COOH} & \text{O} = \text{C} - \text{COOH} \\
\mid & \mid & \mid \\
\text{CH} - \text{COOH} + \text{TPN}^+ \rightleftharpoons \text{TPN} \cdot \text{H} + \text{H}^+ + & \text{CH} - \text{COOH} \xrightarrow{Mn^{++}} & \text{CH}_2 + \text{CO}_2 \\
\mid & \mid & \mid \\
\text{CH}_2 - \text{COOH} & \text{CH}_2 - \text{COOH} & \text{CH}_2 - \text{COOH} \\
\text{Isocitric acid} & \text{Oxalosuccinic} & \alpha\text{-Ketoglutaric} \\
 & \text{acid} & \text{acid}
\end{array}
$$

These reactions represent a connected sequence in which equilibrium lies far to the right. However, if the reactions are coupled with a reaction which utilizes TPN^+ and forms $TPN \cdot H$, they are reversed, so that CO_2 is taken up and "fixed" in oxalosuccinic and isocitric acids. Such a reaction as the following may be coupled to give CO_2 fixation:

$$\text{Glucose-6-phosphate} + \text{TPN}^+ \rightleftharpoons \text{6-phosphogluconic} + \text{TPN} \cdot \text{H} + \text{H}^+$$
$$\text{acid}$$

α-Ketoglutaric acid is formed not only in the citric acid cycle but is fed into the cycle directly by deamination of glutamic acid and indirectly by proline, hydroxyproline, histidine, and arginine which form glutamic acid in their metabolism. Also, α-ketoglutaric acid from the cycle is utilized in the synthesis of glutamic acid and its derivatives.

The conversion of isocitrate to oxalosuccinate is inhibited by diphenyl chloroarsine, while the decarboxylation of oxalosuccinate to α-ketoglutarate is inhibited by pyrophosphate.

5. Oxidative decarboxylation of α-ketoglutaric acid to succinic acid. This is a complex sequence of reactions involving thiamine pyrophosphate (TPP), lipoic acid,

DPN, and coenzyme A, the reactions being catalyzed by an enzyme complex referred to as α-ketoglutaric oxidase or, in general, as oxidative α-ketocarboxylase, since the same enzyme system also oxidatively decarboxylates pyruvic and other α-keto acids by the same mechanisms (55). The series of reactions is considered to proceed as follows in which R represents the group attached to —CO—COOH (CH_3— in pyruvic acid and —$(CH_2)_2$—COOH in α-ketoglutaric acid) and R' represents —$(CH_2)_4COOH$ in lipoic acid:

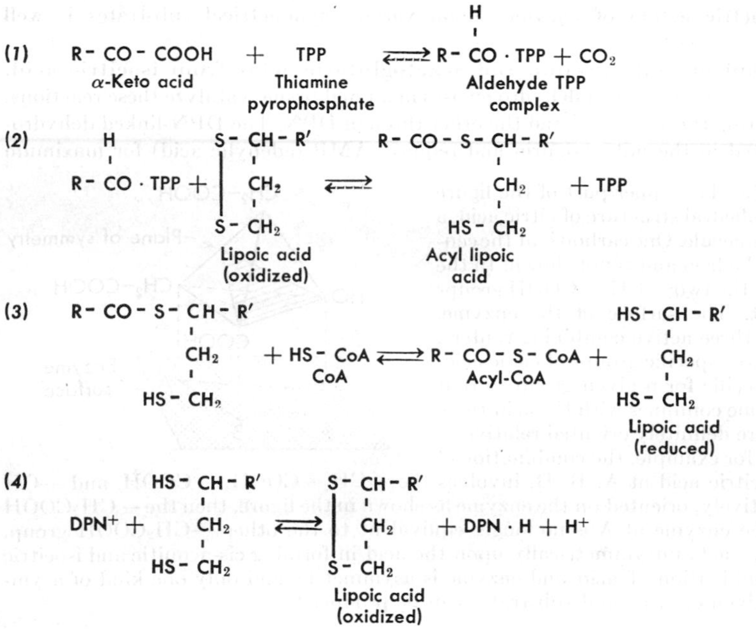

(1)   R— CO— COOH   +   TPP $\rightleftharpoons$ R— CO · TPP + CO_2

        α-Keto acid   Thiamine   Aldehyde TPP
                             pyrophosphate   complex

(2)   H   S— CH— R'   R— CO— S— CH— R'
             | | |
        R— CO · TPP + CH_2 $\rightleftharpoons$ CH_2 + TPP
                            | |
                            S— CH_2 HS— CH_2

                        Lipoic acid   Acyl lipoic
                        (oxidized)   acid

(3)   R— CO— S— CH— R'   HS— CH— R'
             | |
             CH_2 + HS— CoA $\rightleftharpoons$ R— CO— S— CoA + CH_2
             | CoA   Acyl-CoA |
        HS— CH_2 HS— CH_2

                                                        Lipoic acid
                                                        (reduced)

(4)   HS— CH— R'   S— CH— R'
                 | |
        DPN+ + CH_2 $\rightleftharpoons$ CH_2 + DPN · H + H+
                 | |
            HS— CH_2 S— CH_2

                                   Lipoic acid
                                   (oxidized)

(5)   DPN · H is reoxidized to DPN+ by the electron transport chain with the formation of 3 ATP. Then the DPN+, TPP, and oxidized lipoic acid re-enter the cycle.

It will be noted that an acyl—CoA derivative is formed. This is a high-energy compound ($-\Delta F'_0$ of hydrolysis, about 8,500 cal) and may react to form ATP through the following sequence of reactions, using succinyl CoA, formed by oxidation of α-ketoglutaric acid in the above reactions, as an example:

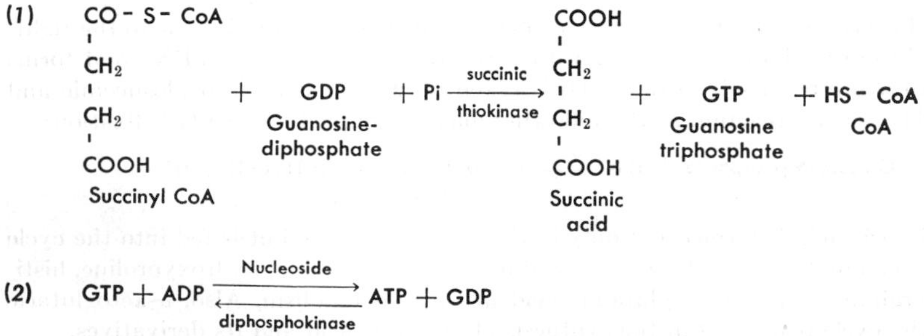

(1)   CO— S— CoA   COOH
        | |
        CH_2 CH_2
        | +   GDP   + Pi $\xrightarrow{\text{succinic}}$ | +   GTP   + HS— CoA
        CH_2 Guanosine-   thiokinase CH_2 Guanosine   CoA
        | diphosphate | triphosphate
        COOH   COOH

        Succinyl CoA   Succinic
                                                        acid

(2)   GTP + ADP $\xrightarrow[\text{diphosphokinase}]{\text{Nucleoside}}$ ATP + GDP

Thus a molecule of succinyl CoA formed in the citric acid cycle provides free energy for the synthesis of a molecule of ATP, and the over-all oxidation of α-ketoglutarate in the citric acid cycle yields a total of four ATP per molecule oxidized.

Succinyl CoA formed in the citric acid cycle may be used for acylating reactions for introduction of a succinyl group. It is also used in other metabolic reactions, such as the synthesis of porphyrins.

Succinyl CoA may be hydrolyzed by the enzyme succinyl CoA deacylase present in tissues:

$$\text{Succinyl - S - CoA} + H_2O \longrightarrow \text{Succinic acid} + HS - CoA$$

This insures operation of the citric acid cycle when other reactions liberating succinic acid are deficient.

The conversion of α-ketoglutarate to succinyl CoA is inhibited by arsenite and hydroxylamine.

The oxidation of α-ketoglutarate apparently represents the only irreversible reaction in the citric acid cycle.

6. Oxidation of succinic acid to fumaric acid. The oxidation of succinic acid to fumaric acid is effected by succinic dehydrogenase, which is a ferriflavoprotein. Succinic acid combined with the enzyme passes H atoms to the FAD group of the enzyme from which they are oxidized by the electron transport chain. For two H atoms oxidized, two ATP are formed:

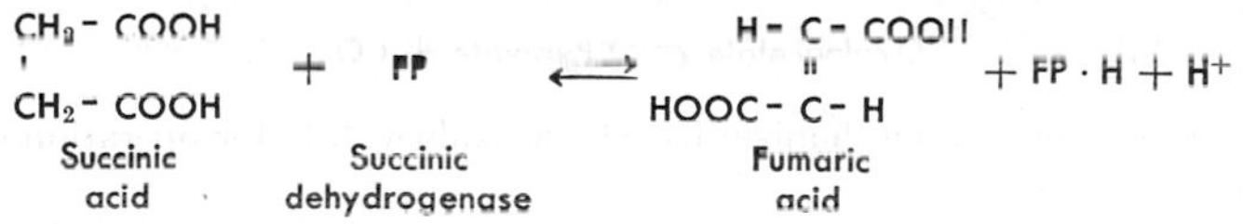

$$\begin{matrix} CH_2 - COOH \\ | \\ CH_2 - COOH \end{matrix} \ + \ FP \ \rightleftharpoons \ \begin{matrix} H - C - COOH \\ || \\ HOOC - C - H \end{matrix} \ + \ FP \cdot H + H^+$$

Succinic acid — Succinic dehydrogenase — Fumaric acid

The cis isomer, maleic acid, is not formed in the reaction, indicating stereo-specificity.

Malonate is a specific competitive inhibitor of the reaction at concentrations around 0.01 M, causing accumulation of succinate and α-ketoglutarate in tissues.

7. The formation of malic acid from fumaric acid. The formation of L-malic acid in the citric acid cycle occurs as the result of the addition of water at the double bond of fumaric acid, and is catalyzed by the enzyme fumarase:

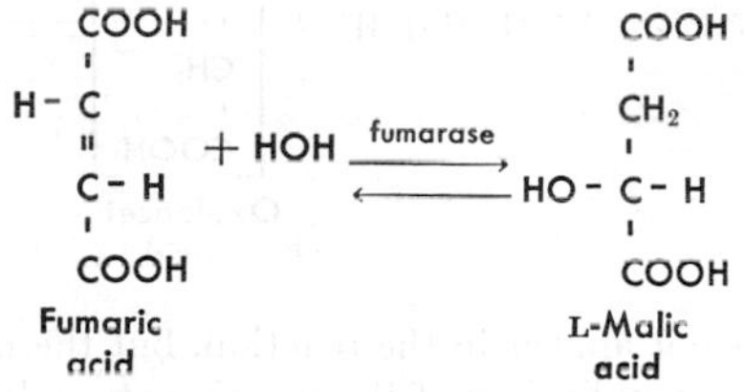

$$\begin{matrix} COOH \\ | \\ H - C \\ || \\ C - H \\ | \\ COOH \end{matrix} \ + \ HOH \ \underset{\longleftarrow}{\overset{fumarase}{\longrightarrow}} \ \begin{matrix} COOH \\ | \\ CH_2 \\ | \\ HO - C - H \\ | \\ COOH \end{matrix}$$

Fumaric acid — L-Malic acid

Fumarase apparently requires a sulfhydryl compound as a cofactor.

8. Oxidation of malic acid to oxaloacetic acid. This oxidation in the citric acid cycle is catalyzed by the enzyme malic dehydrogenase, which acts with the DPN system as cofactor:

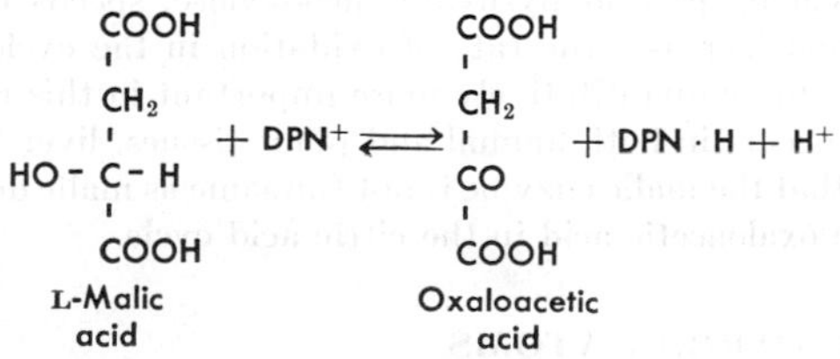

$$\begin{matrix} COOH \\ | \\ CH_2 \\ | \\ HO - C - H \\ | \\ COOH \end{matrix} \ + \ DPN^+ \ \rightleftharpoons \ \begin{matrix} COOH \\ | \\ CH_2 \\ | \\ CO \\ | \\ COOH \end{matrix} \ + \ DPN \cdot H + H^+$$

L-Malic acid — Oxaloacetic acid

The DPN $\cdot$ H is oxidized through the electron transport chain and forms three ATP.

This reaction completes the cycle, forming oxaloacetate, which then may continue in the cycle by reacting with acetyl CoA to form citric acid.

Oxaloacetic acid is reversibly converted to pyruvic acid and CO_2 by liver enzymes (56), and the process appears to take place in two stages. The first reaction is catalyzed by phosphopyruvate carboxylase and the second by phosphopyruvate kinase:

$$
\begin{array}{l}
\text{COOH} \\
| \\
\text{CO} \\
| \\
\text{CH}_2 \\
| \\
\text{COOH}
\end{array}
\quad + \text{ ITP } \rightleftharpoons
\begin{array}{l}
\text{COOH} \\
| \\
\text{C} - \text{O} - \text{PO}_3\text{H}_2 \\
\| \\
\text{CH}_2
\end{array}
+ \text{CO}_2 + \text{IDP}
$$

Oxaloacetic   Phosphopyruvic
acid   acid

$$
\begin{array}{l}
\text{COOH} \\
| \\
\text{C} - \text{O} - \text{PO}_3\text{H}_2 \\
\| \\
\text{CH}_2
\end{array}
+ \text{IDP} \rightleftharpoons
\begin{array}{l}
\text{COOH} \\
| \\
\text{C} - \text{OH} \\
\| \\
\text{CH}_2
\end{array}
\rightleftharpoons
\begin{array}{l}
\text{COOH} \\
| \\
\text{C} = \text{O} \\
| \\
\text{CH}_3
\end{array}
+ \text{ITP}
$$

Pyruvic acid,   Pyruvic acid,
enol form   keto form

The over-all reaction is:

$$\text{Oxaloacetate} \rightleftharpoons \text{Pyruvate} + \text{CO}_2$$

This process represents a mechanism by which oxaloacetate for operation of the citric acid cycle may be formed.

9. Oxidative decarboxylation of malic acid to pyruvic acid by the malic enzyme. Malic acid is reversibly converted to pyruvic acid and CO_2 by the "malic enzyme" (57) which acts with TPN and requires Mn^{++}. The process represents both oxidation and decarboxylation by the same enzyme, as observed in the action of iscitrate dehydrogenase upon isocitric acid, and may be represented:

$$
\begin{array}{l}
\text{COOH} \\
| \\
\text{H} - \text{C} - \text{OH} \\
| \\
\text{CH}_2 \\
| \\
\text{COOH}
\end{array}
+ \text{TPN}^+ \rightleftharpoons \text{TPN} \cdot \text{H} + \text{H}^+ +
\left[
\begin{array}{l}
\text{COOH} \\
| \\
\text{C} = \text{O} \\
| \\
\text{CH}_2 \\
| \\
\text{COOH}
\end{array}
\right]
\overset{Mn^{++}}{\rightleftharpoons}
\begin{array}{l}
\text{COOH} \\
| \\
\text{C} = \text{O} \\
| \\
\text{CH}_3
\end{array}
+ \text{CO}_2
$$

L-Malic   Oxaloacetic
acid   acid

Free oxaloacetic acid does not appear in the reaction, but the malic enzyme decarboxylates oxaloacetic acid. While equilibrium of the reaction strongly favors oxidation of malate, if the TPN^+ formed is removed by coupling with another reaction, then the process is readily reversed, with fixation of CO_2.

When large amounts of citric acid cycle intermediates are introduced into the cycle, the conversion of malic acid to pyruvic acid by the malic enzyme, and of oxaloacetic acid to phosphopyruvic acid by phosphopyruvate carboxylase, speeds up removal of malic acid from the cycle and increases the rate of oxidation in the cycle. The action of the malic enzyme appears to be quantitatively more important in this respect.

The malic enzyme occurs in both animal and plant tissues, liver being a good source.

It should be noted that the malic enzyme is not the same as malic dehydrogenase, which oxidizes malic acid to oxaloacetic acid in the citric acid cycle.

ORIENTATION OF CARBON ATOMS IN THE CITRIC ACID CYCLE

It will be seen in Figure 21.6 (page 864) that certain carbon atoms of oxaloacetate and acetyl CoA are labeled with small letters, 1, 2 and 3, 4. If any of these carbon atoms are

C^{14} or C^{13}, the isotope distribution in the components of the citric acid cycle, up to succinic acid, will be as shown in the figure for the first turn of the cycle. However, as soon as an isotopic atom reaches the symmetrical dicarboxylic acids, succinic and fumaric, it becomes randomized.

Suppose C^{14} acetate, labeled in both carbons, is metabolized. It will enter the cycle as acetyl CoA with both acetyl carbons labeled (3 and 4, Figure 21.6). The α-ketoglutarate formed will be labeled at 3 and 4. When the α-ketoglutaric acid is oxidized and decarboxylated to symmetrical succinic acid, the isotopic atoms become randomized as shown in the following diagram:

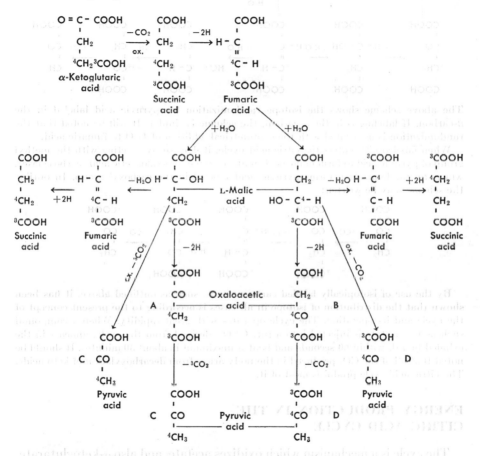

It will be seen from Figure 21.6 and the diagram that:

1. While two molecules of CO_2 are produced in the citric acid cycle, none of the isotopically labeled carbon of acetic acid is lost on the first turn of the cycle, but on the second turn carbon 3 of oxaloacetic acid (A), derived from acetic acid, appears as CO_2 upon oxidative decarboxylation of α-ketoglutaric acid.

2. Randomization of isotope takes place in succinic acid, with the isotopic atoms symmetrically distributed about the plane of symmetry.

3. If oxaloacetic or malic acid is decarboxylated to pyruvic acid, a part of the carboxyl carbon of acetic acid (3) will appear in the carboxyl carbon of pyruvic acid (D), and a part in CO_2. The methyl carbon of acetic acid (4) will be distributed between the carbonyl and methyl groups of pyruvic acid (C and D).

If pyruvic acid is labeled in either the α- or β-carbon, in passing through the dicarboxylic acid "shuttle," isotope appears in both the α- and β-positions:

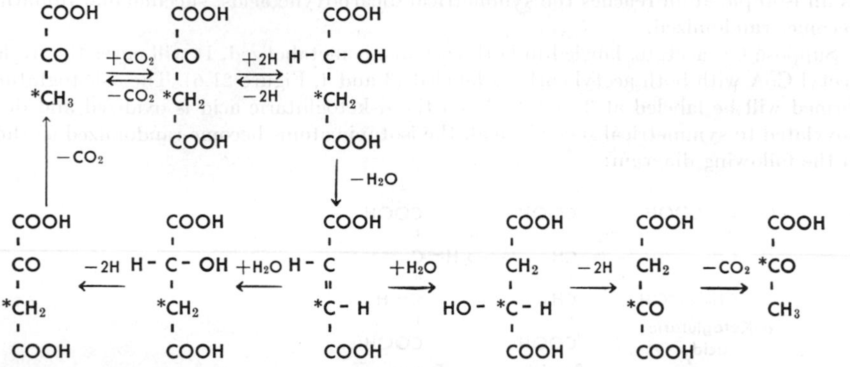

$$
\begin{array}{ccccc}
\text{COOH} & & \text{COOH} & & \text{COOH} \\
| & & | & & | \\
\text{CO} & \overset{+CO_2}{\underset{-CO_2}{\rightleftarrows}} & \text{CO} & \overset{+2H}{\underset{-2H}{\rightleftarrows}} & \text{H} - \text{C} - \text{OH} \\
| & & | & & | \\
*\text{CH}_3 & & *\text{CH}_2 & & *\text{CH}_2 \\
& & | & & | \\
& & \text{COOH} & & \text{COOH}
\end{array}
$$

The above scheme shows the isotope randomization for pyruvic acid labeled in the β-carbon. If labeling is in the α-carbon, the scheme is similar. It will be noted that the randomization is associated with the symmetrical addition of H_2O to fumaric acid.

When labeled CO_2 enters the citric acid cycle, it does so by reacting with the methyl group of pyruvic acid to form malic acid (malic enzyme) or oxaloacetic acid (carboxylase), which by randomization forms pyruvic acid labeled in the carboxyl group. In outline the scheme may be written:

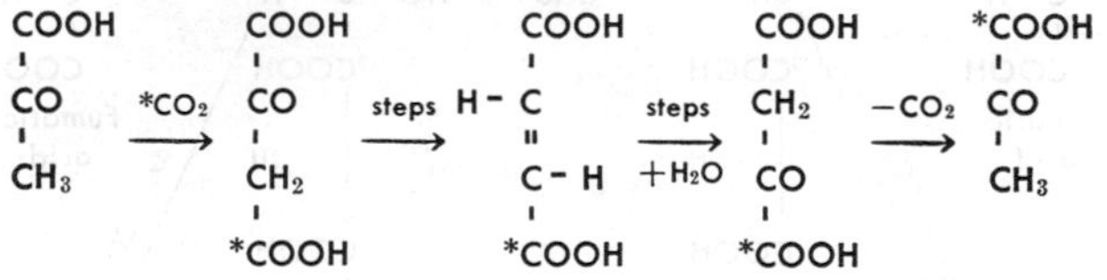

$$
\begin{array}{ccccccccc}
\text{COOH} & & \text{COOH} & & \text{COOH} & & \text{COOH} & & *\text{COOH} \\
| & & | & & | & & | & & | \\
\text{CO} & \overset{*CO_2}{\longrightarrow} & \text{CO} & \overset{steps}{\longrightarrow} & \text{H} - \text{C} & \overset{steps}{\underset{+H_2O}{\longrightarrow}} & \text{CH}_2 & \overset{-CO_2}{\longrightarrow} & \text{CO} \\
| & & | & & \| & & | & & | \\
\text{CH}_3 & & \text{CH}_2 & & \text{C} - \text{H} & & \text{CO} & & \text{CH}_3 \\
& & | & & | & & | & & \\
& & *\text{COOH} & & *\text{COOH} & & *\text{COOH} & &
\end{array}
$$

By the use of isotopically labeled carbon atoms, such as outlined above, it has been shown that the distribution of isotope in all cases is according to the present concept of the cycle and its operation. The cycle operates with great rapidity. When a compound such as C^{14}-acetate is injected into a rat, $C^{14}O_2$, derived from the cycle, appears in the exhaled breath within 60 seconds and is at a maximum in about 30 minutes. It should be noted that all of the CO_2 produced in the body arises from decarboxylation of keto acids. The citric acid cycle produces most of it.

ENERGY PRODUCTION IN THE CITRIC ACID CYCLE

The cycle is a mechanism which oxidizes acetate, and also α-ketoglutarate, fumarate, and malate, which enter the cycle at various stages. The net effect for each turn of the cycle is the oxidation of a molecule of acetate:

$$CH_3COOH + 2O_2 \longrightarrow 2CO_2 + 2H_2O + 209{,}000 \text{ cal}$$

As indicated in Figure 21.6 (page 864), each turn of the cycle produces 12 molecules of ATP, or the oxidation of a mol of acetate yields 12 mols of ATP, which is equivalent to about 84,000 cal. Since the oxidation of a mol of acetic acid produces 209,000 total calories, the biological efficiency of the cycle in producing utilizable free energy stored as ATP is $84{,}000/209{,}000 \times 100 =$ about 40 per cent.

Oxidation of metabolites through combined action of the citric acid cycle and electron transport chain provides definite increments of energy as ATP which are generally utilizable for the many and varied processes of tissues.

Respiration of tissues. The rate at which a tissue utilizes O_2 is expressed in terms of Q_{O_2} values, which represent the milliliters of O_2 under standard conditions consumed per milligram of tissue per unit of time, such as per hour. The Q_{O_2} values are calculated on the basis of tissue dry or wet weight and designated as $-Q_{O_2}$, the minus sign indicating O_2 decrease in the incubating medium.

The rates of O_2 utilization by many tissues have been studied, using tissue slices, etc., in the Warburg apparatus. Rat retina in Ringer's phosphate buffer + glucose has the remarkably high $-Q_{O_2}$ value of 31 per mg of dry tissue per hour. The values found for some other rat tissues under similar conditions are: kidney 21; liver, fasted animal 17, fed animal 12; cerebral cortex 12; adrenal gland 10; lung 8; diaphragm 6; heart 5; skeletal muscle 3; cornea 2; skin 0.8; and lens 0.5.

Under normal circumstances, as pointed out in earlier discussion, the rate of oxidation through the mitochondrial electron transport chain, which largely regulates the rate of oxygen utilization, is determined by the demand for ATP. This oxidation is coupled with phosphorylation of ADP to ATP. If the concentration of ADP is relatively high and ATP low, oxidation and respiration are speeded up to supply ATP to the tissues. Conversely, when most of the ADP has been converted to ATP, oxidation and respiration necessarily must decrease in proportion because of lack of ADP to phosphorylate. We may state then that the rate of respiration is governed by the energy demand of the tissue.

Oxidations which do not proceed through the electron transport chain, such as those catalyzed by oxidases of various types, and which are not coupled with oxidative phosphorylation, proceed at rates determined by the factors which generally influence enzyme activity. Consequently, substances whose oxidation is not coupled with phosphorylation when given to an animal, or incubated with a tissue, are oxidized readily without regard to the tissue demand for ATP. However, if the animal or tissue is given a substance such as glucose, whose oxidation is coupled with phosphorylation, the substance is oxidized only to the extent of tissue demand for ATP, and the excess is stored as glycogen or fat until the tissue demand for energy brings about oxidation of the stored reserves.

GENERAL REFERENCES

Bray, H. G., and White, K.: *Kinetics and Thermodynamics in Biochemistry.* Academic Press, New York, 1957.

Clark, W. M.: *Oxidation-Reduction Potentials of Organic Systems.* Williams & Wilkins Co., Baltimore, 1960.

Clark, W. M.: *Topics in Physical Chemistry,* 2nd ed. Williams & Wilkins Co., Baltimore, 1951.

Dixon, M., and Webb, E. C.: *Enzymes.* Academic Press, New York, 1958.

Howett, L. F.: *Oxidation-Reduction Potentials in Bacteriology and Biochemistry,* 6th ed. E. & S. Livingston, London, 1950.

Krebs, H. A., and Kornberg, H. L.: *Energy Transformations in Living Matter*. Springer-Verlag, Berlin, 1957.

Krebs, H. A.: "The Tricarboxylic Acid Cycle." In Greenberg, D. M. (ed.): *Chemical Pathways of Metabolism*, Vol. I, Academic Press, New York, 1954.

Lardy, H. A.: *Respiratory Enzymes*. Burgess Publishing Co., Minneapolis, 1949.

Mehler, A. H.: *Introduction to Enzymology*. Academic Press, New York, 1957.

Neilands, J. B., and Stumpf, P. K.: *Outlines of Enzyme Chemistry*. John Wiley & Sons, New York, 1955.

Ochoa, S.: *Advances in Enzymol.*, **15**, 183, 1954.

Sumner, J. B., and Myrback, K. (eds.): *The Enzymes*, Vol. II, Part 1. Academic Press, New York, 1951.

SPECIAL REFERENCES

1. Conn, E. E., in Mason, H. S., and Florkin, M. (eds.): *Comparative Biochemistry*, Vol. I, Chap. 11. Academic Press, New York, 1960.
2. Green, D. E.: *Federation Proc.*, **18**, 987, 1959; *Advances in Enzymol.*, **21**, 73, 1959.
3. Chance, B., and Williams, G. R.: *Advances in Enzymol.*, **17**, 65, 1956; *J. Biol. Chem.*, **217**, 429, 1955.
4. Neilands, J. B.: *Ann. Rev. Biochem.*, **27**, 455, 1958.
5. Slater, E. C.: *Advances in Enzymol.*, **20**, 147, 1958.
6. Green, D. E., and Lester, R. L.: *Federation Proc.*, **18**, 987, 1959.
7. Mason, H. S.: *Advances in Enzymol.*, **19**, 79, 1957.
8. Schneider, W. C.: *Advances in Enzymol.*, **21**, 1, 1959. Chance, B., and Williams, G. R.: *Advances in Enzymol.*, **17**, 97, 1956.
9. Lehninger, A. L.; Wadkins, C. L.; and Remmert, L. F. In Wolstenholme, G. E. W., and O'Connor, C. M. (eds.): *Ciba Foundation Symposium, Regulation of Cell Metabolism*, p. 130. Little, Brown & Co., Boston, 1959.
10. Joshi, S.; Newburgh, R. W.; and Cheldelin, V. H.: *Abstr. Pac. Slope Biochem. Congr.*, Berkeley, Cal., 1957.
11. Lang, C. A., and Nason, A.: *J. Biol. Chem.*, **234**, 1874, 1959.
12. Humphrey, G. F.: *Biochem. J.*, **65**, 546, 1957.
13. Kaplan, N. O.; Schwartz, M. N.; Frech, M. E.; and Ciotti, M. M.: *Proc. Natl. Acad. Sci. U. S.*, **42**, 481, 1956.
14. Cooper, C., and Lehninger, A. L.: *J. Biol. Chem.*, **219**, 489, 507, 519, 1956; **224**, 547, 561, 1957. Gamble, J. L., Jr., and Lehninger, A. L.: *J. Biol. Chem.*, **223**, 921, 1956.
15. Green, D. E.: *Advances in Enzymol.*, **21**, 73, 1959.
16. Brodie, A. F.; Davis, B. R.; and Fieser, L. F.: *J. Am. Chem. Soc.*, **80**, 6454, 1958. Brodie, A. F.: *J. Biol. Chem.*, **234**, 398, 1959.
17. Smith, L.: *J. Biol. Chem.*, **215**, 833, 1955.
18. Slater, E. C.: *Advances in Enzymol.*, **20**, 171, 1958.
19. Chance, B., and Williams, G. R.: *Advances in Enzymol.*, **17**, 65, 1956. Chance, B. in Wolstenholme, G. E. W., and O'Conner, C. M. (eds.): *Ciba Foundation Symposium, Regulation of Cell Metabolism*. Little, Brown & Co., Boston, 1959.
20. Harden, A., and Young, W. J.: *J. Physiol.*, **32**, Proc. of Nov., 1904, 1905.
21. Meyerhof, O.: *Z. physiol. Chem.*, **101**, 165, 1917–1918.
22. Schlenk, F.: *Svenska Vet. Akad. Arkiv. Keini*, **12B**, 20, 1936. Schlenk, F., and Euler, H. von: *Naturwissenschaften*, **24**, 794, 1936.
23. Warburg, O., and Christian, W.: *Biochem. Z.*, **254**, 438, 1932.
24. Warburg, O.; Christian, W.; and Griese, A.: *Biochem. Z.*, **282**, 157, 1935.
25. Dixon, M., and Webb, E. C.: *Enzymes*, p. 348. Academic Press, New York, 1958.
26. Warburg, O., and Christian, W.: *Naturwissenschaften*, **20**, 688, 980, 1932; *Biochem. Z.*, **254**, 438, 1932.
27. Singer, T. P., and Kearney, E. B., in Neurath, H., and Bailey, K. (eds.): *The Proteins*, Vol. II, Part A. Academic Press, New York, 1954.
28. Warburg, O., and Christian, W.: *Biochem. Z.*, **298**, 150, 1938.
29. Chance, B., and Williams, G. R.: *Advances in Enzymol.*, **17**, 72, 1956.
30. Theorell, H.: *Biochem. Z.*, **290**, 293, 1937.
31. Theorell, H.: *Advances in Enzymol.*, **20**, 31, 1958.
32. Corran, H. S.; Green, D. E.; and Straub, F. B.: *Biochem. J.*, **33**, 793, 1939.
33. Ziegler, D. M.; Green, D. E.; and Doeg, K. A.: *J. Biol. Chem.*, **234**, 1916, 1959.
34. Crane, F. L.; Hatefi, Y.; Lester, R. L.; and Widmer, C.: *Biochim. et Biophys. Acta*, **25**, 220, 1957.

35. Lester, R. L.; Crane, F. L.; and Hatefi, Y.: *J. Am. Chem. Soc.*, **80**, 4751, 1958. Lester, R. L.; Hatefi, Y.; Widmer, C.; and Crane, F. L.: *Biochim. et Biophys. Acta*, **33**, 170, 1959. Wolf, D. E.; Hoffmann, C. H.; Trenner, N. R.; Arison, B. A.; Schunk, C. H.; Linn, B. O.; and Folkers, K.: *J. Am. Chem. Soc.*, **80**, 4752, 1958.

36. MacMunn, C. A.: *Phil. Trans.*, **177**, 267, 1886.

37. Keilin, D.: *Proc. Roy. Soc.*, B, **98**, 312, 1925; **104**, 206, 1929; **106**, 418, 1930. Keilin, D., and Hartree, E. F.: *ibid.*, **122**, 298, 1937; **125**, 171, 1938; **127**, 167, 1939; **129**, 277, 1940.

38. Wainio, M. W., and Cooperstein, S. J.: *Advances in Enzymol.*, **17**, 329, 1956.

39. Dixon, M., and Webb, E. C.: *Enzymes*, p. 414. Academic Press, New York, 1958.

40. Tuppy, H., and Paleus, S.: *Acta Chem. Scand.*, **9**, 353, 1955.

41. Strittmatter, C. F., and Ball, E. G.: *Proc. Natl. Acad. Sci. U. S.*, **38**, 19, 1952; *J. Cellular Comp. Physiol.*, **43**, 57, 1954.

42. Bailie, M., and Morton, R. K.: *Nature*, **176**, 111, 1955.

43. Chance, B.: *Advances in Enzymol.*, **12**, 153, 1951. Chance, B., and Fergusson, R. R., in McElroy, W. D., and Glass, B. (eds.): *The Mechanism of Enzyme Action*. Johns Hopkins Press, Baltimore, 1954.

44. Tauber, H.: *Proc. Soc. Exptl. Biol. Med.*, **81**, 237, 1952.

45. Bonnischen, R. K.: *Acta Chem. Scand.*, **2**, 561, 1948; *Arch. Biochem.*, **12**, 83, 1947.

46. Thunberg, T.: *Skand. Arch. Physiol.*, **40**, 1, 1920.

47. Krebs, H. A.: *Harvey Lectures*, Ser. **44**, 165, 1948–1949.

48. Martius, C., and Lynen, F.: *Advances in Enzymol.*, **10**, 167, 1950.

49. Krebs, H. A., in Greenberg, D. M. (ed.): *Chemical Pathways of Metabolism*, Vol. I, pp. 109–171. Academic Press, New York, 1954.

50. Ochoa, S.: *Advances in Enzymol.*, **15**, 183, 1954.

51. Lynen, F., and Reichert, E.: *Angew. Chem.*, **63**, 47, 1951. Lynen, F.; Reichert, E.; and Rueff, L.: *Ann. Chem.*, **574**, 1, 1951.

52. Wood, H. G.; Werkman, C. H.; Hemingway, A.; and Nier, A. O.: *J. Biol. Chem.*, **139**, 483, 1941.

53. Wilcox, P. E.; Heidelberger, C.; and Potter, V. R.: *J. Am. Chem. Soc.*, **72**, 5019, 1950.

54. Ogston, A. G.: *Nature*, **162**, 963, 1948.

55. Koike, M., and Reed, L. J.: *J. Am. Chem. Soc.*, **81**, 505, 1959. Reed, L. J.: *Advances in Enzymol.*, **18**, 319, 1957.

56. Utter, M. F., and Wood, H. G.: *J. Biol. Chem.*, **164**, 455, 1946. Utter, M. F.; Kurahashi, K.; and Rose, I. A.: *J. Biol. Chem.*, **207**, 803, 1954; *Federation Proc.*, **14**, 240, 1955.

57. Ochoa, S.; Mehler, A. H.; and Kornberg, A.: *J. Biol. Chem.*, **174**, 979, 1948.

22

Energy metabolism

The study of energy metabolism encompasses a variety of subjects including the caloric value of foods, the respiratory quotient (RQ), direct and indirect calorimetry, basal metabolism and its determination, the body's caloric requirements and the specific dynamic action (calorigenic action) of foods. It is the purpose here to discuss only the fundamental principles involved in the determination of basal metabolism without attempting to consider clinical implications.

Through experimentation and reasoning, Lavoisier was the first to arrive at an understanding of the oxidation of foods in the body. He proposed that carbon and hydrogen of foods are oxidized in the body by oxygen and that in the process heat, along with CO_2 and water, is produced. Many years later it was established that the body tissues are the primary site of the oxidations.

Caloric value of foods. It should be recalled that one calorie (small c) is the amount of heat required to raise the temperature of 1 g of water 1° C (more specifically, from 15° to 16° C). One Calorie (capital C) equals 1000 cal. The large Calorie (Cal) or kilogram-calorie is in general usage in any discussion of energy metabolism. In the following discussion, "Cal" will be used.

The caloric value of any combustible substance, including foods or purified protein, carbohydrate or fat, is readily determined in an apparatus such as a bomb calorimeter. In the operation of a combustion calorimeter, a weighed sample of material is placed in a heavy metal cylinder, and the cap of the cylinder is firmly positioned. Through the cap passes a loop of fine wire (platinum, for instance) which is embedded in the test material. The closed cylinder is put under oxygen pressure (say, 20 atm) and placed in a known amount of water at a known temperature. Upon passing current through the fine wire, the test material becomes completely combusted, and the heat is transferred to the water. Precautions must be observed to obviate transfer of heat to any other substance. From the mass of water and the temperature change the heat production is readily calculated in terms of calories, cal $= m(T_2 - T_1)$, where m = mass of water in grams.

876

By methods involving the above principle the caloric values of a great many foodstuffs (and other materials) have been determined. Table 22.1 gives a few typical examples. In certain instances the values can be no more than averages because of variations in composition of some substances, such as bread or even a fat.

The figures in Table 22.1 represent the heat production upon complete oxidation of the substances tested. In the body the oxidation of absorbed carbohydrate and of absorbed fat is also complete. In the case of protein, however, the oxidation is quite incomplete in the body. One needs only to consider the urinary end products of protein metabolism, urea, creatinine, uric acid, etc., to understand that the body has not obtained all the available calories from protein, since these compounds still contain oxidizable H and C. About 1.3 Cal per gram of protein is lost to the body, and using an average figure

Table 22.1.   Caloric Value of a Few Materials

Substance	Cal per Gram
Hydrogen	34.4
Charcoal	8.0
Glucose	3.75
Sucrose	3.96
Starch	4.2
Fat	9.4
Beefsteak (dry)	5.4
Casein	5.84
Urea	2.5
Creatinine	4.5

of 5.6 Cal per gram for mixed proteins (bomb calorimeter), we arrive at about 4.3 Cal per gram of absorbed protein as the heat available on oxidation in the body. However, ingested protein is not 100 per cent absorbed, nor is fat or carbohydrate. For this reason and also because little error is introduced by rounding off the caloric values, the following are in general usage in nutritional and dietetic work; protein, 4; carbohydrate, 4; and fat, 9—all in Cal per gram ingested.

The energy expenditure of the body, which is continuous throughout life, is the result of the transformation of chemical energy into muscular and other forms of energy, with the accompanying production of heat. It is important to understand the technique used to determine this over-all heat production.

Direct calorimetry. By direct calorimetry is meant the measurement of the actual heat production of an individual or of an animal. It is obvious that an apparatus adaptable to such measurements must be complicated. There is little need to dwell on particulars here. The important consideration is the fact that through direct calorimetry and simultaneous studies on gas exchange (carbon dioxide produced and oxygen consumed) it became evident that an accurate estimate of heat production could be obtained by measuring the gaseous exchange alone (indirect calorimetry).

Any chamber to be used as a calorimeter must be so constructed that there is no heat loss to the outside. The heat produced by the animal or man inside the chamber is picked up by water flowing through pipes. The amount of water passing through the chamber and the temperature change must be ascertained with great accuracy. Any change in the temperature of the subject or of the walls and contents of the chamber must also be known. The heat required to vaporize water appearing in the expired air of the subject is calculated from the water content of H_2SO_4 used to pick up the moisture. To arrive at the gaseous exchange, it is necessary to pump known quantities of air through the chamber and determine the CO_2 produced and oxygen consumed. This is usually done by arranging a closed system and adding oxygen as necessary. Any temperature change in the gases must also be considered in the total heat production. This superficial description gives an idea of the complexity of the animal calorimeter. Details of construction and operation can be found in the classic reference book by Lusk (1).

Atwater and Benedict (cited by Lusk (1), p. 62) showed the remarkable correlation between the direct and indirect methods of determining heat production of humans. Averages of 40-day determinations on three individuals showed only 0.2 per cent difference between the two methods of arriving at total daily caloric output.

The indirect method of determining heat production is far simpler, and since the results are of proved validity, it is today and has for a long time been the method of choice. In order to comprehend how a calculation of energy production can be made from a knowledge of CO_2 production and O_2 consumption (indirect calorimetry), it is essential to understand the respiratory quotient and the relation of urinary nitrogen excretion to this.

Respiratory quotient. The respiratory quotient (RQ) is defined as the volume of CO_2 produced divided by the volume of O_2 consumed over some time period. One can readily calculate the RQ of carbohydrate undergoing oxidation in the body or in a bomb calorimeter, since the end products (and energy production) are the same in either instance. Using glucose as an example, we have:

$$C_6H_{12}O_6 + 6O_2 \longrightarrow 6CO_2 + 6H_2O + 673 \text{ Cal}$$

from which it can be seen that the RQ = 1:

$$RQ = \frac{6CO_2}{6O_2} = 1$$

or multiplying by 22.4,

$$\frac{134.4 \text{ l } CO_2}{134.4 \text{ l } O_2} = 1$$

Since 1 mol of glucose, upon complete oxidation, yields 673 Cal and utilizes 134.4 l of O_2, it follows that in the body each liter of O_2 oxidizing carbohydrate exclusively will account for 5.01 Cal:

$$\frac{673 \text{ Cal}}{134.4 \text{ l}} = 5.01 \text{ Cal per l } O_2$$

In the case of fat, the calculated RQ and the actual RQ vary slightly with the small differences in the ratios of hydrogen, carbon, and oxygen atoms contained in different fat molecules. Using a theoretical fat containing two molecules of stearic and one of palmitic acid, we find the following:

$$2(C_{55}H_{106}O_6) + 157O_2 \longrightarrow 110CO_2 + 106H_2O + 16,353 \text{ Cal}$$

$$RQ = \frac{110CO_2}{157O_2} = 0.701 \quad \text{or} \quad \frac{2464 \text{ l } CO_2}{3516.8 \text{ l } O_2} = 0.701$$

The RQ for triolein is 0.71, and that for tripalmitin, 0.703.

Upon complete oxidation of the 2 mols of fat there would be produced 16,353 Cal and a utilization of 3516.8 l of O_2, from which it is calculated that each liter of O_2 oxidizing fat exclusively in the body accounts for 4.65 Cal:

$$\frac{16,353 \text{ Cal}}{3516.8 \text{ l}} = 4.65 \text{ Cal per l } O_2$$

Slight variations in this figure will be found in different texts. This is a reflection of employing different fat molecules for calculations and arriving at slightly different RQ values.

The RQ for protein oxidation is not so readily obtained, since we are unable to write an accurate equation depicting the oxidation of a protein molecule in the body. However, Loewy (cited by Lusk (1), p. 64) computed the protein RQ from experimental data. An adaptation of his figures follows.

Table 22.2

	100 g Meat Protein Contain, g	Eliminated in Urine and Feces, g	Remaining for Respiration, g
C	52.38	10.877	41.50
H	7.27	2.875	4.40
O	22.68	14.998	7.69
N	16.65	16.65	
S	1.02	1.02	

After deducting the oxygen and an amount of hydrogen (0.961 g) to convert it into water (intramolecular water), there remains for oxidation, 41.5 g of C and 3.439 g of H:

41.5 g C require 110.66 g O_2 and produce 152.17 g CO_2
3.439 g H require 27.52 g O_2
Total   138.18 g O_2 152.17 g CO_2
138.18 g O_2 = 96.7 l and 152.17 g CO_2 = 77.46 l

Then:

$$\frac{77.46}{96.7} = 0.801 = \text{RQ for protein}$$

From the foregoing it is seen that in the body the RQ for carbohydrate oxidation is 1, for fat about 0.701, and for protein about 0.801. Values above 1.0 and below 0.70 have been observed. In geese an RQ of 1.33 was found by Bleibtreu (cited by Lusk (1), p. 396) after stuffing them with grain. Here carbohydrate, an oxygen-rich substance, was being converted into fat, an oxygen-poor substance. The excess oxygen in the carbohydrate would be available for other oxidations in the body, decreasing the quantity required from the inspired air, while the quantity of CO_2 produced was not necessarily altered. Because of the magnitude of this conversion, the volume of expired CO_2 was greater than the volume of O_2 used, and hence an RQ over unity. RQ values below 0.70 have been observed in severe diabetes.

Since food proteins contain, on the average, 16 per cent nitrogen, it follows that every gram of urinary nitrogen represents 6.25 g of protein metabolized

$(100 \div 16 = 6.25)$. It has been demonstrated that the metabolism of an amount of protein sufficient to yield 1 g of urinary nitrogen results in the production of 26.51 Cal and 4.754 l of CO_2, while 5.923 l of oxygen are utilized.

The various values of importance that have been developed in the preceding pages are brought together here for convenience:

	RQ	Cal/g	Cal/l Oxygen
Carbohydrate	1.00	4.0	5.01
Fat	0.70–0.71	9.0	4.65
Protein	0.801	4.0	4.48

One gram urinary nitrogen represents 5.923 l of O_2 used, 4.754 l of CO_2 produced, 6.25 g of protein metabolized, and a production of 26.51 Cal.

From these figures along with certain experimental data on an animal or a man, some rather significant calculations can be made. Knowing the urinary nitrogen excretion, the O_2 consumption, and the CO_2 production of an individual over a definite time period, one can calculate the Cal arising from protein, from fat, and from carbohydrate metabolized, as well as the amounts of each undergoing oxidation during the experimental period.

To illustrate, let us assume that an individual during a one-hour experiment excreted 0.5 g of urinary nitrogen, utilized 20 l of O_2, and produced 16 l of CO_2.

From the urinary nitrogen excretion the following data are readily ascertained:

$$0.5 \times 26.51 \ \text{Cal} = 13.25 \ \text{Cal from protein oxidation}$$
$$0.5 \times 6.25 \ \text{g} = 3.13 \ \text{g protein metabolized}$$
$$0.5 \times 5.923 \ \text{l} = 2.961 \ \text{l } O_2 \text{ used for protein oxidation}$$

Leaving $20 - 2.961 = 17.04$ l O_2 for fat and carbohydrate

$$0.5 \times 4.754 \ \text{l} = 2.377 \ \text{l } CO_2 \text{ produced by protein oxidation}$$

Leaving $16 - 2.377 = 13.623$ l CO_2 from fat and carbohydrate

The nonprotein RQ, calculated from the oxygen consumption and CO_2 production due solely to fat plus carbohydrate oxidation, is:

$$\frac{13.62 \ \text{l}}{17.04 \ \text{l}} = 0.80$$

With a nonprotein RQ of 0.80, the proportions of fat and of carbohydrate metabolized are readily obtainable from Table 22.3. The caloric value of 1 l of O_2 is also given in the table. These values are readily calculated if such a table is not available. Consider the accompanying diagram:

RQ = 0.707	0.80	RQ = 1.00
Fat only		Carbohydrate only

Cal/l O_2 = 4.686   Cal/l O_2 = 5.047

Table 22.3. The Nonprotein Respiratory Quotient Related to Calories per Liter of Oxygen Used and to the Proportions of Carbohydrate and of Fat Metabolized (2)
Equivalents of 1 l of Oxygen

Nonprotein Respiratory Quotient	Grams		Calories
	Carbohydrate	Fat	
0.707	0.000	0.502	4.686
0.71	0.016	0.497	4.690
0.72	0.055	0.482	4.702
0.73	0.094	0.465	4.714
0.74	0.134	0.450	4.727
0.75	0.173	0.433	4.739
0.76	0.213	0.417	4.751
0.77	0.254	0.400	4.764
0.78	0.294	0.384	4.776
0.79	0.334	0.368	4.788
0.80	0.375	0.350	4.801
0.81	0.415	0.334	4.813
0.82	0.456	0.317	4.825
0.83	0.498	0.301	4.838
0.84	0.539	0.284	4.850
0.85	0.580	0.267	4.862
0.86	0.622	0.249	4.875
0.87	0.666	0.232	4.887
0.88	0.708	0.215	4.899
0.89	0.741	0.197	4.911
0.90	0.793	0.180	4.924
0.91	0.836	0.162	4.936
0.92	0.878	0.145	4.948
0.93	0.922	0.127	4.961
0.94	0.966	0.109	4.973
0.95	1.010	0.091	4.985
0.96	1.053	0.073	4.998
0.97	1.098	0.055	5.010
0.98	1.142	0.036	5.022
0.99	1.185	0.018	5.035
1.00	1.232	0.000	5.047

From McClendon, J. F., and Medes, G.: *Physical Chemistry in Biology and Medicine*. W. B. Saunders Company, Philadelphia, 1925, p. 158.

If the nonprotein RQ were just halfway between 0.707 (fat oxidation) and 1.0 (carbohydrate oxidation), the proportions of Cal from these constituents undergoing oxidation would be equal, and the caloric value of 1 l of O_2 would be just halfway between the two extremes. But in our case:

5.047 − 4.686 = 0.36 total difference in Cal per 1 O_2
1.00 − 0.707 = 0.293 total difference in RQ
0.80 − 0.707 = 0.093 difference in RQ (hypothetical case)

so that

$$4.686 + \left(\frac{0.093}{0.293} \times 0.36\right) = 4.80$$

and 4.80 is the caloric value of a liter of O_2 at a nonprotein RQ of 0.80. From this the total caloric output during the test period due to carbohydrate plus fat metabolism is:

$$17.04 \times 4.80 = 81.79 \text{ Cal}$$

But only 0.093/0.293 or 31.7 per cent of these calories was derived from carbohydrate, and the remainder, or 68.3 per cent, from fat:

$$0.317 \times 81.79 = 25.93 \text{ Cal from carbohydrate}$$
$$0.683 \times 81.79 = 55.86 \text{ Cal from fat}$$
$$\text{Previously shown} \quad \underline{13.25} \text{ Cal from protein}$$
$$\text{Total} \quad 95.04 \text{ Cal per hour}$$

To convert Calories to grams, it is necessary to divide Calories by 4 for carbohydrate, and by 9 for fat:

$$\frac{25.93}{4} = 6.48 \text{ g carbohydrate oxidized}$$

$$\frac{55.86}{9} = 6.21 \text{ g fat oxidized}$$

It was previously shown that 3.13 g protein was oxidized, and by another method we find $13.25/4 = 3.3$ g protein oxidized.

The preceding calculations indicate the variety of information obtainable from data on O_2 consumption, CO_2 production, and urinary nitrogen excretion. Such information is seldom necessary or even desirable in the clinical study of an individual's heat production. However, it is of value in gaining an insight into the fundamentals upon which are based our knowledge of basal metabolism.

Basal metabolism. Basal metabolism indicates the rate at which the body is carrying out its over-all cellular metabolism under a set of empirical circumstances known as "basal conditions." The basal metabolic rate (BMR) is calculated in terms of heat production, a by-product of metabolism. The higher the rate of metabolism, the more heat is produced. To be in the basal state, an individual must have no food for some 14 hours (postabsorptive state); he must be physically relaxed and in a comfortable and supine position. His body temperature should be normal, and the environment should be around 70° F. It is also important that the subject not be alarmed over the tests about to be conducted, since mental anxiety, with the accompanying increased muscle tonus, etc., will introduce marked errors.

Under such conditions the heat production of an individual is calculated from a determination of oxygen consumption over a definite time period, say six or ten minutes. From this value alone, the total heat production is obtained, and from the total Calories the Calories per square meter of body surface per hour or per 24 hours are readily obtainable.

How can total heat production be calculated from the O_2 consumption? It should be recalled that for any known RQ, the calorific value of 1 l of O_2 can readily be calculated or found in various tables. From a great many determinations on the RQ of human beings under basal conditions, the average value of 0.82 has been derived. Data from various laboratories with varying age groups and among both sexes are in surprisingly good agreement on this value.

Therefore, since the RQ of an individual under basal conditions is 0.82

and the calorific value of 1 l of O_2 at this RQ is 4.825 Cal, total heat production is readily found if O_2 consumption is determined.

It has further been established that heat production of an individual (or of an animal) is related directly to total body area. For a number of species the total heat per square meter body area per 24 hours is close to 1000 Cal. Heat production correlates poorly with total weight among different species or in one species (including man). There have been developed a number of formulas useful for the calculation of body area from the height and weight of an individual. One of these, the DuBois and DuBois (3) formula is:

$$A = \text{wt}^{0.425} \times \text{ht}^{0.725} \times 71.84$$

in which A = area in square centimeters, wt = weight in kilograms, and ht = height in centimeters. This formula was developed through actual measurements of surface area of a great many individuals. Except among individuals with unusual body build, the error in the calculated area is said rarely to exceed ± 1.5 per cent. More conveniently, the nomogram prepared by Boothby and Sandiford (4) can be used for finding surface area for an individual of known height and weight (Fig. 22.1).

The types of equipment available for determining O_2 consumption are many and varied. For clinical work an apparatus is generally used which allows the subject to breathe oxygen-enriched air from a face mask connected with the O_2 supply. The CO_2 expired is entrained. The system is a closed one, and O_2 consumption is readily found from the drop in the spirometer bell which contains the oxygen supply. Further details of the apparatus will not be given here, since it is the purpose of this discussion to indicate the fundamental principles upon which such determinations are based, and not to detail procedures of operation.

In young normal adult men the BMR is about 40 Cal per square meter body surface per hour. In women of the same age the heat production is 8 to 10 per cent less, or around 36 Cal per square meter per hour. Table 22.4 shows the normal standards of BMR for various age groups of both sexes.

Suppose a young adult man was found to consume 1500 ml O_2 in a six-minute test period. In one hour this would amount to 15 l of O_2, and since the caloric value of 1 l of O_2 under basal conditions is 4.825, then the hourly heat production would be 72.4 Cal. From the man's height, 150 cm, and his weight, 60 kg, the surface area of 1.54 sq m is obtainable from the nomogram referred to previously, and:

$$\frac{72.4}{1.54} = 47.0 \text{ Cal per sq m per hour}$$

From the table of normal standards we see that a man of this age should have a BMR of 41 Cal per sq m per hour, and consequently in this case the BMR is elevated by 6/41, or about 15 per cent high (BMR = +15). If the value calculates to 20 per cent below the standard, then BMR = -20.

It is seen from the above that an individual's BMR is high, low, or

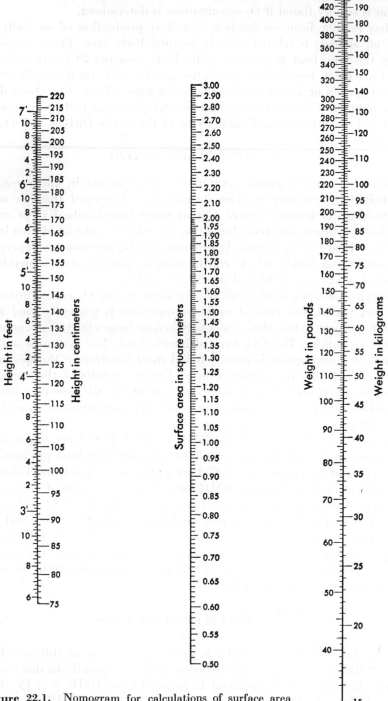

Figure 22.1. Nomogram for calculations of surface area from height and weight. (W. M. Boothby and R. B. Sandiford, *Boston Med. Surg. J.*, **185,** 337, 1921.)

Table 22.4. Standard Values (BMR), Calories per Square Meter per Hour in Relation to Age (5)

Males		Females	
Age last birthday	Mean	Age last birthday	Mean
years		years	
6	53.00	6	50.62
7	52.45	6½	50.23
8	51.78	7	49.12
8½	51.20	7½	47.84
9	50.54	8	47.00
9½	49.42	8½	46.50
10	48.50	9–10	45.90
10½	47.71	11	45.26
11	47.18	11½	44.80
12	46.75	12	44.28
13–15	46.35	12½	43.58
16	45.72	13	42.90
16½	45.30	13½	42.10
17	44.80	14	41.45
17½	44.03	14½	40.74
18	43.25	15	40.10
18½	42.70	15½	39.40
19	42.32	16	38.85
19½	42.00	16½	38.30
20–21	41.43	17	37.82
22–23	40.82	17½	37.40
24–27	40.24	18–19	36.74
28–29	39.81	20–24	36.18
30–34	39.34	25–44	35.70
35–39	38.63	45–49	34.94
40–44	38.00	50–54	33.96
45–49	37.37	55–59	33.10
50–54	36.73	60–64	32.61
55–59	36.10	65–69	32.30
60–64	35.48		
65–69	34.80*		

* Obtained by extrapolation.
From Boothby, W. M.; Berkson, J.; and Dunn, H. L.: *Am. J. Physiol.*, 116, 468, 1936.

normal, depending on how it compares with accepted standard values. Such values have been developed from data obtained on a great many normal people. Slightly different values can be found among the standards developed by various groups of workers.

The BMR is altered by many factors. It can readily be seen in the table of normal standards that age and sex are important determinants. Of lesser importance are such factors as race and climate. Nutritional state is important especially after prolonged fasting. Increased body temperature is said to elevate the BMR by about 7 per cent for each 1° F.

For practical purposes the BMR determination is of most importance in assessing the state of activity of the thyroid gland. As is well known, the thyroid hormone is the primary regulator of the rate of body metabolism. In hyperthyroidism the BMR may be elevated as much as 75 to 100 per cent (extreme cases) and in severe hypofunction, metabolism may be decreased to 40 or 50 per cent below normal. Although other factors and disease states have an effect on the rate of metabolism, the value of the BMR test is primarily in relation to thyroid dysfunction.

The heat loss from the body must balance the heat production, since body temperature is, for all practical purposes, maintained constant. Exact figures for the proportions lost through the various channels are of little value, since they would apply only to a situation with rigidly defined conditions concerning type of clothing, the movement, moisture content and temperature of the air, etc. In general, however, some 70 to 80 per cent of the total heat loss may be through radiation and conduction, 15 to 20 per cent through evaporation of water (skin and lungs), and a few per cent in the expired air and urine and feces.

Caloric requirement. For any individual there is a quite constant heat production (BMR) and a quite inconstant factor, depending on muscle activity. The sum of the two determines the total amount of food or Cal required to maintain body weight or caloric balance (in an adult). During growth more Cal are needed to allow for the increase in body tissues.

The total energy requirement must be sufficient to cover the needs for: (a) basal metabolism, including the work involved in the action of the organs such as the heart, lungs, and kidneys, and the effort due to muscle tonus, as well as the maintenance of body temperature; (b) muscular activity; (c) specific dynamic action; and (d) growth, including reproduction.

A caloric intake of 1300 to 2000 Cal per 24 hours would cover the basal needs of most individuals. And to this must be added sufficient Cal to allow for all the muscular exertion associated with normal activity. This factor varies tremendously from one individual to another or from day to day for the same person.

From 2000 to 3000 Cal per day is sufficient for most individuals represented by a group of college students or faculty. Athletes and many others carrying on considerable physical exertion may require 4000 or even 5000 Cal per day, depending on the time spent and the nature of the physical endeavor.

Without exhaustive experimental work only rough estimates can be made of the caloric requirement for any particular occupation. Actually the value of such information is quite limited except in rare instances. However, in order to indicate the very important part played by exercise in determining our daily food needs, Table 22.5 of estimated requirements is given (6).

There are various methods of arriving at heat production or caloric requirements during exercise. One approach is to study the food intake for a number of days of individuals in some occupation. If there is no change in body weight, the caloric intake can be found from the caloric value of the diet. By this approach the total 24-hour need can be found. Another method is to determine RQ during exercise with the appropriate apparatus, and then calculate the caloric value of 1 l of O_2 for the determined RQ. From this the calorie expenditure of an individual while playing the piano, dancing, etc., may be found. To determine RQ under conditions of exercise

Table 22.5.   The Energy Requirements of Men of the Same Size Engaged in Different Types of Activity

Type of Exercise	Cal per lb of Body wt per Day	Cal per kg of Body wt per Day	Total Cal per Day for a Man Weighing 155 lb or 70 kg
Very light exercise: typist, tailor	13–16	30–35	2100–2450
Moderate exercise: metal worker, furniture painter	18–20	40–45	2800–3150
Severe exercise: stonemason, laborer, mason	22–32	50–70	3500–4900

From Turner, C. E.: *Industrial Hygiene*. Edited by A. J. Lanza and J. A. Goldberg. Oxford University Press, New York, 1939, p. 591.

it is necessary to measure CO_2 production and O_2 consumption as well as urinary nitrogen excretion. Various types of portable apparatus are available for estimating the gaseous exchange.

Table 22.6 (7) indicates a few values reported for various occupations in terms of extra Cal per hour (above basal) required while working.

Table 22.6.   Caloric Requirements for Work

Occupation	Increased Requirement for Work Cal per hour
Shoemaker (2 men)	89 and 90
Tailor (2 men)	44 and 44
Bookbinder (2 men)	89 and 92
Metal worker (2 men)	137 and 145
Painter (2 men)	143 and 146
Carpenter (2 men)	116 and 164
Stonemason (2 men)	319 and 286
Wood sawyer (2 men)	406 and 370
Sewing by hand (2 women)	4 and 7
Sewing by machine (2 women)	24 and 57
Washerwoman (2 women)	214 and 124
Housemaid (2 women)	157 and 81
Bookbinder (2 women)	38 and 63

Newburgh and Robinson (8) found that several young medical students and laboratory workers had a daily caloric output very close to twice the basal heat production. Since these subjects were not engaged in a manual occupation, they questioned some of the earlier reports, which in some instances indicated far less heat production than twice the basal level even for individuals engaged in manual occupations.

A lumberman in a cold environment may expend 8000 Cal per day, and Lusk reported the production of 9000 Cal per day by a 16-hour bicycle rider.

Other investigations (9) of the rate of metabolism while swimming are of interest. A number of college students were tested by the Douglas-Haldane method, and the energy expenditure was calculated from the oxygen debt. This involved the collection and analysis of expired air over a period of time immediately following the exercise. At swimming speeds of over 2 ft per second, metabolism was found to be increased over 10 times the basal level, whereas at speeds beyond 5 ft per second, metabolism was often more than 100 times the basal level. Certainly the latter rate could not be sustained for more than a short period of time. It is also of interest that unskilled swimmers expended from two to five times as much energy as skilled swimmers at comparable speeds and using the same stroke.

Data, such as the foregoing, are to be considered gross approximations when applied to any persons other than those by whom the actual work was performed. Any standard of this nature, although of value in calculating the needs of a population, must be considered merely as an indication of the general magnitude of the caloric requirements of a specific individual.

Except under unusual circumstances most adults maintain a rather constant body weight. It is the appetite which regulates the caloric intake from day to day, and the intake is definitely related to the requirement.

There are many possibilities of applying, in a practical way, knowledge of occupational caloric requirements. A rather amusing example by Cathcart (cited by Lusk (1), p. 473) is as follows. This investigator pointed out that to carry the 1914 equipment of the British soldier at 90 yd per minute required 4.25 Cal per minute, while the newly modified equipment demanded only 3.66 Cal. At two hours a day this would amount to a saving of 70.8 Cal per man per day, or 70,800 Cal per battalion, and over 1,000,000 Cal, or the equivalent of around 1000 loaves of bread, for each division of 15,000 men.

Calorigenic or specific dynamic action of foods. After the ingestion of foods, with all other conditions remaining as defined for the basal state, there is an increased total body heat production. This is known as the "specific dynamic action" or the "calorigenic action" of foods. Even today, the nature of the mechanisms involved in producing the extra heat are poorly understood.

The amount of extra heat produced and the length of the period of elevated heat production depend upon the type and the amount of food eaten. Protein foods show the greatest increment in heat production. After eating considerable protein, the increment in heat production may be as much as 30 per cent of the basal value. The specific dynamic action of carbohydrate and of fat amounts to only a few per cent. In the fasted subject the SDA of foods largely disappears.

Hawkins (10) stresses the point that specific dynamic action should be thought of in relation to basal metabolism. He cites an example which brings out this point very well. An individual has a BMR of 60 Cal per hour. He takes food equivalent to 200 Cal and during the next five hours expends not 300 Cal but 320 Cal, or an extra 10 per cent of the Cal eaten. At this time the BMR is again 60 Cal per hour, and the SDA of the food is over. The basal heat production of this individual is 1440 Cal per day, and this amount of Cal in his daily food would be insufficient to maintain balance, since 10 per cent of this will be lost as SDA. However, 1600 Cal will just allow for caloric balance. Ten per cent of 1600, the amount eaten, is 160 Cal, and this plus 1440 is 1600. If more than 1600 Cal are ingested, positive balance results.

If 2500 Cal were taken, there would be 810 Cal available for activity beyond the basal requirements [2500 − (250 + 1440)].

Work with human beings (11) indicates that the total SDA of a high protein meal (37 per cent) of about 1000 Cal amounts to 17 per cent, and that of an isocaloric low protein (7 per cent), high carbohydrate meal, to 9.6 per cent of the Calories consumed. This was determined in men in the sitting position, and the SDA was arrived at by measurement for 6.5 hours after the meal and then by calculation for the remaining time until the metabolic rate returned to the basal level.

Many individual amino acids exert SDA, and it is about the same if they are taken orally or given intravenously, indicating that the work involved in digestion and absorption does not enter into the picture. The amino acids need not be oxidized in order to exert their SDA, since in a diabetic dog the carbon atoms of administered glycine, for instance, may appear in the urine as sugar and the SDA may amount to about the same as that found in a normal dog following the same dose of amino acid.

There are many aspects of SDA that have not been explained. Various reviews of this large and somewhat confusing field are available (1, 12, 13, 14, 15).

Although there is considerable lack of agreement, a figure of 6 per cent of the basal metabolic rate roughly covers the SDA of the mixed diet consumed by many people. Obviously, this must be given consideration in arriving at caloric requirements.

The explanation for the SDA of foods remains quite incomplete. In the case of amino acids, the great variability in their SDA now appears to be associated largely with the nature of the deamination. Oxidative deamination (transformation into urea) is associated with a large heat increment, while in transamination the heat increment is small (16).

It is well known that glucose is readily converted into fat in the body, and that thiamine is involved in this transformation. In rats it has been demonstrated that glucose administered with thiamine exerts a greater SDA (8.0 per cent) than glucose alone (4.2 per cent) (17). This extra energy output may represent that required to prepare glucose for deposition in the form of fat.

The old plethora theory of Lusk has been revived to help explain the SDA of foods (11). According to this theory, the absorbed digestion products pass from the blood into the tissues and during the time that the rate of inflow exceeds the rate of utilization, there develops a plethora in the tissues. This brings about an accelerated rate of SDA which subsides as the flow of nutrients to the tissues decreases.

SPECIAL REFERENCES

1. Lusk, G.: *Science of Nutrition*, 4th ed. W. B. Saunders Co., Philadelphia, 1928.
2. McClendon, J. F., and Medes, G.: *Physical Chemistry in Biology and Medicine.* W. B. Saunders Co., Philadelphia, 1925, p. 158.
3. Du Bois, D., and Du Bois, E. F.: *Arch. Internal Med.*, **17**, 865, 1916.
4. Boothby, W. M., and Sandiford, R. S.: *Boston Med. Surg. J.*, **185**, 337, 1921.

5. Boothby, W. M.; Berkson, J.; and Dunn, H. H.: *Am. J. Physiol.*, **116**, 468, 1936.
6. Turner, C. E.: *Industrial Hygiene*, edited by A. J. Lanza and J. A. Goldberg. Oxford University Press, New York, 1939, p. 591.
7. Becker, G., and Hämäläinen, J. W.: *Skand. Arch. Physiol.*, **31**, 198, 1914.
8. Newburgh, L. H., and Robinson, W. D.: *Diseases of Metabolism*, 2nd ed., edited by G. G. Duncan, W. B. Saunders Co., Philadelphia, 1947, p. 508.
9. Karpovich, P. V., and Millman, N.: *Am. J. Physiol.*, **142**, 140, 1944.
10. Hawkins, W. W.: *Science*, **116**, 19, 1952.
11. Glickman, N.; Mitchell, H. H.; Lambert, E. H.; and Keeton, R. W.: *J. Nutrition*, **36**, 41, 1948.
12. Borsook, H.: *Biol. Revs., Cambridge Phil. Soc.*, **11**, 147, 1936.
13. Wilhelms, C. M.: *Physiol. Revs.*, **15**, 202, 1935.
14. Kriss, M.: *J. Nutrition*, **21**, 257, 1941.
15. Sadhu, D. P.: *Missouri Agr. Expt. Sta. Research Bull.*, No. 408, 1, 1947.
16. Sadhu, D. P., and Brody, S.: *Am. J. Physiol.*, **151**, 131, 342, 1947.
17. Ring, G. C.: *Am. J. Physiol.*, **138**, 488, 1943.

23

Lipid metabolism

The metabolism of lipids embraces the metabolism of fats, phospholipids, sterols, and glycolipids, though little is known of the metabolism of glycolipids. In fact, our knowledge of lipid metabolism as a whole is incomplete, and much work remains to be done.

The fats are of particular importance, because they represent the bulk of stored energy-producing food in the body. Fats are stored in the adipose tissues or fat depots, of which the fatty subcutaneous layer (panniculus adiposus) is generally the most important. Other depots include the omentum, mesentery, intermuscular connective tissues, and connective tissues around organs such as the kidneys and heart. These adipose tissues may contain as much as 90 per cent fat (triglycerides). Since the storage of carbohydrate (as glycogen) and of proteins in tissues is always accompanied by much water, and since the caloric value of fats is more than twice that of carbohydrate or protein, the storage of fats as a source of energy to the body is most efficient. Subcutaneous fat and fat about organs (perirenal fat, etc.) serve to protect against mechanical trauma and also to insulate against heat loss from the body.

Phospholipids, cholesterol, and glycolipids are not stored in the adipose tissues but are found in the various organs of the body as essential structural constituents.

BLOOD LIPIDS

The blood lipids, as all other blood constituents, are in a continuous state of change, and the quantities present at any given time are the resultant of processes adding lipids to the blood and processes removing them from it.

Lipids are added to the blood by absorption from the intestine, by synthesis, particularly by the liver, and by mobilization from the fat depots. They are removed from the blood by deposition in the depots (fats), by oxidation in the tissues, by utilization as components of tissues and tissue products, and by excretion into the intestine. These different processes of addition and subtraction affect different types of lipids differently. For example, fats are chiefly concerned in additions to and subtractions from the depots and in tissue oxidations, whereas phospholipids, sterols, and glycolipids primarily enter into the composition of tissues. The lipid composition of blood is accordingly a variable quantity, and in order that comparable values may be obtained, it is necessary to determine blood lipids under definitely controlled conditions. In order to obviate the effects of intestinal absorption, samples of blood for analysis are taken in the postabsorptive state (in the morning before breakfast). Since the lipid compositions of plasma and cells are widely different and the plasma lipids more accurately reflect the state of lipid metabolism, it is customary to use only the plasma for analysis.

The student should review the discussion of lipid absorption in Chapter 13 at this time.

Table 23.1. Plasma Lipids of Various Animal Species
Mean and standard deviations of plasma lipid values in fasting
oxalated plasma expressed as milligrams per 100 ml

Species	Man*	Cow	Albino Rat	Cat	Rabbit	Cockerel	Guinea Pig
Number tested	118	3	116	27	89	22	10
Total lipid	530 ± 74	348 ± 51	230 ± 31	376 ± 110	243 ± 89	520 ± 85	169 ± 34
Neutral fat	142 ± 60	105 ± 39	85 ± 30	108 ± 65	105 ± 50	225 ± 77	73 ± 33
Total fatty acids	316 ± 85	202 ± 55	152 ± 23	228 ± 82	169 ± 66	361 ± 74	116 ± 29
Total cholesterol	152 ± 24	110 ± 32	52 ± 12	93 ± 24	45 ± 18	100 ± 23	32 ± 5
Cholesterol esters	106 ± 25	73 ± 15	31 ± 10	63 ± 23	23 ± 12	66 ± 19	21 ± 4
Free cholesterol	46 ± 8	37 ± 15	21 ± 8	30 ± 10	22 ± 13	34 ± 9	11 ± 2
Phospholipids	165 ± 28	84 ± 21	83 ± 24	132 ± 53	78 ± 33	155 ± 34	51 ± 12

* All values are for healthy adults, either males or nonpregnant females.
From Boyd, E. M.: *J. Biol. Chem.*, 142, 131, 1942.

Table 23.1 gives the gross lipid composition of plasmas from several animal species, including healthy adult humans. The variation in plasma lipid concentration for the population as a whole varies much more widely (see Table 15.1, page 495).

Blood and tissue lipids do not contain the water-soluble short-chain fatty acids, which are rapidly oxidized after absorption.

Glycolipids are present in blood at very low concentrations.

The phospholipids of human plasma are composed of lecithins, sphingomyelins, and cephalins in ranges of 100–200, 10–50, and 0–30 mg per 100 ml, respectively.

While there is wide variation in the plasma lipid values within a group of normal persons, the values for any given individual tend to be much less variable. Sperry (1) has shown that although cholesterol may vary 60 per cent on both sides of the mean (107–320 mg per 100 ml) in a large group of the population, individuals generally show no more than 15 per cent variation over a long period of time. A similar relation holds for phospholipids, and to a much lesser extent for fats. Certain apparently normal people maintain low plasma lipid levels, whereas others maintain high levels. The mean plasma lipid values for the population at large may be pathologically high for one person and low for another. When possible, the condition of an individual's plasma lipids at any given time is determined best by comparison with his previously established normal lipid pattern.

Plasma cholesterol and phospholipids tend to rise and fall simultaneously, so that for normal persons the cholesterol to phospholipid ratio is relatively constant. An even more constant ratio is that of free cholesterol to total cholesterol, which in normal plasma varies from about 0.24 to 0.32 and averages about 0.28. It appears therefore that maintenance of the proper ratios between plasma lipids is more important than maintenance of absolute concentrations.

The general lipid composition of erythrocytes differs sharply from that of plasma, and shows much less variation as a result of disease, diet, and other influences. Erythrocytes contain more phospholipid than plasma, with a different distribution, cephalin being present at the highest and lecithin at the lowest concentration. Erythrocyte cholesterol varies from 125 to 150 mg per 100 ml, and in adults is present almost exclusively in the unesterified condition. The cells of children contain appreciable cholesterol esters. Erythrocytes contain practically no fat but more glycolipids than found in plasma.

Many factors influence the quantity and distribution of blood lipids. The plasma of infants and young children contains less total lipid and less of the various fractions than adult plasma. Race and sex do not appear to affect the plasma lipid content or distribution, nor do states of leanness or obesity. During starvation, when the body is obtaining its energy supply largely from fat oxidation, there may be elevation of plasma triglycerides along with greater increases in cholesterol and phospholipids. In severe diabetes and glycogen storage disease there is marked hyperlipemia, which represents increases in all fractions of plasma lipids, especially the triglycerides. Marked reduction in either available carbohydrate, as in fasting, or in capacity to use carbohydrate, as in diabetes, causes elevation of plasma lipids.

The mesenteric and thoracic duct lymph is a clear watery fluid in the postabsorptive state. However, soon after the ingestion of a high-fat meal the lymph becomes a milky fluid very rich in triglycerides, which are present as chylomicrons 0.5–1.0 μ in diameter. The chylomicrons contain 85–90 per cent triglyceride, small amounts of phospholipid and cholesterol (ratio about 2:1), very small amounts of unesterified fatty acid, and 0.2 to 1.0 per cent protein. The chyle passes from the thoracic duct into the left subclavian vein and mixes with the systemic blood. This causes a rapid increase in the plasma lipids, especially the triglycerides, which may be sufficient to impart a milky opalescence to the plasma. This rise in blood lipids is referred to as "alimentary" or "absorptive lipemia."

The lipids of the blood arise from intestinal absorption, mobilization from adipose tissue, and synthesis, especially in the liver.

LIPOPROTEINS OF PLASMA

At this time the student should review the discussion of lipoproteins in Chapter 15. These important substances are considered in articles by Fredrickson and Gordon (2), Lindgren and associates (3), Surgenor (4), Gofman (5), and Oncley (6).

Essentially all of the plasma lipids are present and transported as lipoprotein complexes, which contain phospholipids, cholesterol, and triglycerides united to α- and β-globulins. The unesterified fatty acids of plasma are combined as lipoproteins with the albumin fraction. The protein and phospholipid components of the lipoproteins make them soluble in water. The chylomicrons are stabilized in the watery plasma by the protein and phospholipid present, which, according to interface energetics, should be located in the surface of the chylomicrons with their charged groups oriented to the water phase.

The formation of plasma lipoproteins generally involves 8 to 12 per cent of the total plasma protein.

The α- and β-lipoproteins may be separated from plasma by the low temperature ethanol fractionation of Cohn and associates and purified by ultracentrifugation, electrophoresis, etc.

Oncley and associates studied a purified β-lipoprotein fraction from normal human plasma which had an anhydrous molecular weight of about 1,300,000, and a hydrated molecular weight of around 2,100,000. Each gram of anhydrous β-lipoprotein combines with about 0.6 g of water. It was estimated that each molecule of the hydrated lipoprotein contained about 44,000 molecules of water, 280 molecules of unesterified cholesterol, 760 molecules of cholesterol esters, 500 molecules of phospholipid, and protein representing 2500 amino acid residues. Small amounts of carotenoids also were present.

It has been shown that both the α- and β-lipoproteins of plasma represent mixtures. There are at least three main groups of lipoproteins in plasma. They are: (1) high-density lipoproteins, density > 1.063 (includes α-lipoproteins); (2) low-density lipoproteins, density < 1.063; and (3) chylomicrons. There is not a fine line of demarcation between the smallest chylomicrons and the lighest low density lipoproteins.

Gofman and associates, using their ultracentrifugal flotation technique (see Chapter 15), have studied in particular the low density lipoproteins, and assigned S_f values according to density. Examples of such values are as follows: S_f 0, d $= 1.063$; S_f 2, d $= 1.050$; S_f 4, d $= 1.040$; S_f 6, d $= 1.035$; S_f 8, d $= 1.029$; S_f 10, d $= 1.023$; S_f 13, d $= 1.015$; S_f 17, d $= 0.99$; S_f 40, d $= 0.96$; S_f 40,000 $=$ chylomicrons. The high-density lipoproteins lie between densities of 1.063 and 1.21.

The protein, cholesterol, phospholipid and triglyceride contents of the lipoproteins of different densities vary. The protein content of the S_f 4 class is about 25 per cent and decreases progressively to chylomicrons (S_f 40,000). Cholesterol and its esters vary from about 30 per cent in the S_f 4 class down to around 5 per cent in the S_f 40,000 class. The phospholipid of S_f 0 is about 25 per cent and decreases to about 7 per cent in S_f 40,000. The triglycerides increase from around 6 per cent in S_f 0 to more than 80 per cent in the chylomicrons.

Both phospholipid and cholesterol appear to enter and leave the lipoprotein macromolecules with relative ease under physiologic conditions.

Gofman has shown increased levels of certain lipoprotein groups, especially the S_f 10–20 group, in patients with arteriosclerotic disease.

Women in the 20–40 age group show a higher plasma content of high-density lipoproteins and a lower content of low-density lipoproteins than do men in the same age group. Low-density lipoproteins increase with age in both sexes.

Lipoprotein lipase or "clearing factor." Hahn in 1943 (7) found that following the injection of heparin into the circulation an enzyme appears in the blood, which hydrolyzes the triglycerides of the chylomicrons to glycerol and fatty acids. This enzyme was referred to as the "clearing factor," since it caused opalescent plasma to become clear. Lipoprotein lipase, which hydrolyzes triglycerides united to protein, has been obtained from plasma, adipose tissue, and myocardium and appears to be identical with Hahn's "clearing factor" (8). The enzyme differs from ordinary pancreatic lipase.

Lipoprotein lipase acts primarily on the triglycerides of the low density β-lipoproteins, including the chylomicrons in this category. Plasma albumin serves as an acceptor to bind the fatty acids liberated. It appears that an as yet unknown protein acts as a cofactor (9). The process may be formulated by the general equation:

$$\begin{array}{c} \text{Low density lipoproteins} \\ | \\ \text{Triglyceride} \end{array} + \text{Albumin} \xrightarrow[\text{"Coprotein"}]{\text{Lipoprotein lipase}}$$

Higher density lipoproteins + Albumin (fatty acids)$_n$ + Glycerol + Soluble mono- and diglycerides

Some of the triglycerides are only partly hydrolyzed as indicated, but the products are soluble, probably due to lipoprotein binding. This action of lipoprotein lipase serves to convert low density to high-density lipoproteins.

While there is no doubt about the activity of lipoprotein lipase in plasma after heparin injection, the role played by the enzyme in clearing plasma under normal physiologic conditions is much less certain. However, the fact that protamine, which inhibits the enzyme, can reverse the clearing effect of heparin in alimentary lipemia, and inhibit the action of the enzyme *in vitro* (9) strongly indicates the presence of low levels of the lipase under normal conditions of fat transport.

Origin of plasma lipoproteins and their removal from blood (10). The α- and β-lipoproteins of plasma are maintained at a relatively steady concentration by processes taking place predominantly in the liver. As previously indicated, plasma chylomicrons, representing mainly triglycerides, arise from thoracic lymph. Fat is mobilized from the fat depots, but the forms of its appearance in blood are not well understood. It probably is partly as lipoprotein triglycerides (including some chylomicrons) and unesterified fatty acids (UFA) combined with albumin. It is well established that severely decreased carbohydrate utilization, as seen in prolonged fasting and in diabetes, causes an outpouring of both triglycerides and UFA from adipose tissue. This is inhibited by feeding carbohydrate to the fasting and administering insulin to the diabetic animal, which increase carbohydrate utilization.

It has been shown that lipoproteins are removed from plasma at a rate which balances their entry, maintaining a relatively constant concentration. Lipoproteins, isotopically labeled in phospholipid or cholesterol, when introduced into the circulation, rapidly equilibrate with extravascular lipids. Most of the cholesterol and phospholipid of the lipoproteins is removed by the liver, and a small fraction by other tissues. It has been shown that plasma lipoproteins pass through the pores and leaks of the capillary membranes into the tissue fluid. The pores of the membrane appear to have a mean diameter of 60–90 Å, sufficient to pass the smaller α-lipoproteins (50 Å), while the much less numerous leaks (116–350 Å) permit the passage of the larger β-lipoproteins (185 Å). The liver cells apparently come in direct contact with the blood, thus enabling them more readily to take up the lipoproteins.

Chylomicrons, with diameters of 0.5–1.0 μ, carry on the average some 500 million fatty acid molecules each, yet they are removed exceedingly rapidly from plasma. It has been shown that C^{14}-glyceryl tripalmitate has a plasma half-life in dogs and rats of about 10 minutes (11). A large proportion of the chylomicron fat is taken up by the liver, though some appears in adipose and other tissues.

The mechanisms by which chylomicrons are removed from plasma are poorly understood. Evidence indicates that some chylomicrons pass from the plasma into the lymph though the amount is unknown, some probably are taken up by phagocytosis, though little is known about it, and some are converted to fatty acids by lipoprotein lipase, the fatty acids and glycerol then passing through capillary membranes to cells or being taken up by liver cells.

The unesterified fatty acids (UFA) of plasma arise from adipose tissue, lymph, and the action of lipoprotein lipase or clearing factor upon triglycerides. The UFA lipid fraction is very important metabolically. It serves as a source of fatty acids for oxidation and energy production in tissues. The concentration of plasma UFA falls during acute exercise, and the rate of labeled UFA disappearance from plasma increases (12).

Havel and Goldfien (13) have shown that the mobilization of unesterified fatty acids (UFA) into the circulation from adipose tissue in humans is increased by anxiety or discomfort. It was found that the administration of norepinephrine or epinephrine causes a rapid increase in plasma UFA. A concomitant increase in oxygen utilization with UFA increase was also observed. These workers consider that the sympathetic nervous system exerts a tonic action on the mobilization of fatty acids from adipose tissue, and that this action may be modified by central nervous stimuli and hormones such as insulin (decrease mobilization) and epinephrine and norepinephrine (increase mobilization).

The heart utilizes much UFA as a source of energy. Liver takes up and oxidizes fatty acids from UFA more readily than the fatty acids of chylomicron triglycerides. Cells of adipose tissue also take up fatty acids from UFA.

Havel and Fredrickson found that isotopically labeled fatty acids injected into dogs have a half-life of about two minutes. Similar results have been obtained for man (14).

It appears probable that the fatty acid-albumin complex (UFA) dissociates at the surface of the capillary endothelial cells, and that the fatty acids then pass across the capillary membrane through the endothelial cells to the tissues rather than passing through membrane pores. Such a mechanism appears probable because of the very rapid rate of passage of small lipid-soluble molecules through capillary membranes, a rate incompatible with passage through pores. Of course, liver cells in direct contact with blood would be expected to take up fatty acids of UFA at the high rate found.

TISSUE LIPIDS AND FAT STORAGE

The student is referred to Chapters 6 and 27 for detailed discussion of the composition and distribution of tissue lipids.

For a given animal species on a uniform diet the depot fat contains a relatively constant proportion of various fatty acids. For example, fats such as lard and beef tallow contain essentially the same kinds of fatty acids, but in widely different proportions, lard containing a higher proportion of unsaturated acids. However, the composition of depot fat may be markedly altered by changes in the diet. For example, the fat of pigs fattened on peanuts becomes softer and has a higher than normal iodine number, indicating the incorporation of unsaturated acids from the peanut oil. The ingestion of highly unsaturated fats tends to produce depot fats with acids more unsaturated than normal but less unsaturated than the acids of the fats fed. Conversely, the feeding of the more saturated fats causes the depot fatty acids to be less unsaturated than normal though more unsaturated than the acids of the fed fat. Thus there is a tendency for the body to change both the unsaturated and saturated acids toward the normal condition for the animal. The nature of the depot fat is best altered by diet after a preliminary period of starvation. The animal body readily forms fat from carbohydrate, and this fat contains a relatively high proportion of saturated fatty acids and is hard fat. Ellis and Zeller (15) found the fat formed by pigs on a high carbohydrate, low fat diet (rice and tankage) to be very hard, with large proportions of the glycerides of oleic, palmitic, and stearic acids.

These acids were present in the ratios of 4:2:1, respectively. The relation of diet to the chemical and physical properties of depot fat is of much importance in the animal industry.

Small amounts of free cholesterol are found in depot fat, and this tends to increase in certain pathologic conditions and in old age.

From the above discussion it is apparent that depot fat arises chiefly from dietary fat, and synthesis from carbohydrate, or substances which form carbohydrate such as the sugar-forming amino acids.

While the liver is concerned both with the synthesis of fatty acids and the modification of those from ingested lipids, it is well established from isotopic tracer studies that tissues in general synthesize fatty acids. It is of interest to note that the adipose tissue itself contributes to fat synthesis from carbohydrate. Tuerkischer and Wertheimer (16) showed that glycogen is initially deposited in the fat cells of rats which have been fasted to exhaust fat stores and then fed a high carbohydrate diet. The adipose tissue of such animals contains 0.2 to 0.5 per cent glycogen. This glycogen gradually disappears, with the simultaneous appearance of fat droplets. Mirski (17) found isolated glycogen-containing adipose tissue to have a respiratory quotient of 1.1 to 1.3, indicating conversion of carbohydrate to fat. Shapiro and Wertheimer (18) incubated the adipose tissue of rats with serum containing D_2O (heavy water) and found D to be incorporated into the fatty acids of the tissue. This incorporation of deuterium from D_2O is first into the carbohydrate present, which is then synthesized to fatty acids and fat.

Until recently animal depot fats were considered relatively inert, because the quantity remains relatively constant when the animal is in caloric equilibrium. However, the work of Schoenheimer and Rittenberg (19) has shown, on the contrary, that the depot fats are in a state of rapid flux. This was demonstrated by maintaining mice on a low fat diet to which 2 per cent of deuterized linseed oil (D attached to fatty acid carbon atoms) had been added and determining the rate of D appearance in the body fat, when the total quantity of this fat remained constant. At the end of four days on the deuterized oil the D content of the adipose fat showed that 44 per cent of this fat had been formed from the dietary fat. Since the total amount of depot fat had remained constant, 44 per cent of the depot fat had been removed or mobilized from the adipose tissues.

Stetten and Schoenheimer (20) have shown that the animal body readily alters the composition of fed fatty acids by desaturation and by shortening and lengthening the carbon chain. Rats were fed a normal diet containing 6 per cent of butter and supplemented with 0.56 per cent deuterized palmitic acid as the ethyl ester. After eight days the depot fats contained D corresponding to 44 per cent of that administered. The various fatty acids were isolated, and their D contents were determined. From these values it was calculated that 24.2 per cent of the palmitic acid, 9.3 per cent of the stearic acid, 5.6 per cent of the lauric and myristic acids, 6.3 per cent of the palmitoleic acid, 1.0 per cent of the oleic acid, and 0.0 per cent of the linoleic acid had been derived from the administered deuterized palmitic acid. These results show that the palmitic acid chain was lengthened by two carbons to form stearic acid, shortened by two and four carbons to form myristic and lauric acids, respectively, and desaturated to form palmitoleic acid. The D-containing oleic acid was probably formed by desaturation of the isotopic stearic acid produced. It is interesting to observe that isotopic linoleic acid, which is essential in the diet, was not formed.

That the animal body also can hydrogenate unsaturated fatty acids was shown by Rittenberg and Schoenheimer (21), who fed deuterio oleic acid to mice and found sufficient D in the saturated fatty acids of depot fat to indicate that two-thirds of these saturated acids had originated from the ingested deuterio oleic acid.

Schoenheimer and Rittenberg (22) showed that, when the animal body synthesizes fatty acids from carbohydrate in the presence of D_2O, large amounts of deuterium are incorporated in these acids. They fed a diet of bread to mice, injected them with D_2O, and then gave them sufficient D_2O in the drinking water to keep the D_2O content of the body fluids constant. At intervals animals were killed, and the D content of the total fatty acids was determined. In about a week the D content of the body fats had become constant, indicating equilibrium between synthesis and destruction.

The deuterium appears in the synthesized fatty acids because carbohydrate, such as glucose, takes up D from D_2O of the fluids and releases H. The fatty acids are then synthesized from the deuterized carbohydrate. It has been shown (23) that this synthesis of fatty acids from carbohydrate is accomplished by the coupling of many small molecules derived from the carbohydrate. This was indicated by the fact that the D content of the saturated acids rose to about half of that of the body water, indicating that D atoms were attached to carbon atoms all along the fatty acid chains. This could have occurred only by coupling many small deuterized molecules obtained from carbohydrate.

These workers also fed mice deuterized fat on a high carbohydrate diet with ordinary water to drink. After the feeding of deuterized fat was discontinued, a decrease in the D content of the body fats occurred. It was found that deuterium disappears from body fats at the same rate at which it appears during synthesis, further demonstrating that the processes of deposition and mobilization of depot fat go on simultaneously.

The inability of the body to form the essential unsaturated acids, linoleic and linolenic, was also demonstrated (24). Rats were injected with D_2O, causing D to be incorporated into the depot fats by synthesis from carbohydrate. The fatty acids of the body fat were fractionated, and large amounts of D were found in palmitic and stearic acids, but none in linoleic and linolenic acids. This experiment also demonstrated that there is no exchange of D of the body fluids and H of the fatty acids, but that any D appearing in the fats must arise by synthesis from carbohydrate (which does exchange H for D of the fluids).

It is of interest to note (23) that, when fats are synthesized from carbohydrate in the presence of D_2O, the deuterium is incorporated much more rapidly into the saturated than into the unsaturated acids; this means that the body synthesizes the saturated acids at a faster rate.

The various reversible interconversions and syntheses of fatty acids in the body as indicated by tracer studies may be summarized as follows:

$$
\begin{array}{cccc}
C_{18} & C_{16} & C_{14} & C_{12} \\
\text{Stearic} \rightleftharpoons & \text{Palmitic} \rightleftharpoons & \text{Myristic} \rightleftharpoons & \text{Lauric} \\
\Updownarrow & \Updownarrow & \Updownarrow & \Uparrow \\
\text{Oleic} & \text{Palmitoleic} & \text{Myristoleic} & \Downarrow
\end{array}
$$

$$
\text{Glucose etc.} \longrightarrow \text{Acetic acid} \rightleftharpoons \text{Shorter-chain acids}
$$

The processes of lengthening, shortening, saturating, and desaturating fatty acid chains go on reversibly and continuously.

Later work has definitely shown that fatty acids are synthesized from acetyl CoA molecules so that the carbon chains are built up by increments of two carbons at a time. As will be shown later, fatty acids are broken down in stages of two carbons at a time by splitting off acetyl CoA molecules.

That the chemical processes involved in the alterations of the depot fats are chiefly due to the action of the liver was shown by Bernhard and Schoenheimer (24). These workers found deuterium to be incorporated about seven times faster in liver lipids than in storehouse fats. Mice synthesized more than half of the liver fatty acids in one day, whereas a week was required for a comparable change in depot fatty acids. Stetten and Grail (25) estimated the half-life of liver fats in mice to be 2.6 to 2.8 days, as compared with 5 to 6 days for depot fats, indicating a much higher rate of turnover in the liver fats. Other evidence to be presented later substantiates the importance of the liver in fat metabolism.

The fats in the adipose tissue are being continually mobilized into the blood stream, and fats are continually formed and deposited in the adipose tissues. The liver modifies the blood fats by lengthening and shortening, and saturating and desaturating the fatty acid chains, and also by adding fat synthesized from glucose and other substances.

While the very rapid deposition and mobilization of fat in adipose tissues is well established, the mechanisms which control the processes are imperfectly understood (26).

Shapiro and associates (27) consider that the balance between mobilization and deposition is controlled by a factor acting in the adipose cell. It was found *in vitro* that fat-depleted adipose tissue but not fat-laden cells readily take up serum fat at 38° C. This uptake was prevented by metabolic poisons, such as cyanide, heating to 80° C, and cooling to 20° C, which indicates that penetration of fat into the cells is dependent upon cellular metabolism and represents active transport.

Various hormones have been shown to affect fat mobilization and deposition (26). Best and associates separated a factor from the anterior pituitary, called "adipokinin," which caused mobilization of fat from the depots to the liver and kidney in mice. Preparations of thyrotropic and lactogenic hormones of the anterior pituitary have been found to mobilize fat of adipose tissue, though contamination of these preparations by adipokinin is not excluded. Severance of the nerve supply to adipose tissue was found to abolish the fat-mobilizing action of pituitary preparations. Adrenal cortical hormones, insulin, and thyroid hormones are involved in the processes of fat mobilization and deposition.

Much evidence shows that nerve stimuli play an important role in fat deposition and mobilization (26). Excessive nerve stimulation causes the loss of fat from adipose tissue, while paralysis or denervation leads to increased deposition.

FUNCTIONS OF THE LIVER IN LIPID METABOLISM

The liver is an organ very actively concerned with lipid metabolism. The lipid content of the liver normally averages about 5 per cent and consists chiefly of phospholipids and neutral fat, though small amounts of both free cholesterol and its fatty acid esters are present. Normally, phospholipid fatty acids exceed those combined as neutral fat. It is also interesting to note that liver phospholipid fatty acids are more unsaturated than those of liver neutral fat. Formerly this was supposed to represent desaturation of the fatty acids by the liver preliminary to oxidation. The work of Schoenheimer and associates, however, showed that desaturation of fatty acids in the body appears limited to the introduction of a single double bond. Since liver phospholipids contain considerable amounts of the more unsaturated acids, such as linoleic and linolenic, these acids must represent selective incorporation from the dietary acids.

That the liver shows great activity in the metabolism of lipids is demonstrated by the following facts. The lipid content of the liver increases with mobilization of fat from the depots for any cause. During starvation, when large amounts of fat are being mobilized to supply the energy requirements of the body, the fat content of the liver is increased. High fat diets cause the liver to become loaded with fat. In untreated diabetes, when large amounts of fat are being mobilized, liver fat increases. Liver fatty acids quickly take on the nature of the acids of ingested fat, and during starvation they more nearly resemble the acids of depot fat. The synthesis and breakdown of fatty acids occurs with great rapidity in the liver. There is rapid synthesis and turnover of phospholipids in the liver, as shown by labeling with radioactive phosphorus. Cholesterol and cholesterol ester syntheses take place in the liver. The liver lengthens and shortens carbon chains and desaturates and saturates them. The liver also oxidizes fatty acids to carbon dioxide and water.

ACCUMULATION OF EXCESS LIPIDS IN THE LIVER—FATTY LIVERS

Mammalian liver normally contains about 5 per cent of lipids, but under the influence of various pathologic and physiologic disturbances the lipid content may rise to 25 or 30 per cent.

Many conditions have been found which cause the accumulation of excess fat in the liver; they are reviewed in articles by McHenry and Patterson (28) and Best and Lucas (29).

Conditions which decrease the rate of phospholipid synthesis and turnover in the liver (as shown by labeling with P^{32}) are generally associated with the accumulation of fat in the liver. While the explanation for this is not clear, it may be related, at least in part, to the demand for phospholipids as components of lipoproteins for lipid transport.

The fatty livers produced by various conditions and factors contain more cholesterol, chiefly as esters, more neutral fat, and less phospholipid than normal, though the proportions of these lipids present may vary widely under different conditions.

It has long been recognized that in conditions such as syphilis, alcoholism, and prolonged malarial fevers there may be cirrhosis of the liver associated with marked fat infiltration and deposition.

Injury to the liver by poisons such as phosphorus and carbon tetrachloride may lead to fatty infiltration of the liver. In acute yellow atrophy there may be extremely large accumulations of fat in the liver, at times amounting to 50 per cent of the liver weight. The above conditions appear to cause fatty livers because of tissue injury and decreased capacity of the liver to metabolize the lipids brought to it.

Fatty livers in diabetic animals not receiving insulin. Fatty livers under these conditions have been studied, particularly in depancreatized dogs. Such animals, maintained without insulin, mobilize large amounts of depot fat into the blood stream to supply their energy requirements. This fat, with that of the diet, is transported to the liver for the initial stages of metabolism. In this process some of the fatty acids are converted to phospholipids, some to cholesterol esters, and others undergo the initial stages of oxidation. The result is that the lipids of the blood and liver are increased. The fatty acids of both plasma and liver resemble those of the fat depots or diet, and the distribution of the types of lipids in plasma and liver are within the normal range. The fatty livers occurring under these conditions may be considered physiologic fatty livers. When the animals are given insulin, enabling them to oxidize carbohydrate, the lipids of plasma and liver decrease.

Fatty livers due to dietary deficiencies or alterations. It has been found that fatty livers result from various dietary deficiencies and alterations. For example, they may be produced by carbohydrate deprivation and by a deficiency of unsaturated essential fatty acids, of choline, of methionine, and of the vitamins pyridoxine and pantothenic acid. Fatty livers may also result from the ingestion of excess cholesterol, cystine, serine, guanidoacetic acid, and of the vitamins thiamine, biotin, and niacin. Substances which when given to animals prevent or relieve fatty livers are referred to as "lipotropic substances."

Fatty livers due to carbohydrate deprivation. During starvation the fuel for energy production is chiefly fat, and large amounts are mobilized into the blood stream from the depots and transported to the liver. The content of fat in the liver is increased so long as fat remains in the depots, and the fatty acids of the liver fat resemble those of the depot fat. In the later stages of starvation, when depot fat is exhausted, the fat content of the liver decreases. Carnivorous animals such as the dog do not show the initial fatty livers during starvation, presumably because the nature of the metabolic mixture utilized for energy in starvation is not radically different from that of the normal diet.

When rats or mice are given diets containing much fat, and free from carbohydrate, the livers accumulate large amounts of fat. This condition resembles that due to starvation in which excessive amounts of fat are presented to the liver for metabolism.

The fatty livers due to starvation and high fat, low carbohydrate diets, like those of diabetic animals without insulin, may be considered physiologic fatty livers.

Fatty livers due to deficiency of unsaturated fatty acids. As previously pointed out, the body is incapable of synthesizing the more unsaturated fatty acids and these must be obtained from the diet. Such acids are linoleic, linolenic, and arachidonic, and they are referred to as the "essential fatty acids." Since these fatty acids, along with others, are components of phospholipids of the liver and other tissues, when the quantity supplied by the diet is inadequate there is decreased phospholipid synthesis. The proper metabolism of fat in the liver is associated with a rapid phospholipid synthesis, which represents conversion of fatty acids to phospholipids and possibly is an essential process related to other metabolic changes. At any rate, that an active phospholipid turnover in the liver is necessary for the proper handling of fat in the liver has been well established. A deficiency of the essential fatty acids leads to the accumulation of excess fat in the liver, and presumably this is due to incapacity of the liver to synthesize phospholipids, with consequent inability properly to metabolize fat, which accumulates.

Fatty livers due to choline deficiency. A choline deficiency leads to fatty livers, because choline is required for phospholipid synthesis in the liver, and this is necessary in the processes of fat metabolism in the liver. Any process which slows down the rate of phospholipid synthesis and turnover in the liver tends to cause fatty livers.

Fatty livers due to cholesterol feeding. Best and Ridout (30) have shown that the feeding of cholesterol to rats produces fatty livers which contain an exaggerated proportion of cholesterol as well as excess neutral fat. Choline tends to alleviate the fat infiltration but has much less effect upon the cholesterol. Perlman and Chaikoff (31), using P^{32} as a tracer, showed that cholesterol feeding decreases the rate of phospholipid turnover in the liver, and that this effect of cholesterol could be neutralized by giving choline.

Since in the metabolism of cholesterol in the liver large amounts of cholesterol esters are formed, it appears probable that feeding cholesterol causes the tying up of essential fatty acids as cholesterol esters and creates a deficiency of these acids for phospholipid synthesis. Cholesterol feeding appears to be the most potent stimulant to lipid infiltration into the liver so far discovered.

Cholesterol fatty livers respond to treatment with large doses of choline.

Table 23.2 summarizes many of the causes of fatty livers, with lipotropic agents. As will be shown in Chapter 25, choline is synthesized through the

Table 23.2.   Fatty Livers and Lipotropic Agents

Cause	Lipotropic Agent
Deficiencies	
A. Essential fatty acids. Interfere with phospholipid synthesis.	Essential fatty acids.
B. Choline. Interferes with phospholipid synthesis.	Choline, methionine, betaine.
C. Pyridoxine. Increases demand for inositol and choline.	Inositol. Choline and methionine less effective.
D. Pantothenic acid. Effect unknown.	Choline? methionine?
E. Thyroid hormone. Lowered metabolism.	
Excesses	
A. Cystine. Stimulates appetite and metabolism. Diverts methionine.	Choline, methionine.
B. Cholesterol. Competes for fatty acids essential in phospholipid synthesis.	Choline, methionine.
C. Guanidoacetic acid. Takes up methyl groups to form creatine. Interferes with choline synthesis.	Choline, methionine.
D. Thiamine. Increases appetite and metabolism. Diverts methionine from choline synthesis.	Choline, methionine.
E. Biotin. Increases demand for inositol.	Inositol, lipocaic.
F. Riboflavin. Increases appetite and metabolism.	Choline, methionine.
G. Niacin. Causes choline deficiency by taking choline methyl groups.	Choline, methionine.
H. Anterior pituitary hormone. Effects possibly due to fat-mobilizing factor, adipokinin.	
I. Adrenal cortical hormones. Increase mobilization of fat to liver.	
J. Female sex hormones. Mechanism of action uncertain.	
Liver Poisons. CCl$_4$, P, etc., cause tissue injury and lowered capacity to metabolize lipids brought to liver.	Choline aids in recovery, does not prevent.

methylation of ethanolamine by methionine ("active" methionine). Consequently, methionine acts as a lipotropic agent because it enables the animal to synthesize choline when the latter is deficient. Substances such as cystine, thiamine, and riboflavin in excess increase appetite and metabolism and increase the demand for methionine for protein synthesis. This diverts methionine from the synthesis of choline and leads to fatty livers. Such substances do not cause fatty livers in the presence of adequate choline.

It is of interest that the quantity of choline in the liver tends to remain relatively constant, even in conditions which cause choline deficiency. The essential point is that in choline deficiency the rate at which choline turns over in phospholipid synthesis and breakdown is decreased. Only experiments using the tracer technique could have established this fact.

In general, agents which cause fatty livers also lead to the hemorrhagic degenerative changes in the kidneys discovered by Griffith and associates (32).

GENERAL RELATIONS IN LIPID METABOLISM

By absorption and synthesis the intestine passes fatty acids as glycerides, phospholipids, and cholesterol esters into chyle and blood. Some lipid is excreted from blood into the intestine.

The liver synthesizes fatty acids, fats, phospholipids, cholesterol, cholesterol esters; shortens, lengthens, saturates, and desaturates fatty acid chains;

by β-oxidation oxidizes fatty acids to acetyl CoA, part of which forms citric acid in the citric acid cycle and is completely oxidized to CO_2 and H_2O; condenses part of the acetyl CoA to acetoacetyl CoA, which is converted to acetoacetic acid and passed to the blood for oxidation in the peripheral tissues; and adds lipids to blood and takes them up from blood.

In general, tissues other than the liver also synthesize fatty acids and fats, cholesterol, and phospholipids, and oxidize fatty acids by β-oxidation to acetyl CoA, which is then oxidized in the citric acid cycle.

Blood transports glycerides, phospholipids, cholesterol, and cholesterol esters. Neutral fats from the blood are deposited in the depots and remobilized into the blood. Blood lipids chiefly arise from the intestine, liver, and fat depots.

The fat depots serve as reservoirs of food material, to receive fat from the blood and to add fat to it in proportion to the energy demands of the body. Mobilized depot fats pass to the liver where much of their metabolism takes place:

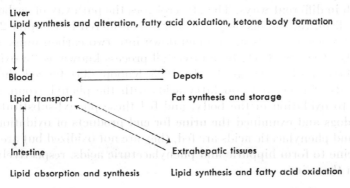

The extent to which extrahepatic tissues other than fat depots take lipids from blood and contribute lipids to it is uncertain.

Most of the over-all processes outlined in the above diagram of general lipid metabolism represent the summation of many different individual metabolic reactions, the mechanisms of some of which are known and will be considered in detail in later sections. Since many of the processes involved in the metabolism of carbohydrates, proteins (amino acids), and lipids are closely interrelated, the more complete understanding of lipid metabolism is achieved only through integration of all of these phases of metabolism. This is attempted in a later chapter.

RATES OF TURNOVER OF LIPIDS IN TISSUES

As indicated previously, the rate of fat turnover in the body has been studied by labeling with deuterium, and the rate of phospholipid turnover has been determined by labeling with P^{32}. The rate of cholesterol turnover has been followed also by labeling with deuterium. The rates of turnover for these lipids in rat whole carcass, liver, and brain are summarized in Table 23.3.

Table 23.3. Rates of Lipid Turnover in Rat Tissues
Expressed as half life in days

Lipid	Carcass	Liver	Brain
Fatty acids	6–9	1–3	10–15
Phospholipid	5–7	1–2	>200
Cholesterol	12–15	5–7	>100

The rapid rate of lipid turnover in the liver and the slow rate of turnover in the brain are good indices of the relative roles played by these diverse tissues in lipid metabolism.

METABOLISM OF FAT

The complete metabolism of fat in the body ultimately leads to oxidation to CO_2 and water, and the liberation of energy equivalent to 9 Cal per gram of fat. The mechanisms by which fat is metabolized involve a long series of successive processes in which the glycerol and fatty acid components are dealt with in different ways. The glycerol goes the pathway of carbohydrate in metabolism, the details of which will be considered in Chapter 24.

The fatty acids of fats are broken down into two carbon units as acetyl CoA, CH_3—CO—S—CoA, by an over-all process known as "β oxidation."

β-Oxidation of fatty acids. In 1905 Knoop (33) tagged the hydrocarbon ends of even and odd fatty acids with the phenyl group, which is resistant to oxidation in the body, and fed these phenyl-substituted fatty acids to dogs and examined the urine for end products of oxidation. When benzoic and phenylacetic acids are fed, they are not oxidized but are coupled with glycine to form hippuric and phenylaceturic acids, respectively, which appear in the urine:

$$\underset{\text{Hippuric acid}}{C_6H_5-\overset{\overset{\text{O}}{\|}}{C}-\overset{\overset{\text{H}}{|}}{N}-CH_2COOH} \qquad \underset{\text{Phenylaceturic acid}}{C_6H_5-CH_2-\overset{\overset{\text{O}}{\|}}{C}-\overset{\overset{\text{H}}{|}}{N}-CH_2COOH}$$

Knoop found that the feeding of phenyl-substituted even carbon acids, such as phenylbutyric, caused the excretion of phenylaceturic acid, while the feeding of phenyl-substituted odd carbon acids, such as phenylpropionic, and phenylvaleric caused the excretion of hippuric acid. In other words, the phenyl-substituted even carbon acids were oxidized to phenylacetic acid in the body, and the phenyl-substituted odd carbon acids were oxidized to benzoic acid.

$$\underset{\text{Phenylbutyric acid}}{C_6H_5-CH_2-CH_2-\ |-CH_2-COOH} \longrightarrow \underset{\text{Phenylacetic acid}}{C_6H_5-CH_2-COOH}$$

$$\underset{\text{Phenylpropionic acid}}{C_6H_5-CH_2-\ |-CH_2-COOH}$$

$$\underset{\text{Phenylvaleric acid}}{C_6H_5-CH_2-\ |-CH_2-CH_2-\ |-CH_2-COOH} \left. \right\} \longrightarrow \underset{\text{Benzoic acid}}{C_6H_5-COOH}$$

Knoop concluded that the oxidation of fatty acids takes place at the carbon atom in the β position to the carboxyl group. Dakin extended and confirmed Knoop's observations and concluded that fatty acids in general are oxidized at the β carbon with the splitting off of the two terminal carbons, leaving a fatty acid chain shorter by two carbons.

As a result of the work of many investigators over a long period of time, the detailed mechanisms of the β oxidation of fatty acids have been established. This work is reviewed in articles by Green (34), Lynen (35), and Kennedy (36).

The processes by which fatty acids are oxidized take place in the cell mitochondria (34) of tissues in general.

The coenzyme A derivatives of fatty acids, fatty acyl CoA derivatives, are first formed. These compounds then undergo a series of successive reactions which leads to the splitting off of acetyl CoA and the formation of an acyl CoA derivative containing two carbon atoms less than the initial acyl CoA compound. Repetition of the process progressively shortens the fatty acid chain until it has all been converted to acetyl CoA, which is oxidized in the citric acid cycle, as shown in Chapter 21.

The detailed reactions involved in β oxidation of fatty acids are outlined below:

I. Activation of fatty acids, formation of acyl coenzyme A derivatives. Fatty acids are converted into acyl CoA derivatives by the action of thiokinase enzymes, coenzyme A (HS—CoA), ATP and Mg^{++}:

$$R- COOH + HS- CoA + ATP \xrightarrow[Mg^{++}]{\text{Thiokinase}} R- CO- S- CoA + AMP + PPi$$

PPi represents inorganic pyrophosphate.

According to the work of Berg (37), the over-all activation process consists of two reactions, the first being the reaction of the fatty acid with ATP to form the fatty acid adenylate:

(a) $\quad$ R- COOH + ATP $\rightleftharpoons$ R- C- O- P- O- ribose- adenine + PPi

$$\underset{\substack{\text{OH} \\ \text{Adenyl or AMP group} \\ \text{Acyl adenylate}}}{}$$

(b) $\quad$ The acyl adenylate (R- CO- AMP) then reacts with HS- CoA:

$$R- CO- AMP + HS- CoA \rightleftharpoons R- CO- S- CoA + AMP$$

Acyl CoA

The acyl adenylates are acid anhydrides, as shown in the partial formula, and consequently are reactive high energy compounds.

Three fatty acid-activating enzymes or thiokinases have been found in animal tissues which are specific for certain chain lengths. Acetic thiokinase activates acetic and propionic acids and has been obtained from yeast, liver, and heart. A second activating enzyme isolated from liver, octanoic thiokinase or short-chain activating enzyme, activates fatty acids C_4 through C_{12}. A long-chain fatty acid-activating enzyme isolated from liver activates acids above C_{12}. Both acetic thiokinase and octanoic thiokinase have been obtained in highly purified form, and it appears that the single enzyme protein catalyzes both reactions of the activation process.

Shorter-chain fatty acids (C_4–C_6) also may be activated or converted into acyl CoA derivatives by reaction with succinyl CoA, the reaction being catalyzed by a thiophorase enzyme:

$$\text{Succinyl} - \text{S} - \text{CoA} + \text{Butyrate} \xrightleftharpoons{\text{Thiophorase}} \text{Succinate} + \text{Butyryl} - \text{S} - \text{CoA}$$

Succinyl CoA is formed in the citric acid cycle (Chapter 21), and also from succinate by a thiokinase and GTP:

$$\text{Succinate} + \text{HS} - \text{CoA} + \text{GTP} \rightleftharpoons \text{Succinyl} - \text{S} - \text{CoA} + \text{GDP} + \text{Pi}$$

It appears that in animal tissues fatty acid activation proceeds chiefly through the thiokinases, while in some microorganisms activation is largely through the thiophorases.

II. Formation of α,β-unsaturated fatty acyl CoA derivatives by acyl dehydrogenases. Acyl dehydrogenases, which are FAD-containing flavoproteins, have been isolated from liver. These enzymes remove H atoms from saturated fatty acyl CoA derivatives to form α-β-unsaturated acyl CoA compounds:

$$\text{R} - \text{CH}_2 - \text{CH}_2 - \text{CO} - \text{S} - \text{CoA} + \text{FP} \longrightarrow \text{R} - \text{CH} = \text{CH} - \text{CO} - \text{S} - \text{CoA} + \text{FP} \cdot \text{H} + \text{H}^+$$

FP and FP · H represent the oxidized and reduced forms of the flavoprotein acyl dehydrogenase enzyme, respectively.

The reduced acyl dehydrogenase, FP · H, is oxidized by a second FAD-containing flavoprotein, the electron-transferring flavoprotein (ETF) (38):

$$\text{FP} \cdot \text{H} + \text{ETF} \rightleftharpoons \text{FP} + \text{ETF} \cdot \text{H}$$

ETF · H may then be oxidized through the electron transport chain with the formation of two ATP (Chapter 21).

Three acyl dehydrogenases have been isolated from liver which act upon acyl CoA derivatives of different chain lengths. They are named according to the chain length for optimum activity. Shorter-chain acyl CoA derivatives are acted upon by butyryl dehydrogenase, which is a green flavoprotein containing copper. Hexanoyl dehydrogenase acts upon acyl CoA derivatives of intermediate chain length, while hexadecanoyl dehydrogenase acts on the long-chain derivatives. Both of these enzymes are yellow flavoproteins.

III. Hydration of α,β-unsaturated acyl CoA derivatives to form β-hydroxyacyl CoA derivatives. Enoyl hydrase (crotonase). The next stage in the β-oxidation process consists in the stereospecific addition of water to the α,β-unsaturated acyl CoA derivatives with the formation of L(+)-β-hydroxyacyl CoA derivatives, the reaction being catalyzed by enoyl hydrase:

$$\text{R} - \text{CH} = \text{CH} - \text{CO} - \text{S} - \text{CoA} + \text{HOH} \rightleftharpoons \text{R} - \overset{\displaystyle \text{OH}}{\underset{\displaystyle \text{H}}{\text{C}}} - \text{CH}_2 - \text{CO} - \text{S} - \text{CoA}$$

Enoyl hydrase, also called "crotonase" because it acts most readily upon crotonyl CoA, has been obtained from liver in crystalline condition (39). The enzyme acts only upon the trans forms of the unsaturated acyl CoA's. It contains one or more —SH groups which are essential for enzymatic activity.

IV. Oxidation of β-hydroxyacyl CoA derivatives to β-ketoacyl CoA derivatives. β-Hydroxyacyl dehydrogenase. The β-hydroxyacyl CoA derivatives are oxidized by the enzyme β-hydroxyacyl dehydrogenase to the β-ketoacyl CoA derivatives, DPN serving as cofactor:

$$\text{R-}\overset{\displaystyle OH}{\underset{\displaystyle H}{\text{C}}}\text{-CH}_2\text{-CO-S-CoA} + \text{DPN}^+ \rightleftharpoons \text{R-CO-CH}_2\text{-CO-S-CoA} + \text{DPN}\cdot\text{H} + \text{H}^+$$

The DPN · H is oxidized through the electron transport chain and forms three ATP (Chapter 21).

β-Hydroxyacyl dehydrogenase has been isolated in highly purified condition from beef liver (40).

V. Thiolytic cleavage of β-ketoacyl CoA derivatives by thiolases. The final stage in the process of β oxidation consists in the cleavage of the β-ketoacyl CoA derivatives by reaction with HS CoA, the reaction being catalyzed by a thiolase enzyme:

$$\text{R-CO-CH}_2\text{-CO-S-CoA} + \text{HS-CoA} \rightleftharpoons \underset{\text{Acetyl CoA}}{\text{CH}_3\text{-CO-S-CoA}} + \underset{\substack{\text{Fatty acyl CoA}\\\text{shorter by 2C}}}{\text{R-CO-S-CoA}}$$

Evidence indicates that there are several thiolases, varying in chain length specificity. It appears that they are thiol enzymes (contain —SH groups), and it seems probable that the thiolytic cleavage occurs in stages something as follows:

(a) $\text{R-CO-CH}_2\text{-CO-S-CoA} + \text{HS-Thiolase} \rightleftharpoons$
    $\text{R-CO-S-Thiolase} + \text{CH}_3\text{-CO-S-CoA}$

(b) $\text{R-CO-S-Thiolase} + \text{HS-CoA} \rightleftharpoons \text{R-CO-S-CoA} + \text{HS-Thiolase}$

The equilibrium of the over-all thiolytic or cleavage reaction lies far to the right and favors production of acetyl CoA.

The oxidation of octanoic acid to CO_2 and H_2O by β oxidation and oxidation in the citric acid cycle is outlined in Figure 23.1, and the general oxidation of fatty acids is shown in Figure 23.2. The student should review the citric acid cycle in Chapter 21 at this time.

The net over-all reaction involved in shortening a fatty acid by two carbons may be represented:

$$\text{R-CH}_2\text{-CH}_2\text{-COOH} + 2\text{HS-CoA} + \text{ATP} + \text{FP} + \text{DPN}^+ \longrightarrow$$
$$\text{R-CO-S-CoA} + \text{AMP} + \text{PPi} + \text{CH}_3\text{-CO-S-CoA} + \text{FP}\cdot\text{H} + \text{DPN}\cdot\text{H} + 2\text{H}^+$$

The acetyl CoA formed in the β oxidation of fatty acids mixes with the pool of acetyl CoA derived from the metabolism of carbohydrate and various

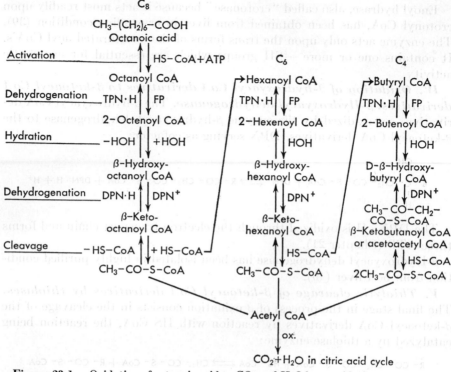

Figure 23.1.   Oxidation of octanoic acid to CO_2 and H_2O by β-oxidation and oxidation in the citric acid cycle.

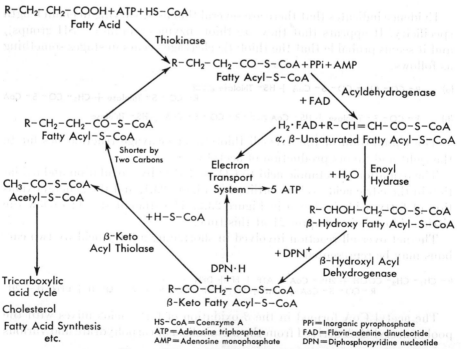

Figure 23.2. β-Oxidation of fatty acids.

amino acids. As will be discussed later acetyl CoA is used for many biological purposes such as synthesis of fatty acids, cholesterol, ketone bodies, and acetyl choline. Its key position as a source of energy production in the citric acid cycle has already been considered in Chapter 21.

ENERGY PRODUCTION IN FATTY ACID OXIDATION

It will be noted from previous discussion of β oxidation that the first stage of oxidation of a fatty acid (II) forms two molecules of ATP per two H atoms oxidized, while the second stage of oxidation (IV) forms three ATP. Thus for each cleavage of a fatty acid five ATP are produced. The oxidation of a molecule of acetyl CoA in the citric acid cycle forms 12 ATP (Chapter 21). Suppose we consider the utilizable energy production (ATP) in the complete oxidation of palmitic acid, $C_{15}H_{31}COOH$, to CO_2 and H_2O. The chain contains 16 carbon atoms, and β oxidation takes place seven times, with the formation of $7 \times 5 = 35$ ATP. Eight molecules of acetyl CoA are formed, which when oxidized in the citric acid cycle yield $8 \times 12 = 96$ ATP. Thus, the total ATP formed in the complete oxidation of a mol of palmitic acid is $35 + 96 = 131$ mols. However, since a mol of ATP per mol of fatty acid is required to "spark" β oxidation through formation of acyl CoA, 130 mols net of ATP are produced. Each mol of ATP represents about 7000 cal of free energy (Chapter 20) stored for metabolic use, so the oxidation of a mol of palmitic acid yields about $130 \times 7000 = 910,000$ cal of utilizable energy.

The combustion of palmitic acid to CO_2 and H_2O liberates a total of 2,330,500 cal per mol. Consequently, the quantity of this total energy converted into the utilizable energy of ATP is $910,000/2,330,500 \times 100 = 39$ per cent.

Oxidation of odd-carbon and branched-chain fatty acids. While the occurrence of odd-carbon fatty acids in natural lipids is rare, some are formed in the metabolism of amino acids, as are some branched-chain fatty acids.

Odd-carbon fatty acids undergo β oxidation according to the same mechanisms operating for even-carbon acids, with the progressive splitting off of molecules of acetyl CoA. However, in the oxidation of odd-carbon fatty acids, the last three carbon atoms of the chain form propionyl CoA.

Branched-chain fatty acids, such as isobutyric and isocaproic, also are oxidized to form propionic acid (propionyl CoA), probably in outline as follows, the acyl CoA derivatives not indicated but being understood as involved:

$$\begin{array}{c} CH_3 \\ | \\ CH-CH_2-CH_2-COOH \longrightarrow CH_3-COOH + \\ | \\ CH_3 \end{array} \qquad \begin{array}{c} CH_3 \\ | \\ CH-COOH \longrightarrow \\ | \\ CH_3 \end{array}$$

Isocaproic acid   Acetic acid   Isobutyric acid

$$\begin{array}{c} COOH \\ | \\ CH_3-CH-COOH \longrightarrow CH_3-CH_2-COOH + CO_2 \end{array}$$

Methylmalonic acid   Propionic acid

Metabolism of propionic acid. The metabolism of propionic acid proceeds by various pathways through succinic acid, and involves the "fixation" of CO_2 (41):

(a)   Propionic acid $+$ HS $-$ CoA $+$ ATP $\xrightarrow{\text{Thiokinase}}$ AMP $+$ PPi $+$ Propionyl CoA

(b) $CH_3 - CH_2 - CO - S - CoA + CO_2 \xrightarrow{\text{Carboxylase}}$
       Propionyl CoA

$$CH_3 - \underset{\displaystyle CO - S - CoA}{\overset{\displaystyle COOH}{CH}}$$

Methyl
malonyl CoA

(c)
$$CH_3 - \underset{\displaystyle CO - S - CoA}{\overset{\displaystyle COOH}{CH}} \xrightarrow{\text{Isomerase}} \underset{\displaystyle \underset{\displaystyle CO - S - CoA}{CH_2}}{\overset{\displaystyle COOH}{\underset{\displaystyle CH_2}{\mid}}}$$

Methyl malonyl CoA   Succinyl CoA

Succinyl CoA is converted to succinic acid and oxidized in the citric acid cycle (Chapter 21), or through pyruvic acid it may form carbohydrate. It is utilized in introducing the succinyl group into substances such as sulfanilamide (to form succinyl-sulfanilamide), in the formation of the CoA derivatives of shorter-chain fatty acids (fatty acid activation), in the synthesis of porphyrins (Chapter 15), and in the generation of ATP (Chapter 21).

FORMATION AND METABOLISM OF THE KETONE BODIES
KETOSIS

Generally the intermediate compounds involved in the oxidation of fatty acids do not accumulate in the tissues and body fluids. However, under circumstances in which carbohydrate utilization is severely restricted and fat metabolism proportionately increased to supply the energy demands of the body—such as starvation, very high fat diets, phlorizin diabetes, and diabetes mellitus—the so-called ketone bodies may accumulate in quantities (ketosis). The term "ketone bodies" is applied to the ketone acid, acetoacetic acid, and acetone and β hydroxybutyric acid, which are derived from acetoacetic acid:

(a) $CH_3 - CO - CH_2 - COOH \longrightarrow CH_3 - CO - CH_3 + CO_2$
       Acetoacetic acid   Acetone

(b) $CH_3 - CO - CH_2 - COOH + DPN \cdot H + H^+ \xrightarrow[\text{dehydrogenase}]{\substack{\beta \text{ Hydroxybutyric} \\ \text{in liver}}} CH_3 - \underset{\displaystyle H}{\overset{\displaystyle OH}{C}} - CH_2 - COOH + DPN^+$
       Acetoacetic acid

D($-$)-β-Hydroxybutyric
acid

The proportions of acetoacetic and D($-$)-β-hydroxybutyric acids in blood vary widely, acetoacetate predominating when liver glycogen is relatively low and β-hydroxybutyrate when liver glycogen is relatively high.

It is of interest that reduction of acetoacetyl CoA in the β oxidation process by β-hydroxyacyl dehydrogenase and DPN · H yields L(+)-β-hydroxybutyryl CoA. The acid excreted in urine is D(−)-β-hydroxybutyric acid, formed by reduction of acetoacetic acid as indicated above.

It will be seen from Figure 23.1 that acetoacetyl CoA is an intermediate in the β oxidation of fatty acids and is also formed from acetyl CoA (of any origin) by reversal of the cleavage reaction:

$$2CH_3-CO-S-CoA \underset{\text{Thiolase}}{\overset{}{\rightleftarrows}} CH_3-CO-CH_2-CO-S-CoA + HS-CoA$$

Free acetoacetic acid is formed from acetoacetyl CoA largely in the liver, which is rich in deacylase enzyme. The over-all process is:

$$CH_3-CO-CH_2-CO-S-CoA + HOH \xrightarrow{\text{Deacylase}} HS-CoA + CH_3-CO-CH_2-COOH$$

The reaction may proceed as above or in two steps as follows:

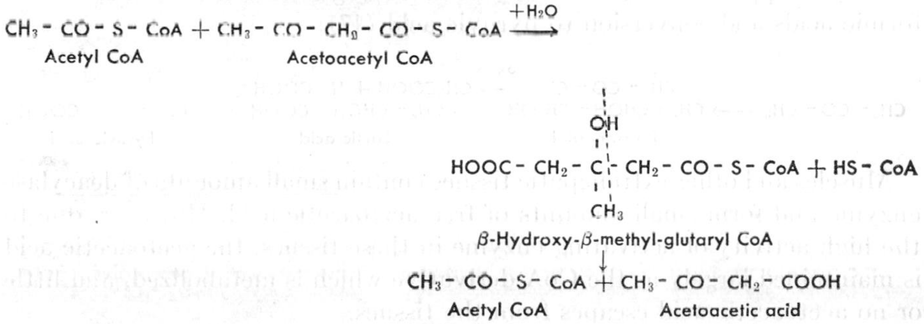

$$\underset{\text{Acetyl CoA}}{CH_3-CO-S-CoA} + \underset{\text{Acetoacetyl CoA}}{CH_3-CO-CH_2-CO-S-CoA} \xrightarrow{+H_2O}$$

$$\underset{\beta\text{-Hydroxy-}\beta\text{-methyl-glutaryl CoA}}{HOOC-CH_2-\overset{\overset{OH}{|}}{\underset{\underset{CH_3}{|}}{C}}-CH_2-CO-S-CoA + HS-CoA}$$

$$\downarrow$$

$$\underset{\text{Acetyl CoA}}{CH_3-CO-S-CoA} + \underset{\text{Acetoacetic acid}}{CH_3-CO-CH_2-COOH}$$

The sum of the reactions is:

$$\text{Acetoacetyl CoA} + H_2O \longrightarrow \text{Acetoacetic acid} + HS-CoA$$

Potentially the liver may form several molecules of acetoacetic acid from each molecule of long-chain fatty acid. For example, each molecule of palmitic acid (C_{16}) forms eight acetyl CoA from which four molecules of acetoacetyl CoA and acetoacetic acid may be formed as a maximum.

That the liver is the chief source of ketone bodies has been thoroughly established. Embden and associates (42) and Snapper and associates (43) perfused livers, skeletal muscles, lungs, and kidneys and found that only liver forms appreciable quantities of ketone bodies. Jowett and Quastel (44) found that slices of spleen, testis, brain, and kidney produced small amounts of ketone bodies, but liver slices formed 10 to 40 times more. Mirsky and Broh-Kahn (45) found that ketosis could not be produced in eviscerated rats (in absence of liver). Stadie, Zapp, and Lukens (46) incubated liver slices and muscle minces together and found that the muscle used up the ketone bodies formed by the liver.

When free acetoacetic acid is once formed in the liver, it is not efficiently reconverted to acetoacetyl CoA (activated) in the liver, because liver is deficient in the activating enzyme system. Consequently much of the free acetoacetic acid cannot be further metabolized in the liver but passes into the circulation and is transported to the muscles and other peripheral tissues which reconvert it to acetoacetyl CoA by reaction with succinyl CoA:

Acetoacetyl

Acetoacetic acid + Succinyl CoA $\xrightleftharpoons[\text{succinicthiophorase}]{}$ Acetoacetyl CoA + Succinic acid

The acetoacetyl CoA is then split into acetyl CoA by cleavage enzyme (thiolase), and the acetyl CoA is oxidized in the citric acid cycle or used for other purposes:

Thiolase

$$CH_3- CO- CH_2- CO- S- CoA + HS- CoA \xrightarrow{} 2CH_3- CO- S- CoA$$

Thus, the liver converts acetoacetyl CoA formed in it into acetoacetic acid, which then is further metabolized by the peripheral tissues.

Acetone, which is slowly formed spontaneously by decarboxylation of acetoacetic acid, and which makes up a very small fraction of the ketone bodies, is apparently metabolized both through oxidation to acetic and formic acids and conversion to pyruvic acid (47):

ox

$$CH_3- CO- CH_3 \longrightarrow CH_3COOH + H \cdot COOH$$
$$CH_3- CO- CH_3 \longrightarrow CH_3- CHOH- CH_2OH \longrightarrow CH_3- CHOH- COOH \longrightarrow CH_3- CO- COOH$$
$$\text{Propanediol} \qquad\qquad \text{Lactic acid} \qquad\qquad \text{Pyruvic acid}$$

Muscles and other extrahepatic tissues contain small amounts of deacylase enzyme and form small amounts of free acetoacetic acid. However, due to the high activity of activating enzyme in these tissues, the acetoacetic acid is maintained largely as the CoA derivative which is metabolized, and little or no acetoacetic acid escapes from the tissues.

Normally, the blood contains not more than a few milligrams per cent of ketone bodies and less than 0.1 g is excreted in the urine per day, which means that the rate at which the peripheral tissues utilize ketone bodies balances their rate of production in the liver. However, when the quantity of fatty acid metabolized is greatly increased due to starvation, very high fat diets, or severe diabetes, the rate of ketone body production in the liver exceeds the capacity for their utilization in the peripheral tissues. Under these conditions the ketone body content of blood increases (ketonemia), urinary excretion increases (ketonuria), and a condition of ketosis exists. If severe, the breath may smell strongly of acetone.

The very severe diabetic may excrete as much as 120 g of ketone bodies in the urine per day, chiefly as acetoacetic and β-hydroxybutyric acids, acetone accounting for only a very small fraction. Breusch and Ulusoy (48) estimate the maximum production of ketone bodies by human liver to be about 150 g per kilogram per day, so the liver of a 75-kg severely diabetic man weighing about 2 kg could form about 300 g of ketone bodies per day, which represents the metabolism of about 200 g of fat. This amount of ketone body production greatly exceeds the metabolic capacity of the peripheral tissues, and the difference between production and utilization is excreted in the urine. If such an individual excretes 120 g of ketone bodies his tissues then may be oxidizing around 180 g per day (300 − 120).

Susceptibility to ketosis varies widely with animal species and age, as well as with sex. The decreasing order of susceptibility with species may be given as follows: human beings and monkeys > steers, goats, rabbits, and rats > dogs. Dogs are exceedingly resistant to starvation ketosis. Rats and others of this group show much less ketosis upon starvation than human beings and monkeys do.

Heinbecker (49) studied the effects of starvation upon ketosis in Arctic Eskimos subsisting on a meat diet (high fat and protein, low carbohydrate) and found less ketone bodies excreted in the urine than in the case of Americans or Europeans. The maximum excretion on the seventh day of starvation was only 3.4 g. Other racial differences in susceptibility to ketosis appear not to have been observed.

The blood ketones gradually rise during the first day of starvation. Crandall (50) studied the blood ketones of six subjects and found an average of 0.3 mg per cent in the postabsorptive state. The average values for the succeeding two days of starvation were 11 and 21 mg per cent, respectively.

Deuel and Gulick (51) studied the effect of fasting on the ketonuria of men and women. These workers found the average daily total ketone body excretion of male subjects, expressed as grams per square meter of body surface, for a control day followed by four fasting days to be: control day 0.02; first fasting day 0.05; second fasting day 0.86; third fasting day 1.90; and fourth fasting day 2.66. The maximum total excretions by one male subject were, respectively, in grams, 0.04, 0.28, 5.01, 8.06, and 8.94. The normal female subjects showed considerably more ketone bodies in the urine than the males. The average values for the females, expressed similarly as for the males, were, 0.02, 0.54, 4.25, 8.47, and 6.56. The maximum excretions for a woman in grams per day for the control day and the three succeeding fast days were 0.03, 0.05, 4.02, and 20.67. The women were much less able to withstand starvation than were the men.

Various studies on subjects fasting up to 30 days have shown ketone body excretion approximately of the same order as found by Deuel and Gulick on the fourth day of fasting. Butts and Deuel (52) showed that fasting causes lower liver glycogen levels in female than in male rats.

The very great difference in ketosis (ketonemia and ketonuria) caused by fasting and by severe diabetes mellitus is worthy of note, fasting causing the excretion of only 5–10 g of ketone bodies per day, while in severe diabetes the excretion may amount to more than 100 g. In each case the body is obtaining most of its energy by the oxidation of fatty acids, but the diabetic puts out many times as much ketone bodies as does the fasting subject. The difference may be related to a decreased capacity of diabetic muscle (and other tissues) to metabolize ketone bodies. The skeletal muscle of diabetic rats has been shown to utilize acetoacetate much less readily than the muscle of normal rats (53).

It appears that any condition which lowers the liver glycogen below a certain level is associated with ketosis. This is explainable upon the basis that in the absence of carbohydrate more fat must be metabolized to provide energy for the liver in particular and for the body as a whole. The availability of carbohydrate to the liver for oxidation is generally proportional to that for the body in general except in cases of liver damage. When oxidation of carbohydrate in the liver is curtailed, more fat is oxidized, producing more ketone bodies which pass in the blood to the peripheral tissues and are there oxidized to spare carbohydrate oxidation in these tissues. Thus the level of carbohydrate oxidation in the liver serves as a regulatory mechanism for the oxidation of fat in general. Decreased oxidation of carbohydrate in the liver is associated with increased fat oxidation throughout the body, and vice versa.

Ketosis is abolished by increasing the metabolism of carbohydrate in the liver. In diabetes this is accomplished by giving insulin, and in ketosis due to carbohydrate deprivation by giving glucose or substances readily convertible to glucose and glycogen.

Infants and young children are much more subject to starvation ketosis than are adults, probably because of less stabilized mechanisms for maintaining their liver glycogen levels.

Ketosis generally occurs in conditions of alkalosis. MacKay and coworkers (54) showed that the administration of bicarbonate to fasting rats increases the ketosis. Booher and Killian (55) demonstrated ketosis in patients with alkalosis caused by giving bicarbonate and by loss of hydrochloric acid due to vomiting. The reasons for alkalosis ketosis are not clear. However, MacKay and associates found the liver glycogen of their fasted rats given bicarbonate to be low and postulated that an alkalosis inhibits formation of glucose from protein.

Since both β-hydroxybutyric and acetoacetic acid are relatively strong organic acids, their accumulation in quantities in the body produces a metabolic acidosis. Their excretion in the urine involves the loss of Na^+ in particular, leading to total electrolyte and Na^+ deficiency. The severe diabetic excretes large quantities of both ketone bodies and glucose in the urine, with an obligatorily large quantity of water, producing dehydration in addition to the electrolyte deficiency. The symptoms of the severely diabetic patient—such as central nervous system depression, leading to coma, hyperpnea, and loss of tissue turgor—are related to the acidosis, electrolyte deficiency, and dehydration. In combating the condition carbohydrate metabolism must be restored by administration of insulin (and at times glucose), which decreases ketone body production, and the electrolytes and fluids of the body must be restored. This is generally accomplished by intravenous injection of isotonic solutions of sodium salts, such as NaCl, $NaHCO_3$, or sodium lactate. Occasionally the addition of potassium salts also is desirable.

BIOSYNTHESIS OF FATTY ACIDS

The naturally occurring fatty acids of animal tissues contain chains of even numbers of carbon atoms from C_4 to C_{24} and increase by increments of two carbon atoms. As previously pointed out, the body synthesizes most of these fatty acids and converts them into the various types of lipids or oxidizes them. Much evidence from experiments with tissue slices and other preparations, as well as with intact animals, has shown that fatty acids can be synthesized from any substance in the body capable of forming acetate. This includes carbohydrates, many amino acids, ethyl alcohol, and, of course, fatty acids themselves:

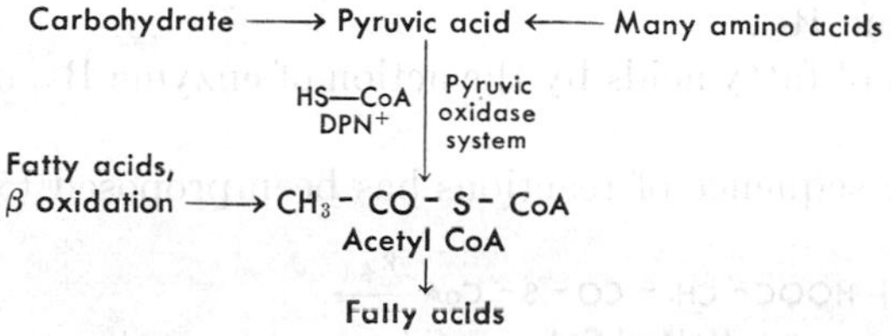

$$\text{Carbohydrate} \longrightarrow \text{Pyruvic acid} \longleftarrow \text{Many amino acids}$$

$$\begin{array}{c} \text{HS—CoA} \\ \text{DPN}^+ \end{array} \Bigg| \begin{array}{c} \text{Pyruvic} \\ \text{oxidase} \\ \text{system} \end{array}$$

$$\begin{array}{l} \text{Fatty acids,} \\ \beta \text{ oxidation} \longrightarrow \text{CH}_3 - \text{CO} - \text{S} - \text{CoA} \\ \qquad\qquad\qquad\quad \text{Acetyl CoA} \\ \qquad\qquad\qquad\qquad\;\; \downarrow \\ \qquad\qquad\qquad\;\; \text{Fatty acids} \end{array}$$

The β-oxidation of fatty acid chains takes place in the mitochondria as previously outlined. Wakil and associates (50) have demonstrated the synthesis of long chain fatty acids from acetyl CoA by liver mitochondrial enzymes incubated with C^{14}-acetyl CoA, TPN $\cdot$ H, DPN $\cdot$ H and ATP. This synthesis appears to represent essentially the reversal of the β-oxidation processes.

While some fatty acid synthesis may take place in the above manner, it appears probable that most synthesis is effected by a different system of reactions, localized in the cytoplasm, discovered by Gibson, Wakil and associates (51). These workers have isolated and purified two enzyme systems from liver, R_{1g} and R_{2g}, which, acting in sequence, form long chain fatty acids from acetyl CoA. TPN $\cdot$ H, ATP, Mn^{++}, and HCO_3^- are required as cofactors. The enzyme R_{1g} contains biotin as an essential component.

Fatty acid synthesis through the action of enzymes R_{1g} and R_{2g} appears to proceed as follows:

1. Formation of malonyl CoA from acetyl CoA and CO_2 through the action of enzyme R_{1g}:

$$\text{CH}_3 - \text{CO} - \text{S} - \text{CoA} + \text{CO}_2 + \text{ATP} \xrightarrow[\text{Mn}^{++}]{R_{1g}} \begin{array}{c} \text{COOH} \\ | \\ \text{CH}_2 \\ | \\ \text{CO} - \text{S} - \text{CoA} \\ \text{Malonyl CoA} \end{array} + \text{ADP} + \text{Pi}$$

Lynen and associates (52) have obtained evidence that CO_2 is activated as follows:

$$\text{ATP} + \text{Biotin-enzyme} \rightleftharpoons \text{ADP-Biotin-enzyme} + \text{Pi}$$
$$\text{CO}_2 + \text{ADP-Biotin-enzyme} \xrightarrow{R_{1g}} \text{CO}_2\text{-Biotin-enzyme} + \text{ADP}$$

The CO_2-biotin-enzyme complex then reacts with acetyl CoA to form malonyl CoA:

$$CH_3 - CO - S - CoA + CO_2\text{-Biotin-enzyme} \rightleftharpoons \begin{array}{c} COOH \\ | \\ CH_2 \\ | \\ CO - S - CoA \end{array} + \text{Biotin-enzyme}$$

Malonyl CoA

That the CO_2 taken up in the reaction to form malonyl CoA does not appear in the synthesized fatty acids has been shown by the use of $C^{14}\text{-HCO}_3$ in the tissue incubation medium (57). It is eliminated in the reactions catalyzed by enzyme R_{2g}.

2. Formation of fatty acids by the action of enzyme R_{2g} upon acetyl CoA and malonyl CoA.

The following sequence of reactions has been proposed (53):

$$CH_3 - CO - S - CoA + HOOC - CH_2 - CO - S - CoA \xrightarrow{R_{2g}}$$
Acetyl CoA   Malonyl CoA

$$CH_3 - CO - CH(COOH) - CO - S - CoA \xrightarrow{TPN \cdot H} CH_3 - CHOH - CH(COOH) - CO - S - CoA \xrightarrow{-H_2O}$$
α-Carboxyacetoacetyl CoA   α-Carboxy-β-hydroxybutyryl CoA

$$CH_3 - CH = C(COOH) - CO - S - CoA \xrightarrow{TPN \cdot H} CH_3 - CH_2 - CH(COOH) - CO - S - CoA \xrightarrow{-CO_2}$$
α-Carboxycrotonyl CoA   α-Carboxybutyryl CoA

$$CH_3 - CH_2 - CH_2 - CO - S - CoA$$
Butyryl CoA

Butyryl CoA may then react with malonyl CoA in a similar series of reactions with the formation of hexanoyl CoA. Thus, by cycling the acetyl CoA through the reaction sequence, the fatty acid chain is built up two carbons at a time through condensation with malonyl CoA.

From recent work of Brady (54) it appears probable that, in the above sequence of reactions, the CO_2 is split out at the stage of the first reaction when acetyl CoA reacts with malonyl CoA rather than in the last reaction as shown. Brady was unable to obtain evidence for the presence of acetylmalonyl CoA as an intermediate. In this case the scheme of synthesis becomes:

$$CH_3 - CO - S - CoA + \begin{array}{c} COOH \\ | \\ CH_2 \\ | \\ CO - S - CoA \end{array} \xrightarrow{R_{2g}} CO_2 + HS - CoA + CH_3 - CO - CH_2 - CO - S - CoA \xrightarrow{TPN \cdot H}$$
Acetyl CoA   Malonyl CoA   Acetoacetyl CoA

$$CH_3 - CHOH - CH_2 - CO - S - CoA \xrightarrow{-H_2O} CH_3 - CH = CH - CO - S - CoA \xrightarrow{TPN \cdot H}$$
β-Hydroxybutyryl CoA   Crotonyl CoA

$$CH_3 - CH_2 - CH_2 - CO - S - CoA$$
Butyryl CoA

The over-all synthesis of palmitic acid from acetyl CoA and malonyl CoA may be represented:

$$\text{Acetyl CoA} + 7 \text{ malonyl CoA} + 14 \text{ TPN} \cdot H \xrightarrow{R_{2g}} \text{Palmityl CoA} + 14 \text{ TPN}^+ + 7 CO_2 + 7 \text{ HS} - CoA$$

Catravas and Anker (55,56) have demonstrated the presence of a substance, lipogenin, in liver, which, in exceedingly small quantities, stimulates lipogenesis by liver both *in vitro* and *in vivo*. This substance may be of significance in the normal regulation of lipogenesis.

The reactions proposed for the synthesis of fatty acids are summarized in Figure 23.3. Much work remains to be done in clarifying the details of fatty acid synthesis.

Normally most of the acetyl CoA utilized for fatty acid and lipid synthesis in general is derived from carbohydrate through pyruvate. It appears that in the normal rat some 30 per cent of the dietary carbohydrate is utilized

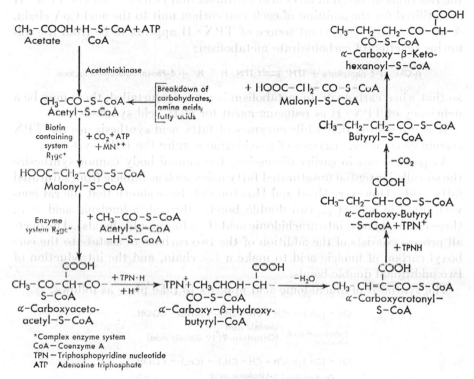

Figure 23.3.   Biosynthesis of fatty acids.

for lipid synthesis. An animal maintained in a steady state on a high carbohydrate lipid-free diet mobilizes and oxidizes depot fat and replaces it by synthesis from carbohydrate.

Convincing evidence has accumulated to show that the major site of carbohydrate conversion to fat is in the adipose tissue (63). Slices of adipose tissue convert glucose to fatty acids at a rate faster than that of liver slices. This, together with the fact that the adipose tissue of man weighs about six times more than liver, indicates that the adipose tissue itself and not the liver is the major site of fat synthesis.

The rate of lipogenesis in an animal falls markedly on a restricted diet insufficient to maintain body weight. The synthesis of fat in thiamine-deficient and pyridoxine-deficient animals is decreased, apparently due to the fact that thiamine pyrophosphate is necessary for the conversion of pyruvic acid to acetyl CoA (Chapter 24), and pyridoxal phosphate is necessary in the deamination of certain amino acids (Chapter 25) to form keto acids that are converted to acetyl CoA. Thus, lipid synthesis is decreased by any factor which decreases the supply of acetyl CoA.

Lipogenesis is markedly decreased in the diabetic state apparently for at least two reasons. Because of the drastic reduction in carbohydrate metabolism, little acetyl CoA is derived from carbohydrate. It will be noted from the reactions involved in fatty acid synthesis that two molecules of TPN · H are utilized for the addition of each two carbon unit to the acyl CoA chain. A quantitatively important source of TPN · H appears to be from the following reaction of carbohydrate metabolism:

$$\text{D-Glucose-6-phosphate} + \text{TPN}^+ \rightleftharpoons \text{TPN} \cdot \text{H} + \text{H}^+ + \text{6-Phosphoglucono-δ-lactone}$$

so that when carbohydrate metabolism is severely curtailed, there may be a deficiency of TPN · H as reducing agent for fatty acid synthesis.

It is interesting that while enzymes of fatty acid synthesis use the TPN system as cofactor, enzymes of β oxidation require the DPN system.

As pointed out in earlier discussion, the animal body cannot synthesize the so-called essential unsaturated fatty acids such as linoleic from saturated fatty acids. However, Mead and Howton (64) have shown that the rat converts linoleic acid (C_{18}, two double bonds) through γ-linolenic acid (C_{18}, three double bonds) into arachidonic acid (C_{20}, four double bonds). The overall process consists of the addition of the two carbons of acetate to the carboxyl carbon of linoleic acid to make a C_{20} chain, and the introduction of two additional double bonds.

The synthesis of arachidonic acid appears to take place as follows:

$$CH_3 - (CH_2)_4 - (CH = CH - CH_2)_2 - (CH_2)_6 - COOH$$

	Linoleic acid
Dehydrogenated, introduce =	(Octadeca-9:12-dienoic acid)

$$CH_3 - (CH_2)_4 - (CH = CH - CH_2)_3 - (CH_2)_3 - COOH$$

	γ-Linolenic acid
Condensation with acetate, adds 2C	(Octadeca-6:9:12-trienoic acid)

$$CH_3 - (CH_2)_4 - (CH = CH - CH_2)_3 - (CH_2)_5 - COOH$$

	Eicosa-8:11:14-trienoic acid
Dehydrogenated, introduce =	

$$CH_3 - (CH_2)_4 - (CH = CH - CH_2)_4 - (CH_2)_2 - COOH$$

Arachidonic acid
(Eicosa-5:8:11:14-tetraenoic acid)

BIOSYNTHESIS OF TRIGLYCERIDES AND PHOSPHATIDES (PHOSPHOLIPIDS)

The chemistry of the phosphatides or phospholipids has been considered in Chapter 6 which the student should review.

The mechanisms by which the phosphatides and triglycerides are synthesized in tissues have been established by a number of workers and are reviewed by Kennedy (65).

Synthesis of triglycerides. The synthesis of triglycerides from fatty acyl CoA derivatives and glycerol proceeds as follows (65):

$$
\begin{array}{l}
\text{CH}_2\text{OH} \\
|\\
\text{ATP} + \text{CHOH} \xrightarrow[\text{kinase}]{\text{Glycero-}} \\
|\\
\text{CH}_2\text{OH} \\
\text{Glycerol}
\end{array}
\quad
\begin{array}{l}
\text{CH}_2\text{OH} \\
|\\
\text{HO} - \text{C} - \text{H} \\
|\\
\text{CH}_2 - \text{O} - \text{PO}_3\text{H}_2 \\
\text{L-}\alpha\text{-Glycerophosphate}
\end{array}
\quad + \text{ADP}
$$

$$
\begin{array}{l}
\text{CH}_2\text{OH} \\
|\\
\text{HO} - \text{C} - \text{H} \\
|\\
\text{CH}_2 - \text{O} - \text{PO}_3\text{H}_2 \\
\text{L-}\alpha\text{-Glycerophosphate}
\end{array}
+ 2\,\text{R} - \text{CO} - \text{S} - \text{CoA} \xrightarrow{\text{Enzyme}}
\begin{array}{l}
\text{CH}_2 - \text{O} - \text{CO} - \text{R} \\
|\\
\text{R} - \text{CO} - \text{O} - \text{C} - \text{H} \\
|\\
\text{CH}_2 - \text{O} - \text{PO}_3\text{H}_2 \\
\text{L-}\alpha\text{-Phosphatidic acid}
\end{array}
+ 2\,\text{HS} - \text{CoA}
$$

Acyl CoA

$$
\begin{array}{l}
\text{CH}_2 - \text{O} - \text{CO} - \text{R} \\
|\\
\text{R} - \text{CO} - \text{O} - \text{C} - \text{H} \\
|\\
\text{CH}_2 - \text{O} - \text{PO}_3\text{H}_2 \\
\text{L}\alpha\text{Phosphatidic acid}
\end{array}
+ \text{HOH} \xrightarrow{\text{Phosphatase}}
\begin{array}{l}
\text{CH}_2 - \text{O} - \text{CO} - \text{R} \\
|\\
\text{R} - \text{CO} - \text{O} - \text{C} - \text{H} \\
|\\
\text{CH}_2 - \text{OH} \\
\text{D-1,2-Diglyceride}
\end{array}
+ \text{Pi}
$$

$$
\begin{array}{l}
\text{CH}_2 - \text{O} - \text{CO} - \text{R} \\
|\\
\text{R} - \text{CO} - \text{O} - \text{C} - \text{H} \\
|\\
\text{CH}_2 - \text{OH} \\
\text{D-1,2-Diglyceride}
\end{array}
+ \text{R} - \text{CO} - \text{S} - \text{CoA} \xrightarrow{\text{Enzyme}}
$$

Acyl CoA

$$
\begin{array}{l}
\text{CH}_2 - \text{O} - \text{CO} - \text{R} \\
|\\
\text{R} - \text{CO} - \text{O} - \text{C} - \text{H} \\
|\\
\text{CH}_2 - \text{O} - \text{CO} - \text{R} \\
\text{Triglyceride}
\end{array}
+ \text{HS} - \text{CoA}
$$

Synthesis of phosphatides. The synthesis of lecithins (65) involves the introduction of a phosphorylcholine group into a D-1,2-diglyceride (see above). The compound cytidine diphosphate choline (CDP-choline) reacts with the 1,2-diglyceride to form lecithin (phosphatidyl choline):

Cytidine monophosphate group (CMP)

Phosphorylcholine group

Cytidine diphosphate choline (CDP-choline)

The formation of a lecithin takes place as follows:

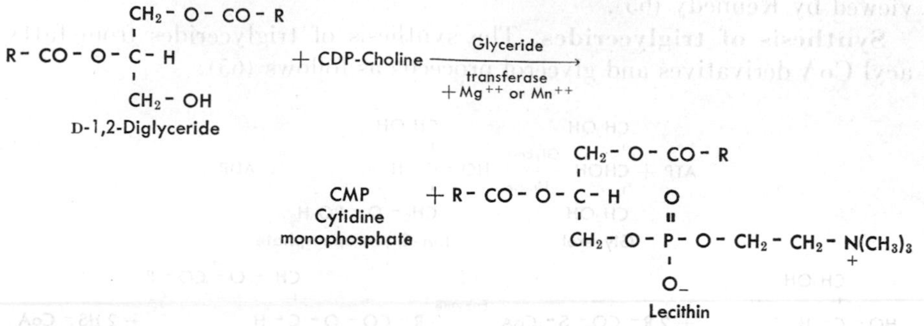

$$
\begin{array}{c}
CH_2-O-CO-R \\
| \\
R-CO-O-C-H \\
| \\
CH_2-OH \\
\text{D-1,2-Diglyceride}
\end{array}
\quad + \text{ CDP-Choline} \xrightarrow[\substack{+ Mg^{++} \text{ or } Mn^{++}}]{\text{Glyceride transferase}}
$$

$$
\begin{array}{c}
CH_2-O-CO-R \\
| \\
CMP \quad + R-CO-O-C-H \qquad O \\
\text{Cytidine} \qquad\qquad\qquad | \qquad\qquad \| \\
\text{monophosphate} \qquad CH_2-O-P-O-CH_2-CH_2-N(CH_3)_3 \\
\qquad\qquad\qquad\qquad\qquad | \qquad\qquad\qquad\quad + \\
\qquad\qquad\qquad\qquad\qquad O_- \\
\qquad\qquad\qquad\qquad\qquad\qquad \text{Lecithin}
\end{array}
$$

Cytidine diphosphate choline is formed by the following sequence of reactions:

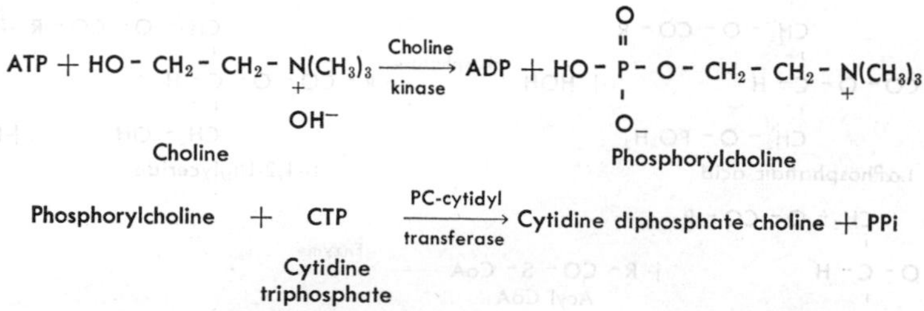

$$
ATP + HO-CH_2-CH_2-\underset{+}{N(CH_3)_3} \xrightarrow[\text{kinase}]{\text{Choline}} ADP + HO-\overset{\overset{\displaystyle O}{\|}}{P}-O-CH_2-CH_2-\underset{+}{N(CH_3)_3}
$$
$$
\underset{\text{Choline}}{OH^-} \qquad\qquad\qquad\qquad\qquad \underset{\text{Phosphorylcholine}}{O_-}
$$

$$
\text{Phosphorylcholine} \quad + \quad CTP \xrightarrow[\text{transferase}]{\text{PC-cytidyl}} \text{Cytidine diphosphate choline} + PPi
$$
$$
\begin{array}{c}\text{Cytidine} \\ \text{triphosphate}\end{array}
$$

PC-cytidyl transferase represents the enzyme phosphorylcholine-cytidine transferase.

The CMP formed in the reaction of the 1,2-diglyceride and CTP to give lecithin is rephosphorylated to CTP by ATP.

The phosphatidyl ethanolamines (cephalins) are synthesized by reactions entirely analogous to those for the synthesis of lecithins. Phosphoethanolamine is converted to cytidine diphosphate ethanolamine, which reacts with D-1,2-diglycerides to form the phosphatidyl ethanolamine.

$$
\begin{array}{c}
OH \\
| \\
HO-P-O-CH_2-CH_2NH_3^+ \\
| \\
O_- \\
\text{Phosphoethanolamine}
\end{array}
$$

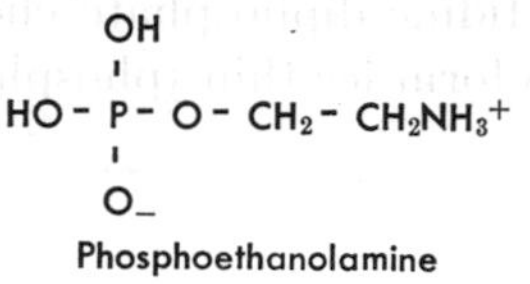

The sphingomyelins are synthesized by reaction of N-acylsphingosine (ceramide) with cytidine diphosphate choline (66):

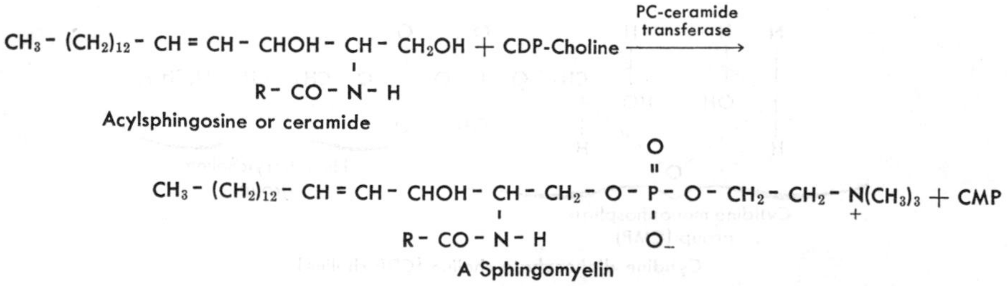

$$
\begin{array}{c}
CH_3-(CH_2)_{12}-CH=CH-CHOH-CH-CH_2OH + \text{CDP-Choline} \xrightarrow[\text{transferase}]{\text{PC-ceramide}} \\
| \\
R-CO-N-H \\
\text{Acylsphingosine or ceramide}
\end{array}
$$

$$
\begin{array}{c}
\qquad\qquad\qquad\qquad\qquad\qquad O \\
\qquad\qquad\qquad\qquad\qquad\qquad \| \\
CH_3-(CH_2)_{12}-CH=CH-CHOH-CH-CH_2-O-P-O-CH_2-CH_2-\underset{+}{N(CH_3)_3} + CMP \\
| \qquad\qquad\qquad | \\
R-CO-N-H \qquad\qquad O_- \\
\qquad\qquad \text{A Sphingomyelin}
\end{array}
$$

The acylsphingosines presumably are formed by reaction of fatty acyl CoA derivatives with sphingosine.

Brady et al. (67) have presented evidence that the synthesis of sphingosine through the action of an enzyme of rat brain involves reduction of palmityl CoA to palmitaldehyde, condensation of palmitaldehyde with serine to form dihydrosphingosine and oxidation of dihydrosphingosine to sphingosine:

(a) $CH_3 - (CH_2)_{14} - CO - S - CoA + TPN \cdot H + H^+ \xrightarrow{\text{enzyme}}$
Palmityl CoA

$$CH_3 - (CH_2)_{14} - CHO + TPN^+ + HS - CoA$$
Palmitaldehyde

(b) $CH_3 - (CH_2)_{14} - CHO + HO - CH_2 - CH(NH_2) - COOH \xrightarrow[\text{pyridoxal phosphate}]{\text{enzyme, Mn}^{++}}$
Palmitaldehyde   Serine

$$CO_2 + CH_3 - (CH_2)_{12} - CH_2 - CH_2 - CHOH - CH - CH_2OH + FP \xrightarrow{\text{enzyme}}$$
$$\underset{NH_2}{|}$$
Dihydrosphingosine

$$CH_3 - (CH_2)_{12} - CH = CH - CHOH - CH - CH_2OH + FP \cdot H + H^+$$
$$\underset{NH_2}{|}$$
Sphingosine

The syntheses of choline and ethanolamine are given in Chapter 25.

It is of interest that CTP (to form the diphosphate choline derivative), but not ATP or any of the other purine or pyrimidine triphosphates, is active in the above syntheses. Also the synthesis of the phosphatidyl cholines and ethanolamines requires the D-1,2-diglyceride specifically.

The synthesis of inositol phosphatide by an enzyme system present in the insoluble residue of guinea pig mitochondria has been reported by Brady and associates (68). The synthesis involves interaction of phosphatidic acid, cytidine diphosphate choline, and inositol in the presence of Mg^{++}. The sequence of proposed reactions is:

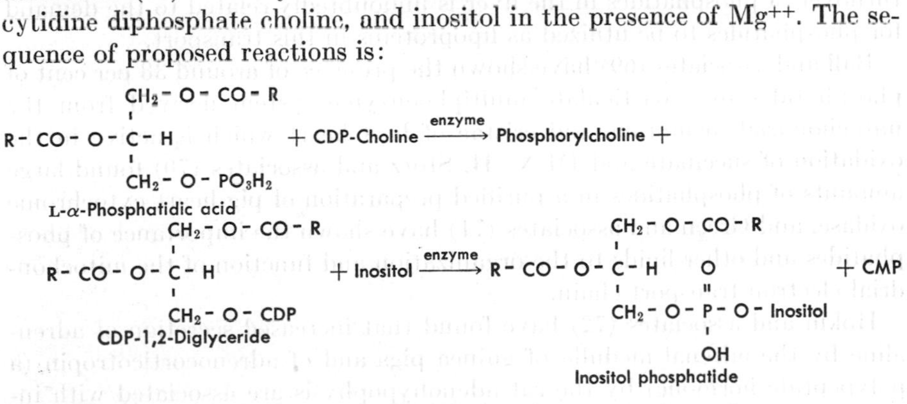

$$CH_2 - O - CO - R$$
$$|$$
$$R - CO - O - C - H \quad + CDP\text{-Choline} \xrightarrow{\text{enzyme}} \text{Phosphorylcholine} +$$
$$|$$
$$CH_2 - O - PO_3H_2$$
L-α-Phosphatidic acid

$$CH_2 - O - CO - R$$
$$|$$
$$R - CO - O - C - H \quad + \text{Inositol} \xrightarrow{\text{enzyme}} $$
$$|$$
$$CH_2 - O - CDP$$
CDP-1,2-Diglyceride

$$CH_2 - O - CO - R$$
$$|$$
$$R - CO - O - C - H \qquad O \qquad + CMP$$
$$| \qquad\qquad ||$$
$$CH_2 - O - P - O - Inositol$$
$$|$$
$$OH$$
Inositol phosphatide

While the syntheses of phosphatidyl serines and plasmalogens are unknown, it appears probable that mechanisms similar to those involved in the synthesis of other phosphatides may be involved.

Figure 23.4 outlines some of the main reactions involved in the synthesis of lipids.

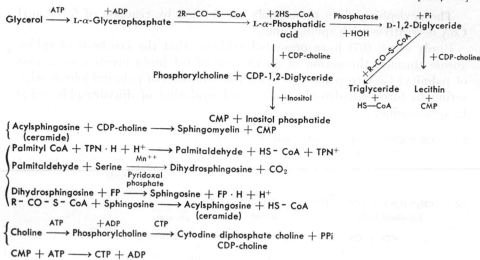

Figure 23.4. Synthesis of lipids and some associated reactions.

FUNCTIONS OF THE PHOSPHATIDES

Phosphatides are present in the plasma and cells of blood and in all tissue cells, though in greatly varying amounts in different tissues (Chapter 6). They generally exist to a large extent in combination with proteins and other lipids as lipoprotein complexes. Such complexes in cells contribute to cellular organization and structure. The lipoproteins of plasma, rich in phosphatides, are essential to the transport of fat and other lipids. The rapid synthesis and turnover of phosphatides in the liver is undoubtedly related to the demand for phosphatides to be utilized as lipoproteins in this transport.

Ball and associates (69) have shown the presence of around 38 per cent of phosphatides in a particulate multiple-enzyme system derived from the mitochondrial membrane and cristae of beef heart which is active in the oxidation of succinate and DPN · H. Stotz and associates (70) found large amounts of phosphatides in a purified preparation of pig heart cytochrome oxidase, and Green and associates (71) have shown the importance of phosphatides and other lipids to the organization and function of the mitochondrial electron transport chain.

Hokin and associates (72) have found that increased secretion of adrenaline by the adrenal medulla of guinea pigs and of adrenocorticotropin (a polypeptide hormone) by the rat adenohypophysis are associated with increased incorporation of P^{32} into the tissue phosphatides, indicating functional activity of the phosphatides in relation to these secretions.

Other evidence (57) indicates that phosphatides aid in maintaining the polarization and excitability of nerve and are involved in the selective cation transport across the erythrocyte membrane. It appears probable that phosphatides are important components of cell membranes in general.

As pointed out in Chapter 15, phosphatide is an essential component of thromboplastin, a factor in blood coagulation.

STEROL METABOLISM

The metabolism of sterols in the body is concerned with cholesterol and its derivatives. Unmodified plant sterols are very poorly absorbed from the gastrointestinal tract.

The biosynthesis of cholesterol. The biosynthesis of cholesterol is reviewed by Cornforth (59), and in Ciba Foundation Symposium, *Biosynthesis of Terpenes and Sterols* (Wolstenholme, G. E. W., and O'Connor, C. M., eds. Little, Brown & Co., Boston, 1959).

That cholesterol is synthesized in the animal body has been shown by many investigators. Dam (73) fed chicks low cholesterol diets and found more cholesterol in their bodies and excreta than contained in their food and the eggs from which they were hatched. Imhäuser (74) found more sterol in the feces of a human subject than was contained in the food eaten. Schoenheimer and Breusch (75) maintained mice on a low cholesterol diet (bread, or bread and fat) and found that they synthesized as much cholesterol in a month as was contained in their bodies at the beginning of the experiment.

It has been thoroughly established by the use of labeled compounds that acetate and compounds which produce acetate in their metabolism are utilized in the synthesis of cholesterol (76). It has also been shown that all of the carbon atoms in cholesterol may be derived from acetate (77) in the form of acetyl CoA. While not all of the fine details relative to the biosynthesis of cholesterol have been worked out, the main pathway appears to be established, and involves a succession of reactions: acetyl CoA $\longrightarrow$ acetoacetyl CoA $\longrightarrow$ mevalonic acid $\longrightarrow$ squalene $\longrightarrow$ lanosterol $\longrightarrow$ zymosterol $\longrightarrow$ desmosterol $\longrightarrow$ cholesterol, a number of stages being involved in some of the processes.

The first process consists in: activation of acetate to acetyl CoA (see previous discussion); or generation of acetyl CoA from fatty acids, carbohydrate (through pyruvate), or the deaminated chains of amino acids.

The second process is the condensation of acetyl CoA to acetoacetyl CoA (see previous discussion).

Acetoacetyl CoA reacts with acetyl CoA to form β-hydroxy-β-methylglutaryl CoA (HMG—S—CoA), the reaction being catalyzed by the HMG—S—CoA condensing enzyme (78):

$$CH_3 - CO - CH_2 - CO - S - CoA + CH_3 - CO - S - CoA \rightleftharpoons$$

Acetoacetyl CoA   Acetyl CoA

$$HOOC - CH_2 - \overset{\overset{\displaystyle CH_3}{|}}{\underset{\underset{\displaystyle OH}{|}}{C}} - CH_2 - CO - S - CoA + HS - CoA$$

β-Hydroxy-β-methyl-glutaryl CoA

Mevalonic acid is formed by reduction of β-hydroxy-β-methyl-glutaryl CoA by TPN $\cdot$ H (79):

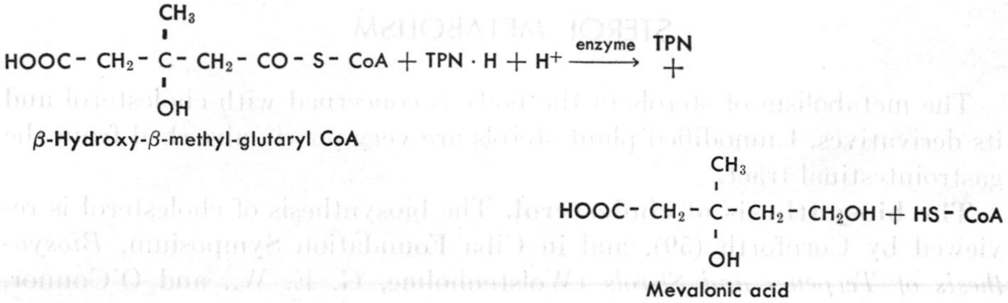

$$\underset{\text{OH}}{\overset{\text{CH}_3}{\text{HOOC}-\text{CH}_2-\text{C}-\text{CH}_2-\text{CO}-\text{S}-\text{CoA}}} + \text{TPN}\cdot\text{H} + \text{H}^+ \xrightarrow{\text{enzyme}} \overset{\text{TPN}}{+}$$

β-Hydroxy-β-methyl-glutaryl CoA

$$\underset{\text{OH}}{\overset{\text{CH}_3}{\text{HOOC}-\text{CH}_2-\text{C}-\text{CH}_2-\text{CH}_2\text{OH}}} + \text{HS}-\text{CoA}$$

Mevalonic acid

Mevalonic acid is converted to 5-phosphomevalonic acid by ATP through the action of mevalonic kinase (80):

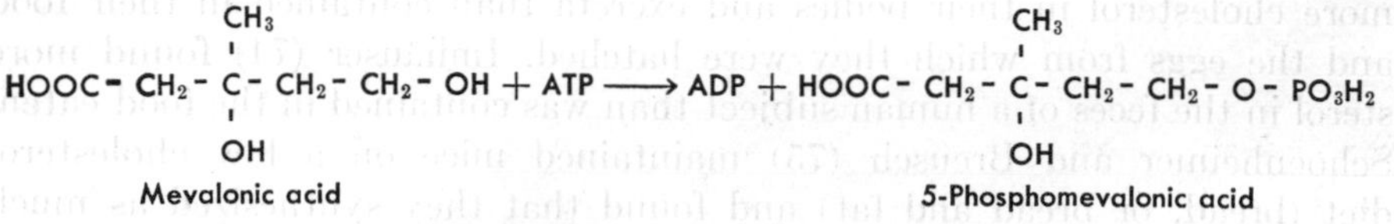

$$\underset{\text{OH}}{\overset{\text{CH}_3}{\text{HOOC}-\text{CH}_2-\text{C}-\text{CH}_2-\text{CH}_2-\text{OH}}} + \text{ATP} \longrightarrow \text{ADP} + \underset{\text{OH}}{\overset{\text{CH}_3}{\text{HOOC}-\text{CH}_2-\text{C}-\text{CH}_2-\text{CH}_2-\text{O}-\text{PO}_3\text{H}_2}}$$

Mevalonic acid   5-Phosphomevalonic acid

The 5-phosphomevalonic acid is converted to 5-diphosphomevalonic acid (mevalonic acid-5-pyrophosphate) by reaction with ATP (81):

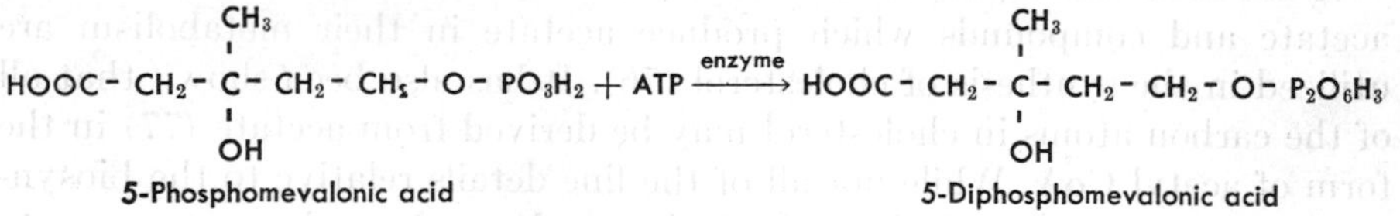

$$\underset{\text{OH}}{\overset{\text{CH}_3}{\text{HOOC}-\text{CH}_2-\text{C}-\text{CH}_2-\text{CH}_2-\text{O}-\text{PO}_3\text{H}_2}} + \text{ATP} \xrightarrow{\text{enzyme}} \underset{\text{OH}}{\overset{\text{CH}_3}{\text{HOOC}-\text{CH}_2-\text{C}-\text{CH}_2-\text{CH}_2-\text{O}-\text{P}_2\text{O}_6\text{H}_3}}$$

5-Phosphomevalonic acid   5-Diphosphomevalonic acid

5-Diphosphomevalonic acid then loses CO_2 and H_2O to form isopentenyl pyrophosphate (82):

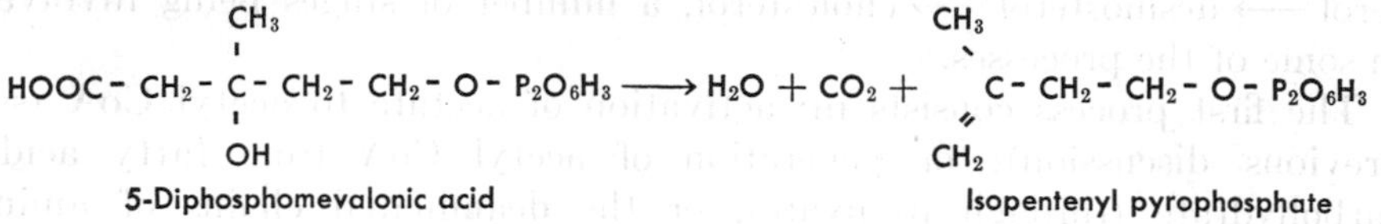

$$\underset{\text{OH}}{\overset{\text{CH}_3}{\text{HOOC}-\text{CH}_2-\text{C}-\text{CH}_2-\text{CH}_2-\text{O}-\text{P}_2\text{O}_6\text{H}_3}} \longrightarrow \text{H}_2\text{O} + \text{CO}_2 + \underset{\text{CH}_2}{\overset{\text{CH}_3}{\text{C}-\text{CH}_2-\text{CH}_2-\text{O}-\text{P}_2\text{O}_6\text{H}_3}}$$

5-Diphosphomevalonic acid   Isopentenyl pyrophosphate

This latter reaction requires ATP, and Block has postulated the formation of 3-phospho-5-diphosphomevalonic acid as an intermediate, though as yet its existence has not been proved.

Isopentenyl pyrophosphate is isomerized to 3,3-dimethylallyl pyrophosphate in the next stage of cholesterol synthesis. This isomerization by yeast enzyme has been reported (83):

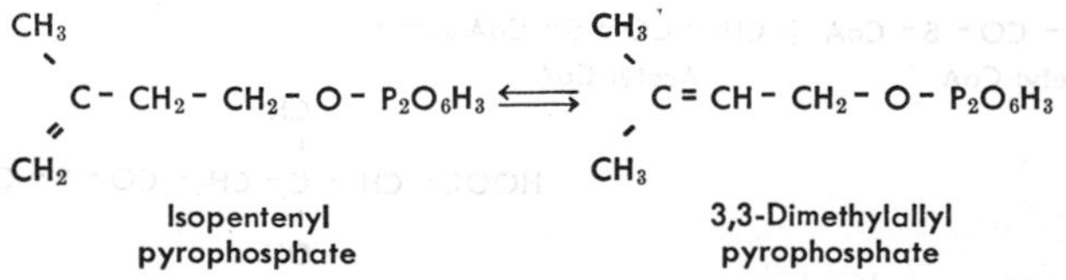

$$\underset{\text{CH}_2}{\overset{\text{CH}_3}{\text{C}-\text{CH}_2-\text{CH}_2-\text{O}-\text{P}_2\text{O}_6\text{H}_3}} \rightleftharpoons \underset{\text{CH}_3}{\overset{\text{CH}_3}{\text{C}=\text{CH}-\text{CH}_2-\text{O}-\text{P}_2\text{O}_6\text{H}_3}}$$

Isopentenyl   3,3-Dimethylallyl
pyrophosphate   pyrophosphate

A molecule of the 3,3-dimethylallyl pyrophosphate then reacts with a molecule of isopentenyl pyrophosphate to form geranyl pyrophosphate:

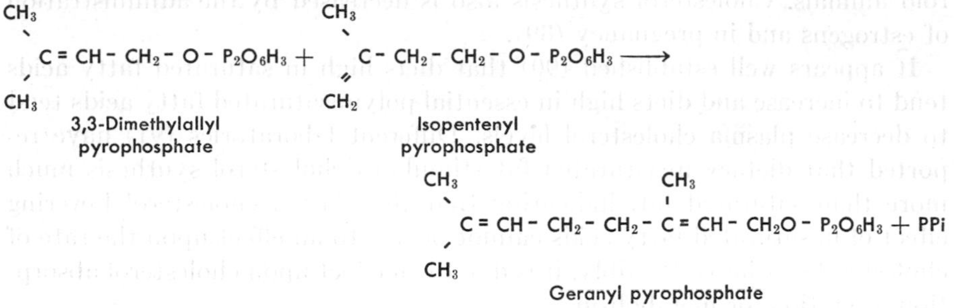

$$CH_3\backslash C = CH - CH_2 - O - P_2O_6H_3 \; + \; CH_3\backslash C - CH_2 - CH_2 - O - P_2O_6H_3 \longrightarrow$$

3,3-Dimethylallyl
pyrophosphate

Isopentenyl
pyrophosphate

$$C = CH - CH_2 - CH_2 - C = CH - CH_2O - P_2O_6H_3 + PPi$$

Geranyl pyrophosphate

A molecule of isopentenyl pyrophosphate reacts with geranyl pyrophosphate to form farnesyl pyrophosphate:

$$C = CH - CH_2 - CH_2 - C = CH - CH_2 - O - P_2O_6H_3 \; + \; C - CH_2 - CH_2 - O - P_2O_6H_3 \longrightarrow$$

Geranyl pyrophosphate

Isopentenyl
pyrophosphate

$$C = CH - CH_2 - CH_2 - C = CH - CH_2 - CH_2 - C = CH - CH_2 - O - P_2O_6H_3 + PPi$$

Farnesyl pyrophosphate

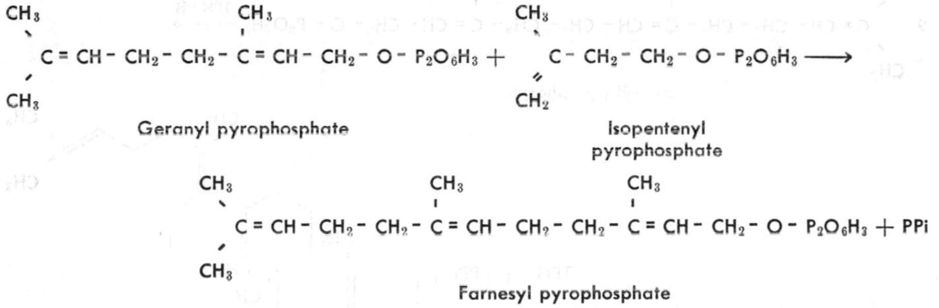

Two molecules of farnesyl pyrophosphate condense to form squalene, TPN · H being required, since reduction is involved (84). Squalene then undergoes cyclization and oxidation to lanosterol in a very complex reaction (85). Completion of the synthesis of cholesterol appears to take place as indicated (86) on pages 928 and 929.

The main steps in the biosynthesis of cholesterol are summarized in Figure 23.5.

Cholesterol synthesis has been shown to take place in many tissues, such as liver, skin, intestinal mucosa, adrenals, kidney, ovary, young brain, and testis. The liver appears to be the chief source of endogenous plasma cholesterol. The enzymes for cholesterol synthesis are associated with cytoplasmic particles (microsomes) and may be obtained in water-soluble form. These enzymes of the microsomes require cofactors present in the supernatant fluid from sedimentation of the microsomes for their activity.

Gould and Taylor (87) found that liver slices of dogs and rabbits fed a high cholesterol diet for six weeks converted C^{14}-acetate into cholesterol at rates only a few per cent of the rate found with liver slices of control animals. It appears that cholesterol synthesis in the liver decreases with increased dietary intake, and vice versa, to keep the supply relatively constant.

The rate of cholesterol synthesis is reduced by fasting and increased on a high carbohydrate diet. Liver slices from diabetic rats prefed glucose form much more cholesterol than do liver slices from prefed controls, and prefeeding with fructose brings cholesterogenesis back to normal (88). Hepatic cholesterol synthesis is increased in hyperthyroid and decreased in hypothyroid animals. Cholesterol synthesis also is decreased by the administration of estrogens and in pregnancy (89).

It appears well established (90) that diets high in saturated fatty acids tend to increase and diets high in essential polyunsaturated fatty acids tend to decrease plasma cholesterol levels. Different laboratories (91) have reported that dietary unsaturated fat stimulates cholesterol synthesis much more than saturated fat, indicating that the plasma cholesterol lowering effect of unsaturated fatty acids cannot be due to an effect upon the rate of cholesterol synthesis. Possibly, it is due to an effect upon cholesterol absorption, excretion, or metabolism.

Since cholesterol deposition in the walls of arteries is prominently associ-

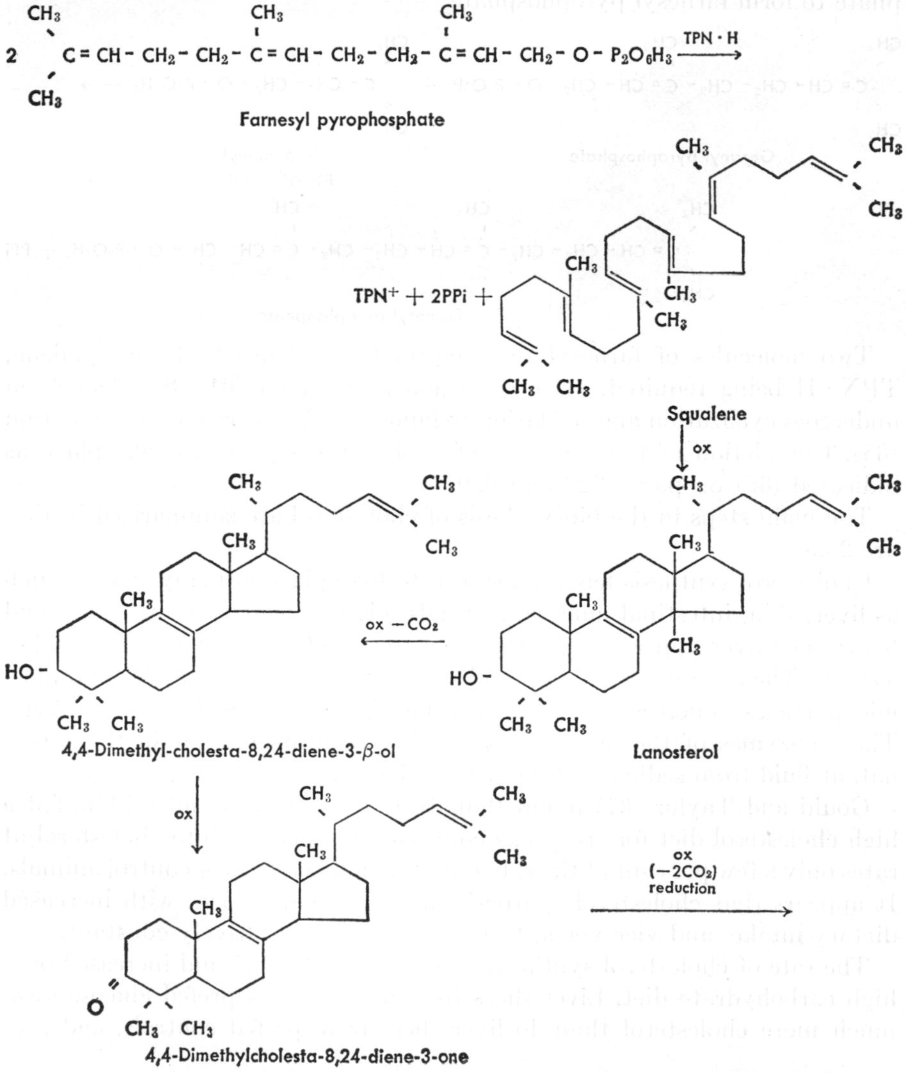
2 (CH3)2C=CH-CH2-CH2-C(CH3)=CH-CH2-CH2-C(CH3)=CH-CH2-O-P2O6H3
TPN · H
Farnesyl pyrophosphate
TPN+ + 2PPi +
Squalene
ox
Lanosterol
ox −CO2
HO
4,4-Dimethyl-cholesta-8,24-diene-3-β-ol
ox
ox
(−2CO2)
reduction
4,4-Dimethylcholesta-8,24-diene-3-one

ated with atherosclerosis and coronary artery disease, the mechanisms leading to this deposition are of much medical importance, though as yet they
are little understood. High plasma cholesterol levels in man predispose to
development of atherosclerosis, although there is not a clear-cut direct
relationship.

The lipid deposits (about 25 per cent in dry intima) in atherosclerotic
arteries are complex, consisting of a mixture of sterols, phospholipids, and
glycerides, with sterols, chiefly cholesterol, making up about 80 per cent of
the total lipid. The proportion of cholesterol esters to free cholesterol in the
deposits is approximately the same as found in plasma.

The fact that atherosclerosis can be developed in some experimental animals, notably the rabbit, by feeding cholesterol and developing hypercholesterolemia, points to elevated plasma cholesterol as being an important
causative agent of the disease. Undoubtedly various other factors, as yet
little understood, are also of importance and vary with animal species. While
it appears probable that plasma cholesterol is the chief source of cholesterol
deposits in arteries, the fact that the arterial walls themselves synthesize
cholesterol must be taken into consideration (92).

Intestinal absorption of sterols (93). Much attention has been given
to the intestinal absorption of dietary cholesterol, because it has been found
that feeding cholesterol to certain experimental animals (particularly rabbits
and chickens) causes atherosclerosis.

While the amounts of cholesterol and other sterols absorbed vary with
animal species, in general cholesterol is absorbed to a much greater extent
than are the other sterols. Practically all of the cholesterol transport from
the intestine is by the thoracic duct lymph.

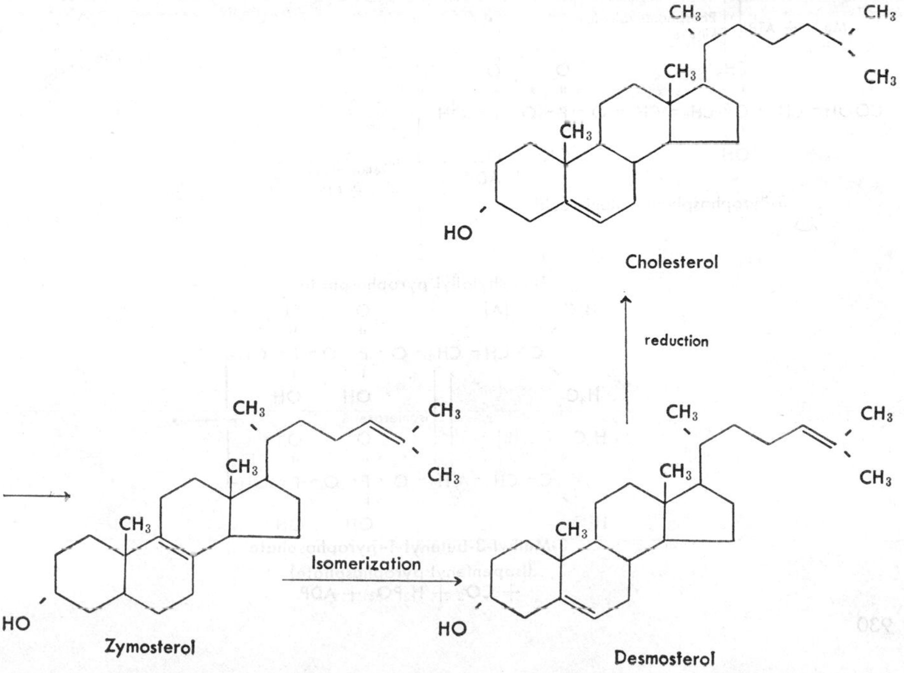

Cholesterol

reduction

Zymosterol

Isomerization

Desmosterol

Figure 23.5.
Biosynthesis of cholesterol.

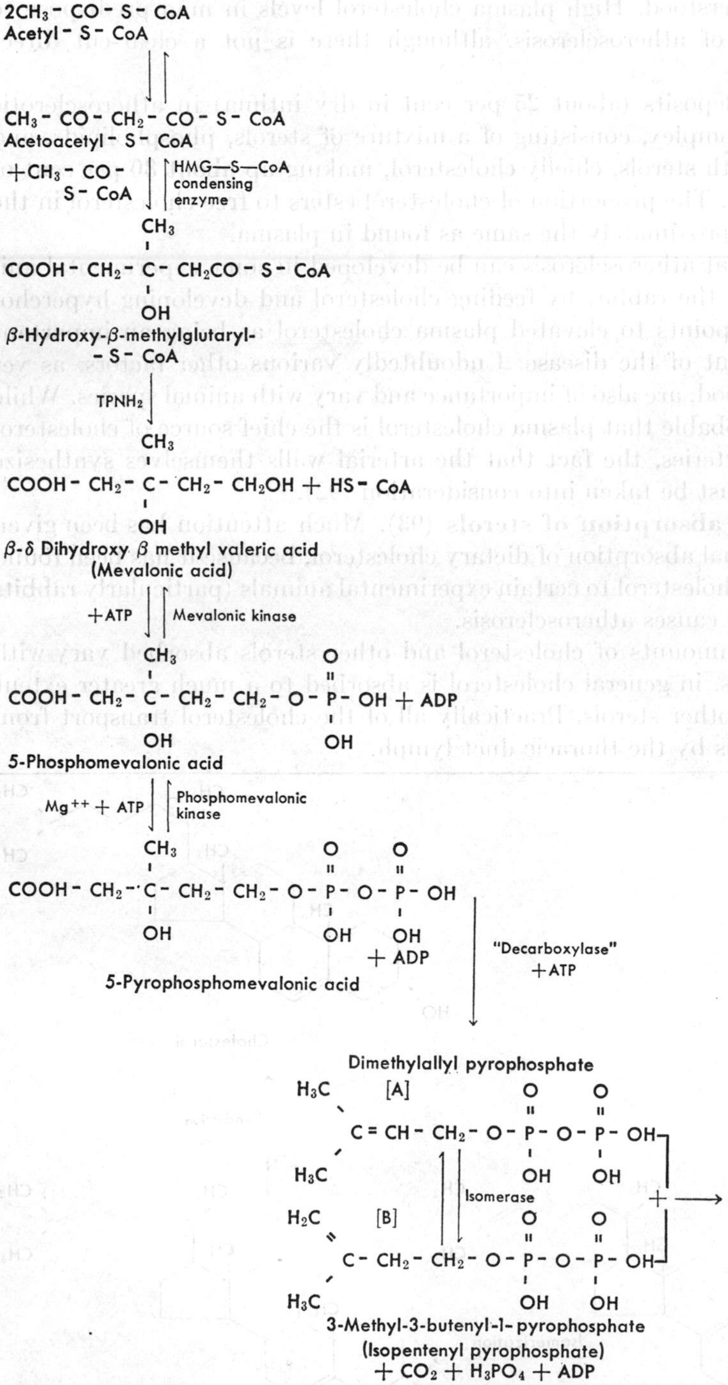

$2CH_3 - CO - S - CoA$
Acetyl $-$ S $-$ CoA

$CH_3 - CO - CH_2 - CO - S - CoA$
Acetoacetyl $-$ S $-$ CoA

$+CH_3 - CO -$ | HMG—S—CoA
$\quad\quad\quad S - CoA$ | condensing enzyme

$\quad\quad\quad CH_3$
$\quad\quad\quad |$
$COOH - CH_2 - C - CH_2CO - S - CoA$
$\quad\quad\quad |$
$\quad\quad\quad OH$
β-Hydroxy-β-methylglutaryl-
$\quad\quad - S - CoA$

TPNH$_2$

$\quad\quad\quad CH_3$
$\quad\quad\quad |$
$COOH - CH_2 - C - CH_2 - CH_2OH + HS - CoA$
$\quad\quad\quad |$
$\quad\quad\quad OH$
β-δ Dihydroxy β methyl valeric acid
(Mevalonic acid)

$+ATP$ | Mevalonic kinase

$\quad\quad\quad CH_3 \quad\quad\quad\quad O$
$\quad\quad\quad | \quad\quad\quad\quad\quad ||$
$COOH - CH_2 - C - CH_2 - CH_2 - O - P - OH + ADP$
$\quad\quad\quad | \quad\quad\quad\quad\quad |$
$\quad\quad\quad OH \quad\quad\quad\quad OH$
5-Phosphomevalonic acid

$Mg^{++} + ATP$ | Phosphomevalonic kinase

$\quad\quad\quad CH_3 \quad\quad\quad\quad O \quad\quad O$
$\quad\quad\quad | \quad\quad\quad\quad\quad || \quad\quad ||$
$COOH - CH_2 - C - CH_2 - CH_2 - O - P - O - P - OH$
$\quad\quad\quad | \quad\quad\quad\quad\quad | \quad\quad |$
$\quad\quad\quad OH \quad\quad\quad\quad OH \quad OH$
$\quad\quad\quad\quad\quad\quad\quad\quad\quad + ADP$
5-Pyrophosphomevalonic acid

"Decarboxylase"
$+ATP$

Dimethylallyl pyrophosphate

$H_3C \quad\quad [A] \quad\quad\quad\quad O \quad\quad O$
$\quad\quad\quad\quad\quad\quad\quad\quad\quad || \quad\quad ||$
$\quad\quad C = CH - CH_2 - O - P - O - P - OH$
$\quad\quad\quad\quad\quad\quad\quad\quad\quad | \quad\quad |$
$H_3C \quad\quad\quad\quad\quad\quad\quad OH \quad\quad OH$

Isomerase

$H_2C \quad\quad [B] \quad\quad\quad\quad O \quad\quad O$
$\quad\quad\quad\quad\quad\quad\quad\quad\quad || \quad\quad ||$
$\quad\quad C - CH_2 - CH_2 - O - P - O - P - OH$
$\quad\quad\quad\quad\quad\quad\quad\quad\quad | \quad\quad |$
$H_3C \quad\quad\quad\quad\quad\quad\quad OH \quad\quad OH$
3-Methyl-3-butenyl-1-pyrophosphate
(Isopentenyl pyrophosphate)
$+ CO_2 + H_3PO_4 + ADP$

$+ \longrightarrow$

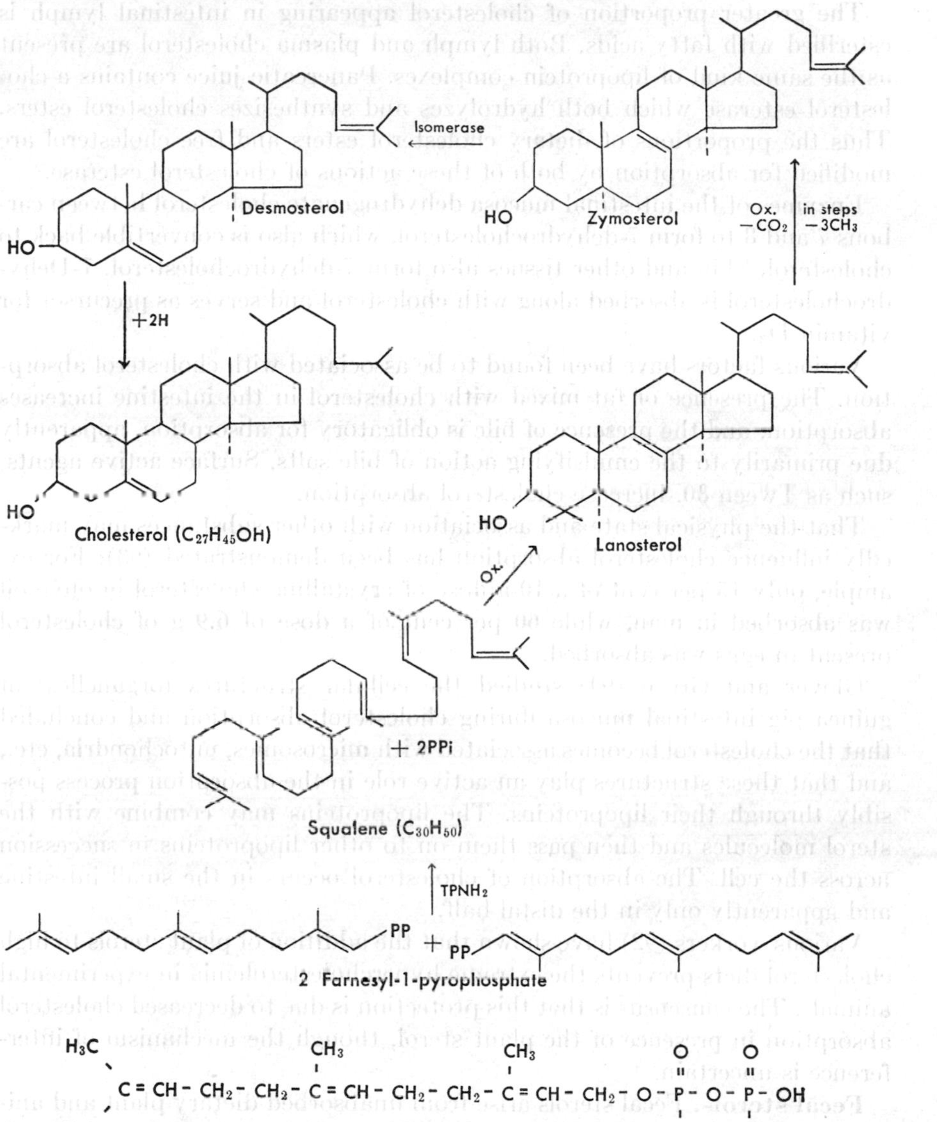

Isomerase

Desmosterol

HO

HO Zymosterol

Ox. in steps
$-CO_2$ $-3CH_3$

$+2H$

HO

Cholesterol ($C_{27}H_{45}OH$)

HO

Lanosterol

O*

$+ 2PPi$

Squalene ($C_{30}H_{50}$)

TPNH$_2$

PP $+$ PP

2 Farnesyl-1-pyrophosphate

$$H_3C\diagdown$$
$$C = CH - CH_2 - CH_2 - C = CH - CH_2 - CH_2 - C = CH - CH_2 - O - \overset{O}{\underset{OH}{P}} - O - \overset{O}{\underset{OH}{P}} - OH$$
$$H_3C\diagup \quad\quad\quad CH_3 \quad\quad\quad CH_3$$

Farnesyl-1-pyrophosphate (C_{15})

$+ PPi$

$+$Isopentenyl
pyrophosphate

$$H_3C\diagdown \quad [A] \quad\quad\quad CH_3\ [B]$$
$$C = CH - CH_2 - CH_2 - C = CH - CH_2 - O - \overset{O}{\underset{OH}{P}} - O - \overset{O}{\underset{OH}{P}} - OH$$
$$H_3C\diagup$$

$+ PPi$

Geranyl-1-pyrophosphate (C_{10})

The greater proportion of cholesterol appearing in intestinal lymph is esterified with fatty acids. Both lymph and plasma cholesterol are present as the same kind of lipoprotein complexes. Pancreatic juice contains a cholesterol esterase which both hydrolyzes and synthesizes cholesterol esters. Thus the proportions of dietary cholesterol esters and free cholesterol are modified for absorption by both of these actions of cholesterol esterase.

Enzymes of the intestinal mucosa dehydrogenate cholesterol between carbons 7 and 8 to form 7-dehydrocholesterol, which also is convertible back to cholesterol. Skin and other tissues also form 7-dehydrocholesterol. 7-Dehydrocholesterol is absorbed along with cholesterol and serves as precursor for vitamin D_3.

Various factors have been found to be associated with cholesterol absorption. The presence of fat mixed with cholesterol in the intestine increases absorption, and the presence of bile is obligatory for absorption, apparently due primarily to the emulsifying action of bile salts. Surface active agents, such as Tween 80, increase cholesterol absorption.

That the physical state and association with other substances may markedly influence cholesterol absorption has been demonstrated (93). For example, only 15 per cent of a 10-g dose of crystalline cholesterol in olive oil was absorbed in man, while 60 per cent of a dose of 6.9 g of cholesterol present in eggs was absorbed.

Glover and Green (94) studied the cellular structures (organelles) of guinea pig intestinal mucosa during cholesterol absorption and concluded that the cholesterol becomes associated with microsomes, mitochondria, etc., and that these structures play an active role in the absorption process possibly through their lipoproteins. The lipoproteins may combine with the sterol molecules and then pass them on to other lipoproteins in succession across the cell. The absorption of cholesterol occurs in the small intestine and apparently only in the distal half.

Various workers (92) have shown that the addition of plant sterols to high cholesterol diets prevents the extreme hypercholesterolemia in experimental animals. The consensus is that this protection is due to decreased cholesterol absorption in presence of the plant sterol, though the mechanism of interference is uncertain.

Fecal sterols. Fecal sterols arise from unabsorbed dietary plant and animal sterols, mucus and intestinal secretions, and intestinal mucosa. Small amounts may be derived from bile sterols.

In a 70-kg normal adult man on a mixed diet the fecal sterol excretion amounts to about 500 mg per day or about 7 mg per kg body weight.

In man and other omniverous animals the chief fecal sterol is coprostanol, though small amounts of cholestanol; Δ^5-, Δ^7-, and $\Delta^{5,7}$-cholestenols; coprostanone and other ketones; and di- and trihydroxysterols have been found. The type of diet may have an effect upon the fecal sterols, apparently due to changes in bacterial flora. For example, both infants and adults on a milk diet excrete mainly cholesterol in the feces.

The formation of coprostanol from cholesterol is effected by bacterial action in the large intestine and appears to be the result of a direct sterospecific hydrogenation of the double bond of cholesterol (95).

Loss of sterols in sebum. As previously pointed out, the skin is active in cholesterol synthesis. Animals lose sterols in the skin fat or sebum continuously. The loss is highly variable, but in man it amounts to about 100 mg per day. Somewhat more squalene is lost in the sebum.

Synthesis of bile acids (92). The synthesis of bile acids in the liver represents quantitatively the major pathway of cholesterol metabolism. In the over-all process the three terminal carbons atoms of the cholesterol chain are split off, the double bond is reduced, and hydroxyl groups are introduced into the ring system.

Two biosynthetic pathways operate in the synthesis of cholic acids. These are shown for the formation of some of the cholic (cholanic) acids in Figure 23.6. The cholic acids are converted into bile acids (taurine and glycine derivatives) through their coenzyme A derivatives:

(a)   Cholic acid + ATP + HS - CoA $\longrightarrow$ Cholyl - S - CoA + AMP + PPi

$$
\begin{array}{cc}
\text{H} & \text{H} \\
| & | \\
\text{(b)} \quad \text{Cholyl - S - CoA} \ | \ \text{H - N - CH}_2\text{ - COOH} \longrightarrow \text{Cholyl - N - CH}_2\text{ - COOH} + \text{HS - CoA} \\
\text{Glycine} & \text{Cholylglycine}
\end{array}
$$

Glycocholic acid,
a bile acid

Taurocholic acids are formed similarly from taurine.

When C^{14}-cholesterol is introduced into the body by intravenous or intraperitoneal injection, or feeding, it mixes rapidly with the cholesterol of liver and blood and a bit more slowly with that in the intestine and other viscera. The metabolism of this C^{14}-cholesterol may be taken as representative of the metabolism of cholesterol in rapid equilibrium with blood cholesterol, which represents the cholesterol pool. This metabolism consists largely in the oxidative removal of the three carbon isopropyl group from the side chain, formation of bile acids, and eventual excretion of bile acid metabolites in the feces. No $C^{14}O_2$ has been found in the respiratory CO_2 of animals given cholesterol labeled in the ring system (C^{14} at C_4), while it appears relatively rapidly when cholesterol-26-C^{14} is administered. The over-all metabolism of C^{14}-cholesterol in rats has been shown to lead to the ultimate excretion of about 85 per cent as bile acid metabolites (steroid acids), 10 per cent as fecal sterols, and only 1 per cent in urine, presumably as metabolites of steroid hormones (92). The bile acid metabolites (steroid acids) excreted in feces are formed by action of bacteria on the bile acids.

Bile acids entering the intestine in bile are very rapidly and efficiently absorbed into the portal blood, removed by the liver, and reutilized. This represents what is called the "enterohepatic circulation" of bile salts. There are similar enterohepatic circulations for other substances, such as cholesterol and urobilinogen.

Synthesis of steroid hormones (89). Cholesterol serves as the precursor of adrenal cortical steroids (corticosteroids), such as aldosterone, corticos-

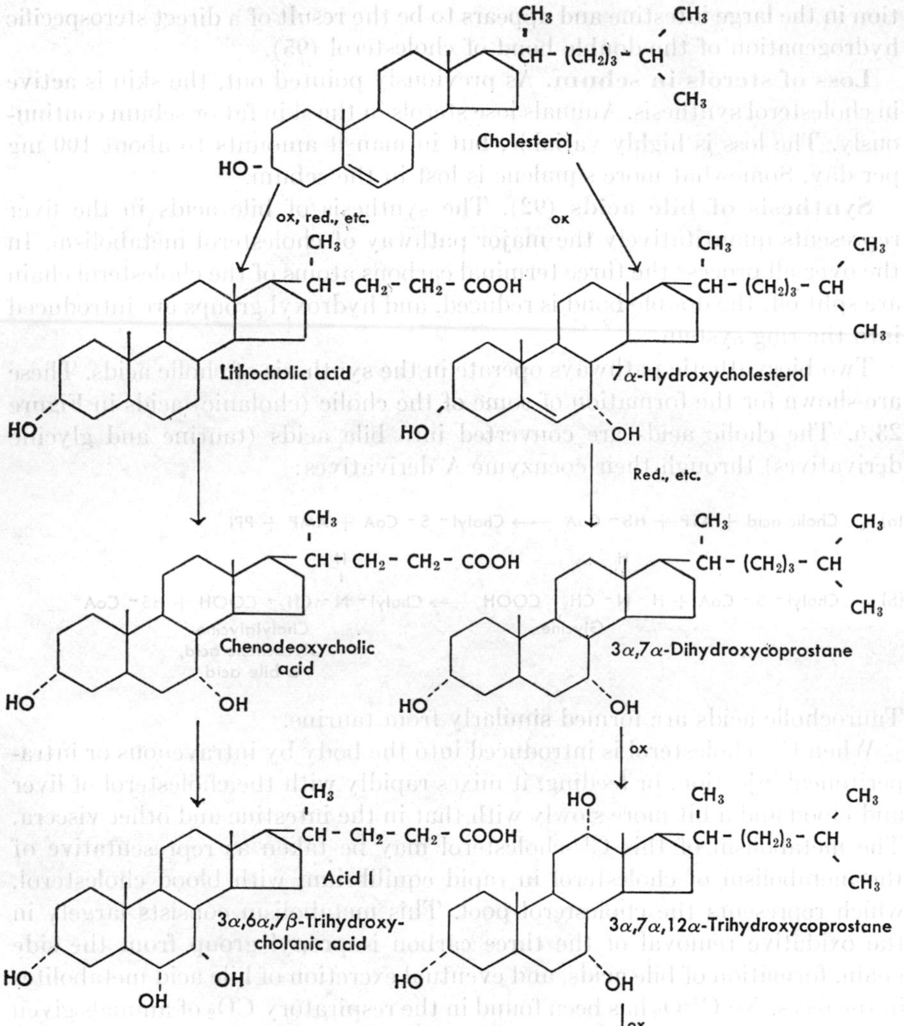

Figure 23.6. Outline of pathways in formation of bile acids. Acids I and II are epimers of hyocholic acid.

terone, and deoxycorticosterone; of the male sex hormones or androgens; and of the female sex hormones or estrogens. The initial stage in the synthesis of all these steroid hormones appears to be the formation of pregnenolone from cholesterol. The second stage is the formation of progesterone from pregnenolone, after which progesterone serves as the common precursor.

Cholesterol is converted to pregnenolone by enzymes of the adrenal cortex:

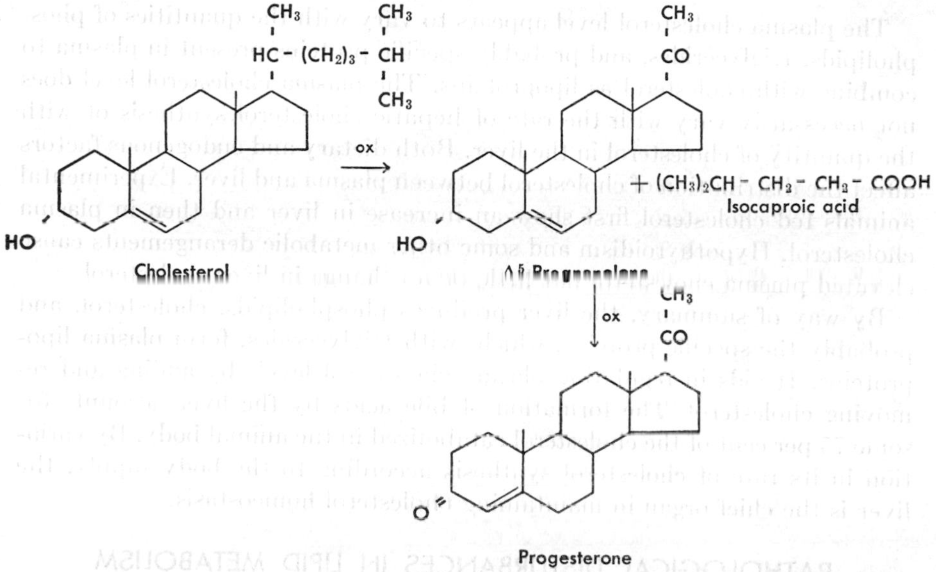

Progesterone

Further consideration of the relation of cholesterol to the steroid hormones will be found in Chapter 34.

Quantitatively only small amounts of cholesterol are required for hormone synthesis as compared to bile acid synthesis.

Role of the liver in regulating cholesterol metabolism (92). The liver plays the dual role of regulating both the plasma cholesterol level and the total body cholesterol.

The total body content of cholesterol is determined by the balance between the amount synthesized plus that absorbed from the diet and the amount converted to other substances plus that excreted in the feces. As the amount of cholesterol absorbed from the diet increases, the amount synthesized by the liver goes down and may reach very low levels. Thus synthesis of cholesterol in the liver appears to be controlled by a kind of feedback mechanism related to the intestinal absorption of cholesterol.

As pointed out above, a large proportion of cholesterol metabolized is converted to bile acids in the liver. The rate of bile acid synthesis appears to be regulated chiefly by the quantity of bile acids in the body. Synthesis is increased many fold if the enterohepatic circulation of bile salts is broken by diversion of bile through a fistula, causing rapid depletion of bile acids in the body. The more efficient the enterohepatic circulation in absorbing and reutilizing bile acids, the slower is their turnover in the body and the slower their production from cholesterol. This decrease in bile acid synthesis decreases the utilization of cholesterol, which is reflected in decreased cholesterol synthesis. Here we appear to have a chain of consecutive feedback controlled processes:

$$\text{Acetyl CoA} \longrightarrow \text{Cholesterol} \longrightarrow \text{Bile acids}$$

The plasma cholesterol level appears to vary with the quantities of phospholipids, triglycerides, and probably specific proteins present in plasma to combine with cholesterol as lipoproteins. The plasma cholesterol level does not necessarily vary with the rate of hepatic cholesterol synthesis or with the quantity of cholesterol in the liver. Both dietary and endogenous factors affect the distribution of cholesterol between plasma and liver. Experimental animals fed cholesterol first show an increase in liver and then in plasma cholesterol. Hypothyroidism and some other metabolic derangements cause elevated plasma cholesterol but little or no change in liver cholesterol.

By way of summary, the liver produces phospholipids, cholesterol, and probably the specific proteins, which, with triglycerides, form plasma lipoproteins. It aids in regulating plasma cholesterol levels by adding and removing cholesterol. The formation of bile acids by the liver accounts for some 75 per cent of the cholesterol catabolized in the animal body. By variation in its rate of cholesterol synthesis according to the body supply, the liver is the chief organ in maintaining cholesterol homeostasis.

PATHOLOGICAL DISTURBANCES IN LIPID METABOLISM

Normally the various kinds of lipids of the various tissues are synthesized, deposited, mobilized, and catabolized at rates which tend to maintain a relatively steady state. The most common disturbances in lipid metabolism involve the deposition and mobilization of triglycerides in the fat depots, leading to obesity when deposition exceeds mobilization, and ultimately to cachexia when mobilization exceeds deposition.

Obesity. The amount of fat in the storage depots is determined by the balance between the rates of deposition and mobilization. An animal becomes fat when the rate of deposition exceeds the rate of mobilization and lean when the processes are reversed. It has been established that obesity results purely from the ingestion of more food than is necessary to meet energy requirements; in other words, it is a question of the appetite being improperly balanced (or controlled) with energy needs. Alterations in the energy demand of an animal without simultaneous change in appetite may occur for various reasons. This may be true with decreased muscular activity. Also, endocrine disturbances may decrease activity and lead to obesity. Castration is often associated with obesity because of lowered activity, as is hypothyroidism, which depresses the rate of food oxidation. In some cases neither of these conditions causes obesity because the appetite is proportionately lowered. Certain pituitary deficiencies may lead to abnormal distribution of body fat without changing the total quantity. Some cases of hyperinsulinism become obese because of the greatly stimulated appetite. It has been demonstrated that the hypothalamic region of the brain is concerned with regulation of appetite. Injuries to this region in experimental animals may lead to great obesity due to appetite stimulation.

Many experiments have shown that the processes of fat metabolism in obese individuals are normal.

Cachexia. There are a number of conditions which lead to abnormally high rates of mobilization from fat depots relative to the rates of deposition, causing, in severe cases, disappearance of most of the adipose tissue. Such situations may be observed in carcinoma, malnutrition, certain chronic infectious diseases, hyperthyroidism, and severe uncontrolled diabetes. The greatly increased mobilization of body fat to supply the increased energy demand is the primary cause of the wasting away or cachexia of hyperthyroidism. Two processes operate to cause the cachexia of severe uncontrolled diabetes. In the first place, due to inability to utilize appreciable carbohydrate, energy is supplied through the mobilization and utilization of excessive amounts of depot fat. In the second place, the capacity of the diabetic to synthesize fat for deposit is drastically reduced.

Severe thiamine deficiency leads to decreased capacity to convert carbohydrate to fat and also decreased appetite, with depletion of fat depots. Of course, in plain starvation the net effect is fat mobilization to supply energy without deposition.

Idiopathic hyperlipemia (Buerger-Grütz disease) (96). This hereditary disease is characterized by very high serum lipid levels. Total fatty acids, largely as fat, may be ten times normal. Also, there are marked elevations of cholesterol and phospholipids. The fasting serum is milky white. Widely distributed cutaneous xanthomas, consisting of soft yellow papules and nodules, are a prominent feature of the disease. The principal complications are episodes of relapsing pancreatitis and atherosclerosis. Many patients in the teens and twenties suffer from angina pectoris or myocardial infarction.

Little is known about the cause of the disease, though there is some evidence that the turnover of plasma fatty acids is decreased and that blood lipase is deficient.

Gaucher's disease (96). Gaucher first observed this hereditary disease in a patient in whom the splenic pulp had been replaced entirely by large pale cells, which now are known as "Gaucher cells." The Gaucher cells are found particularly in spleen, brain, and bone marrow. Gaucher cells have been found to contain abnormally large amounts of: (a) a cerebroside composed of galactose, sphingosine, and lignoceric acid (kerasin); (b) a cerebroside containing glucose instead of galactose; and (c) a water-soluble glycolipid made up of sphingosine or a sphingosine-like base, long-chain saturated fatty acids, and one or more hexose groups. This substance has been named "polycerebroside."

Thannhauser considers that in Gaucher's disease there is an imbalance between the rates of cerebroside formation and catabolism, leading to the accumulation of cerebrosides in certain cells to form Gaucher cells.

Niemann-Pick disease (96). This disease has many clinical features in common with Gaucher's disease. It is characterized by a very generalized distribution of large pale cells (Niemann-Pick cells) having a foamy-appearing vacuolated cytoplasm. The spleen, lung, lymph nodes, liver, and bone marrow are primarily involved, though organs in general are infiltrated. The ganglion cells of the central nervous system and elsewhere undergo degeneration. There is an immense accumulation of lipid in the Niemann-Pick cells, of which sphingomyelin is the major component. Thannhauser has postulated that in Niemann-Pick disease the conversion of ceramide (acylsphingosine) to sphingomyelin is normal but the reverse process is defective. A hereditary condition of infants which in many respects resembles Niemann-Pick disease is Tay-Sachs disease. Both conditions occur most frequently in individuals of the Jewish race; in both conditions there is a cherry-red spot in the macula and macular degeneration; the histologic changes in the brain are similar in both conditions; and cases of Niemann-Pick and Tay-Sachs disease have been observed in siblings of the same families. In Tay-Sachs disease the chief pathology is related to degeneration of ganglion cells of the central nervous system and retina. Apparently this degeneration is caused by the accumulation of lipid in the cells. However, sphingomyelin does not appear to be a prominent component of this lipid.

There are a number of other pathologic states associated with abnormal lipid metabolism.

GENERAL REFERENCES

Cook, R. P.: *Cholesterol. Chemistry, Biochemistry and Pathology.* Academic Press, New York, 1958.
Deuel, H. J., Jr.: *The Lipids*, Vol. III, Biosynthesis, Oxidation, Metabolism, and Nutritional Value. Interscience, New York, 1957.
Dole, V. P.: "Transport of Non-esterified Fatty Acids in Plasma," in *Chemistry of Lipids as Related to Atherosclerosis, A Symposium.* Charles C Thomas, Publisher, Springfield, Ill., 1958.
Engelberg, H.: "Heparin Lipemia Clearing Reaction and Fat Transport in Man. A Summary of Available Knowledge," *Am. J. Clin. Nutrition*, 8, 21, 1960.
Hsia, D. Y.: *Inborn Errors of Metabolism.* Yearbook Publishers, Chicago, 1959.
Katzman, P. A.; Doisy, E. A., Jr.; Matschiner, J. T.; and Doisy, E. A.: *Ann. Rev. Biochem.*, 28, 257, 1959.
Kennedy, E. P.: "Metabolism of Lipides," *Ann. Rev. Biochem.*, 26, 119, 1957.
Kritchevsky, D.: *Cholesterol.* John Wiley & Sons, New York, 1958.
Lynen, F.: "Lipide Metabolism," *Ann. Rev. Biochem.*, 24, 653, 1955.
Mead, J. F.: "The Metabolism of the Polyunsaturated Fatty Acids," *Am. J. Clin. Nutrition*, 8, 55, 1960.
"Metabolism of Lipids" (many authors), *British Med. Bull.*, 14, 197–275, 1958.
Page, I. H. (ed.): *Chemistry of Lipids as Related to Atherosclerosis, A Symposium.* Charles C Thomas, Publisher, Springfield, Ill., 1958.
Pincus, G. (ed.): *Hormones and Atherosclerosis.* Academic Press, New York, 1959.
Popják, G., and Le Breton, E. (eds.): *Biochemical Problems of Lipids.* Butterworth & Co., Ltd., London, 1956.
Sinclair, H. M. (ed.): *Essential Fatty Acids.* Academic Press, New York, 1958.
Schoenheimer, R.: *The Dynamic State of Body Constituents.* Harvard University Press, Cambridge, Mass., 1942.

"Symposium on Lipid Metabolism" (many authors), *Am. J. Clin. Nutrition*, **8,**, 1–111, 1960.

Wolstenholme, G. E. W., and O'Connor, C. M.: *Biosynthesis of Terpenes and Sterols, Ciba Foundation Symposium*. Little, Brown & Co., Boston, 1959.

Zilversmit, D. B.: "Metabolism of Complex Lipides," *Ann. Rev. Biochem.*, **24,** 157, 1955.

SPECIAL REFERENCES

1. Sperry, W. M.: *J. Biol. Chem.*, **117,** 391, 1937.
2. Fredrickson, D. S., and Gordon, R. S., Jr.: *Physiol. Revs.*, **38,** 585, 1958.
3. Lindgren, F. T.; Elliott, H. A.; and Gofman, J. W.: *J. Phys. and Colloid Chem.*, **55,** 80, 1951.
4. Surgenor, D. M.: *Symposium on Atherosclerosis, Natl. Acad. Sci.-Natl. Res. Council,* Pub. 338, p. 203, 1954.
5. Gofman, J. W.: *J. Gerontology*, **6,** 105, 1951.
6. Oncley, J. L.: *Harvey Lectures*, Series L, 1954–1955, 1956.
7. Hahn, P. F.: *Science*, **98,** 19, 1943.
8. Robinson, D. S., and French, J. E.: *Quart. J. Exptl. Physiol.*, **42,** 151, 1957.
9. Anfinsen, C. B.: *Symposium on Atherosclerosis, Natl. Acad. Sci.-Natl. Res. Council,* Pub. 338, p. 217, 1955.
10. French, J. E.; Morris, B.; and Robinson, D. S.: *British Med. Bull.*, **14,** 234, 1958.
11. Havel, R. J., and Fredrickson, D. S.: *J. Clin. Invest.*, **35,** 1025, 1956. French, J. E., and Morris, B.: *J. Physiol.*, **138,** 326, 1957.
12. Friedberg, S. J.; Harlan, W. R., Jr.; Trout, D. L.; and Estes, E. H., Jr.: *J. Clin. Invest.*, **39,** 215, 1960.
13. Havel, R. J., and Goldfien, A.: *J. Lipid Research*, **1,** 102, 1959.
14. Laurell, S.: *Acta Physiol. Scand.*, **41,** 158, 1957.
15. Ellis, N. R., and Zeller, J. H.: *J. Biol. Chem.*, **89,** 185, 1930.
16. Tuerkischer, E., and Wertheimer, E.: *J. Physiol.*, **104,** 361, 1946.
17. Mirski, A.: *Biochem. J.*, **36,** 232, 1942.
18. Shapiro, B., and Wertheimer, E.: *J. Biol. Chem.*, **173,** 725, 1948.
19. Schoenheimer, R., and Rittenberg, D.: *J. Biol. Chem.*, **111,** 175, 1935.
20. Stetten, De W., Jr., and Schoenheimer, R.: *J. Biol. Chem.*, **133,** 329, 1940.
21. Rittenberg, D., and Schoenheimer, R.: *J. Biol. Chem.*, **117,** 485, 1937.
22. Schoenheimer, R., and Rittenberg, D.: *J. Biol. Chem.*, **114,** 381, 1936.
23. Rittenberg, D., and Schoenheimer, R.: *J. Biol. Chem.*, **121,** 235, 1937.
24. Bernhard, K., and Schoenheimer, R.: *J. Biol. Chem.*, **133,** 707, 713, 1940.
25. Stetten, De W., Jr., and Grail, G. F.: *J. Biol. Chem.*, **148,** 509, 1943.
26. Deuel, H. J.: *The Lipids*, Vol. II. Interscience, New York, 1955.
27. Shapiro, B.; Weissmann, D.; Bentor, V.; and Wertheimer, E.: *Nature*, **161,** 482, 1948.
28. McHenry, E. W., and Patterson, J. M.: *Physiol. Revs.*, **24,** 128, 1944.
29. Best, C. H.: *Federation Proc.*, **9,** 506, 1950. Best, C. H., and Lucas, C. C.: *Vitamins and Hormones*, **1,** 1, 1943.
30. Best, C. H., and Ridout, J. H.: *J. Physiol. (London)*, **78,** 415, 1933.
31. Perlman, I., and Chaikoff, I. L.: *J. Biol. Chem.*, **127,** 211, 1939.
32. Griffith, W. H., and Wade, N. J.: *J. Biol. Chem.*, **131,** 567, 1939; 132, 627, 1940. Griffith, W. H., and Mulford, D. J.: *J. Nutrition*, **21,** 633, 1941.
33. Knoop, F.: *Beitr. chem. Physiol. Path.*, **6,** 150, 1905.
34. Green, D. E.: *Biological Reviews*, **29,** 330, 1954.
35. Lynen, F.: *Ann. Rev. Biochem.*, **24,** 653, 1955.
36. Kennedy, E. P.: *Ann. Rev. Biochem.*, **26,** 119, 1957.
37. Berg, P.: *J. Biol. Chem.*, **222,** 991, 1956; *Science*, **129,** 895, 1959.
38. Crane, F. L., and Beinert, H.: *J. Biol. Chem.*, **218,** 717, 1956.
39. Stern, J. R.; del Campillo, A.; and Raw, I.: *J. Biol. Chem.*, **218,** 971, 1956. Stern, J. R., and del Campillo, A.: *J. Biol. Chem.*, **218,** 985, 1956.
40. Wakil, S. J.; Green, D. E.; Mii, S.; and Mahler, H. R.: *J. Biol. Chem.*, **207,** 631, 1954.
41. Kennedy, E. P.: *Ann. Rev. Biochem.*, **26,** 126, 1957.
42. Embden, G., and Kalberlah, F.: *Beitr. chem. Physiol. Path.*, **8,** 121, 1906. Embden, G., and Engel, H.: *ibid.*, **11,** 323, 1908.
43. Snapper, I., and Grunbaum, A.: *Biochem. Z.*, **201,** 464, 1928. Neuberg, J.: *ibid.*, **167,** 100, 1926.

44. Jowett, M., and Quastel, J. H.: *Biochem. J.*, **29**, 2159, 2181, 1935.
45. Mirsky, I. A., and Broh-Kahn, R. H.: *Am. J. Physiol.*, **120**, 446, 1937.
46. Stadie, W. C.; Zapp, J. A., Jr.; and Lukens, F. D. W.: *J. Biol. Chem.*, **132**, 423, 1940.
47. Huff, E., and Rudney, H.: *Federation Proc.*, **12**, 221, 1953.
48. Breusch, F. L., and Ulusoy, E.: *Arch. Biochem.*, **14**, 183, 1947.
49. Heinbecker, P.: *J. Biol. Chem.*, **80**, 461, 1928; **93**, 327, 1931; **99**, 279, 1932–1933.
50. Wakil, S. J.; McLain, L. W., Jr.; and Warshaw, J. B.: *J. Biol. Chem.*, **235**, No. 8, PC 31, 1960.
51. Gibson, D. M.; Titchener, E. B.; and Wakil, S. J.: *Biochim. et Biophys. Acta*, **30**, 376, 1958. Wakil, S. J.; Porter, J. W.; and Gibson, D. M.: *ibid*, **24**, 453, 1957. Porter, J. W.; Wakil, S. J.; Tietz, A.; Jacob, M. I.; and Gibson, D. M.: *ibid*, **25**, 35, 1957. For reviews of fatty acid synthesis see: Green, D. E., and Gibson, D. M., in *Metabolic Pathways*, Vol. I, p. 301, Greenberg, D. M., ed. Academic Press, New York, 1960; and Stumpf, P. K., *Ann. Rev. Biochem.*, **29**, 261, 1960.
52. Lynen, F.; Knappe, J.; Lorch, E.; Jütting, G.; and Ringelmann, E.: *Angew. Chem.*, **71**, 481, 1959.
53. Stumpf, P. K.: *Ann. Rev. Biochem.*, **29**, 261, 1960.
54. Brady, R. O.: *J. Biol. Chem.*, **235**, 3099, 1960.
55. Catravas, G. N., and Anker, H. S.: *J. Biol. Chem.*, **232**, 669, 1958.
56. Catravas, G. N., and Anker, H. S.: *Proc. Natl. Acad. Sci. U. S.*, **44**, 1097, 1958.
57. Kennedy, E. P.: *Ann. Rev. Biochem.*, **26**, 119, 1957.
58. Hele, P.: *British Med. Bull.*, **14**, 201, 1958.
59. Cornforth, J. W.: *J. Lipid Research*, **1**, 3, 1959.
60. Wakil, S. J., and Ganguly, J.: *J. Am. Chem. Soc.*, **81**, 2597, 1959.
61. Green, D. E.: *Scientific American*, **202**, 46, 1960.
62. Gibson, D. M.; Titchener, E. B.; and Wakil, S. J.: *J. Am. Chem. Soc.*, **80**, 2908, 1958.
63. Siperstein, M. D.: *Amer. J. Med.*, **26**, 685, 1959.
64. Mead, J. F., and Howton, D. R.: *J. Biol. Chem.*, **229**, 575, 1957.
65. Kennedy, E. P.: *Federation Proc.*, **16**, 847, 1957; *Ann. Rev. Biochem.*, **26**, 119, 1957.
66. Sribney, M., and Kennedy, E. P.: *J. Biol. Chem.*, **233**, 1315, 1958.
67. Brady, R. O.; Formica, J. V.; and Koval, G. J.: *J. Biol. Chem.*, **233**, 1072, 1958.
68. Agranoff, B. W.; Bradley, R. M.; and Brady, R. O.: *J. Biol. Chem.*, **233**, 1077, 1958.
69. Joel, C. D.; Karnovsky, M. L.; Ball, E. G.; and Cooper, O.: *J. Biol. Chem.*, **233**, 1565, 1958.
70. Marinetti, G. V.; Erbland, J.; Kochen, J.; and Stotz, E.: *J. Biol. Chem.*, **233**, 740, 1958.
71. Green, D. E., and Lester, R. L.: *Federation Proc.*, **18**, 987, 1959.
72. Hokin, M, R.; Hokin, L. E.; Saffran, M.; Schally, A. V.; and Zimmermann, B. U.: *J. Biol. Chem.*, **233**, 811, 1958. Hokin, M. R.; Benfey, B. G.; and Hokin, L. E.: *ibid.*, **233**, 814, 1958.
73. Dam, H.: *Biochem. Z.*, **220**, 158, 1930.
74. Imhäuser, K.: *Klin. Wochschr.*, **9**, 71, 1930.
75. Schoenheimer, R., and Breusch, F.: *J. Biol. Chem.*, **103**, 439, 1933.
76. Block, K., and Rittenberg, D.: *J. Biol. Chem.*, **143**, 297, 1942; **145**, 625, 1959. Block, K.; Borek, E.; and Rittenberg, D.: *J. Biol. Chem.*, **162**, 441, 1946. Block, K.: *Recent Progress in Hormone Research*, **6**, 111, 1951. Hellman, L.; Rosenfeld, R. S.; and Gallagher, T. F.: *J. Clin. Invest.*, **33**, 142, 1954. Gould, R. G.: *Am. J. Med.*, **11**, 209, 1951.
77. Popják, G.: *Chemistry, Biochemistry and Isotopic Tracer Technique.* Lectures, Monographs, and Reports No. 2, p. 59. The Royal Inst. of Chem. W. Heffer & Sons, Ltd., Cambridge, England, 1955.
78. Rudney, H.: *J. Am. Chem. Soc.*, **76**, 2595, 1954; **77**, 1698, 1955. Rudney, H.: "The Biosynthesis of β-Hydroxy-β-methyl-glutaryl Coenzyme A and Its Conversion to Mevalonic Acid." In Wolstenholme, G. E. W., and O'Connor, C. M. (eds.): *Biosynthesis of Terpenes and Sterols*, p. 75. Little, Brown & Co., Boston, 1959.
79. Lynen, F.; Knappe, J.; Eggerer, H.; Henning, U.; and Aranoff, B. W.: *Federation Proc.*, **19**, 1099, 1959.
80. Tchen, T. T.: *J. Biol. Chem.*, **233**, 1100, 1958.
81. Block, K.; Chaykin, S.; Low, J.; Phillips, A. N.; and Tchen, T. T.: *Proc. Natl. Acad. Sci. U. S.*, **44**, 998, 1958.
82. Tavormina, P. A., and Gibbs, M. H.: *J. Am. Chem. Soc.*, **78**, 6210, 1956.

83. Agranoff, B. W.; Eggerer, H.; Henning, U.; and Lynen, F.: *J. Am. Chem. Soc.*, **81**, 1254, 1959.
84. Lynen, F.; Eggerer, H.; Henning, U.; and Kassel, J.: *Angew. Chem.*, **70**, 738, 1959.
85. Block, K., and Tchen, T. T.: *J. Biol. Chem.*, **226**, 921, 931, 1957.
86. Schwenk, E.; Alexander, G. J.; Fish, C. A.; and Stoudt, T. H.: *Federation Proc.*, **14**, 752, 1955. Block, K., and Johnston, J. P.: *J. Am. Chem. Soc.*, **79**, 1145, 1957.
87. Gould, R. G., and Taylor, C. B.: *Federation Proc.*, **9**, 179, 1950.
88. Hotta, S.; Hill, R.; and Chaikoff, I. L.: *J. Biol. Chem.*, **206**, 835, 1954.
89. Kritchevsky, D.: *Cholesterol.* John Wiley & Sons, New York, 1958.
90. Bronte-Stewart, B.: *British Med. Bull.*, **14**, 243, 1958.
91. Kritchevsky, D.: *Am. J. Nutrition*, **8**, 53, 1960.
92. Cook, R. P.: *Cholesterol*, p. 248. Academic Press, New York, 1958.
93. Cook, R. P. (ed.): *Cholesterol.* Academic Press, New York, 1958. Glover, J., and Morton, R. A.: *British Med. Bull.*, **14**, 226, 1958.
94. Glover, J., and Green, C., in Popják, G., and Le Breton, E. (eds.): *Biochemical Problems of Lipids*, p. 359. Academic Press, New York, 1956.
95. Rosenman, R. H.; Byers, S. O.; and Friedman, M.: *Circulation Research*, **2**, 160, 1954. Snog-Kjaer, A.; Prange, I.; and Dam, H.: *J. Gen. Microbiol.*, **13**, 256, 1956.
96. Hsia, D. Y.: *Inborn Errors of Metabolism.* Year Book Publishers, Chicago, 1959.

24

Carbohydrate metabolism

Carbohydrate metabolism in the animal body is essentially the metabolism of glucose and of substances related to glucose in their metabolic processes.

The characteristic sugar of blood and of tissue fluids is glucose. The digestion of food carbohydrates, such as starch, sucrose, and lactose, produces the monosaccharides glucose, fructose, and galactose, which pass into the blood stream. Galactose and fructose then are converted to glucose in the liver. There is evidence that the intestinal mucosa may play a role in converting fructose to glucose as the fructose is absorbed.

The glucose of circulating blood and tissue fluids is drawn upon by all the cells of the body and used for the production of energy. Normally, carbohydrate metabolism supplies more than half of the energy requirements of the body. In fact the brain depends largely upon carbohydrate metabolism as a source of energy and quickly ceases to function properly when the blood glucose level falls much below normal.

The glycogen of liver, muscles, and other tissues is formed primarily from glucose and serves as a source of immediately available or reserve energy. Normally, much of the reserve fat in the body depots is formed from glucose. The mammary gland synthesizes lactose from blood glucose. Tissue glycolipids and mucopolysaccharides are formed from glucose.

The metabolism of many of the protein amino acids proceeds by the glucose pathway, and some of the products of glucose metabolism are utilized by the body for the synthesis of amino acids.

Thus it is apparent that glucose occupies the central position in carbohydrate metabolism, and that carbohydrate metabolism is intimately related to the metabolism of both lipids and proteins.

The absorption of sugars into the blood stream from the intestine has been considered in Chapter 13, which the student should review at this time.

THE SUGAR OF BLOOD AND OTHER BODY FLUIDS

Blood sugar. As previously indicated, the sugar of blood and tissue fluids normally is glucose, with the exception that very small amounts of galactose and fructose may be present after absorption from the intestine and before their conversion to glucose. Disaccharides, such as sucrose, lactose, and maltose, usually are completely hydrolyzed to the monosaccharides in the process of digestion and do not enter the blood stream. If lactose and sucrose are absorbed or enter the blood by injection, they are treated as foreign substances and excreted in the urine, since there are no enzymes present for their hydrolysis to utilizable monosaccharides. It appears that if maltose enters the blood it may be partly hydrolyzed and used. Bollman, Mann, and Magath (1) obtained evidence in hepatectomized animals that glycogen injected intravenously may be hydrolyzed and converted to blood glucose.

The sugar of blood and other biologic fluids is commonly determined on blood filtrates with a copper sugar reagent. For many years most clinical sugar analyses have been performed on Folin tungstic acid filtrates. Somogyi (2) showed that the values obtained on such filtrates are usually too high by some 20 to 25 mg per cent, because of the presence of nonsugar-reducing substances, such as glutathione and ergothioneine. The true glucose of blood may be determined by yeast fermentation of blood filtrates, or by the use of filtrates prepared by zinc, iron, cadmium, or mercury precipitations, which remove most of the nonsugar-reducing substances. Somogyi's zinc filtrates are most commonly used for the determination of true blood sugar.

The postabsorptive (12–14 hours after the last meal) true blood sugar in man normally varies from about 60 to 90 mg per cent and may attain levels of 130 mg per cent or higher after meals high in carbohydrate. The values for other warm-blooded animals are generally of the same order. Somogyi (3) and Klinghoffer (4) have shown that in man blood glucose is distributed uniformly throughout the water of red cells and plasma. Since the erythrocytes contain much less water than plasma, the concentration of sugar per unit volume in cells is less than for plasma. This equal concentration of glucose in cell and plasma water apparently holds only for the anthropoids. For example, pig and rat erythrocytes appear to be practically devoid of glucose.

The arteriovenous (AV) difference in the glucose content of blood is ordinarily obtained by analysis of capillary and venous blood samples taken simultaneously. Foster (5) showed that the sugar content of capillary blood is the same as that of arterial blood. As expected, the glucose content of venous is uniformly less than that of arterial blood owing to sugar utilization in the tissues. Somogyi (6) found that the AV glucose difference of postabsorptive normal persons varies from about 1.5 to 8 mg per cent. It is increased in the normal animal by elevation of the blood sugar and by insulin administration, and is decreased in conditions such as diabetes, when the utilization of glucose by the tissues is below normal.

The liver in blood sugar regulation. The liver is the organ primarily responsible for the regulation of blood glucose concentration, since it alone possesses a supply of glycogen directly convertible to glucose and since it is the only organ capable of forming glucose from noncarbohydrate sources, such as amino acids, in quantities sufficient to meet bodily needs. Soskin and associates (7) demonstrated that as the blood glucose level rises the output of glucose by the liver decreases, whereas a fall in blood glucose results in an increased output of sugar by the liver.

Much of our information relative to the role of the liver in maintaining blood glucose has been obtained on dogs and other animals hepatectomized according to the procedure of Mann (8) or a modification of this procedure. The blood sugar of such animals rapidly falls to hypoglycemic levels that produce convulsions and death unless glucose is continually given intravenously. If this is done, the animals may survive for many hours but finally die from causes unrelated to hypoglycemia. Although fructose is somewhat effective in alleviating the hypoglycemia, this appears to be true only if the intestines are present for the conversion of this sugar to glucose, since Bollman and Mann and others (9) showed that only glucose is effective in completely eviscerated animals. The liverless animal cannot form glucose from noncarbohydrate substances, such as lactic acid and amino acids, which are readily converted to glucose by the normal animal.

That muscle glycogen cannot serve directly as a source of blood glucose was shown by the experiments of Bollman, Mann, and Magath (1), who found an appreciable amount of glycogen in the muscles of their hepatectomized dogs when blood glucose had fallen to very low levels. Soskin (10) demonstrated that the muscle glycogen of liverless dogs is not converted to blood glucose by subjecting the animals to the effects of epinephrine, ether anesthesia, and asphyxia. These procedures cause hyperglycemia only when the liver is present and contains glycogen. Muscle glycogen can become blood glucose only through first being broken down to lactic acid, which is transported by the blood to the liver, where it is converted to glucose.

The kidneys as a source of blood glucose. Although the liver plays the predominant role in blood glucose regulation, there is considerable evidence that the kidneys are able to form glucose from a number of carbohydrate intermediates and also from amino acids. Russell and Wilhelmi (11) showed that kidney slices form carbohydrate from pyruvate, succinate, and α-ketoglutarate, and from the amino acids alanine and glutamic acid. All the evidence indicates that while the kidneys undoubtedly possess some capacity for gluconeogenesis and maintenance of blood glucose, this capacity is very minor as compared with that of the liver.

Variations in blood sugar. The blood sugar level is variable throughout the day and at any given time represents the balance between the processes adding glucose to the blood and those removing glucose from it.

The diagram below illustrates the situation.

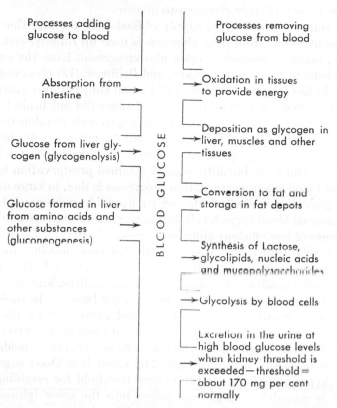

Processes adding glucose to blood		Processes removing glucose from blood
Absorption from intestine →	**BLOOD GLUCOSE**	→ Oxidation in tissues to provide energy
Glucose from liver glycogen (glycogenolysis) →		→ Deposition as glycogen in liver, muscles and other tissues
Glucose formed in liver from amino acids and other substances (gluconeogenesis) →		→ Conversion to fat and storage in fat depots
		→ Synthesis of Lactose, glycolipids, nucleic acids and mucopolysaccharides
		→ Glycolysis by blood cells
		Excretion in the urine at high blood glucose levels → when kidney threshold is exceeded — threshold = about 170 mg per cent normally

As will be explained later, glycogen is both formed from glucose and converted into glucose in the liver. When the blood is rich in glucose after meals, a part of it is converted to liver glycogen, which is later returned to the blood as glucose when the blood sugar level falls.

The processes involving both addition and subtraction of blood glucose proceed simultaneously, and it is the degree to which these different processes are operating that determines the blood glucose level at any given time.

The chief variations in the blood sugar level in the normal animal are generally the result of variations in absorption rate from the intestine (highest after meals, lowest just before meals). As the blood glucose rises after meals (alimentary hyperglycemia), the pancreas is stimulated to secrete more insulin; this causes the rates of tissue oxidation and of glycogen and fat formation and deposition to increase, tending to lower the sugar level of the blood. When the rate of sugar absorption from the intestine no longer equals the tissue demand for glucose and the blood glucose begins to fall toward hypoglycemic levels (low blood sugar), the liver increases its rate of glucose addition to the blood by increasing the rate of glycogen breakdown and also the rate of glucose synthesis from amino acids and other substances (gluconeogenesis). Hypoglycemia stimulates the adrenal medulla to increase its secretion of the hormone epinephrine into the blood, which increases the rate of breakdown of liver glycogen to glucose.

During starvation, when the supply of food from the intestine is cut off, the glucose available from liver glycogen is used up rapidly, and the blood sugar level becomes dependent upon gluconeogenesis from the amino acids of tissue proteins. Lennox, O'Connor, and Bellinger (12) observed the daily variations in blood sugar in a group of human subjects over starvation periods of 11 to 16 days. Generally the blood sugar did not begin to fall until the end of 48 hours of fasting. A definite hypoglycemia developed during the first week, the blood sugar averaging about 65 mg per cent, but in some instances it fell to 50 mg per cent or lower. The sugar level tended to rise during the second week but infrequently attained prestarvation levels. This recovery of blood sugar as starvation progresses is due, in large measure, to increased gluconeogenesis. Infants and young children are much less able to maintain normal blood sugar levels during starvation than are adults, apparently because of less efficient gluconeogenesis.

The islet cells of the pancreas produce the hormone insulin, which is essential for the utilization of most of the glucose by the tissues. Failure to produce sufficient insulin results in the disease diabetes mellitus, and in severe cases there may be drastic changes in the blood sugar balance. In such cases the rate of glucose removal from the blood and utilization by the tissues is greatly reduced without reduction in the total amount of glucose added to the blood. In fact, the process of gluconeogenesis from amino acids generally is increased markedly in the disease. The result is a blood sugar level so elevated (hyperglycemia) that the kidney threshold for retaining sugar in the blood is exceeded, and glucose passes into the urine (glucosuria). Although a deficiency of insulin causes hyperglycemia, an excessive amount of insulin causes the rate of glucose utilization to exceed the rate at which glucose normally can be added to the blood, with resulting hypoglycemia and insulin shock, unless extra carbohydrate is provided. Such situations occasionally result from overproduction of insulin by the pancreas and overdosage with insulin in the treatment of diabetes.

The anterior pituitary gland secretes hormones which inhibit carbohydrate utilization. The formation of excessive amounts of these hormones by the animal or injection of them causes hyperglycemia.

The adrenal cortex also secretes hormones related to the formation and utilization of glucose. One action of such hormones is to regulate gluconeogenesis from amino acids in the liver. The injection or formation of excessive amounts of these hormones may stimulate gluconeogenesis sufficiently to cause hyperglycemia.

The adrenal medulla secretes the hormone epinephrine, which promotes the breakdown of liver glycogen to glucose. The sudden secretion of excessive amounts during tense emotional states may produce hyperglycemia sufficient to cause glucosuria.

When blood is drawn and allowed to stand, the glucose is slowly broken down to lactic acid through a series of reactions involving sugar phosphates.

This process is referred to as "glycolysis." In the broader sense "glycolysis" also refers to similar processes in which glycogen or other carbohydrates are converted to lactic acid by tissues. The glycolysis of blood glucose is due to the action of both red cells and leucocytes. Per cell the latter are more active, though normally red cells are responsible for the greater portion of glycolysis, due to their far greater numbers. In some forms of leukemia, where the number of certain leucocytes is greatly increased, the rate of glycolysis is largely determined by the leucocytes. Such appears to be true in cases of myelogenous leukemia. Glycolysis in blood is inhibited by chilling and increased by warming. It is stopped by heating to 58° C, due to enzyme inactivation. Glycolysis is markedly inhibited by the enzyme poisons monoiodoacetate and fluoride, the latter being employed as a preservative of blood for sugar analysis. Oxalate retards glycolysis, as does the process of laking. Glycolysis increases with rising pH and becomes maximum at pH values from 8 to 9. The action of insulin is not essential for glycolysis, since the process occurs at the same rates in diabetic and normal bloods. Normally, from 10 to 20 mg per cent of glucose per hour is glycolyzed in blood at body temperature, and this rate of breakdown appears to be rather independent of the initial blood glucose level. It is reasonable to suppose that glycolysis of sugar in blood proceeds *in vivo* at a rate equal to that *in vitro*, and if this is true, about 1 g of lactic acid per hour would be formed in the blood of a normal adult by the glycolytic process.

Sugar of fluids other than blood. The concentration of glucose in lymph, transudates, and edema fluid per unit of water is the same as found in plasma, indicating the free diffusibility of glucose across vascular and lymphatic membranes. The glucose content of spinal fluid is generally 20 to 30 mg per cent less than that of blood, though variations in blood glucose are reflected in variations in the sugar of spinal fluid. The relation here is more than represented by simple diffusion between the two fluids. The aqueous humor of the eye also contains less glucose per unit of water than does the plasma, though glucose readily enters the aqueous humor from the plasma. The concentration of glucose within tissue cells per unit of water is less than in blood and varies with different tissues and physiologic states. The glucose of liver may be higher than that of blood, although generally it is lower. The glucose of both liver and kidneys has been shown by Cori and associates (13) to vary with blood glucose over wide ranges. Muscle and brain sugar show much less variation with plasma changes. Cori found muscle glucose to vary only from 6 to 52 mg per cent, with plasma variations from 19 to 272 mg per cent. That tissue glucose generally should be less than plasma sugar is to be expected because of the high rate of tissue utilization of glucose.

Entrance of sugars into tissue cells. In order to explain the widely different concentrations of glucose often observed in extracellular and intracellular fluids and the differential passage of various sugars into cells, it has long been evident that the permeability of cells to sugars must be controlled by special mechanisms. While the problem of the entrance of sugars into cells has not been fully resolved, considerable evidence as to some of the principles involved has been obtained.

Levine and associates (14) have shown that the administration of insulin markedly increases the entrance of glucose and other sugars into tissue cells, and it is now considered that this probably represents the primary action of insulin.

Insulin has been shown to increase the penetration into cells of many monosaccharides including D-galactose, D-glucose, D-mannose, D-fructose, D-xylose, L-arabinose, and D-fucose, but not of the sugar alcohols such as mannitol and sorbitol (15). Insulin also increases the entry of the nonmetabolizable methylated sugar 3-O-methyl glucose (3-OMG) into cells. The insulin effect has been demonstrated in rat, rabbit, dog, cat, and man and on erythrocytes and diaphragm and heart and skeletal muscle, but not in brain. It is of interest that insulin is not necessary to the metabolism of brain tissue.

Park and associates have reviewed the action of insulin on the transport of sugars through the cell membrane (16).

In relation to the action of insulin in increasing the passage of sugars into cells, Stadie and associates (17) have shown that several tissues which respond to insulin *in vitro* bind insulin to their surfaces, and that the insulin response, under appropriate conditions, is proportional to the amount of insulin bound. This means that the target tissue may build up local concentrations of insulin on its surface far greater than the concentrations existing in blood.

Park and collaborators (16) have developed the concept of a membrane carrier system as the functional mechanism governing the transport of glucose and other sugars across cell membranes. The theory is based upon work using both erythrocytes and muscle. The essential features of the theory are given in Figure 24.1. Sugar on the outside of the cell membrane surface, S_0, is postulated to form a complex SC with a "carrier" substance C in the membrane. The complex SC then moves across the membrane, dissociates, and releases free sugar, S_1, into the cell, the process being reversible. The free carrier, C_1, may either combine with free sugar in the cell and transport it to the extracellular fluid (reversal), or it may move back to the outside membrane surface to complex with free sugar, S_0, and transport it into the cell.

Evidence such as the following supports the carrier scheme:

1. D-Galactose rapidly enters the cell, while L-galactose is excluded. Because these sugars are of similar size and solubility, it appears highly improbable that this striking differential permeation can be the result of simple diffusion through membrane pores.

2. When the entrance of a sugar such as glucose into cells is measured against the extracellular sugar concentration, the transport rate of the sugar into the cells increases rapidly at low concentrations but at higher concentrations levels off and approaches a plateau. This kind of curve is best interpreted as due to a limited number of combining sites in the membrane which become saturated as the extracellular sugar concentration rises. Each sugar appears to have a definite affinity for the combining sites and to give a characteristic permeability curve. For example, the following orders of affinity have been found: 3-OMG > D-galactose > D-xylose. All of these sugars have high affinities for the combining sites. They all show rapid transport at low concentrations and early saturation at high concentrations. On the other hand, D-fructose, L-arabinose, and several other pentoses have affinities so low that saturation cannot be demonstrated at any usable concentration of the sugar.

3. When pairs of sugars are present, there is competitive inhibition of transport. Under certain conditions this competition can lead to movement of one of the sugars

against a concentration gradient. In order to show this, muscle is perfused with 3-OMG alone until close to maximum concentration of the sugar in the cells has been reached. The rates of entrance into and exit from the cells are about equal. Now if glucose is added to the perfusing fluid, the 3-OMG leaves the cells against a concentration gradient, which appears to provide very strong evidence against a simple diffusion process, and for a mechanism such as that postulated in the carrier scheme as outlined in Figure 24.1. According to the carrier mechanism postulated, the above facts may be explained as follows. Glucose effectively competes with 3-OMG at the external membrane surface of the cell and reduces 3-OMG entry. However, inside the cell the glucose is metabolized and consequently does not compete with 3-OMG exit. The 3-OMG exit from the cell

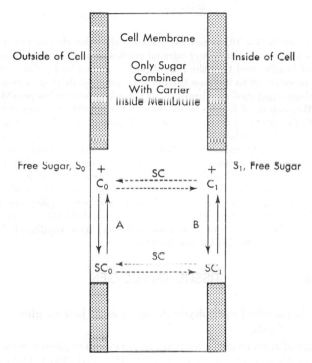

Figure 24.1.   Membrane carrier system for sugar transport, adapted from Park et al. (16). S_0 and S_1 represent free sugar on outside and inside surfaces of cell membrane respectively, and C_0 and C_1 similarly represent carrier. Reactions A and B are very rapid. Movement of SC across the membrane is the rate-limiting process.

thus exceeds its entrance into the cell until the concentration of 3-OMG in the cell falls sufficiently to establish a new equilibrium of transport rates. The energy for the process is supplied originally by the inward movement of glucose down its concentration gradient from the extracellular to the intracellular fluid. Since the glucose is used up in the cell, there is a higher concentration of carrier available to transport 3-OMG from the inside to the outside than from the outside to the inside of the membrane, thus giving a carrier gradient.

The over-all energy requirement in the postulated carrier system is met by the kinetic or thermal energy of the molecules in solution, and not by metabolic energy generated in the cell, since sugar transport into cells and the effect of insulin on this transport take place anaerobically. This differentiates the process from "active transport" as found in the kidney, gastrointestinal tract, etc., which is dependent upon metabolic energy.

Nothing is known about the chemical nature of the carrier C. Presumably it may be of a lipid character possessing membrane solubility. While the carrier hypothesis is still an hypothesis, an increasing amount of evidence appears to support some such mechanism.

Since the primary action of insulin in metabolism appears to be its effect in greatly increasing the rate of entrance of sugar into tissue cells, if the carrier theory of sugar transport is valid, then the action of insulin may be upon some phase of the carrier system.

The initial stage in the metabolism of sugars generally involves phosphorylation by ATP to the sugar phosphate in a reaction catalyzed by a hexokinase enzyme. In the case of glucose the reaction is:

$$\text{Glucose} + \text{ATP} \xrightarrow{\text{Glucokinase}} \text{Glucose-6-phosphate} + \text{ADP}$$

Cori and associates (18, 19) presented evidence that the glucose hexokinase reaction is inhibited by anterior pituitary and adrenal cortical hormones (which are antagonistic to the action of insulin) and that the inhibition is removed by insulin. Such an effect of insulin would be expected to increase the diffusion gradient driving glucose into the cells as a result of glucose metabolism. However, later work in general has provided inadequate evidence for this action of insulin (20), though Kipnis (21) has reported that insulin stimulates both the entry of 2-deoxyglucose into diaphragm muscle cells and its conversion to the 6-phosphate by the hexokinase reaction. Since the phosphate is not metabolized further, it accumulates. More recently Helmreich and Cori (22) have shown that insulin increases the passage of D-arabinose and D-lyxose into cells, but also that muscle stimulation has the same effect as insulin. These workers consider that increased metabolic activity due to either insulin or muscular work may change the cell membrane to make it more permeable to sugars. According to this view, the permeability effect of insulin is secondary to its metabolic effect. It seems probable that both this explanation and that of a carrier theory for the entry of sugars into cells may have validity. It is obvious that much additional work is needed for clarification.

TISSUE GLYCOGEN

Glycogen is the chief carbohydrate of tissues, just as glucose is of blood and other body fluids.

The storage of reserve carbohydrate as glycogen in tissues was first demonstrated by the French physiologist Claude Bernard (1813–1878). As demonstrated by Bernard (23), liver glycogen is reversibly convertible to blood glucose and normally serves to maintain the blood sugar level when the supply of carbohydrate from intestinal absorption is inadequate. The glycogen of muscle and other tissues is utilized directly as a source of energy, the energy being liberated when glycogen is broken down through a long series of phosphorylated intermediates and finally oxidized to carbon dioxide and water. The formation of fat from carbohydrate is effected from breakdown products of glycogen or glucose.

The amounts of glycogen present in tissues varies widely among different tissues and with diet and physiologic states. In general, liver tissue contains the largest amount, up to 10 to 15 per cent in animals fed a high carbohydrate diet, with an average of about 5 per cent. Skin and brain contain least glycogen, ordinarily 0.1 per cent or less. The glycogen content of mammalian skeletal muscle normally is around 0.5 per cent. Soskin and Levine (24) tabulated the distribution of carbohydrate in the tissues of rat, dog, and man, and these values are given in Table 24.1, in which the figures represent ranges or averages observed on a mixed diet.

The total carbohydrate as glucose in the body of the average-sized man probably does not exceed 20 to 30 g, whereas that present as glycogen amounts to 300 g or more. Although normally the per cent glycogen in liver is higher than in muscle, the total quantity in muscle is generally much greater because of the larger muscle mass.

The glycogen of heart muscle tends to be maintained at normal or elevated values under conditions causing severe depletion of liver and skeletal muscle glycogen. Macleod and Prendergast (25) found the glycogen of heart muscle to be increased above normal after starvation, and Junkersdorf (26) found 0.8 per cent glycogen in the heart of a fasted phlorizinized dog, as compared with only 0.02 and 0.03 per cent in the liver and skeletal muscles,

Table 24.1. Distribution of Carbohydrate in Various Tissues of Rat, Dog, and Man

Tissue	Rat		Dog		Man	
	Glycogen (per cent)	Glucose (mg per cent)	Glycogen (per cent)	Glucose (mg per cent)	Glycogen (per cent)	Glucose (mg per cent)
Skeletal muscle	0.81–1.06	50–70	0.55	40–60	0.4–0.6	
Liver	2.5–8.3		6.1		1.5–6.0	
Heart	0.3–0.6		0.47			
Kidney			0.15		0.4	
Brain	0.08		0.1	57		
Skin	0.07	77	0.08	71	0.08	60–82
Blood and extra- cellular fluids		90–129		60–80		60–90

From Soskin and Levine: *Carbohydrate Metabolism.* The University of Chicago Press, Chicago, 1946.

respectively. The maintenance of heart glycogen levels under adverse circumstances is in keeping with the vital function of the organ.

Tissue glycogen is generally determined by some modification of the original method of Pflüger, according to which the quickly excised tissue is placed first in strong KOH solution and heated until it is disintegrated and dissolved. The glycogen is then precipitated from the solution by the addition of alcohol, centrifuged off, and hydrolyzed to glucose with mineral acid. The glucose formed from the glycogen is then estimated.

The use of a strongly alkaline solution in the disintegration of tissue for glycogen analysis appears necessary in order to liberate some of the glycogen from its combination with tissue protein.

A very satisfactory modification of Pflüger's method is that of Good, Kramer, and Somogyi (27).

PRECURSORS OF TISSUE GLYCOGEN

The convertibility of a substance into glycogen in the tissues of the body may be studied by various procedures, of which several are outlined as follows.

1. Administration of substances to fasted animals. A procedure which has been commonly used is to starve a group of rats for 24 to 48 hours, after which liver glycogen values have generally fallen to a few tenths of 1 per cent. The substance to be tested is then given by stomach tube to some of the animals, with others being reserved as controls. After a few hours the liver glycogen of the experimental and control groups is determined and the effect of the test substance noted.

2. Administration of substances to depancreatized or phlorizinized animals. It is assumed, logically, that substances convertible to glucose are also glycogen precursors in the body. The liver glycogen of completely depancreatized animals and of animals treated with the glucoside phlorizin is low. While such animals are unable to store much tissue glycogen (heart excepted), they readily convert various substances into glucose which they excrete in the urine. Carbohydrate utilization by the depancreatized animal is inhibited because of lack of insulin, and, as a result, glucose accumulates in the blood to hyperglycemic levels which exceed the kidney threshold, and glucose passes into the urine. In animals treated with phlorizin the situation is quite different. Phlorizin prevents reabsorption of glucose from the glomerular filtrate by the tubular cells and thus abolishes the kidney threshold to glucose, with the net effect that glucose is drained from the body to produce a severe hypoglycemia. The result is that the glucose concentration of the body fluids bathing the tissues is so low that little carbohydrate can be utilized. It appears that phlorizin-treated animals utilize less carbohydrate than depancreatized animals.

Starved depancreatized or phlorizinized animals continue to excrete glucose and nitrogen in the urine at a relatively constant rate. The ratio of glucose to nitrogen excreted is called the "G:N ratio" (also written "D:N" for dextrose:nitrogen). Minkowski (28) and others showed that the G:N ratio of fasting depancreatized dogs seldom exceeds 2.8, while Lusk (29) found this ratio for fasting phlorizinized dogs to average about 3.6 to 3.65. However, the variations of the G:N ratio in both types of animals is rather wide. It is interesting to note that the G:N ratio for man in severe pancreatic diabetes is about the same as for the phlorizinized dog.

Because phlorizin treatment generally causes the excretion of more glucose than does pancreatectomy and is a simpler procedure, phlorizinized animals are commonly used in testing the conversion of administered substances to glucose. Deuel, Wilson, and Milhorat (30) observed the average urinary excretion of 91 per cent of the glucose given to phlorizinized dogs, and other workers have recovered 75 to 95 per cent of the sugar administered. These results show that such animals possess little capacity to utilize glucose.

When a fasted phlorizinized animal is fed lean meat, both the urinary nitrogen and glucose increase without essential change in the G:N ratio. This fact is taken as evidence that the metabolism of protein produces glucose as well as nitrogenous waste products, and that both the glucose and nitrogen excreted by the fasting phlorizinized animal originate from tissue protein. If the G:N ratio is 3.65 for such an animal when starving or fed lean meat, this means that 3.65 g of glucose are formed in the body when protein equivalent to 1 g of nitrogen is metabolized (6.25 g of protein). This would represent about 58 per cent (3.65/6.25 × 100) conversion of protein to glucose.

When proteins, individual amino acids, or other metabolizable nitrogenous compounds are given to a fasted phlorizinized animal, the basal nitrogen excretion for a given period of time is increased to about the amount represented by the nitrogen of the substance given, while the increase in basal glucose excretion, if any, represents the degree of conversion of the substance to glucose. The administration of nonnitrogenous compounds may cause increased excretion of glucose, with a rise in the G:N ratio. The increase in glucose excretion above the basal value for a given period may be used to calculate the degree of conversion of the substance to glucose in the body.

Since the origin of glucose from protein is due to the presence of certain sugar-forming amino acids, it is not surprising that different proteins produce different amounts of glucose in phlorizinized animals. Janney (31) observed the following percentage quantities of glucose to be derived from proteins: casein 48, serum albumin 55, ovalbumin 54, gelatin 65, fibrin 53, zein 53, edestin 65, and gliadin 80.

Results obtained as above on phlorizinized animals are approximate only, but serve to indicate gross conversion of a substance to glucose. The method is inadequate when the tested substance is a very poor sugar former.

3. *In vitro* synthesis by tissue slices. Many observations upon the conversion of substances to glucose or glycogen by tissue slices suspended in the proper medium have been carried out. This procedure affords a method of estimating the capacity of a specific tissue in effecting the conversion, as contrasted with administration to the intact animal. By the tissue slice technique it can be shown, for example, that the liver, and to some extent the kidneys, are able to deaminize certain amino acids and form glucose and glycogen from the deaminated residues, while muscle and other tissues are unable to do this, although they do form glycogen from glucose.

4. Use of isotopic tracers. The incorporation of deuterium and radioactive (C^{14}) or heavy carbon (C^{13}) into substances is proving a valuable aid in determining the convertibility of such substances into glycogen by the animal body, as well as the rates of glycogen turnover. Of these tracer procedures those utilizing the isotopes of carbon appear to be most promising, though even here the results are often difficult to interpret because of the complexity of the chemical processes involved. An illustration of the use of C^{13} as a tracer in carbohydrate metabolism is afforded by work such as that of Wood, Lifson, and Lorber (32), in which they fed $NaHCO_3$ containing the isotope, and also the shorter-chain fatty acids labeled with C^{13} in various positions. They isolated the liver glycogen, converted it to glucose, and by suitable means of glucose degradation determined the positions in the glucose molecule occupied by C^{13}. The mechanisms involved in this and other tracer work relating to carbohydrate metabolism will be discussed in a later section.

5. Perfusion of surviving organs. The perfusion of substances through surviving organs, particularly the liver, with determination of the glucose content of afferent and efferent blood, has been utilized in studying their convertibility to glucose (and glycogen).

Table 24.2 lists many of the substances which are recognized to be precursors of glycogen in the animal body.

Table 24.2. Substances Convertible into Glycogen in the Animal Body

D-Glucose	α-Ketoglutaric acid
D-Fructose	Citric acid
D-Galactose	Isocitric acid
D-Mannose	cis-aconitic acid
D-Sorbose and L-sorbose	Glycine
D-Glyceraldehyde	Alanine
Dihydroxyacetone	Serine
Glycerol	Valine
Mannitol	Threonine
Sorbitol	Isoleucine
Inositol	Norleucine
Propionic acid and odd C fatty acids oxidized to propionic	Glutamic acid
Lactic acid	Aspartic acid
Pyruvic acid	Cysteine
Succinic acid	Cystine
Fumaric acid	Methionine
Malic acid	Histidine
Oxaloacetic acid	Arginine
Glyceric acid	Citrulline

Most tissues appear capable of forming glycogen from both glucose and lactic acid (through pyruvic acid), the extent of formation from each depending upon the tissue and the concentration of glucose or lactate. Heart muscle utilizes blood lactate quite readily as a source of energy and for glycogen formation.

RATE OF GLYCOGEN FORMATION

The rate of formation of tissue glycogen from its various precursors when administered orally is dependent upon the rates of absorption from the intestine, the competitive processes for the metabolism of each substance, the chemical changes necessary for conversion, and the physiologic state of the test animal. The time at which tissue glycogen is determined after administration of the test substance is also important. The following experiments may be cited for illustration of some of these points.

Cori (33) found much more glycogen in the livers of rats four hours after feeding fructose than after feeding glucose, and least after feeding galactose, the inference being that galactose is a poor former of liver glycogen. However, Harding, Grant, and Glaister (34) fed galactose to rats and in one hour found nearly all the sugar had been converted to liver glycogen. Now the relative rates of absorption from the intestine are galactose > glucose > fructose. Galactose is absorbed more rapidly than the other sugars, and the increase in liver glycogen from it comes sooner than from glucose and fructose, and in four hours the liver glycogen formed from galactose has been largely converted to blood glucose and lost from the liver. The apparent formation of more liver glycogen from fructose than glucose four hours after feeding is the result of the relatively slower rate of fructose absorption and the fact that after fructose enters the blood stream it is converted largely to glycogen in the liver before conversion to blood glucose and utilization by the other tissues (true of galactose also), while absorbed glucose may be utilized by all the tissues of the body directly without preliminary conversion to liver glycogen.

The effect of the physiologic state of the test animal upon conversion of a substance to liver glycogen is seen in the experiments of Deuel and associates (35), who found that rats fasted 48 hours formed liver glycogen more rapidly from glucose than from galactose, whereas if kept on an ordinary diet glycogen was formed faster from galactose. When animals are starved for a sufficient time, their capacity to oxidize glucose is decreased. In the above experiments the normally fed animals converted all the galactose to liver glycogen before utilization but oxidized much of the glucose directly without forming glycogen, while the starved rats, being unable to oxidize the glucose normally, converted much of it to glycogen. The results of these experiments show that the liver forms glycogen more readily from glucose than from galactose.

The utilization of carbohydrate by the normal animal is correlated with the amount of glycogen in the liver. This is true because liver glycogen, through conversion to blood glucose, serves as a source of carbohydrate for the muscles and other tissues, and also because conditions of diet and physiologic states which regulate carbohydrate supplies to the liver generally affect other tissues similarly.

The glycogen content of tissues varies under the influence of numerous physiologic, pathologic, and experimental conditions, some of which deplete while others increase it.

FACTORS AFFECTING TISSUE GLYCOGEN

1. Dietary state. The glycogen content of liver and muscles as well as of other tissues may be markedly altered by changes in the dietary condition of the animal.

Schöndorff (36) fed seven dogs a diet rich in carbohydrate for several days and found maximal and minimal glycogen values, respectively, as follows: liver 18.69–7.3, muscle 3.72–0.72, heart 1.32–0.104. These values, for liver and muscle especially, are much higher than found on an ordinary diet.

Mirski and associates (37) have shown that when high carbohydrate and high protein diets are fed to different groups of rats, those fed the high carbohydrate diet have about three times as much liver glycogen and a little more muscle glycogen than those fed the high protein diet. However, the rats fed the high protein diet maintain liver and muscle glycogen much better during starvation, and under other conditions tending to lower tissue glycogen, than do the animals receiving a high carbohydrate diet. This effect is referred to as the "protein effect" and is probably due to stimulation of liver gluconeogenesis from amino acids by the high protein diet. Gluconeogenesis is depressed on a high carbohydrate diet. The liver of an animal which has been on a high protein diet consequently continues to form glucose at a rapid rate from the amino acids of tissue protein when fasted or placed under other conditions of stress, while the stimulus for gluconeogenesis is lacking in the liver of an animal previously fed a high carbohydrate diet.

As previously indicated, both liver and muscle glycogen are reduced by starvation. The starvation effect varies with time. Fischer and Lackey (38) found 0.26 and 0.09 per cent of glycogen in the liver and muscles, respectively, of dogs fasted five days, while Külz (39) found values of 0.59 and 0.21 after eleven days of fasting. In the animals fasted for the longer period of time, gluconeogenesis from tissue protein has become better established and yields larger quantities of glucose to the tissues.

2. Exercise. Severe exercise greatly accelerates the oxidation of carbohydrate in the tissues and tends to deplete glycogen stores of both the muscles and the liver. The glycogen stores of an animal may be reduced to minimal values by strychnine convulsions, which impose a maximum of muscular contraction and carbohydrate utilization in the body. Prolonged severe chilling causes violent shivering and exercise of the muscles, and this too leads to drastic reduction of muscle and liver glycogen.

3. Insulin. Insulin is necessary for both the oxidation of glucose and its conversion to glycogen. The liver and muscle glycogen values of depancreatized animals are low, but may be restored to normal by insulin administration.

The injection of insulin into normal animals generally causes a fall in both muscle and liver glycogen and hypoglycemia, on account of an increase in the rate of carbohydrate oxidation. If, however, the blood glucose is maintained during insulin action by giving sugar, the muscle glycogen is increased. When convulsive doses of insulin are given to normal animals, the glycogen of liver is decreased, essentially all the muscle glycogen is lost, and heart glycogen may markedly increase, as shown by the following results of Dudley and Marrian (40), obtained with rabbits:

Tissue	Normal Animals Glycogen Per Cent	Animal after Insulin Convulsions Glycogen Per Cent
Skeletal muscles	0.57	0
Liver	5.53	1.86
Heart	0.26	0.54

Best, Hoet, and Marks (41) showed that the skeletal muscle glycogen is maintained under convulsive doses of insulin if the muscles are denervated to prevent contraction.

4. Epinephrine and glucagon. The injection of epinephrine or the secretion of excessive amounts in tense emotional states accelerates the breakdown of liver glycogen to increase blood glucose and of muscle glycogen to increase blood lactic acid.

The injection of glucagon, the hormone of the α-cells of the pancreas, causes very rapid breakdown of liver glycogen to glucose. Glucagon, unlike epinephrine, does not affect muscle glycogen.

5. Adrenal cortical hormones. The adrenal cortex secretes hormones which stimulate gluconeogenesis from amino acids. Adrenalectomized animals cannot maintain blood glucose and tissue glycogen levels when starved or placed under stress due to this failure of glucose formation from protein. Muscle glycogen is affected less than liver glycogen. The injection of proper adrenal cortical extracts or steroids into adrenalectomized animals maintains blood glucose and tissue glycogen levels. If given to well-fed normal animals, the liver glycogen may be increased much above normal.

6. Anterior pituitary hormones. The anterior pituitary secretes hormones which are antagonistic to the action of insulin and inhibit carbohydrate utilization. When animals are hypophysectomized and fasted, the blood sugar and liver and muscle glycogen become depleted, though these can be prevented by proper feeding. Excessive amounts of these hormones secreted by or injected into an animal may severely retard carbohydrate utilization and in addition cause degeneration of the islet cells of the pancreas with the production of typical diabetes mellitus. The relation of the anterior pituitary hormones to carbohydrate metabolism is complex and will be discussed later.

7. Phlorizin. As stated earlier, a very severe form of diabetes is caused by the injection of phlorizin in which the kidney threshold to glucose is abolished and the carbohydrate reserves of the body are drained off. Under these conditions little carbohydrate can be utilized, and the liver and muscle glycogen reserves fall to low levels. However, Deuel, Wilson, and Milhorat (30) showed that if the kidneys are removed from phlorizinized dogs to prevent glucose excretion and maintain the blood sugar level, the tissues metabolize carbohydrate in an essentially normal manner.

8. Acidosis. Elias (42) showed that the intravenous injection of acid into dogs causes the rapid breakdown of liver glycogen with hyperglycemia and glucosuria and suggested that the acidosis of diabetes may be an important factor in reducing liver glycogen.

9. Tissue anoxia. Conditions such as asphyxia and ether anesthesia, which cut off or severely limit the supply of oxygen to tissues, cause the rapid loss of liver and muscle glycogen. An adequate supply of oxygen is necessary for glycogen synthesis. Also, anoxia produces tissue acidosis, which, as indicated above in case of the liver, increases the rate of glycogen breakdown.

GENERAL PROCESSES OF CARBOHYDRATE METABOLISM

At this point it appears desirable to present an over-all summary of the chief phases of carbohydrate metabolism both as a sequel to previous discussion of blood sugar and tissue glycogen in which many relations of carbohydrate metabolism were indicated and preliminary to the discussion of the detailed chemical mechanisms involved in carbohydrate metabolism to follow. Such an over-all summary is presented in the diagram of Figure 24.2.

The chief primary materials for carbohydrate metabolism supplied to the blood from the intestine are the monosaccharides from the digestion of food carbohydrate and most of the amino acids in excess of the amounts required for the synthesis of tissue proteins in growth and maintenance. The materials absorbed into the portal blood pass to the liver, where fructose and

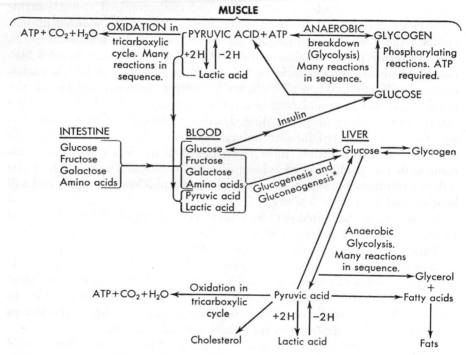

* The term gluconeogenesis is generally used to indicate glucose formation from noncarbohydrate substances such as amino acids.

Figure 24.2.   Diagram of carbohydrate metabolism.

galactose are converted to glucose and glycogen and some of the amino acids are deaminized to form keto acids which are also converted to these carbohydrates. Lactic and pyruvic acids are always present in the blood as a result of metabolism in the muscles and other tissues. These acids are continually being passed into the liver, where they also are converted to glucose and glycogen. All the processes by which the liver converts nonglucose substances into glucose constitute the gluconeogenetic mechanism of the liver. Although the kidneys have some capacity for gluconeogenesis, it is very limited as compared with that of the liver. Gluconeogenesis is constantly taking place but at widely varying rates. It is increased on high protein diets when large amounts of amino acids are absorbed into the blood, and decreased on high carbohydrate diets when there is an abundance of pre-formed glucose. It is increased during exercise, when large amounts of lactic and pyruvic acids escape from the working muscles and there is need to keep up the blood glucose and replenish the muscle glycogen supply. Under these conditions the liver acts to recover and return to them sources of energy lost by the muscles. During starvation gluconeogenesis from the amino acids of tissue protein is the chief source of blood sugar and tissue glycogen. In dia-betic states the rate of gluconeogenesis from both food and tissue protein may be greatly increased, contributing to body emaciation.

The liver stores glucose as glycogen when the supplies of blood glucose and glucose precursors are liberal and reconverts this glycogen to glucose for addition to the blood when the blood sugar falls. The liver thus acts as a glucostatic mechanism to maintain the blood glucose within normal physio-logic limits. The conversion of glucose to glycogen by the liver (as well as other tissues) requires preliminary phosphorylation of the glucose, for which ATP is essential. Chemical energy in the form of ATP is required also for many other liver processes. Part of this ATP is provided through oxidation of fatty acids, previously considered in Chapter 23, and a part by oxidation of some of the glycogen. In this latter process the glycogen first undergoes breakdown or glycolysis through a long series of phosphorylated intermedi-ates to pyruvic acid. In this process some useful energy as ATP is stored up. The pyruvic acid is then oxidized through the tricarboxylic or citric acid cycle to CO_2 and H_2O, with the formation of most of the ATP which is pro-duced from glycogen. While both lactic and pyruvic acids are formed in the liver cells, essentially none escapes into the blood (in contrast with muscle). This is due to the efficiency of reconversion to glycogen in case the oxidation of pyruvic acid cannot keep up with the rate of its formation in the glycolytic stage. Lactic acid is first converted to pyruvic acid in the liver, and the pyruvic acid is then converted to glycogen. These processes thus constitute the mechanism of glucogenesis from lactic and pyruvic acids.

It will be noted from the diagram that glycerol is formed in the glycolytic phase of glycogen breakdown in the liver. Fatty acids are synthesized from pyruvic acid, which upon combination with the glycerol form the glycerides of fats. In this way the liver forms fat from carbohydrate. The liver also synthesizes cholesterol from the pyruvic acid of glycogen breakdown. This synthesis proceeds through acetic acid (acetyl CoA) as an intermediate stage, as also does the synthesis of fatty acids from pyruvic acid. Acetic acid, as acetyl CoA formed from pyruvic acid, is used by the liver in acetylating amines in the process of detoxication.

The chemical mechanisms involved in liver gluconeogenesis from nonglu-cose monosaccharides and amino acids will be pointed out in later discussions.

Carbohydrate metabolism in muscle is highly specialized and designed primarily for the production of ATP as a source of energy for the contraction process. Muscle is limited essentially to blood glucose for its carbohydrate supply. In muscle, glucose is converted to glycogen through the same phosphorylating reactions involved in the formation of liver glycogen. This glycogen yields energy as ATP through glycolysis and oxidation of pyruvic acid in the tricarboxylic cycle, just as does liver glycogen. Muscle also forms glycogen from lactic acid through pyruvic acid and reversal of the glycolytic reactions. Meyerhof (43), in his classical work on frog muscle, demonstrated the reconversion to glycogen of part of the lactic acid formed from glycogen in muscle contraction. In violent exercise the rate of production of pyruvic and lactic acids in muscle greatly exceeds the rate at which they can be oxidized or reconverted to glycogen, and much escapes into the blood stream. Any condition such as asphyxia, which causes tissue anoxia or which limits the oxidative processes in tissues, likewise causes the rapid breakdown of muscle glycogen and escape of these acids into the blood. Most of the acids not picked up from the blood and utilized by the muscles and other peripheral tissues are transported to the liver and converted to glycogen, which is passed back into the blood as glucose when the blood sugar level falls. However, the conservation by the liver of lactic and pyruvic acids escaping from muscle is not complete, since as the blood level of the acids rises appreciable amounts may be lost in the urine.

While pyruvic acid is the primary product of glycolysis, it is reversibly convertible to lactic acid under the influence of the enzyme lactic dehydrogenase. The point of equilibrium of the reaction lies toward lactic acid, and the blood of normal resting adults generally contains about 10 mg of lactic acid and 1 mg of pyruvic acid per 100 ml. The lactate-pyruvate ratio then is about 10:1. These values vary with exercise and disturbances in normal tissue oxidative processes.

CHEMICAL MECHANISMS INVOLVED IN CARBOHYDRATE METABOLISM

The chemical reactions involved in carbohydrate metabolism in the body represent complex groups, sequences, and cycles of reactions which integrate at various points with the reactions concerned in the metabolism of lipids and of proteins. Also, there is much overlapping of reactions in carbohydrate metabolism, so that reactions involved in one stage of metabolism may represent necessary changes preliminary to another stage of metabolism. An illustration of this is seen in the glycolytic breakdown of glucose or glycogen through many phosphorylated intermediates to pyruvic acid, and the subsequent oxidation of this pyruvic acid through the sequence of reactions in the tricarboxylic acid cycle previously considered in Chapter 21. Here we find that the reactions of glycolysis must take place preliminary to the reactions of carbohydrate oxidation. The synthesis of fat from carbohydrate involves synthesis of fatty acids from pyruvic acid formed by glycolysis and combination of these fatty acids with glycerol, which is also a product of glycolytic reactions. Another interesting aspect of carbohydrate metabolism is that the reactions involved in one phase of metabolism may represent essentially the reverse of the reactions concerned in a second phase of metabolism. For example, the process of glucogenesis from pyruvic acid in the liver consists chiefly in reversal of the glycolysis reactions by which the liver converts glucose to pyruvic acid. Thus it is seen that while we may differentiate carbohydrate metabolism into various phases—such as glucogenesis, glycolysis (breakdown of carbohydrate, generally glycogen or glucose), glycogenesis (glycogen synthesis), glycogenolysis (breakdown of glycogen specifically), carbohydrate oxidation, and fat synthesis from carbohydrate—it is impossible to segregate into definite distinct groups the chemical reactions concerned with these phases of carbohydrate metabolism.

The major types of chemical processes involved in carbohydrate metabolism may be grouped as follows:

1. The reversible process, glucose $\rightleftharpoons$ glycogen.

2. The processes by which sugars such as fructose, mannose, and galactose are converted to glucose.

3. The reversible processes by which glucose is converted to pyruvic acid.

4. The oxidation of pyruvate to CO_2 and H_2O in the citric acid cycle.

5. Reduction of —CHOH— groups to —CH_2— groups and reverse, such as the conversion of carbohydrate carbon (—CHOH—) to fatty acid carbon (—CH_2—), and of amino acid carbon (—CH_2—) to carbohydrate carbon (—CHOH—).

RELATIONS OF SUGARS AND GLYCOGEN IN CARBOHYDRATE METABOLISM

Glucose is primarily the carbohydrate supplied by the diet and utilized by the tissues. Other sugars, such as fructose, galactose, and mannose, are convertible into glucose and glycogen and undergo metabolism largely through such conversions. The interconversions of sugars and their conversion to glycogen are effected through enzymatic reactions of the sugar phosphates.

For orientation purposes, general relations of the sugars in metabolism are shown in Figure 24.3.

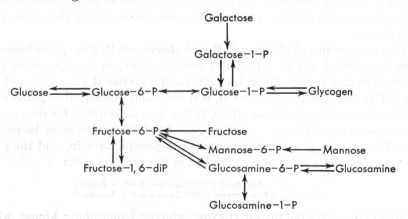

Figure 24.3. General relations of the sugars. Detailed mechanisms are given in the text. ↔ represents a reversible reaction, while ⇄ represents processes reversible by separate reactions (in this diagram specifically).

The metabolism of sugars takes place through their phosphates to pyruvic (and lactic) acid in a process called "glycolysis," which may proceed anaerobically. Pyruvic acid is then converted to acetyl CoA, which is oxidized to CO_2 and H_2O in the citric acid cycle. Discussion in this section will deal particularly with the metabolism of sugars relating to their conversion to sugar phosphates, and with the relation of these phosphates to each other.

The hexokinase reactions. As previously indicated, the first reaction involved in the metabolism of a sugar is phosphorylation by ATP, which is catalyzed by a hexokinase enzyme:

$$\text{Sugar} + \text{ATP} \xrightarrow{\text{Hexokinase}} \text{Sugar phosphate} + \text{ADP}$$

The hexokinase reaction was first discovered in yeast (44), and yeast hexokinase (glucokinase) has been obtained in crystalline form (molecular weight about 97,000) (45). The enzyme catalyzes the phosphorylation of glucose, mannose, fructose, glucosamine, and 2-deoxyglucose to the 6-phosphates. A glucokinase specific for glucose is present in animal tissues and bacteria (46). It forms glucose-6-P. Liver and muscle contain a fructokinase which forms fructose-1-P instead of the 6-phosphate. Galactokinase present in yeast and animal tissues forms galactose-1-P. Liver galactokinase also acts upon galactosamine.

The free energy liberated in the hexokinase reaction is relatively large (about 4 kcal for glucose), and the reaction lies far to the right.

$$\text{Glucose} + \text{ATP} \underset{\longleftarrow}{\overset{\text{Glucokinase}}{\longrightarrow}} \text{Glucose-6-P} + \text{ADP}$$

Though reversibility of the reaction has been demonstrated (47), it is slight and of no appreciable metabolic importance. Glucose-6-P in the liver is hydrolyzed to glucose and Pi by a specific enzyme glucose-6-phosphatase. While glucose-6-P is formed in muscle, it is not converted to glucose because of the absence of glucose-6-phosphatase. Hydrolysis of glucose-6-P in liver represents the final reaction in the formation of glucose from glycogen and from other sugar phosphates. The enzyme is deficient in Von Gierke's disease, a glycogen storage disease, which leads to massive accumulation of glycogen in the liver.

Interconversion of glucose-1-P and glucose-6-P. Phosphoglucomutase. As pointed out in a previous section, glycogen is synthesized from glucose-1-P and broken down into glucose-1-P. After the formation of glucose-6-P in the hexokinase reaction, it is reversibly converted to glucose-1-P by the enzyme phosphoglucomutase. It has been shown that for the reaction to proceed a catalytic amount of glucose-1,6-diphosphate must be present (48). The enzyme phosphoglucomutase is a phosphoprotein, and the phosphate group of the enzyme participates in the reaction (49):

$$\text{Glucose-1-P} + \text{Enzyme-P} \rightleftharpoons \text{Glucose-1,6-diP} + \text{Enzyme}$$
$$\text{Glucose-1,6-diP} + \text{Enzyme} \rightleftharpoons \text{Glucose-6-P} + \text{Enzyme-P}$$

Muscle and yeast contain an enzyme, glucose-1-phosphate kinase, which catalyzes the phosphorylation of glucose-1-P to glucose-1,6-diP by ATP

(50). Also, muscle and bacteria contain glucose-1-phosphate transphosphorylase (51), which forms glucose-1,6-diP by the reaction:

$$2 \text{ Glucose-1-P} \rightleftharpoons \text{Glucose-1,6-diP} + \text{Glucose}$$

These processes supply the amounts of glucose-1,6-diP necessary for the phosphoglucomutase reaction.

Interconversion of glucose-6-P and fructose-6-P. Phosphohexose isomerase (phosphoglucose isomerase). Glucose-6-P is reversibly converted to fructose-6-P by a phosphohexose isomerase enzyme (52):

$$\text{Glucose-6-P} \rightleftharpoons \text{Fructose-6-P}$$

At equilibrium (30° C, pH 8) there is about 30 per cent fructose-6-P and 70 per cent glucose-6-P. The reaction appears to proceed through an enol intermediate:

$$\underset{R-\ CH-\ CHO}{\overset{OH}{|}} \longleftrightarrow \underset{R-\ C-\ CHOH}{\overset{OH}{|}} \longrightarrow R-\ CO-\ CH_2OH$$

Phosphorylation of fructose-6-P to fructose-1,6-diP. Phosphofructokinase. The phosphorylation of fructose-6-P to fructose-1,6 diphosphate by ATP is catalyzed by the enzyme phosphofructokinase, and resembles the hexokinase reaction:

$$\text{Fructose-6-P} + \text{ATP} \longrightarrow \text{Fructose-1,6-diP} + \text{ADP}$$

The reaction, like the hexokinase reaction, is inappreciably reversible, and fructose-1,6-diphosphate is converted back to fructose-6-P through hydrolysis by a specific enzyme, fructose-1,6-diphosphatase:

$$\text{Fructose-1,6-diP} + H_2O \longrightarrow \text{Fructose-6-P} + \text{Pi}$$

Ling and Lardy (53) have shown that fructose-6-P may be phosphorylated to fructose-1,6-diphosphate also by inosine triphosphate (ITP) and uridine triphosphate (UTP).

Metabolism of fructose. Fructose is phosphorylated by ATP through the action of two different fructokinases. As previously indicated, glucokinase forms fructose-6-P:

$$\text{Fructose} + \text{ATP} \longrightarrow \text{Fructose-6-P} + \text{ADP}$$

The fructose-6-P may then be converted to glucose-6-P and glucose, or to glucose-1-P through glucose-6-P, and then to glycogen. It may also be phosphorylated to fructose-1,6-diP, which undergoes conversion to lactic and pyruvic acid through glycolysis, with final conversion of pyruvic acid (by oxidation, etc.) to acetyl CoA, which is oxidized to CO_2 and H_2O in the citric acid cycle. Other sugars are metabolized similarly by being converted to fructose-1,6-diphosphate, so that this compound represents a common meeting point in the metabolic stream of the sugars.

Another fructokinase in animal tissues, as previously indicated, with ATP phosphorylates fructose to fructose-1-P:

$$\text{Fructose} + \text{ATP} \longrightarrow \text{Fructose-1-P}$$

Hers and Kusaka (54) have shown that fructose-1-P is converted to fructose-1,6-diphosphate as follows:

$$\text{Fructose-1-P} \xrightleftharpoons{\text{Aldolase}} \text{Dihydroxyacetone-P} + \text{Glyceraldehyde}$$

$$\text{Glyceraldehyde} + \text{ATP} \xrightarrow{\text{Kinase}} \text{Glyceraldehyde-3-P} + \text{ADP}$$

$$\text{Glyceraldehyde-3-P} + \text{Dihydroxyacetone-P} \xrightleftharpoons{\text{Aldolase}} \text{Fructose-1,6-diphosphate}$$

Metabolism of mannose. Mannose enters the carbohydrate stream through phosphorylation in the hexokinase reaction and then conversion to fructose-6-P:

$$\text{Mannose} + \text{ATP} \xrightarrow{\text{Glucokinase}} \text{Mannose-6-P} + \text{ADP}$$

$$\text{Mannose-6-P} \xrightleftharpoons[\substack{\text{isomerase} \\ \text{(muscle)}}]{\text{Phosphomannose}} \text{Fructose-6-P}$$

Metabolism of galactose (55). Galactose enters the blood stream from the intestine, being formed in the digestion of lactose. It is converted into glucose-1-P by the following series of reactions:

$$\text{Galactose} + \text{ATP} \xrightarrow{\text{Galactokinase}} \text{Galactose-1-P} + \text{ADP}$$

$$\text{Galactose-1-P} + \text{UDP-Glucose} \xrightleftharpoons[\text{uridyl transferase}]{\text{Phosphogalactose}} \text{UDP-galactose} + \text{Glucose-1-P}$$

$$\text{UDP-galactose} \xrightleftharpoons[\text{Epimerase}]{\text{UDP-galactose}} \text{UDP-glucose}$$

(Sum) $$\text{Galactose} + \text{ATP} \longrightarrow \text{Glucose-1-P} + \text{ADP}$$

The glucose-1-P then may undergo the transformations indicated in previous discussion.

Kalckar (55) has shown that congenital absence of the enzyme phosphogalactose uridyl transferase is the cause of the disease galactosemia in children. This means that in galactosemia the conversion of galactose to galactose-1-P takes place but the conversion of galactose-1-P to glucose-1-P does not. Under these conditions galactose-1-P accumulates in erythrocytes and other tissues, causing damage particularly to the liver, brain, and optic lens. Treatment consists in feeding galactose (lactose)-free diets. UDP-galactose is required in forming tissue glycolipids and lactose in the adult female. In galactosemia this is formed from glucose through the epimerase reaction:

$$\text{UDP-glucose} \xrightleftharpoons{\text{Epimerase}} \text{UDP-galactose}$$

An alternate route for the metabolism of galactose is due to the presence of the enzyme uridine diphosphate galactose pyrophosphorylase, which catalyzes the formation of UDP-galactose from galactose-1-P:

$$\text{Galactose-1-P} + \text{UTP} \xrightleftharpoons{} \text{UDP-galactose} + \text{PPi}$$

UDP-galactose pyrophosphorylase is present in low activity in infant liver but increases with age, so the galactosemic adult is able to metabolize appreciable quantities of galactose.

The synthesis of lactose from UDP-galactose is discussed in Chapter 27.

Metabolism of sorbitol. The sugar alcohol sorbitol is formed from glucose in seminal vesicles by reduction of glucose:

$$\text{Glucose} + \text{TPN} \cdot \text{H} + \text{H}^+ \xrightleftharpoons{\text{Dehydrogenase}} \text{Sorbitol} + \text{TPN}^+$$

The seminal vesicles are rich in fructose, and it appears probable that it

RELATION OF SUGARS AND GLYCOGEN IN CARBOHYDRATE METABOLISM

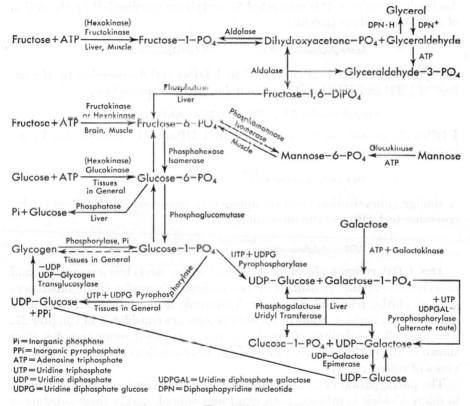

Figure 24.4

is formed there by the action of sorbitol dehydrogenase (56) upon sorbitol:

$$\text{Sorbitol} + \text{DPN}^+ \xrightleftharpoons[\text{dehydrogenase}]{\text{Sorbitol}} \text{Fructose} + \text{DPN} \cdot \text{H} + \text{H}^+$$

Many of the interrelations of the carbohydrates discussed above are shown in Figures 24.3 and 24.4.

Formation and metabolism of hexosamines (57). The hexosamines D-glucosamine, D-mannosamine, and D-galactosamine, as their acetyl derivatives, are important constituents of the mucopolysaccharides of tissues and other substances. Glucosamine-6-P is formed from fructose-6-P:

$$\text{Fructose-6-P} + \text{Glutamine} \xrightarrow{\text{Enzyme}} \text{Glucosamine-6-P} + \text{Glutamic acid} + \text{H}_2\text{O}$$

Glucosamine is also converted to glucosamine-6-P by ATP and glucokinase:

$$\text{Glucosamine} + \text{ATP} \xrightarrow{\text{Glucokinase}} \text{Glucosamine-6-P} + \text{ADP}$$

Glucosamine-6-P is converted to N-acetylglucosamine-6-P through the action of acetyl CoA and the enzyme glucosamine-6-P acetylase:

$$\text{Glucosamine-6-P} + \text{CH}_3 - \text{CO} - \text{S} - \text{CoA} \longrightarrow \text{N-Acetylglucosamine-6-P} + \text{HS} - \text{CoA}$$

Acetylglucosamine-6-P is converted to acetylglucosamine-1-P by the action of a phosphomutase enzyme:

$$\text{Acetylglucosamine-6-P} \xleftrightarrow{\text{Phosphomutase}} \text{Acetylglucosamine-1-P}$$

Acetylglucosamine-1-P is converted to UDP-acetylglucosamine by the action of UTP and UDP-acetylglucosamine pyrophosphorylase:

$$\text{Acetylglucosamine-1-P} + \text{UTP} \rightleftarrows \text{UDP-acetylglucosamine} + \text{PPi}$$

UDP-acetylglucosamine is converted to UDP-acetylgalactosamine by an epimerase enzyme:

$$\text{UDP-acetylglucosamine} \xleftrightarrow{\text{Epimerase}} \text{UDP-acetylgalactosamine}$$

A similar epimerization reaction apparently also converts UDP-acetylglucosamine to UDP-acetylmannosamine:

$$\text{UDP-acetylglucosamine} \xleftrightarrow{\text{Epimerase}} \text{UDP-acetylmannosamine}$$

The UDP compounds of acetylglucosamine, acetylgalactosamine, and acetylmannosamine are utilized in the synthesis of complex tissue substances such as chitin, bacterial cell walls, hyaluronic acid, sialic acid, and other mucopolysaccharides. Some of these syntheses are considered in Chapter 27. The over-all metabolism of the hexosamines is much more complex than shown in the outline above. Comprehensive discussions are given in the reviews of reference (57).

The participation of uridine diphosphate (UDP) and similar compounds in many biologic syntheses, both plant and animal, makes these substances of unusual significance. Recent comprehensive reviews have been written by Strominger (58) and Leloir, Cardini, and Cabib (59).

GLYCOGENESIS AND GLYCOGENOLYSIS

The mechanisms by which glycogen is formed and broken down in tissues have been worked out by the Coris and their associates (60) and by Leloir, Cardini, and associates (61).

Phosphorylases. It has been shown that animal tissues such as liver and muscle contain enzymes, the phosphorylases, which break the glucosidic bonds of glycogen by a process of phosphorolysis, in which inorganic phosphate splits these bonds to form glucose-1-phosphate (Cori ester). Previously the breakdown of glycogen in tissues was considered to involve hydrolysis of the glucosidic bonds. Purified phosphorylase preparations were obtained and the reaction studied *in vitro*. The process was found to be readily reversible, and at equilibrium—pH 7 and 25° C—77 per cent of the carbohydrate is present as glycogen and 23 per cent as glucose-1-phosphate (glucose-1-P):

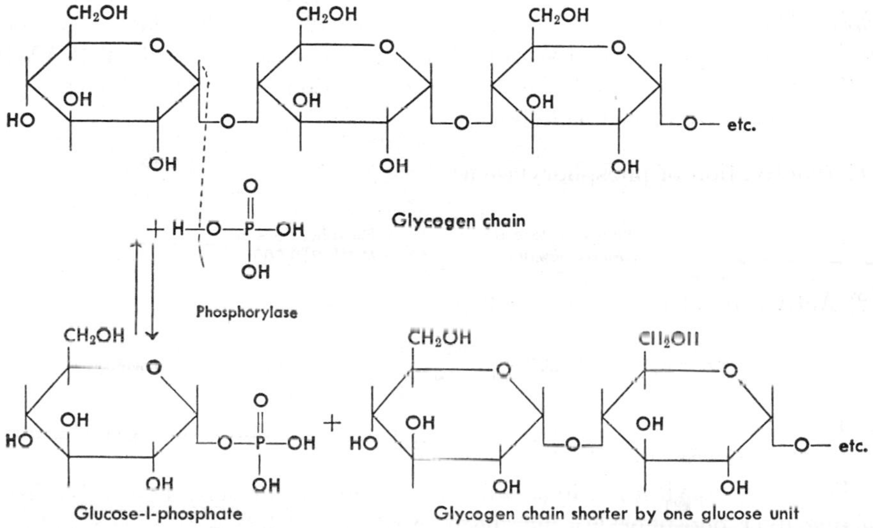

Glycogen chain

Phosphorylase

Glucose-1-phosphate

Glycogen chain shorter by one glucose unit

In order to synthesize glycogen *in vitro* by the phosphorylase reaction it is necessary to prime the reaction by adding glycogen or another branched-chain polysaccharide, such as amylopectin or branched dextrin, to the mixture. Phosphorylase causes the addition of glucose residues to the nonreducing ends of the branches of the activating polysaccharide to lengthen them. Also, it splits glucose units from the nonreducing ends. When phosphorylase of muscle acts on glucose-1-P, it does not form branched glycogen but a straight-chain amylose type of polysaccharide containing 80 to 200 glucose units. This substance has little or no activating effect. Phosphorylase is limited to the formation and splitting of $\alpha(1 \longrightarrow 4)$ glucosidic bonds. The efficiency of activation is proportional to the number of end groups present (degree of branching) in the polysaccharide.

Crystalline phosphorylase was obtained from rabbit muscle in 1943, and found to have a molecular weight of about 500,000 (62). It was found that the crystalline enzyme named "phosphorylase a" is converted by a tissue enzyme, "phosphorylase rupturing enzyme" (PR enzyme) or phosphorylase phosphatase, into inactive "phosphorylase b," with a molecular weight of about 250,000 (63). The inactivation process appears to be due to proteolytic splitting of a peptide bond, since trypsin converts phosphorylase a to phosphorylase b without appreciable destruction of potential phosphorylase activity.

Crystalline muscle phosphorylase a contains 4 mols of pyridoxal phosphate per mol of enzyme, and removal of the pyridoxal phosphate inactivates it. The activity is restored by addition of the cofactor (64). Phosphorylase b contains 2 mols of pyridoxal phosphate per mol.

Inactive phosphorylase b of muscle is converted to active phosphorylase a by reaction with ATP in the presence of Mg^{++}, the reaction being catalyzed by a phosphokinase. It has been shown that activity of the phosphokinase is greatly increased by cyclic-3',5'-adenylic acid (cyclic-3',5'-AMP) (65). Epinephrine increases the concentration of active phosphorylase in muscle, and it appears to do this by promoting the formation of cyclic-3',5'-AMP.

The above processes relating to interconversion of the phosphorylases of muscle may be outlined as follows:

(*1*) Inactivation of phosphorylase a:

$$\text{Phosphorylase a} \xrightarrow{\text{PR enzyme}} \text{2 Phosphorylase b}$$
$$\text{M.W. 500,000} \qquad\qquad\qquad \text{M.W. 250,000}$$

(2) Activation of phosphorylase b (66):

$$\text{2 Phosphorylase b} + \text{4ATP} \xrightarrow[\text{Mg}^{++}, \text{ cyclic-3',5'-AMP}]{\text{Phosphokinase}} \text{Phosphorylase a} + \text{4ADP}$$

In the activation process the phosphorylase b is phosphorylated (2 P groups per mol) and also dimerized.

The phosphorylases of liver differ from those of muscle. The active form of dog liver phosphorylase has been purified and has a particle weight of around 240,000 (67). The liver enzyme is inactivated by an enzyme, phosphorylase phosphatase, which splits out 2 mols of inorganic phosphate (Pi) per mol of phosphorylase:

$$\begin{array}{c}\text{Phosphorylase} \\ \text{active}\end{array} \xrightarrow{\text{Phosphatase}} \begin{array}{c}\text{Phosphorylase} + \text{2Pi} \\ \text{inactive}\end{array}$$

This suggests that active liver phosphorylase is a phosphoprotein which is dephosphorylated by the inactivating enzyme.

Inactive liver phosphorylase is converted back to the active form by a phosphokinase enzyme, dephosphophosphorylase phosphokinase, ATP, and Mg^{++}. Cyclic-3',5'-AMP increases the activity of the phosphokinase:

$$\begin{array}{c}\text{Phosphorylase} + \text{2ATP} \\ \text{Inactive}\end{array} \xrightarrow[\text{Mg}^{++}, \text{ Cyclic-3',5'-AMP}]{\text{Phosphokinase}} \begin{array}{c}\text{Phosphorylase} + \text{2ADP} \\ \text{Active}\end{array}$$

Both epinephrine and glucagon (hormone of pancreatic α-cells) activate liver phosphorylase, apparently by increasing the formation of cyclic-3',5'-AMP. Only epinephrine promotes the activation of muscle phosphorylase, glucagon being without effect. Accordingly, the administration of epinephrine to an animal causes the rapid breakdown of both liver and muscle glycogen, while glucagon causes the breakdown of only liver glycogen.

Phosphorylases have been found in various animal tissues (muscle, liver, heart, brain), in yeast, and in higher plants, such as peas and potatoes. The phosphorylases of plants act upon starch similarly as those of animals act upon the glycogens.

Amylo (1,4 ⟶ 1,6)-transglucosidase and amylo-1,6-glucosidase. Branching and debranching enzymes. As indicated above, the phosphorylases split (reversibly) only the α-1,4 bonds and are not capable of synthesizing branched polysaccharides. Cori and associates obtained preparations of a branching enzyme, amylo (1,4 ⟶ 1,6)-transglucosidase, from liver and muscle which produce 1,6 glucose linkages, and this enzyme acting with phosphorylase forms branched polysaccharides.

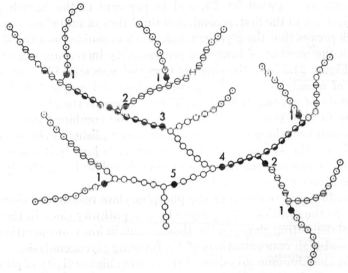

Figure 24.5. Model of segment of muscle glycogen based on results obtained by stepwise enzymatic degradation. ⊙, ⊖, and ⊜ glucose residues removed by first, second, and third degradation with phosphorylase, respectively. ●, glucose residues removed by amylo 1,6-glucosidase. Of five tiers three were degraded, corresponding to 122 out of 150 glucose residues.

Larner (68) showed that the combined action of phosphorylase and branching enzyme upon glucose-1-phosphate to form glycogens is something as follows. Phosphorylase produces chains with 1-4 glucose linkages, and then the branching enzyme acts upon these chains to convert some of the 1-4 linkages to 1-6 linkages, thus forming branches. Larner prepared glycogens with outer branches of different lengths by enzymatic methods and found that those preparations with an average outer chain length of 6 glucose units could not be branched by the branching enzyme, while glycogens with average outer chain lengths of 11 to 21 glucose units could all be branched by the enzyme.

Since the branching enzyme transposes glucose units from 1-4 linkages to 1-6 linkages it has been designated "amylo-(1,4 → 1,6)-transglucosidase."

The synthesis of the starches in plants proceeds according to the general pattern of glycogen synthesis in animals. However, in this case the branching enzyme is designated the Q enzyme, and it produces longer branches than does the animal branching enzyme.

The enzymatic breakdown of the branched structure of glycogen in animal tissues involves the enzymes phosphorylase and amylo-1, 6-glucosidase. The phosphorylase splits off the 1-4 linked glucose residues from the outer branches as glucose-1-phosphate, and then the glucosidase hydrolyzes out the 1-6 linked glucose units at the branch points as glucose, thereby exposing another tier of branches to be broken down by phosphorylase. Cori and associates (69) degraded both glycogens and amylopectins by the successive actions of phosphorylase and amylo-1, 6-glucosidase to the extent of about 90 per cent. They found 50, 20, and 10 per cent of the branch points of muscle glycogen in the first, second, and third tiers of branches, respectively. This work proves that the glycogen molecule is organized as a tree-like structure, with the number of branches progressively increasing toward the periphery. Figure 24.5 from the paper of Cori and associates illustrates the degradation of muscle glycogen by phosphorylase and amylo-1, 6-glucosidase.

Synthesis of glycogen from uridine diphosphate glucose (UDPG). While the *in vitro* synthesis of glycogen by the combined action of phosphorylase and branching enzyme is readily accomplished, evidence indicates that in tissues the synthesis of glycogen proceeds largely if not exclusively by a different process, the function of phosphorylase being chiefly the conversion of glycogen to glucose-1-P.

The equilibrium condition of the phosphorylase reaction in tissues is not favorable to the synthesis of glycogen by this pathway (58). In the fed resting animal depositing glycogen the tissues contain low concentrations of glucose-1-P and high concentrations of Pi, favoring glycogenolysis.

Robbins and Lipmann (61) showed that during high activity of phosphorylase a in muscle the incorporation of glucose into glycogen almost completely ceased. However, with the steady decrease of phosphorylase activity to practically zero, the incorporation of glucose into glycogen showed a marked increase, indicating that glycogen synthesis not involving phosphorylase was taking place. Niemeyer (70) postulated that phosphorylase may function exclusively as a glycogen-splitting agent, and that glycogen synthesis may be catalyzed by a different enzyme involving possibly uridine diphosphate glucose (UDPG). The exceedingly rapid and massive glycogenolysis caused by glucagon and epinephrine, which activate phosphorylase, indicate the preponderance of glycogen breakdown over glycogen synthesis in the phosphorylase reaction in tissues.

Leloir and Cardini (61) have shown that glycogen is synthesized in both liver and muscle through the action of UDPG and the enzyme glycogen synthetase or UDPG-glycogen transglucosylase. Glucose units are added to the nonreducing ends of glycogen by 1,4 bonds, as in the case of phosphorylase action. The process may be represented:

$$\text{UDP-G} + (\text{Glucose})_n \longrightarrow (\text{Glucose})_{n+1} + \text{UDP}$$
$$\qquad\quad \text{Glycogen} \qquad\qquad \text{Glycogen}$$

This action must take place in conjunction with the branching enzyme in order to maintain the branched structure of the glycogen tree as it is built up. UDPG synthesis of glycogen also requires a primer, though in this case even maltose will serve.

In contrast to the phosphorylase reaction the UDPG reaction for the synthesis of glycogen is practically irreversible. The UDPG-glycogen trans-glucosylase activity of muscle is high (61, Robbins and Lipmann).

It appears that the relations in the synthesis and breakdown of glycogen in tissues may be represented:

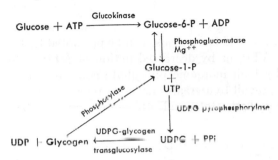

The great biologic importance of the uridine diphosphate glycosides is shown by the fact that, in addition to glycogen and starch synthesis, these compounds are intermediates in the formation of a large proportion of other natural carbohydrates. They act as carriers of active sugar (glycosyl) groups which are transferred to other substances under the catalytic action of trans-glycosylase enzymes. Uridine diphosphate glycosides are involved in the synthesis of sucrose, lactose, uronic acids, glucuronides, glycolipids, pento-sans, mucopolysaccharides, bacterial cell wall carbohydrates, cellulose, chi-tin, and other substances. Some of these syntheses are considered in Chapter 27, on specialized tissues, and later in this chapter. Strominger has written a comprehensive review on the uridine diphosphate compounds (58).

The composition of bacterial cell wall structural material is of interest and importance. The synthesis of the cell wall of *S. aureus* in particular has been studied (58). The funda-mental building unit of the cell wall material in *S. aureus* is a peculiar sugar derivative, acetylmuramic acid, which is made up of an acetylhexosamine (probably glucosamine), lactic acid, and a peptide:

The cell wall structure is built up from UDP-acetylmuramic acid molecules so that the acetylmuramic acid groups are united by 1,4 glycoside bonds. Lysozyme—an enzyme found in egg white, tears, and gastrointestinal secretions—lyses the bacteria by splitting these 1,4 bonds of the cell wall structure. Penicillin and some other antibiotics block metabolic processes in the cell wall synthesis.

According to the above scheme of sugar-glycogen relations, the reactions for the conversion of sugar to glycogen will be shifted toward glycogen synthesis by mass effect when the blood sugar concentration is high, as after carbohydrate meals, and when the ATP concentration is high, as found in the resting normal well-fed animal. Conversely, according to mass effect, the breakdown of liver glycogen to glucose, and of muscle and other tissue glycogen to pyruvic and lactic acids, will be promoted by low concentrations of glucose and ATP, or by decreased action of ATP as found in diabetes mellitus, and by high inorganic phosphate concentrations. Some or all of these relations prevail to a greater or lesser degree as the result of exercise, starvation, the diabetic state, and other pathologic conditions.

GLYCOLYSIS. THE BREAKDOWN OF SUGARS TO PYRUVIC AND LACTIC ACIDS. EMBDEN-MEYERHOF PATHWAY

The process of glycolysis in tissues consists in the breakdown of glycogen, glucose, or other sugars to pyruvic and lactic acids and is a process of carbohydrate metabolism generally characteristic of animal cells. Although one stage of glycolysis requires oxidation by dehydrogenation, this may be accomplished without oxygen, so the process as a whole may be anaerobic. As already indicated, glycolysis proceeds through a sequence of phosphorylated sugars and sugar derivatives, some of which have been considered in the previous section.

The glycolytic process is necessary for most phases of carbohydrate metabolism except the interconversion of glycogen and sugars. It is obligatory to one pathway of carbohydrate oxidation, since the pyruvic acid formed by glycolysis is then oxidized to CO_2 and H_2O in the tricarboxylic acid cycle. This oxidation is the source of most of the utilizable energy (ATP) derived from carbohydrate metabolism. Fat formation from carbohydrate is effected by synthesis from products formed in the glycolytic reactions. Glycolysis also yields some energy in the form of ATP which can be utilized for muscle contraction and other functions. This is particularly important during sudden strenuous exercise, when energy must be made available in excess of that which can be provided by oxidative processes.

The sequence of chemical changes preliminary to and directly and indirectly concerned in glycolysis is indicated in the diagrams of Figures 24.6 and 24.7.

The glycolytic process taking place in animal tissues involves the sequence of intermediates on page 975.

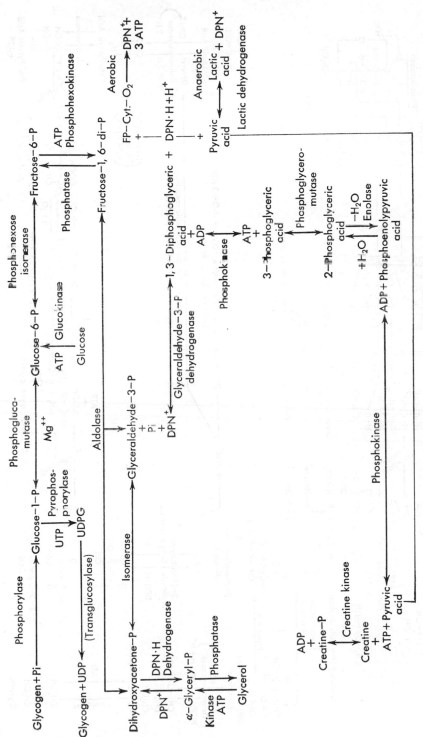

Figure 24.6. Glycolysis. Embden-Meyerhof pathway.

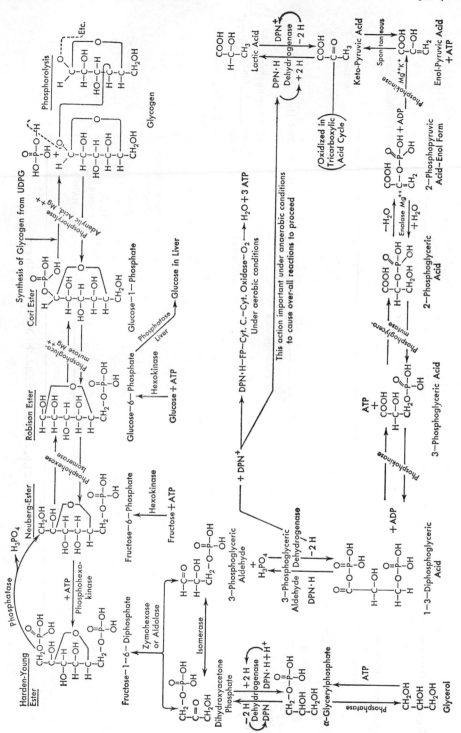

Figure 24.7.   Glycolysis, showing the formulas of intermediates.

Glycogen ⟶ glucose-1-P
              ↓
glucose ⟶ glucose-6-P ⟶ fructose-6-P ⟶
fructose-1,6-diP ⟶ glyceraldehyde-3-P + dihydroxyacetone-P[⟶ glyceraldehyde-3-P] ⟶
3-phosphoglyceric acid ⟶ 2 phosphoglyceric acid ⟶ phosphoenolpyruvic acid ⟶
pyruvic acid ⟶ lactic acid

Since the transformations through fructose-1,6-diphosphate have been considered previously, the following discussion will concern only the remaining processes.

Fructose-1,6-diP is cleaved by the enzyme aldolase between the third and fourth carbon atoms to form two triose phosphate molecules, glyceraldehyde-3-P and dihydroxyacetone phosphate.

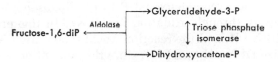

Crystalline aldolase has been prepared from rabbit muscle (71). Isotopic studies indicate that aldolase combines with dihydroxyacetone-P to form a complex which labilizes one of the two H atoms on carbon 3 in a stereospecific manner (72).

It will be noted that the reaction is reversible. Glyceraldehyde-3-P and dihydroxyacetone-P are freely interconvertible through the action of triose-P isomerase.

Glycerol is formed from dihydroxyacetone-P by the reactions:

$$\text{Dihydroxyacetone-P} + \text{DPN} \cdot \text{H} + \text{H}^+ \xrightarrow{\text{Dehydrogenase}} \alpha\text{-Glycerophosphate} + \text{DPN}^+$$

$$\alpha\text{-Glycerophosphate} + \text{H}_2\text{O} \xrightarrow{\text{Phosphatase}} \text{Glycerol} + \text{Pi}$$

Glycerol enters the metabolic pathway through phosphorylation by ATP to α-glycerophosphate:

$$\text{Glycerol} + \text{ATP} \xrightarrow[\text{phosphokinase}]{\text{Glycerol}} \alpha\text{-Glycerophosphate} + \text{ADP}$$

The next step in the main stream of glycolysis consists of the combined phosphorylation and oxidation of glyceraldehyde-3-P to 1,3-diphosphoglyceric acid, which is catalyzed by the enzyme glyceraldehyde-3-P dehydrogenase:

$$\text{Glyceraldehyde-3-P} + \text{Pi} + \text{DPN}^+ \rightleftharpoons \text{1,3-Diphosphoglyceric acid} + \text{DPN} \cdot \text{H} + \text{H}^+$$

Racker and Krimsky (73) have shown that the dehydrogenase contains firmly bound glutathione, and that the —SH group of glutathione takes part in the reactions. The process requires that ADP or another acceptor, such as creatine (74) be present to accept the high-energy carboxyl phosphate of the 1,3-diphosphoglyceric acid formed. The reaction is further promoted by the presence of an acceptor for high-energy phosphate from ATP, such as creatine or glucose, which causes regeneration of ADP:

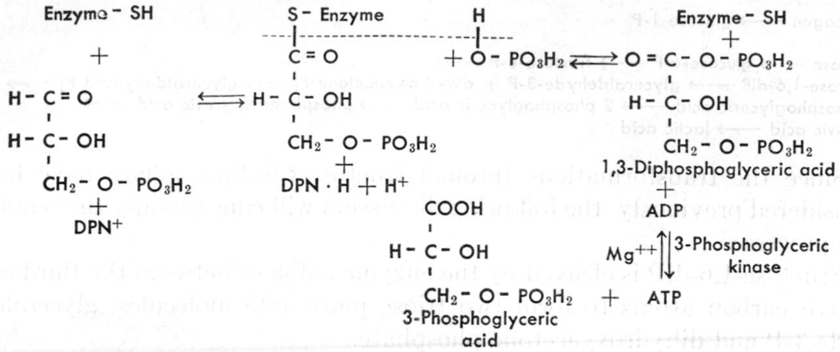

Enzyme - SH   S - Enzyme   H   Enzyme - SH
                               ---|-----------------|----   +
       +   C = O   + O - PO₃H₂ ⇌ O = C - O - PO₃H₂
                                  | |
  H - C = O   ⇌   H - C - OH   H - C - OH
      | | |
  H - C - OH   CH₂ - O - PO₃H₂   CH₂ - O - PO₃H₂
      | +   1,3-Diphosphoglyceric acid
  CH₂ - O - PO₃H₂   DPN · H + H⁺   +
       +   ADP
     DPN⁺   COOH
                                  | Mg⁺⁺⇅ 3-Phosphoglyceric
                             H - C - OH   kinase
                                  |
                             CH₂ - O - PO₃H₂   +   ATP
                             3-Phosphoglyceric
                                   acid

The conversion of glyceraldehyde-3-P to 1,3-diphosphoglyceric acid proceeds anaerobically through oxidation by DPN⁺. In this process DPN⁺ is
converted to DPN · H, and the reaction would soon cease without a mechanism to reoxidize DPN · H to DPN⁺, since the amount of coenzyme present
is very small. Anaerobically DPN · H is oxidized to DPN⁺ by pyruvic acid,
with the formation of lactic acid:

$$\text{Pyruvic acid} + \text{DPN} \cdot \text{H} + \text{H}^+ \xrightleftharpoons[\text{dehydrogenase}]{\text{Lactic}} \text{Lactic acid} + \text{DPN}^+$$

Substances other than pyruvic acid may serve also to oxidize DPN · H
to DPN⁺. Among these are dihydroxyacetone-P, which is reduced to α-glycerophosphate, and oxaloacetic acid, which is reduced to malic acid. Reduction by these substances is of importance in starting the glycolytic process
before sufficient pyruvic acid has been formed to function in the regeneration
of DPN⁺. No ATP is formed in the oxidation of DPN · H by pyruvic acid.

When the supply of oxygen to the tissues and the oxidative mechanisms
are adequate, the DPN · H is oxidized to DPN⁺ through the mitochondrial
electron transport chain:

$$\text{DPN} \cdot \text{H} - \text{FP} - \text{Cytochromes} - \text{O}_2 \longrightarrow \text{DPN}^+ + \text{H}_2\text{O} + 3\text{ATP}$$

Consequently, lactic acid accumulates in tissues only when oxidation by O_2
cannot keep up with glycolytic reactions and pyruvic acid is reduced to
lactic acid.

It will be noted that in this stage of glycolysis we have the first generation
of utilizable energy as ATP, 1 mol of ATP per triose phosphate mol when
DPN · H is oxidized anaerobically (by pyruvate), and 4 mols per triose phosphate mol when DPN · H is oxidized by O_2. This means that the utilizable
energy obtained varies with the proportions of DPN · H oxidized by pyruvate and by O_2.

The next stage of glycolysis consists in the conversion of 3-phosphoglyceric
acid to 2-phosphoglyceric acid by the enzyme phosphoglyceromutase, which
requires catalytic amounts of 2,3-diphosphoglyceric acid (75). The process
is entirely analogous to the action of 1,6-glucose-P in the phosphoglucomutase reaction:

3-Phosphoglyceric acid + Enzyme - P ⇌ 2,3-Diphosphoglyceric acid + Enzyme
2,3-Diphosphoglyceric acid + Enzyme ⇌ 2-Phosphoglyceric acid + Enzyme - P

Glycolysis proceeds by the conversion of 2-phosphoglyceric acid to phosphoenolpyruvic acid through action of the enzyme enolase (76). The reaction involves dehydration of 2-phosphoglyceric acid and is freely reversible:

$$
\begin{array}{ccc}
\text{COOH} & & \text{COOH} \\
| & & | \\
\text{H} - \text{C} - \text{O} - \text{PO}_3\text{H}_2 & \rightleftharpoons & \text{C} - \text{OPO}_3\text{H}_2 + \text{H}_2\text{O} \\
| & & || \\
\text{CH}_2 - \text{OH} & & \text{CH}_2
\end{array}
$$

2-Phosphoglyceric acid   Phosphoenolpyruvic acid
Low-energy phosphate group   Phosphopyruvic acid
                              High-energy phosphate group

The loss of water converts the low-energy phosphate group of 2-phosphoglyceric acid to the high-energy phosphate group of phosphopyruvic acid, yet the total energy change in the reaction is relatively small (-0.64 kcal). This indicates a redistribution of energy in the molecule resulting from the loss of water.

Because of the high-energy phosphate group present in phosphopyruvic acid, it reacts with ADP to form ATP and pyruvic acid to complete glycolysis proper. The reaction is catalyzed by the enzyme ATP-phosphopyruvic transphosphorylase or pyruvate kinase, which requires Mg^{++} and K^{+} for activation (in muscle, but only Mg^{++} in yeast) (77):

$$
\begin{array}{ccccc}
\text{COOH} & & \text{COOH} & & \text{COOH} \\
| & & | & & | \\
\text{C} - \text{OPO}_3\text{H}_2 + \text{ADP} \rightleftharpoons \text{ATP} + & \text{C} - \text{OH} & \rightleftharpoons & \text{CO} \\
|| & & || & & | \\
\text{CH}_2 & & \text{CH}_2 & & \text{CH}_3
\end{array}
$$

Phosphopyruvic   Enolpyruvic   Ketopyruvic
acid   acid   acid

The free energy change in the reaction, $\Delta F'$, amounts to about -6 kcal, which means that equilibrium lies far to the right toward formation of ATP and pyruvic acid. This reaction accounts for the formation of 2 mols of ATP per mol of sugar glycolyzed.

PYRUVATE METABOLISM

The reactions of glycolysis in animal tissues lead to the end products pyruvic and lactic acids, lactic acid being readily and reversibly converted into pyruvic acid.

Pyruvic acid is oxidized and converted to acetyl CoA by an oxidative α-ketodecarboxylase enzyme, and the over-all reaction is:

$$\text{CH}_3 - \text{CO} - \text{COOH} + \text{HS} - \text{CoA} + \text{DPN}^+ \longrightarrow \text{CH}_3 - \text{CO} - \text{S} - \text{CoA} + \text{DPN} \cdot \text{H} + \text{H}^+ + \text{CO}_2$$

The mechanism of the reaction, which is complex, is given in Chapter 21. Oxidation of the $\text{DPN} \cdot \text{H}$ in the electron transport chain yields 3ATP per mol (Chapter 21).

The acetyl CoA formed from pyruvic acid is oxidized in the citric acid cycle (see Chapter 21) to CO_2 and H_2O, with the formation of 12ATP per mol.

Pyruvic acid occupies a key position in metabolism, where numbers of reactions converge in its production and others lead from it to form various substances. As indicated above, it is the end product in the main line of glycolysis (lactic acid is a side issue), and from it acetyl CoA is formed to run the citric acid cycle, to synthesize fatty acids and cholesterol (Chapter 23), and for acetylation reactions. Alanine upon deamination directly forms pyruvic acid, and amination of pyruvic acid forms alanine. Several amino acids in their metabolism are indirectly converted to pyruvic acid (Chapter 25). Decarboxylation of oxaloacetic acid forms pyruvic acid, as does oxidation of malic acid by the malic enzyme. The metabolism of pyruvic acid is outlined in Figure 24.8.

PYRUVATE METABOLISM

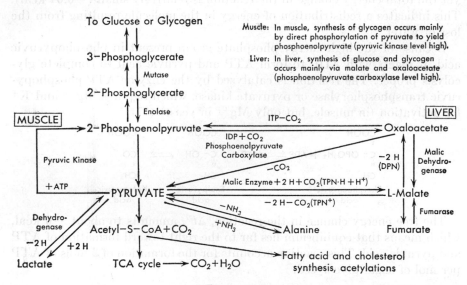

Figure 24.8

Energy production from carbohydrate metabolism through glycolysis and oxidation in the citric acid cycle. As indicated in previous discussion, relatively little ATP is formed in the glycolysis process, most of it being produced by oxidation in the citric acid cycle. The energy yielding processes and the mols of ATP formed per hexose unit metabolized are as follows:

	ATP yield per hexose unit
1. Glycogen $\longrightarrow$ Fructose-1,6-diphosphate	-1
2. Glucose $\longrightarrow$ Fructose-1,6-diphosphate	-2
3. 2 Triose-P $\longrightarrow$ 2,3-Phosphoglyceric acid $+$ 2DPN$\cdot$H	$+2$
2DPN$\cdot$H $\longrightarrow$ 2DPN$^+$	$+6$
4. 2 Phosphopyruvic acid $\longrightarrow$ 2 Pyruvic acid	$+2$
5. 2 Pyruvic acid $\longrightarrow$ 2 Acetyl CoA $+$ 2CO$_2$ $+$ 2DPN$\cdot$H	
2DPN$\cdot$H $\longrightarrow$ 2DPN$^+$	$+6$
6. 2 Acetyl CoA $\longrightarrow$ 4CO$_2$	$+24$
Net: C$_6$H$_{12}$O$_6$ $+$ 6O$_2$ $\longrightarrow$ 6CO$_2$ $+$ 6H$_2$O	38

It will be noted that 2 mols of ATP are utilized in the metabolism of a mol of glucose, while only one ATP is utilized per hexose unit of glycogen metabolized. Accordingly there is a net production of 39ATP per glycogen hexose unit metabolized.

The above energy yield is based upon the fact that the DPN · H formed in Reaction 3 is oxidized by O_2 rather than by pyruvic acid. As pointed out in earlier discussion, the oxidation of DPN · H by pyruvate with the formation of lactic acid does not form ATP. Consequently, if the glycolysis process is purely anaerobic, the ATP production is reduced by 6 mols per mol of hexose metabolized. Accordingly, the net energy production varies with the degree of anaerobiosis under which glycolysis proceeds. Also, the amount of lactic acid accumulating varies proportionately.

The complete oxidation of glucose to CO_2 and H_2O yields 686,500 cal per mol. Of this energy glycolysis proper (glucose to pyruvic acid) yields as a net maximum about 56,000 cal (8ATP) of utilizable energy if DPN · H (Reaction 3) is oxidized to DPN^1 by O_2, and only 14,000 cal (2ATP) if DPN · H is oxidized by pyruvic acid. Oxidation of pyruvic acid to acetyl CoA plus oxidation in the citric acid cycle yields about 210,000 cal (30ATP) of utilizable energy. Accordingly, the formation of 38ATP as a maximum in the metabolism of glucose through these pathways represents about 266,000 cal of utilizable energy, and an efficiency of (266,000/686,500 × 100) about 39 per cent.

A comprehensive discussion of the energy changes in the metabolism of carbohydrates, fats, and proteins is given by Krebs and Kornberg (78).

YEAST FERMENTATION

The fermentation of monosaccharides by yeast involves exactly the same chemical reactions as glycolysis in animal tissues down to the production of pyruvic acid. Yeast then decarboxylates the pyruvic acid to acetaldehyde and reduces the latter to ethyl alcohol:

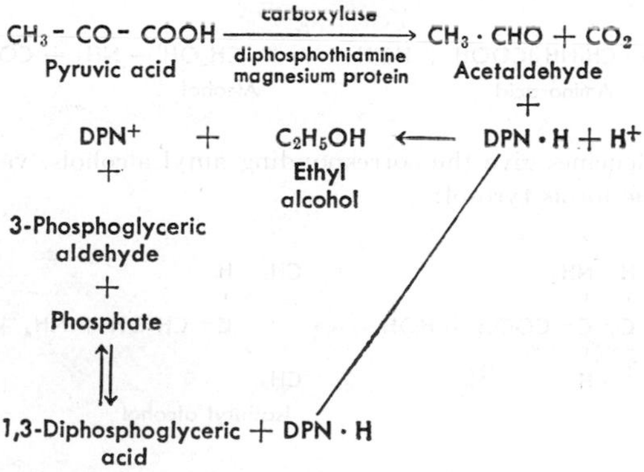

$$
\begin{array}{c}
\text{CH}_3\text{-CO-COOH} \xrightarrow[\substack{\text{diphosphothiamine} \\ \text{magnesium protein}}]{\text{carboxylase}} \text{CH}_3 \cdot \text{CHO} + \text{CO}_2 \\
\text{Pyruvic acid} \qquad\qquad \text{Acetaldehyde} \\
+ \\
\text{DPN}^+ \quad + \quad \text{C}_2\text{H}_5\text{OH} \longleftarrow \text{DPN} \cdot \text{H} + \text{H}^+ \\
+ \qquad\qquad \text{Ethyl} \\
\text{alcohol} \\
\text{3-Phosphoglyceric} \\
\text{aldehyde} \\
+ \\
\text{Phosphate} \\
\Updownarrow \\
\text{1,3-Diphosphoglyceric} + \text{DPN} \cdot \text{H} \\
\text{acid}
\end{array}
$$

The reduction of acetaldehyde to alcohol in yeast fermentation converts DPN · H to DPN^+. This keeps up the supply of DPN^+ for the oxidation of 3-phospho-glyceric aldehyde to 1-3-diphosphoglyceric acid, just as this supply is maintained in muscle by the reaction of pyruvic acid with DPN · H to form DPN⁺ and lactic acid. The formation of ATP in the yeast fermentation of sugar takes place through the same glycolytic reactions that cause its formation in animal tissues. The chief uses of this ATP are for the phosphorylation of sugars to hexose mono- and diphosphates to promote the fermentation process, and for other synthetic processes vital to yeast cells.

Yeast fermentation generally produces small amounts of glycerol in addition to alcohol. This glycerol is formed by reduction of dihydroxyacetone-P to α-glycerol phosphate by DPN · H under the influence of dehydrogenase, followed by hydrolysis of the α-glycerol phosphate to glycerol and phosphate by phosphatase.

$$\text{Dihydroxyacetone-P} + \text{DPN} \cdot \text{H} + \text{H}^+ \underset{\text{Dehydrogenase}}{\overset{}{\rightleftharpoons}} \alpha\text{-Glycerol-P} + \text{DPN}^+$$
$$+$$
$$\text{Pi} + \text{Glycerol} \underset{\text{Phosphatase}}{\overset{}{\longleftarrow}} \text{H}_2\text{O}$$

This process is important in the initiation of yeast fermentation to regenerate DPN⁺ for the oxidation of 3-phosphoglyceric aldehyde to 1-3-diphosphoglyceric acid, an essential step preliminary to the formation of acetaldehyde. After acetaldehyde is formed, the DPN⁺ is largely regenerated by the reaction between DPN · H and acetaldehyde. As indicated above, only small amounts of glycerol are normally formed. However, if sodium bisulfite is added to the fermenting mixture, it reacts with the acetaldehyde formed to produce acetaldehyde bisulfite which cannot be reduced to alcohol. Under these conditions DPN⁺ is regenerated through the reactions leading to the formation of glycerol, with one molecule of phosphoglyceric aldehyde being converted through dihydroxyacetone-P to glycerol and one to phosphoglyceric acid which then forms acetaldehyde. This acetaldehyde is combined with bisulfite. The addition of bisulfite thus provides a method for changing yeast fermentation from the production of alcohol to the production of glycerol. A similar result is accomplished by keeping the fermenting mixture alkaline, which causes two molecules of acetaldehyde to be dismuted to one molecule each of acetic acid and alcohol without reaction with DPN · H. Under these conditions DPN⁺ also must be regenerated through the reactions producing glycerol.

Yeast fermentation, as applied commercially to the production of alcoholic beverages, generally produces some of the higher alcohols such as isoamyl and isobutyl alcohol. These higher alcohols of yeast fermentation are called "fusel oil" and arise from the action of yeast upon amino acids present in fermenting solutions. Yeast enzymes deaminate amino acids in a peculiar manner, which consists of hydrolytic decarboxylation:

$$\underset{\text{Amino acid}}{\text{R} \cdot \text{CH(NH}_2)\text{COOH}} + \text{HOH} \longrightarrow \underset{\text{Alcohol}}{\text{R} \cdot \text{CH}_2\text{OH}} + \text{NH}_3 + \text{CO}_2$$

In this way the leucines give the corresponding amyl alcohols, valine yields isobutyl alcohol, and tyrosine forms tyrosol:

$$\underset{\text{Valine}}{\begin{array}{c} \text{CH}_3 \quad \text{H} \quad \text{NH}_2 \\ \diagdown \ | \ | \\ \text{C} - \text{C} - \text{COOH} \\ \diagup \quad | \\ \text{CH}_3 \quad \text{H} \end{array}} + \text{HOH} \longrightarrow \underset{\text{Isobutyl alcohol}}{\begin{array}{c} \text{CH}_3 \quad \text{H} \\ \diagdown \ | \\ \text{C} - \text{CH}_2\text{OH} \\ \diagup \\ \text{CH}_3 \end{array}} + \text{NH}_3 + \text{CO}_2$$

These higher alcohols of fusel oil are more powerful narcotics than ethyl alcohol and when present in alcoholic beverages in appreciable quantities are responsible for accentuated unpleasant effects.

PASTEUR EFFECT

In many tissue preparations and microorganisms glycolysis, as measured by glucose utilization and lactic acid production, is decreased by the presence of oxygen. It appears that the chief factor involved in the effect is the competition between the glycolytic and citric acid cycle processes for inorganic phosphate and ADP (79). Anaerobically, all of the Pi and ADP necessary for the glycolytic reactions to proceed at a fast rate is available in the cell. Upon the admission of oxygen, competition for the ADP and Pi is established between the glycolytic processes and the oxidative processes of the citric acid cycle, which are coupled with phosphorylation of ADP by Pi to form ATP. This results in a decreased supply of ADP and Pi for glycolytic processes. This explanation of the "Pasteur effect" is reinforced by the fact that addition to glycolyzing systems of 2,4-dinitrophenol, which uncouples oxidative phosphorylation and permits accumulation of Pi and ADP, abolishes the Pasteur effect.

Another possible factor relating to the decreased formation of lactic acid in the presence of oxygen is that the supply of DPN · H for the reduction of pyruvic to lactic acid may be decreased, since, as pointed out previously, the DPN · H formed in the oxidative conversion of glyceraldehyde-3-P to 1,3-diphosphoglyceric acid may either reduce pyruvic to lactic acid or be oxidized by O_2 through the electron transport chain, with the formation of ATP. If the DPN · H is oxidized in this way, the supply for the reduction of pyruvic to lactic acid will be decreased. This oxidative phosphorylation also uses up both Pi and ADP.

The opposite of the "Pasteur effect" is the "Crabtree effect," which represents decreased respiration of cellular systems, such as ascites tumor cells, caused by high concentrations of glucose. The "Crabtree effect" appears to be due to increased competition of glycolytic processes for inorganic phosphate, and possibly pyridine nucleotides, leaving less for oxidative phosphorylation reactions.

RATES OF GLYCOLYSIS AND TRICARBOXYLIC ACID OXIDATION

It is of interest to consider how the rates of the reactions of glycolysis and tricarboxylic acid oxidation are controlled to meet the needs of the animal. During periods of exercise, when the demands for ATP for muscle contraction and other processes are high, the ATP is rapidly used up to form ADP and inorganic phosphate. Creatine phosphate is broken down through ATP at the same time:

$$\text{creatine phosphate} + \text{ADP} \longleftrightarrow \text{creatine} + \text{ATP}$$

Increased inorganic phosphate accelerates the rate of glycogen breakdown, and increased ADP provides increased acceptor for the production of more ATP in the oxidation of phosphoglyceric aldehyde, from phosphopyruvic acid, and by oxidations in the tricarboxylic cycle. Increased glycolysis causes increased production of pyruvic and lactic acids, which in turn increase the rates of reaction in the cycle, with an increase in the rate of ATP formation. Thus we see that an increase in physiologic processes which increases the use of ATP automatically increases the rate of ATP production. In this process phosphate continually and rapidly passes around the cycle:

Glycolysis and tricarboxylic oxidation

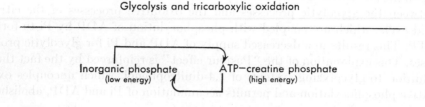

Inorganic phosphate   ATP—creatine phosphate
(low energy)   (high energy)

Muscle contraction and other processes

which extracts chemical energy from foods for muscle contraction and other processes.

When exercise ceases and the demand for ATP diminishes, the rates of ADP and inorganic phosphate production decrease; this slows the rates of the glycolytic and tricarboxylic cycle reactions. These reactions, however, proceed at an elevated rate for a time after exercise stops because of the elevated ADP and inorganic phosphate concentrations at that time, so that when recovery from exercise is complete, the tissues are again well supplied with ATP and creatine phosphate. In other words, the high-energy phosphate battery is left in a well-charged condition.

CONVERSION OF SUBSTANCES TO GLUCOSE AND GLYCOGEN BY REVERSAL OF GLYCOLYTIC PROCESSES. GLUCOGENESIS AND GLYCOGENESIS

Pyruvic acid occupies a key position in the formation of glucose and glycogen from many substances through reversal of glycolytic reactions, as shown in Figure 24.8.

In an earlier section it was pointed out that many nonsugar substances are convertible into glucose and glycogen in the body. With an understanding of the reactions of glycolysis and the tricarboxylic acid cycle, it is now possible to explain the mechanisms by which many of these conversions are accomplished.

All the glycolytic reactions are reversible, directly or indirectly, as are most of the reactions of the cycle, and it is upon the reversibility of these reactions that the conversion of various substances into glucose and glycogen largely depends.

The processes involved in the conversion of lactic and pyruvic acids, of glycerol, and of all intermediate products of glycolysis into glucose and glycogen are evident from an inspection of the glycolysis diagram. Substances such as glyceric aldehyde, glyceric acid, and dihydroxyacetone are phosphorylated to their phosphates by ATP (as is glycerol) and then enter the reverse glycolysis stream at the proper intervals. As has been pointed out in Chapter 23, the metabolism of the odd carbon fatty acids leads to the production of some liver glycogen. In the final stage of the β-oxidation of these acids one molecule of propionic acid is formed. This substance is a glycogen-former, apparently through preliminary oxidation to pyruvic acid followed by reversed glycolysis.

All the members of the tricarboxylic cycle and all substances convertible into members of the cycle form glycogen in the body. For example, the conversion of succinic acid to glycogen involves the successive conversions: Succinic acid $\longrightarrow$ fumaric acid $\longrightarrow$ malic acid $\longrightarrow$ oxaloacetic acid $\longrightarrow$ pyruvic acid $\longrightarrow$ glycogen. The conversion of citric acid proceeds also through pyruvic acid and includes the members of the tricarboxylic cycle.

There are three stages at which the glycolytic reactions are not readily reversible, and which present blocks to glucose synthesis through pyruvate. One is the reaction:

$$\text{Glucose} + \text{ATP} \longrightarrow \text{Glucose-6-P} + \text{ADP}$$

The block is removed by hydrolysis of glucose-6-P by liver glucose 6 phosphatase (80). This block is not involved in glycogen synthesis. The following reaction also is essentially irreversible:

$$\text{Fructose-6-P} + \text{ATP} \longrightarrow \text{Fructose-1,6-diphosphate} + \text{ADP}$$

However, this block is removed through hydrolysis of fructose-1,6-diphosphate by fructose-1,6-diphosphatase, forming fructose-6-P.

The third block to carbohydrate synthesis by reversal of glycolysis is the reaction:

$$\begin{array}{ccc}
\text{COOH} & & \text{COOH} \quad\quad \text{COOH} \\
| & \text{Pyruvic} & | \quad\quad\quad\quad\quad | \\
\text{C} - \text{O} - \text{PO}_3\text{H}_2 + \text{ADP} \underset{\text{kinase}}{\rightleftharpoons} \text{ATP} + \text{C} - \text{OH} \rightleftharpoons \text{CO} \\
\| & & \| \quad\quad\quad\quad\quad\quad | \\
\text{CH}_2 & & \text{CH}_2 \quad\quad\quad \text{CH}_3
\end{array}$$

The free energy decrease of this reaction, $\Delta F'$, is about 6 kcal, which means that the equilibrium point lies far to the right. Accordingly, the phosphorylation of pyruvic acid to phosphoenolpyruvic acid for glycogen synthesis by reversal of this reaction is opposed by a large energy barrier (78). Notwithstanding, it appears that in muscle glycogen synthesis from pyruvate does proceed largely through reversal of this reaction (81). In liver, however, phosphoenolpyruvate is formed chiefly by a shunt mechanism (81) represented by the following reactions:

$$\text{Pyruvate} + \text{TPN} \cdot \text{H} + \text{H}^+ + CO_2 \xrightleftharpoons[\text{Enzyme}]{\text{Malic}} \text{Malate} + \text{TPN}^+$$

$$\text{Malate} + \text{DPN}^+ \xrightleftharpoons[\text{dehydrogenase}]{\text{Malic}} \text{Oxaloacetate} + \text{DPN} \cdot \text{H} + \text{H}^+$$

$$\text{Oxaloacetate} + \text{ITP} \longrightarrow \text{Phosphoenolpyruvate} + CO_2 + \text{IDP}$$

(Sum) $\text{Pyruvate} + \text{TPN} \cdot \text{H} + \text{H}^+ + \text{DPN}^+ + \text{ITP} \longrightarrow$
$$\text{Phosphoenolpyruvate} + \text{DPN} \cdot \text{H} + \text{TPN}^+ + \text{IDP}$$

Since the total energy barrier in going from pyruvic acid to phosphoenolpyruvic acid is the same regardless of pathway, the latter mechanism must provide means of overcoming the barrier, which it does. Some 6 kcal of energy per mol is necessary to phosphorylate pyruvic acid, and this may be supplied by linking the over-all endergonic reaction:

$$\text{Pyruvate} + \text{TPN} \cdot \text{H} + \text{H}^+ + \text{DPN}^+ + \text{ITP} \longrightarrow \text{Phosphoenolpyruvate} + \text{DPN} \cdot \text{H} + \text{TPN}^+ + \text{IDP}$$

with exergonic reactions which increase TPN · H, DPN$^+$, and ITP and decrease DPN · H, TPN$^+$, and IDP to drive the reaction to the right, with formation of phosphoenolpyruvate. Such reactions are:

$$\text{Glucose-6-P} + \text{TPN}^+ \rightleftharpoons \text{6-Phosphogluconolactone} + \text{TPN} \cdot \text{H}$$

which is quantitatively important in liver metabolism. This reaction increases TPN · H and decreases TPN$^+$.

Krebs (78) cites evidence for the production of TPN · H in liver by reversal of oxidative phosphorylation:

$$\text{FP} \cdot \text{H} + \text{TPN}^+ + \text{ATP} \rightleftharpoons \text{FP} + \text{TPN} \cdot \text{H} + \text{ADP} + \text{Pi}$$

IDP is converted to ITP by reaction with ATP:

$$\text{ATP} + \text{IDP} \rightleftharpoons \text{ADP} + \text{ITP}$$

Thus it appears that the formation of liver glycogen (and glucose) from pyruvate is made possible by the coupling of an endergonic process with exergonic reactions which make the over-all phosphorylation of pyruvic acid an exergonic process capable of taking place.

At this point it is pertinent to inquire as to the conditions leading to the accumulation of tissue glycogen as a result of reverse reactions through the tricarboxylic and glycolytic systems. The reactions leading to oxidation and the production of energy will predominate during exercise, and members of these systems and substances feeding into them obviously will tend to be oxidized. However, during rest in the well-fed animal, when the supply of food is liberal and the oxidative requirements are minimal, much tissue glycogen may be formed by reversal of the reactions of these systems. During starvation, when the supply of food carbohydrate is cut off, the glucose of blood is maintained at low normal values, and small amounts of glycogen are present in liver and muscles. This carbohydrate is formed in the liver (gluconeogenesis) from amino acids through mechanisms such as those discussed above. It is of interest to note that while the utilization of glucose by the diabetic is reduced, the ability of the animal to convert nonsugar substances such as amino acids into glucose appears to be unimpaired. This explains the hyperglycemia and glucosuria of the starving severely diabetic animal.

THE METABOLISM OF ALCOHOL IN THE BODY

Because of the consumption of very considerable amounts of alcoholic beverages by a large proportion of the population, the mechanisms involved in alcohol metabolism are of interest and importance. While the metabolism of alcohol in all its relations may not be fully understood, the chief pathway of its oxidation appears to be established.

That the liver is the organ primarily concerned in the initial oxidation of alcohol is well established. Mirsky and Nelson (82) found that partial removal of the liver diminished the capacity for alcohol oxidation in proportion to the amount of liver removed.

While it appears well established that alcohol is oxidized in the liver to acetaldehyde and acetate (acetyl CoA), there is still considerable uncertainty as to the over-all mechanisms of its metabolism.

The only enzyme in the body known to act upon ethyl alcohol is alcohol dehydrogenase, almost exclusively present in the liver, which converts alcohol to acetaldehyde. Stotz (83) found the blood acetaldehyde to be elevated during the metabolism of alcohol in some animal species. Block and Rittenberg (84) fed deuterioethanol to rats along with phenyl-aminobutyric acid and found D in the acetyl groups of the excreted acetylated acid, proving that alcohol had been converted to acetic acid (acetyl CoA) in its metabolism.

Burton and Stadtman (85) have obtained a purified aldehyde dehydrogenase preparation from *Clostridium kluyveri*, which catalyzes the oxidation of acetaldehyde in the presence of DPN and coenzyme A to acetyl CoA, apparently according to the reactions:

$$C_2H_5OH + DPN^+ \xrightarrow[\text{dehydrogenase}]{\text{alcohol}} DPN \cdot H + H^+ + CH_3 - CHO$$

Alcohol   Acetaldehyde

$$CH_3 - CHO + DPN^+ + HS - CoA \xrightarrow[\text{dehydrogenase}]{\text{aldehyde}} DPN \cdot H + H^+ + CH_3 - CO - S - CoA$$

Acetaldehyde   Acetyl CoA

The acetyl CoA formed may then be oxidized in the citric acid cycle, converted to cholesterol and fatty acids, or utilized for acetylations just as the acetyl CoA from any other source.

It is interesting to note that Westerfeld, Stotz, and Berg (86) found the administration of pyruvate to dogs greatly increased the capacity of the animals to metabolize alcohol. It was also found that pyruvate metabolism was increased during alcohol metabolism. These facts are in keeping with observations that increased carbohydrate metabolism, which increases the supply of pyruvate, facilitates the metabolism of alcohol. The feeding of large amounts of carbohydrate increases the rate of alcohol oxidation, as does the administration of insulin, particularly when sugar is given at the same time. It has also been found that alcohol increases blood sugar at the expense of liver glycogen, and that when the liver glycogen is depleted by fasting, the rate of alcohol metabolism is decreased and parallels the rate of carbohydrate oxidation. Leloir and Muñoz (87) found that pyruvate accelerates the oxidation of alcohol by liver slices.

It is of interest to note that not only does the metabolism of pyruvate increase the rate of alcohol metabolism but the metabolism of alcohol also increases the rate of pyruvate metabolism (86).

BIOLOGIC ACETYLATION

Acetylation is utilized by the body in detoxication of amines and of drugs containing the amino group, such as sulfanilamide, and in the synthesis of essential substances such as acetylhexosamines and acetylcholine. Acetyl CoA, with the proper transacetylase enzyme, represents the active acetylating agent. The administration to an animal (or tissue preparation) of an amino compound such as phenylaminobutyric acid, which is acetylated in the body, along with an isotopically labeled substance, provides a test for the conversion of the labeled substance to acetate. For example, if ethanol labeled with C^{14} is given to a rat along with phenylaminobutyric acid, the urine will contain acetylphenylaminobutyric acid, and the acetyl group, obtained by hydrolysis, will be labeled with C^{14}, having been formed through oxidation of the alcohol.

While the metabolism of many substances yields acetyl CoA that may be used for acetylation, the oxidative decarboxylation of pyruvic acid, with acetyl CoA formation, represents a major source.

ISOTOPES IN THE STUDY OF CARBOHYDRATE METABOLISM

Considerable information relative to carbohydrate synthesis from nonsugar substances in the body has been obtained through the use of isotopic atoms, only a small part of which can be considered here.

Stetten and associates (88) have utilized deuterium as an indicator in studying the conversion of various substances to glycogen. The method employed consisted in injecting D_2O into the animal or feeding it so as to keep the D_2O content of the body fluids constant. The rate at which deuterium was introduced into glycogen as the result of synthesis from substances which exchange H for D of the body fluid D_2O was then determined by sacrificing the animals at different times and determining the D content of the tissue glycogen. It was found that about 33 per cent of the H atoms of glycogen are easily exchanged for D of D_2O or the H of H_2O. Consequently, the glycogen isolated for analysis could contain as a maximum only about 67 per cent of the concentration of D present in the body D_2O. Now the small molecules, such as lactic acid, from which glycogen may be formed exchange much more H for D of body fluids in the process of conversion to glycogen than do glucose and other hexoses. This is due to the greater number of processes involving enolization and the gain and loss of water in the conversion of the smaller molecules to glycogen. It was found that the liver glycogen of rats fed a high carbohydrate diet, at a given time, contained much less D than the liver glycogen of fasted rats, indicating that glycogen was formed from smaller molecules in the latter animals. Also, when rats were given lactate, the glycogen formed contained much D. It is of interest to note that the D content of muscle glycogen varied very much less than that of liver glycogen under the different experimental conditions. This is in keeping with a previous statement that gluconeogenesis is primarily the function of the liver and that mammalian muscle appears largely limited to glucose for glycogen formation.

These workers also determined the amount of D appearing in the liver fatty acids of rats fed a high carbohydrate diet as compared with the amount present in glycogen. Since the D of fatty acids is rather stably bound, it must have originated by exchange between the D_2O of body fluids and H of the small molecules of glucose metabolism on their way to fatty acid synthesis. It was found that the fatty acids contained a surprising amount of D, indicating that fat synthesis represents a major pathway of carbohydrate metabolism in the well-fed animal. As pointed out previously, the synthesis of fatty acids from carbohydrate proceeds through pyruvic and acetic acids (acetyl CoA).

A number of experiments relative to the mechanisms of carbohydrate metabolism have been carried out by the use of compounds containing isotopic carbon. One of the first of such experiments was that of Hastings and associates (89), who gave $NaHCO_3$ containing radioactive C^{11} to rats and observed the appearance of C^{11} in the liver glycogen. This conversion of CO_2 to glycogen involves a series of reactions which places some of the C^{11} in pyruvate. These reactions may be pictured as follows:

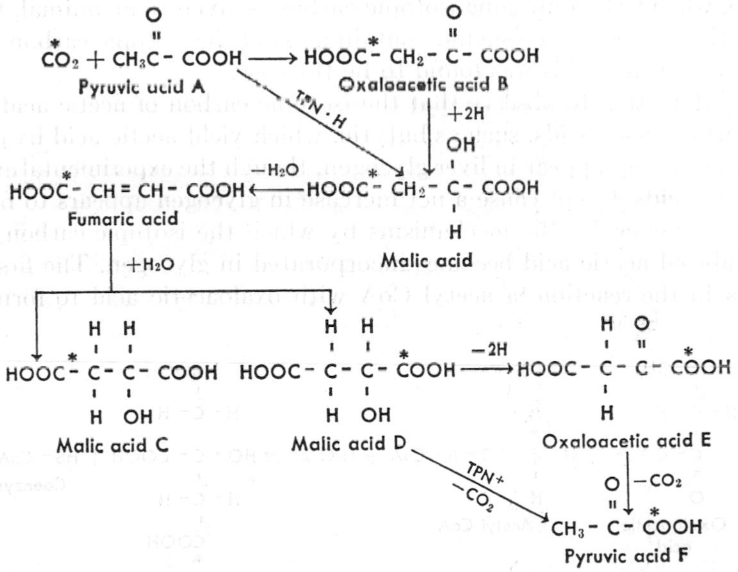

The $\overset{*}{C}O_2$ is first fixed in oxaloacetic acid by reaction with pyruvic acid or into malic acid through action of the malic enzyme. By conversion to malic acid and reconversion to oxaloacetic acid through reversal of the reactions, some of the C^{11} becomes fixed in the carboxyl group adjacent to the carbonyl group of oxaloacetic acid. This oxaloacetate yields pyruvic acid containing C^{11} in the carboxyl group. The pyruvic acid is then converted to glycogen by reversal of the glycolytic reactions.

Wood and associates (90) developed a method by which the position of isotopic carbon in glucose may be determined. By this method, which depends upon a combination of bacterial and chemical degradation, it is possible to determine the distribution of isotopic C between the various carbon positions of glucose. These workers fed $NaHCO_3$ containing C^{13} and fatty acids from acetic to butyric labeled with C^{13} in various positions to rats and determined the positions of the C^{13} in the glucose derived from liver glycogen formed during the experiment. It was found that the C^{13} was localized in the glucose in positions predicted on the basis of formation through reactions of the tricarboxylic acid cycle and of glycolysis. While the review by Wood (91) should be consulted for a detailed discussion, some of the reasoning involved is presented below.

As pointed out above, Hastings and associates showed that the carbon of CO_2 is incorporated into liver glycogen. The manner in which this C may become the C of the carboxyl group of pyruvic acid was also demonstrated. By inspection of the glycolysis diagram, it will be seen that this C becomes the C of the aldehyde group of 3-phosphoglyceric aldehyde and of the free primary alcohol group of dihydroxyacetone phosphate. These groups are combined in the formation of fructose-1-6-diphosphate from the glyceric aldehyde phosphate and dihydroxyacetone phosphate. According to this scheme, when CO_2 containing isotopic carbon is given to an animal, the glucose of the liver glycogen should contain most of the isotopic carbon in positions 3 and 4, and this was found to be the case.

It is interesting to observe that the isotopic carbon of acetic acid and of even-carbon fatty acids, such as butyric, which yield acetic acid by β oxidation was found to appear in liver glycogen, though the experimental evidence that such acids do not cause a net increase in glycogen appears to be good. Suppose we consider the mechanisms by which the isotopic carbon of carboxyl-labeled acetic acid becomes incorporated in glycogen. The first stage consists in the reaction of acetyl CoA with oxaloacetic acid to form citric acid:

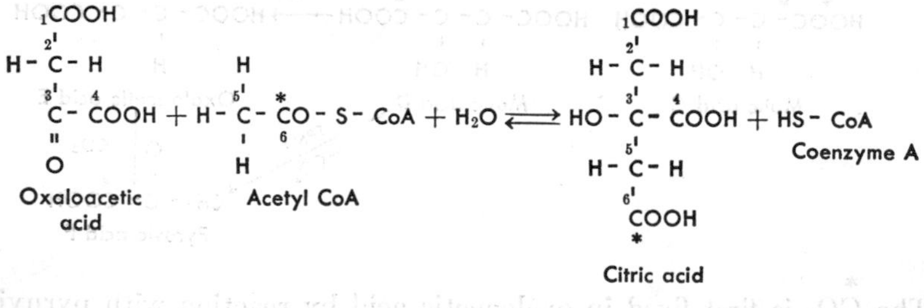

Carbon atoms 5 and 6 (labeled) represent the acetic acid carbon atoms, and 1, 2, 3, and 4 the oxaloacetic acid carbon atoms. Now the enzyme aconitase acts unsymmetrically upon the symmetrical citric acid molecule to remove water from carbon atoms 2 and 3 with the formation of cis-aconitic acid, which then undergoes changes as follows, yielding finally pyruvic acid, one-half of the molecules of which contain labeled C in the carboxyl group:

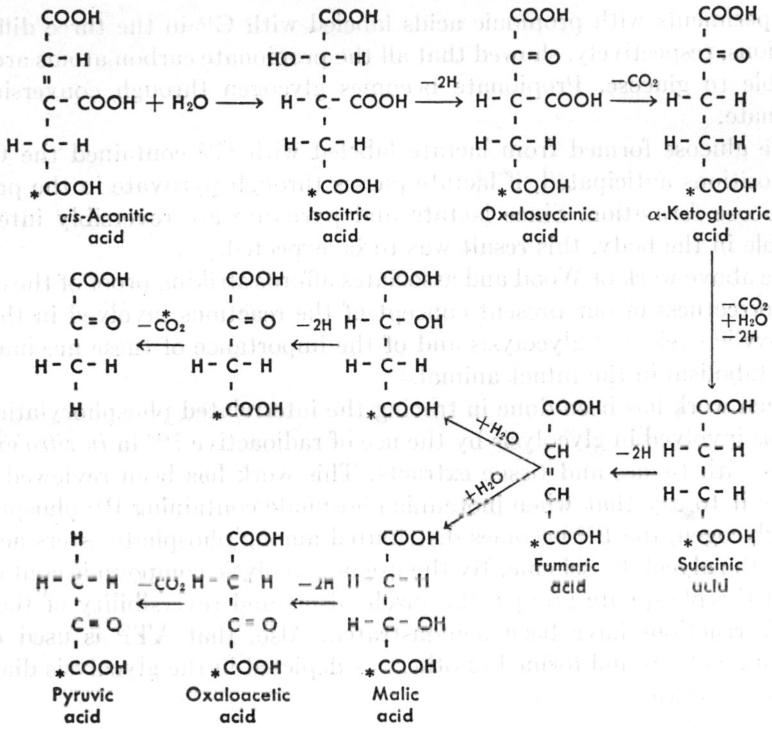

COOH   COOH   COOH   COOH

C‑H   HO‑C‑H   C=O   C=O

C‑COOH + H_2O ⟶ H‑C‑COOH $\xrightarrow{-2H}$ H‑C‑COOH $\xrightarrow{-CO_2}$ H‑C‑H

H‑C‑H   H‑C‑H   H‑C‑H   H‑C‑H

*COOH   *COOH   *COOH   *COOH

cis‑Aconitic acid   Isocitric acid   Oxalosuccinic acid   α‑Ketoglutaric acid

COOH   COOH   COOH

C=O $\xleftarrow{-\overset{*}{CO_2}}$ C=O $\xleftarrow{-2H}$ H‑C‑OH

H‑C‑H   H‑C‑H   H‑C‑H

H   *COOH   *COOH

$\left. \begin{array}{c} -CO_2 \\ +H_2O \\ -2H \end{array} \right.$

COOH   COOH

CH   H‑C‑H

CH $\xleftarrow{-2H}$ H‑C‑H

*COOH   *COOH

Fumaric acid   Succinic acid

H   COOH   COOH

H‑C‑H $\xleftarrow{-CO_2}$ H‑C‑H $\xleftarrow{-2H}$ H‑C‑H

C=O   C=O   H‑C‑OH

*COOH   *COOH   *COOH

Pyruvic acid   Oxaloacetic acid   Malic acid

The carboxyl-labeled pyruvic acid then forms glucose with labeled C in positions 3 and 4 through reversal of the glycolytic reactions, as shown in Figure 24.7 (p. 974).

If acetic acid is labeled with isotopic C in the methyl group, it can be seen, by following the reactions of the tricarboxylic cycle, that pyruvic acid containing C* in both the carbonyl and methyl groups will result. Such a compound, upon forming glucose by reversal of the glycolytic reactions, will place C* in the 1, 2 and 5, 6 positions of the glucose.

Wood and associates found that the glucose formed from acetate labeled with C^{13} in the carboxyl group forms glucose with C^{13} chiefly in the 3, 4 positions, while methyl-labeled acetate gives glucose with C^{13} mainly in the 1, 2 and 5, 6 positions. However, while carbon atoms of acetic acid may become incorporated in liver glycogen by the mechanisms indicated, the process of incorporation would not give a net increase in glycogen. This is true because when acetate is condensed with oxaloacetate and passed through the tricarboxylic cycle, two carbon atoms are lost as CO_2, which are equivalent to the two carbon atoms of acetate which may be incorporated into glycogen. If the oxidative decarboxylation of pyruvic acid to acetic acid were reversible, then there would be a mechanism for the net conversion of acetic acid and the higher even carbon fatty acids to glucose and glycogen. However, this apparently is not true.

Experiments with propionic acids labeled with C^{13} in the three different positions, respectively, showed that all the propionate carbon atoms are convertible to glucose. Propionate becomes glycogen through conversion to succinate.

The glucose formed from lactate labeled with C^{13} contained the C^{13} in the positions anticipated, if lactate passes through pyruvate in the process of glucose formation. Since lactate and pyruvate are reversibly interconvertible in the body, this result was to be expected.

The above work of Wood and associates affords striking proof of the essential correctness of our present concept of the reactions involved in the tricarboxylic cycle and glycolysis and of the importance of these mechanisms to metabolism in the intact animal.

Much work has been done in tracing the interrelated phosphorylation reactions involved in glycolysis by the use of radioactive P^{32} in *in vitro* experiments with tissues and tissue extracts. This work has been reviewed (92). Suffice it to say that when inorganic phosphate containing P^{32} phosphorylates glycogen, the P^{32} becomes distributed among phosphate esters according to the glycolytic scheme. By the use of glycolytic compounds containing P^{32} in the phosphate groups, the mechanisms and reversibility of the glycolytic reactions have been demonstrated. Also, that ATP is used up in certain reactions and formed in others as depicted in the glycolysis diagram has been shown.

ALTERNATE PATHWAYS OF CARBOHYDRATE METABOLISM

Although the Embden-Meyerhof glycolytic pathway coupled with oxidation in the citric acid cycle (TCA-cycle) undoubtedly represents the principal route of carbohydrate breakdown and oxidation in animal tissues and some microorganisms, much evidence has accumulated for the operation of alternate pathways which importantly supplement the glycolytic-TCA pathway. These alternate pathways include what is variously called the "hexose monophosphate shunt" or the "pentose phosphate pathway" or the "pentose cycle" or the "phosphogluconate oxidative pathway" or the "Warburg-Dickens-Lipmann pathway." This pathway will be called the "pentose phosphate pathway" in the following discussion. Another pathway is called the "glucuronic acid cycle" or "glucuronate pathway." Still other routes of metabolism are the "Entner-Doudoroff pathway" and the "glyoxylate cycle."

THE PENTOSE PHOSPHATE PATHWAY

The initial studies of Warburg, Dickens, Lipmann, and Dische established the existence of the pentose phosphate pathway, and the intricate reactions involved in it have been worked out especially by Horecker, Cohen, and Racker (93).

The mechanisms of the pentose phosphate pathway are interrelated in a most complex manner so that following the main stream of metabolism is difficult. It involves phosphates of heptose, hexose, pentose, tetrose, and triose sugars and of a sugar lactone and sugar acids in a complex cycle which effects the complete oxidation of glucose to CO_2 and H_2O with the formation of 36 mols of ATP per mol of sugar oxidized. In order that the student may obtain a general over-all picture of the process, it is given in word outline in Figure 24.9.

The enzymes operating in the pentose phosphate pathway and the products of their action, which, all integrated together compose the pathway, are given below.

FORMATION OF PENTOSE PHOSPHATES

Glucose-6-P-dehydrogenase. This enzyme is widely distributed in animal tissues, plants, and microorganisms. It catalyzes the oxidation of glucose-6-P to 6-phosphogluconolactone:

$$TPN^+ \qquad\qquad TPN \cdot H + H^+$$

Glucose-6-P		6-Phosphoglucono-δ-Lactone		6-Phosphogluconic acid
H–C–OH	Glucose-6P dehydrogenase →	CO	Lactonase +H₂O → −H₂O ←	COOH
H–C–OH		H–C–OH		H–C–OH
HO–C–H		HO–C–H		HO–C–H
H–C–OH		H–C–OH		H–C–OH
H–C–		H–C–		H–C–OH
CH₂–O–PO₃H₂		CH₂–O–PO₃H₂		CH₂–O–PO₃H₂

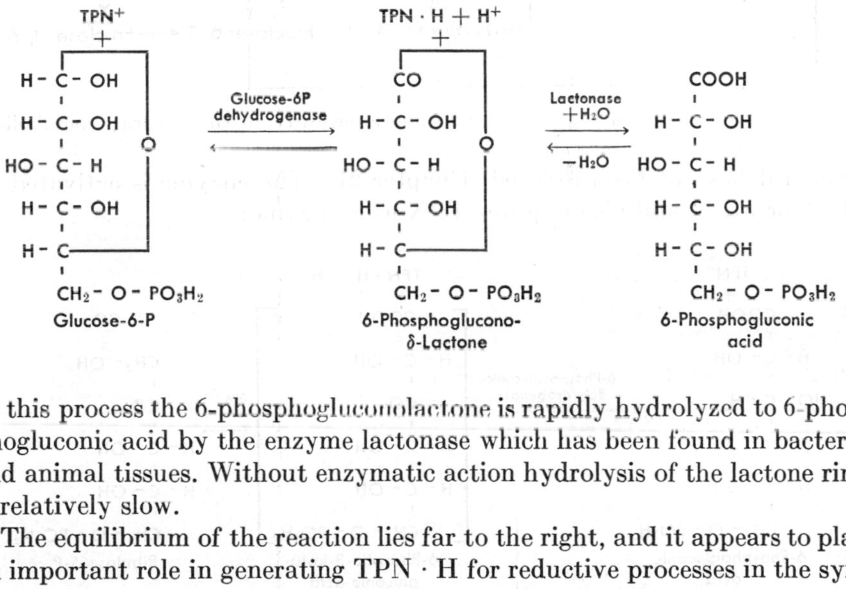

In this process the 6-phosphogluconolactone is rapidly hydrolyzed to 6-phosphogluconic acid by the enzyme lactonase which has been found in bacteria and animal tissues. Without enzymatic action hydrolysis of the lactone ring is relatively slow.

The equilibrium of the reaction lies far to the right, and it appears to play an important role in generating $TPN \cdot H$ for reductive processes in the synthesis of fatty acids and cholesterol. The reaction is used in *in vitro* systems as a source of $TPN \cdot H$ for other reactions (coupled).

6-Phosphogluconic acid dehydrogenase. This enzyme is found in animal and plant tissues, and bacteria. It oxidizes 6-phosphogluconic acid to ribulose-5-P, apparently through 3-keto-6-phosphogluconic acid, though the latter has not been isolated. Presumably it is decarboxylated to ribulose-5-P as it is formed on the enzyme surface. The enzymatic action appears to be quite analogous to the oxidative decarboxylation of malate to pyruvate by the malic enzyme, in which oxaloacetic acid appears to be an intermediate

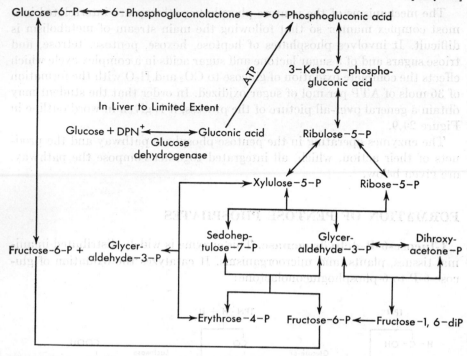

Figure 24.9. Outline of the pentose phosphate pathway of carbohydrate metabolism.

though it has not been isolated (Chapter 21). The enzyme is activated by Mg^{++} or Mn^{++} and also requires TPN as coenzyme:

$$
\begin{array}{ccc}
\text{TPN}^+ & \text{TPN} \cdot \text{H} + \text{H}^+ & \\
+ & + & \\
\text{COOH} & \text{COOH} & \text{CO}_2 \\
| & | & + \\
\text{H}-\text{C}-\text{OH} & \text{H}-\text{C}-\text{OH} & \text{CH}_2-\text{OH} \\
| & | & | \\
\text{HO}-\text{C}-\text{H} & \text{CO} & \text{CO} \\
| & | & | \\
\text{H}-\text{C}-\text{OH} & \text{H}-\text{C}-\text{OH} & \text{H}-\text{C}-\text{OH} \\
| & | & | \\
\text{H}-\text{C}-\text{OH} & \text{H}-\text{C}-\text{OH} & \text{H}-\text{C}-\text{OH} \\
| & | & | \\
\text{CH}_2-\text{O}-\text{PO}_3\text{H}_2 & \text{CH}_2-\text{O}-\text{PO}_3\text{H}_2 & \text{CH}_2-\text{O}-\text{PO}_3\text{H}_2 \\
\text{6-Phosphogluconic} & \text{6-Phospho-3-keto-} & \text{Ribulose-5-P} \\
\text{acid} & \text{gluconic acid} &
\end{array}
$$

labels: 6-Phosphogluconic dehydrogenase; Mn^{++}

It will be noted that this reaction also yields TPN · H, which may serve as reducing agent in other reactions coupled with it, such as those of fatty acid and cholesterol synthesis.

PENTOSE PHOSPHATE REACTIONS

Ribose-5-phosphate isomerase. This enzyme is widely distributed and converts the ketose phosphate, ribulose-5-P, to the aldose phosphate, ribose-5-P. The reaction is similar to that of phosphohexose isomerase in converting glucose-6-P to fructose-6-P:

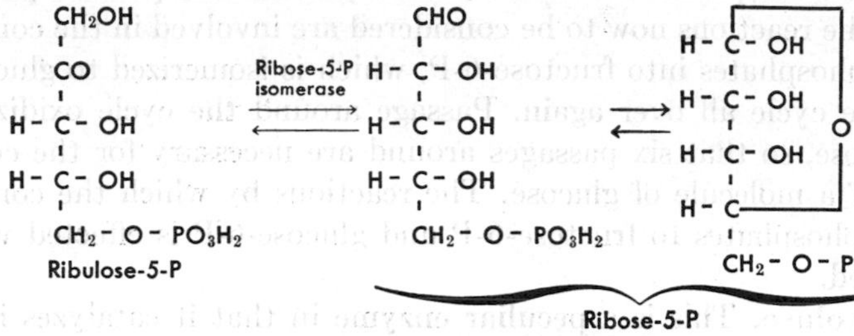

$$
\begin{array}{ccc}
\text{CH}_2\text{OH} & & \text{CHO} \\
| & & | \\
\text{CO} & \xrightarrow[\text{isomerase}]{\text{Ribose-5-P}} & \text{H} - \text{C} - \text{OH} \\
| & & | \\
\text{H} - \text{C} - \text{OH} & \rightleftharpoons & \text{H} - \text{C} - \text{OH} \\
| & & | \\
\text{H} - \text{C} - \text{OH} & & \text{H} - \text{C} - \text{OH} \\
| & & | \\
\text{CH}_2 - \text{O} - \text{PO}_3\text{H}_2 & & \text{CH}_2 - \text{O} - \text{PO}_3\text{H}_2 \\
\text{Ribulose-5-P} & & \text{Ribose-5-P}
\end{array}
$$

Ribose-5-P is converted to ribose-1-P by phosphoglucomutase which exhibits "phosphoribomutase" activity:

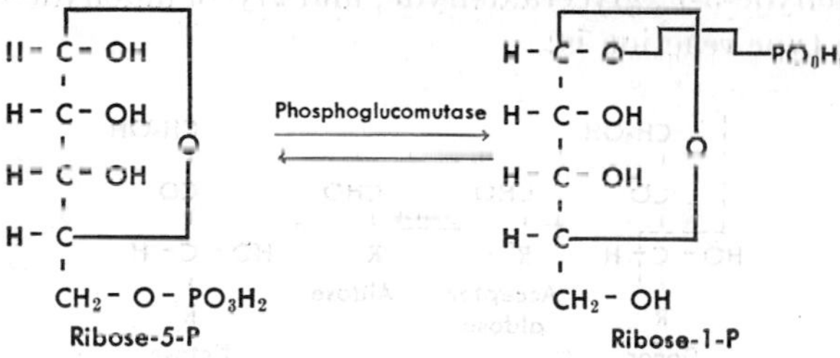

$$
\begin{array}{ccc}
\text{H} - \text{C} - \text{OH} & & \text{H} - \text{C} - \text{O} - \!\!-\!\!-\text{PO}_3\text{H}_2 \\
| & & | \\
\text{H} - \text{C} - \text{OH} & \xrightarrow{\text{Phosphoglucomutase}} & \text{H} - \text{C} - \text{OH} \\
| & & | \\
\text{H} - \text{C} - \text{OH} & \rightleftharpoons & \text{H} - \text{C} - \text{OH} \\
| & & | \\
\text{H} - \text{C} & & \text{H} - \text{C} \\
| & & | \\
\text{CH}_2 - \text{O} - \text{PO}_3\text{H}_2 & & \text{CH}_2 - \text{OH} \\
\text{Ribose-5-P} & & \text{Ribose-1-P}
\end{array}
$$

The above reactions provide ribose-5-P and ribose-1-P for the synthesis of nucleic acids (Chapter 26).

Phosphopentose epimerase. This enzyme, which is found in animal and plant tissues and in microorganisms, interconverts ribose-5-P, ribulose-5-P, and xylulose-5-P:

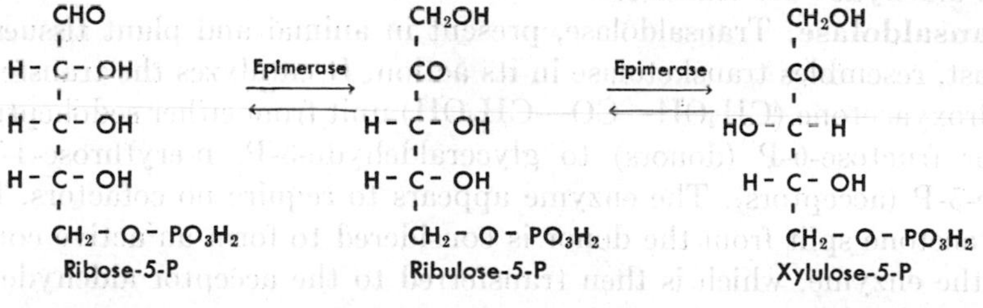

$$
\begin{array}{ccccc}
\text{CHO} & & \text{CH}_2\text{OH} & & \text{CH}_2\text{OH} \\
| & & | & & | \\
\text{H} - \text{C} - \text{OH} & \xrightarrow{\text{Epimerase}} & \text{CO} & \xrightarrow{\text{Epimerase}} & \text{CO} \\
| & & | & & | \\
\text{H} - \text{C} - \text{OH} & \rightleftharpoons & \text{H} - \text{C} - \text{OH} & \rightleftharpoons & \text{HO} - \text{C} - \text{H} \\
| & & | & & | \\
\text{H} - \text{C} - \text{OH} & & \text{H} - \text{C} - \text{OH} & & \text{H} - \text{C} - \text{OH} \\
| & & | & & | \\
\text{CH}_2 - \text{O} - \text{PO}_3\text{H}_2 & & \text{CH}_2 - \text{O} - \text{PO}_3\text{H}_2 & & \text{CH}_2 - \text{O} - \text{PO}_3\text{H}_2 \\
\text{Ribose-5-P} & & \text{Ribulose-5-P} & & \text{Xylulose-5-P}
\end{array}
$$

The reactions are similar to the interconversions of glucose-6-P and fructose-6-P by hexose phosphate isomerase, and of glyceraldehyde-3-P and dihydroxyacetone-P by triose phosphate isomerase.

CONVERSION OF PENTOSE PHOSPHATES TO HEXOSE PHOSPHATES

It will be noted that carbohydrate oxidation takes place only in the first two reactions discussed above—that is, in the conversion of glucose-6-P to

6-phosphoglucono-δ-lactone, and the formation of ribulose-5-P from 6-phosphogluconic acid. One molecule of CO_2 is split out in the latter reaction. No other oxidation or production of CO_2 takes place in the pentose phosphate pathway. The reactions now to be considered are involved in the conversion of pentose phosphates into fructose-6-P, which is isomerized to glucose-6-P to begin the cycle all over again. Passage around the cycle oxidizes only C-1 of glucose, so that six passages around are necessary for the complete oxidation of a molecule of glucose. The reactions by which the conversion of pentose phosphates to fructose-6-P and glucose-6-P is effected will now be considered.

Transketolase. This is a peculiar enzyme in that it catalyzes in effect the transfer of a ketol group, —CO—CH$_2$OH, from xylulose-5-P to an aldehyde acceptor. As a matter of fact, what it transfers is the equivalent of glycol aldehyde, H—CO—CH$_2$OH. A number of aldehydes—such as ribose-5-P, glyceraldehyde-3-P, glyceraldehyde, and glycol aldehyde—can serve as acceptor. The type reaction is:

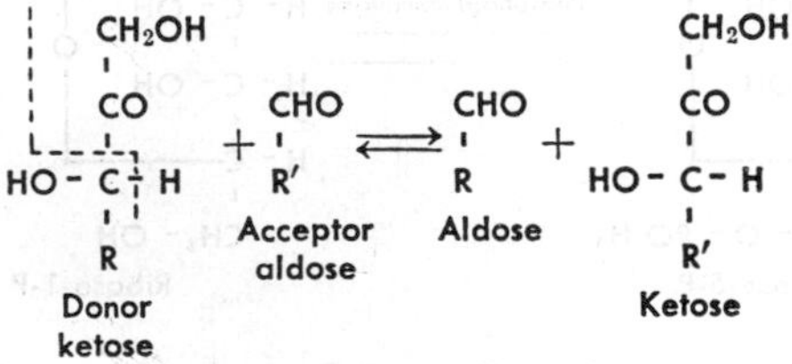

Transketolase is widely distributed and has been obtained from yeast in crystalline condition. It contains thiamine pyrophosphate (TPP), which, with Mg^{++}, is essential for its activity. Glycol aldehyde is thought to be split from the xylulose-5-P and probably bound to the thiamine as "active glycol aldehyde" for transfer.

Transaldolase. Transaldolase, present in animal and plant tissues and in yeast, resembles transketolase in its action. It catalyzes the transfer of a dihydroxyacetone (CH$_2$OH—CO—CH$_2$OH) unit from either sedoheptulose-7-P or fructose-6-P (donors) to glyceraldehyde-3-P, D-erythrose-4-P, or ribose-5-P (acceptors). The enzyme appears to require no cofactors. Dihydroxyacetone split from the donor is considered to form an active complex with the enzyme, which is then transferred to the acceptor aldehyde. The type reaction is:

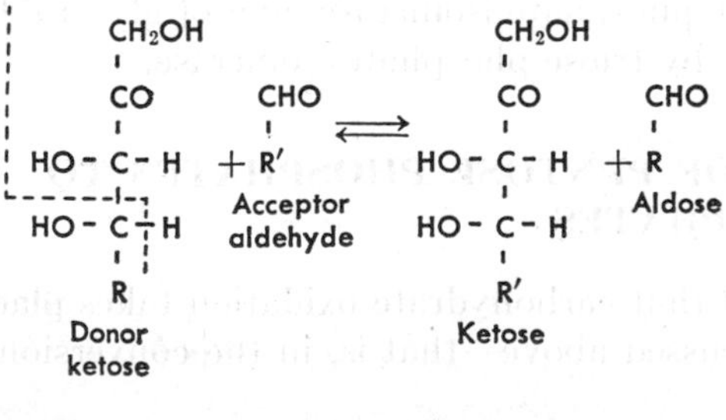

Two transketolase reactions and a transaldolase reaction are involved in the pentose phosphate pathway as follows:

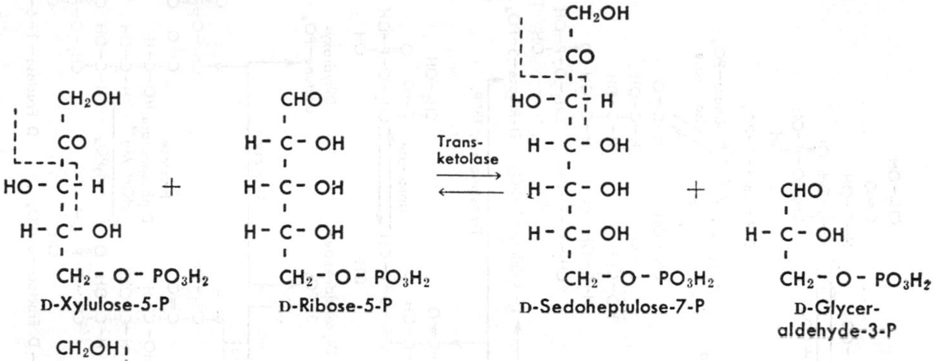

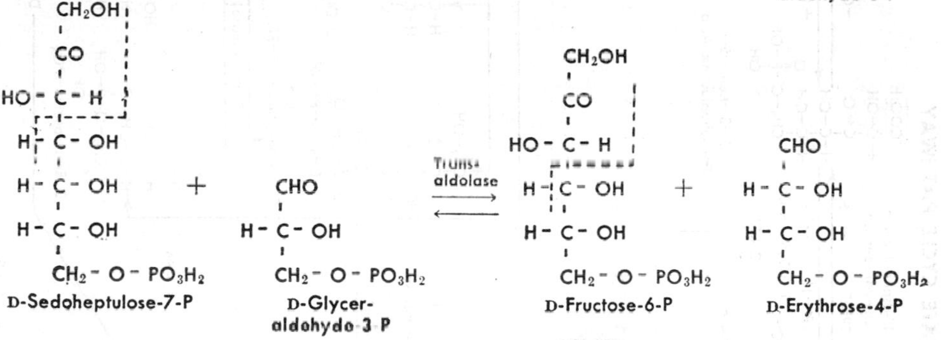

$$
\text{D-Xylulose-5-P} + \text{D-Ribose-5-P} \xrightleftharpoons[\text{Trans-}]{\text{ketolase}} \text{D-Sedoheptulose-7-P} + \text{D-Glyceraldehyde-3-P}
$$

D-Xylulose-5-P

$$
\begin{array}{c}
CH_2OH \\
| \\
CO \\
| \\
HO-C-H \\
| \\
H-C-OH \\
| \\
CH_2-O-PO_3H_2
\end{array}
$$

D-Ribose-5-P

$$
\begin{array}{c}
CHO \\
| \\
H-C-OH \\
| \\
H-C-OH \\
| \\
H-C-OH \\
| \\
CH_2-O-PO_3H_2
\end{array}
$$

D-Sedoheptulose-7-P

$$
\begin{array}{c}
CH_2OH \\
| \\
CO \\
| \\
HO-C-H \\
| \\
H-C-OH \\
| \\
H-C-OH \\
| \\
H-C-OH \\
| \\
CH_2-O-PO_3H_2
\end{array}
$$

D-Glyceraldehyde-3-P

$$
\begin{array}{c}
CHO \\
| \\
H-C-OH \\
| \\
CH_2-O-PO_3H_2
\end{array}
$$

D-Sedoheptulose-7-P + D-Glyceraldehyde-3-P $\xrightleftharpoons[\text{aldolase}]{\text{Trans-}}$ D-Fructose-6-P + D-Erythrose-4-P

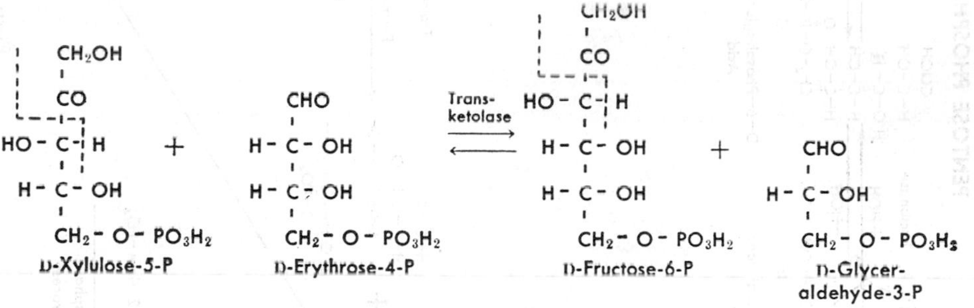

D-Sedoheptulose-7-P

$$
\begin{array}{c}
CH_2OH \\
| \\
CO \\
| \\
HO-C-H \\
| \\
H-C-OH \\
| \\
H-C-OH \\
| \\
H-C-OH \\
| \\
CH_2-O-PO_3H_2
\end{array}
$$

D-Glyceraldehyde-3-P

$$
\begin{array}{c}
CHO \\
| \\
H-C-OH \\
| \\
CH_2-O-PO_3H_2
\end{array}
$$

D-Fructose-6-P

$$
\begin{array}{c}
CH_2OH \\
| \\
CO \\
| \\
HO-C-H \\
| \\
H-C-OH \\
| \\
H-C-OH \\
| \\
CH_2-O-PO_3H_2
\end{array}
$$

D-Erythrose-4-P

$$
\begin{array}{c}
CHO \\
| \\
H-C-OH \\
| \\
H-C-OH \\
| \\
CH_2-O-PO_3H_2
\end{array}
$$

D-Xylulose-5-P + D-Erythrose-4-P $\xrightleftharpoons[\text{ketolase}]{\text{Trans-}}$ D-Fructose-6-P + D-Glyceraldehyde-3-P

D-Xylulose-5-P

$$
\begin{array}{c}
CH_2OH \\
| \\
CO \\
| \\
HO-C-H \\
| \\
H-C-OH \\
| \\
CH_2-O-PO_3H_2
\end{array}
$$

D-Erythrose-4-P

$$
\begin{array}{c}
CHO \\
| \\
H-C-OH \\
| \\
H-C-OH \\
| \\
CH_2-O-PO_3H_2
\end{array}
$$

D-Fructose-6-P

$$
\begin{array}{c}
CH_2OH \\
| \\
CO \\
| \\
HO-C-H \\
| \\
H-C-OH \\
| \\
H-C-OH \\
| \\
CH_2-O-PO_3H_2
\end{array}
$$

D-Glyceraldehyde-3-P

$$
\begin{array}{c}
CHO \\
| \\
H-C-OH \\
| \\
CH_2-O-PO_3H_2
\end{array}
$$

The two molecules of D-glyceraldehyde-3-P form fructose-1,6-diP as follows:

$$
\text{Glyceraldehyde-3-P} \xrightarrow{\text{Isomerase}} \text{Dihydroxyacetone-P}
$$

$$
\text{Glyceraldehyde-3-P} + \text{Dihydroxyacetone-P} \xrightarrow{\text{Aldolase}} \text{Fructose-1,6-diP}
$$

The fructose-1,6-diphosphate is then hydrolyzed to fructose-6-P and Pi by fructose-1,6-diphosphatase.

Fructose-6-P formed in the above reactions is converted to glucose-6-P by hexosephosphate isomerase for recycling through the pentose phosphate pathway.

The manner in which the above reactions are integrated into the pentose phosphate pathway is shown in Figure 24.10.

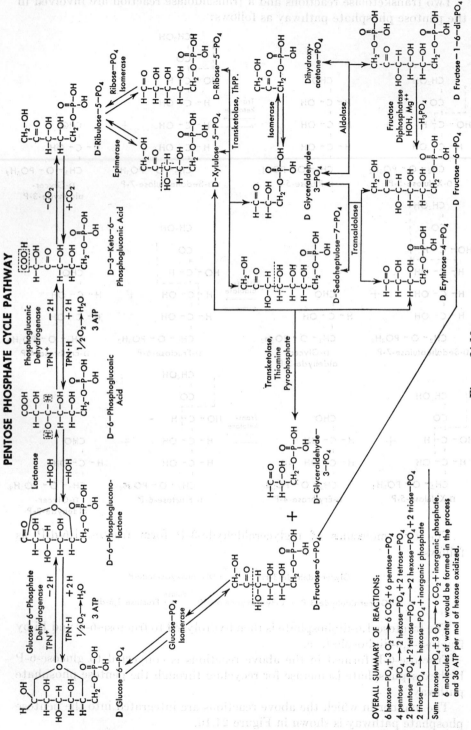

PENTOSE PHOSPHATE CYCLE PATHWAY

Figure 24.10

OVERALL SUMMARY OF REACTIONS:

6 hexose—PO_4 + 3 O_2 ⟶ 6 CO_2 + 6 pentose—PO_4
6 pentose—PO_4 ⟶ 2 hexose—PO_4 + 2 pentose—PO_4
4 pentose—PO_4 ⟶ 2 hexose—PO_4 + 2 tetrose—PO_4
2 pentose—PO_4 + 2 tetrose—PO_4 ⟶ 2 hexose—PO_4 + 2 triose—PO_4
2 triose—PO_4 ⟶ hexose—PO_4 + inorganic phosphate

Sum: Hexose—PO_4 + 3 O_2 ⟶ 6 CO_2 + inorganic phosphate.
    6 molecules of water would be formed in the process
    and 36 ATP per mol of hexose oxidized.

SIGNIFICANCE OF THE PENTOSE PHOSPHATE PATHWAY

While the enzymes necessary for the pentose phosphate pathway have been found widely distributed in animal and plant tissues and microorganisms, it is not possible at present to evaluate the quantitative significance of this oxidative pathway relative to that of glycolysis and the citric acid cycle. Attempts to do this have been based upon the metabolism of glucose and other substances labeled with C^{14}. One approach has been to determine the $C^{14}O_2$ production when glucose-1-C^{14} and glucose-6-C^{14} are metabolized by tissues. For example, Bloom and Stetten (94) found that the yields of $C^{14}O_2$ from glucose-1-C^{14} and glucose-6-C^{14} were about equal when incubated with kidney slices. However, liver slices yielded much more $C^{14}O_2$ from glucose-1-C^{14} than from glucose-6-C^{14}. A similar result was obtained by Muntz and Murphy in the liver of rats in vivo (95). The reasoning here is that C^{14}-1 and C^{14}-6 of glucose both form the methyl group of pyruvic acid in glycolysis (Figure 24.7) and consequently give the same amount of $C^{14}O_2$ through oxidation in the citric acid cycle. However, in the oxidation of glucose-1-C^{14} and glucose-6-C^{14} by the pentose phosphate pathway C-1 is split off as $C^{14}O_2$ in the first cycle, and C-6 becomes C-3 of glyceraldehyde-P. The latter may enter the glycolysis pathway and undergo various metabolic changes. Thus, if the pentose phosphate pathway is operating in a biologic system, glucose-1-C^{14} would be expected to yield more $C^{14}O_2$ than glucose-6-C^{14}.

Wood (96) has pointed out the many difficulties involved in assaying the quantitative contributions of these alternate pathways to carbohydrate metabolism. It appears that oxidation of glucose by the pentose phosphate pathway is of some quantitative significance in liver and takes place to a greater extent than oxidation by the glycolysis-TCA cycle route in certain specialized tissues such as lactating mammary glands, leucocytes, and adrenal cortex (97). Isotopic experiments indicate that carbohydrate oxidation in muscle proceeds by the pathway of glycolysis and the TCA-cycle.

A factor controlling the extent to which the pentose phosphate pathway operates in a tissue may be the supply of TPN available.

THE GLUCURONIC ACID CYCLE

This cycle involves the formation of glucuronic acid from glucose-6-P, the formation of xylulose from the glucuronic acid, conversion of the xylulose to xylulose-5-P, and, finally, formation of glucose-6-P from xylulose-5-P by the pentose phosphate cycle. Accordingly, the glucuronic acid cycle is a combination of cycles. Holzer (98) has reviewed the recent literature on this cycle. It is outlined in the diagram of Figure 24.11.

Pentosuria. It will be seen from Figure 24.11 that L-xylulose is converted to xylitol by the TPN system and xylitol dehydrogenase. In the hereditary condition of essential pentosuria there is a deficiency of the enzyme and a block in the conversion of L-xylulose to xylitol. As a result, persons with this metabolic defect normally excrete 2 to 4 g of L-xylulose per day in the urine. Small amounts of L-arabitol, apparently formed by reduction of L-xylulose is also excreted. The condition appears to be of no clinical importance (99) but is only a harmless biochemical anomaly. Touster and associates (100) showed that L-xylulose is formed from glucuronic acid by administering C¹³-labeled glucuronolactone to a pentosuric human and recovering C¹³ in the urinary L-xylulose. Touster and Harwell (101) administered D-glucuronolactone-1-C¹³ to a pentosuric human and isolated L-arabitol labeled with C¹³ from the urine, indicating formation from L-xylulose. The validity of the proposed glucuronic acid cycle in guinea pigs and rats has been demonstrated by giving xylitol-1-C¹⁴ and determining the pattern of glycogen labeling (labeling of glucose from the glycogen) in the animals (102). The glycogen is formed from glucose-6-P of the cycle. Other isotopic experiments in animals have confirmed these results (103).

Synthesis of ascorbic acid. It will be noted from Figure 24.11 that the synthesis of ascorbic acid is effected from L-gulonic acid of the cycle:

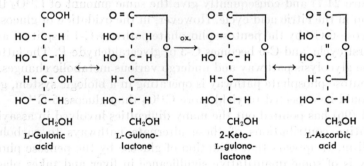

It has been shown by isotopic studies that man, monkey, and guinea pig can carry out all of the processes for the synthesis of ascorbic acid except the conversion of L-gulonolactone to ascorbic acid, which means that they lack the dehydrogenase enzyme for oxidation of the L-gluconolactone to 2-keto-L-gulonolactone. It may be said that these animals develop scurvy on an ascorbic acid-deficient diet because of hereditary deficiency of the enzyme (104).

It is very interesting that a variety of drugs such as barbital, chlorobutanol (Chloretone), aminopyrine, antipyrine, meprobamate, and arphenadrine markedly increase the rate at which glucose enters the glucuronic acid pathway (104). Such substances cause greatly increased excretion of ascorbic acid in the rat and increased excretion of L-xylulose in the pentosuric human. The mechanism of action is unknown, though this stimulation of the cycle may represent adaptation by the body to foreign compounds, since the activity of liver enzymes which metabolize foreign compounds is increased.

It is interesting to note that in the animal capable of synthesizing ascorbic acid, C-1 of glucose-1-C¹⁴ becomes C-6 in ascorbic acid, and C-6 in glucose-6-C¹⁴ becomes C-1 in ascorbic acid. This is due to the fact that designation of the ends of the carbon chains is reversed in passing from glucose to glucuronic acid:

$$CH_2OH - \overset{|}{C} - \overset{|}{C} - \overset{|}{C} - \overset{|}{C} - \overset{\overset{H}{|}}{C} = O \quad \text{D-Glucose}$$

C-6   C-1

$$O = \overset{\overset{H}{|}}{C} - \overset{|}{C} - \overset{|}{C} - \overset{|}{C} - \overset{|}{C} - COOH \quad \text{D-Glucuronic acid}$$

C-1   C-6

Glucuronides and detoxication. Glucuronic acid detoxifies numerous substances in the body by the formation of glucuronides. As shown in Figure 24.11, UDP-glucuronic acid (UDP-GA) is the active form of glucuronic acid utilized (58). The substances detoxified include phenols, (e.g., morphine,

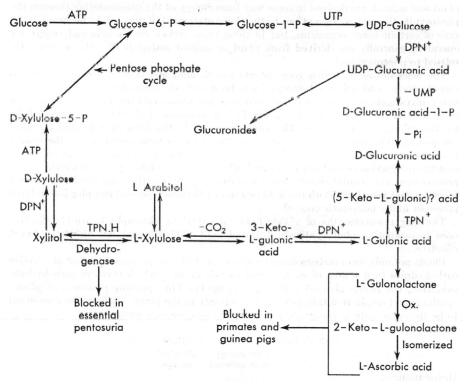

Figure 24.11. The glucuronic acid cycle of carbohydrate metabolism.

steroids, p-nitrophenol), alcohols (e.g., tertiary amyl), carboxylic acids (benzoic, bilirubin) and amines (aniline). Both O-glucuronides and N-glucuronides are formed. The glucuronides are formed in the liver. An example of the formation of the glucuronide of phenol is:

$$UDP\text{-}GA + HO \cdot C_6H_5 \longrightarrow GA\text{-}O\text{-}C_6H_5 + UDP$$
Phenylglucuronide

Other pathways of carbohydrate metabolism have been demonstrated in microorganisms, such as the Entner-Doudoroff pathway and the glyoxylate cycle (98, Holzer), but will not be considered here.

PHOTOSYNTHESIS

Recent reviews of processes involved in photosynthesis have been written by Vishniac, Horecker, and Ochoa (105), Noggle (106) and Calvin (107), and monographs by Hill and Whittingham (108) and Franck and Loomis (109).

Both figuratively and literally, photosynthesis is the most important chemical process under the sun. In the narrower sense it represents the chemical processes according to which plants containing the pigment chlorophyll absorb light energy and utilize it in converting atmospheric carbon dioxide to various carbohydrates. In the broader sense it represents the process basic to formation of all the organic compounds of plants, such as proteins, fats, acids, alkaloids, and vitamins, as well as carbohydrates.

Since directly or indirectly the animal world feeds upon the plant world, the organic compounds and energy involved in the structure and functioning of living things, both plant and animal, are derived in some way from energy of the sun operating through the photosynthetic process. Exceptions to the above statement, if any, might be found in the case of certain lower organisms, but in these cases carbon compounds and energy for operation generally are derived from plant or animal materials directly or indirectly related to photosynthesis.

The mechanisms by which green plants absorb light and convert carbon dioxide to carbohydrates and other substances have been and are being intensively studied by many investigators. It is well established that the photosynthetic process is composed essentially of two general processes. The first process consists in the absorption of light by the chlorophyll system, which provides energy in the form of activated chemical compounds. The reactions in this case are the so-called light reactions. In the second process carbon dioxide is reduced by the active molecules formed in the light reactions, and the production of carbohydrates and other substances takes place. Since this latter process does not require simultaneous illumination, the reactions involved are referred to as the dark reactions. Both the light and dark reactions represent complex interrelated processes under enzymatic control.

The longer wavelengths of visible light (absorbed by chlorophyll) are the effective ones in promoting photosynthesis. Infrared light (800–850 mμ) has also been found effective.

Plants not only form carbohydrate by absorbing CO_2 and giving off O_2, but also utilize carbohydrate as a source of energy, and in this process, which involves carbohydrate oxidation, the plants give off CO_2 and take up O_2. The opposing processes of photosynthesis and respiration take place independently in the plant. If glucose is considered to be the carbohydrate concerned in these processes, we may write:

Photosynthesis:

$$6CO_2 + 6H_2O + 677 \text{ Cal} \longrightarrow C_6H_{12}O_6 + 6O_2$$

Light energy   Chemical
(large calories)   energy

Respiration:

$$C_6H_{12}O_6 + 6O_2 \longrightarrow 6CO_2 + 6H_2O + 677 \text{ Cal}$$

Chemical   Chemical
energy   energy

These reactions represent over-all processes, each of which is composed of a number of consecutive interdependent reactions.

Each mol of CO_2 changed to carbohydrate in photosynthesis converts about 113 Cal of light energy to chemical energy stored in the carbohydrate formed, while in respiration the plant obtains 113 Cal of chemical energy for each mol of CO_2 formed. The extent to which plant respiration may represent reversal of photosynthetic reactions is unknown. It is highly probable, however, that the two processes overlap, at least to some degree.

It will be observed that the over-all oxidation of glucose in the plant is the same as in the animal.

Oxidations both through mechanisms of the citric acid cycle and the pentose phosphate pathway appear to be involved in the respiration of plants.

The respiratory quotients of both plant photosynthesis and respiration have been found to be close to unity, in general agreement with the above equations.

Chlorophyll. It is certainly true that the pigment chlorophyll, which absorbs light to serve as energy for photosynthesis, is one of the world's most important substances. It is accordingly not surprising that the chemistry of chlorophyll has been the subject of investigation for more than a hundred years.

The chloroplasts are the pigment-bearing structures of plants. Their solids are composed approximately of protein 45 per cent, lipids 25 per cent, and pigments 5 to 10 per cent. Considerable copper and iron are present in the chloroplast. The pigments consist of chlorophylls, the xanthophylls, and the carotenes. A red protein-containing pigment, phycoerythrin, occurs in the chloroplasts of most red algae. A similar blue pigment, phycocyanin, is present in most blue-green algae and in some red algae. These various pigments exhibit characteristic light absorption and are identified by their spectral absorption curves.

Emerson and Lewis (110) showed that light energy absorbed by phycocyanin as well as that absorbed by chlorophyll participates in photosynthesis by the blue-green alga *Chroococcus*. Participation of light absorbed by the carotenoid pigments was also indicated.

Four different forms of chlorophyll, a, b, c, d, have been found in plants. Chlorophyll a occurs in all groups of plants, while b, c, and d are of more limited distribution. Only a and b occur in higher plants. The occurrence ratio of chlorophyll a to chlorophyll b is generally about three to one.

Chlorophyll is bound to protein in the chloroplast as a protein-chlorophyll complex which was found by sedimentation velocity measurements in the ultracentrifuge to have a minimal molecular weight of 265,000.

Chlorophyll may be extracted from leaves with solvents such as alcohol and acetone. It is a bluish black substance with a strong metallic luster. When powdered, it is greenish black or bluish black. It dissolves in absolute alcohol to a blue-green solution. The melting points of different samples vary (93–106° C). The color of chlorophyll is changed to olive-brown by acids, which split magnesium from the molecule.

The structure of chlorophyll has been largely solved through the work of Willstätter and associates (111), and of H. Fischer and co-workers (112).

According to Fischer, the formula of chlorophyll a is as follows:

Phytol $C_{55}H_{72}O_5N_4Mg$

Chlorophyll a

Chlorophyll b differs from chlorophyll a only in having the CH_3— group on carbon

$$\overset{\text{H}}{\underset{\text{I}}{}}$$

3 replaced by a - C = O group.

It will be observed that the magnesium atom is held in the chlorophyll molecule by both normal covalent and coordinate covalent linkages (two of each). The magnesium linkage consequently is not ionic.

Chlorophyll is hydrolyzed by the enzyme chlorophyllase to produce chlorophyllid a and the unsaturated alcohol phytol. Phytol has the structure:

$$CH_3 - CH - (CH_2)_3 - CH - (CH_2)_3 - CH - (CH_2)_3 - C = CH - CH_2OH$$
$$\quad\;\; | \qquad\qquad\qquad | \qquad\qquad\quad | \qquad\qquad\quad |$$
$$\quad\;\; CH_3 \qquad\qquad\;\; CH_3 \qquad\qquad CH_3 \qquad\qquad CH_3$$

The structure of the phorbin ring system of the chlorophylls is very similar to that of the porphin ring system of heme, the colored group present in the hemoglobins.

The porphin ring is composed of four pyrrol rings. The phorbin ring also contains four pyrrol rings but in addition has a cyclopentane ring.

It has been estimated that the agricultural crops of the United States alone produce more than 6,000,000 tons of chlorophyll annually.

Energy relations in photosynthesis. The conversion of 6 mols of CO_2 to 1 mol of glucose requires approximately 690 kcal of energy, which is obtained from the radiant energy of visible light (4,000 to 7,000 Å) absorbed by chlorophyll. Light is emitted in "packets" of waves called "photons." The energy of a photon is equal to the product of its frequency ν, (reciprocal of wavelength in cm) and Planck's constant $h(6.55 \times 10^{-27}$ erg second); that is, $E = h\nu \cdot E$ may be expressed in ergs or calories (1 absolute cal = 4.184×10^7 ergs). According to Einstein's law of photochemical equivalence, a molecule can react only after absorbing one photon, which means that a mol of substance must absorb 6.02×10^{23} (N) photons in a photochemical reaction, and the energy required per mol equals $N h\nu$, which is called an "Einstein." Obviously the value of an Einstein varies with the wavelength and frequency of the light. For example, the value of $N h\nu$ for light of wave length 4900 Å and a frequency of $6.12 \times 10^{14} = 6.02 \times 10^{23} \times 6.55 \times 10^{-27} \times 6.12 \times 10^{14}/4.84 \times 10^7 = 57,800$ cal, while the value of $N h\nu$ for light of wavelength 6,500 Å = 43,480 cal. From Einstein's law of photochemical equivalence there should be a direct relation between the absorption spectra of the chlorophylls and the photosynthetic efficiency of different wavelengths of light. The wavelengths absorbed most strongly should be most effective in photosynthesis. However, while this is largely the case, the situation is complicated by the fact that light absorbed by the carotenoids and other plant pigments also provides energy for photosynthesis. It appears that light absorbed by carotenoids is transferred to chlorophyll-b and then to chlorophyll a which finally provides the energy for photosynthesis.

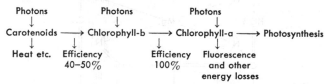

Warburg (113), in studies with chlorella (blue-green algae), found 4 quanta of red light (6560 Å) to be required per mol of O_2 formed in photosynthesis, which would represent 24 quanta and about 1000 kcal per mol of hexose synthesized:

$$6CO_2 + 6H_2O \longrightarrow C_6H_{12}O_6 + 6O_2$$

Theoretically the free energy to synthesize a hexose molecule is about 690 kcal. According to Warburg, the efficiency in his experiments was around 65 per cent. Other workers have found 6 to 12 quanta to be required per mol of O_2 formed—36 to 72 quanta per mol of hexose synthesized—and proportionately less efficiency.

The light or Hill reaction. Hill (114) in 1937 found that when suspensions of chloroplasts are illuminated in the complete absence of CO_2, water is split to give O_2 if a substrate for reduction, such as Fe^{+++}, quinone, or organic dye, is present to act as hydrogen acceptor (A):

$$A + 2H_2O \xrightarrow[\text{Light}]{\text{Chloroplasts}} AH_2 + O_2$$

The identity of the primary hydrogen acceptor in photosynthesis is unknown, though DPN · H and TPN · H apparently represent the reducing agents involved in photosynthesis. Their over-all production from the Hill reaction may be represented:

$$2DPN^+(\text{or } TPN^+) + 2H_2O \xrightarrow[\text{Light}]{\text{Chloroplasts}} 2DPN \cdot H(\text{or } TPN \cdot H) + 2H^+ + O_2$$

Light splits H_2O into O_2 and active hydrogen, which then serves as the reducing agent, though various intermediate steps are probably involved. Ultimately, however, energy as DPN · H and TPN · H is stored up for the synthetic process.

It has been shown that oxidative phosphorylation coupled with oxidation of pyridine nucleotides (DPN · H, TPN · H) is effected by chloroplasts and grana to form ATP (115). It appears that light energy converted into the energy of DPN · H and TPN · H and ATP primarily provides the energy for photosynthesis.

Fixation of carbon dioxide and carbohydrate formation in photosynthesis. After the light or Hill reaction has taken place, the fixation of CO_2 and synthesis of carbohydrate take place. These processes can proceed in the dark and are sometimes referred to as the dark reactions. Energy stored up by the Hill or light reaction drives the endergonic dark reactions.

Calvin and associates (107) studied photosynthesis by algae in the presence of $C^{14}O_2$. The algae preparations were exposed to light for very short periods of time (seconds) and then the distribution of C^{14} in the reaction products was determined by paper chromatography. From these experiments the pathway of CO_2 in photosynthesis has been worked out.

The initial reaction in the photosynthetic fixation of CO_2 appears to be reaction of CO_2 with ribulose-1,5-diphosphate to form two molecules of 3-phosphoglyceric acid. The reaction is catalyzed by a carboxylation enzyme (carboxydismutase enzyme system):

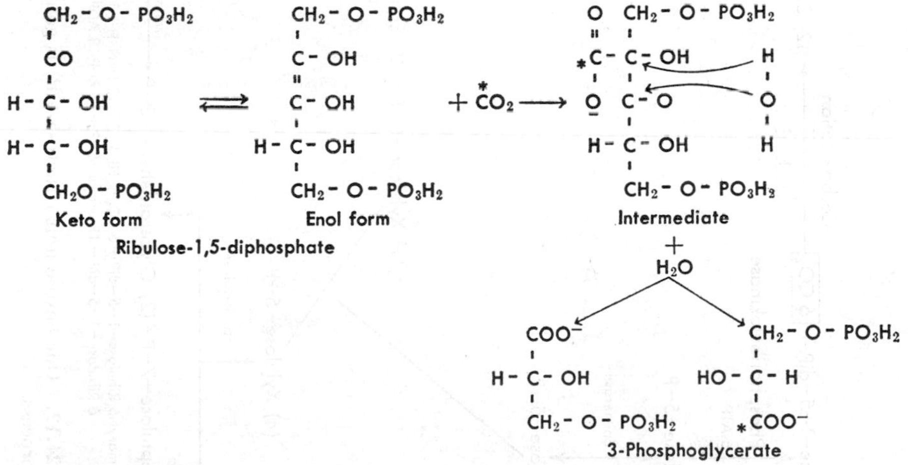

The 3-phosphoglycerate is then converted to 1,3-diphosphoglycerate, which is acted upon by phosphoglyceraldehyde dehydrogenase and DPN · H or TPN · H to form glyceraldehyde-3-P:

1,3-Diphosphoglycerate + DPN · H + H$^+$ ⟶ Glyceraldehyde-3-P + DPN$^+$ + Pi

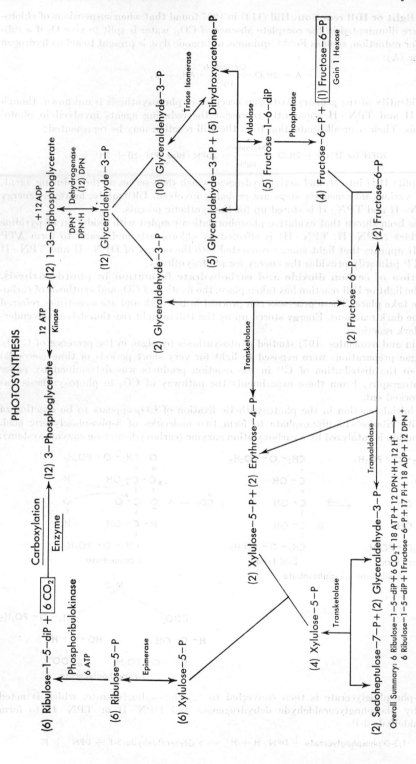

Figure 24.12. One hexose unit (fructose-6-P) is gained in the cycle for each 6 CO_2 and 6 ribulose-1-5-diphosphate reacting in the photosynthetic process.

The glyceraldehyde-3-P then continues in the cycle of reactions shown in Figure 24.12. The reaction of $6CO_2$ with 6-ribulose-1,5-diP leads to the formation of a net molecule of fructose-6-P. Six molecules of ribulose-1,6-diP are regenerated in the cycle to keep the process going.

Fructose-6-P formed in the cycle is converted to glucose-6-P by isomerase, and glucose-6-P to glucose-1-P by phosphoglucomutase. Glucose-1-P is converted to UDP-glucose by action with UTP.

Sucrose is synthesized in plants by two reactions (59):

$$\text{UDP-glucose} + \text{Fructose} \Longleftrightarrow \text{Sucrose} + \text{UDP}$$

$$\text{UDP-glucose} + \text{Fructose-6-P} \Longleftrightarrow \text{UDP} + \text{Sucrose-P} \xrightarrow[\text{H}_2\text{O}]{\text{Phosphatase}} \text{Sucrose} + \text{Pi}$$

The synthesis of starches in plants is very similar to the synthesis of glycogen in animal tissues. It may proceed either through glucose-1-P and phosphorylase action or through UDP-glucose and transglycosylase action (with branching enzyme in each case).

The synthesis of cellulose and pentosans in plants appears also to depend upon the action of UDP-glucose and transglycosylase enzymes, though little is known about the reactions:

$$\text{UDP-glucose} \longrightarrow \text{Cellulose} + \text{UDP}$$
$$\text{UDP-xylose} \longrightarrow \text{Xylan (pentosan)} + \text{UDP}$$
$$\text{UDP-arabinose} \longrightarrow \text{Araban (pentosan)} + \text{UDP}$$

It appears that inulin, which is fructosan with a molecular weight of about 5000, is synthesized in Jerusalem artichokes and dahlias by the action of an invertase which also acts as a transglycosylase (transfructosylase):

$$n \text{ Sucrose} \longrightarrow (\text{Fructose})_n + n \text{ Glucose}$$
$$\text{Inulin (a levan)}$$

In this case fructosyl groups are built up into a linear chain. An enzyme in *L. mesenteroides* transfers glycosyl groups from sucrose (transglucosylase) to form the dextrans:

$$n \text{ Sucrose} \longrightarrow (\text{Glucose})_n + n \text{ Fructose}$$
$$\text{Dextran}$$

In the synthesis of inulin fructosyl groups are transferred, while in the synthesis of dextran glucosyl groups are transferred.

FREE ENERGY RELATIONS IN CARBOHYDRATE SYNTHESIS

In general the synthesis of compound sugars depends upon reactions of substances containing bonds of higher free energy with the formation of compounds containing bonds of lower free energy. Table 24.3 gives the approximate free energies of hydrolysis of a number of carbohydrates and derivatives (59, 116)

The driving force in a reaction is represented by the decrease in free energy in the reaction. The free energy decrease in the hydrolysis of UDP-glucose (−7.6 kcal) is greater than the free energy decrease in the hydrolysis of glucose-1-P (−5 kcal). This means that the driving force in the transfer of a glucosyl group from UDP-glucose is greater than that from glucose-1-P.

The glycosyl (sugar group) transfer potentials of key substances in carbohydrate synthesis are in the decreasing order UDP-sugar > Sucrose > aldose-1-P.

Atkinson and Morton give a comprehensive discussion of the synthesis of phosphates of biologic importance and the energy relations involved (116).

Table 24.3.   Standard Free Energies of Hydrolysis of Some
Carbohydrates and Derivatives

Compound	$\Delta F'$ (kcal)	pH
UDP-glucose	−7.6	7.4
Glucose-1-P	−5.0	7.0
Glucose-6-P	−2.9	8.5
Galactose-1-P	−4.5	
Galactose-6-P	−3.0	8.5
Mannose-6-P	−2.7	8.5
Fructose-1-P	−2.8	8.5
Fructose-6-P	−3.4	8.5
Sucrose	−6.6	
Lactose	−3.0	
Maltose	−3.0	
Glycogen and Starch	−4.3	
Levan	−4.6	
Dextran	−2.0	

INTEGRATION OF CARBOHYDRATE, FAT, AND PROTEIN METABOLISM
THROUGH THE TRICARBOXYLIC ACID CYCLE

The reactions of the tricarboxylic acid cycle afford the mechanism for the final oxidation of fatty acids through the oxidation of acetyl CoA and that for the oxidation of carbohydrate through oxidation of pyruvic acid. Earlier discussion has pointed out that the final stages of the oxidation of a number of the amino acids (protein metabolism) are effected through reactions of the tricarboxylic cycle. The diagram of Figure 24.13 represents an attempt to depict the integration of fat, carbohydrate, and protein metabolism in the cycle. Although this picture is not complete, it seems to bring together much of our information about the chemical mechanisms of metabolism in general.

According to the integration diagram, certain of the amino acids, such as leucine, tyrosine, and phenylalanine are deaminated and oxidized to form acetoacetic acid, which then is oxidized through the cycle. Acetyl CoA formed from these amino acids may also be used for the synthesis of fatty acids and cholesterol and for acetylations. Other amino acids, such as alanine, cystine, cysteine, and serine, form pyruvic acid which then may be oxidized in the cycle, or be converted to glucose and glycogen by reverse glycolysis, or converted to acetyl CoA and utilized for the synthesis of fatty acids and cholesterol, and in the acetylation process.

Aspartic and glutamic acids directly enter the tricarboxylic cycle at the oxaloacetate and α-ketoglutarate stages from which their oxidations proceed to completion in two or more turns of the cycle. These substances also may lead to increased production of pyruvate with sugar and glycogen formation, and also through pyruvate to acetyl CoA, which can yield fatty acids and cholesterol and be utilized for acetylations. The same statements are true for arginine, histidine, ornithine, and proline, which enter the cycle indirectly through glutamic acid at the α-ketoglutarate stage.

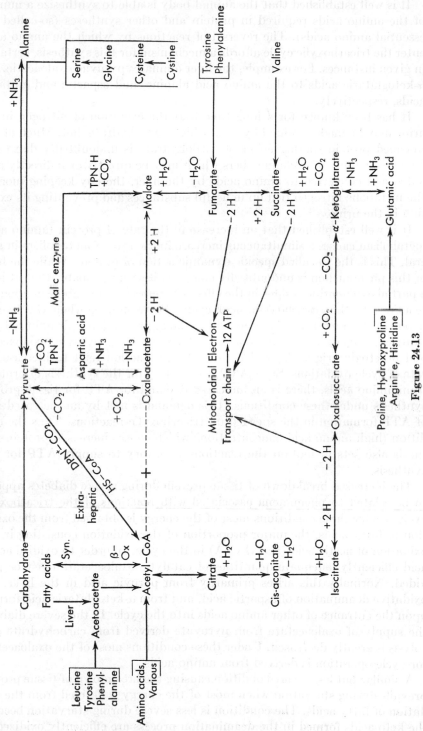

INTEGRATION OF CARBOHYDRATE, FAT AND PROTEIN METABOLISM THROUGH THE TRICARBOXYLIC OR CITRIC ACID CYCLE

Figure 24.13

It is well established that the animal body is able to synthesize a number of the amino acids required in protein and other syntheses (so-called unessential amino acids). The reversal of reactions by which the amino acids enter the tricarboxylic cycle affords a mechanism for this synthesis, certainly in given instances. For example, the liver aminates pyruvic, oxaloacetic, and α-ketoglutaric acids to the amino acid alanine, and aspartic and glutamic acids, respectively.

It has been known for a long time that the excretion of nitrogen in the urine may be made minimal by a very high carbohydrate diet. Much of this so-called protein sparing effect of carbohydrate is undoubtedly due to an increased supply of cycle members which may be directly or indirectly aminated and converted to amino acids by the liver, thereby keeping more of the metabolic nitrogen tied up in useful substances and preventing its excretion in the urine.

It is well established that an increase in the rate of protein (amino acid) metabolism causes a simultaneous increase in the rate of metabolism in general. This is the so-called specific dynamic action of protein. While the basis of this phenomenon is undoubtedly complex, it seems probable that at least a partial explanation resides in the effect of amino acid metabolism upon the reactions of the tricarboxylic acid cycle. For example, when the liver is flooded with a mixture of amino acids, a large proportion is deaminized and oxidized, causing marked increases in the amounts of pyruvic, oxaloacetic, and α-ketoglutaric acids, which through mass action tend to increase the rate of cycle oxidations. Since ATP is necessary for the synthesis of proteins from amino acids, there is an increased demand for ATP for tissue protein synthesis under these conditions. This demand is met by an increased rate of ATP formation in the speeded up tricarboxylic reactions. Thus the condition (high amino acid concentration) which causes increased protein synthesis also sets in motion the reactions necessary to supply ATP for this synthesis.

The increased breakdown of tissue protein during severe diabetes appears to be related to phenomena associated with reactions of the tricarboxylic cycle. Under these conditions most of the energy is obtained from the oxidation of fatty acids, the major proportion of the oxidation consisting in the oxidation of acetic acid (acetyl CoA) in the cycle. In order to oxidize acetic acid efficiently, adequate quantities of catalytic oxaloacetate must be provided. Normally this arises primarily from pyruvic acid in the liver, the oxidative deamination of aspartic acid, and from α-ketoglutaric acid formed upon the entrance of other amino acids into the cycle. In the severe diabetic the supply of oxaloacetate from pyruvate derived from carbohydrate glycolysis is greatly decreased. Under these conditions most of the oxaloacetate for cycle operation is derived from amino acids.

A similar but less severe condition causing the breakdown of tissue protein prevails during starvation when most of the energy is derived from the oxidation of fatty acids. The condition is less severe during starvation because the keto acids formed in the deamination process are efficiently oxidized to yield energy, whereas in the severe diabetic a large proportion of these acids is converted to glucose in the liver and excreted in the urine.

The formation of oxaloacetate and other cycle members from amino acids takes place largely in the liver, from which they pass by way of the blood stream to other tissues and are used in their tricarboxylic acid oxidations.

RELATIONS OF THE ENDOCRINE GLANDS TO CARBOHYDRATE METABOLISM

Most of the processes of carbohydrate metabolism are regulated, directly or indirectly, through the hormones secreted by endocrine glands. These hormonal relations are exceedingly complex and, as yet, are imperfectly understood. This complexity is due to a number of causes. In the first place, the major control of carbohydrate metabolism is effected through both opposing and complementary actions of the hormones of the pancreas, anterior pituitary, and adrenal cortex. In the second place, each endocrine gland generally secretes more than one hormone affecting carbohydrate metabolism, and these hormones may exert apparently opposing effects. Lastly, the anterior pituitary not only produces hormones directly affecting the metabolic processes, but also through its tropic hormones regulates the activity of other endocrines such as the adrenals and thereby exerts a secondary effect upon carbohydrate metabolism.

As indicated in previous discussion, carbohydrate metabolism proceeds by several intricate pathways involving numerous reactions and enzymes which catalyze them. Also, the metabolic paths of carbohydrate metabolism intersect and integrate with the pathways of fat and amino acid (protein) metabolism to constitute a dynamic, generally reversible, network of metabolic reactions. Factors which primarily affect one reaction in a pathway may exert a strong secondary effect upon other reactions in the integrated network, and often it is very difficult to distinguish secondary from primary effects.

The detailed mechanisms by which hormones exert their control over enzymatic processes are little understood, though in some cases the evidence points to effects upon specific enzymes and reactions. A hormone may, in some manner, directly affect an enzyme system so as to make it more or less effective. It may indirectly affect an enzyme system as in the action of epinephrine (and glucagon) to activate phosphorylase by increasing the production of cyclic-3′,5′-AMP, which is required in the conversion of inactive phosphorylase b to active phosphorylase a. However, we know nothing about how epinephrine and glucagon increase the formation of cyclic-3′,5′-AMP! Since the enzymes which catalyze metabolic reactions are proteins, and some of the hormones which regulate these reactions are proteins, factors, including hormones, which affect protein synthesis also have an effect upon the control of metabolic pathways by regulating the supply of enzymes and hormones.

Since the pathways of carbohydrate, fat, and protein metabolism are closely interrelated, severe primary disturbances in carbohydrate metabolism, as seen in diabetes, also cause profound alterations in the metabolism of fats and proteins as secondary consequences.

Methods used in the study of hormonal regulation of carbohydrate metabolism. Because of the enormous complexity of the problem of hormonal control of carbohydrate metabolism, it has been approached in many different ways.

Carbohydrate metabolism is primarily under the control of insulin from the pancreas, which promotes the metabolism of glucose, and of the hormones of the anterior lobe of the hypophysis (adenohypophysis), and of the adrenal cortex which oppose the action of insulin. Thus, a normal balance between these hormones maintains normal carbohydrate metabolism, and imbalance of the hormones results in abnormal carbohydrate metabolism.

Removal of the action of insulin in an animal by pancreatectomy, or destruction of the β-cells of the islets of Langerhans with alloxan, produces severe diabetes in which carbohydrate metabolism is primarily under the control of hypophyseal and adrenal cortical hormones:

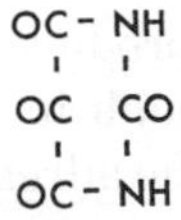

$$
\begin{array}{c}
\text{OC} - \text{NH} \\
\mid \qquad \mid \\
\text{OC} \quad \text{CO} \\
\mid \qquad \mid \\
\text{OC} - \text{NH}
\end{array}
$$

Alloxan

Adrenalectomy or hypophysectomy yields animals in which carbohydrate metabolism is regulated primarily by insulin and either cortical hormones (hypophysectomy) or hypophyseal hormones (adrenalectomy).

Pancreatectomy and adrenalectomy of an animal results in carbohydrate metabolism controlled primarily by growth hormone of the anterior pituitary (adenohypophysis). Besides growth hormone (somatotropin) active in controlling carbohydrate metabolism, the anterior pituitary also supplies adrenocorticotropic hormone (ACTH) which controls the development of the adrenals and their production of hormones affecting carbohydrate metabolism. In the absence of the pancreas and adrenals, chiefly the growth hormone of the hypophysis is active in regulating carbohydrate metabolism.

Pancreatectomy and hypophysectomy of an animal places carbohydrate metabolism primarily under the control of the adrenal glands. However, because of the absence of ACTH, the adrenals soon atrophy and exhibit subnormal activity.

Essentially all hormonal control of carbohydrate metabolism is abolished by pancreatectomy, adrenalectomy, and hypophysectomy.

As to be expected, removal of anti-insulin action by adrenalectomy or hypophysectomy should make an animal more sensitive to the action of insulin. This is especially the case with the hypophysectomized animal, and the combination of hypophysectomy and adrenalectomy renders an animal extremely sensitive to insulin, so that small doses which have no appreciable effect on a normal animal may produce hypoglycemic convulsions. The rat made diabetic with alloxan and then adrenalectomized and hypophysectomized is so sensitive to the action of insulin that it has been used by Bornstein (117) for the quantitative estimation of insulin in very low concentrations.

It can be seen from the above discussion that the effects of hormone deficiency on carbohydrate metabolism, singly and in varied combination, may be observed through removal of the proper endocrine glands. The positive effects of hormones on metabolism may be assayed by injecting them into animals from which the corresponding endocrine glands have been removed. Also, the effect of a hormone upon an animal retaining the corresponding endocrine gland but from which another has been removed may be observed, as in the administration of growth hormone to a depancreatized animal. In such a case the controlling effect of growth hormone upon metabolism is magnified by adding exogenous hormone to the animal's own endogenous supply.

Various metabolic studies on the action of hormones have been conducted on completely or partly eviscerated preparations in which the heart and lungs are functional but certain or all visceral organs have been removed. Under these conditions metabolism is largely concentrated in the skeletal muscle mass, and the influence of organs such as the kidneys, liver, etc., may be ruled out.

Much study on the hormonal control of carbohydrate metabolism has been based upon the effect of the various hormones upon the in vitro metabolism of excised tissues, such as the rat diaphragm and epididymal fat pads incubated in suitable media. The excised rat diaphragm, in which the edges are cut all around, has been used extensively. The diaphragm is generally cut to give two hemidiaphragms, one being used to test the effect of a hormone upon the metabolism of the tissue and the other as a control in medium not containing the hormone.

A hormone may be given to an appropriate animal and permitted to act in the animal on the diaphragm or other tissue before excision of the tissue for in vitro studies. If a hormone shows an effect upon the metabolism of a tissue when added to the incubating medium, it is considered that the hormone has a direct primary action on the tissue. This is seen when rat diaphragm is incubated in medium containing glucose with and without insulin. The insulin-containing preparation takes up more glucose from the medium and forms more glycogen in the tissue than the control without insulin. However, when direct addition of a hormone to an in vitro tissue preparation has no effect, but administration of the hormone to the animal for a time before excision of the tissue does have an effect, then it is considered that the hormonal action upon the tissue is indirect.

In the discussion which follows, reference to Figure 24.14 may aid in better understanding the relation of the endocrine glands to carbohydrate metabolism.

Discussions of the relation of endocrine glands to carbohydrate metabolism may be found in the reviews of De Bodo and Altszuler (118), Stadie

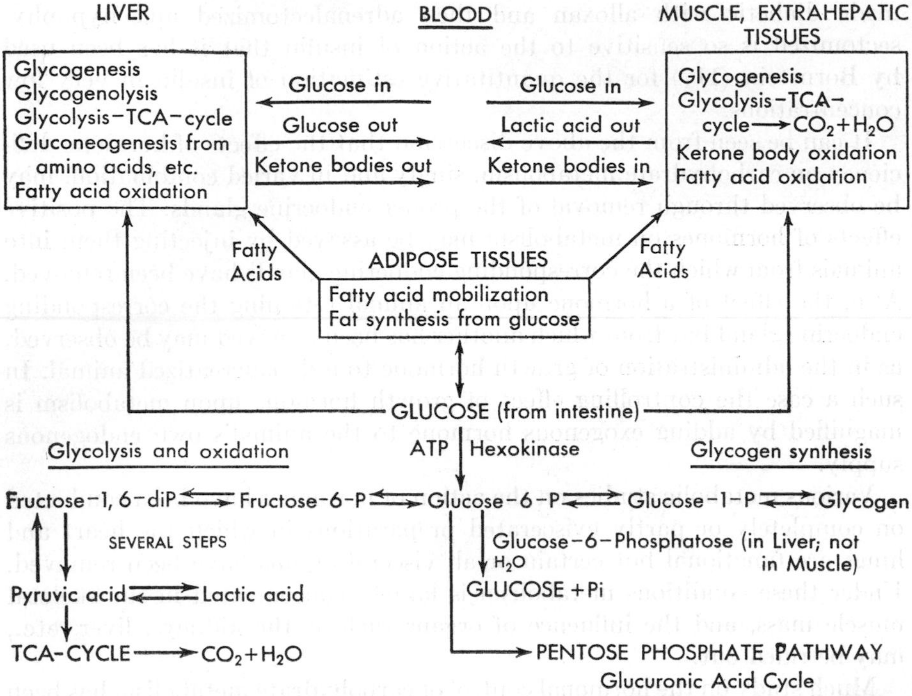

Figure 24.14. Major tissues and some processes involved in hormonal control of metabolism. Glucose enters metabolism as glucose-6-P formed in the hexokinase reaction. Glucose is formed in the liver from glucose-6-P by the action of glucose-6-phosphatase.

(119), Field, Park and associates, and Berthet (120), and a group of specialists in the field (121). The book Diabetes, edited by Williams, gives a comprehensive discussion (122).

PANCREAS

The pancreas secretes two hormones, insulin and glucagon, which participate in the control of carbohydrate metabolism.

The relation of the pancreas to carbohydrate metabolism was first clearly indicated by von Mering and Minkowski (123), who produced diabetes in dogs by removal of the pancreas. Banting and Best (124) and Macleod (125) demonstrated the presence of the hormone insulin in the islands of Langerhans, and Banting and associates (126) succeeded in preparing extracts suitable for clinical use. Somogyi, Doisy, and Shaffer (127) developed a method based upon acid-alcohol extraction of pancreas tissue followed by isoelectric precipitation which yielded insulin of high activity. Abel and associates (128) succeeded in crystallizing insulin from a strongly buffered pyridine solution. This crystalline insulin is combined with zinc, and it seems probable that the metal is present in the hormone as secreted by the gland, since the pancreas contains appreciable quantities of zinc.

Secretion of insulin. Insulin is a small protein with a minimal molecular weight of 6000 (129). The amino acid sequence and structure of insulin are given in Chapter 8.

The amount of insulin secreted by the pancreas per day to maintain normal carbohydrate metabolism has been estimated at about 1 unit per kilogram of body weight, which, for a human subject weighing 60 kg would be about 2.5 mg. This agrees well with the required dose of 60 to 70 units per day for the severe diabetic. However, some diabetic cases resistant to insulin may require several thousand units per day.

The body of evidence shows that the rate of secretion of insulin by the pancreas is largely controlled by the blood sugar level, the rate increasing with a rise and decreasing with a fall in this level. The secretion of insulin according to the blood sugar level provides an automatic mechanism for the disposal of sugar according to the supply of sugar available for metabolism.

Some evidence indicates that possibly the nervous system may exert the finer control of insulin secretion by means of fibers in the right vagus leading to the pancreas.

Effect of pancreatectomy. The diabetic state. The removal of the pancreas has somewhat different effects in different animals. The depancreatized dog exhibits characteristic metabolic changes similar to those observed in severe cases of human diabetes mellitus. These changes may be summarized as follows:

1. The blood sugar increases to profound hyperglycemic levels which result in pronounced glucosuria. The hyperglycemia and glucosuria persist during fasting.

2. The liver glycogen falls to extremely low levels, generally less than 0.1 per cent. Muscle glycogen is decreased, but relatively much less than liver glycogen.

3. Ingested glucose is excreted almost quantitatively in the urine in the period immediately following pancreatectomy, though appreciable quantities may be retained during the terminal stages.

4. The respiratory quotient (RQ) falls to around 0.71, the value for fat oxidation, and is not raised by the ingestion of glucose.

5. The rate of tissue protein breakdown is markedly accelerated, as shown by the increased urinary nitrogen excretion of fasted depancreatized animals as compared with fasted normal animals. The G:N ratio of fasted depancreatized animals is around 3 and indicates that a relatively constant proportion of the amino acids derived from tissue protein (or dietary protein) is converted to glucose.

6. The injection of glucose into normal animals causes a rise in blood pyruvate (and lactate). Bueding and associates (130) showed that this does not occur with depancreatized animals. Himwich and Himwich (131) confirmed this in dogs and also demonstrated a similar relation in diabetic patients. They found that while muscle glycogen is broken down to pyruvate during exercise in the diabetic, glucose gives no increase in pyruvate.

7. Large quantities of ketone bodies (acetoacetic and β-hydroxybutyric

acids and acetone) are formed, causing ketonemia and ketonuria. This increase in ketone bodies, as indicated previously in Chapter 23, is the result of increased metabolism of fats. The ketone acids lead to severe acidosis and finally to coma and death in four to fourteen days.

8. The excretion of large amounts of sugar and ketone bodies in the urine necessitates the simultaneous excretion of much water, which causes dehydration and severe thirst.

9. In severe diabetes there is a strikingly increased rate of mobilization of triglycerides and unesterified fatty acids (UFA) from adipose tissue into the blood and transport to the liver and other tissues. In severe cases of human diabetes with pronounced acidosis or coma the plasma level of UFA may rise to two or three times the normal value. Upon adequate treatment with insulin there is a prompt drop of UFA to normal, which parallels the fall in blood glucose. Insulin markedly increases the rate of conversion of glucose to fat in adipose tissue, and in its absence the rate of mobilization of triglycerides and UFA from adipose tissue is greatly increased.

The injection of insulin promptly corrects all the above metabolic disturbances, and depancreatized animals, when properly fed and treated with insulin, may be maintained in good health for long periods of time.

As previously indicated, the effects of pancreatectomy vary with animal species. Some of these variations are tabulated below.

Although pancreatectomy causes some alterations in the carbohydrate metabolism of most animals, and in the dog and cat produces changes similar to those of severe diabetes mellitus in human beings, many of the metabolic reactions appear to proceed in a normal manner even in the severe diabetic state. Also, the metabolic rate is maintained in the diabetic, indicating that energy is being produced at a normal rate. The capacity of the diabetic liver

Table 24.4

Animal	Effect of Pancreatectomy
Cat	Essentially as in the dog.
Goat	Only slight hyperglycemia, glucosuria, and ketosis. Urinary N increases, but less than in dog.
Pig	Like the goat, except marked ketosis.
Rabbit	Profuse glucosuria without ketosis. Survives for a long time without insulin.
Duck	Little or no metabolic disturbance detected.
Monkey	When fed shows marked glucosuria and only mild ketosis. Serious ketosis when fasted.
Owl	Extreme hyperglycemia when well fed. May die in hypoglycemia if fasted.

to deaminate amino acids and form sugar is at least normal. In general, this process is greatly increased in the diabetic. The capacity of the liver to deposit and hold this glucose as glycogen is practically lost in the diabetic. Apparently the capacity of the diabetic to glycolyze glucose is impaired, since, as previously indicated, the administration of glucose to the diabetic fails to cause an increase in blood pyruvate, the end product of the glycolysis reaction. The glycolysis of muscle glycogen, however, readily takes place, as does the breakdown of liver glycogen to glucose.

That the diabetic animal's capacity to phosphorylate glucose in the hexo-kinase reaction is seriously impaired has been conclusively shown. This appears largely due to a decreased rate of glucose transport into tissue cells (particularly muscle) in the absence of insulin.

A serious defect in the diabetic, other than decreased phosphorylation of glucose in the hexokinase reaction, is the greatly increased glucose-6-phos-phatase activity of the liver, which increases the rate at which glucose-6-P, formed in the hexokinase reaction and by glycogenolysis and gluconeogene-sis, is hydrolyzed to glucose. Since glucose metabolism in general proceeds through sugar phosphates, this increased glucose-6-phosphatase activity in the liver of the diabetic appears to be a chief reason for decreased carbohy-drate metabolism in the liver and failure to store liver glycogen.

It appears very likely that the action of insulin in the presence of abundant glucose may lead to a considerable decrease in intracellular pH as a result of increasing the concentration of sugar phosphates, which are stronger acids than phosphoric acid (Table 24.5).

Table 24.5.   Acid Strengths of Phosphate Esters

	pK_1	pK_2	pK_3
α-Glycerol phosphoric	1.40	6.44	—
Glyceraldehyde phosphoric	2.10	6.75	—
Dihydroxyacetone phosphoric	1.77	6.45	—
Fructose-6-phosphoric	0.97	6.11	—
Glucose-6-phosphoric	0.94	6.11	—
Glucose-1-phosphoric	1.10	6.13	—
Fructose-1,6-diphosphoric	1.48	6.32	—
Enolpyruvic phosphoric	—	3.5	6.38
3-Phosphoglyceric	1.42	3.42	5.98
H_3PO_4	1.96	6.7	12.4

Presumably the reason why products of glycolysis, such as pyruvic and lactic acids, and members of the tricarboxylic cycle cause increased produc-tion and excretion of glucose when administered to the diabetic is that these substances are taken from the blood by the liver and converted to glucose before appreciable quantities penetrate into the muscle cells. That the mus-cles of the diabetic have the capacity to form glycogen from products of glycolysis such as lactic acid and hexose phosphate has been shown by Lukens (132).

As previously indicated, the liver of the diabetic animal fails to deposit glycogen. The deposition of liver glycogen depends upon the interrelation of the following and associated processes:

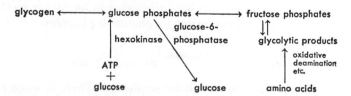

In the diabetic animal the rate of glucose formation from amino acids and other small molecules is greatly accelerated (gluconeogenesis), and the rate at which glycogen is broken down to glucose is increased (glycogenolysis), with the result that glucose from any source tends to accumulate in the blood. That the diabetic liver can still form glycogen was shown by Mirsky and associates (133), who diminished ketonuria and nitrogen excretion by intravenous injection of glucose into depancreatized dogs, a result due to building up the glycogen reserves of the liver. Also, de Bodo and associates (134) demonstrated increased liver glycogen by direct analysis under these conditions. Thus, if the concentration of blood glucose is sufficiently high, its mass effect will shift the above reactions to cause a deposition of some liver glycogen. This is in accord with the idea of Soskin (135) that the high blood sugar of the diabetic represents a compensation through mass action to further the utilization of sugar. That this mechanism largely fails is indicated by the body of evidence.

It has been found that fructose is metabolized to a greater extent than glucose by the diabetic animal and human (136). Apparently the phosphorylation of fructose by tissues of the diabetic is essentially normal; however, due to conversion of fructose to glucose in the liver, the efficiency of fructose utilization is also impaired. It has been shown that liver from alloxan diabetic rats oxidizes fructose but not glucose at a normal rate, and that alloxan diabetic rats utilize more fructose than glucose. As pointed out in earlier discussion, liver and muscle contain a fructokinase which catalyzes the formation of fructose-1-phosphate instead of fructose-6-phosphate, which is converted to fructose-1,6-diphosphate as follows:

$$\text{Fructose-1-P} \underset{\text{Aldolase}}{\overset{}{\rightleftarrows}} \text{Dihydroxyacetone-P} + \text{Glyceraldehyde}$$

$$\text{Glyceraldehyde} + \text{ATP} \xrightarrow{\text{Kinase}} \text{Glyceraldehyde-3-P} + \text{ADP}$$

$$\text{Glyceraldehyde-3-P} + \text{Dihydroxyacetone-P} \underset{\text{Aldolase}}{\overset{}{\rightleftarrows}} \text{Fructose-1,6-diP}$$

There is the possibility that the processes involved in this pathway of fructose metabolism are not affected or are less affected by insulin lack than the pathway involving phosphorylation in position 6 of the sugar. It is of interest that the aldolase catalyzing the reversible conversion of fructose-1-P to dihydroxyacetone-P and glyceraldehyde, 1-phospho-fructo-aldolase, is specific for fructose-1-P (118, p. 82). The problem of fructose metabolism appears to require further investigation.

Metabolic effects of insulin. One of the most important effects of insulin is to increase the transport of glucose and other sugars across the cell membrane into the cell, which has been discussed in an earlier section. This provides glucose for phosphorylation to glucose-6-phosphate in the hexokinase reaction:

$$\text{Glucose} + \text{ATP} \xrightarrow{\text{Glucokinase}} \text{Glucose-6-P} + \text{ADP}$$

which is the starting point in metabolic sequences. There is some evidence, though possibly not conclusive, that insulin in some manner also promotes this reaction (121, Kipnis). It appears, however, that the main action of insulin is to increase the transport of glucose into cells.

The *in vitro* action of insulin on tissue preparations shows that it exerts major direct effects upon tissues having membranes offering a high degree of resistance to glucose penetration into the cell, such as skeletal and heart muscle, the lens and blood-aqueous barrier, and probably adipose tissue and leucocytes, which are extremely sensitive to the action of insulin (122, p. 129). There appears to be essentially no direct effects of insulin upon tissues offering much less resistance to glucose penetration, such as brain, kidney, and intestinal mucosa. The carbohydrate metabolism of these tissues appears to be essentially normal in diabetic animals.

Tissues which contain appreciable levels of free intracellular glucose, such as erythrocytes, kidney, and probably brain, are not directly responsive to the action of insulin. The above facts suggest that the primary action of insulin is upon the transport of glucose into cells rather than stimulation of phosphorylation in the hexokinase reaction.

In the whole animal the quantitatively most important over-all effect of insulin is to increase the rate of glycogen formation and oxidation of carbohydrate in muscle.

The effects of insulin upon liver are complex. Liver tissue obtained from diabetic animals shows many gross metabolic abnormalities, such as decreased glucose phosphorylation, glycogen synthesis, and lipogenesis and increased glycogenolysis and gluconeogenesis. All of these processes appear to be brought back to normal by injecting insulin into the animal (rat) 12 to 24 hours previous to removal of the liver tissue.

Direct effect of insulin upon liver tissue *in vitro* has been shown in the synthesis of glycogen from glucose, of fatty acids from acetate, and of protein from amino acids (122, p. 142). However, these effects have been more difficult to demonstrate and of smaller magnitude than such effects in extrahepatic tissues such as skeletal muscle.

De Bodo and associates (121) gave dogs a priming dose of glucose-C^{14} and then perfused with glucose containing sufficient glucose-C^{14} to establish a constant C^{14} activity. From dilution of administered glucose-C^{14} activity, the glucose pool size was obtained. From changes in the glucose pool size and plasma-C^{14} specific activity, it was possible to calculate the rate of glucose removal from the pool and of addition to the pool by liver gluconeogenesis under various hormonal conditions. It was found that insulin-induced hypoglycemia is primarily due to increased uptake of glucose by extrahepatic tissues. These workers also obtained evidence that prolonged infusion of small amounts of insulin appeared to exert a "restraining" effect upon the increased hepatic gluconeogenesis which normally accompanies hypoglycemia. Other workers (137, 138) have obtained evidence that insulin decreases glucose output by the liver (decreased gluconeogenesis).

It has been shown in the rat that the glucose-6-phosphatase activity of the liver is markedly increased in diabetes, and that the injection of insulin (not *in vitro*) decreases the activity to normal (139). This increase in glucose-6-phosphatase activity in diabetes, which increases the rate at which glucose is formed in the liver, coupled with decreased formation of glucose-6-phosphate by the hexokinase reaction, appears to account primarily for the hyperglycemia and glucosuria of the diabetic state. Also, since glucose-6-phosphate is the key compound of carbohydrate metabolism, its deficient formation and exaggerated hydrolysis in the diabetic reduces the supply for the processes of carbohydrate metabolism in general; glycolysis and TCA-cycle oxidation; pentose phosphate pathway and formation of TPN · H for fat and cholesterol synthesis; glucuronic acid pathway; etc. Thus most of the effects of insulin deficiency appear to be related to these changes in the synthesis and hydrolysis of glucose-6-phosphate.

The effect of insulin upon lipogenesis has been discussed in Chapter 23, where it was shown that the synthesis of fatty acids almost ceases in severe diabetes (absence of insulin). It has been shown (122) that fatty acid synthesis in adipose tissue, liver, and mammary gland is stimulated *in vitro* by the addition of glucose alone or of glucose plus insulin. Apparently insulin without glucose is ineffective, due to the fact that products of glycolysis, glycerol and pyruvate, are utilized for fat synthesis, and the production of TPN · H in the pentose phosphate pathway is obligatory in the synthesis of fatty acids.

Insulin has been found to have important effects on the tissue synthesis of proteins (122, p. 121), the mechanisms of which are incompletely understood. In the first place, insulin appears to increase the transport of amino acids into cells independent of its effect upon glucose transport, and probably to release from inhibition an enzyme or enzymes involved in protein synthesis. There is also an indirect effect of insulin associated with its action in increasing the rate of glucose oxidation in tissues, with the formation of ATP, which is necessary to supply energy for protein synthesis. Insulin also appears to restore the capacity of the diabetic liver to synthesize protein by aiding in restoring the machinery (possibly enzymes) for protein synthesis.

Optimal action of insulin in promoting protein synthesis is dependent upon the action also of the pituitary growth hormone (somatotropin).

Insulin antagonists in plasma (122). Insulin at concentrations as low as 10^{-4} unit per milliliter increases the glucose uptake of isolated rat diaphragm when added to the incubation medium. This sensitive response of the isolated diaphragm to insulin is used as the basis of an *in vitro* assay of insulin (or insulin like substances) in plasma.

As measured by the rat diaphragm assay method, an antagonist to insulin action, which is present in the β-lipoprotein fraction of plasma, appears to be formed by combined growth hormone and adrenal steroid action. The antagonist was not present in the plasma of adrenalectomized-hypophysectomized (ADH) or alloxan-diabetic hypophysectomized rats but was present in the plasma of ADH rats treated with both cortisone and growth hormone, though not when the animal was treated with only one hormone. The hormones singly or together had no effect *in vitro*. There is no evidence as to whether the antagonist is formed from adrenal steroid and growth hormone (possibly a β-lipoprotein containing the steroid and growth hormone protein) or from other substances under the influence of the hormones.

Another antagonist to the action of insulin appears to be an antibody in the γ-globulin fraction of serum from diabetic patients who have been treated with heterologous insulin (insulin from another animal) for several months. This antibody appears to combine with insulin and render it biologically inactive, and may be a factor in cases of diabetes showing insulin resistance.

A third type of insulin antagonist has been detected in the α-globulin fraction of serum of diabetics resistant to insulin (requiring several hundred or thousand units daily) and with severe ketotic acidosis. It has also been found in the plasma of depancreatized cats. Since the antagonist is in the α-globulin fraction of plasma, it appears not to be an antibody. Its origin is obscure but does not appear related to growth hormone or adrenal steroid. The antagonist appears significantly concerned in cases of insulin-resistant diabetes.

It is of interest that certain obese diabetics are insulin-resistant (require several thousand units of insulin daily) yet show no insulin antagonist in the serum or its protein fractions, suggesting that this kind of insulin resistance may be due to changes in the tissue cells.

Breakdown of insulin in tissues (122, p. 283). It has been found that radioactive I^{131} may be very easily substituted into the insulin molecule (tyrosine groups) without detectable loss in biologic activity. Such labeled insulin has permitted studies on the binding of insulin (118) and its breakdown (140) by tissues.

An insulin degrading enzyme in liver was discovered in 1949 by Mirsky and Broh-Kahn (141), and since that time insulin has been shown to be degraded *in vitro* by preparations of a wide variety of tissues, and by plasma. It appears that liver contains two insulin-degrading systems, one heat-stable and a reducing agent, such as glutathione, which inactivates insulin by splitting disulfide bonds ($-S-S- \longrightarrow -SH + -SH$), and the other heat-labile and probably a proteolytic enzyme. The inactivating enzyme has been termed "insulinase." It exhibits limited insulin specificity since it acts upon some other proteins. As yet little is known about the enzyme and its action, and the extent to which it may be concerned in contributing to insulin resistance in diabetics. However, it has been found that while insulin degradation is normal in untreated diabetics, it is decreased in persons treated with insulin for considerable time.

Insulin degradation is decreased by nephrectomy and hepatectomy, indicating the role of the kidneys and liver. It is also decreased by hypophysectomy, which may be a factor in the insulin sensitivity of hypophysectomized animals. Degradation is increased by thyroxin and decreased by thyroidectomy, which is in accord with the increased insulin requirements of hyperthyroid diabetics. An insulinase inhibitor, apparently a peptide, has been partially purified from the liver, and may play a role in regulating the rate of insulinase inactivation of insulin.

Stimulation of insulin secretion by pancreatic β-cells with drugs (122, p. 481). Certain sulfonamides and sulfonamide derivatives, the sulfonylureas, have been found to stimulate the pancreatic β-cells to increased insulin production. Some of the sulfonylureas are effective in the oral treatment of certain types of diabetes, particularly diabetes found in many older patients. Compounds of special interest at the present time are tolbutamide, chlorpropamide, and metahexamide:

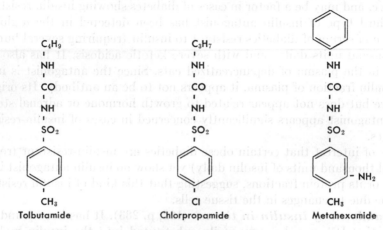

Tolbutamide   Chlorpropamide   Metahexamide

The sulfonamides and sulfonylureas appear to act primarily by increasing the secretion of insulin by the β-cells. They are inactive in depancreatized animals, and their efficacy in the oral treatment of diabetes is dependent upon the presence of functional islet tissue.

Glucagon—the hyperglycemic-glycogenolytic factor (HGF). The production of a hormone by the pancreas which causes the rapid breakdown of liver glycogen to glucose (glycogenolysis) was discovered when it was found that the injection of some commercial preparations of insulin caused a transient hyperglycemia preceding the hypoglycemia while other preparations did not show the hyperglycemic effect. Staub and associates (142) prepared crystalline glucagon from a fraction obtained in the commercial purification of insulin. Glucagon is a small-protein hormone composed of 15 different common amino acids, and contains 29 amino acid residues (129). The sequence of amino acids is:

$$NH_2$$
$$|$$
His.Ser. Glu. Gly. Thr. Phe. Thr. Ser. Asp. Tyr. Ser. Lys.
$$NH_2NH_2NH_2$$
$$|||$$
Tyr.Leu.Asp.Ser.Arg.Arg.Ala - Glu. Asp.Phe.Val. Glu.Tyr.Leu.Met. Asp.Thr.

The structure of glucagon is quite different from that of insulin in that only a few dipeptide sequences are similar, and there are no disulfide bridges in glucagon as in insulin (Chapter 8).

Though accumulated evidence indicates that glucagon is secreted by the α-cells of the pancreatic islets, it does not conclusively prove this to be the case (122, p. 42).

Metabolic effects of glucagon. The injection of extremely small quantities of glucagon rapidly causes the breakdown of liver glycogen to glucose and hyperglycemia but does not cause the breakdown of muscle glycogen. As pointed out previously, glucagon causes the conversion of inactive liver phosphorylase b to active phosphorylase a through increasing the formation of cyclic-3',5'-AMP. This action in reactivating phosphorylase, the enzyme which causes glycogenolysis, has been shown to occur in liver preparations at a glucagon concentration of about 1×10^{-8} M.

It may be stated that glucagon functions chiefly to mobilize liver glycogen into blood glucose, which is then utilized in extrahepatic tissues under the influence of insulin. It appears that glucagon has no readily demonstrable effect upon extrahepatic glucose utilization. However, it has been reported (143) that repeated injection of glucagon suspension in rats has a diabetogenic action, with hyperglycemia, glucosuria, increased urinary nitrogen excretion, loss of weight, and death in five to ten days. Also, continuous treatment with large doses in man produces similar diabetogenic effects.

The diabetogenic action of glucagon is indicated by the fact that alloxan diabetic animals, which produce normal amounts of glucagon, require less insulin for maintenance after pancreatectomy, which cuts off the supply of glucagon. Also, the insulin requirements of severe human diabetics is decreased following pancreatectomy.

It appears probable that large doses of glucagon stimulate the adrenal cortex to produce steroid hormones that increase gluconeogenesis from amino acids, with resultant rise in urinary nitrogen excretion. However, it has been reported that glucagon causes increased nitrogen excretion in adrenalectomized rats, in which the adrenal hormones are absent.

It has been demonstrated that glucagon has less hyperglycemic effects when injected into hypophysectomized dogs (118, p. 429) with normal liver glycogen supplies. However, the response to glucagon was restored by treating the animals with ACTH, which stimulates the adrenals to form steroid hormones, or by giving the adrenal cortical hormones cortisone or cortisol to the animals. Thus, it appears that the action of cortical hormones is essential for this normal tissue response to glucagon.

Various other effects of glucagon have been reported, some of them undoubtedly secondary to its primary effect upon the breakdown of liver glycogen and the resulting hyperglycemia and stimulated gluconeogenesis. Berthet (144) has recently reviewed the glucagon problem.

Glucagon may be made radioactive with I^{131} similarly to insulin. Glucagon-I^{131} has been used in studying the distribution and rate of breakdown of glucagon in tissues (122, p. 67). Glucagon is broken down, chiefly in the liver, by proteolysis. Its half-life in tissues appears to be less than 10 minutes (144).

THE ADRENAL GLANDS

The adrenal cortex forms a large number of steroids that have hormonal activity. The ones primarily concerned with carbohydrate metabolism, the glucocorticoids, are corticosterone (11-dehydrocorticosterone), cortisone (17-hydroxy, 11-dehydrocorticosterone), and cortisol (17-hydroxycorticosterone) in order of increasing potency (122, p. 194). The chief glucocorticoids secreted by the adrenal cortex are corticosterone and cortisol, cortisol secretion predominating in man, dog, and monkey.

The adrenal medulla secretes two hormones, epinephrine and norepinephrine, of which epinephrine is significantly involved in the control of carbohydrate metabolism.

That the adrenal glands play an important role in metabolism has been apparent since Addison pointed out that what is now known as "Addison's disease" results from a pathologic condition of these glands.

The experimental work of Long and associates has contributed much to our knowledge of the relations of the adrenal cortex to carbohydrate metabolism (145).

Effects of adrenalectomy upon carbohydrate metabolism. The chief effects of the removal of the adrenal glands upon carbohydrate metabolism are due to removal of the cortex and the hormones secreted by it. These may be summarized as follows:

1. The effects of adrenalectomy upon carbohydrate metabolism are similar in many respects to the effects of hypophysectomy.

2. The blood sugar and tissue glycogen levels of adrenalectomized animals tend to be low. The feeding of adequate carbohydrate enables the blood sugar level to be maintained, but when fasted the animals go into hypoglycemia with severe depletion of liver glycogen. Muscle glycogen is maintained better than in hypophysectomized animals, but is depleted in the severe stages of adrenalectomy. Administration of sodium salts with the food does much to help maintain the carbohydrate levels and life of adrenalectomized animals.

3. Adrenalectomized animals excrete less nitrogen when fasted than do normal animals. Also, phlorizin causes the excretion of less glucose and nitrogen by the fasted adrenalectomized animal than by the fasted normal animal. These facts indicate that cortical hormones function to increase the rate of glucose formation from tissue protein (gluconeogenesis).

4. When normal rats are fasted at low oxygen pressures, their liver glycogen and urinary nitrogen excretion are increased. Adrenalectomized rats do not give these responses. These facts indicate that the cortical hormones function to increase gluconeogenesis from tissue protein when the animal is under stress.

5. Adrenalectomy acts very much as does hypophysectomy in alleviating pancreatic diabetes. Adrenalectomy lowers the blood sugar, sometimes to hypoglycemic levels, and the excretions of glucose, ketone bodies, and nitro-

gen in the urine decrease. The G:N ratio of the adrenalectomized-depancreatized fasting animal may be quite low, though it rises when protein is fed, but to lower values than found in simple depancreatized animals.

Effects of the injection of cortical hormones. 1. The injection of cortical extracts into fasting normal or adrenalectomized animals causes mild hyperglycemia, a striking increase in liver glycogen, and no appreciable change in muscle glycogen. This increase in body carbohydrate is the result of increased gluconeogenesis from tissue protein, as indicated by the increased urinary nitrogen excretion.

2. When cortical extracts are given to a normal animal fed glucose, less of the glucose is oxidized than in the normal untreated animal, but more glycogen is deposited in the liver. The liver glycogen of mice has been found to reach 12 per cent when the animals are liberally fed and given cortical extracts.

3. Insulin convulsions in mice may be prevented by the injection of cortical hormones, which provide sugar through stimulating gluconeogenesis.

4. The diabetic state is increased in severity by the injection of cortical extracts.

5. The injection of cortical extracts prevents the rapid depletion of blood glucose and liver glycogen in fasted hypophysectomized rats and restores these substances if their levels are already depleted. However, the extracts have little effect upon the muscle glycogen of these animals.

Russell (146) restored the muscle glycogen of adrenalectomized rats without appreciably affecting liver glycogen by giving anterior pituitary extracts. Thus it appears that a factor of the adrenal cortex is primarily concerned with maintaining liver glycogen, while a factor of the anterior pituitary is essential for the maintenance of muscle glycogen.

The metabolic effects of adrenal cortical hormones (glucocorticoids). Numerous experiments have shown that the glucocorticoids increase glucose production by the liver by increasing gluconeogenesis from amino acids. When administered to intact fasting animals, liver glycogen stores are markedly increased and blood sugar levels are elevated. At the same time urinary nitrogen increases due to increased breakdown of amino acids. Experiments by De Bodo and associates (118), using the glucose-C^{14} technique described previously, in dogs, indicated a marked decrease in hepatic gluconeogenesis in glucocorticoid deficient animals and a marked increase upon the administration of the hormones.

Glucocorticoids added directly to liver slices in *in vitro* preparations have no significant effect upon gluconeogenesis (direct effect). However, their administration to animals, both normal and diabetic, increases gluconeogenesis (122, p. 199).

The mechanism by which glucocorticoids increase gluconeogenesis from amino acids is uncertain. Do they decrease protein synthesis and make more amino acids available for gluconeogenesis, or do they actively promote tissue protein breakdown into amino acids? It has been reported that adrenalectomy decreases and adrenal extracts increase the amino acid level in the serum of hepatectomized animals (122, p. 205). It also has been reported that adrenalectomy reduces the release of amino nitrogen by the isolated rat diaphragm, and that previous administration of adrenal extracts to the animal restores the release of amino nitrogen by the diaphragm to normal. Evidence has been presented that glucocorticoids enable the rat liver to concentrate amino acids more efficiently. It is of interest that when patients with Cushing's syndrome (adrenal cortical hyperfunction) who show evidence of decreased glucose tolerance (some do not) are compared with cases of severe diabetes, the depletion of body proteins in the hyperadrenal patients is the most striking metabolic difference. This suggests a protein catabolic effect of the cortical hormones.

It is of interest that increased liver transaminase activity has been observed in animals given glucocorticoids for several days. These enzymes are involved in the deamination of amino acids to keto acids in the process of gluconeogenesis.

Although rat diaphragm muscle from adrenalectomized and from diabetic-adrenalectomized rats appears to utilize more glucose than diaphragm from normal and diabetic animals, respectively, no effect of glucocorticoid administration on this utilization has been demonstrated.

Patients with Addison's disease, in which the adrenals are hypofunctional, and show fasting hypoglycemia and decreased urinary nitrogen excretion, are brought toward normal by glucocorticoid administration.

It has been observed that the impaired synthesis of fat by the liver from diabetic animals is restored almost to normal by adrenalectomy, but this is not true of fat synthesis in adipose tissue. The inhibitory effect of glucocorticoids on lipogenesis appears to be of secondary origin and is possibly related to the gluconeogenesis and marked reversal of glycolytic reactions which supply substrates for fat synthesis (122, p. 202).

It has been shown by Scow and associates (147) that cortisone administration to depancreatized rats markedly increases the level of blood ketone bodies, which may be related to increased mobilization of fat from adipose tissues through action of the hormone.

It has long been known that the adrenalectomized animal is hypersensitive to insulin, which is corrected by the glucocorticoids, and that overdosage with the hormones results in decreased sensitivity to insulin. De Bodo and Altszuler (118) suggest that the chronic hyperglycemia resulting from glucocorticoid action leads to chronic hyperinsulinism, and that decreased response is to be expected from the administration of relatively small doses of exogenous insulin. In the adrenalectomized animal with glucocorticoid deficiency the reverse would be expected.

It has been shown (118) that administration of cortisone to rats for five days markedly increases the glucose-6-phosphatase activity of liver homogenates and nuclear, microsomal, and mitochondrial fractions. Since hydrolysis of glucose-6-phosphate is involved in gluconeogenesis through the glycolytic pathway, increased glucose-6-phosphatase activity should favor gluconeogenesis. However, increase in the enzymatic activity appears to be secondary to increased gluconeogenesis, since gluconeogenesis is affected earlier than the activity of the enzyme.

It is very important that the glucocorticoids and other adrenal cortical hormones in their over-all effects put the tissues of an animal in better condition to withstand stress in general. Adrenalectomized animals (cortical insufficiency) exhibit greatly decreased resistance to a variety of stresses, such as temperature changes, infection, trauma, many toxic substances, fasting, and exercise. It is of interest that the responsiveness of tissues to the action of epinephrine is increased within a matter of minutes after the injection of glucocorticoids.

Administration of adrenal 11-oxy steroids, such as cortisone, quickly decreases the production of the anterior pituitary hormone, adrenocorticotropin (ACTH), which stimulates the secretion of the cortical hormones. Thus, the amount of cortical hormones available to the tissues tends to be stabilized by a feedback system.

The metabolic effects of the glucocorticoids are reviewed by Renold and Ashmore (122).

The adrenal medulla. As indicated previously, the adrenal medulla secretes two hormones, epinephrine (adrenaline) and norepinephrine (noradrenaline). These hormones also are formed in postganglionic nerve fibers (chiefly norepinephrine) and are present in the central nervous system. Epinephrine is the hormone of the medulla particularly related to carbohydrate metabolism:

Epinephrine, or adrenaline

Norepinephrine,
Noradrenaline, or Arterenol

It appears that epinephrine and norepinephrine are secreted by the medulla in a ratio of about 5:1. Epinephrine, within the physiologic range, acts as an over-all vasodilator and increases blood pressure by increasing cardiac output, while norepinephrine increases blood pressure by an over-all vasoconstrictor effect, with no or a slight decrease in cardiac output. The action of norepinephrine in breaking down liver glycogen to glucose (hyperglycemic effect) is very much less than that of epinephrine (about one-eighth).

The major effect of epinephrine injection upon carbohydrate metabolism (148) is the rapid breakdown (glycogenolysis) of liver glycogen to glucose with the production of hyperglycemia, and of muscle glycogen to lactic acid, which causes a rapid increase in blood lactate. The lactate is carried to the liver, where it, along with glucose, is slowly converted to glycogen, the level of which may exceed that before epinephrine injection. Part of the lactate reenters the tissues and is oxidized. The hyperglycemic response to epinephrine is not seen when the liver is cut out of the circulation, indicating that only liver glycogen forms glucose as a result of epinephrine action.

The over-all effect of injecting epinephrine into an animal is to quickly raise the blood glucose and lactic acid contents of blood, and in the slower recovery phase to transfer muscle glycogen to liver glycogen (via lactic acid).

The chief physiological function of epinephrine in relation to carbohydrate metabolism is to cause the liberation of extra glucose into the blood stream under conditions of violent effort and emotion, which increase secretion of the hormone through action of the nervous system upon the adrenal glands. This secretion of epinephrine and its metabolic effects thus represent an important reaction to stress. The hormone is not essential to the life of the animal as in case of the cortical hormones. Glucagon of the pancreas apparently is concerned more with the normal physiologic release

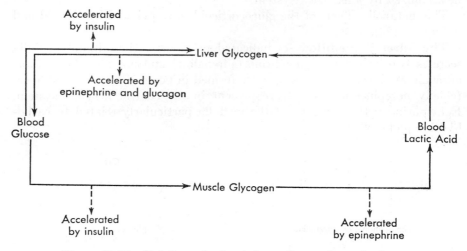

Figure 24.15.   Relations of epinephrine to liver and muscle glycogen.

of glucose from the liver to the blood stream by glycogenolysis than is epinephrine. Epinephrine may be said to represent more of an emergency hormone than does glucagon.

The general effects of epinephrine upon carbohydrate metabolism are shown in Figure 24.15.

As pointed out in discussion of the phosphorylases, the primary action of epinephrine in carbohydrate metabolism is to accelerate the conversion of inactive phosphorylase b to active phosphorylase a by increasing the rate of formation of cyclic-3',5'-AMP, which is required in the conversion. This means that epinephrine, by increasing phosphorylase activity in both muscle and liver, increases the rate of formation of glucose-1-P and glucose-6-P. In liver, glucose-6-P is rapidly hydrolyzed to glucose by the enzyme glucose-6-phosphatase. However, muscle does not contain glucose-6-phosphatase, and consequently the glucose-6-P formed through the action of epinephrine (or otherwise) goes the pathway of glycolysis and produces lactic acid.

Some evidence has accumulated that epinephrine may inhibit the peripheral utilization of glucose, but apparently this action is still rather uncertain (118).

It has been reported that epinephrine increases fat mobilization from adipose tissue (149) and also causes increased formation of ketone bodies and decreased lipogenesis in liver slices (150).

THE ANTERIOR PITUITARY (ADENOHYPOPHYSIS)

The anterior lobe of the pituitary gland secretes a number of hormones having effects upon metabolism. Some of these effects are indirect and caused by tropic hormones, such as adrenocorticotropin (ACTH), which regulates the activity of the adrenal glands and thus controls the production of the glucocorticoids that have pronounced effects upon metabolism which have already been considered. Another tropic hormone having an indirect metabolic effect is the thyrotropic hormone which regulates activity of the thyroid gland and production of thyroxin. Hormones of the anterior pituitary which exert more direct effects upon metabolism are the growth hormone (somatotropin) and prolactin (luteotropin).

It has been known for a long time that the anterior pituitary exerts an effect upon carbohydrate metabolism. Cushing (151) in 1912 noted that acromegalics (pituitary hyperfunction) show reduced carbohydrate tolerance, which at times may approach the severity of true diabetes, and that the capacity of animals to metabolize carbohydrate may be lowered by injection of extracts of the anterior lobe of the pituitary. Geiling and associates (152) showed that hypophysectomized dogs are peculiarly sensitive to the hypoglycemic action of insulin. That insulin and anterior pituitary hormones exert antagonistic effects upon carbohydrate metabolism was strikingly shown by Houssay (153), who demonstrated that removal of the pituitary markedly ameliorates the diabetic state in depancreatized dogs and cats. Houssay also found that the injection of alkaline extracts of the anterior pituitary causes hyperglycemia and glucosuria in a large variety of animals.

The Houssay dog (hypophysectomized-depancreatized) exhibits the following characteristics:

1. When fasted, the Houssay dog has a normal or low blood sugar and excretes little or no glucose in the urine.

2. The administration of glucose orally or by injection, however, causes severe and prolonged hyperglycemia, and glucosuria.

3. The Houssay animal is extremely sensitive to the hypoglycemic action of insulin. The hypophysectomized animal is thrown into hypoglycemic convulsions by a dose of insulin only about one-tenth that required to affect the blood sugar of a normal animal. This sensitivity of the hypophysectomized animal to insulin is abolished by the injection of anterior pituitary extracts. Such extracts given to normal animals produce a condition of

insensitivity to insulin, enabling them to withstand injection of potent doses without appreciable effect upon the blood sugar level.

4. In spite of the sensitivity to insulin, the fed Houssay dog requires insulin to prevent hyperglycemia and glucosuria.

5. Liver glycogen is maintained better by the Houssay animal than by one which has been depancreatized only.

6. The Houssay animal excretes less nitrogen and ketone bodies than the depancreatized animal. When the Houssay animal is fed protein, a considerable amount of the glucose formed from the protein is excreted in the urine. However, the G:N ratios of both fasting and protein-fed Houssay animals are lower than those of depancreatized animals.

7. The injection of saline or alkaline anterior pituitary extracts causes the Houssay animal to revert to the totally diabetic state.

Thus it is seen that hypophysectomy of the diabetic animal ameliorates the diabetic state in that it decreases the blood glucose level, glucosuria, the rate of urinary nitrogen excretion, and the ketosis.

Mathison (154) has reported the case of a severe diabetic female who required 115 units of insulin per day for control. After a severe infection which destroyed the function of the anterior pituitary, she became very sensitive to insulin, required only 8 to 10 units per day, and was subject to repeated attacks of hypoglycemia. This patient represents the human counterpart of an Houssay animal.

Much of our knowledge of the relations of the anterior pituitary to carbohydrate metabolism has been obtained from experiments on hypophysectomized rats and rats injected with anterior pituitary extracts. A review of this work is given by Russell (155).

Metabolic effects of growth hormone. A principal effect of growth hormone, from which it derives its name, is its action in promoting protein synthesis and generalized growth, which will be discussed later on.

The metabolic effects of growth hormone (somatotropin) upon carbohydrate metabolism have been reviewed by De Bodo and Altszuler (118) and by Young and Korner (122, p. 216).

Diabetogenic effect. That the injection of growth hormone has diabetogenic effects in partially depancreatized dogs and cats, and in normal animals has been demonstrated. Young and associates (156) found that normal adult cats treated with purified growth hormone developed a diabetic condition. Evans and associates (157) observed diabetes in normal dogs subjected to prolonged treatment with growth-promoting extracts of the anterior pituitary, and Young (122, p. 218) showed that a permanent diabetic state could be induced in adult dogs by short periods of treatment with such extracts. Campbell and associates (158) produced both temporary and permanent diabetes in dogs by treatment with large doses of growth hormone.

It has been found that growth hormone has marked effects upon pancreatic islet tissue. These include cellular proliferation, β-cell degranulation associated with an increased rate of insulin secretion, and, finally, hydropic degeneration and atrophy. Consequently, it appears that the production of diabetes through treatment of animals with large doses of growth hormone is related to overstimulation and exhaustion atrophy of the β-cells.

It appears possible that the insulin antagonist of the B_1-lipoprotein fraction of plasma, formed under the influence of growth hormone and glucocorticoids (see discussion page 1018) may contribute to the diabetogenic action of large repeated doses of growth hormone.

The administration of growth hormone to hypophysectomized-adrenalectomized dogs was found to ameliorate or abolish insulin hypersensitivity, showing that the adrenal steroids are not necessary for this effect. However, in using growth hormone for replacement therapy in hypophysectomized dogs, it was found that relatively large doses decreased the capacity to use glucose; also, the animals exhibited anorexia (loss of appetite), vomiting, lethargy, and weakness, and some died. Also, with continued treatment the animals showed a progressive decrease in response to the hormone (118). These untoward effects were abolished by prior and concomitant administration of adrenal glucocorticoids. The supply of glucocorticoids in hypophysectomized animals is deficient because of the absence of the adrenal-stimulating ACTH of the hypophysis.

Numerous experiments have been carried out on the effects of growth hormone upon the carbohydrate metabolism of isolated rat diaphragm (118). Park and associates found that intraperitoneal or intravenous injection of small doses of growth hormone into 18 to 24 hour fasted hypophysectomized rats caused immediate hypoglycemia, and also stimulation of glucose uptake by diaphragms from the animals. (This effect may be due to the action of growth hormone protein in protecting insulin in the tissues from degradation (159).) However, in normal rats much greater doses of growth hormone failed to produce hypoglycemia and increased glucose uptake by the diaphragm. The above workers also observed inhibition of glucose uptake by diaphragms from hypophysectomized and normal rats with growth hormone treatment under certain conditions. The effects of growth hormone on glucose utilization by isolated tissues is very complicated and controversial (118).

Glycostatic effect. Russell and associates (160) showed that the gastrocnemius muscle of fasting hypophysectomized rats lost an abnormal amount of glycogen, which was prevented by administration of growth hormone (161). However, in contrast, growth hormone had little effect upon the muscle glycogen of adrenalectomized rats. The effect of growth hormone in maintaining muscle glycogen levels was designated the "glycostatic effect" by Russell.

Effect on glucose production. De Bodo and associates (118), using normal, hypophysectomized, and adrenalectomized dogs on a growth hormone regimen (1 mg per kilogram per day for four or five days), studied the rate of glucose production by the liver with their glucose-C^{14} technique previously described. They found that the hormone raised blood sugar levels and the size of the glucose pools. In addition, the rate of flow of glucose from the liver into the tissues nearly doubled in the normal dog, was raised to normal in the hypophysectomized dog, and was significantly increased in the adrenalectomized animal, which was deficient in steroid hormones.

It appears that the increased release of glucose into the blood under the influence of growth hormone stimulates increased secretion of insulin, which promotes more rapid uptake of glucose by the peripheral tissues.

Effect on fat metabolism (118, p. 406). The tissues of animals treated with anterior pituitary extract or growth hormone showed increased protein formation and decreased fat. Calorimetry and respiratory studies on animals treated with growth hormone showed increased energy production and markedly lowered R.Q. values, signifying increased fat oxidation. Many experiments have shown that the injection of growth hormone is quickly followed by mobilization of fat in the adipose tissues and transport to the liver. Experiments also indicate that treatment with growth hormone *in vivo* inhibits the synthesis of fat from carbohydrate and of fatty acids from acetate.

The over-all effects of growth hormone relative to carbohydrate and fat metabolism in the whole animal may be summarized as follows. Growth hormone causes: (*a*) increased glucose output by the liver, (*b*) increased insulin activity in plasma, (*c*) increased glucose uptake by the peripheral tissues, (*d*) increased mobilization of fat in adipose tissue to the blood with increased transport to the liver, and (*e*) repeated large doses exert a powerful diabetogenic action probably resulting from exhaustion atrophy of the islet β-cells.

Prolactin (luteotropin). Prolactin, also produced in the adenohypophysis, primarily functions to stimulate growth and lactation of the mammary glands. However, it has effects on carbohydrate metabolism resembling some of the effects of growth hormone (118).

Prolactin exerts an antiinsulin effect as shown by amelioration of the insulin hypersensitivity of hypophysectomized animals. De Bodo and associates found that administration of prolactin to hypophysectomized dogs raised the blood sugar level toward normal and reduced the sensitivity of the animals to insulin. However, the effects of prolactin were less marked than those of growth hormone. Houssay and Penhos (162) have demonstrated a diabetogenic effect of prolactin in adrenalectomized-hypophysectomized dogs which had also been partially depancreatized (15–18 per cent of pancreas remaining). Such animals were used to rule out the effect of any ACTH contaminating the prolactin preparation.

By way of summary, it may be stated that prolactin exerts a diabetogenic action which is much less pronounced than that of growth hormone. The mechanisms by which prolactin exerts its effects require clarification.

OTHER HORMONES IN CARBOHYDRATE METABOLISM

Thyroid. Thyroid hormone increases the absorption of glucose, especially galactose, from the intestine, raising the blood sugar level. Observations that patients suffering from hyperthyroidism exhibit hyperglycemia after meals at first were interpreted to indicate reduced capacity to metabolize carbohydrate. However, Althausen (163) showed that this effect is the result of an accelerated rate of sugar absorption from the intestine due to increased thyroid hormone. The postabsorptive blood sugar level of animals treated with thyroxine is normal. The rate of sugar absorption from the intestine is decreased in hypothyroidism.

Excess thyroid hormone causes hypertrophy and hyperplasia of the islet β-cells in rats and some other animals but has little or no effect in others (dogs). Administration of thyroid hormone increases the severity of experimental and human diabetes, glucosuria and ketosis being markedly increased. In patients with both hyperthyroidism and diabetes, thyroidectomy markedly decreases the intensity of the diabetes. At least a part of the diabetogenic action of thyroid hormone is probably related to its stimulation of the general metabolic rate, which in the diabetic, particularly, increases the rate of fat metabolism and production of ketone bodies. Since the rate of protein catabolism is also increased by excessive thyroid hormone, this would lead to increased gluconeogenesis from amino acids in the liver, with increased hyperglycemia and glucosuria.

Sex hormones (122, p. 247). Female sex hormones, or estrogens, such as estrone and estradiol (Chapter 34), ameliorate the diabetic state. They rather rapidly produce hypertrophy and hyperplasia of the islets of Langerhans and β-cells of the pancreas, with increased formation of insulin.

It is of interest that while estrogen treatment of rats increases the insulin content of the pancreas, this does not occur in hypophysectomized animals.

The estrogens have also been found to be diabetogenic in animals with hormonal deficiencies.

The male sex hormone testosterone (an androgen, Chapter 34), markedly increases the severity of diabetes in castrated male and female animals.

CARBOHYDRATE TOLERANCE

The student will realize from the previous discussion of carbohydrate metabolism that the capacity of an animal to metabolize carbohydrate is dependent upon many factors. This capacity for carbohydrate utilization is commonly evaluated by so-called carbohydrate tolerance tests, and the results are expressed in the form of tolerance curves. There are a number of variations in the procedure of conducting tolerance tests, but all depend upon the administration of a definite quantity of glucose, with blood sugar determinations at definite time intervals thereafter. The blood sugar is determined previous to sugar administration in order to provide a basal value. The blood sugar values are then plotted against time to give the tolerance curve.

The so-called standard glucose tolerance test is conducted on patients as follows. The patient, who for three days has eaten a diet containing at least 300 g of carbohydrate per day, reports in the morning without breakfast (postabsorptive state). A sample of venous blood is taken for analysis, and immediately 100 g of glucose in 300 ml of water are given by mouth. Blood samples for sugar analysis are taken at one-half-, one-, two-, and three-hour intervals after the sugar is given. The tolerance curves of Figure 24.16 are characteristic of the normal, mild diabetic, and severe diabetic states. In general, the postabsorptive blood sugar of a normal individual is below 100 mg per cent before the sugar is given, does not rise above 160 mg per cent, and falls to normal values within two hours. The diabetic generally has a postabsorptive blood sugar above 100 mg per cent, which rises higher

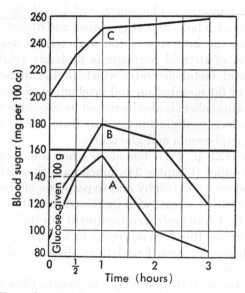

Figure 24.16. Three glucose tolerance curves. *A* depicts the normal glycemic response to the oral administration of 100 g of glucose. The rise in the blood sugar level is rapid, but a normal value is restored in two hours. In *B* the glycemic response is slower, and normal values are not restored until the third hour as is found in mild diabetes. *C* depicts the fasting hyperglycemia and the continued increase in the blood sugar level even at the third hour as seen in severe diabetes. Glycosuria usually occurs when the blood sugar level is maintained (for several hours) above 160 mg per 100 ml as depicted by the heavy black line. (G. G. Duncan, *Diseases of Metabolism*, 2nd ed. W. B. Saunders Company, Philadelphia, 1947.)

than normal after sugar is given and remains elevated for a longer period of time. Minor individual variations in both normal and diabetics are observed. Tolerance curves run on arterial blood from the finger tip are similar to those on venous blood, except that all the sugar values are higher. The difference between the arterial and venous curves is a measure of the rate of sugar utilization in the tissues. This difference decreases with decreased capacity for utilization.

The blood sugar values of a tolerance test are determined by the balance between the rate of sugar absorption from the intestine and the rate at which sugar is removed from the blood by the metabolic processes. As previously indicated, the absorption rate may be increased in hyperthyroidism and decreased in hypothyroidism, and tests run under these conditions must be interpreted accordingly. The difficulty may be circumvented by administering the sugar intravenously, which, however, gives a different type of curve.

Some of the major factors, other than diabetic states, which influence carbohydrate tolerance are given below.

1. Carbohydrate starvation. It is well established that starvation or the ingestion of high fat diets lowers the capacity of the body to utilize carbohydrate, and the ingestion of sugar or high carbohydrate meals after prolonged carbohydrate deprivation may cause hyperglycemia and glucosuria. Tolerance tests conducted under such conditions may give typical diabetic curves. Accordingly, a patient should have a liberal supply of carbohydrate in his diet for a few days before a tolerance test is run. Since it has been demonstrated that secretion of insulin by the pancreas is related to the blood sugar level, increasing with hyperglycemia, it would appear reasonable to assume that the decrease in capacity to utilize carbohydrate as the result of carbohydrate starvation is related to decreased insulin secretion. Although this may be part of the explanation, other factors are concerned. It seems probable that starvation diabetes may represent not only some decreased capacity to secrete insulin, but also decreased efficiency of some or all of the enzyme systems concerned with carbohydrate metabolism.

2. Effect of exercise. Severe exercise for an hour and a half immediately after the ingestion of glucose decreases the hyperglycemia and hastens return of the blood sugar to normal levels. This effect appears to be due to increased carbohydrate utilization as the result of exercise. Violent exercise just before ingestion of glucose, however, exaggerates the hyperglycemia. The exaggerated hyperglycemic response due to exercise before glucose is abolished by the ingestion of large amounts of carbohydrate on the preceding day.

3. Hyperinsulinism. Greatly accelerated utilization of carbohydrate is observed in cases of so-called hyperinsulinism, which may be due to benign or malignant tumors of the islets of Langerhans or to functional hypertrophy and hyperplasia of the islets. Excessive amounts of insulin are secreted under these conditions. Such cases may suffer severe hypoglycemic attacks, which can be alleviated by the administration of carbohydrate. However, in the long-time treatment it has been found best to provide dietary carbohydrate in slowly assimilable forms (starches) and to give a rather high protein diet so that glucose may be slowly formed from the absorbed amino acids. The object is to avoid stimulation of the pancreas by alimentary hyperglycemia as much as possible.

4. Diseases of the liver. Cases of acute yellow atrophy, infectious hepatitis, and other extensive diseases of the liver exhibit abnormal carbohydrate metabolism because of failure of liver function. In such cases the reduced capacity of the liver to form and store glycogen is likely to result in hypoglycemia. The tolerance curves are characterized by a low initial postabsorptive blood sugar level (hypoglycemia) which, after glucose is taken, may resemble the curves of diabetes mellitus. The deficiency here resides in the failure of the liver to convert glucose to glycogen and not in the general capacity to oxidize it in the peripheral tissues.

In 1929 von Gierke described a disease known as glycogenosis, glycogen storage disease, or von Gierke's disease, in which the liver and often the heart contain excessive amounts of glycogen. The disease is congenital and hereditary, and is characterized by retardation of growth and development, fasting hypoglycemia, and a tendency to ketosis. In spite of the tendency to severe fasting hypoglycemia, the blood sugar after oral glucose remains elevated longer than normal, though it does not rise to excessive values. Sufferers from the disease are extremely sensitive to insulin, though epinephrine causes less than normal hyperglycemia. The livers in fatal cases of von Gierke's disease contain practically no glucose-6-phosphatase, the enzyme which converts glucose-6-phosphate derived from glycogen to glucose. The structure of the liver glycogen is normal in these cases. Here we have a disease caused by a deficiency of a specific enzyme.

In some cases of glycogen storage disease, abnormal types of glycogen are present. In one case both liver and muscle glycogens were abnormal. The liver glycogen had very short outer branches, while the muscle glycogen had almost no outer branches. In another case the liver glycogen was less branched and had longer inner and outer chains than normal glycogen, and in general resembled amylopectin. These cases with abnormal glycogens indicate a different type of enzyme deficiency and show that there are different types of the disease.

Acute and chronic infections. That a great variety of infections may decrease carbohydrate tolerance is well established. Hyperglycemia, glucosuria, and reduced carbohydrate tolerance characteristic of moderately severe diabetes may be associated with pyodermic infections such as carbunculosis and furunculosis. The sugar tolerance curve in most infections is generally more or less of the diabetic type, but becomes normal when the infection is cleared up.

Thiamine deficiency. Although various vitamin deficiencies may contribute to some extent to decreased carbohydrate tolerance, only in cases of severe thiamine deficiency is a direct effect apparent. Under these conditions the glucose tolerance curves are abnormally elevated and prolonged. Such an effect is probably related to the function of thiamine pyrophosphate as coenzyme in the oxidation of pyruvic acid.

Nervous disorders. Claude Bernard discovered that puncture of the floor of the fourth ventricle of the brain induces glucosuria, and this condition is referred to as piqûre diabetes. However, a great variety of other injuries to the brain have been found to cause hyperglycemia and glucosuria. In hypophyseal cachexia or Simmond's disease, which is caused by atrophy or degeneration of the anterior lobe of the pituitary, the blood sugar falls to hypoglycemic levels. This effect would be expected as a result of decreasing the anti-insulin effects of the anterior pituitary hormones.

Hypoglycemia and abnormal carbohydrate tolerance curves may be observed in various psychoses (e.g., schizophrenia), general paralysis, and subdural hemorrhage.

Hypoglycemia and increased carbohydrate tolerance may be associated with certain disturbances of the sympathetic nervous system such as neurocirculatory asthenia, vagotonia, and various neuroses. The glucose tolerance curves are abnormally flat (plateau curves) and fall to mild hypoglycemic levels several hours after glucose is given.

Effects of anesthetics and other drugs. General anesthetics and ether in particular raise the blood sugar and diminish carbohydrate utilization. This hyperglycemic effect appears to be due largely to increased epinephrine secretion with resultant increased liver glycogenolysis. Morphine also causes hyperglycemia through stimulation of the adrenal medulla. As expected, ephedrine and other drugs resembling adrenaline exert a similar effect upon carbohydrate metabolism, though they generally have less hyperglycemic action when given in therapeutic doses. Dinitrophenol, which exerts a general calorigenic action upon metabolism, has been found to increase blood sugar and lactic acid and to increase the rate of carbohydrate oxidation.

EFFECTS OF SHOCK ON CARBOHYDRATE METABOLISM

It appears that an effect of shock in general is to cause the rapid depletion of high-energy phosphates in the shocked tissue. Severe shock is generally associated with circulatory collapse and anoxia. This accentuates the breakdown of tissue glycogen and the accumulation of lactic acid.

Effects on the brain are of paramount importance. Anoxia, electric shock, drugs causing convulsions, and cyanide poisoning cause decreases in brain glycogen, glucose, phosphocreatine, and ATP. Brain lactic acid is increased.

GENERAL REFERENCES

Atkinson, M. R., and Morton, R. K.: Free Energy and the Biosynthesis of Phosphates In Florkin, M., and Mason, H. S. (eds.): *Comparative Biochemistry*, Vol. II. Academic Press, New York, 1960.

Calvin, M.: Energy Reception and Transfer in Photosynthesis, and Free Radicals in Photosynthetic Systems. In Oncley, J. L. (ed.): *Biophysical Science—A Study Program.* John Wiley & Sons, New York, 1959, pp. 147–161.

Cori, C. F.: Enzymatic Reactions in Carbohydrate Metabolism, *Harvey Lectures*, **41**, 253, 1945–1946.

Cori, G. T.: Glycogen Structure and Enzyme Deficiencies in Glycogen Storage Disease, *Harvey Lectures*, **48**, 145–171, 1952–1953.

De Bodo, R. C., and Altszuler, N.: Insulin Hypersensitivity and Physiological Insulin Antagonists, *Physiol. Revs.*, **38**, 389, 1958.

Forsham, P. H. (ed.): Current Trends in Research and Clinical Management of Diabetes, *Ann. N. Y. Acad. Sci.*, **82**, Art. 2, 191–644, 1959.

Greenberg, D. M.: *Metabolic Pathways*, Vol. I. Academic Press, New York, 1960.

Hill, R., and Whittingham, C. P.: *Photosynthesis*. John Wiley & Sons, New York, 1955.

Kalckar, H. M., and Maxwell, E. S.: Biosynthesis and Metabolic Function of Uridine Diphosphoglucose in Mammalian Organisms and Its Relevance to Certain Inborn Errors, *Physiol. Revs.*, **38**, 77, 1958.

Korkes, S.: Carbohydrate Metabolism, *Ann. Rev. Biochem.*, **25**, 685, 1956.
Leloir, L. F.; Cardini, C. E.; and Cabib, E.: Utilization of Free Energy for the Biosynthesis of Saccharides. In Florkin, M., and Mason, H. S. (eds.): *Comparative Biochemistry*, Vol. II. Academic Press, New York, 1960.
Mehler, A. H.: *Introduction to Enzymology*. Academic Press, New York, 1957.
Rabinowitch, E.: *Photosynthesis and Related Processes*, Vol. I, 1945; Vol II, Part 1, 1951; Vol. II, Part 2, 1956. Interscience, New York.
Stadie, W. C.: Current Concepts of the Action of Insulin, *Physiol. Revs.*, **34**, 52, 1954.
Stetten, D., Jr. (ed.): Symposium on Disorders of Carbohydrate Metabolism, *Amer. J. Med.*, **26**, 659–760, 1959.
Strominger, J. L.: Mononucleotide Acid Anhydrides and Related Compounds as Intermediates in Metabolic Reactions, *Physiol. Revs.*, **40**, 55, 1960.
Utter, M. F.: Carbohydrate Metabolism, *Ann. Rev. Biochem.*, **27**, 245, 1958.
Vishniac, W.; Horecker, B. L.; and Ochoa, S.: Enzymic Aspects of Photosynthesis, *Advances in Enzymol.*, **19**, 1, 1957.
Williams, R. H. (ed.): *Diabetes*. Paul B. Hoeber, Inc., New York, 1960.

SPECIAL REFERENCES

1. Bollman, J. L.; Mann, F. C.; and Magath, T. B.: *Am. J. Physiol.*, **74**, 238, 1925.
2. Somogyi, M.: *J. Biol. Chem.*, **75**, 33, 1927; **83**, 157, 1929.
3. Somogyi, M.: *J. Biol. Chem.*, **78**, 117, 1928; **103**, 665, 1933.
4. Klinghoffer, K. A.: *Am. J. Physiol.*, **111**, 231, 1935; **130**, 89, 1940.
5. Foster, G. L.: *J. Biol. Chem.*, **55**, 291, 1923.
6. Somogyi, M.: *J. Biol. Chem.*, **179**, 217, 1949.
7. Soskin, S.; Allweiss, M. O.; and Cohn, D. J.: *Am. J. Physiol.*, **109**, 155, 1934. Soskin, S., and Mirsky, I. A.: *ibid.*, **112**, 649, 1935; Soskin, S.; Zimmerman, L. M.; and Heller, R. C.; *ibid.*, **114**, 648, 1936.
8. Mann, F. C.: *Am. J. Med. Sci.*, **161**, 37, 1921.
9. Bollman, J. L., and Mann, F. C.: *Am. J. Physiol.*, **96**, 683, 1931. Drury, D. R., and Salter, W. T.; *ibid.*, **107**, 406, 1934. Griffiths, J. P., and Waters, E. T.: *ibid.*, **117**, 34, 1936.
10. Soskin, S.: *Am. J. Physiol.*, **81**, 382, 1927.
11. Russell, J. A., and Wilhelmi, A. E.: *J. Biol. Chem.*, **140**, 747, 1941.
12. Lennox, W. G.; O'Connor, M.; and Bellinger, M.: *Arch. Internal. Med.*, **38**, 553, 1926.
13. Cori, C. F., and Cori, G. T.: *J. Pharmacol. Exptl. Therap.*, **24**, 465, 1924–25. Cori, G. T.; Closs, J. O.; and Cori, C. F.: *J. Biol. Chem.*, **103**, 13, 1933.
14. Levine, R.; Goldstein, M. S.; Klein, S.; and Huddlestun, B.: *J. Biol. Chem.*, **179**, 985, 1949; *Am. J. Physiol.*, **163**, 70, 1950. Levine, R., and Goldstein, M. S.: *Brookhaven Symposia in Biol.*, **5**, 73, 1952. Goldstein, M. S.; Henry, W. L.; Huddlestun, B.; and Levine, R.: *Am. J. Physiol.*, **173**, 207, 1953.
15. De Duve, C., and Hers, H. G.: *Ann. Rev. Biochem.*, **26**, 149, 1957.
16. Park, C. R.; Reinwein, D.; Henderson, M. J.; Cadenas, E.; and Morgan, H. E.: *Amer. J. Med.*, **26**, 674, 1959.
17. Stadie, W. C.; Haugaard, N.; and Vaughn, M.: *J. Biol. Chem.*, **200**, 745, 1953.
18. Colowick, S. P.; Cori, G.; and Slein, M. W.: *J. Biol. Chem.*, **168**, 583, 1947.
19. Cori, C. F.: Influence of hormones on enzymatic reactions. *First International Congress Biochemistry*, p. 9, 1949.
20. Stadie, W. C.: *Physiol. Revs.*, **34**, 52, 1954.
21. Kipnis, D. M.: *Federation Proc.*, **17**, 254, 1958.
22. Helmreich, E., and Cori, C. F.: *Ciba Foundation Colloquia on Endocrinology*, **9**, 227, 1956.
23. Bernard, C.: *Lecons Sur le diabetes sucre*. Paris, 1877; *Compt. rend. acad. sci.*, **82**, 1351, 1405, 1876; **83**, 369, 407, 1876.
24. Soskin, S., and Levine, R.: *Ccarbohydrate Metabolism*. University of Chicago Press, Chicago, 1946, p. 12.
25. Macleod, J. J. R., and Prendergast, D. J.: *Trans. Roy. Soc. Can.*, **15**, (V), 37, 1921.
26. Junkersdorf, P.: *Pflügers Arch. ges. Physiol.*, **200**, 443, 1923.
27. Good, C. A.; Kramer, H.; and Somogyi, M.: *J. Biol. Chem.*, **100**, 485, 1933.
28. Minkowski, O.: *Arch expt. Path. Pharmakol.*, **31**, 85, 1893.

29. Lusk, G.: *The Science of Nutrition.* W. B. Saunders Co., Philadelphia, 1928, p. 632.
30. Deuel, H. J., Jr.; Wilson, H. E. C.; and Milhorat, A. T.: *J. Biol. Chem.*, **74**, 265, 1927.
31. Janney, N. W.: *J. Biol. Chem.*, **20**, 321, 1915.
32. Wood, H. G.; Lifson, N.; and Lorber, V.: *J. Biol. Chem.*, **159**, 475, 1945; **161**, 411, 1945.
33. Cori, C. F.: *J. Biol. Chem.*, **70**, 577, 1926.
34. Harding, V. J.; Grant, G. A.; and Glaister, D.: *Biochem. J.*, **28**, 257, 1934.
35. Deuel, H. J., Jr.; MacKay, E. M.; Jewel, P. W.; Gulick, M.; and Grunewald, C. F.: *J. Biol. Chem.*, **101**, 301, 1933.
36. Schöndorff, B.: *Pflügers Arch. ges. Physiol.*, **99**, 191, 1903.
37. Mirski, A.; Rosenbaum, I.; Stein, L.; and Wertheimer, E.: *J. Physiol. (London)*, **92**, 48, 1938.
38. Fischer, N. F., and Lackey, W. R.: *Am. J. Physiol.*, **72**, 43, 1925.
39. Külz, E.: *Festschrift zu Ludwig.* Marburg, Germany, 1891, p. 109.
40. Dudley, H. W., and Marrian, G. F.: *Biochem. J.*, **17**, 435, 1923.
41. Best, C. H.; Hoet, J. P.; and Marks, H. P.: *Proc. Roy. Soc. (London)*, B100, 32, 1926.
42. Elias, H.: *Biochem. Z.*, **48**, 120, 1912–13.
43. Meyerhof, O.: *Pflügers Arch. ges. Physiol.*, **175**, 82, 1919.
44. Euler, H. von, and Adler, E.: *Z. Physiol. Chem.*, **235**, 122, 1935.
45. Berger, L.; Slein, M. W.; Colowick, S. P.; and Cori, C. F.: *J. Gen. Physiol.*, **29**, 141, 1946.
46. Racker, E.: *Advances in Enzymology*, **15**, 141, 1954.
47. Gamble, J. L., Jr., and Najjar, V. A.: *J. Biol. Chem.*, **217**, 595, 1955.
48. Leloir, L. F.: *Phosphorus Metabolism*, **1**, 67, 1951.
49. Najjar, V. A., and Pullman, M. E.: *Science*, **119**, 631, 1954.
50. Palladini, A. C.; Caputto, R.; Leloir, L. F.; Trucco, R. E.; and Cardini, C. E.: *Arch. Biochem.*, **23**, 55, 1949.
51. Sidbury, J. B., Jr.; Rosenberg, L. L.; and Najjar, V. A.: *J. Biol. Chem.*, **222**, 89, 1956.
52. Lohmann, K.: *Biochem. Z.*, **262**, 137, 1933.
53. Ling, K., and Lardy, H. A.: *J. Am. Chem. Soc.*, **76**, 2842, 1954.
54. Hers, H. G., and Kusaka, T.: *Biochim. et Biophys. Acta*, **11**, 427, 1953.
55. Kalckar, H. M.: *Advances in Enzymology*, **20**, 111, 1958. Kalckar, H. M., and Maxwell, E. S.: *Physiol. Revs.*, **38**, 77, 1958. Strominger, J. L.: *Physiol. Revs.*, **40**, 55, 1960.
56. Blakley, R. L.: *Biochem. J.*, **49**, 257, 1951. Hers, H. G.: *Biochim. et Biophys. Acta*, **22**, 202, 1956.
57. Roseman, S.: *Ann. Rev. Biochem.*, **28**, 545, 1959. See also ref. 54.
58. Strominger, J. L.: *Physiol. Revs.*, **40**, 55, 1960.
59. Leloir, L. F.; Cardini, C. E.; and Cabib, E.: In *Comparative Biochemistry*, Vol. II, p. 97, Florkin, M., and Mason, H. S., (eds.). Academic Press, New York, 1960.
60. Cori, C. F.: Enzymatic Reactions in Carbohydrate Metabolism, *Harvey Lectures*, 41, 253, 1945–46. Cori, G. T., and Larner, J.: *J. Biol. Chem.*, **188**, 17, 1951.
61. Leloir, L. F., and Cardini, C. E.: *J. Am. Chem. Soc.*, **79**, 6340, 1957. Leloir, L. F., and Goldenberg, S. H.: *J. Biol. Chem.*, **235**, 919, 1960. See also Robbins, P. W., and Lipmann, F.: Recent Observations on the Mechanism of Glycogen Synthesis in Muscle in Regulation of Cell Metabolism, *Ciba Foundation Symposium*, Wolstenholme, G. E. W., and O'Connor, C. M. (eds.) Little, Brown & Co., Boston, 1959, p. 188.
62. Green, A. A., and Cori, G. T.: *J. Biol. Chem.*, **151**, 21, 1943.
63. Keller, P. J., and Cori, G. T.: *J. Biol. Chem.*, **214**, 127, 135, 1955.
64. Cori, C. F., and Illingworth, B.: *Proc. Natl. Acad. Sci. U.S.*, **43**, 547, 1957.
65. Rall, T. W., and Sutherland, E. W.: *J. Biol. Chem.*, **232**, 1065, 1077, 1958; *J. Am. Chem. Soc.*, **79**, 3608, 1957.
66. Krebs, E. G.; Kent, A. B.; and Fischer, E. H.: *J. Biol. Chem.*, **231**, 73, 1958.
67. Sutherland, E. W., and Wosilait, W. D.: *J. Biol. Chem.*, **218**, 459, 1956.
68. Larner, J.: *J. Biol. Chem.*, **202**, 491, 1953.
69. Cori, G. T., and Larner, J.: *J. Biol. Chem.*, **188**, 17, 1951. Larner, J.; Illingworth, B.; Cori, G. T.; and Cori, C. F.: *J. Biol. Chem.*, **199**, 641, 1952. Also see Stetten, D., Jr., et al.: *J. Biol. Chem.*, **213**, 723, 1955; **222**, 587, 1956.

70. Niemeyer, H.: *Metabolismo de los hidratos de carbono en el higado*. (Imprenta Universitaria, Santiago, Chile, 159 pp., 1955.) See De Duve, C., and Hers, H. G.: *Ann. Rev. Biochem.*, **26**, 168, 1957.
71. Leuthardt, F., and Wolf, H. P.: *Helv. Physiol. et Pharmacol. Acta*, **13**, C20, 1955.
72. Rose, I. A., and Rieder, S. V.: *J. Am. Chem. Soc.*, **77**, 5764, 1955. Bloom, B., and Topper, Y. J.: *Science*, **124**, 982, 1956.
73. Racker, E., and Krimsky, I.: *J. Biol. Chem.*, **198**, 731, 1952.
74. Cori, O.; Traverso-Cori, A.; Lagarrigue, M.; and Marcus, F.: *Biochem. J.*, **70**, 633, 1958.
75. Sutherland, E. W.; Posternak, T.; and Cori, C. F.: *J. Biol. Chem.*, **181**, 153, 1949.
76. Warburg, O., and Christian, W.: *Biochem. Z.*, **310**, 384, 1942.
77. Oesper, P., and Meyerhof, O.: *Arch. Biochem.*, **27**, 223, 1950.
78. Krebs, H. A., and Kornberg, H. L.: *Energy Transformations in Living Matter. A Survey*. Springer, Berlin, 1957.
79. Lynen, F.: *Ann. Chem.*, **546**, 120, 1941. Johnson, M. J.: *Science*, **94**, 200, 1941.
80. Ashmore, J., and Weber, G.: *Vitamins and Hormones*, **17**, 91, 1959.
81. Hiatt, H. H.; Goldstein, M.; Lareau, J.; and Horecker, B. L.: *J. Biol. Chem.*, **231**, 303, 1958.
82. Mirski, I. A., and Nelson, N.: *Am. J. Physiol.*, **127**, 308, 1939.
83. Stotz, E.: *J. Biol. Chem.*, **148**, 585, 1943.
84. Block, K., and Rittenberg, D.: *J. Biol. Chem.*, **155**, 243, 1944.
85. Burton, R. M., and Stadtman, E. R.: *J. Biol. Chem.*, **202**, 873, 1953.
86. Westerfeld, W. W.; Stotz, E.; and Berg, R. L.: *J. Biol. Chem.*, **144**, 657, 1952.
87. Leloir, L. F., and Muñoz, J. M.: *Biochem. J.*, **32**, 299, 1938.
88. Stetten, D., Jr., and Boxer, G. E.: *J. Biol. Chem.*, **155**, 231, 237, 1944; **156**, 271, 1944. Stetten, D., Jr., and Stetten, M. R.: *ibid.*, **165**, 147, 1946. Stetten, D., Jr., and Klein, B. V.: *ibid.*, **165**, 157, 1946.
89. Solomon, A. K.; Vennesland, B.; Klemperer, F. W.; Buchanan, J. M.; and Hastings, A. B.: *J. Biol. Chem.*, **140**, 171, 1941.
90. Wood, H. G.; Lifson, N.; and Lorber, V.: *J. Biol. Chem.*, **159**, 475, 1945; **161**, 411, 1945.
91. Wood, H. G.: In *Symposium on the Use of Isotopes in Biology and Medicine*, p. 209, University of Wisconsin Press, Madison, 1948.
92. Meyerhof, O.: *Bull. soc. chim. biol.*, **31**, 1096, 1939. Parnas, J. K.: *Enzymologia*, **5**, 166, 1938–1939; *Bull. soc. chim. biol.*, **31**, 1059, 1939. Hevesy, G.: *Enzymologia*, **5**, 138, 1938–1939; *Ann. Rev. Biochem.*, **9**, 641, 1940.
93. Racker, E.: *Advances in Enzymol.*, **15**, 141, 1954; *Harvey Lectures*, **51**, 143, 1957. Horecker, B. L., and Mehler, A. H.: *Ann. Rev. Biochem.*, **24**, 207, 1955. Cohen, S. S., in *Chemical Pathways in Metabolism*, Vol. I, p. 173, Greenberg, D. M. (ed.). Academic Press, New York, 1954. Wood, H. G.: *Physiol. Revs.*, **35**, 841, 1955.
94. Bloom, B., and Stetten, D., Jr.: *J. Am. Chem. Soc.*, **75**, 5446, 1953.
95. Muntz, J. A., and Murphy, J. R.: *J. Biol. Chem.*, **224**, 971, 1957.
96. Wood, H. G.: *Physiol. Revs.*, **35**, 841, 1955.
97. Abraham, S.; Hirsch, P. F.; and Chaikoff, I. L.: *J. Biol. Chem.*, **211**, 31, 1954. Coxon, R. V., and Robinson, R. J.: *Proc. Roy. Soc.*, **145B**, 232, 1956.
98. Holzer, H.: *Ann. Rev. Biochem.*, **28**, 171, 1959. Touster, O.: *Amer. J. Med.*, **26**, 724, 1959. Burns, J. J.: *ibid.*, **26**, 740, 1959.
99. Touster, O.: *Amer. J. Med.*, **26**, 724, 1959.
100. Touster, O.; Mayberry, R. H.; and McCormick, D. B.: *Biochim. et Biophys. Acta*, **25**, 196, 1957.
101. Touster, O., and Harwell, S. O.: *J. Biol. Chem.*, **230**, 1031, 1958.
102. McCormick, D. B., and Touster, O.: *J. Biol. Chem.*, **229**, 451, 1957.
103. Dayton, P. G.; Eisenberg, F., Jr.; and Burns, J. J.: *Federation Proc.*, **17**, 209, 1958.
104. Burns, J. J.: *Amer. J. Med.*, **26**, 740, 1959.
105. Vishniac, W.; Horecker, B. L.; and Ochoa, S.: *Advances in Enzymol.*, **19**, 1, 1957.
106. Noggle, G. R.: In *The Carbohydrates*, Pigman, W. (ed.), p. 733. Academic Press, New York, 1957.
107. Calvin, M.: In *Biophysical Science—A Study Program*, Oncley, J. L. (ed.), pp. 147, 157. John Wiley & Sons, New York, 1959.
108. Hill, R., and Whittingham, C. P.: *Photosynthesis*. Metheun & Co., London, 1955.
109. Franck, J., and Loomis, W. E.: *Photosynthesis in Plants*. Iowa State College Press, Ames, 1949.

110. Emerson, R., and Lewis, C. M.: *J. Gen. Physiol.*, **25**, 579, 1942.
111. Willstätter, R.: *J. Am. Chem. Soc.*, **37**, 323, 1915.
112. Fischer, H., and Breitner, S.: *Ann.*, **522**, 151, 1936. Bauer, K.: *ibid.*, **523**, 235, 1936.
113. Warburg, O., et al.: *Z. Naturforsch.*, **8b**, 675, 1953; **11b**, 654, 1956.
114. Hill, R.: *Advances in Enzymol.*, **12**, 1, 1951.
115. Vishniac, W., and Ochoa, S.: *J. Biol. Chem.*, **198**, 501, 1952.
116. Atkinson, M. R., and Morton, R. K.: In *Comparative Biochemistry*, Vol. II p. 1, Florkin, M., and Mason, H. S. (eds.). Academic Press, New York, 1960.
117. Bornstein, J.: *Australian J. Exp. Biol. Med. Sci.*, **28**, 87, 1950.
118. De Bodo, R. C., and Altszuler, N.: *Physiol. Revs.*, **38**, 389, 1958.
119. Stadie, W. C.: *Physiol. Revs.*, **34**, 52, 1954.
120. Symposium on Disorders of Carbohydrate Metabolism, *Amer. J. Med.*, **26**, 662–760, 1959.
121. Current Trends in Research and Clinical Management of Diabetes, *Ann. N. Y. Acad. Sci.*, **82**, Art. 2, 195–643, 1959.
122. Williams, R. H. (ed.): *Diabetes*. Paul B. Hoeber, Inc., New York, 1960.
123. Mering, J. von: *Verhandl. Kong. Inn. Med.*, **5**, 185, 1886. Minkowski, O.: *Arch. exptl. Path. Pharmakol.*, **31**, 85, 1893.
124. Banting, F. G., and Best, C. H.: *J. Lab. Clin. Med.*, **7**, 251, 1922.
125. Macleod, J. J. R.: *J. Metabolic Research*, **2**, 149, 1922.
126. Banting, F. G.; Best, C. H.; Collip, J. B.; Hepburn, J.; MacLeod, J. J. R.; and Noble, E. C.: *Trans. Roy. Soc., Canada*, 16(V), 1, 1922.
127. Somogyi, M.; Doisy, E. A.; and Shaffer, P. A.: *J. Biol. Chem.*, **60**, 31, 1924.
128. Abel, J. J.: *Proc. Natl. Acad. Sci. U.S.*, **12**, 132, 1926. Abel, J. J., et al.: *J. Pharmacol. Exptl. Therap.*, **31**, 65, 1927.
129. Behrens, O. K., and Bromer, W. W.: *Ann. Rev. Biochem.*, **27**, 57, 1958.
130. Bueding, E.; Fazekas, J. F.; Herrlich, H., and Himwich, H. E.: *J. Biol. Chem.*, **148**, 97, 1943.
131. Himwich, W. A., and Himwich, H. E.: *J. Biol. Chem.*, **165**, 513, 1946.
132. Lukens, F. D.: *Ann. Internal Med.*, **8**, 727, 1934.
133. Mirsky, I. A.; Heiman, J. D.; and Broh-Kahn, R. H.: *Am. J. Physiol.*, **118**, 290, 1937.
134. De Bodo, R. C.; CoTui, R.; and Farber, L.: *Am. J. Physiol.*, **103**, 18, 1933.
135. Soskin, S., and Levine, M. D.: *Carbohydrate Metabolism*. University of Chicago Press, Chicago, 1946.
136. Day, H. G., and Pigman, W.: Carbohydrates in Nutrition, in *The Carbohydrates*, p. 787, Pigman, W. (ed.). Academic Press, New York, 1957.
137. Madison, L. L.; Combes, B.; Strickland, W.; Unger, R.; and Adams, R.: *Metabolism*, **8**, 469, 1959.
138. Reichard, C. A., Jr.; Jacobs, A. G.; Friedman, B.; Kimbel, P. R.; Hochella, N. J.; and Weinhouse, S.: *Metabolism*, **8**, 486, 1959.
139. Ashmore, J.; Hastings, A. B.; and Nesbett, F. B.: *Proc. Natl. Acad. Sci. U.S.*, **40**, 673, 1954. Langdon, R. G., and Weakley, D. R.: *J. Biol. Chem.*, **214**, 167, 1955. Ashmore, J., and Weber, G.: *Vitamins and Hormones*, **17**, 91, 1959.
140. Behrens, O. K., and Bromer, W. W.: *Ann. Rev. Biochem.*, **27**, 64, 1958.
141. Mirsky, I. A., and Broh-Kahn, R. H.: *Arch. Biochem. Biophys.*, **20**, 1, 1949.
142. Staub, A.; Sinn, L. G.; and Behrens, O. K.: *J. Biol. Chem.*, **214**, 619, 1955.
143. Salter, J. M.; Davidson, I. W. F.; and Best, C. H.: *Diabetes*, **6**, 248, 1957.
144. Berthet, J.: *Amer. J. Med.*, **26**, 703, 1959.
145. Long, C. N. H.: *Harvey Lectures*, **32**, 194, 1936–37; *Endocrinology*, **30**, 870, 1942.
146. Russell, J. A.: *Am. J. Physiol.*, **128**, 552, 1940.
147. Scow, R. O.; Chernick, S. S.; and Guarco, B. A.: *Federation Proc.*, **17**, 144, 1958.
148. Cori, C. F., and Cori, G. T.: *J. Biol. Chem.*, **74**, 473, 1927; **79**, 309, 321, 343, 1928.
149. Wool, I. G.; Goldstein, M. S.; Ramey, E. R.; and Levine, R.: *Am. J. Physiol.*, **178**, 427, 1954.
150. Haugaard, E. S., and Stadie, W. C.: *J. Biol. Chem.*, **199**, 741, 1952; **200**, 753, 1953. Haugaard, E. S., and Haugaard, N.: *ibid.*, **206**, 641, 1954.
151. Cushing, H.: *The Pituitary Body and Its Disorders*. J. B. Lippincott Co., Philadelphia, 1912.
152. Geiling, E. M. K.; Campbell, D.; and Ishikawa, Y.: *J. Pharmacol. Exp. Therap.*, **31**, 247, 1927.
153. Houssay, B. A.: *New Engl. J. Med.*, **214**, 971, 1936.

154. Mathison, H. S.: *Acta Med. Scand.*, **145**, 326, 1953.
155. Russell, J. A.: *Physiol. Revs.*, **18**, 1, 1938.
156. Cotes, P. M.; Reid, E.; and Young, F. G.: *Nature (London)*, **164**, 209, 1949.
157. Evans, H. M.; Meyer, K.; Simpson, M. E.; and Reichert, F. L.: *Proc. Soc. Exp. Biol. Med.*, **29**, 857, 1932.
158. Campbell, J.; Davidson, I. W. F.; and Lei, H. P.: *Endocrinology*, **46**, 588, 1950.
Campbell, J.; Davidson, I. W. F.; Snair, W. D.; and Lei, H. P.: *ibid.*, **46**, 273, 1950.
159. Narahara, H. T., and Williams, R. H.: *J. Biol. Chem.*, **233**, 1034, 1958.
160. Russell, J. A., and Bennett, L. L.: *Am. J. Physiol.*, **118**, 196, 1937.
161. Russell, J. A., and Wilhelmi, A. E.: *Endocrinology*, **47**, 26, 1950.
162. Houssay, B. A., and Penhos, J. C.: *Endocrinology*, **59**, 637, 1956.
163. Althausen, T. L.: *J. Clin. Invest.*, **16**, 658, 1937.

25

Protein metabolism

Proteins are the chief organic components of cellular structure and organization. Each animal species and each type of tissue is characterized by its own specific kinds of proteins. In fact, it may be stated that variations in proteins, directly or indirectly, form the basis for the variations in animal species and tissue types. Just as proteins are primary constituents of the body machinery, they are also the constituents of tissues, in the forms of enzymes and hormones, which are chiefly concerned with regulating the chemical processes that operate this body machinery. The proteins of blood plasma aid in controlling the distribution of fluids in the body and also provide antibodies (plasma γ-globulins) to combat disease. The chief protein of the erythrocytes of blood, hemoglobin, serves to transport oxygen from the lungs to the tissues. In addition to these functions, proteins, like carbohydrates and fats, serve as a source of energy for the body.

The metabolism of proteins essentially is the metabolism of amino acids. Food proteins are digested to amino acids in the gastrointestinal tract, and these amino acids then pass into the portal blood stream and to the liver. The liver removes a certain proportion of amino acids to supply its own needs and adds amino acids which it has synthesized to the blood. Also, the tissue proteins are continually undergoing breakdown (catabolism), which adds amino acids to the blood. The blood amino acids thus arise from absorption, synthesis, and tissue catabolism and represent an amino acid pool which can be drawn upon for all purposes of protein metabolism. Each tissue of the body takes from this pool the specific amino acids in the proper proportions and synthesizes them into the kinds of proteins which are required for growth, maintenance, and proper function. Also, many nitrogenous nonprotein substances essential to tissue operation, such as creatine, choline, and glutathione, are formed from amino acids drawn from the pool. Amino acids in excess of the requirements for the formation of structural tissue proteins, enzymes, hormones, etc., are deaminized in the liver to form ammonia and keto acids. The ammonia is converted to urea, which is excreted in the urine. The liver converts some of the keto acids to ketone bodies and others to glucose, which are metabolized according to the processes of fat and carbohydrate metabolism already considered. All the keto acids derived from amino acids eventually are oxidized to carbon dioxide and water and yield utilizable energy in the form of ATP.

Some of the amino acids, cystine, methionine, and cysteine, contain sulfur, which is split out in the processes of metabolic breakdown.

The metabolism of the nucleic acids of nucleoproteins yields phosphate and purine bases, adenine, and guanine, which in man and some other animals are converted to uric acid and excreted as such in the urine.

A part of the urinary phosphate arises from the phosphoric acid of phosphoproteins in their metabolic breakdown. It appears that the phosphorus of phosphoproteins is largely if not entirely represented by the phosphate ester of serine present in the proteins.

Excepting carbon dioxide, most of the waste products of protein metabolism are excreted in the urine. Urea represents the larger proportion of the nitrogen excreted, the remainder being in the form of uric acid, creatinine, ammonia, and very small amounts of many other nitrogenous substances.

Since nitrogen is the most characteristic and constant element of proteins and of the products of protein metabolism, and since it is readily determined by the Kjeldahl method of analysis, it is possible to determine the over-all protein metabolism of an animal by determining the so-called nitrogen balance. In order to do this, the nitrogen contents of the food eaten and of the waste products excreted (urine and feces) in a given time are obtained. If the nitrogen of the food exceeds that excreted, the body is retaining nitrogen, chiefly as tissue protein, and the animal is said to be in positive nitrogen balance. Animals are in positive nitrogen balance during the period of growth and during recovery from emaciating illnesses when the processes of tissue formation (anabolism) exceed those of tissue breakdown (catabolism). If the nitrogen excreted equals that of the food eaten, the animal is in nitrogen balance; this means that the rates of tissue anabolism and catabolism are equal. This is the condition of the normal adult. If the nitrogen excreted exceeds that of the food eaten, the animal is in negative nitrogen balance; the tissue proteins are being broken down faster than they are formed. Negative nitrogen balances are observed during emaciating illnesses, starvation, and when an animal is fed a diet containing an insufficient amount of protein or protein of poor quality (lacking essential amino acids). The question of nitrogen balance in relation to dietary protein will be discussed in detail in Chapter 28.

The general relations of protein metabolism are given in Figure 25.1.

Figure 25.1. Protein metabolism.

AMINO ACIDS OF BLOOD, TISSUES, AND URINE

Blood. As already indicated, the amino acids of blood arise from absorption, synthesis, and tissue breakdown. Some or all of these processes are continually adding amino acids to blood. Also, amino acids are continually being withdrawn from blood for the synthesis of tissue proteins and other nitrogenous compounds and for oxidation to yield energy. Consequently, the amino acid level of blood, like the levels of blood sugar and all other blood constituents, is determined by the balance between the rates of addition and removal.

Table 25.1 gives the free amino acid content (range) of human blood plasma (1).

Table 25.1.   Free Amino Acids of Human Blood Plasma (mg/100 ml)

Amino Acid		Amino Acid	
Alanine	3.4–4.2	Leucine	1.7–2.4
α-Aminobutyric	0.2–0.3	Lysine	2.2–3.0
Arginine	1.5–2.5	Methionine	0.3–0.9
Asparagine	1.0–1.4	Ornithine	0.6–0.8
Aspartic acid	0.01–0.07	Phenylalanine	0.8–1.9
Citrulline	0.5	Proline	2.4–2.9
Cystine	1.0–2.0	Serine	1.0–1.3
Glutamic acid	0.7–4.4	Threonine	1.3–3.1
Glutamine	5.8–9.7	Tryptophan	1.1–1.7
Glycine	1.1–2.8	Tyrosine	1.0–1.5
Histidine	1.0–2.1	Valine	2.7–3.4
Isoleucine	0.9–1.8		
Total		32.3–55.1	

The amino acids of erythrocytes are not in simple diffusion equilibrium with those of plasma. Messing (2) found that the amino acid concentration of dog erythrocytes did not rise until the plasma amino acid level was far above normal. Leucocytes contain more amino acids than do erythrocytes. The amide of glutamic acid, glutamine, represents a relatively very large proportion of the amino acid content of plasma. Its concentration in tissues is also high.

Hier (3) has followed the plasma level of arginine, histidine, leucine, isoleucine, methionine, phenylalanine, tyrosine, threonine, tryptophan, and valine in dogs when each of the amino acids was given by stomach tube. The plasma concentration of an amino acid rose after being given, generally reached a maximum in 60 minutes, and fell to normal in 24 hours.

It is interesting to note the effects, in certain cases, of administering one amino acid upon the plasma level of others. For example, when leucine was given, the plasma levels of arginine, isoleucine, methionine, phenylalanine, threonine, tyrosine, and valine were decreased, though only the urinary excretion of leucine was increased. This effect may be the result of a mass action of leucine in increasing the rates of syntheses involving the other amino acids.

The administration of phenylalanine caused an increase in plasma tyrosine, but the reverse was not true. This is in accord with the fact that the animal can form tyrosine from phenylalanine but cannot reverse the process.

The effect of methionine was interesting in that the plasma level of the amino acid remained many times above normal even 24 hours after administration, indicating a slow rate of metabolism.

Various factors affect the blood amino acid level. The ingestion of a protein meal in the postabsorptive state generally increases the whole blood amino nitrogen 2 to 6 mg per cent, the rise beginning shortly after the meal and usually falling to normal within 4 hours. Age and sex appear to have little effect, though values for infants and young children appear to be definitely lower than for adults. This is probably related to the more rapid utilization of amino acids for tissue formation by the young than by the adult. Prolonged starvation does not lower the blood amino acids below the postabsorptive level but, on the contrary, appears to cause a slight increase. This is probably due to an increased rate of tissue protein utilization for energy production in the starving animal. The injection of insulin causes a marked fall in blood amino acids paralleling the fall in blood sugar. Small increases in blood amino acids have been observed in diabetes. Diseases of the liver, such as acute yellow atrophy, in which there is a large amount of liver destruction, may cause a very great increase in blood amino acids due to failure of the deamination process. Also, blood amino acids may be elevated in the terminal stages of chronic glomerular nephritis and advanced arterial disease with renal failure. Man (4) has found the blood amino acids to be low after severe injury and operations and during serious infections.

The fact that hydrolysis of protein-free filtrates of blood causes some increase in α-amino nitrogen is taken as evidence for the presence of peptides.

Tissue amino acids. In general, tissues contain 5 to 10 times as much amino acids as blood. Van Slyke and Meyer (5) found that the muscles of the dog can take up amino acid nitrogen to a saturation level of about 75 mg per cent (about 500 mg per cent of amino acids), and the liver can take up much more. The amino acids of tissues and blood rapidly exchange, though this exchange is not due to simple diffusion because the concentration in tissues is always much higher than in blood. Tissue amino acids do not represent a storage reserve as glycogen does, since during starvation their concentration may actually be increased above normal. This is probably a reflection of the increased rate of tissue protein catabolism during starvation.

It may be considered that each type of tissue contains an amino acid pool from which amino acids are taken by the tissue cells for metabolic processes and to which amino acids are added by catabolism of tissue proteins, synthesis by certain tissues, and absorption from the blood (through the interstitial fluid). The amino acid pool of the body is thus composed of many separate and distinct tissue pools linked through the blood and interstitial fluid pools.

Amino acids of urine. In general, the free α-amino nitrogen of urine amounts to only 1 to 2 per cent of the total nitrogen. Hier and associates (6) have determined the 24-hour urinary excretion of a number of amino acids by 18 normal human subjects, generally on a normal diet. Both free and combined amino acids (liberated by hydrolysis) were determined. Their results are summarized in Table 25.2. It will be noted that many of the amino acids

Table 25.2.   Amino Acid Excretion in the Urine of Normal Human Subjects
Figures represent mean values in milligrams per 24 hours.

Amino Acid	Total	Free	Combined
Arginine	23.7	21.3	2.4
Histidine	203.3	188.3	15.0
Lysine	73.2	33.6	39.6
Aspartic acid	164.5	1.3	163.2
Glutamic acid	351.4	35.8	315.6
Glycine	463.0	—	—
Serine (egg diet)	27.0	—	—
Leucine	21.2	9.6	11.6
Isoleucine	21.3	5.9	15.4
Methionine	8.6	7.8	0.8
Cystine	—	87.7	—
Phenylalanine	23.3	16.4	6.9
Tyrosine	52.5	20.8	31.7
Proline	42.8	8.5	34.3
Threonine	53.8	24.4	29.4
Tryptophan	41.4	24.6	16.8
Valine	19.8	4.5	15.3
Totals	1590.8	490.5	698.0

From Woodson, H. W.; Hier, S. W.; Solomon, J. D.; and Bergeim, O.: *J. Biol. Chem.*, **172**, 615, 1948.

were excreted largely in the combined form. This amounted to about 99 per cent of the aspartic acid, 90 per cent of the glutamic acid, 71 per cent of the isoleucine, 80 per cent of the proline, and 77 per cent of the valine. The combined amino acids represented peptides and conjugates such as glycine with benzoic acid (hippuric acid).

Considering the very large quantities of amino acids transported by the blood per day, the tubular reabsorption of amino acids in the kidney is relatively efficient, but not so efficient as the reabsorption of glucose. Table 25.2 shows that the capacity of the kidneys to reabsorb varies widely with different amino acids—for example, only 1.3 mg of free aspartic acid being excreted, as compared with the excretion of 188 mg of free histidine.

The urinary excretion of amino acids increases with increased blood levels and without any definite kidney threshold as exhibited for glucose.

Dunn and associates (7) studied the urinary excretion of free tryptophan, histidine, and cystine by 57 pathologic individuals and found it to be high in diabetes, pregnancy, acute infection, and liver disease, in all of which elevated blood amino acid levels are to be expected.

Transport of amino acids into cells. Christensen (8) has reviewed the problem of amino acid transport into tissue cells. As previously noted, the amino acid concentration in cells generally is much higher than in the extracellular fluid, which means that the amino acids are moved into the cells against concentration gradients, requiring energy; that is, the process is an example of what is called active transport. Factors such as anoxia, lowered temperature, and tissue respiratory inhibitors, which decrease energy production, also decrease amino acid transport into cells. The degree to which amino acids are concentrated in cells over their levels in plasma varies widely with the chemical composition of the amino acid and the type of cell. Christensen and associates have presented evidence that pyridoxal promotes transport of amino acids into cells, possibly through combination with the amino acids. The movement of amino acids from extracellular to intracellular fluid is accompanied by a flow of water into the cell, a passage of K^+ from the cell, and a compensatory movement of Na^+ into the cell. Also, a high concentration of extracellular K^+ inhibits amino acid transport into cells. Thus, it appears that there is a mutual interference between the active transport processes of amino acids and of Na^+ and K^+.

The amino acid pool. As previously pointed out, amino acids are continuously being added to body fluids by absorption from the intestine, synthesis, and the breakdown of tissue proteins. Also, they are being removed continually for synthesis of tissue protein and other uses. The size of the amino acid pool (amount of free amino acids in the body) represents the balance between these processes. Pietro and Rittenberg (9) administered N^{15}-labeled glycine and aspartic acid to human beings and determined the metabolic pool of these amino acids and the rate of their use in protein synthesis. One individual (68 kg) showed a glycine nitrogen pool of 0.61 g and the utilization of 39.4 g of glycine nitrogen in protein synthesis per day. Another subject (68 kg) had an aspartic acid nitrogen pool of 0.84 g and used 29 g of aspartic acid nitrogen for synthesis per day. It was shown that the total free amino acid nitrogen pools of such subjects were only somewhat more than 2 g. Thus the amino acid nitrogen pool is small and turns over very rapidly. The metabolically active proteins of the body (plasma, liver, other internal organs; muscle proteins turn over much more slowly) in one of these 68-kg subjects amounted to 141 g of protein nitrogen, about equal to the protein nitrogen of plasma, liver, and other internal organs. This protein nitrogen was calculated to have a half-life of 2.5 days, indicating a very rapid synthesis and breakdown.

It is necessary to emphasize that the total amino acid pool of the body represents the sum total of the many different pools of the different tissues.

PROTEIN SYNTHESIS, BREAKDOWN, AND STORAGE

GENERAL CONSIDERATIONS

Although some 20 amino acids enter into the structures of proteins, the animal requires only the so-called essential amino acids in the diet for tissue formation, since it can synthesize the remainder.

The synthesis of body proteins from amino acids is obvious in the increase of tissue mass during growth, in the regeneration of injured tissues, and in the maintenance of the tissue mass of the adult animal. However, we know little about the specific mechanisms by which amino acids are linked together in the proper arrangement to form proteins. A group of proteolytic enzymes, the cathepsins, is widespread in tissues. The cathepsins, I, II, III, and IV, are similar to pepsin, trypsin, aminopeptidase, and carboxypeptidase, respectively, in their proteolytic activities. The catheptic enzymes appear to be concerned in the breakdown of tissue proteins to amino acids generally throughout the body.

The processes of tissue protein synthesis from amino acids and of breakdown of tissue proteins into amino acids go on simultaneously with opposite net results, regardless of whether or not they represent the operation of some of the same reversible chemical mechanisms. Although both processes are constituted of many stages, the over-all operations may be represented:

$$\text{amino acids} \underset{\substack{\text{enzymes} \\ \text{(catabolism)}}}{\overset{\substack{\text{(anabolism)} \\ \text{enzymes}}}{\rightleftarrows}} \text{proteins}$$

During growth the rate of synthesis exceeds the rate of breakdown, and the animal is in positive nitrogen balance. During starvation and emaciating conditions the reverse is true, and the animal is in negative nitrogen balance. These processes exactly balance in the normal adult to give a state of nitrogen balance.

Caspersson and associates (10) showed that nucleic acids are necessary for cellular protein synthesis. Apparently the ribonucleic acids, which alone are present in the cytoplasm, regulate the synthesis of the cytoplasmic proteins. Deoxyribonucleic acids are present only in the nucleus. The nucleolus has been shown to contain both ribonucleic and deoxyribonucleic acids. Davidson and Waymouth (11) showed that the ribonucleic acids are concentrated in the central portion and the deoxyribonucleic acids in the peripheral region of rat liver cell nucleoli. The deoxyribose nucleic acids of the nucleus control the synthesis of chromatin proteins. Although the synthesis of cytoplasmic proteins is under direct control of the ribonucleic acids, this synthesis is indirectly controlled by the deoxyribonucleic acids of the nucleus.

Novikoff and Potter (12) determined the nucleic acids of developing chick embryos and found their concentrations highest at the time of most rapid protein synthesis. These workers also removed about two-thirds of the liver of rats and determined the pentose and deoxypentose nucleic acids during regeneration of the liver to its original size, which occurred in several days. The concentration of pentose nucleic acid increased during the period of most rapid regeneration, while that of the deoxypentose nucleic acid did not change consistently.

Protein synthesis is also regulated to a greater or lesser degree by hormonal action. Thyroxine of the thyroid gland is necessary for proper growth of the young, a severe deficiency causing a low metabolic rate, failure to grow, and imbecility (cretinism). Failure of protein synthesis is a chief cause of growth failure. The relation of thyroxine to growth appears to be due to its effect in increasing the rate of energy production and speeding up metabolic reactions in general, and not to any specific action upon protein synthesis. Excess thyroxine as found in cases of hyperthyroidism (Graves' disease) may have the opposite effect and cause an increased rate of tissue protein breakdown with marked emaciation. It appears that in these cases the rate of oxidation of foods is so increased that amino acids which normally would go into protein synthesis are destroyed by oxidation.

The hormone specifically concerned with protein synthesis is the growth hormone of the anterior pituitary. Gigantism and acromegaly are due to overproduction of the growth hormone, whereas dwarfism is the result of underproduction, and these conditions are associated with excessive and deficient rates of protein synthesis. Lee and Schaffer (13) speeded up the growth rate of young rats by giving anterior pituitary extracts and determined the composition of the growth gain as compared with that of controls fed the same quantity and kind of food. The tissue gain of the treated animals contained a much larger proportion of protein than did that of the controls. Evans and associates (14) found that hypophysectomized rats when treated with purified growth hormone gained more weight than untreated controls with identical food intakes. That the effect was general throughout the body was indicated by the fact that all internal organs examined were heavier in the treated group. The male sex hormones or androgens also stimulate protein synthesis (Chapter 34).

Bartlett (15) has shown that growth hormone increases the rate of protein synthesis and causes marked increases in the size of the nitrogen pool (amino acid pool) in the tissues of adult dogs. This effect in increasing the amino acid pool of tissues may represent the chief effect of the hormone in regulating intracellular protein synthesis.

Clark (16) has shown that cortisone of the adrenal cortex inhibits protein synthesis. He also found that increased protein synthesis (anabolism) is associated with an increase in the nonprotein nitrogen of tissues, whereas increased protein breakdown (catabolism) is associated with a decrease in the nonprotein nitrogen. These findings agree with those of Bartlett relative to the correlation of increased protein synthesis and an increase in the nitrogen pool (amino acid pool).

Although each tissue of the body takes the appropriate amino acids from the blood and synthesizes its own characteristic proteins *in situ*, the liver also synthesizes fibrinogen and albumin, and much of the globulin fraction of blood plasma. Lymphoid tissue may be the site of synthesis of at least a part of the globulin fraction, since lymphocytes have been shown to contain a protein identical with plasma γ-globulin. The formation of plasma proteins is given in more detail in the chapter on blood (Chapter 15).

PROTEIN STORAGE AND BREAKDOWN

The body has little or no capacity to store protein as such comparable with the storage of glycogen and fat. When the protein intake of an animal in nitrogen equilibrium is raised suddenly, decreasing amounts of the extra nitrogen are retained for several successive days until nitrogen equilibrium is again reached, but at a higher level. Some of the retained nitrogen apparently forms body protein. A part of the nitrogen is retained as nonprotein nitrogen. On the other hand, if the intake of protein is decreased, though still adequate for maintenance, more nitrogen will be excreted than taken in for a few days until nitrogen balance at a lower level is achieved. Such results indicate the fluidity of body protein structures enabling them to be rather rapidly built up or broken down within limits according to the

Table 25.3.   Metabolism of Benedict's Fasting Subject L.

Days of Fast	Weight at Start of Each Period Kilograms	Total Urine Nitrogen Grams per Day	NH₃ Nitrogen Grams per Day	Total Calories Produced	Per Cent of Calories from Protein
Average, days:					
3 before fast	—	14.0	—	—	—
1–7	60.6	9.9	1.1	1650	15
8–14	55.1	10.3	1.3	1450	18
15–21	52.8	8.4	1.4	1290	17
22–28	50.1	7.8	1.2	1250	16
29–31	48.1	7.2	1.1	1260	15
3 following fast	47.4	3.8	0.5	—	—

From Peters, J. P., and Van Slyke, D. D.: *Quantitative Clinical Chemistry*, Vol 1, *Interpretations*. The Williams and Wilkins Company, Baltimore, 1931, p. 274.

supply of dietary protein. The only kind of protein storage in a normal animal would be represented by the difference in tissue protein of an animal when at nitrogen balance on high protein and lower protein diets. The protein causing an increase in tissue protein on a high protein diet, however, appears to be identical with the structural and functional cellular proteins, so that we cannot differentiate any protein in the body as representing storage protein.

Addis and coworkers (17) showed that when the dietary protein of the rat is increased the greatest increase in tissue protein occurs in the liver, kidneys, and blood. These workers also found that a seven-day fast caused the loss of 40 per cent of the liver protein; 8 per cent each of the muscle, skin, and skeletal protein; and 5 per cent of the brain protein. Because of the greater mass, almost two-thirds of the protein loss came from sources other than the liver. The liver lost 20 per cent of its protein during a two-day fast when the body as a whole lost only 4 per cent. These results indicate that liver protein is the body protein which can be most quickly broken down to supply amino acids. Liver protein also is formed most rapidly.

The rate of tissue protein breakdown in the human during a 31-day fast has been determined by Benedict on his famous fasting subject L. (18). Table 25.3 summarizes several of the metabolic findings. The constancy of the nitrogen excretion relative to body weight during the latter half of the fast was remarkable. It was also found that after the fourth day of fast essentially all the carbohydrate reserves available for fuel were used up, and energy from then on was derived from fat and protein metabolism, with fat supplying about 85 per cent. It has been found in animal experiments that a sharp premortal rise in nitrogen excretion occurs shortly before death. At this time the fat reserves have been exhausted and the body must utilize tissue protein alone as a source of energy with resulting large increase in the rate of tissue destruction which rapidly leads to death.

SYNTHESIS OF PEPTIDE BONDS AND PROTEINS

The synthesis of tissue proteins involves the joining of many different amino acids in definite and characteristic sequences by peptide bonds into large polypeptide chains and then the organization of these peptide chains into specific kinds of proteins varying from globular to fibrous types.

Much progress has been made in recent years in establishing the mechanisms by which peptide bond formation is effected in biologic systems, though as yet we know very little as to how the sequence of amino acids characteristic for each protein is determined and the factors controlling the specific manner in which the peptide chains are organized in natural proteins. Recent reviews dealing with the synthesis of peptides and proteins are those of Chantrenne (19), Zamecnik and associates (20), and Meister (21).

Synthesis of peptide bonds. The synthesis of a peptide bond between a carboxyl group and an amino group is an endergonic reaction. The standard free energy of hydrolysis of the peptide bond in a dipeptide:

$$\begin{array}{ccccc}
NH_2 & & & NH_2 & NH_2 \\
| & & & | & | \\
HC-CO-NH-CH-COOH + HOH \rightleftharpoons & HC-COOH + HC-COOH \\
| & | & & | & | \\
R & R' & & R & R'
\end{array}$$

is about -3000 cal per mol and that for longer peptides somewhat less. At one time reversal of enzymatic hydrolytic reactions was considered of importance in protein synthesis. However, conditions in cells (amino acid concentration, etc.), the energy requirements of forming peptide bonds, and the determination of amino acid sequence in the synthesis of peptide chains made it obvious that other mechanisms are operative.

Many investigations (19) have shown that peptide bond formation is effected through reactions of energy-rich compounds. Apparently there are three types of energy-rich or "activated" compounds utilized directly in peptide bond formation: the acyl adenylates, which are acid anhydride derivatives of AMP (adenylic acid); acyl derivatives of coenzyme A; and acyl phosphates. In all cases activation consists in forming an energy-rich bond at a carboxyl group, acid anhydride bonds in the acyl adenylates and phosphates, and thio-ester bonds in the acyl-CoA compounds. In the formation of these "active" compounds the energy of their high-energy bonds is derived from breaking a pyrophosphate bond of ATP. The phosphate bond energy of ATP is largely conserved in the bond energy of the adenylates, acyl CoA compounds, and acyl phosphates and is used in peptide bond formation. In general, it may be stated that one ATP is required for the synthesis of each peptide bond regardless of the final reaction mechanism.

Acyl activated compounds such as those discussed above react with hydroxylamine to form hydroxamic acids which give a red complex with Fe^{+++} in acid solution. The reaction has been of much value in testing for the presence of such substances:

$$CH_3—CO—S—CoA + H_2N—OH \longrightarrow CH_3—CO—NH—OH + HS—CoA$$

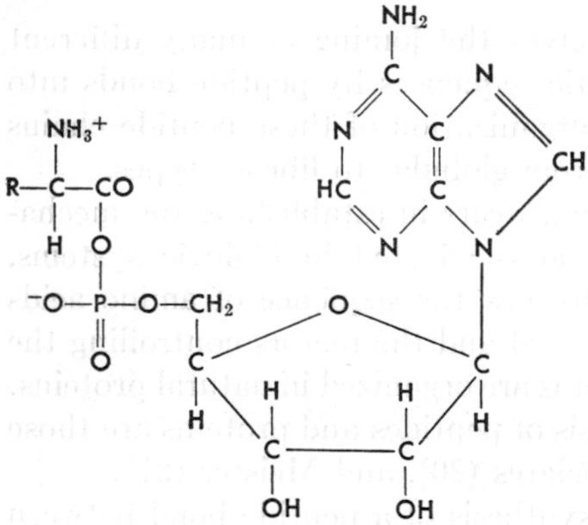

Acethydroxamic acid

Amino-acyl-adenylate

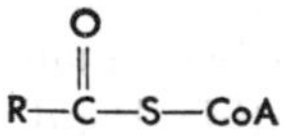

$$R—\overset{O}{\underset{}{C}}—S—CoA$$

Acyl CoA

$$R—\overset{O}{\underset{}{C}}—O—\overset{O}{\underset{OH}{P}}—OH$$

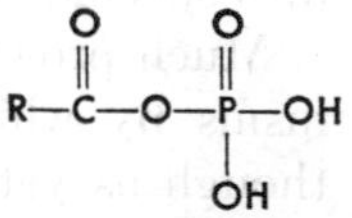

Acyl phosphate

The type of energy-rich compound used in peptide bond formation varies with the kind of peptide synthesized.

I. Peptide bond formation through acyl CoA compounds. In the biological acetylation of amines, and the formation of substances such as hippuric acid (benzoyl glycine), and phenylacetyl glutamine, the peptide bond is formed by reaction of an acyl CoA compound with an amino group. The acyl—CoA appears to be formed as follows, using acetyl CoA as an example:

Acetate + ATP $\xrightarrow[\text{Enzyme}]{\text{Activating}}$ Adenyl~acetate + PP

Adenyl~acetate + HS⁻CoA $\longleftrightarrow$ Acetyl⁻S⁻CoA + AMP

One enzyme catalyzes both of these reactions.

The adenyl~acetate has not been isolated from the reaction medium and must remain tightly bound to the enzyme protein. The energy in the thio-ester bond of acetyl—S—CoA, which is available for peptide bond formation, originates from the second pyrophosphate bond in ATP. The acetyl—S—CoA reacts with an amine to form a peptide bond:

$$CH_3-CO-S-CoA + H_2N-R \xrightarrow[\text{acetylase}]{\text{Trans-}} \overset{\overset{\displaystyle H}{|}}{CH_3-CO-N-R} + HS-CoA$$
$$\text{Acetylated amine}$$

In bacteria acetyl CoA may be formed from acetate through acetyl phosphate, as is the case with *E. coli*:

$$\text{ATP} + \text{Acetate} \underset{}{\overset{\text{Enzyme}}{\longleftrightarrow}} \text{Acetyl} \sim \text{phosphate} + \text{ADP}$$

$$\text{Acetyl} \sim \text{phosphate} + HS-CoA \xrightarrow[\text{transacetylase}]{\text{Phospho-}} \text{Acetyl}-S-CoA + Pi$$

Acetyl phosphate, unlike the adenyl acetate, is not firmly bound to the enzyme and may accumulate in the medium.

The synthesis of hippuric acid in the liver also takes place through an acyl CoA compound:

$$\text{Benzoate} + \text{ATP} \underset{}{\overset{\text{Activating Enzyme}}{\longleftrightarrow}} \text{Adenyl} \sim \text{benzoate} + \text{PP}$$

$$\text{Adenyl} \sim \text{benzoate} + HS-CoA \longleftrightarrow \text{Benzoyl}-S-CoA + \text{AMP}$$

$$\overset{\overset{\displaystyle H}{|}}{C_6H_5-CO-S-CoA} + H-N-CH_2-COOH \xrightarrow[\text{Enzyme}]{\text{Condensing}} C_6H_5-\overset{\overset{\displaystyle O}{\|}}{C}-\overset{\overset{\displaystyle H}{|}}{N}-CH_2-COOH + HS-CoA$$
$$\text{Benzoyl CoA} \qquad \text{Glycine} \qquad \qquad \text{Benzoyl glycine}$$
$$\text{or Hippuric acid}$$

The condensation of phenylacetic acid with glutamine in the liver to form phenylacetyl glutamine seems to be peculiar to man and the chimpanzee. The processes involved appear to be quite analogous to those of hippuric acid synthesis. Phenylacetic acid is converted to phenylacetyl—S—CoA, which condenses with the amino group of glutamine:

$$C_6H_5-CH_2-CO-\overset{\overset{\displaystyle H}{|}}{\underset{\underset{\displaystyle H}{|}}{N}}-\overset{\overset{\displaystyle COOH}{|}}{C}-CH_2-CH_2-CO-NH_2$$
$$\text{Phenylacetylglutamine}$$

II. Peptide bond formation through acyl phosphates.

The syntheses of glutamine and glutathione involve acyl phosphates as energy-rich reactants, which appear to be firmly bound to the enzyme protein.

Glutamine is widely distributed in animal and plant tissues. The enzyme which catalyzes glutamine synthesis, glutamine synthetase, occurs in various animal tissues, such as liver, kidney, brain, and retina. The over-all synthesis of glutamine from glutamic acid, NH$_3$, and ATP may be represented by the reaction:

$$\text{L-Glutamic acid} + NH_3 + \text{ATP} \underset{Mg^{++}}{\overset{\text{Glutamine synthetase}}{\longleftrightarrow}} \text{Glutamine} + \text{ADP} + \text{Pi}$$

It appears that the mechanism of the process probably is as follows, one enzyme catalyzing both activation of the glutamic acid carboxyl group and also bringing about the condensation reaction:

$$\text{Glutamic acid} + \text{ATP} + \text{Enzyme} \longleftrightarrow (\gamma\text{-Glutamyl} \sim P)\text{-Enzyme} + \text{ADP}$$
$$(\gamma\text{-Glutamyl} \sim P)\text{-Enzyme} + NH_3 \longleftrightarrow \gamma\text{-Glutamylamide} + \text{Pi} + \text{Enzyme}$$
$$\gamma\text{-Glutamine}$$

The tripeptide glutathione (γ-glutamylcysteinylglycine) is a widely distributed and important constituent of tissues, both plant and animal. The synthesis of the peptide bonds of glutathione appears to be effected in a manner analogous to the synthesis of the peptide bond (amide bond) in glutamine. Two enzymes are involved, which are represented as Enz_1 and Enz_2 in the following reactions:

$$Enz_1 + \text{Glutamic acid} + ATP \longleftrightarrow (\gamma\text{-Glutamyl}\sim P)\text{-}Enz_1 + ADP$$
$$(\gamma\text{-Glutamyl}\sim P)\text{-}Enz_1 + \text{Cysteine} \longrightarrow \gamma\text{-Glutamyl-Cysteine} + Pi + Enz_1$$

The γ-glutamylcysteine (γ-Glu-Cys) then reacts with Enz_2:

$$Enz_2 + \gamma\text{-Glu-Cys} + ATP \longleftrightarrow (\gamma\text{-Glu-Cys}\sim P)\text{-}Enz_2 + ADP$$
$$(\gamma\text{-Glu-Cys}\sim P)\text{-}Enz_2 + \text{Glycine} \longrightarrow \gamma\text{-Glu-Cys-Glycine} + Pi + Enz_2$$
$$\text{Glutathione}$$

III. Synthesis of peptide bonds through amino-acyl-adenylates.
The enzymatic synthesis of the dipeptide carnosine (β-alanyl histidine) from β-alanyl adenylate and histidine has been demonstrated by Kalyankar and Meister (22):

$$\beta\text{-Alanine} + Enz + ATP \longleftrightarrow (\beta\text{-Alanyl adenylate})\text{-}Enz + PP$$
$$(\beta\text{-Alanyl adenylate})\text{-}Enz + \text{Histidine} \longrightarrow \beta\text{-Alanylhistidine} + AMP + Enz$$
$$\text{Carnosine}$$

IV. Amino-acyl-adenylates and protein synthesis (19,20). Evidence leading to our present partial understanding of the reaction mechanisms of protein synthesis has been obtained largely by studies on the incorporation of labeled amino acids into proteins by tissue slices, homogenates, and cell-free extracts. It has been firmly established that respiration, and particularly oxidative phosphorylation (ATP production), is necessary for *in vitro* incorporation of amino acids into proteins by tissues. In tissue homogenates and cell-free extracts incorporation is dependent upon ATP or the presence of systems capable of generating it.

Zamecnik and associates (20) obtained by centrifugation cell-free preparations of liver containing the microsome and soluble cytoplasmic fractions capable of synthesizing protein from amino acids in the presence of ATP. The microsome fraction could be centrifuged out at 100,000 g, and further separated into a larger fraction rich in lipoprotein membranes and a smaller fraction made up of ribonucleoprotein particles. Very interestingly, it was found that this ribosomal nucleoprotein fraction is the site of the highest early specific radioactivity of protein formed from C^{14}-labeled amino acids, suggesting its fundamental role in the process. It was also shown that this ribonucleoprotein of the microsomes (ribosome) appears to be the earliest site for the formation of a complete long peptide chain, suggesting that it may represent a template determining the sequential arrangement of amino acids prior to their linkage through peptide bond formation. It was also found that the protein synthesized *in vitro* from labeled amino acids was composed of the amino acids joined by α-peptide bonds as in native proteins.

Berg (23) and Hoagland and associates (24) demonstrated the enzymatic activation of amino acids by reaction with ATP to form the amino acid adenylates (amino-acyl-adenylates), which are largely bound to the enzyme protein. Karasek and associates (25) reported isolation of the first enzymatically produced amino acid adenylate, tryptophanyl-adenylate. Work on the amino acid adenylates is reviewed by Meister (21).

It was found (20) that the liver cell preparation contained soluble ribonucleic acid (S—RNA) which did not sediment in the centrifuge at 105,000 g. Using labeled amino acids, it was found that they were first combined with the S—RNA and then transferred to the ribonucleoprotein particles of the microsomes (ribosome), where they were synthesized into protein. After synthesis the protein passed from the ribosomes into the soluble cytoplasmic protein mixture.

Evidence indicated that combination of amino acids (activated forms) with cytoplasmic S—RNA was dependent upon preliminary reaction of RNA with two molecules of CTP (cytidine triphosphate) to introduce two cytidine monophosphate groups (CMP) into the end of the S—RNA molecule (by esterification at free ribose hydroxyl groups in the end of the S—RNA chain) and then linkage of a terminal AMP group to the CMP group by reaction with ATP. S—RNA which had the terminal mononucleotide groups split off enzymatically was inactive in combining with either amino acids or AMP unless first treated with CTP. Thus, the process of adding CMP and AMP to the ends of S—RNA molecules constitutes an activation process preliminary to combination of S—RNA with activated amino acids. The activated amino acids apparently react with the 2' or 3' ribose hydroxyl group of the terminal AMP to form an ester linkage joining the amino acid to the AMP.

It was found that a single labeled amino acid could be added in increasing amounts until saturation for it was reached, but that this did not affect the combination of S—RNA for other amino acids. This indicated the presence of a specific S—RNA coded to combine with a specific amino acid, the coding mechanism being arranged internal to the activated nucleotide end groups of S—RNA, since this component is uniform for the different S—RNA molecules.

Activation of amino acids to the adenylates apparently proceeds as follows, the action being catalyzed by specific activating enzymes present in the cytoplasm:

$$
\begin{array}{c}
\underset{\substack{\text{AD}-\text{O}-\text{P}-\text{O}-\text{P}-\text{O}-\text{P}-\text{OH}}}{\overset{\overset{\displaystyle O}{\|}\quad\overset{\displaystyle O}{\|}\quad\overset{\displaystyle O}{\|}}{}} + \underset{\text{Amino acid}}{\overset{\overset{\displaystyle O\ \ H}{\|\ \ |}}{\text{O}-\text{C}-\text{C}-\text{NH}_3^+}} + \text{Enz}_1 \longrightarrow
\end{array}
$$

AD- O- P- O- P- O- P- OH + ⁻O- C- C- NH₃⁺ + Enz₁ ⟶
with O⁻, O⁻, O⁻ below phosphates and R below the carbon

ATP, Adenosine triphosphate   Amino acid

$$
\text{Enz}_1 - \text{AD} - \text{O} - \overset{O}{\underset{O^-}{\overset{\|}{P}}} - \text{O} - \overset{O\ H}{\underset{R}{\overset{\|\ |}{C - C}}} - \text{NH}_3^+ + \text{HO} - \overset{O}{\underset{O^-}{\overset{\|}{P}}} - \text{O} - \overset{O}{\underset{O^-}{\overset{\|}{P}}} - \text{OH}
$$

Enzyme-amino-acyl-adenylate complex   Pyrophosphate

Activation of S—RNA to receive the activated amino acid may be represented:

$$S-RNA + 2CTP \overset{Enz_2}{\rightleftharpoons} S-RNA-CMP-CMP + 2PP$$
$$S-RNA-CMP-CMP + ATP \rightleftharpoons S-RNA-CMP-CMP-AMP + PP$$

The activated amino acid then reacts with its specific activated S—RNA:

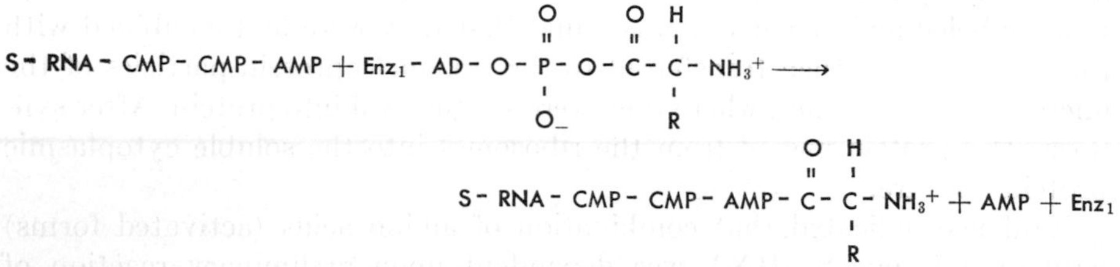

$$S-RNA-CMP-CMP-AMP + Enz_1-AD-O-\overset{O}{\underset{O_-}{\overset{\|}{P}}}-O-\overset{O}{\overset{\|}{C}}-\overset{H}{\underset{R}{\overset{|}{C}}}-NH_3^+ \longrightarrow$$

$$S-RNA-CMP-CMP-AMP-\overset{O}{\overset{\|}{C}}-\overset{H}{\underset{R}{\overset{|}{C}}}-NH_3^+ + AMP + Enz_1$$

Activated S— RNA amino acid complex

The activated S—RNA amino acid complexes may be referred to as "transfer RNAaa," or as T—RNAaa. The T—RNAaa molecules pass to the microsomal RNA, where each T—RNAaa molecule transfers its specific amino acid to a definite site on the microsomal RNA determined by the coding system of the microsomal RNA, the process being catalyzed by enzyme₃(Enz₃). This places the amino acids in the proper sequence for the specific protein being synthesized. The process of transfer of amino acids from T—RNAaa to microsomal RNA requires guanosine triphosphate (GTP) and ATP, though their functions are unknown. The amino acids lined up in proper sequence on the microsomal RNA are now joined by peptide bond formation into a peptide chain, which then is organized into a specific protein structure.

The process of protein formation according to this theory may be stated in outline as follows:

1. Amino acids are converted to amino acid adenylates by specific activating enzymes in the cytoplasm, and remain bound to the enzymes.

2. Small specific soluble RNA molecules in the cytoplasm react first with 2CTP and then ATP to form specific amino acid carriers of the type RNA—CMP—CMP—AMP, where CMP and AMP represent the mononucleotide groups cytidine monophosphate and adenosine monophosphate, respectively. The reactions are enzymatic.

3. Specific RNA—CMP—CMP—AMP molecules then react with specific enzyme-amino acid adenylates to form transfer complexes, the amino acids being linked to the end AMP group of the carrier (RNA—CMP— CMP—AMP— amino acid). These transfer complexes may be designated T—RNAaa.

4. The T—RNAaa molecules then transfer their amino acids to specific sites for specific amino acids on the microsomal RNA, which, through its coding system, determines the sequence of amino acids attached to it as a template. The amino acids are then joined by peptide bonds into peptide chains, and the chains are organized into the structure characteristic of the

specific protein being synthesized and are released from the microsomal template.

While there are still various unknown and unsubstantiated points about this theory, the body of evidence seems to indicate the probable correctness of a large proportion of it (20). It very prominently suggests specific critical roles for nucleic acids in protein metabolism, for which there is considerable evidence.

Nothing is known as to how the deoxyribonucleic acids of the nucleus control synthesis of chromatin proteins and other proteins of the nucleus. That the synthesis of cytoplasmic proteins is under the direct control of RNA appears well established, but also the synthesis of cytoplasmic proteins is under the indirect control of DNA by some unknown mechanism.

It has been proposed that one gene of the chromosomes composed of DNA, determines the synthesis of one protein (26), which possibly represents an overly simplified generalization. However, Horowitz and associates (27) have shown that mutation of a single genetic locus in *Neurospora* causes the formation of an abnormal type of tyrosinase protein, which indicates the relation here of only one gene to the synthesis of a specific protein. Certainly it appears that a relatively very small segment of chromosomal DNA represents the hereditary structure which controls the synthesis of a specific protein.

The close relation of nucleic acids to protein synthesis has been demonstrated through studies on the induction of bacterial enzymes. Various microorganisms adapt to the utilization of a substance added to the culture medium by forming an enzyme which is not present in detectable amounts in the absence of the added substance. The phenomenon is called "enzyme induction," and the substance added which causes the enzyme production is an "enzyme inducer." For example, *E. coli*, grown in the presence of lactose, through induction forms the enzyme β-galactosidase, which hydrolyzes β-galactosides such as lactose. It is of interest that β-methyl-D-thiogalactoside also induces the formation of β-galactosidase by *E. coli*, though the compound is not hydrolyzed by the induced enzyme, so the enzyme inducer may be a compound not acted upon by the enzyme induced.

Gale and associates (28) have shown that cells of *S. aureus*, partially disrupted by sonic vibration, are still capable of forming β-galactosidase through induction, but this property is lost when the cells are treated with ribonuclease which breaks down the RNA.

The theory relative to protein synthesis outlined above considers that the sequential arrangement of amino acids in the peptide chains is determined by essentially simultaneous peptide bond formation between amino acids lined up at specific sites on RNA as a template. Undoubtedly the nucleic acids carry the code in determining the way in which the peptide chains are organized. While the template theory is in accord with some of the evidence, it cannot be considered as proved. It may be that synthesis of proteins takes place in which single amino acids are successively added on to the growing peptide chain, or that small peptides are added on to the peptide chain.

While peptide intermediates have not been found in tissues, it may be that they are highly reactive and have only a transient existence, as is true of the intermediates in fatty acid synthesis. Experiments on the incorporation of amino acids into ovalbumin by hen's oviduct by Anfinsen and associates (29) have shown nonuniform labeling of a given amino acid along the peptide chains, suggesting synthesis by successive amino acid addition. On the other hand, Velick and associates (30) injected five labeled amino acids into rabbits and isolated the enzymes aldolase and glyceraldehyde-3-phosphate dehydrogenase from the muscle. Each labeled amino acid in aldolase was 1.8 times as radioactive as it was in the dehydrogenase, a result in conformity with template synthesis. Possibly protein synthesis involving both processes may take place, though the template process appears more logical from the standpoint of mechanism for coding the location of different amino acids in peptide chains. Much work remains to be done on the problem.

Formation of peptides by transpeptidation. Many peptides have been synthesized through the transfer of a peptide group by proteolytic or other enzymes (19, 31).

I. Transglutamylation. Enzymes from plants, microorganisms, and various animal tissues catalyze the exchange of the amide group of γ-glutamine with the NH_2^- of hydroxylamine.

$$\gamma\text{-Glutamine} + H_2N-OH \xrightarrow{\text{Enzyme}} \gamma\text{-Glutamylhydroxamic acid} + NH_3$$

Animal tissues (kidney, pancreas) contain an enzyme which catalyzes the transfer of the glutamyl group in reversible reactions such as the following:

$$\gamma\text{-Glutamylglycine} + \text{Cysteinylglycine} \xrightleftharpoons{\text{Enzyme}} \gamma\text{-Glutamylcysteinylglycine} + \text{Glycine}$$
$$\text{Glutathione}$$

Hydrolysis of the peptides occurs along with transpeptidation.

II. Transpeptidation from amides. A number of transpeptidation reactions from amides, catalyzed by proteolytic enzymes of both plants and animals (cathepsins, chymotrypsin, trypsin, papain, ficin, etc.), have been observed. For example, beef spleen cathepsin catalyzes a reaction such as the following:

Glycyl-phenylalanylamide + Glycyl-phenylalanylamide $\longrightarrow$
Glycyl-phenylalanyl-glycyl-phenylalanylamide + NH_3

This reaction can be repeated with the addition of more glycylphenylalanyl groups to form octa- or decapeptide amides.

Transpeptidations transpose but do not form new peptide bonds. Their biological importance is unknown. They may be involved in changing the terminal amino acid groups of peptide chains.

DEAMINATION, TRANSAMINATION, AND AMINATION

The metabolism of the amino acids involves deamination and formation of the corresponding keto acids preliminary to oxidation and the production of energy. The synthesis of amino acids in tissues involves amination of keto acids derived from carbohydrate, protein, and fat metabolism. Also, amino groups of certain amino acids may be transferred to the keto acids corresponding to other amino acids, thereby effecting amino acid-keto acid interconversion. The latter process is called "transamination" and is one process of amination and of amino acid synthesis. As to be expected, the processes of deamination and amination are often inseparable, since amination may represent simply the reverse of deamination.

Site of deamination. That the liver is responsible for most of the deamination of amino acids has been shown by the work of Mann and associates (32). These workers found that the blood amino acid level remained high after the injection of amino acids into hepatectomized dogs, and also that there was failure of urea production. Krebs (33) has studied the deamination of amino acids by tissue slices and found kidney as well as liver to be very active. Much other work has confirmed these findings.

The various types of deamination are discussed in reviews by Cohen (34) Meister (35) and Krebs (36).

Oxidative deamination. Krebs (37) found that kidney and liver of many animals contain enzymes which oxidatively liberate ammonia from amino acids, approximately 2 mols of NH_3 being formed for each mol of O_2 taken up:

$$R - CH(NH_2) - COOH + \tfrac{1}{2}O_2 \longrightarrow R - CO - COOH + NH_3$$

Krebs also demonstrated the presence of D- and L-amino acid oxidases which act upon D- and L-amino acids, respectively. The D-amino acid oxidases could be readily extracted with water, but the L-amino acid oxidases were bound to tissue particles. Blanchard and associates (38), however, obtained from rat kidney and liver preparations of L-amino acid oxidases. The D-amino acid oxidases are flavoproteins containing FAD. The L-amino acid oxidases of kidney and liver are also flavoproteins but contain FMN (flavin mononucleotide). However, an L-amino acid oxidase from mocassin venom was found to contain FAD. Both D- and L-amino acid oxidases are found in microorganisms.

It is rather peculiar that despite the absence of D-amino acids in tissues, the activity of the D-amino acid oxidases is generally much greater than that of the L-oxidases. The function of the D-oxidases is unknown.

The mechanism of oxidative deamination may be represented by the following equations:

$$
\begin{array}{ccccc}
R - CH - COOH & + & FP & \longrightarrow & R - C - COOH + FP \cdot H_2 \\
\quad | & & & & \quad \| \\
\quad NH_2 & & & & \quad NH \\
\text{Amino acid} & & \text{Flavoprotein} & & \text{Imino acid} \qquad \text{Reduced} \\
& & \text{enzyme} & & \qquad\qquad\quad \text{enzyme}
\end{array}
$$

$$
\begin{array}{cc}
R - C - COOH + H_2O \rightleftharpoons & R - C - COOH + NH_3 \\
\quad \| & \quad \| \\
\quad NH & \quad O \\
\text{Imino acid} & \text{Keto acid}
\end{array}
$$

This reaction takes place spontaneously.

$$FP \cdot H_2 + O_2 \longrightarrow FP + H_2O_2$$

$$2H_2O_2 \xrightarrow{\text{Catalase}} 2H_2O + O_2$$

Evidence for intermediate formation of the imino acid in the process has been obtained by Pitt (39).

It is of interest that L-glutamic acid is not deaminated by L-amino acid oxidase but by L-glutamic dehydrogenase, which is widely distributed. The crystallized enzyme from beef liver contains zinc:

$$
\underset{\substack{| \\ H_2N-CH-COOH \\ \text{L-Glutamic acid}}}{\overset{\substack{DPN^+ \\ + \\ CH_2-CH_2-COOH}}{}} \Longleftrightarrow
\underset{\substack{| \\ HN=C-COOH \\ \alpha\text{-Iminoglutaric acid}}}{\overset{\substack{DPN\cdot H + H^+ \\ + \\ CH_2-CH_2-COOH + H_2O}}{}} \Longleftrightarrow
\underset{\substack{| \\ O=C-COOH \\ \alpha\text{-Ketoglutaric acid}}}{\overset{\substack{CH_2CH_2-COOH + NH_3}}{}}
$$

Either DPN or TPN may serve as cofactor.

The fact that this deamination is reversible is of much biologic importance, since it represents a mechanism by which NH_3 is taken up by α-ketoglutaric acid, a member of the citric acid cycle, and converted to glutamic acid. The $-NH_2$ group of glutamic acid may then be reversibly converted into the $-NH_2$ groups of other amino acids by transamination. Thus, the reaction serves as a mechanism for incorporating ammonia into the amino acids and links protein and carbohydrate metabolisms through the citric acid cycle. It also constitutes, in the forward direction, an important pathway for the removal of the $-NH_2$ groups of amino acids as NH_3 through glutamic acid.

Although the L-amino acid oxidases of animal tissues deaminate many of the naturally occurring amino acids, the generally low level of oxidase activity indicates that oxidative deamination is, in general, of minor importance quantitatively in removing the amino groups of amino acids as NH_3. However, the reversible oxidative deamination of glutamic acid appears to be of major importance in this respect.

Glycine, which is not deaminated by either D- or L-amino acid oxidase, is deaminated by a specific glycine oxidase present in the kidney and liver of mammals, and in bacteria:

$$
\underset{\text{Glycine}}{H_2N-CH_2-COOH} + \tfrac{1}{2}O_2 \longrightarrow \underset{\text{Glyoxylic acid}}{OHC-COOH} + NH_3
$$

Nonoxidative deamination. *1. Amino acid dehydrases.* The hydroxy amino acids serine, threonine, and homoserine, are deaminated by specific enzymes which catalyze a primary dehydration followed by spontaneous deamination. These enzymes are called "amino acid dehydrases":

$$
\underset{\substack{| \\ NH_2 \\ \text{Serine}}}{HO-CH_2-CH-COOH} \xrightarrow{-H_2O}
\underset{\substack{| \\ NH_2 \\ \text{Intermediate}}}{CH_2=C-COOH} \Longleftrightarrow
\underset{\substack{\| \\ NH \\ \text{Imino acid}}}{CH_3-C-COOH} \underset{\pm H_2O}{\rightleftarrows}
\underset{\substack{\| \\ O \\ \text{Pyruvic acid}}}{CH_3-C-COOH} + NH_3
$$

The dehydrases require pyridoxal phosphate as cofactor. Dehydrases for L-amino acids are found in mammalian liver, while dehydrases active with both D- and L- amino acids are present in various microorgansims.

2. Amino acid desulfhydrases. The sulfur-containing amino acids cysteine and homocysteine are deaminated by a primary desulfhydration $(-H_2S)$ forming an imino acid, which is then spontaneously hydrolyzed:

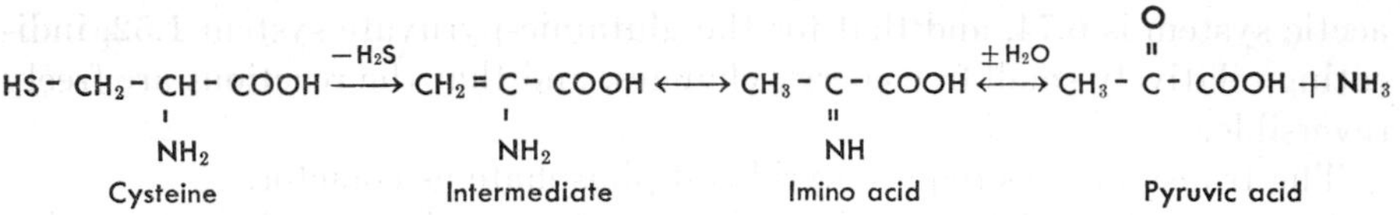

$$\underset{\substack{| \\ NH_2 \\ \text{Cysteine}}}{HS-CH_2-CH-COOH} \xrightarrow{-H_2S} \underset{\substack{| \\ NH_2 \\ \text{Intermediate}}}{CH_2=C-COOH} \longleftrightarrow \underset{\substack{\| \\ NH \\ \text{Imino acid}}}{CH_3-C-COOH} \overset{\pm H_2O}{\longleftrightarrow} \underset{\text{Pyruvic acid}}{CH_3-\overset{\overset{O}{\|}}{C}-COOH + NH_3}$$

Desulfhydrases require pyridoxal phosphate as cofactor, and are found in animal tissues such as kidney, pancreas and liver. They are also present in some microorganisms.

A peculiar nonoxidative deamination, known as the "Stickland reaction," is catalyzed by enzymes of certain anaerobic microorganisms, particularly the *Clostridiae*. The reaction involves two amino acids, in which one acts as a hydrogen donor and the other as a hydrogen acceptor. An example is:

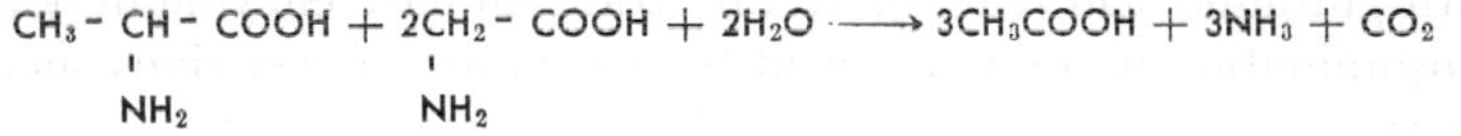

$$\underset{\substack{| \\ NH_2}}{CH_3-CH-COOH} + \underset{\substack{| \\ NH_2}}{2CH_2-COOH} + 2H_2O \longrightarrow 3CH_3COOH + 3NH_3 + CO_2$$

Transamination. A process of combined deamination and amination according to which the amino group of one amino acid may be reversibly transferred to the keto acid of another amino acid, thus effecting amino acid-keto acid interconversion, was discovered by Braunstein and Kritzmann (40). The process represents intermolecular transfer of amino groups without the splitting out of ammonia. The reaction is reversible and is catalyzed by transaminase enzymes, which have been found in practically all animal tissues, but especially in heart, brain, kidney, testicle, and liver. Transaminase enzymes are also operative in higher plants and microorganisms.

The subject of transamination is reviewed by Meister (35,42), Cohen (42), and Braunstein (40).

The general process of transamination may be represented:

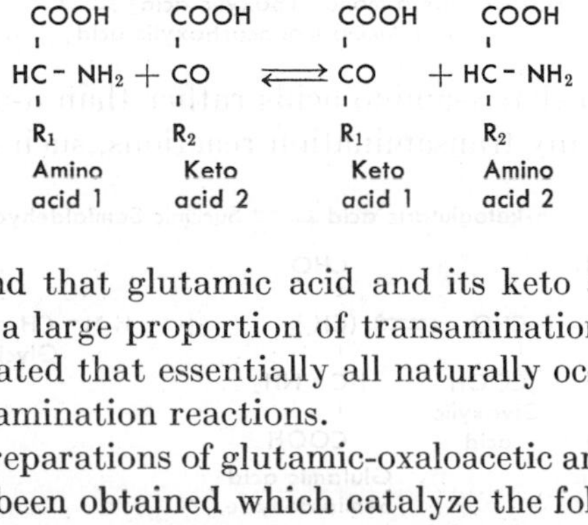

$$\underset{\substack{| \\ R_1 \\ \text{Amino} \\ \text{acid 1}}}{\overset{COOH}{HC-NH_2}} + \underset{\substack{| \\ R_2 \\ \text{Keto} \\ \text{acid 2}}}{\overset{COOH}{CO}} \rightleftarrows \underset{\substack{| \\ R_1 \\ \text{Keto} \\ \text{acid 1}}}{\overset{COOH}{CO}} + \underset{\substack{| \\ R_2 \\ \text{Amino} \\ \text{acid 2}}}{\overset{COOH}{HC-NH_2}}$$

It was early found that glutamic acid and its keto acid, α-ketoglutaric acid, participate in a large proportion of transaminations, though more recent work has indicated that essentially all naturally occurring amino acids participate in transamination reactions.

Highly purified preparations of glutamic-oxaloacetic and glutamic-pyruvic transaminase have been obtained which catalyze the following reactions:

$$\text{L-Glutamic acid} + \text{Pyruvic acid} \xleftrightarrow{\text{Transaminase}} \alpha\text{-Ketoglutaric acid} + \text{L-alanine}$$

$$\text{L-Glutamic acid} + \text{Oxaloacetic acid} \xleftrightarrow{\text{Transaminase}} \alpha\text{-Ketoglutaric acid} + \text{L-Aspartic acid}$$

It has been found that the equilibrium constant for the glutamic-oxalo-acetic system is 6.74, and that for the glutamic-pyruvate system 1.52, indicating relatively small free energy changes, and that the reactions are freely reversible.

The transaminases require pyridoxal phosphate as cofactor.

It appears that the glutamic-oxaloacetic transaminase is the most active and widely distributed of the transaminases. The most common general type of transamination in animals, plants, and microorganisms appears to be represented by the equation:

$$\text{L-Amino acid} + \alpha\text{-Ketoglutaric acid} \longleftrightarrow \alpha\text{-Keto acid} + \text{L-Glutamic acid}$$

While the evidence indicates the operation of a number of transaminases, not much progress has been made in their separation and characterization. This work is complicated by the fact that small contamination of a preparation with glutamic acid and a glutamic transaminase enzyme may catalyze the transamination of an amino acid by a coupling of reactions such as the following:

$$\text{Pyruvic acid} + \text{Glutamic acid} \rightleftharpoons \text{Alanine} + \alpha\text{-Ketoglutaric acid}$$
$$\text{Amino acid} + \alpha\text{-Ketoglutaric acid} \rightleftharpoons \alpha\text{-Keto acid} + \text{Glutamic acid}$$

which in effect but not in mechanism may be represented by:

$$\text{Amino acid} + \text{Pyruvic acid} \rightleftharpoons \alpha\text{-Keto acid} + \text{Alanine}$$

In general, the transaminases of animal tissues and higher plants appear to be specific for L-amino acids. However, it has been found that certain bacteria, such as *B. subtilis*, possess transaminases specific for both D- and L-amino acids.

While glutamic and α-ketoglutaric acids are most commonly involved in transamination reactions, α-amino monocarboxylic acids and α-keto mono-carboxylic acids may also transaminate:

$$\text{L-}\alpha\text{-Amino monocarboxylic acid}_1 + \alpha\text{-Keto monocarboxylic acid}_2 \rightleftharpoons$$
$$\text{L-}\alpha\text{-Amino monocarboxylic acid}_2 + \alpha\text{-Keto monocarboxylic acid}_1$$

It has been found that ω-amino acids rather than α-amino acids serve as —NH_2 donors in many transamination reactions, such as the following:

$$\gamma\text{-Amino butyric acid} + \alpha\text{-ketoglutaric acid} \rightleftharpoons \text{Succinic Semialdehyde} + \text{L-Glutamic acid}$$

$$\begin{array}{ccccc}
CH_2NH_2 & & CHO & & \\
| & & | & & \\
(CH_2)_2 & + \;CHO & \rightleftharpoons \;(CH_2)_2 & + & H_2N-CH_2-COOH \\
| & | & | & & \text{Glycine} \\
HC-NH_2 & COOH & HC-NH_2 & & \\
| & \text{Glyoxylic} & | & & \\
COOH & \text{acid} & COOH & & \\
\text{Ornithine} & & \text{Glutamic acid} & & \\
& & \text{Semialdehyde} & &
\end{array}$$

Transamination reactions between glutamine or asparagine with keto acids take place in which the amide group of glutamine or asparagine is split off by hydrolysis:

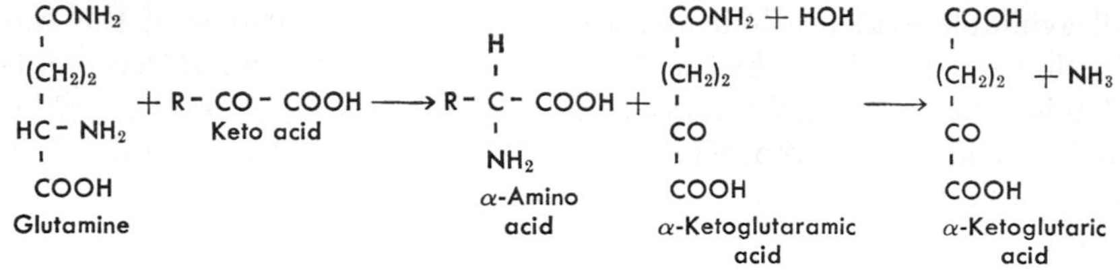

$$
\begin{array}{ccccccc}
\text{CONH}_2 & & & & \text{CONH}_2 + \text{HOH} & & \text{COOH} \\
| & & \text{H} & & | & & | \\
(\text{CH}_2)_2 & & | & & (\text{CH}_2)_2 & & (\text{CH}_2)_2 + \text{NH}_3 \\
| & + \text{R}-\text{CO}-\text{COOH} \longrightarrow & \text{R}-\text{C}-\text{COOH} + & | & \longrightarrow & | \\
\text{HC}-\text{NH}_2 & \text{Keto acid} & | & & \text{CO} & & \text{CO} \\
| & & \text{NH}_2 & & | & & | \\
\text{COOH} & & \alpha\text{-Amino} & & \text{COOH} & & \text{COOH} \\
\text{Glutamine} & & \text{acid} & & \alpha\text{-Ketoglutaramic} & & \alpha\text{-Ketoglutaric} \\
& & & & \text{acid} & & \text{acid}
\end{array}
$$

This reaction involves both transamination and deamidination.

Mechanism of transamination. As previously indicated, transaminases require pyridoxal phosphate as cofactor. Pyridoxamine phosphate has also been found to be effective as a cofactor in transaminations. Snell (43) found that transamination occurs in nonenzymatic model systems when pyridoxal and glutamic acid or pyridoxamine and α-ketoglutaric acid are heated. This led to the theory (44) that pyridoxal phosphate and pyridoxamine phosphate are involved in transamination reactions according to the equations:

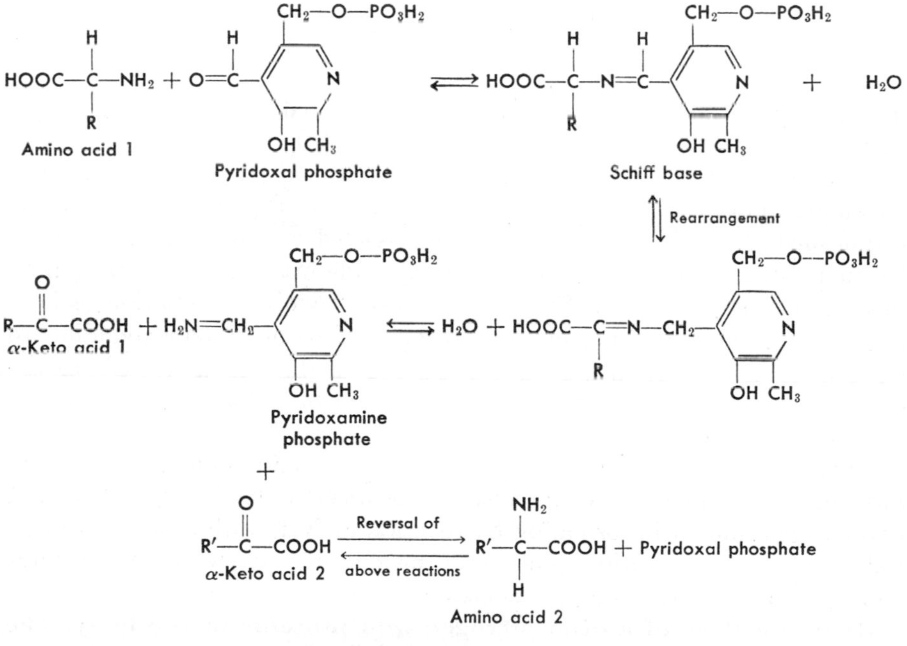

According to this scheme, pyridoxamine phosphate donates the —NH$_2$ group of amino acid 1 to keto acid 2 with the formation of keto acid 1 and amino acid 2, and the reverse process also takes place. This is equivalent to the reaction:

Amino acid 1 + Keto acid 2 $\rightleftharpoons$ Keto acid 1 + Amino acid 2

It is of some interest that the glutamic-oxaloacetic (also called "glutamic-aspartic") transaminase activity of serum rises sharply following myocardial infarction, and the rise appears to be proportional to the size of the infarcted area (45).

All available evidence indicates the very great importance of the transamination reaction in amino acid and protein metabolism. It represents a mechanism for the deamination of amino acids, and also for the synthesis of amino acids from keto acids and glutamic acid. The key role of glutamic acid and α-ketoglutaric acid in amino acid and protein metabolism is obvious.

Amino acid decarboxylation. A number of enzymes which decarboxylate amino acids, decarboxylases, have been found in animal tissues, especially in liver, kidney, and brain. These enzymes also require pyridoxal phosphate as a cofactor. Pyridoxamine phosphate is not involved. The mechanism by which pyridoxal phosphate enters into the process is unknown. The general reaction is:

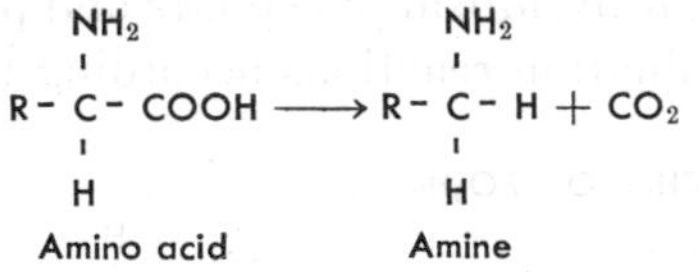

$$\underset{\text{Amino acid}}{R - \underset{\underset{H}{|}}{\overset{\overset{NH_2}{|}}{C}} - COOH} \longrightarrow \underset{\text{Amine}}{R - \underset{\underset{H}{|}}{\overset{\overset{NH_2}{|}}{C}} - H} + CO_2$$

The process is important in the body in the formation of histamine from histidine and in the production of other amines from amino acids.

Amination, amino acid synthesis. That the synthesis of amino acids by amination is a general and important process in the animal body is well established. Animals can synthesize the so-called nonessential amino acids by combining the nitrogen of the essential acids with the appropriate nonnitrogenous organic acids. That this synthesis involves amination of keto acids is indicated by the fact that certain keto acids corresponding to essential amino acids may successfully replace the essential acids in the diets. Such a case in point is the substitution of indole pyruvic acid for tryptophan.

Since N^{15}—NH_3 administered to animals is rapidly incorporated into most of the amino acids of proteins, it appears that this incorporation first involves glutamic acid formation by reaction of NH_3 with α-ketoglutarate, followed by transamination reactions of the glutamic acid with the keto acids corresponding to various amino acids.

Dynamic state of amino nitrogen and proteins of the body. The work of Schoenheimer and associates (46) showed that the amino nitrogen of amino acids in the body is continually shifting from one amino acid to another (lysine excepted) as a result of simultaneous processes of deamination and reamination. Their work has shown also that amino acids continually are being drawn from the amino acid pool and incorporated into tissue proteins and split from tissue proteins and returned to the pool.

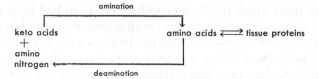

Foster, Schoenheimer, and Rittenberg gave ammonium citrate containing N^{15} to rats and found this N^{15} widely distributed among the amino acids of tissue proteins. Lysine did not contain the isotope, apparently indicating the absence of a keto acid or other product capable of being aminated to the amino acid. As expected, glutamic and aspartic acids contained a large proportion of the isotope. Schoenheimer and associates fed tyrosine containing N^{15} to a rat, maintained in nitrogen equilibrium, for ten days. Only about half of the N^{15} appeared in the urine, showing that much of it had replaced ordinary nitrogen of tissue proteins, which was then excreted. The liver proteins contained about three times as much of the N^{15} as found in the rest of the body proteins. The N^{15} was distributed among various amino acids. In a later experiment leucine labeled with deuterium and N^{15} was fed over a period of three days to rats in nitrogen balance. More than half (57 per cent) of the N^{15} was found in body proteins. The proteins were hydrolyzed, and some 22 different amino acids isolated. Excess N^{15} was found in all the amino acids except lysine, showing that the leucine amino nitrogen had been distributed among all these amino acids. Aside from leucine, glutamic and aspartic acids contained the most isotope. A comparison of the ratios of deuterium to N^{15} in the fed and tissue leucine showed that more than a third of the N^{15} of the dietary leucine had been replaced with ordinary nitrogen.

The fact that such a large proportion of the fed isotopic nitrogen appeared in the dicarboxylic amino acids glutamic and aspartic indicates the importance of these acids and of the transamination reactions in the taking up and redistribution of amino nitrogen.

UREA FORMATION

The deamination of amino acids forms large amounts of ammonia which, if allowed to accumulate, would be highly toxic. Normally, the blood contains only 0.1 to 0.2 mg per cent of ammonia nitrogen, an amount so small that special techniques are required for its determination. A concentration of 5 mg per cent is fatal to the rabbit. In view of the toxicity of ammonia, it is not surprising that the animal body detoxifies it rapidly in the liver before release into the systemic circulation. In man and other mammals detoxication is achieved largely by conversion to urea, whereas in reptiles and birds uric acid is formed. Considerable ammonia nitrogen may be excreted in the urine, but this is formed in the kidney for excretion in the urine and does not appreciably increase the ammonia content of the systemic blood.

Site of urea formation. Conclusive evidence that the liver is the site of urea formation was afforded by the work of Bollman, Mann, and Magath

(47) on dogs from which the liver or kidneys or both had been removed. If the kidneys alone were removed, preventing excretion, the blood urea rose rapidly. If the liver was removed, and the kidneys were left intact, the blood urea fell. If both the kidneys and liver were removed, the blood urea remained constant, since urea was neither being formed nor excreted.

In vitro work has shown that the enzymes concerned in the conversion of ammonia to urea are localized in the liver.

CHEMICAL MECHANISMS OF UREA FORMATION

Krebs-Henseleit cycle. Krebs and Henseleit (48), working with liver slices, established the general chemical mechanisms by which ammonia is converted to urea. These workers incubated liver slices with ammonium salts, bicarbonate as a source of carbon dioxide, and lactate as a source of energy, and studied the rate of urea formation. They found that the addition of ornithine greatly increased the rate of urea production. Citrulline had a similar effect. The amino acid, arginine, was found to be an intermediate product of the reaction. The liver contains the enzyme, arginase, which hydrolyzes arginine to ornithine and urea. Balance experiments showed that during urea synthesis the sum of the concentrations, ornithine + arginine, did not decrease appreciably, while the quantity of ammonia disappearing was approximately equivalent to the urea formed. The ornithine was not used up, showing its action to be catalytic. Although citrulline was involved in the synthesis, it did not act catalytically, since one of its nitrogen atoms appeared in the urea formed.

On the basis of the above observations Krebs and Henseleit proposed a cyclic mechanism for urea synthesis involving ornithine, citrulline, arginine, ammonia, and carbon dioxide as follows:

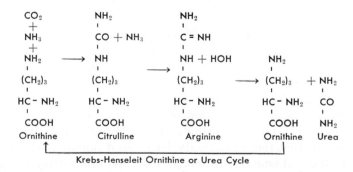

Krebs-Henseleit Ornithine or Urea Cycle

Two molecules of NH_3 and one molecule of CO_2 are converted to a molecule of urea for each turn of the cycle, and the ornithine is regenerated. The synthesis of urea involves the primary "fixation" of both CO_2 and NH_3.

Although the over-all process of urea synthesis as outlined in the Krebs-Henseleit cycle has been shown to be correct, it has been found that formation of citrulline, and the conversion of citrulline to arginine, are complex processes (49). Cohen (34,42) has recently reviewed urea formation.

Formation of carbamyl phosphate. The first stage in the synthesis of urea in animals may be considered to be the formation of carbamyl phosphate, the reaction being catalyzed by carbamyl phosphate synthetase (50):

$$NH_4^+ + HCO_3^- + 2ATP \xrightarrow[\text{Acyl glutamate}]{Mg^{++}} H_2N-\overset{\overset{\textstyle O}{\|}}{C}-O-PO_3H_2 + 2ADP + Pi$$

Carbamyl phosphate

Carbamyl phosphate is a reactive high-energy compound.

The standard free energy change, $\Delta F°'$, in the reaction is about -2 kcal. The enzyme carbamyl phosphate synthetase is present in the particulate fraction of the livers of vertebrates but is absent from avian liver, which forms uric acid instead of urea from NH_3. The enzyme requires an acyl glutamate such as N-acetyl glutamate as a cofactor, though its specific function is unknown.

Formation of citrulline from ornithine. Ornithine is converted to citrulline through the action of carbamyl phosphate and the liver enzyme ornithine transcarbamylase:

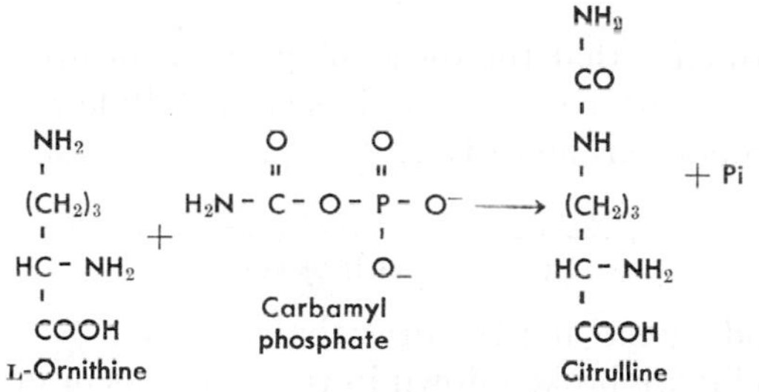

The reaction, as it operates in the liver, is not reversible.

Formation of arginine from citrulline. The synthesis of arginine from citrulline is effected in two stages. The first stage is the condensation of citrulline with aspartic acid to form argininosuccinic acid by the enzyme argininosuccinate synthetase. The argininosuccinate is then split into arginine and fumarate by the cleavage enzyme arginine synthetase.

The synthesis of urea is outlined in Figure 25.2.

Formation of urea from arginine. Arginine is hydrolyzed to ornithine and urea by the enzyme arginase as shown in the above equations. Arginase appears to occur only in the livers of animals which excrete urea; for example, it is not in the livers of birds, which excrete uric acid, but in the kidneys.

It will be observed from the above reactions that of the two N atoms in a molecule of urea, one is derived from ammonia, through carbamyl phosphate, and the other from aspartic acid, through argininosuccinic acid.

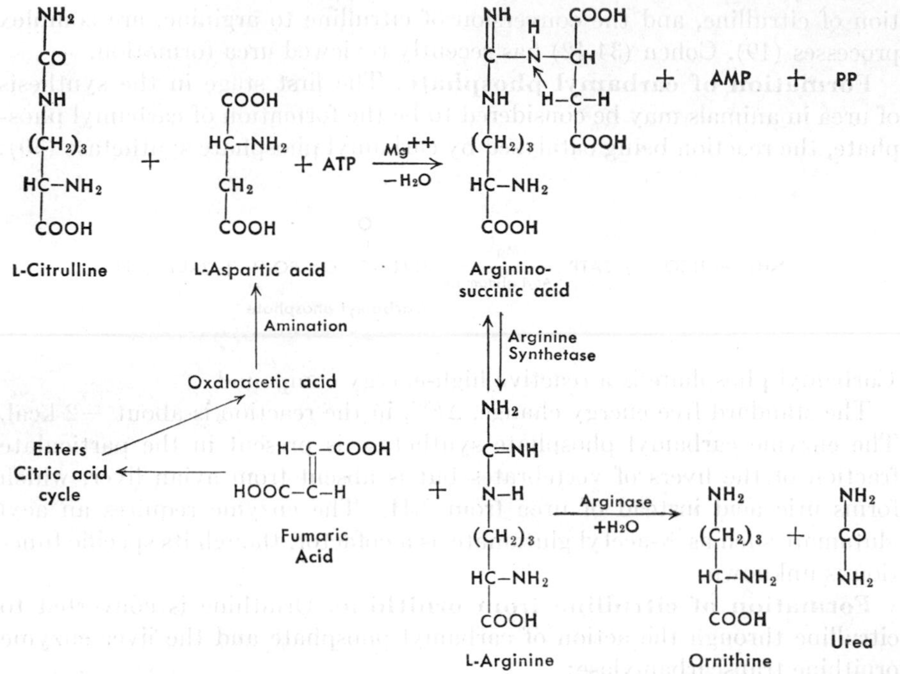

Figure 25.2. Urea synthesis.

Cohen (50) estimates that the over-all synthesis of urea from NH_4^+ and HCO_3^- through the ornithine cycle requires around 10 kcal of energy per mol under standard conditions and pH 7.

$$NH_4^+ + HCO_3^- + Aspartate^{\pm} \longrightarrow 2H_2O + Urea + Fumarate^{2-} + H^+$$
$$(\Delta F^{o'}_{298} = +10.04 \text{ kcal})$$

The process is endergonic and requires that energy be supplied to make it go. Since three ATP are broken down in the reactions of urea synthesis, the over-all process:

$$NH_4^+ + HCO_3^- + Aspartate^{\pm} + H_2O + 3ATP \longrightarrow$$
$$Urea + Fumarate^= + 2ADP + AMP + PP + Pi + H^+ (\Delta F^{o'} = -13.15 \text{ kcal})$$

is strongly exergonic.

MECHANISM OF AMINO GROUP AND AMMONIA INTERCONVERSION

It appears that the L-amino acid oxidases of tissues do not have the quantitative capacity or breadth of specificity enabling them to account for the oxidative removal of the amino groups as NH_3 from all the amino acids as a group. After NH_3 is introduced as —NH_2 groups into an amino acid, then the N is distributed throughout the other amino acids of the tissues by transamination reactions. Also, the —NH_2 groups of amino acids may be removed as NH_3. It appears that a coupling of transamination reactions and the reversible oxidative deamination of glutamic acid to α-ketoglutaric acid and NH_3 constitutes the mechanism which largely controls the removal of $-NH_2$ groups from amino acids as NH_3, and also "fixes" NH_3 into amino acids as $-NH_2$ groups (51).

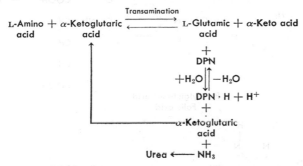

Thus, $-NH_2$ groups from amino acids in general first become the $-NH_2$ groups of glutamic acid molecules, and then become NH_3 through the action of glutamic acid dehydrogenase. Conversely, NH_3 becomes $-NH_2$ groups of amino acids, first by conversion to the $-NH_2$ of glutamic acid by reversal of the dehydrogenase reaction, and then distribution by transamination with α-keto acids corresponding to different amino acids.

THE UREA POOL OF THE BODY

Pietro and Rittenberg (52) injected N^{15}-labeled urea into human subjects and, by measuring the dilution of the N^{15}-labeled urea in the plasma (by body urea) or the rate of excretion of the labeled urea in the urine, calculated the size of the urea pool of the body. Urea readily passes through all membranes of the body and rapidly equilibrates with all the body water. A 68-kg subject had 5.74 g of urea nitrogen in his body pool, which represented a urea space (volume of body fluids containing 5.74 g of urea N) of 33.8 l. This represented 50 per cent of the body weight. The half-life of the urea pool (time for half to be excreted in the urine) for this subject was calculated to be 8.9 hours.

ONE-CARBON METABOLISM

Active formate and active formaldehyde. It has been shown that the metabolism of various amino acids and other compounds yields "active" formyl, formaldehyde, and formimino derivatives which are utilized for the incorporation (often reversibly) of one-carbon groups into other compounds. The metabolism involving these groups has been called "one-carbon" or "1-carbon" metabolism.

It has been found that the vitamin folic acid functions as a carrier of active one-carbon groups. The subject has been recently reviewed by Huennekens and Osborn (53).

The structures of folic acid and the various folic acid derivatives which serve as carriers of active one-carbon groups are given below:

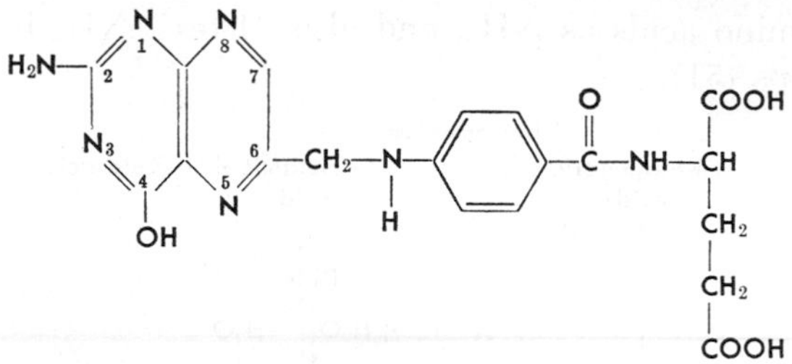

Pteroylglutamic acid
Folic acid

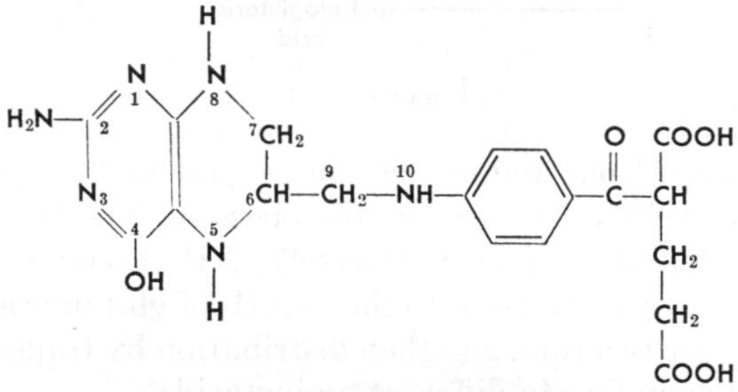

Tetrahydrofolic acid (FH₄)

Tetrahydrofolic acid (FH_4) is generally the carrier of the active one-carbon group. Since this function involves the part of the molecule containing N^5 and N^{10}, only this part is shown in the structures below:

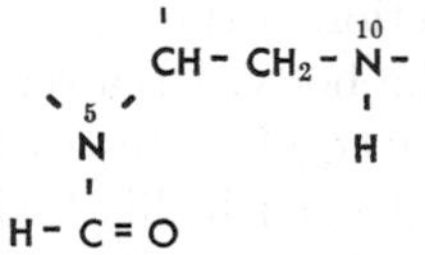

N^5-Formyltetrahydrofolic acid ($FH_4 \cdot CHO^5$)
Folinic acid

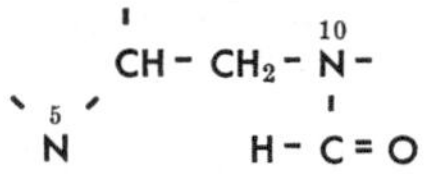

N^{10}-Formyltetrahydrofolic acid ($FH_4 \cdot CHO^{10}$)

The above compounds are carriers of the formyl group, $-\overset{\overset{\displaystyle H}{|}}{C}{=}O$ derived from $H \cdot COOH$, and represent what is called "active formate." The N^5 and N^{10} formyl derivatives are commonly designated as $f \cdot {}^5FH_4$ and $f \cdot {}^{10}FH_4$, respectively. However, for teaching purposes designations as $FH_4 \cdot CHO^5$ and $FH_4 \cdot CHO^{10}$, will be used in later discussion. These symbols merely indicate the N^5 and N^{10} formyl derivatives of FH_4, because one H to nitrogen is replaced by the formyl group:

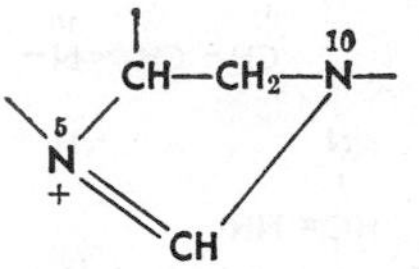

N⁵,N¹⁰-Methenyltetrahydrofolic acid
Anhydroleucovorin ($FH_4 \cdot CH^{5-10}$)

$FH_4 \cdot CHO^5$ and $FH_4 \cdot CHO^{10}$ are reversibly interconvertible through anhydroleucovorin:

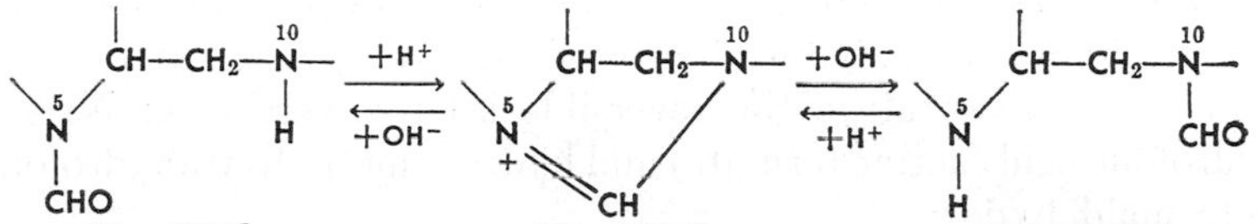

In enzymatic reactions it appears that N^{10} formyltetrahydrofolic acid, $FH_4 \cdot CHO^{10}$, or the bridge compound, anhydroleucovorin, $FH_4 \cdot CH^{5-10}$, is the formyl donor or "active formate."

$FH_4 \cdot CHO^5$ is enzymatically converted to $FH_4 \cdot CHO^{10}$ by a reaction involving ATP:

$$FH_4 \cdot CHO^5 + ATP \xrightarrow[\text{Mg}^{++}]{\text{Enzyme}} FH_4 \cdot CHO^{10} + ADP + Pi$$

$FH_4 \cdot CHO^{10}$ is formed by the formate activating enzyme (tetrahydrofolic formylase) of liver and microorganisms from FH_4, formate, and ATP:

$$H \cdot COOH + FH_4 + ATP \xrightarrow{\text{Mg}^{++}} FH_4 \cdot CHO^{10} + ADP + Pi$$

Formate is readily incorporated into the "active formate" pool by this reaction.

Tetrahydrofolic acid (FH_4) readily reacts with formaldehyde to form hydroxymethyl-tetrahydrofolic acid. It may be considered that the FH_4 first adds to the —NH— at N^5 or N^{10} to form a —CH_2OH group, which then loses water with the other —NH-group to form a methylene bridge compound. This may be represented as follows, where only the N^5 and N^{10} atoms are shown:

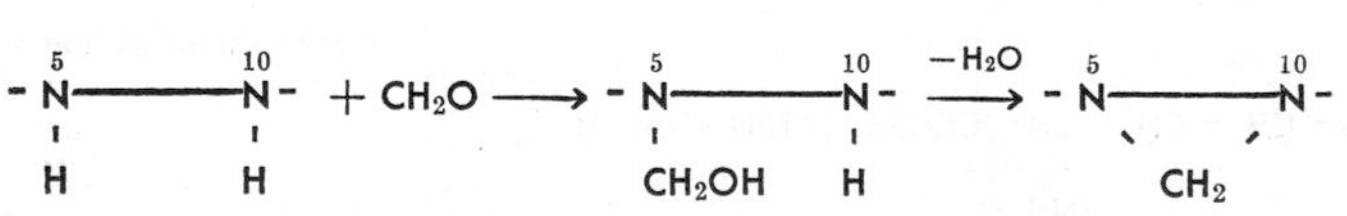

The formulation of the hydroxymethyl compound as a methylene bridge derivative is based upon its stability to air oxidation and other properties (53). In enzymatic reactions the bridge compound in effect provides hydroxymethyl groups, —CH_2OH. The bridge methylene form will be designated $FH_4 \cdot CH_2^{5-10}$, and the open form $FH_4 \cdot CH_2OH$. The substance represents what is called "active formaldehyde":

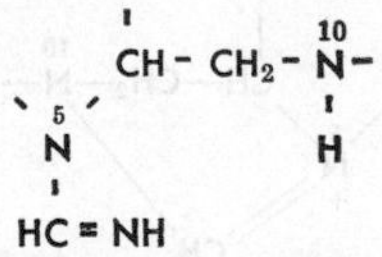

$$\begin{array}{c} \underset{5}{\overset{|}{CH}} - CH_2 - \overset{10}{\underset{|}{N}} - \\ \diagdown \; N \qquad\qquad H \\ \overset{|}{HC = NH} \end{array}$$

N⁵-Formiminotetrahydrofolic acid
$FH_4 \cdot CH = NH$

N^5-Formiminotetrahydrofolic acid, designated here as $FH_4 \cdot CH{=}NH$, is a carrier of formimino groups, $-CH{=}NH$, in a variety of metabolic reactions.

Interconversion of "active formate" and "active formaldehyde." An enzyme, hydroxymethyltetrahydrofolic dehydrogenase, found in liver, has been shown to catalyze the reversible interconversion of N^{10}-formyltetrahydrofolic acid (active formate) and hydroxymethyltetrahydrofolic acid (active formaldehyde):

$$FH_4 \cdot CH_2OH + TPN^+ \rightleftarrows FH_4 \cdot CHO^{10} + TPN \cdot H + H^+$$

While in crude enzyme preparations $FH_4 \cdot CHO^{10}$ is formed, it appears from studies with purified enzyme that the bridge structures are involved in the primary reaction:

$$FH_4 \cdot CH_2{}^{5-10} + TPN^+ \rightleftarrows FH_4 \cdot CH^{5-10} + TPN \cdot H$$

Active formaldehyde   Active formate

Synthesis of the methionine methyl group from "active formaldehyde" (53, p. 423). It has been shown that an enzyme of liver catalyzes the incorporation of a methyl group, derived from the $-CH_2OH$ group of serine, into homocysteine with the formation of methionine. The reactions are complex and require FH_4, ATP, TPN, and Mg^{++}. In outline the process appears to be represented as follows, no attempt being made to indicate a function for ATP (unknown):

$$HO-CH_2-\underset{\underset{NH_2}{|}}{CH}-COOH + FH_4 \xrightleftharpoons[\text{hydroxymethylase}]{\text{Serine}} FH_4 \cdot CH_2OH + H_2N-CH_2-COOH$$

Serine   Glycine

$$FH_4 \cdot CH_2OH + HS-CH_2-CH_2-\underset{\underset{NH_2}{|}}{CH}-COOH \xrightleftharpoons{\text{Enzyme}} FH_4 + HO-CH_2-S-CH_2-CH_2-\underset{\underset{NH_2}{|}}{CH}-COOH$$

Homocysteine   Hydroxymethyl-homocysteine

$$HO-CH_2-S-CH_2-CH_2-\underset{\underset{NH_2}{|}}{CH}-COOH + TPN \cdot H + H^+ \xrightleftharpoons{\text{Enzyme}}$$

Hydroxymethyl-homocysteine

$$CH_3-S-CH_2-CH_2-\underset{\underset{NH_2}{|}}{CH}-COOH + TPN^+$$

Methionine

Methionine is the chief direct donor of methyl groups in biologic methylations after conversion to "active" S-adenosylmethionine, which is formed by the reaction of methionine with ATP, the reaction being catalyzed by the "methionine activating enzyme" (54):

$$\text{Adenosine triphosphate} + CH_3\text{—}S\text{—}CH_2\text{—}CH_2\text{—}CH\text{—}COOH \xrightarrow{Mg^{++}}$$
$$\underset{\text{ATP}}{} \qquad\qquad\qquad\qquad\qquad \underset{\substack{| \\ NH_2 \\ \text{Methionine}}}{}$$

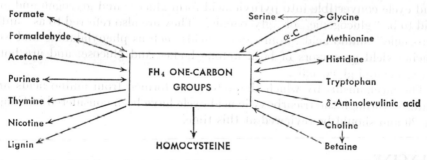

S-Adenosylmethionine

The $CH_3\text{—}\overset{+}{S}$ bond of S-adenosylmethionine is a high-energy bond, and the compound serves as a methylating agent in the synthesis of various methyl-containing compounds (creatine, choline, anserine, adrenaline, etc.).

Most of the S-adenosylmethionine in the animal body is generally formed from methionine of the diet; however, under unusual circumstances the one-carbon pool may be drawn upon as a source of methyl groups through the reactions outlined.

It is of interest that the formation of methyl groups from the one carbon pool requires not only the participation of tetrahydrofolic acid derivatives but also, in some unknown way, vitamin B_{12} or cyanocobalamine (55).

Formate
Formaldehyde
Acetone
Purines
Thymine
Nicotine
Lignin

Serine ⟷ Glycine
α-C
Methionine
Histidine
Tryptophan
δ-Aminolevulinic acid
Choline
Betaine

FH₄ ONE-CARBON GROUPS

HOMOCYSTEINE

Figure 25.3. Relation of tetrahydrofolic acid "activated compounds" in metabolism.

The one-carbon pool. The one-carbon derivatives of tetrahydrofolic acid are of much biologic importance in reactions involving amino acids, purines, pyrimidines, etc. The diagram of Figure 25.3 shows the relations of tetrahydrofolic acid derivatives to the synthesis or breakdown of a number of biologically important compounds. One-carbon derivatives of tetrahydrofolic acid are both utilized in the synthesis of compounds such as purines, methionine, and histidine and are formed in the breakdown of these compounds. In other cases the breakdown of substances only yields one-carbon FH_4 derivatives (tryptophan, betaine, acetone). FH_4 derivatives are utilized in the synthesis of some compounds but apparently are not formed directly in their breakdown (thymine, choline, and nicotine). Thus, it is seen that many compounds, in conjunction with one-carbon tetrahydrofolic acid derivatives, constitute a mobile active "one-carbon pool" that is involved in many biological reactions.

METABOLISM OF INDIVIDUAL AMINO ACIDS

Since the amino acids involved in protein metabolism represent some 20 different chemical structures, the metabolic processes of the amino acids are highly diversified. As previously indicated, the mechanisms of deamination are rather much the same for the amino acids as a group. The intricacies of amino acid metabolism become apparent in a consideration of the interconversions of amino acids, in their utilization for special syntheses, and in the pathways of the oxidative degradation of the keto acids resulting from deamination. The present discussion will deal with these phases of amino acid metabolism.

In general, the metabolism of the keto acids formed by deamination of amino acids leads to the formation of substances such as acetyl CoA, acetoacetic acid, pyruvic acid, α-ketoglutaric acid, oxaloacetic acid, and fumaric acid, some of which may be converted to fatty acids and cholesterol, others to glucose and glycogen, and all may be oxidized to CO_2 and H_2O through the citric acid cycle. Amino acids which yield acetyl CoA or acetoacetic acid and increase the excretion of ketone bodies in diabetic animals are said to be ketogenic. Amino acids which form pyruvic acid or a member of the citric acid cycle convertible into pyruvic acid form glucose and glycogen and are said to be "glucogenic" or "glycogenic." They are also referred to as "antiketogenic" amino acids. Some amino acids such as phenylalanine and isoleucine yield precursors of both ketone bodies and glucose, and are both ketogenic and glycogenic.

The mechanisms by which the keto acids formed from amino acids are oxidized through the tricarboxylic acid cycle have been considered in Chapter 20 and should be reviewed at this time.

GLYCINE

Glycine alone of the natural amino acids does not contain an asymmetric carbon atom and consequently does not exist in isomeric forms. Most of our information relative to glycine metabolism has been obtained through the use of isotopic tracer atoms.

Deamination and amination. That glycine is readily deaminized in the body has been shown by feeding glycine labeled with N^{15} and finding the N^{15} distributed among the various tissue amino acids and urea. Conversely, amination of a carbon compound to give glycine, directly or indirectly, is shown by the fact that N^{15} of ammonia or labeled amino acids fed to an animal appears in the tissue glycine.

The general amino acid D- and L-oxidases do not act upon glycine, which is oxidatively deaminized by a specific glycine oxidase, a flavoprotein (FP):

$$H_2N-CH_2-COOH + \underset{\substack{Glycine \\ oxidase}}{FP} \longrightarrow \underset{Imino\ acid}{HN=\overset{H}{C}-COOH} + FP \cdot 2H$$

$$FP \cdot 2H + O_2 \longrightarrow FP + H_2O_2$$

$$2H_2O_2 \xrightarrow{catalase} 2H_2O + O_2$$

$$\downarrow +HOH$$

$$\underset{Glyoxylic\ acid}{O=\overset{H}{C}-COOH} + NH_3$$

Glyoxylic acid may be aminated back to glycine by transamination with glutamine, glutamate, ornithine, etc. This, of course, also provides a pathway of glycine deamination.

Weinhouse and associates (56) have shown that glyoxylic acid is rapidly oxidized to formic and oxalic acids and CO_2 by rat liver slices:

(1) $$O=\overset{H}{C}-COOH + H_2O_2 \longrightarrow H \cdot COOH + CO_2$$
(2) $$H \cdot COOH + H_2O_2 \longrightarrow CO_2 + 2H_2O$$

(3) $$O=\overset{H}{C}-COOH + \tfrac{1}{2}O_2 \longrightarrow HOOC-COOH$$

It appears that little oxalate is formed unless the concentration of glyoxylate is high, and this production of oxalate appears normally to be of little metabolic importance. The oxidation of formate to CO_2 and H_2O proceeds very rapidly.

The above relations in glycine metabolism may be represented as follows:

$$\underset{Glycine}{H_2N-CH_2-COOH} \rightleftharpoons \underset{Glyoxylic\ acid}{O=\overset{H}{C}-COOH} + NH_3$$

$$\underset{Oxalic\ acid}{HOOC-COOH} \qquad \underset{Formic\ acid}{H \cdot COOH + CO_2}$$

$$\downarrow$$

$$CO_2 + H_2O$$

Since glycine is glycogenic and glyoxylic and oxalic acids are not, much glycine must be metabolized through other pathways. As shown below, an important pathway of glycine metabolism is through conversion to serine, which is glycogenic.

It will be noted that the α-carbon of glycine is converted to formate, which enters the one-carbon pool, and thus it may serve as a source of one carbon units for the synthesis of other compounds.

Interconversion of glycine and serine. Greenberg and associates (57) incubated glycine containing C^{14} in the α-position with liver homogenate and found most of the C^{14} taken up by the tissue proteins to be present in serine, indicating conversion of glycine to serine. Sakami (58) gave glycine labeled with C^{13} in the carboxyl group and formate labeled with C^{14} to rats simultaneously. The serine isolated from liver proteins contained a large amount of C^{13} in the carboxyl group and C^{14} in the β-carbon position.

This evidence indicates that serine is produced in the body by interaction of glycine and formate:

$$
\underset{\text{Formic acid}}{\overset{\overset{O}{\|}}{H-C^{14}-OH}} + \underset{\underset{H}{|}}{\overset{\overset{NH_2}{|} \ \overset{O}{\|}}{H-C\text{---}C^{13}-OH}} \xrightarrow{+2H} \underset{\underset{H \quad H}{|}}{\overset{\overset{OH \ NH_2 \ O}{|} \ \ \ \ |}{H-C^{14}-C\text{---}C^{13}-OH}} + H_2O
$$

Glycine   Serine

Sakami (59) later showed that formate for this reaction is derived also from glycine. He administered glycine labeled with C^{14} in the methylene group to rats and determined the isotope distribution in the liver serine formed. Almost as much C^{14} was present in the β- as in the α- carbon position of serine, showing that the β-carbon must have originated from formate formed from the methylene carbon of glycine:

$$
\underset{\underset{\text{Glycine}}{\underset{H}{|*}}}{\overset{\overset{COOH}{|}}{H-C-NH_2}} \xrightarrow[\text{deam}]{ox} \underset{\underset{\text{Glyoxylic}}{\underset{H}{|*}}}{\overset{\overset{COOH}{|}}{C=O}} \xrightarrow{ox} \underset{\underset{\text{Formic}}{\underset{*}{}}}{\overset{\overset{O}{\|}}{H-C-OH}} + CO_2
$$

acid

$$
\underset{\underset{\text{Formic}}{\text{acid}}}{\overset{\overset{O}{\|}}{H-C-OH}} + \underset{\underset{\text{Glycine}}{\underset{H}{|*}}}{\overset{\overset{NH_2}{|}}{H-C-COOH}} \xrightarrow{+2H} \underset{\underset{\text{Serine}}{\underset{H \quad H}{|*}}}{\overset{\overset{OH \ \ NH_2}{|} \ \ \ |}{H-C\text{---}C-COOH}} + H_2O
$$

It has been shown (60) that the β-carbon of serine, presumably through formate or formaldehyde, may arise from a number of different sources which include the α-carbon of glycine, the methyl groups of choline and methionine, the methyl groups of acetone, the C_2 of the imidazole group of histidine, and the methyl group of sarcosine (N-methylglycine) (61). It was shown by Mitoma and Greenberg (61) that formaldehyde is a product of the oxidation of the methyl group of sarcosine, and that a formaldehyde-like compound is the intermediary one-carbon compound in the formation of the β-carbon of serine from both glycine and sarcosine.

Mackenzie and associates (62) have shown that liver homogenates oxidize dimethylaminoethanol, dimethylglycine, methylglycine (sarcosine), and methanol to give formaldehyde. Dimethylglycine formed sarcosine, and sarcosine gave glycine, in addition to formaldehyde. It is probable that all methyl compounds oxidized in the body to yield formaldehyde also provide this formaldehyde for the synthesis of serine from glycine.

The formation of glycine from serine has been demonstrated by Shemin (63). He injected serine containing N^{15} in the amino group and C^{13} in the carboxyl group into guinea pigs and rats. The ratio of C^{15} in the carboxyl group to N^{15} of the amino group in the glycine formed was about the same as this ratio for the serine injected. This demonstrated that the body forms glycine from serine by removing the β-carbon of serine, presumably as formate.

The interconversion of serine and glycine is effected through the action of the liver enzyme serine hydroxymethylase, which requires pyridoxal phosphate, glutathione, tetrahydrofolic acid (FH_4), TPN or DPN, and Mn^{++}. N^{10}-Hydroxymethyl-tetrahydrofolic acid ($FH_4 \cdot CH_2OH^{10}$) is formed in the process, which may be represented as follows:

(1)
$$FH_4 + HO-CH_2-\underset{\underset{\text{Serine}}{\overset{|}{NH_2}}}{CH}-COOH \underset{+Mn^{++}}{\overset{\overset{\text{Pyridoxal}}{\text{Phosphate}}}{\rightleftharpoons}} FH_4 \cdot CH_2OH^{10} + H_2N-CH_2-COOH$$
$$\underset{\text{GSH}}{} \qquad \underset{\text{Glycine}}{}$$

Formate, from the one-carbon pool, is utilized for the synthesis of serine from glycine by reaction with FH_4 to form N^{10}-formyltetrahydrofolic acid, $FH_4 \cdot CHO^{10}$, which is then reduced to $FH_4 \cdot CH_2OH^{10}$ as follows:

(2)
$$FH_4 \cdot CHO^{10} + TPN \cdot H + H^+ \rightleftharpoons FH_4 \cdot CH_2OH^{10} + TPN^+$$

Glycine then reacts with $FH_4 \cdot CH_2OH^{10}$ to form serine and FH_4 by reversal of Reaction (1).

When carboxyl-labeled alanine was given to the rat, carboxyl-labeled glycine was formed (64). Carboxyl-labeled pyruvate also gave carboxyl-labeled glycine, while pyruvic acid labeled in the α-C gave glycine labeled in the α-carbon (65). These findings may be integrated through serine as follows:

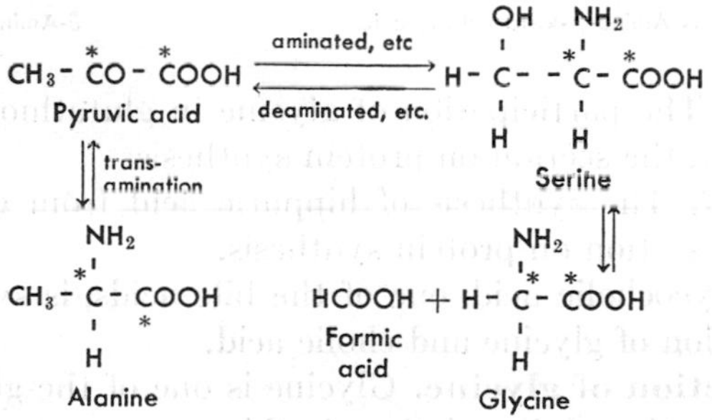

$$\underset{\text{Pyruvic acid}}{CH_3-\overset{*}{C}O-\overset{*}{C}OOH} \underset{\text{deaminated, etc.}}{\overset{\text{aminated, etc}}{\rightleftharpoons}} \underset{\text{Serine}}{\overset{OH \quad NH_2}{H-\overset{|}{\underset{|}{C}}-\overset{*|}{\underset{|}{C}}-\overset{*}{C}OOH}}$$

$$\Big\updownarrow \underset{\text{amination}}{\text{trans-}} \qquad\qquad\qquad \Big\updownarrow$$

$$\underset{\text{Alanine}}{CH_3-\overset{*|}{\underset{\underset{H}{|}}{C}}-COOH} \qquad \underset{\substack{\text{Formic} \\ \text{acid}}}{HCOOH} + \underset{\text{Glycine}}{H-\overset{*}{\underset{\underset{H}{|}}{C}}-\overset{*}{C}OOH}$$

According to these relations, any substance convertible into pyruvic acid and serine may form glycine. This means that pyruvic acid from carbohydrate breakdown, from the metabolism of many amino acids, and from the members of the citric acid cycle may contribute the carbon atoms for serine and glycine synthesis. Also, it is obvious that glycine, through the pathway of serine and pyruvic acid, is integrated with carbohydrate and fatty acid metabolism.

Relation of glycine to the synthesis of other biologically important substances. *Creatine.* Glycine is utilized by the body in the formation of creatine. Bloch and Schoenheimer (66) administered glycine labeled with N^{15} to rats and found a high concentration of N^{15} in the sarcosine (methylglycine) portion of the creatine formed. This synthesis will be given in more detail in later discussion.

Purines. Glycine has been shown (67) to provide carbon atoms 4 and 5, and the nitrogen at position 7, of the purine ring. This means that other substances convertible into glycine contribute to the synthesis:

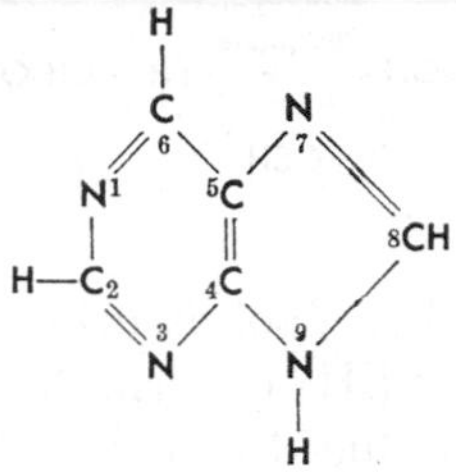

Purine

Heme. As pointed out in Chapter 12, glycine is involved in heme synthesis through its participation in the synthesis of the intermediate, δ-aminolevulinic acid (67).

$$H_2N - CH_2 - COOH + HOOC - CH_2 - CH_2 - CO - S - CoA \longrightarrow HS - CoA +$$

Succinyl CoA

$$\underset{\alpha\text{-Amino-}\beta\text{-keto-adipic acid}}{HOOC - \underset{\underset{NH_2}{|}}{CH} - CO - CH_2 - CH_2 - COOH} \overset{-CO_2}{\longrightarrow} \underset{\delta\text{-Aminolevulinic acid}}{H_2N - CH_2 - CO - CH_2 - CH_2 - COOH}$$

Glutathione. The participation of glycine in glutathione synthesis has been considered in the section on protein synthesis.

Hippuric acid. The synthesis of hippuric acid from glycine has been considered in the section on protein synthesis.

Bile acids. Glycocholic acid, one of the bile acids, is synthesized in the liver by conjugation of glycine and cholic acid.

Glycogenic action of glycine. Glycine is one of the glycogenic (glucogenic) amino acids, though its relations in this respect are complex. The fact that glycine is converted to serine and serine to pyruvic acid accounts for the incorporation of glycine carbon atoms into glucose and glycogen.

That glycine has an important indirect action in stimulating glycogen formation from other substances, which in effect exceeds the direct production from glycine, appears to be established. Olsen, Hemingway, and Nier (68) fed mice glycine labeled with C^{13} in the carboxyl group and after 16 hours determined the liver glycogen and the amount of C^{13} present. Despite the fact that there was a large increase in the amount of liver glycogen due to the metabolism of glycine, the quantity of C^{13} present indicated that a relatively small proportion of the glycine carbon atoms had been incorporated into the glycogen. The work of Todd and associates (69) provided excellent support for the concept that glycine metabolism stimulates glycogen formation from other substances. These workers fed one group of rats a control diet and another group the control diet containing 10 per cent glycine substituted for dextrin. Insulin was administered to both groups, and after five hours the carbohydrates of the body were determined. The glycine-fed rats had 2.5 times as much muscle glycogen and 10 times as much liver glycogen as the control animals and also showed much less depression of the blood sugar. A determination (70) of the glycine contents of such animals prior to the action of insulin showed that the glycine present could account for only a small fraction of the carbohydrate formed, and the remainder must have been produced through the stimulating action of glycine upon the formation

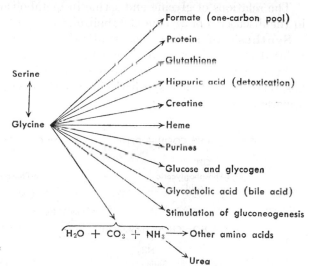

Figure 25.4. Glycine metabolism.

of glycogen from other substances. This action apparently is due to a stimulation of adrenal cortical activity (and gluconeogenesis) by glycine, since adrenalectomized rats do not respond with increased carbohydrate formation after glycine, as do normal animals (71).

Mirski and coworkers (72) observed that animals maintained on a high protein diet and then fasted or subjected to other strenuous conditions maintain their glycogen reserves better than animals fed a high carbohydrate diet. This was termed the "protein effect." That the protein effect is related to the stimulating action of protein upon gluconeogenesis was indicated by disappearance of the effect after adrenalectomy. Todd and associates have shown that glycine is responsible for much of this protein effect.

Summary of glycine metabolism. Glycine, the simplest of the amino acids, to date has been found to be utilized in more different ways in the animal body than practically any other amino acid. Whether this situation is true or only apparent awaits isotopic studies on other amino acids as extensive as those carried out on glycine.

The diagram of Figure 25.4 summarizes most of the known metabolic functions of glycine.

SERINE

Serine, α-amino-β-hydroxypropionic acid, need not be included in the diet for growth and maintenance and consequently is readily synthesized by the body. It is a glycogenic amino acid. As previously indicated, serine and glycine are interconvertible in the body, and serine also is involved in the synthesis of cysteine. Serine is a component of phosphatidyl serine, a member of the cephalin group of phospholipids. Ethanolamine, the immediate precursor of choline, is formed by decarboxylation of serine.

The relations of glycine and serine in metabolism have been pointed out in the discussion of glycine metabolism.

Synthesis of serine. The synthesis of serine from glycine has been pointed out. Ichihara and Greenberg (73) have reported the synthesis of serine by enzymes of rat liver from 3-phosphoglyceric acid, and Davies (74) has reported a similar synthesis in pea epicotyls. The reactions involved apparently are as follows:

$$P-O-CH_2-\underset{\underset{OH}{|}}{CH}-COOH + DPN^+ \underset{\xleftarrow{}}{\overset{Enzyme}{\longrightarrow}} P-O-CH_2-\underset{\underset{O}{\|}}{C}-COOH + DPN \cdot H + H^+$$

3-Phosphoglyceric acid   3-Phosphohydroxypyruvic acid

$$\Big\updownarrow \begin{array}{l} \text{Transamination} \\ \text{with glutamate} \end{array}$$

$$Pi + HO-CH_2-\underset{\underset{NH_2}{|}}{CH}-COOH \xleftarrow[+H_2O]{\underset{\text{phosphatase}}{\text{Phosphoserine}}} P-O-CH_2-\underset{\underset{NH_2}{|}}{CH}-COOH$$

Serine   3-Phosphoserine

Deamination. Serine is deaminated by L-serine dehydrase of liver which requires pyridoxal phosphate as cofactor (35, p. 277).

$$\underset{\underset{COOH}{|}}{\overset{CH_2OH}{\underset{|}{HC-NH_2}}} \xrightarrow{-H_2O} \underset{\underset{COOH}{|}}{\overset{CH_2}{\underset{\|}{C-NH_2}}} \rightleftharpoons \underset{\underset{COOH}{|}}{\overset{CH_3}{\underset{\|}{C=NH}}} \xrightarrow[Mg^{++}]{+H_2O} \underset{\underset{COOH}{|}}{\overset{CH_3}{\underset{|}{CO}}} + NH_3$$

Serine   Imino acid   Pyruvic acid

Serine is also deaminated by a transamination with pyruvic acid (75) catalyzed by liver transaminase:

L-Serine + Pyruvic acid $\rightleftharpoons$ Hydroxypyruvic acid + L-Alanine

The reverse of this reaction represents serine synthesis.

Specialized functions of serine. Stetten and Grail (76) fed serine containing N^{15} to rats and found the isotope present in the serine of the phospholipid fraction (phosphatidyl serine) and in ethanolamine and tissue protein cystine in amounts indicating conversion of serine to ethanolamine and cystine. Since ethanolamine is converted to choline by methylation (by methionine), N^{15} was also present in the choline formed but in lesser amounts than in ethanolamine. Ethanolamine is formed from serine by decarboxylation:

$$
\underset{\text{Serine}}{HO-\overset{\overset{\displaystyle H}{|}}{\underset{\underset{\displaystyle H}{|}}{C}}-\overset{\overset{\displaystyle NH_2}{|}}{\underset{\underset{\displaystyle H}{|}}{C}}-COOH} \xrightarrow{\text{decarboxylase}} \underset{\text{Ethanolamine}}{HO-\overset{\overset{\displaystyle H}{|}}{\underset{\underset{\displaystyle H}{|}}{C}}-\overset{\overset{\displaystyle H}{|}}{\underset{\underset{\displaystyle H}{|}}{C}}-NH_2 + CO_2}
$$

The mechanism of conversion of serine to cystine will be considered in the discussion of cysteine and methionine.

The metabolisms of serine and glycine are intimately associated in the formation of choline and related compounds, as shown in the diagram of

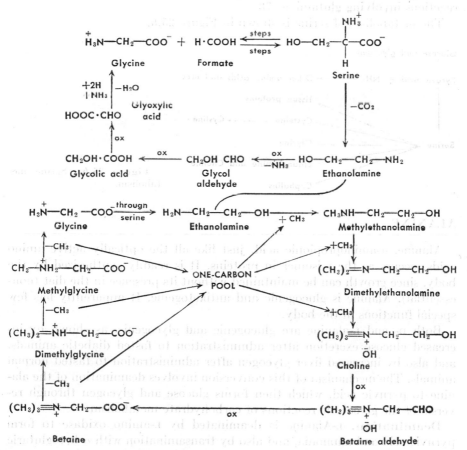

Figure 25.5. Synthesis of choline and betaine.

Figure 25.5, which represents two interconnected cycles. As indicated, one-carbon metabolism is prominent in the transformations, which involve one-carbon derivatives of tetrahydrofolic acid. In the methylation of ethanol-amine to choline, it appears that the first two methyl groups are derived from hydroxymethyltetrahydrofolic acid, $FH_4 \cdot CH_2OH$ (77), while the third methyl is derived from methionine through S-adenosyl-methionine.

It is of interest that certain molds form serine derivatives which are antibiotics:

N_2CH_2—CO—O—CH$_2$—CH—COOH
                              |
                            NH$_2$

o-Diazoacetylserine
Azaserine

Cycloserine
Oxamycin

Azaserine is of interest because it inhibits the growth of tumors and produces cell mutation. It interferes with purine synthesis through blocking reactions involving glutamine (78).

The metabolism of serine is shown in Figure 25.6.

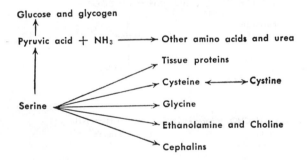

Figure 25.6. Serine metabolism.

ALANINE

Alanine, α-aminopropionic acid, just like all the optically active amino acids, occurs as the L-isomer in proteins. It is readily synthesized by the body, since growth can be maintained without its presence in the diet (non-essential). Alanine is glucogenic and antiketogenic. It apparently has few special functions in the body.

Both D- and L-alanine are glucogenic and glycogenic, as shown by increased glucose excretion after administration to fasted diabetic animals, and also by increased liver glycogen after administration to fasted normal animals. The mechanism of this conversion involves deamination of the alanine to pyruvic acid, which then forms glucose and glycogen through reversal of the glycolytic reactions of carbohydrate metabolism.

Deamination. L-Alanine is deaminated by L-amino oxidase to form pyruvic acid and ammonia, and also by transamination with α-ketoglutaric acid:

$$CH_3 - CH - COOH + FP \longrightarrow CH_3 - C - COOH + FP \cdot H_2$$

$$\begin{array}{ccc} | & \quad & || & \quad + \\ NH_2 & & NH & O_2 \\ \text{L-Alanine} & & \text{Imino acid} & \downarrow \\ & & + & FP + H_2O_2 \\ NH_3 + CH_3 - CO - COOH & \longleftarrow & H_2O & \\ & \text{Pyruvic acid} & & \end{array}$$

$$\text{L-Alanine} + \alpha\text{-Ketoglutaric acid} \xrightarrow{\text{Transaminase}} \text{Pyruvic acid} + \text{L-Glutamic acid}$$

Reversal of this reaction leads to the synthesis of alanine from pyruvic acid.

The unnatural isomer D-alanine is apparently well utilized by animals through deamination to pyruvic acid by D-amino acid oxidase followed by transamination of the pyruvic acid to L-alanine.

It is of interest that D-alanine is present as a polypeptide in the cell wall of *L. casei* (79).

The metabolic relations of alanine are shown in Figure 25.7.

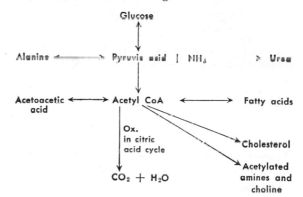

Figure 25.7. Metabolism of alanine.

THREONINE

Threonine, α-amino-β-hydroxy-n-butyric acid, possesses two asymmetric carbon atoms and exists in four isomeric forms:

$$\begin{array}{cccc}
\text{COOH} & \text{COOH} & \text{COOH} & \text{COOH} \\
| & | & | & | \\
H-C-NH_2 & H_2N-C-H & H-C-NH_2 & H_2N-C-H \\
| & | & | & | \\
HO-C-H & H-C-OH & H-C-OH & HO-C-H \\
| & | & | & | \\
CH_3 & CH_3 & CH_3 & CH_3
\end{array}$$

$$\text{D} \quad \text{Threonines} \quad \text{L} \qquad\qquad \text{D} \quad \text{Allothreonines} \quad \text{L}$$

The configurational relation of the asymmetric carbon attached to the amino group of natural threonine is the same as found in L-serine and in L-glyceric aldehyde of the sugar series. Accordingly, it is designated "L-threonine."

Synthesis of threonine. Threonine has been shown to be indispensable in the diet of man as well as the rat, and accordingly is not synthesized in the body. However, its synthesis by microorganisms such as *Neurospora crassa*, *E. coli*, and yeast from aspartic acid according to the following reactions appears to be established (80, 81):

$$\text{HOOC} - CH_2 - \underset{\underset{NH_2}{|}}{CH} - COOH + ATP \underset{\xrightarrow{\hspace{2.5cm}}}{\overset{\beta\text{-Aspartokinase}}{\rightleftharpoons}} ADP + H_2O_3P - O - \overset{\overset{O}{\|}}{C} - CH_2 - \underset{\underset{NH_2}{|}}{CH} - COOH$$

$$\underset{\text{L-Aspartic acid}}{} \qquad\qquad\qquad\qquad\qquad \underset{\beta\text{-Aspartyl phosphate}}{}$$

$$+$$

$$TPN \cdot H + H^+$$

$$\Big\updownarrow \text{Dehydrogenase}$$

$$H^+ + DPN \cdot H + O = \overset{\overset{}{}}{\underset{\underset{H}{|}}{C}} - CH_2 - \underset{\underset{NH_2}{|}}{CH} - COOH + TPN^+ + Pi$$

$$\underset{\text{Aspartic-}\beta\text{-Semialdehyde}}{}$$

$$\Big\updownarrow \overset{DPN \cdot H + H^+}{\text{Dehydrogenase}}$$

$$\underset{\substack{\text{ATP, pyridoxal}\\\text{phosphate, enzyme}}}{}$$

$$CH_3 - \underset{\underset{OH}{|}}{CH} - \underset{\underset{NH_2}{|}}{CH} - COOH \longleftarrow\!\!\!\!\!\!\!\!\xrightarrow{\hspace{3.5cm}} HO - CH_2 - CH_2 - \underset{\underset{NH_2}{|}}{CH} - COOH + DPN^+$$

$$\underset{\text{Threonine}}{} \qquad\qquad\qquad\qquad\qquad\qquad\qquad \underset{\text{Homoserine}}{}$$

A second pathway for the synthesis of threonine in microorganisms involves the reversible reaction of glycine and acetaldehyde (81):

$$\underset{\underset{\underset{\text{Glycine}}{NH_2}}{|}}{CH_2 - COOH} + CH_3 - CHO \underset{\underset{\substack{\text{Pyridoxal}\\\text{phosphate}}}{\xleftarrow{\hspace{1.5cm}}}}{\overset{\text{Glycinogenase}}{\xrightarrow{\hspace{1.5cm}}}} CH_3 - \underset{\underset{\underset{\text{Threonine}}{OH \quad NH_2}}{|\quad\;\;|}}{CH - CH} - COOH$$

$$\underset{\text{Acetaldehyde}}{}$$

Mammalian liver contains an enzyme catalyzing this reaction. However, the animal apparently does not synthesize threonine because of lack of acetaldehyde. In the animal the reaction represents a pathway of threonine breakdown with the formation of glycine.

Catabolism of threonine (82). Threonine apparently is deaminated only by threonine dehydrase. It does not undergo transamination. As indicated above, threonine is split into glycine and acetaldehyde. The two established pathways of threonine breakdown by liver enzymes may be represented as follows:

$$\underset{\underset{\text{Acetaldehyde}}{CHO}}{\overset{CH_3}{|}} \xleftarrow{\text{Glycino-}} \overset{\text{genase}}{} \quad \underset{\underset{\underset{\text{L-Threonine}}{COOH}}{\underset{H - C - NH_2}{|}}}{\overset{\underset{HO - C - H}{|}}{\overset{CH_3}{|}}} \underset{+H_2O}{\overset{\text{Dehydrase}}{\underset{\xleftarrow{\hspace{1cm}}}{\overset{-H_2O}{\rightarrow}}}} \underset{\underset{COOH}{\underset{C - NH_2}{\|}}}{\overset{\overset{CH}{\|}}{\overset{CH_3}{|}}} \rightleftharpoons \underset{\underset{\underset{\text{Imino}\atop\text{acid}}{COOH}}{\underset{C = NH}{|}}}{\overset{\overset{CH_2}{|}}{\overset{CH_3}{|}}} + H_2O \longrightarrow \underset{\underset{\underset{\alpha\text{-Ketobutyric}\atop\text{acid}}{COOH}}{\underset{CO}{|}}}{\overset{\overset{CH_2}{|}}{\overset{CH_3}{|}}} + NH_3$$

$$\underset{\underset{\underset{\text{Glycine}}{COOH}}{\overset{CH_2 - NH_2}{|}}}{\xleftarrow{\hspace{1cm}}}$$

$$\underset{\underset{\underset{CO}{|}}{\overset{CH_2}{|}}}{\overset{CH_3}{|}} \xrightarrow{\text{ox}} CO_2 + \underset{\text{Propionic acid}}{CH_3 - CH_2 - COOH} \longrightarrow \text{Glucose}$$

$$\underset{\underset{\alpha\text{-Ketobutyric}\atop\text{acid}}{COOH}}{} \underset{\text{Transamination}}{\overset{\xrightarrow{\hspace{1.5cm}}}{\xleftarrow{\hspace{1.5cm}}}} CH_3 - CH_2 - \underset{\underset{NH_2}{|}}{CH} - COOH$$

$$\underset{\alpha\text{-Aminobutyric acid}}{}$$

The metabolism of threonine in the animal body may be summarized as shown in Figure 25.8.

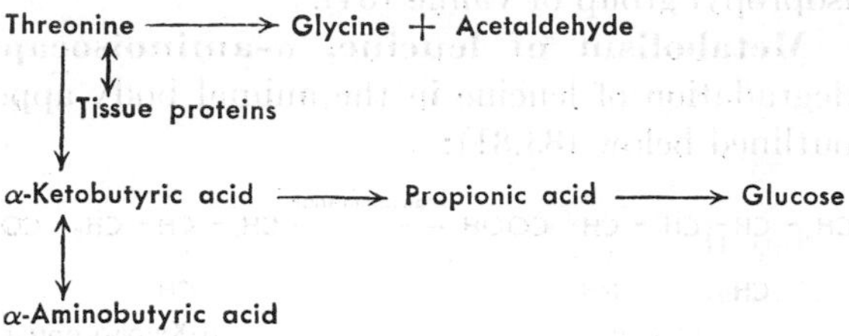

$$\text{Threonine} \longrightarrow \text{Glycine} + \text{Acetaldehyde}$$

$$\big\updownarrow \ \text{Tissue proteins}$$

$$\alpha\text{-Ketobutyric acid} \longrightarrow \text{Propionic acid} \longrightarrow \text{Glucose}$$

$$\big\downarrow$$

$$\alpha\text{-Aminobutyric acid}$$

Figure 25.8. Metabolism of threonine.

VALINE, LEUCINE, AND ISOLEUCINE

These three amino acids are not synthesized by the mammal, and all are essential in the mammalian diet. Since they all contain branched chain aliphatic groups and have metabolic features in common their metabolisms are considered together. Much of the evidence as to their metabolic pathways is due to Coon and associates (83).

All of these amino acids form the corresponding keto acids by transamination reactions. The keto acids may replace the essential amino acids in the diets of growing rats, indicating conversion to the L-acid.

Metabolism of valine, α-amino-isovaleric acid. The metabolic breakdown of valine in the animal body may be represented as follows (83,81):

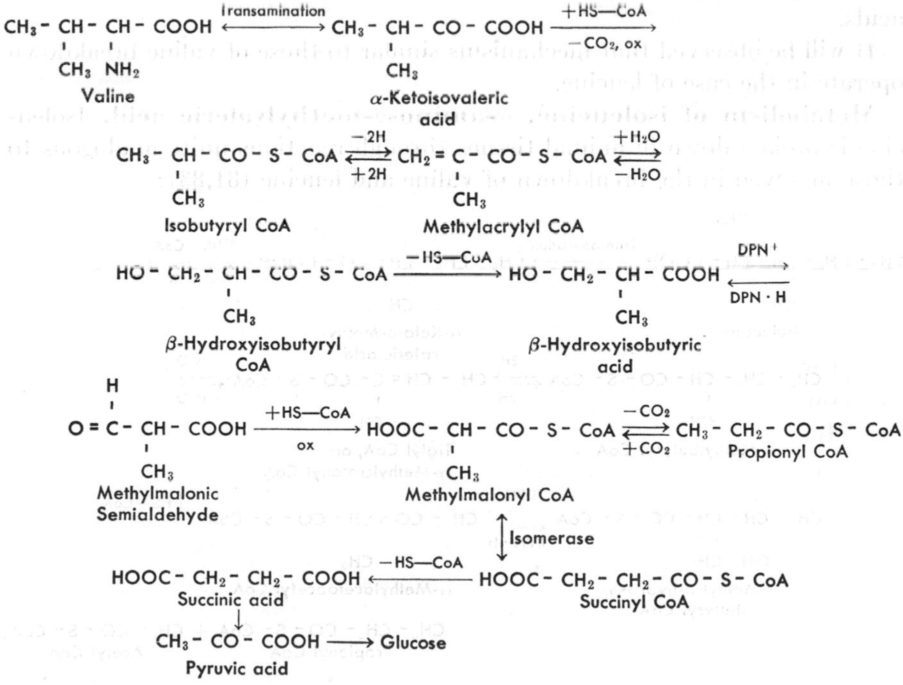

$$\underset{\substack{\text{CH}_3 \ \text{NH}_2 \\ \text{Valine}}}{\text{CH}_3 - \text{CH} - \text{CH} - \text{COOH}} \ \underset{\text{Iransamination}}{\overset{}{\longleftrightarrow}} \ \underset{\substack{\text{CH}_3 \\ \alpha\text{-Ketoisovaleric acid}}}{\text{CH}_3 - \text{CH} - \text{CO} - \text{COOH}} \ \underset{-\text{CO}_2,\ \text{ox}}{\overset{+\text{HS—CoA}}{\longrightarrow}}$$

$$\underset{\substack{\text{CH}_3 \\ \text{Isobutyryl CoA}}}{\text{CH}_3 - \text{CH} - \text{CO} - \text{S} - \text{CoA}} \ \underset{+2\text{H}}{\overset{-2\text{H}}{\rightleftharpoons}} \ \underset{\substack{\text{CH}_3 \\ \text{Methylacrylyl CoA}}}{\text{CH}_2 = \text{C} - \text{CO} - \text{S} - \text{CoA}} \ \underset{-\text{H}_2\text{O}}{\overset{+\text{H}_2\text{O}}{\rightleftharpoons}}$$

$$\underset{\substack{\text{CH}_3 \\ \beta\text{-Hydroxyisobutyryl CoA}}}{\text{HO} - \text{CH}_2 - \text{CH} - \text{CO} - \text{S} - \text{CoA}} \ \overset{-\text{HS—CoA}}{\longrightarrow} \ \underset{\substack{\text{CH}_3 \\ \beta\text{-Hydroxyisobutyric acid}}}{\text{HO} - \text{CH}_2 - \text{CH} - \text{COOH}} \ \underset{\text{DPN} \cdot \text{H}}{\overset{\text{DPN}}{\longleftrightarrow}}$$

$$\underset{\substack{\text{CH}_3 \\ \text{Methylmalonic Semialdehyde}}}{\overset{\text{H}}{\underset{}{\text{O} = \text{C} - \text{CH} - \text{COOH}}}} \ \underset{\text{ox}}{\overset{+\text{HS—CoA}}{\longrightarrow}} \ \underset{\substack{\text{CH}_3 \\ \text{Methylmalonyl CoA}}}{\text{HOOC} - \text{CH} - \text{CO} - \text{S} - \text{CoA}} \ \underset{+\text{CO}_2}{\overset{-\text{CO}_2}{\rightleftharpoons}} \ \underset{\text{Propionyl CoA}}{\text{CH}_3 - \text{CH}_2 - \text{CO} - \text{S} - \text{CoA}}$$

$$\big\updownarrow \ \text{Isomerase}$$

$$\underset{\text{Succinic acid}}{\text{HOOC} - \text{CH}_2 - \text{CH}_2 - \text{COOH}} \ \overset{-\text{HS—CoA}}{\longleftarrow} \ \underset{\text{Succinyl CoA}}{\text{HOOC} - \text{CH}_2 - \text{CH}_2 - \text{CO} - \text{S} - \text{CoA}}$$

$$\big\downarrow$$

$$\underset{\text{Pyruvic acid}}{\text{CH}_3 - \text{CO} - \text{COOH}} \longrightarrow \text{Glucose}$$

This scheme of metabolism of valine is in accord with the observation that three carbons of valine yield glucose in the diabetic animal. Isotopic experiments have shown that these three carbon atoms are derived from the isopropyl group of valine (84).

Metabolism of leucine, α-aminoisocaproic acid. The metabolic degradation of leucine in the animal body appears to follow the pathways outlined below (83,81):

$$\underset{\substack{|\\ CH_3 \\ \text{Leucine}}}{CH_3-CH-CH_2-CH-COOH} \overset{\text{Transamination}}{\underset{\substack{|\\ NH_2}}{\longleftrightarrow}} \underset{\substack{|\\ CH_3 \\ \alpha\text{-Ketoisocaproic acid}}}{CH_3-CH-CH_2-CO-COOH} \overset{+HS-CoA}{\underset{-CO_2,\,ox}{\longrightarrow}}$$

$$\underset{\substack{|\\ CH_3 \\ \text{Isovaleryl CoA}}}{CH_3-CH-CH_2-CO-S-CoA} \underset{+2H}{\overset{-2H}{\rightleftarrows}} \underset{\substack{|\\ CH_3 \\ \text{Dimethylacrylyl CoA, or}\\ \beta\text{-Methylcrotonyl CoA}}}{CH_3-C=CH-CO-S-CoA} \overset{+H_2O}{\underset{-H_2O}{\rightleftarrows}}$$

$$\underset{\substack{|\\ CH_3 \\ \beta\text{-Hydroxyisovaleryl CoA}}}{\overset{\substack{OH\\|}}{CH_3-C-CH_2-CO-S-CoA}} \overset{+ATP}{\underset{+CO_2}{\longrightarrow}} \underset{\substack{|\\ CH_3 \\ \beta\text{-Hydroxy-}\beta\text{-Methylglutaryl CoA}}}{\overset{\substack{OH\\|}}{HOOC-CH_2-C-CH_2-CO-S-CoA}} \longrightarrow$$

$$\underset{\text{Acetoacetic acid}}{CH_3-CO-CH_2-COOH} + \underset{\text{Acetyl CoA}}{CH_3-CO-S-CoA}$$

Since acetyl CoA is convertible to ketone bodies, the metabolism of a mol of leucine can yield 1.5 mols of acetoacetic acid in the diabetic animal, which is in accord with observations. Leucine is the most ketogenic of all the amino acids.

It will be observed that mechanisms similar to those of valine breakdown operate in the case of leucine.

Metabolism of isoleucine, α-amino-β-methylvaleric acid. Isoleucine is broken down in animal tissues through reactions quite analogous to those involved in the breakdown of valine and leucine (81,83):

$$\underset{\substack{|\\ CH_3 \\ \text{Isoleucine}}}{\overset{\substack{NH_2\\|}}{CH_3-CH_2-CH-CH-COOH}} \overset{\text{Transamination}}{\longleftrightarrow} \underset{\substack{|\\ CH_3 \\ \alpha\text{-Keto-}\beta\text{-Methy-}\\ \text{valeric acid}}}{CH_3-CH_2-CH-CO-COOH} \overset{+HS-CoA}{\underset{CO_2,\,ox}{\longrightarrow}}$$

$$\underset{\substack{|\\ CH_3 \\ \alpha\text{-Methylbutyryl CoA}}}{CH_3-CH_2-CH-CO-S-CoA} \underset{+2H}{\overset{-2H}{\rightleftarrows}} \underset{\substack{|\\ CH_3 \\ \text{Tiglyl CoA, or}\\ \alpha\text{-Methylcrotonyl CoA}}}{CH_3-CH=C-CO-S-CoA} \overset{+H_2O}{\underset{-H_2O}{\rightleftarrows}}$$

$$\underset{\substack{|\quad|\\ OH\ \ CH_3 \\ \alpha\text{-Methyl-}\beta\text{-hydroxy-}\\ \text{butyryl CoA}}}{CH_3-CH-CH-CO-S-CoA} \overset{DPN^+}{\underset{DPN\cdot H}{\rightleftarrows}} \underset{\substack{|\\ CH_3 \\ \alpha\text{-Methylacetoacetyl CoA}}}{CH_3-CO-CH-CO-S-CoA} \overset{+HS-CoA}{\longrightarrow}$$

$$\underset{\substack{\text{Propionyl CoA}\\ \downarrow\\ \text{Glucose}\\ \text{(Antiketogenic)}}}{CH_3-CH_2-CO-S-CoA} + \underset{\substack{\text{Acetyl CoA}\\ \downarrow\\ \text{Acetoacetic acid}\\ \text{(Ketogenic)}}}{CH_3-CO-S-CoA}$$

From the pathway of isoleucine metabolism it is seen that two carbon atoms may lead to the formation of acetyl CoA and three carbon atoms to the formation of glucose. Consequently, isoleucine is both weakly ketogenic and antiketogenic in the diabetic animal.

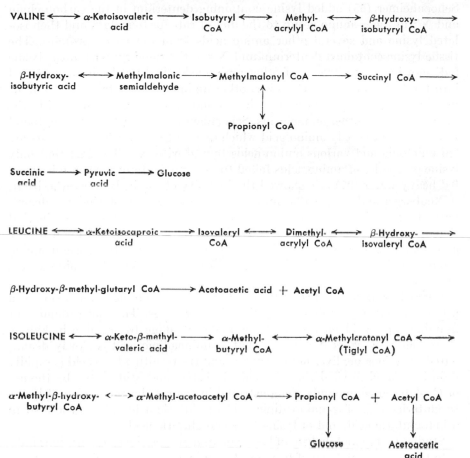

Figure 25.9. Metabolisms of valine, leucine, and isoleucine.

The synthesis of valine, leucine, and isoleucine by microorganisms such as *Neurospora*, *E. coli*, and yeasts has been demonstrated, and pathways proposed (81).

The metabolisms of valine, leucine, and isoleucine are outlined in Figure 25.9.

LYSINE

L-Lysine (α- ϵ-diaminocaproic acid) cannot be synthesized by any animal investigated and is an essential amino acid. The requirement of L-lysine in the diet is very specific, since only it—and some derivatives with substituents in the ε-amino group such as ε-N-acetyllysine and ε-N-methyllysine—support the growth of rats.

Deamination and metabolism. Lysine is deaminated in the body but cannot be synthesized by reamination of the carbon chain. Weissman and Schoenheimer (85) added lysine containing deuterium in the carbon chain and N^{15} in the α-amino group to the diet of rats for four days and then isolated lysine and several other amino acids from the tissue proteins. The tissue lysine contained deuterium and N^{15} in the same ratio as in the lysine fed, showing that nitrogen of other amino acids had not been incorporated into the lysine molecule. However, other amino acids contained N^{15}, showing that the lysine had been deaminized and the nitrogen exchanged in the amino groups of other amino acids. Schoenheimer and Rittenberg (86) found that lysine is the only amino acid which does not take up N^{15} when rats are fed ammonia and various amino acids tagged with N^{15}. The fact that only lysine of a series of amino acids failed to take up deuterium when mice were fed heavy water (87) also showed the inability of the body to synthesize it.

Neuberger and Sanger (88) found that neither D- nor L-lysine was deaminated by D- and L-amino acid oxidases, respectively. However, they did find that the ε-acetyl derivatives of both D- and L-lysine are acted upon by the corresponding amino acid oxidases and suggested that the epsilon amino group may require modification in some such way before the amino acid is metabolized.

Borsook and associates (89) have identified α-aminoadipic acid as a product of lysine metabolism by liver homogenates. They also found that α-aminoadipic acid may serve to aminate citrulline to arginine in kidney slices. These workers (90) found that α-aminoadipic acid is slowly deaminated by guinea pig liver homogenates, and the resulting keto acid is rapidly decarboxylated to yield glutaric acid. Rothstein and Miller (91), by the use of C^{14}-labeled compounds, demonstrated in the rat the conversion of lysine to glutaric acid, of α-aminoadipic acid to glutaric acid, of glutaric acid to α-ketoglutaric acid, and of lysine to α-ketoglutaric acid.

Studies on the metabolism of lysine in animals and liver preparations indicate that the breakdown of lysine in the animal body proceeds as shown on the following page (81). According to this pathway lysine is potentially glycogenic and antiketogenic.

Lysine is synthesized by certain bacteria and yeasts, and pathways have been proposed (81,92).

Hydroxylysine, α-ε-diamino-δ-hydroxycaproic acid. Hydroxylysine has been obtained only from hydrolysates of collagen and gelatin, and appears to have a very limited distribution.

Sinex and Van Slyke (93) fed C^{14}-labeled lysine to growing rats and found identical specific radioactivities and position labeling in the lysine and hydroxylysine isolated from skin collagen. This indicates the synthesis of hydroxylysine from lysine by hydroxylation in the δ-position. It was found also that lysine is converted to hydroxylysine after the lysine has been incorporated into protein.

$$
\begin{array}{c}
\text{CH}_2\text{—NH}_2 \\
| \\
\text{CH}_2 \\
| \\
\text{CH}_2 \\
| \\
\text{CH}_2 \\
| \\
\text{H—C—NH}_2 \\
| \\
\text{COOH}
\end{array}
\quad
\xrightarrow{-\text{NH}_3}
\quad
\begin{array}{c}
\text{CH}_2\text{—NH}_2 \\
| \\
\text{CH}_2 \\
| \\
\text{CH}_2 \\
| \\
\text{CH}_2 \\
| \\
\text{CO} \\
| \\
\text{COOH}
\end{array}
\quad
\underset{+\text{H}_2\text{O}}{\overset{-\text{H}_2\text{O}}{\rightleftarrows}}
\quad
\begin{array}{c}
\text{CH}_2 \\
\diagup \quad \diagdown \\
\text{H}_2\text{C} \qquad \text{CH}_2 \\
| \qquad\qquad | \\
\text{H}_2\text{C} \qquad \text{C—COOH} \\
\diagdown \quad \diagup \\
\text{N}
\end{array}
\quad
\xrightarrow{+2\text{H}}
\quad
\begin{array}{c}
\text{CH}_2 \\
\diagup \quad \diagdown \\
\text{H}_2\text{C} \qquad \text{CH}_2 \\
| \qquad\qquad | \\
\text{H}_2\text{C} \qquad \text{CH—COOH} \\
\diagdown \quad \diagup \\
\text{N} \\
| \\
\text{H}
\end{array}
\quad
\xrightarrow{-2\text{H}}
$$

L-Lysine   α-Keto-ε-amino-caproic acid   Δ¹-Piperidine-2-carboxylic acid   Pipecolic acid

$$
\begin{array}{c}
\text{CH}_2 \\
\diagup \quad \diagdown \\
\text{H}_2\text{C} \qquad \text{CH}_2 \\
| \qquad\qquad | \\
\text{HC} \qquad \text{CH—COOH} \\
\diagdown \quad \diagup \\
\text{N}
\end{array}
\quad
\xrightarrow{+\text{H}_2\text{O}}
\quad
\begin{array}{c}
\text{COOH} \\
| \\
\text{H}_2\text{N—C—H} \\
| \\
\text{CH}_2 \\
| \\
\text{CH}_2 \\
| \\
\text{CH}_2 \\
| \\
\text{CHO}
\end{array}
\quad
\xrightarrow{\text{ox}}
\quad
\begin{array}{c}
\text{COOH} \\
| \\
\text{H}_2\text{N—C—H} \\
| \\
\text{CH}_2 \\
| \\
\text{CH}_2 \\
| \\
\text{CH}_2 \\
| \\
\text{COOH}
\end{array}
\quad
\xrightarrow{-\text{NH}_3}
\quad
\begin{array}{c}
\text{COOH} \\
| \\
\text{CO} \\
| \\
\text{CH}_2 \\
| \\
\text{CH}_2 \\
| \\
\text{CH}_2 \\
| \\
\text{COOH}
\end{array}
\quad
\underset{\text{ox}}{\xrightarrow{-\text{CO}_2}}
\quad
\begin{array}{c}
\text{COOH} \\
| \\
\text{CH}_2 \\
| \\
\text{CH}_2 \\
| \\
\text{CH}_2 \\
| \\
\text{COOH}
\end{array}
\quad
\xrightarrow{\text{ox}}
$$

Δ⁶-Piperidine-2-carboxylic acid   α-Amino-adipic-ε-semialdehyde   L-α-Amino-adipic acid   α-Keto-adipic acid   Glutaric acid

$$
\begin{array}{c}
\text{COOH} \\
| \\
\text{CO} \\
| \\
\text{CH}_2 \\
| \\
\text{CH}_2 \\
| \\
\text{COOH}
\end{array}
\quad
\xrightarrow{+\text{NH}_3}
\quad
\begin{array}{c}
\text{COOH} \\
| \\
\text{H}_2\text{N—C—H} \\
| \\
\text{CH}_2 \\
| \\
\text{CH}_2 \\
| \\
\text{COOH}
\end{array}
$$

α-Ketoglutaric acid   L-Glutamic acid

ASPARTIC AND GLUTAMIC ACIDS

Aspartic acid, α-aminosuccinic acid, and glutamic acid, α-aminoglutaric acid, are readily synthesized by the body and are nonessential. Metabolically, they are the most reactive of the amino acids. As previously indicated, these amino acids are active agents in the processes of deamination and amination through their participation in transamination reactions. Glutamic acid, as acetyl glutamate, participates in the conversion of ornithine to citrulline, and aspartic acid participates in the conversion of citrulline to arginine, in the Krebs-Henseleit cycle of urea formation. Glutamic acid also is converted to glutamine, which is the source of urinary ammonia and which also appears to serve as a reservoir of amino nitrogen in the body. These relations have been considered in previous sections, to which the student is referred.

Since deamination of aspartic and glutamic acids yields oxaloacetic and α-ketoglutaric acids, respectively, both of which are components of the citric acid cycle, these amino acids form glucose and glycogen in the animal body and are antiketogenic.

Deamination and metabolism. Both aspartic acid and glutamic acid are deaminated and synthesized by transamination reactions:

$$\text{Glutamic acid} + \text{Pyruvic acid} \underset{\substack{\text{Pyridoxal} \\ \text{phosphate}}}{\overset{\text{Transaminase}}{\rightleftharpoons}} \alpha\text{-ketoglutaric acid} + \text{alanine}$$

$$\text{Aspartic acid} + \alpha\text{-ketoglutaric acid} \underset{\substack{\text{Pyridoxal} \\ \text{phosphate}}}{\overset{\text{Transaminase}}{\rightleftharpoons}} \text{Oxaloacetic acid} + \text{Glutamic acid}$$

A major pathway for the formation of glutamic acid is provided by the action of liver glutamic dehydrogenase requiring DPN or TPN:

$$\alpha\text{-ketoglutaric acid} + NH_4^+ + DPN \cdot H + H^+ \rightleftharpoons \text{L-Glutamate} + DPN^+ + H_2O$$

Brain contains much glutamic acid (100 to 150 mg per 100 g). An enzyme in brain, glutamic decarboxylase, converts glutamic acid to γ-amino butyric acid:

$$\underset{\substack{| \\ NH_2 \\ \text{L-Glutamic acid}}}{HOOC - CH - CH_2 - CH_2 - COOH} \underset{\substack{\text{Pyridoxal} \\ \text{phosphate}}}{\overset{\text{Decarboxylase}}{\longrightarrow}} \underset{\text{γ-Aminobutyric acid}}{H_2N - CH_2 - CH_2 - CH_2 - COOH} + CO_2$$

It is of interest that brain tissue contains large amounts of N-acetyl-L-aspartic acid (ca. 100 mg per 100 g), the function of which is unknown.

As previously indicated, glutamic acid is a constituent of the tripeptide glutathione (γ-glutamylcysteinylglycine).

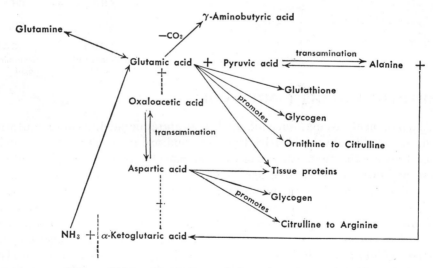

Figure 25.10. Metabolisms of glutamic and aspartic acids.

As will be seen later, aspartic acid participates in the synthesis of purines and pyrimidines.

The conversion of glutamic acid to glutamine and the metabolism of glutamine will be considered in the following section.

The metabolism of glutamic and aspartic acids are shown in the diagram of Figure 25.10.

GLUTAMINE

As pointed out earlier in this chapter, glutamine is synthesized in tissues through the action of the enzyme glutamine synthetase:

$$\text{Glutamic acid} + NH_3 + ATP \xrightarrow[Mg^{++}]{\text{Enzyme}} \text{Glutamine} + ADP + Pi$$

Synthesis takes place in tissues such as liver, kidney, brain, retina, etc. Blood glutamine probably is synthesized largely in the liver.

Hamilton (94) found in dog tissues the following amounts of glutamine expressed as milligrams per 100 g of tissue: heart, 225; diaphragm muscle, 183; skeletal muscle, 122; brain, 64; liver, 45; kidney, 11.3. The value for heart muscle, 225 mg per cent, represented more than half of the total free amino nitrogen. Human and dog plasma were found to contain 6 to 12 mg per cent of glutamine, representing 18 to 25 per cent of the total free amino nitrogen of the plasma.

Glutamine is hydrolyzed by the enzyme glutaminase, which is found in various tissues (brain, kidney, liver, retina, etc.):

$$\text{Glutamine} + H_2O \xrightarrow{\text{Glutaminase}} \text{Glutamic acid} + NH_3$$

Glutamine and glutamic acid are readily interconverted.

Glutamine constitutes a large proportion of the free amino nitrogen of tissues and blood, and of the metabolic nitrogen pool. It serves as an important reservoir of ammonia nitrogen in tissues which can be drawn upon for synthetic purposes. The amide nitrogen of glutamine is utilized in the synthesis of glucosamine-6-phosphate (Chapter 24), and of purines (Chapter 26), for example. Ammonia formed in deamination processes may be stored as glutamine without raising the ammonia content of blood and tissues to the toxic level.

As noted earlier, glutamine, like glutamic acid, participates in transamination reactions.

The importance of glutamine as a source of ammonia (through hydrolysis by glutaminase) for the conservation of Na$^+$ in the kidney has been pointed out in Chapter 17.

Glutamine is of particular importance in brain metabolism, as indicated in Chapter 27. While many cell membranes and the blood-brain barrier are relatively impermeable to glutamic acid, glutamine penetrates readily. Thus glutamine serves as an important source of glutamic acid to tissues, and it probably represents practically all of the supply to the brain. Mammalian tissue cultures appear to require glutamine, which is probably related to its ability to enter the cells *in vitro* and serve as a source of glutamic acid.

As pointed out in earlier discussion, man and the chimpanzee conjugate phenylacetic acid with glutamine to form phenylacetylglutamine, which is excreted in the urine.

Bartlett (95) has reported that the administration of growth hormone to dogs causes marked increases in the plasma glutamine level along with the nitrogen storage and weight gain. Hypophysectomized rats given growth hormone had more glutamine in their kidneys than did untreated hypophysectomized controls. These results suggest the probable importance of glutamine in tissue protein synthesis.

PHENYLALANINE AND TYROSINE

Phenylalanine is an essential amino acid in mammals, while tyrosine is formed from phenylalanine and is not essential. The feeding of tyrosine decreases the need for phenylalanine (sparing action) by reducing the quantity of phenylalanine converted to tyrosine. The deamination product of phenylalanine, phenylpyruvic acid, may replace phenylalanine in the diet indicating its reamination to phenylalanine.

Despite the fact that tyrosine is dispensable, it is utilized with marked economy. Butts and associates (96) found that administration of tyrosine to rats did not increase urinary nitrogen. Greene and Johnston (97) found that tyrosine given intravenously to dogs (0.2 g per kilogram) very rapidly disappeared from the blood but was not excreted in the urine. Medes (98) gave 50 g of tyrosine in divided doses to a normal human subject over a two-day period and found no increase in the amino acid nitrogen, tyrosine, or intermediary products of tyrosine metabolism in the urine. Schoenheimer and associates (99) found the largest fraction of N^{15} to be present in tissue protein tyrosine after giving isotopic tyrosine to rats.

The organism is less conservative in the use of phenylalanine, since Butts and associates found this amino acid to increase urinary nitrogen when given to rats.

Both phenylalanine and tyrosine yield ketone bodies in their metabolism, and both are glycogenic in fasting rats.

The metabolisms of these amino acids are complex. Besides entering into the formation of body proteins, the amino acids participate in the synthesis of other important substances. Tyrosine is utilized in the formation of the hormones of the adrenal medulla, epinephrine (adrenaline) and arterenol (demethylated epinephrine); of the thyroid hormone thyroxine; and of the pigment melanin. Since phenylalanine is convertible to tyrosine, it also participates in all these syntheses.

Metabolic breakdown of phenylalanine and tyrosine (100, 101). The general pathway of breakdown of phenylalanine and tyrosine in the animal body was rather early established by finding intermediate products of metabolism in the urine of humans with the hereditary conditions of alkaptonuria, tyrosinosis, and phenylketonuria (100). More recently the pathway has been substantiated and elaborated through the use of isotopically labeled compounds in intact animals and with tissue preparations.

In the metabolism of phenylalanine the amino acid is first irreversibly hydroxylated to tyrosine, and then tyrosine undergoes a series of changes leading through p-hydroxphenylpyruvic acid, homogentisic acid, maleylacetoacetic acid, and fumarylacetoacetic acid to fumaric acid and acetoacetic acid. Fumaric acid, being a component of the citric acid cycle, is convertible through pyruvic acid to glucose and glycogen. The ketone body, acetoacetic acid, goes the pathway of fatty acid metabolism, being convertible into acetyl CoA. Thus, phenylalanine and tyrosine are both glycogenic and ketogenic.

The conversion of phenylalanine to tyrosine represents a complex process involving an enzyme system commonly called "phenylalanine oxidase," but which in reality is composed of two enzymes. The over-all reaction is generally represented as follows:

$$\text{L-Phenylalanine} + \text{TPN} \cdot \text{H} + \text{H}^+ + \text{O}_2 \longrightarrow \text{L-Tyrosine} + \text{H}_2\text{O} + \text{TPN}^+$$

Recent work of Kaufman and Levenberg (102) has shown that tetrahydrofolic acid (tetrahydropteroylglutamic acid) and other tetrahydropteridines, such as 2-amino-4-hydroxy-6-methyltetrahydropteridine, may serve as cofactor in the hydroxylation, though the natural cofactor has not been identified. It appears that the hydroxylation involves two reactions which may be represented:

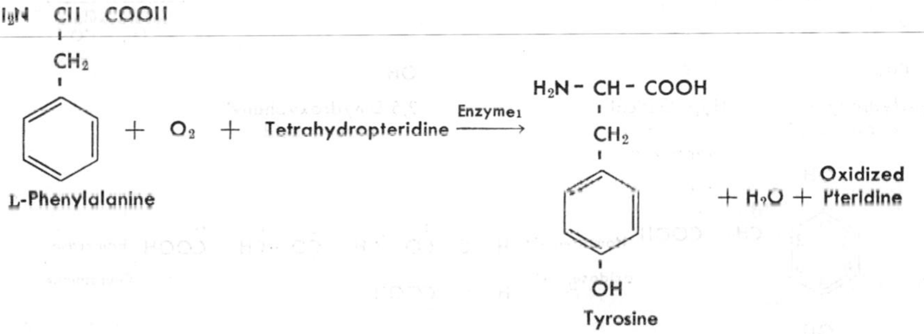

(2) $\text{Oxidized pteridine} + \text{TPN} \cdot \text{H} + \text{H}^+ \xrightarrow{\text{Enzyme}_2} \text{Tetrahydropteridine} + \text{TPN}^+$

The regenerated tetrahydropteridine re-enters the cycle. Its exact function is as yet unknown.

Tyrosine is converted to *p*-hydroxyphenylpyruvic acid by tyrosine-*α*-ketoglutaric transaminase of liver (103):

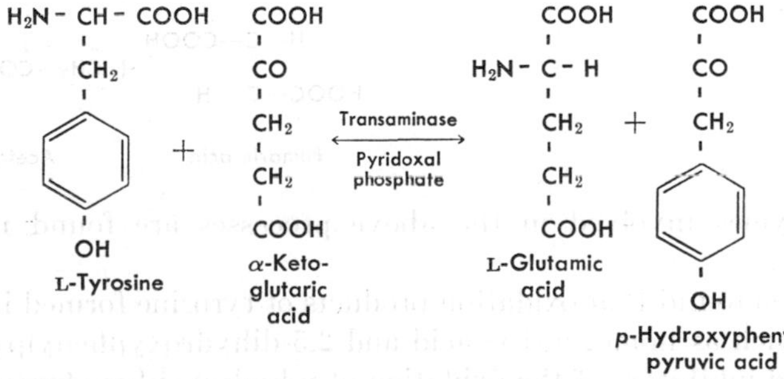

p-Hydroxyphenylpyruvic acid is oxidized to homogentisic acid through the action of *p*-hydroxyphenylpyruvic oxidase. Two reactions appear to be involved: first the oxidation of p-hydroxyphenylpyruvic acid to 2,5-dihydroxyphenylpyruvic acid by enzyme$_1$, in the presence of ascorbic acid and vitamin B$_{12}$, and then the oxidation of 2,5-dihydroxyphenylpyruvic acid to homogentisic acid through the action of enzyme$_2$ (104). The process, as shown·by isotopic labeling, involves a shift in the side chain of the p-hydroxyphenylpyruvic acid in the formation of 2,5-dihydroxyphenylpyruvic acid (101, 105). Homogentisic acid is then broken down to fumaric and acetoacetic acids through maleylacetoacetic acid and fumarylacetoacetic acid. The above processes are shown in the following equations, in which the numbers indicate the metabolic fates of the carbon atoms and are not related to the positions of substituents:

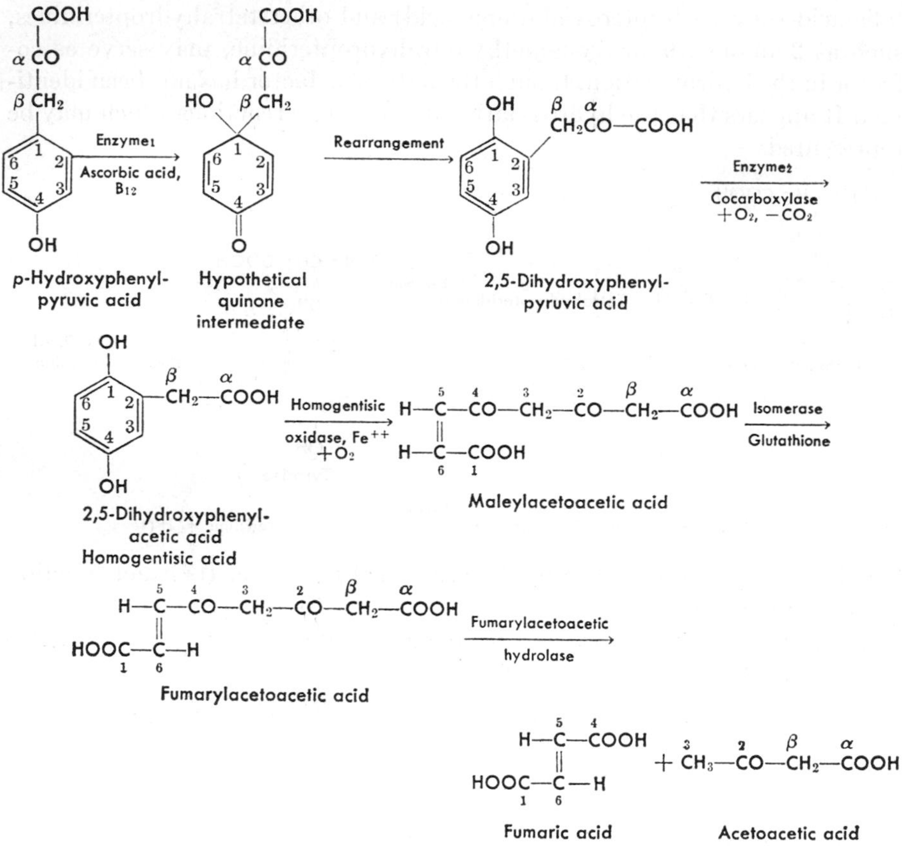

p-Hydroxyphenyl-
pyruvic acid

Hypothetical
quinone
intermediate

2,5-Dihydroxyphenyl-
pyruvic acid

2,5-Dihydroxyphenyl-
acetic acid
Homogentisic acid

Maleylacetoacetic acid

Fumarylacetoacetic acid

Fumaric acid   Acetoacetic acid

The enzymes involved in the above processes are found in the liver particularly.

It has been found that oxidation products of tyrosine formed in the above reactions, such as homogentisic acid and 2,5-dihydroxyphenylpyruvic acid, are powerful inhibitors of the oxidation of p-hydroxyphenylpyruvic acid by its oxidase, and that this inhibition is removed by ascorbic acid and other reducing agents (106). Ascorbic acid thus apparently plays the role of only a rather nonspecific reducing agent in the metabolism of phenylalanine and tyrosine.

There are several rather incidental transformations of phenylalanine and tyrosine which are not connected with the main pathways of metabolism but which, under certain conditions, lead to the excretion of derivatives in the urine.

Phenylalanine undergoes transamination to form phenylpyruvic acid, which is reduced to phenyllactic acid and oxidized to phenylacetic acid:

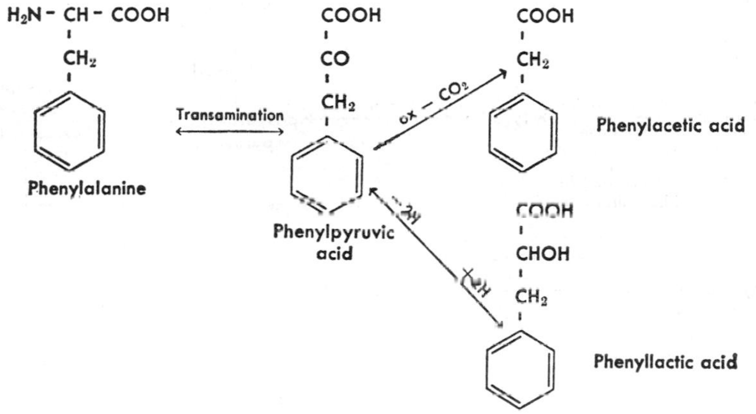

These acids normally are converted back to tyrosine and metabolized.

Normally, phenylpyruvic acid and phenyllactic acid are converted back to phenylalanine and then are metabolized through tyrosine and homogentisic acid. Phenylacetic acid is conjugated with glutamine to form phenylacetylglutamine (in man) and excreted in the urine. When the oxidation of phenylalanine to tyrosine is blocked, as in phenylketonuria, then the concentrations of phenylalanine and its derivatives in blood increase and the excretion of all of the above substances is greatly increased.

p-Hydroxyphenylpyruvic acid is reversibly reduced to p-hydroxyphenyllactic acid:

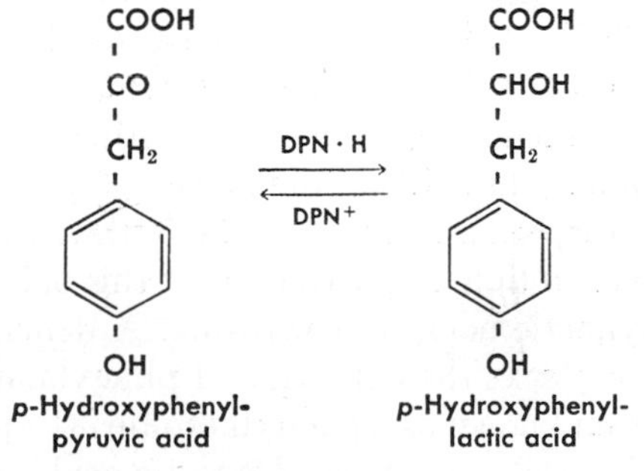

These acids normally are converted back to tyrosine and metabolized.

The processes involved in the main pathway of phenylalanine and tyrosine metabolism are outlined in the diagram of Figure 25.11.

Hereditary defects in phenylalanine and tyrosine metabolism.
Three well-established hereditary defects in the metabolism of phenylalanine
and tyrosine through the main pathway outlined in Figure 25.11 are alcaptonuria, tyrosinosis, and phenylketonuria or phenylpyruvic oligophrenia. In

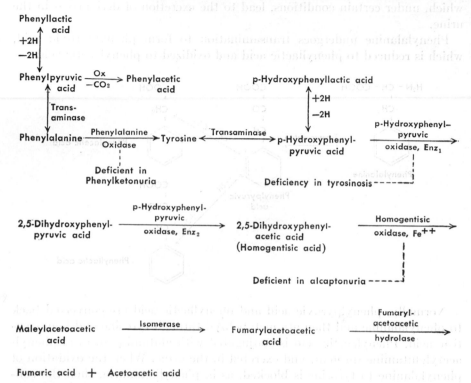

Figure 25.11. Main pathway of phenylalanine and tyrosine metabolism.

each case the defect is due to the hereditary absence or deficit of a specific
enzyme involved in a specific reaction (107). These conditions belong to
what Garrod called "inborn errors of metabolism."

As shown in Figure 25.11, alcaptonuria is caused by the absence or deficiency of the enzyme homogentisic oxidase, which causes a block in the
metabolic pathway at homogentisic acid, resulting in its accumulation in
the blood and excretion in the urine. A deficiency of p-hydroxyphenylpyruvic
oxidase, as in tyrosinosis, causes a block in the pathway at p-hydroxyphenyl-
pyruvic acid and the excretion, in particular, of this acid, its reduction product, p-hydroxyphenyllactic acid, and tyrosine. A deficiency of the enzyme
phenylalanine oxidase blocks the oxidation of phenylalanine to tyrosine and
represents the condition known as "phenylketonuria" (phenylpyruvic oligophrenia), in which phenylalanine, phenylpyruvic acid, and phenyllactic acid
are excreted.

Alcaptonuria (alkaptonuria). Alcaptonuria is an inborn error of phenylalanine and
tyrosine metabolism first described by Bodeker in 1858. The condition is characterized

by the excretion of urine which upon standing gradually becomes darker in color and may finally turn black. The urine is also strongly reducing and gives a violet color with ferric chloride. The substance responsible for the formation of the black pigment and other reactions has been identified as 2,5-dihydroxyphenylacetic acid, or homogentisic acid.

Administration of phenylalanine, tyrosine, or their corresponding keto acids to an alcaptonuric causes a marked increase in homogentisic acid excretion. Medes (98) has shown that homogentisic acid given to normal persons is not excreted in the urine and does not cause the excretion of related compounds, indicating that it is well metabolized. Alcaptonuria shows a familial tendency and is inherited as a recessive Mendelian character. It is a rather rare condition.

Experimental alcaptonuria. Alcaptonuria was produced in rats by Papageorge and Lewis (108) by feeding phenylalanine for several days. Sealock and Silberstein (109) found that the feeding of tyrosine to scorbutic guinea pigs caused the excretion not only of homogentisic acid but also of other intermediates of tyrosine metabolism, p-hydroxyphenylpyruvic and p-hydroxyphenyllactic acids (formed by reduction of the keto acid). The administration of ascorbic acid completely prevented excretion of these substances, showing that the vitamin is necessary for phenylalanine and tyrosine metabolism.

Ascorbic acid does not relieve cases of spontaneous alcaptonuria in human beings.

p-Hydroxyphenylketonuria and p-hydroxyphenyllacticuria. Levine and associates (110) found that premature infants on a high protein diet of cow's milk, low in vitamin C, excrete excessive amounts of p-hydroxyphenylpyruvic and p-hydroxyphenyllactic acids in the urine, and, as in the case of experimental alcaptonuria in rats and guinea pigs, the administration of ascorbic acid relieved the condition. Homogentisic acid was not excreted, and the condition does not represent alcaptonuria. These workers caused a similar effect in full-term infants by giving phenylalanine and tyrosine (111). It was found that the feeding of phenylalanine in large doses (1 g per kilogram) caused the excretion also of very large amounts of tyrosine and its related keto and hydroxy acids. However, when tyrosine was fed, there was no significant excretion of phenylalanine and its keto acid, though tyrosine and its keto and hydroxy acids were excreted abundantly. These results show that the animal body converts phenylalanine to tyrosine but not the reverse, which is in accord with the fact that tyrosine cannot be substituted for phenylalanine in the diet.

Fishberg (112) identified the reversible oxidation product of homogentisic acid, benzoquinoneacetic acid, in the urine of a case of "autotoxic enterogenous cyanosis" and found that this substance causes cyanosis by oxidizing hemoglobin to methemoglobin. Administration of ascorbic acid caused cessation of excretion:

Homogentisic acid   Benzoquinoneacetic acid

Benzoquinoneacetic acid was found in the urines of cases of scurvy and rheumatic fever and of scorbutic guinea pigs, indicating that it is probably a normal metabolism intermediate. Since it accumulates only in cases of vitamin C deficiency, it would appear that ascorbic acid plays a role in the further metabolism of this substance.

Tyrosinosis. The first authentic case of tyrosinosis was described by Medes (98) in 1932, and two other cases have been found by Felix and associates (13). Blatherwick failed to detect a case in the examination of 26,000 urines (114), indicating the extreme rareness of the condition.

The case of Medes was characterized by excretion in the urine of tyrosine, p-hydroxyphenylpyruvic and p-hydroxyphenyllactic acids, and small amounts of 3,4-dihydroxyphenylalanine. The administration of tyrosine caused greatly increased excretion of all these substances, with least effect upon 3,4-dihydroxyphenylalanine excretion. The administration of phenylalanine caused these substances to be excreted later and in smaller quantities. When p-hydroxyphenyllactic acid was given, some of the substance appeared in the urine after the second day, but tyrosine and p-hydroxyphenylpyruvic acid were not excreted. The administration of p-hydroxyphenylpyruvic acid caused excretion of large quantities of the acid and also of some tyrosine and p-hydroxyphenyllactic acid. After 3,4-dihydroxyphenylalanine was given, some of the compound was promptly excreted whereas p-hydroxyphenylpyruvic acid did not appear until the fourth day. The patient oxidized homogentisic acid completely. The primary defect in tyrosinosis consists in the inability to oxidize p-hydroxyphenylpyruvic acid, the deamination product of tyrosine.

Phenylketonuria or phenylpyruvic oligophrenia. This condition is characterized by inferior mental ability and excretion in the urine of phenylpyruvic acid and excessive amounts of phenylalanine with smaller quantities of phenyllactic acid (reduction product of phenylpyruvic acid). Jervis (115) showed that administration of phenylalanine, phenylpyruvic acid, or phenyllactic acid increases the excretion of phenylpyruvic acid. However, administration of tyrosine does not affect the excretion of these substances. Jervis and associates found very high levels of phenylalanine in the blood of 16 cases examined. The ingestion of proteins, phenylalanine, and phenylpyruvic or phenyllactic acid caused a rise in phenylalanine alone, with no determinable increase in related acids.

Jervis showed that the primary metabolic defect in phenylketonuria is the inability of the body to convert phenylalanine to tyrosine. He found that ingestion of phenylalanine by fasting human subjects caused an increase in blood tyrosine. Patients suffering from phenylketonuria did not show this effect. The main pathway of phenylalanine breakdown must proceed through tyrosine.

Closs and Fölling (116) found small amounts of phenylpyruvic acid in the urine of rats in thiamine deficiency, indicating that the vitamin is involved in the oxidation of the acid. Since this oxidation also includes decarboxylation, and thiamine is a constituent of the carboxylase enzyme system, there is a relation of thiamine to the oxidation of phenylpyruvic acid and also to the oxidation of other keto acids derived from amino acids.

Phenol formation. Tyrosine and phenylalanine (through tyrosine) are acted upon by bacteria in the gut to form phenol and paracresol, which are absorbed, conjugated in the liver with sulfuric and glucuronic acids, and excreted in the urine. Some phenols appear to arise from the metabolism of the amino acids in the tissues, since they do not disappear from the blood and urine during starvation and they increase when the amino acids are given intravenously.

Tyramine and epinephrine formation. Decarboxylation of tyrosine forms the corresponding amine, tyramine. This process occurs in the gut as a result of bacterial action, and Schuler and associates (117) showed that tyramine is formed by the action of kidney slices upon tyrosine. The reaction is favored by oxygen deficiency. In the presence of sufficient oxygen the tissue deaminated tyrosine instead.

Tyramine and related amines elevate blood pressure.

Formation of epinephrine (adrenaline) and norepinephrine (arterenol). According to present evidence (118), the synthesis of epinephrine and norepinephrine in the adrenal medulla from tyrosine proceeds through 3,4-dihydroxyphenylalanine (dopa) and 3,4-dihydroxyphenylethylamine (hydroxytyramine), both of which have been found in extracts of the adrenal gland (Figure 25.12).

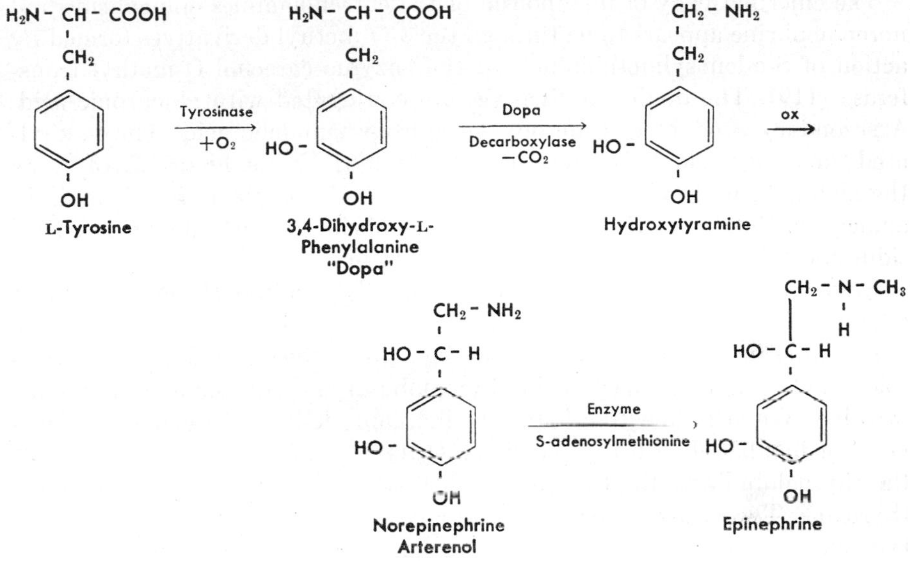

Figure 25.12. Norepinephrine and epinephrine formation.

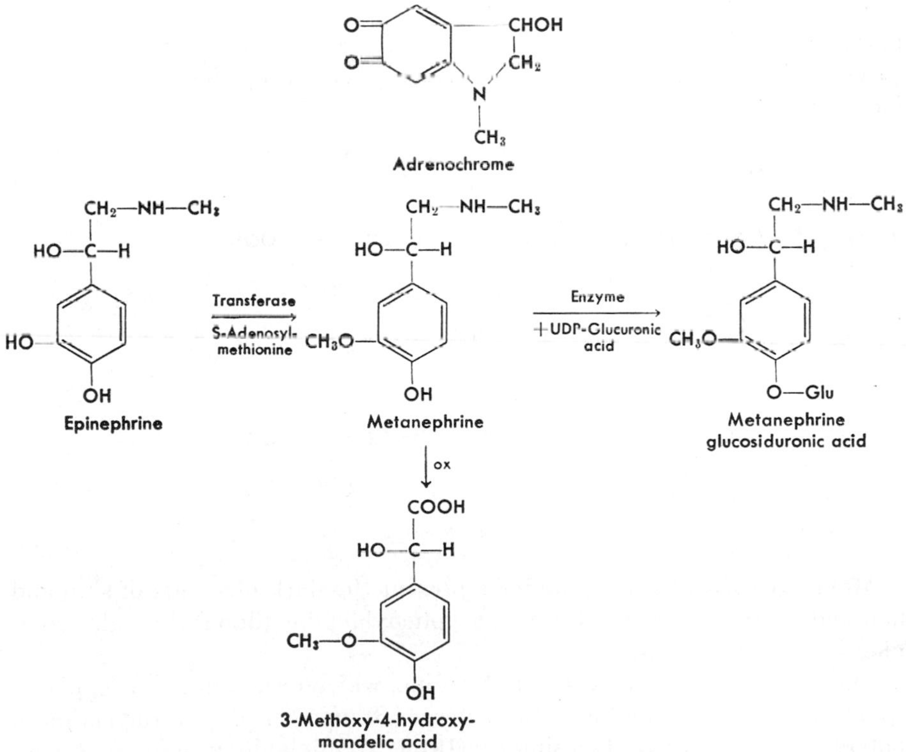

Figure 25.13. Metabolism of epinephrine.

The chief pathway of metabolism of the catecholamines epinephrine and norepinephrine appears to be through the 3-O-methyl derivatives formed by action of S-adenosylmethionine and the enzyme catechol O-methyl transferase (119). The methyl derivatives are conjugated with glucuronic acid. A secondary product is 3-methoxy-4-hydroxy-mandelic acid. The methylated glucuronic acid derivatives are excreted in the urine. Figure 25.13 shows the metabolism of epinephrine, to which that of norepinephrine is entirely analagous, the derivatives being normetanephrine, normetanephrine glucosiduronic acid, and also 3-methoxy-4-hydroxy-mandelic acid.

Epinephrine is oxidized by ferric compounds to adrenochrome, which at alkaline pH values polymerizes to brown pigments.

Formation of thyroxine. Thyroxine, the active hormone of the thyroid gland, occurs as a part of the thyroglobulin molecule along with diiodotyrosine. When radioactive iodine as inorganic iodide is given to animals (120) or incubated with thyroid tissue (121), it is rapidly incorporated into the thyroglobulin of the thyroid gland, first as diiodotyrosine and later as thyroxine. Turner and associates (122) have shown that proteins containing tyrosine may be treated with iodine to form iodinated proteins containing thyroxine.

In the formation of thyroxine tyrosine of the protein appears to be first iodinated to diiodotyrosine, from which thyroxine is formed by a series of complex reactions (100). 3,3′,5-Triiodothyronine, which contains one less iodine than thyroxine, is also formed in the thyroid gland, and is more active physiologically than thyroxine. It is possibly formed by the removal of one iodine atom from thyroxine (100):

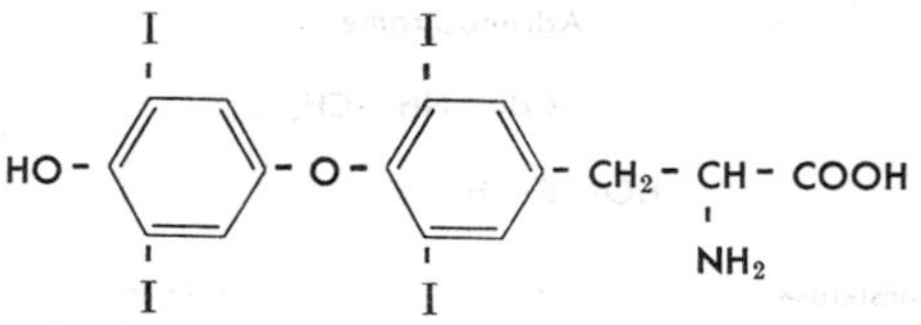

Thyroxine

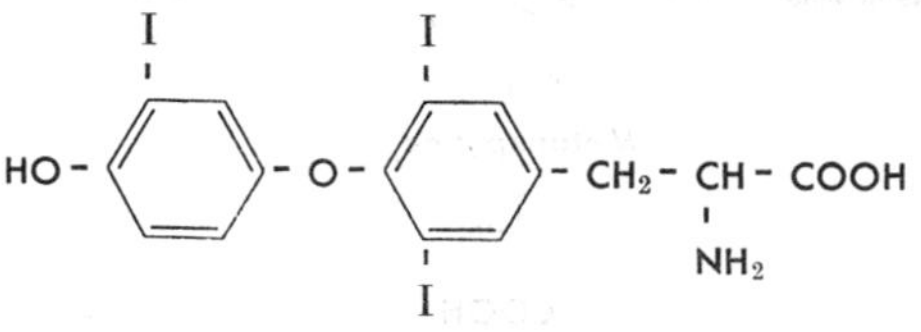

Triiodothyronine

Melanin formation. Melanins represent the dark pigments of skin and hair and are formed from 3,4-dihydroxyphenylalanine (dopa) through a complex series of reactions.

The formation of melanins from tyrosine, which occurs in animals, plants (potato, mushroom), and certain bacteria (*B. niger*), is due to the action of polyphenol oxidases or tyrosinases (101,123). Melanin formation is considered to proceed according to the outline in Figure 25.14.

Previously it was believed that an enzyme, dopa oxidase, catalyzes the formation of melanins from dopa. Lerner (101) considers that the enzyme tyrosinase is responsible for the entire process. Tyrosinase is a copper protein, and in the oxidation of tyrosine to dopa and dopa quinone the copper goes through a cycle, $Cu^{++} \longrightarrow Cu^{+} \longrightarrow Cu^{++}$, during which it acts as a catalyst of the oxidations.

While the melanins of human beings are derived from tyrosine through dopa, most polyhydroxyphenyl and aminophenyl compounds having ortho or para groups can be oxidized to pigmented polymers, and the type of melanin is best shown by indicating the substance from which the melanin is

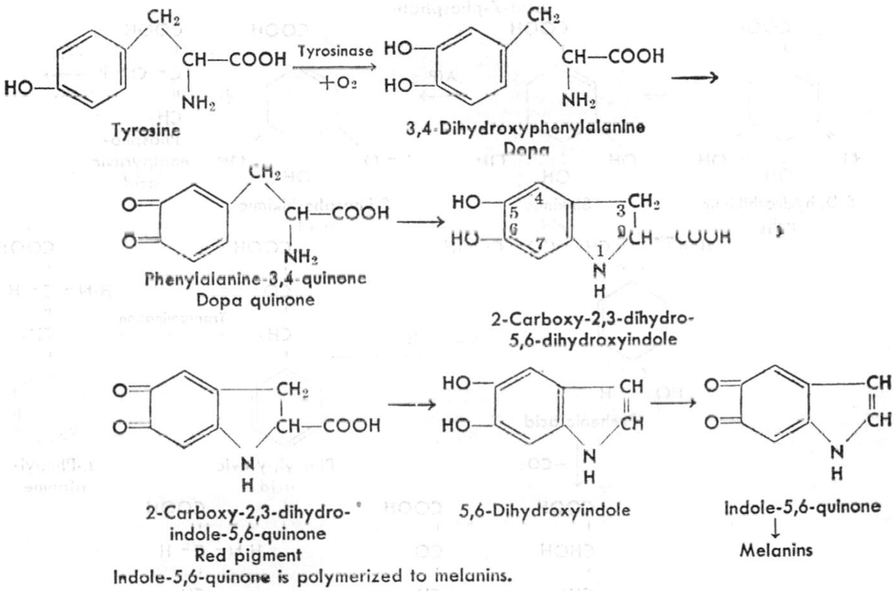

Figure 25.14. Melanin formation.

formed. Thus we may have dopa-melanin, adrenaline-melanin, homogentisic acid-melanin, *p*-phenylenediamine-melanin, etc.

Melanin forms a reversible oxidation-reduction system, in which the reduced form is tan and the oxidized form is black.

Melanins appear in tissues as regular, spheroid granules and represent formed elements rather than precipitated aggregates.

Melanins are produced in pigment-forming cells, the melanocytes, and their formation is stimulated by adrenal cortical and especially pituitary hormones (124).

The melanins are very complex substances of high molecular weight and are insoluble in most solvents. In tissues they are generally combined with protein.

Melanins are formed in large quantities by melanosarcomas, and melanin precursors may be excreted in the urine as a result of these tumors.

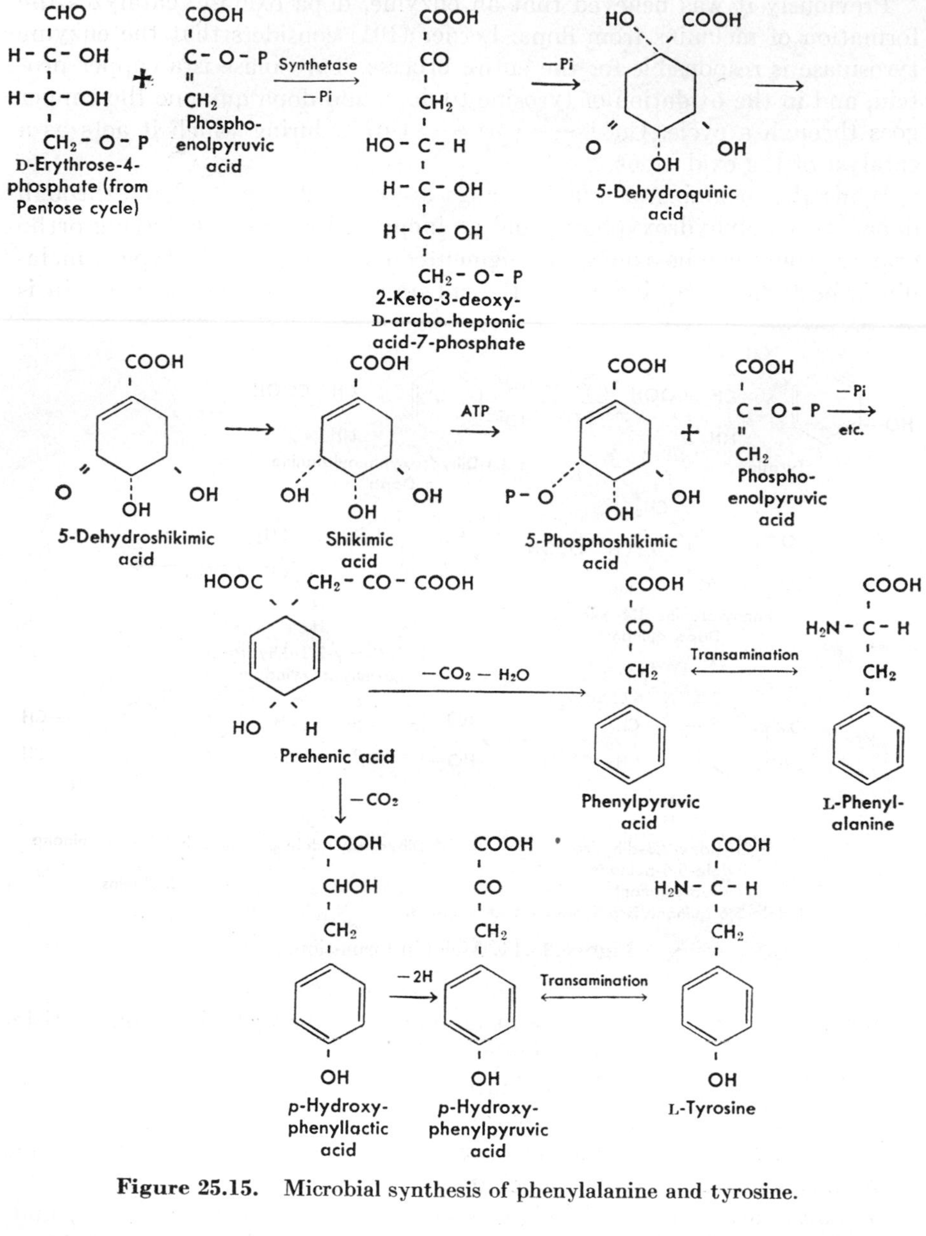

Figure 25.15.   Microbial synthesis of phenylalanine and tyrosine.

Total albinism is a hereditary condition in which there is complete absence of pigment in the skin, eyes, and hair. It is due to absence of tyrosinase in the melanocytes (107) and is transmitted as a simple recessive. There are various types of hereditary albinism in which pigment is only lacking from certain parts of the body, such as the eye, areas of the skin, and areas of the hair.

Biosynthesis of phenylalanine and tyrosine. While mammals are unable to synthesize phenylalanine, various microorganisms such as *Neurospora, E. coli,* and *A. aerogenes* synthesize both phenylalanine and tyrosine, the amino acids being derived from a common precursor, prehenic acid. The accumulated evidence (125) indicates that microbial synthesis of the amino acids is effected as outlined in Figure 25.15.

For simplicity the relations of phenylalanine and tyrosine metabolism are recapitulated below in Figure 25.16.

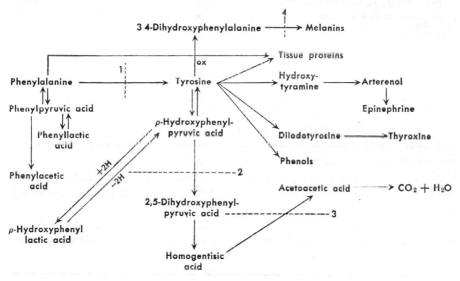

1. Blocked in phenylketonuria (phenylpyruvic oligophrenia).
2. Blocked in tyrosinosis.
3. Blocked in alcaptonuria.
4. Blocked in albinism.

Figure 25.16. Metabolism of phenylalanine and tyrosine.

The possibility exists that phenylalanine may be converted to tyrosine through oxidation of phenylpyruvic acid to *p*-hydroxyphenylpyruvic acid and amination of this acid. Also, phenylpyruvic acid may be oxidized through 2,5-dihydroxyphenylpyruvic acid to homogentisic acid. However, the probability that such processes play an important part in phenylalanine metabolism appears remote in view of the difficulty with which phenylpyruvic acid is metabolized.

TRYPTOPHAN

Tryptophan, α-amino-β-indolepropionic acid, is the only amino acid containing the indole ring. It is an essential amino acid. Omission of tryptophan from the diet of man or animals is promptly followed by tissue wasting and negative nitrogen balance. In rats the appetite fails and the serum albumin and globulin fall markedly. Hemoglobin also diminishes and the animals develop cataracts.

Tryptophan undergoes reversible deamination in the body, since its corresponding keto acid, β-3-indolepyruvic acid, can replace it in the diet, and the amino and keto acids yield the same end products in the body.

Tryptophan does not give demonstrable increases in liver glycogen in fasted rats or glucose or ketone body excretion in phlorizinized animals. Accordingly, it is considered to be neither glycogenic nor ketogenic. However, that some of the carbon atoms of tryptophan may be converted to glucose has been shown by Sanadi and Greenberg (126), who administered DL-tryptophan labeled with C^{14} at the β position to phlorizinized rats and found sufficient C^{14} in the glucose excreted to indicate that some of the carbon atoms of tryptophan had been incorporated into the glucose. The radioactivity of the glucose was greater than that of the carbon dioxide of the body pool. The ketone bodies excreted did not contain C^{14}.

The D- and L-isomers of tryptophan maintain nutrition and growth equally well (127), indicating that the unnatural D-isomer is inverted to L-tryptophan through the common indolepyruvic acid. The hydroxy acid, indolelactic acid, has also been reported to be capable of replacing tryptophan in the diet (128), and it must function by conversion to L-tryptophan through indolepyruvic acid.

Schayer (129) gave rats D-tryptophan labeled with N^{15} in the indole N and found L-tryptophan similarly labeled in the tissue proteins, proving the conversion of the D- to the L- form.

Despite the highly essential nature of tryptophan, Albanese and associates (130) showed that it is very inefficiently utilized in the body. These workers found a considerable amount of the tryptophan ingested by normal men to be excreted in the urine. From 6 to 9 mg of tryptophan per kilogram of body weight was necessary to prevent negative nitrogen balance. Half or more of the tryptophan required for maintenance may be excreted in the urine.

Many intermediate products of tryptophan metabolism have been identified. Among these are formylkynurenine, kynurenine, kynurenic acid, 3-hydroxykynurenine, 3-hydroxyanthranilic acid, xanthurenic acid, quinolinic acid, and nicotinic acid.

Metabolic breakdown of tryptophan. As indicated above, the keto acid and hydroxy acid corresponding to tryptophan are utilized in place of tryptophan in the diet. The following relations have been demonstrated between tryptophan, indolepyruvic acid, indoleacetic acid, indolelactic acid, and tryptamine (128,131):

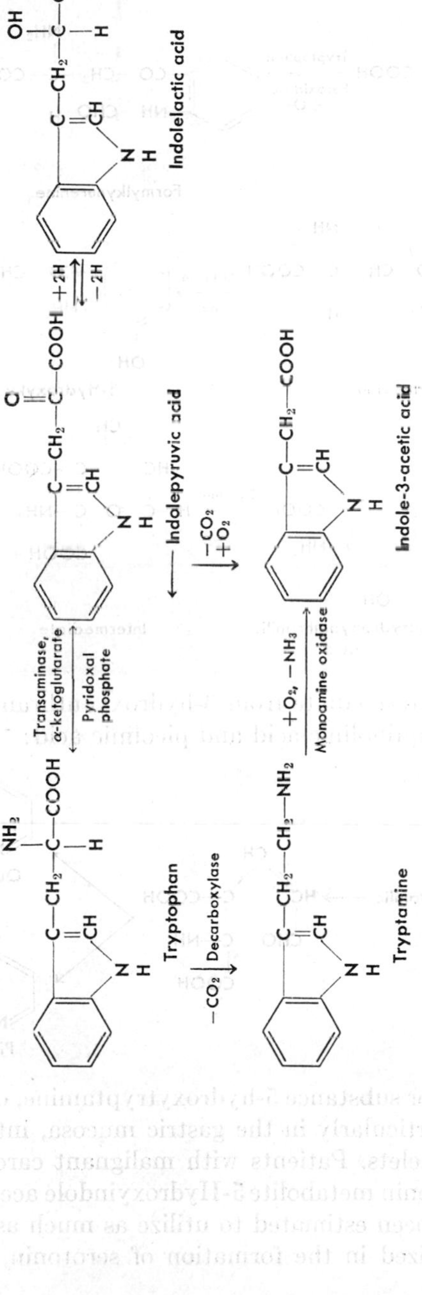

The daily urinary excretion of indoleacetic acid in man generally amounts to 5 to 18 mg but may reach 200 mg per day in certain pathologic conditions and after tryptophan administration (feeding).

The main line of tryptophan breakdown proceeds through formylkynurenine, kynurenine, 3-hydroxykynurenine, and 3-hydroxy anthranilic acid to nicotinic acid (cf. 1182,1234).

Indolelactic acid

Indolepyruvic acid

Indole-3-acetic acid

$+2H \downdownarrows -2H$

Transaminase, α-ketoglutarate

Pyridoxal phosphate

$-CO_2 +O_2$

$+O_2, -NH_3$ Monoamine oxidase

Tryptophan

$-CO_2$ Decarboxylase

Tryptamine

The vasoconstrictor substance, 5-hydroxytryptamine, or serotonin, is present in the blood, particularly in the gastric mucosa, intestine, brain, mast cells, and blood platelets. Patients with malignant carcinoid excrete large amounts of the serotonin metabolite 5-Hydroxyindole acetic acid in the urine. Such patients have been estimated to utilize as much as 60 per cent of the tryptophan metabolized in the formation of serotonin, as compared with

The daily urinary excretion of indoleacetic acid in man generally amounts to 5 to 18 mg but may reach 200 mg per day in certain pathologic conditions and after tryptophan administration (loading).

The main line of tryptophan breakdown proceeds through formylkynurenine, kynurenine, 3-hydroxykynurenine, and 3-hydroxy anthranilic acid to nicotinic acid (132,133):

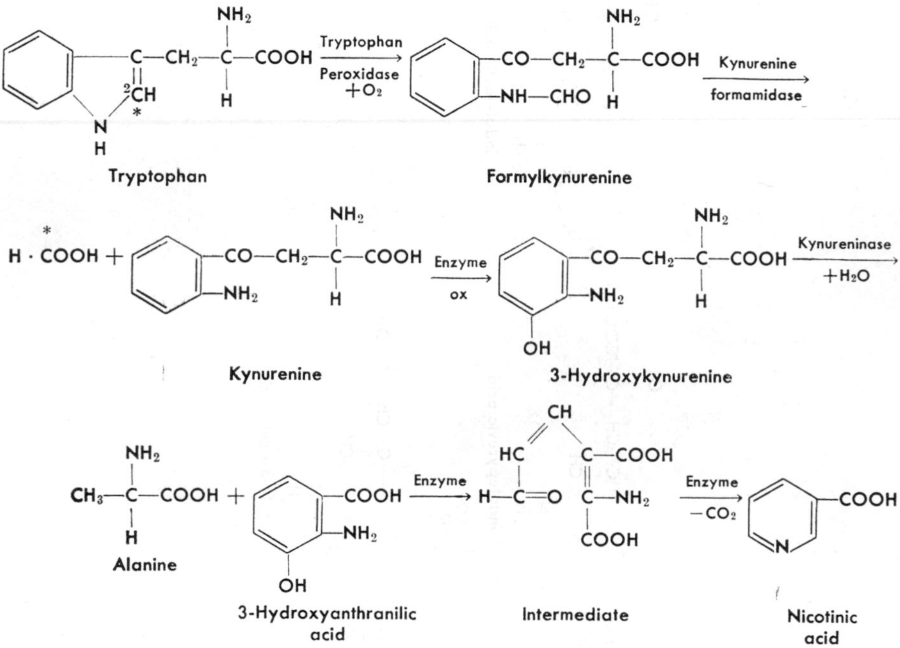

Tryptophan $\xrightarrow[\text{Peroxidase} +O_2]{\text{Tryptophan}}$ Formylkynurenine $\xrightarrow[\text{formamidase}]{\text{Kynurenine}}$

Kynurenine $\xrightarrow{\text{Enzyme ox}}$ 3-Hydroxykynurenine $\xrightarrow[+H_2O]{\text{Kynureninase}}$

Alanine + 3-Hydroxyanthranilic acid $\xrightarrow{\text{Enzyme}}$ Intermediate $\xrightarrow[-CO_2]{\text{Enzyme}}$ Nicotinic acid

The open-chain intermediate from 3-hydroxyanthranilic acid apparently is also converted to quinolinic acid and picolinic acid:

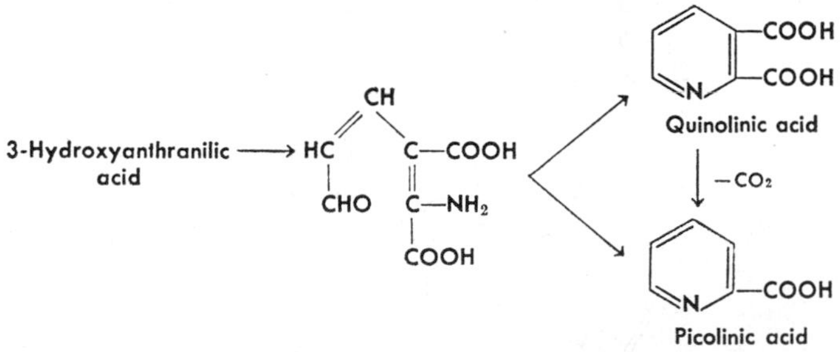

3-Hydroxyanthranilic acid ⟶ Intermediate → Quinolinic acid $\xrightarrow{-CO_2}$ Picolinic acid

The vasoconstrictor substance 5-hydroxytryptamine, or serotonin, is present in the blood, particularly in the gastric mucosa, intestine, brain, mast cells, and blood platelets. Patients with malignant carcinoid excrete large amounts of the serotonin metabolite 5-Hydroxyindole acetic acid in the urine. Such patients have been estimated to utilize as much as 60 per cent of the tryptophan metabolized in the formation of serotonin, as compared with

1 per cent for the normal individual (132, p. 408). Serotonin is considered to function as a neurohumoral agent.

The formation of serotonin from tryptophan has been established by the use of C^{14} tryptophan (134,135):

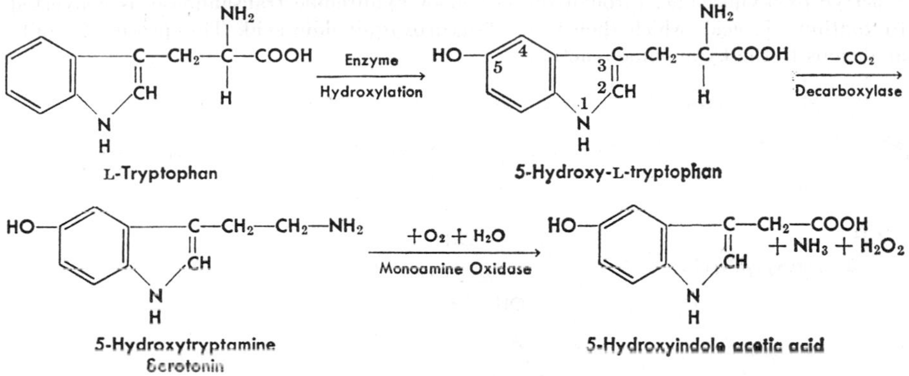

L-Tryptophan   5-Hydroxy-L-tryptophan

5-Hydroxytryptamine
Serotonin

5-Hydroxyindole acetic acid

From the above reactions it will be seen that three carbons of tryptophan form alanine, which may form pyruvic acid and glucose, and that carbon 2 of the pyrrol ring yields formic acid; thus tryptophan contributes to the one-carbon pool. Also, the metabolism of tryptophan yields nicotinic acid, which is converted to the vitamin niacin (nicotinamide) in the animal body.

Kynurenine and 3-hydroxykynurenine, from the main line metabolism of tryptophan, are converted into a number of related substances in the animal (132).

Kynurenine is converted to anthranilic acid and alanine by kynureninase:

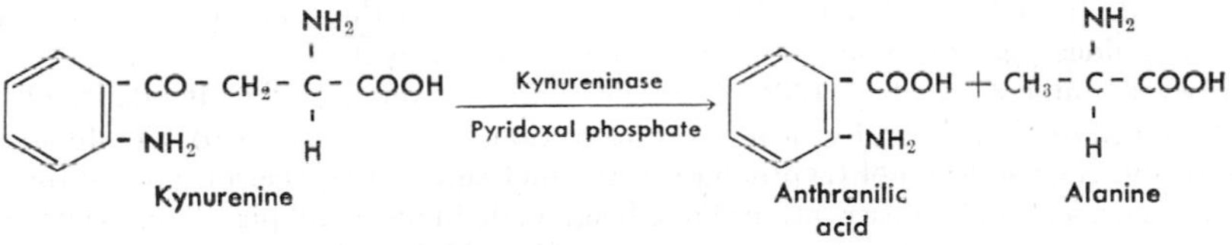

Kynurenine   Anthranilic
acid   Alanine

Kynurenine transaminates to form the corresponding ketoacid, which spontaneously forms kynurenic acid. Kynurenic acid is converted to quinaldic acid by dehydroxylation:

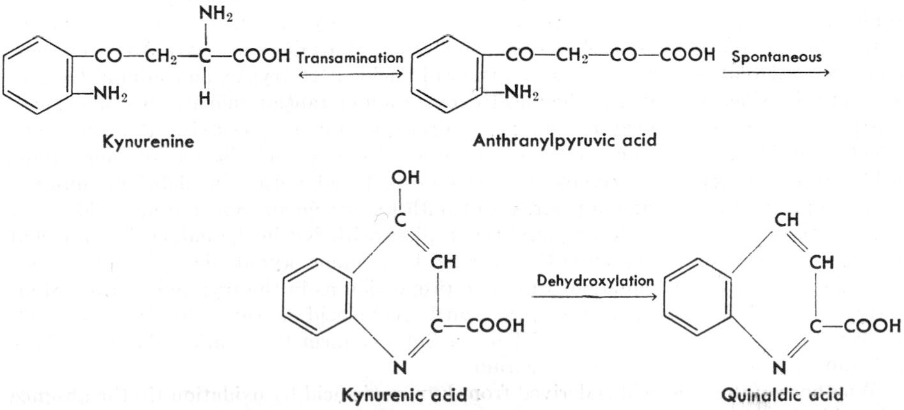

Kynurenine   Anthranylpyruvic acid

Kynurenic acid   Quinaldic acid

Both humans and rats excrete quinaldic acid in the urine after ingestion of kynurenic acid.

3-Hydroxykynurenine undergoes reactions analagous to those of kynurenine. For example, 3-hydroxykynurenine is converted to 3-hydroxyanthranilic acid by kynureninase, as shown above in the main line of tryptophan metabolism.

3-Hydroxykynurenine, through the action of kynurenine transaminase, is converted to xanthurenic acid, which then forms 8-hydroxyquinaldic acid. This process is quite analogous to the kynurenine reaction:

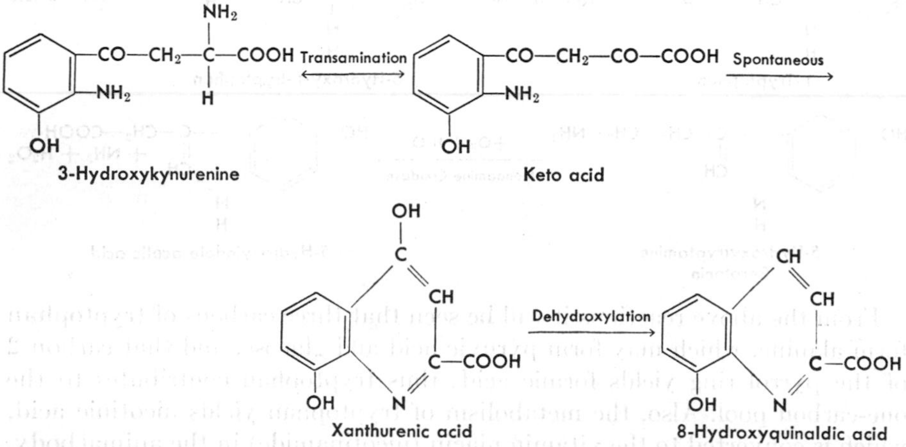

3-Hydroxykynurenine   Keto acid

Xanthurenic acid   8-Hydroxyquinaldic acid

The 8-methyl ether of xanthurenic acid and 8-hydroxyquinaldic acid have been identified in urine (132).

Matsuoka and Yoshimatsu (136) found kynurenine in the urine of rabbits injected with tryptophan. Kynurenine was converted into kynurenic acid when given to rabbits. Gordon and associates (134) have found kynurenic acid in the urines of rats, dogs, coyotes, and guinea pigs, but none in the urines of cats and men.

Lepkovsky and associates (138) observed that rats on a pyridoxine-deficient diet excrete xanthurenic acid in the urine, the excretion being abolished by pyridoxine administration. The addition of tryptophan to the diet caused reappearance of xanthurenic acid in the urine. Similar observations have been made in mice and pigs. That kynurenine is an intermediate in the formation of xanthurenic acid from tryptophan was shown by the fact that kynurenine, as well as tryptophan, caused increased excretion of xanthurenic acid by pyridoxine-deficient rats (139). Indolepyruvic and indolelactic acids were without effect, indicating that these products derived from tryptophan by deamination (indolelactic from indolepyruvic) are not precursors of kynurenine or xanthurenic acid. Lepkovsky and associates (140) have also shown that young dogs on a pyridoxine-deficient diet excreted both kynurenine and xanthurenic acid after tryptophan administration. When pyridoxine was added to the diet the excretion of xanthurenic acid was abolished, but kynurenine excretion continued and kynurenic acid now appeared in the urine. The effect of pyridoxine was to cause the excretion of kynurenic acid instead of xanthurenic acid. Since kynurenine is excreted by both normal and pyridoxine-deficient animals, kynurenine must be a common precursor of both kynurenic and xanthurenic acids.

Foster and associates (141) prepared tryptophan with N^{15} in the indole ring, injected it into rats and rabbits, and found the excreted kynurenine, kynurenic acid, and xanthurenic acid to contain N^{15} in about the same proportion as in the tryptophan ring. Similarly, N^{15}-labeled kynurenine produced xanthurenic acid in rats with the same N^{15} concentration as in the kynurenine. These results confirm the relations between these substances indicated in the above diagram.

Whether xanthurenic acid is derived from kynurenic acid by oxidation (in the absence of pyridoxine) is unknown.

The conversion of tryptophan to the vitamin nicotinic acid has been demonstrated by many workers. Sydenstricker and associates (142) found that the administration of tryptophan to rats caused a large increase in the excretion of nicotinic acid and methyl-nicotinic acid in the urine. Perlzweig and associates (143) found that the administration of tryptophan causes increased excretion of methylnicotinamide in the urines of both infants and adults. Duel and associates (144) found that 3-hydroxyanthranilic acid given to rats caused increased excretion of nicotinamide (niacin) and N'-methylnicotinamide.

Biosynthesis of tryptophan. Yanofsky (145) has obtained evidence which indicates that the synthesis of tryptophan by *E. coli* proceeds as follows through shikimic acid, anthranilic acid, and indole. Shikimic acid is synthesized from glucose by microorganisms:

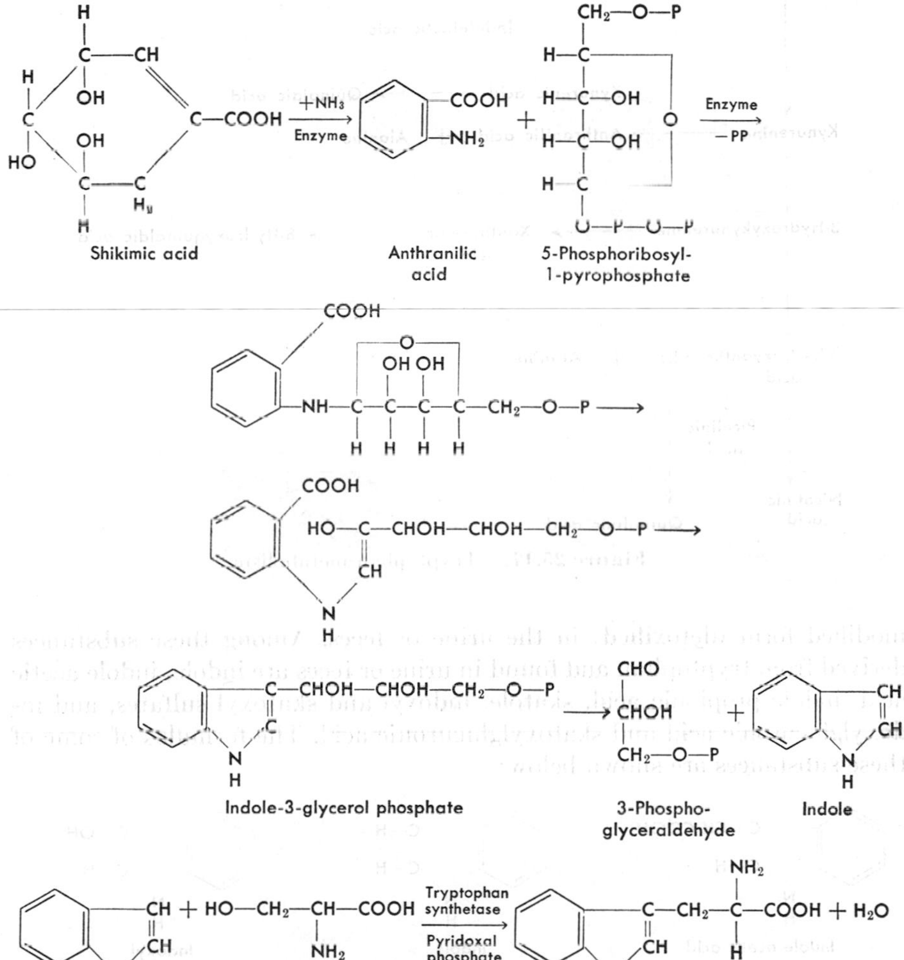

Shikimic acid → Anthranilic acid + 5-Phosphoribosyl-1-pyrophosphate

Indole-3-glycerol phosphate → 3-Phosphoglyceraldehyde + Indole

Indole + Serine (Tryptophan synthetase, Pyridoxal phosphate) → Tryptophan + H₂O

The last process, catalyzed by tryptophan synthetase in the presence of pyridoxal phosphate, involves several steps, with pyridoxal phosphate acting as carrier of a serine residue to indole (146,147).

Bacterial putrefaction. The action of bacteria upon tryptophan in the gut produces a large number of substances which are excreted as such or in

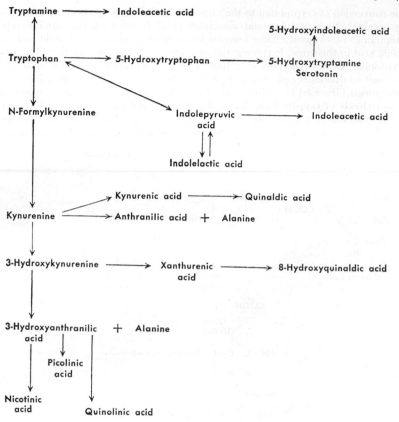

Figure 25.17. Tryptophan metabolism.

modified form (detoxified) in the urine or feces. Among these substances derived from tryptophan and found in urine or feces are indole, indole acetic acid, indole propionic acid, skatole, indoxyl and skatoxyl sulfates, and indoxylglucuronic acid and skatoxylglucuronic acid. The formulas of some of these substances are shown below:

The formation of indoxyl and skatoxyl from indole and skatole and their conjugation with sulfuric and glucuronic acids take place in the liver and represent detoxication processes.

The metabolism of tryptophan is outlined in Figure 25.17.

The fate of indole pyruvic acid in the body, other than its conversion to tryptophan, is unknown.

HISTIDINE

Histidine, α-amino-β-imidazolepropionic acid, is characterized among the amino acids by the presence of the imidazole ring.

Histidine appears to be essential for growth but not for the maintenance of nitrogen equilibrium in rats. Rose and associates (148) found that human adults maintained nitrogen equilibrium on diets deficient only with respect to histidine. Schoenheimer and associates (149) found N^{15} in the histidine of tissue proteins of rats which had received isotopic ammonia. The N^{15} was localized in the α-amino group. The absence of N^{15} from the imidazole group indicated that the animal body cannot synthesize it. Leiter (150) injected histidine into dogs and found only a small amount to be excreted in the urine, despite very high blood levels, and no other imidazole derivatives could be recovered. These results indicate that histidine, like tyrosine, is utilized with marked economy, or else that it is metabolized in such a manner that the imidazole ring is completely broken up (both may be true). Tesar

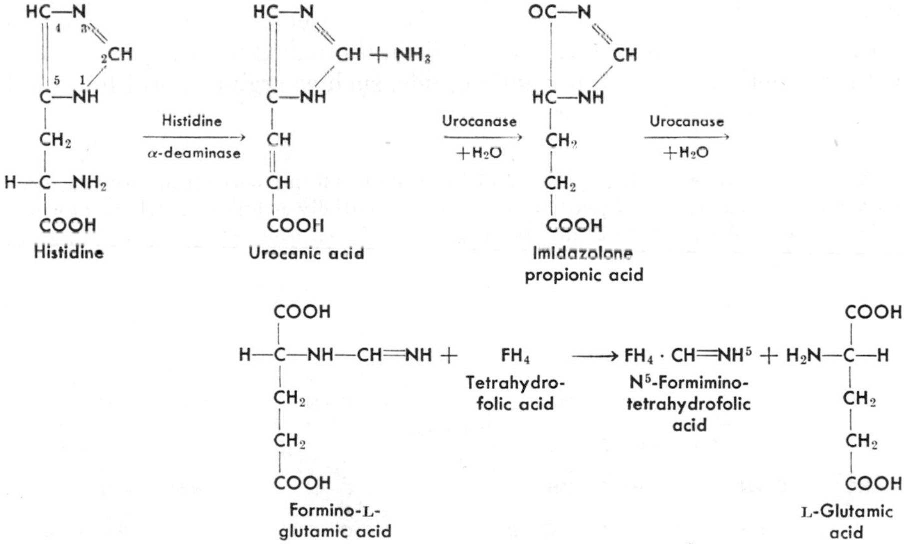

$$FH_4 \cdot CH{=}NH^5 + H_2O \longrightarrow FH_4 \cdot CHO^{10} + NH_3$$

N^5-Formimino- tetrahydrofolic acid

N^{10}-Formyl- tetrahydrofolic acid

$$FH_4 \cdot CHO^{10} + ADP + Pi \overset{Mg^{++}}{\rightleftharpoons} FH_4 + H{-}COOH + ATP$$

and Rittenberg (151) fed histidine labeled with N^{15} in the imidazole ring to rats and found N^{15} to be distributed among the tissue amino acids and other substances very much as found in the case of the nitrogen of ammonia and the α-amino nitrogen of other amino acids when they are fed. This indicated that the imidazole ring is broken up during metabolism.

The fact that both imidazole pyruvic acid and imidazole lactic acid may replace histidine for growth purposes indicates that the keto acid may be aminated to histidine. Conrad and Berg (151) increased the quantity of L-histidine in the bodies of growing rats by feeding the unnatural isomer, D-histidine. This inversion probably was effected through deamination of D-histidine to the keto acid and amination of the latter to L-histidine.

Metabolic breakdown of histidine. The breakdown of histidine in mammalian liver proceeds through urocanic acid, imidazolonepropionic acid, and α-formimino-L-glutamic acid (formamido-glutamic acid) to glutamic acid, formic acid, and ammonia (152,153) as shown on page 1111.

The breakdown of N^5-formimino-tetrahydrofolic acid to ammonia and N^{10}-formyl-tetrahydrofolic acid involves several steps (153, p. 406).

The breakdown of histidine by microorganisms appears to follow the same pathway as in mammalian liver down to formiminoglutamic acid, which then is broken down to glutamic acid, NH_3, and $H \cdot COOH$ by pathways not requiring folic acid derivatives.

It will be noted from the above reactions of histidine breakdown that carbon 2 of histidine enters the one-carbon pool, and in animals is available for the synthesis of one-carbon groups in other compounds. Since the metabolism of histidine yields glutamic acid, it is glucogenic and antiketogenic in the animal body. Also, histidine metabolism, through glutamic acid, is linked with the metabolisms of other amino acids, such as arginine, ornithine, and proline, to be considered later.

Histidine synthesis. The synthesis of histidine in all microorganisms studied, such as *Neurospora*, bacteria, and yeast, appears to be essentially as follows (81,153), in which imidazoleglycerol phosphate is an intermediate, is formed from AMP, ribose-5-P, ATP, and glutamine:

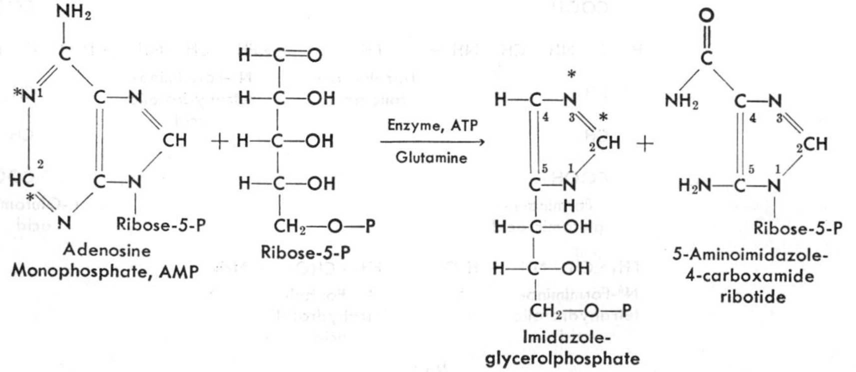

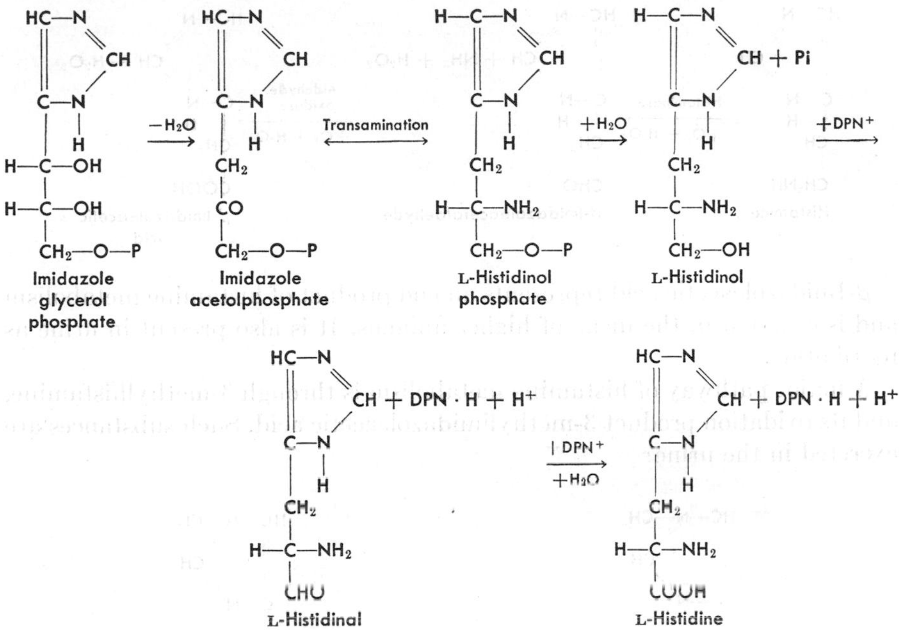

$$
\begin{array}{ccccc}
\text{(Imidazole glycerol phosphate)} & \xrightarrow{-H_2O} & \text{(Imidazole acetolphosphate)} & \xrightleftharpoons{\text{Transamination}} & \text{(L-Histidinol phosphate)} & \xrightarrow{+H_2O} & \text{(L-Histidinol)} \xrightarrow{+DPN^+}
\end{array}
$$

Imidazole glycerol phosphate — Imidazole acetolphosphate — L-Histidinol phosphate — L-Histidinol

L-Histidinal — L-Histidine

$\text{CH} + \text{DPN}\cdot\text{H} + \text{H}^+$ (L-Histidinal)

$\xrightarrow[+H_2O]{|\ DPN^+}$

$\text{CH} + \text{DPN}\cdot\text{H} + \text{H}^+$ (L-Histidine)

It appears that nitrogen 1 and carbon 2 of the purine ring of AMP become nitrogen 3 and carbon 2 of the imidazole ring of histidine, and that the five-carbon chain of histidine is derived from the ribose carbons. Nitrogen 1 of the imidazole group of histidine apparently is derived from the amide group of glutamine.

As indicated previously, the adult human maintains nitrogen balance without histidine in the diet. It has been suggested that microbial synthesis in the intestine might provide histidine for the human. However, it seems rather improbable that sufficient amounts of the amino acid could be supplied in this way, which, if true, would lead to the conclusion that man synthesizes histidine. However, nothing is known regarding such synthesis except that human liver apparently can incorporate formate carbon into position 2 of the imidazole ring but rat liver cannot do this.

Small amounts of methylhistidines, 1-methylhistidine and 3-methylhistidine, have been found in the urines of some animals.

Histamine. Histamine is formed in the gut by bacterial decarboxylation of histidine. It is also formed in injured tissues and apparently is continually formed in small amounts in normal tissue. Allergic reactions appear to be related to the explosive liberation of histamine caused by entrance of the sensitizing substance into the tissues. Its excessive liberation may be related to traumatic shock. Histamine markedly depresses blood pressure, and large doses may cause extreme vascular collapse. Histamine strongly stimulates the secretion of both pepsin and acid by the stomach and is administered in studies of gastric secretion.

An enzyme, histaminase (diamine oxidase), in mammalian tissues oxidizes histamine to β-imidazoleacetaldehyde, which in the liver is further oxidized to β-imidazoleacetic acid by aldehyde oxidase:

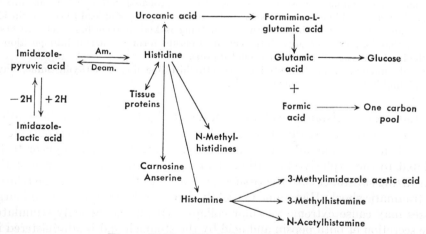

β-Imidazoleacetic acid represents an end product of histamine metabolism and is excreted in the urine of higher animals. It is also present in urine as its ribotide.

A major pathway of histamine metabolism is through 3-methylhistamine, and its oxidation product 3-methylimidazoleacetic acid. Such substances are excreted in the urine:

N-Acetylhistamine, in which the —NH_2 group is acetylated, is excreted in the urine of man and other higher animals.

Figure 25.18.   Metabolism of histamine.

Other histidine derivatives. The dipeptides carnosine (β-alanylhistidine), and anserine (β-alanyl-1-methylhistidine) are constituents of muscle. Apparently the methyl group of anserine is derived from methionine.

Ergothioneine is the betaine of thiolhistidine and was first isolated from ergot. It is present in blood (ca. 10 mg per 100 ml) and in liver and brain. Practically all of the ergothioneine of blood is in the red cells. Ergothioneine of animal tissues is derived from the diet and is not synthesized by animals. It is formed by fungi:

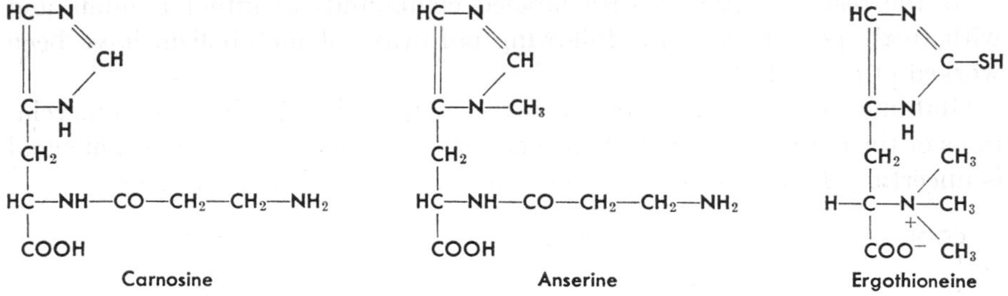

Carnosine   Anserine   Ergothioneine

The metabolism of histamine is outlined in Figure 25.18.

ARGININE, ORNITHINE, PROLINE, AND HYDROXYPROLINE

The metabolisms of these amino acids are considered together since they are intimately related.

Arginine and ornithine. Arginine, α-amino-δ-guanidovaleric acid, and ornithine, α,δ-diaminovaleric acid are closely related in the formation of urea through the Krebs-Henseleit cycle previously discussed. While arginine is a constituent of proteins, ornithine apparently is not. Ornithine serves catalytically in the formation of arginine, which is then hydrolyzed to ornithine and urea.

Arginine is utilized in the synthesis of creatine, to be considered in a later section.

Arginine transamidinates with glycine to form ornithine and guanidoacetic acid, as described under creatine metabolism.

Arginine also transamidinates with γ-aminobutyric acid in brain to form γ-guanidobutyric acid.

Essential nature of arginine. Although arginine is commonly classed as an essential amino acid, its essentiality is somewhat equivocal. Rose (154) found that the omission of arginine from otherwise adequate diets retarded growth but did not entirely stop it. Scull and Rose (155) found more arginine in the bodies of growing rats than had been provided in their diets. Whipple and associates (156) found that dogs on diets deficient only in arginine maintained nitrogen equilibrium for a week or two but could not regenerate serum proteins at a normal rate. Albanese and associates (157) maintained nitrogen balance in men for ten days on an arginine-deficient diet, but at the end of this time found spermatogenesis to be severely impaired. The condition was corrected only gradually after arginine was added to the diet. Sperm nucleoproteins are rich in arginine.

The above evidence shows that, while arginine may be synthesized by a number of animal species, the rate of synthesis is too slow to provide for normal growth and maintenance.

The synthesis of arginine by the body may be effected from proline, which is convertible to ornithine and then to arginine. Also, ornithine is convertible to proline in the body.

Interrelations of arginine, ornithine, and proline. The metabolisms of all these amino acids yield glutamic acid in the animal body.

As the result of studies with labeled compounds in intact animals and with tissue preparations the following pathways of metabolism have been worked out (132,158).

Glutamic acid γ-semialdehyde is a key intermediate in the metabolic relations of the amino acids, and its mechanism of formation from glutamic acid is uncertain. However, it may be formed by the following reaction:

$$
\begin{array}{ccccc}
\text{COOH} & & \text{CO - O - PO}_3\text{H}_2 & & \text{CHO} \\
| & & | & & | \\
\text{CH}_2 & \xrightarrow[\text{Mg}^{++}]{\text{Enzyme}} & \text{CH}_2 & \xrightarrow[]{\text{Dehydrogenase}} & \text{CH}_2 \\
| & & | & & | \\
\text{CH}_2 \quad + \text{ATP} & \rightleftharpoons & \text{CH}_2 \quad + \text{TPN}\cdot\text{H} + \text{H}^+ & \rightleftharpoons & \text{CH}_2 \quad + \text{TPN}^+ + \text{Pi} \\
| & & | & & | \\
\text{H - C - NH}_2 & & \text{H - C - NH}_2 & & \text{H - C - NH}_2 \\
| & & | & & | \\
\text{COOH} & & \text{COOH} & & \text{COOH} \\
\text{Glutamic} & & \gamma\text{-Glutamyl} & & \text{Glutamic acid-} \\
\text{acid} & & \text{phosphate} & & \gamma\text{-semialdehyde}
\end{array}
$$

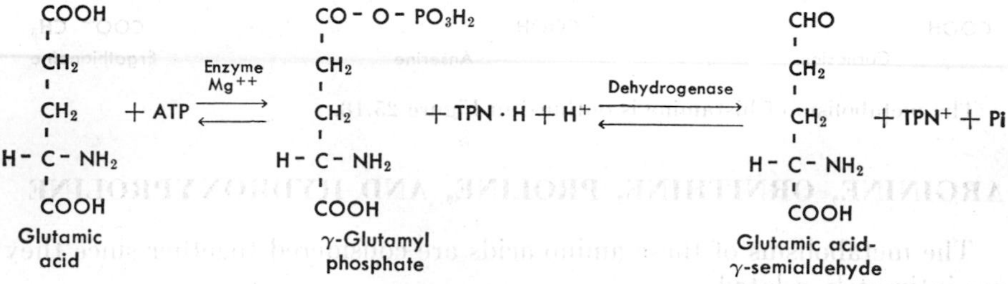

since a similar reaction involving aspartic acid has been found in yeast (81, p. 288).

Glutamic acid is converted to proline by the following reactions (132):

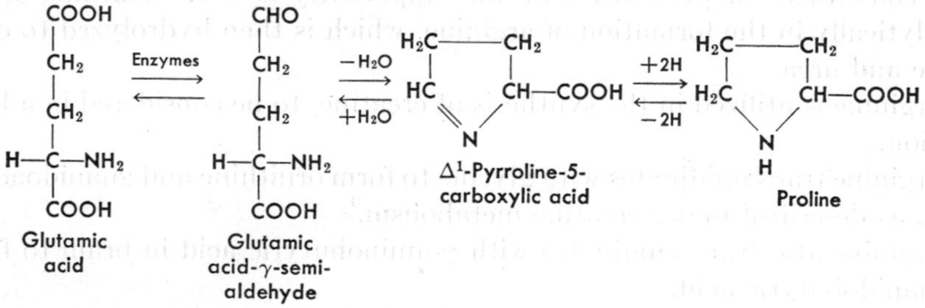

$$
\begin{array}{ccccc}
\text{COOH} & & \text{CHO} & & \\
| & & | & & \\
\text{CH}_2 & \xrightarrow[\text{Enzymes}]{} & \text{CH}_2 & \xrightarrow[+\text{H}_2\text{O}]{-\text{H}_2\text{O}} & \Delta^1\text{-Pyrroline-5-carboxylic acid} \xrightarrow[-2\text{H}]{+2\text{H}} \text{Proline} \\
| & & | & & \\
\text{CH}_2 & & \text{CH}_2 & & \\
| & & | & & \\
\text{H-C-NH}_2 & & \text{H-C-NH}_2 & & \\
| & & | & & \\
\text{COOH} & & \text{COOH} & & \\
\text{Glutamic} & & \text{Glutamic} & & \\
\text{acid} & & \text{acid-}\gamma\text{-semi-} & & \\
& & \text{aldehyde} & &
\end{array}
$$

All of the reactions are reversible.

Glutamic acid semialdehyde is converted to ornithine by transamination:

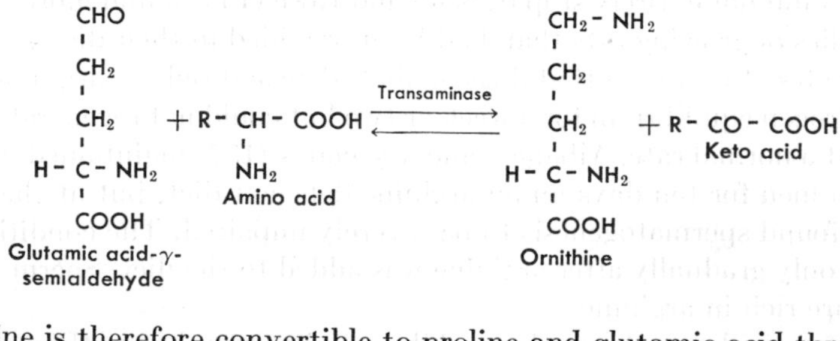

$$
\begin{array}{ccccc}
\text{CHO} & & & & \text{CH}_2\text{- NH}_2 \\
| & & & & | \\
\text{CH}_2 & & \xrightarrow[\text{Transaminase}]{} & & \text{CH}_2 \\
| & & & & | \\
\text{CH}_2 \quad + \text{R - CH - COOH} & \rightleftharpoons & & & \text{CH}_2 \quad + \text{R - CO - COOH} \\
| \qquad\qquad | & & & & | \qquad\qquad \text{Keto acid} \\
\text{H - C - NH}_2 \quad \text{NH}_2 & & & & \text{H - C - NH}_2 \\
| \qquad\qquad \text{Amino acid} & & & & | \\
\text{COOH} & & & & \text{COOH} \\
\text{Glutamic acid-}\gamma\text{-} & & & & \text{Ornithine} \\
\text{semialdehyde} & & & &
\end{array}
$$

Ornithine is therefore convertible to proline and glutamic acid through glutamic acid-γ-semialdehyde.

* Ornithine is converted to arginine through the Krebs-Henseleit urea cycle.

Hydroxyproline is formed by hydroxylation of proline. When hydroxyproline containing N^{15} is fed to rats, no appreciable amount is incorporated in body proteins in contrast to other labeled amino acids (159). Also, after feeding labeled hydroxyproline the tissue proline contained only a trace of N^{15}, indicating that hydroxyproline is not converted to proline. However, when N^{15}-proline is fed, much more N^{15}-hydroxyproline is found in tissue proteins, indicating the conversion of proline to hydroxyproline. These results also indicate that proline is hydroxylated after incorporation into tissue proteins, and that this is the case has been shown by other isotopic evidence (160). Ascorbic acid has been shown to stimulate formation of hydroxyproline in guinea pigs (161).

It appears that hydroxyproline is broken down through γ-hydroxyglutamic acid semialdehyde and γ-hydroxyglutamic acid (162) to form alanine:

CHO
CHOH
CH₂
H—C—NH₂
COOH
γ-Hydroxy-glutamic acid semialdehyde

Hydroxyproline

Δ¹-3-hydroxy-pyrroline-5-carboxylic acid

COOH
CHO·H
CH₂
H—C—NH₂
COOH
γ-Hydroxy-glutamic acid

CH₃
H—C—NH₂
COOH
Alanine

COOH
CHO
Glyoxylic acid

Cleavage Enzyme

Since arginine, ornithine, and proline yield glutamic acid, and hydroxy-proline gives alanine, both of which are convertible to glucose, all of the amino acids are glucogenic and antiketogenic.

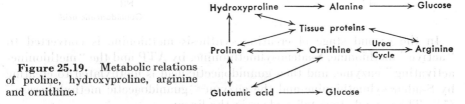

Figure 25.19. Metabolic relations of proline, hydroxyproline, arginine and ornithine.

Hydroxyproline ⟶ Alanine ⟶ Glucose
Tissue proteins
Proline ⟷ Ornithine ⟷ Arginine Urea Cycle
Glutamic acid ⟶ Glucose

As indicated previously, arginine is partially essential in animals, apparently because of slow rate of synthesis. Proline, hydroxyproline, and ornithine are not essential amino acids in the diets of animals, since they can be synthesized in adequate quantities.

An outline of the metabolic relations of arginine, ornithine, proline, and hydroxyproline is given in Figure 25.19.

CREATINE

Formation of creatine. The importance of creatine phosphate as a reservoir of high-energy phosphate readily convertible to ATP in muscles and other tissues has been pointed out. The synthesis of creatine involves the amino acids glycine, arginine, and methionine (as S-adenosylmethionine). Guanidoacetic acid is first formed by a transamidination reaction between glycine and arginine, in which the amidine group of arginine is transferred to glycine (163,164). The transamidinase enzyme is found in mammalian kidney and pancreas (165) but appears to be absent from such other tissues as liver, heart, skeletal muscle, blood, brain, and spleen.

$$
\underset{\text{Arginine}}{\text{HOOC}-\underset{\underset{\text{NH}_2}{|}}{\overset{\overset{\text{H}}{|}}{\text{C}}}-\text{CH}_2-\text{CH}_2-\text{CH}_2-\underset{\overset{|}{\text{H}}}{\text{N}}-\underset{\overset{\|}{\text{NH}}}{\text{C}}-\text{NH}_2} + \underset{\text{Glycine}}{\text{H}_2\text{N}-\text{CH}_2-\text{COOH}} \underset{}{\overset{\text{Transamidinase}}{\rightleftharpoons}}
$$

$$
\underset{\substack{\text{Guanidoacetic acid,}\\ \text{or Glycocyamine}}}{\text{H}_2\text{N}-\underset{\overset{\|}{\text{NH}}}{\text{C}}-\text{NH}-\text{CH}_2-\text{COOH}} + \underset{\text{Ornithine}}{\text{HOOC}-\underset{\underset{\text{NH}_2}{|}}{\overset{\overset{\text{H}}{|}}{\text{C}}}-\text{CH}_2-\text{CH}_2-\text{CH}_2-\text{NH}_2}
$$

It is of interest that Walker (164) obtained evidence that an amidine derivative of the transamidinase enzyme is an intermediate in the reaction. The process may be represented as follows:

$$
\underset{\text{Arginine}}{\text{R}-\text{NH}-\underset{\overset{\|}{\text{NH}}}{\text{C}}-\text{NH}_2} + \text{Enzyme} \rightleftharpoons \underset{\text{Enzyme-amidine}}{\text{Enzyme}-\underset{\overset{\|}{\text{NH}}}{\text{C}}-\text{NH}_2} + \underset{\text{Ornithine}}{\text{R}-\text{NH}_2}
$$

$$
\underset{}{\text{Enzyme}-\underset{\overset{\|}{\text{NH}}}{\text{C}}-\text{NH}_2} + \underset{\text{Glycine}}{\text{H}_2\text{N}-\text{CH}_2-\text{COOH}} \rightleftharpoons \text{Enzyme} + \underset{\substack{\text{Guanidoacetic acid}}}{\text{H}_2\text{N}-\underset{\overset{\|}{\text{NH}}}{\text{C}}-\underset{\overset{|}{\text{H}}}{\text{N}}-\text{CH}_2-\text{COOH}}
$$

In the second stage of creatine synthesis methionine is converted to "active" methionine, S-adenosylmethionine, by ATP and the "methionine-activating" enzyme, and then guanidoacetic acid is methylated to creatine by S-adenosylmethionine and the enzyme "guanidoacetic methylpherase" (54). The second stage takes place in the liver:

$$
\underset{\text{L-Methionine}}{\text{CH}_3-\text{S}-\text{CH}_2-\text{CH}_2-\underset{\overset{|}{\text{NH}_2}}{\text{CH}}-\text{COOH}} + \text{ATP} \xrightarrow[\text{Enzyme}]{\text{Activating}} \underset{\text{S-Adenosyl-L-methionine}}{\text{Adenosyl}-\overset{+}{\underset{\overset{|}{\text{CH}_3}}{\text{S}}}-\text{CH}_2-\text{CH}_2-\underset{\overset{|}{\text{NH}_2}}{\text{CH}}-\text{COOH}} + \text{PP} + \text{Pi}
$$

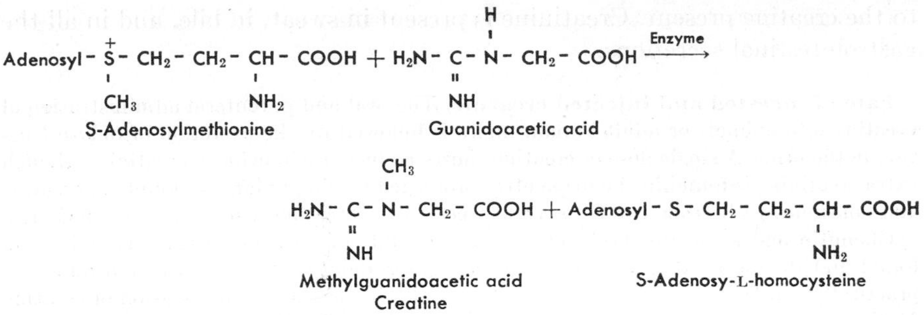

$$\text{Adenosyl} - \overset{+}{\underset{\underset{\text{S-Adenosylmethionine}}{CH_3}}{S}} - CH_2 - CH_2 - \underset{NH_2}{CH} - COOH + H_2N - \underset{\underset{\text{Guanidoacetic acid}}{NH}}{\overset{H}{C}} - N - CH_2 - COOH \xrightarrow{\text{Enzyme}}$$

$$H_2N - \underset{NH}{\overset{CH_3}{C}} - N - CH_2 - COOH + \text{Adenosyl} - S - CH_2 - CH_2 - \underset{NH_2}{CH} - COOH$$

Methylguanidoacetic acid   S-Adenosy-L-homocysteine
Creatine

The methyl group of creatine is not transferred to other compounds, as is the methyl of S-adenosylmethionine and of betaine (later discussion). Also, the methyl group of creatine is not oxidized to formaldehyde or formate and, consequently, does not contribute to the one-carbon pool. However, the methyl groups of creatine may be formed from the one-carbon pool (through methionine).

Creatine occurs generally in the tissues of the body, though in uneven distribution. The highest concentrations are found in striated muscle, heart muscle, testes, liver, and kidneys, and somewhat lesser quantities in the brain. Very small amounts are present in blood, about 0.2 to 0.6 mg per cent in plasma and around 3 mg per cent in the cells. The muscles contain about 98 per cent of the total body creatine (ca. 0.5 per cent).

Most of the creatine in normal tissues (red cells excepted) occurs as the high-energy compound creatine phosphate.

The urine of normal adult persons contains only small amounts of creatine, but much creatinine, the anhydride of creatine. Creatinine apparently serves no useful function in the body but simply represents a waste product of creatine metabolism. Borsook and Dubnoff (166) showed that most of the creatinine formed in the body arises from the spontaneous decomposition of creatine phosphate according to the equation:

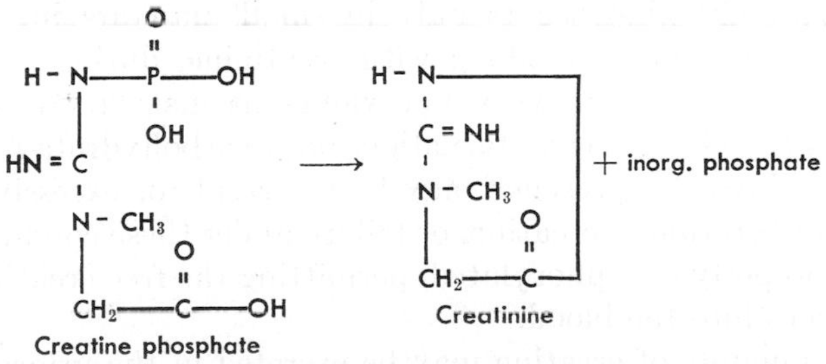

Creatine phosphate   Creatinine   + inorg. phosphate

The blood plasma contains about 0.6 to 1.0 mg per cent of creatinine, while the concentration in the red cells has been found to be less, about 0.5 to 0.65 mg per cent. It appears that creatinine, unlike creatine, is distributed between the plasma and cells in proportion to their respective water contents, indicating free diffusibility. Baker and Miller (167) found 0.1 to 4.7 mg of creatinine per 100 g to be present in rat tissues, amounts proportional to the creatine present. Creatinine is present in sweat, in bile, and in all the gastrointestinal secretions.

Fate of ingested and injected creatine. The oral and parenteral administration of creatine into animals or adult human males is followed by the excretion of only a fraction in the urine. A single dose of creatine causes no increase in urinary creatinine, though extra creatinine is found in the urine after prolonged feeding of large amounts of creatine and continues to be excreted for several weeks after creatine ingestion is discontinued.

Chanutin and associates (168) gave large amounts of creatine to rats and mice and found that the muscle creatine increased sharply for about a day, after which it remained practically constant. Liver and kidney creatine also increased. Upon cessation of creatine feeding, the excess creatine rapidly disappeared from the tissues except the muscles, which retained excessive amounts for some time.

Bloch and Schoenheimer (119) showed that N^{15}-labeled creatine fed to rats was deposited in the tissues, and the urinary creatinine excreted contained amounts of N^{15} indicating its origin from creatine. These workers also fed isotopic creatinine and found the prompt excretion of most of it in the urine. Also, no N^{15} was found in the body creatine, indicating that the conversion of creatine to creatinine is biologically irreversible.

Hoberman and associates (170) labeled the tissue creatine of a human subject on a creatine-free diet with N^{15} by feeding isotopic creatine for 38 days and then isotopic guanidoacetic acid for ten days. Nonisotopic creatine then was given for five days and the urine analyzed for 28 days. The rate of turnover of endogenous creatine, as determined by the N^{15} concentration of excreted creatinine (and creatine) after nonisotopic creatine was given, showed that 1.64 per cent of the tissue creatine (endogenous creatine) turned over per day. A balance between the amount of creatine retained in the body, and the amounts deposited in the tissues or excreted as extra creatinine in the urine could not be achieved. These workers suggest that the synthesis of endogenous creatine is retarded by the presence of exogenous creatine (administered). The amount of creatinine excreted per day as determined from its N^{15} content was directly proportional to the amount of creatine in the body.

Hoberman and associates (171) have shown, by the use of N^{15}-labeled creatine, that the administration of the hormone methyltestosterone increases the rate of creatine synthesis in the body.

Bloch and Schoenheimer (169) gave isotopic creatinine (N^{15}) to rats and found 75 per cent of the N^{15} in urinary creatinine. The remaining 25 per cent could not be accounted for in either tissues or urine.

Creatinuria. Creatine occurs only in small amounts in the urine of normal adults. It is present, along with creatinine, during the process of growth, and it decreases to very low values as maturity is approached. Creatinuria is found in fevers, starvation, on a carbohydrate-free diet, and in diabetes mellitus. Its presence may be the result of excessive tissue destruction and liberation of creatine, or failure under these conditions to keep the creatine properly phosphorylated, permitting the free creatine to diffuse from the tissues into the blood.

Excessive amounts of creatine may be excreted in the urines of patients with muscular dystrophy or hyperthyroidism.

Constancy of creatinine—creatine excretion. Shaffer (177) showed that the daily excretion of creatinine by the adult male and of creatinine + creatine in subjects with physiologic creatinuria (such as growing children) is remarkably constant. It is little affected by diet (excluding diets high in creatine and creatinine), exercise, or urine volume. The creatinine (or creatinine + creatine) excretion apparently is characteristic of a healthy individual and is proportional to size and particularly to muscle mass. The daily excretion of creatinine is sufficiently constant for a given individual under ordinary conditions that the accuracy of 24-hour urine collections may be checked by its determination.

Creatinine coefficient. The creatinine coefficient (or creatinine + creatine coefficient) represents the milligrams of creatinine (or creatinine + creatine) per kilogram of body weight excreted daily. The creatinine coefficient normally averages 20 to 26 for men and 14 to 22 for women.

The urine of premature infants and of normal infants during the first few days of life contains little creatine, and the creatinine coefficients are low.

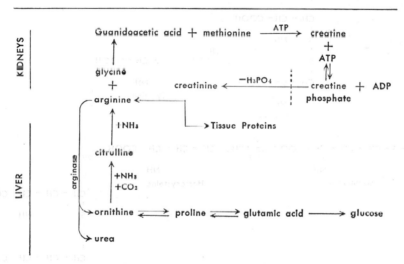

Figure 25.20.   Relations of arginine and creatine.

Creatinuria and creatinine coefficients gradually increase during the first month of life.

McClugage and associates (173) found the daily creatinine excretion of obese persons to be low in relation to weight, but normal in relation to their ideal weight. Upon weight reduction through dietary control, the creatinine excretion remained constant. Underweight persons were found to have abnormally low creatinine coefficients.

Hodgson and Lewis (174) consider the difference in creatinine coefficients of males and females to be related to the differences in muscular development rather than sex differences, since they found women with unusual muscular development to have creatinine coefficients comparable with those of males.

The relations between the metabolism of arginine and of creatine are summarized in the diagram of Figure 25.20.

THE SULFUR-CONTAINING AMINO ACIDS, METHIONINE AND CYSTINE, AND RELATED AMINO ACIDS, HOMOCYSTEINE AND CYSTEINE

Most of the sulfur of proteins is represented by the methionine and cystine present, though small amounts of cysteine, the reduction product of cystine, may be present also. This is indicated by the presence of free —SH groups in a large number of enzyme and other proteins.

Demethylation of methionine produces homocysteine, which may be re-methylated to methionine. Cystine is reversibly convertible to cysteine and homocystine to homocysteine by oxidation-reduction. The chemical relations between these amino acids may be shown as follows:

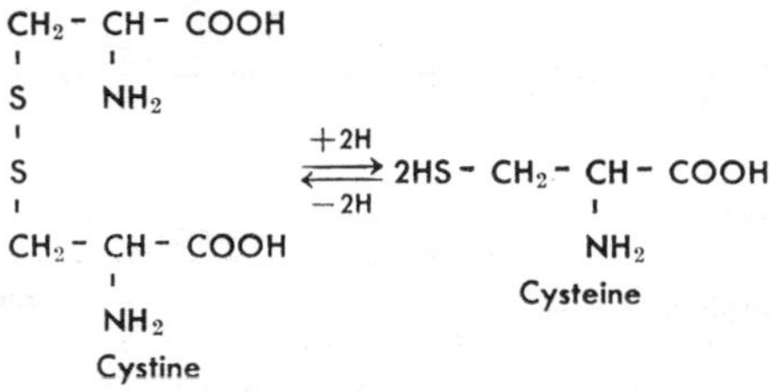

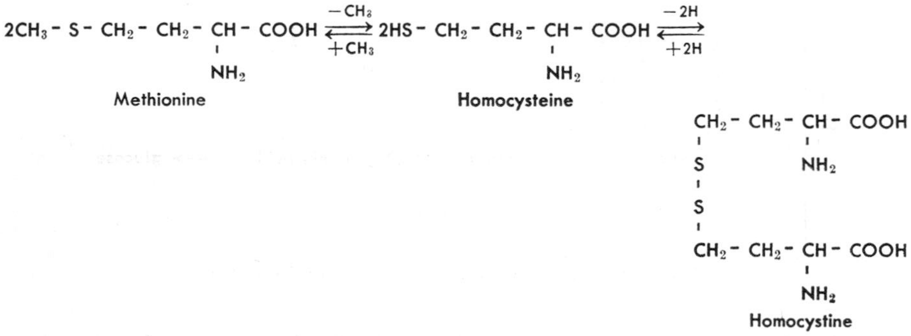

$$
\begin{array}{l}
\text{CH}_2-\text{CH}-\text{COOH} \\
\;\;|\qquad\;\; | \\
\;\;\text{S}\qquad \text{NH}_2 \\
\;\;| \qquad\qquad\qquad \overset{+2H}{\underset{-2H}{\rightleftharpoons}} \; 2\text{HS}-\text{CH}_2-\text{CH}-\text{COOH} \\
\;\;\text{S} \qquad\qquad\qquad\qquad\qquad\qquad\qquad | \\
\;\;|\qquad\qquad\qquad\qquad\qquad\qquad\quad \text{NH}_2 \\
\text{CH}_2-\text{CH}-\text{COOH}\qquad\qquad\quad \text{Cysteine} \\
\qquad\;\; | \\
\qquad\; \text{NH}_2 \\
\qquad \text{Cystine}
\end{array}
$$

$$
2\text{CH}_3-\text{S}-\text{CH}_2-\text{CH}_2-\text{CH}-\text{COOH} \underset{+CH_3}{\overset{-CH_3}{\rightleftharpoons}} 2\text{HS}-\text{CH}_2-\text{CH}_2-\text{CH}-\text{COOH} \underset{+2H}{\overset{-2H}{\rightleftharpoons}}
$$

$$
\begin{array}{cc}
\qquad\qquad\qquad\quad | & \qquad\qquad\qquad | \\
\qquad\qquad\qquad\;\; \text{NH}_2 & \qquad\qquad\; \text{NH}_2 \\
\qquad\quad \text{Methionine} & \qquad\; \text{Homocysteine}
\end{array}
$$

$$
\begin{array}{l}
\text{CH}_2-\text{CH}_2-\text{CH}-\text{COOH} \\
\;\;| \qquad\qquad\qquad | \\
\;\;\text{S} \qquad\qquad\quad \text{NH}_2 \\
\;\;| \\
\;\;\text{S} \\
\;\;| \\
\text{CH}_2-\text{CH}_2-\text{CH}-\text{COOH} \\
\qquad\qquad\qquad\;\; | \\
\qquad\qquad\qquad \text{NH}_2 \\
\qquad\qquad \text{Homocystine}
\end{array}
$$

Cysteine is nonenzymatically and reversibly oxidized to cystine by glutathione present in cells generally:

$$
\text{Cysteine} + \text{G}-\text{S}-\text{S}-\text{G} \rightleftharpoons 2\text{GSH} + \text{Cystine}
$$

The methyl group of methionine is removed through S-adenosylmethionine in the formation of creatine and choline (discussed earlier). A methyl group is added to homocysteine to form methionine, as pointed out in the discussion of one-carbon metabolism.

Since cysteine and cystine and homocysteine and homocystine are readily interconvertible, processes which lead to the formation of one of either pair of these compounds may be considered also to form the other pair.

Methionine but not cystine is an essential amino acid in the diet of all animals investigated. The dietary requirements for L-methionine may be met by feeding the corresponding keto acid, α-keto-γ-methylthiobutyric acid, which is aminated to L-methionine, or by feeding D-methionine, which is converted to L-methionine through the keto acid. While the animal can convert the corresponding keto acid (and hydroxy acid through the keto acid) to methionine, it cannot synthesize the keto acid.

Since cystine is not an essential amino acid, this indicates the formation of cystine from methionine. The presence of cystine in the diet reduces the requirement for methionine (sparing action).

Pathways of methionine metabolism (81). Methionine undergoes transamination in the liver with α-ketoglutaric acid to yield the keto acid α-keto-γ-methylthiobutyric acid.

$$CH_3 - S - CH_2 - CH_2 - \underset{\underset{NH_2}{|}}{CH} - COOH + HOOC - CH_2 - CH_2 - CO - COOH \xrightarrow[\text{Pyridoxal phosphate}]{\text{Transaminase}}$$

Methionine   α-Ketoglutaric acid

$$CH_3 - S - CH_2 - CH_2 - CO - COOH + HOOC - CH_2 - CH_2 - \underset{\underset{NH_2}{|}}{CH} - COOH$$

α-Keto-γ-methylthiobutyric acid   Glutamic acid

The main pathway of methionine metabolism leads through cysteine and homoserine.

Tarver and Schmidt (175) fed rats methionine labeled with S^{35} and found the isotope in the cystine of tissue proteins, proving the utilization of methionine S in the formation of cystine. Stetten (176) fed N^{15}-serine to rats and found a high concentration of N^{15}-cystine in the tissue proteins, indicating that serine is involved in the formation of cystine from methionine. Brand and associates (177) gave homocysteine to a patient with cystinuria and observed an increase in urinary cystine excretion. These workers suggested that cystathionine, formed from homocysteine and serine, is an intermediate in the formation of cysteine (cystine) in the animal. That this is the case was proved by the work of Du Vigneaud and associates (178). The processes involved in the main pathway of methionine metabolism may be represented as shown in Figure 25.21.

It will be noted from the reactions of Figure 25.21 that only the sulfur of methionine is used in the synthesis of cysteine (cystine), the rest of the cysteine molecule being derived from serine. The remainder of the methionine molecule is converted to homoserine, which is broken down through α-keto-butyric acid to propionic acid. The S of methionine goes the pathway of cysteine metabolism, to be considered later.

As indicated in Figure 25.21, pyridoxal phosphate is required in the formation of cystathionine, and liver preparations from pyridoxine (vitamin

B_6)-deficient rats do not form cysteine from homocysteine and serine unless pyridoxal phosphate is added (179).

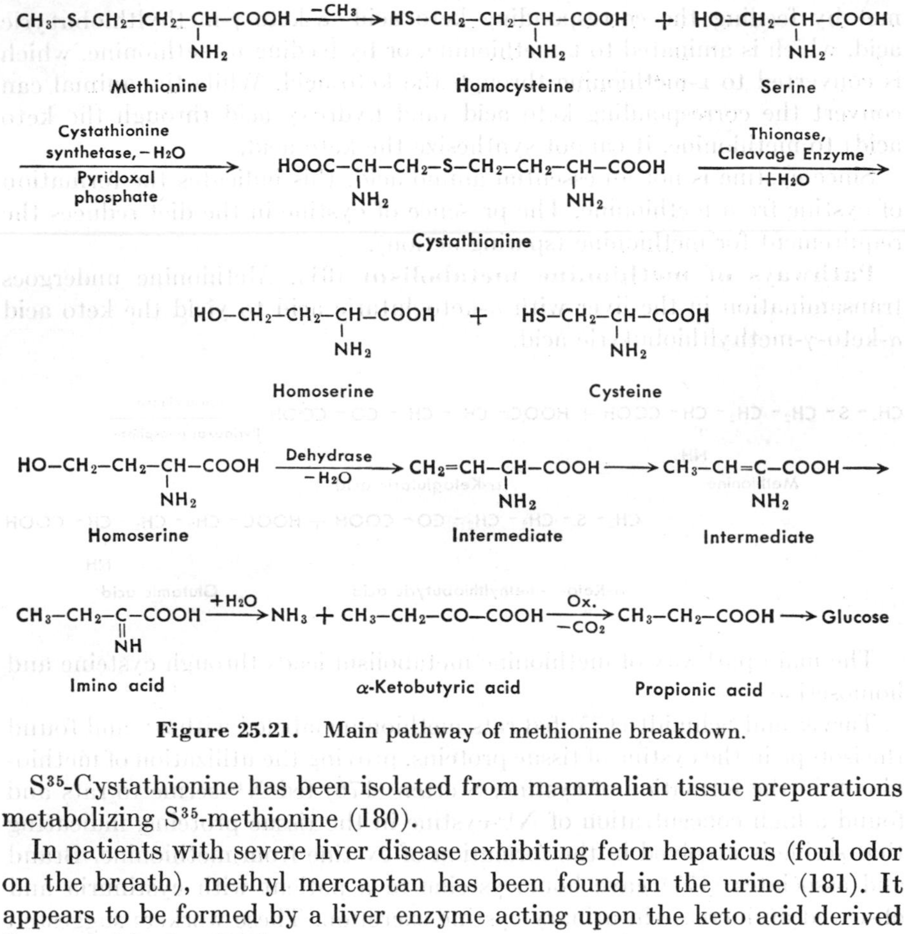

$$CH_3-S-CH_2-CH_2-CH-COOH \xrightarrow{-CH_3} HS-CH_2-CH_2-CH-COOH \;+\; HO-CH_2-CH-COOH$$
$$\qquad\qquad\qquad\quad NH_2 \qquad\qquad\qquad\qquad\qquad NH_2 \qquad\qquad\qquad\qquad NH_2$$

Methionine   Homocysteine   Serine

$$\xrightarrow[\substack{Pyridoxal\\phosphate}]{\substack{Cystathionine\\synthetase,-H_2O}} HOOC-CH-CH_2-S-CH_2-CH_2-CH-COOH \xrightarrow[+H_2O]{\substack{Thionase,\\Cleavage\ Enzyme}}$$
$$\qquad\qquad\qquad\qquad\qquad\quad NH_2 \qquad\qquad\qquad\quad NH_2$$

Cystathionine

$$HO-CH_2-CH_2-CH-COOH \;+\; HS-CH_2-CH-COOH$$
$$\qquad\qquad\qquad NH_2 \qquad\qquad\qquad\qquad\quad NH_2$$

Homoserine   Cysteine

$$HO-CH_2-CH_2-CH-COOH \xrightarrow[-H_2O]{Dehydrase} CH_2=CH-CH-COOH \longrightarrow CH_3-CH=C-COOH \longrightarrow$$
$$\qquad\qquad\qquad NH_2 \qquad\qquad\qquad\qquad\qquad NH_2 \qquad\qquad\qquad\qquad NH_2$$

Homoserine   Intermediate   Intermediate

$$CH_3-CH_2-C-COOH \xrightarrow{+H_2O} NH_3 + CH_3-CH_2-CO-COOH \xrightarrow[-CO_2]{Ox.} CH_3-CH_2-COOH \longrightarrow Glucose$$
$$\qquad\qquad\; \| $$
$$\qquad\qquad NH$$

Imino acid   α-Ketobutyric acid   Propionic acid

Figure 25.21.   Main pathway of methionine breakdown.

S^{35}-Cystathionine has been isolated from mammalian tissue preparations metabolizing S^{35}-methionine (180).

In patients with severe liver disease exhibiting fetor hepaticus (foul odor on the breath), methyl mercaptan has been found in the urine (181). It appears to be formed by a liver enzyme acting upon the keto acid derived from methionine (182):

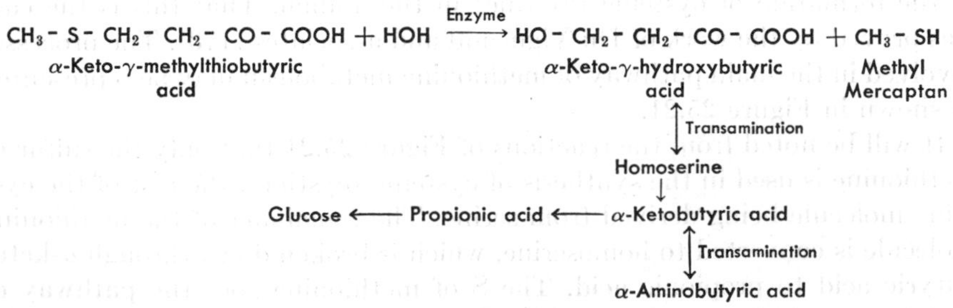

$$CH_3-S-CH_2-CH_2-CO-COOH + HOH \xrightarrow{Enzyme} HO-CH_2-CH_2-CO-COOH + CH_3-SH$$

α-Keto-γ-methylthiobutyric   α-Keto-γ-hydroxybutyric   Methyl
acid   acid   Mercaptan

$\uparrow$ Transamination

Homoserine

$\downarrow$

Glucose $\longleftarrow$ Propionic acid $\longleftarrow$ α-Ketobutyric acid

$\uparrow$ Transamination

α-Aminobutyric acid

In the "Fanchoni syndrome," which is characterized by a low renal threshold for amino acids, aminobutyric acid, formed from α-ketobutyric acid as indicated above, is excreted in the urine.

Homocysteine is convertible by a liver desulfhydrase enzyme, thionase, into α-ketobutyric acid, NH_3, and H_2S:

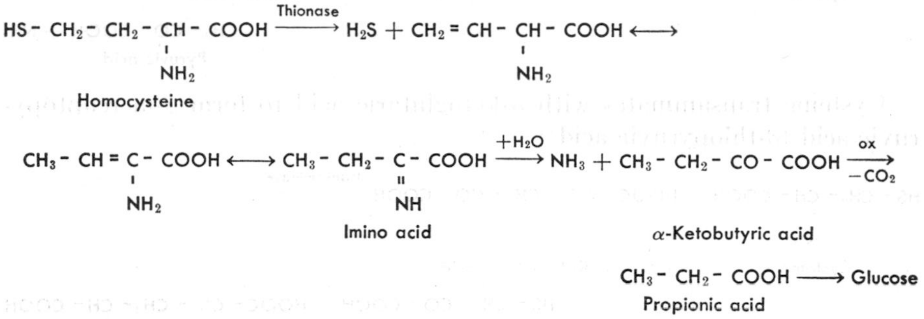

$$HS-CH_2-CH_2-\underset{\underset{NH_2}{|}}{CH}-COOH \xrightarrow{\text{Thionase}} H_2S + CH_2=CH-\underset{\underset{NH_2}{|}}{CH}-COOH \longleftrightarrow$$

Homocysteine

$$CH_3-CH=\underset{\underset{NH_2}{|}}{C}-COOH \longleftrightarrow CH_3-CH_2-\underset{\underset{NH}{||}}{C}-COOH \xrightarrow{+H_2O} NH_3 + CH_3-CH_2-CO-COOH \xrightarrow[-CO_2]{ox}$$

Imino acid $\qquad\qquad\qquad\qquad$ α-Ketobutyric acid

$$CH_3-CH_2-COOH \longrightarrow \text{Glucose}$$
Propionic acid

Most of the H_2S formed is oxidized to sulfate and a smaller proportion to thiosulfate.

Du Vigneaud and associates (183) prepared methionine containing C^{14} in the methyl group and fed it to a rat. After 52 hours 32 per cent of the administered C^{14} had been given off in exhaled CO_2, showing that the methyl group of methionine is oxidized in the body.

Metabolism of cysteine and cystine. Cystine metabolism appears to proceed entirely through cysteine, into which it is readily converted. When cystine, cysteine, or methionine is given to animals, a large proportion of the sulfur of the amino acids is rapidly oxidized to sulfate and excreted in the urine.

Urinary sulfur is derived almost entirely from the metabolism of the sulfur amino acids. It consists of: (a) inorganic sulfate sulfur, about 80 per cent; (b) ethereal sulfate sulfur, about 5 per cent; and (c) organic sulfide sulfur, 15 to 20 per cent. Oxidation of the sulfur of the sulfur-containing amino acids to sulfate represents the final stage of sulfur oxidation in the body. Ethereal sulfates generally represent compounds formed in the detoxication of phenols, such as phenylsulfuric acid, indican, and skatoxylsulfuric acid. A small portion of the organic sulfide sulfur is made up of unchanged sulfur-containing amino acids, and some may be mercaptan sulfur, especially in certain liver diseases, but the nature of most of this fraction of urinary sulfur is unknown. It is undoubtedly a highly complex mixture of substances.

The ethereal sulfate compounds are formed by reaction of "active sulfate," 3'-phosphoadenosine-5'-phosphosulfate (Chapter 20), with ROH compounds.

The formation of cysteine from methionine has been discussed. Since in this process only the S of methionine is converted to the S of cysteine, the metabolism of cysteine involves the S but not the carbon chain of methionine.

Cysteine is metabolized in animals by several pathways (81).

Cysteine is converted to pyruvic acid, H_2S, and NH_3 by a desulfhydrase enzyme found in liver, kidney, and pancreas (184):

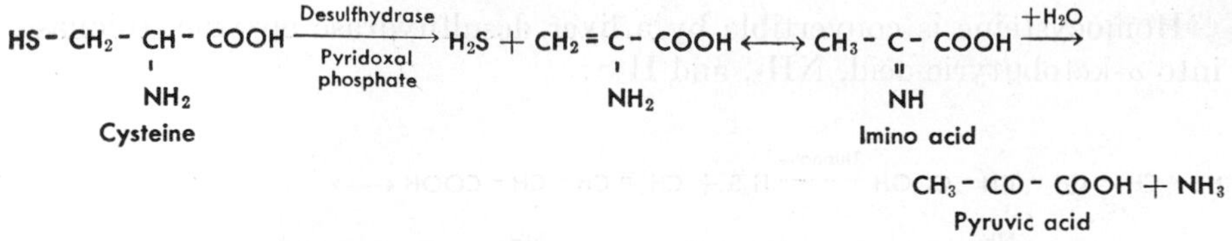

$$HS - CH_2 - CH - COOH \xrightarrow[\text{Pyridoxal phosphate}]{\text{Desulfhydrase}} H_2S + CH_2 = C - COOH \longleftrightarrow CH_3 - C - COOH \xrightarrow{+H_2O}$$

$$\underset{NH_2}{|} \qquad\qquad\qquad\qquad \underset{NH_2}{|} \qquad\qquad \underset{NH}{\|}$$

Cysteine   Imino acid

$$CH_3 - CO - COOH + NH_3$$
Pyruvic acid

Cysteine transaminates with α-ketoglutaric acid to form β-mercaptopy-ruvic acid (β-thiopyruvic acid):

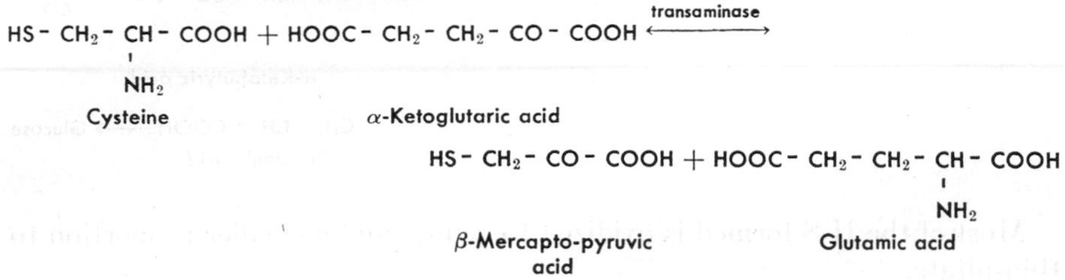

$$HS - CH_2 - CH - COOH + HOOC - CH_2 - CH_2 - CO - COOH \xleftarrow{\text{transaminase}}$$

$$\underset{NH_2}{|}$$

Cysteine α-Ketoglutaric acid

$$HS - CH_2 - CO - COOH + HOOC - CH_2 - CH_2 - CH - COOH$$

$$\underset{NH_2}{|}$$

β-Mercapto-pyruvic   Glutamic acid
acid

β-Mercaptopyruvic acid is converted to pyruvic acid and S by enzymes of animal tissues and bacteria (81):

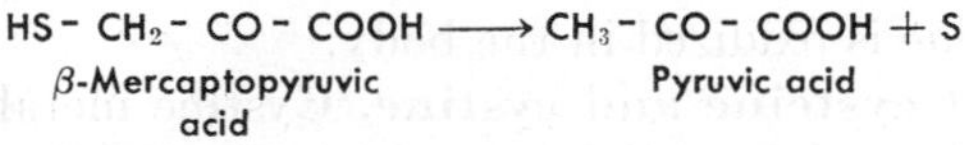

$$HS - CH_2 - CO - COOH \longrightarrow CH_3 - CO - COOH + S$$
β-Mercaptopyruvic   Pyruvic acid
acid

The S is converted to H_2S by reducing agents such as cysteine and gluta-thione:

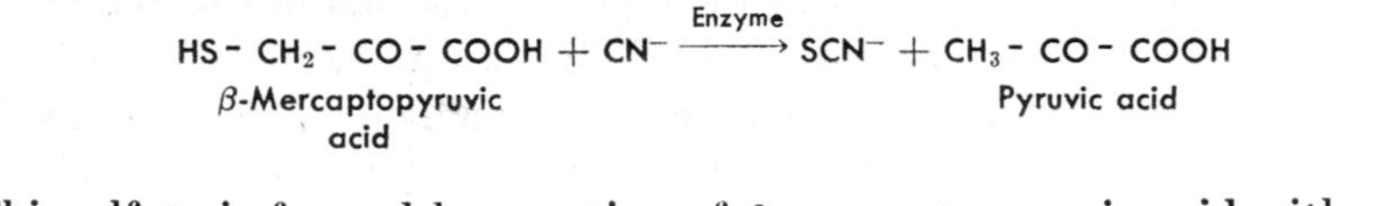

$$2HS - CH_2 - CH - COOH + S \rightleftharpoons HOOC - CH - CH_2 - S - S - CH_2 - CH - COOH + H_2S$$

$$\underset{NH_2}{|} \qquad\qquad\qquad \underset{NH_2}{|} \qquad\qquad\qquad \underset{NH_2}{|}$$

Cysteine   Cystine

β-Mercaptopyruvic acid transfers sulfur to the cyanide ion to form sulfo-cyanate. The reaction is catalyzed by a liver transulfurase enzyme:

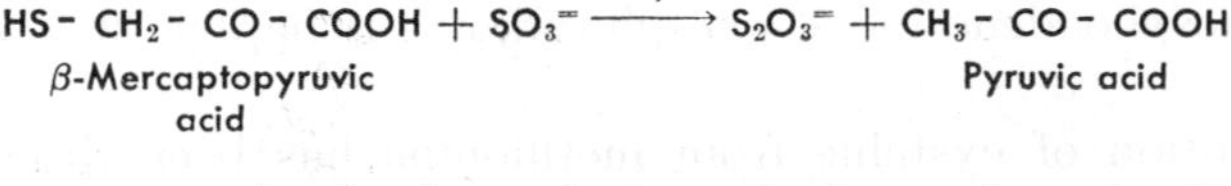

$$HS - CH_2 - CO - COOH + CN^- \xrightarrow{\text{Enzyme}} SCN^- + CH_3 - CO - COOH$$
β-Mercaptopyruvic   Pyruvic acid
acid

Thiosulfate is formed by reaction of β-mercaptopyruvic acid with sulfite through the action of a transulfurase enzyme found in kidney and liver:

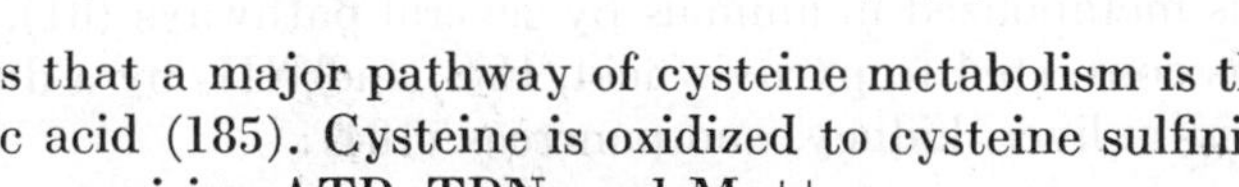

$$HS - CH_2 - CO - COOH + SO_3^= \xrightarrow{\text{Enzyme}} S_2O_3^= + CH_3 - CO - COOH$$
β-Mercaptopyruvic   Pyruvic acid
acid

Sulfocyanate may also be formed through the action of a liver enzyme, rhodanese, from CN^- and S, and from CN^- and $S_2O_3^=$:

$$CN^- + S \longrightarrow SCN^- \qquad\qquad\qquad CN^- + S_2O_3^= \longrightarrow SCN^- + SO_3^=$$

It appears that a major pathway of cysteine metabolism is through cys-teine sulfinic acid (185). Cysteine is oxidized to cysteine sulfinic acid by a liver enzyme requiring ATP, TPN, and Mg^{++}:

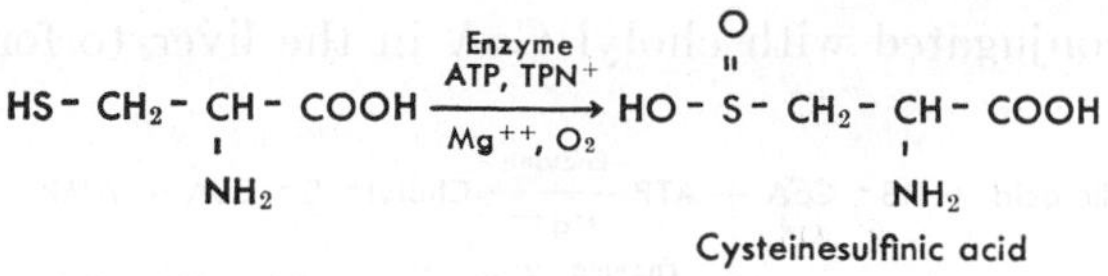

$$HS-CH_2-CH-COOH \xrightarrow[\text{Mg}^{++}, \text{O}_2]{\substack{\text{Enzyme} \\ \text{ATP, TPN}^+}} HO-\overset{\overset{\text{O}}{\|}}{S}-CH_2-CH-COOH$$

with NH$_2$ below the left structure and NH$_2$ below the right structure

Cysteinesulfinic acid

Cysteine sulfinic acid rapidly transaminates to form B-sulfinylpyruvic acid, which then loses SO$_2$ and forms pyruvic acid:

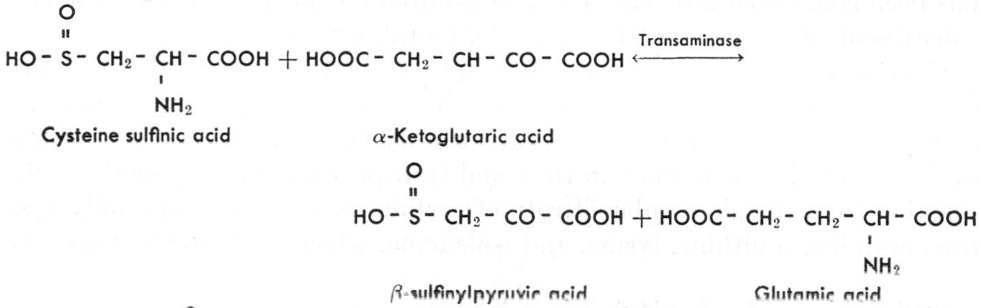

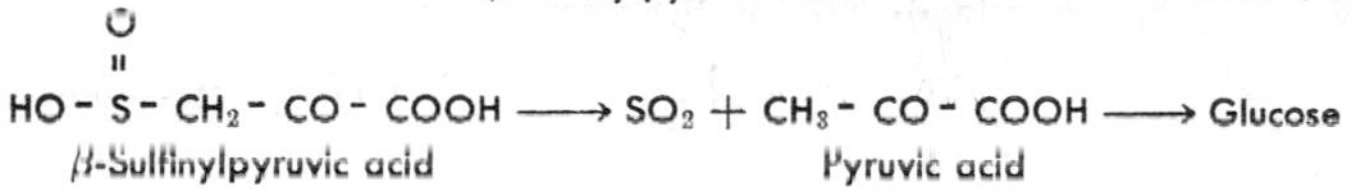

$$HO-\overset{\overset{\text{O}}{\|}}{S}-CH_2-CH-COOH + HOOC-CH_2-CH-CO-COOH \underset{}{\overset{\text{Transaminase}}{\longleftrightarrow}}$$

NH$_2$ below first structure

Cysteine sulfinic acid   α-Ketoglutaric acid

$$HO-\overset{\overset{\text{O}}{\|}}{S}-CH_2-CO-COOH + HOOC-CH_2-CH_2-CH-COOH$$

NH$_2$ below second structure

β-sulfinylpyruvic acid   Glutamic acid

$$HO-\overset{\overset{\text{O}}{\|}}{S}-CH_2-CO-COOH \longrightarrow SO_2 + CH_3-CO-COOH \longrightarrow Glucose$$

β-Sulfinylpyruvic acid   Pyruvic acid

It will be noted that the loss of SO$_2$ from β-sulfinyl pyruvic acid to form pyruvic acid is quite analagous to the decarboxylation of oxaloacetic acid to form pyruvic acid.

The SO$_2$ (sulfite) is oxidized to sulfate by a liver enzyme, sulfite oxidase, which appears to require hypoxanthine and lipoic acid (186).

Taurine appears to be formed from cysteine sulfinic acid in the liver by two pathways. One is by oxidation to cysteic acid and then decarboxylation of the cysteic acid:

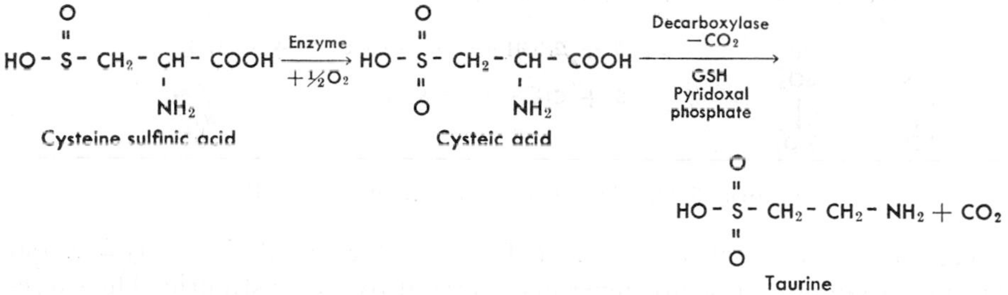

$$HO-\overset{\overset{\text{O}}{\|}}{S}-CH_2-CH-COOH \xrightarrow[+\frac{1}{2}O_2]{\text{Enzyme}} HO-\overset{\overset{\text{O}}{\|}}{\underset{\overset{\|}{O}}{S}}-CH_2-CH-COOH \xrightarrow[\substack{\text{GSH} \\ \text{Pyridoxal} \\ \text{phosphate}}]{\substack{\text{Decarboxylase} \\ -CO_2}}$$

NH$_2$ below first; NH$_2$ below second

Cysteine sulfinic acid   **Cysteic acid**

$$HO-\overset{\overset{\text{O}}{\|}}{\underset{\overset{\|}{O}}{S}}-CH_2-CH_2-NH_2 + CO_2$$

Taurine

The other pathway involves first the decarboxylation of cysteine sulfinic acid to hypotaurine and then oxidation of hypotaurine to taurine:

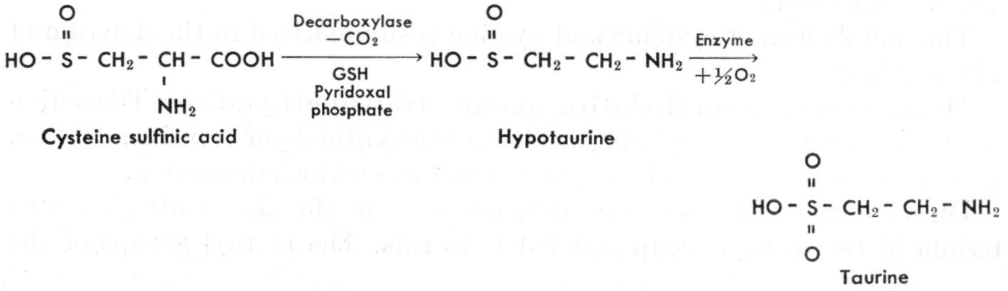

$$HO-\overset{\overset{\text{O}}{\|}}{S}-CH_2-CH-COOH \xrightarrow[\substack{\text{GSH} \\ \text{Pyridoxal} \\ \text{phosphate}}]{\substack{\text{Decarboxylase} \\ -CO_2}} HO-\overset{\overset{\text{O}}{\|}}{S}-CH_2-CH_2-NH_2 \xrightarrow[+\frac{1}{2}O_2]{\text{Enzyme}}$$

NH$_2$ below first structure

Cysteine sulfinic acid   **Hypotaurine**

$$HO-\overset{\overset{\text{O}}{\|}}{\underset{\overset{\|}{O}}{S}}-CH_2-CH_2-NH_2$$

Taurine

Taurine is conjugated with cholyl CoA in the liver to form taurocholic acid:

$$\text{Cholic acid} + \text{HS - CoA} + \text{ATP} \xrightarrow[\text{Mg}^{++}]{\text{Enzyme}} \text{Cholyl - S - CoA} + \text{AMP} + \text{PP}$$

$$\text{Taurine} + \text{Cholyl - S - CoA} \xrightarrow{\text{Enzyme}} \text{Taurocholic acid} + \text{HS - CoA}$$

The role of cysteine in the formation of mercapturic acids for detoxication has been considered in Chapter 14. As pointed out previously, cysteine is a constituent of the important tripeptide, glutathione.

Cystinuria. Cystinuria, in which appreciable amounts of cystine are excreted in the urine, is one of the congenital or hereditary defects originally described as an inborn error of metabolism by Garrod. The defect in cystinuria consists in a deficiency in the renal transport mechanism for the reabsorption from the glomerular filtrate of certain amino acids, especially cystine, arginine, ornithine, lysine, and isoleucine, which leads to their urinary

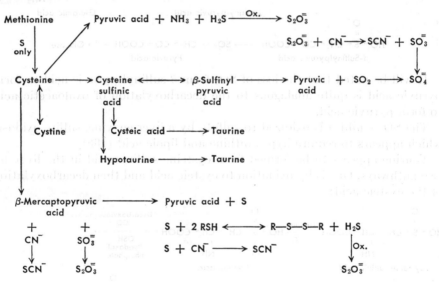

Figure 25.22. Metabolism of cysteine and cystine.

excretion in abnormal amounts. In fact, greater quantities of lysine and arginine than of cystine are generally excreted by the cystinuric. The excretion of cystine was observed first because of its insolubility, leading to the occurrence of cystine crystals in the urine and cystine calculi in the kidneys and urinary tract.

The metabolism of cysteine and cystine is summarized in the diagram of Figure 25.22.

Methionine as a methylating agent—transmethylation. The action of methionine as a methylating agent in the synthesis of creatine, choline, and other compounds has been pointed out in previous discussion.

Du Vigneaud and associates (187) prepared methionine containing deuterium in the methyl group and fed it to rats. The methyl groups of the choline, creatine, and creatinine formed in the body contained deuterium, showing that methionine had served as the methylating agent in forming these substances. Simmonds and du Vigneaud (188) also showed that the choline and creatinine formed in an adult human male after taking methionine, with deuterium in the methyl group, contained deuterium.

That choline may methylate homocysteine to methionine (reverse the reaction) has been shown by feeding to rats choline with the methyl group labeled with deuterium, with and without homocystine. In both cases tissue methionine contained the deuterium in the methyl group (189). Du Vigneaud and associates (190) also showed that homocystine + choline could be substituted for methionine in the diet, showing synthesis of methionine from homocystine (through homocysteine).

While choline through betaine can methylate homocysteine directly to methionine, the utilization of a choline methyl group to convert guanidoacetic acid to creatine necessitates preliminary formation of methionine from betaine and homocysteine (191). The methionine then, as active methionine, methylates the guanidoacetic acid to creatine. The methyl group of creatine is not utilizable for methylations.

In methylations by choline it has been shown that choline must first be oxidized to betaine, which serves directly as the methylating agent. Choline is oxidized to betaine aldehyde by the enzyme choline oxidase which is a flavoprotein (FP) containing FAD. Betaine aldehyde is oxidized to betaine by betaine aldehyde dehydrogenase and DPN (192,193).

$$(CH_3)_3 \equiv N - CH_2 - CH_2 - OH + FP \longrightarrow FP \cdot H_2 + (CH_3)_3 \equiv N - CH_2 - CHO + DPN^+ \xrightarrow{\text{Dehydrogenase}}$$

Choline   Choline oxidase   Betaine aldehyde

$$(CH_3)_3 \equiv N - CH_2 - COO^- + DPN \cdot H + H^+$$

Betaine

Betaine methylates homocysteine to methionine, the reaction being catalyzed by "betaine-homocysteine transmethylase":

$$(CH_3)_3 \equiv N - CH_2 - COO^- + HS - CH_2 - CH_2 - CH - COOH \longrightarrow$$
$$NH_2$$

Betaine   Homocysteine

$$CH_3 - S - CH_2 - CH_2 - CH - COOH + (CH_3)_2 \equiv N - CH_2 - COOH$$
$$NH_2$$

Methionine   Dimethylglycine

The methionine formed is converted into "active methionine," S-adenosyl-methionine, by reaction with ATP:

$$\text{L-Methionine} + \text{ATP} \xrightarrow[\substack{\text{Glutathione} \\ \text{Mg}^{++}}]{\text{Enzyme}} \text{S-Adenosylmethionine} + \text{PP} + \text{Pi}$$

Dimethylglycine is oxidized to formaldehyde and glycine:

$$(CH_3)_2 = N - CH_2 - COOH \xrightarrow[+O_2]{\text{Demethylase}}$$

Dimethylglycine

$$CH_2O + CH_3 - \overset{H}{\underset{|}{N}} - CH_2 - COOH \xrightarrow[+O_2]{\text{Demethylase}} CH_2O + H_2N - CH_2COOH$$

Sarcosine   Glycine

$$\downarrow ox \qquad\qquad\qquad\qquad\qquad \downarrow ox$$

$$H \cdot COOH \qquad\qquad\qquad\qquad\qquad H \cdot COOH$$

Du Vigneaud has termed the interchange of methyl groups between methyl donors such as betaine and methionine transmethylation.

Maw and du Vigneaud (194) found that dimethylthetin and dimethylpropiothetin are active methyl donors. While the presence of these substances in animal tissues has not been proved, dimethylpropiothetin occurs in a marine alga, and it may be that such compounds play a role as methyldonors in animal tissues:

$$(CH_3)_2 = \overset{+}{S} - CH_2 - COO^- \qquad\qquad (CH_3)_2 = \overset{+}{S} - CH_2 - CH_2 - COO^-$$

Dimethylthetin   Dimethylpropiothetin

It is interesting to note that all the active methyl donors have methyl attached to a positively charged "onium" atom, the quaternary ammonium N of betaine, and the sulfonium atoms of active methionine and the thetins. Cantoni (195) has pointed out that these methyl-onium bonds are high-energy bonds—an explanation of methylating capacity.

The body synthesizes labile methyl groups from many precursors. As has been pointed out earlier, the metabolism of a number of compounds produces formaldehyde and formate, and it has been shown that formate and formaldehyde carbon are incorporated into the methyl group of methionine. Substances such as serine, glycine, acetone, sarcosine, methanol, dimethylglycine and other methyl compounds, and histidine and tryptophan, in their metabolism yield one-carbon units which can be utilized for the synthesis of labile methyl groups. In all these cases it appears that the methyl group is produced from formate or formaldehyde.

The relation of tetrahydrofolic acid derivatives and vitamin B_{12} to the genesis of methyl groups has been pointed out earlier in the discussion of one-carbon metabolism.

Cantoni (195) has written a review dealing with the synthesis and transfer of labile methyl groups.

Methylations, and methylating agents such as methionine and choline are of extreme importance in the body for both the production of essential body constituents and detoxication processes (detoxication of amines). The importance of choline and methionine to metabolism has also been indicated in the chapter on lipid metabolism.

Du Vigneaud has written a review of transmethylation and the role of methyl groups in nutrition (196).

The metabolism of methionine is outlined in Figure 25.23.

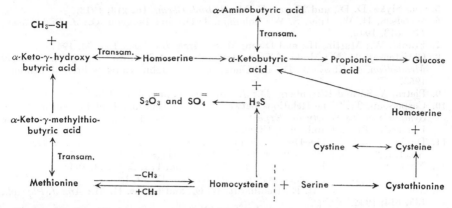

Figure 25.23. Methionine metabolism. The sulfur amino acids are glycogenic due to the formation of pyruvic acid (cystine and cysteine) and propionic acid (methionine) in their metabolic breakdown.

GENERAL REFERENCES

Cohen, G. N., and Gros, F.: Protein Biosynthesis, *Ann. Rev. Biochem.*, **29**, 525, 1960.

Cohen, P. P., and Brown, G. W., Jr.: Ammonia Metabolism and Urea Biosynthesis, in *Comparative Biochemistry*, Vol II, Florkin, M., and Mason, H. S. (eds.). Academic Press, New York, 1960.

Dalgliesh, C. E.: Metabolism of the Aromatic Amino Acids, *Advances in Protein Chemistry*, **10**, 31–150, 1955.

Davis, D. B.: Intermediates in Amino Acid Biosynthesis, *Advances in Enzymol.*, **16**, 247–312, 1955.

Du Vigneaud, V.: A Trail of Research, in *Sulfur Chemistry and Metabolism and Related Fields*, Cornell University Press, Ithaca, 1952.

Edsall, J. T.: *Amino Acids, Proteins, and Cancer Biochemistry: Jesse P. Greenstein Memorial Symposium*. Academic Press, New York, 1960.

Garrod, A. E.: *Inborn Errors of Metabolism*, 2d ed. H. Frowde & Hodder & Stoughton, London, 1923.

Greenberg, D. M. (ed.): *Chemical Pathways of Metabolism*, Vol. II. Academic Press, New York, 1954.

Hsia, D. Y.: *Inborn Errors of Metabolism*. Year Book Publishers, Inc., Chicago, 1959.

Huennekens, F. M., and Osborn, M. J.: Folic Acid Coenzymes and One-Carbon Metabolism, *Advances in Enzymol.*, **21**, 369, 1959.

McElroy, W. D., and Glass, B. (eds.): *Amino Acid Metabolism*. Johns Hopkins Press, Baltimore, 1955.

Mehler, A. H.: *Introduction to Enzymology*. Academic Press, New York, 1957.

Meister, A.: *Biochemistry of the Amino Acids*. Academic Press, New York, 1957.

Schoenheimer, R.: *The Dynamic State of Body Constituents*. Harvard University Press, Cambridge, 1942.

Udenfriend, S.; Weissbach, H.; and Mitoma, C.: Metabolism of Amino Acids, *Ann. Rev. Biochem.*, **29**, 207, 1960.

Young, L., and Maw, A.: *The Metabolism of Sulphur Compounds*. John Wiley & Sons, New York, 1958.

SPECIAL REFERENCES

1. Stein, W. H., and Moore, S.: *J. Biol. Chem.*, **211**, 915, 1954.
2. Messing, B.: *Biochem. Z.*, **218**, 54, 1930.
3. Hier, S. W.: *J. Biol. Chem.*, **171**, 813, 1947.
4. Man, E. B., cited in *Quantitative Clinical Chemistry*, Vol. I, *Interpretations*, p. 808, by Peters, J. P., and Van Slyke, D. D. Williams & Wilkins Co., Baltimore, 1946.

5. Van Slyke, D. D., and Meyer, G. M.: *J. Biol. Chem.*, **16**, 213, 1913.
6. Woodson, H. W.; Hier, S. W.; Solomon, J. D.; and Bergeim, O.: *J. Biol. Chem.*, **172**, 613, 1948.
7. Frankl, W.; Martin, H.; and Dunn, M. S.: *Arch. Biochem.*, **13**, 103, 1947.
8. Christensen, H. N.: Mode of Transport of Amino Acids into Cells, in *Amino Acid Metabolism*, McElroy, W. D., and Glass, B. (eds.). Johns Hopkins Press, Baltimore, 1955.
9. Pietro, A. S., and Rittenberg, D.: *J. Biol. Chem.*, **201**, 457, 1953.
10. Caspersson, T.: "The Relations between Nucleic Acid and Protein Synthesis," in *Symposia of the Society for Experimental Biology*, No. I, *Nucleic Acid*. Cambridge University Press, Cambridge, England, 1947.
11. Davidson, J. N.: "The Distribution of Nucleic Acids in Tissues," in *Nucleic Acid*, No. I, p. 82. Cambridge University Press, Cambridge, England, 1947.
12. Novikoff, A. B., and Potter, V. R.: *J. Biol. Chem.*, **173**, 223, 233, 1948.
13. Lee, M. O., and Schaffer, N. K.: *J. Nutrition*, **7**, 337, 1934.
14. Marx, W.; Simpson, M. E.; Reinhardt, W. O.; and Evans, H. M.: *Am. J. Physiol.*, **135**, 614, 1942.
15. Bartlett, P. D.: *Federation Proc.*, **11**, 184, 1952.
16. Clark, I.: *J. Biol. Chem.*, **200**, 69, 1953.
17. Addis, T.; Lee, D. D.; Lew, W.; and Poo, L. J.: *J. Nutrition*, **19**, 199, 1940. Addis, T.; Poo, L. J.; and Lew, W.: *J. Biol. Chem.*, **115**, 111, 177, 1936.
18. Benedict, F. G.: *Carnegie Inst. Wash. Publ.*, 203, 1915.
19. Chantrenne, H., in Florkin, M., and Mason, H. S. (eds.): *Comparative Biochemistry*, Vol. II, p. 139. Academic Press, New York, 1960; *Ann. Rev. Biochem.*, **27**, 35, 1958.
20. Zamecnik, P. C.: *The Harvey Lectures*, **54**, 256, 1958–1959. Stephenson, M.; Hecht, L. I.; Littlefield, J. W.; Loftfield, R. B.; and Zamecnik, P. C.: In *Subcellular Particles*, p. 160, Hayashi, T. (ed.). Ronald Press, New York, 1959.
21. Meister, A., in *Amino Acids, Proteins, and Cancer Biochemistry: Jesse P. Greenstein Memorial Symposium*. Academic Press, New York, 1960.
22. Kalyankar, G. D., and Meister, A.: *J. Am. Chem. Soc.*, **81**, 1515, 1959.
23. Berg, P.: *J. Am. Chem. Soc.*, **77**, 3163, 1955; *J. Biol. Chem.*, **222**, 1025, 1956.
24. Hoagland, M. B.: *Biochim. et Biophys. Acta*, **16**, 288, 1955. Hoagland, M. B.; Keller, E. B.; and Zamecnik, P. C.: *J. Biol. Chem.*, **218**, 345, 1956.
25. Karasek, M.; Castelfranco, P.; Krishnaswamy, P. R.; and Meister, A.: *J. Am. Chem. Soc.*, **80**, 2335, 1958; *Symposium on Microsomal Particles and Protein Synthesis*, p. 109.
26. Anfinsen, C. B.: *The Molecular Basis of Evolution*, p. 36. John Wiley & Sons, New York, 1959.
27. Horowitz, N. H., and Fling, M., in *Enzymes, Units of Biological Structure and Function*, p. 139, Gaebler, O. G. (ed.). Academic Press, New York, 1956.
28. Gale, E. F.: *Harvey Lectures*, **51**, 25, 1957.
29. Anfinsen, C. B., and Steinberg, D.: *J. Biol. Chem.*, **189**, 739, 1951; **199**, 25, 1952. Anfinsen, C. B., and Flavin, M.: *Federation Proc.*, **12**, 170, 1953.
30. Simpson, M. V., and Velick, S. F.: *J. Biol. Chem.*, **208**, 61, 1954. Heimberg, M., and Velick, S. F.: *J. Biol. Chem.*, **208**, 725, 1954.
31. Fruton, J. S.: *Harvey Lectures*, **51**, 64, 1957.
32. Bollman, J. L.; Mann, F. C.; and Magath, T. B.: *Am. J. Physiol.*, **69**, 371, 1924.
33. Krebs, H. A.: *Biochem. J.*, **29**, 1620, 1935; *Klin. Wochschr.*, **11**, 1744, 1932; *Z. Physiol. Chem.*, **217**, 191, 1933.
34. Cohen, P. P., in *Comparative Biochemistry*, Vol. II, Florkin, M., and Mason, H. S. (eds.), pp. 161–231. Academic Press, New York, 1960; in *Chemical Pathways of Metabolism*, Vol. II, Greenberg, D. M. (ed.), pp. 1–46. Academic Press, New York, 1954.
35. Meister, A.: *Biochemistry of the Amino Acids*. Academic Press, New York, 1957; *Advances in Enzymol.*, **16**, 185, 1955.
36. Krebs, H. A., in *The Enzymes*, Sumner, J. B., and Myrbäck, K. (eds.), Vol. II, Part I, pp. 499–535. Academic Press, New York, 1951.
37. Krebs, H. A.: *Biochem. J.*, **29**, 1620, 1935.
38. Blanchard, M.; Green, D. E.; Nocito, V.; and Ratner, S.: *J. Biol. Chem.*, **155**, 421, 1944; **161**, 583, 1945.
39. Pitt, B. M.: *J. Am. Chem. Soc.*, **80**, 3799, 1958.

40. Braunstein, A. E.: *Advances in Protein Chem.*, **3**, 1, 1947.
41. Meister, A.: *Advances in Enzymol.*, **16**, 185, 1955.
42. Cohen, P. P., in *Chemical Pathways of Metabolism*, Vol. II, Greenberg, D. M. (ed.), pp. 1–46. Academic Press, New York, 1954.
43. Snell, E. E.: *J. Am. Chem. Soc.*, **67**, 194, 1945.
44. Shlenk, F., and Fisher, A.: *Arch. Biochem.*, **12**, 69, 1947.
45. Nydick, I.; Wroblewski, F.; and La Due, J. S.: *Circulation*, **12**, 161, 1955.
46. Schoenheimer, R.: *The Dynamic State of Body Constituents*. Harvard University Press, Cambridge, Mass., 1942.
47. Bollman, J. L.; Mann, F. C.; and Magath, T. B.: *Am. J. Physiol.*, **64**, 371, 1924.
48. Krebs, H. A., and Henseleit, H.: *Z. Physiol. Chem.*, **210**, 33, 1932.
49. Grisolia, S.: *Phosphorus Metabolism*, Vol. I, 619, 1951. Ratner, S.: *ibid.*, 601.
50. Cohen, P. P., in *Comparative Biochemistry*, Vol. II, Florkin, M., and Mason, H. S. (eds.), pp. 161–231. Academic Press, New York, 1960.
51. Hughes, D. E.: *Biochem. J.*, **46**, 231, 1950. Braunstein, A. E., and Azarkh, R. M.: *Biokhimiya*, **5**, 1, 1939.
52. Pietro, A. S., and Rittenberg, D.: *J. Biol. Chem.*, **201**, 445, 1953.
53. Huennekens, F. M., and Osborn, M. J.: *Advances in Enzymol.*, **21**, 369, 1959.
54. Cantoni, G. L.: *J. Biol. Chem.*, **204**, 403, 1953. Cantoni, G. L., and Vignos, P. J.: *ibid.*, **209**, 647, 1954. Cantoni, G. L., and Durell, J.: *ibid.*, **225**, 1033, 1957.
55. Bennett, M. A.; J. Biol. Chem., **107**, 751, 1950. Davis, B. D., and Mingioli, E. S.: *J. Bact.*, **60**, 17, 1950. Shive, W.: *Ann. N. Y. Acad. Sci.*, **52**, 1212, 1950. Stekol, J. A.; Weiss, S.; Anderson, E. I.; Hsu, P. T.; and Watjen, A.: *J. Biol. Chem.*, **226**, 95, 1957.
56. Weinhouse, S., in *Amino Acid Metabolism*, McElroy, W. D., and Glass, B. (eds.) p. 637. Johns Hopkins Press, Baltimore, 1955.
57. Winnick, T.; Moring-Claesson, I.; and Greenberg, D. M.: *J. Biol. Chem.*, **175**, 121, 1948.
58. Sakami, W.: *J. Biol. Chem.*, **176**, 995, 1948.
59. Sakami, W.: *Federation Proc.*, **8**, 246, 1949.
60. Tarver, H.: *Ann. Rev. Biochem.*, **21**, 309, 1952.
61. Mitoma, C., and Greenberg, D. M.: *J. Biol. Chem.*, **196**, 599, 1952.
62. Frisell, W. R., and Mackenzie, C. G.: *Federation Proc.*, **12**, 206, 1953. Mackenzie, C. G.; Johnston, J. M.; and Frisell, W. R.: *J. Biol. Chem.*, **203**, 743, 1953. Mackenzie, C. G., and Abeles, R. H.; *ibid.*, **222**, 145, 1956.
63. Shemin, D.: *J. Biol. Chem.*, **162**, 297, 1946.
64. Shemin, D.: *Cold Spring Harbor Symposia Quant. Biol.*, **14**, 161, 1949.
65. Anker, H. S.: *J. Biol. Chem.*, **176**, 1337, 1948.
66. Bloch, K., and Schoenheimer, R.: *J. Biol. Chem.*, **138**, 179, 1941.
67. Brown, G. B.; Roll, P. M.; and Weinfeld, H.: *Phosphorus Metabolism*, 2, 389, 1952.
68. Olsen, N. S.; Hemingway, A.; and Nier, A. D.: *J. Biol. Chem.*, **148**, 611, 1943.
69. Cunningham, L.; Barnes, J. M.; and Todd, W. R.: *Arch. Biochem.*, **16**, 403, 1948.
70. Todd, W. R., and Talman, E.: *Arch. Biochem.*, **22**, 386, 1949.
71. Todd, W. R.; Barnes, J. M.; and Cunningham, L.: *Arch. Biochem.*, **13**, 261, 1947.
72. Mirski, A.: Rosenbaum, I.; Stein, L.; and Wertheimer, E.: *J. Physiol.*, **92**, 48, 1938.
73. Ichihara, A., and Greenberg, D. M.: *J. Biol. Chem.*, **224**, 331, 1957.
74. Davies, D. D.: *Nature*, **182**, 532, 1958.
75. Sallach, H. J., in *Symposium on Amino Acid Metabolism*, Baltimore, 1954.
76. Stetten, D., Jr., and Grail, G. F.: *J. Biol. Chem.*, **144**, 501, 1942.
77. Stekol, J. A.; Weiss, S.; and Anderson, E. I.: *J. Am. Chem. Soc.*, **77**, 5192, 1955. Pilgeram, L. O.; Hamilton, R. E.; and Greenberg, D. M.: *J. Biol. Chem.*, **227**, 107, 1957.
78. Hartman, S. C., and Buchanan, J. M.: *Ann. Rev. Biochem.*, **28**, 365, 1959.
79. Snell, E. E.; Radin, N. S.; and Ikawa, M.: *J. Biol. Chem.*, **217**, 803, 1955.
80. Black, S., and Wright, N. G., in *Amino Acid Metabolism*, McElroy, W. D., and Glass, B. (eds.). Johns Hopkins Press, Baltimore, 1955.
81. Meister, A.: *Biochemistry of the Amino Acids*. Academic Press, New York, 1957.
82. Greenberg, D. M. (ed.): *Chemical Pathways of Metabolism*, Vol. II. Academic Press, New York, 1954.
83. Coon, M. J.; Robinson, W. G.; and Bachhawat, B. K.: in *Amino Acid Metabolism*, McElroy, W. D., and Glass, B. (eds.). Johns Hopkins Press, Baltimore, 1955.

84. Fones, W. S.; Waalkes, T. P.; and White, J.: *Arch. Biochem. and Biophys.*, **32**, 89, 1951. Peterson, E. A.; Fones, W. S.; and White, J.: *ibid.*, **36**, 323, 1952.
85. Weissman, N., and Schoenheimer, R.: *J. Biol. Chem.*, **140**, 799, 1941.
86. Schoenheimer, R., and Rittenberg, D.: *Physiol. Revs.*, **20**, 218, 1940.
87. Foster, G. L.; Rittenberg, D.; and Schoenheimer, R.: *J. Biol. Chem.*, **125**, 13, 1938.
88. Neuberger, A., and Sanger, F.: *Biochem. J.*, **38**, 119, 1944.
89. Borsook, H.; Deasey, C. L.; Haagen-Smit, A. J.; Keighley, G.; and Lowy, P. H.: *J. Biol. Chem.*, **173**, 423, 1948. Borsook, H., and Dubnoff, J. W.: *ibid.*, **141**, 717, 1943; **173**, 425, 1948.
90. Borsook, H.; Deasey, C. L.; Haagen-Smit, A. J.; Keighley, G.; and Lowy, P. H.: *J. Biol. Chem.*, **176**, 1383, 1395, 1948.
91. Rothstein, M., and Miller, L. L.: *J. Biol. Chem.*, **206**, 243, 1954.
92. Work, E., in *Amino Acid Metabolism*, McElroy, W. D., and Glass, B. (eds.). Johns Hopkins Press, Baltimore, 1955.
93. Sinex, F. M., and Van Slyke, D. D.: *J. Biol. Chem.*, **216**, 245, 1955; *ibid.*, **232**, 797, 1958.
94. Hamilton, P. B.: *J. Biol. Chem.*, **158**, 397, 1945.
95. Bartlett, P. D.: *Federation Proc.*, **8**, 182, 1949.
96. Butts, J. S.; Dunn, M. S.; and Hallman, L. F.: *J. Biol. Chem.*, **123**, 711, 1938.
97. Greene, J. A., and Johnston, G. W.: *Am. J. Physiol.*, **136**, 460, 1942.
98. Medes, G.: *Biochem. J.*, **26**, 917, 1932.
99. Schoenheimer, R.; Ratner, S.; and Rittenberg, D.: *J. Biol. Chem.*, **127**, 333, 1939.
100. Dalgliesh, C. E.: *Advances in Protein Chemistry*, **10**, 31, 1955.
101. Lerner, A. B.: *Advances in Enzymol.*, **14**, 73, 1953.
102. Kaufman, S.: *J. Biol. Chem.*, **234**, 2677, 1959. Kaufman, S., and Levenberg, B.: *ibid.*, **234**, 2683, 1959.
103. Kenney, F. T.: *J. Biol. Chem.*, **234**, 2707, 1959.
104. Uchida, M.; Suzuki, S.; and Ichihara, K.: *J. Biochem. (Japan)*, **41**, 41, 1954.
105. Weinhouse, S., and Millington, R. H.: *J. Biol. Chem.*, **175**, 995, 1948; **181**, 645, 1949. Schepartz, B., and Gurin, S.: *ibid.*, **180**, 663, 1949. Lerner, A. B.: *ibid.*, **181**, 281, 1949. Ravdin, R. G., and Crandall, D. I.: *ibid.*, **189**, 137, 1951.
106. Zannoni, V. G., and La Du, B. N.: *J. Biol. Chem.*, **234**, 2925, 1959.
107. Hsia, D. Y.: *Inborn Errors of Metabolism*, Year Book Publishers, Inc., Chicago, 1959.
108. Papageorge, E., and Lewis, H. B.: *J. Biol. Chem.*, **123**, 211, 1938.
109. Sealock, R. R., and Silberstein, H. E.: *J. Biol. Chem.*, **135**, 251, 1940.
110. Levine, S. Z.; Marples, E.; and Gordon, H. H.: *J. Clin. Invest.*, **20**, 199, 209, 1941.
111. Levine, S. Z.; Dann, M.; and Marples, E.: *J. Clin. Invest.*, **22**, 551, 1943.
112. Fishberg, E. H.: *J. Biol. Chem.*, **172**, 155, 1948.
113. Felix, L.; Leonhardi, G.; and Glaseivapp, I.: *Z. physiol. Chem.*, **287**, 141, 1951.
114. Blatherwick, N. R.: *J. Am. Med. Assoc.*, **103**, 1933, 1934.
115. Jervis, G. A.: *J. Biol. Chem.*, **126**, 305, 1938; **169**, 651, 1947. Jervis, G. A.; Block, R. J.; Bolling, D.; and Kanze, E.: *ibid.*, **134**, 105, 1940.
116. Closs, K., and Fölling, A.: *Z. physiol. Chem.*, **254**, 258, 1938.
117. Schuler, W.; Bernhardt, H.; and Reindel, W.: *Z. physiol. Chem.*, **243**, 90, 1936. Schuler, W., and Wiedmann, A.: *ibid.*, **235**, 235, 1935.
118. Udenfriend, S., and Wyndgaarden, J. B.: *Biochim. et Biophys. Acta*, **20**, 48, 1956. Goodall, M., and Kirshner, N.: *J. Biol. Chem.*, **226**, 213, 1957; *Biochim. et Biophys. Acta*, **24**, 658, 1957.
119. Axelrod, J.; Senoh, S.; and Witkop, B.: *J. Biol. Chem.*, **233**, 697, 1958.
120. Mann, W.; Leblond, C. P.; and Warren, S. L.: *J. Biol. Chem.*, **142**, 905, 1942.
121. Morton, M. E., and Chaikoff, I. L.: *J. Biol. Chem.*, **144**, 565, 1942.
122. Reinecke, E. P.; Williamson, M. B.; and Turner, C. W.: *J. Biol. Chem.*, **143**, 285, 1942.
123. Mason, H. S.: *J. Biol. Chem.*, **172**, 83, 1948. Cromartie, R. J. T., and Harley-Mason, J.: *Biochem. J.*, **66**, 713, 1957.
124. Lerner, A. B., and Fitzpatrick, T. B.: *Physiol. Revs.*, **30**, 91, 1950.
125. Davis, B. D., and Mingioli, E. S.: *J. Bact.*, **66**, 129, 1953. Davis, B. D.: *Advances in Enzymol.*, **16**, 247, 1955. Weiss, U.; Gilvarg, C.; Mingioli, E. S.; and Davis, B. D.: *Science*, **119**, 774, 1954; *J. Am. Chem. Soc.*, **78**, 2894, 1956. Metzenberg, R. L., and Mitchell, H. K.: *Arch. Biochem. and Biophys.*, **64**, 51, 1956. Srinivasan, P. R., and Sprinson, D. B.: *J. Biol. Chem.*, **234**, 716, 1959.

126. Sanadi, D. R., and Greenberg, D. M.: *Federation Proc.*, **8**, 394, 1949.
127. Berg, C. P., and Potgieter, M.: *J. Biol. Chem.*, **94**, 661, 1932.
128. Jackson, R. W., and Chandler, J. P.: *Ann. Rev. Biochem.* **8**, 249, 1939.
129. Schayer, R. W.: *J. Biol. Chem.*, **187**, 777, 1950.
130. Holt, L. E., Jr.; Albanese, A. A.; Frankston, J. E.; and Irby, V.: *Bull. Johns Hopkins Hosp.*, **75**, 353, 1944.
131. Weissbach, H.; King, W.; Sjoerdsma, A.; and Udenfriend, S.: *J. Biol. Chem.*, **234**, 81, 1959.
132. Coon, M. J., and Robinson, W. G.: *Ann. Rev. Biochem.*, **27**, 561, 1958.
133. Gholson, R. K.; Henderson, L. M.; Mourkides, G. A.; Hill, R. J.; and Koeppe, R. E.: *J. Biol. Chem.*, **234**, 96, 1959.
134. Udenfriend, S.; Titus, E.; Weissbach, H.; and Peterson, R. E.: *J. Biol. Chem.*, **219**, 335, 1956. Udenfriend, S.; Weissbach, H.; and Bogdanski, D. F.: *ibid.*, **224**, 803, 1957.
135. Gaddum, J. H., and Giarman, N. J.: *Brit. J. Pharmacol.*, **11**, 88, 1956.
136. Matsuoka, Z., and Yoshimatsu, N.: *Z. Physiol. Chem.*, **143**, 206, 1925.
137. Gordon, W. G.; Kaufman, R. E.; and Jackson, R. W.: *J. Biol. Chem.*, **113**, 125, 1936.
138. Lepkovsky, S.; Roboz, E.; and Haagen-Smit, A. J.: *J. Biol. Chem.*, **149**, 195, 1943.
139. Reid, D. F.; Lepkovsky, S.; Bonner, D.; and Tatum, E. L.: *J. Biol. Chem.*, **155**, 299, 1944.
140. Axelrod, H. E.; Morgan, A. F.; and Lepkovsky, S.: *J. Biol. Chem.*, **160**, 155, 1945.
141. Schayer, R. W.; Foster, G. L.; and Shemin, D.: *Federation Proc.*, **8**, 248, 1949.
142. Singal, S. A.; Briggs, A. P.; Sydenstricker, V. P.; and Littlejohn, J. M.: *J. Biol. Chem.*, **166**, 573, 1946.
143. Porlzweig, W. A.; Rosen, F., Levitas, N.; and Robinson, J.: *J. Biol. Chem.*, **167**, 511, 1947.
144. Albert, P. W.; Scheer, B. T.; and Deuel, H. J., Jr.: *J. Biol. Chem.*, **175**, 479, 1948.
145. Yanofsky, C.: *J. Biol. Chem.*, **223**, 171, 1956; **224**, 783, 1957.
146. Tatum, E. L., and Shemin, D.: *J. Biol. Chem.*, **209**, 671, 1954.
147. Metzler, D. E.; Ikawa, M.; and Snell, E. E.: *J. Am. Chem. Soc.*, **76**, 648, 1954.
148. Rose, W. C.; Haines, W. J.; Johnson, J. E.; and Warner, D. T.: *J. Biol. Chem.*, **148**, 457, 1943.
149. Foster, G. L.; Schoenheimer, R.; and Rittenberg, D.: *J. Biol. Chem.*, **127**, 319, 1939. Schoenheimer, R.; Ratner, S.; and Rittenberg, D.: *ibid.*, **130**, 703, 1939.
150. Leiter, L.: *J. Biol. Chem.*, **64**, 125, 1925.
151. Tesar, C., and Rittenberg, D.: *J. Biol. Chem.*, **170**, 35, 1947.
152. Borek, B. A., and Waelsch, H.: *J. Biol. Chem.*, **205**, 459, 1953. Miller, A., and Waelsch, H.: *ibid.*, **228**, 365, 1957. Tabor, H., and Mehler, A. H.: *ibid.*, **210**, 559, 1954. Mehler, A. H., and Hayaishi, T.: *Biochem. Preparations*, **4**, 50, 1955.
153. Huennekens, F. M., and Osborn, M. J.: *Advances in Enzymol.*, **21**, 369, 1959.
154. Rose, W. C.: *Physiol. Revs.*, **18**, 109, 1938.
155. Scull, C. W., and Rose, W. C.: *J. Biol. Chem.*, **89**, 109, 1930.
156. Madden, S. C.; Carter, J. R.; Kattus, A. A., Jr.; Miller, L. L.; and Whipple, G. H.: *J. Exptl. Med.*, **77**, 277, 1943.
157. Holt, L. E., Jr.; Albanese, A. A.; Shettles, L. B.; Kajdi, C.; and Wangerin, D. M.: *Federation Proc.*, **1**, 116, 1942.
158. Stetten, M. R., and Schoenheimer, R.: *J. Biol. Chem.*, **153**, 113, 1944. Stetten, M. R.: *ibid.*, **189**, 499, 1951. Sallach, H. J.; Koeppe, R. E.; and Rose, W. C.: *J. Am. Chem. Soc.*, **73**, 4500, 1951.
159. Stetten, M. R.: *Federation Proc.*, **8**, 256, 1949; *J. Biol. Chem.*, **181**, 31, 1949.
160. Wolf, G., and Berger, C. R. A.: *J. Biol. Chem.*, **230**, 231, 1958.
161. Gould, B. S.: *J. Biol. Chem.*, **232**, 637, 1958.
162. Wolf, G.; Heck, W. W.; and Leak, J. C.: *J. Biol. Chem.*, **223**, 95, 1956.
163. Borsook, H., and Dubnoff, J. W.: *J. Biol. Chem.*, **138**, 389, 1941; *ibid.*, **132**, 559, 1940.
164. Walker, J. B.: *J. Biol. Chem.*, **224**, 57, 1957.
165. Walker, J. B.: *Proc. Soc. Exptl. Biol. Med.*, **98**, 7, 1958.
166. Borsook, H., and Dubnoff, J. W.: *J. Biol. Chem.*, **168**, 493, 1947.
167. Baker, Z., and Miller, B. F.: *J. Biol. Chem.*, **130**, 393, 1939.
168. Chanutin, A.: *J. Biol. Chem.*, **89**, 765, 1930. Beard, H. H.: *ibid.*, **78**, 167, 1928. Chanutin, A., and Silvette, H.: *ibid.*, **80**, 589, 1928.

169. Block, K., and Schoenheimer, R.: *J. Biol. Chem.*, **131,** 111, 1939.
170. Hoberman, H. D.; Sims, E. A. H.; and Peters, J. H.: *J. Biol. Chem.*, **172,** 45, 1948.
171. Hoberman, H. D.; Sims, E. A. H.; and Engstrom, W. W.: *J. Biol. Chem.*, **173,** 111, 1948.
172. Shaffer, P. A.: *Am. J. Physiol.*, **23,** 1, 1908–09.
173. McClugage, H. B.; Booth, G.; and Evans, F. A.: *Am. J. Med. Sci.*, **181,** 349, 1931.
174. Hodgson, P., and Lewis, H. B.: *Am. J. Physiol.*, **87,** 288, 1926.
175. Tarver, H., and Schmidt, C. L. A.: *J. Biol. Chem.*, **130,** 67, 1939.
176. Stetten, D., Jr.: *J. Biol. Chem.*, **144,** 501, 1942.
177. Brand, E.; Cahill, G. F.; and Block, R. J.: *J. Biol. Chem.*, **110,** 399, 1935. Brand, E.; Block, R. J.; Kassell, B.; and Cahill, G. F.: *Proc. Soc. Exptl. Biol. Med.*, **35,** 501, 1936.
178. Du Vigneaud, V.; Brown, G. B.; and Chandler, J. P.: *J. Biol. Chem.*, **143,** 59, 1942. Binkley, F.; Anslow, W. P., Jr.; and du Vigneaud, V.: *ibid.*, **143,** 559, 1942. Binkley, F., and du Vigneaud, V.: *ibid.*, **144,** 507, 1942. Anslow, W. P., Jr., and du Vigneaud, V.: *ibid.*, **170,** 245, 1947. Binkley, F., and Okeson, D.: *ibid.*, **182,** 273, 1950. Rachele, J. R.; Reed, L. J.; Kidwai, A. R.; Ferger, M. F.; and du Vigneaud, V.: *ibid.*, **185,** 817, 1950.
179. Braunstein, A. E., and Goryachenkova, E. V.: *Doklady Akad. Nauk, S.S.S.R.*, **74,** 529, 1950.
180. Hess, W. C.: *Arch. Biochem. and Biophys.*, **40,** 127, 1942. Tarver, H., and Tabachnik, M.: *Federation Proc.*, **12,** 279, 1953.
181. Challenger, F., and Walshe, J. M.: *Biochem. J.*, **59,** 372, 1955.
182. Cannellakis, E. S.: *Federation Proc.*, **11,** 194, 1952. Cannellakis, E. S., and Tarver, H.: *Arch. Biochem. and Biophys.*, **42,** 387, 1953.
183. Mackenzie, C. G.; Chandler, J. P.; Keller, E. B.; Rachelle, J. R.; Cross, N.; Melville, D. B.; and du Vigneaud, V.: *J. Biol. Chem.*, **169,** 757, 1947.
184. Tarr, H. L. A.: *Biochem. J.*, **27,** 1869, 1933.
185. Formageot, C.: *Harvey Lectures*, 1953–54 Series, 1, 1955.
186. Fridovich, I., and Handler, P.: *J. Biol. Chem.*, **223,** 321, 1956; 228, 67, 1957.
187. Du Vigneaud, V.; Chandler, J. P.; Cohn, M.; and Brown, G. B.: *J. Biol. Chem.*, **134,** 787, 1940; also see 140, 625, 1941.
188. Simmonds, S., and du Vigneaud, V.: *J. Biol. Chem.*, **146,** 685, 1942.
189. Simmonds, S.; Cohn, M.; Chandler, J. P.; and du Vigneaud, V.: *J. Biol. Chem.*, **149,** 519, 1943.
190. Du Vigneaud, V.; Chandler, J. P.; Moyer, A. W.; and Keppel, D. M.: *J. Biol. Chem.*, **131,** 57, 1939.
191. Du Vigneaud, V.: *Biol. Symposia*, **5,** 243, 1941.
192. Rothschild, H. A.; Cori, O.; and Barron, E. S. G.: *J. Biol. Chem.*, **208,** 41, 1954. Rothschild, H. A., and Barron, E. S. G.: *ibid.*, **209,** 511, 1954.
193. Klein, J. R., and Handler, P.: *J. Biol. Chem.*, **144,** 537, 1942.
194. Maw, G. A., and du Vigneaud, V.: *J. Biol. Chem.*, **174,** 381, 1948.
195. Cantoni, G. L.: *Phosphorus Metabolism*, **2,** 129, 1952.
196. Du Vigneaud, V.: *A Trail of Research.* Cornell University Press, Ithaca, N. Y., 1952.

26

Metabolism of nucleoproteins, nucleic acids, and nucleotides

The chemistry of the purines, pyrimidines, nucleic acids, and nucleoproteins has been given in Chapter 9, which the student should review as background material for the following discussion.

The protein components of nucleoproteins go the pathways of amino acids in their metabolism. The metabolism characteristic of the nucleoproteins is related to the synthesis and breakdown of the nucleic acids.

The body does not require purines and pyrimidines in the diet but can synthesize them *de novo* from the products of protein and carbohydrate metabolism. Miescher (1) demonstrated that salmon during the spawning season, while fasting, form much nucleoprotein in the generative organs from muscle protein. Kossel (2) showed that the purine content of hen's eggs increases during incubation. Burian and Schur (3) found that suckling rabbits and puppies stored more purine nitrogen than contained in the food. Kollmann (4) found that an adult woman on a low purine diet for 50 days gained 4 kg in weight and excreted more purines than consumed.

DIGESTION AND ABSORPTION OF NUCLEOPROTEINS

The protein component of nucleoproteins is hydrolyzed by gastric and intestinal enzymes into the constituent amino acids. The liberated nucleic acids are not broken down in the stomach but are acted upon by pancreatic nucleases in the intestine (5). Ribonuclease of pancreatic juice hydrolyzes ribonucleic acids (RNA) splitting off particularly pyrimidine mononucleotides. Pancreatic deoxyribonuclease, in the presence of Mg^{++} or Mn^{++}, hydrolyzes deoxyribonucleic acids (DNA) to oligonucleotides (composed of a few mononucleotides). Other nucleases from the intestinal mucosa such as phosphodiesterase complete the hydrolysis of nucleic acids to mononucleotides. The mononucleotides are further hydrolyzed by intestinal phosphatases (nucleotidases) to inorganic phosphate and nucleosides. It appears that nucleosides are not hydrolyzed in the intestine but are absorbed as such.

Nucleosidases, which split the glycosidic bond of nucleosides to form D-ribose, D-deoxyribose, and purine and pyrimidine bases, are found in extracts of various tissues such as liver, kidney, spleen, bone marrow, etc. Little is known about the nucleosidases, since they have not been studied extensively or purified. It is probable that there are nucleosidases specific for different types of nucleosides.

Nucleosides are split not only by nucleosidases but also by nucleoside phosphorylases, discovered by Kalckar (6):

$$\text{Uracil riboside} + H_2O \xrightarrow{\text{Nucleosidase}} \text{Uracil} + \text{Ribose}$$
$$\text{Uridine}$$

$$\text{Guanine riboside} + Pi \xleftrightarrow{\substack{\text{Nucleoside} \\ \text{Phosphorylase}}} \text{Guanine} + \alpha\text{-D-Ribose-1-P}$$
$$\text{Guanosine}$$

Nucleoside phosphorylase is present in liver and other tissues and acts upon various nucleosides. The reactions catalyzed by it are reversible, with equilibrium points such that the enzyme may function in both synthesis and breakdown of nucleosides.

SYNTHESIS OF PURINES IN THE BODY

Barnes and Schoenheimer (7) gave ammonia labeled with N^{15} to rats and pigeons and found the N^{15} to be rapidly incorporated into the purines and pyrimidines of nucleic acids of the internal organs. Plentl and Schoenheimer (8) fed N^{15}-labeled guanine and also uracil and thymine (pyrimidines). Guanine was not incorporated into the nucleic acids of either pigeons or rats but was excreted as uric acid by pigeons and as allantoin by the rats. The isotopic pyrimidines, fed to rats, also were not found in the tissue nucleic acids, but their N^{15} was excreted as ammonia and urea in the urine, indicating that the pyrimidine ring had been broken up.

Brown and associates (9) fed adenine labeled with N^{15} in the pyrimidine part of the purine ring to rats and found high concentrations of N^{15} in both the adenine and the guanine of tissue nucleic acids. When they fed isotopic guanine, however, it was not utilized for nucleic acid formation, confirming the work of Plentl and Schoenheimer. It appears, therefore, that dietary adenine, but not guanine, may be used for nucleic acid formation in the body, and that adenine is converted to guanine after the adenine has been incorporated into the nucleotide structures.

Kalckar and Rittenberg (10) gave ammonia labeled with N^{15} to rats and found the isotope to be rapidly incorporated into the 6-amino group of adenine in adenylic acid. This process was much faster than N^{15} incorporation into glutamic acid. The 6 position of adenine in the nucleotide undergoes very rapid reversible deamination-amination:

$$\text{adenylic acid} \underset{+NH_3}{\overset{-NH_3}{\rightleftharpoons}} \text{inosinic acid}$$

Brown and associates (11) have shown that hypoxanthine cannot be incorporated into nucleotide structures. They fed N^{15}-labeled hypoxanthine to rats and did not find the isotope in muscle adenylic acid or tissue nucleic acids. Most of the N^{15} appeared in urinary allantoin. Isotopic xanthine gave similar results.

SYNTHESIS OF PURINE NUCLEOTIDES

The mechanisms of purine synthesis have been recently reviewed by Buchanan (12) and by Hartman and Buchanan (13).

By feeding labeled compounds to pigeons, which excrete uric acid labeled in definite positions, and by studying purine synthesis in cell-free systems of pigeon liver, it has been established that purine biosynthesis is effected de novo from several small molecules (12). It was found that the various components of the purine ring are derived from formate, CO_2, glutamine, aspartic acid, and glycine as shown in Figure 26.1.

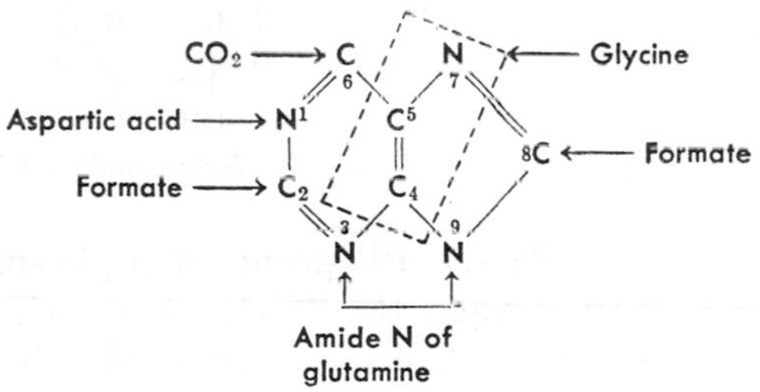

Figure 26.1.   Sources of the purine ring.

The pathways of purine biosynthesis have been established particularly by studies of the action of pigeon liver preparations and of enzyme preparations from microorganisms such as *E. coli* and *Neurospora crassa* upon labeled compounds, and isolation of labeled intermediates (12,13). Various enzymes which catalyze specific reactions in the synthetic pathway have been separated and extensively purified.

It is of interest that the pathways of purine synthesis in microorganisms are essentially the same as those found in the livers of animals.

The purines are synthesized *de novo* not as free purines but first as the nucleotide inosinic acid (hypoxanthine-ribose-5'-phosphate), which is then converted into the adenine and guanine nucleotides. The purine ring is synthesized on to ribose-5-phosphate through numerous intermediates to form inosinic acid. The reactions involved in nucleotide synthesis have been established through the work of many investigators, particularly by Buchanan, G. R. Greenberg, A. Kornberg, and their associates (12,13,14).

The synthesis of inosinic acid begins with D-ribose-5-phosphate, which is formed in the pentose cycle (Chapter 24). D-Ribose-5-P is converted to 5-phosphoribosyl-1-pyrophosphate by the action of ATP and a kinase enzyme:

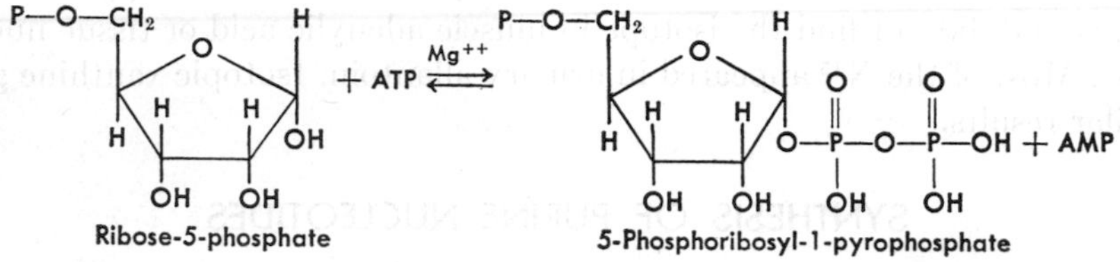

Ribose-5-phosphate   5-Phosphoribosyl-1-pyrophosphate

This appears to be the only known instance in which a kinase causes the transfer of a pyrophosphate group to a compound from ATP.

5-Phosphoribosyl-1-pyrophosphate then reacts with glutamine to replace the pyrophosphate group (PP) by an —NH_2 group, with the formation of 5-phosphoribosyl-1-amine. The enzyme catalyzing this reaction is 5-phosphoribosyl pyrophosphate amidotransferase.

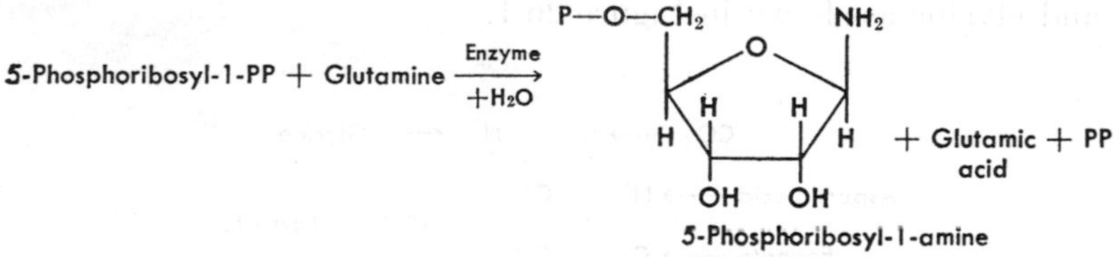

5-Phosphoribosyl-1-amine

It will be noted that while the PP group of 5-phosphoribosyl-1-PP is joined to the sugar by an α-linkage, the —NH_2 group which replaces PP to form the amine is joined by a β-linkage, representing inversion of spatial configuration at C-1' of the ribose.

The next step in the synthesis consists in the formation of glycinamide ribotide from 5-phosphoribosyl-1-amine, glycine, and ATP, the reaction being catalyzed by the enzyme 2-amino-N-ribosylacetamide-5'-phosphate kinosynthase (glycinamide ribotide kinosynthase) (15):

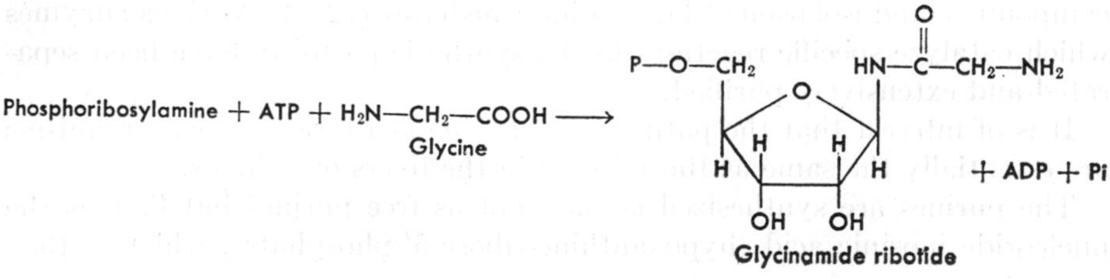

Glycinamide ribotide

Glycinamide ribotide is converted to formylglycinamide ribotide by N^5, N^{10}-anhydroformyltetrahydrofolic acid (N^5, N^{10}-anhydroformyl-FH_4) and the enzyme glycinamide ribotide transformylase:

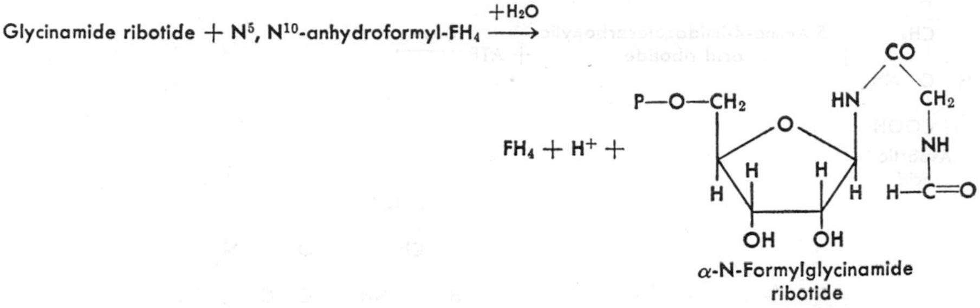

$$\text{Glycinamide ribotide} + N^5, N^{10}\text{-anhydroformyl-}FH_4 \xrightarrow{+H_2O}$$

$$FH_4 + H^+ +$$

α-N-Formylglycinamide
ribotide

Formylglycinamide ribotide then reacts with glutamine and ATP to form formylglycinamidine ribotide, which then undergoes ring closure to give 5-aminoimidazole ribotide:

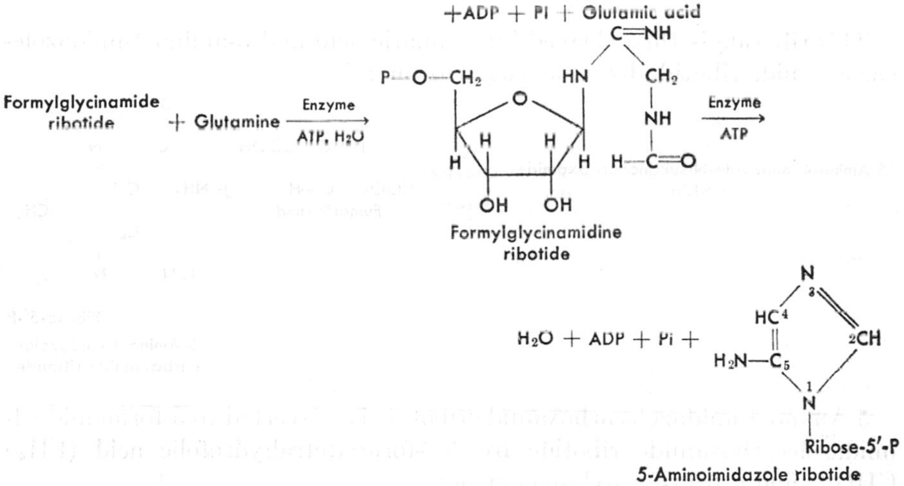

Formylglycinamide ribotide + Glutamine $\xrightarrow[\text{ATP, }H_2O]{\text{Enzyme}}$

Formylglycinamidine
ribotide

$$\xrightarrow[\text{ATP}]{\text{Enzyme}}$$

$$H_2O + ADP + Pi +$$

Ribose-5'-P
5-Aminoimidazole ribotide

5-Aminoimidazole ribotide then is carboxylated to 5-amino-4-imidazole-carboxylic acid ribotide by the enzyme aminoimidazole ribotide carboxylase:

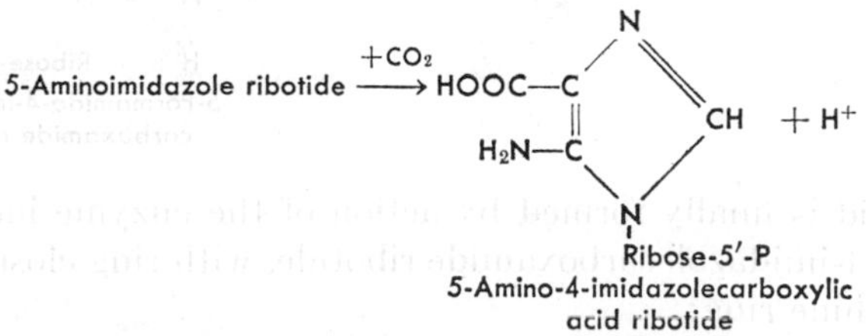

$$\text{5-Aminoimidazole ribotide} \xrightarrow{+CO_2} $$

$$+ H^+$$

Ribose-5'-P
5-Amino-4-imidazolecarboxylic
acid ribotide

The compound 5-amino-4-imidazolecarboxylic acid ribotide reacts with aspartic acid and ATP to form 5-amino-4-imidazole-N-succinocarboxamide ribotide:

COOH
|
CH₂   5-Amino-4-imidazolecarboxylic   Enzyme
| +   acid ribotide   + ATP ⟶
H—C—NH₂
|
COOH
Aspartic
acid

COOH
|
CH₂   O   N
| ‖   ╱ ╲
H—C—NH——C—C   CH + ADP + Pi
| ‖
COOH   H₂N—C
           │
           N
           │
      Ribose-5′-P
5-Amino-4-imidazole-N-succinocarboxamide
            ribotide

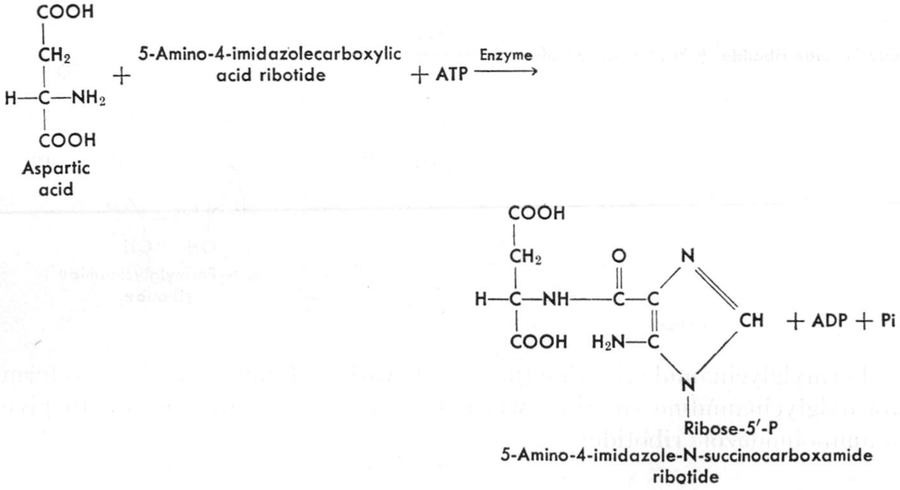

This ribotide is then cleaved into fumaric acid and 5-amino-4-imidazole-carboxamide ribotide by a cleavage enzyme:

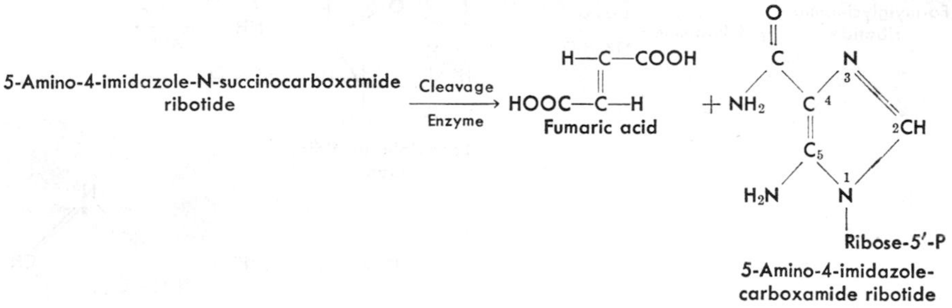

5-Amino-4-imidazole-N-succinocarboxamide   Cleavage   H—C—COOH   O
            ribotide   ⟶   HOOC—C—H   + NH₂   C   N
                                          Enzyme   Fumaric acid   C ⁴   ³
                                                                  C₅   ₂CH
                                                                  │
                                                              H₂N   N
                                                                     │
                                                                Ribose-5′-P
                                                           5-Amino-4-imidazole-
                                                           carboxamide ribotide

5-Amino-4-imidazolecarboxamide ribotide is converted to 5-formamido-4-imidazolecarboxamide ribotide by N^{10}-formyltetrahydrofolic acid ($FH_4 \cdot CHO^{10}$) and a transformylase enzyme:

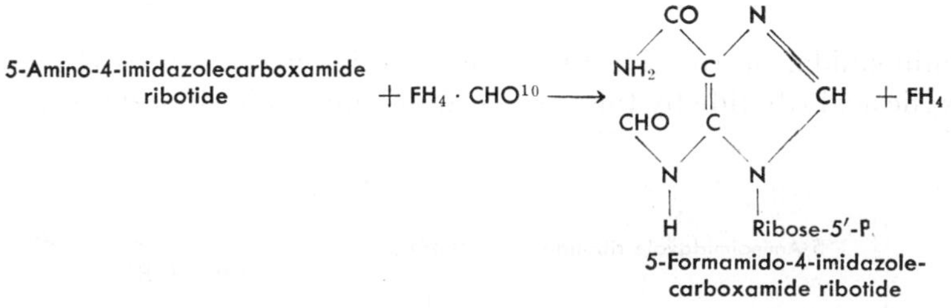

5-Amino-4-imidazolecarboxamide   CO   N
        ribotide   + FH₄ · CHO¹⁰ ⟶   NH₂   C
                                                  ‖   CH + FH₄
                                               CHO   C
                                                ╲   ╱ ╲
                                                 N   N
                                                 │   │
                                                 H   Ribose-5′-P
                                            5-Formamido-4-imidazole-
                                            carboxamide ribotide

Inosinic acid is finally formed by action of the enzyme inosinicase upon 5-formamido-4-imidazolecarboxamide ribotide, with ring closure completing the hypoxanthine ring:

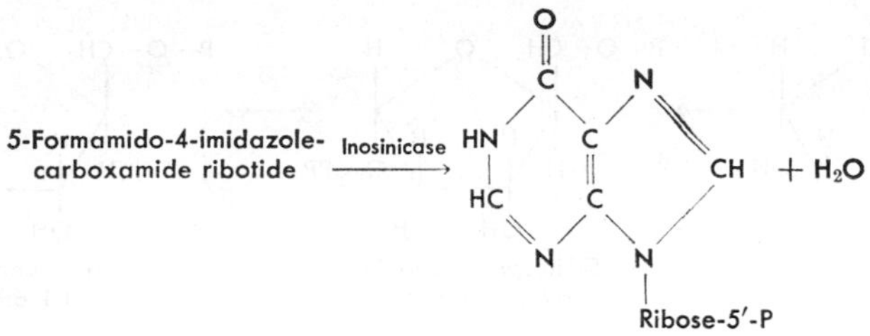

5-Formamido-4-imidazole-carboxamide ribotide $\xrightarrow{\text{Inosinicase}}$

Inosine-5'-phosphate
Inosinic acid

$+ H_2O$

Formation of adenylic acid (adenosine-5'-phosphate). Adenylic acid is formed from inosinic acid through adenylosuccinic acid, two reactions being involved. Adenylosuccinic acid is formed from inosinic acid, aspartic acid, and guanosine triphosphate (GTP):

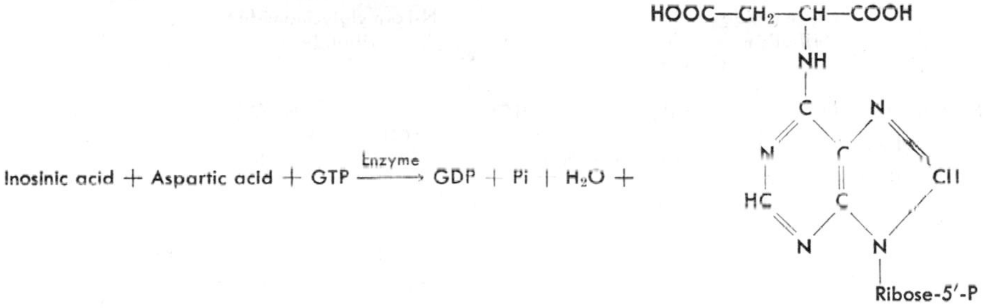

Inosinic acid + Aspartic acid + GTP $\xrightarrow{\text{Enzyme}}$ GDP + Pi + H$_2$O +

Adenylosuccinic acid

Adenylosuccinic acid is split by the enzyme adenylosuccinase into fumaric acid and adenylic acid:

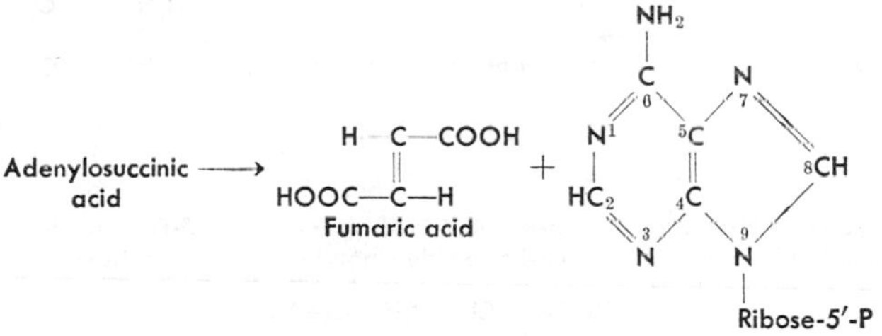

Adenylosuccinic acid $\longrightarrow$

Fumaric acid

Adenosine-5'-phosphate
Adenylic acid

Formation of guanylic acid (guanosine-5'-phosphate). The mononucleotide guanylic acid is synthesized from inosinic acid through xanthylic acid:

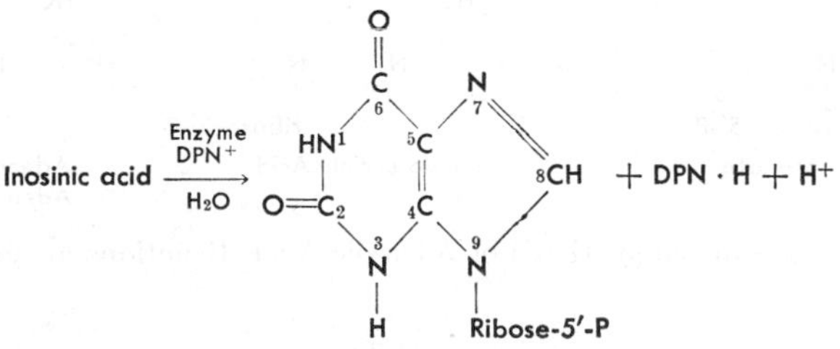

Inosinic acid $\xrightarrow[\text{H}_2\text{O}]{\substack{\text{Enzyme} \\ \text{DPN}^+}}$

$+ DPN \cdot H + H^+$

Xanthylic acid

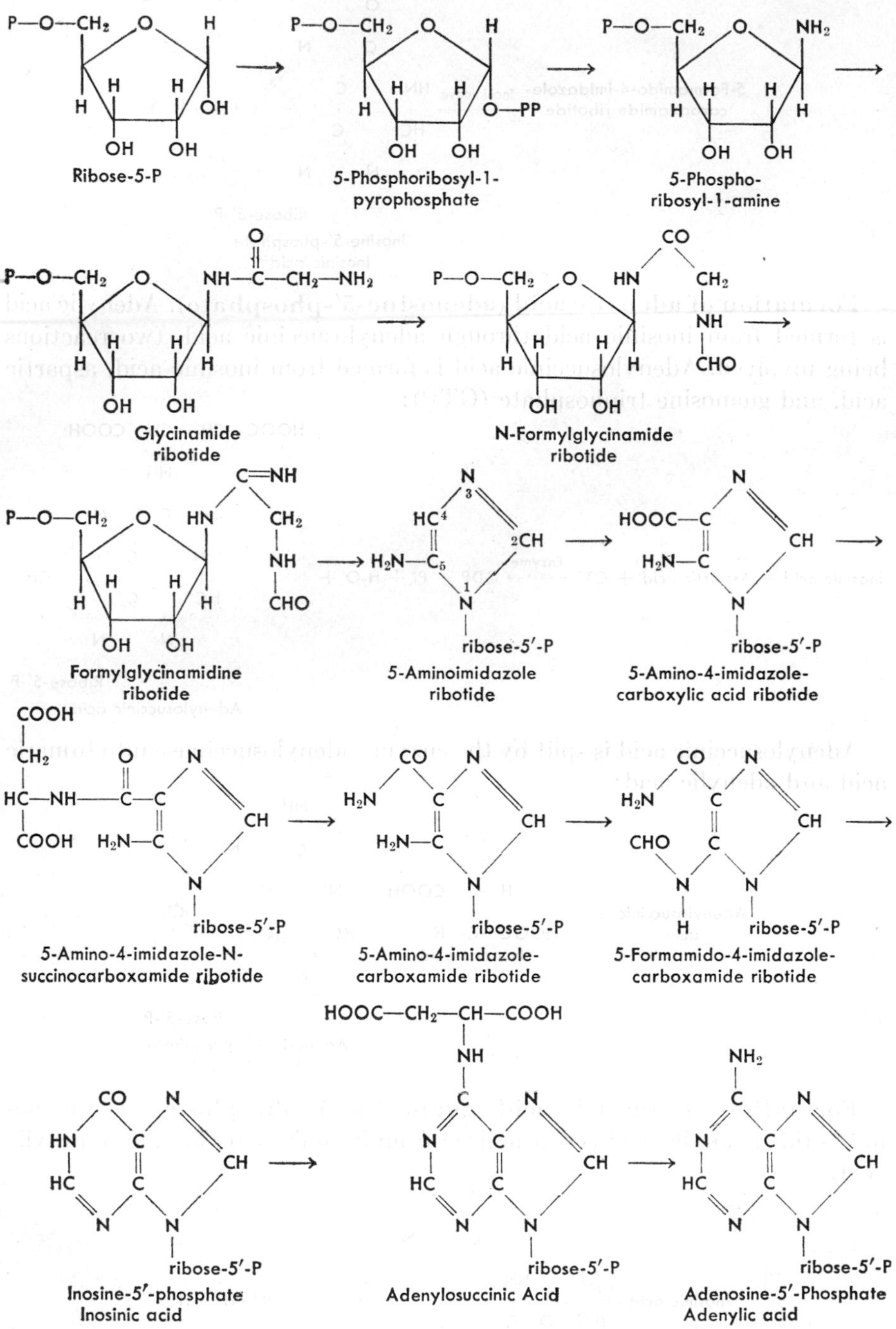

Figure 26.2. Stages in the synthesis of Adenylic Acid. Reactions are given in the text.

Xanthylic acid is then aminated in the 2 position by the action of glutamine and ATP:

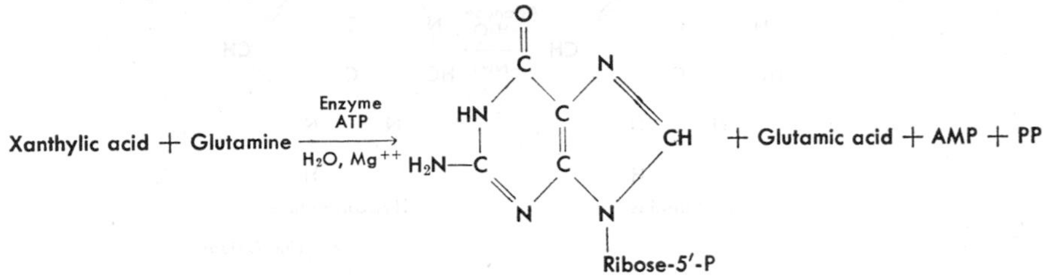

$$\text{Xanthylic acid} + \text{Glutamine} \xrightarrow[\text{H}_2\text{O, Mg}^{++}]{\substack{\text{Enzyme}\\\text{ATP}}}$$

Guanosine-5'-Phosphate
Guanylic acid

$$+ \text{Glutamic acid} + \text{AMP} + \text{PP}$$

Salvage pathways of nucleotide synthesis. The major pathway of nucleotide synthesis has been outlined above. However, nucleosides and nucleotides may be synthesized from purine bases by reactions such as the following:

$$\text{Adenine} + \text{Phosphoribosyl-pyrophosphate} \xrightarrow{\text{Enzyme}} \text{Adenylic acid} + \text{PP}$$

Similar reactions are given by guanine and hypoxanthine.

Nucleosides may be formed by reaction with ribose-1-phosphate:

$$\text{Adenine} + \text{Ribose-1-P} \xrightarrow{\text{Phosphorylase}} \text{Adenosine} + \text{Pi}$$

The nucleoside then may be phosphorylated to the nucleotide by ATP:

$$\text{Adenosine} + \text{ATP} \xrightarrow[\text{kinase}]{\text{Adenosine}} \text{Adenylic acid} + \text{ADP}$$

While it appears that in animals adenylic acid may be formed by a so-called salvage pathway from adenine, as outlined above, and incorporated into nucleic acids, such seems not to be the case with guanine. The synthesis of nucleotides from the free bases appears to be more important for certain microorganisms than for animals.

Stages in the synthesis of adenylic acid are shown in Figure 26.2.

PURINE CATABOLISM

The stages in the breakdown of purines are shown in Figure 26.3.

The end products of purine metabolism vary widely with different animal species. Man and other primates, the Dalmatian dog, birds, and certain reptiles convert purines to uric acid. Mammals other than primates (Dalmatian dog excepted) and gastropods carry the breakdown still farther and excrete allantoin, which is formed by the action of uricase upon uric acid. Some teleost fishes excrete allantoic acid, which is formed from allantoin by the action of allantoinase. Most fishes, amphibia, and fresh water lamellibranchs carry the breakdown still farther by converting allantoic acid to urea and glyoxylic acid through the action of allantoicase. And, finally, marine lamel-

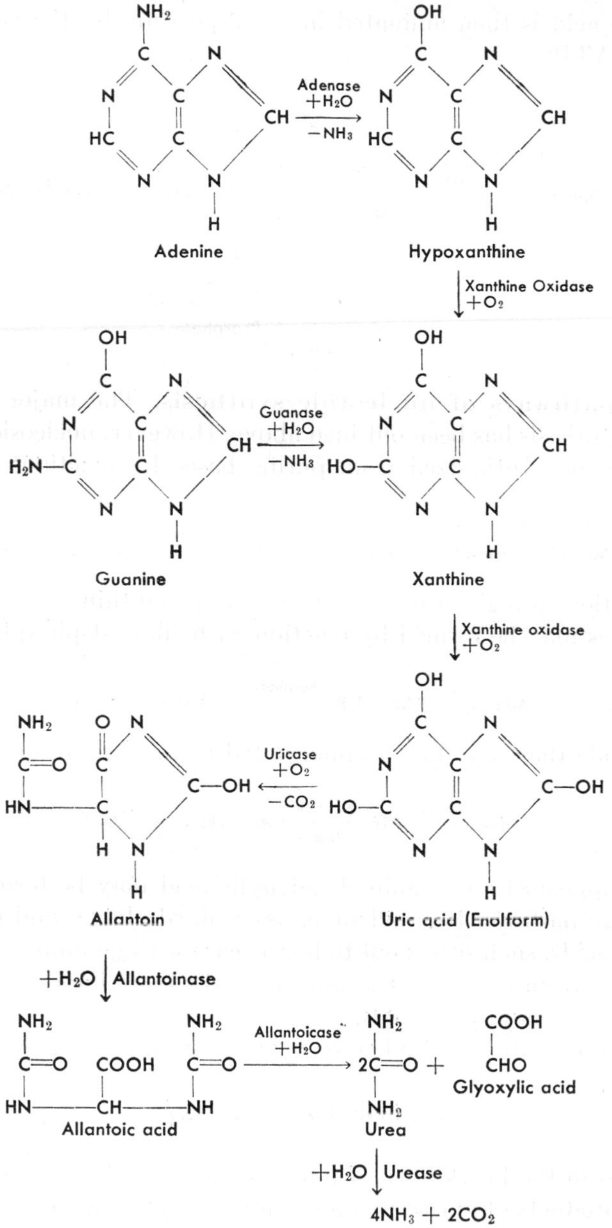

Figure 26.3.   Purine catabolism. End products vary with animal species (see text).

libranchs, crustacea, and gephyrean worms convert the purines through urea to ammonia and carbon dioxide.

Guanase is present in animal organs such as the liver, spleen, pancreas, and kidneys. However, it is not present in pig liver and spleen but is present in other tissues. Adenase is seldom found in animal tissues, though it is present in cow muscle and milk. Adenase appears to be absent from the tissues of man.

It appears that adenine and some guanine may be deaminized to hypoxanthine and xanthine while still in nucleoside combination, since adenosine deaminase and guanosine deaminase are present in liver and other tissues. The conversion of adenine to hypoxanthine while combined as adenylic acid in muscle by the enzyme, adenylic deaminase, is well established:

$$\text{adenylic acid} \underset{+NH_3}{\overset{-NH_3}{\rightleftharpoons}} \text{adenylic acid deaminase inosinic acid}$$

Xanthine oxidase, the enzyme that oxidizes hypoxanthine to xanthine and xanthine to uric acid, is present in the liver of man, and in several organs and the milk of the cow, but is absent from liver of the dog and hedgehog.

In man and other primates and the Dalmatian dog, purine metabolism largely stops with uric acid, which is then excreted in the urine. As indicated previously, other animal species carry purine metabolism beyond the uric acid stage according to the presence of requisite enzymes. In one case, that of the pig, conversion of purines to uric acid is deficient, because of insufficient guanase, and the pig excretes guanine as well as allantoin in the urine. The pig may suffer from guanine gout on account of deposition of guanine crystals in the joints, just as man suffers from gout due to deposition of the monosodium salt of uric acid.

Wyngaarden and Stetten (16) gave 1000 mg of uric acid-1,3-N^{15} intravenously to a normal man and found 17 per cent of the N^{15} excreted as urea N^{15} in the urine. Ammonia N^{15} accounted for a bit less than 1 per cent of the uric acid N^{15}. About 6 per cent of the uric acid was excreted in the feces, and 78 per cent was eliminated unchanged in the urine. These results show a rather surprising and hitherto unsuspected degree of breakdown of the purine ring in man.

It is of interest that a riboside of uric acid has been found in animal tissues (17), indicating that guanine or adenine may be converted to uric acid while still attached to sugar.

The Dalmatian dog excretes largely uric acid rather than allantoin. However, his liver is fairly rich in uricase, the enzyme which converts uric acid to allantoin. Apparently, uric acid excretion is due to a low kidney threshold for it.

Birds not only convert purines to uric acid, but also form uric acid from the ammonia split out in the deamination of amino acids. They are unable to form urea because arginase is not present in the liver. The uric acid is excreted through the cloaca, mostly in solid form. This permits birds to economize greatly in their use of water.

Uric acid of blood and tissues. The range of uric acid in normal human plasma appears to be from 2 to 6 mg per cent, averaging 4 mg per cent. Values for females average about 3.5 and for males 4.5 mg per cent. Red cells appear to contain about half as much uric acid as plasma.

Uric acid appears to be very irregularly distributed in tissues. Folin and associates (18) observed an uneven distribution of uric acid in the tissues of the dog after injecting the substance. Injections which caused the uric acid of kidneys to rise to 200 mg per cent had practically no effect upon muscle uric acid. Human muscle has been reported to contain about half as much uric acid as blood per 100 g. Feces contain about the same uric acid concentration as blood.

Effect of diet. Uric acid excretion continues at a rather steady rate during starvation and during a purine-free diet owing to the so-called endogenous (tissue) purine metabolism. The ingestion of foods high in nucleoprotein, such as glandular organs, produces a marked increase. A diet of milk, eggs, and cheese, all of which are very low in purine content, causes practically no increase in uric acid excretion over the endogenous level.

Pathologic states. Blood uric acid generally is more or less elevated in gout, a disease in which large amounts of monosodium urate may be deposited in the joints and tissues (tophi).

It has been shown that in a normal man the uric acid pool amounts to about 1 g (17) in a volume approximately equal to that of the extracellular fluids. A much larger uric acid pool was found in the gouty patient. Also, the gouty patient incorporated glycine-N^{15} more rapidly into uric acid than the normal subject, indicating an abnormally high rate of uric acid synthesis. The increased uric acid blood level in gout probably is partly due to impaired renal excretion.

In terminal stages of acute yellow atrophy, the blood uric acid is markedly reduced, apparently as a result of inability of the liver to form it from the purines.

In leukemia and pneumonia, the blood uric acid may be elevated owing to the increased rate of purine metabolism accompanying the disintegration of leucocytes and tissue autolysis.

The blood uric acid is often increased in arteriosclerosis with hypertension and in cardiac decompensation. In some instances this may be due to renal insufficiency. Increases have been observed in severe diabetes and in acute infections of children.

SYNTHESIS OF PYRIMIDINE NUCLEOTIDES

Reichard has written a recent review on the biosynthesis of the pyrimidines (19).

The mechanisms of pyrimidine synthesis have been established largely through studies with microbial and liver enzymes acting upon labeled compounds.

The pyrimidines, like the purines, are synthesized as the nucleotides.

The discovery which in particular aided in the study of pyrimidine synthesis was that orotic acid (6-carboxyuracil) could satisfy the pyrimidine requirements of several bacteria (20):

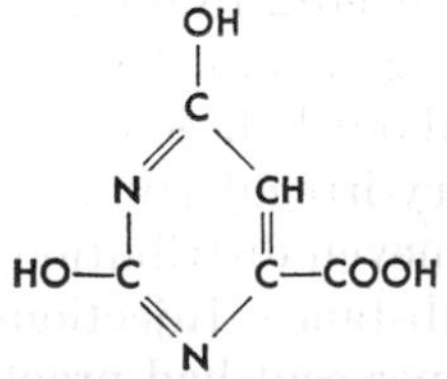

6-Carboxyuracil
Orotic acid

It was found by both *in vitro* and *in vivo* experiments, using orotic acids labeled with C^{14} and N^{15}, that mammalian tissues utilize orotic acid for the synthesis of pyrimidines of both DNA and RNA (21), and Reichard demonstrated that rat liver slices synthesize orotic acid (22).

The first process in the synthesis of pyrimidine nucleotides is the reaction of carbamyl phosphate with aspartic acid to form carbamyl aspartate or ureidosuccinic acid.

The reaction is catalyzed by the enzyme aspartate carbamyl transferase:

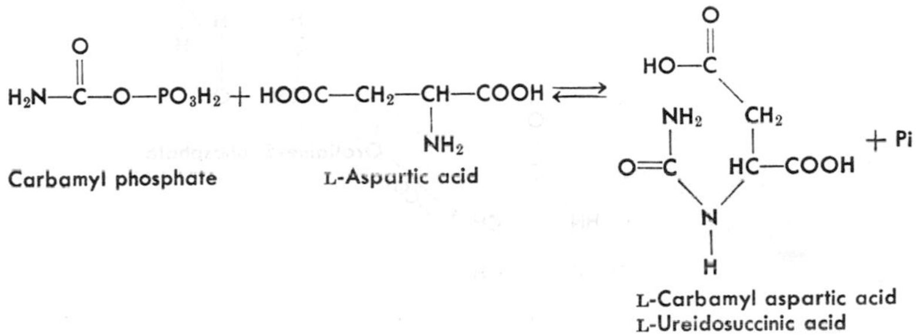

$$H_2N-\overset{\overset{O}{\|}}{C}-O-PO_3H_2 + HOOC-CH_2-\underset{\underset{NH_2}{|}}{CH}-COOH \rightleftharpoons$$

Carbamyl phosphate   L-Aspartic acid

(product structure) + Pi

L-Carbamyl aspartic acid
L-Ureidosuccinic acid

The equilibrium of this reaction lies far toward synthesis of carbamyl aspartate.

The enzyme dihydroorotase acts upon L-carbamyl aspartic acid to give ring closure with the formation of L-dihydroorotic acid. Dihydroorotic acid is then oxidized to L-orotic acid by the enzyme dihydroorotic dehydrogenase, which requires DPN:

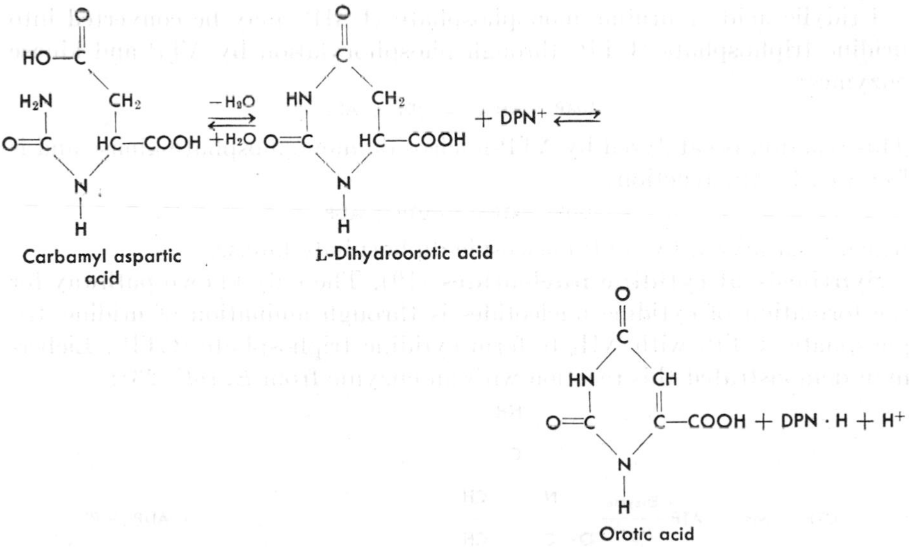

Carbamyl aspartic acid $\overset{-H_2O}{\underset{+H_2O}{\rightleftharpoons}}$ L-Dihydroorotic acid $+ DPN^+ \rightleftharpoons$

Orotic acid $+ DPN \cdot H + H^+$

Orotic acid is converted into the nucleotide orotodine-5′-phosphate by reaction with 5-phosphoribosyl-1-pyrophosphate. The reaction is catalyzed by the enzyme orotidine-5′-phosphate pyrophosphorylase. Orotidine-5′-phosphate is decarboxylated to uridylic acid (uridine-5′-phosphate) by the enzyme orotidine-5′-phosphate decarboxylase:

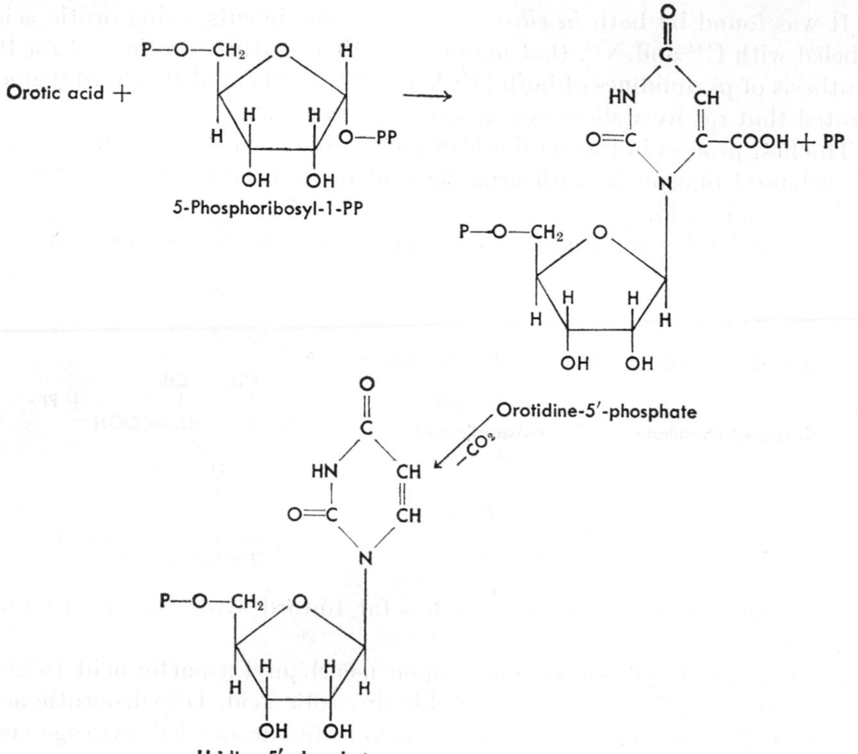

Orotic acid +

5-Phosphoribosyl-1-PP

$\longrightarrow$

Orotidine-5'-phosphate

$-CO_2$

Uridine-5'-phosphate
Uridylic acid (UMP)

Uridylic acid or uridine monophosphate (UMP) may be converted into uridine triphosphate (UTP) through phosphorylation by ATP and kinase enzymes:

$$UMP + ATP \rightleftharpoons UDP + ADP$$

This reaction is catalyzed by ATP-nucleoside monophosphate kinase and is followed by the reaction:

$$UDP + ATP \rightleftharpoons UTP + ADP$$

which is catalyzed by ATP-nucleoside diphosphate kinase.

Synthesis of cytidine nucleotides (19). The only known pathway for the formation of cytidine nucleotides is through amination of uridine triphosphate (UTP) with NH_3 to form cytidine triphosphate (CTP). Lieberman demonstrated this reaction with an enzyme from *E. coli* (23):

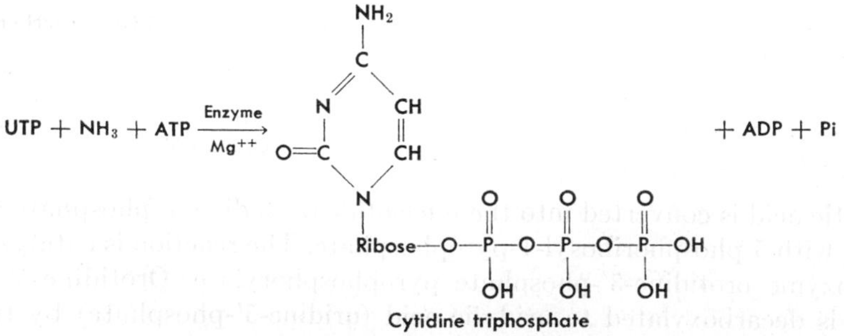

$$UTP + NH_3 + ATP \xrightarrow[Mg^{++}]{\text{Enzyme}} \qquad + ADP + Pi$$

Cytidine triphosphate

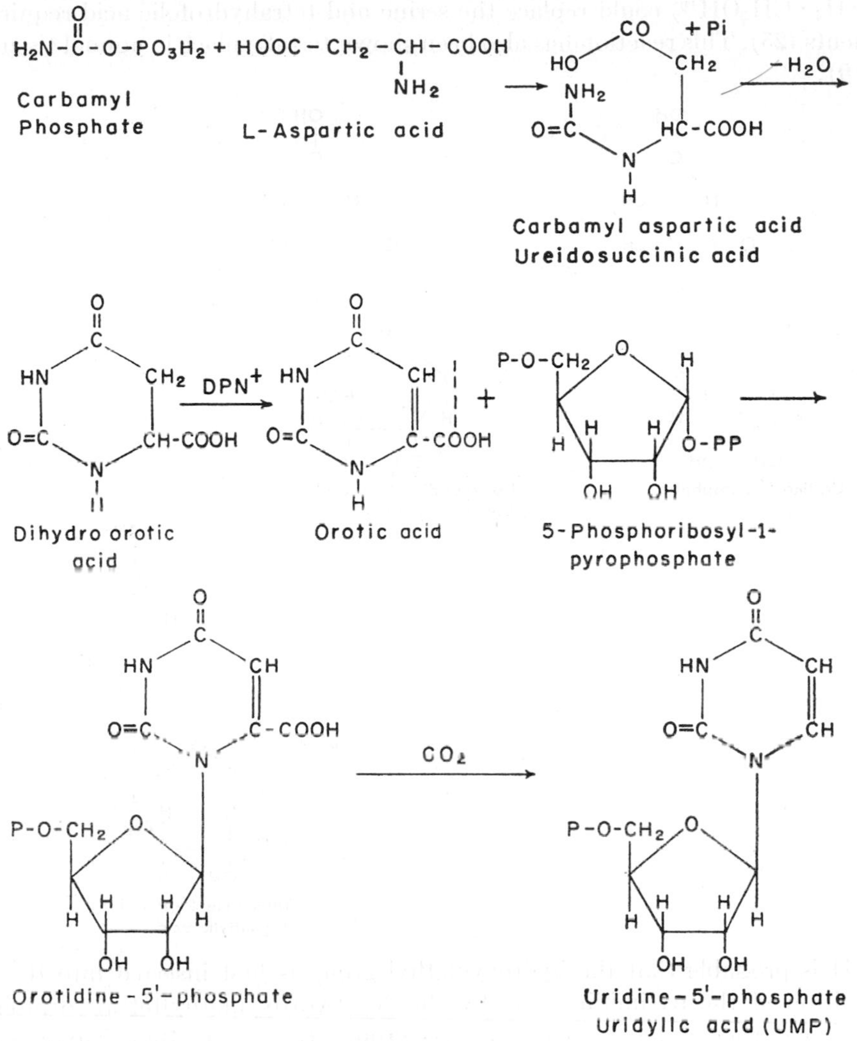

Figure 26.4. Stages in the synthesis of uridylic acid. More complete reactions given in the text.

Cytidine diphosphate (CDP) and monophosphate (CMP) may be formed by reactions such as the following, catalyzed by the appropriate kinases:

$$CTP + AMP \rightleftharpoons CDP + ADP$$
$$CDP + ADP \rightleftharpoons CMP + ATP$$

Synthesis of thymine nucleotides (19). The synthesis of thymine nucleotides involves both conversion of a ribotide to a deoxyribotide and also methylation of the pyrimidine ring. Friedkin and Kornberg (24) found that an enzyme from *E. coli* converted deoxyuridylic acid labeled with C^{14} or P^{32} to thymidylic acid in the presence of serine, tetrahydrofolic acid, ATP, and Mg^{++}. It was found that N^{10}-hydroxymethyltetrahydrofolic acid

($FH_4 \cdot CH_2OH^{10}$) could replace the serine and tetrahydrofolic acid requirements (25). This reaction has also been shown to take place in animal tissues
(19):

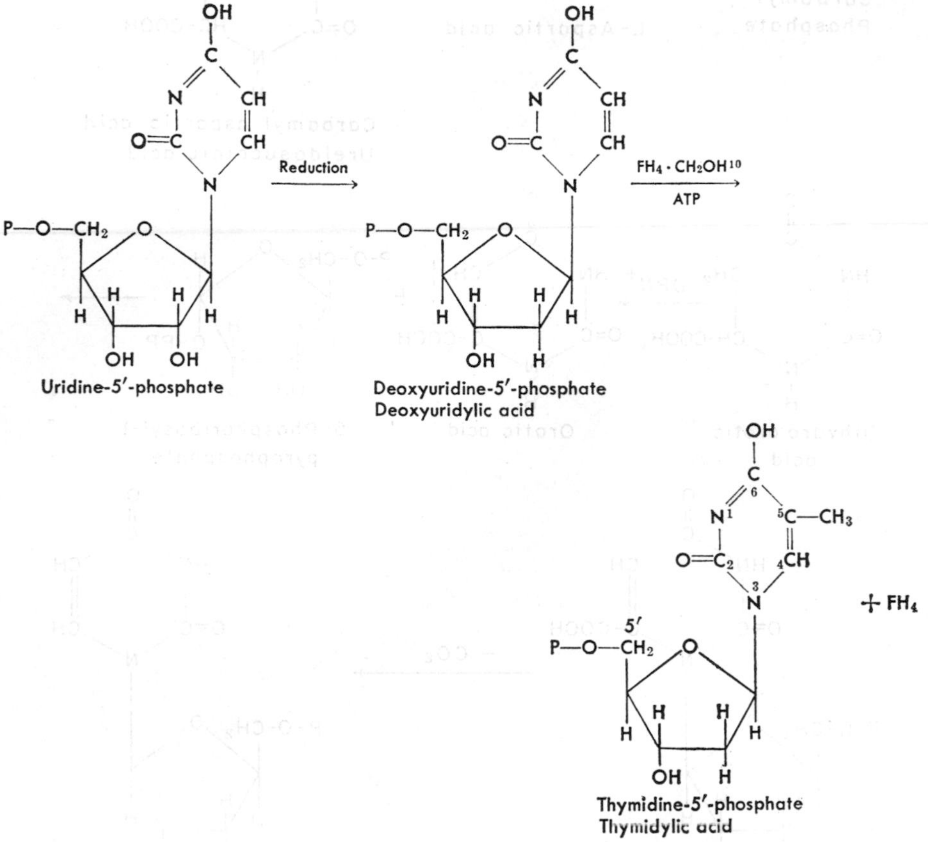

Uridine-5'-phosphate

Deoxyuridine-5'-phosphate
Deoxyuridylic acid

Thymidine-5'-phosphate
Thymidylic acid

It is probable that the hydroxymethyl group is first inserted into the 5
position of the pyrimidine ring by the N^{10}-hydroxymethyltetrahydrofolic
acid and then reduced to the methyl group. It appears that 5-hydroxy-
methylcytosine is formed by an analogous process from deoxycytidine-5'-
phosphate through the introduction of a hydroxymethyl group by N-^{10}hy-
droxymethyltetrahydrofolic acid (19).

The synthesis of uridylic acid is outlined in Figure 26.4.

PYRIMIDINE CATABOLISM

Pyrimidine nitrogen is largely excreted in the urine as urea and ammonia,
just as is the nitrogen of amino acids. This indicates complete disruption of
the pyrimidine ring.

That pyrimidine breakdown may occur while the pyrimidine is still
attached as the nucleotide or nucleoside appears established. Sweet and
Levene (26) found that more than half of the thymine fed to a dog could be

recovered in the urine, but if an equivalent amount of thymine was fed as nucleic acid, none could be found in the urine. Deuel (27) found that, when large amounts of thymine or uracil (1–3 g) were given to dogs, a considerable proportion was excreted in the urine. If the same quantities were given in small divided doses over a period of days, pyrimidines could not be detected

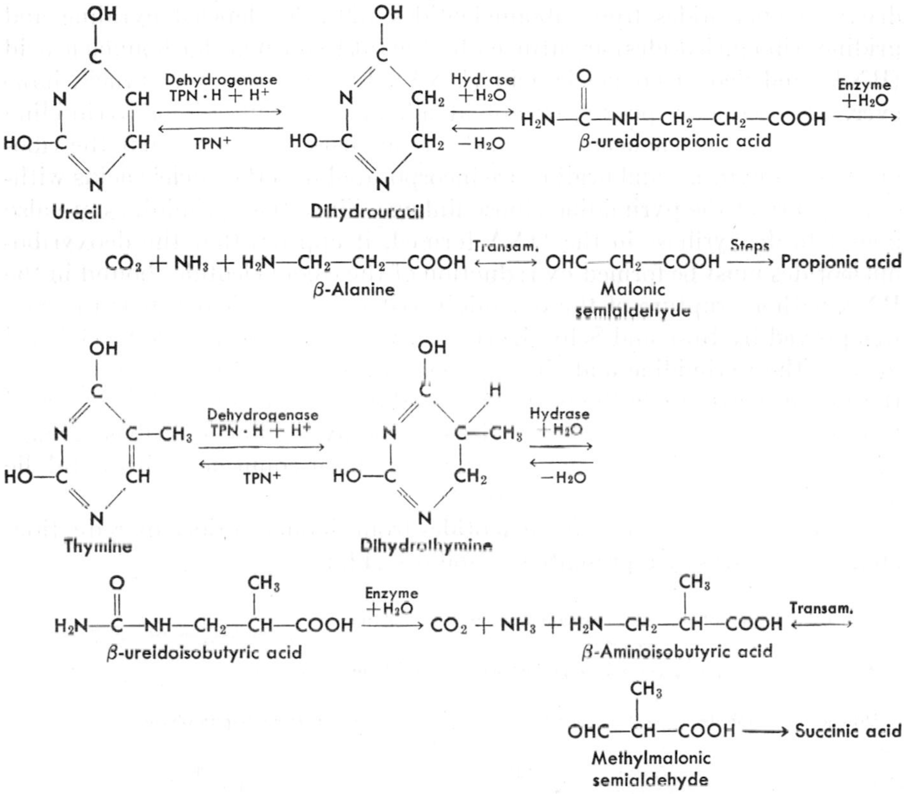

Figure 26.5.   Metabolic breakdown of uracil and thymine.

in the urine, indicating complete metabolism. Deuel was unable to isolate any pyrimidines from 150 l of normal human urine, though the ingestion of large amounts (50 g) of thymus nucleic acid led to the excretion of free pyrimidines.

The pathway of metabolism of the free pyrimidines has been studied by feeding them to animals (loading) and by *in vitro* experiments with liver preparations. Uracil is broken down to β-ureidopropionic acid and β-alanine, while thymine forms β-ureidoisobutyric acid and β-aminoisobutyric acid (28).

The first stage in the breakdown of uracil consists in reduction to dihydrouracil by TPN · H. Dihydrouracil is then hydrolyzed to β-ureidopropionic acid which yields β-alanine and NH_3. Thymine is broken down by analogous reactions, which are shown in Figure 26.5.

SYNTHESIS OF DEOXYRIBONUCLEOTIDES

There is no evidence that nucleotides containing deoxyribose are synthesized by pathways similar to the main pathways outlined above for the synthesis of ribonucleotides. However, there is evidence that the rat can form deoxyribonucleotides from ribonucleotides (29). N^{15}-labeled cytidine and uridine (ribonucleosides) are utilized by the rat to form both ribonucleic acid (RNA) and deoxyribonucleic acid (DNA). Free cytosine and uracil, however, are used very poorly, or not at all, for the synthesis of pyrimidine nucleotides in nucleic acids (10,30,31). It appears, therefore, that the ribonucleosides cytosine and uridine are incorporated into the nucleic acids without rupture of the pyrimidine-ribose linkage. Since the pyrimidines are also bound to deoxyribose in the DNA formed, it appears that the deoxyribonucleotides must be formed by reduction of the ribonucleotides bound in the RNA without rupture of the pyrimidine-ribose bond. That this is the case was proved by Rose and Schweigert (32), who injected cytidine-C^{14} labeled in both the pyrimidine and ribose groups into rats and found the ratio of the specific activities in the pyrimidine and deoxyribose of the DNA formed to be the same as the specific activities of the pyrimidine and ribose groups of the injected cytidine. These results have been confirmed with cytidylic acid, uridylic acid, and uridine (19).

The formation of deoxyribonucleotides from ribonucleotides by reduction, etc., may be grossly represented as follows (14):

Guanosine-5'-phosphate $\xrightarrow{+2H}$ Deoxyguanosine-5'-phosphate

Adenosine-5'-phosphate $\xrightarrow{+2H}$ Deoxyadenosine-5'-phosphate

Uridine-5'-phosphate $\xrightarrow{+2H}$ Deoxyuridine-5'-phosphate $\longrightarrow$ Thymidine-5'-phosphate

$\downarrow +NH_3$ $\qquad\qquad\qquad$ $\downarrow +NH_3$

Cytidine-5'-phosphate $\xrightarrow{+2H}$ Deoxycytidine-5'-phosphate $\longrightarrow$ Methyldeoxycytidine-5'-phosphate

SYNTHESIS OF NUCLEIC ACIDS

The synthesis of nucleic acids has been reviewed by Kornberg (14), Heppel and Rabinowitz (33), and Hartman and Buchanan (13).

Ribonucleic acid synthesis. Ochoa and associates found in *Azotobacter vinelandii* an enzyme, polynucleotide phosphorylase, which reversibly converts 5'-nucleoside diphosphates (nucleoside pyrophosphates) to polynucleotides (34). The reaction was also demonstrated by Kornberg and associates using an enzyme preparation from *E. coli* (14). Such enzymes also cause the formation of polymers from ATP and other nucleoside triphosphates but less readily from the diphosphates. The action of polynucleotide phosphorylases on nucleoside diphosphates may be represented by the general equation:

$$n \text{ Nucleoside-PP} \rightleftharpoons (\text{Nucleoside-P})_n + n \text{ Pi}$$

The reaction as shown is reversible and polynucleotides are both broken down and synthesized by the enzymes. Polynucleotides may be formed from single nucleoside diphosphates or mixtures of them. It has been found in many cases that more or less specific polynucleotide primers are essential to start polynucleotide formation. For example, the polymerization of ADP by the enzyme from *A. vinelandii* to form polyadenylic acid (poly-A) has a long initial lag period which is abolished by adding polyadenylic acid but not by adding polyuridylic acid (poly-U). The polymerization of ADP or UDP may be started by adding oligonucleotides (di-, tri-, and tetra-nucleotides) of adenylic acid.

Polynucleotide phosphorylases which form polyribonucleotides have been obtained from yeast as well as bacteria, though little is known about such enzymes in animal tissues. However, it appears that they probably function there also (8).

The polyribonucleotides synthesized by the polynucleotide pyrophosphorylases are often viscous substances of high molecular weight, and are nondialyzable (33). Their particle size may be controlled by variation in the ratio of substrate to enzyme. X-ray diffraction studies of fibers drawn from the polynucleotide mixtures have indicated both two-stranded and three-stranded helical structures.

Deoxyribonucleic acid synthesis. Kornberg and associates (33,35) have obtained from *E. coli* a highly purified polynucleotide pyrophosphorylase enzyme which catalyzes the incorporation of deoxyribonucleoside triphosphates into polynucleotides of high molecular weight. Incorporation of any one of the triphosphates of deoxyadenosine (APPP), deoxyguanosine (GPPP), deoxycytidine (CPPP), or deoxythymidine (TPPP), requires the presence of all four deoxynucleoside triphosphates, and also highly polymerized DNA and Mg^{++}.

In these studies the deoxynucleoside triphosphates were labeled with P^{32}. Kornberg formulates the polymerization reaction as follows:

$$n(TP^{32}PP + CP^{32}PP + GP^{32}PP \mid AP^{32}PP) + DNA \rightleftharpoons DNA - (TP^{32} - CP^{32} - GP^{32} - AP^{02})_n + 4(N)PP$$

The product formed was digested by pancreatic DNAase and yielded dinucleotides possessing the typical 3′,5′-phosphodiester linkages found in tissue DNA. In the ultracentrifuge the material showed the same sedimentation characteristics as natural DNA.

It is uncertain whether the DNA added as primer has nucleotide chains added to it or functions as a template for the formation of new chains. The affinities between the substrates are so great that concentrations of only 10^{-3} M need be used in the reaction.

Inhibition of nucleic acid synthesis. The synthesis of nucleic acids is inhibited by a number of substances which interfere with specific enzymatic reactions. For example, azaserine and 6-diazo-5-keto-L-norleucine inhibit utilization of glutamine in the formation of formylglycinamidine for purine synthesis. Structural analogs of folic acid (pteroylglutamic acid) interfere with formylation reactions involved in purine and pyrimidine synthesis. Several purine derivatives such as 8-azaguanine and 6-mercaptopurine interfere with nucleic acid synthesis, probably through incorporation into the nucleic acids with the formation of abnormal nucleic acids. Pyrimidine structural analogues such as 4-azathymine appear to act similarly.

Because the growth of tumor cells is closely related to the rapid synthesis of both DNA and RNA, much research has been directed toward finding inhibitors of nucleic acid synthesis in tumor cells, of low toxicity to the host, for use in the treatment of human cancers (36). Unfortunately, the toxicity of most substances so far discovered to inhibit tumor growth precludes their successful therapeutic use in patients:

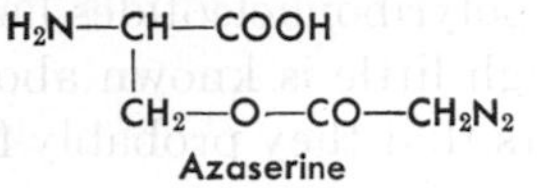

$$H_2N—CH—COOH$$
$$CH_2—O—CO—CH_2N_2$$
Azaserine

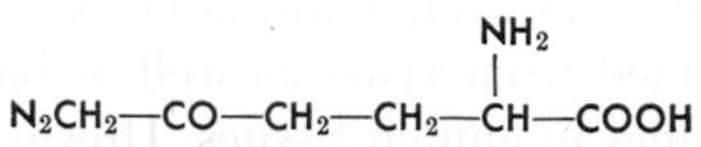

$$NH_2$$
$$N_2CH_2—CO—CH_2—CH_2—CH—COOH$$
6-Diazo-5-keto-L-norleucine

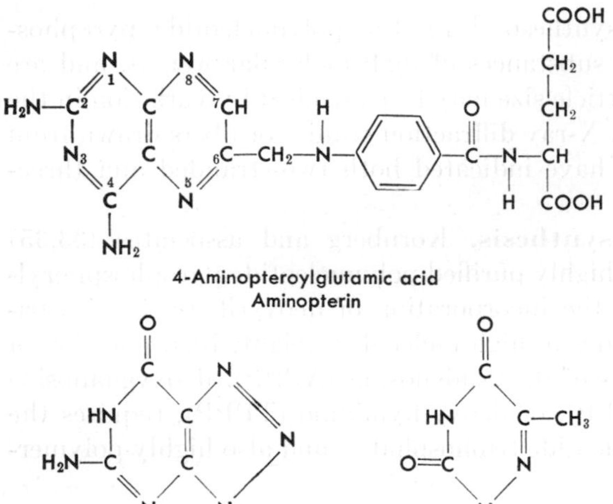

4-Aminopteroylglutamic acid
Aminopterin

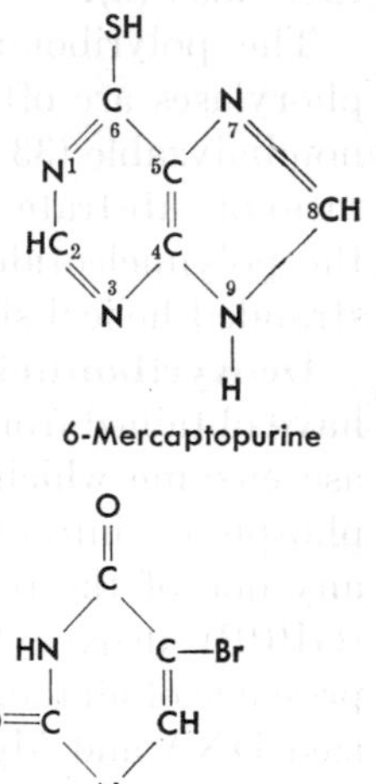

6-Mercaptopurine

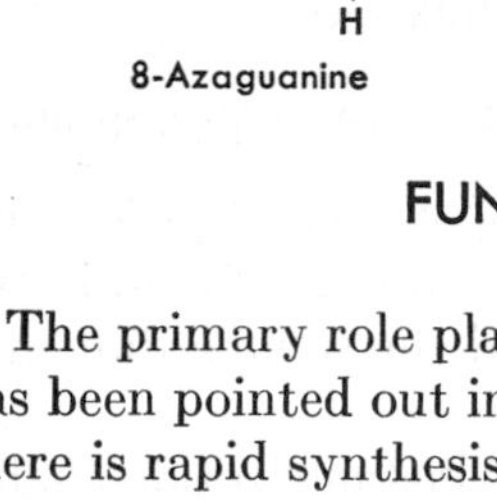

8-Azaguanine

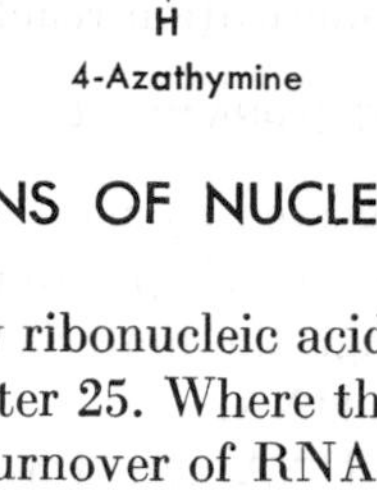

4-Azathymine

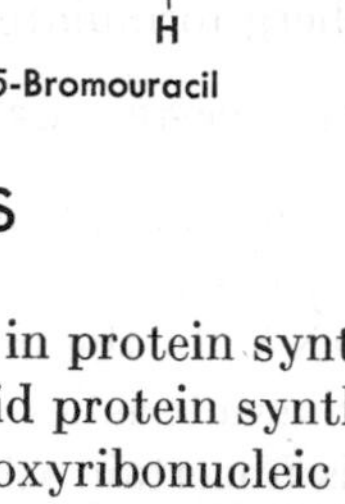

5-Bromouracil

FUNCTIONS OF NUCLEIC ACIDS

The primary role played by ribonucleic acids (RNA) in protein synthesis has been pointed out in Chapter 25. Where there is rapid protein synthesis, there is rapid synthesis and turnover of RNA. That deoxyribonucleic acids (DNA) of the cell nuclear chromosomes in some way carry the genetic information determining the synthesis of proteins by RNA appears well established. This undoubtedly means that in some way DNA controls the kinds of RNA synthesized, which in turn determines the kinds of cytoplasmic proteins synthesized.

That DNA controls protein synthesis in cell nuclei has been demonstrated by Allfrey and Mirski and their associates (37). These investigators isolated thymus nuclei and demonstrated that they incorporated labeled amino acids into nuclear protein. It was also found that treatment of the nuclei with

DNAase, which depolymerized the DNA, decreased protein synthesis in proportion to the loss of DNA. One of the most striking features of this research was that the addition of DNA from various sources as well as alkali denatured DNA and larger split products of DNA to nuclei deprived of DNA by DNAase treatment restored the capacity to incorporate amino acids into protein. RNA, but not its alkali split products, was also effective.

That DNA is closely related to nuclear synthesis of ATP, and to the incorporation of orotic acid into nuclear RNA pyrimidines and of adenosine into nuclear RNA purines, was shown by the above workers. Treatment of the nuclei with DNAase impaired all of these functions.

That the chromosomes of the germ cells are the primary structures concerned with the storage and transmission of hereditary characteristics is subject to no question. Also, deoxyribonucleic acids are the substances in the chromosomal strands most directly involved in these functions.

As pointed out in Chapter 9, it has been shown that for a given species the DNA content of somatic cells (diploid) is constant from tissue to tissue, but that sperm cells (haploid) contain just half as much, which is consonant with genetic mechanisms.

While the turnover rate of RNA is generally rather rapid, metabolic changes in DNA are remarkably slow (38). It appears that the DNA content of chromosomes remains constant during the stages of division, and the structural components of DNA do not equilibrate with extranuclear DNA precursors. Howard and Pelc (39) labeled the chromosomal DNA of *Vicia fabia* roots with P^{32} by growing the plants in the presence of radioactive phosphate. Autoradiographs of the root tips were prepared which showed the incorporation of P^{32} into the nuclei at stages of rest and division. It was found that incorporation of P^{32} (into DNA) took place only in the resting interphase nucleus, and that prophase and metaphase nuclei were not actively synthesizing nucleic acids. It was also found that the labeled nucleic acids of the chromosomes were passed on to the daughter cells without breakdown and resynthesis, showing the metabolic stability of gene structure.

Taylor and associates (40) labeled the DNA of the chromosomes of roots (*Crepis, Bellevalia*) by growing them in the presence of tritium-labeled thymidine, which is incorporated into DNA. The distribution of label in the chromosomes upon division was followed by the preparation of autoradiographs. After the labeled thymidine had been incorporated, the first cell division showed the two daughter chromosomes to be equally labeled. When the labeled chromosomes passed through a first and second duplication after removal of the labeled thymidine, one labeled and one unlabeled daughter cell were formed in the second duplication. In the first duplication in the presence of labeled thymidine each daughter cell received equal amounts of labeled thymidine. However, when these labeled chromosomes divided in the absence of the label, the two units separated and an unlabeled unit was built along each strand. Consequently, in the next duplication a labeled and an unlabeled daughter were produced.

The genetic role of DNA is shown from studies on "transformation" in microorganisms discovered in 1928 by F. Griffith (38). Pneumococci exist in two forms. One form grows as "smooth" colonies on agar plates, possesses a capsule containing a type-specific polysaccharide, and is virulent. The other form grows as "rough" colonies, possesses no capsule or specific polysaccharide, and is nonvirulent. Smooth forms are genetically stable and do not spontaneously mutate to other smooth forms. Smooth organisms, however, do mutate to rough organisms, apparently irreversibly.

Griffith found that when he injected into mice living, nonencapsulated, rough organisms mixed with killed, smooth, encapsulated organisms, he could isolate living, smooth, encapsulated organisms from the animals. These smooth organisms were shown to give rise to smooth organisms through successive generations. It was later shown that the active substance causing the transformation of rough unencapsulated to smooth encapsulated organisms was DNA derived from the killed smooth encapsulated bacteria. This means that the genetic factor controlling the synthesis of capsular material is carried in the DNA molecule. Similar genetic transformations have been carried out with other microorganisms.

There is much evidence which indicates that changes in DNA are associated with mutation, whether caused by irradiation or chemical agents. Zamenhof and associates (41) have shown that incorporation of the thymine analog, 5-bromouracil, into the DNA of a cell greatly increases the frequency of mutation. This effect is probably due in some way to alteration of the chemical structure of DNA, the carrier of genetic information.

The mechanism by which DNA may be synthesized and its structure duplicated according to the Watson-Crick concept has been pointed out in Chapter 9.

SYNTHESIS OF COENZYME NUCLEOTIDES

Diphosphopyridine and triphosphopyridine nucleotides, DPN and TPN (42). ATP phosphorylates nicotinamide mononucleotide (NMN) to DPN, the reaction being catalyzed by DPN pyrophosphorylase:

$$ATP + NMN \rightleftharpoons DPN + PP$$

However, since a pathway for NMN synthesis has not been found it appears that DPN is formed as follows (43):

$$\text{Nicotinic acid} + \text{5-Phosphoribosyl-1-pyrophosphate} \xrightarrow{\text{Enzyme}} \text{Phosphoribosyl-nicotinic acid}$$

Phosphoribosyl-nicotinic acid is converted to desamido-DPN by ATP and the enzyme desamido-DPN pyrophosphorylase:

$$\text{Phosphoribosyl-nicotinic acid} + ATP \rightleftharpoons \text{Desamido-DPN} + PP$$

Desamido-DPN is then aminated to DPN by glutamine and ATP:

$$\text{Desamido-DPN} + \text{Glutamine} + ATP \xrightarrow{\text{Pyrophosphorylase}} DPN + AMP + PP + \text{Glutamic acid}$$

DPN is phosphorylated to TPN by ATP- and DPNkinase.

Flavin adenine dinucleotide, FAD (42). Flavin adenine dinucleotide is synthesized from ATP, riboflavin phosphate, and a specific pyrophosphorylase:

$$
\text{ATP} + \text{Riboflavin-P} \rightleftharpoons \text{Adenosine} - \overset{\overset{O}{\|}}{\underset{\underset{OH}{|}}{P}} - O - \overset{\overset{O}{\|}}{\underset{\underset{OH}{|}}{P}} - \text{riboflavin} + \text{PP}
$$

Flavin adenine dinucleotide (FAD)

Coenzyme A (42). Coenzyme A is synthesized from pantetheine-4-phosphate by the action of ATP and a specific pyrophosphorylase:

$$
\text{Pantetheine-4-phosphate} + \text{ATP} \rightleftharpoons \text{Dephospho-CoA} + \text{PP}
$$
$$
\text{Dephospho-CoA} + \text{ATP} \longrightarrow \text{Coenzyme A} + \text{ADP}
$$

GENERAL REFERENCES

Anfinsen, C. B.: *The Molecular Basis of Evolution*. John Wiley & Sons, New York, 1959.

Buchanan, J. M.: The Enzymatic Synthesis of the Purine Nucleotides, *Harvey Lectures*, Series, 54, 104, 1960.

Buchanan, J. M., and Hartman, S. C.: Enzymatic Reactions in the Synthesis of the Purines, *Advances in Enzymol.*, 21, 199, 1959.

Chantrenne, H.: The Genetic Control of Protein Synthesis, *Ann. Rev. Biochem.*, **27**, 35, 1958.

Chargaff, E., and Davidson, J. N. (eds.): *The Nucleic Acids*, Vols. I and II. Academic Press, New York, 1955.

Kornberg, A.: Pyrophosphorylases and phosphorylases in Biosynthetic Reactions, *Advances in Enzymol.*, **18**, 191, 1957.

McElroy, W. D., and Glass, B (eds.)· *The Chemical Basis of Heredity*. Johns Hopkins Press, Baltimore, 1955.

Reichard, P.: The Enzymic Synthesis of Pyrimidines, *Advances in Enzymol.*, 21, 263, 1959.

Strominger, J. L.: Mononucleotide Acid Anhydrides and Related Compounds as Intermediates in Metabolic Reactions, *Physiol Revs.*, **40**, 55, 1960.

SPECIAL REFERENCES

1. Miescher, F.: *Verhandl., naturforsch. Ges. Basel*, **6**, 138, 1874.
2. Kossel, A.: *Z. physiol. Chem.*, **10**, 248, 1886.
3. Burian, R., and Schur, H.: *Z. physiol. Chem.*, **23**, 55, 1897.
4. Kollmann, G.: *Biochem. Z.*, **123**, 235, 1921.
5. Schmidt, G., in *The Nucleic Acids*, Vol. I, Chap. 15, Chargaff, E., and Davidson, J. N. (eds.). Academic Press, New York, 1955.
6. Kalckar, H. M.: *J. Biol. Chem.*, **158**, 723, 1945; **167**, 477, 1947.
7. Barnes, F. W., Jr., and Schoenheimer, R.: *J. Biol. Chem.*, **151**, 123, 1943.
8. Plentl, A. A., and Schoenheimer, R.: *J. Biol. Chem.*, **153**, 203, 1944.
9. Brown, G. B.: *Cold Spring Harbor Symposia Quant. Biol.*, **13**, 43, 1948. Brown, G. B.; Petermann, M. L.; and Furst, S. S.: *J. Biol. Chem.*, **174**, 1043, 1948. Brown, G. B.; Roll, P. M.; and Plentl, A. A.: *ibid.*, **172**, 469, 1948.
10. Kalckar, H. M., and Rittenberg, D.: *J. Biol. Chem.*, **170**, 455, 1947.
11. Brown, G. B.: *Cold Spring Harbor Symposia Quant. Biol.*, **13**, 48, 1948.
12. Buchanan, J. M.: *Harvey Lectures*, Series 54, 104, 1960.
13. Hartman, S. C., and Buchanan, J. M.: *Ann. Rev. Biochem.*, **28**, 365, 1959. Buchanan, J. M., and Hartman, S. C.: *Advances in Enzymol.*, 21, 199, 1959.
14. Kornberg, A.: Pathways of Enzymatic Synthesis of Nucleotides and Polynucleotides, in *The Chemical Basis of Heredity*, McElroy, W. D., and Glass, B. (eds.). Johns Hopkins Press, Baltimore, 1957.
15. Hartman, S. C., and Buchanan, J. M.: *J. Biol. Chem.*, **233**, 451, 456, 1958.
16. Wyngaarden, J. B., and Stetten, D., Jr.: *J. Biol. Chem.*, **203**, 9, 1953.

17. Brown, G. B.: *Ann. Rev. Biochem.*, **22**, 161, 1953.
18. Folin, O.; Berglund, H.; and Derick, C.: *J. Biol. Chem.*, **60**, 361, 1924.
19. Reichard, P.: *Advances in Enzymol.*, **21**, 263, 1959.
20. Loring, H. S., and Pierce, J. G.: *J. Biol. Chem.*, **153**, 61, 1944. Rogers, H. J.: *Nature*, **153**, 251, 1944. Chattaway, F. W.: *Nature*, **153**, 250, 1944.
21. Reichard, P.: Biosynthesis of Purines and Pyrimidines, Chap. 23 in *The Nucleic Acids*, Chargaff, E., and Davidson, J. N. (eds.). Academic Press, New York, 1955.
22. Reichard, P.: *J. Biol. Chem.*, **197**, 391, 1952.
23. Lieberman, I.: *J. Am. Chem. Soc.*, **77**, 2661, 1955; *J. Biol. Chem.*, **222**, 765, 1956.
24. Friedkin, M., and Kornberg, A., in Chemical Basis of Heredity, McElroy, W. D., and Glass, B., (eds.), p. 609. Johns Hopkins Press, Baltimore, 1957.
25. Jaenicke, L.: *Federation Proc.*, **15**, 281, 1956.
26. Sweet, J. E., and Levene, P. A.: *J. Exptl. Med.*, **9**, 229, 1907.
27. Deuel, H. J., Jr.: *J. Biol. Chem.*, **60**, 749, 1924.
28. Fink, K.: *J. Biol. Chem.*, **218**, 9, 1956. Fink, R. M.; McGaughey, C.; Cline, R. E.; and Fink, K.: *ibid.*, **218**, 1, 1956. Canellakis, E. S.: *ibid.*, **221**, 315, 1956. Fritzson, P., and Pihl, A.: *ibid.*, **226**, 223, 229, 1957.
29. Hammarsten, E.; Reichard, P.; and Saluste, E.: *J. Biol. Chem.*, **183**, 105, 1950.
30. Bendich, A.; Getler, H.; and Brown, G. B.: *J. Biol. Chem.*, **177**, 565, 1949.
31. Rutman, R. J.; Cantarow, A.; and Paschkis, K. E.: *Cancer Research*, **14**, 119, 1954.
32. Rose, I. A., and Schweigert, B. S.: *J. Biol. Chem.*, **202**, 635, 1953.
33. Heppel, L. A., and Rabinowitz, J. C.: *Ann. Rev. Biochem.*, **27**, 613, 1958.
34. Grunberg-Manago, M., and Ochoa, S.: *J. Am. Chem. Soc.*, **77**, 3165, 1955. Grunberg-Manago, M.; Ortiz, P. J.; and Ochoa, S.: *Science*, **122**, 907, 1955; *Biochim. et Biophys. Acta*, **20**, 269, 1956.
35. Kornberg, A.: *Advances in Enzymol.*, **18**, 191, 1957.
36. Rhoads, C. P.: *Antimetabolites and Cancer*. American Association for the Advancement of Science, Washington, D.C., 1955.
37. Allfrey, V., and Mirsky, A. E., in *Subcellular Particles*, Hayashi, T., (ed.), p. 186. Ronald Press, New York, 1959.
38. Anfinsen, C. B.: *The Molecular Basis of Evolution*. John Wiley & Sons, New York, 1959.
39. Howard, A., and Pelc, S. R.: *Exptl. Cell Research*, **2**, 178, 1951.
40. Taylor, J. H., and Woods, P. S., in *Subcellular Particles*, Hayashi, T., (ed.), p. 172. Ronald Press, New York, 1959.
41. Zamenhof, S.: DeGiovanni, R.; and Rich, K. J.: *Bacteriology*, **71**, 60, 1956.
42. Strominger, J. L.: *Physiol. Revs.*, **40**, 55, 1960.
43. Preiss, J., and Handler, P.: *J. Biol. Chem.*, **233**, 488, 493, 1958.

27

Composition and metabolism of specialized tissues

MUSCLE

GENERAL CONSIDERATIONS

Muscle, striated and smooth, represents very highly and specially organized tissue, both morphologically and biochemically, designed for the production of chemical energy and its conversion into mechanical motion and work. Excellent discussions of muscle structure and function are given in the articles by Perry (1).

Most of the biochemical work on striated vertebrate muscle has been done on rabbit skeletal muscle. The biochemistry of smooth muscle has been much less investigated and is less well understood.

The muscle cells of both striated and smooth muscle contain fibrous elements, the myofibrils, which are oriented along the fiber axis and surrounded by the sarcoplasm. Embedded in the sarcoplasm also are the nucleus and sarcosomes, which include mitochondria and granular elements such as are found in other cells. The sarcoplasmic reticulum represents membranous structures of the sarcoplasm, similar to endoplasmic reticulum of other cells.

GENERAL COMPOSITION OF MUSCLE

Table 27.1 gives a number of substances present in fresh mammalian muscle, many of which are present in tissues generally. The composition of muscle and of other tissues varies with nutrition and physiologic state. The

1161

formulas of some of the more unusual organic compounds present are given below:

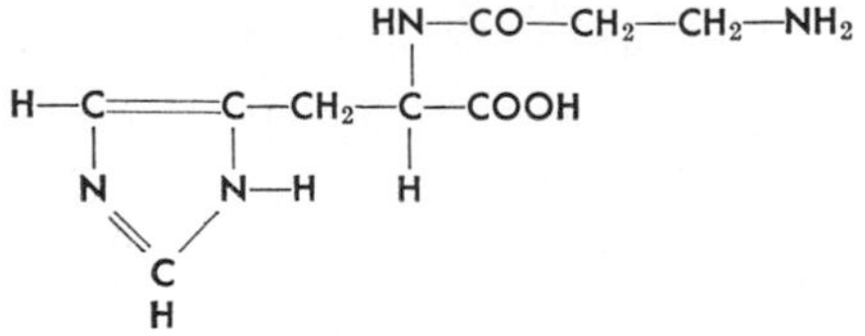

$$HN—CO—CH_2—CH_2—NH_2$$
$$H—C = C—CH_2—C—COOH$$
$$N \quad N—H \quad H$$
$$C$$
$$H$$

β-Alanylhistidine
carnosine

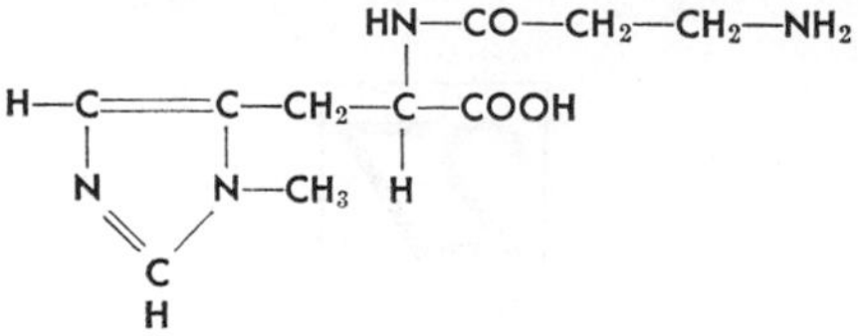

$$HN—CO—CH_2—CH_2—NH_2$$
$$H—C = C—CH_2—C—COOH$$
$$N \quad N—CH_3 \quad H$$
$$C$$
$$H$$

Methylcarnosine
anserine

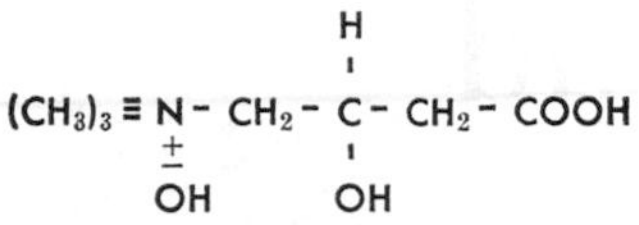

$$(CH_3)_3 \equiv N — CH_2 — C — CH_2 — COOH$$
$$\overset{+}{} \quad OH \quad OH$$

Carnitine

$$CH_2 — COOH$$
$$H — N — CH_3$$

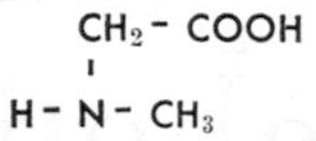

Methylglycine sarcosine

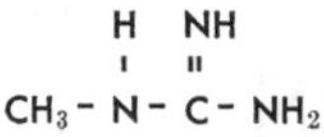

$$CH_3 — N — C — NH_2$$
$$H \quad NH$$

Methylguanidine

$$H_2N — (CH_2)_3 — N — (CH_2)_4 — N — (CH_2)_3 — NH_2$$
$$H \quad H$$

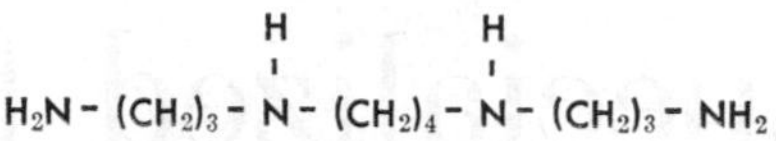

Spermine

Spermine is found in many tissues as the phosphate (1 to 30 mg per cent), in human semen (90 to 200 mg per cent), and in human prostate (130 mg per cent).

STRUCTURES OF MUSCLE

Myofibrils. A great amount of evidence indicates that the myofibrils represent the contractile units of striated muscle, while much less evidence and analogy with striated muscle make it most likely that the myofibrils are also the contractile units of smooth muscle.

The myofibrils of skeletal muscle are cross-striated by the A and I bands as shown in the diagram of Figure 27.1. The A band is the wider of the bands and contains the H disc with the M line. The narrower I band contains the N and Z lines. The A bands are strongly birefringent (anisotropic), apparently due to the high concentration of myosin in them, while the I bands are only weakly birefringent (isotropic). The diameter of skeletal muscle myofibrils generally is within the range 0.5–2.0 μ.

Huxley (2) from his studies on the myofibrils of rabbit skeletal muscle concludes that they are made up of two types of filament, the A and I filaments. The A filaments, diameter 110 Å, pass continuously throughout the A band, and thicken to 140 Å in the H space. The I band is made up exclusively of filaments, diameter 40 Å, which pass continuously into the A band up to the edge of the H space. Where the A and I filaments overlap in the A band, they constitute a twofold hexagonal arrangement (Figure 27.2).

The sarcomere represents a complete functional segment of a myofibril, such as the region between the centers of two I bands. The sarcomere of rabbit skeletal muscle is 2.5 μ long at rest, of which the I band material makes up 1.0 and the A band 1.5 μ, the A band thus constituting the greater proportion of the sarcomere.

Smooth muscle myofilaments do not exhibit the longitudinal periodicity or cross striations of skeletal and heart muscle myofibrils, and show wide variation in diameter from the same tissue (100–200 Å in human and rat uterine muscle). The myofilaments of smooth muscle do not appear to be organized into well-defined bundles, but are distributed throughout the

Table 27.1. Some Substances Present in Fresh Mammalian Muscle
Values Are Approximate

Substance	Per Cent	Substance	Per Cent
Water	75	Hypoxanthine	0.005
		Inosinic acid	0.01
Solids	25	Methylguanidine	0.005
		Sarcosine	+
Proteins	20	Spermine	+
		Taurine	0.07
Stroma proteins, insoluble	4	Thiamine (vitamin B₁)	0.00002
Intracellular proteins,		Urea, frog muscle	0.01
soluble	16		
Myoglobin, muscle		Non-nitrogenous extractives	
hemoglobin	0.15	Acetoacetic acid	+
Flavoproteins	+	Ascorbic acid (vitamin C)	0.004
Cytochromes	+	Citric acid	+
Enzymes, various	+	Ethyl alcohol	0.00003
		Fumaric acid	+
Lipids		Glucose	0.05
Phospholipids	2	Hexose phosphate	0.06
Cerebrosides	1	β-Hydroxybutyric acid	+
Cholesterol, free and ester	1	Inositol	0.02
Neutral fat	1	α-Ketoglutaric acid	+
Glycogen, widely variable	0.5–1.8	Lactic acid, highly variable	
		with activity	
Nitrogenous extractives		Succinic acid	0.02
Acetylcholine	+		
Adenosine triphosphate		Inorganic constituents	
(ATP)	0.37	Calcium	0.007
Adenylic acid	+	Magnesium	0.02
Amino acids, free	0.3	Potassium	0.32
Anserine	0.4	Sodium	0.08
Carnitine	0.02	Iron	0.004
Carnosine	0.1	Cobalt	+
Coenzymes I and II		Copper	+
Diphosphopyridine		Nickel	+
nucleotide (DPN)	+	Zinc	+
Triphosphopyridine		Manganese	+
nucleotide (TPN)	+	Chlorine	0.06
Creatine phosphate +		Phosphorus, total	0.2
creatine	0.5	Phosphorus, as phosphate	0.15
Creatinine	0.02	Phosphorus, organic	0.05
Glutathione	0.05	Sulfur, chiefly in proteins	0.2
Histamine	+	Sulfate	+

whole cell as a single loose bundle within which there are clefts of different size containing sarcoplasm, the nucleus, mitochondria, and other sarcosomes. The myofilaments are not aligned strictly parallel to one another as in striated muscle, and cross sections do not show the regular hexagonal pattern characteristic of striated muscle.

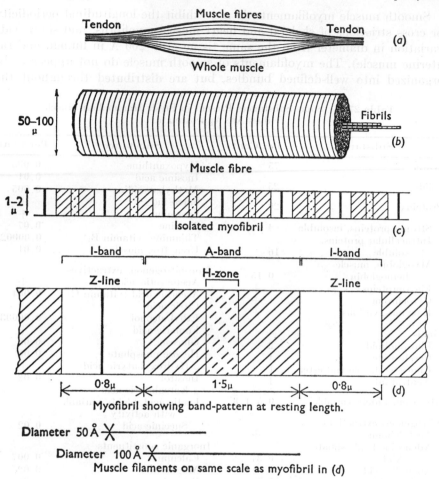

Figure 27.1. The structure of muscle at different levels of organization; dimensions shown are those for rabbit psoas muscle. (From Huxley, H. E.: *Endeavour*, **15**, 177, 1956.)

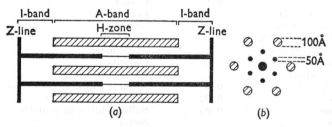

Figure 27.2. Diagrammatic representation of arrangement of filaments in striated muscle: (a) longitudinal, (b) sectional. (From Huxley, H. E.: *Endeavour*, **15**, 177, 1956.)

While smooth muscle exhibits spontaneous activity, skeletal striated muscle does not. Cardiac muscle of vertebrates, while showing myofibrillar striation similar to that of skeletal muscle, is built into a syncytium and shows spontaneous activity. Thus heart muscle, morphologically and functionally, lies somewhere between skeletal and smooth muscle.

While the myofibrils of skeletal muscle, irrespective of source, are practically identical in appearance, histologic differences have been observed leading to the identification of two types of striated muscle cell, known as the red and white fibers. Both types are found in all muscles of the majority of animals, including man, each muscle being characterized by the predominant type. The rabbit is peculiar in that its muscles generally are made up of only the red or white fibers, giving rise to patently red or white muscles.

There are certain functional differences between white and red muscle. White muscle reacts more quickly to stimulus than does red muscle, and is capable of short periods of intense activity, but it fatigues more rapidly than does red muscle. In general, muscles which contract slowly and repetitively, such as heart muscle and vertebrate postural muscles, are red; however, not all red muscles are slow, as in the case of flight muscles of birds and insects.

Red muscles generally are capable of sustained activity, and they have a higher rate of oxygen utilization than do white muscles, which correlates with their relative content of more and larger mitochondria, more myoglobin, and more cytochrome and succinic oxidase activities. The color of red muscles is due to their contents of myoglobin and cytochromes.

White muscle, in contrast to red, generally contains larger high-energy phosphate reserves and higher capacity to derive energy from glycolytic reactions, accounting for its quick response with much energy for a short period of time. White muscle is organized to yield much energy (ATP) quickly by anaerobic processes, while red muscle is more dependent upon the continuous production of energy (ATP) through mitochondrial oxidative phosphorylation reactions.

It is of some interest that white muscle contains large amounts of the dipeptide anserine while red muscle contains little or none (3). Davey (4) considers that the high concentration of anserine in white muscle, where glycolytic activity and acid production are high, serves as a buffer to counteract large changes of pH in the muscle.

Sarcolemma. The sarcolemma, which covers muscle fibers, consists of an outer layer of reticular fibers closely adhering to an inner membrane built up of granular material and a network of fine filaments about 100 Å in diameter. The filaments apparently are not collagenous.

The sarcolemma is attached at its inner surface to the Z line of the myofibrils, and possibly at other sites, such as the M line. The outer reticular fibers of the sarcolemma are arranged in whorls and apparently are collagenous, which would explain its stretchability.

The sarcolemma is polarized (100 mv, outside positive), as are cell membranes in general, and stimulation to contraction is associated with depolarization. Huxley and Taylor (5) have obtained evidence that the influence of depolarization leading to contraction is passed to the myofibrils from the sarcolemma at the Z line attachment.

The permeability of the sarcolemma to extracellular ions and molecules determines the extent to which these substances enter the muscle. Active transport, such as represented by the sodium pump, takes place through the sarcolemma.

MUSCLE PROTEINS

Proteins of the sarcoplasm. The sarcoplasm, which bathes all of the formed elements of the muscle cell, contains a complex mixture of proteins, chiefly with the properties of albumins, in relatively high concentration. Concentrated sarcoplasm may be obtained by pressing minced muscle which has been permitted to stand for 30 minutes.

Sarcoplasmic proteins may be extracted by buffers of low ionic strength (0.1–0.15) which do not dissolve proteins of the myofibrils. These proteins are referred to collectively as the "myogens," from which have been separated protein fractions such as myogens A and B and globulin X, which, according to later work (6), are mixtures of proteins.

Electrophoretic analysis of sarcoplasmic extracts of rabbit skeletal muscle separated from sarcosomes by high-speed centrifugation has indicated the presence of at least 11 components (7). Only a small beginning has been made on the separation and identification of the sarcoplasmic proteins. Obviously they must include all the enzymes involved in glycolysis, as well as enzymes such as creatine phosphokinase, myokinase, phosphorylase, and adenylic deaminase. Myoglobin also is a protein of the sarcoplasm. In skeletal muscle the sarcoplasmic proteins make up 20–30 per cent of the total muscle protein.

The myofibrils are immersed in the sarcoplasm, from which they obtain substrates required for contraction (such as ATP), and to which the products of the enzymatic reactions associated with contraction diffuse. The evidence indicates no boundary membrane around the myofibrils. Penetration of substances into the myofibrils from the sarcoplasm is determined by charge and molecular size. Thus, inorganic ions, ATP, and creatine phosphate readily penetrate into the myofibril, as does inulin. It appears probable also that small proteins—such as the relaxing factor, which inhibits myosin ATPase—pass into the myofibril.

Presumably the microsomes distributed in the sarcoplasm are responsible for the synthesis of muscle proteins, just as microsomes have the function of synthesizing proteins in the liver. Experiments with labeled glycine (8) indicate that the over-all average turnover rate of muscle protein, including the myofibrillar proteins, is quite slow. However, a protein fraction present in low concentration, possibly the microsomal protein, has a relatively high turnover rate.

Proteins of the myofibrils. Proteins make up 90 to 95 per cent of rabbit myofibrillar solids, while small amounts of lipids, nucleic acids, and inorganic salts amount to 4 to 7 per cent.

The well-established proteins of the myofibril are myosin, actin, and tropomyosin, the actin and myosin generally being associated more or less into a complex, actomyosin, from which actin and myosin may be separated.

The dry rabbit myofibril contains approximately the following percentages of the above proteins: myosin, 50–55; actin, 20–25; tropomyosin, 10–15.

Various other proteins, lipids, etc., constitute 5 to 10 per cent of the dry myofibril.

The contractility of muscle is based upon the unique properties and morphologic arrangements of the myofibrillar proteins.

Proteins of the myofibril are generally extracted and separated by the use of solutions of salts (such as KCl and LiCl) of different ionic strengths, which may contain buffers or other substances.

Table 27.2.   Chief Proteins of the Myofibril

Muscle	Protein	Sed. Constant (10^{-13})	Diffusion Constant $(10^{-7}$ cm.^{2} sec.$^{-1})$	Mol. Wt.	Molecular Shape
Rabbit, skeletal	Actin G	2.7–4.0	2.5	120,000–150,000 (dimer)	24 × 590 Å
Rabbit, skeletal	Actin F	50–65			
Cod, skeletal	Actin G	1.0	2.3	160,000 (dimer)	Axial ratio 25
Rabbit, skeletal	L-Myosin	7.1	0.87	840,000 (dimer)	23 × 2300 Å
Dog, heart	L-Myosin	3.5–4.9		100,000	Frictional ratio 1.2
Rabbit, skeletal	H-Meromyosin*			232,000	
Rabbit, skeletal	L-Meromyosin*			96,000	
Rabbit, skeletal	Tropomyosin	2.6	2.4	53,000	
Pig, heart	Tropomyosin			89,000	

* Formed by brief action of trypsin on L-myosin. L-Myosin appears to be composed of two L-meromyosin groups and one H-meromyosin group joined by peptide bonds giving a molecular weight (monomer) of 424,000. The L-myosin of the table (dimer) represents association of two monomer units.

1. L-Myosin. The term "L-myosin" is used in reference to "actin-free" myosin (9).

Myosin appears to make up most of the protein of the myofibrillar A band. When rigor mortis muscle is extracted with 0.53 M KCl containing 0.01 M sodium pyrophosphate at pH 6.5, the A band disappears and myosin free from actin is obtained (10).

Rabbit L-myosin gives clear viscous solutions in the presence of neutral salts such as KCl (0.3 M), and precipitates to form gels when the solutions are diluted. When the myosin gel is washed to remove electrolytes, it swells due to the Donnan effect and passes into a pseudosol state.

The myosin molecule is very asymmetric, representing a structure about 2300 Å long and 23 Å in diameter. It appears that the true minimum molecular weight of myosin is about 420,000, but that two of the smaller molecules may associate into a dimer with a molecular weight of 840,000.

Myosin has the enzymatic property of an ATPase and splits ATP into ADP and inorganic phosphate.

Rabbit skeletal L-myosin is split by trypsin and chymotrypsin into one molecule of H-meromyosin (mol. wt. 232,000) and two molecules of L-meromyosin (mol. wt. 96,000) (9), whose combined molecular weights represent the molecular weight of the L-myosin molecule (monomer).

The L-myosin properties of combining with actin and enzymatically splitting ATP are exhibited by H-meromyosin but not by L-meromyosin.

Apparently only the meromyosins from rabbit muscle have been reported.

Tsao (11) has broken up myosin into subunits by treatment with concentrated urea solution, which does not break peptide bonds. These subunits, which are organized into the myosin molecule, apparently represent cyclic polypeptides, since no terminal amino acid group could be found. The subunits did not combine with actin or show ATPase activity.

2. Actin. The method developed by Straub and Feuer (12) for the extraction of actin from rabbit muscle is based upon an initial extraction of some of the myosin, then dehydration of the tissue with an organic solvent, such as acetone, and finally extraction of actin with water. The clear actin solutions of low viscosity contain globular or G-actin. When salts are added to these solutions, they become very viscous, apparently due to polymerization of the G-actin to fibrous or F-actin. This polymerization is dependent upon free —SH groups of G-actin, and the presence of small amounts of a divalent ion such as Mg^{++} or Ca^{++}. F-actin is depolymerized to G-actin by KI, and chelating agents such as ethylenediaminetetraacetate and hexametaphosphate, which bind the bivalent ion. Molecular weights for such actin have been obtained varying from 70,000 to 150,000.

It appears that G-actin occurs as the monomer (mol. wt. 70,000), and also as the dimer (mol. wt. 140,000) consisting of two monomer units combined through a divalent ion such as Mg^{++} or Ca^{++} (9), and that F-actin is formed by polymerization of the G-actin dimer.

It is interesting that G-actin preparations always contain small quantities of bound nucleotide, chiefly ATP, which is dephosphorylated to ADP when G-actin is converted to F-actin.

Direct extraction experiments appear to indicate that actin is largely concentrated in the I band of the myofibril (9). However, appreciable quantities are also present in the A band.

3. Actomyosin. Actin and myosin undergo a specific type of interaction with the production of actomyosin. Also, actomyosin of variable purity may be extracted directly from muscle.

The combination of actin and myosin to form actomyosin requires the free —SH groups of myosin but appears not to involve the —SH groups of actin.

Actomyosin dissolves in KCl solutions stronger than 0.3 M at pH 7. Such solutions are very viscous but show a marked fall in viscosity upon the addition of ATP. The ATP is then hydrolyzed by the ATPase activity of the myosin component.

Evidence indicates that the action of ATP upon actomyosin causes dissociation into actin and myosin (13), which causes the decrease in viscosity. Upon subsequent hydrolysis of ATP, the actin and myosin recombine to form actomyosin, which causes the viscosity to increase.

Dilution of the KCl solution of actomyosin to a KCl concentration of around 0.05 M at pH 7 causes precipitation of a gel, which in the presence of low concentrations of Mg^{++} or Ca^{++} synereses or contracts upon the addition of ATP, the water content of the gel dropping from 97–98 per cent to around 50 per cent. The particles decrease in size, increase in density, and rapidly settle out, giving rise to the phenomenon known as "superprecipitation."

If a solution of actomyosin in 0.3 M KCl is squirted as a fine stream into a very weak salt solution, the actomyosin separates as threads which shorten when ATP is added.

Washed isolated myofibrils undergo pronounced shortening and settle from suspension when ATP is added, the phenomenon resembling the superprecipitation observed with actomyosin solutions.

Glycerated muscle fibers are prepared by placing thin strips of muscle at resting length in 50 per cent glycerol at $-10°$ C for several days. This treatment removes most of the endogenous ATP and some of the sarcoplasmic proteins. It leaves the myofibrillar structures apparently intact. When fiber bundles are teased from such glycerated fibers, they contract violently upon the addition of ATP and in the presence of proper concentrations of ions such as K^+, Ca^{++}, and Mg^{++}. The tensions developed by such fibers approximate those developed by the living muscle fibers from which they were prepared (0.5 kg per square centimeter to 5 kg per square centimeter).

Finally, the application of ATP to resting normal muscle produces contraction.

The precipitation, shortening, and contraction phenomena caused by ATP in the above preparations are associated with hydrolysis of ATP to ADP and inorganic phosphate and the liberation of energy. Thus it has become quite evident that the normal process of muscle contraction must be related to interactions of actin, myosin, and ATP.

4. Tropomyosin. Tropomyosin may be extractd from muscle by the method of Bailey (14). In this method the sarcoplasmic proteins are first extracted, and the fibers are dried and then extracted with M KCl. The tropomyosin is precipitated in the range of 40–70 per cent saturation of the extract with ammonium sulfate. Other methods of preparation have been used (9), and tropomyosins associated with nucleic acid (usually RNA) have been obtained, called "nucleotropomyosin." These complexes may represent artifacts formed during the process of extraction.

Evidence indicates that tropomyosin is concentrated along with actin in the I band of the myofibril (15).

The tropomyosin of rabbit skeletal muscle has been most studied. It forms highly polymerized viscous solutions at neutral pH in the absence of electrolytes and is reversibly depolymerized by salts. It crystallizes relatively easily as plates and is the only muscle protein which has been crystallized in the true sense. It is resistant to denaturation by organic solvents and acids.

The monomer unit of tropomyosin has a molecular weight of about 50,000 at high ionic strengths, at pH values around 2 and 12, and in strong urea solutions. It has an axial ratio greater than 20 and apparently has its charge distributed so that one end is positive and the other negative, facilitating end-to-end aggregation.

5. Other proteins of the myofibril. Several proteins other than those mentioned above have recently been obtained from the myofibrils in small amounts (9). Some of these protein fractions, while associated with the major myofibrillar proteins in extracts, may not be present as such in the myofibrils, but represent sarcoplasmic contaminants. Some have been shown to represent mixtures. These minor protein fractions have been known by such names as "component C," "delta-protein," "metamyosin," "contractin," "X-protein," and "Y-protein." Little is known as to their properties or functions.

Gitlin and associates (16) have reported evidence that the myoalbumin of muscle is identical with serum albumin and is not formed by the muscle cell, but is a component of muscle interstitial fluid. These workers also identified a muscle globulin as being the same as serum γ-globulin. Thus, it appears that a considerable proportion of the soluble protein extracted from muscle represents plasma proteins present in muscle interstitial fluid.

NUCLEOTIDES OF MUSCLE

Most of the muscle nucleotide is represented by ATP and ADP, and the major proportion of the ATP is in the sarcoplasm, originating through oxidative phosphorylation in the mitochondria, and through the processes of anaerobic glycolysis. Other nucleoside triphosphates—such as inosine triphosphate (ITP), guanosine triphosphate (GTP), and uridine triphosphate (UTP)—are present in small amounts.

Well-washed myofibrils of rabbit skeletal muscle contain bound adenosine phosphates of which 70 to 80 per cent is ADP. This bound nucleotide ranges from 9 to 14 mg of acid-labile P per 100 g of myofibrils isolated from skeletal and cardiac muscle of the rabbit and skeletal muscle of the rat. Evidence indicates that the bound nucleotide is concentrated in the I band of resting muscle, and presumably it is attached to the actin component. It is of interest that *in vitro* the ADP bound to the myofibril is not catalyzed to react by myokinase and is not converted to ATP by creatine phosphate and creatine phosphokinase. It thus is not available for reaction, as is the ADP of the sarcoplasm, and must play an important structural role in the myofibril.

It is unknown whether or not the bound ADP is completely phosphorylated to ATP in the contraction-relaxation cycle.

ENZYMES OF THE MYOFIBRILS

L-Myosin ATPase. As previously indicated, the myofibrillar protein L-myosin is an ATPase, which catalyzes the hydrolysis of ATP:

$$ATP + H_2O \longrightarrow ADP + Pi \text{ (inorganic phosphate)}$$

Myosin also hydrolyzes other nucleoside triphosphates, such as ITP, UTP, and GTP, small amounts of which are associated with ATP in muscle and other tissues. Myosin contains free —SH groups which are essential for its ATPase activity.

Preparations of L-myosin ATPase are activated by Ca^{++}, and this activation is strongly inhibited by Mg^{++}. However, the evidence indicates that *in situ* in the myofibril myosin ATPase is strongly activated by both magnesium and calcium. Magnesium is significantly related to the contraction-relaxation cycle of muscle. It is necessary for the optimum contraction of both glycerated fibers and isolated myofibrils when they are treated with ATP. Magnesium also is essential for muscle relaxation. While myofibrillar ATPase is activated by Ca^{++}, contraction does not occur in the absence of Mg^{++}.

It is of interest that the active ATPase centers of L-myosin appear to be also the active centers at which myosin combines with actin to form actomyosin (6).

Myokinase. The enzyme myokinase is closely associated with myosin ATPase in the myofibril, and sarcoplasm is rich in the enzyme. It acts upon ADP to form AMP and ATP:

$$2ADP \rightleftarrows AMP + ATP$$

Nucleoside diphosphokinase or "nudiki." This enzyme is widely distributed in muscle and other tissues. It catalyzes the reversible transfer of phosphate from the triphosphate of one nucleoside to the diphosphate of another nucleoside:

$$ATP + UDP \rightleftarrows UTP + ADP$$
$$ATP + GDP \rightleftarrows GTP + ADP$$
$$ATP + IDP \rightleftarrows ITP + ADP$$

and thereby renders available the free energy of all of the nucleoside triphosphates through any one of them.

Myosin and actomyosin solutions catalyze the exchange of phosphate between ADP and ATP, as shown by isotopic experiments (6):

$$ADP^{32} + ATP \rightleftharpoons ADP + ATP^{32}$$

The reaction is probably catalyzed by nucleoside diphosphokinase, and may be of importance in the rephosphorylation of ADP bound to the myofibril, converting it to ATP.

Adenylic deaminase. This enzyme is present in muscle sarcoplasm, and much may also be firmly associated with the myofibril. It hydrolyzes the amino group from adenylic acid, replacing it with a hydroxyl group. The products are inosinic acid and ammonia:

$$\underset{\text{AMP}}{\text{Adenylic acid}} + H_2O \longrightarrow \text{Inosinic acid} + NH_3$$

The function of the enzyme in muscle operation is not clear. It has been suggested that it prevents the escape of AMP from muscle to the blood, where it has powerful action on the heart and other organs. Another suggestion is that it supplies NH_3 to help decrease the acidity due to the large accumulation of lactic acid in prolonged muscular activity.

Sarcoplasmic or granular ATPase. This enzyme has been isolated from rabbit muscle and shown to differ from myosin in physical, and to some extent enzymatic, properties. It appears to be associated with sarcoplasmic granules, such as mitochondria and microsomes. It, like myosin ATPase, is inhibited by agents which react with and block —SH groups such as compounds of mercury. Granular ATPase has a broader substrate specificity than does myosin; in addition to hydrolyzing ATP, it slowly hydrolyzes ADP.

MUSCLE ENERGY

The over-all energy for muscle activity is provided as ATP and is formed by: (a) anaerobic glycolysis taking place in the soluble sarcoplasm, leading to the breakdown of glucose and glycogen to pyruvic and lactic acids, and (b) oxidation of lactic acid to pyruvic acid and further oxidation of pyruvate via acetyl–CoA in the tricarboxylic acid cycle by the mitochondria. Oxidation of fatty acids (β oxidation and oxidation of acetyl–S–CoA by the TCA cycle in mitochondria) also contributes to the ATP supply of muscle.

ATP in excess of immediate needs reacts with creatine under the catalytic action of creatine phosphokinase to form creatine phosphate:

$$\text{Creatine} + ATP \rightleftharpoons \text{Creatine} - P + ADP$$

The reaction is freely reversible, and during activity the ATP concentration is maintained at the expense of the creatine phosphate store.

Thus, all of the muscle ATP is formed in the sarcoplasm, but it provides energy for both myofibrillar and sarcoplasmic processes.

Figure 27.3 shows the over-all metabolic processes by which muscle obtains energy as ATP for the performance of work. The same processes, of course, operate for other tissues also.

Processes which lead to the breakdown of ATP in muscle with the liberation of energy are: (a) the contraction-relaxation cycle; (b) a great many synthetic reactions, such as synthesis of peptides and proteins, CO_2 fixation, formation of glycogen, and various key metabolic intermediates; (c) secretory processes of the cell, active transport, and polarization of the sarcolemma; (d) hydrolysis by myosin ATPase in the myofibril, and by granular ATPase in the sarcoplasm.

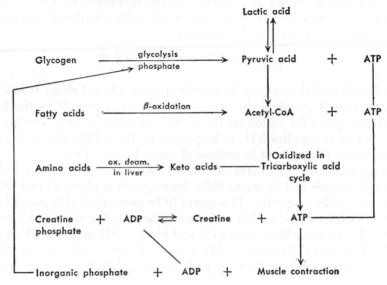

Figure 27.3.   Energy production in muscle.

MUSCLE CONTRACTION

The activity of muscle is associated with shortening of the myofibrils in the contraction phase and lengthening in the relaxation phase. ATP applied to *in vitro* models or *in vivo* causes contraction (discussed previously) and inorganic phosphate increases, though in living muscle a decrease in ATP may not be demonstrable, probably because of the rapid rephosphorylation of ADP to ATP.

Perry points out (9) that the experimental evidence is in agreement with the concept that ATP is hydrolyzed to ADP and inorganic phosphate whenever contraction occurs, but that it is as yet uncertain as to whether the transfer of energy to the myofibrils takes place during the binding of ATP to the myofibrils or when the ATP is hydrolyzed. Chance and Connelly (17) have demonstrated an increase in ADP after a single twitch of the perfused frog sartorius muscle, and progressive increase with repeated stimulation. Thus it appears established that ATP provides the energy for muscle contraction. However, the possibility that some high-energy phosphate other than ATP, which is maintained in equilibrium with ATP, may be the immediate source of energy for contraction has not been ruled out.

The facts relative to the contraction process of muscle indicate that the hydrolysis of ATP takes place whenever contraction occurs. If hydrolysis of ATP is prevented by inhibiting myosin ATPase with a substance such as salyrgan, contraction does not occur, but added ATP under these conditions causes relaxation.

The relaxation of muscle appears to be due to what Gergeley (18) calls the relaxing factor system (RFS). RFS consists of sarcoplasmic granules and a soluble, dialyzable cofactor, the exact nature of which is as yet unknown. RFS in the presence of Mg^{++} and the proper concentration of ATP inhibits the actomyosin ATPase of the myofibrils. The activity of RFS is strongly inhibited by Ca^{++} and also carnosine. It is very interesting that pyridoxal phosphate, just as RFS, inhibits myofibrillar ATPase; in fact, it has effects resembling those of the complete RFS. Carnosine also inhibits the action of pyridoxal phosphate. Parker and Gergeley (19) showed that incubation of granules, ATP, and cofactor formed a nonprotein substance (relaxing substance) having the effects of the complete relaxing system. Whether the active relaxing substance produced may be pyridoxal phosphate or some other phosphate is as yet unknown, though the requirement for ATP in forming the relaxing substance seems to suggest that such may be the case.

According to the present view, then, muscle relaxation appears to be caused by a relaxing substance formed by the relaxing factor system. This substance inhibits the actomyosin ATPase of the myofibrils and permits a concentration of ATP to be built up on the myofibrils which causes relaxation, presumably by dissociation of actomyosin into its components actin and myosin.

In the unstimulated muscle with high ATP concentration (which in itself inhibits myosin ATPase), the proper Mg^{++}, Ca^{++}, and K^+ concentrations, and the presence of relaxing substance, the myosin ATPase does not hydrolyze ATP and the muscle is relaxed. Upon stimulation, the balance of ions and other components of the myofibrils is disturbed, putting the relaxing substance out of action; the myosin ATPase hydrolyzes ATP and the muscle contracts. After stimulation and contraction, the ionic balance, etc., is restored, ATPase activity is inhibited by the relaxing substance, and the ATP concentration increases and causes relaxation. Thus contraction is dependent upon hydrolysis of ATP, while relaxation is caused by the action of ATP upon the myofibrils without hydrolysis.

It may be that the carnosine of muscle plays a role in inhibiting and controlling the action of the relaxing factor system, because Hayashi (20) found that intracellular injection of carnosine causes muscular contraction.

The path of muscle research is strewn with discarded theories as to how the interactions of myosin and actin (actomyosin), ATP, and inorganic ions operate in the contraction-relaxation cycle. These mechanisms are discussed by Perry (9) and Wilkie (21).

Two main types of mechanism have been suggested to explain the shortening and relaxation of the myofibrils, the folding and sliding theories.

One folding theory considers that the myofibril is kept extended (relaxed) by electrostatic positive charges distributed along its length. Morales and associates postulate that negatively charged ATP neutralizes these charges and permits the myofibrillar elements to fold and shorten. The ATP is then hydrolyzed and released from the charged points, which then cause re-extension (relaxation).

Weber considers that the myofibril is phosphorylated by ATP at certain points, A, along the fiber, and that the phosphate groups at A form bonds with groups at B further along the fiber, thus drawing the A and B points toward each other all along the fiber, thereby causing shortening. The phosphate groups at A then split out as inorganic phosphate, and the muscle relaxes.

Huxley and Hanson (22), from electron microscope studies on isolated myofibrils contracted with ATP, proposed a sliding mechanism. The theory is based upon the changes in the A bands (myosin rich) and I bands (actin and tropomyosin, nucleotide rich) which take place on contraction and relaxation. According to this theory, upon contraction, the I band filaments which run continuously into the A bands and between the A filaments slide deeper into the A band and cause disappearance of the H space (see Figure 27.2). Upon further contraction (around 60 per cent), the I band disappears as the I filaments are drawn into the A band, presumably with folding, until the Z lines are close to the outside edges of the A band. Relaxation consists of the sliding of the I filaments out from between the A filaments to the edge of the H space. The changes causing I filaments to be pulled in between the A filaments in contraction and to slide out in relaxation are supposed to be related in some way to the action and hydrolysis of ATP. Various theories have been proposed for the manner in which ATP acts, but since none are established, they will not be considered here.

The sliding theory explains the contraction of striated muscle down to 60 per cent of its length, in which the myosin or A bands are not shortened. However, *in vitro* the myofibrils can shorten to 20 to 25 per cent of their original length, under which conditions the A band filaments (myosin) must shorten. The theory is not generally applicable to smooth muscle, since the two-filament system appears to be absent in some smooth muscle and, when present, both filament systems appear to be continuous. Smooth muscle contraction, accordingly, must involve filament folding.

Much work remains to be done in order to clarify the mechanisms involved in muscular contraction.

RIGOR MORTIS

Rigor mortis is the stiffening of muscles that occurs after death; it is associated with the fall in ATP level as the rate of breakdown of ATP by muscle ATPase exceeds the rate of ATP synthesis. A decrease in creatine phosphate is first observed, due to its utilization in maintenance of the ATP level. The ATP level begins to fall when about 70 per cent of the creatine phosphate has been hydrolyzed, the signs of rigor appear when the ATP level has fallen to 85 per cent of its initial value, and it is practically complete when the ATP has fallen to 15 per cent of this value (23).

Rigor is associated with a decrease in extractability of myosin by KCl and phosphate solutions, undoubtedly due to combination of actin and myosin into the less soluble complex actomyosin. ATP breaks the linkages between actin and myosin and permits relaxation. In the absence of sufficient ATP, the actin and myosin filaments (I and A filaments) become locked together by interaction of the active groups of the proteins, resulting in a partially contracted state, the state of rigor. It appears that factors other than decreased ATP levels may be involved in rigor, but these are imperfectly understood.

It is of interest that the muscles of an animal subjected to severe exercise just prior to death go into rigor much more quickly than the muscles of an unexercised animal. This is due to depletion of ATP reserves in the exercised muscles.

NERVOUS TISSUE

It has been estimated by Donaldson that nervous tissue constitutes about 2.4 per cent of the body weight of man and that the brain alone represents about 2 per cent of the body weight. He gives the following distribution of nervous tissue in the body of a man weighing 68 kg and 68 inches tall.

	Grams
Brain	1,400
Spinal nerves	151
Sympathetic nerves	30
Spinal cord	27
Cranial nerves	12
Total	1,620

Nervous tissue is highly specialized in both function and composition. The German chemist J. L. W. Thudichum laid the foundation of our knowledge of the composition of the brain. His work was published in 1884 in his book entitled *A Treatise on the Chemical Composition of the Brain, Based Throughout on Original Researches*. Thudichum's findings have been supplemented by the later work of W. Koch and various other investigators.

The passage of substances to the brain from the blood is restricted and regulated by the blood-cerebrospinal fluid barrier (Chapter 15) and the blood-brain barrier, which appears to consist of an extra layer of glial cells surrounding the capillaries. These barriers in particular limit the passage of negatively and positively charged ions, both organic and inorganic, from the blood to the brain, as well as the passage of large organic molecules, such as lipids, polypeptides, and polysaccharides.

It is of importance that the blood-brain barrier of persons with brain tumors permits the passage of the dye iodofluoroscein labeled with I^{131} which accumulates in the tumors and thus permits localization of the tumors through radioactivity measurements.

These barriers to the free interchange of substances between blood and brain limit studies of metabolism *in vivo* to a much greater extent than in the case of most other organs. A large proportion of our knowledge relative to brain metabolism of necessity has been obtained by *in vitro* studies on brain preparations.

The limited exchange between blood and brain imposes a greater degree of metabolic autonomy upon brain than is found for most other tissues. As will be seen from following discussion, the composition of brain is very different from the compositions of other tissues, in keeping with its very different function.

The most striking fact about the composition of brain (and nerves) is the large amount of lipid material relative to protein in the brain solids. Brain contains more lipid by far than any other tissue excepting adipose tissue itself. The composition of the different parts of the brain may vary within wide limits. For example, the water content of the gray matter of adult human brain is about 85 per cent, while that of the white matter is only 70 per cent. The white matter thus contains about twice as much solids as the gray matter (30:15 per cent). The water content of brain also varies with age, being highest in young brains. The high solid content of the white matter of brain is largely due to its very great content of lipids. The lipids of brain (and nerves) are chiefly composed of cholesterol, phospholipids, glycolipids (cerebrosides), and sulfolipids or sulfatides. Relatively little neutral fat is present.

The composition of brain varies widely with age. Adult brain contains less water, much more lipid, less protein, less organic extractives, and less mineral material than the brain of a child.

SUBCELLULAR STRUCTURES OF THE NEURONS AND THEIR FUNCTIONS

The neurons represent the fundamental brain cells in which the metabolic activities of the brain are concentrated. The neurone subcellular structures, their composition characteristics, and their functions are outlined below according to McIlwain (24).

1. Nucleus. The nucleus contains nearly all of the DNA of the cell and about a third of the RNA. It also contains cerebroside but little cholesterol. It contains much ATPase. The nucleus contains relatively small quantities of glycolytic and respiratory enzymes, and its utilization of oxygen is small.

2. Nucleolus. The nucleolus contains much RNA, basic protein, and thiamine pyrophosphatase. Increased cellular activity greatly increases the size of the nucleolus.

3. Nucleolus-associated chromatin. This chromatin is within the nucleus and adjoins the nucleolus, which appears to arise from it. In contrast to the nucleolus, this chromatin contains much DNA and also basic protein. Acid phosphatase is present.

4. Chromocentre substances. These substances are associated with the nucleolus of larger neurons and are characterized by their containing basic proteins and small amounts of RNA. These substances increase in quantity after the stimulation of sensory neurons.

5. Mitochondria. The mitochondria contain about half of the cell phospholipids and a fifth of the cellular nitrogen. They contain the organized electron transport systems of the cell and form ATP by oxidative phosphorylation. Both alkaline phosphatase and ATPase contents are high.

6. Microsomes. The microsomes contain much RNA and synthesize a large proportion of brain proteins.

7. Nissl bodies. The Nissl bodies contain RNA and also appear to contain microsomes. Presumably they participate in protein synthesis.

8. Golgi apparatus. The Golgi apparatus is identified by silver staining due to the presence of reducing material. It contains protein and lecithin but not cholesterol.

9. Cytoplasm. The cytoplasm contains the enzymes of glycolysis, phosphokinases, and phosphatases, as well as electrolytes and metabolites. It is the chief site involved in the breakdown of carbohydrate to pyruvate and lactate.

10. Myelin sheath. The myelin sheath contains large amounts of cerebrosides, sphingomyelin, and cholesterol. It has the function of serving as insulation and is metabolically relatively inactive.

BRAIN LIPIDS

The lipids of brain most specific to it are found in the myelin sheath and at cell boundaries. Brain cells, the neurons, contain lipids in their subcellular structures, just as do other cells; and some lipids are present in nonneuronal components.

The largest proportion of brain lipid is present in the myelin sheath of white matter, where it serves as an electrical insulator and permits rapid ionic conduction of impulses over sections of nerve fibers. Cerebrosides, cholesterol, and sphingomyelin appear to be the chief lipids of the myelin sheath; they increase in quantity in white matter during the myelination period. Plasmalogens also are components of the myelin sheath. The lipid molecules in the myelin sheath of peripheral nerve appear to be oriented to the fiber axis in laminated structures associated with protein molecules (25). The proteolipids may represent a part of these lipid-protein structures.

The lipids of the myelin sheath represent structural rather than metabolic components and, as expected, are metabolically relatively inert—as shown by their greater stability under conditions of metabolic stress, such as starvation and dietary deficiencies. However, breakdown of the myelin sheath structure occurs as the result of damages from various causes, such as anoxia, glucose deprivation, many avitaminoses, mechanical injury, and allergic reactions involving nervous tissue.

Table 27.3 gives the approximate lipid content of the gray and white matter of adult mammalian brain (21). The student will find a discussion of the chemistry of the various types of brain lipids in Chapter 6.

The brain cells apparently synthesize all of their lipid components by processes outlined in Chapter 23. This synthesis must depend upon utilization of products derived from brain carbohydrate metabolism (acetate, glycerol), phosphate, inositol, choline, etc., from the blood supply, and the reutilization of lipid breakdown products.

Brain tissues have been shown to oxidize several fatty acids, but only to

Table 27.3.   Lipid Content of Adult Mammalian Brain

	Approximate Per Cent of Fresh Weight		
Lipid	Whole brain	Gray matter	White matter
Fats	0.6		
Cholesterol esters	0.05		
Cholesterol, free		1.0	4.0
Phospholipids:		3.5	7.4
Phosphatidylcholine		1.0	1.4
Phosphatidylethanolamine		1.3	1.5
Phosphatidylserine		0.5	2.1
Diphosphoinositide		0.2	0.4
Plasmalogens	0.5		
Sphingomyelin		0.5	2.0
Cerebrosides		0.9	4.8
Sulfatides		0.2	1.2
Gangliosides		0.07	0.14
Strandin		0.7	0.07
Proteolipids			2.7
Total lipids		9.87	27.7

a limited extent. Such oxidation can contribute only a very minor fraction of the energy requirements of the brain which are supplied chiefly through carbohydrate metabolism.

BRAIN PROTEINS

Proteins make up about 40 per cent of the dry weight of whole brain and 8 per cent of the weight of whole fresh brain.

The association of brain proteins with much lipid material and the presence of protein-lipid complexes have made the extraction and separation of relatively pure brain proteins a difficult task, most of which remains to be done. Brain proteins have been separated into groups by extraction with different solvents, and six or more apparently distinct proteins have been identified by electrophoresis in extracts. Table 27.4, taken from McIlwain (24), lists protein fractions separated from brain, the types of proteins in the fractions, and their distribution in the brain. Many of the fractions represent overlapping and are poorly defined.

The brain synthesizes proteins according to the processes outlined in Chapter 25. Most of this synthesis takes place in the microsomes.

It has been found that conditions of severe stress cause marked decreases in the cytoplasmic proteins and nucleic acids of the brain cells of guinea pigs, with restoration in 48 hours.

The young unipolar neuroblast, which consists of about two-thirds nucleus, contains much DNA and little RNA. As the cell develops through the various stages to the adult nerve cell, the DNA content remains unchanged while the contents of RNA and protein show parallel increases. These processes agree with the concept that DNA is the primary genetic material which controls the synthesis of RNA, which, in turn, controls protein synthesis.

Table 27.4. Cerebral Proteins

Fraction	Type of protein in fraction	Approximate proportion of the total proteins of whole brain, or of grey and white matter, per cent
Soluble in barbitone, ph 8.6	Two, albumin-like	15
	Three, globulin-like	35
Soluble in saline	Two globulins, nucleoprotein	—
Soluble in 4.5% KCl	Isoelectric point pH 5.6	28 (gray); 24 (white)
Soluble in water	Isoelectric point pH 4.6	30 (gray); 19 (white)
Soluble in water	A phosphoprotein	12
Soluble in dilute alkali	Phosphoprotein	25
Insoluble in water, acid or alkali	—	50
Insoluble in water after treatment with pepsin and trypsin	Neurokeratin	4 (gray); 15 (white)
Insoluble in 0.1 N NaOH at room temperature; soluble on autoclaving with water	Collagen	3.3
Insoluble in 0.1 N NaOH at 100°	Elastin	3.5
Insoluble in water; soluble in chloroform-methanol	Proteolipids	20 (gray); 50 (white)

From McIlwain, H.: *Biochemistry and the Central Nervous System*, 2nd ed. Little, Brown & Co., Boston, 1959.

Porter and Folch (26) have demonstrated a fraction of brain proteins combined with copper, and from it isolated a purified protein, cerebrocuprein I, with a molecular weight of about 35,000 and containing two atoms of copper.

Wilson's disease or hepatolenticular degeneration is a hereditary disease which shows pathologic changes of the liver, kidneys, and central nervous system, the latter being localized especially in the lenticular bodies. The disease is associated with excessive absorption of copper from the intestine, increased urinary excretion of copper, and low levels of plasma copper combined with an α-globulin known as "ceruloplasmin." The level of uncombined plasma copper is high, which apparently permits the observed deposition of excessive amounts of copper in the kidneys, liver, and brain. Presumably the intellectual deterioration associated with Wilson's disease is related to this excess brain copper, and probably to increased protein-bound copper.

Amino acids of brain. The total free amino acid concentration of brain is high relative to that of plasma, being some six times higher in rat brain and eight times higher in human brain than in plasma.

Amino acids are selectively concentrated in brain tissue (24). For example, the concentration of glutamic acid plus glutamine in cat brain is about 200 mg per cent, but in cat plasma it is only about 12 mg per cent. Threonine is about twice as concentrated in cat brain as in plasma (10:5). On the other hand, the group of amino acids represented by leucine, isoleucine, valine, methionine, arginine, lysine, histidine, proline, tryptophane, tyrosine, and phenylalanine is present at a lower concentration in brain (16 mg per cent) than in plasma (27 mg per cent).

The brain contains, compared to plasma, very large amounts of the following amino compounds: γ-aminobutyric acid, aspartic acid, N-acetylaspartic acid, taurine, and glutathione (33, 41, 84, 65 mg per cent, respectively, in cat brain, as compared to 1 mg per cent in plasma).

Marked increases in plasma amino acid concentration due to administering amino acids may cause several-fold increase in the amino acids of muscle, liver, and kidney with no appreciable effect upon brain amino acid concentration.

Table 27.5 gives a comparison of the gross compositions of muscle and brain.

Table 27.5. Approximate Composition of Muscle and Brain

Component	Skeletal muscle, per cent	Whole brain, per cent
Water	75	77 to 78
Inorganic salts	1	1
Soluble organic substances	3 to 5	2
Carbohydrate	1	1
Protein	18 to 20	8
Lipids: Simple fats	1	1
Cholesterol	1	2 to 3
Phosphatides	2	5 to 6
Cerebrosides	1	2

From McIlwain, H.: *Biochemistry and the Central Nervous System*, 2nd ed. Little, Brown & Co., Boston, 1959.

CARBOHYDRATE AND OXYGEN METABOLISM OF BRAIN

Brain exhibits a very high rate of oxygen metabolism, which accounts for some 25 per cent of the total oxygen utilized by the body at rest. The brain tissue of children (mean age 6.2 years) (24) uses about 5 ml O_2 per 100 g per minute, while brain tissue of adult subjects at rest uses about 3.5 ml O_2 per 100 g per minute, in all cases at normal blood sugar levels (about 80 mg per 100 ml). At low blood sugar levels of insulin hypoglycemia (arterial glucose 19 mg per 100 ml) the utilization of O_2 falls to around 2.6 ml per 100 g per minute, and in insulin coma (arterial glucose 9 mg per 100 ml) to 1.9 ml per 100 g per minute.

The respiratory quotient of brain metabolism is very close to unity, indicating that carbohydrate is the predominant oxidative substrate of brain.

Brain contains very little glycogen, about 0.1 per cent, and while this glycogen is quickly broken down and metabolized upon demand, nearly all of the carbohydrate for brain metabolism is supplied by the circulating blood glucose.

Although brain tissue *in vitro* readily oxidizes the compounds of the tricarboxylic acid cycle, and also fructose and various other compounds, these substances are relatively ineffective in restoring brain metabolism in hypoglycemic coma, whereas glucose is highly effective. The failure of substances other than glucose to relieve hypoglycemic coma is probably due to their failure to pass from the blood to the brain in adequate quantities.

Marked decrease in either the O_2 supply to the brain (hypoxia) or the glucose supply to the brain leads to greatly decreased oxidative metabolism, with precipitate decreases in high-energy compounds, such as ATP and creatine phosphate, and large increases in lactic acid and inorganic phosphate. Poisoning with cyanide, which blocks the cytochrome oxidase system, has similar effects.

Agents which produce anesthesia or sleep cause increases in high-energy phosphates and decreases in inorganic phosphate and lactic acid, as well as a decrease in oxygen utilization. This means that the decreased utilization of high-energy compounds more than balances their rate of production, leading to a net increase.

Contrary to the effects of central nervous system depressants, greatly increased cerebral activity, such as occurs in convulsions induced by convulsive drugs, leads to quick depletion of high-energy phosphates and the accumulation of much inorganic phosphate and lactic acid.

While the brain contains enzymes involved in the pentose cycle mechanism of carbohydrate oxidation, the evidence indicates that most of the carbohydrate metabolism of brain proceeds through glycolysis and tricarboxylic acid cycle oxidation.

ELECTROLYTES OF BRAIN

Table 27.6 shows the chief electrolytes of brain in comparison with those of plasma and cerebrospinal fluid (27).

Table 27.6.   Cations and Anions of Brain Cerebrospinal Fluid and Plasma
Values represent meq per l or kg

Cations	Plasma	Cerebrospinal fluid	Brain
Ca^{++}	5	2.5	2
Na^+	141	141	57
K^+	5	2.5	96
Total cations*	153	148	166
Anions			
Cl^-	101	127	37
Phosphates	2	1	16
HCO_3^-	27	18	12
N-Acetylaspartate	0.1?	—	12
Other org. acids	2	2	10
Proteins	20	0	40†
Lipids	0	0	40†
Total anions	152	148	167

* Mg^{++} not included.
† Represents probable contributions to anions from proteins and lipids in balancing cations. Distribution between proteins and lipids uncertain.

The composition of cerebrospinal fluid is taken to approximate that of brain interstitial fluid, though these fluids originate from blood chiefly by different routes.

Nearly all of the brain chloride, as well as most of the Na^+, appears to be present in the interstitial fluid. The intracellular concentration of Na^+ is estimated to be about $0.02\ M$ and that of K^+ about $0.14\ M$. Maintenance of high intracellular K^+ and low intracellular Na^+ against the concentration gradients between the brain cells and interstitial fluid represents active transport, presumably due to the sodium pump mechanism discussed in Chapter 5, and requires the continual expenditure of energy provided by the oxidation of glucose.

ACETYLCHOLINE AND THE NERVE IMPULSE

As pointed out in the above discussion of electrolytes in nervous tissue, the concentration of K^+ is much higher inside the neurons than in the surrounding interstitial fluid, while the concentrations of Na^+ show the reverse relations. These differential ionic concentrations are maintained by active transport across the cell membrane, probably through operation of a sodium pump mechanism.

The differential distributions of K^+ and Na^+ set up a polarization across the nerve cell membrane amounting to some 75 mv, the inner surface of the membrane being relatively negative. During transmission of an impulse, a wave of electrical negativity passes along the nerve fiber. Associated with this activity is a marked decrease in electrical resistance, with influx of Na^+ during the ascending phase of the action potential, followed by an equivalent outflow of K^+ during the descending phase. The permeability of the axonal membrane to Na^+ increases some 500 times during nerve activity (28). The impulse travels along the fiber as a chain process. As each local region of the fiber becomes depolarized with movement of Na^+ and K^+, it becomes refractory or inactive until energy from metabolic processes can restore the original distributions of these ions. The impulse passes along the fiber as a succession of locally initiated depolarization currents after the initial stimulus has started the impulse.

It appears from the work of Nachmansohn and others (29) that acetyl choline functions as a depolarizing agent of nerve membranes to facilitate the generation and propagation of nerve impulses.

Acetylcholine and acetylcholine esterase, which very rapidly hydrolyzes and inactivates acetylcholine, are present generally in nerves and are localized near the axon surface. Acetylcholine is rapidly synthesized in nervous tissue by the enzyme choline acetylase from choline and acetyl coenzyme A:

$$\text{Choline} + CH_3CO-S-CoA \longrightarrow \text{Acetylcholine} + HS-CoA$$

Both the synthesis of acetylcholine to depolarize the membranes and its hydrolysis by acetylcholine esterase to stop its action appear to take place with sufficient rapidity to function in the generation and transmission of the nerve impulse.

The acetylcholine of nerve tissue in the resting state is in a bound (probably to protein) and inactive form (storage form). Upon stimulation, free acetylcholine is released from the bound or storage form and acts upon an acetylcholine receptor to cause membrane depolarization and generation of the electric potential at the site involved. The acetylcholine at this site is then hydrolyzed by acetylcholine esterase, permitting repolarization of the membrane by movement of Na^+ and K^+ ions. The reactions take place so rapidly that the whole process is accomplished in microseconds. Each local depolarization and current generation liberates free acetylcholine in the adjacent area (in the direction of impulse transmission) with repetition of the process. Thus, the impulse passes along the fiber as a succession of locally initiated depolarization currents after the initial stimulus has started the impulse.

It is of interest that the plates of the electric organs of *Torpedo* and *Electrophorus electricus*, which are powerful bioelectric generators, contain high concentrations of acetylcholine esterase. The discharge from *Electrophorus electricus* averages 400–600 v. There is a direct proportionality between the esterase content of the plates of the electric organs and the discharge voltage.

Nerve conduction is abolished by inhibitors of acetylcholine esterase due to failure of membrane repolarization. Conduction also stops when the enzyme activity falls to about 20 per cent of its initial value.

Wilson (30) has presented evidence that acetylcholine esterase possesses two functionally and spatially separated active sites: an anionic site, which attracts and binds the cationic nitrogen of acetylcholine and aids in orienting the molecule, and an esteratic site, which binds the ester group of acetyl choline. Thus, acetylcholine is bound to the enzyme at both ends of the molecule. Upon hydrolysis of acetylcholine by the enzyme, choline is first split from the enzyme-acetylcholine complex, and acetyl enzyme is formed, which is then hydrolyzed to acetate and enzyme.

Methyl derivatives of ammonia (methyl amines) and of ethanolamine combine reversibly with the anionic site of acetylcholine esterase and are competitive inhibitors. On the other hand, alkyl phosphates, such as diisopropylfluorophosphate (DFP), form stable combinations with the esteratic site of the enzyme and thus irreversibly inhibit its action and stop nervous activity. Such substances are violent poisons and are used in insectisides and as the "nerve gases" of chemical warfare agents:

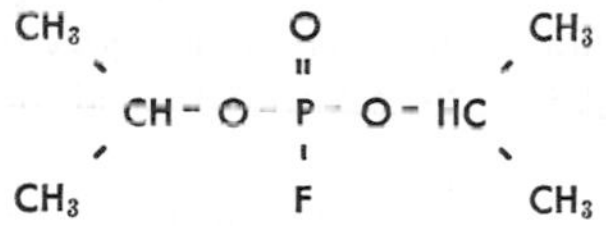

Diisopropylfluorophosphate

Wilson (31), from his studies on the active sites of acetylcholine esterase, was able to prepare substances capable of displacing the alkyl phosphates from the esteratic site and relieving the inhibition, the most effective substance being 2-pyridine aldoxime methiodide. This substance:

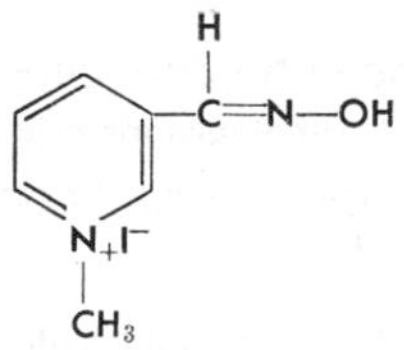

2-Pyridine aldoxime methiodide

is an effective antidote to DFP poisoning.

SPECIAL PHASES OF BRAIN METABOLISM

Glutamic acid and glutamine. Glutamic acid and glutamine represent about 80 per cent of the free α-amino nitrogen of the brain; their concentrations in brain are higher than in most other tissues, and some 15 times higher than in plasma.

Glutamic acid and glutamine undergo rapid metabolism in brain, as they do in other tissues.

The blood-cerebrospinal fluid and blood-brain barriers permit exceedingly little glutamic acid to pass to the brain, but these barriers are readily penetrated by glutamine. As shown in the following scheme of reactions, the brain can derive glutamic acid from glutamine and vice versa:

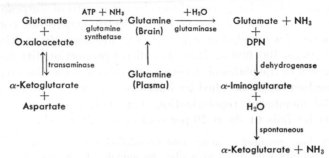

The brain rapidly deaminizes glutamic acid to α-ketoglutaric acid and oxidizes it in the tricarboxylic acid cycle. Because of the very active metabolism of glutamic acid in brain, it has been administered to influence mental states. It has been found to decrease petit mal attacks, and to improve to a small degree the condition of some mental defectives.

Brain ammonia. While brain tissue *in vitro* may produce relatively enormous quantities of ammonia (56 mg NH_3 per 100 g of tissue), the ammonia content of brain *in vivo* is relatively small and constant, suggesting that reactions involving glutamate and glutamine provide the necessary regulation.

In animals convulsions caused by decapitation, electrical stimulation, or convulsive drugs very rapidly increase brain ammonia. The administration of ammonium salts causes convulsions when the cerebral ammonia is raised to around 9 mg per cent.

γ-Aminobutyric acid. Brain tissue, particularly gray matter, contains an α-glutamic decarboxylase which splits out CO_2 from glutamic acid and forms γ-aminobutyric acid:

$$\underset{\substack{| \\ NH_2 \\ \text{Glutamic acid}}}{HOOC-CH-CH_2-CH_2-COOH} \xrightarrow[\substack{\text{pyridoxal} \\ \text{phosphate}}]{\text{decarboxylase}} \underset{\gamma\text{-Aminobutyric acid}}{H_2N-CH_2-CH_2-CH_2-COOH} + CO_2$$

An enzyme of brain catalyzes transamination of γ-aminobutyric acid with α-keto-glutarate to form succinic semialdehyde:

$$\underset{\gamma\text{-Aminobutyric acid}}{H_2N-CH_2-CH_2-CH_2-COOH} + \underset{\alpha\text{-Ketoglutaric acid}}{HOOC-CO-CH_2-CH_2-COOH} \xrightarrow{\text{transaminase}}$$

$$\underset{\substack{| \\ H \\ \text{Succinic semialdehyde}}}{O=C-CH_2-CH_2-COOH} + \underset{\substack{| \\ NH_2 \\ \text{Glutamic acid}}}{HOOC-CH-CH_2-CH_2-COOH}$$

γ-Aminobutyric acid occurs in brain to the extent of 0.2–0.4 mM per 100 g of tissue, and has been shown to inhibit transmission of impulses, apparently through direct action upon the neurons (32). The substance has been found to prevent fatal strychnine convulsions in mice when injected intraperitoneally (100 mg per kg).

It appears that γ-aminobutyric acid plays an important role in regulating impulse generation in the central nervous system, thereby serving as an anticonvulsive agent.

Serotonin or 5-hydroxytryptamine. This substance is found in the brain and other tissues (stomach, intestine, mast cells, blood platelets, etc.) and is a constituent of various venoms. It is a potent vasoconstrictor. Serotonin is formed in the brain and other tissues by 5-hydroxylation of tryptophan followed by decarboxylation:

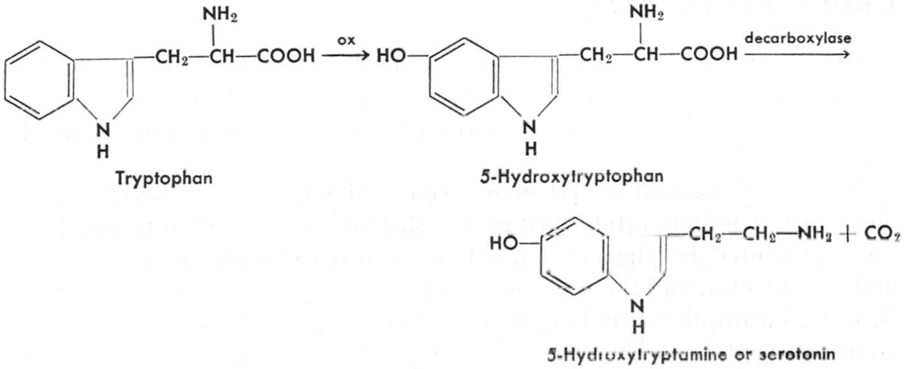

Tryptophan   5-Hydroxytryptophan

5-Hydroxytryptamine or serotonin

When 5-hydroxytryptophan is administered to an animal, it is followed by an increase in brain serotonin, with marked central nervous system actions, such as catatonia, rage, and fear. To produce such results, serotonin must be given intraventricularly or in high dosage intravenously, since it does not readily pass from blood to brain.

Serotonin is rapidly broken down by brain amine oxidase, and excites the neurones during the short interval between formation and destruction. Much of the serotonin of brain is in a bound form localized in the hypothalamus. Reserpine displaces bound serotonin from its sites in the brain and other tissues; this appears to be related to the tranquilizing effects of the drug.

Lysergic acid diethylamide in very small doses causes a schizophrenic-like condition in man, which is prevented by serotonin.

Serotonin appears to be an important transmitting agent in the sympathetic nerves of the autonomic nervous system (33).

It is of interest that serotonin is a potent stimulator of smooth muscle and causes contraction of the uterus and ileum.

While our knowledge of serotonin is rather fragmentary, the substance undoubtedly is important in regulating the activity of brain and other tissues.

CONNECTIVE TISSUE

Distribution. Connective tissue is distributed throughout the body and, as its name implies, literally connects the body together. It makes up the capsules and frameworks of organs and the sheaths of tendons and muscles. The skin is attached to the rest of the body by connective tissue (dermis), and connective tissue forms the supporting framework of blood and lymph vessels and nerves. It anchors organs in position.

Connective tissues provide barriers against infective agents and are of primary importance in wound healing. They are involved in the so-called collagen diseases.

Composition. Connective tissue is made up of three parts—namely, ground substance, fibers, and cells, which are composed of fibroblasts (osteocytes in bone and chondrocytes in cartilage), mast cells, and reticuloendothelial cells. The fibers, which constitute the supporting mechanism of connective tissue, are embedded in the ground substance along with the cells, which ultimately are the source of both ground substance and fibers.

GROUND SUBSTANCE

The ground substance is composed essentially of acid mucopolysaccharides associated and combined with proteins. The ground substance also contains tissue fluid, which originates from the plasma, metabolites formed by the cells, and lipids.

Meyer and associates (34) give seven acid mucopolysaccharides which have been definitely established as constituents of connective tissue. These are represented by the nonsulfated mucopolysaccharides hyaluronic acid and chondroitin, and the sulfated mucopolysaccharides chondroitin sulfates A, B, C, keratosulfate, and heparitin sulfate. The chemistry of all these substances except heparitin sulfate has been given in Chapter 7, which the student should review at this time. Heparitin sulfate is a polymer made up of equimolecular proportions of uronic acid, glucosamine and sulfate, though the detailed structure is unknown.

The mucopolysaccharides are formed by the mast cells of connective tissue.

The uronic acid components of the mucopolysaccharides are formed from UDP-glucose and UDP-galactose, etc. (35), as illustrated below:

$$\text{UDP-Glucose} \xrightleftharpoons[\text{epimerase}]{} \text{UDP-Galactose}$$

$$\downarrow +2\text{DPN} \qquad\qquad \downarrow +2\text{DPN}$$

$$\text{UDP-Glucuronic acid} \qquad\qquad \text{UDP-Galacturonic acid}$$

Similarly, the hexosamine components are formed from the UDP-derivatives as shown below:

$$\text{D-Glucose-6-P} + \text{Glutamine} \rightleftharpoons \text{Glucosamine-6-P} + \text{Glutamic acid}$$

$$\text{Glucosamine-6-P} + \text{Acetyl} - \text{S} - \text{CoA} \rightleftharpoons \text{N-Acetyl-glucosamine-6-P} \xrightleftharpoons[]{\text{mutase}}$$

$$\text{N-Acetyl-glucosamine-1-P} + \text{UTP} \longrightarrow$$

$$\text{UDP-N-Acetylglucosamine} \xrightleftharpoons[\text{epimerase}]{} \text{UDP-N-Acetylgalactosamine}$$

Hyaluronic acid synthesis appears to proceed as follows:

$$\text{UDP-Glucuronic acid} + \text{UDP-N-Acetylglucosamine} \longrightarrow \text{hyaluronic acid}$$

Chondroitin sulfate formation involves sulfation by "active sulfate" (Chapter 20):

$$\text{UDP-Glucuronic acid} + \text{UDP-N-Acetylgalactosamine} + \text{Active sulfate} \longrightarrow \text{Chondroitin sulfate}$$

Hyaluronic acid is broken down by hyaluronidases found in microorganisms, snake venom, and mammalian tissues, the testis being particularly rich in hyaluronidase. Hyaluronidases in general hydrolyze the bond between carbon one of glucosamine and carbon four of glucuronic acid. Testicular hyaluronidase forms a mixture of tetra- and disaccharides. Microbial hyaluronidase forms a disaccharide containing a double bond ($\Delta 4$—5) in the glucuronic acid group. Bacterial hyaluronidases acting upon the hyaluronic acid of connective tissues break down tissue barriers and permit the infection to spread; consequently, the hyaluronidases are referred to as "spreading factors." The hyaluronidase of sperm appears to promote fertilization by breaking down hyaluronic acid barriers.

Chondroitin sulfates A and C are hydrolyzed by exhaustive action of testicular hyaluronidase chiefly to sulfated tetrasaccharides, while chondroitin sulfate B is not hydrolyzed by the enzyme.

The mucopolysaccharides of connective tissue exhibit very active metabolism. Radioactive S^{35} ($S^{35}O_4^=$) and glucose—C^{14} are rapidly incorporated into hyaluronic acid and chondroitin sulfate. Rheumatic joints show proliferation of connective tissue with partially depolymerized or incompletely polymerized hyaluronic acid in the synovial fluid. Normal hyaluronic acid is restored by adrenal cortical hormones. The rate of turnover of isotope-labeled connective tissue mucopolysaccharides is decreased by adrenal corticosteroids. Growth hormone stimulates production of the acid mucopolysaccharides (36). The synthesis of mucopolysaccharides is decreased in scorbutic animals (37). The turnover rate of skin mucopolysaccharides is decreased in the diabetic animal and restored toward normal by insulin administration. The increased susceptibility to infections, slow wound healing, and tendency to atherosclerosis seen in diabetics is probably, in part, related to deficiency in synthesis of mucopolysaccharides caused by insulin deficiency.

FIBERS OF CONNECTIVE TISSUE

Connective tissue contains collagen, reticulin, and elastic fibers.

Collagen. Collagen fibers predominate in connective tissue, and collagen, the protein of which the fibers are formed, is of the albuminoid type and is the most abundant protein in the body. The amino acid composition of collagen is given in Table 8.3. Collagen is unique in containing hydroxyproline (14 per cent) and hydroxylysine (1.1 per cent); in fact, the collagen of tissues is obtained by determination of their hydroxyproline contents. Collagen also contains much proline (15 per cent) and glycine (27 per cent). Cystine and cysteine are absent, and very little methionine is present (0.8 per cent). The collagen units from which the fibers are organized appear to consist of three peptide chains joined by hydrogen bonds into a helix with a gradual right-handed twist.

When collagen fibers are treated with hot water, they are disaggregated and converted into soluble gelatin. The amino acid compositions of collagen and gelatin are essentially identical.

Formation of collagen fibers. Collagen fibers are formed by fibroblasts (osteoblasts, chondroblasts, etc.) in a series of stages described by Jackson (38). Fractions of collagen may be extracted from a tissue such as skin by neutral salt solutions (NaCl), acid citrate buffer, and dilute acetic acid, each extracting a different proportion of the collagen present. However, precipitation and purification of the collagen from all of these extracts gives material with the same physico-chemical properties and which behaves as a single molecular species. This collagen is a rod-shaped particle 3000 Å long, with a diameter of 15 Å, and has a molecular weight of about 320,000. It is very interesting that neutral solutions of such collagen when warmed to 37° C produce collagen gels made up of fibrils with cross striations about 640 Å apart and the interband periodicity found in native collagen fibers. Jackson labeled the collagen of guinea pig skin and of carrageenin granulomas grown in the same animals with glycine-C^{14} and extracted the collagen exhaustively in succession with increasing concentrations of NaCl—0.14, 0.28, 0.45, 1.0, 2.0 M, all at pH 7.4—and then with 0.2 M citrate buffer at pH 3.6, and finally converted the insoluble collagen to gelatin with hot water. From the quantities of collagen and the specific activities (C^{14}) in each fraction, it was possible to formulate the process of collagen fibrogenesis as follows.

The fibroblast (or osteoblast, chondroblast, etc.) synthesizes collagen protein intracellularly (tropocollagen) and moves it to the cell surface, where some of it forms very small collagen fibrils and the remainder passes into the extracellular space. This first fibrillar and extracellular collagen, called "neutral collagen," is extracted by 0.14 M NaCl. The small fibrils formed at the cell surface serve as templates for fiber development and grow in length and thickness by the addition of extracellular collagen units held together by hydrogen bonds, probably to a large extent by bonds between the hydroxyl hydrogen of hydroxyproline and the C=O groups of the peptide chains. The normal length of the collagen fiber is attained first, and then the process consists essentially in the addition of collagen molecules along the fiber to increase its thickness. As the collagen fibers grow in diameter, and age, they become more firmly united by cross linkages between the peptide chains, until finally the mature very strong collagen fibers are formed.

The so-called neutral collagen, represented by the first fibrils and the nonfibrillar extracellular collagen, as well as collagen newly deposited on the outside of the growing fibers, is extracted by 0.14 M NaCl. This collagen is weakly cross-linked. However, as the depth of the collagen molecules in the fibers increases (and their age), there is increased cross-linking to hold these collagen molecules more firmly. They can be extracted only with increasing concentrations of NaCl, or by citrate buffer; and, finally, the old most strongly cross-linked collagen deep in the fiber cannot be extracted by these solvents. The cross linkages of these collagen molecules are broken up by hot water, and the collagen changed into soluble gelatin. Thus, the different fractions of collagen extracted by different solvents do not represent different collagens, but collagen molecules at different stages of organization into collagen fibers, each stage representing the disruption of collagen molecules bound by cross-linkage forces within certain limits of strength (see Figure 27.4).

As previously pointed out, collagen is unique among tissue proteins in containing hydroxyproline and hydroxylysine.

It has been demonstrated (39) that fibroblasts incorporate C^{14}-labeled hydroxyproline into collagen when supplied with C^{14}-labeled proline, while C^{14}-labeled hydroxyproline fed to rats is not incorporated into collagen (40). This appears to indicate that the hydroxyproline of collagen is formed from proline after the latter is bound, presumably in peptide linkage. A similar relation has been found for lysine and the hydroxylysine of collagen (41).

The importance of ascorbic acid to wound healing is well established, which indicates a relation to connective tissue metabolism. Impaired hydroxyproline synthesis is a very early manifestation of ascorbic acid withdrawal, while there is rapid formation of hydroxyproline (collagen) in scorbutic animals following administration of ascorbic acid (42). Thus, it appears that ascorbic acid in some manner is necessary for the hydroxylation of protein-bound proline in the formation of collagen, which is fundamental in the wound-healing process.

The enzyme collagenase, which hydrolyzes both collagen and gelatin, has been found in various bacteria, and the enzyme from *Clostridium histolyticum* has been appreciably purified. It has a molecular weight around 100,000, digests collagen and gelatin to relatively small peptides, and shows a high degree of specificity.

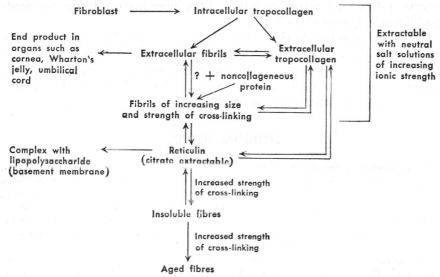

Figure 27.4. Formation of collagen fibers. (Courtesy of Dr. David S. Jackson.)

Reticulin. There appear to be two types of reticulin in connective tissue (43). One type is present in developing connective tissue and represents thin collagen fibers, soluble in acid citrate buffer, which precede the thicker collagen fibers. The other is associated with basement membranes of parenchymatous organs, and is present around nerve and muscle fibers and between connective tissue and epithelium. This reticulin is very insoluble and appears to be a complex of collagen, lipid, and a polysaccharide. This reticulin, under normal physiologic conditions, does not develop into typical collagen fibers.

Elastin. Elastin is the protein composing highly stretchable strong fibers of connective tissue and has an amino acid composition quite different from that of collagen (44). The proportion of nonpolar amino acids is high, causing elastin to be extremely insoluble and rubbery and to show little swelling in aqueous solvents, in contrast to collagen. When elastin is subjected to a short hydrolysis with oxalic acid, two products are formed (45), one of which is called "α-elastin" (mol. wt. 60,000–80,000) and the other "β-elastin" (mol. wt. around 6000). α-Elastin solutions form gels under various conditions of pH and temperature.

Elastin fibers may be separated from collagen in connective tissues by mild alkaline hydrolysis, which dissolves the collagen and other materials. The elastin fibers may be digested from connective tissue, leaving the collagen, by elastase, a specific enzyme system found in pancreatic juice. Elastase apparently forms α- and β-elastins from elastic fibers.

The work of Hall and associates (46) led them to consider elastic fibers to be made up of two phases, an amorphous phase, containing mucoprotein, which surrounds a fibrous phase and protects it from solution. The outer amorphous phase consists of α-elastin peptide chains (mol. wt. around 6000) cemented together by mucopolysaccharide, which is removed by the elastase enzyme system, and permits solution of the inner fibrous elastin core made up of linear polymers of β-elastin.

The structure of the elastic fiber is more complex and less well worked out than that of the collagen fiber. However, this structure must be such as to provide stretchability along the long fiber axis, and great lateral and longitudinal strength, probably through cross linkages between the peptide chains. Hall has written a review on elastin (47).

EPITHELIAL TISSUES

These tissues comprise the epidermis and related structures, such as hair, nails, horns, hoofs, and feathers. They are composed largely of keratins, which are highly insoluble proteins of the albuminoid type. The keratins are insoluble in all the ordinary protein solvents. They are dissolved by strong alkalies and acids but with decomposition. When keratins are subjected to the simultaneous action of a reducing agent, such as thioglycollic acid, and a protein-denaturing agent, such as guanidine hydrochloride, in neutral solution, they are dissolved. The thioglycollic acid reduces —S—S— linkages of the keratins to —SH groups, whereupon the keratins are dissolved by the denaturing agent. Reduction of the —S—S— groups of keratins to —SH groups has also been found to increase digestibility by proteolytic enzymes. This reduction takes place very readily in alkaline solution. The digestion of finely powdered wool, feathers, and other keratins in the intestine is probably dependent upon the preliminary reduction of —S—S— to —SH groups.

Block (48) has studied the amino acid composition of many keratins and for certain ones has found a striking relation between the molecular ratios of histidine, lysine, and arginine.

The keratins have been classified into two main groups. The eukeratins are characterized by being insoluble in water, dilute alkalies, and acids and not digested by the common proteolytic enzymes, and by containing histidine, lysine, and arginine in the molecular ratios of approximately 1:4:12. The eukeratins are found in tissues such as hair, feathers, horn, and snake skin. Pseudokeratins, like eukeratins, are highly insoluble but, unlike eukeratins, are somewhat digestible by proteolytic enzymes. They also contain less arginine relative to histidine and lysine, and the histidine-lysine-arginine ratios are much less constant than for the eukeratins.

Pseudokeratins are found in structures such as human skin, whale baleen, pelican excrescence, and turtle scutes.

Table 27.7 gives Block's analysis of several keratins with approximate molecular ratios of the amino acids. It will be noted that the ratios of histidine, lysine, and arginine in the eukeratins are remarkably constant, generally 1:4:12. These ratios for the pseudokeratins are much less constant. In general, the sulfur content of the keratins is relatively high. Cystine represents most of the sulfur, though methionine may be present in considerable amounts.

In general, the eukeratins are found in structures which may be readily shed or removed from the animal, whereas pseudokeratins are present in structures which cannot be removed without injury.

The skins of human beings and other higher animals are more highly diversified anatomically and chemically than other keratinous structures. Anatomically skin is composed of two composite layers; the dermis, or inner layer, and the epidermis, or outer layer. The keratins of skin are localized in the epidermis, which consists of several layers. The lower epidermal layer, the stratum germinativum, is composed of the most active cells and is the highest of the epidermal layers in water content. The cells of the stratum germinativum lose water and are forced by new cells toward the surface, where they successively become components of the stratum spinosum, stratum granulosum, stratum lucidium, and stratum corneum. The cells of the stratum granulosum contain granules of an albuminoid protein keratohyaline, which is considered the precursor of the protein eleidin found in the stratum lucidum. In the stratum corneum the cells have lost their nuclei and are composed chiefly of pseudokeratin, presumably formed from the eleidin of the stratum lucidum.

Table 27.7.   Percentage Amino Acid Composition of Some Keratins with Approximate Molecular Ratios

Keratin	Histidine	Lysine	Arginine	Cystine	Methionine*	Tyrosine	Tryptophan	Phenylalanine	Glycine	Nitrogen	Sulfur
	1†	4	12	16	7	4	1	5	22		
Human hair	0.6	2.5	8.0	14.7	5.1	2.9	0.7	2.0	4.2	14.9	5.0
	1	4	12	20	3	4	1	11	44		
Hen feathers	0.3	1.6	6.0	6.9	1.4	2.2	0.7	4.1	9.5	15.5	2.1
	1	4	12	25							
Fingernails	0.5	2.6	8.5	12.0							
	1	4	12	10	7	4	1	5	29		
Cattle horn	0.64	2.8	9.4	5.7	4.7	3.7	0.7	3.8	9.8	16.1	2.5
	1	5	12	13	6	12	2	0	66		
Snake skin	0.42	1.9	5.6	4.1	2.3	5.7	1.0	3.5	13.1	15.2	1.6
	1	4	7	3		4	2				
Human skin	0.8	4.3	6.5	3.8		3.4	1.8			14.2	
	1	6	6	6	4	4	1	3			
Whale baleen	1.0	3.7	6.2	9.5	3.7	5.0	1.0	2.8		14.1	
	1	1	2	3		6	1	3			
Turtle scutes	1.8	2.2	4.2	8.6		13.1	2.3	5.2		14.1	
	1	2	3	1		2	3	2			
Horse burrs	1.7	3.9	5.2	2.6		3.7	0.7	4 3		15.3	

* Methionine calculated from noncystine S.
† Molecular ratios.
Selected data from Block, R. J., *Cold Spring Harbor Symposia Quant. Biol.*, **6**, 80–82, 1938.

The dermal layer of skin contains the albuminoid collagen and elastin and reticulin, which also are albuminoids.

Humphrey, Neuberger, and Perkins (49) have demonstrated the presence of plasma proteins (albumin and globulins) in extracts of rabbit and rat skin. These workers found about 0.7 g/per 100 g in rabbit skin, which for the total skin represented about 2 g, equivalent to 25 to 30 per cent of the proteins in the circulating plasma. It was also found that around 60 per cent of the skin albumin is replaced daily by the circulating plasma albumin. Thus, it appears that the skin contains a relatively large proportion of the plasma proteins of the body which are in dynamic exchange with the plasma. These proteins are present in the skin interstitial fluid.

The color of the skin is largely determined by the quantity of melanin pigments present, the pigmentation varying from practically zero in the albino to high values in the colored races. The melanins are complex derivatives of tyrosine (see Chapter 25). The color of skin may be modified by the presence of other pigments, notably the yellow pigment carotene.

The lipids extractable from the surface of the skin are largely mixtures of cholesterol and its esters of fatty acids.

Suntzeff and Carruthers (50) have carried out mineral analyses of normal human epidermal cells by improved techniques.

The average percentage composition is as follows:

Potassium	0.322
Sodium	0.122
Magnesium	0.018
Calcium	0.015

Hair is composed almost entirely of eukeratin characterized by higher contents of cystine and methionine than other keratin. The color of hair, like that of skin, is due mainly to melanin pigments.

LIVER

The major role played by the liver in the metabolism of sugars, fats, and amino acids, in detoxication processes, and in the synthesis of many substances has been pointed out in the chapters on metabolism and elsewhere. In order to accomplish these functions, the liver has a high rate of energy production and utilization. Its protein is very labile, with a high rate of turnover. Liver protein very rapidly decreases during starvation, along with decreases in cytoplasm, mitochondria, microsomes, and enzymes. RNA levels are lowered, but the DNA content is not affected. Glycogen and phospholipid levels are greatly decreased. However, upon resumption of food intake, the liver rapidly recoups its losses and returns to normal.

Hepatectomy leads to drastic upsets in the metabolism of the animal, with rapid fall in the blood glucose level, hypoglycemic convulsions, and death. The animal may be kept alive for a few days if given glucose. However, in absence of the liver, with administered glucose, much of the protein and lipid metabolism ceases; the blood ammonia and amino acid levels rise, while urea and uric acid levels rapidly fall; and the animal dies, presumably because of ammonia intoxication.

Many pathologic states are associated with hepatic damage and dysfunction, which has lead to the proposal of many so-called liver function tests, no one of which is an index of the general condition of the liver because each test measures only a limited part of liver function. Liver function tests are based upon such procedures as determination of plasma proteins, excretion of hippuric acid after ingestion of benzoic acid, plasma-free and esterified cholesterol, and clearance of dyes, such as bromsulfalein, which are excreted in the bile. The details of such tests are to be found in texts on clinical pathology.

MAMMARY GLAND

Much work has been done to ascertain the biochemical mechanisms by which the mammary gland forms and secretes the various components of milk. Barry has written a recent review (51).

Because the blood leading to and from the mammary gland can be easily sampled, and most of the metabolic products of the gland pass into the milk rather than into the blood, metabolic studies on the gland are greatly facilitated.

Measurements indicate that approximately 500 l of blood flow through the mammary gland of the cow for each liter of milk secreted. If one knows the quantity of a substance in a liter of cow's milk and in a liter of blood, it is possible to estimate approximately the maximum amount of the substance that could be contributed to milk from blood without synthesis in the gland. Thus, Stein and Moore (52) have shown that peptides of blood can as a maximum supply less than 10 per cent of each amino acid of milk proteins.

Mammary gland metabolism varies with species, especially between ruminants and other mammals. For example, rat mammary gland oxidizes glucose more rapidly than acetate, while sheep gland oxidizes acetate more rapidly than glucose (53). Ruminants absorb much acetate from the intestine, but almost no glucose, while in rats the reverse is the case. It appears that cow mammary tissue oxidizes glucose through the pentose phosphate cycle practically exclusively, and only slowly. However, the rat tissue readily oxidizes glucose both through the glycolysis-tricarboxylic-acid-cycle and pentose-phosphate-cycle pathways.

Tracer experiments on cows and goats have shown that most of the amino acids for the synthesis of milk proteins are derived from blood, though such experiments also have shown that a small fraction of amino acids is synthesized by the mammary gland (54). Tracer experiments have shown that while α-lactalbumin is formed largely or exclusively from amino acids of blood in the gland, the immune globulin and serum albumen of milk are derived unchanged from the blood. However, the immune globulin of cow's colostrum appears to be made by plasma cells of the gland from free amino acids.

The origins of the fats and fatty acids of milk are diverse and have been studied chiefly in ruminants, largely by the use of labeled compounds. The injection into a cow of glycerides containing labeled stearic acid results in the appearance of much of the labeled stearic acid in milk fat, while very little of the labeled acid appears in the fat after the injection of labeled glucose or acetate. This work indicates that the mammary gland obtains at least a large proportion of long-chain fatty acid from the blood. Folley and associates (53), working with the goat, injected labeled acetate and determined the distribution of activity in the various fatty acids of milk fat. From these results it appears that a large proportion of the shorter-chain acids and a smaller fraction of long-chain acids are derived by synthesis from acetate in the gland. The utilization of acetate by the gland is shown by the arteriovenous difference of the blood supply, and by the fact that slices of the gland rapidly incorporate labeled acetate into fatty acids. It is of some interest that ruminant milk contains traces of odd-carbon acids (C_7 to C_{17}), which arise by condensation in the gland of acetate with propionate to form a C_5 acid, which by further condensation with acetate gives the higher odd-carbon acids.

Little is known as to the origin of the glycerol component of ruminant milk, though Wood and associates have shown that about 17 per cent of the glycerol carbon of cow milk fat arises from blood glucose (54). That there is a rapid exchange of glyceride fatty acids and free fatty acids in mammary cells is shown by the presence of both long-chain acids (derived from blood) and short-chain acids (synthesized in the gland) in the same glyceride molecule.

The lactose of milk is formed from blood glucose. Glucose is utilized by the mammary gland, as shown by arteriovenous difference, and when uniformly labeled C^{14}-glucose is injected into a goat or cow, both the glucose and galactose groups of the milk lactose become rapidly, uniformly, and equally labeled. Barry showed that the C^{14} of injected C-1 labeled glucose appeared almost exclusively in C-1 of the glucose and galactose groups of lactose; consequently, the synthesis of lactose does not involve breaking the glucose chain of carbon atoms.

Because so little glucose is absorbed into the blood from the gut of ruminants, it appears that a large proportion must be synthesized from fatty acids. Some is formed from propionate, but the amounts possible from this source appear to be hardly sufficient to supply the glucose for lactose production. Rogers and Kleiber (55) obtained good evidence for the formation of glucose from butyrate.

The established pathway for the production of lactose by the mammary gland (Chapter 24) involves the sequences:

glucose $\longrightarrow$ glucose-6-P $\longrightarrow$ glucose-1-P $\longrightarrow$ UDP-glucose $\longrightarrow$ UDP-galactose
UDP-galactose + glucose-1-P $\longrightarrow$ lactose-1-P $\longrightarrow$ lactose

The tracer experiments of Wood and associates, however, led them to suggest that lactose in the cow is formed largely by reaction of UDP-galactose with free glucose. Accordingly, the problem as yet is not fully clarified.

CARTILAGE

Cartilage consists of cells (chondroblasts), connective tissue fibers (predominantly collagen), and an organic matrix secreted by the cells. Cartilage is the chief constituent of the internal skeletons of cartilaginous fish and forms parts of the skeletal structures of higher animals.

When cartilage is heated with water under pressure, the organic matrix and collagen fibers are disrupted to yield gelatin (from collagen) and chondromucoid. Chondromucoid is a mucoprotein made up of the mucopolysaccharide, chondroitin sulfuric acid, united to protein. Chondroalbuminoid, the insoluble protein remaining after extraction of the other proteins, resembles elastin in properties. Cartilage contains relatively small quantities of chondroalbuminoid.

The blood and interstitial fluid supply to cartilage is very limited, and food is supplied to it and waste products eliminated from it largely by slow diffusion. This results in cartilage being one of the less metabolically active tissues.

BONE

Bone, like cartilage, consists of cells (osteoblasts and osteoclasts) and an organic matrix, formed by the osteoblasts, in which characteristic bone mineral is deposited in orderly arrangement. Some bones are formed by mineral deposition in cartilage, while others arise by ossification of fibrous tissue. Hollow bones may contain much marrow, which is high in lipid content (up to 25 per cent). All bones contain more or less lipid, most of which is fat. The water content of marrow-free bones generally amounts to 20 to 25 per cent. Both the lipid and water contents of bones vary with age and the nutritive state of the animal.

Dry lipid-free bone is composed of about one-third organic matrix and two-thirds bone mineral. The great strength of bone is due to the hardness of the mineral component and the toughness of the protein matrix in which the mineral is embedded.

The organic matrix of bone is composed chiefly of a mixture of the three proteins ossein, osseoalbuminoid, and osseomucoid. Ossein is present in greatest amount. It is apparently identical with collagen, since it yields gelatin. Osseoalbuminoid is present as a very tough elastic and fibrous substance and resembles the elastin of connective tissue and tendons. Osseoalbuminoid contains more nitrogen and less sulfur than chondroalbuminoid of cartilage.

Osseoalbuminoid is supposed to be a constituent of the lining of the Haversian canals.

Osseomucoid, like chondromucoid, is a mucoprotein and contains chondroitin sulfuric acid as the prosthetic group. Osseomucoid closely resembles tendomucoid in properties.

While the proteins of bone are of the same type as those found in cartilage, it is apparent that in the ossification of cartilage to form bone some changes in the cartilage proteins do take place.

Most of the mineral matter of bone may be dissolved out by prolonged soaking in dilute HCl, leaving the soft protein matrix. When bone is strongly heated, the organic substances are burned and 60 to 70 per cent of bone ash is left.

Most of our knowledge of the composition of bone mineral has been obtained by analysis of bone ash. However, the process of ashing does cause some changes in chemical composition. Bone and tooth mineral may be prepared more satisfactorily for analysis by boiling the tissue in a solution of KOH in ethylene glycol, which leaches out the organic matter.

The composition of bone mineral is relatively constant. Average values for the chief components are:

	Per Cent of Total
Calcium	36.6
Magnesium	0.62
Phosphorus	16.6
Carbon dioxide	4.3

Considerable amounts of sodium and appreciable amounts of potassium are also present, as well as a small amount of fluorine. The phosphorus is present as phosphate ion, and carbon dioxide as the carbonate ion. Gabriel found 3.7 per cent combined water in bone mineral of the ox and 3.48 per cent in mineral of the teeth. The ratio of calcium atoms to phosphate groups $(Ca:PO_4)$ in bone mineral is a bit less than 10:6, the ratio in the apatite mineral $CaCO_3 \cdot 3Ca_3(PO_4)_2$.

Bone contains appreciable quantities of citric acid (about 1 per cent) which is present as citrate.

The composition of bone mineral shows little variation with animal species.

Hevesy and associates (56) have shown that the mineral component of bones and teeth is in a dynamic state, being continually formed and broken down. These workers gave radioactive phosphorus as phosphate to rats and observed the rate of its accumulation in the bones and teeth of the animals, and also the rate at which it disappeared. Thirty per cent of the phosphorus atoms deposited in the adult rat skeleton were eliminated in 20 days. In experiments on a human subject it was found that an average of only about one of 300,000 administered radiophosphorus atoms enters a single tooth. The replacement of 1 per cent of the phosphorus atoms of human teeth by phosphorus atoms from the food was calculated to require about 250 days.

The gross analysis of bone mineral suggests that it is composed largely of tricalcium phosphate, $Ca_3(PO_4)_2$, with a smaller proportion of calcium carbonate. However, it has long been recognized that bone mineral is not simply a mixture of these substances, but a complex salt.

Rosebury, Hastings, and Morse (57) have studied the structure of bone mineral by x-ray analysis. They found the x-ray diagrams to correspond to those of apatite minerals such as $CaF_2 \cdot 3Ca_3(PO_4)_2$ and $CaCO_3 \cdot 3Ca_3(PO_4)_2$, which are complex salts of similar crystal pattern. The formula $CaCO_3 \cdot [n \ Ca_3(PO_4)_2]$ represents the $Ca:PO_4$ ratio of bone mineral when n is not less than 2 or more than 3.

The carbonate apatite mineral $CaCO_3 \cdot 3Ca_3(PO_4)_2$ is preferably written $Ca_{10}(PO_4)_6(CO_3)$, since x-ray diagrams of it are quite distinct from those of $CaCO_3$ and $Ca_3(PO_4)_2$. This is also true for bone mineral. In other words, bone mineral does not contain $CaCO_3$ and $Ca_3(PO_4)_2$ as such, but Ca^{++}, $PO_4^{\equiv}$, and $CO_3^{=}$ ions arranged in a definite crystal lattice characteristic of apatite minerals. The apatite structure accounts for minor constituents of bone mineral and variations in composition under different nutritive and pathologic conditions. Any compound possessing the apatite crystal lattice may undergo exchange reactions by which one or more groups in the lattice may be substituted by certain other groups without significant change in crystal structure. Thus OH^- and F^- ions may be interchanged in equivalent numbers, as may Mg^{++} and Ca^{++} ions, without causing significant changes in the diffraction pattern. Hendricks and Hill (58) found that $4CO_3^{=}$ ions may replace $3PO_4^{\equiv}$ ions with accompanying changes such as replacement of Ca^{++} by Na^+ ions. These workers prepared tricalcium phosphate by hydrolysis of $CaHPO_4 \cdot 2H_2O$ in solutions more acid than pH 5 and at 100° C. Analysis gave the empirical formula $Ca_3(PO_4)_2 \cdot \frac{2}{3}H_2O$. The substance possesses the apatite crystalline structure. The water in the compound is held up to a temperature of 600° C; this indicates that it is probably present as H^+ and OH^- ions in the crystal lattice. These facts appear to be explained best by the apatite structure:

$$[Ca_9^{++} \cdot (H^+)_2](PO_4^=)_6 \cdot (OH^-)_2$$

which contains the elements in the proportion of $Ca_3(PO_4)_2 \cdot \frac{2}{3}H_2O$.

The formula above is equivalent to that of a carbonate apatite, $CaCO_3 \cdot 3Ca_3(PO_4)_2$ written in the apatite form:

$$[Ca_{10}^{++}](PO_4^=)_6 \cdot (CO_3)$$

in which Ca^{++} has been replaced by $2H^+$ and $CO_3^=$ by $2OH^-$.

In order to account for the composition of bone mineral as shown by the most trustworthy analyses, Hendricks and Hill suggested the following apatite type of structure in which the positive ions are represented by Ca^{++}, Mg^{++}, Na^+, and H^+, and the negative ions by PO_4^-, CO_3^-, and OH^- in the proportions shown:

$$[Ca_{8.5}^{++} \cdot Mg_{0.25}^{++} \cdot Na_{0.19}^+ \cdot H_2^+](PO_4^=)_{5.07}(CO_3^=)_{1.24}(OH^-)_2$$

Such a formula explains the apatite crystal structure of bone mineral and also permits considerable variation in composition by ionic substitution. Normal bone contains a small amount of fluorine (0.03–0.065 per cent) which, as F^-, replaces an equivalent amount of OH^-. The carbonate content of bone may be increased and the phosphate decreased by placing animals on a high-calcium low-phosphate diet which leads to the substitution of $CO_3^=$ for $PO_4^=$ ions. The reverse occurs in low-calcium diets. Increasing the vitamin D intake also lowers the carbonate-calcium ratio in bones. Sobel, Rockenmacher, and Kramer (59) point out that the carbonate-calcium ratio in bones is related to changes in the serum carbonate phosphate ratio, which in turn varies with the dietary calcium-phosphate ratio, vitamin D intake, and other factors.

While the above suggested apatite crystal lattice for bone appears to be valid, it should be pointed out that such a structure must provide adsorption centers for both cations and anions, and that variable quantities of ions such as Na^+, K^+, F^-, citrate$^=$, etc., may be present due to adsorption.

Calcium ions in bone mineral are replaced by lead ions in cases of chronic lead poisoning and are mobilized into the blood under conditions which cause bone calcium to be mobilized (diets low in calcium and phosphorus, excessive doses of vitamin D, parathyroid hormone, acidosis). Similarly, ionic exchange causes the deposition of strontium, radium, beryllium, potassium, and various other elements in bone.

The dynamic state of bone mineral is also strikingly evident in conditions imposing large demands upon blood calcium and phosphorus, such as heavy lactation and pregnancy, when dietary calcium and phosphorus are inadequate. Under these conditions much calcium and phosphorus may pass from bone mineral into the blood to serve for the production of milk or bone mineral of the fetus.

The breakdown or resorption of bone mineral is brought about by the osteoclasts through mechanisms not well explained. It appears that the initial process may involve depolymerization of the mucopolysaccharides.

Formation of bone. Details relative to bone metabolism are given in Chapter 30, and only an outline of special phases are presented below.

Osteoblasts are the cells primarily concerned with bone formation and produce the proteins and mucopolysaccharides making up the connective tissue fibers and the cementing gel in which the fibers and mineral components are embedded. This organic matrix of fibers and cementing substance is first formed, and then deposition of bone mineral takes place. This mineral deposition in orderly arrangement appears to be related to the association of chondroitin sulfate with the collagen fibers, the chondroitin sulfate serving as a cation exchanger which binds Ca^{++} and other cations for deposition with phosphate and other anions as bone mineral between the collagen fibers. Little is known about the finer details of this deposition. It appears that mineral deposition takes place concomitantly with the process of glycolysis and the production of organic phosphates in the osteoblasts. The osteoblasts generally contain much alkaline phosphatase, and it may be that this enzyme hydrolyzes an organic phosphate at the site of mineralization to provide $PO_4^{\equiv}$ ions for the process.

The metabolic processes of the bone lead to the synthesis of citrate, presumably via the tricarboxylic acid cycle, which is probably retained in the bone largely through adsorption to the mineral crystal lattice, from which it may be released to the circulation.

TEETH

Teeth represent complex calcified structures in which calcification is differentiated in three distinct anatomical regions: enamel, dentine, and cementum. Dentine is the major tooth component; into it extends the pulp cavity containing the blood vessels and nerves. The dentine is covered with a layer of cementum in the root and a layer of enamel in the exposed part of the tooth. Enamel is the most highly calcified and also the hardest tissue of the body. Dentine is softer than enamel but harder than bone and shows an intermediate degree of calcification. Cementum and bone represent comparable degrees of calcification and hardness. The mineral phase constitutes about 98 per cent of enamel, 77 per cent of dentine, and 70 per cent of cementum. The general composition of cementum is analogous to that of bone.

The protein matrix of dry enamel amounts to about 1 per cent(0.49–1.95 per cent) of the tissue and is composed chiefly of a protein which in some respects resembles keratin. Pincus (60), however, states that it is not a true keratin because of its deficiency in sulfur and its anomalous solubility. The protein of enamel is of epidermal origin. Dry dentine contains, on the average, 22 per cent of protein matrix, which is largely collagen, and is of mesodermal origin. All phases of tooth structure contain some lipid material.

Armstrong (61) has collected analyses of the inorganic constituents of whole teeth and of enamel and dentine. Table 27.8 presents selected values from his tabulation. The fluorine content of enamel has been reported to be about 0.011 per cent, and of dentine 0.009 per cent.

The considerable variations in composition reported by different workers are related not only to different samples of teeth but also to differences in the preparation of the samples for analysis and the use of different analytical methods.

Table 27.8.   Chief Constituents of Whole Teeth, Enamel, and Dentine of the Human

Material	Ca Per Cent	Mg Per Cent	P Per Cent	CO_2 Per Cent
Inorganic residue of:				
Whole teeth	37.5 ± 9.8	0.32 ± 0.25	16.3 ± 0.9	
Whole teeth	35.2 ± 0.7		16.8 ± 0.3	3.45 ± 0.26
Whole teeth, fetal	$34.5 + 2.3$	1.1 ± 0.6	16.9 ± 0.5	3.3 ± 0.1
Enamel (deciduous)	36.0 ± 2.0		17.8 ± 1.2	
Dentine (deciduous)	33.3 ± 4.6		16.5 ± 1.2	
Enamel (Precolumbian specimens)	37.13 ± 0.99		17.62 ± 0.49	1.98 ± 0.39
Dentine (Precolumbian specimens)	35.70 ± 1.31		16.63 ± 0.94	3.31 ± 0.56
Dry ether alcohol extracted:				
Enamel	35.41 ± 0.96	0.30 ± 0.05	17.45 ± 0.51	3.00 ± 0.24
Dentine	26.18 ± 0.34	0.83 ± 0.08	12.74 ± 0.48	$3.57 + 0.1$
Fresh enamel	35.80	0.25	16.91	2.75
Fresh dentine	26.30	0.83	12.70	3.17

Note: Inorganic residue prepared by KOH-glycol extraction.

In addition to the common constituents of teeth, spectroscopic analysis has indicated the presence of traces of barium, strontium, tin, zinc, manganese, titanium, nickel, vanadium, aluminum, silicon, boron, iron, chromium, platinum, and silver.

Murray and Bowes (62) have made comprehensive analyses of enamel and dentine of sound human teeth. Their results are summarized in Table 27.9.

The mineral components of enamel and dentine show definite variations in composition. The mineral of enamel contains more calcium and phosphate and less magnesium and carbonate than the mineral of dentine. If the equivalents of calcium phosphate and carbonate in the minerals of enamel and dentine are calculated, the ratio of calcium phosphate to calcium carbonate in enamel is 4.05 and in dentine 2.38, according to Armstrong and Brekhus. These workers also have found a higher fluorine content in dentine than in enamel (63). Since the proportions of cementum, dentine, and enamel may vary appreciably in different teeth, analysis of the whole tooth cannot be relied upon to indicate variations in the composition of any of these components.

Table 27.9.   Composition of Enamel and Dentine of Human Teeth in Per Cent

Constituent	Dry Enamel	Dry Dentine
Ash	95.38	71.09
Combined water calcd.	1.35	
Nitrogen	0.156	3.43
Protein calcd.	0.97	21.44
Calcium	37.07	27.79
Magnesium	0.46	0.83
Sodium	0.25	0.19
Potassium	0 05	0.07 or less
Phosphorus	17.22	13.81
Combined CO_2	1 95	3.17
Chlorine	0.30	none
Fluorine	0.025	0.0246
Silicon	0.003	
Ca/P	2.153	2.012
Ca/Mg	79.89	33.29
Ca/Na	148.28	146.0
P/CO$_2$	8.88	4.35
P/F	688.8	561.4

The apatite crystal structure is characteristic of the minerals of enamel and dentine, as it is of bone mineral. Hendricks and Hill have suggested the following apatite compositions for these minerals. The composition of bone mineral is repeated for comparison:

Bone mineral:

$$[Ca_{8.5}{}^{++} \cdot Mg_{0.25}{}^{++} \cdot Na_{0.19}{}^{+} \cdot H_2{}^{+}](PO_4{}^{\equiv})_{5.07} \cdot (CO_3{}^{=})_{1.24} \cdot (O\bar{H})_2$$

Dentine mineral:

$$[Ca_{8.36}{}^{++} \cdot Mg_{0.45}{}^{++} \cdot Na_{0.16}{}^{+} \cdot H_2{}^{+}](PO_4{}^{\equiv})_{5.34} \cdot (CO_3{}^{=})_{0.88} \cdot (OH^{-})_2$$

Enamel mineral:

$$[Ca_{9.48}{}^{++} \cdot Mg_{0.18}{}^{++} \cdot Na_{1.11}{}^{+} \cdot H_{0.46}{}^{+}](PO_4{}^{\equiv})_{5.67} \cdot (CO_3{}^{=})_{0.45} \cdot (OH^{-})_2$$

The mineral of enamel is more basic than that of dentine.

The small amount of F^- in teeth exchanges with OH^-, as it does in bone. Similarly, traces of many elements may be present in teeth as in bone through ionic exchange without appreciable alteration of the crystal lattice. However, exchange reactions proceed more slowly in teeth than in bone. Hevesy and associates first demonstrated that radioactive P given to rats appears in tooth mineral but at a much slower rate than in bone mineral. Its disappearance from teeth was also much slower than from bone. These observations have been confirmed and extended by other workers. In normal teeth the uptake of radioactive P is greatest in the dentine immediately surrounding the pulp and is higher in root dentine than in crown dentine. Enamel takes up only 20 to 35 per cent as much as crown dentine. In general, the rate of the uptake of radioactive P is inversely proportional to the density of the tooth structure. The rate of exchange of radioactive P in dentine is about 16 times faster and in bone more than 100 times faster than in enamel. The rate at which tooth mineral is formed and resolved is accordingly much slower than in the case of bone mineral. This fact is evident in conditions that may cause much resolution of bone mineral without appreciable effect upon tooth structure, such as pregnancy and lactation without adequate dietary calcium and phosphorus.

Although the amount of fluorine in teeth is very small, it appears to be highly important. The ingestion of small amounts of fluorides has been shown to have a definite effect in the prevention of caries. Excessive amounts are harmful and may cause mottled teeth. The proper number of F^- ions in the enamel crystal structure appears to make it more resistant to solution in acids. It is claimed that the topical application of fluoride solutions to teeth renders them less soluble in acids and reduces the incidence of caries.

GENERAL REFERENCES

BONE

Bourne, G. H.: *The Biochemistry and Physiology of Bone.* Academic Press, New York, 1956.
Neuman, W. F., and Neuman, M. W.. *The Chemical Dynamics of Bone Mineral.* University of Chicago Press, Chicago, 1958.
Wolstenholme, G. E. W., and O'Connor, C. M. (eds.): *Bone Structure and Metabolism.* Little, Brown & Co., Boston, 1956.

CONNECTIVE TISSUE

Asboe-Hansen, G. (ed.): *Connective Tissue in Health and Disease.* Ejnar Munksgaard, Copenhagen, 1954.
Asboe-Hansen, G.: "Hormonal Effects on Connective Tissue," *Physiol. Revs.,* **38,** 446, 1958.
Jackson, D. S.: "Some Biochemical Aspects of Fibrinogenesis and Wound Healing," *New Engl. J. Med.,* **259,** 814, 1958.
Tunbridge, R. E. (ed.): *Connective Tissue.* Blackwell, Oxford, 1957.
Wolstenholme, G. E. W., and O'Connor, M. (eds.): *Chemistry and Biology of Mucopolysaccharides.* Little, Brown & Co., Boston, 1958.

MUSCLE

Bourne, G. H. (ed.): *Structure and Function of Muscle,* Vols. I, II, III. Academic Press, New York, 1960.
"Conference on Muscular Contraction," *Ann. N. Y. Acad. Sci.,* **81,** Art. 2, 401, 1959.

NERVOUS TISSUE

"Conference on Physicochemical Mechanism of Nerve Activity," *Ann. N. Y. Acad. Sci.,* **81,** Art. 2, 215, 1959.
Korey, S. R., and Nurnburger, J. I. (eds.): *Neurochemistry.* Paul B. Hoeber, Inc., New York, 1956.
McIlwain, H.: *Biochemistry and the Central Nervous System,* 2nd ed. Little, Brown & Co., Boston, 1959.
Nachmansohn, D.: "Metabolism and Function of the Nerve Cell," *The Harvey Lectures,* 1953–1954. Academic Press, New York, 1955.
Richter, D. (ed.): *Metabolism of the Nervous System.* Pergamon Press, New York, 1957.
Waelsch, H. (ed.): *Biochemistry of the Developing Nervous System.* Academic Press, New York, 1955.
Waelsch, H. (ed.): *Progress in Neurobiology,* Vol. II, Ultrastructure and Cellular Chemistry of Neural Tissue. Paul B. Hoeber, Inc., New York, 1957.

SPECIAL REFERENCES

1. Perry, S. V.: *Physiol. Revs.*, **36**, 1, 1956. Perry, S. V., in Mason, H. S., and Florkin, M. (eds.): *Comparative Biochemistry*, Vol. II, Chap. 5. Academic Press, New York, 1960.
2. Huxley, H. E.: *J. Biophys. Biochem. Cytol.*, **3**, 631, 1957.
3. Davey, C. L.: *Nature*, **179**, 209, 1957.
4. Davey, C. L.: Ph.D. Dissertation, Cambridge University, 1957.
5. Huxley, A. F., and Taylor, R. E.: *Nature*, **176**, 1068, 1955.
6. Perry, S. V.: *Physiol. Revs.*, **36**, 1, 1956.
7. Jacob, J. J. C.: *Biochem. J.*, **41**, 83, 1947.
8. Bidinost, L. E.: *J. Biol. Chem.*, **190**, 423, 1951.
9. Perry, S. V., in Mason, H. S., and Florkin, M. (eds.): *Comparative Biochemistry*, Vol. II, Chap. 5. Academic Press, New York, 1960.
10. Hasselbach, W. Z.: *Naturforsch.*, **8b**, 449, 1953.
11. Tsao, T. C.: *Biochim. et Biophys. Acta*, **11**, 368, 1953.
12. Straub, F. B., and Feuer, G.: *Biochim. et Biophys. Acta*, **4**, 455, 1950.
13. Weber, A.: *Biochim. et Biophys. Acta*, **19**, 345, 1956. Gergeley, J.: *J. Biol. Chem.*, **220**, 917, 1956.
14. Bailey, K.: *Biochem. J.*, **43**, 271, 1948.
15. Perry, S. V., and Corsi, A.: *Biochem. J.*, **68**, 5, 1958.
16. Gitlin, D.; Nakasato, D.; and Richardson, W. R.: *J. Clin. Invest.*, **34**, 935, 1955.
17. Chance, B., and Connelly, C. M.: *Nature*, **179**, 1235, 1957.
18. Gergeley, J.: "Second Conference on Muscular Contraction," *Ann. N. Y. Acad. Sci.*, **81**, Art. 2, 490, 1959.
19. Parker, C. J., Jr., and Gergeley, J.: *Abstr. 135th Meeting Am. Chem. Soc.*, 7C, 1959.
20. Hayashi, T.: *Chemical Physiology of Excitation in Muscle and Nerve*. Nakayama-Shoten, Ltd., Tokyo, Japan.
21. Wilkie, D. R.: *Progr. in Biophys. and Biophys. Chem.*, **4**, 288, 1954.
22. Huxley, H. E., and Hanson, J.: *Nature*, **173**, 973, 1954. Huxley, H. E.: *Endeavour*, **15**, 177, 1956.
23. Bate-Smith, E. C., and Bendall, J. R.: *J. Physiol.*, **110**, 47, 1949.
24. McIlwain, H.: *Biochemistry and the Central Nervous System*, 2nd ed. Little, Brown & Co., Boston, 1959.
25. Elkes, J., and Finean, J. B.: *Exptl. Cell Research*, **4**, 69, 82, 1953.
26. Porter, H., and Folch, J.: *J. Neurochem.*, **1**, 260, 1957.
27. Manery, J. F., in *The Biology of Mental Health and Disease*. Cassell, London, 1952. Harrison, G. A.: *Chemical Methods in Clinical Medicine*, 4th ed. Churchill, London, 1957. Tallan, H. H.: *J. Biol. Chem.*, **224**, 41, 1957.
28. Wilson, I. B., and Altamirano, M., in Korey, S. R., and Nurnberger, J. I. (eds.): *Neurochemistry*. Paul B. Hoeber, Inc., New York, 1956.
29. Nachmansohn, D.: *The Harvey Lectures, 1953–1954*. Academic Press, New York, 1955.
30. Wilson, I. B., in McElroy, W. D., and Glass, B. (eds.): *The Mechanism of Enzyme Action*. Johns Hopkins Press, Baltimore, 1954, p. 642.
31. Wilson, I. B.: *J. Biol. Chem.*, **199**, 113, 1952. Meislich, E. K.: *J. Am. Chem. Soc.*, **75**, 4628, 1953.
32. Florey, E., and McLennan, H.: *J. Physiol.*, **129**, 384; **130**, 446, 1955. McLennan, H.: *ibid.*, **139**, 79, 1957.
33. Brodie, B. B., and Shore, P. A., in Hoagland H. (ed.): *Hormones, Brain Function and Behavior*. Academic Press, New York, 1957.
34. Meyer, K.; Hoffman, P.; and Linker, A.: "The Acid Mucopolysaccharides of Connective Tissue." In Tunbridge, R. E. (ed.): *Connective Tissue*. Blackwell, Oxford, 1957; Charles C Thomas, Publisher, Springfield, Ill., 1957.
35. Leloir, L. F.; Cardini, C. E.; and Cabib, E., in Mason, H. S., and Florkin, M. (eds.): *Comparative Biochemistry*, Vol. II, Chap. 2. Academic Press, New York, 1960.
36. Asboe-Hansen, G.: *Physiol. Revs.*, **38**, 446, 1958.
37. Kent, P. W., and Whitehouse, M. W.: *Biochemistry of the Amino Sugars*. Academic Press, New York, 1955.
38. Jackson, D. S.: *J. Biophys. Biochem. Cytol.*, **7**, 37, 1960.

39. Mitoma, C., and Smith, T. E.: *Federation Proc.*, **16**, 222, 1957.
40. Stetten, M. R.: *J. Biol. Chem.*, **181**, 31, 1949.
41. Sinex, F. M., and Van Slyke, D. D.: *Federation Proc.*, **16**, 250, 1957.
42. Gould, B. S., and Woessner, J. F.: *J. Biol. Chem.*, **226**, 289, 1957.
43. Robb-Smith, A. H. T., in Tunbridge, R. E. (ed.): *Connective Tissue.* Blackwell, Oxford, 1957, p. 177.
44. Partridge, S. M., and Davis, H. F.: *Biochem. J.*, **61**, 21, 1955.
45. Partridge, S. M.; Davis, H. F.; and Adair, G. S.: *Biochem. J.*, **61**, 11, 1955.
46. Hall, D. A.; Reed, R.; and Tunbridge, R. E.: *Nature*, **170**, 264, 1952.
47. Hall, D. A., in Tunbridge, R. E. (ed.): *Connective Tissue.* Blackwell, Oxford, 1957.
48. Block, R. J.: *Cold Spring Harbor Symposia Quant. Biol.*, **6**, 79, 1938.
49. Humphrey, J. H.; Neuberger, A.; and Perkins, D. J.: *Biochem. J.*, **66**, 390, 1957.
50. Suntzeff, Z., and Carruthers, C.: *J. Biol. Chem.*, **160**, 567, 1945.
51. Barry, J. M.: *Endeavour*, **18**, 173, 1959.
52. Stein, W. H., and Moore, S.: *J. Biol. Chem.*, **211**, 915, 1954.
53. Folley, S. J.: *The Physiology and Biochemistry of Lactation.* Oliver & Boyd, London, 1956.
54. Wood, H. G.; Gillespie, R.; Joffe, S.; Hansen, R. G.; and Hardenbrook, H.: *J. Biol. Chem.*, **233**, 1271, 1958.
55. Rogers, T. A., and Kleiber, M.: *Biochim. et Biophys. Acta*, **22**, 284, 1956.
56. Chievitz, O., and Hevesy, G.: *Kgl. Danske Videnskab. Selskab Biol. Medd.*, **13**, No. 9, 1937. Hevesy, G.; Holst, J. J.; and Krogh, A.: *ibid.*, **13**, No. 13, 34, 1937. Hahn, L.; Hevesy, G.; and Lundsgaard, E.: *Biochem. J.*, **31**, 1705, 1937.
57. Roseberry, H. H.; Hastings, A. B.; and Morse, J. K.: *J. Biol. Chem.*, **90**, 395, 1931.
58. Hendricks, S. B., and Hill, W. L.: *Science*, **96**, No. 2489, 255, 1942.
59. Sobel, A. E.; Rockenmacher, M.; and Kramer, B.: *J. Biol. Chem.*, **158**, 475, 1945.
60. Pincus, P.: *Biochem. J.*, **33**, 694, 1939.
61. Armstrong, W. D.: *Ann. Rev. Biochem.*, **11**, 441, 1942.
62. Murray, M. M., and Bowes, J. H.: *Biochem. J.*, **29**, 2721, 1935; **30**, 977, 1936.
63. Armstrong, W. D., and Brekhus, P. J.: *J. Biol. Chem.*, **120**, 677, 1937; *J. Dental Research*, **17**, 27, 1938.

28

Nutritional aspects of proteins and amino acids

The quantitative dietary protein requirement of man is still a matter of controversy. This is due largely to the difficulties involved in human nutritional experimentation. Far more data are available concerning the requirements of farm and experimental animals than of man.

The term "nutritional requirement" is very comprehensive. The protein intake, for example, is concerned not only with growth, and maintenance after growth, but also in several other life processes. Enzymes and certain hormones are proteins and must be synthesized in the body from amino acids. Many specific metabolic reactions involve, and indeed require, specific amino acids from ingested protein. The osmotic pressure relationships between blood and tissue fluids and between cells and extracellular fluid are governed to an important degree by the nature and amount of protein present. Requirements also may be altered by changes in activity, temperature of environment, and state of health. During pregnancy and lactation and for egg production the increased protein demand must be met by increased consumption.

Protein quality. The earlier work on dietary protein was concerned primarily with the quantity in the diet, but recently the type of protein has assumed equal significance. In other words, the quality of the protein must be considered in any attempt to arrive at requirements. This came about with the realization by chemists that proteins from various sources differ widely in their amino acid makeup, and that their value in nutrition depends largely on the presence of specific amino acids. The failure of animals to grow properly on diets containing certain proteins was demonstrated to result from deficiencies in the proteins of one or more of these amino acids.

It should be emphasized that the requirement of animals and man is not for protein *per se*, but for specific amounts of specific amino acids, the so-called essential, or indispensable, amino acids. The development of our knowledge of their relation to nutrition is one of the highlights in recent biochemical research.

1204

As late as 1930 only five amino acids were generally accepted as essential for the growth of rats (1). These were lysine, cystine, tryptophan, tyrosine, and histidine. These results were established for the most part by two methods of approach.

In the first method, rats were fed water and a ration containing fat, carbohydrate, a salt mixture compounded to simulate the inorganic matter of cow's milk, and some individual protein. In many such experiments the protein was fed at a level of about 18 per cent. If the animals showed good growth over a considerable period of time, the protein was considered a complete biologic protein; i.e., it was considered to contain all the essential amino acids in sufficient quantity for rat growth. If the animals grew poorly, various amino acids were added to the diet, singly or in combination, in attempts to establish which of these were required by the animals, and consequently the ones which were absent or deficient in the protein employed. In some cases a second protein known to contain one or more of the amino acids in question was added instead of the amino acids.

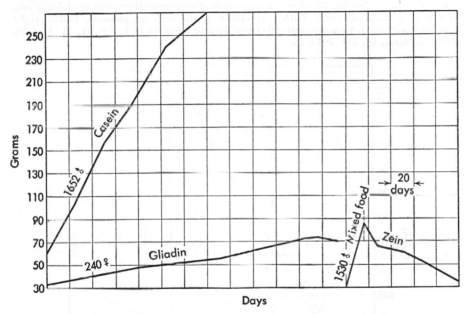

Figure 28.1. Growth curves of rats maintained on diets containing a single protein. Note poor growth with gliadin as the protein (lysine deficient), and with zein (lysine and tryptophan deficient). Excellent growth is obtained with a casein diet. (L. B. Mendel, *Harvey Lectures*, **10**, 111, 1914–15.)

The supplementary effect of several proteins for other proteins was established in this way. Actually the results pointed out the essential or indispensable nature of various amino acids.

Osborne and Mendel (2) were pioneers in this field and are particularly responsible for our early information on this subject. Casein of milk has long been respected as a complete biologic protein; at a level of 18 per cent or slightly less, it supplies sufficient quantities of all the amino acids required for growth and reproduction of rats and other experimental animals. In much of the early work, therefore, the nutritive worth of many proteins was assessed by comparing their growth-promoting value to that of casein. Figures 28.1, 28.2, and 28.3 indicate the growth of rats on rations containing various purified proteins as the only source of dietary amino acids and the effect of the addition of amino acids or of other protein. The other constituents of the rations were in general the same, so that the only limiting factor was the intake of amino acids as they occur in the various proteins studied. Thus gliadin of wheat is seen to be a poor biologic protein.

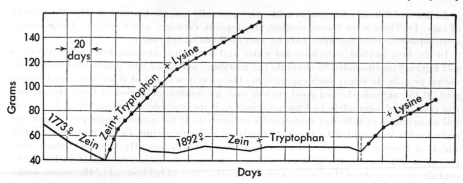

Figure 28.2. Showing the effect on rat growth of supplementing a diet containing zein with tryptophan and lysine. With tryptophan as the only supplement, body weight is maintained; growth ensues only after the further addition of lysine. (L. B. Mendel, *Harvey Lectures*, **10**, 111, 1914–15.)

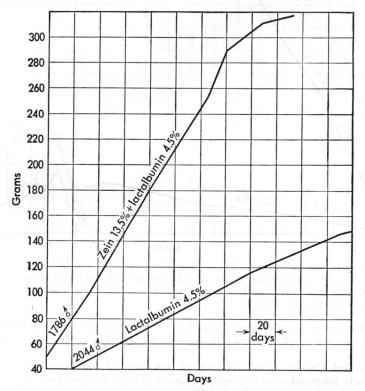

Figure 28.3. The effect on rat growth of supplementing a zein diet with lactalbumin. (L. B. Mendel, *Harvey Lectures*, **10**, 112, 1914–15.)

It is known to be very low in the amino acid lysine. Zein from corn does not support growth until both lysine and tryptophan are added to the diet, although the addition of tryptophan alone allows maintenance of weight. Supplementing this protein with lactalbumin from milk, which is high in these two amino acids, also corrects the deficiency so that good growth is obtained. Chemical analysis bears out the lack of these two amino acids in zein.

A partial list of the proteins which Osborne and Mendel showed to be adequate and some which were found to be inadequate for the growth of rats appears in Table 28.1. It should be understood that the proteins listed under "adequate," when fed as the only source of amino acids in the diet and at the proper level, allow growth of rats, and that those listed under "inadequate" fail to do so.

In the second method of approach to this problem other investigators employed hydrolysates of various proteins as the source of amino acids in their experimental diets. In some instances one or more of the amino acids were removed from such mixtures, and if they then did not support growth, the "essentiality" of the removed amino acid was demonstrated. On the other hand, if some protein hydrolysate proved inadequate for growth, various amino acids were added until the mixture supported growth. In 1912 Abderhalden fed enzymatically hydrolyzed meat to a dog as the only source of nitrogen in the diet over a period of 100 days. The animal maintained health and gained weight on this regime. Obviously, a similar experiment employing a hydrolysate of one of the biologically poor proteins such as zein would be unsuccessful.

Table 28.1. Proteins for Growth of Rats

Adequate	Inadequate
Animal proteins	Gliadin of wheat
Casein of milk	Legumin of pea
Lactalbumin of milk	Zein of corn
Ovalbumin of egg	Hordein of barley
	Gelatin of horn
Vegetable proteins	Legumelin of soybean
Globulin of cottonseed	
Glutenin of wheat	
Edestin of hempseed	
Excelsin of Brazil nut	

An excellent example of the use of such a procedure is the work of St. Julian and Rose (3). These authors studied the dispensable nature of the acidic amino acids glutamic and aspartic. They removed these compounds from an acid hydrolysate of casein, supplemented the remaining mixture with tryptophan and cystine, and fed this to rats as the only source of nitrogen in an otherwise complete diet. Growth of the rats was equal to that of litter mates receiving the dibasic amino acids in addition. Such evidence points to the dispensable nature of these protein constituents.

It should be pointed out that acid hydrolysis of protein destroys tryptophan, but enzyme hydrolysis does not. At the time of this experiment cystine was considered an essential amino acid and casein was known to be very low in this component. This explains why these investigators supplemented their diet with tryptophan and cystine.

Essential amino acids. As valuable as much of this early experimental work proved to be, the fact is inescapable that the main virtue lay not in the information given to science, but in the impetus to further and more adequate experimentation.

Commenting on this early work, Rose (4), stated that definite proof of indispensability existed for only the three amino acids, tryptophan, lysine, and histidine. Since the data regarding other amino acids was so conflicting, he felt that it was hazardous to draw definite conclusions regarding them.

A new technique for studying protein requirements has recently been developed. It involves the determination of the essential or nonessential nature of each amino acid known to occur in proteins and of the amount of each required. This can be accomplished only by employing pure amino acids in the diets. By such means the experimenters avoid the uncertainties of feeding whole proteins or protein hydrolysates, which in most instances contain unknown and undeterminable materials. It is also difficult, if not impossible, in many instances to rid a digest completely of one or more amino acids or to determine the presence in a digest of minute amounts of certain of these substances. Thus the work previous to about 1930 was attended by great difficulties and unavoidable errors.

It was Rose who finally perfected the technique of substituting mixtures of purified amino acids for protein in the diets of experimental animals. It was Rose also who, with many collaborators, applied this procedure to the study of the individual amino acids known to occur in proteins, and, as a result, he is credited with developing much of our present knowledge of indispensable amino acids.

In the early experiments in Rose's laboratory the amino acid mixtures were made to simulate the composition of casein. Nineteen different acids were available. When such a mixture was fed to rats at 18 to 21 per cent of a ration containing the other known essential constituents, the demands of growth were not met. At this time Rose was of the opinion that the ration was devoid of some essential component, and his view was strengthened when he showed that the substitution of 5 per cent casein for an equal amount of the amino acid mixture greatly improved the nutritive quality of the ration. It was only natural that attempts were instituted at once to determine what substance or substances in casein might be responsible for the improvement. To this end, casein was hydrolyzed and then separated into five fractions of amino acids as follows: less soluble acids, dibasic acids, diamino acids, alcohol soluble acids, and monoamino acids. Only the last fraction, when incorporated into the diet, exerted an appreciable effect on growth. The effect was greater than that due to an equivalent amount of casein.

Rose and his associates required four years to establish the nature of the component in the monoamino acid fraction of casein hydrolysates responsible for inducing growth in rats when added to the ration originally employed. The work was attended by many complications which at the time could not have been anticipated. A great deal of credit is due them for their continued patience in the face of great difficulties and a "baffling situation." Finally, in 1934 the component was isolated in pure form (5). It proved to be α-amino-β-hydroxy-n-butyric acid, a heretofore unknown growth essential. The spatial arrangement of the groups was later shown to be identical with that of the sugar, $d(-)$ threose, and consequently the newly discovered amino acid was given the name $d(-)$threonine. The naturally occurring threonine is now known as $l(-)$threonine, or, according to the newer usage, L-threonine.*

* The change in prefix from d to l was made in conformity with a report of the Committee on Nomenclature, Spelling and Pronunciation of the American Chemical Society (Committee Report, *Chem. Eng. News*, 25, 1364, 1947). Prefix terminology in carbohydrate chemistry as well as in amino acid chemistry is based upon the glyceraldehydes. The dextrorotatory isomer is by convention designated d-glyceraldehyde. Consequently any sugar with a similar configuration about the highest numbered asymmetric carbon atom

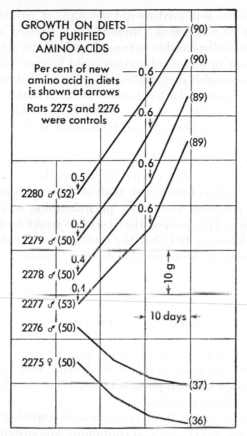

Figure 28.4. Effect on rat growth of addition of threonine to diet. Figures in parentheses indicate initial and final weights of the rats. (R. H. McCoy, C. E. Meyer, and W. C. Rose, *J. Biol. Chem.*, **112**, 283, 1935–36.)

These two compounds are shown below:

```
        COOH                          CHO
         |                             |
  H₂N - C - H                        HOCH
         |                             |
        HCOH                          HCOH
         |                             |
        CH₃                          CH₂OH
    l(—)Threonine                  d(—)Threose
    L-threonine                    D-threose
```

These workers were now able to compound a ration which allowed good growth in rats with the nitrogen supplied entirely by a mixture of purified amino acids. This had not previously been accomplished. Figure 28.4 demon-

is designated a *d* sugar. However, in naming amino acids, the configuration about the lowest numbered asymmetric carbon atom, the α-carbon atom, determines whether the compound shall be designated *d* or *l*. On this basis naturally occurring threonine is an *l* compound. W. C. Rose, its discoverer, has accepted the change. According to newer terminology both sugars and amino acids are designated by small capital letters—i.e., D-glucose, D-alanine.

strates that the amino acid mixture did not support growth of rats until the amino acid threonine was added. Obviously this allowed an ideal approach to the study of the indispensable nature of each of the amino acids in their mixture, for any one or any combination could be removed and the growth properties of the remaining diet studied. If growth failed on the removal of a certain acid and was resumed after its addition, then that acid, after sufficient confirmation of the results, was classed as indispensable for growth of the rat. An acid likewise was classed as dispensable if its removal from the diet did not affect the growth rate.

Soon after developing this technique, the disputed question of the interchangeability of tyrosine and phenylalanine in the rat was settled. Rats failed to grow on a ration from which both of these acids had been removed, and growth was resumed when only phenylalanine was returned to the amino acid mixture. This proved that tyrosine could be formed in the rat body from phenylalanine, but that the reaction could not be reversed, and thus phenylalanine is an indispensable dietary component:

$$C_6H_5CH_2CHNH_2COOH \xrightarrow{\text{ox}} OHC_6H_4CH_2CHNH_2COOH$$

Phenylalanine can be oxidized by the rat to tyrosine. The reverse cannot occur.

This conversion has been confirmed by Moss and Schoenheimer (6), who fed phenylalanine containing stably bound deuterium in the phenyl ring. Tyrosine containing a high proportion of deuterium was later isolated from the liver and other body proteins.

It is now known, however, that tyrosine exerts a sparing action on phenylalanine. On diets low in tyrosine and containing suboptimal levels of phenylalanine, the addition of tyrosine stimulates growth of animals eating such diets. This means that in a deficiency of tyrosine some of the dietary phenylalanine must be converted to the former compound, since it is essential in the body, though not in the food. The addition of tyrosine, then, eliminates the necessity of this conversion, and more of the phenylalanine of the diet is available to meet its functions in growth.

In 1936 it was demonstrated that leucine and isoleucine are indispensable, whereas norleucine is not required in the diet of the rat.

For many years cystine had been considered indispensable. This was difficult, if not impossible, to reconcile with two well-established facts: (a) casein is biologically an excellent protein, and (b) it is practically devoid of cystine. Such a situation was readily explained by Rose and coworkers when they demonstrated that cystine is dispensable but that the other sulfur-containing amino acid, methionine, is indispensable for rat growth. Casein is known to contain considerable methionine, and hence the facts and observations were brought into agreement. It was later established, however, that when cystine was added to a diet containing suboptimum levels of methionine, the growth of rats was stimulated. This amounts to a sparing action of cystine on methionine and is similar to the relationship of tyrosine to phenylalanine.

Direct evidence for the conversion of methionine to cystine was supplied by the use of isotopic sulfur. Tarver and Schmidt (7) fed methionine containing the radioactive sulfur isotope S^{35} to rats and later isolated cystine containing this isotope from hair and skin.

The absence of valine in the diet of rats causes the development of an unusual syndrome in the animals, which, among other symptoms, is characterized by a lack of muscular coordination. After the addition of this amino acid to the ration, the condition disappears. Valine is an indispensable amino acid.

In 1930 Scull and Rose established that rats are able to synthesize arginine. By analyzing the entire bodies of animals at the beginning of the experiment and of litter mates after feeding a diet very low in arginine, they showed

Table 28.2.   Classification of the Amino Acids with Respect to Their Growth Effects in the Rat

Essential	Nonessential
Lysine	Glycine
Tryptophan	Alanine
Histidine	Serine
Phenylalanine	Cystine †
Leucine	Tyrosine ‡
Isoleucine	Aspartic acid
Threonine	Glutamic acid §
Methionine	Proline §
Valine	Hydroxyproline
Arginine *	Citrulline

* Arginine can be synthesized by the rat, but not at a sufficiently rapid rate to meet the demands of maximum growth. Its classification, therefore, as essential or nonessential is purely a matter of definition.
† Cystine can replace about one-sixth of the methionine requirement but has no growth effect in the absence of methionine.
‡ Tyrosine can replace about one-half the phenylalanine requirement but has no growth effect in the absence of phenylalanine.
§ Glutamic acid and proline can serve individually as rather ineffective substitutes for arginine in the diet. This property is not shared by hydroxyproline.
From Rose, W. C.; Oesterling, M. J.; and Womack, M.: *J. Biol. Chem.*, **176**, 753, 1948.

that the tissues contained two or three times as much of this substance as could be accounted for by the total intake in the food. The mouse likewise is able to synthesize arginine.

Later in Rose's laboratory it was demonstrated that rats on a ration devoid of arginine show 70 to 80 per cent as much growth as other animals supplied with this amino acid.

An indispensable dietary component, according to Rose, is one which cannot be synthesized by the animal from available food molecules rapidly enough to meet the demands for normal growth. This definition applies to growth only, and, according to it, arginine is classed as essential. Table 28.2, taken from an article by Rose and coworkers (8) indicates the indispensable and the dispensable amino acids for the growth of rats.

The name MATT VILPHLy is an aid in remembering the ten essential amino acids for growth: M for methionine, A for arginine, Ly for lysine, etc.

As Rose stated, feeding trials containing only the ten indispensable amino acids as a source of protein nitrogen "exceeded our expectations." The rats showed growth gains comparable to those on diets containing all the known amino acids. The former diet, while containing around 18 to 21 per cent of the amino acid mixture, contained only 11.2 per cent of the natural isomers. It should be emphasized that the animals were able to synthesize at least twelve other amino acids from the ten that were supplied, since it is well established that the amino acid pattern of developing protein tissue is essentially unalterable by diet. This means that the new protein tissue of growing rats always contains the same arrangement of the same amino acids even though, in this case, their diet supplied only ten of the twenty-two amino acids (at least) used in its construction.

Table 28.3 indicates Rose's (9) values for the minimum quantity of each essential amino acid required for normal rat growth. These values were

Table 28.3. Minimum Amount of Each Essential Amino Acid Necessary to Support Normal Growth When the Nonessentials Are Included in the Food

Amino Acid	Per Cent	
Lysine	1.0	
Tryptophan	0.2	
Histidine	0.4	
Phenylalanine	0.7	0.9*
Leucine	0.8	
Isoleucine	0.5	
Threonine	0.5	
Methionine	0.4	
Valine	0.7	
Arginine	0.2	
Total	5.8	

* In a diet devoid of tyrosine, the phenylalanine requirement is 0.9 per cent (10).
From Rose, W. C.: *Science*, **86**, 298, 1937. Rose, W. C.; Smith, L. C.; Womack, M.; and Shane, M.: *J. Biol. Chem.*, **181**, 307, 1949.

arrived at by varying the level of one acid while the others were maintained at a constant level. They represent the level of the naturally occurring amino acids required when the nonessentials are liberally supplied in the diet, and the values are to be considered only tentative.

A more detailed classification of the amino acids has been offered by Block and Bolling (11). In Table 28.4 it will be seen that arginine is removed from the indispensable list and classed as semi-indispensable. As pointed out previously, rats can synthesize some of this amino acid, but not sufficient for optimum growth. Glycine is under the same heading, because it has been shown to be essential for growth in some species of fowls. Cystine and tyrosine are classed as semi-indispensable because of their sparing action on methionine and phenylalanine respectively.

Berg (12) has reviewed the subject of utilization of D-amino acids (unnatural forms) by rats, mice and men. The bulk of the studies have been conducted on rats, using growth as the criterion of utilization. Since no animal proteins are known to contain D-amino acids, it follows that animals making use of such isomers must convert them to the L-form (natural form). Of the ten essential amino acids for rat growth, some utilization has been observed for the D-form of tryptophan, methionine, phenylalanine, leucine, valine, histidine, and arginine. Also, D-tyrosine, but not D-cystine, of the semi-indispensable amino acids, was found to be used to some extent. In man D-methionine (13) and D-phenylalanine (14) only were reported to be used, while the other six amino acids of the eight required for nitrogen balance maintenance for adult humans (see further) were found to be unusable.

Table 28.4.   Tentative Classification of Amino Acids

| Dispensable | Semi-Indispensable | | Indispensable |
	Group A	Group B	
Glutamic acid	Arginine	Cystine	Histidine
Aspartic acid	Glycine	Tyrosine	Lysine
Alanine			Tryptophan
Serine			Phenylalanine
Proline			Methionine
Hydroxyproline			Threonine
			Leucine
			Isoleucine
			Valine

From Block, R. J., and Bolling, D.; *J. Am. Dietet. Assoc.*, 20, 69, 1944.

The rat is able to bring about many rearrangements to produce essential amino acids from related compounds supplied in the diet. For instance, β-imidazole lactic acid can replace histidine, and α-keto-γ-methylvaleric acid can replace leucine:

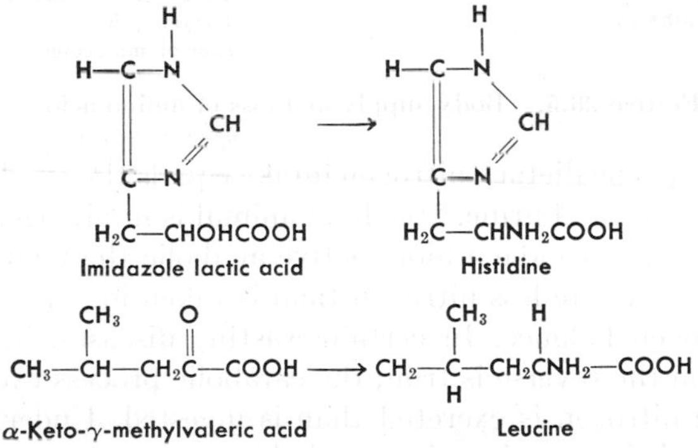

Imidazole lactic acid   Histidine

α-Keto-γ-methylvaleric acid   Leucine

For the sake of brevity, a few other examples will be cited without showing corresponding formulas. The α-keto or the α-hydroxy analogs of all essential acids, except lysine, threonine, and isoleucine, may be substituted for the corresponding amino acids. Certain N-methyl derivatives can be demethylated to yield the amino acid; among these are methylated tryptophan, methionine, and histidine. Likewise, acyl derivatives, and esters and amides in some instances, can be converted to the corresponding amino acids.

On the other hand, a variety of derivatives do not yield the desired amino acid in the body. The N-methyl derivatives of lysine, for instance, cannot be converted to this amino acid. Similarly, rats are unable to insert an amino group at the ϵ position of α-amino caproic acid to form lysine.

Chicks require the ten essential amino acids (rat growth) plus glycine and glutamic acid for best growth. Around 1 or 1.5 per cent glycine is often added to commercial diets. Higher intake of glycine (2 or more per cent) is toxic (15) to chicks. Almquist (16) has reviewed the amino acid intake of some domestic animals.

So far the amino acid requirements for growth only have been considered. Attention must now be turned to other physiologic aspects of protein nutrition, such as maintenance of nitrogen equilibrium in the adult and plasma protein formation.

Nitrogen balance. In a healthy adult animal the processes of catabolism, or breaking down of tissues, and of anabolism, or building up of tissues,

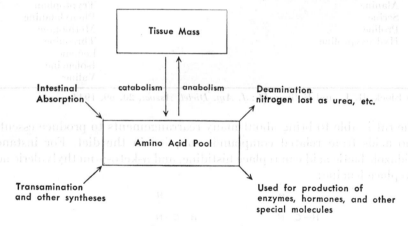

Figure 28.5.   Body supply and loss of amino acids.

are in equilibrium. The dietary nitrogen intake equals the combined nitrogen excretion of the feces and urine.* Such an animal is in nitrogen equilibrium. A growing animal must have a more active anabolic than catabolic process and consequently excrete less nitrogen than is taken in. This is an example of positive nitrogen balance. In certain wasting diseases, in old age, and during starvation the reverse is true; the catabolic process exceeds the anabolic, and more nitrogen is excreted than is ingested. Under such circumstances the body is in negative nitrogen balance.

Consider Figure 28.5. The amino acid pool, though not well defined, represents the available supply of these substances throughout the body fluids and tissues. It is supplied by the catabolic processes, the absorption from the intestine of food amino acids, and by synthesis. It should be emphasized that the indispensable amino acids are not synthesized in appreciable amounts.

* In all but long-time experiments other body losses of nitrogen, such as sweat and fur and horn growth, are generally disregarded.

Suppose a normal adult animal eats more protein than it requires in a day. The extra amino acids accumulating in the pool are largely deaminated, and the nitrogen is excreted in the urine, primarily as urea. This again represents nitrogen equilibrium. But now suppose the animal consumes no protein for a day. Urinary nitrogen excretion continues. The animal is in negative nitrogen balance, since excretion exceeds intake. The mechanism involved here is the critical point of this discussion.

Indispensable as well as dispensable amino acids are continually removed from the pool for purposes other than tissue protein rebuilding. It is obvious, then, that a constant supply to the pool, other than through tissue breakdown, must be available. Normally this is met by absorption of amino acids from the intestine, but in the animal not eating protein this source of supply is eliminated.

The catabolism of tissue protein continues. The anabolism cannot, since the loss of amino acids from the pool continues but their supply to it does not. As pointed out elsewhere, the amino acid arrangement of tissue protein is essentially unalterable, and consequently, in a deficiency of even one essential amino acid, tissue synthesis slows down.

Under these conditions the body finds itself with a supply of amino acids which in large part cannot be utilized for synthesis. Consequently, they are deaminated, and the nitrogen appears in the urine as urea. This, in general, is the mechanism of a negative nitrogen balance.

For the maintenance of nitrogen equilibrium in adult rats, all the ten amino acids indispensable for growth, except arginine, are necessary (17). The removal of any one of the other nine acids from the diet results in a negative nitrogen balance, and on replacing the missing amino acid the animals return to a state of nitrogen equilibrium. It is not surprising that arginine can be dispensed with for adult maintenance, since, as pointed out previously, rats synthesize a considerable amount of this amino acid.

Rose and Rice (18) demonstrated that adult dogs require the ten growth amino acids, except arginine, for maintenance of nitrogen equilibrium.

Elman, Davey, and Loo (19) starved dogs several days and then supplied them with their nonprotein needs by gavage (stomach tube). This food consisted primarily of Ringer's solution, Karo syrup, and a vitamin supplement. An amino acid mixture containing all the ten essential amino acids except arginine was dissolved in water and injected intravenously as a 5 per cent solution. On this regime dogs maintained nitrogen equilibrium. If histidine was removed from the mixture and glycine substituted to yield the same nitrogen intake, positive balances were maintained for a period of three days, after which nitrogen excretion increased markedly, leading to negative balances. This is in contrast to the results found when an acid hydrolysate of casein instead of the mixture of pure amino acids was injected. Such a hydrolysate, as pointed out previously, contains no tryptophan, since this is destroyed during hydrolysis. The dogs showed a marked negative balance for each day of the experiment rather than only after the third day, as in the case of the histidine deficiency.

Human requirement. One of the outstanding aftermaths of the animal work discussed has been the application of the methods used and the results obtained to studies of human requirements for amino acids. During this work a number of important physiologic functions of individual amino acids have come to light. Some of these constitute important advances in medicine.

The technique developed by the Johns Hopkins group (Holt and co-workers) for the study of human amino acid requirements is in general as follows. An acid hydrolysate of casein is prepared which contains the amino acids of this protein with the exception of tryptophan, which is destroyed during the process. Cystine is added to the extent of 1 per cent, and this mixture is used to supply 90 per cent of the dietary nitrogen; the remaining 10 per cent is obtained from certain low nitrogen foods such as tomatoes,

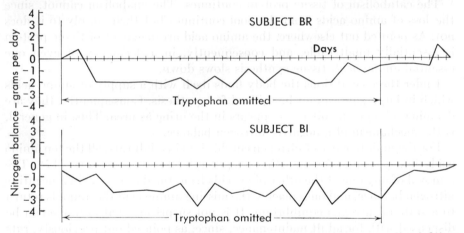

Figure 28.6. Observations of nitrogen balance in human subjects on a diet deficient in tryptophan. (Holt, L. E., Jr.; Albanese, A. A.; Brumback, J. E., Jr.; Kadji, C.; and Wangerin, D. M.: *Proc. Soc. Exptl. Biol. & Med.*, **48**, 726, 1941.)

carrots, apples, and oranges. Fats, starches, and sugars are supplied as well as vitamin supplements. The completed diet supplies the adult subject with 2400 to 2700 Cal per day, and the nitrogen intake is adjusted to the weight of the subjects to supply 0.1 g per kilogram per day.

Such a ration is practically devoid of tryptophan and was employed to establish the essential nature of this amino acid for maintenance of nitrogen equilibrium in adult human subjects. For a week preceding the experimental period and for a week following it the subjects were given the above diet except that it was supplemented with tryptophan to the extent of 1.5 per cent. Throughout the experiments the food and the excreta of the subjects were analyzed for nitrogen content. Nitrogen balances were calculated for each two-day period.

Figure 28.6 shows a curve of the nitrogen balance of subjects on this experiment. It is seen that when tryptophan was absent from the diet, a continued negative nitrogen balance resulted, whereas, upon the addition of this amino acid to the diet, nitrogen equilibrium was shortly attained. It must be assumed from this that tryptophan is a dietary essential for human beings. Certain other amino acids can be removed from or destroyed in casein hydrolysates. By feeding mixtures prepared by this method, workers at Johns Hopkins have demonstrated the essential nature of various amino acids for maintenance of nitrogen equilibrium in human adults.

After a few days on a lysine-deficient diet (20) there occurred a sharp rise in nonketo organic acids in the urine, and the subjects complained of nausea, dizziness, and hypersensitivity to metallic sounds. Negative nitrogen balances prevailed. At this point the lysine-deficient hydrolysate of the diet was replaced by an hydrolysate of casein containing this amino acid. After four days the subjective symptoms were relieved, nonketo acid excretion fell to normal, and nitrogen equilibrium was restored.

Three male subjects subsisting on a diet deficient in arginine maintained nitrogen equilibrium for ten days (21). However, on the ninth day of the experiment the seminal plasma of each of the men revealed a reduction in spermatozoa to approximately one-tenth of the normal value. A change to a similar diet, but containing arginine, resulted in an increased spermatozoa count, although several weeks on a normal diet were required to restore the original values. It must be concluded that arginine is a dietary essential for human beings, although nitrogen equilibrium can be maintained in its absence for short periods at least.

Holt and Albanese (22) gave a partial review of their work and brought out the interesting point that arginine therapy resulted in definite stimulation of spermatogenesis in two of five cases of idiopathic hypospermia.

Rose (23,24,25) has attacked the problem of human amino acid requirements by using mixtures of pure acids as the source of nitrogen in his diets. As in his animal studies, one or more of these constituents was omitted. In these experiments the maintenance of nitrogen balance was used as a criterion of the essential nature of an amino acid. The original diet consisted of starch, sucrose, washed centrifugated butter, inorganic salts, vitamins, and the ten amino acids essential for rat growth. The amino acid mixture supplied the normal adult subjects with approximately 7 g of nitrogen per day. Nitrogen equilibrium was maintained on such diets for six to eight days. This indicates that the twelve amino acids previously shown to be dispensable for animals are similarly not essential for man.

After this experiment individual amino acids were omitted from the diets, and the effects on nitrogen equilibrium were studied. By such means it was demonstrated that valine, methionine, threonine, leucine, isoleucine, phenylalanine, tryptophan, and lysine are essential for the maintenance of nitrogen equilibrium. The removal of any one of the above acids from the diet was followed by a marked negative nitrogen balance which was corrected on the readdition of the amino acid to the food mixture.

The removal of histidine from the diets was not attended by alterations in nitrogen balance. This finding was quite unexpected, since animals require histidine. Repetition of the tests with various individuals led to the same conclusion. Similarly, negative nitrogen balances were not observed after the removal of arginine from the diet. It thus appears that neither histidine nor arginine is necessary in human adults for the maintenance of nitrogen equilibrium.

It is now established that to maintain nitrogen equilibrium in adults eight amino acids are required in the diet; viz., methionine, threonine, tryptophan, valine, isoleucine, leucine, phenylalanine, and lysine.

A review of their human experiments is given by Rose and others (26). Table 28.5 from this paper indicates tentative quantitative requirements of amino acids for nitrogen balance maintenance in adults. Realizing the individual variations in human response, Rose has set the safe intake of the amino acids at twice the minimum daily need. Comprehensive reviews by Rose (27) and another by Leverton (28) are available.

Table 28.5. Summary of Amino Acid Requirements of Man

All values were determined with diets containing the eight essential amino acids and sufficient extra nitrogen to permit the synthesis of the nonessentials.

Amino acid	No. of quantitative experiments	Range of requirements observed	Value proposed *tentatively* as minimum	Value which is definitely a safe intake	No. of subjects maintained in N balance on safe intakes or less
		gm. per day	*gm. per day*	*gm. per day*	
L-Tryptophan	3*	0.15–0.25	0.25	0.50	42
L-Phenylalanine	6	0.80–1.10†	1.10	2.20	32
L-Lysine	6	0.40–0.80	0.80	1.60	37‡
L-Threonine	3§	0.30–0.50	0.50	1.00	29
L-Methionine	6	0.80–1.10‖	1.10	2.20	23
L-Leucine	5	0.50–1.10	1.10	2.20	18
L-Isoleucine	4	0.65–0.70	0.70	1.40	17
L-Valine	5	0.40–0.80	0.80	1.60	33

* Fifteen other young men were maintained in nitrogen balance on daily intakes of 0.20 g, though their exact minimal needs were not established. Of the 42 subjects maintained on the *safe* level of intake, thirty-three received 0.30 g daily or less.

† These values were obtained with diets which were devoid of tyrosine. In two experiments, the presence of tyrosine in the food was shown to spare the phenylalanine requirement to the extent of 70 to 75 per cent (29).

‡ Ten of these individuals received daily intakes of 0.80 g or less.

§ In addition to these three subjects, four young men received rations containing 0.60 g of L-threonine daily and 16 others received doses of 0.80 g daily. No attempt was made to determine the exact minimal requirements of these 20 individuals, but all were in positive balance on the doses indicated.

‖ These values were determined with cystine-free diets. In three experiments, the presence of cystine was found to exert a sparing effect of 80 to 89 per cent upon the minimal methionine needs of the subjects (30).

The human infant requires the eight essential amino acids necessary for adults. The quantitative needs are far different, as might be expected, since the adult is in nitrogen equilibrium and the infant in a marked positive balance. Interesting aspects of this matter are discussed by Albanese (31,32).

Madden (33) reported that parenterally administered amino acids are able to maintain nitrogen balance and sustain weight in man for as long as 75 days.

Plasma protein synthesis. Another function of amino acids in the body which has been studied (34) is that of regeneration of plasma proteins and of hemoglobin. Whipple and associates believe that, under normal circumstances, in the dog plasma protein molecules are constantly passing out of the blood and into the tissues, and tissue protein molecules are replacing those lost from the blood. It appears that at least half the circulating protein may undergo such an exchange in 24 hours! Also, the manufacture of new plasma protein molecules from orally or parentally supplied amino acids can be demonstrated to take place in as short a time as one hour. These observations indicate a close relationship between food, plasma, and tissue proteins.

A hypoproteinemia can readily be induced in dogs by bleeding the animals and reinjecting the washed cells. This process is known as "plasmapheresis" and is valuable in studying the ability of amino acids and of various food proteins to rebuild plasma proteins.

In plasmapheresed animals the replacement of dietary protein by the ten amino acids essential for rat growth is followed by excellent plasma protein production, and the weight and nitrogen balances of the animals are maintained. The mixture is as effective as most dietary proteins in these respects. The amino acid mixture can be dissolved and given intravenously with equally good results. An odd finding is that cystine can replace methionine for plasma protein production for seven to ten days, but apparently at the expense of body tissues, since under these conditions there is body weight loss and a negative nitrogen balance.

Whipple and associates (35,36) have studied hemoglobin and plasma protein production simultaneously. Dogs were fed low protein diets to induce low plasma protein levels and were bled periodically to produce anemia. When such dogs were given digests of dog plasma or serum, they invariably produced more hemoglobin than plasma protein. Dog or sheep hemoglobin injected intraperitoneally was well utilized to form both. Of considerable interest is the finding that the amino acid mixture of Rose was as effective by mouth or vein for hemoglobin and plasma protein production as were digests of hemoglobin, casein, or serum. In fact, new hemoglobin formation was favored more by the amino acid mixture than by any other material tested.

Risser and coworkers (37) demonstrated that adult dogs could be kept in nitrogen equilibrium by the intravenous injection of a casein hydrolysate fortified with tryptophan and cystine. The requirement was established to be 120 mg of nitrogen per kilo of body weight per day. A fortified partial hydrolysate in which only one-third of the amino acids were in a free state also maintained nitrogen equilibrium when given similarly and at the same level of nitrogen intake. Thus it appears that intravenously administered peptide nitrogen in this form is available for maintaining nitrogen balance in dogs.

Barrows and Chow (38) have reviewed the field of plasma proteins and other protein syntheses in relation to diet.

Amino acid deficiency. A rather new field in nutrition involves studying the symptoms of a sustained single amino acid deficiency in animals. Admittedly the experiments so far reported have serious limitations due to the loss of appetite and the consequent inanition of the animals. But, since the paired feeding technique* has generally been used, the differences in animals on the deficient diets and on the control diets may largely represent changes due to the single amino acid deficiency.

Maun and coworkers (39,40,41) have reported on the morphologic findings in rats subjected to a deficiency of each of three amino acids. On a deficiency of either phenylalanine or leucine for one month, rats showed at autopsy thymic atrophy, atrophy and decreased lipid content of the adrenal cortex, degeneration and atrophy of the seminiferous tubular epithelium, and a thinning of the epiphyses of long bones. Certain ocular changes were noted in the leucine-deficient animals. Plasma proteins and hemoglobin were reduced in animals on a phenylalanine-deficient diet.

After 28 days on a histidine-deficient diet, rats showed decreased hemoglobin, atrophy of the thymus gland, and vascularization and metaplasia of the cornea.

These results are cited in order to indicate the diversity of pathologic findings from a single essential amino acid deficiency. They open a fruitful avenue of research.

The possible relations of these results to human deficiencies offer a field for speculation and study. It is possible to show by calculation that certain restricted diets used in human diseases are deficient in some essential amino acid. This will probably become more apparent as our limited knowledge of the quantitative human requirements is expanded.

Block and Bolling (11) made estimations of the amino acid content of certain food proteins and have calculated the available essential amino acids in 100-g portions of various foods. These values are compared with the estimated human requirements in Table 28.6, taken from their paper. It should be understood that 100 g of protein is more than the average per capita consumption, even in the United States. It should be noted that 100 g of white flour supplies only 40 per cent of the daily requirement of lysine. Certainly few, if any, persons in the United States obtain their total daily protein requirement from wheat, but were corn to be used in conjunction with wheat, the situation would not be improved. Consider also that a great many individuals ingest perhaps only 40 to 50 g of protein daily. It then becomes imperative that a variety of different proteins be included in the diet, and especially some animal protein, if amino acid deficiencies are to be avoided. It is certainly quite true that generally the American diet is comprised of foods sufficiently varied that amino acid deficiencies are largely avoided. But it would be folly to assume that human amino acid deficiencies are not current and, among certain groups of people, widespread in the United States.

---

* The paired feeding technique is a valuable tool in experimental nutrition work. In each pair of animals used, one receives the deficient diet and the other receives the same diet plus the nutrient under study. The latter animal's daily food intake is adjusted to equal the intake of the animal on the deficient diet. Thus, the two animals of one pair have the same over-all intake, with the exception of one or more substances under study. Obviously, modifications make the procedure highly adaptable to a variety of circumstances.

Interesting observations on the relation of dietary protein and cholinesterase enzyme activity of rat tissues was reported by Barrows (42).

Biologic value of proteins. The biologic value of a protein is an expression of a number of the nutritional characteristics of the substance. Among these are: (a) the digestibility, (b) the availability of the digested products, and (c) the presence and amounts of the various essential amino acids. The values obtained for the nutritive or the biologic value of a protein are empirical and are useful for comparing proteins from various sources or comparing a combination of proteins such as might be found in a mixed feed or diet.

One of the early methods for estimating the biologic value of proteins, and one which is still used today, is the nitrogen retention method developed

Table 28.6. Percentage of Optimal Daily Requirement for Each of the Essential Amino Acids Supplied by 100 g Protein Obtained from Each of the Specified Foods

Amino Acid	Average Requirement Calculated grams	Supplied by 100 g Protein per cent					
		Meat	Milk	White Flour	"Enriched" Bread*	Corn	Soy-beans
Arginine	3.5	210	125	110	110	115	165
Histidine	2.0	105	125	110	113	120	115
Lysine	5.2	145	140	40	55	40	105
Tyrosine	3.9	80	140	100	113	155	105
Tryptophan	1.1	110	175	90	120	55	145
Phenylalanine	4.4	100	130	125	115	105	125
Cystine + methionine	3.8	110	105	110	110	130	80
Threonine	3.5	125	135	80	80	105	120
Leucine	9.1	135	180	130	120	240	90
Isoleucine	3.3	105	135	110	100	115	125
Valine	3.8	90	145	90	80	120	115

* "Enriched" bread contained 6 per cent milk solids and high vitamin yeast.
From Block, R. J., and Bolling, D.: *J. Am. Dietet. Assoc.*, 20, 69, 1944.

especially by H. H. Mitchell and his many collaborators at the University of Illinois. This technique was developed in 1924. Certain refinements in technique have been added (43).

Mitchell's method is time-consuming and difficult to carry out, since it involves nitrogen balance experiments on specially prepared growing rats or other animals. His definition of biologic value (later called "protein value") is the per cent of absorbed food nitrogen not eliminated in the urine. It can be seen that this is an expression of the efficiency of utilization of ingested amino acids. Of course, a number of rats must be used, and the experiments are generally conducted for at least five days so that average values may be obtained.

The following data from some of Mitchell's early work (44) will illustrate the calculations. A rat ingested 127 mg of nitrogen per day (10.0 g of ration containing 1.27 per cent nitrogen). The fecal nitrogen was 22 mg, of which 18 mg was calculated to be of body origin, indicating that 4 mg of the food nitrogen was lost to the animal. So the animal had a net absorption of 123 mg. The urinary nitrogen averaged 58 mg per day, of which 34 mg was calculated to be of endogenous origin, and, consequently, 24 mg represented food nitrogen lost in the urine. Of the 123 mg of nitrogen absorbed, 99 mg was retained by the animal, and thus $100 \times (99 \div 123) = 81$, which is the determined biologic value of the dietary protein studied in this experiment.

A good deal of valuable information has been developed by this technique, not only by Mitchell and his group but also by many other investigators.

The supplementary action of one food protein on another is of special interest, since only in experimental work is a human being or an animal limited to a single dietary protein. Two proteins fed together often show a higher biologic value than (a) the biologic value of either protein fed alone at a comparable level or (b) the calculated value from the individual values and the proportion of each fed. This is known as the "supplementary action" of protein, and an insight into the cause of it is fundamental to an understanding of the nutritive or biologic value of proteins.

Suppose a single protein showed a biologic value of 70 (70 per cent of the food nitrogen absorbed retained by the experimental animal) and another protein a value of 50. By calculation, then, if the total protein content of the ration were maintained the same but was derived from half of each of these proteins, the value should be 60, provided that no supplementary effect occurred. If the mixture showed a value of 66, however, a supplementary effect of one protein on the other would be indicated. Fundamentally this would mean that one of the proteins contains one or more essential amino acids deficient in the other protein.

Recall at this point that catabolism and anabolism of protein are going on continuously in the body. In order to carry out the latter process efficiently, all the essential amino acids must be available in sufficient quantity. If they are not, excess nitrogen is lost in the urine, since the catabolic processes continue. Under such circumstances it is obvious that less absorbed food nitrogen is retained by the body and low biologic values result from proteins or mixtures of proteins deficient in essential amino acids.

Another approach to the appraisal of the biologic value of protein is the method devised about 1915 by Osborne and Mendel (45) and improved upon later by these and other investigators. The modern version of the method involves the determination of the growth rate of young animals on a basal ration devoid of protein, but nutritionally complete in other respects, to which has been added 10 per cent of the protein or its equivalent in the food to be tested. The nutritive value of the protein is calculated as the ratio of gain in body weight to the weight of protein ingested during the experimental period—i.e., gain in body weight in grams per gram of protein consumed.

It is readily seen that this method has certain advantages over the nitrogen balance method; no nitrogen determinations need be made on urine and feces. The experimental period is considerably longer however, usually about four weeks. Certainly the method affords good comparisons of biologic values between various proteins or between the proteins of various mixed foods and feeds.

The following data from Hove and Harrel (46) illustrate the calculations used in this method.

Four young rats on the experimental ration containing 10.2 per cent protein (N × 6.25) from wheat germ showed an average gain in weight over 4 weeks of 86 g and consumed an average of 300 g of the ration during this time. The biologic value averaged 2.8. This was calculated by dividing the growth (86 g) by the protein consumption, 10.2 per cent of 300 g = 30.6 g.

Obviously the level of protein fed in the experiments must be expressed for the biologic value to have any significance. Compare, for instance, with the figures above, the value of 2.12 for the protein of wheat germ when fed at a level of 4.7 per cent.

A number of attempts to assign some type of value to proteins on the basis of amino acid analysis have been made. Thus Mitchell and Block (47) devised a system of "chemical scores" based on the quantity of the essential amino acid in greatest deficit in a protein (compared to a standard protein). Block and Bolling (48) made some remarkable comparisons between biologic value of proteins and the determined amino acid content.

Onor (49,50) proposed the Essential Amino Acid index (EAA index) to indicate the value of specific proteins. The EAA index is based on a comparison of the amount of each essential amino acid in the protein compared to the amount of each in whole egg protein. Close agreement between predicted and observed biologic values are found in most instances.

An interesting sidelight relating to amino acid composition and biologic value of proteins is found in work by Melnick and coworkers (51). It has been known for some time that the biologic value of soybean proteins is markedly improved by heat treatment. Since the degree of digestibility and the amino acid composition are unchanged by heating, no explantion for the improvement was available. It is also known that the addition of methionine to soybean proteins increases the biologic value, and it was assumed that heating in some way increases the availability of this amino acid.

These workers indicate that the rate of liberation of methionine and not the extent may be the limiting factor. Without heat treatment the soy flour used showed a biologic value of 53, and after autoclaving a value of 71 (nitrogen retention method). The degree of digestibility was about the same, and in each case only about one-half the methionine present was absorbed. But in vitro work showed that methionine in the untreated preparation was liberated at a much slower rate by enzymes.

They conclude that in vivo methionine is released later from the unheated soy meal and that absorption occurs so late in the intestinal transit that this amino acid as well as others are not well utilized for synthesis. They presume that for optimum utilization of protein all the essential amino acids must be liberated during digestion at rates allowing mutual supplementation.

The conclusions are predicated partly on the established fact that feeding a diet devoid of one essential amino acid leads to poor nitrogen utilization (negative balance) and that injecting the missing amino acid separately eight hours after giving the basic diet does not improve nitrogen retention.

The experiments of Geiger (52) are of interest in this connection. He fed young rats on diets containing incomplete amino acid mixtures for 12 hours of each day, and then for the alternate 12 hours he gave them the same diet in which the missing amino acid or acids were substituted for the original amino acid mixture. So, during each day the rats had access to an adequate supply of essential amino acids. Since the rats showed little or no growth compared to control animals eating the diet containing the complete mixture of amino acids, it was assumed that storage of amino acids, even for short periods, did not occur. It follows from these experiments that delayed supplementation of a missing essential amino acid does not allow good utilization for growth of the amino acids previously eaten by young rats, at least when 12-hour time intervals are employed, as in this study. It has not been demonstrated that delayed supplementation of each essential amino acid results in inefficient utilization of other food amino acids, but Geiger's study indicates that this is the case with regard to methionine, tryptophan, and lysine.

Antibody formation. Among the globulins of blood plasma proteins there is a distinct fraction called the "γ-globulin fraction." A number of specific antibodies have been found in this fraction of the blood serum of normal individuals (53). Cohn (54) and others demonstrated the value of the γ-globulin fraction of human serum in preventing measles. Fraction II of the γ-globulin fraction primarily has been employed in the study of the control of infectious diseases. This fraction represents about 5 per cent of the total plasma protein. Cohn stated that the γ-globulin fraction may come to be recognized as the most important fraction of the plasma from the point of view of public health. The further importance of these protein antibodies in disease resistance cannot be dwelt on here, but the relation of diet to their formation may well be discussed briefly.

Elsewhere in this chapter the relation of dietary amino acids and proteins to plasma protein regeneration has been discussed. It is apparent that antibody formation is an important part of this problem. Cannon, in a review (55), pointed out that the problem of antibody production is certainly the problem of plasma globulin synthesis.

It has been amply demonstrated that food amino acids enter actively into the metabolism of the various plasma protein fractions, including the γ-globulin fraction. Also, correlation between nutritive value of proteins and their value in antibody production has been indicated. This is not unexpected, since analytical data suggest a close similarity between antibody globulin and normal plasma globulin.

In protein-depleted animals the hypoalbuminemia leads to various conditions including edema, while the hypoglobulinemia results in lowered resistance to infection. Cannon and coworkers (56) studied antibody formation in normal and hypoproteinemic rats. They injected red cells from sheep and measured the hemolysin (an antibody) output. Their results indicated that the animals with normal protein reserves and an adequate protein intake formed, on the average, approximately ten times as much antibody as did the rats with depleted reserves.

These workers further demonstrated that replenishing the protein reserves in depleted animals by feeding high quality protein for a period of only seven days renewed the animals' capacity to form specific antibodies in almost normal quantities. Further work from the same laboratory (57,58) extends these findings.

Dubos and Schaedler (59) studied resistance to infection in mice subsisting on diets containing various proteins at a number of levels. The qualitative character of the protein and the amount fed were found to be important in determining resistance. Amino acid supplements were also used. It was observed that resistance varied independently of the growth curve, and the authors concluded that resistance to bacterial infections is controlled by nutritional factors different from those concerned with gain in weight.

The problem of decreased resistance to disease and its relation to protein nutrition in human beings is of tremendous importance. Although data on human beings indicating a close relationship between these factors are largely circumstantial, it is only necessary to consider the known correlation of disease incidence and famine in order to appreciate that such a relationship does exist. Cannon (55) reviewed this problem in a general way in his discussion of protein metabolism and antibody formation previously mentioned.

Amino acid imbalance. It follows that a high biologic value protein contains a balance of amino acids in proportions required by the body and that as the balance of amino acids in a protein diverges from these figures, the biologic value falls. According to Harper (60), the concept of amino acid imbalance has developed from many studies in animals in which adverse effects, beyond the expected decrease in protein utilization, have been observed as a result of feeding low protein diets, unbalanced by the addition to the diet of amino acids or unbalanced protein. The decreased growth rate or other effect can be reversed by supplying an additional quantity of the amino acid that is most limiting in the diet.

Amino acid imbalance may also be thought of as a relative essential amino acid deficiency resulting from ingesting an excess of one or more amino acids when the diet is barely adequate with respect to protein. As an example, Elvehjem and coworkers (61) fed weaning rats on diets containing only 6 per cent of the protein fibrin. When the diet was supplemented with methionine and phenylalanine, the acids calculated to be most limiting for growth, there resulted a growth depression rather than a stimulation. Additional supplements of histidine, leucine, isoleucine, and valine improved growth considerably. No adequate explanation for the imbalance phenomenon is available. Other discussions indicate further complexities of the problem (62,63,64).

Protein requirement. Since man's protein requirement is actually an amino acid requirement, and since the quantitative aspects of dietary amino acids are almost wholly unknown, it is impossible to do more than estimate the protein needs. Early workers set the needed protein intake much higher than the values generally employed today. Voit, for instance, studied the intake of a number of German working men and arrived at a figure of 118 g per day, which became the standard requirement. Many other workers soon attempted to show that this figure is too high. In this country Chittenden studied many adult diets, especially in relation to protein intake, and showed that nitrogen equilibrium could be maintained on protein intakes of 35 to 50 g per day. Other workers feel that 1 g of protein per kilogram of body weight per day better expresses man's requirement. This figure is in agreement with the recommended standard (Table 18.5, page 696) set forth by the Food and Nutrition Board, National Research Council, of 70 g per day for a moderately active adult man.

It should be kept in mind that the type of protein is of prime importance, and the above values are based on the assumption that the protein is derived from a variety of foods, including meat, eggs, and milk. It is also assumed that fat and carbohydrate are present in the diet to supply sufficient additional calories.

The student undoubtedly recognizes that man's protein requirement has not been studied in detail. Few reports are available on human requirements.

One recent study should be mentioned here. Mitchell and associates (65) have carefully determined the biologic value of proteins and the protein requirement for nitrogen balance in women by the nitrogen retention technique. They studied milk, white flour, soy flour, a soy-white flour combination (13 and 87 per cent), and a well-balanced mixture of foods. The indicated biologic values were, in the same order: 74, 41, 65, 55, and 65.

They also reported that, after making due allowances for probable dermal losses of nitrogen and for growth of tissues during adult life, the average daily requirements of protein for an adult calculated to 70 kg body weight, 1.8 square meters body surface, and a basal metabolism of 1650 Cal daily are for the proteins of: milk, 43 g; white flour, 74 g; soy flour, 47 g; soy-white flour combination, 54 g; and mixed foods, 50 g. These values are requirements and are not to be considered optimum intakes for human beings.

SPECIAL REFERENCES

1. Mathews, A. P.: *Physiological Chemistry*, 5th ed. Wm. Wood & Co., New York, 1930, p. 872.
2. Mendel, L. B.: *Harvey Lectures*, 10, 101, 1914–15.
3. St. Julian, R. R., and Rose, W. C.: *J. Biol. Chem.*, 98, 439, 1932.
4. Rose, W. C.: *Physiol. Revs.*, 18, 109, 1938.
5. McCoy, R. H.; Meyer, C. E.; and Rose, W. C.: *J. Biol. Chem.*, 112, 283, 1935.
6. Moss, A. R., and Schoenheimer, R.: *J. Biol. Chem.*, 135, 415, 1940.
7. Tarver, H., and Schmidt, C. L. A.: *J. Biol. Chem.*, 130, 67, 1939.
8. Rose, W. C.; Oesterling, M. J.; and Womack, M.: *J. Biol. Chem.*, 176, 753, 1948.
9. Rose, W. C.: *Science*, 86, 298, 1937.
10. Rose, W. C., and Womack, M.: *J. Biol. Chem.*, 166, 103, 1946.
11. Block, R. J., and Bolling, D.: *J. Am. Dietet. Assoc.*, 20, 69, 1944.
12. Berg, C. P., in *Protein and Amino Acid Nutrition*, Albanese, A. A. (ed.). Academic Press, New York, 1959, p. 57.
13. Rose, W. C.; Coon, M. J.; Lockhart, H. B.; and Lambert, G. F.: *J. Biol. Chem.*, 215, 101, 1955.
14. Rose, W. C.; Leach, B. E.; Coon, M. J.; and Lambert, G. F.: *J. Biol. Chem.*, 213, 913, 1955.
15. Almquist, H. J.; Stokstad, E. L. R.; Mecchi, E.; and Manning, P. V. D.: *J. Biol. Chem.*, 134, 213, 1940.
16. Almquist, H. J., in *Protein and Amino Acid Nutrition*, Albanese, A. A. (ed). Academic Press, New York, 1959, p. 349.

17. Wolf, P. A., and Corley, R. C.: *Am. J. Physiol.*, **127**, 589, 1939.
18. Rose, W. C., and Rice, E. E.: *Science*, **90**, 186, 1939.
19. Elman, R.; Davey, H. W.; and Loo, Y.: *Arch. Biochem.*, **3**, 45, 1943.
20. Albanese, A. A.; Holt, L. E., Jr.; Frankston, J. E.; Kajdi, C. N.; Brumback, J. E., Jr.; and Wangerin, D. M.: *Proc. Soc. Exptl. Biol. Med.*, **52**, 209, 1943.
21. Holt, L. E., Jr.; Albanese, A. A.; Shettles, L. B.; Kajdi, C. N.; and Wangerin, D. M.: *Federation Proc.*, **1**, 116, 1942.
22. Holt, L. E., Jr., and Albanese, A. A.: *Trans. Assoc. Am. Physicians*, **58**, 143, 1944.
23. Rose, W. C.; Haines, W. J.; and Johnson, J. E.: *J. Biol. Chem.*, **146**, 683, 1942.
24. Rose, W. C.: *Federation Proc.*, **8**, 546, 1949.
25. Rose, W. C.: *Chem. Eng. News*, **30**, 2385, 1952.
26. Rose, W. C.; Wixom, R. L.; Lockhart, H. B.; and Lambert, G. F.: *J. Biol. Chem.*, **217**, 987, 1955.
27. Rose, W. C.: *Nut. Abstracts and Revs.*, **27**, 63, 1957.
28. Leverton, R. M., in *Protein and Amino Acid Nutrition*, Albanese, A. A. (ed.). Academic Press, New York, 1959, p. 477.
29. Rose, W. C., and Wixom, R. L.: *J. Biol. Chem.*, **217**, 95, 1955.
30. Rose, W. C., and Wixom, R. L.: *J. Biol. Chem.*, **216**, 763, 1955.
31. Albanese, A. A.: *Protein and Amino Acid Requirements of Mammals*. Academic Press, New York, 1950, p. 115.
32. Albanese, A. A., in *Protein and Amino Acid Nutrition*, Albanese, A. A. (ed.). Academic Press, New York, 1959, p. 419.
33. Madden, S. C.: *Proc. Inst. Med. Chicago*, **15**, 25, 1944.
34. Madden, S. C.; Carter, J. R.; Kattus, A. A., Jr.; Miller, L. L.; and Whipple, G. H.: *J. Exptl. Med.* **77**, 277, 1943.
35. Whipple, G. H.: *Am. J. Med. Sci.*, **203**, 477, 1942.
36. Robscheit-Robbins, F. S.; Miller, L. L.; and Whipple, G. H.: *J. Exptl. Med.*, **77**, 375, 1943.
37. Risser, W. C.; Schenk, J. R.; and Frost, D. V.: *Science*, **103**, 362, 1946.
38. Barrows, C. H., Jr., and Chow, B. F., in *Protein and Amino Acid Nutrition*, Albanese, A. A. (ed.). Academic Press, New York, 1959, p. 117.
39. Maun, M. E.; Cahill, W. M.; and Davis, R. M.: *Arch. Path.*, **39**, 294, 1945.
40. Maun, M. E.; Cahill, W. M.; and Davis, R. M.: *Arch. Path.*, **40**, 173, 1945.
41. Maun, M. E.; Cahill, W. M.; and Davis, R. M.: *Arch. Path.*, **41**, 25, 1946.
42. Barrows, C.: *J. Nutrition*, **66**, 515, 1958.
43. Mitchell, H. H.; Hamilton, T. S.; and Beadles, J. R.: *J. Nutrition*, **29**, 13, 1945.
44. Mitchell, H. H., and Carman, G. G.: *J. Biol. Chem.*, **68**, 183, 1926.
45. Osborne, T. B., and Mendel, L. B.: *J. Biol. Chem.*, **20**, 351, 1915; **22**, 241, 1915.
46. Hove, E. L., and Harrel, C. G.: *Cereal Chem.*, **20**, 141, 1943.
47. Mitchell, H. H., and Block, R. J.: *J. Biol. Chem.*, **163**, 599, 1946.
48. Block, R. J., and Bolling, D.: *J. Am. Dietet. Assoc.*, **20**, 69, 1944.
49. Oser, B. L.: *J. Am. Dietet. Assoc.*, **27**, 396, 1951.
50. Oser, B. L., in *Protein and Amino Acid Nutrition*, Albanese, A. A. (ed.). Academic Press, New York, 1959, p. 281.
51. Melnick, D.; Oser, B. L.; and Weiss, S.: *Science*, **103**, 326, 1946.
52. Geiger, E.: *J. Nutrition*, **34**, 97, 1947.
53. Enders, J. F.: *J. Clin. Invest.*, **23**, 510, 1944.
54. Cohn, E. J.: *Science*, **101**, 51, 1945.
55. Cannon, P. R.: *Advances in Protein Chem.*, **2**, 135, 1945.
56. Cannon, P. R.; Wissler, R. W.; Woolridge, R. L.; and Benditt, E. P.: *Ann. Surg.*, **120**, 514, 1944.
57. Wissler, R. W.; Woolridge, R. L.; Steffee, C. H., Jr.; and Cannon, P. R.: *J. Immunol.*, **52**, 267, 1946.
58. Wissler, R. W.; Steffee, C. H.; Woolridge, R. L.; Benditt, E. P.; and Cannon, P. R.: *J. Am. Dietet. Assoc.*, **23**, 841, 1947.
59. Dubos, R. J., and Schaedler, R. W.: *Science*, **126**, 1230, 1957.
60. Harper, A. E.: *J. Nutrition*, **68**, 405, 1959.
61. Deshpande, P. D.; Harper, A. E.; and Elvehjem, C. A.: *J. Biol. Chem.*, **230**, 327, 1958.
62. Salmon, W. D.: *Am. J. Clin. Nutrition*, **6**, 487, 1958.
63. Fisher, H.; Griminger, P.; Leveille, G. A.; and Shapiro, R.: *J. Nutrition*, **71**, 213, 1960.
64. *Nutrition Revs.*, **17**, 122, 1959.
65. Bricker, M.; Mitchell, H. H.; and Kinsman, G. M.: *J. Nutrition*, **30**, 269, 1945.

29

Nutritional aspects of the lipids and the carbohydrates

LIPIDS IN NUTRITION

All fractions of the large class of compounds known as lipids have important and essential roles in animal nutrition. Of these various types of substances, it appears that only certain fatty acids must be ingested preformed; the other fatty acids and lipid fractions can be synthesized from constituents of the diet in amounts sufficient to carry out their metabolic roles.

Lipids are necessary constituents of all body tissues. Many specific metabolic functions are known, and these are discussed under the metabolism of fats. More general functions may be mentioned here. One gram of fat supplies 9 Cal, more than twice the heat obtainable from the same weight of either carbohydrate or protein, and so acts as a primary source of body energy. This is of special significance, since considerable fat is generally stored in the body and is available as a source of energy during food shortages. Fats pad and thus protect vital organs of the body; they act in the capacity of heat insulators. In their natural forms, many fats are nutritionally important for the vitamins they contain.

Essential fatty acids. It is well known that the animal body can convert carbohydrate into fat. Hogs are regularly fattened on corn, a high carbohydrate food. Rats deposit fat on a diet very low in fat and high in carbohydrate. Humans also have this capacity. On the other hand, certain fatty acids are necessary in the diet of animals and man.

In 1929 two papers appeared on the growth and development of rats ingesting rations extremely low in fat. A report from Mendel's laboratory (1) indicated that growth is poor on such a ration, and Burr and Burr (2) described a new deficiency disease in rats resulting from the exclusion of fat from the diet. The latter investigators prepared fat free casein by exhaustive solvent extraction. Sucrose was found to be suitable without further treatment. A salt mixture was added to the casein and sugar, and this constituted the bulk of the ration. The vitamin B complex was supplied by ether-extracted yeast and the nonsaponifiable fraction of cod liver oil constituted the source of vitamins A and D.

Rats reared on such a ration after weaning showed a peculiar scaly condition of the skin between the seventieth and ninetieth days of life. Some time later the tip of the tail

1228

developed an inflamed and swollen condition and was soon heavily scaled and ridged. A necrotic condition usually ensued resulting in the loss of 1 to 3 cm of tail. Other symptoms were hemorrhagic spots on the skin of the tail, red and swollen feet, alopecia about the face, back, and throat, and often sores on the body. Growth of the animals was poor, and they died if they were maintained on this diet for a prolonged period.

At autopsy a pathologic condition of the urinary tract and kidney was consistently found, and this was considered to be an important factor in the death of the animals.

The daily administration of as little as 10 drops of melted lard or 13 drops of fatty acids isolated from lard protected the animals completely from the deficiency disease, or cured the disease after it had developed. The nonsaponifiable fraction plus glycerine afforded no protection. Additional vitamin supplements were without effect.

This condition constituted a hitherto unknown deficiency disease.

In 1930 the same authors (3) showed that linoleic acid ($C_{17}H_{31}COOH$) in small quantities protected against and also cured the condition, while certain fats and oils devoid of acids more unsaturated than oleic, and also purified saturated acids, had no beneficial effect. They proposed that linoleic acid is an essential fatty acid for rats.

Burr and coworkers (4) later demonstrated that either linoleic or linolenic acid protects rats against the deficiency symptoms. The individual fatty acids are generally prepared and fed as methyl esters. These are utilized by rats almost as effectively as the glycerides. A mixture of the two esters was found to be no more effective than either one alone. This is interesting, since, as the authors point out, tissues generally have a mixture of the two acids.

Later work has shown that arachidonic acid (four double bonds) also is highly effective in preventing the fat deficiency disease.

Other species for which a linoleic acid requirement has been demonstrated include dog, rabbit, guinea pig, mouse, pig, man, and some insects, although it has not been possible to develop deficiency symptoms in adults of all these species.

At the present time three fatty acids are known which show high biologic activity in curing essential fatty acid (EFA) deficiency symptoms and in promoting growth in fat-deficient rats. These are γ-linolenic acid, CH_3-$(CH_2)_4(CH\!\!=\!\!CH\!\!-\!\!CH_2)_3(CH_2)_3COOH$ (6,9,12-octadecatrienoic acid); linoleic acid, $CH_3(CH_2)_4(CH\!\!=\!\!CH\!\!-\!\!CH_2)_2(CH_2)_6COOH$ (9,12-octadecadienoic acid); and arachidonic acid, $CH_3(CH_2)_4(CH\!\!=\!\!CH\!\!-\!\!CH_2)_4(CH_2)_2$ $COOH$ (5,8,11,14-eicosatetraenoic acid). Some other unsaturated acids, including α-linolenic (9,12,15-octadecatrienoic acid), stimulate growth but are not effective in curing the dermal manifestations of deficiency.

The presence of double bonds at the 6,7 and at the 9,10 positions (counting from the terminal CH_3— group) is essential for biologic activity. More double bonds on the CH_3— side of those positions results in decreased activity, and additional double bonds on the —COOH side may augment activity.

Comparative biopotencies of the active compounds are discussed in detail in the comprehensive review by Deuel (5). Arachidonic acid is apparently the most active of the EFA.

Actually, since mammals can synthesize arachidonic acid (6) and γ-linolenic acid from linoleic, the latter only is essential in the true sense. Studies with C^{14} compounds proved these interconversions in rats (7) and demonstrated that linolenic acid is an intermediate in the conversion of linoleic to arachidonic (8). The pathway would then appear to be (9):

$$\text{linoleic} \xrightarrow{-2H} \text{linolenic} \xrightarrow{+C_2} \text{homo-linolenic} \xrightarrow{-2H} \text{arachidonic}$$

Heat and alkali treatment isomerize fatty acids. Unnatural cis, trans or trans, trans linoleic acids are without EFA activity and may even possess antimetabolic action (10).

The relation of essential fatty acids to human nutrition has received some experimental attention and a good deal of speculation, especially in regard to certain types of eczema. In humans EFA deficiency symptoms are less clear-cut, and most of the symptoms found in animals have not been found in man.

Hansen (11) determined the iodine number of the fatty acids of blood serum lipids in a series of infants and children exhibiting various degrees of eczema. The values were considerably lower than those found in normal subjects of comparable age, and it was determined that neither previous diet nor infection were contributing factors. After the oral administration of large doses of an oil with a high iodine number, the iodine number of the serum lipids rose significantly, and a coincident clinical improvement was noted in the patients.

In England during World War II industrial dermatitis increased according to Bodman and Felix (12). These authors pointed out the possibility that this might be due in part to the decreased consumption of fats. They prepared on ointment for topical treatment and an emulsion for oral use, both high in unsaturated acids. These were found to be valuable in treating some types of dermatitis.

An interesting report (13) deals with the effects of experimental fat deprivation in human nutrition. An adult male was maintained for six months on a diet which supplied him with only 0.03 g of fat per kilogram of body weight per day. No harmful effects were noted. The diet was low enough in fat so that when rats were placed on it, they developed the typical fat deficiency symptoms. In the man the iodine number of the total blood serum fatty acids was decreased from an average of 123 before the experiment to 93 during the period of fat restriction. The linoleic and arachidonic acid levels of the serum fell to around one-half of the original values. This decrease in unsaturated fatty acids as a result of the low fat diet at least indicates that man, like the rat, cannot synthesize these unsaturated fatty acids and that they should therefore be supplied in the diet.

Hansen and coworkers (14) found lowered levels of dienoic, tetraenoic, and hexaenoic acids in a group of poorly nourished infants and children, compared to the values found in well-nourished subjects.

It would appear that EFA are required by man but that this species, like the pig, is much less susceptible to production of deficiency symptoms than the rat or dog.

Outstanding vegetable sources of essential fatty acids are safflower oil, cottonseed oil, sunflower seed oil, wheat germ oil, soybean oil, peanut oil, and corn oil. Safflower oil, for instance, contains about 78 per cent linoleic acid, soybean oil about 58 per cent, cottonseed oil 50 per cent, and corn oil 39 per cent. The EFA content of animal fats depends considerably on the diet of the animals. Egg yolk, chicken fat, and pig fat are outstanding sources of linoleic acid, while many fish fats have large amounts of linolenic acid. Butter is not a prominent source of EFA, and, of course, hydrogenation of vegetable oils (margarines and solid shortening products) reduces the quantities originally present. Comprehensive tables on the EFA content of many products are given in the review by Deuel (5).

Lipids: atherosclerosis relations. "Atherosclerosis" refers to a type of arteriosclerosis characterized by hyperplasia of connective tissue and elasticomuscular layers and generally associated with fatty degeneration of the arterial wall. In many studies correlation has been observed between: (a) fat content of the diet and blood cholesterol levels and (b) blood cholesterol levels and incidence of atherosclerosis. It is not established whether the hypercholesterolemia is the cause of the disease or whether it simply accompanies the condition. On the basis of these observations a great many studies have been reported concerning dietary (and other) means of altering blood cholesterol levels in animals and in humans. It is now established that a correlation exists between the degree of unsaturation of dietary fat and the blood cholesterol level. Especially when the cholesterol level is elevated, adding polyunsaturated fats, such as corn oil or safflower oil to the diet brings about a decrease in blood cholesterol. Unsaturated fatty acids, such as ethyl or methyl ester, likewise are effective in this respect.

Holman (15) feels that essential fatty acids are closely related to the overall problem, although Ahrens and coworkers (16) obtained a reduction of plasma cholesterol in patients by feeding menhaden oil, which is poor in essential fatty acids but high in other unsaturated acids. Much of the data indicate that it is not necessarily the essential fatty acid type of unsaturation that is involved here (9).

A variety of other factors are involved in lipid metabolism and blood levels of various lipids, such as cholesterol. Included are dietary proteins and lipotropic substances, hormones, vitamins, phospholipids, and others.

No theory to account for the relation of dietary fat and blood cholesterol has met with general acceptance. Various factors are discussed by Olson (9) and by Klein (17).

Other lipid fractions, such as phospholipids, glycolipids, and sterols, play important, essential roles in nutrition. All these compounds can be synthesized in the animal body from constituents occurring even in diets containing highly purified carbohydrate (sucrose or other sugars), protein (pure amino acid mixtures), fat (purified fatty acids), minerals, and highly purified vitamins.

It is obvious that the essential role of many of the small molecules in such a diet involves the synthesis of some of these lipids. The synthesis of lecithin may serve to illustrate this point. The two molecules of fatty acid contained in lecithin may be formed from carbohydrate in the diet, an important consideration in the absence of sufficient dietary fatty acids. Glycerol also is formed readily in the body from carbohydrate. The phosphoric acid residue can be obtained from dietary minerals. Choline is synthesized in the body if the diet contains a source of labile methyl groups, such as methionine (an essential amino acid) and serine from which ethanolamine is formed. Fatty acid, glycerol, phosphoric acid and choline are the substances required for the synthesis of lecithin which, we know, need not be fed preformed in the diet. We must not lose sight of the fact that, although the body is endowed with this remarkable synthetic power, it can carry it out only when the proper precursors are at hand.

Digestibility. The digestibility coefficient of a fat is the per cent of ingested fat that is absorbed. The melting point of a fat and the amount in the diet have important effects on digestibility. There are also marked variations among different animal species. The rat compares favorably with man in its ability to utilize high-melting-point fats.

Evans and Lepkovsky (18), using rats, studied the relation of melting point to digestibility of a number of simple triglycerides. They reported digestibilities as follows: caprylin (mp 7–8° C) 97.5, caprin (mp 25–26° C) 96.5, laurin (mp 43° C) 96, myristin (mp 53–54° C) 91, and palmitin (mp 58–60° C) 73.4.

Holt and associates (19) studied the digestibilities of various food fats in infants. They reported the following values; corn oil 96.9, olive oil 95.1, soybean oil 93.7, butter fat 92, breast milk fat 92.4, and coconut oil 88.7. This extensive paper considers in detail many of the important factors concerned with fat digestibility in humans.

Normal fat requirements. In the human diet fat and carbohydrate can replace each other within wide limits. It is impossible at the present time to set a value for the amount of fat that must be eaten. Many factors are concerned in regulating the quantity that is eaten, such as availability, climate, work, habit, preference, and methods of food preparation. In World War I the United States soldiers in training camps consumed 31 per cent of their total calories (3700 Cal per day) in the form of fat. Certainly considerably more or less than this is compatible with good nutrition.

Outstanding sources of fat in the human diet are dairy products and eggs, meat products—especially pork—and cooking fats and oils of both plant and animal origin. Edible nuts contain from about 50 to over 70 per cent fat with the exception of chestnuts, which are quite low in fat. In general, whole grains contain little fat, but wheat bran and wheat germ have around 5 and 10 per cent, respectively. Soybean flour, generally classed with the grains, contains 20 per cent fat, and oatmeal has around 7 per cent.

There are no data indicating that the other lipids, such as phospholipids, glycolipids, sterols, and waxes, need be taken in the diet. This simply means that the body has the ability to synthesize them from other dietary constituents.

CARBOHYDRATES IN NUTRITION

The principal carbohydrates in the human diet are the starches and the sugars. Glycogen and starch hydrolysis products, such as the dextrins, are consumed in lesser quantity.

Grains and vegetables constitute the primary sources of the starches, while fruits may contain considerable of the sugars. Small amounts of glycogen are consumed in meat and sea foods.

The proportions of the various carbohydrates ingested by man are largely determined by: (*a*) availability of different foods, (*b*) food habits, and (*c*) economic status. It is generally true that high carbohydrate foods, such as the grains and potatoes, offer more calories per dollar than such low carbohydrate foods as meat, eggs, and fruits. On the other hand, it is obvious that in some climates little carbohydrate food is available, while in other climates the abundance and low price of such foods make them the principal dietary component.

Certain groups of people have taken their nourishment almost entirely from meat and fish for many generations. Even though small amounts of glycogen and other carbohydrate molecules are consumed with such a diet, there is no direct proof that the human requires preformed dietary carbohydrate.

In the United States carbohydrate constitutes some 50 to 60 per cent of the total caloric intake. This value varies within wide limits. Such wide variations are compatible with good nutrition, and it seems apparent that little attention need be paid to balancing the dietary proportions of the three major foodstuffs in healthy individuals.

From the foregoing it should be obvious that the nutritional problems involving carbohydrates have given investigators far less concern than the dietary problems concerning either proteins or fats. This may or may not be due to the fact that important considerations in this field have not yet come to light.

It is of interest to consider briefly the major sources of food carbohydrates.

Starches, dextrins, and glycogen. These polysaccharides are hydrolyzed to glucose and absorbed primarily by the portal blood. The glucose contributes to the blood sugar, to the tissue glycogen, and to many other carbohydrate-containing molecules.

Sucrose. Glucose and fructose are the hydrolysis products of this disaccharide. From the standpoint of abundance it is the most important of the sugars in the diet of most civilized people. The fructose is converted into glucose by the liver and probably to some extent in the intestinal mucosa.

Lactose. The digestion products of lactose are glucose and galactose. The liver and other tissues convert galactose to glucose. Lactose provides nearly the total carbohydrate intake of infants and animals ingesting only milk. This attests to the nutritive value of the sugar.

Certain unexplained findings in regard to the experimental feeding of lactose or of galactose are of interest. It has been known for some time that feeding rats diets high in lactose (20) or galactose (21) leads to the development of a type of cataract. Day (22) amply confirmed these observations and also determined blood sugar in rats eating diets containing 60 per cent of various carbohydrates. The fasting blood sugar levels were similar regardless of the type of carbohydrate previously fed. However, in unfasted rats consuming the 60 per cent lactose or the 60 per cent galactose ration, the mean blood sugar levels were 160 and 372 mg per cent, respectively. The values represent total sugar and were taken to be the sum of glucose plus galactose. Rats eating 60 per cent glucose or starch rations showed 121 and 123 mg per cent of blood sugar.

Of 18 rats on the lactose ration, 17 developed cataract at an average time of 44 days. Three rats given the galactose ration showed cataracts on the eleventh day. None of the animals eating the rations containing sucrose, glucose, or starch showed cataracts. The cataracts were said to be readily distinguishable from the cataracts that develop in rats as a result of riboflavin deficiency (see Chapter 18). The relationship between the incidence of cataract and high blood sugar is not clear. In diabetes mellitus the incidence of cataract is apparently higher than in healthy individuals.

The poor nutritive value of lactose when it constitutes the sole carbohydrate of rations of animals past the weaning age is attested to by many reports. Growth of such animals is invariably poorer with this sugar constituting the dietary carbohydrate than when sucrose, glucose, or starch is employed.

Young rats fed on diets containing 43 per cent of the calories as lactose had 40 per cent less body fat than control animals given a glucose-, sucrose-, dextrin-, or glucose-galactose-containing diets (23). The authors found the ceca of the lactose fed rats were enlarged and the contents acid—a condition noted in rats fed incompletely digested and absorbed carbohydrates, such as sorbitol and cellobiose.

The disease galactosemia is an enzymatic defect resulting in injury to the central nervous system, cataracts, and hepatic disease in infants if it goes unrecognized. This inborn error of metabolism is discussed in Chapter 24.

Pentoses. These five carbon sugars are not utilized by the body in the sense that the hexoses are. When ingested as such, the pentoses are largely excreted in the urine. However, the pentose ribose is a constituent of a number of important molecules in the body, such as the nucleic acids, riboflavin, and certain coenzymes. It can be synthesized from glucose as the occasion demands.

Organic acids. Many fruits contain appreciable quantities of various organic acids, such as citric and malic acids. Lactic acid is found in sauerkraut and some pickles. Though the above acids are not carbohydrates, they contribute to the total intake because of their rapid conversion to carbohydrate in the body. Acetic acid, especially in foods containing vinegar, holds a unique place in carbohydrate and fat metabolism (see Chapters on fat and on carbohydrate metabolism).

SPECIAL REFERENCES

1. McAmis, A. J.; Anderson, W. E.; and Mendel, L. B.: *J. Biol. Chem.*, **82**, 247, 1929.
2. Burr, G. O., and Burr, M. M.: *J. Biol. Chem.*, **82**, 345, 1929.
3. Burr, G. O., and Burr, M. M.: *J. Biol. Chem.*, **86**, 587, 1930.
4. Burr, G. O.; Burr, M. M.; and Miller, E. S.: *J. Biol. Chem.*, **97**, 1, 1932.
5. Deuel, H. J., Jr.: *The Lipids*, Vol. III. Interscience Publishers, Inc., New York, 1957, p. 783.
6. Widmer, C., Jr., and Holman, R. T.: *Arch. Biochem.*, **25**, 1, 1950.
7. Steinberg, G.; Slaton, W. H., Jr.; Howton, D. R.; and Mead, J. F.: *J. Biol. Chem.*, **220**, 257, 1956.
8. Mead, J. F., and Howton, D. R.: *J. Biol. Chem.*, **229**, 575, 1957.
9. Olson, R. E.: *Ann. Rev. Biochem.*, **28**, 467, 1959.
10. Holman, R. T., and Aaes-Jorgensen, E.: *Proc. Soc. Exptl. Biol. Med.*, **93**, 175, 1956.
11. Hansen, A. E.: *Am. J. Diseases Children*, **53**, 933, 1939.

12. Bodman, J., and Felix, E.: *Med. Press and Circ.*, **209**, 331, 1943.
13. Brown, W. R.; Hansen, A. E.; Burr, G. O.; and McQuarrie, I.: *J. Nutrition*, **16**, 511, 1938.
14. Hansen, A. E.; Sinclair, J. G.; and Wiese, H. F.: *J. Nutrition*, **52**, 541, 1954.
15. Holman, R. T.: *Am. J. Clin. Nutrition*, **8**, 95, 1960.
16. Ahrens, E.; Insull, W.; Hirsch, J.; Stoffel, W.; Peterson, M.; Farquhar, J.; Miller, T.; and Thomasson, H.: *Lancet*, **1**, 115, 1959.
17. Klein, P. D.: *Am. J. Clin. Nutrition*, **8**, 104, 1960.
18. Evans, H. M., and Lepkovsky, S.: *J. Biol. Chem.*, **96**, 179, 1932.
19. Holt, L. E., Jr.; Tidwell, H. C.; Kirk, C. M.; Cross, D. M.; and Neale, S.: *J. Pediat.*, **6**, 427, 1935.
20. Mitchell, H. S.: *J. Nutrition*, **9**, 37, 1935.
21. Mitchell, H. S.: *Proc. Soc. Exptl. Biol. Med.*, **32**, 971, 1935.
22. Day, P. L.: *J. Nutrition*, **12**, 395, 1936.
23. Tomarelli, R. M.; Hartz, R.; and Bernhart, F. W.: *J. Nutrition*, **71**, 221, 1960.

The metabolism of the inorganic elements

The metabolism of the food minerals does not involve the radical changes of molecular form that are found in protein, carbohydrate, and lipid metabolism. The positive mineral ions, such as Ca^{++}, Mg^{++}, K^+, and Na^+, taken in our food as salts of organic or inorganic acids or associated with proteins or lipids, are, after absorption, associated with just such negative ions in the body. Tricalcium phosphate, for instance, may be changed to the more soluble secondary phosphate before absorption and then circulate partly as this salt in the body after absorption. The calcium ion may partly become associated with plasma protein, protoplasmic protein, or organic (or other inorganic) acids. The phosphate radical can be converted into any of a great number of organic esters in the blood or tissue cells. The positive and negative mineral ions not used as body structural units undergo, in general, no greater chemical alteration than an exchange of partners during metabolism and excretion.

CALCIUM AND PHOSPHORUS

The normal level of blood calcium in humans and many other animal species ranges from 9 to 11 mg per 100 ml of serum. The cells contain negligible amounts. About one-half of the serum calcium is protein-bound, and the remainder is in a diffusible state. The latter fraction is spoken of as the "diffusible," the "ultrafiltrable," or the "ionized" blood calcium. It is not certain that all the calcium which will diffuse through a parchment membrane or one of cellophoane or collodion is ionized, but for practical purposes such an assumption appears to be logical. It is also assumed that the ionic calcium is the physiologically active fraction.

1236

Total calcium is readily and simply determined in serum (not plasma). The most generally used methods employ oxalate precipitation from diluted serum and titration of the oxalic acid, freed from the separated calcium oxalate by acid, with potassium permanganate. The diffusible or ionized calcium can be determined by ultrafiltration methods. Undiluted serum is forced through various semipermeable membranes with either positive or negative pressure, and the calcium content of the filtrate is determined (1,2). A biologic method (3) based on the response of the frog heart to Ca^{++} in serum perfused through it has also been used. In general, the different methods are in reasonable agreement with 50 to 60 per cent of the total blood calcium found to be in the diffusible or ionic state (4). For a number of years there has been little activity in the study of the types of blood calcium. This seems to have come about largely because of the lack of correlation between the levels of the various types of calcium and conditions of upset calcium-phosphorus metabolism in disease.

The blood phosphorus is always determined as phosphate but is calculated and reported as elemental phosphorus. Several types of phosphorus compounds occur in the blood and other tissues. Many compounds of the body exist as phosphate esters, and we know of mono-, di-, and triphosphoric acid esters. The phosphate generally determined in blood, however, is the inorganic phosphate and exists in blood, for instance, in a definite ratio of HPO_4^- to $H_2PO_4^-$ depending on blood pH (Hasselbalch equation). The charges on these radicals are offset by the metal ions Ca^{++}, Mg^{++}, Na^+, and K^+. Phosphorus exists normally in animal and plant tissues only in the form of one of the phosphate radicals, never as phosphite, elemental phosphorus, or other form. In infants the inorganic phosphorus ranges from 4.5 to 6.0 mg per 100 ml. of serum or plasma. With increasing age the quantity decreases, and adults normally have 3 to 4 mg per cent. All the blood inorganic phosphate appears to be ultrafiltrable if the calcium and phosphorus levels are within normal limits. With an increased level of either calcium or phosphate a colloidal calcium phosphate complex is thought to exist in blood.

The human body contains in the neighborhood of one-twelfth blood by weight. A 70-kg man might have 6 kg or 6 l of blood of which roughly one-half is plasma. Each 100 ml of plasma contains 10 mg of calcium, so this man has in his circulatory system about 300 mg of calcium, of which only one-half is physiologically active. The inorganic phosphorus would be about one-third of this or 100 mg. Consider that the daily urinary excretion of calcium can and often does exceed 300 mg, and that an individual may eat far less than this amount of calcium for a day or for several days. In health the blood level of calcium does not change even with minimal calcium ingestion for considerable periods of time.

It is obvious from the above that certain neat mechanisms are at work to maintain the level of blood calcium within very narrow limits. Significant alterations produce a number of undesirable effects. Some of the factors known to be involved in the maintenance of the blood calcium level will now be reviewed. The actions of the parathyroid glands and of vitamin D in this respect are discussed in Chapter 18. This section should be referred to in connection with the following.

Factors affecting the level of blood calcium. 1. *The absolute levels of calcium and phosphorus and the Ca:P ratio of food.* A low intake of either element over long periods of time leads to decreased blood levels. For short periods a deficiency of these minerals in food is compensated by the body very readily; the bones supply both calcium and phosphate or the soft tissues are called upon to supply phosphate. The resulting negative balance of either or both elements is of little consequence if the deficiency is of short duration, or if the deficiency is slight and of a longer duration. On the other hand, under protracted and severe circumstances, the bones may become rarefied and fracture easily.

The ratio of calcium to phosphorus in the diet has an important bearing on the degree of absorption, and thus on blood levels of both elements. With a marked excess of either in the diet, the fecal excretion of both increases. This is usually explained on the basis of the formation of insoluble calcium phosphate which is not readily available for absorption. Certainly a better explanation should be sought. In fact, one report indicates that additional dietary phosphate in man does not adversely affect calcium absorption (5), although various other reports are in disagreement with this finding. At any rate, a ratio of Ca:P in the diet within the limits of 1:2 to 2:1 allows for the optimum utilization of both elements and with ratios outside these limits absorption is decreased. In young rats a severe degree of rickets can be produced by feeding a vitamin D low diet with a Ca:P ratio of about 4.5:1. This is done by the simple expedient of adding sufficient $CaCO_3$ to the mixture of wheat gluten, ground corn, and salt (Steenbock rachitic ration 2965).

2. *Fat digestion and amount in diet.* Under normal circumstances more or less fat has a minimal effect on the absorption of calcium from the intestine. But in certain abnormal circumstances there may be a marked loss of food calcium as a result of impaired fat absorption. It should be recalled that the fatty acid salts of calcium (calcium soaps) are insoluble. If food fats are hydrolyzed, yielding fatty acids, and these acids are not absorbed, there is bound to be a loss of food calcium in the feces. The loss of unhydrolyzed fat in the feces does not bring about calcium loss to the body. In diarrhea and in steatorrhea the loss of calcium can be marked, depending on the severity and duration of the condition.

An interesting report in this connection deals with a man who had lost surgically all but about 34 in of small intestine (6). Balance studies on protein, fat, carbohydrate, calcium, and phosphorus were carried out on this individual for three different periods of study. The man consumed large amounts of fat and lost a great proportion of it in the feces. The fat was largely hydrolyzed to fatty acids and as such removed a great deal of the food calcium and administered calcium consumed. Blood calcium levels were generally low, and signs of tetany were present much of the time. In a later study the diet was controlled, and less than half the amount of fat was allowed daily. Fat absorption was poor in this period also, but the quantity of fatty acids excreted in the feces was markedly reduced, and, as a consequence, the absorption of calcium improved and tetany was more easily controlled. High levels of calcium and vitamin D were not sufficient to keep the blood calcium at normal levels during the period of high fat consumption.

3. Phytic acid, iron, and oxalates. A large excess of iron is generally not used therapeutically over long periods except in rare instances. It might be well to give due consideration to calcium and phosphorus metabolism under such circumstances. In rats a sufficiently high iron intake will result in a low phosphate rickets. This comes about through decreased phosphate absorption, since ferric phosphate is highly insoluble. The net result is an upset in the Ca:P ratio.

Oxalates in certain foods precipitate calcium in the intestine as the insoluble calcium oxalate. This is not of practical importance, since few foods are high in oxalate and these are not foods eaten regularly. Rhubarb is a high oxalate food.

Of some significance may be the presence of phytic acid in foods. This compound, the hexaphosphate of inositol (see Chapter 18), is widespread in cereals. It may contribute to the total phosphate ingestion and may also have a marked influence on calcium absorption. In humans the ingestion of large amounts of phytic acid in foods or added to foods led to negative calcium balances (7,8). In these studies it was found that the phytic acid formed insoluble salts with calcium (phytin) in the intestine and thus the calcium was unavailable for absorption:

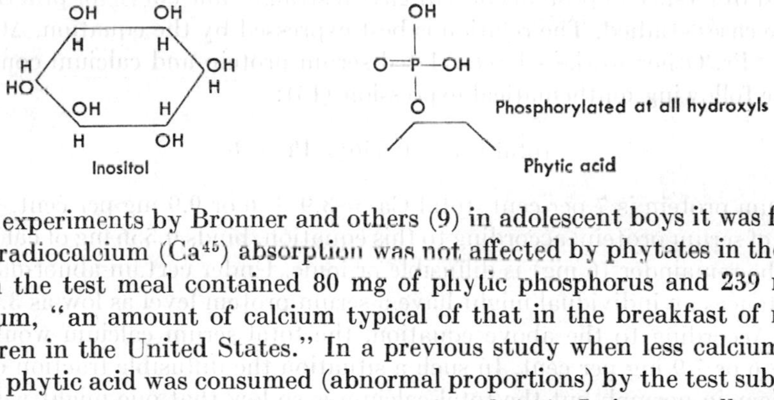

Inositol   Phytic acid

Phosphorylated at all hydroxyls

In experiments by Bronner and others (9) in adolescent boys it was found that radiocalcium (Ca^{45}) absorption was not affected by phytates in the diet when the test meal contained 80 mg of phytic phosphorus and 239 mg of calcium, "an amount of calcium typical of that in the breakfast of many children in the United States." In a previous study when less calcium and more phytic acid was consumed (abnormal proportions) by the test subjects, a depression of calcium absorption was found (10). It is generally agreed that food phytic acid becomes a nutritional problem only under special conditions of very low calcium intake or excessive phytic acid intake or both.

4. Acidity relations. The pH of the intestine, though not subject to marked variations normally, has a direct bearing on calcium and phosphorus absorption. Acid residue diets promote absorption. $CaCl_2$ by mouth brings about a prompt increase in urinary calcium through increased absorption. Increased gastric acidity also increases the solubility of the calcium salts in the intestine and so favors their absorption. It is known that the ingestion of lactose increases calcium absorption. This is generally explained on the basis of the acidifying effect of the lactic acid formed from the sugar by microorganisms.

5. Protein in the diet. It has been adequately demonstrated that certain calcium salts are much more soluble in an aqueous solution of amino acids than in water. It has also been reported that calcium absorption increases with increased protein consumption (11). It was pointed out in this paper that Eskimos are largely carnivorous and that their calcium intake is low compared to our standards. In general, however, they appear to have no calcium deficiency as judged by growth and bone and tooth formation. The authors suggest that a very high protein diet allows for excellent absorption of the small amount of dietary calcium.

The five factors just discussed affect the level of blood calcium indirectly through their regulatory action on the degree of calcium absorption from the intestine. The following factors have a direct effect on blood calcium level not related to the absorptive process.

6. Vitamin D and the parathyroid glands. These factors are discussed in the section on vitamin D in Chapter 18. The student should review this section.

7. Serum protein level. The total calcium content of serum and of certain other body fluids is related and in part governed by the amount of protein present. In a study (12) of the calcium and the protein content of serum and of body transudates (pleural and ascitic fluid) it was demonstrated that the difference in calcium content of serum and transudate plotted against difference in protein content gave a straight line curve for practically all the cases studied. The relation is best expressed by the equation, $\Delta Ca = 0.561 \, \Delta Pr$. Other workers have related serum protein and calcium contents by the following mathematical expression (13):

$$\text{total Ca} = 0.556\% \text{ Pr} + 6$$

If serum protein is 7 per cent, total Ca = 3.9 + 6 or 9.9 mg per cent. Each gram of serum protein, according to this equation, binds 0.556 mg of calcium, and the remainder (6 mg) is diffusible or ionic. Under certain abnormal circumstances an individual might have a serum protein level as low as 3.4 per cent. According to the above equation, the total serum calcium would be 1.9 + 6 or 7.9 mg per cent. In such a situation the diffusible fraction could well remain normal, but the total calcium is so low that one might wonder why the individual is not exhibiting symptoms of tetany. The explanation lies in the small amount of protein-bound calcium.

Later work by Rawson and Sunderman (14) with human serum indicated that each gram of serum protein binds 0.84 mg of calcium, so that:

$$\text{total Ca} = 0.84\% \text{ Pr} + D$$

where D = diffusible calcium. At the pH of blood, one might expect 1 g of serum albumin (isoelectric pH 4.7) to bind more calcium than 1 g of serum globulin (isoelectric pH 5.4) because the albumin would be dissociated to a greater degree as a negative ion. It was found by the above workers, however, that the binding capacity of the two proteins is practically identical.

The relation of calcium to protein in body fluids is further illustrated by the levels in spinal fluid. The total calcium (all ionic) is normally about the same as the ionic calcium of serum, and there is practically no protein in spinal fluid to bind calcium.

8. Reciprocal relation of serum calcium and phosphorus. It is often stated that a reciprocal relationship exists in blood between the concentrations of calcium and phosphorus. No doubt this is quite true within certain narrow limits and under conditions not involving serious upsets in calcium-phosphorus metabolism. On the other hand, it is not uncommon in certain types of kidney disease to find a patient with a normal serum calcium (and protein) level and an inorganic phosphorus concentration of 10 or even 20 mg per cent. It is obvious that the mechanisms controlling the reciprocal relation are not functioning in such a condition.

9. Kidney threshold. It is certain that the kidney threshold is important in regulating the blood calcium level, but our knowledge of how this operates and why it often fails to operate normally is indeed meager. In a normal adult any extra calcium absorbed from the intestine is readily excreted in the urine. The intravenous administration of calcium gluconate, for instance, is followed by an immediate increased kidney excretion. And this excretion is efficient to the point that there is generally no lowering in plasma phosphate through the reciprocal relationship discussed above. On the other hand, the serum calcium may remain at a level low enough to bring on muscle and nerve hyperirritability or tetany, even though calcium (from food or administered salts) is undergoing absorption from the intestine and appearing in the urine. Such a situation generally involves hypoparathyroid function, but obviously the normal kidney threshold does not obtain. In hypercalcemia kidney threshold also is abnormal.

10. Sex hormones. During the menopause many women develop a negative calcium and phosphorus balance leading to a type of osteoporosis (undermineralization of bone). This is often attended by pain and the bones are abnormally subject to fracture. The part played by sex hormones in regulating calcium and phosphorus levels and the metabolism of these elements in such individuals has been studied especially by Albright and coworkers (15). They have demonstrated that the negative balances are markedly improved by the administration of estrogens, either estradiol benzoate or the synthetic diethylstilbesterol, or by androgens such as testosterone. A combination of estrogens and androgens is more effective than either one alone. Both fecal and urinary calcium and phosphorus excretions were decreased usually as soon as six days after initiating treatment. The maximum effect was noted in about 30 days, and the action persisted for over a month after the hormone treatment was stopped. Serum phosphorus, which tends to be high in these cases, was lowered in most instances. Albright feels that older women with fractures (hip especially) respond better with such hormone therapy.

11. Other factors. It can be said unequivocally that unknown or little understood factors are important in regulating the levels of blood calcium and phosphorus. An individual's acid-base status is an example. Does hyperacidity in the body affect kidney threshold, the parathyroid gland, or some other mechanism to bring about the attendant increased urinary calcium excretion? In alkalosis muscle and nerve hyperirritability may become marked, and the picture often simulates the hyperirritability resulting from low blood calcium. At one time the postulate was offered that increased blood alkalinity brings about increased dissociation of plasma proteins as negative ions, resulting in the binding of more calcium, thus lowering the ionized fraction. The result of lowering ionized plasma calcium would indeed bring on hyperirritability, but it has never been shown that even in severe alkalosis this fraction of blood calcium is decreased. It is best perhaps, in the absence of a clear explanation for this, to think of the regulation of muscle and nerve irritability, not by calcium ion alone but by the ratios of the various ions, such as Ca^{++}, Mg^{++}, Na^+, and K^+, as well as H^+ and OH^-, all of which are definitely involved. The degree of hydration is also an important factor in this connection. McQuarrie and coworkers (16) studied certain factors other than hypocalcemia in relation to hyperirritability in a case of idiopathic hypoparathyroidism. The individual was given a diet low in mineral content and during another period of study a diet high in minerals. Interesting among the findings reported by these workers was the fact that the convulsive tendency (tetany) was more marked on the low mineral diet. By various means convulsions could be brought on during the period of low mineral diet but not during the high mineral intake, although the serum calcium and phosphorus were essentially the same during both periods.

Functions of calcium. The essential nature of calcium and phosphorus in bone and tooth formation is obvious. Our knowledge of the mechanisms involved in the calcification process is fragmentary and quite unsatisfactory. A brief discussion of the process can be found in the section on vitamin D. Without bone development there cannot be growth, so calcium is intimately related with and indeed essential for growth.

The blood-clotting process requires Ca^{++} ion, and this is discussed in the section on blood. Milk clotting also requires Ca^{++} ion.

A number of enzymes, including lipase, succinic dehydrogenase, adenosine triphosphatase, and certain proteolytic enzymes, are activated by calcium. Whether such an activation is essential or even of importance to the normal metabolic processes is not known.

The Ca^{++} ion is directly related to muscle contraction. In the absence of calcium all types of muscle lose their ability to contract. But in an excess of calcium the isolated heart stops in contraction. Of course, the ratios of calcium to other cations is also of importance in muscle contraction. The transmission of nerve impulses also involves a functional role of calcium.

Membrane permeability generally is decreased by calcium, and this effect balances the opposite action of sodium and potassium. Capillary permeability, on the other hand, can be markedly increased by perfusing with solutions low in calcium because a constant supply of calcium is required to maintain the integrity of the intercellular cement substance.

The physicochemical action of calcium in the regulation of water balance (osmotic effect) and acid-base balance are minimal because of the small amounts present in body fluids compared to the other regulatory ions, such as Na^+, K^+, Cl^-, and HCO_3^-.

Phosphorus plays essential roles other than in bone and tooth formation. The place of phosphate in the high-energy bonds, such as ATP, is amply discussed in the sections on intermediary metabolism. Phosphates are used in the synthesis of phospholipids, constituents of cell membranes, nervous tissue, etc. All through the body phosphates contribute significantly to buffer systems. The phosphate-containing compounds RNA and DNA are significant from the standpoint of protein synthesis and genetics. A variety of coenzymes are phosphate compounds.

Calcium and phosphorus requirement. A statement of dietary calcium need for a group of people must be an approximate one. This is obvious in view of the many factors regulating calcium absorption in the intestine and individual variations which may not be related to these factors.

In the earlier literature it will be found that Sherman (17,18) reported a minimum intake of 0.45 g of calcium daily for an adult to maintain calcium balance. He proposed a 50 per cent increase over this figure as a margin of safety, which set his idea of adult requirements at about 0.68 g daily. In growing children the requirement was established at something over 1 g daily, and it was pointed out that the calcium of milk was generally more available than that of vegetables.

Balance studies have been used to arrive at requirements of a variety of nutrients including calcium and phosphorus. In one such study (19) adult men were placed on low calcium diets, and their balances were determined. The calcium intake was then increased, either as additional food calcium or salt supplements, and the balances again established. From such data the per cent utilization of calcium from food or other sources can be estimated. The diets used in these studies supplied about 60 per cent of the calcium intake in milk products or equally available calcium salts. It was found that about 32 per cent of the food calcium was utilized by the subjects. Their calculations indicate a requirement for young adults (college students and staff) of 10 mg per kilogram body weight per day on diets supplying one-half to two-thirds of the calcium intake from dairy products.

Hegsted has questioned the validity of generalizing about requirements from data obtained in specific balance experiments. Thus Hegsted and co-workers (20) showed that the maintenance requirement for calcium is low in men who had been on low calcium intake over an extended period. In ten men the average intake found to maintain equilibrium (balance studies) was 216 mg per day. In individuals subsisting on much higher intakes balance data might indicate a requirement of two or three times this amount. Hegsted concluded from his own and many other reports that calcium balance experiments in adults represent a study of calcium status in relation to previous intake and bear no relation to requirements (21). The same conclusion was reached in balance studies on dogs (22).

In the report of a symposium (23) on high calcium intakes it was pointed out that some individuals adapt readily to a low calcium intake while others may have difficulty or not adapt at all (24). This simply points up the established observations of individual variations in efficiency of the absorption processes and makes clear the fact that minimal calcium intake may be well suited to some people but that normal calcification in all children may not follow continued low intakes.

The Recommended Dietary Allowances, National Research Council, sets the intake of 0.8 g per day for men and women. During pregnancy it is 1.5 g and during lactation 2.0 g per day (Table 18.5, p. 696). Most women are in negative calcium balance during lactation even with markedly increased intake. This may be a normal physiologic process, and little evidence exists that attempts to obviate the negative balance are nutritionally sound.

There is good reason for the continued interest and study relating to calcium requirements. No doubt many individuals, both children and adults, are subsisting on diets supplying suboptimal calcium intakes. Part of this is due to food habit or dislikes, but to a large extent it stems from economic inability to obtain foods rich in this element (dairy products). There was some agitation a few years ago in favor of fortifying patent flour with some low-priced calcium salt, such as $CaCO_3$, which would automatically raise the calcium intake of a very large proportion of the population. White flour is now fortified with iron and certain vitamins of the B complex.

Dairy products remain one of the most important dietary sources of calcium. Whole milk contains about 115 mg per cent, and the various cheese products vary from less than this to as much as 1100 mg per cent. The grains in general are low in calcium. White flour has about 20 mg, and whole wheat around 40 mg per 100 g. Meats generally are poor calcium sources, containing 10 to 20 mg per cent. Many seafoods, especially shellfish, are high in this element, and some canned fish, because of the bone content, may supply up to 300 or 400 mg per cent. The vegetables are not outstanding calcium sources, although many green tops, such as turnip greens, are excellent sources.

Many calcium salts have been used to augment the dietary intake. In general, the availability of calcium from the salts in popular use does not vary markedly. It is of interest to compare the amount of calcium contained in the various compounds. Table 30.1 shows the approximate calcium content of several salts. Not all people tolerate some of the compounds listed. Certain salts may act as a cathartic in some people, while others may have the opposite effect. The chloride has a definite acidifying action, and the carbonate is an antiacid, since it neutralizes gastric HCl, especially when taken alone.

It is doubtful if the national dietary is low in phosphorus except in isolated instances. This is not due to a lower phosphorus requirement but to its more widespread distribution in foods. Because of this situation the study of human requirements for this element have not been pursued as extensively as studies regarding calcium needs. Early work by Sherman indicates an adult requirement of about 0.88 g of phosphorus daily. At present it is generally considered that an adult should consume around 1.5 times as much phosphorus as calcium and that children and women during pregnancy and lactation should have a phosphorus intake equal to that of calcium. Proteins supply considerable phosphorus, and generally, if the protein and calcium intake from foods are adequate, the phosphorus requirement will be met. Milk, because of its general and liberal use, is an important source of phosphorus with 93 mg per cent, while various cheeses, depending on their water content, contain 200 to 900 mg per cent. White flour has about the same phosphorus content as whole milk, while whole wheat flour may contain four times as much. Many meat cuts supply 100 to 200 mg per cent of phosphorus, and fish products contain somewhat similar amounts.

Table 30.1

Source	Approximate Per Cent Calcium
CaCO₃	40
CaCl₂ (various hydrates)	18–28
Ca (CH₃CHOHCOO)₂ · 5H₂O (lactate)	13
Ca (C₆H₁₁O₇)₂ H₂O (gluconate)	9
Ca₃(PO₄)₂ (tertiary)	13
Ca (HPO₄) · 2H₂O (secondary	23

In health some 60 to 80 per cent of ingested phosphorus is excreted by the kidney while the remainder is excreted by the bowel. The situation is about reversed in the case of calcium: some 65 to 80 per cent is excreted in the feces and the remainder in the urine. These figures are rough indeed, since the excretion of these elements is governed by so many factors. In various conditions of altered calcium-phosphorus metabolism or under specific dietary conditions the amounts of calcium and phosphorus excreted by the two pathways may be reversed, or practically all of one element may be excreted via one of the pathways.

For reviews of various aspects of calcium metabolism, see (23) and (25).

MAGNESIUM

The essential nature of magnesium in animal nutrition has been established for 25 years. Still we know little regarding specific functional roles for this element in the body. Blood serum contains 2 to 3 mg per cent of magnesium, and the erythrocytes slightly more. On a dry basis bone contains about 1.5 per cent $Mg_3(PO_4)_2$. Soft tissues contain three to five times as much magnesium as calcium. Rat muscle, for instance, has 29.6 mg of magnesium and 5.7 mg of calcium per 100 g of wet tissue (26). All plant tissues contain magnesium. A large number of enzymes concerned with metabolic processes involving fats, proteins, and carbohydrates require Mg^{++} as an activating ion. These relations are clearly indicated in the sections on intermediary metabolism.

The widespread occurrence of this element in both plant and animal tissue insures an adequate intake except under extreme conditions. Low levels of blood magnesium, like low levels of calcium, produce a tetany. In rats a low magnesium tetany was produced by feeding a diet purified to such an extent that it contained only 1.8 parts magnesium per million (27,28). The animals exhibited redness of exposed skin surfaces due to hyperemia, hyperirritability, cardiac arrhythmia, and finally tetany. Magnesium deficiency symptoms in rats and guinea pigs were found to be accentuated by high phosphorus diets (29). Thyroxine feeding impairs growth of rats. It was observed by Vitale and coworkers (30) that this growth inhibition could be partially alleviated by additional dietary magnesium.

In cattle "grass tetany" is observed in isolated areas. It is a result of upset magnesium metabolism, with accompanying hypomagnesemia. Some success in treatment of the disease by feeding magnesium supplements (31) or by fertilizing pasture lands with magnesium compounds (32) has been reported.

Of the few cases of reported human tetany from a magnesium deficiency all but one have been largely discounted because other causes of human tetany were not clearly eliminated. In one case, however, the data perhaps justify a diagnosis of low magnesium tetany (33). The plasma magnesium during an attack was markedly low (0.6 mg per cent), the calcium was normal, and magnesium sulfate by mouth was highly effective in alleviating the hyperirritability. The plasma magnesium level was normal after two weeks of treatment.

Excess plasma magnesium decreases muscle and nerve irritability, and high levels (20 mg per cent in blood) induce anesthesia. This was earlier used for anesthetizing rabbits to remove muscle for the preparation of ATP, since there is minimal struggling with magnesium anesthesia.

It is not safe to assume that factors governing the absorption and excretion of calcium are those that govern magnesium metabolism. The parathyroid hormone(s), so important in regulating calcium blood levels and excretion, has little effect on magnesium in these respects. On the other hand, magnesium (like calcium) absorption from the intestine is markedly decreased on a diet containing excess phytic acid (34).

It is immediately obvious that our over-all knowledge of magnesium metabolism is meager. But since abnormal metabolism of this element in humans is almost unknown and quite rare in other animals, it is logical that workers in the field of mineral metabolism have largely directed their attentions to other mineral ions.

A detailed description of deficiency symptoms including microscopic findings in various animal species is given by Follis (35).

SODIUM, POTASSIUM, AND CHLORINE

It is practical to discuss the metabolic and nutritional aspects of these three elements together, since they are so intimately related, and also it is obvious that individual treatment would lead to considerable repetition.

It is unnecessary to dwell on the essential nature of these three elements for man, beast, and plant life. The literature regarding animal experimental deprivation of these ions is large; a good summary of the findings can be found in the last edition of McCollum and coworkers' book on nutrition (36).

In animal tissue both sodium and potassium occur in relatively large amounts as chlorides and other inorganic salts, as well as protein and organic acid salts. In plant material, however, the potassium content is high compared with the sodium concentration. Since excess potassium intake by animals causes excess sodium excretion, herbivorous animals must be supplied with extra NaCl. Wild herbivora have been known to travel hundreds of miles to a salt lick. Cattle or sheep deprived of NaCl for even short periods of time have been known, when confronted with sufficient salt, to consume lethal quantities.

Young rats restricted to synthetic rations containing only 0.002 per cent sodium (37) grow slowly for a time and then lose weight. After six to eight weeks on the diet, definite eye changes develop in the animals. Many other changes found at autopsy were reported in this paper. Among these were lack of fat deposits, muscle and testicular atrophy, lung infection, retarded bone growth, and a deficiency of osteoid tissue.

On diets very low in potassium (38) young rats grow slowly. Both sexes become sterile. The heart rate is slow. On histologic examination a scarring of heart muscle and kidney hypertrophy are found. Bone growth is retarded, and the bones are excessively fragile.

Dogs (39) grow poorly and develop a paralysis on potassium-deficient diets. These abnormal symptoms are corrected by the administration of potassium salts.

A dietary chlorine deficiency (37) produced no symptoms over a 90-day test period in young rats except a subnormal growth rate.

Under normal dietary conditions human beings are not subject to a deficiency of sodium, potassium, or chlorine. However, excessive diarrhea, pernicious vomiting, or an extreme degree of sweating over long periods may bring about a sodium chloride deficiency. It is common practice now to supply workers subjected to excessive heat with extra sodium chloride in the form of salt water or salt tablets.

In the United States the per capita sodium chloride consumption is around 10 g per day (about 4 g of sodium) supplied primarily as seasoning. This is many times the requirement. In health the excess salt consumed is excreted by the kidney, since it is fairly completely absorbed from the intestine. The human potassium intake is around 2 to 4 g per day, all supplied by the food we eat. Again this is far more than our requirement, and the excess is excreted in the urine.

The primary functions of these mineral ions in the animal body include the part they play in maintaining normal osmotic pressure relations throughout the body, the maintenance of the normal state of acid-base and water balance, and the intricate role in gaseous transport. These matters are adequately discussed in appropriate sections. See also under adrenal corticohormones. Both sodium and potassium are important in maintaining muscle and nerve irritability at the proper level. They are antagonistic to calcium and magnesium ions, so the ratios of the various ions are of importance as well as the absolute amounts in body fluids and cells. In blood plasma sodium and potassium chlorides have the outstanding function not only of keeping the globulins in physical solution, but also of regulating the degree of hydration of the plasma proteins, so important to the maintenance of the proper viscosity of blood.

Gastric HCl is derived from the sodium chloride of the blood, and the base in other digestive fluids, such as the pancreatic juice and bile, is derived from blood sodium and potassium salts.

SULFUR

The metabolism of sulfur is essentially a matter of cystine and methionine metabolism. This is discussed in Chapter 25. Practically all our sulfur intake is from these amino acids as they occur in the various food proteins. The essential nature of sulfur in nutrition is attested to by the fact that all animal species studied, including man, require the sulfur-containing amino acid methionine. All body proteins and special protein molecules, such as enzymes and hormones that have been studied, are found to contain methionine. Glutathione, bile salts, and chondroitin sulfuric acid are other important molecules containing sulfur. Sulfur, as sulfate, is used in the body for the detoxification of a variety of molecules, including indoxyl and phenol. Excess sulfur is excreted in the urine as sulfate.

If the dietary methionine or the cystine and methionine requirement is met, the sulfur need is amply satisfied. Since wool contains about 13 per cent cystine, the dietary intake of the sulfur-containing amino acids in wool-bearing animals is now under careful study.

THE "TRACE ELEMENTS"

A number of inorganic ions are essential for plant and animal life in rather minute quantities compared with the amounts of calcium and phosphorus required. For this reason they are referred to as "trace elements." Included in the group of elements studied to determine their dispensable and indispensable nature in animal and in plant nutrition are the following: Fe, Cu, Co, Ni, Mn, Mo, Al, As, Zn, B, Si, I, Br, and Se. Most of the above elements have proved essential either for plants or animals or for both.

IRON

Iron functions in the body as an essential part of many oxidation-reduction enzymes and is contained in several other biologically significant proteins. Table 30.2 shows some of the enzymes and proteins that contain iron.

Iron absorption. Part of the iron of our foodstuffs is converted to iron salts by the gastric HCl and then is reduced by the various food reducing agents such as glutathione, ascorbic acid, and many —SH (sulfhydryl) groups of protein amino acids. The absorption takes place largely in the small intestine and as ferrous ions. It is now established that iron absorption is governed largely by the content of ferritin in the intestinal mucosal wall.

Ferritin is composed of a protein (apoferritin) and colloidal micelles of ferric hydroxide-ferric phosphate. These micelles are tightly held to the surfaces of the protein and have a composition approaching $(FeOOH)_8(FeOO-PO_3H_2)$. The iron content varies in ferritin up to as high as 25 per cent on the dry basis. Apoferritin has a molecular weight of around 465,000. The metabolism and actions of ferritin were reviewed by Shorr (40).

Table 30.2. Iron-Containing Mammalian Enzymes and Other Proteins

Hemoglobin	Cytochromes	Xanthine oxidase
Myoglobin	Cytochrome reductase	Homogentisicase
Ferritin	Cytochrome oxidase	Hydroxyanthranilic oxidase
Hemosiderin	Catalases	Phenylalanine hydroxylase
Siderofilin, or Transferrin	Peroxidases	Tryptophan oxidase

Mazur and coworkers (41) postulate two types of ferritin: inactive ferritin, containing ferric iron, and active ferritin, containing some ferrous iron stabilized by sulfhydryl groups. Ferrous iron, which is dissociable from the active ferritin, is the type of iron involved in transport of iron across membranes including liver cell wall (into plasma), intestinal mucosal cells (in absorption), placental membrane, and cell membranes involved in iron storage, such as liver, spleen and bone marrow. The incorporation of plasma-bound iron into ferritin has been shown to involve ATP and ascorbic acid (*in vitro* work with rat tissues) (42).

Both ferritin and apoferritin have been crystallized (43). Granick (44) proposes that iron in the ferrous form enters the mucosal cells and is stored in ferritin as ferric hydroxide. An equilibrium may exist in the cells between ferrous ions (chemical combination unknown) and the ferric ions of ferritin. When the blood serum iron level decreases, ferritin iron is converted to ferrous ions which enter the blood stream.

When the content of iron in ferritin decreases to some critical point, more iron from the intestine is absorbed into the mucosal cells. A further part of the postulate holds that more iron would be absorbed only when the cells are no longer "physiologically saturated" with respect to ferrous iron.

The assumptions that iron absorption is largely controlled by the intestine (45) and that absorption proceeds only when there is a body need for iron (46) have been upheld by several studies using radioactive iron. It was shown that in anemic dogs (through bleeding) but not in normal animals, radioactive iron was readily absorbed (47). In normal adults absorption was found by Moore (48) to be 10 per cent or less of the dose (Fe^{59}), while in iron deficient patients the absorption was over 10 per cent. The simultaneous ingestion of ascorbic acid increased absorption in normal people and to a greater extent in those with iron deficiency. It is of interest that in other studies using bread prepared from flour enriched with Fe^{59} the absorption was found to vary from 1 to 12 per cent in a group of normal adults, from 26 to 38 per cent in four individuals thought to have had suboptimal iron stores, and from 45 to 64 per cent in patients with iron deficiency anemia (49). A review on absorption by Moore covers his work and that of other investigators (50).

In human subjects iron was found to be readily absorbed in conditions of known body deficiency, but in anemias not accompanied by a deficiency state, such as pernicious anemia, little iron was absorbed (51). The concept is now generally held that the total body iron is controlled by absorption in the intestine, since this tissue does not excrete iron to an appreciable degree. However, rats maintained on a corn grit and lard ration with a large excess of added ferric citrate absorbed abnormal amounts of iron. The blood iron was very high, and the livers contained four to six times as much iron as animals fed a stock diet with or without added iron. Massive hemosiderin deposits were observed in the tissues (52). Hemosiderin is an iron-protein complex, the iron apparently being derived from hemoglobin of disintegrating red cells as well as from dietary or administered iron. On excessive destruction of red cells many tissues become loaded with hemosiderin. Further work by these investigators indicated that the abnormal absorption of iron on the corn and lard diet was largely due to a deficiency of minerals, principally phosphate (53). In pyridoxine deficiency the absorption of both iron and copper appears to be abnormal (54). It may be necessary to state that body iron stores are governed by intestinal absorption except under certain abnormal conditions.

Iron storage and transport. Ferrous iron entering the blood is oxidized to the ferric state. It is associated with a β_1-globulin fraction of plasma proteins called siderophilin or transferrin. This protein binds two iron atoms per mole and has a molecular weight of around 90,000.

Normally, the plasma iron level in man is around 130 μg per cent (50-180 μg range), and various types or fractions of plasma iron have been postulated. The liver, spleen, and bone marrow are the principal iron storage depots.

These tissues contain ferritin and hemosiderin. Shoden and coworkers (55) have demonstrated some interesting relationships between these two iron storage compounds. In human and rabbit tissues a slight preponderance of ferritin over hemosiderin iron was found at physiologic iron levels. With increased tissue iron levels and at very high levels, hemosiderin stores were in excess. Radioiron given parenterally or orally was stored in both compounds, and mobilized iron was derived from both fractions. It was postulated that the two forms are functionally indistinguishable and may represent only different physical forms. The data seemed to be consistent with the concept that hemosiderin is an aggregate of ferritin molecules.

Normally these compounds along with other smaller stores may amount to one-fifth of the total body iron. They are drawn upon in time of iron need for the production of hemoglobin and other heme-containing molecules. Interestingly enough, the iron of hemoglobin derived from disintegrating red blood cells appears to be used preferentially, but obviously this is unable to meet the demand in time of need such as following hemorrhage or in any instance of rapid regeneration of red cells.

Action of iron. Many species of animals are subject to a hypochromic, microcytic anemia characteristic of iron deficiency. Iron administered in such instances is rapidly used for the production of hemoglobin and new red blood cells. The ferrous ion is incorporated into protoporphyrin, forming heme which combines with the protein, globin, to form hemoglobin.

The synthesis of porphyrins and the insertion of iron into protoporphyrin to form heme is discussed in Chapter 12.

A hepatic vasodepressor principle (VDM) involved in regulation of peripheral circulation was concentrated from beef, dog, horse, and human liver (56). The VDM activity of the concentrates was found to be proportional to the ferritin content. The active principle was identified as ferritin, and both purified ferritin and apoferritin (protein part) were shown to exert similar effects. So ferritin, aside from its importance in the absorption, storage, and transport of iron in the body, exhibits the unusual role of a regulator of peripheral circulation.

The concept that iron deficiency is without effect on iron-containing enzymes has been challenged by Beutler (57).

Sources and availability of iron. There has long been disagreement on the relative availability of ferrous and ferric iron compounds. Since only ferrous ions are absorbed, the discrepancies in the reported degrees and rates of absorption of the two forms of iron may actually reflect differences in efficiency of the processes involved in reducing ferric to ferrous iron. Definite species variations are now established; while rats absorb both forms about equally well, human beings absorb ferrous better than ferric iron.

Inorganic iron of food is readily available for absorption in all animal species studied. The organic food iron, which consists primarily of hematin-like iron, is not effective in iron deficiency anemia in man or animals, because the iron in such combinations is not available for absorption (at least not more than to a small degree). The iron of hematin or hemoglobin by vein, but not by mouth, is utilized for new hemoglobin formation. Based on such findings workers developed the concept of "available" food iron as opposed to total food iron.

It was shown by Hill (58) that α,α-dipyridyl reacts with ferrous ions to give an intense red color to the solution, whereas organically bound iron, including hematin iron, does not react. Elvehjem and coworkers (59) and others (60) determined the biologic value of food iron by noting the response in "standardized" anemic rats. Fairly good agreement between the amount of iron reacting with the dipyridyl reagent and the biologically available iron has been noted in many foods. In other words, the hemoglobin response indicates about the same amount of iron in a food as that which is found to react with the α,α-dipyridyl. In certain foods the data from the chemical and biologic methods do not correlate well (61). The available iron varies in foods from 15 or 20 per cent of the total to 90 or so per cent. Spinach contains around 56 mg of iron per 100 g of dry sample of which only about 20 per cent is available (59). Liver, other meats, spinach, eggs, dried fruits, and parsley are good sources of food iron.

Iron from hemoglobin breakdown is reutilized efficiently in the body before or following storage as ferritin. This source of available iron reduces the dietary requirement markedly.

Iron requirement. The human iron requirement has been studied by many workers employing a variety of techniques and criteria. Exact information is not easily obtained. Studies with school children on absorption of administered radioactive iron led to interesting data (62). The uptake was found to be 7.7 to 17.7 per cent of a test dose of 2 to 3 mg of radioactive ferrous iron. It was shown that the uptake correlated with the estimated yearly increases in body iron during growth. From these and other data the investigators estimated that children 7 to 10 years old require 2.3 to 3.8 mg per day of absorbable iron. Obviously the total food iron requirement is higher, since, as pointed out previously, variable quantities of the iron in different foods are wholly unavailable.

From various reports and calculations it was indicated by Moore and others (49) that adult men consuming 12 to 15 mg of food iron daily should maintain iron balance. Women, however, are in a less favorable position due to menstruation and pregnancy and deficiency states with the above indicated intakes may develop. Aside from this the National Research Council Allowance (Table 18.5, p. 696) of 7 to 15 mg daily for children and 10 to 12 mg (15 in pregnancy) for adults appear to be liberal.

COPPER

When young rats are restricted to a diet of cow's milk, they develop rather rapidly a nutritional anemia. The addition of iron salts, purified to remove copper, does not correct the condition. But upon addition of iron and copper, or at this time copper alone, a prompt reticulocyte response follows. Several species of animals, including rats, rabbits, pigs, chickens, and dogs, are known to require copper for hemoglobin formation. The earlier literature on the controversial "essential" nature of copper in this respect has been reviewed by Elvehjem (63).

A copper-deficiency syndrome, including anemia, in sheep pasturing on copper-deficient grazing land in western Australia has been studied in detail (64). The anemia responds to copper therapy.

In infants copper has been demonstrated to be a beneficial adjunct to iron therapy in the treatment of nutritional anemia. In adults the value of copper in this condition is controversial. It is difficult to study because of the small quantities that might be required, the normal distribution of copper in food, and the usual copper contamination of iron preparations used in therapy (19).

The mode of action of copper in hemoglobin formation is unknown. Perhaps something of significance will some day develop from the observations that in copper deficiency the marrow of rat bones is markedly decreased in cytochrome oxidase and that the enzyme concentration increases upon the administration of copper (65). It is well established that in rats suffering from an iron and copper deficiency anemia, the administration of iron results in an accumulation of this element, especially in the liver and spleen. If at such a time copper is given in place of iron, the stored iron leaves the liver, and hemoglobin synthesis is rapid (66). If follows that copper functions somehow in the mobilization of stored iron.

Work by Wintrobe and others (67) indicates a functional role of copper in the absorption of iron and a requirement for tissue copper in the utilization of administered iron for hemoglobin synthesis. Cartwright (68) demonstrated a decreased red blood cell survival time and a concomitant rate of new cell production insufficient to compensate for the increased red cell destruction in copper deficient pigs.

In adults the copper content of whole blood is something over 100 μg per 100 ml. In nutritional anemia the value may become very low. It appears that the copper is rather evenly distributed between cells and plasma. A protein, given the name "hemocuprein," has been isolated from red blood cells and from plasma. It contains 0.34 per cent copper. Another protein, isolated from liver and named "hepatocuprein," contains the same amount of copper (69). Neither was found to exhibit any of the catalytic properties of enzymes. Erythrocuprein from red cells and cerebrocuprein from brain are other copper protein complexes. Ceruloplasmin holds 90 per cent or more of the plasma copper. This protein has weak peroxidase activity *in vitro*. Morrell and others (70) reported that ceruloplasmin could be separated into copper and protein and that the reaction is reversible *in vivo*. This finding is in agreement with the theory that ceruloplasmin operates by releasing and binding copper at the proper sites in the body, thus aiding the regulation of copper absorption and transport. The isotope Cu^{64} was used in these studies, and the observation was made that ceruloplasmin copper and ionic copper exchanged only when ceruloplasmin was reduced by ascorbic acid. Hemocyanin, the well-known oxygen-carrying blood pigment of cephalopods, contains copper as an essential part of the molecule. Polyphenol oxidase (tyrosinase) and ascorbic acid oxidase are two plant enzymes containing copper.

An interesting observation by Mills (71) indicated that certain copper-containing preparations of herbage fed to copper-deficient rats showed greater responses in growth, hemoglobin levels, and liver copper stores than equivalent amounts of inorganic copper ($CuSO_4$). Further purification resulted in a material effective at much lower levels than inorganic copper. The implication is that some organic form of copper is more active or more available (or both) than cupric ion (72).

Copper is widely distributed in foods, and it is unlikely that human beings, with the exception of infants on an exclusive milk diet, ever develop a dietary deficiency. In milligrams per cent of copper, liver contains around 4 to

5, certain nuts and dry legumes around 1, while tubers and some leafy vegetables are as low as 0.1. The copper content of cow's milk is only about 0.1 mg per liter.

The interesting nutritional interrelations of copper and molybdenum will be brought out in the discussion of the latter element.

COBALT

It has been known for over 20 years that the supplementation of a rat's diet with cobalt produces a polycythemia. Since that time this effect of cobalt has been demonstrated in other species, including chickens, pigs, rabbits, and dogs (73). In copper- and iron-deficient rats, no response to cobalt is found. Cobalt-deficiency anemia has not been produced in rats experimentally, even though they were maintained on rations containing less than 0.03 ppm of cobalt (74). Perhaps this reflects the minute amounts required and the difficulty of removing the last traces from natural foods.

Around 95 per cent of a small dose of cobalt given either orally or parenterally to rats is excreted in four days (75). Only 40 to 50 μg of cobalt is found in the entire body of a rat at the height of the polycythemia.

It has been demonstrated that cobalt stimulates erythropoieten production. This "hormone" is a factor in plasma of anemic animals which accelerates erythropoiesis when injected into test animals. The injection of cobaltous chloride into rats brings about a very rapid increase in the blood level of this "hormone." The mechanism of its production remains obscure (76). This may represent a beginning in our understanding of how cobalt brings on polycythemia.

In various parts of the world cattle and sheep suffer from a cobalt deficiency. In these areas the grazing land is deficient in this element, and a supplementation of cobalt often corrects the condition. In this country several reports have appeared regarding cobalt deficiency in cattle. In one instance the cattle were unthrifty and anemic. The addition of $CoSO_4$ to the grain ration or to the water supply (about 3 mg Co per animal per day) corrected the condition.

Administration of vitamin B_{12} (see Chapter 28) is likewise effective in cobalt deficient ruminants (77). It is now clear that a cobalt deficiency in these animals results in a vitamin B_{12} deficiency. Vitamin B_{12} contains around 4 per cent cobalt by weight. Cobalt deficiency has not been demonstrated in species other than the ruminants, although, of course, B_{12} deficiency has.

In nature B_{12} is synthesized only by certain microorganisms, and ruminants depend upon such synthesis in the gastrointestinal tract for a supply of the vitamin. Thus, oral cobalt is dramatically effective in cobalt-deficient animals, while parental administration is without effect. Parental vitamin B_{12} is highly effective, as would be expected.

Therefore, ruminants require dietary cobalt for the purpose of supplying microorganisms with the element in order that the organisms may synthesize

B_{12} to furnish the host with this required nutrient. A comprehensive review by Underwood (78) is available.

ZINC

All naturally growing materials contain zinc. The essential nature of this element for plant growth is well established. Various plant diseases are now known to be related to zinc deficiency. Much of this material is brought together in a review (79). Zinc is likewise an essential element in animal nutrition. In 1934 zinc-deficiency symptoms in rats were reported (80). Poor body and fur growth were the prominent symptoms seen in the animals maintained on diets containing only 1.6 mg of zinc per kilo of ration. These observations have been amply confirmed (81,82). Similar symptoms and also a marked decrease in the catalase activity of kidney and liver have been reported in mice (83) placed at weaning time on diets very low in zinc.

It was formerly held rather generally that zinc is an integral and essential part of the insulin molecule. However, at the present time active zinc-free insulin preparations are available. It is not clear whether or not zinc is incorporated into the molecules of this material after administration, or whether it retains its activity without zinc.

Highly purified carbonic anhydrase, a vital enzyme in many animal species, contains zinc (84). It is essential to the activity of the enzyme and thus to life in these species (including man). Dehydropeptidase (85), a phosphatase (86), and uricase (87) are other enzymes which appear to contain zinc.

Vallee and coworkers have reported on the functional aspect of zinc in several dehydrogenases (88) and in pancreatic carboxypeptidase (89).

Even though the physiologic functions of zinc appear to be diverse, little progress has been made in relations of deficiency symptoms and enzyme levels in animals.

An unusual development in the last few years involves the unexpected interrelation of zinc and calcium. It was observed that additional zinc was required for good growth on some practical swine rations and that additional calcium supplements were deleterious. The further addition of zinc at this time to such a ration brought about a dramatic alleviation of the symptoms, principally parakeratosis (abnormal development of the corneous layer of the epidermis) and lowered growth rate (90).

The practical implications in swine nutrition and the academic implications of such findings led to intensive investigations in this area. Explanations for the interference of calcium in zinc metabolism have not been forthcoming. In a review of this problem, Forbes (91) concludes that although the skin lesions cannot be explained on the basis of known catalytic or enzymatic functions of zinc, it seems most probable, on the basis of present evidence, that calcium interference in zinc function occurs at the cellular level.

The wide distribution of zinc in foods of both plant and animal origin accounts for the unlikelihood of deficiency symptoms developing spontaneously in man or animals.

Oysters and certain other seafoods, liver, wheat germ, yeast, and lettuce are high in zinc. Milk contains only 2 or 3 mg per liter.

A comprehensive review by Vallee on the biochemistry, physiology, and pathology of zinc is available (92).

MANGANESE

The essential nature of manganese in plant nutrition has long been known. This element is routinely added to the nutrient solution employed in hydroponics (soil-less plant growth).

The evidence that manganese belongs in the list of essential elements in animal nutrition is altogether convincing. In 1931 it was established that rats reared on manganese-deficient diets fail to suckle their young and that males develop testicular degeneration leading, in time, to complete sterility (93). Growth is poor, bone formation abnormal, hemoglobin regeneration interfered with, and blood serum phosphatase markedly elevated in rats on purified diets supplying only 5 μg of manganese daily (94). Liver arginase is decreased (95). Other species studied show characteristic symptoms of manganese deficiency. In the chick a perosis develops (96), in cattle sterility may ensue (97), while in pigs a lameness has been reported (98).

Manganese as Mn^{++} activates a number of plant and animal enzymes, including arginase, phosphoglucomutase, hexokinase, isocitric dehydrogenase, pyrophosphatase, and various decarboxylases. In certain instances other bivalent ions may be effective activators, but Mn^{++} may be specific for some—i.e., arginase. Liver arginase decreases in a deficiency of the element, and upon addition of manganese salts to liver preparations from deficient animals, the activity of arginase can be increased substantially. If manganese functions in hemoglobin formation, the mechanism by which it does so is entirely unknown.

The evidence of Borg and Cotzias (99) that mammalian (including human) red cells have one or more porphyrins containing manganese is of paramount interest in this connection.

The name "transmanganin" was given to a β_1-globulin of human plasma which binds manganese (100). The protein is different from transferrin (iron-binding protein).

Requirements are established for some animals, but human requirements are largely unknown and figures stated are estimates at best. Thus Cotzias (101) estimated man's requirement to range from 3 to 9 mg per day.

The universal distribution of manganese in plant and animal tissues contraindicates spontaneous deficiency in man and most animals except under extraordinary conditions. The requisite addition of the element to poultry rations is based upon sound experimental evidence.

Reviews on manganese include that of Cotzias (101) and a shorter paper by the same author (102).

MOLYBDENUM

It was demonstrated by Westerfeld and Richert (103) that intestinal xanthine oxidase (xanthine $\longrightarrow$ uric acid) is dependent upon a dietary factor called the "xanthine oxidase factor." The same workers (104) later identified this factor as the trace element molybdenum. It was shown that purified milk xanthine oxidase contains 0.03 per cent molybdenum. Animals subsisting for seven to ten days on a diet extremely low in this element showed a marked decrease in the activity of the enzyme in intestinal tissue, and upon the addition of sodium molybdate to the diet, the enzyme activity returned to normal in several days.

Two other flavoprotein enzymes, nitrate reductase of plants and microorganisms (105) and a hydrogenase of bacterial origin (106), likewise contain and require molybdenum.

The element is essential in plant growth on the basis of its role in nitrogen fixation. So far, deficiency symptoms in rats have not been observed in spite of the virtual elimination of molybdenum and xanthine oxidase from rat tissues by feeding low Mo diets and tungstate (Mo antagonist) (107). In chicks, deficiency symptoms are established (108). This species difference may reflect the greater need for xanthine oxidase for the production of more uric acid, the end product of protein metabolism in chickens.

Molybdenum:copper:sulfate interrelations. The intriguing interrelations of molybdenum and copper in nutrition came to light when the deleterious effects of increased dietary molybdenum in cattle and sheep were found to respond dramatically to copper sulfate by mouth. The mechanism of such a profound action is not known (109). There is a marked species variation in response to molybdenum toxicity. Cattle and sheep are the most susceptible, horses and pigs the least, and rats and rabbits intermediate (110). The significant observation that dietary sulfate decreased or even removed the deleterious effects of molybdenum (111) is in part due to the resulting lowered blood molybdenum levels.

The influence of molybdenum on copper metabolism in sheep is evident only in the presence of dietary sulfate (112). Molybdenum or sulfate separately does not interfere with copper retention. Thus, copper poisoning has been reported in sheep on moderate copper intakes and very low intakes of sulfate and of molybdenum. On the other hand, copper deficiency symptoms have been observed with depletion of tissue copper when copper intake was normal but molybdenum and sulfate intakes were elevated (113). No explanation of such findings is available. Some speculation on the matter is of interest (109).

Comparable relations in human nutrition are not known at this time.

BORON

Since there has long been agreement regarding the essential nature of boron in plant life (114), it follows that investigators would study the requirement of this element in animal nutrition. To date there is no clear demonstration that animals normally need boron. If the rat requires boron, it would seem that as little as 0.6 μg per day satisfies the need (115). A report regarding the beneficial effect of boron on growth and survival time of rats eating diets deficient in potassium (116) was not confirmed by other workers (117).

Boric acid has been rather widely used in the treatment of extensive burns in human beings. It has again been pointed out (118) that boric acid is a cumulative poison, and the authors suggest that its use be discontinued.

ARSENIC

Although arsenic is widely distributed in plant and animal tissues, it has not been demonstrated as an essential element in animal nutrition. The earlier claim for a functional role of arsenic in hemoglobin formation has not been corroborated in later work.

Since cow's milk is low in arsenic (32 to 60 μg per liter), it has been used as an experimental diet to study the possible role of arsenic in the nutrition of the rat (119). In this study it was reported that arsenic, added to the milk diet with iron or with iron and copper, was without effect on the regeneration of hemoglobin or red blood cells of anemic rates. The conclusion was reached that if arsenic is essential for growth or for hemoglobin or red cell production in the rat, then 2 μg, the quantity normally present in about 50 ml of milk, satisfies this requirement.

Sickness and death in cattle in a specific area of New Zealand was reported to result from excessive arsenic intake. The soil was high in arsenic, and the drinking water was found to contain 2.6 grains of As_2O_5 per gallon (120).

ALUMINUM

The early proponents of the theory of "toxicity" from aluminum cooking ware and from aluminum salts used in baking powder have derived little solace from the scientific data subsequently developed on the subject. The rather widespread occurrence of aluminum in plant and animal tissues is generally accepted at present (121). In moderate amounts this element has not been shown to exert deleterious effects in man or animals.

Rats on a mineralized milk ration showed no significant growth differences upon the addition of aluminum. It was concluded that if the rat needs aluminum during its most rapid period of growth, 1 μg per day satisfies the requirement (122). It has been concluded from balance studies in preschool children that aluminum is not an essential constituent of their diet (123).

FLUORINE

Though fluorine is practically always present in soil, it is not known to be required for plant growth. At present the data are conflicting on the essential nature of this element in animal nutrition.

Rats grow and reproduce well on whole milk mineralized with iron, copper, and manganese. Such a diet supplies very little fluorine—about 50 μg per day per kilogram body weight based on a content of 0.1 to 0.2 ppm in the milk (124). Additional fluorine (0.1–20 ppm to the milk) brought about no improvement in the animals. On the other hand, it has been reported that rats on a "fluorine-free" diet died of starvation because caries destroyed all the effective chewing surfaces of the molar teeth and the animals stopped eating (125). It was concluded that fluorine is necessary in a diet that has to be chewed. In a later publication from the same laboratory it was reported that growth and reproduction in rats on the "fluorine-free" diet were not so good as in rats on the same diet with a source of fluorine added (126). The rations used in these studies were composed primarily of foods grown by hydroponics. No reports corroborating the claim for an essential role of fluorine in rat nutrition have been found, and it is rather generally accepted that this element probably has no essential function in the rat (127).

It is well established that, on certain caries-producing rations, fluorine in some way acts as a caries-preventive agent in rats. Also established is the fact that fluorides by mouth (drinking water or diet) are more effective than by topical application or stomach tube and that by parenteral injection they are not effective. A review covering much of the experimental fluorine work on rats and hamsters is available (128).

Perhaps the most interesting aspect of the fluorine problem is related to dental caries in human beings. The development of our present knowledge on the subject has an interesting history and is reviewed in a number of places [see, for instance, the book referred to in (128)].

As early as 1916 it was proposed that mottled enamel (enamel becomes stratified and shows pits and other depressions) resulted from something in the drinking water. That this "something" is fluoride was established by various workers in 1931 (129). The exact concentration of fluoride in drinking water required to produce mottling in children may vary somewhat with other factors. At any rate, it appears that, in general, a small percentage of children show mild mottling at a level of 1.2 ppm or greater, and the severity of the condition increases with increasing levels of fluorine intake.

In areas of endemic mottling the incidence of dental caries was found to be markedly reduced. This led to the discovery that fluoride is associated with caries inhibition in human beings. Of the many epidemiologic studies carried out to integrate this relationship, one of the most informative is that of Dean and associates (130) reported in 1942. This particular work is known as the "21 cities study," and was designed to answer among other questions whether or not a communal water supply might be high enough in fluoride to reduce dental caries markedly, and low enough so as to eliminate the complication of mottling. Over 7000 children—12, 13, and 14 years of age—who had been continuously exposed to the communal water supplies of these cities were subjected to dental examinations.

The relation between caries incidence and fluoride intake is dramatically demonstrated in the accompanying graph (Figure 30.1). Fluorosis (mottled enamel) was found to be negative or borderline and of no esthetic significance in several cities where caries incidence was minimal. The fluoride varied from 0.9 to 1.2 ppm in the water supply of these cities.

These and many other observations of a like nature led to experimental topical application of fluorides to children's teeth, as well as to the experimental addition of NaF to low fluoride communal water supplies in attempts to arrest the rampant caries so prevalent in many parts of the country.

Notwithstanding isolated reports to the contrary, it is established that the periodic topical application of NaF solution to the teeth of children does reduce the subsequent incidence of dental caries (131). Since this approach is quite new, the length of time of inhibition due to topical fluoride application is as yet not well established. However, a group of 39 patients in which one quadrant of the teeth had been treated with a 0.1 per cent solution of NaF six times during two years was re-examined three years after cessation

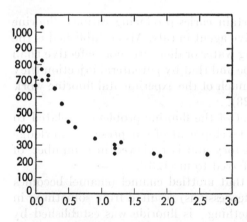

Figure 30.1. Relation between dental caries in permanent teeth per 100 children and fluoride content of drinking water (ppm, horizontal scale). A study of 21 cities in 4 states, observations of 7257 selected 12- to 14-year-old white school children. (H. T. Dean, F. A. Arnold, and E. Elvolve, *Pub. Health Rept.*, 57, 115, 1942.)

of the treatments. Over this three-year period the development of new decay was found to be about 30 per cent less in the teeth of the previously treated quadrants (131).

A progress report on the Newburgh-Kingston Fluorine Demonstration, now in progress under the New York State Department of Health (132) has appeared (133). In this experiment the water supply of Newburgh, New York, has been supplemented with 1 ppm fluoride (as NaF) since May, 1945, while in the comparable city of Kingston the water is fluoride-free. A total of about 3400 children from Newburgh and 2800 from Kingston have undergone periodic dental examinations. The data indicate a markedly lower incidence of caries experience (decayed, missing, or filled teeth) among the children living in Newburgh. The younger the children were at the beginning of the experiment, the greater the benefit from the fluoridated water. This study as well as others of a similar nature are reviewed editorially (134). Blayney (135) reviews the results of 13 years' experience with fluoridation of the water supply in Evanston, Illinois. The data are in accord with the many other studies indicating the tremendous practical value in children of ingesting fluoride. One statement provides a rather unique outlook toward the problem. The author states that, in terms of teeth, 30,250 have been saved from decay that would have been attacked had the water not been fluoridated (according to the 1946 prefluoridation standard).

A study of the relation of fluoride intake and caries incidence in adults supported the conclusion that the cariostatic effect is exerted in adults who are native to localities in which the water supply contains fluoride (136).

The mechanism by which fluorine inhibits caries production is unknown. There is little or no evidence to support the theory that it acts antienzymatically. Although mottled teeth do have increased levels of fluoride in both dentine and enamel, it is doubtful if carious teeth in any one person's mouth contain, either in the enamel or dentine, less fluoride than the sound teeth. Even in teeth treated topically with NaF, the fluoride concentration of enamel appears to be unaltered. Perhaps the methods are not sufficiently sensitive to show slight changes in fluoride concentration. If there is an increase, this might answer many questions, since decreased enamel solubility, etc., then could be postulated (137).

The highly toxic nature of excessive fluoride ion in animals has long been a subject of investigation. Definite harmful effects on growth and bone and tooth development in cattle from supplemental feeding of fluoride-containing rock phosphates are well known. In experimental work with rats it was reported that a reduction in the hemoglobin level was brought about by giving the animals drinking water containing 50 ppm fluoride as NaF. More recently this claim has been contested by other workers who found no effect on hemoglobin concentration or hematocrit value in rats given water containing the same source and concentration of fluoride ion (137).

In man relatively large quantities of fluoride are required to produce toxic symptoms. A very extensive study of the hazards to man and animals from fluorisis associated with the industrial production of aluminum in Scotland was published in 1949 (138). In one furnace room in this factory fluoride concentrations as high as 3.6 mg per cubic meter of air were found. Although some of the older workers, exposed for many years to such an atmosphere, showed x-ray findings generally associated with fluorosis, none of them suffered clinical disability. It was established also that considerable fluorine was liberated from the factory, but rather intensive clinical and laboratory examination of inhabitants in the area failed to reveal any signs of injury to health.

A re-evaluation of fluoride toxicity in man is underway. The following example illustrates this. A group of 70 patients with various forms of cancer were given large doses of NaF in enteric-coated capsules. Among the adults, the average intake was 80 mg NaF four times a day. The children received 20 to 50 mg four times a day. It was reported that the ingestion of as much as 320 mg of NaF daily for periods of five to six months resulted in no evidence of acute or chronic toxicity in man. One individual was given a total of 5600 mg of NaF intravenously in 400- or 500-mg doses over nine days with no apparent signs of toxicity (139).

SELENIUM

"Alkali disease" in cattle was known to the early settlers of the Great Plains area. The name is a misnomer, since alkali water and forage from alkali soils are not toxic. It was not until 1931 that the harmful agent in the forage of certain of these areas was found to be selenium. In rather specific areas the selenium content of the soil is such that the forage and many of the crops under cultivation have a selenium content ranging up to 13 or more ppm. It is now well established that cattle, sheep, and other farm animals on such feed develop typical symptoms which often become debilitating and may lead to death. Experimentally it has been demonstrated that similar symptoms can be developed by feeding animals diets containing added selenium. Human beings in these areas are likewise subject to selenium poisoning. In the section on detoxication mechanisms a brief discussion can be found regarding the detoxication of selenium in animals and man.

In general, the forage crops concentrate soil selenium more than cultivated crops, although, oddly enough, crop plants growing in close proximity to seleniferous forage plants may become highly toxic themselves, supposedly because the forage crops in some way convert soil selenium to a more readily absorbable form.

It has been postulated that selenium might replace sulfur in amino acids of proteins. Experimental support of this hypothesis was offered by the work of Moxon and coworkers (140). They found about the same magnitude of toxicity in rats by feeding seleniferous wheat, sodium selenite, or selenium-cystine, and L-selenium-cystine was far more toxic than the unnatural D-form. It is of interest that arsenic gave full protection to the animals against the selenium of the selenium-cystine. The arsenic was given in the drinking water (10 ppm as sodium arsenite). Milk from cattle in selenium areas contains considerable amounts of this element. In rats the incorporation of inorganic selenium into organic combination has been demonstrated. Upon the administration of radioactive selenium to nursing rats radioactivity was found in the milk proteins, and very little activity in the milk whey (141).

Attempts to treat seleniferous soil with arsenic or sulfates in order to reduce the selenium content of the crops have not in general proved successful.

Of great interest was the announcement in 1957 of the essential role of selenium in the nutrition of the rat and the chicken. As early as 1935 a deficiency disease characterized by liver necrosis in rats was recognized. In chickens an exudative diathesis developed on diets free of vitamin E and containing a specific yeast as source of protein. In either case vitamin E was protective and "Factor 3," isolated from certain yeasts, also was protective (142). Schwarz and Foltz announced that active preparations of "Factor 3" contain organically bound selenium (143). Inorganic selenium as selenite or selenate was found to protect rats completely against necrotic liver degeneration in quantities as small as a few tenths of a microgram per animal daily.

It was also shown that minute quantities of selenium added to rations known to produce exudative diathesis in chickens afforded complete protection (144). It remains to be seen whether selenium will prove to be an essential element under conditions other than those for which such a demonstration has been made.

The subject has been reviewed by Underwood (109) and by Schwarz (145).

BROMINE

Bromine occurs regularly in plant tissue. This is not surprising in view of the fact that most soils and waters contain small amounts of this element. The presence of bromine in animal tissues, long denied, is now generally accepted.

Growth inhibition in mice occasioned by feeding a synthetic diet supplemented with succinylsulfathiazole and physiologically active iodinated casein was reversed by supplements of trace element sea salt or the ash of whey. Bromine was demonstrated to be the active principle in the supplements (146). A slight growth response to NaBr in chicks was noted under controlled feeding conditions (147). These data are of academic interest only at this time.

The bromine content of various animal tissues has been reported (148). In man the blood of some 100 samples from persons never treated with bromine-containing medicine showed a bromine content of 0.15 to 0.35 mg per 100 ml. In ten manic depressives normal values for bromine were found in both blood and urine.

IODINE

As early as 1820 it was postulated that iodine, earlier discovered by Courtois in seaweed, was a curative for goiter. Since iodine-deficiency goiters were common in many parts of the world, the news traveled, and the use of iodine and iodine-containing substances (burned sponge, etc.) became so popular it is little wonder that such a widespread health measure was attended by numerous instances of injudicious treatment. In time man developed discrimination in the use of this "wonder drug," and the beneficial effect of salt rich in iodine advanced the prophylactic and therapeutic treatment of goiter.

The discovery of Baumann in 1896 that the thyroid gland is far richer in iodine than other tissues led to controlled experimentation with animals and human beings on the relation of dietary iodine and thyroid function. Earlier postulates of a higher incidence of thyroid enlargement among peoples in areas where the soil and water are low in iodine were corroborated and extended. In various animal species goiter was produced by restricting dietary iodine and relieved by supplementation with iodide salts or foods rich in this element.

Marine early came to the conclusion that thyroid hyperplasia (simple goiter) is a compensatory mechanism on the part of the body in response to a deficiency of iodine. The hyperplasia may be thought of as a futile attempt on the part of the body to produce the thyroid hormone by increasing the number of the cells in the thyroid gland. Obviously without available iodine the iodine-containing hormone cannot be fabricated.

In the United States various areas have been designated as "goiter belts." The central plain states, especially around the Great Lakes, and the Pacific Northwest were outstanding for the high incidence of endemic goiter before the advent of iodized salt, the educational programs over the past years, plus the leveling effect of the tremendous increase in intersectional transport of both fresh and canned foods. It is generally true that in a given locality the iodine content of the drinking water and the incidence of goiter show an inverse relation, not that drinking water is directly an important source of dietary iodine, but it is an index of the iodine in the earth's surface and thus in the vegetation.

Marine and associates undertook the first large-scale, controlled treatment of simple goiter in human beings when they began their classic studies with school children in Akron, Ohio, (149). These investigators administered NaI (ten doses of 0.2 g over two weeks) each autumn and spring. The results were dramatic. In a two-and-a-half year study five children in a group of 2190 given NaI developed thyroid enlargement, while of 2305 children not given treatment 495 developed enlargement of the thyroid. Of 1182 children showing thyroid enlargement at the outset who were given treatment, 773 showed a decrease in thyroid size. Of 1048 pupils showing enlargement at the outset who were not treated, 145 showed a decrease in thyroid size. The prophylactic as well as the curative effect of iodine is well demonstrated in this study.

Similar treatment was soon instituted in large and small cities throughout the so-called goiter belts of the country. It became obvious that some plan was needed whereby the intake of iodine would become not only more widespread but in a sense automatic. What better approach could be found than to add iodine to common table salt?

In this country the early trials in Michigan were highly successful (50). After a ten-year period in which iodized salt (0.01–0.02 per cent NaI added) was used in several counties, the incidence of thyroid enlargement was found to have decreased about 74 to 90 per cent. The showing might have been even better were it not for the fact that the iodized salt was used sporadically or not at all by some of the people examined before and after this ten-year study.

It is of interest to look at a survey by Hamwi and coworkers (151) of some 27,000 Ohio school children planned to study the progress in controlling simple goiter since 1925. A survey in 1954 was conducted in the same four counties in Ohio in which children had been examined in 1925. Similar criteria were used in both instances. Table 30.3, modified from Hamwi and coworkers, shows the incidence of enlarged thyroid glands found in the two studies. The over-all decrease in simple goiter from 32 per cent in 1925 to around 4 per cent in 1954 is due largely to the use of iodized salt, and to the increased use of foods with elevated iodide content (i.e., seafood) over the years.

Occasionally fears are expressed regarding the continuous ingestion of iodine by hyperthyroid individuals. There seems to be little basis for alarm, however (152).

It is probably true that all cells of the body contain iodine, but normally an adult has a total body content of only about 50 mg. The tremendous concentrating ability of the thyroid gland for iodine is demonstrated by the fact that about one-fifth of the body store is localized in this gland, which weighs around 25 g. The blood in normal man varies in iodine content, depending

Table 30.3. Comparison of the Incidence of Enlarged Thyroid Gland in Ohio School Children as Shown by Goiter Surveys Made in Four Counties in 1925 and 1954

County		Total Cases Studied	Per Cent Goiter All Children
Butler	1925	10,679	31.5
Butler	1954	12,905	3.0
Marion	1925	5352	33.1
Marion	1954	4231	4.6
Union	1925	1302	31.0
Union	1954	1412	5.2
Washington	1925	4247	33.8
Washington	1954	3854	5.9
Total	1925	21,580	32.3
	1954	22,402	4.0

Modified from Hamwi, G. J., and coworkers: *Am. J. Public Health*, 45, 1344, 1955.

somewhat on intake. The range is around 5 to 12 μg per 100 ml of serum. A marked interest has recently developed in blood iodine levels, especially the various fractions, as a diagnostic aid in thyroid diseases. It is thought that protein-bound iodine of serum represents principally the circulating thyroid hormone. Thus the protein-bound iodine was reported to be: in normal children, 4.0 to 7.0; in normal adults, 6.0 to 8.4; in cretinism (juvenile hypothyroidism), 1.8 to 3.0; and in thyrotoxicosis (hyperthyroidism), 9.2 to 14.5, all in micrograms per 100 ml of serum (153). The protein-bound iodine of serum drops rapidly after thyroidectomy in rats. This was followed by the use of radioactive iodine, and it was shown that after 12 hours the level may fall to 30 per cent or less of normal (154).

Another recent development is the use of iodinated proteins as a dietary supplement in animal husbandry. In this new field much of the data are conflicting, but it appears that by the judicious use of iodinated casein, for example, it is possible to stimulate increased milk production in cows, improve libido and fertility in inactive bulls, induce a slight advantage in growth rate and economy of gain in young pigs, and possibly improve egg production, especially during the summer slack, in chickens. The physiologic effects of iodinated proteins are due largely to their thyroxine content.

The dietary requirement of iodine is difficult to assess. The various approaches to the problem are reviewed (152), and the conclusion is reached that around 3 μg per kilogram body weight per day, or 2 μg for an average adult, suffices. The Food and Nutrition Board, National Research Council, sets the Recommended Daily Dietary Allowance at 0.15 to 0.30 mg of iodine daily for an adult. By a simple calculation it can be seen that even on a minimal intake of iodized salt (0.02 per cent NaI) the above allowances will be amply met.

The functions and metabolism of the iodine-containing thyroid hormone are discussed in Chapter 34.

SPECIAL REFERENCES

1. Nicholas, H. O.: *J. Biol. Chem.*, **97**, 457, 1932.
2. Logan, M. A.: *Physiol. Revs.*, **20**, 522, 1940.
3. McLean, F. C., and Hastings, A. B.: *J. Biol. Chem.*, **108**, 285, 1935.
4. Todd, W. R.: *J. Biol. Chem.*, **140**, CXXXIII, 1941.
5. Malm, O. J.: *Scandinav. J. Clin. & Lab. Invest.*, **5**, 75, 1953.
6. West, E. S.; Montague, J. R.; and Judy, F. R.: *Am. J. Digestive Diseases*, **5**, 690, 1938. Todd, W. R.; Dittebrandt, M.; Montague, J. R.; and West, E. S.: *ibid.*, **7**, 295, 1940.
7. McCance, R. A., and Widdowson, E. M.: *J. Physiol.*, **101**, 44, 1942.
8. McCance, R. A., and Walsham, C. M.: *Brit. J. Nutrition*, **2**, 26, 1948.
9. Bronner, F.; Harris, R. S.; Maletskos, C. J.; and Benda, C. E.: *J. Nutrition*, **59**, 393, 1956.
10. Bronner, F.; Harris, R. S.; Maletskos, C. J.; and Benda, C. E.: *J. Nutrition*, **54**, 523, 1954.
11. McCance, R. A.; Widdowson, E. M.; and Lehman, H.: *Biochem. J.*, **36**, 686, 1942.
12. Miller, M.: *J. Biol. Chem.*, **122**, 59, 1937–38.
13. Peters, J. P., and Eiserson, L.: *J. Biol. Chem.*, **84**, 155, 1929.
14. Rawson, A. J., and Sunderman, F. W.: *J. Clin. Invest.*, **27**, 82, 1948.
15. Reifenstein, E. C., Jr., and Albright, F.: *J. Clin. Invest.*, **26**, 24, 1947.
16. McQuarrie, I.; Hansen, A. E.; and Ziegler, M. R.: *J. Clin. Endocrinol.*, **1**, 789, 1941.
17. Sherman, H. C.: *J. Biol. Chem.*, **44**, 21, 1920.
18. Sherman, H. C., and Hawley, E.: *J. Biol. Chem.*, **53**, 375, 1922.
19. Steggerda, F. R., and Mitchell, H. H.: *J. Nutrition*, **31**, 407, 1946.
20. Hegsted, D. M.; Moscoso, I.; and Collazos, C. C.: *J. Nutrition*, **46**, 181, 1952.
21. *Nutrition Revs.*, **15**, 257, 1957.
22. Gershoff, S. N.; Legg, M. A.; and Hegsted, D. M.: *J. Nutrition*, **64**, 303, 1958.
23. American Institute of Nutrition, Symposium on Effects of High Calcium Intakes, *Federation Proc.*, **18**, 1075, 1959.
24. Ohlson, M. A., and Stearns, G.: *Federation Proc.*, **18**, 1076, 1959.
25. Nicolaysen, R.; Eeg-Larsen, N.; and Malm, O. J.: *Physiol. Revs.*, **33**, 424, 1953.
26. Tufts, E. V., and Greenberg, D. M.: *J. Biol. Chem.*, **122**, 693, 1938.
27. Kruse, H. D.; Orent, E. R.; and McCollum, E. V.: *J. Biol. Chem.*, **96**, 519, 1932.
28. Kline, H.; Orent, E. R.; and McCollum, E. V.: *Am. J. Physiol.*, **112**, 256, 1935.
29. O'Dell, B. L.; Morris, E. R.; and Regan, W. O.: *Federation Proc.*, **17**, 487, 1958.
30. Vitale, J. J.; Hegsted, D. M.; Nakamura, M.; and Conners, P.: *J. Biol. Chem.*, **226**, 597, 1957.
31. Allcroft, R.: *Vet. Record*, **66**, 517, 1954.
32. Parr, W. H., and Allcroft, R.: *Vet. Record*, **69**, 1041, 1957.
33. Miller, J. F.: *Am. J. Diseases Children*, **67**, 117, 1944.
34. McCance, R. A., and Widdowson, E. M.: *J. Physiol.*, **101**, 44, 304, 1942–43.
35. Follis, R. H., Jr.: *Deficiency Disease*, Charles C Thomas, Springfield, Ill., 1958, p. 35.
36. McCollum, E. V.; Orent-Keiles, E.; and Day, H. G.: *The Newer Knowledge of Nutrition.* The Macmillan Co., New York, 1939, Chap. 8.

37. Orent-Keiles, E.; Robinson, A.; and McCollum, E. V.: *Am. J. Physiol.*, 119, 651, 1937.
38. Orent-Keiles, E., and McCollum, E. V.: *Am. J. Pathol.*, 18, 29, 1942.
39. Ruegamer, W. R., and Elvehjem, C. A.: *Proc. Soc. Exptl. Biol. Med.*, 61, 234, 1946.
40. Shorr, E.: *Harvey Lectures*, 50, 112, 1954–55.
41. Mazur, A.; Baez, S.; and Shorr, E.: *J. Biol. Chem.*, 213, 147, 1955.
42. Mazur, A.; Green, S.; and Carleton, A.: *Federation Proc.*, 19, 335, 1960.
43. Granick, S.: *Chem. Revs.*, 38, 379, 1946.
44. Granick, S.: *Science*, 103, 107, 1946.
45. McCance, R. A., and Widdowson, E. M.: *J. Physiol.*, 94, 148, 1938.
46. Robscheit-Robbins, F. S., and Whipple, G. H.: *Am. J. Physiol.*, 83, 76, 1927.
47. Hahn, P. F.; Bale, W. F.; Lawrence, E. O.; and Whipple, G. H.: *J. Am. Med. Assoc.*, 111, 2285, 1938.
48. Moore, C. V.: *Am. J. Clin. Nutrition*, 3, 3, 1955.
49. Steinkemp, R.; Dubach, R.; and Moore, C. V.: *Arch. Internal Med.*, 95, 181, 1955.
50. Moore, C. V.: *Scand. J. Clin. and Lab. Invest.*, 9, 292, 1957.
51. Balfour, W. M.; Hahn, P. F.; Bale, W. F.; Pommerenke, W. T.; and Whipple, G. H.: *J. Exptl. Med.*, 76, 15, 1942.
52. Kinney, T. D.; Hegsted, D. M.; and Finch, C. A.: *J. Exptl. Med.*, 90, 137, 1949.
53. Hegsted, D. M.; Finch, C. A.; and Kinney, T. D.: *J. Exptl. Med.*, 90, 147, 1949.
54. Gubler, C. J.; Cartwright, G. E.; and Wintrobe, M. M.: *J. Biol. Chem.*, 178, 989, 1949.
55. Shoden, A.; Gabrio, B. W.; and Finch, C. A.: *J. Biol. Chem.*, 204, 823, 1953.
56. Mazur, A., and Shoor, E.: *J. Biol. Chem.*, 176, 771, 1948.
57. Beutler, E., and Blaisdell, R. K.: *Blood*, 15, 30, 1960.
58. Hill, R.: *Proc. Roy. Soc. (London)*, B107, 205, 1930.
59. Sherman, W. C.; Elvehjem, C. A.; and Hart, E. B.: *J. Biol. Chem.*, 107, 383, 1934.
60. Smith, M. C., and Otis, L.: *J. Nutrition*, 14, 365, 1937.
61. Borgen, D. R., and Elvehjem, C. A.: *J. Biol. Chem.*, 119, 725, 1937.
62. Darby, W. J.; Hahn, P. F.; Kaser, M. M.; Steinkamp, R. C.; Densen, P. M.; and Cook, M. B.: *J. Nutrition*, 33, 107, 1947.
63. Elvehjem, C. A.: *Physiol. Revs.*, 15, 471, 1935.
64. Bennetts, H. W., and Beck, A. B.: *Bull. 147, Council for Scientific and Industrial Research, Commonwealth of Australia*, Melbourne, 1942.
65. Schultze, M. O.: *J. Biol. Chem.*, 138, 219, 1941.
66. Elvehjem, C. A., and Sherman, W. C.: *J. Biol. Chem.*, 98, 309, 1932.
67. Wintrobe, M. M.; Cartwright, G. E.; and Gubler, C. J.: *J. Nutrition*, 50, 395, 1953.
68. Cartwright, G. E.: *Am. J. Clin. Nutrition*, 3, 11, 1955.
69. Mann, T., and Keilen, D.: *Proc. Roy. Soc. (London)*, B126, 303, 1938–39.
70. Morrell, A. G., and Scheinberg, I. H.: *Science*, 127, 588, 1958.
71. Mills, C. F.: *Biochem. J.*, 63, 190, 1956.
72. *Nutrition Revs.*, 16, 78, 1958.
73. Grant, W. C., and Root, W. S.: *Physiol. Revs.*, 32, 449, 1953.
74. Houk, A. E. H.; Thomas, A. W.; and Sherman, H. C.: *J. Nutrition*, 31, 609, 1946.
75. Greenberg, D. M.; Copp, D. H.; and Cuthbertson, D. H.: *J. Biol. Chem.*, 147, 749, 1943.
76. Goldwasser, E.; Jacobson, L. O.; Fried, W.; and Plzak, L. F.: *Blood*, 13, 55, 1958.
77. Smith, S. E., and Loosli, J. K.: *J. Dairy Sci.*, 40, 1215, 1957.
78. Underwood, E. J.: *Trace Elements in Human and Animal Nutrition*. Academic Press, Inc. New York, 1956.
79. Chandler, W. H.: *Botan. Gaz.*, 98, 625, 1937.
80. Todd, W. R.; Elvehjem, C. A.; and Hart, E. B.: *Am. J. Physiol.*, 107, 146, 1934.
81. Hove, E.; Elvehjem, C. A.; and Hart, E. B.: *Am. J. Physiol.*, 124, 750, 1938.
82. Day, H. G., and McCollum, E. V.: *Proc. Soc. Exptl. Biol. Med.*, 45, 282, 1940.
83. Day, H. G., and Skidmore, B. E.: *J. Nutrition*, 33, 27, 1947.
84. Keilen, D., and Mann, T.: *Nature*, 144, 442, 1939.
85. Yudkin, W. H., and Fruton, J. S.: *J. Biol. Chem.*, 170, 421, 1947.
86. Cloetens, R.: *Biochem. Z.*, 308, 37, 1941.
87. Holmberg, C. G.: *Biochem. J.*, 33, 1901, 1939.
88. Vallee, B. L.; Hoch, F. L.; Adelstein, S. J.; and Wacker, E. C.: *J. Am. Chem. Soc.*, 78, 5879, 1956.

89. Vallee, B. L., and Neurath, H.: *J. Am. Chem. Soc.*, **76**, 5006, 1954.
90. Tucker, H. F., and Salmon, W. D.: *Proc. Soc. Exptl. Biol. Med.*, **88**, 613, 1955.
91. Forbes, R. M.: *Federation Proc.*, **19**, 1960.
92. Vallee, B. L.: *Physiol. Revs.*, **39**, 443, 1959.
93. Orent, E. R., and McCollum, E. V.: *J. Biol. Chem.*, **92**, 651, 1931.
94. Wachtel, L. W.; Elvehjem, C. A.; and Hart, E. B.: *Am. J. Physiol.*, **140**, 72, 1943.
95. Boyer, P.; Shaw, J.; and Phillips, P. H.: *J. Biol. Chem.*, **143**, 417, 1942.
96. Wilgus, H. S.; Norris, L. C.; and Heuser, G. F.: *J. Nutrition*, **14**, 155, 1937.
97. Tutt, J. F. D.: *Vet. J.*, **90**, 355, 1934.
98. Miller, R. C.; Keith, T. B.; McCarty, M. A.; and Thorp, W. T. S.: *Proc. Soc. Exptl. Biol. Med.*, **45**, 50, 1940.
99. Borg, D. C., and Cotzias, G. C.: *Nature*, **182**, 1677, 1959.
100. Bertinchamps, A. J., and Cotzias, G. C.: *Federation Proc.*, **18**, 469, 1959.
101. Cotzias, G. C.: *Physiol. Revs.*, **38**, 503, 1958.
102. Cotzias, G. C.: *Federation Proc.*, **19**, 1960.
103. Westerfeld, W. W., and Richert, D. A.: *J. Biol. Chem.*, **192**, 35, 1951; **199**, 393, 1952.
104. Richert, D. A., and Westerfeld, W. W.: *J. Biol. Chem.*, **203**, 915, 1953.
105. Nicholas, D. J. O., and Nason, A.: *J. Biol. Chem.*, **207**, 353, 1954.
106. Shug, A. L.; Wilson, P. W.; Green, D. E.; and Mahler, H. R.: *J. Am. Chem. Soc.*, **76**, 3355, 1954.
107. Higgins, E. S.; Richert, D. A.; and Westerfeld, J.: *J. Nutrition*, **59**, 539, 1956.
108. Reid, B. L.; Kurnick, A. A.; Burroughs, R. N.; Svacha, R. L.; and Couch, J. R.: *Proc. Soc. Exptl. Biol. Med.*, **94**, 737, 1957.
109. Underwood, E. J.: *Ann. Rev. Biochem.*, **28**, 499, 1959.
110. Miller, R. F., and Engel, R. W.: *Federation Proc.*, **19**, 1960.
111. Dick, A. T.: *Australian Vet. J.*, **29**, 18, 1953.
112. Dick, A. T.: *Australian Vet. J.*, **28**, 30, 1953.
113. Wynne, K. N., and McClymont, G. L.: *Australian J. Agri. Research*, **7**, 45, 1956.
114. Brenchley, W. E., and Thornton, H. G.: *Proc. Roy. Soc.* (*London*), **B98**, 373, 1925.
115. Teresi, J. D.; Hove, E.; Elvehjem, C. A.; and Hart, E. B.: *Am. J. Physiol.*, **140**, 513, 1944.
116. Skinner, J. T., and McHargue, J. S.: *Am. J. Physiol.*, **143**, 385, 1945.
117. Follis, R. H., Jr.: *Am. J. Physiol.*, **150**, 520, 1947.
118. Pfeiffer, C. C.; Hallman, L. F.; and Gersh, I.: *J. Am. Med. Assoc.*, **128**, 266, 1945.
119. Hove, E.; Elvehjem, C. A.; and Hart, E. B.: *Am. J. Physiol.*, **124**, 205, 1938.
120. Grimmett, R. E. R.; McIntosh, I. G.; Wall, E. M.; and Jones, G. B.: *New Zealand J. Sci. Technol.*, **21A**, 150, 1939.
121. Kehoe, R. A.; Cholak, J.; and Story, R. V.: *J. Nutrition*, **20**, 85, 1940.
122. Hove, E.; Elvehjem, C. A.; and Hart, E. B.: *Am. J. Physiol.*, **123**, 640, 1938.
123. Scoular, F. I.: *J. Nutrition*, **17**, 393, 1939.
124. Evans, R. J., and Phillips, P. H.: *J. Nutrition*, **18**, 353, 1939.
125. McClendon, J. F.: *Federation Proc.*, **3**, 94, 1944.
126. McClendon, J. F., and Foster, W. C.: *Federation Proc.*, **4**, 159, 1945.
127. McClure, F. J.: *Ann. Rev. Biochem.*, **18**, 335, 1949.
128. Hodge, H. C., and Sognnaes, R. F.: *Dental Caries and Fluorine*. American Association for the Advancement of Science, Washington, D. C., 1946, p. 53.
129. Smith, M. C.; Lantz, E. M.; and Smith, H. V.: *Science*, **74**, 244, 1931.
130. Dean, H. T.; Arnold, F. A., Jr.; and Elvove, E.: *Pub. Health Repts.*, **57**, 1155, 1942.
131. Bibby, B. G., and Turesky, S. S.: *J. Dental Research*, **26**, 105, 1947.
132. Ast, D. B.: *Pub. Health Reports*, **58**, 857, 1943.
133. Ast, D. B.; Finn, S. B.; and McCaffrey, I.: *Am. J. Pub. Health*, **40**, 716, 1950. Schlesinger, E. R.; Overton, D. E.; and Chase, H. C.: *ibid.*, **40**, 725, 1950.
134. *Nutrition Revs.*, **9**, 21, 1951.
135. Blayney, J. R.: *J. Am. Dental Assoc.*, **61**, 76, 1960.
136. Russell, A. L., and Elvove, E.: *Pub. Health Reports*, **66**, 1389, 1951.
137. McClure, F. J.: *J. Am. Med. Assoc.*, **139**, 711, 1949.
138. *Report to the Fluorosis Committee, Medical Research Council, Memorandum No. 22*. His Majesty's Stationery Office, London, 1949.
139. Black, M. M.; Kleiner, I. S.; and Bolker, H.: *N. Y. State J. Med.*, **49**, 1187, 1949.
140. Moxon, A. L.; Du Bois, K. P.; and Potter, R. L.: *J. Pharmacol. Exptl. Therap.*, **72**, 184, 1941.

141. McConnell, K. P.: *J. Biol. Chem.*, **173**, 653, 1948.
142. Scott, M. L.; Bieri, J. G.; Briggs, G. M.; and Schwarz, K.: *Poultry Sci.*, **36**, 1155, 1957.
143. Schwarz, K., and Foltz, C. M.: *J. Am. Chem. Soc.*, **79**, 3292, 1957.
144. Stockstad, E. L. R.; Patterson, E. L.; and Milstrey, R.: *Poultry Sci.*, **36**, 1060, 1957.
145. Schwarz, K.: *Nutrition Revs.*, **18**, 193, 1960.
146. Huff, J. W.; Bosshardt, D. K.; Miller, O. P.; and Barnes, R. H.: *Proc. Soc. Exptl. Biol. Med.*, **92**, 216, 1956.
147. Bosshardt, D. K.; Huff, J. W.; and Barnes, R. H.: *Proc. Soc. Exptl. Biol. Med.*, **92**, 219, 1956.
148. Ucko, H.: *Biochem. J.*, **30**, 992, 1936.
149. Marine, D., and Kimball, O. P.: *J. Am. Med. Assoc.*, **77**, 1068, 1921.
150. "First Official Report of the 1935 Goiter Survey of Michigan," *J. Michigan State Med. Soc.*, **36**, 647, 1935.
151. Hamwi, G. J.; van Fossen, A. W.; Whetstone, R. E.; and Williams, I.: *Am. J. Public Health*, **45**, 1344, 1955.
152. Curtis, G. M., and Fertman, M. B.: *J. Am. Med. Assoc.*, **139**, 28, 1949.
153. Talbot, N. B.; Butler, A. M.; Saltzman, A. H.; and Rodriguez, P. M.: *J. Biol. Chem.*, **153**, 479, 1944.
154. Chaikoff, I. L.; Taurog, A.; and Reinhardt, W. O.: *Endocrinology*, **40**, 47, 1947.

31

Foods

Although various aspects of foods are discussed in several other chapters, it is the purpose here to bring together, in brief form, the composition and certain pertinent facts regarding a few nutritionally important, naturally occurring foods and food products derived from them. There is perhaps little virtue in learning the specific composition of a variety of foods, but it has long been a source of amazement to the writers how many beginning medical students are able to state a more satisfactory approximate composition of solder than of cow's milk.

DAIRY PRODUCTS

The principal dairy products used in this country are whole milk, evaporated milk, dried milk (whole or skim), cream, butter, cheese, and ice cream. Under each of these general terms we find various types and speciality products. There are innumerable varieties of cheese available for instance, and several grades of milk and cream. It is not the purpose to discuss the various types of cheeses, etc., but to treat the dairy products from a general viewpoint.

Table 31.1 gives the approximate composition of a number of foods obtained from cow's milk. The values in the table are subject to considerable variation. The fat content of milk varies with the breed of cow from 3 to 6 per cent. Cream is marketed with a fat content of as low as 18 per cent and as high as 40 per cent or even over. Butter without added salt has a mineral content of only 0.1 or 0.2 per cent. Salt is added in quantities of from 1 to 5 per cent in manufacture. The fat content varies usually between 80 and 85 per cent because of the amount of water and salt worked into the butter.

1270

The greatest variations are probably found among the hundreds of types of cheeses. Here the fat content may run from less than 1 per cent (cottage cheese made from skim milk) to 40 per cent in a cream cheese. The protein also varies from 20 to 40 per cent, depending largely on the amount of water allowed to remain in the final product. The composition of ice cream produced commercially at the present time is subject to some variations. Local and other government requirements must be met (especially in regard to fat content), and economically it is not generally feasible to produce ice cream with more fat than is required. Most states require a minimum of 10 or 12 per cent fat. Of importance to the consumer is the fact that ice cream today is sold on a weight and not a volume basis, since it has a large quantity of air incorporated into it.

Milk. No other single food has as many nutritional virtues as milk. It is not, however, a perfect food, since it lacks iron and copper among other

Table 31.1.   Approximate Composition of Some Typical Dairy Products

	Water (per cent)	Protein (per cent)	Lactose (per cent)	Fat (per cent)	Mineral Ash (per cent)	Cal/100 g
Whole milk	87	3.4	4.8	3.5	0.7	65
Evaporated milk	74	6.8	9.7	7.9	1.4	140
Dried milk, whole	3.5	26.0	38.0	27.0	6.0	495
Dried milk, skim	3.5	36.0	52.0	1.0	8.0	360
Cream	52–74	2–3	2.5–4.8	20–40	0.5	200–388
Butter	16	1.0	0.4	82	2.5	730
Cheese, cheddar	35	26	2.0	34	3	400
Cheese, cottage	72	21	4.0	1.0	1.8	108
Ice cream	61	4	21	13	1.0	217

essential nutrients. The proteins of milk are casein, lactalbumin, and lactoglobulin. About 80 per cent of the total is due to casein, a phosphoprotein of high biologic value.

Table 31.2 from Block and Bolling (1) and Block and Weiss (2) gives the approximate amino acid composition of casein. The composition of milk fat is governed to some extent by the breed and the diet of the cow, period of gestation, etc. In general, the fat contains fatty acids from C_4 through C_{20}. It is unusual to find appreciable quantities of the low molecular weight acids in natural fats. The approximate fatty acid content of butter fat is as follows: butyric 3.0, caproic 1.5, caprylic 1.0, capric 1.8, lauric 6.5, myristic 21, palmitic 19, stearic 15, oleic 30, and linoleic plus linolenic 0.4—all in per cent of total fatty acids. Other lipids in the "fat" include cholesterol and phospholipids in small quantities.

Lactose constitutes the principal carbohydrate of milk. It is a disaccharide composed of glucose and galactose, and though it is an excellent carbohydrate from a biologic standpoint, it appears to have little special virtue compared to sucrose, for instance.

The mineral constituents of milk are present in a rather unique proportion. Early workers simulated this composition for a mineral mixture to be used in synthetic experimental animal diets, and, indeed, such mixtures are widely used for this purpose today. The calcium-phosphorus ratio is such that excellent utilization of these elements is possible in man and animals, and the calcium content is higher than in practically any other important food. Table 31.3 lists the approximate mineral composition of whole milk and of milk ash.

Table 31.2.   Approximate Amino Acid Composition of Casein
Calculated to 16 per cent nitrogen

Amino Acids	Per Cent
Arginine	4.1 ± 0.2
Histidine	2.5 ± 0.3
Lysine	6.9 ± 0.7
Tyrosine	6.4 ± 0.4
Trytophan	1.8 ± 0.2
Phenylalanine	5.2 ± 0.5
Cystine	0.36 ± 0.04
Methionine	3.5 ± 0.3
Serine	6–7
Threonine	3.9 ± 0.1
Leucine	12.1
Isoleucine	6.5
Valine	7.0
Glutamic acid	22.8
Aspartic acid	6.3
Glycine	0.5
Alanine	5.6
Proline	8.2
Hydroxyproline	2

Small amounts of sulfur, iron, copper, zinc, manganese, etc., are also found in milk. The copper and iron content of milk is low; both humans and experimental animals develop a dietary anemia on an exclusive milk diet if care is observed to obviate metallic contamination. A milk diet is regularly used to produce anemia in rats for experimental study.

Table 31.3.   The Approximate Mineral Composition of Whole Milk and of Milk Ash

Element	Whole Milk (per cent)	Milk Ash (per cent)
Ca	0.12	16
P	0.09	12
Mg	0.02	1.8
Na	0.048	5.4
K	0.13	21
Cl	0.11	13

Milk is a good source of vitamin A. It contains very little vitamin D, unless it is fortified to produce one of the types of "vitamin D milk." The ascorbic acid concentration is low, and pasteurization destroys around one-half the original content. Milk has rather low concentrations of the B vitamins, but because of the relatively large amounts consumed by the majority of children, this source is quite significant in the over-all intake.

Since all dairy products contain milk in one form or another, it is not necessary to discuss further the nutritive value or the composition of these.

Human milk differs markedly from cow's milk in a number of ways. The protein content of human milk is far lower, while the lactose is much higher. Table 31.4 compares the general composition of human and cow's milk.

Table 31.4. Comparison of Human Milk and Cow's Milk
Approximate composition

	Water (per cent)	Protein (per cent)	Lactose (per cent)	Fat (per cent)	Mineral Ash (per cent)	Cal/100 g
Human milk	87	1.5	7.2	3.6	0.2	67
Cow's milk	87	3.5	4.8	3.5	0.7	65

For infant feeding, cow's milk generally is diluted with water to bring the protein content down and then fortified with carbohydrate so that the composition of mother's milk with respect to these constituents is approached.

MEAT AND FISH

Meat and fish, because of their fine flavor, have been sought after by man since the beginning of history. There is no doubt that they play a most important part in our nutrition. The principal nutrient supplied is protein, although from the quantity standpoint many meat cuts contain a higher percentage of fat. In general, the proteins of meat and of fish are of good biologic value, and especially important as supplements to the proteins of grains, many of which, by themselves, are rather poor biologically.

Table 31.5 lists the approximate, partial composition of some typical meat and fish products. Here again the values in the table are subject to

Table 31.5. Approximate Composition of Some Meat and Fish Products
Fresh basis

Product	Water (per cent)	Protein (per cent)	Fat (per cent)	Cal/100 g
Beef roast	62	16	21	253
Veal roast	65	18	15	207
Lamb roast	60	16	22	263
Beef liver	70	20	3.5	111
Salmon steak	65	20	10	170
Halibut filet	74	21	5	130

variations; this is especially true of the figures for fish. In the case of salmon the fat content may be a small fraction of 10 per cent or a good deal more, depending on variety, time of year, and where the fish are caught.

Muscle meat, in itself, is not a complete food; it is seriously deficient in calcium, and the high phosphorus content makes the calcium-phosphorus ratio out of balance. Ascorbic acid, the fat-soluble vitamins, and certain B vitamins are likewise deficient. In general there is practically no carbohydrate present. An extensive compilation in book form, by Waisman and Elvehjem (3), can be consulted for the content of the various vitamins in most meat cuts.

THE GRAINS

Since wheat is by far our most important grain crop, the following discussion will be limited to this food commodity. About 30 per cent of the protein intake of the average American diet comes from wheat flour. Some years ago our government made the enrichment of white flour with iron, thiamine, riboflavin, and niacin a compulsory measure. The amounts added are such that the final concentration in white flour approaches that of whole wheat flour with respect to these nutrients. Table 31.6 from Dunlap (4) shows this very well.

Table 31.6. Comparison of Composition of White, Enriched, and Whole Wheat Flours

	White Flour (mg/lb)	Enriched Flour (mg/lb)	Whole Wheat Flour (mg/lb)
Calcium	82.0	82.0*	140.0
Phosphorus	400.0	400.0	1600.0
Iron	3.2	13.0–16.5	17.5
Thiamine	0.35	2.0–2.5	2.25
Riboflavin	0.15	1.2–1.5	0.55
Niacin	3.5	16.0–20.0	22–29
Pantothenic acid	2.2–2.7	2.2–2.7	4.5–5.4
Pyridoxine	0.9–1.1	0.9–1.1	1.8–2.2

* If calcium is added as an optional ingredient, enriched flour contains 500–625 mg per pound. Phosphated and self-rising flours, widely used in the South, contain much more calcium per pound.
From Dunlap, F. L.: *White Versus Brown Flour.* Wallace and Tiernen Company. Newark, 1945, p. 7.

The minimum government standards at the present time for enriched white flour are in milligrams per pound: thiamine 2, riboflavin 1.2, niacin 16, and iron 13. The addition of calcium is optional.

White flour contains approximately the following in percentage: water 10 to 12, protein 10 to 12, fat 1 to 2, carbohydrate 72 to 76, and ash 0.5. Whole wheat flour has slightly more protein, fat, and ash, while the available carbohydrate is somewhat lower. Thus, aside from the valuable protein source, this food offers an abundance of carbohydrate. Because of the enrichment program and the relatively large amounts consumed, wheat flour products constitute an important dietary adjunct to our intake of various members of the vitamin B complex.

The primary proteins of wheat are glutenin (a glutelin) and gliadin (a prolamin). Together they form the so-called wheat gluten. The biologic value of wheat proteins is lower than for milk, egg, or meat proteins. The essential amino acid lysine is especially deficient in wheat proteins, so that on supplementation with this amino acid or with another protein liberally supplied with it the biologic value can be markedly improved. Fortunately, in our own diet this supplementation with other proteins is exactly what is practiced.

EGGS

For most people, eggs are a palatable and enjoyable food. From a nutritive standpoint, the egg stands with dairy products and meat. The proteins of egg are high on the scale of biologic values. The calcium, phosphorus, and available iron content are especially noteworthy. Certain of the vitamins are supplied in highly significant amounts. Although the egg contains very little carbohydrate, the lipids (fat, phospholipids, and cholesterol) constitute a worthy supplement to our diet. The approximate composition of the whole egg (edible part), white and yolk, is given in Table 31.7. The shell amounts to about one-tenth of the egg weight.

Table 31.7.   Approximate Composition of Hens' Eggs

	Whole Egg	Yolk	White
Water	73	49	85
Lipid	12	33	Trace
Protein	12.5	16	11.5
Carbohydrate	0.5	0.5	0.6
Ash	1.0	1.5	0.5
Calories per 100 g	160	360	47

In the white of the egg are found the proteins ovalbumin and ovoglobulin, and the yolk contains the phosphoprotein ovovitellin. Together these proteins offer an excellent supply of all the essential amino acids for growth, repair, and reproduction in animals, and, as far as we know, for human beings as well (see under biological value in Chapter 28).

The fat of the egg yolk is readily and thoroughly digested and absorbed. It contains appreciable amounts of linoleic acid, one of the essential fatty acids. Lecithin and cephalin are the principal phospholipids of the yolk.

Few foods supply as much available iron as do eggs. It appears to be present practically all in inorganic form.

Eggs are a good source of vitamins A and D only if the hen eats feed high in these nutrients. In the case of vitamin A, the various carotene precursor pigments, if present in the diet, are transferred to the yolk. Since grain is one of the important constituents of the laying hen's ration, various B vitamins, especially riboflavin, from it are found in significant amounts in eggs.

ACID AND ALKALINE RESIDUE FOODS

All naturally occurring foods contain some acid and some base-forming elements. In certain foods one or the other may predominate to a slight or to a marked extent. In general, the organic matter of foods does not leave an acid or an alkaline residue on oxidation in the body.

Most proteins contain sulfur and many also contain phosphorus. On metabolism of the protein, these elements remain as sulfuric and phosphoric acids and must be neutralized by ammonia, calcium, sodium, and potassium for excretion by the kidney. From this it follows that high protein foods in general are acid residue foods. This is also true of most grains.

In fruits and most vegetables, on the other hand, the organic acids are present partly as salts (K, Na, Ca, Mg), depending on the pH and in accordance with the Hasselbalch equation. Since the organic acids are oxidized to CO_2 and water, the alkaline metallic elements remain and must be neutralized by body acids. Exceptions to this statement can be found in the case of benzoic and oxalic acids, which occur in a few foods and are not oxidized to any great extent in the body, thus necessitating cations for their excretion.

Quantitatively the acidity or alkalinity of a given food is expressed as ml of 0.1 N acid or alkali equivalent to the residue of 100 g of the food. On this basis lean beef, wheat flour, and eggs have an acid residue of around 10. Many common fruits and vegetables have an alkaline residue varying from around 2 or 3 to 10 or 15.

For an excellent and detailed source of information on food composition and allied matters see the compilation by Burton (5).

SPECIAL REFERENCES

1. Block, R. J., and Bolling, D.: *The Amino Acid Composition of Proteins and Foods.* Charles C Thomas, Springfield, Ill., 1945, p. 303.
2. Block, R. J., and Weiss, K. W.: *Amino Acid Handbook.* Charles C Thomas, Springfield, Ill., 1956.
3. Waisman, H. A., and Elvehjem, C. A.: *The Vitamin Content of Meat.* Burgess Publishing Co., Minneapolis, 1941.
4. Dunlap, F. L.: *White versus Brown Flour.* Copyrighted by Wallace & Tiernan Co., Inc., Newark, N.J., 1945, p. 7.
5. Burton, B. T. (ed.): *The Heinz Handbook of Nutrition.* McGraw-Hill Book Co., Inc. New York, 1959.

32

Antimetabolic agents

An outstanding scientific achievement of the past years has been the development in the preparation and use of the sulfonamide drugs and the antibiotics. Without the integrated cooperation of chemists, bacteriologists, pharmacologists, clinical practitioners, and big business, the phenomenal advances leading to our present state of knowledge in these fields would have been retarded many years. During World War II, because of the already indicated value of these drugs, certain governments, including our own, utilized tremendous amounts of money and man power to hasten the availability of certain of the "wonder drugs" for both military and civilian use. That such a foresighted program "paid off" in saving lives and minimizing suffering needs no further comment.

The term "antibiotic" came into widespread use after the discovery of penicillin and other antibacterial substances produced by living microorganisms. It has been used primarily to differentiate this class of compounds from the laboratory-synthesized sulfonamide drugs. Such a distinction is disappearing since certain of the antibiotics and many derivatives of the naturally occurring substances are now synthesized in the laboratory. It is obvious that a reclassification of the chemotherapeutic agents is needed.

SULFONAMIDE DRUGS

With few exceptions the use of drugs for blood stream infections before 1930 or so failed because the drug was toxic to the host or because the host altered (detoxified) the drug so that it no longer was effective in halting the growth of microorganisms.

The first important advance in sulfonamide therapy was during the early 1930's, when the compound Prontosil was found to be active in mice against β-hemolytic streptococci. Previous to this time many drugs were known that were bacteriostatic in the test tube but not in the body. It was not until 1935 that the important paper of Domagk (1) appeared in the literature, although much of the work on the use of Prontosil in animal infections had been done two or three years previously.

In the same year, French workers (2) announced that one part of the compound— namely, p-aminobenzenesulfonamide (sulfanilamide)—had about the same antibacterial action as the larger dye molecule Prontosil. Later work demonstrated that the antibac-

terial action was not associated with the dye molecule but was, in fact, due to sulfanilamide, a cleavage product in the body:

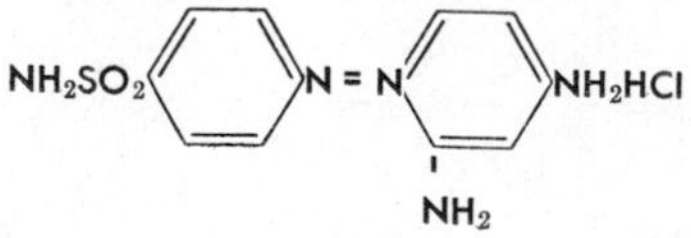

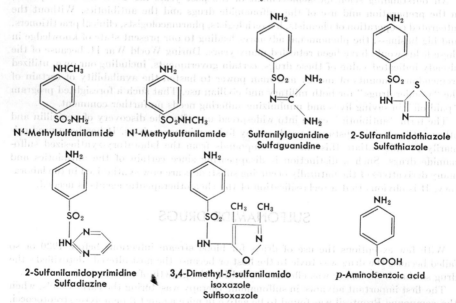

NH$_2$SO$_2$ — N = N — NH$_2$HCl

NH$_2$

Prontosil

Prontosil is now of historical interest only as a chemotherapeutic drug.

At the present time thousands of sulfonamide derivatives have been synthesized by
the organic chemist, of which relatively few have proved of value in combating infections.
The sulfonamides can be considered as derivatives of p-aminobenzenesulfonamide. The
accompanying formulas indicate a few of the well-known drugs and also a part of the
system of nomenclature developed by Northey and associates (3). See also the outstanding monograph by Northey on the sulfonamide drugs (4):

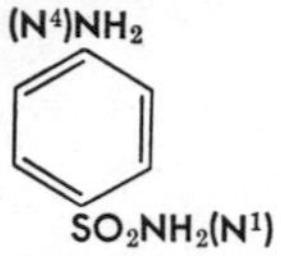

(N^4)NH$_2$

SO$_2$NH$_2$(N^1)

p-Aminobenzenesulfonamide
sulfanilamide

NH$_2$

SO$_2$NH—

Sulfanilamido
group

NH$_2$

SO$_2$—

Sulfanilyl
group

Derivatives may have attachment at N^4 or N^1 or at both positions. They may be
derivatives of the sulfanilamido or of the sulfanilyl radicals:

NHCH$_3$

SO$_2$NH$_2$

N^4-Methylsulfanilamide

NH$_2$

SO$_2$NHCH$_3$

N^1-Methylsulfanilamide

NH$_2$

SO$_2$ NH$_2$

N=C

NH$_2$

Sulfanilylguanidine
Sulfaguanidine

NH$_2$

SO$_2$

S

HN

N

2-Sulfanilamidothiazole
Sulfathiazole

NH$_2$

SO$_2$

HN

N

N

2-Sulfanilamidopyrimidine
Sulfadiazine

NH$_2$

SO$_2$ CH$_3$ CH$_3$

HN

N

O

3,4-Dimethyl-5-sulfanilamido
isoxazole
Sulfisoxazole

NH$_2$

COOH

p-Aminobenzoic acid

Sulfisoxazole (Gantrisin) is presently one of the most widely used sulfonamide drugs.

The sulfonamide drugs are effective by mouth, and in the case of those with higher
solubilities, the blood concentration can be raised to the desired level, which depends
on the drug and the infection, and can be maintained there by oral administration. They
are also used topically in a microcrystalline form in dressings for surgery or other wounds.

Among the infections responding well to various of these agents are gonorrhea, men-
ingitis, urinary tract infections, pneumonia, and various septic wounds.

Many of the sulfonamide drugs are excreted partly as the N^4-acetyl derivative in the urine. When sulfanilamide was used, as much as half of that excreted often appeared in this form. Glucuronide formation is also used by the body in detoxication.

The determination of sulfonamide drugs in blood or in urine is quite simple. The most commonly used method, that of Bratton and Marshall (5), employs diazotization of the free amino group (with nitrous acid) and coupling with N-(1-naphthyl)-ethylenediamine. This forms a dye: the color is intense for only small amounts of the drug and may be compared to standard solutions of the drug similarly treated for quantitative estimations. Protein-free filtrates of blood must be used. Only the drugs with a free p-amino group will react; hence acetylated or other N^4 derivatives must be hydrolyzed before they can be determined by this method.

The mechanism by which sulfonamide drugs act to suppress bacterial growth is not well understood, although some observations point up what must be part of the metabolic machinery involved. Only microorganisms which synthesize their own folic acid are sensitive to sulfonamide drug action. Such microorganisms use p-aminobenzoic in this synthesis. Organisms that require the vitamin in the growth medium are not effected by the drugs. Note the close chemical relationship of sulfanilamide and p-aminobenzoic acid. According to theory, the sulfonamide drug in some way inactivates an enzyme system or systems involved in handling p-aminobenzoic acid (a component of the vitamin molecule) in folic acid synthesis. Stated another way, the sulfonamide drug competes with p-aminobenzoic acid for specific receptor sites on enzyme molecules concerned with the normal metabolism of p-aminobenzoic acid. Either folic acid (noncompetitively) or p-aminobenzoic acid (competitively) is able to overcome the sulfonamide inhibition in sensitive microorganisms. Also, it is quite clear that p-aminobenzoic acid has other functions than as a part of the folic acid molecule. Folic acid is discussed in Chapter 18 and enzyme inhibition in Chapter 11. In humans and animals metabolic pathways are not altered by sulfonamides. They do not synthesize folic acid. They require a dietary source. It would be expected that since p-aminobenzoic acid is apparently not metabolized in these species, the sulfonamide drugs are not toxic.

ANTIBIOTICS

As previously stated, the term "antibiotic" is used to indicate a substance that is produced by a microorganism and is detrimental to the existence of other microorganisms. In this group of substances are penicillin, streptomycin, chlortetracycline (Aureomycin), chloramphenicol (Chloromycetin), and a host of others. Members of this class of substances are often highly active against organisms not affected by sulfonamides or other drugs.

Penicillin. As early as 1929, Fleming (6) noticed that when a specific strain of the mold *Penicillium* was grown on a synthetic medium, there was produced a specific substance endowed with antibacterial powers. Fleming showed that the active substance could be extracted from the medium and that it was not toxic to animals. He gave it the name "penicillin." For some reason this important announcement did not stimulate immediate research activity in this field.

However, in 1939 Dubos (7) isolated an active material from the culture medium of a soil aerobe. He named the antibiotic "tyrothrycin." From this time on activity in the field of antibiotics expanded at a tremendous rate.

The penicillin problem was again taken up by Florey and coworkers (8,9) some ten years after Fleming's original report. They substantiated the earlier work and outlined conditions for the production of penicillin as well as a method of assay. They pointed out that bacteriostatic concentrations could be maintained in the blood of humans and animals without causing any toxic symptoms, and that the growth of various pathogenic organisms was thereby prevented. Growth of certain organisms *in vitro* was prevented by "purified penicillin" at a dilution of one to a million or more. Proof was presented that pus, blood, and tissue derivatives did not lessen the activity of penicillin against the organisms studied.

At the present time many different penicillins are known; about a dozen are known to be produced biosynthetically, while a large number of derivatives have been prepared in the laboratory. Only five different penicillins have been produced and used in quantity. These commonly known compounds have the same basic structure, but the side chain, represented by R in the accompanying formula, differs in each of the penicillins, as indicated in Table 32.1:

$$
\begin{array}{c}
\quad\;\; O\;\;\; H\;\; H\;\; H\qquad CH_3 \\
\quad\;\; \parallel\;\;\; |\;\;\; |\;\;\; |\qquad\; | \\
R-C-N-C-C-S-C-CH_3 \\
\qquad\quad |\;\;\; |\qquad\quad | \\
\qquad\quad O=C-N-\;-\;C-COOH \\
\qquad\qquad\qquad\quad\;\; H
\end{array}
$$

Penicillin basic structure

Table 32.1.   Common Penicillins

Penicillin, Common Name	R	
	Name	Formula
G	Benzyl-	$C_6H_5—CH_2—$
X	p-Hydroxybenzyl-	$OH—C_6H_4—CH_2—$
F	2-Pentenyl-	$CH_3—CH_2—CH=CH—CH_2—$
Dihydro F	n-Pentanyl (n-amyl)	$CH_3—CH_2—CH_2—CH_2—CH_2—$
K	n-Heptyl-	$CH_3—CH_2—CH_2—CH_2—CH_2—CH_2—CH_2—$

By custom, the term "penicillin" alone refers to one of the salts (Na, K, or Ca) of penicillin G. This is the most widely used of the penicillins at the present time.

Penicillin G is a fairly strong monobasic acid ($pK = 2.5$) with an optical rotation, $[\alpha]_D^{23} = +280$. It is soluble in the common fat solvents and in water.

The instability of penicillin preparations, until quite recently, was a real industrial and medical problem. In the dry state salts of penicillin are now of such a purity that they are stable practically indefinitely. In solution, however, penicillin is subject to deterioration. The inactivation is generally due to hydrolysis, and the products formed are determined largely by the pH of the solution. Two molecules of water hydrolyze penicillin into penicillamine (dimethylcysteine), and other products. On acid hydrolysis, penillic acid is formed. Alkali and the enzyme penicillinase inactivate it with the formation of penicilloic acid:

Penicilloic acid   Penicillamine

The sodium and potassium salts of penicillin are most stable in solutions of pH 6.0 to 6.8. In solution outside this pH range, activity is soon lost.

Although various penicillins have been synthesized in the laboratory (10), the commercial production is carried out biosynthetically by an appropriate mold—for example *Penicillium chrysogenum*, mutant strain Q-176, growing in a carefully prepared culture medium.

The older definitions of the penicillin units are of historical interest only. Since pure compounds have become available for standards in the assay, it is practical to define on a weight basis. Thus, one unit equals 0.0006 mg (0.6 γ or μg) of the sodium salt of penicillin G (benzyl penicillin).

The biologic assays are based on the inhibition of growth of a pure strain of a sensitive bacteria (11,12). Colorimetric methods (13) and spectrophotometric methods (14) are constantly being improved.

The bulk of the evidence on the mode of action of penicillin indicates that it is bacteriostatic (or bacteriolytic or bactericidal) because it interferes in one or more essential metabolic processes; it appears to be a metabolic antagonist.

Penicillin is bacteriostatic at a threshold concentration, and bactericidal at concentrations beyond this. The effects are greatest on rapidly growing organisms, and in this case respiration is inhibited (15).

The mode of action of penicillin is not clearly defined. The many facts observed concerning metabolic alterations and other findings in microorganisms treated with penicillin argue in favor of the hypothesis that the primary action of the drug is interference with reactions concerned with cell wall synthesis. Many microorganisms are lysed by the drug, and in others there is found an accumulation of uridine nucleotides and peptides. It is thought that these molecules may be precursors of cell wall substance (16).

Chain (17) and also Burkholder (18) have reviewed various aspects of the antibiotics.

Streptomycin. Since penicillin is ineffective against gram-negative organisms and the tuberculosis organism, it was indeed a great stride forward when, in 1944, Waksman and associates (19) discovered an antibiotic highly active toward these bacteria. This substance was isolated from the medium in which an organism resembling *Streptomyces griseus*, a soil organism, was under culture. The active principle was named "streptomycin." It was reported to resemble streptothrycin (previously isolated) as to water solubility, mode of isolation, and concentration from culture medium, selective activity toward gram-negative bacteria, and limited toxicity to animals. Differences were noted in the bacterial spectrum (number of different organisms acted upon) and the quantities required to show a satisfactory antibacterial action. It was suggested that the two are closely related compounds. Streptomycin has been found to have decided clinical advantages over streptothrycin, and consequently the latter is not in general use.

Many workers have added to the knowledge of the structure of strepto-mycin. It consists essentially of two parts, a nitrogen-containing disaccharide known as "streptobiosamine" and a base, streptidine. Streptidine is 1,3-diguanidino,2-4-5-6-tetrahydroxycyclohexane. Streptobiosamine consists of the two hexoses, streptose, and N-methylglucosamine which is 2-(methyl-amino) glucose. The point of attachment of the two primary parts of the molecule remained unsettled for some time (20), but now appears to be at carbon 4 of the streptidine ring (21):

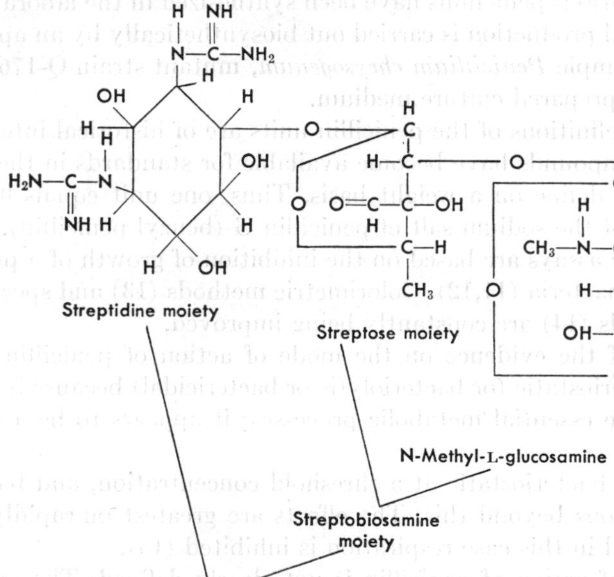

It is of interest that streptomycin is a glycoside and that the products of hydrolysis are not endowed with antibiotic activity. The two guanidine residues are not uncommon (arginine, creatine, etc.) in biological compounds. Nor is the remainder of the streptidine molecule, for note the relation of this to inositol (a B complex vitamin). The fact that the N-methyl-L-glucosamine has an L configuration is indeed surprising.

At the present time the unitage of streptomycin is on a weight basis; 1 μg of pure base equals one unit (1,000,000 units per gram). Commercial preparations, as used clinically, are usually the trihydrochloride or the tri-hydrosulfate salt because of the basic nature of the compound. Consequently, 1 g of such material contains less than 1,000,000 units of streptomycin.

At the present time a reduced form, dihydrostreptomycin, is used almost exclusively because of its reduced toxicity. In this molecule the aldehyde structure in the streptose moiety is reduced to an alcohol.

The mechanism by which streptomycin acts involves permeability of the cell membrane. The effect increases the outward permeability to nucleic acids and to amino acid and the inward permeability to streptomycin itself. It appears that the action is not on already formed cell wall but on the wall formed in the presence of the drug, in studies with *E. coli* (22,23).

The tetracyclines. In 1948 Duggar discovered an antibiotic produced by the fungus *Streptomyces aureofaciens* (24). It was given the trade name Aureomycin and is known officially as chlortetracycline. It has a wide spectrum, including various gram-positive and gram-negative organisms, but has been largely replaced by newer drugs. The structure was announced by Waller and coworkers (25) and is similar to the structure of oxytetracycline (Terramycin), a valuable drug of this class. The drug tetracycline (Achromycin), which was synthesized by Boothe and coworkers (26) in 1959, is also widely used:

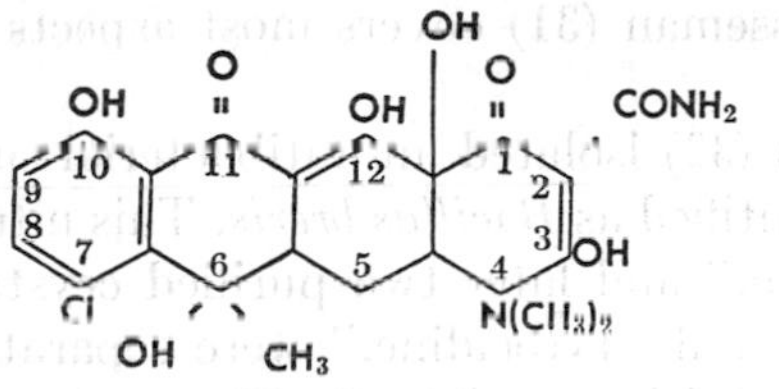

Chlortetracycline

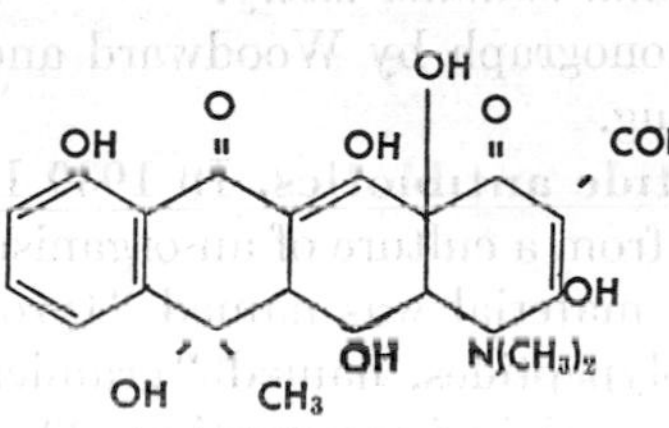

Oxytetracycline

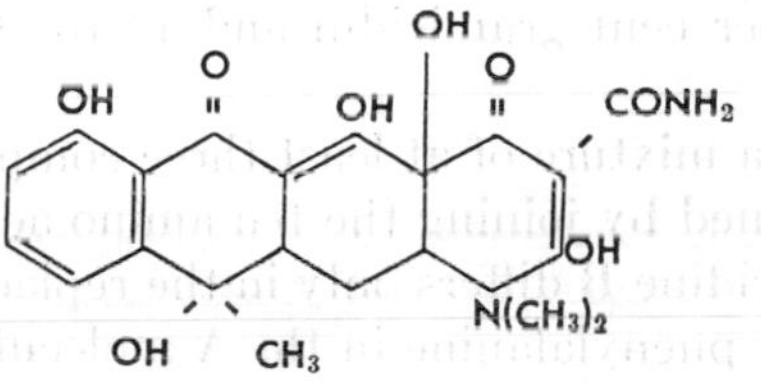

Tetracycline

The mechanism of action of the tetracyclines may involve chelation of heavy metals, such as Mg, Fe, and Mn, in enzyme systems required for the synthesis of protein by growing bacteria (17).

Chloramphenicol. In 1947 Ehrlich and coworkers (27) discovered chloramphenicol (Chloromycetin), a drug produced by *Streptomyces venezuelae*. The structure was determined (28) and synthesis accomplished (29) rather soon after its discovery and demonstration of its clinical value. The present commercial source of chloramphenicol is through laboratory synthesis; most other antibiotics are produced through biosynthesis. The compound is shown herewith. It is, oddly enough, a nitro compound with the name 1-*p*-nitrophenyl-2-dichloroacetamido-1,3-propandiol:

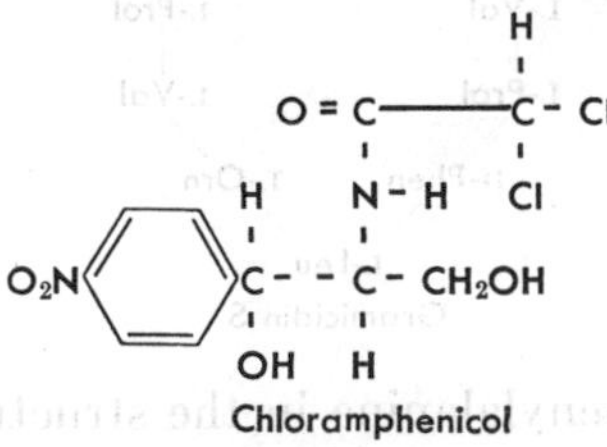

Chloramphenicol

Chloramphenicol is slightly soluble in water (2.5 mg per milliliter) and more soluble in the common fat solvents. It does not form salts either with acids or with bases; hence solubility is not increased appreciably in acid or alkaline solution. A water solution is quite stable even at 100° C.

The drug is especially active against some of the rickettsial infections in man (typhus, Rocky Mountain spotted fever, etc.), and has been used successfully in relapsing fever, undulant fever, and in various infections due to gram-negative bacteria. The toxicity of chloramphenicol is exceptionally low, although in some individuals the drug has precipitated an aplastic anemia (30).

Micorbiologic methods similar to those used for other antibiotics are used in the assay of this drug. Chemical methods may be practical if the pure compound is under assay.

A monograph by Woodward and Wisseman (31) covers most aspects of this drug.

Peptide antibiotics. In 1939 Dubos (32) isolated an antibacterial substance from a culture of an organism identified as *Bacillus brevis*. This nitrogenous material was named "tyrothricin," and later two purified crystalline polypeptides, named "gramicidin" and "tyrocidine," were separated from the original preparation (33). Tyrothricin as originally prepared, contains some 10 to 20 per cent gramicidin and 40 to 60 per cent tyrocidine hydrochloride.

Crude tyrocidine is a mixture of at least three components. Tyrocidine A is a cyclic peptide formed by joining the ten amino acid residues in peptide linkage (34), and tyrocidine B differs only in the replacement of tryptophan of the B compound by phenylalanine in the A molecule, as indicated in the formulas proposed by Craig and co-workers (35):

```
           L-Orn                                      L-Orn
          /     \                                    /     \
     L-Val      L-Leuc                          L-Val       L-Leuc
       /            \                             /             \
   L-Tyr            D-Phen                    L-Tyr             D-Phen
     |                |                         |                 |
  L-Glutam          L-Prol                  L-Glutam           L-Prol
       \            /                             \             /
      L-Asp      L-Tryp                          L-Asp       L-Phen
          \     /                                    \     /
          D-Phen                                     D-Phen
       Tyrocidine B                              Tyrocidine A
```

```
                    L-Leu
                   /     \
              L-Orn       D-Phen
               /              \
           L-Val              L-Prol
             |                  |
           L-Prol             L-Val
              \               /
             D-Phen        L-Orn
                 \        /
                  L-Leu
              Gramicidin S
```

Note the presence of D-phenylalanine in the structures. This is one of the few instances in which the unnatural or D form of an amino acid has been found in a naturally occurring substance.

Gramicidin as isolated from the tyrothrycin mixture contains at least four related substances. Three of these, gramicidins A, B, and C, have been crystallized. They all contain 2-aminoethanol along with amino acids and are apparently cyclic structures since no free carboxyl or amino groups are present. Gramicidin A, for instance, contains the amino acids D-leucine, L-tryptophan, both D- and L-valine, L-alanine and glycine (36).

Gramicidin S is produced by a different strain of B. brevis from the one producing tyrothrycin and chemically resembles the tyrocidines more than the gramicidines. It is a decapeptide in a cyclic structure containing a twice repeated five-amino acid sequence, as shown herewith. The synthesis of the molecule (37) confirmed the postulated structure (38).

Bacitracin was isolated from an organism of the B. subtilis group by Johnson and coworkers (39). It is a mixture of several substances, and complete separation has not been attained. Bacitracin A has been studied considerably and structures and amino acid sequences proposed (17,40).

Other peptide antibiotics are the polymixins and the actinomycins. The book by Goldberg (41) and the review by Chain (17) give further details.

In general the peptide antibiotics are not used for oral treatment, due to toxicity and to the fact that some destruction of the drugs occurs in the intestine.

Additional uses for antibiotics. Antibiotics are used as supplements in animal feeds. Poultry, pigs, and mink fed small amounts of the proper antibiotic in their feed show increased food efficiency, faster growth, and decreased mortality rates. Such desirable effects may result from suppression of certain intestinal microorganisms, thus decreasing the production of toxins and possibly increasing the quantity of some essential growth factors to the host.

Many foods are preserved with antibiotics. Meats can be aged at higher temperatures and other foods last longer without spoilage after such treatment. Large quantities are used in veterinary medicine and for control of some plant diseases. Berkholder (18) states that in 1956 the total antibiotic production for all uses in the United States was 2.7 million pounds.

Reviews on antibiotics include those by Verwey (42), Eagle and Saz (43), and Jawetz (44).

INSECTICIDES AND HERBICIDES

The sulfonamides and the antibiotic compounds just discussed appear to operate, in general, by inhibiting normal metabolism of microorganisms. It might be well to add here a few of the compounds that interfere in some way with the metabolism of certain plants and animals.

DDT. Although the compound, 1,1,1-trichloro-2,2-bis(p-chlorophenyl) ethane (DDT) was synthesized in 1874, it was not until 1939 that Swiss workers demonstrated the marked toxicity of it for certain insects. This information spread slowly, and it was not until 1942 that samples of the material reached the United States. According to Frear (45), about 33,000,000 lb were produced in the United States during 1945.

DDT is generally prepared through the reaction of chloral and chlorobenzene in the presence of H_2SO_4 (to remove water):

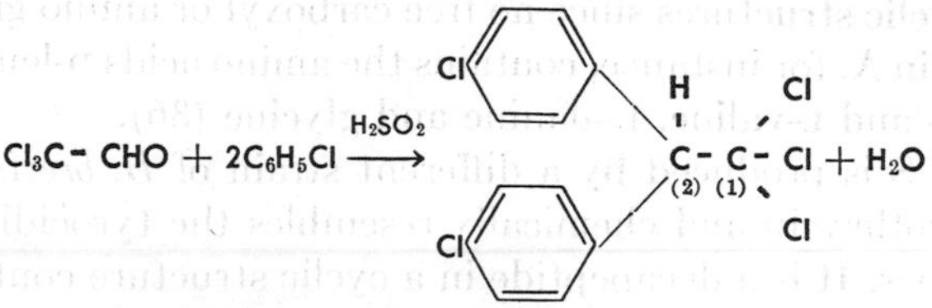

$$Cl_3C\text{-} CHO + 2C_6H_5Cl \xrightarrow{H_2SO_2}$$

2,2-bis(p-Chlorophenyl)-1,1,1-trichloroethane
(DDT)

The material is used as an insecticide in spray form, dissolved in one or a mixture of organic solvents. Deodorized kerosene has been used among other things. It is also used as a dust in which from 1 to 10 per cent of DDT is incorporated into a mixture with talc, etc. Another manner of use is the so-called aerosol method in which a solution containing spreading and emulsifying agents is sprayed from an air pressure tank as a very finely divided aerosol.

Fortunately, DDT is highly lethal toward a number of disease-carrying insects that attack man—i.e., mosquitoes, lice, and ticks. Also fortunate is the fact that with cautious use there is slight danger to humans from the drug.

Little critical information is available on the mechanism of DDT action. The compound unstabilizes the nervous system of insects and thus causes hyperneuromuscular activity. It was pointed out in a review on the mode of action of insecticides (46) that there is evidence for an accumulation of acetylcholine in treated insects but that there still is no indication of the way in which DDT may produce this or the other effects associated with its action.

It is interesting that one type of resistance to DDT involves enzymatic detoxication of DDT to form 1,1-dichloro-2,2-bis(p-chlorophenyl)ethylene. The enzyme (DDT-dehydrochlorinase) has been isolated and purified (47).

Chlordan. Chlordan, as produced for insecticidal use, is a viscous liquid containing around 60 or 70 per cent of the active principle. It is generally used as a spray dissolved in an organic solvent. Dusting preparations have also been employed. In the case of a number of insects it has about the same killing power as DDT, although there are marked species variations. The structure is thought to be as shown:

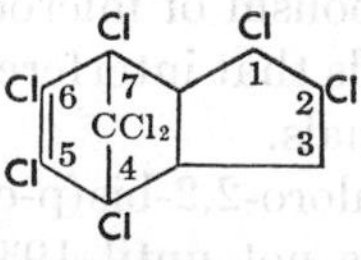

Octachloro-4,7-Methanotetrahydroindane
Chlordan

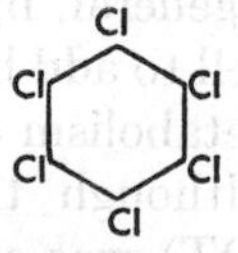

1,2,3,4,5,6-Hexachlorocyclohexane
Gammexane

Gammexane. Chemically Gammexane is 1,2,3,4,5,6-hexachlorocyclohexane. This compound has often been incorrectly referred to as "hexachlorobenzene" (C_6Cl_6). The γ isomer is the most toxic to insects, and the compound is an important one in pest control.

For some insects Gammexane is more toxic than DDT (housefly, for instance), and it is effective toward insects that have developed a resistance to DDT.

Organic phosphates. TEPP, tetraethylpyrophosphate, is a commonly used insecticide. Hundreds of organic phosphates have been studied. In general these compounds (sometimes referred to as nerve gases) are anticholinesterases; they inhibit the enzyme cholinesterase so that acetylcholine is not hydrolyzed normally at nerve endings following passage of nerve impulses at these junctions. Chemical combination of drug and enzyme has been demonstrated in some instances. As an example, diisopropylfluorophosphate plus cholinesterase yields diisopropylphosphoryl cholinesterase, which has been studied in connection with active centers of enzymes (48):

$$
\begin{array}{ccc}
\text{C}_2\text{H}_5 & \text{C}_2\text{H}_5 & \text{(CH}_3\text{)}_2\text{CH} \\
\diagdown & \diagdown & \diagdown \\
\text{O} \quad \text{O} \quad \text{O} \quad \text{O} & & \text{O} \quad \text{F} \\
\diagdown \text{P} - \text{O} - \text{P} \diagup & & \text{P} \\
\text{O} & \text{O} & \text{O} \quad \text{O} \\
\diagup & \diagdown & \diagup \\
\text{C}_2\text{H}_5 & \text{C}_2\text{H}_5 & \text{(CH}_3\text{)}_2\text{CH}
\end{array}
$$

Tetraethylpyrophosphate (TEPP)   Diisopropylfluorophosphate (DFP)

2,4-Dichlorophenoxyacetic acid (2-4-D). One of the most used and most successful herbicides is 2-4-D and, of course, a great variety of its derivatives. This compound has such a selective action that it has found wide use in destroying weeds in gardens, grain fields, etc. It kills a great variety of wide-leaf plants and is innocuous to grasses (including most grains) (49). The free acid is insoluble in water, but may be used as a spray emulsified in water, or the sodium salt, which is soluble, can be used. About 0.1 per cent of the active principle is generally employed. Spreading and wetting agents are commonly added to increase the effectiveness.

The compound is simply prepared by the reaction of 2,4-dichlorophenol and monochloracetic acid in the presence of NaOH. This yields the sodium salt and the free acid can be obtained on acidification with HCl:

$$
\text{Cl} - \bigcirc - \text{OH} + \text{Cl} - \text{CH}_2\text{COOH} \xrightarrow{\text{2NaOH}} \text{Cl} - \bigcirc - \text{O} - \text{CH}_2\text{COONa} + 2\text{H}_2\text{O} + \text{NaCl}
$$

2,4-Dichlorophenol   Monochloracetic acid   2,4-Dichlorophenoxyacetic acid—sodium salt

A further advantage is the fact that 2-4-D is relatively nontoxic for man and animals.

Many other phenoxy derivatives of acetic acid—such as 4-chloro-2-methylphenoxy acetic acid, 2,4,5-trichlorophenoxy acetic acid, and various esters of these—are important herbicides.

The mechanism of action of these weed killers remains unknown. It seems reasonable to assume that they inhibit one or more specific enzyme systems essential to normal metabolism in the sensitive plants. It is possible that in plants not affected by them the enzyme system or systems are absent, or these plants are able to by-pass the metabolic link involved and thus maintain the integrity of their metabolism.

In a comprehensive discussion of the herbicides by Woodford and others (50) no definite conclusion was reached to account for the action of 2-4-D and related compounds.

MISCELLANEOUS ANTIMETABOLITES

A few drugs of special interest which act as antimetabolites will be mentioned briefly.

Disulfiram, Antabuse, tetraethylthiuram disulfide. The compound known popularly as "Antabuse" or "Disulfiram" has been used in the clinical treatment of alcoholism with some success (51). It is also called "bis(diethylthiocarbamyl) disulfide" and has the structure shown.

$$(C_2H_5)_2 - N - \overset{\overset{S}{\|}}{C} - S - S - \overset{\overset{S}{\|}}{C} - N - (C_2H_5)_2$$

Disulfiram, bis(diethylthiocarbamyl) disulfide

In the presence of this substance in the body, the ingestion of alcohol results in an accumulation of acetaldehyde. The compound acts in some way as an inhibiter to an enzyme or enzymes involved in the normal metabolism of the aldehyde resulting from early step in the oxidation of alcohol. The toxic nature of the accumulated acetaldehyde is manifested in a variety of unpleasant symptoms which theoretically deter a treated individual from taking alcoholic beverages.

It was shown by Graham (52) that acetaldehyde dehydrogenase of rat liver is strongly inhibited by low concentrations of the drug. This worker felt that the substance acts as a competitive inhibitor, competing with diphosphopyridine nucleotide for active centers of the apoenzyme. Xanthine oxidase and succinoxidase of rat liver homogenate are also inhibited. These enzymes are probably not concerned directly in acetaldehyde metabolism, but since they are structurally similar to acetaldehyde dehydrogenase, it is perhaps not surprising that they are inhibited by disulfiram (53).

Isonicotinyl hydrazine. At the present time a drug widely used in treating human tuberculosis is isonicotinyl hydrazine. The mechanism of action in combating the growth of the tubercle bacillus is not known. However, one is probably on safe ground in assuming that the compound interferes in some key enzyme system within the microorganism. The structure of the drug is given here:

Diphenhydramine

Isonicotinyl hydrazine
(Isoniazid)

Antihistamines. As the name implies, the antihistamines are compounds which act in opposition to the physiologic effects of histamine. How they do this is not known. It has been established, however, that animals can be protected against histamine shock by the proper pretreatment with one of the various active compounds (54). At the present time there is such a variety of compounds with antihistamine activity that it is impractical here to attempt any thorough discussion of the diverse chemical structures involved. Many people taking one of these drugs obtain marked relief of symptoms, thought to result from overproduction of histamine in the body from food, beverage, or other cause.

One of the commonly employed drugs in this group is diphenhydramine (Benadryl), with the structure shown. Chemically it can be visualized as the hydrochloride of the diphenylmethyl ether of β-dimethylamino ethanol.

SPECIAL REFERENCES

1. Domagk, G.: *Deut. med. Wochschr.*, **61**, 250, 1935.
2. Trefouel, J.; Nitti, F.; and Bouet, D.: *Compt. rend. soc. biol.*, **120**, 756, 1935.
3. Crossley, M. L.; Northey, E. H.; and Hultquist, M. E.: *J. Am. Chem., Soc.*, **60**, 2217, 1938.
4. Northey, E. H.: *The Sulfonamides and Allied Compounds.* Am. Chem. Soc. Monograph Series, Reinhold, New York, 1948.
5. Bratton, A. C., and Marshall, E. K.: *J. Biol. Chem.*, **128**, 537, 1939.
6. Fleming, A.: *Brit. J. Exptl. Path.*, **10**, 226, 1929.
7. Dubos, R.: *Proc. Soc. Exptl. Biol. Med.*, **40**, 311, 1939; *J. Exptl. Med.*, **70**, 1, 11, 1939.
8. Chain, E.; Florey, H. W.; Gardner, A. D.; Heatley, N. G.; Jennings, M. A.; Orr-Ewing, J.; and Sauders, A. G.: *Lancet*, **2**, 226, 1940.
9. Abraham, E. P.; Chain, E.; Fletcher, C. M.; Gardner, A. D.; Heatley, N. G.; Jennings, M. A.; and Florey, H. W.: *Lancet*, **2**, 177, 1941.
10. Du Vigneaud, V.; Carpenter, F. H.; Holley, R. W.; Livermore, A. H.; and Rachele, J. R.: *Science*, **104**, 431, 1946.
11. Heilman, D. H., and Herrell, W. E.: *Am. J. Clin. Path.*, **15**, 7, 1945.
12. Rammelkamp, C. H.: *Proc. Soc. Exptl. Biol. Med.*, **51**, 95, 1942.
13. Boxer, G. E., and Everett, P. M.: *Anal. Chem.*, **21**, 670, 1949.
14. Levy, G. B.; Shaw, D.; Parkinson, E. S.; and Fergus, D.: *Anal. Chem.*, **20**, 1159, 1948.
15. Krampitz, L. O., and Werkman, C. H.: *Arch. Biochem.*, **12**, 57, 1947.
16. Park, J. T., and Strominger, J. L.: *Science*, **125**, 99, 1957.
17. Chain, E. B.: *Ann. Rev. Biochem.*, **27**, 167, 1958.
18. Burkholder, P. R.: *Science*, **129**, 1457, 1959.
19. Schatz, A.; Bugie, E.; and Waksman, S. A.: *Proc. Soc. Exptl. Biol. Med.*, **55**, 66, 1944.
20. Carter, H. E.; Loo, Y. H.; and Skell, P. S.: *J. Biol. Chem.*, **168**, 401, 1947.
21. Kuehl, F. A., Jr.; Peck, R. L.; Hoffhine, C. E., Jr.; Peel, E. W.; and Folkers, K.: *J. Am. Chem. Soc.*, **69**, 1234, 1947.
22. Anand, N., and Davis, B. D.: *Nature*, **185**, 22, 1960.
23. Anand, N.; Davis, B. D.; and Armitage, A. K.: *Nature*, **185**, 23, 1960.
24. Duggar, B. M.: *Ann. N. Y. Acad. Sci.*, **51**, 177, 1948.
25. Waller, C. W.; Hutchings, B. L.; Broschard, R. W.; Goldman, A. A.; Stein, W. J.; Wolf, C. F.; and Williams, J. H.: *J. Am. Chem. Soc.*, **74**, 4981, 1952.

26. Boothe, J. H.; Kende, A. S.; Fields, T. L.; and Wilkinson, R. G.: J. Am. Chem. Soc. 81, 1006, 1959.
27. Ehrlich, J.; Bartz, Q. R.; Smith, R. M.; Joslyn, D. A.; and Burkholder, P. R.: Science, 106, 417, 1947.
28. Bartz, Q. R.: J. Clin. Invest., 28, 1051, 1948.
29. Controulis, J.; Rebstock, M. C.; and Crooks, H. M., Jr.: J. Am. Chem. Soc., 71, 2463, 1949.
30. Rheingold, J. J., and Spurling, C. L.: J. Am. Med. Assoc., 149, 1301, 1952.
31. Woodward, T. E., and Wisseman, C. L., Jr.: Chloromycetin. Medical Encyclopedia, Inc., New York, 1957.
32. Dubos, R. J., and Cattenoe, C.: J. Exptl. Med., 70, 249, 1939.
33. Hotchkiss, R. D., and Dubos, R. J.: J. Biol. Chem., 141, 155, 1941.
34. Paladini, A., and Craig, L. C.: J. Am. Chem. Soc., 76, 688, 1954.
35. King, T. P., and Craig, L. C.: J. Am. Chem. Soc., 77, 6624, 6627, 1955.
36. Gregory, J. D., and Craig, L. C.: J. Biol. Chem., 172, 839, 1948.
37. Schwyzer, R., and Sieber, P.: Helv. Chim. Acta, 40, 624, 1957.
38. Consden, R.; Gorgon, A. H.; Martin, A. J. P.; and Synge, R. L. M.: Biochem. J., 41, 596, 1947.
39. Johnson, B. A.; Anker, H.; and Meleney, F. L.: Science, 102, 376, 1945.
40. Weisiger, J. R.; Harsmann, W.; and Craig, L. C.: J. Am. Chem. Soc., 77, 3123, 1955.
41. Goldberg, H. S. (ed.): Antibiotics, Their Chemistry and Non-Medical Uses. D. Van Nostrand Co., Inc., New York, 1959.
42. Verwey, W. F.: Ann. Rev. Microbiol., 13, 177, 1959.
43. Jawetz, E.: Ann. Rev. Microbiol., 10, 85, 1956.
44. Eagle, H., and Saz, A. K.: Ann. Rev. Microbiol., 9, 173, 1955.
45. Frear, D. E. H.: Chemistry of Insecticides, Fungicides and Herbicides. Van Nostrand, New York, 1948.
46. Winteringham, F. P. W., and Lewis, S. E.: Ann. Rev. Entomol., 4, 303, 1959.
47. Lipke, H., and Kearns, C. W.: J. Biol. Chem., 234, 2123, 1959.
48. Schaffer, N. K.; May, S. C.; and Summerson, W. H.: J. Biol. Chem., 206, 201, 1954.
49. Marth, P. C., and Mitchell, J. W.: Botan. Gaz., 106, 244, 1944.
50. Woodford, E. K.; Holly, K.; and McCready, C. C.: Ann. Rev. Plant Physiol., 9, 311, 1958.
51. Martensen-Larsen, O.: Quart. J. Studies Alc., 14, 406, 1953.
52. Graham, W. D.: J. Pharm. Pharmacol., 3, 160, 1951.
53. Richert, D. A.; Vanderlinde, R.; and Westerfeld, W. W.: J. Biol. Chem., 186, 261, 1950.
54. Staub, A. M., and Bovet, D.: Compt. rend. soc. biol., 125, 818, 1937.

33

Composition of urine

GENERAL CONSIDERATIONS

At this time the student should review the discussion of renal function in Chapter 16 in order that he may have a better basis for understanding the composition of urine.

The chief waste products of the body are carbon dioxide, derived from the oxidation of all organic foods; various nitrogenous substances, such as urea, uric acid, and creatinine, from protein metabolism; sulfur compounds and phosphates, also largely from protein metabolism; and excess quantities of water, sodium, potassium, calcium, magnesium, and chloride. Many other substances in small amounts are eliminated from the body in urine.

Carbon dioxide is largely excreted by the lungs (Chapter 15). The intestine excretes most of the calcium, magnesium, and iron, and some other substances. The skin normally eliminates considerable water by insensible evaporation but during active perspiration may excrete massive quantities of water containing large amounts of sodium and chloride, appreciable potassium, considerable quantities of urea, and smaller amounts of other substances. However, it is the kidneys upon which falls the burden of excreting most of the solid waste products of the body (normal average about 75 g per 24 hours for an adult) and excess body water.

The composition of urine is determined by the quantities of substances which must be removed from the body by the kidneys in order to maintain the composition of blood and other body fluids within physiologic limits.

Aside from water, the preponderant amount of waste products in urine arises from the metabolism of protein derived from food and tissues. In general, then, the gross amount of substances excreted in urine is proportional to the protein eaten, and the major waste product from protein is urea. During starvation the qualitative composition of urine remains essentially unchanged, but the quantitative relations of the constituents are markedly altered. A few substances, such as creatinine, are formed largely as the result of tissue metabolism (endogenous metabolism) and show relatively less variation with diet than do substances, such as urea, which normally are mainly the result of metabolism of food (exogenous metabolism).

The composition of urine in pathologic states generally differs from the normal in the relative amounts of constituents. For example, the urine of a normal person contains an average of only about 0.1 g of glucose per 24-hour sample, while the daily urine of a diabetic may contain 150 g or more. Similarly, only traces of the ketone bodies are present in normal urine, while 50 g or more may be excreted daily by the severe diabetic. Normally less than 100 mg of protein per day are excreted by normal persons, but the urine of the nephrotic patient may contain many grams.

There are two chief objects in studying the composition of urine. One of these is to aid in understanding, through the end products formed and excreted in the urine, the processes of body metabolism, details of which have been considered in the chapters on metabolism. The other object is to obtain evidence, through the presence of abnormal substances or substances in abnormal amounts, that may be of aid in the diagnosis and treatment of pathologic states.

Detailed composition of urine. Because the volume of urine relative to contained solutes varies widely, expression of the amount of substance per 100 ml of urine is generally of little value. Rather, it is necessary to calculate the amount of substance contained in the total volume of urine excreted per 24 hours or other definite period of time.

When the quantities of urinary substances per 24 hours are to be determined, the sample is usually collected as follows. Upon arising at a definite time in the morning, the bladder is emptied and the urine is discarded. During the ensuing day and night, and upon arising (at the same time as the day before), all samples of urine are collected in a bottle or flask containing a suitable preservative, such as toluene. This mixed sample represents the urine corresponding to a 24-hour metabolic period. Collections for shorter periods are carried out similarly. Detailed methods for the analysis of urine are to be found in laboratory manuals and works on clinical chemistry.

Since the quantities of most of the constituents of urine depend largely upon the nature and amount of the food eaten, it is impossible to give average values that are of much significance. Table 33.1 gives values such as may be found for a 24-hour sample of urine from an individual on a diet containing an average quantity of proteins. In addition, values for the chief nitrogenous substances on high and low protein diets are included. Detailed discussions of the urinary excretion of many of the substances are to be found in the chapters dealing with metabolism, acid-base and electrolyte-water balances, and nutrition. In addition to the components indicated in the table, urine contains many other substances, some of which are poorly defined. The book by Sunderman and Boerner gives comprehensive data on the composition of urine.

The values indicated for the very low protein diet represent the distribution of urinary substances resulting from a diet very high in carbohydrate

Table 33.1.   Composition of Urine
Figures represent grams per 24-hour sample unless otherwise specified

	Ordinary Diet	High Protein Diet	Very Low Protein Diet
Volume, ml	1250	1550	950
Total nitrogen	13.20	23.28	4.20
Urea	24.30	43.80	6.20
Urea nitrogen	11.40	20.40	2.90
Ammonia	0.50	1.00	0.20
Ammonia nitrogen	0.40	0.80	0.17
Creatinine	1.64	1.72	1.60
Creatinine nitrogen	0.61	0.64	0.60
Uric acid	0.60	0.90	0.30
Uric acid nitrogen	0.20	0.30	0.10
Total amino acids	1.5, less than half free		
Amino acid nitrogen	0.2		
Hippuric acid	0.6		
Indican	0.01		
Allantoin	0.015		
Creatine	0.0–0.06		
Undetermined nitrogen	0.60	1.10	0.50
Glucose	0.10		
Nonglucose reducing substances calculated as glucose	1.0		
Phenols	0.20		
Citric acid	0.30		
Ascorbic acid	0.025		
Oxalic acid (oxalates)	0.015		
Acetone bodies	0.01		
Thiamine	0.0001		
Total sulfur	1.0		
Inorganic sulfates	0.80		
Ethereal sulfates	0.08		
Neutral sulfur	0.12		
Chlorine as chloride	7.0		
Phosphorus as phosphate	1.0		
CO_2 as $HCO_3^- + H_2CO_3$	Varies with urinary pH		
Sodium	5.0		
Potassium	2.5		
Calcium	0.2		
Magnesium	0.15		
Copper	0.00004		
Iron	0.00003		
Iodine	0.00005		
Water	90–95 per cent		

and containing very little protein. The nitrogen excretion under such conditions is decidedly less than found during starvation, due to the protein-sparing action of a high carbohydrate diet. Table 33.2, taken from Lusk, shows the composition of the urine of Victor Beauté on different days of a prolonged fast. It is of interest to note the increased rate of tissue protein breakdown on the third day of starvation, causing a sharp rise in nitrogen output. The greatly decreased excretion of cations and chloride in the urine during starvation indicates their conservation to the plasma by the kidneys in order to maintain the ionic balance and osmotic pressure of blood.

Urine specific gravity and volume. The specific gravity of urine normally varies between 1.015 and 1.025 but is subject to wide fluctuations under various conditions. It may fall to 1.003 or lower as the result of copious water drinking and rise to 1.040 or higher because of hemoconcentration due to excessive perspiration. The specific gravity is increased by the excretion of large amounts of sugar in diabetes and of protein in nephrosis. The posterior pituitary secretes an antidiuretic hormone pitressin, which regulates the absorption of water by the tubules. Deficiency of this hormone leads to

Table 33.2. Composition of Urine During Fasting
Values represent grams per 24 hours

	Day of Fasting			
	1st	3rd	12th	14th
Total N	10.51	13.72	8.77	7.78
Urea N	8.96	12.26	6.62	5.99
Ammonia N	0.40	0.73	1.05	0.73
Uric acid N	0.12	0.06	0.17	0.17
Purine base N	0.029	0.032	0.023	
Creatinine N	0.42	0.34	0.30	0.24
Creatine N	0.02	0.09	0.09	0.10
Total S	0.614	0.801	0.577	0.536
Total P_2O_5	2.26	2.98	1.55	1.25
Cl	3.2	1.5	0.18	0.24
Ca		0.216		0.096
Mg		0.131		0.037
K		1.33		0.515
Na		0.865		0.096

From Lusk, G.: *The Science of Nutrition*, 4th ed. W. B. Saunders Co., Philadelphia, Pa., 1928.

the condition known as "diabetes insipidus," in which enormous volumes of urine are excreted (up to 30 l per 24 hours) having a specific gravity of 1.001 to 1.003. In such cases the solute concentration of urine may be less than that of blood plasma.

The specific gravity of urine is directly proportional to the solute content and generally varies inversely with the volume. The solute content of urine may be calculated by the use of Long's formula, in which the last two figures of the specific gravity (to the third decimal) are multiplied by the factor 2.6. This gives approximately the solids in grams per liter of urine. For example, suppose we wish to calculate the total solids in 1250 ml of urine with a specific gravity of 1.020. The solids per liter would be:

$$20 \times 2.6 = 52 \text{ g}$$

and per 1250 ml:

$$\frac{1250}{1000} \times 52 = 65 \text{ g}$$

The osmolar concentration of urine may be calculated from the freezing point depression which generally varies from $-1.3°$ to $-2.3°$ C, but as a maximum may reach $-2.6°$ C. Since a depression of $-1.86°$ C represents a concentration of 1 osmol, a depression of $-2.6°$ C represents $-2.6/-1.86 = 1.4$ osmols per liter. This value of 1.4 osmols represents the maximum concentrating capacity of the normal kidney and may be used in calculating the minimal water requirement for the excretion of a given quantity of waste products. Suppose an individual excretes 1250 ml of urine per 24 hours, showing a freezing point depression of $-1.49°$ C. The osmolar concentration per liter is: $-1.49/-1.86 = 0.80$, and the milliosmolar concentration is $0.80 \times 1000 = 800$. The total milliosmols excreted, then, would be $1250/1000 \times 800 = 1000$. Assuming the kidneys of the individual to be capable

Table 33.3.   Minimal Volumes of Urine Required to Excrete Definite Quantities of Waste Products

Waste Products Total Milliosmols	Minimal Urine Volume in Milliliters for Excretion	
	At 1.4 Conc Cap	At 0.4 Conc Cap
200	143	500
400	286	1,000
600	429	1,500
800	571	2,000
1,000	714	2,500
1,200	857	3,000
1,400	1,000	3,500
1,600	1,140	4,000

of concentrating to 1.4 osmols per liter (1400 milliosmols), the minimal quantity of urine required for excretion of waste products would be:

$$\frac{\text{total milliosmols of waste products}}{1.4} = \frac{1000}{1.4} = 714 \text{ ml}$$

Similarly, the minimal quantity of urine required for the excretion of any given quantity of waste products for any given kidney concentrating capacity may be calculated. Table 33.3 lists these values for different quantities of urine solutes at kidney concentrating capacities of 1.4 and 0.4 osmols per liter. An individual on an ordinary diet generally excretes about 1200 milliosmols of solutes, which is greatly increased on diets high in protein and salt, and which may fall to 200 on diets high in carbohydrate (very low protein) and low in salt. It can be seen from the table that when the concentrating capacity of the kidneys is severely reduced, as may be the case in diseased states, the volume of water required for excretion of waste products may be very greatly increased. A number of tests for kidney function are based upon kidney concentrating capacity under controlled conditions.

Urine secretion and work. In general, the solute concentration of urine is much greater than is plasma. This concentration of urine over plasma is effected through the reabsorption of water and solutes from the glomerular fluid as it passes through the tubules. This concentrating process represents osmotic work done by the kidneys (tubules) upon the glomerular fluid.

The minimum osmotic work, W_{min}, in small calories, involved in transferring solute from a concentration C_1 in plasma to a concentration C_2 in urine is given by the thermodynamic equation:

$$W_{min} = NRT \ln \frac{C_2}{C_1} = 2.3NRT \log \frac{C_2}{C_1}$$

in which C_1 and C_2 are expressed as mols per kilogram of water, $T =$ the absolute temperature, $N =$ the molar concentration in urine, $R =$ the gas constant in calories (1.987), $\ln =$ the natural logarithm, $\log =$ the logarithm to base 10, and 2.3 = the factor for the conversion of natural to base 10 logarithms.

This equation may be applied to any constituent of plasma and urine. For example, if the concentration of Cl^-, C_1, in plasma is 0.104 mol per kilogram of water, and in urine C_2 is 0.166 mol per kilogram of water, the minimum osmotic work done by the kidneys at 37° C (310° A) is given by the expression:

$$\overset{N \qquad R \qquad T}{W_{min} = 2.3 \times 0.166 \times 1.987 \times 310 \log \frac{0.166}{0.104}}$$

$$= 2.3 \times 0.166 \times 1.987 \times 310 \times 0.2 = 47 \text{ cal}$$

Suppose the concentration of urea in plasma, C_1, is 0.005 mol, and in urine C_2 is 0.333 mol per kilogram of water. Then the minimum work involved in its excretion would be:

$$W_{min} = 2.3 \times 0.333 \times 1.987 \times 310 \times \log \frac{0.333}{0.005}$$

$$= 2.3 \times 0.333 \times 1.987 \times 310 \times 1.82 = 861 \text{ cal}$$

Since the concentration of water is higher in plasma than in urine, the work done is negative. The value of N for pure H_2O is $1000/18 = 55.55$. Suppose the concentration of H_2O, C_1, in plasma is about 55.2, and in urine about 54.8. Then the minimum work done would be:

$$W_{min} = 2.3 \times 54.8 \times 1.987 \times 310 \times \log \frac{54.8}{55.2}$$

$$= 2.3 \times 54.8 \times 1.987 \times 310 \times (-0.0032) = -240 \text{ cal}$$

It is of interest that the concentration of Na^+ in plasma normally is about the same as the concentration in urine so that essentially no net work is required for its excretion.

The concentration of HCO_3^- is generally lower in urine than in plasma and contributes about -2 cal to the work of excretion. Normally, then, the excretion of only water and HCO_3^- represents negative work calories.

The net over-all work done by the kidneys in forming urine from plasma is the difference between the sums of the positive calories and negative calories represented by the various substances excreted. This net over-all work is about 800 to 900 cal per liter when the concentrations of solutes are normal. The work of the kidneys varies with the concentrations of solutes in the urine which in turn are affected by the diet (especially NaCl and protein) and water intake. The concentration of Cl⁻ in urine may be less than in plasma and thus contribute negative calories. With large urine volumes the concentration of water in the urine may become greater than in plasma and contribute positive calories.

It will be noted, as to be expected, that most of the work of the kidneys is performed in the excretion of urea.

The efficiency of the kidneys in performing concentration work in the secretion of urine may be expressed by the equation:

$$\text{efficiency} = \frac{\text{concentration work}}{\text{total energy consumption}} \times 100$$

The total energy consumption may be arrived at from the O_2 utilization. It is estimated that the total energy consumption of the kidneys in forming 1 l of normal urine is about 65,000 cal, and the minimum concentration work, W_{min}, done is around 850 cal. This gives:

$$\text{efficiency} = \frac{850}{65,000} \times 100 = 1.3 \text{ per cent}$$

By comparison, the efficiency of the salivary glands in forming saliva is $250/5000 \times 100 = 5.0$ per cent, that of the stomach in forming gastric juice is $900/12,000 \times 100 = 7.5$ per cent, and that of the pancreas in forming pancreatic juice is $55/75,000 \times 100 = 0.073$ per cent.

The above efficiency values are calculated on the basis of all the energy expended being utilized for one purpose, which generally is not true, since each organ utilizes energy for various purposes. However, these values do indicate the proportion of total energy expenditure which is utilized for the specific purpose of forming a given fluid.

Urine acidity and pH. The kidneys may secrete urine with a pH value as low as 4.5 and as high as 8.2 under extreme conditions. The mean pH of the normal mixed 24-hour sample is about 6.0.

The titratable acidity of urine (to phenolphthalein) in terms of milliliters of 0.1 N alkali required to neutralize the 24-hour sample generally varies from 200 to 500 and averages around 300. It is dependent almost entirely upon the nature of the diet, being high on a high protein diet, which yields much sulfuric and phosphoric acids upon metabolism, and low on a high vegetable and fruit diet, which when metabolized yields a basic residue from oxidation of the potassium and sodium salts of organic acids present.

While the acidity of normal urine is due to a complex mixture of organic acids and acid phosphates (BH_2PO_4), the latter contribute most of the acidity. In severe diabetes mellitus the ketone acids acetoacetic and β-hydroxybutyric may represent major proportions of the titratable acidity. The ingestion of ammonium salts of strong acids, such as NH_4Cl, increases urinary acidity due to the fact that the ammonia is converted to neutral urea in the liver, releasing HCl, which lowers the pH of blood and of the urine formed from it.

The pH of urine may be raised above 7 and the titratable acidity reduced to 0 (alkaline urine) by the ingestion of sodium bicarbonate or salts of organic acids such as sodium citrate which, when metabolized, yield sodium bicarbonate. Urine collected shortly after meals may be alkaline on account of the so-called alkaline tide. Occasionally urine as voided may be ammoniacal and alkaline due to bacterial action upon urea in the bladder or other parts of the urinary tract.

The usual titration of urine to phenolphthalein, pH around 9, is considerably above the normal pH of blood, 7.4. Samples of urine with pH values above that of blood may still show appreciable titratable acidity when titrated to phenolphthalein. More significant values are obtained by titrating electrometrically to pH 7.4 with the glass electrode. This procedure is necessary when accurate studies of urinary acidity in relation to blood pH are carried out.

In the titration of urine to phenolphthalein neutral potassium oxalate is added to precipitate the calcium as oxalate to prevent its interference with titration of acid phosphates. The chief reaction in the titration is:

$$H_2PO_4^- + \bar{O}H \longrightarrow H_2O + HPO_4^=$$

If the $H_2PO_4^-$ is present as the Na^+ or K^+ salt, the titration proceeds normally. However, in the presence of Ca^{++} ions the relatively insoluble and unstable salt, $CaHPO_4$, is formed as the pH is raised and the concentration of $HPO_4^=$ ions increases. The $CaHPO_4$ then slowly undergoes transformation as follows:

$$4CaHPO_4 \longrightarrow Ca_3(PO_4)_2 + Ca(H_2PO_4)_2$$

The triple phosphate $Ca_3(PO_4)_2$ precipitates out, leaving the acid salt $Ca(H_2PO_4)_2$ in solution; this makes the solution more acid and requires additional alkali. In effect, the presence of Ca^{++} ions causes the titration of some of the $H_2PO_4^-$ to $PO_4^=$ instead of stopping at $HPO_4^=$, the desired stage. Unless the calcium is removed before titration, samples of urine of the same acidity may show widely different values due to this calcium effect.

The acidity of the urine formed is chiefly dependent upon the degree to which the Na^+ ions of the glomerular filtrate are replaced by H^+ ions supplied by the carbonic acid-carbonic anhydrase system of the distal tubules, and also upon the extent to which these cations are substituted by NH_4^+ ions. The reabsorption of $HC\bar{O}_3$ ions into the blood is dependent upon the availability of Na^+ ions for simultaneous reabsorption with the $HC\bar{O}_3$ ions. In an acidosis such as caused by diabetic ketosis, the kidneys are flooded with so much of the Na^+ salts of the ketone acids that sufficient H^+ and NH_4^+ cannot be substituted to conserve the Na^+, and excessive amounts of these ions are lost in the urine, and the body supply is depleted. With depletion of Na^+ ions in the plasma and glomerular filtrate the reabsorption of the basic $HC\bar{O}_3$ ions into the blood is decreased, and the condition of acidosis becomes established. In the acidosis of chronic nephritis the damaged kidney tubules are unable to exchange H^+ and NH_4^+ for Na^+ sufficiently rapidly to conserve the Na$^+$, the reabsorption of basic HC$\bar{\text{O}}_3$ into the blood is decreased, and a condition of acidosis results.

Normally the reabsorption of glomerular fluid HC$\bar{\text{O}}_3$ back into the blood by the tubules is so efficient that only about 0.1 per cent escapes into the urine. However, after the ingestion of bicarbonate, large quantities can be excreted in the urine with only a slight increase in plasma level.

The drug acetazolamide (Diamox) (2-acetylamino-1,3,4-thiadiazole-5-sulfonamide) is a powerful inhibitor of carbonic anhydrase, and when administered decreases the concentration of H_2CO_3 in the distal tubule cells and the capacity to exchange H$^+$ for Na$^+$. This results in a copious excretion of Na$^+$, HC$\bar{\text{O}}_3$, and water, a rise in urinary pH (urine may become alkaline) and a fall in blood pH. Diamox is used to promote the excretion of Na$^+$ and water in the reduction of edema due to heart failure.

The student will find a discussion of the renal tubular mechanisms involved in regulating urinary acidity in Chapter 16.

Turbidity of urine. Normally samples of freshly voided urine are clear. However, less acid urines upon standing may become cloudy owing to the precipitation of insoluble phosphates (calcium and magnesium phosphates). This precipitation is the result of an increase in pH into the zone of formation of the insoluble phosphates resulting from the loss of dissolved CO_2 or to the formation of ammonia by the bacterial decomposition of urea when the sample of urine is not preserved. This precipitate of phosphates readily dissolves upon acidification with acetic acid.

Turbidity also may appear in urine upon standing due to the separation of a cloud (nebecula) composed chiefly of mucoid or nucleoprotein and epithelial cells. Grossly pathologic urine containing pus may be densely turbid.

Odor of urine. The odor of normal urine, characteristic and faintly aromatic, is due to a number of substances, among which are certain volatile organic acids in small amounts. Some of the odor has been attributed to a neutral ill-smelling substance called "urinod," C_6H_8O. The urine voided after eating asparagus possesses a typical odor said to be due to the presence of methylmercaptan, CH_3SH, which may arise from an unstable precursor in urine. The ingestion of substances such as turpentine, tolu, and copaiba give excretory products which impart rather characteristic odors to urine. When urine undergoes so-called alkaline fermentation in which urea is hydrolyzed to ammonia, it develops a strongly ammoniacal odor. This may be associated with a putrid odor, if pus and decomposing tissue cells are present.

Color of urine. The color of normal urine shows a wide variation from the light straw color of highly dilute urine to the reddish yellow color of concentrated urine. Acid urines are generally darker than alkaline urines.

The color of normal urine is due chiefly to pigment called "urochrome," which appears to be a compound of urobilin and a peptide. Fresh urine contains little if any free urobilin, though upon storage at ordinary temperature or heating free urobilin, a brown substance, is liberated, causing the urine to become darker in color. Also, a colorless reduction product of urobilin, urobilinogen, is present in urine and is oxidized to the colored urobilin upon exposure to air. Urobilinogen originates through bacterial action upon bile pigments in the intestine. Urochrome is present in urine partly as the colorless reduction product, urochromogen, which is oxidized to urochrome upon exposure to air.

Urobilin is also excreted in the feces, where it is generally known as "stercobilin," to the extent of 100 to 200 mg per day. The urobilin of urine, as urochrome and urobilinogen, generally amounts to 70 to 80 mg per day, all but a few milligrams of which are represented by urochrome. The total urobilin of feces and urine is considered to be a measure of the rate of hemoglobin breakdown in the body.

The amount of urochrome excreted per day appears to vary with the metabolic rate and accordingly is increased in fevers.

The vitamin riboflavin is excreted in urine and contributes to its yellow color.

Hemoglobin, myoglobin, and bile pigments may be present in urine as the result of pathologic conditions or injury and contribute to its color. In the rare condition of alcaptonuria the urine contains homogentisic acid, which, upon making the urine alkaline, is oxidized to a black pigment (see tyrosine metabolism). Melanotic tumors may cause the excretion of melanin precursors in the urine and give it a brown or black color.

The ingestion of certain foods and drugs may cause characteristic changes in the color of urine. Rhubarb, cascara, and senna color urine a reddish brown which turns to blood red upon addition of alkali. Methylene blue causes pale green to greenish blue coloration. Phenol and some of its derivatives lead to dark green or brownish black colors, especially upon standing exposed to air.

NORMAL AND ABNORMAL CONSTITUENTS OF URINE

The origins of most of the usual constituents of urine have been considered in the chapters on metabolism, and the following discussion is concerned primarily with additional facts relative to the chemistry of these constituents and to their importance as urinary components.

Urea. Urea is the principal end product of protein (amino acid) metabolism in the human, mammals in general, and in certain lower forms. In the human it usually represents 80 to 90 per cent of the total urinary nitrogen. In general, the proportion of nitrogen as urea increases as the total urinary nitrogen increases, and vice versa. On very low protein diets urea may represent 60 per cent or less of the total nitrogen.

The quantity of urea excreted, in general, is proportional to the total protein metabolism, whether this protein represents food protein or the protein of tissues undergoing catabolism. The excretion of urea is decreased in certain liver diseases, such as acute yellow atrophy and cirrhosis, in which the capacity to form urea is decreased. In cases of severe acidosis the amount of urea excreted may be considerably reduced because of diversion of amino nitrogen to ammonia formation. Excretion of urea also may be decreased in nephritis when the ability of the kidneys to excrete it is severely impaired. This may cause greatly increased concentrations of urea in the blood (uremia) and other body fluids.

Ammonia. The mechanism of ammonia formation by the kidneys and the regulation of the amount formed have been considered in detail in the chapters dealing with protein metabolism and acid-base balance, to which the student is referred.

Ammonia, normally, is the second most important nitrogenous substance of urine quantitatively. Ordinarily, 2.5 to 4.5 per cent of the total urinary nitrogen is composed of ammonium salts. On the average this represents about 0.7 g per day.

Since both urinary ammonia and urea are derived from the amino groups of the amino acids, for a given quantity of nitrogen excreted an increase in the amount of the one leads to a decrease in the amount of the other.

As previously pointed out, ammonia is formed in the kidney to be substituted for Na^+ and K^+ so that they may be conserved to the plasma. Accordingly, the quantity of urinary ammonia per day varies from practically 0 in alkalosis to 8 to 10 g in cases of severe diabetic acidosis.

Urinary ammonia may be markedly decreased in cases of severe nephritis in which the capacity of the kidneys to form it has been impaired. This reduces the capacity of the kidneys to conserve base and contributes to the development of acidosis.

The quantity of ammonia in the urine may be enormously increased through hydrolysis of urea by bacteria in the bladder (cystitis) or other parts of the urinary tract. This bacterial production of ammonia from urea in normal urine may take place if the samples are stored without preservative (alkaline fermentation).

Uric acid and other purines. Uric acid is the chief end product of purine metabolism in man, the higher apes, and the Dalmatian dog (see the discussion of nucleoprotein metabolism). The quantity of uric acid in human urine is generally from 0.5 to 1.0 g per 24 hours, though the amount is subject to wide variations. On a purine-free diet the uric acid excretion may fall to 0.1 g per day, while on a high purine diet the daily excretion may rise to 2 g.

Uric acid is very sparingly soluble in water (0.06 g in 100 ml of hot water) and is insoluble in alcohol and ether.

Through its enol form uric acid acts as a weak dibasic acid and forms both neutral and acid salts. The neutral lithium and potassium salts are the most soluble urates. The acid salts of the alkali metals are rather insoluble. Ammonium urate is difficultly soluble. The alkaline earth urates are insoluble. The acid salts of sodium and potassium form most of the sediment which separates from concentrated acid urine upon standing and cooling.

Crystals of uric acid are readily precipitated from urine by acidifying with HCl. Such preparations are colored reddish brown by associated urine pigments, which may be removed by solution in concentrated H_2SO_4 and precipitation of the uric acid by careful dilution with water or alcohol. Uric acid separates from pure solution as transparent, colorless, rhombic plates, while from urine it gives a variety of colored crystal forms.

The two pK_a values ($-\log K_a$) of uric acid are approximately 5.7 and 9.8.

In very acid urines the proportion of free uric acid is considerable, while in urines of average pH (6 ± 0.5) the sodium and potassium acid salts, which are much more soluble than uric acid, predominate. Alkaline urines contain a large proportion of the soluble sodium and potassium salts. Acid urates tend to separate from urines more acid than normal when permitted to stand, and free uric acid may separate from strongly acid urines.

Uric acid reduces alkaline copper and silver but not bismuth solutions. It also reduces sodium phosphotungstate in alkaline solution and arseno-phosphotungstate in the presence of cyanide to give blue colors. The latter reaction is commonly used in the quantitative estimation of uric acid.

When uric acid is oxidized with concentrated nitric acid and the mixture made alkaline with NH_4OH, a reddish purple color appears because of the formation of ammonium purpurate, also called "murexide." The murexide test is given by various purines:

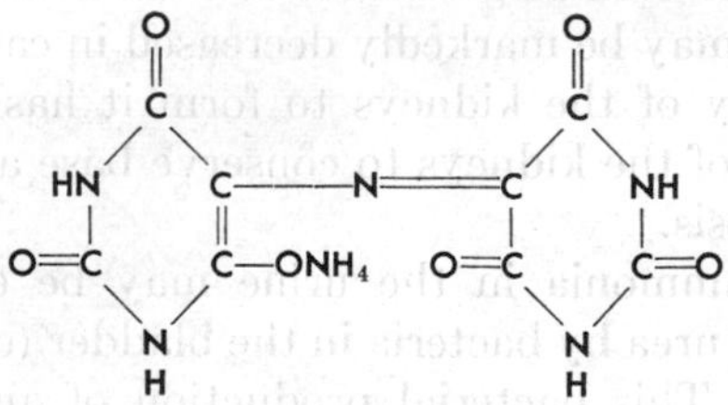

Ammonium purpurate
Murexide

Uric acid is converted to allantoin by the enzyme uricase:

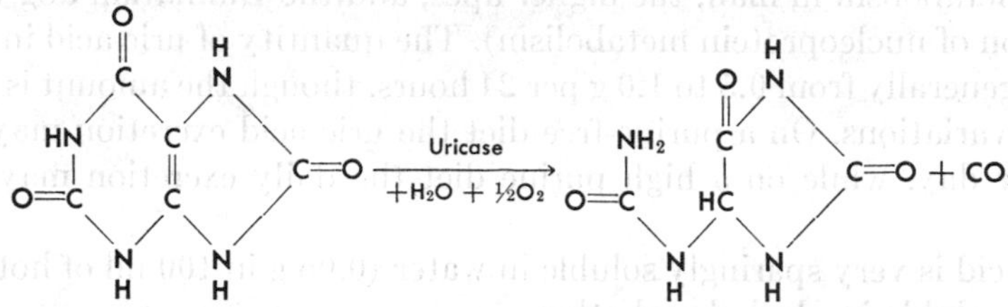

Uric acid (keto form)   Allantoin (keto form)

This reaction with uricase has been made the basis of a specific quantitative method for uric acid (1), the principle of which is to run colorimetric estimations with arsenophosphotungstic acid on samples before and after treatment with uricase, which specifically destroys the uric acid and leaves the other substances which give a color with the reagent. Uric acid is represented by the difference between the uric acid equivalents of the color values before and after treatment with uricase.

The excretion of uric acid in pathologic conditions varies widely. Conditions involving the breakdown of large quantities of nuclear material such as is found in the destruction of leucocytes in leukemia may cause the excretion of large amounts of uric acid (10 g or more). In gout the uric acid content of blood may rise to 15 mg per cent, apparently partly due to decreased kidney elimination. The uric acid of the urine tends to decrease prior to an attack of gout and to increase during the crisis and recovery, sometimes to twice the normal value.

Small amounts of various purines other than uric acid are excreted in urine (2). These substances include 1-methylguanine, N²-methylguanine, 1-methylhypoxanthine, 8-hydroxy-7-methylguanine, guanine, hypoxanthine, adenine, 7-methylguanine, 1-methylxanthine, 7-methylxanthine, and 1,7-dimethylxanthine (paraxanthine). The latter three compounds are present only after the ingestion of coffee, tea, etc. The total excretion of these purines averages around 30 mg per day and varies widely in a group and in an individual case. The excretion is little affected by diet, indicating an endogenous source.

Creatinine and creatine. The formation and metabolism of these substances have been considered in the chapter on protein metabolism:

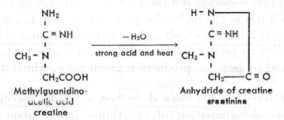

Methylguanidino-
acetic acid
creatine

Anhydride of creatine
creatinine

The quantity of creatinine excreted in urine by the normal adult generally is from 1.2 to 1.7 g per 24 hours and depends partly upon the amount of creatinine (from meats and soups) in the diet, since this is excreted unchanged in the urine. The quantity excreted on a creatinine-free diet is practically constant for a given individual over long periods of time and is independent of the total nitrogen output. Shaffer (3) defines the creatinine coefficient as the milligrams of creatinine, or creatine plus creatinine (when creatine is present), excreted per kilogram of body weight per day. The creatinine coefficient averages 20 to 26 in normal men and 14 to 22 in women. It varies in proportion to muscular development, is not significantly altered by variations in diet (when these do not involve the ingestion of much preformed creatinine), exercise, urine volume, and many pathologic conditions. Prolonged illness and old age, both of which are associated with loss of muscular tone and activity, may cause marked decreases in the creatinine coefficient.

The statement is commonly made that creatine is absent from the urine of normal adult males. However, Albanese and Wangerin (4) and Wilder and Morgulis (5), using improved methods of analysis, have shown that normal adult males regularly excrete a small amount of creatine. Wilder and Morgulis found that 60 to 150 mg of creatine per day are excreted, which on the average amounts to about 6 per cent of the total creatinine output.

Adult females show much greater variation in creatine excretion, although in the great majority of cases it amounts to two or two and a half times as much as for adult males. In about one-fifth of the females the creatine excretion is similar to that for the males.

The excretion of creatine is greatly increased in infants and children, during starvation, and particularly in patients with certain muscular dystrophies.

Creatinine crystallizes as colorless, glistening, monoclinic prisms. It is soluble in water and alcohol. Its nitrogen atoms are weakly basic, and it forms salts only with strong acids. It forms an important compound with zinc chloride which has the formula $(C_4H_7N_3O)_2ZnCl_2$. Creatinine reduces alkaline copper solutions and forms an insoluble cuprous-creatinine salt. It is responsible for some of the reducing action of urine, and consequently may cause errors in urinary sugar determinations by certain methods.

Creatinine reacts with picric acid in alkaline solution to form a red substance (Jaffe reaction), which is the basis for the method commonly used for its quantitative determination. Greenwald (6) has studied the nature of this colored product and considers it a complex of creatinine, picric acid, sodium hydroxide, and water in the molecular proportions of 2-1-3-3, respectively. When creatinine is treated with alkali and sodium nitroprusside, a red color changing to yellow is produced. The addition of acetic acid to the yellow solution, followed by heating, produces a green color, which finally changes to blue.

Sullivan and Irreverre (7) have described a highly specific method for the quantitative determination of creatinine based upon the carmine color formed when creatinine reacts with 1,4-naphthoquinone-2-potassium sulfonate.

Creatine is converted to creatinine by heating its solutions with strong acid. The difference in creatinine before and after heating urine and other biologic fluids with acid gives the amount of creatine present, calculated as creatinine. The method is not very accurate.

Amino acids. The total amino acid excretion in urine per 24 hours normally amounts to about 1.5 g, of which more than half is in peptide or other combinations from which the free amino acids are liberated by acid hydrolysis (8).

The quantity of urinary amino acids may be increased in diseases associated with excessive tissue destruction such as severe diabetes, typhoid fever, and acute yellow atrophy of the liver. In the latter condition the capacity of the liver to deaminize amino acids is impaired sufficiently to cause their excessive accumulation in blood and excretion in the urine.

Hippuric acid. Hippuric acid, so called because it was first found in the urine of horses, is a peptide of benzoic acid and glycine, benzoylglycine:

$$\text{C}_6\text{H}_5 - \overset{\overset{\text{O}}{\|}}{\text{C}} - \overset{\overset{\text{H}}{|}}{\text{N}} - \text{CH}_2\text{COOH}$$

Hippuric acid

Hippuric acid represents a detoxication product of benzoic acid. Benzoic acid is present in many fruits and vegetables, especially in cranberries and prunes. Some food products, such as ketchups, are preserved with 0.1 per cent of sodium benzoate and contribute to the benzoic acid intake. Benzoic acid also may be formed by the oxidative breakdown of phenylalanine through bacterial action in the intestine.

The amount of hippuric acid excreted per day in the urine averages about 0.7 g and ranges from 0.1 to 1.0 g. In the dog hippuric acid formation occurs in the kidneys, but in man and the rabbit synthesis appears to take place largely in the liver. The capacity of an individual to synthesize hippuric acid after a test dose of sodium benzoate is used as a clinical test of liver function.

Hippuric acid is readily soluble in alcohol and hot water and is sufficiently soluble in ether to permit extraction from aqueous solution with this solvent. Armstrong and associates (9) have demonstrated the presence of m-hydroxy-hippuric and β-m-hydroxyphenylhydracrylic acids in urine:

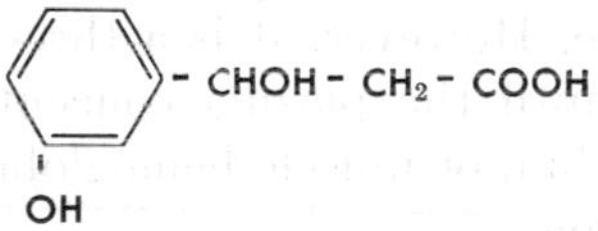

$$\text{◯} - \text{CHOH} - \text{CH}_2 - \text{COOH}$$
$$\text{OH}$$

β-m-Hydroxyphenylhydracrylic acid

Allantoin. Allantoin occurs, in varying amounts, in the urine of practically all mammals. The urines of man, anthropoid apes, and the Dalmatian dog contain very small amounts, while those of other mammals contain allantoin in quantity, where it represents the chief end product of purine metabolism.

Allantoin is formed in the liver by the action of the enzyme uricase upon uric acid (see uric acid above), and the quantity of the substance in urine varies with the amount or activity of this enzyme. Extirpation of the liver of a dog causes allantoin excretion to be changed to uric acid excretion.

Human urine generally contains 10 to 25 mg of allantoin per 24-hour specimen.

Proteins. Normally, human urine contains exceedingly little protein (20–80 mg per 24 hours), which is composed of a small quantity of insoluble nebecula (mucoid or nucleoprotein), albumin, and enzymes. However, in various kidney diseases large quantities of protein may be excreted in the urine, as much as 20 g per day in cases of nephrosis.

The kinds of protein that may be found in urine under various pathologic conditions include serum albumin and globulin, nucleoprotein, fibrin, myoglobin, hemoglobin, and related substances, proteoses and peptones, and Bence Jones protein. Of these proteins serum albumin and globulin are most frequently present in urine, with albumin predominating, apparently because of its smaller molecular size and more ready passage through the glomerular membrane. Protein in the urine is usually referred to as "albuminuria."

Nucleoproteins in appreciable amounts may appear in the urine in conditions involving inflammation of the urinary epithelia such as cystitis (in the bladder) and pyelitis (in the kidney).

Bence Jones protein, considered a low-molecular-weight globulin, may occur in the urines of patients with multiple myeloma, which is a tumorlike growth in bone marrow, and at times in the urines of leukemia patients. Bence Jones protein is characterized by precipitating when the urine is warmed to 40 to 60° C and dissolving almost completely when the urine is further heated to boiling. Upon cooling the precipitate reappears.

The excretion of proteoses and peptones in the urine may occur in conditions involving destruction of much tissue protein, such as pneumonia, carcinoma, and diphtheria.

Blood cells and other constituents may be present in urine because of hemorrhage into the urinary tract (hematuria). Hemoglobinuria, the presence of hemoglobin in urine, results when appreciable quantities of hemoglobin are released into the blood (hemoglobinemia) through hemolysis of the red cells. Hemoglobin dissolved in plasma is treated as a foreign protein and excreted in the urine. However, it is a threshold substance and is retained by the kidneys until the plasma concentration rises above about 150 mg per cent. Myoglobin, or muscle hemoglobin, may occur in the urine after severe muscle trauma.

Functional proteinurias, not related to diseased states, may be observed after violent exercise, cold baths, and as a result of standing upright (postural proteinuria). Postural proteinuria is probably due to interference with the blood supply to the kidneys, causing venous stasis, since the condition disappears when the individual is lying down. The amounts of protein excreted in functional proteinurias are generally small.

The subject of proteinuria is large and complex, and for detailed discussions the student should consult books dealing with clinical pathology.

Carbohydrates in urine. Normal urine contains a variety of carbohydratelike substances which reduce sugar reagents. When calculated as glucose, these ordinarily amount to 1.0 to 1.5 g per 24 hours. Much of this material consists of nonglucose substances present in foods or formed from them during cooking. The quantity of glucose present generally averages about 140 mg per 24-hour specimen, though it is subject to considerable variation.

The presence of appreciable quantities of glucose in urine is known as "glucosuria" (or "glycosuria"). The most severe glucosurias are seen in severe diabetes mellitus, when the urine may contain 10 per cent or more of glucose. In such conditions both the urine volume and specific gravity are high. Such glucosurias are due to elevated blood sugar levels (hyperglycemia) exceeding the renal threshold.

In renal diabetes the blood sugar is normal, but the renal threshold is below normal, so that some glucose is excreted in the urine, particularly after meals.

Emotional glucosuria is the result of the rapid breakdown of liver glycogen through adrenaline action, causing a hyperglycemia which exceeds the kidney threshold.

Pentoses such as arabinose may occur in urine (pentosuria) as the result of ingestion of large amounts of foods rich in pentoses such as cherries, grapes, prunes, and plums. This type of pentosuria is alimentary. In cases of idiopathic or essential pentosuria, which represents an "inborn error of metabolism," the major pentose excreted is L-xylulose. Futterman and Roe (10) have identified both D-ribulose and L-xylulose, in very small amounts, as constituents of normal human urine. D-Ribulose is formed in the pentose cycle of carbohydrate metabolism, and L-xylulose in the metabolism of D-glucuronic acid (11).

Lactose is frequently present in the urine of lactating women as the result of the passage of the sugar from the mammary gland into the blood. Since lactose as such cannot be utilized by the body, it is excreted as a foreign substance in the urine. It is important to differentiate lactose from glucose in such cases, since a lactosuria is of no significance whereas the presence of glucose may indicate diabetes mellitus. The sugars are best differentiated by reduction tests before and after fermentation with bakers' yeast which removes glucose but not lactose. If both sugars are present, as may be the case, quantitative determination of fermentable sugar indicates the proportions of each. Lactose may be qualitatively detected in urine through the osazone and mucic acid tests.

Galactosuria has been observed following the ingestion of large amounts of galactose in nursing infants with gastrointestinal disturbances, and in both infants and adults with liver disease.

Fructosuria or levulosuria may occur in severe cases of diabetes mellitus, in which fructose accompanies glucose. Alimentary fructosuria may result after the ingestion of large quantities of fructose by patients with liver disease. Essential levulosuria or fructosuria, in which fructose is excreted in the urine from birth, is a rare condition which may be considered as an "inborn error of metabolism." In some cases there is complete inability to metabolize ingested fructose; the sugar is quantitatively excreted in the urine. Insulin has no effect upon the condition, and carbohydrates other than fructose are metabolized normally.

Fat in urine. Fat may be present in the urine of normal persons after a high fat meal (lipuria), or after the ingestion of large amounts of fatty oils such as cod liver oil. Lipuria may occur in cases of severe diabetes mellitus, in which the plasma lipid concentration is markedly elevated, in nephrosis, in cases of traumatic injury to the bone marrow, and when there has been extensive crushing of superficial fat. Lipuria has been reported in cases of alcohol and phosphorus poisoning. Obstruction of lymph flow in the thoracic duct may cause distension and rupture of lymph vessels of the kidney and bladder with resulting lymphuria or chyluria, and the presence of lipids in the urine. Fat may appear in the urine as the result of fatty degeneration of epithelial cells and leucocytes in conditions such as pyelonephritis and nephrosis.

Glucuronic acid. Glucuronic acid occurs in urine conjugated with a wide variety of substances under both normal and pathologic conditions and after the administration of certain drugs. These conjugates represent detoxication products of the body (see Chapter 13).

The glucoside conjugates are formed from aromatic alcohols and phenols such as naphthol, phenol, and borneol, while ester conjugates are formed particularly from aromatic acids such as benzoic and phenylacetic.

Both free glucuronic acid and ester conjugates reduce alkaline sugar reagents, the latter being hydrolyzed to glucuronic acid by the alkali. Glucoside conjugates are not hydrolyzed by alkali and show reduction only after acid hydrolysis. Glucuronic acid and its conjugates are not fermentable. Peculiarly, free glucuronic acid is dextrorotatory while its conjugates are levorotatory.

The total glucuronic acid content of urine normally amounts to 0.5 to 1.0 g per day and is present chiefly as conjugates of phenol, indoxyl, skatoxyl, and the estrogenic hormones.

The urinary glucuronates may be greatly increased by the administration of substances such as antipyrine, camphor, chloral hydrate, borneol, menthol, aspirin, morphine, phenolphthalein, most of the sulfonamide drugs, and turpentine. Decreases in glucuronate excretion have been observed in the rat associated with vitamin deficiencies. Riboflavin deficiency, however, appears to cause increased excretion.

Glucuronic acid and glucuronates give a color reaction with naphthoresorcinol when heated with strong HCl, which is used for their qualitative detection and quantitative estimation.

Ketone bodies. The ketone bodies found in urine are derived chiefly from the metabolism of fatty acids (see Chapter 23) and consist of acetone, acetoacetic acid, and β-hydroxybutyric acid:

$$CH_3 - \overset{OH}{\underset{H}{C}} - CH_2 - COOH \qquad CH_3 - \overset{O}{C} - CH_2 - COOH \qquad CH_3 - \overset{O}{C} - CH_3$$

β-Hydroxybutyric acid   Acetoacetic acid   Acetone

Acetoacetic acid is the primary ketone body from which β-hydroxybutyric acid is formed by reduction and acetone by decarboxylation. The liver is the site of formation of the ketone acids.

A normal person on a mixed diet generally excretes less than 100 mg of ketone bodies per 24 hours. Typical ketonuria results whenever the rate of production of ketone bodies in the liver exceeds the capacity of the body tissues to oxidize them. This occurs on very high fat diets, during starvation when a large amount of body fat is metabolized, in diabetes mellitus, in both normal and toxemic pregnancies, during ether anesthesia, and often in conditions of alkalosis. In severe diabetic acidosis 75 g or more of ketone bodies may be excreted in the 24-hour urine.

Nitroprusside reacts with acetoacetic acid in the presence of NH_4OH

and $(NH_4)_2SO_4$ to give a permanganate color (Rothera's test), which is commonly used as a test for the substance in urine. Acetone also reacts, but less readily. Acetoacetic acid also gives a Bordeaux red color with ferric chloride.

Acetone gives iodoform when treated with alkaline iodine solution. In testing urines for acetone the latter should first be separated by distillation.

β-Hydroxybutyric acid, when oxidized with hydrogen peroxide and treated with a mixture of ferric and ferrous chlorides, gives a rose color (Black's reaction). The acid must be separated from urine before applying the test.

Citric acid. Citric acid is formed continually in carbohydrate metabolism through operation of the tricarboxylic or citric acid cycle, and small amounts, 0.2 to 1.2 g per 24 hours, are excreted in the urine. The excretion is increased in conditions of alkalosis. Citric acid excretion is increased after the administration of estrogens. A marked increase follows hepatectomy.

Lactic acid. Lactic acid accumulates in the tissues and blood under all conditions in which the supply of oxygen to the tissues is deficient, and small amounts escape in the urine. The urinary lactic acid increases in cases of pneumonia, eclampsia, ether anesthesia, carbon monoxide poisoning, acute yellow atrophy of the liver, and epileptic attacks. As expected, severe muscular exercise may markedly increase urinary lactic acid.

Normal urine generally contains 50 to 200 mg of lactic acid per 24-hour specimen.

Oxalic acid. Normal urine contains 10 to 30 mg of oxalic acid as oxalates per 24-hour sample. Although it appears that some oxalic acid may arise from metabolic processes, the larger proportion generally is derived from the oxalates present in foods such as asparagus, spinach, rhubarb, lettuce, apples, and other vegetables and fruits.

Oxalic acid separates from urine as insoluble calcium oxalate. Many urinary calculi are largely calcium oxalate.

The oxalic acid content of urine is increased in diabetes mellitus, in certain liver diseases, and in various conditions involving deficient tissue oxidations.

Oxaluric acid, $H_2N—CO—NH—CO—COOH$, a combination of oxalic acid and urea, occasionally is present in traces in normal urine. It breaks up into urea and oxalic acid upon hydrolysis.

Sulfur compounds. Sulfur is excreted in the urine in three combinations: inorganic sulfate, organic ester or ethereal sulfate, and so-called neutral sulfur.

Most of the urinary sulfur arises from the metabolism of protein, specifically from the S-containing amino acids, cystine, cysteine, and methionine, and varies with the protein intake and the rate of tissue protein breakdown. The total urinary sulfur varies ordinarily from about 0.8 to 1.4 g per 24 hours, and averages about 1.0 g. Generally the urinary N:S ratio ranges from 13 to 16 on a high meat diet and during fasting.

Inorganic sulfate sulfur generally makes up the greater proportion of urinary sulfur and ordinarily amounts to 0.7 to 1.0 g per day. It normally represents from 85 to 95 per cent of the total sulfur excreted. The sulfate sulfur excretion may be diminished in conditions of renal functional impairment and is increased on high protein diets and when there is excessive tissue breakdown such as occurs in high fevers.

Ethereal sulfate sulfur excretion in the urine generally ranges from 0.06 to 0.12 g per day. It consists of the sodium and potassium salts of sulfuric acid esters of phenols such as indoxyl, skatoxyl, phenol, and cresol. These ethereal sulfates represent detoxication compounds of phenols and are formed in the liver. Some of the phenolic substances originate through bacterial action in the intestine (see Chapter 13), and some appear to be formed in tissue metabolism. Indoxyl and skatoxyl are formed practically entirely by the putrefactive decomposition of tryptophan in the intestine. Both substances are esterified with sulfuric acid in the liver and excreted in the urine as sodium and potassium salts:

Skatoxylsulfuric acid

Indoxylsulfuric acid
K salt is called "indican"

The amount of indican, potassium indoxyl sulfate, excreted in the urine is taken as a rough index of intestinal putrefaction.

Indican is oxidized to the dye indigo blue by hypochlorite (Jaffe test) and by ferric chloride in strong HCl solutions (Obermayer test):

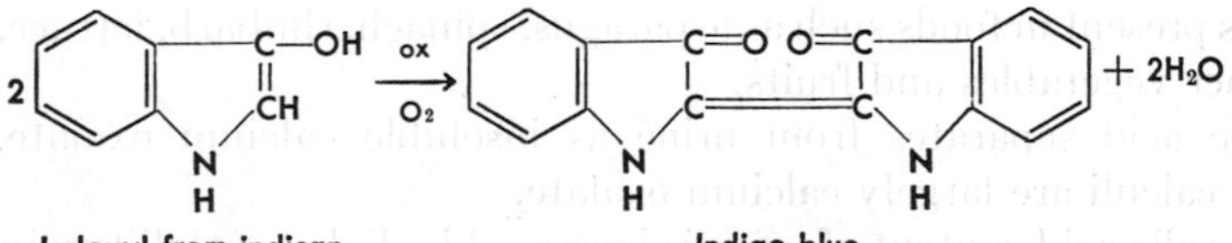

Indoxyl from indican

Indigo blue

These tests are used for the detection of indican in urine.

The neutral sulfur fraction of urine, ordinarily ranging from 0.08 to 0.16 g per day, is composed of a heterogeneous mixture of sulfur compounds. These include cystine, methionine, oxyproteic acids, urochrome, thiosulfates, thiocyanates, bile acids, and taurine and its derivatives.

Urinary neutral sulfur is increased in cystinuria, melanuria, and in obstructive and hepatocellular jaundice due to the excretion of bile acids.

A comprehensive discussion of sulfur excretion is given by Peters and Van Slyke (12).

Chlorides. Next to urea, chlorides make up the chief solid constituent of urine, generally amounting to 6 to 9 g per day of Cl⁻, and equivalent to 10 to 15 g of NaCl, which is the chief chloride present. However, the daily excretion varies widely with the dietary intake.

The excretion of chlorides in the urine may be markedly decreased by excessive perspiration owing to loss in the sweat. During fasting, chloride excretion may fall to a trace, even though the concentration of blood chlorides is approximately normal. This shows the remarkable capacity of the kidneys to conserve electrolyte for the maintenance of the osmotic pressure of body fluids. Excessive water drinking and the resulting diuresis cause increased chloride excretion. Under such conditions a fasting subject is no longer able to maintain normal blood chloride concentrations. Since cations, chiefly Na^+, are excreted with the Cl^-, such a condition also leads to a cation deficit in the body.

The excretion of chlorides in the urine is decreased when blood chloride levels are lowered by loss through diarrhea and excessive vomiting.

During pneumonia and other infectious diseases hypochloremia results from the withdrawal of blood chlorides into exudates, and the excretion of chlorides in the urine falls. Upon resolution of the exudates excretion of chlorides increases.

Patients with edema from practically any cause (nephrosis, nephritis, malnutrition, or cardiac decompensation) show decreased urine chlorides rather independent of blood chloride concentration.

Urine chlorides may be extremely low in cases of severe diabetes insipidus.

Excessive amounts of sodium and chloride are excreted in the urine in cases of adrenal cortical insufficiency (Addison's disease), while the excretion of these substances is decreased in cortical hyperfunction (Cushing's syndrome).

Phosphates. Phosphate ions generally rank next in amount to chloride ions among the anions of urine. The amount of urinary phosphate varies widely, depending largely upon the diet, and is generally equivalent to 0.8 to 1.3 g of P per day (average about 1.1 g). Most of this is present as inorganic phosphate (B_2HPO_4 and BH_2PO_4), organic phosphates making up only 1 to 4 per cent of the total.

Urinary phosphate arises largely from the breakdown of phospholipids, nucleoproteins, nucleotides, and phosphoproteins of foods and tissues. Much of the phosphate is hydrolyzed from foods in the intestine. The reaction of the intestinal contents has much to do with the quantity of phosphate absorbed into the blood and excreted in the urine. Increased alkalinity in the presence of food calcium, magnesium, and iron causes the precipitation of insoluble phosphates which pass out in the feces. A more acid condition increases the intestinal absorption of phosphorus.

As previously indicated, the inorganic phosphates of urine are composed of a mixture of B_2HPO_4 and BH_2PO_4, the amount of BH_2PO_4 being responsible for most of the titratable acidity of urine. The proportions of B_2HPO_4 and BH_2PO_4 are in proportion to urinary pH (see Chapter 16).

When urines are made alkaline, insoluble phosphates of calcium and magnesium separate. In conditions of "phosphaturia" the urine contains a crystalline precipitate of magnesium ammonium phosphate, $MgNH_4PO_4$, also called triple phosphate. This is due to decreased acidity of urine. Such precipitation of insoluble phosphates is responsible for the formation of calculi in the kidney and bladder (kidney and bladder stones). Treatment is directed toward increasing the acidity and decreasing the phosphate content of the urine.

Urinary phosphate excretion is increased in diseases of the bones such as rickets, osteomalacia, and periostosis. It is also increased by the excessive amounts of parathyroid hormone in cases of parathyroid hyperfunction. Conversely, it is decreased in parathyroid hypofunction.

Decreases in urinary phosphates may be observed in pregnancy as the result of utilization of maternal phosphate in the formation of fetal bones, in acute infections, and in nephritis, when the capacity of the kidneys to eliminate phosphates is decreased.

Sodium and potassium. The excretion of these elements has been considered in detail in Chapter 17.

The quantity of sodium excreted in the urine normally ranges from 4 to 5 g per day, although it varies widely and generally parallels the chloride excretion. Urinary potassium ordinarily amounts to 2.5 to 3.0 g per day, and the ratio K:Na is generally about 3:5. During fasting, however, because of lack of NaCl intake and the release of much more K^+ than Na^+ in the catabolism of tissues, more potassium than sodium is excreted in the urine.

The urinary excretion of potassium relative to sodium is increased in acute febrile conditions involving tissue destruction and, like sodium excretion, is increased in acidosis. In Addison's disease with adrenal cortical deficiency, the excretion of sodium is increased and of potassium decreased.

Calcium and magnesium. Ordinarily the greater proportions of calcium and magnesium are excreted in the feces. Generally, the urinary excretion of calcium lies between 0.1 and 0.3 and of magnesium between 0.1 and 0.2 g per day.

As indicated above in the discussion of phosphates, increased alkalinity of intestinal contents causes precipitation of increased amounts of insoluble calcium and magnesium phosphates which are lost in the feces, with less of these elements being absorbed into the blood and excreted in the urine. Conversely, increased acidity of the intestinal contents causes more calcium and magnesium to be absorbed and excreted in the urine.

The urinary excretion of both calcium and magnesium normally is primarily dependent upon the nature of the diet.

It is of some interest that while the excretion of calcium in osteomalacia is increased as the result of bone decalcification, the excretion of magnesium may be decreased. The injection of $MgSO_4$ or citrate^{3-} into rats has been found to increase by several times the urinary calcium excretion, presumably due to mobilization from bones (13).

The excretion of these elements is considered in Chapter 29.

URINARY SEDIMENTS

Urinary sediments are obtained by centrifuging the urine or permitting it to stand. These precipitates ordinarily are composed of so-called organized and unorganized sediments.

Organized sediments may contain erythrocytes, epithelial cells, pus cells, bacteria, animal parasites, spermatozoa, urethral filaments, tissue debris, and contaminating foreign substances.

The organized sediments of urine are examined microscopically in the clinical laboratory as an aid to the diagnosis of various urinary tract diseases.

The most common unorganized sediments contain calcium oxalate and phosphate, magnesium ammonium phosphate (triple phosphate), uric acid, and ammonium and sodium urates. Less common constituents are calcium sulfate and carbonate, magnesium phosphate, amino acids (cystine, leucine, and tyrosine), xanthine, melanin, bilirubin, indigo, and hippuric acid. These substances separate from urine under conditions in which their solubilities in urine are exceeded.

Calcium phosphate separates from urines more alkaline than pH 6, and calcium oxalate from urines of any pH. Ammonium magnesium phosphate, ammonium urate, and calcium carbonate separate from urines made both alkaline and ammoniacal by "ammoniacal fermentation" due to bacterial action.

Uric acid and sodium acid urate separate from the more acid urines.

Urinary calculi, concretions found pathologically, generally in the kidney and bladder, are of much medical importance. They are of simple and compound forms, the former being composed of a single compound and the latter of two or more substances. Calculi generally consist of a central nucleus surrounded by a succession of concentric layers, which often but not always represent different components.

Urinary calculi often appear secondary to urinary tract infections. Clumps of pus and epithelial cells and bacteria may serve as foreign body nuclei upon which calcium phosphate and magnesium ammonium phosphate precipitate due to the alkaline ammoniacal medium caused by bacterial decomposition of urea.

The majority of stones arise over long periods of time in the absence of infection and are composed of a number of substances, generally with one predominating.

Calculi are generally classified according to their principal constituent. The most common types in man are uric acid and urate calculi, phosphatic calculi, and calcium oxalate calculi. Calcium carbonate calculi are frequently found in herbivorous animals, but very rarely in man. Cystine calculi occur rarely, generally making up less than 1 per cent of calculi. Xanthine calculi are more rare than those of cystine. Indigo and cholesterol calculi are extremely rare, as are urostealith calculi, which are composed principally of fat and fatty acids. Fibrin calculi may be formed by blood coagulation in the urinary tract. A comprehensive discussion of urinary sediments and calculi may be found in Lippman's *Urine and Urinary Sediments* (Charles C Thomas, publisher, Springfield, Ill., 1952). Also, see *Practical Physiological Chemistry* by Hawk, Oser, and Summerson, 13th ed., p. 854. (McGraw-Hill Book Co., Inc., New York, 1954.)

GENERAL REFERENCES

Cantarow, A., and Trumper, M.: *Clinical Biochemistry*, 5th ed. W. B. Saunders Co.,
Philadelphia, 1955.

Hawk, P. B.; Oser, B. L.; and Summerson, W. H.·*Practical Physiological Chemistry*,
13th ed. McGraw-Hill Book Co., Inc., New York, 1954.

Peters, J. P., and Van Slyke, D. D.: *Quantitative Clinical Chemistry*, Vol I, Interpretations. Williams & Wilkins Co., Baltimore, 1931.

Sunderman, F. W., and Boerner, F.: *Normal Values in Clinical Medicine*. W. B. Saunders
Co., Philadelphia, 1949.

SPECIAL REFERENCES

1. Buchanan, O. H.; Block, W. D.; and Christman, A. A.: *J. Biol. Chem.*, 157, 181, 1945.
   Schaffer, N. K.: *J. Biol. Chem.*, 153, 163, 1944.
2. Weissmann, B.; Bromberg, P. A.; and Gutman, A. B.: *J. Biol. Chem.*, 224, 407, 423,
   1957.
3. Shaffer, P. A.: *Am. J. Physiol.*, 23, 1, 1908–09.
4. Albanese, A. A., and Wangerin, D. M.: *Science*, 100, 58, 1944.
5. Wilder, V. M., and Morgulis, S.: *Arch. Biochem. Biophys.*, 42, 69, 1952.
6. Greenwald, I.: *J. Biol. Chem.*, 77, 539, 1928.
7. Sullivan, M. X., and Irreverre, F.: *J. Biol. Chem.*, 233, 530, 1958.
8. Woodson, H. W.; Hier, S. W.; Solomon, J. D.; and Bergeim, O.: *J. Biol. Chem.*,
   172, 613, 1948.
9. Armstrong, M. D.; Wall, P. E.; and Parker, V. J.: *J. Biol. Chem.*, 218, 921, 1956.
   Armstrong, M. D., and Shaw, K. N. F.: *ibid*, 225, 269, 1957.
10. Futterman, S., and Roe, J. H.: *J. Biol. Chem.*, 215, 257, 1955.
11. Touster, O.; Hutcheson, R. M.; and Rice, L.: *J. Biol. Chem.*, 215, 677, 1955.
12. Peters, J. P., and Van Slyke, D. D.: *Quantitative Clinical Chemistry*, Vol. I, Inter-
    pretations. Williams & Wilkins Co., Baltimore, 1931.
13. Clark, I., and Geoffroy, R.: *J. Biol. Chem.*, 233, 203, 1958.

34

The hormones

GENERAL CONSIDERATIONS

The hormones are substances secreted by specific tissues. They travel by way of the blood stream to remote organs or structures and there exert control over various body processes. Although ductless glands usually are designated as the principal source of hormones, other tissues such as the gut are known to be associated with hormone production. In the field of plant biochemistry, hormone-like substances are elaborated by nonglandular tissues. Because the hormones act at sites distant to their origin, their function may be likened to that of chemical messengers. Since only minute amounts are usually secreted at any one time, the profound physiologic changes elicited indicate the great potency of the hormones. Because of this high degree of activity, the hormones are considered to act catalytically in helping control various chemical reactions concerned with the maintenance and operation of the body.

The field of endocrinology, the study of hormonal phenomena, is rapidly expanding, and at present difficulty is encountered in the definition of hormone origin and function. Selye (1) has presented a thorough discussion of definitions and generalizations on the nature of hormone action.

Difficulty is occasionally encountered in differentiating hormone action from the action of vitamins. As pointed out above, the hormones are formed within the body and there exert their effects. Vitamins to a large extent are supplied in the diet. For many of the vitamins, moreover, a direct metabolic role has been assigned. Their participation in specific enzyme systems has been established. In addition, these enzyme systems are generally widespread throughout the body. The as yet unknown specific roles of most of the hormones, together with the fact that often specific tissues are regulated, further differentiate hormones and vitamins.

In some phases of biochemistry the student is concerned only with one particular family or group of compounds, such as carbohydrates, fats, or proteins. The chemistry of the hormones, however, knows no such close confines, for the hormones belong to various types of organic compounds. As pointed out by Li (2), the hormones can be grouped according to their chemical similarities as: (a) phenol derivatives—adrenaline, noradrenaline, thyroxine; (b) proteins—insulin, anterior pituitary hormones, human chorionic gonadotropin, pregnant mare serum gonadotropin, thyroglobulin, and secretin; (c) peptides—corticotropin (ACTH), vasopressin, and ocytocin; (d) steroids—estrogens, androgens, progesterone, and adrenal corticoids. The hormones then are studied as a group, not because of chemical similarities, but because of their related physiologic role of regulation and coordination of vital processes.

In the following sections, reference will often be made to review articles and books rather than to the original reference. This practice has been necessary because of the extensive bibliography available for each of the hormones. In the case of most hormones, entire books have been written on one or more phases of the biochemistry, physiology, and endocrinology of the hormone.

Details of the effects of the hormones upon metabolic processes will be found in the chapters on metabolism, where these effects can be presented in the light of the metabolic sequences involved.

METHODS OF STUDY OF HORMONE FUNCTION

Since, with few exceptions, a single isolated tissue is responsible for the synthesis of any particular hormone, one of the oldest and most important proofs of hormone function is obtained through removal of the gland or tissue suspected of secreting a hormone. For many years surgical removal of the gland was the only method available to deprive the animal of its source of hormone. Within recent years, with the advent of thiourea and thiouracil derivatives, it has been possible to inhibit the production of the thyroid hormone. Alloxan also has been of great utility in destroying pancreatic tissue responsible for the elaboration of insulin. After the surgical or chemical ablation of a gland, the deficiency symptoms that result furnish strong evidence for the role of the substances secreted by the gland.

Chemical fractionation of tissue suspected of secreting hormones often yields pure or semipure material with hormonal activity. Such material can be administered to the deficient animal described above. Alleviation of the deficiency symptoms offers strong proof for the presence of an active principle. In addition, such extracts may be given to the normal animal and the effects observed. Since most endocrine glands contain only small amounts of hormone at any one time, the chemical fractionation of such tissue is generally laborious and time-consuming.

A number of additional techniques have been used in hormone studies. At times it is possible to demonstrate the presence of hormones in venous blood coming from the endocrine organ. This technique is particularly useful when it is possible to stimulate the gland and effect an increase in the circulating hormone. Transplantation of endocrine tissue within the body and explantation of such tissue to culture or perfusion assemblies *in vitro* are useful procedures. Surgical establishment of a cross circulation between two animals (parabiosis), one of which is deficient in hormone, has been used particularly in studies of gonad function.

The final proof of the presence of a hormone in a particular tissue is the isolation of the hormone in pure form. The pure product must be able to replace or relieve the symptoms of hormone deficiency. Since a number of the hormones are proteins, it has been most difficult to obtain unequivocal proof of their chemical purity. The goal of all such hormone chemistry is the eventual chemical synthesis of the hormone that has been isolated. This has been accomplished in a number of instances.

Biologic evaluation of hormonal potency is of much importance. It is beyond the scope of this discussion to give the technical details necessary for the successful use of bioassay methods, but in general, the quantitative administration of graded amounts of hormone to test animals or tissues should produce specific effects which can be quantitatively graded.

THE PITUITARY GLAND

The pituitary gland (hypophysis) is enclosed in the hypophyseal fossa and is attached to the base of the brain by a thin stalk emerging from the tuber cinereum. In the adult human the gland weighs about 0.5 to 0.6 g, being somewhat larger in the female than in the male. The gland may be roughly divided into three functional units: the anterior, intermediate, and posterior lobes.

The remoteness of location and the small size of the gland early led to much erroneous speculation as to its physiologic function. It was not until the early 1900's that this structure's true function as an endocrine organ became apparent, and it was not until 1940 that a pure hormone was finally isolated from the gland.

All the recognized hormones of the pituitary are proteins. Because of the great difficulties associated with the fractionation and purification of proteins, and also because of the small size of the gland and its low hormone content, our knowledge of the chemistry of the pituitary hormones has developed slowly.

In spite of the brilliant and intensive work on the role of the pituitary, the number of hormones actually synthesized by the gland still is unknown. All biologically active preparations available for study have been made from extracts of the gland. Since the protein hormones isolated from these extracts were being synthesized by the gland at the time of its removal, it has been suggested that the various fractions so identified are in reality only fragments of some larger or master hormone, or that the isolated material may in reality be an active precursor of some other final hormone. Evans (3) suggests that the isolation of the hormones from the blood stream will clarify the problem of the identity of the true hormones of the pituitary gland.

Although the chemistry of these hormones remains to be clarified, considerable information is available with respect to the physiologic functions of the pituitary fractions.

Table 34.1 lists the various hormones considered to have been isolated from the pituitary with the synonyms commonly found in the literature.

Table 34.1.   Pituitary Hormones

Name	Synonyms	Source
Follicle-stimulating hormone (FSH)	Follicle stimulator Thylakentrin	Largely basophil cells of anterior pituitary
Interstitial cell-stimulating hormone (ICSH)	Luteinizing (LH) Metakentrin	Largely basophil cells of anterior pituitary
Prolactin	Luteotropin Lactogenic Mammotropin Luteotropic hormone Galactin	Largely basophil cells of anterior pituitary
Adrenocorticotropic hormone (ACTH)	Corticotropic Adrenotropin Corticotropin Adrenotropic hormone	Largely basophil cells of anterior pituitary
Thyroid-stimulating hormone (TSH)	Thyrotropin Thyreotropic hormone Thyrotropic	Anterior lobe
Growth hormone	Somatotropin Somatotropic	Anterior lobe, eosinophil cells
(See Selye for a list of 25 poorly defined but potentially important other factors thought to be elaborated by the anterior pituitary)		
Melanocyte-stimulating hormone (MSH)	Melanotropin Chromatophorotropic hormone Intermedin	Intermediate lobe
Vasopressin	Pitressin Vasopressor principle Antidiuretic principle	Posterior pituitary
Oxytocin	Pitocin Oxytocic hormone	Posterior pituitary

HORMONES OF THE ANTERIOR LOBE (ADENOHYPOPHYSIS)

Six hormones have been isolated from the anterior lobe of the pituitary. Four of these—the lactogenic or luteotropic, interstitial cell-stimulating (ICSH), adrenocorticotropic (ACTH), and growth hormones—have been purified sufficiently to be considered pure. The follicle-stimulating (FSH) and thyrotropic (TSH) hormones, although highly purified, are not considered to be entirely homogeneous.

These six hormones can be classified into two groups (3): the gonadotropic hormones (follicle-stimulating, interstitial cell-stimulating, and luteotropic or lactogenic hormones) and the so-called metabolic hormones (adrenocorticotropic, thyrotropic, and growth hormones). These protein hormones also may be divided into two chemical groups, since the adrenocorticotropic, luteotropic, and growth hormones are simple proteins, while the thyrotropic, follicle-stimulating, and interstitial cell-stimulating, or luteinizing hormones are glycoproteins.

The anterior pituitary hormones are obtained by complex extraction and differential salt and isoelectric precipitation procedures, the details of which are specific for each hormone.

The somatotropic or growth hormone. The growth hormone (4) has been shown to be a simple protein containing 15.6 per cent nitrogen. The protein has a molecular weight of around 47,000 and an isoelectric point at pH 6.85. On the basis of analysis for specific amino acids, as well as C, H, N, and S determinations, it has been estimated that the hormone contains some 396 amino acid residues, 15 amino acids accounting for 82 per cent of the protein N. The amount of each amino acid is within the normal range for other protein hormones (5).

It has been suggested (4) that the growth hormone has a branched polypeptide chain (Y-shaped) having phenylalanine and alanine as the two N-terminal residues and only one C-terminal residue, phenylalanine.

Studies on the effect of heat and enzymes upon the hormone indicate (3) that biologic activity resides in the protein molecule as such. The hormone is more stable in alkali than in acid and is stable up to 60° C.

Of prime consideration in evaluating the biologic effects of this hormone upon growth is the fact that the hormone will support growth in hypophysectomized animals. Daily dosage, however, is required for normal growth in such animals. Normal rats, having reached a plateau of growth development, can be caused to resume growth under the influence of repeated injections of this hormone to produce giant animals (3). Hypophysectomized animals are more sensitive than normal animals to the hormone and are more useful for assay purposes.

One phase of growth that is particularly affected by the specific action of the hormone is the growth of the epiphyseal cartilages of the long bones of hypophysectomized animals. This particular response has been utilized by Evans and coworkers (5) as a method of bioassay and has been shown to be sensitive and specific to growth hormone activity.

It is extremely difficult to evaluate the physiologic role of the growth hormone. Hypophysectomy of young rats causes a great decrease in growth rate. In addition, many metabolic functions are seriously deranged. Administration of growth hormone restores the growth rate and alleviates some of the metabolic symptoms. The removal of the entire pituitary, however, with concomitant loss of effect of the other pituitary hormones, makes it difficult to assign a specific role to the growth hormone. Attempted stimulation of intact animals by single hormonal principles has proved of value in this connection.

The increase in total body substance associated with growth necessarily involves an accumulation of protein. It was early found (6) that growth hormone-rich fractions cause a lowering of blood nonprotein nitrogenous substances in experimental animals. This effect on blood NPN was correlated (7) with a decrease in urinary nitrogen. It was later shown that the growth hormone acts to bring about protein anabolism. Li and Evans (7) summarize these effects as follows. The growth hormone causes: (a) nitrogen retention, (b) lowering of blood amino acids, (c) an increase of protein content and a decrease of fat content in the carcass, (d) an increase in alkaline phosphatase and inorganic P, (e) enlargement of the liver and thymus, and (f) a slight increase in the ribonucleic acid content of the liver.

Growth hormone exhibits marked species specificity. It is necessary to use human or monkey growth hormone to demonstrate typical metabolic changes in man. Although both monkey and human growth hormone produce metabolic signs of growth in man, these two preparations are chemically different.

Continued studies (8,9) have failed to reveal the exact role of the growth hormone on nitrogen metabolism. Many of these studies have centered around the calculation of the rates of protein synthesis and breakdown and the "turnover" of amino acids through the several amino acid pools. The relationship of these processes may be visualized as:

$$\text{Body proteins} \rightleftharpoons \text{Amino Acids} \longrightarrow \text{Urinary nitrogen}$$
$$\uparrow$$
$$\text{Diet}$$

Each of the arrows indicates a pathway of nitrogen metabolism for which there may be calculated a reaction rate, K. Each of the substances—i.e., body protein, amino acids, etc.—represents a compartment or "pool." The determination of reaction rates and the size and/or homogeneity of the compartments or pools has been difficult. There is now general agreement (8) that the growth hormone does increase protein synthesis and decrease urea formation, but the determination of the mechanism of this effect is not final.

Pituitary preparations long have been known to affect carbohydrate metabolism. Much of this work has been done with fractions rich in growth hormone, but the actual contribution of the growth hormone as such to the observed effects is uncertain. Marx and Evans (10) have summarized 13 known effects of the pituitary as a whole upon carbohydrate metabolism. In general, pituitary extracts have a diabetogenic effect in both normal and operated animals. The growth hormone may be at least partly responsible for the diabetogenic properties of such extracts. Li and Harris (11) state that the glycotropic, pancreatropic, glycostatic, diabetogenic, and ketogenic effects of pituitary preparations can all be largely explained by intrinsic properties of the growth hormone.

It has been shown (8) that the growth hormone increases the output of glucose by the liver and the uptake of glucose by the tissues. The plasma insulin activity is also increased, and the diabetes that results from growth hormone treatment may be due to the increased output of insulin and subsequent exhaustion of the beta cells of the pancreas. The effects of the growth hormone upon fat metabolism appear to be mediated through the adrenocortical and thyroid hormones (8), an early effect of the administration of the hormone being a mobilization of carcass fat to the liver followed by an increased fat breakdown and increased production of ketone bodies. The relation of the pituitary to the hexokinase reaction, as described in Chapter 24, may explain to a large extent the findings of disturbed carbohydrate metabolism in animals injected with pituitary extracts.

Thyrotropic hormone (TSH). Although the thyrotropic or thyroid stimulating hormone has been studied extensively, pure preparations have not as yet been made. Although most TSH preparations still contain demonstrable amounts of other pituitary hormones (3,12), one of the purest preparations to date (4) appears to contain only ICSH as contaminant.

The hormone may have a molecular weight of about 10,000 (13), but proteolytic degradation of the hormone reveals that activity is not destroyed even though the hormone becomes dialyzable. The hormone may be a mucoprotein. N-terminal amino acid study has been inconclusive, the carbohydrate moiety perhaps being attached to the terminal amino acid(s) (13).

The physiologic effects of the hormone can be studied either by its direct effect upon the thyroid gland or by the secondary effects of thyroid gland stimulation such as increased rate of metabolism. The direct methods have as their criteria: alterations in the histologic appearance of the thyroid gland, changes in the iodine content of the gland, and increases in its weight (12).

Considerable variation is seen in the response of various animals to TSH stimulation, the chicken and guinea pig being the most sensitive. The frog, rat, and dog are much more resistant to the hormone, man being intermediate between these groups (14,15). It is of interest that those animals showing the greatest sensitivity to TSH have the lowest content of TSH in their own pituitaries. Conversely, animals more refractory to TSH have the highest content of TSH in their pituitaries.

TSH effects on the thyroid gland are multiple in nature. The first effect may be to cause the thyroid to discharge its hormone into the circulation (16). As thyroid iodine values fall, there are increases in thyroid acinar cell height, thyroid weight, and finally in the capacity of the thyroid to concentrate iodine. Just which of these responses are primary and which are compensatory is not certain.

Although the mechanism of TSH stimulation is imperfectly understood, some evidence indicates that the hormone is inactivated by the thyroid as the gland is stimulated. It has been suggested that the loss of physiologic TSH activity that occurs during stimulation is due to oxidation since experiments have shown that reducing agents may potentiate the effects of TSH (16).

A dynamic balance may exist between the secretion of TSH by the hypophysis and the secretion of its hormone by the thyroid. Thyroidectomy is thought to cause an increase of TSH as may goiterogenic drugs such as thiourea and thiouracil. On the other hand, administration of exogenous thyroxine may cause decreased secretion of TSH. That the physiologic control of this balance is more complex than suggested above is clear from much reported work (14).

Prolactin, lactogenic or luteotropic hormone (luteotropin). The luteotropic hormone of the anterior pituitary was the first hormone of this gland to be isolated in a pure form, Lyons, White, Li, Evans, and others (3,17) being the principal investigators. The hormone is a protein, having limited solubility in water, an isoelectric pH of 5.5, and a molecular weight around 30,000. Prolactin does not contain carbohydrate (2,4) or phosphorus, and the nitrogen content (15.86 per cent) can be accounted for by the amino acid content. Sheep and beef pituitary glands are the best source of the hormone. Preparations from sheep glands have solubility characteristics and a tyrosine content different from those of beef glands. Although the activity of the hormone may be destroyed by heat, it is unique in withstanding a temperature of 100° C for short periods when in solutions at pH values of 1 to 8. Amino acid analysis of a homogenous prolactin preparation has been reported by Li (2,18) and reveals the amino acid composition to be: Thr Pro Val Thr Pro Arg_{10} Asp_{22} CyS_3 Glu_{18} Gly_{12} His_7 (Ileu and Leu)$_{35}$ Lys_{10} Met_7 Phe_9 Pro_{12} Ser_{18} Thr_9 Tyr_7 Try_2 $(—NH_2)_2$ Val_{11}.

In each of the three major phases of lactation—(a) development of the mammary gland, (b) secretion of milk, and (c) evacuation of the gland— hormones play major roles (19). Since many of the hormones of the body affect some phase of the lactation phenomenon, the subject of lactation is a complex one. Development of the mammary gland, which is essentially a growth process, is influenced by a number of pituitary factors, but prolactin plays an important role in the process.

The hormone is effective in stimulating lactation, but only after complete morphologic development of the mammary gland by the combined effects of the ovarian hormones. The ovarian hormones, in preparing the gland for lactation, also inhibit maximal production of luteotropin by the pituitary. Release of the pituitary, at parturition, from a high concentration of ovarian hormones associated with the pregnant state allows pituitary formation of luteotropin with consequent mammary gland stimulation (20). The immature or male breast, if first suitably treated with ovarian hormones, may be caused to lactate after luteotropin administration. The crop gland of the pigeon or dove is particularly sensitive to luteotropin, its weight increase serving for the convenient bioassay of the hormone.

The presence of mammogens I and II, duct growth and lobule-alveolar growth factors in the pituitary, has been postulated by Turner (21) and others. These factors are thought to be lipid-soluble hormones that influence mammary gland development and function. Present evidence does not support the necessity for these additional lactogenic factors.

Prolactin plays an important role in stimulating progesterone formation by corpora lutea. The following section discusses the relation of this hormone to primary and secondary sex function.

Follicle-stimulating (FSH) and interstitial cell-stimulating (ICSH) hormones. Removal of the pituitary gland before maturity causes a cessation of sexual development (22). In the mature animal, following hypophysectomy, the gonads and the reproductive system atrophy. Softening and a decrease in size of the testes may be seen as early as four or five days after the surgery. The ovaries also atrophy and degenerative changes are seen in the follicles. Primordial follicles may show some growth but develop only to the stage of beginning antrum formation. Hypophysectomy during pregnancy has a variable effect in different animals (23). In dogs, cats, and rabbits abortion is induced, while in mice, rats, and guinea pigs, if the operation is performed in the second half of gestation, a prolonged gestation period may result. Lactation usually abruptly ceases following hypophysectomy.

The early work of Smith, and Zondek and Aschheim (23), indicated that these sex functions are controlled by secretions of the pituitary. Fevold, Hisaw, and Leonard (24) first showed the multiple nature of the secretion and separated pituitary extracts into a follicle-stimulating fraction (FSH) and a luteinizing fraction (LH). The follicle-stimulating material was shown to cause spermatogenic activity in the testes, and the luteinizing fraction to cause Leydig cell development and function with production of the male hormone testosterone. This latter fraction is usually called "interstitial cell-stimulating hormone" (ICSH), but it is the same as luteinizing hormone (LH).

At the present time, it is possible to replace all gonadotropic function of the pituitary by purified preparations of FSH, ICSH, and luteotropin, although some claim is still made for the concept of a single hormonal control of these functions (3).

Highly purified FSH preparations have been made, the hormone apparently being a glucoprotein with a molecular weight of 67,000 and an isoelectric point at pH 4.5. It contains some 2 to 5 per cent hexose represented by mannose and glucose, and 1 to 2 per cent hexoseamine. The activity of purified FSH can be destroyed by certain amylase preparations, by heat, and by trypsin. Digestion at pH 4.0 with pepsin (11) to the extent of 65 per cent yields a dialyzable fraction that contains the follicle-stimulating potency. Pancreatin digested FSH preparations have activities about ten times as great as previous undigested preparations (18). FSH is the only pituitary hormone that is soluble in 50 per cent ammonium sulfate, most isolation procedures depending upon this fact.

Several laboratories have prepared pure ICSH from both sheep and swine pituitaries. In contrast to other hormone preparations from different animals, sheep and swine ICSH appear to be grossly different substances. Sheep ICSH has a molecular weight of 40,000 and an isoelectric pH of 4.6, while swine ICSH has a molecular weight of 100,000 and an isoelectric pH of 7.45. In addition to containing different amounts of mannose and hexoseamine, the proteins have been shown to be immunologically different. Although these two hormones are truly interstitial-stimulating hormones they differ somewhat in biologic potency as indicated by a variety of assay methods (2,3).

Relation of FSH, ICSH, and prolactin to reproductive physiology. Development of ovarian follicles to the antrum stage and to functional macroscopic follicles is due to ovarian stimulation by FSH. Early preparations of this hormone were able to cause complete follicular development and ovulation, but it is now known that contamination of FSH with ICSH activity was responsible for this effect. When the follicle has reached macroscopic size, increasing amounts of ICSH cause further development to a secretory state, and the follicle puts out estrogens. Finally, under the synergistic effect of FSH and ICSH the follicle ruptures, and the ovum is discharged. In the final stages of follicular development FSH effects become minimal. After ovulation, the predominant hormone, ICSH, now causes the development of corpora lutea. As with the FSH effects noted above, it was once held that ICSH alone is responsible for the development of secreting corpora lutea. The third gonadotropin, prolactin, is now known to be responsible for luteal development. ICSH, with the aid of prolactin, causes the corpora lutea to secrete progesterone. If fertilization does not occur, atrophy of the corpora lutea takes place. If fertilization occurs, continued prolactin action causes increased production of progesterone, which is essential for early placental and fetal development.

These effects have been summarized by Fevold (24) as follows:

(1)   Nonantra-containing follicles + FSH ———→ macroscopic follicles
(2)   Macroscopic follicles + FSH + ICSH ———→ secreting follicles (estrogen)
(3)   Secreting follicles + FSH + ICSH ———→ preovulatory swelling and ovulation
(4)   Mature follicles + ICSH ———→ corpora lutea
(5)   Corpora lutea + prolactin ———→ secreting corpora lutea (progesterone)

It early was noted that the injection of estrogenic hormones lowers the over-all gonadotropic effect of the pituitary. Conversely, in the absence of the ovary or its secretions, gonadotropic secretion of the pituitary is increased. It became obvious that a dynamic balance or interplay of hormones is responsible for the cyclic nature of female sex phenomena. As will be shown in a later section, uterine and mammary gland development and other sex characteristics are under the influence of the ovarian hormones. The interplay of ovarian and pituitary hormones, then, is responsible for the cyclic or rhythmic uterine development in the human menstrual cycle. The effects of the ovarian hormones on the pituitary may be summarized as follows:

(1)   Anterior pituitary + increasing estrogen ———→ increasing ICSH and prolactin + decreasing FSH
(2)   Anterior pituitary + decreasing estrogen ———→ decreasing ICSH + increasing FSH
(3)   Anterior pituitary + progesterone ———→ decreasing ICSH

The pituitary gonadotropins have equally important functions in male and female physiology. Hypophysectomy of the male animal causes a varied response, depending upon the nature of the breeding cycle, etc. In general the testes become flabby, the seminiferous tubules undergo regressive changes, germ cell maturation does not occur, and accessory reproductive organs undergo atrophy (24). FSH is responsible for stimulation of the tubules to spermatogenic activity although it may be that FSH action is necessary only after the germ cells have reached the spermatogonium stage. Secretion of the male hormone by the interstitial elements of the testes is due largely to stimulation by the gonadotropin, ICSH. That testosterone, the hormone of the testes, may exert control over pituitary gonadotropins is indicated by decreased urinary gonadotropins (25) when large doses of testosterone are injected into normal males. Heller and Nelson (25) have discussed the possibility of testicular inactivation of hypophyseal gonadotropins. They state that, within physiologic limits, testosterone has little effect upon pituitary elaboration of gonadotropins.

Since the adrenal cortex and possibly the testes and ovaries may liberate both male and female sex hormones, and these may in turn influence pituitary secretions, the sex hormone relations of the body are exceedingly complex, and much work is yet required for clarification.

Gonadotropic activity of human pregnancy urine was discovered by Aschheim and Zondek in 1927. Since that time human blood and urine and pregnant mare serum have been found to contain gonadotropins differing from FSH, ICSH, and luteotropin. Levin (26) has reviewed the physiology of these substances, and Li (27) has presented the chemistry of several of these hormone-like materials.

Pregnant mare serum gonadotropin (PMSG or PMS) is a glycoprotein with an isoelectric point at pH 2.60 to 2.65. Biologically PMSG behaves in the rat like a mixture of FSH and ICSH, but it is claimed that a single gonadotropin is responsible for this action.

Human chorionic gonadotropin (HCG) appears in the urine of pregnancy as early as two to four weeks after fertilization of the ovum and reaches a maximum 40 to 50 days later, after which time it falls to lower levels. This hormone-like material causes little or no follicular growth but acts chiefly upon the theca tissue inducing a few enlarged corpora lutea. As Levin (26) points out, little is known as to the function of nonhypophyseal gonadotropins in normal physiology, but determination of relative gonadotropin excess is of great value in the diagnosis of pregnancy.

Adrenocorticotropic hormone, corticotropin (ACTH). Smith (22) first observed a direct relation between the pituitary and the adrenal cortex, hypophysectomy causing atrophy of the cortex but not of the medulla. Injection of pituitary extracts causes hyperplasia of all three cell layers of the cortex.

As late as 1952, ACTH was considered to be a protein hormone with a molecular weight of around 20,000. Intensive investigations by a large number of workers reveals that the principal biologic activity resides in a polypeptide structure with a molecular weight of about one-fourth of the above figure. Polypeptides have been isolated from both sheep and pig pituitary glands, the sheep preparation (α-corticotropin) having a molecular weight, calculated from analytical data, of 4541 and an isoelectric point at pH 6.6 (12 mg of α-corticotropin may be isolated from 1 kg of sheep pituitary glands). Corticotropin-A has been prepared from pig pituitary tissue by several research groups, and the analytical data from these groups for the hormone differ. Lee (28) has reviewed the problems of terminology and of structural comparisons. Until the problem of ultimate structure is solved, the term "corticotropin" and the abbreviation ACTH may be used to describe the group of preparations now possessing a variety of special names.

α-Corticotropin and the corticotropin-A isolated by the group at Armour (28) appear to contain 39 amino acids, with serine as the N terminal residue and phenylalanine as the C terminal residue. The complete amino acid sequences for the hormones have been established. α-Corticotropin appears to contain one more serine than corticotropin-A, and the latter contains one more leucine than the former. Although these hormones with 39 amino acid residues appear to be pure, further enzymic and acid hydrolysis appears capable of splitting off amino acid residues, permitting the isolation of biologically active fragments. Further work will likely resolve the minimum molecular structures required for full activity, and perhaps also the nature of the structure that causes the biologic effects at specific tissue sites.

Biological functions of ACTH. By both *in vivo* and *in vitro* techniques, it can be shown that ACTH stimulates the secretion of steroid hormones by the adrenal cortex. Heckter and Pincus (29) have shown that a major *in vitro* effect of ACTH is at the stage of conversion of cholesterol to progesterone during corticoid formation. ACTH is also capable of altering the pattern of corticosteroid secretion and of causing growth and development of the adrenal cortex (30). A number of these actions can be related to the problem of protein (enzyme, hormone, tissue) synthesis, and it is possible that effects on protein metabolism may be a major function of ACTH. Within two minutes after the injection of ACTH into hypophysectomized dogs the secretion of 17-hydrocorticosterone has been found to be increased. When ACTH is injected, it rapidly disappears from the circulation. Although the mechanism for the removal of the hormone from the circulation is not known, it has been calculated that the biologic half-life of ACTH in the blood of the adrenalectomized rat is about one minute and the average life of the molecule is 17 minutes. Because of these short times, it is desirable to introduce some delaying agent into injectable preparations of ACTH.

Purified ACTH preparations exhibit melanotropic activity. As described under the section on MSH, this activity may be due to the presence of a certain amino acid sequence, one that is common to ACTH and to MSH.

An interesting relation between ACTH stimulation and the cholesterol and ascorbic acid values of the adrenal cortex has been found (31). Within three hours after the injection of ACTH the cholesterol content of the adrenal drops to 50 per cent of its initial value. Ascorbic acid values fall further and more rapidly. These observations have led to the development of assay procedures based upon cholesterol or ascorbic acid decreases. Stresses such as those due to noxious agents, bleeding, and disease agents also cause decreases in cholesterol and ascorbic acid values.

Administration of cortical hormones causes pituitary inhibition. If such hormones are given at the time of stress, no change is seen in adrenal activity. Particularly active in pituitary inhibition are the 17-hydroxy derivatives of corticosterone. A dynamic balance exists between the pituitary and the adrenal cortex similar to that between the ovary and pituitary systems, but the rate of secretion of ACTH appears to be controlled by multiple factors (32). The role of the sympathetic nervous system may be one of direct neurologic stimulation, but a neurohumoral mechanism involving epinephrine is also possible.

The relation of ACTH to the diabetogenic action of the anterior pituitary is discussed in Chapter 24.

Melanocyte-stimulation hormone (MSH). This hormone is also called "melanotropin" and is found in the intermediate lobe of the hypophysis, in the posterior lobe and/or the anterior lobe (2,18), depending upon the species of animals studied. Although earlier studies on the hormone were largely confined to amphibia, the recent isolation of a number of active principles from pig and bovine glands and the demonstration of the biologic activity of the preparation in a number of species, including man, suggest that this hormone plays a role as one of the factors controlling pigmentation (33). β—MSH from pig glands has been shown to be a polypeptide with 18 amino acids. The amino acid sequence Asp. Glu. Gly. Pro. Tyr. Lys. Met. Glu. His. Phe. Arg. Tyr. Gly. Ser. Pro. Pro. Lys. Asp. shows in part a remarkable similarity to a portion of the ACTH structure. The sequence 7 to 13 (18) is identical to that between 4 and 10 in ACTH, this similarity possibly accounting for the MSH activity of ACTH.

β- MSH---Pro. Tyr. Lys.	Met. Glu. His. Phe. Arg. Tyr. Gly.	Ser.---
4　5　6	7　8　9　10　11　12　13	14

ACTH　　Ser. Tyr. Ser.	Met. Glu. His. Phe. Arg. Tyr. Gly.	Lys.---
1　2　3	4　5　6　7　8　9　10	11

Lerner and his collaborators (33) have isolated α-MSH hormone from pituitary tissue, but the structural characterization of this hormone is not yet complete (34).

HORMONES OF THE POSTERIOR LOBE (NEUROHYPOPHYSIS)

Surgical removal of the posterior lobe without damage to associated tissue is difficult. This fact plus the differences that exist in the anatomic and histologic make-up of the gland from one animal to another make difficult the exact definition of posterior hormone function. Information obtained largely from the injection of preparations of the posterior lobe, reveals that this tissue (35,36,37) causes contraction of the mammalian uterus, diuresis and antidiruesis in mammals, and pressor and other effects such as milk letdown, changes in membrane permeability, avian vaso depression, etc.

A number of active principles have been isolated from posterior lobe extracts, but it is not yet known whether such materials exist in and are singly secreted by the gland or the gland secretes a master hormone having multiple functions. Although a protein preparation having a molecular weight of some 30,000, and possessing multiple hormonal properties has been isolated (35,36,37), clear-cut evidence for the physiologic role of this preparation is not available.

Much of the biologic activity of crude gland preparations can be duplicated by two octapeptides, oxytocin and vasopressin. Injection of the vasopressor material causes an immediate, sharp rise in blood pressure due to constriction of the peripheral vessels; larger doses may cause a slowing of the heart rate due to constriction of the coronary artery.

Posterior lobe extracts, as well as vasopressin preparations, have a profound effect upon salt and water balance. Loss of posterior lobe function induces the condition known as diabetes insipidus, characterized by excessive water excretion. Injection of the purest pressor preparations have shown that this hormone has both diuretic and antidiuretic effects (36), the antidiuretic effect being demonstrable only when the urine is dilute, as in the case of diabetes insipidus or after the administration of large amounts of water (36). The diuretic action may be secondarily related to the increased blood pressure caused by the hormone.

The posterior lobe hormone known as the "oxytocic principle" causes marked contraction of smooth muscle, particularly that of the uterus and of certain portions of the gastrointestinal tract. Although the effect of oxytocin on smooth muscle may be modified by many factors (35), the hormone generally causes uterine contractions. Routine obstetrical use is made of this fact in initiating labor, the gravid uterus at or near term being particularly susceptible to such stimulation. The stimulating effect of oxytocin upon the contractions of isolated smooth muscle strips serves as an assay method for the hormone. Crude posterior pituitary preparations as well as purified oxytocin and vasopressin have effects other than those above (18,37,38). Each of the octapeptides, moreover, has some biologic activity usually assigned to the other.

Du Vigneaud and associates have obtained purified preparations of the oxytocic principle. The hormone was shown to be an octapeptide with a molecular weight of about 1000. Complete hydrolysis showed the presence of one equivalent each of leucine, isoleucine, tyrosine, proline, glutamic acid, aspartic acid, glycine, and cystine, as well as three equivalents of ammonia.

Oxytocin has the amino acid composition and sequence:

$$Cy.Tyr.Ileu.Glu. - (NH_2).Asp. - (NH_2).Cy. Pro. Leu. Gly. - (NH_2)$$
$$S-\!\!\!-S$$

and the structure:

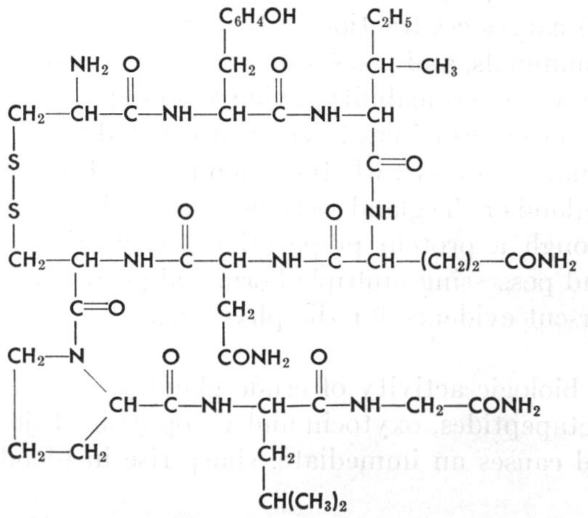

Vasopressin prepared from beef glands has six of the same amino acids, as does oxytocin, and is represented as:

Cy. Tyr. Phe. Glu. - (NH₂).Asp. - (NH₂).Cy. Pro. Arg. Gly. - (NH₂)

S————————————————————S

with the structure:

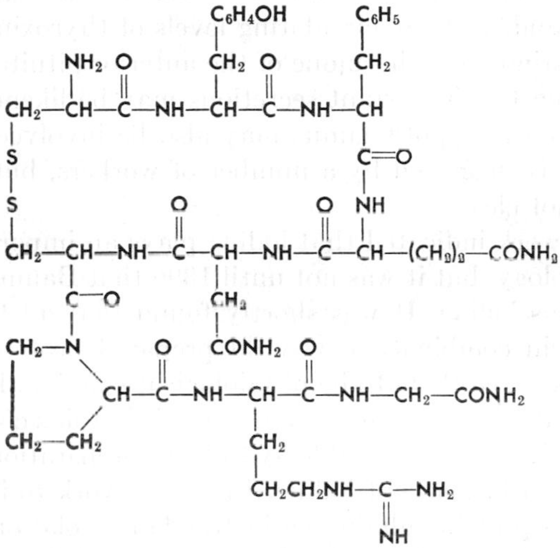

$$
\begin{array}{c}
\quad C_6H_4OH \quad\quad C_6H_5 \\
\quad\quad | \quad\quad\quad\quad | \\
NH_2 \; O \quad CH_2 \; O \quad CH_2 \\
| \quad\quad || \quad\quad | \quad\quad || \quad\quad | \\
CH_2-CH-C-NH-CH-C-NH-CH \\
| \quad\quad\quad\quad\quad\quad\quad\quad | \\
S \quad\quad\quad\quad\quad\quad\quad\quad C=O \\
| \quad\quad\quad\quad\quad\quad\quad\quad | \\
S \quad\quad\quad O \quad\quad\quad O \; NH \\
| \quad\quad\quad || \quad\quad\quad || \; | \\
CH_2-CH-NH-C-CH-NH-C-CH-(CH_2)_3-CONH_2 \\
| \\
C=O \quad\quad\quad CH_2 \\
| \\
CH_2-N \quad\quad O \quad CONH_2 \; O \\
| \quad\quad\quad\quad || \quad\quad\quad\quad || \\
\quad CH-C-NH-CH-C-NH-CH_2-CONH_2 \\
CH_2-CH_2 \quad\quad\quad CH_2 \\
| \\
CH_2CH_2NH-C-NH_2 \\
|| \\
NH
\end{array}
$$

Hog vasopressin has the same structure as beef vasopressin except that lysine replaces arginine.

Of great interest and biochemical importance was the announcement (38,39) of the synthesis of the octapeptides, thus confirming the structures previously suggested.

THE THYROID GLAND

The thyroid gland in the normal adult human generally weighs about 25 g but may vary considerably, depending upon the season, climate, geographical location, age, food, and sex. The gland usually consists of a right and left lobe connected by an isthmus. However, a third lobe is occasionally found as well as accessory thyroid tissue. The gland is even more vascular than the kidney, and it is estimated that some 5 l of blood flow through the thyroid per hour (1).

Histologically (40) the thyroid consists of aggregates of follicles or acini which are lined by a single layer of epithelium, the cells of which are generally medium cuboidal. The lumen of the follicle contains variable amounts of colloid material, depending upon the functional state of the gland. Since the epithelium has no basement membrane, free-floating epithelial cells are often seen in the lumen of the gland. A great deal of work has been done in attempts to associate Golgi bodies, vacuoles, mitochondria, and intracellular lipoid material with the functional activity of the gland.

As will be shown below, the follicular colloid represents the gland's store of hormone. Because of this, the thyroid is unique, for it is the only endocrine gland to store appreciable amounts of hormone.

Thyroid gland activity is controlled, at least in part, by the thyrotropic hormone of the anterior pituitary. Stimulation by the pituitary hormone causes secretory alterations of the cytologic components of the follicular cells. hypertrophy and hyperplasia of the epithelium, vacuolization and resorption of colloid, loss of hormonal iodine, and increases in vascularity and size of the thyroid gland. In turn, circulating levels of thyroxine appear to control the thyroid-stimulating hormone of the anterior pituitary. This balance of control between two important secretions may be likened to a feedback mechanism. That the hypothalamus may also be involved in the thyroid-pituitary system is suggested by a number of workers, but the mechanism of this effect is not clear.

Early clinical work indicated that iodine plays an important role in thyroid gland physiology, but it was not until 1896 that Baumann showed that the gland contains iodine. It was shortly found that all the iodine of the gland is in protein combination. Oswald prepared protein fractions from the thyroid and showed them to be physiologically active. His "iodothyreoglobulin" preparations from human and animal thyroids contained from 0.1 to 0.9 per cent iodine, but by suitable hydrolysis, preparations could be made that contained 7 to 14 per cent iodine. Intensive work to isolate the active component of this protein culminated in Kendall's isolation (41) of thyroxine. Harington and coworkers (42) improved upon Kendall's method of isolation and determined the structure of the compound. The subsequent synthesis of thyroxine (43) confirmed the earlier work. Thyroxine has the following formula:

$$HO - \bigcirc - O - \bigcirc - CH_2 - CHNH_2 - COOH \quad (C_{15}H_{11}O_4NI_4)$$

its complete chemical name being $\beta(3,5$ diiodo-4[3',5' diiodo-4'-hydroxyphenoxy])phenyl-α-aminopropionic acid, the naturally occurring material having the L configuration.

D,L-Thyroxine, as crystallized from aqueous-alcoholic sodium hydroxide by acidification with acetic acid, separates in rosettes and sheaves of colorless microscopic needles. It contains 65 per cent iodine and melts with decomposition at 231 to 232° C. It is rather insoluble in all solvents, but in the form of its salts is slightly soluble in water. The compound is stable toward alkalies but is decomposed by strong acids.

The portions of the thyroxine molecule necessary for biologic activity have been studied with the use of structural analogs (43,44,45). The side chain must be a polar group, such as glycine, propionic acid or acetic acid, but alanine appears to be the most active side group. The —OH group should be free and be in the ortho or para position. 3' and 5' substitution by two halogens, preferably iodine, is required for maximal activity. The diphenyl ether grouping is important, but sulfur may be substituted for oxygen in the ether linkage.

In addition to thyroxine, there have also been isolated from the thyroid gland, 3 monoiodotyrosine, 3:5 diiodotyrosine, 3:5 diiodothyronine, 3:3':5' triiodothyronine, 3:3' diiodothyronine, and 3:5:3' triiodothyronine, (43,46). The structural formula of the 3:5:3' isomer of iodothyronine is:

$$HO - \langle\!\!\!\bigcirc\!\!\!\rangle - O - \langle\!\!\!\bigcirc\!\!\!\rangle - CH_2 - CHNH_2 - COOH$$

3:3:3' Triiodothyronine

The biologic activities of the various compounds isolated from the gland have been compared by a variety of assay methods. In addition, many compounds related to the natural material have been prepared and assayed biologically. Although the activities of the compounds vary depending upon the assay procedure, it is clear that the two compounds possessing the greatest activity (on oxygen consumption) are thyroxine and the 3:5:3' isomer of triiodothyronine. The 3:3':5' isomer and the mono and diiodo derivatives of tyrosine have only slight biological activity (43).

The interrelationship of these compounds has received intensive study, and research progress has been rapid through the use of radioactive iodine together with techniques of chromatography. It was early found that the thyroid gland has a unique ability to remove and concentrate blood iodide. The uptake of tracer iodide is dependent somewhat upon the amount of iodide used in the study and upon the presence of anterior pituitary TSH. The iodide taken up by the gland is held in a bound form, likely one of association with protein. By following the comparative radioactivities of organic iodine compounds it has been possible to describe the time course of the formation of circulating hormone. These studies well illustrate the power of the radio-tracer technique. Taurog and Chaikoff (47) showed that some 26 per cent of the total thyroid iodine is represented by thyroxine iodine. As early as 15 minutes after the injection of radioiodine 95 per cent of the radioactivity was present in organic combination in the thyroid, and of this about 80 per cent was found in the diiodotyrosine fraction and 10 to 15 per cent in the thyroxine fraction. By following similarly injected animals over a period of time, Chaikoff and Taurog (48) found a progressive decrease in the diiodotyrosine fraction and an increase in the thyroxine fraction.

Leblond and Gross (49) found that one hour after the injection of radioiodine, radioautographs indicated the presence of protein-bound iodine in the apex of the follicular epithelial cells, with small amounts in the periphery of the colloid. Twenty-four hours later, similar animal preparations showed a uniform distribution of organically bound radioiodine throughout the colloid material.

The sequence of reactions associated with thyroid function cannot be given in detail but are summarized as follows:

1. Uptake of blood iodide by the thyroid.
2. Storage of this iodide as inorganic iodide.
3. Enzymic oxidation of iodide to iodine.
4. Iodination of protein bound tyrosine to monoiodo- and diiodotyrosine (protein bound).
5. Coupling of the iodotyrosine units to form thyroxine and formation of triiodothyronine through coupling of mono and diiodotyrosine units (or by deiodination of thyroxine).
6. Release of thyroid hormones from thyroglobulin by thyroid protease.
7. Secretion of thyroxine and triiodothyronine into blood.
8. Association of thyroxine and triiodothyronine with blood protein.
9. Distribution to tissues.
10. Metabolism (deiodination) of the hormones.

Thyroid gland secretion and the circulating hormone. It is well established that the active hormones thyroxine and triiodothyronine are bound and stored in the gland as a part of the protein thyroglobulin (43,50, 51,52). The thyroid glands of a number of laboratory animals and of man as well, contain a protease that can liberate (43,53) free hormone from the protein combination. As stated by Pitt-Rivers (43); only thyroxine and tri-iodothyronine are, under normal conditions, secreted into the blood by the gland, and of these two compounds, thyroxine is present to the extent of some 90 per cent of the circulating organic iodine. Thyroxine enters the blood at the rate of some 50 to 200 μg per day and is bound to both albumin and α globulin serum proteins. Blood thyroxine levels are thus commonly determined on protein bound iodine fractions (PBI). It is beyond the scope of this text to discuss the variations in organic bound iodine output or the variations found in the binding of iodo compounds in the blood.

Although the circulating hormone is bound firmly enough to resist disassociation by dialysis and by treatment with trichloroacetic acid, ethanol and butanol do dissolve the hormone and serve as a means of extraction of thyroxine from blood.

Determination of total blood iodine (normal 5-15 μg per cent) is of little value in the diagnosis of hyperthyroidism, but determination of the iodine precipitated with plasma proteins (thyroxine) is of importance in this connection.

Antithyroid compounds. A number of compounds are known which inhibit the formation of thyroxine by the thyroid gland. Astwood (54) groups these as follows: (a) thyroxine, (b) iodine, (c) thiocyanate, (d) antithyroid substances proper.

The effect of thyroxine in inhibiting the gland's response to TSH when both are administered simultaneously remains unexplained. Iodine on the one hand causes additional thyroxine synthesis by an iodine-deficient gland but on the other suppresses this synthesis by a hyperfunctioning gland (54,55). This latter effect is as yet unexplained. Thiocyanate inhibits the accumulation of iodine by the thyroid gland and thus may cause thyroid enlargement (thiocyanate goiter). Under these conditions the thyroid can synthesize little thyroxine. In general, when the supply of iodine to the gland is deficient, compensatory enlargement of the gland occurs in an attempt to relieve the thyroxine deficiency.

The antithyroid substances such as thiourea, thiouracil, and sulfa drugs, and derivatives of these three classes of substances are potent inhibitors of the thyroid gland. These compounds apparently exert their action by inhibiting the synthesis of thyroxine. It has been suggested that this may be due to a blocking of the conversion of iodide to iodine, since it is likely that thyroid iodide must first be converted to iodine, I_2, before it can iodinate tyrosine residues. This step, as well as the coupling of diiodotyrosine molecules to form thyroxine, is an oxidative one. If the above postulate is correct, the antithyroid compounds may act either by removing I_2, or by blocking the oxidative enzyme reactions essential for the formation of I_2 from iodide, $2I^- \xrightarrow{-2e} I_2$ (54).

The thiourea and thiouracil compounds are important in both experimental hormone work and clinical medicine. These substances may be used for the chemical ablation of the thyroid gland, or in smaller quantities, for the suppression of a hyperfunctioning gland:

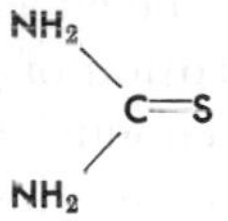

NH₂
\
C=S
/
NH₂
Thiourea

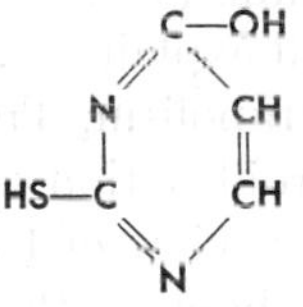

Thiouracil

Physiologic effects of thyroxine. Hypofunction of the thyroid, or thyroidectomy of the young animal, results in cessation of growth, abeyance of reproductive activity, psychic changes, metabolic disturbances, and changes in the hair and skin, because lack of thyroxine leads to hypofunction of all tissues and glandular structures. *In utero* thyroxine deficiency causes cretinism that does not respond well to treatment. If hypothyroidism occurs in early childhood, it is often possible to arrest and relieve the symptoms by adequate thyroid therapy. The cretin is usually a dwarf and an idiot, with clumsy gait and flaccid muscles.

Hypothyroidism in the adult is known as "myxedema." The disease is more prevalent in women than in men and is not an unusual condition. Myxedema is usually insidious, with gradual retardation of physical and mental functions (43,56). The basal metabolic rate (rate of energy production) is lowered, the skin becomes dry and thick, the face appears puffed, the eyelids protrude, the tongue is enlarged, speech becomes slurred, the voice may be husky, hair and teeth are lost, reproductive activity is lessened, and there is general mental deterioration. Because of the great reduction in energy production, the body temperature is low, and various metabolic chemical processes are deranged. Such patients generally show high blood cholesterol values. Complete reversal of these gross changes usually may be accomplished by suitable therapy with thyroid preparations.

Simple or endemic goiter is a condition of thyroid enlargement usually associated with lack of iodine. The high incidence of goiter in geographical areas known to be deficient in dietary iodine has led to the prophylactic and therapeutic use of iodine with favorable results.

Toxic goiter, whether diffuse (Graves' disease) or nodular (toxic adenoma) in which the gland is hyperactive, results in clinical manifestations of hyperthyroidism. Such patients usually show increased basal metabolic rate, tachycardia (fast heart rate), exophthalmos, tremor, loss of weight, dyspnea, and psychoses. The protruding eyeballs of the patient with exophthalmos give the appearance of surprise or terror (58). Iodine therapy, surgery, or treatment with the antithyroid drugs all serve for the relief of this disease.

The metabolic effects of the thyroid hormones have been extensively studied (43,57), but in spite of this, few specific effects of the hormones are known. The effect of the hormones upon tissue oxidation seems to be the single most important effect. The hormones seem to increase oxygen consumption and caloric production by uncoupling oxidative phosphorylation as evidenced by a lowered $P:O$ ratio. Thyroxine and triiodothyronine have about the same activity in changing the $P:O$ ratio. The mechanism of this effect may well be through an alteration in permeability of the mitochondrial membrane (43). A variation in mitochondrial membrane permeability also may well explain a number of the other less specific effects of thyroxine on tissue metabolism. The increased intestinal absorption of glucose attributed to thyroid action may be related to the mitochondrial permeability. For a broad review of the metabolic effects of thyroxine the student is referred to the book of Pitt-Rivers (43).

THE PARATHYROID GLANDS

Although the parathyroid glands are generally considered to secrete a hormone, the chemistry and physiology of this material is poorly understood.

The parathyroid glands, two or four in number, are located along the dorsolateral border of the thyroid gland. The parathyroids have a thin connective tissue capsule with delicate trabeculae penetrating the gland, blood being supplied to the parenchyma through sinusoids (58). Complete removal of the parathyroids is difficult because of accessory parathyroid tissue scattered throughout the neck region and often found within the thymus gland. Total parathyroid tissue in man weighs only 0.1 to 0.2 g.

Ablation of the parathyroids results in neuromuscular symptoms and changes in mineral balance. Removal of the parathyroids in the dog, 16 hours postoperatively, results in fibrillary twitchings of muscles followed by disordered and involuntary muscle contractions which end in climatic and unrestrained violence (tetany). After this period symptoms may disappear only to reappear in a more violent state. This cycle of events is repeated at shorter intervals until exhaustion is severe and the animal lapses into a torpor (39,58). Death, which follows in the absence of treatment, is usually due to asphyxia caused by spastic contraction of the laryngeal and respiratory musculature.

The outstanding metabolic changes seen in parathyroid hormone deficiency are low serum calcium (hypocalcemia), high blood phosphorus (hyper-phosphatemia) low urine calcium, and low urine phosphorus.

Greep (39,58) reviewed the principal metabolic disturbances related to parathyroid hormone (PTH) function and the several theories advanced to account for them. PTH appears to exert its action on calcium metabolism by its influence upon the mobilization of this element from bones and tissues. The effects upon phosphorus may be related to a direct action of PTH upon the kidney. For a discussion of the interrelations of calcium and phosphorus metabolism and the factors that influence both; see Chapter 30.

The chemistry of PTH is poorly understood. The hormone apparently is a protein since it is susceptible to inactivation by proteolytic enzymes. Ross and Wood (59) found that about half of the hormonal activity resided in a protein fraction of high molecular weight, and that the remainder of the activity was in a protein of low molecular weight. L'Heureux, Tepperman, and Wilhelmi (60), however, found that only low molecular weight fractions possessed activity.

In the human, the use of PTH appears to have clinical value, but adequate control of calcium metabolism can be accomplished without this material. (See Chapter 30.)

Little is known regarding possible pituitary parathyroid interrelations.

THE ADRENAL GLANDS

The adrenal glands in the human adult are situated close to the upper pole of the kidneys and average 45x25x6 mm in size and weigh about 10 g each. The adrenal gland is divided both histologically and physiologically into two distinct portions. The medulla contains largely polygonal cells 18 to 30 μ in size, characterized by distinct staining reactions. The cortex, the outer portion of the gland, contains three structurally distinct layers, the zona glomerulosa, the zona fasciculata, and the zona reticularis. In some lower animals there is little differentiation between the medulla and the various layers of the cortex.

THE MEDULLARY HORMONES

The first hormone isolated from the adrenal medulla was epinephrine. Shortly after this discovery in 1901, it was suspected that an additional substance was present in medullary tissue and present in certain nerve endings. In 1946 (61,62), it was established that this second substance was norepinephrine (arterenol) which had been synthesized and studied as early as 1904:

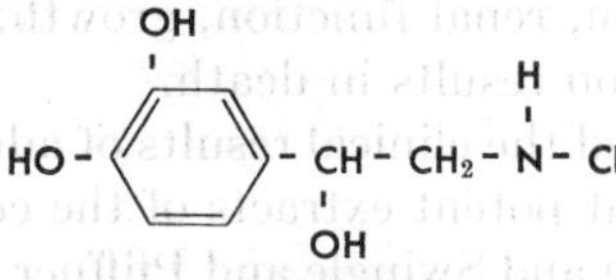

Epinephrine
(Adrenaline)

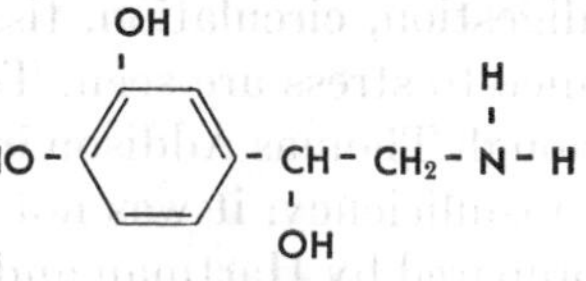

Norepinephrine
(Arterenol)

These two hormones, belonging to the catechol amine class of organic compounds, have potent physiologic activity in both metabolic and physiologic regulation. Norepinephrine and epinephrine are present to the extent of less than 2 μg per liter of blood and in urine to the extent of some 20 μg per 24-hour output (62). Human adrenals have been shown to contain some 0.089 mg per gram norepinephrine and 0.49 mg per gram epinephrine. Other species have different levels of these amines.

Epinephrine is slightly soluble in cold water, insoluble in most organic solvents, and precipitated by ammonia. The orthophenolic groups give rise to a number of color reactions, the color produced with ferric chloride being used in staining procedures. Epinephrine is unstable in the presence of oxygen, giving rise to black pigments.

The characteristic chromaffin granules of the medulla are thought to be epinephrine or its precursor.

Epinephrine secretion is governed largely by the sympathetic nervous system. Stimulation of the adrenal nerves quickly causes histologic changes in the chromaffin granules and an immediate release of epinephrine into the circulation. Such stimulation does not appear to cause any change in the cortex.

The action of epinephrine on muscle and blood vessels is sympathomimetic, for its effects are similar to sympathetic nerve stimulation. Depending upon the amount administered, the hormone may have both pressor and depressor effects upon the circulation. Upon carbohydrate metabolism, epinephrine has the effect of causing liver and muscle glycogenolysis, hyperglycemia, and glucosuria. The hormone causes increased oxygen consumption, its effect being more rapid than that of thyroxine.

The biochemical actions of epinephrine are discussed in Chapter 24, and its biosynthesis is given in the discussion of phenylalanine and tyrosine in Chapter 25.

Norepinephrine causes an increase in blood pressure by causing an increase in peripheral resistance. The hormone has however little effect on carbohydrate metabolism.

The finer points of the action of these substances upon various types of muscles and nerves is beyond the scope of this book. Reviews of this subject by Gaddum (61) and Euler (62) should be consulted for specific effects.

ADRENAL CORTICAL HORMONES

Loss of adrenal cortex function, either from surgery or disease, results in profound changes in biochemical and physiologic functions (63). Effects upon digestion, circulation, tissue metabolism, renal function, growth, and resistance to stress are seen. Total deprivation results in death.

Although Thomas Addison in 1855 described the clinical results of adrenal cortex insufficiency, it was not until 1930 that potent extracts of the cortex were prepared by Hartman and Brownell (64) and Swingle and Pfiffner (65).

Active extracts of the gland early were named "cortin," and this name has persisted to the present time, although now "cortin" usually refers to unfractionated extracts of the cortex or to semipurified yet unidentified fractions of the gland.

After the demonstration of physiologic activity of adrenal cortical extracts it soon became evident that the activity was not due to a single hormonal substance. Pfiffner, Wintersteiner, and Kendall in the United States and Reichstein in Switzerland began to report the isolation of crystalline compounds. Each group named the compounds found in their laboratory by some letter designation peculiar to the specific laboratory. It was not until the chemical identities of the various materials were established that it was possible to correlate the results of the investigations in the several laboratories. Heard (66) tabulated pertinent information regarding the naming and structure of 26 crystalline cortical compounds.

Typical of isolation procedures is that of Kuizenga (67). Starting with 1000 lb of beef adrenals he isolated 9 g of a final product which had a biologic potency equivalent to 2.5 g of Kendall's compound E (17-hydroxy-11-dehydrocorticosterone), or 75,000 rat units. It is obvious that to attempt to isolate and characterize all the fractions of the gland is a great task.

After all crystallizable material has been removed from cortical extracts there remains behind an "amorphous fraction" which has 14 to 30 per cent of the activity (based on life maintenance) of the original whole extract.

From this residual material, aldosterone (electrocortin) has now been isolated. This crystalline material appears to account for the bulk of the biologic activity of the "amorphous fraction."

All the compounds thus far isolated from the adrenal cortex are steroids and are related to the parent substances allopregnane and androstane, the formulas of which are given below:

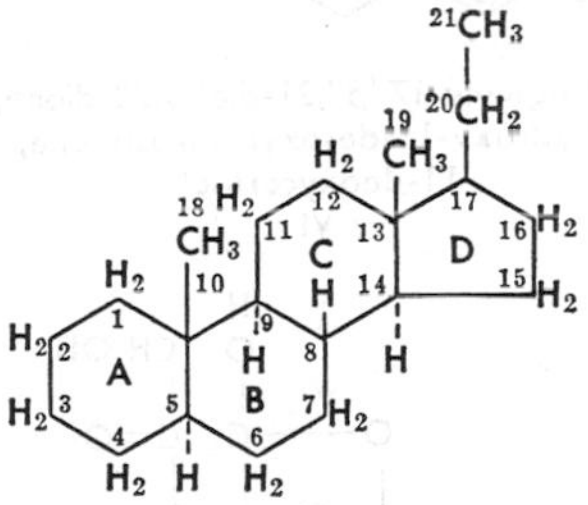

Allopregnane 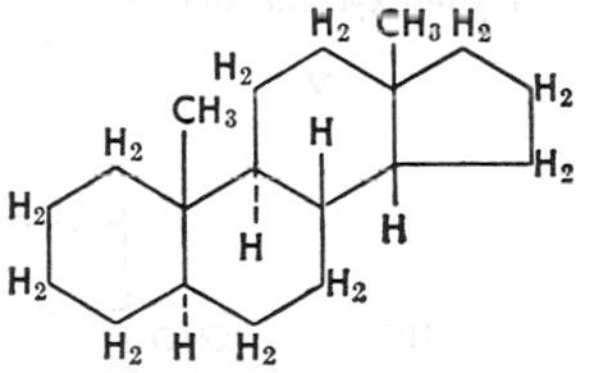   Androstane

Although 30 or more steroids have been isolated from the gland, seven of them account for most of the activity of the original extracts. Three steroids have been demonstrated in venous blood leaving the human adrenal gland, corticosterone, 17-hydroxycorticosterone, and aldosterone. There is marked species variation in the types of steroids normally secreted by the adrenal:

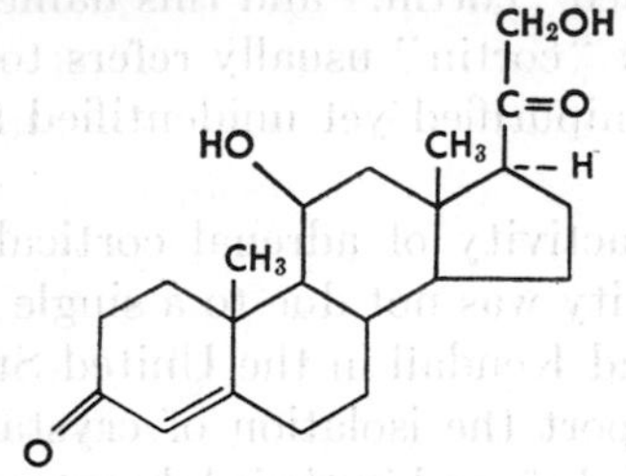

Δ⁴-Pregnene-11β,21-diol-3,20-dione,
corticosterone

I

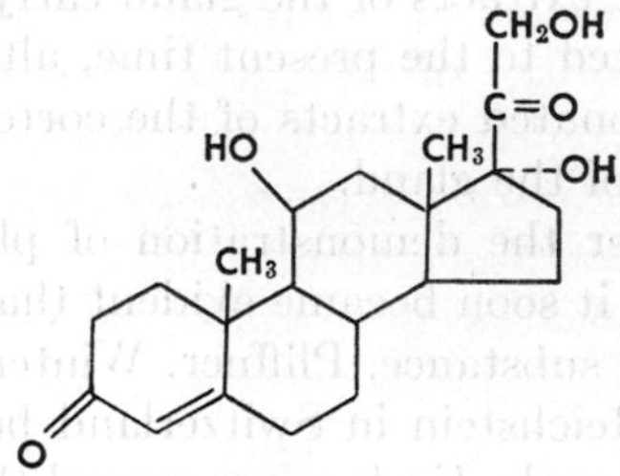

Δ⁴-Pregnene-11β,17"β",21-triol-3,20-dione,
17-hydroxycorticosterone,
cortisol

II

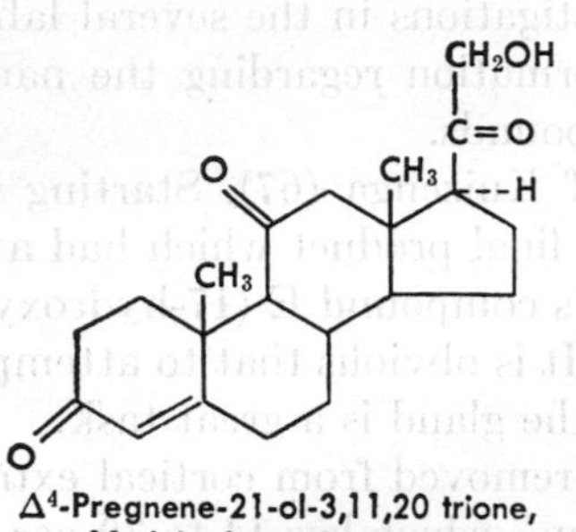

Δ⁴-Pregnene-21-ol-3,11,20 trione,
11-dehydrocorticosterone

III

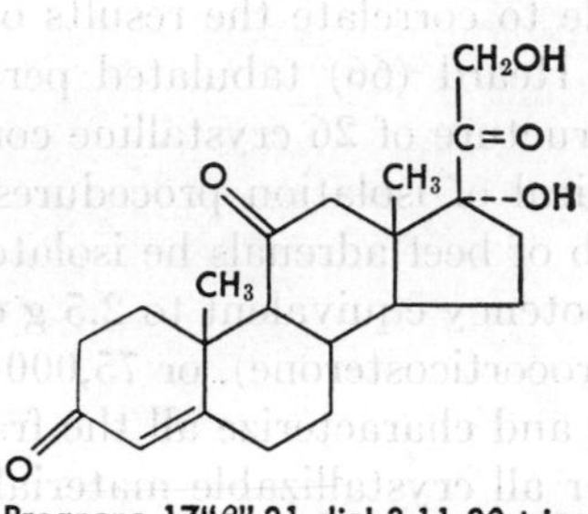

Δ⁴-Pregnene-17"β",21-diol-3,11-20 trione,
17-hydroxy-11-dehydrocorticosterone,
cortisone

IV

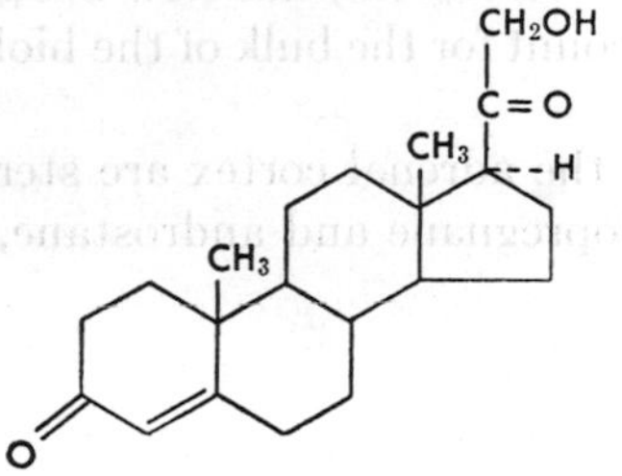

Δ⁴-Pregnene-21-ol-3,20-dione,
11-desoxycorticosterone

V

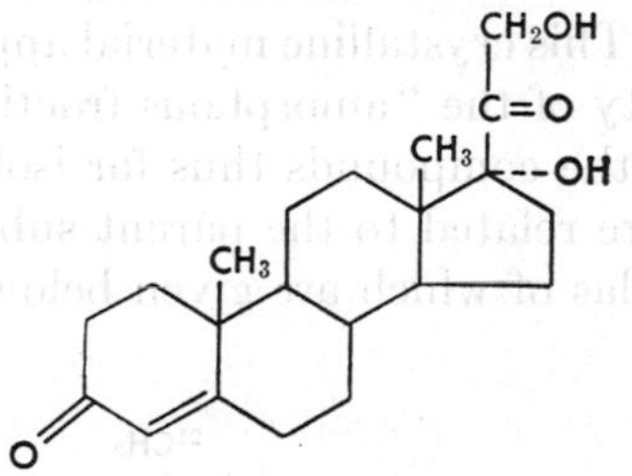

Δ⁴-Pregnene-17"β",21-diol-3,20-dione,
17-hydroxy-11-desoxycorticosterone,
11-deoxycortisol

VI

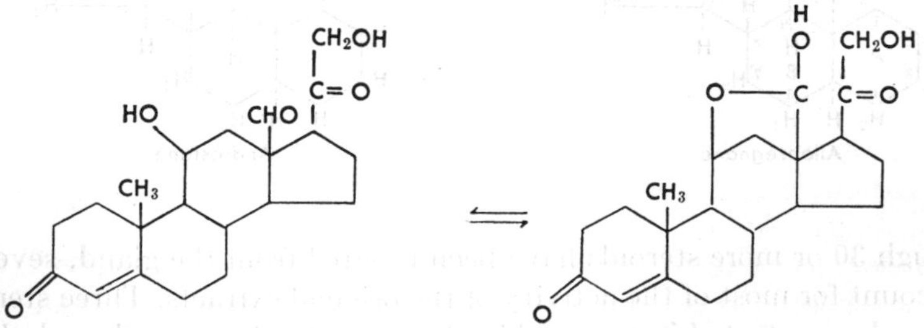

(aldehyde)   (hemiacetal)

Aldosterone
VII

Relation of structure to physiologic activity. The physiologic activity of the adrenal corticosteroids varies with variations in chemical structure. Four key structural features are of paramount importance. The physiologic activity of these substances is related largely to the following structures: (*a*) the α,β-unsaturated ketone group on C-3, (*b*) the ketonic oxygen atom at C-20 adjacent to the primary hydroxyl group at C-21, (*c*) the space orientation of the side chain at C-17, (*d*) an alcoholic or ketonic oxygen at C-11.

Although each of the above qualifications is not met by all adrenal steroids, it is through variations in one or more of these functional groups that biological individuality is given to the various structures.

The α,β unsaturation associated with the ketone group on C-3 (the 4,5 ethylenic linkage in ring A) is found in all active adrenal steroids. If either the ketonic group or the ethylenic linkage is reduced, with the consequent loss of resonance associated with this system, a significant loss of activity is noted.

The α-ketol group of the side chain (CH_2—OH · CO—) is essential to all activity except life maintenance. Compounds with this grouping are similar to fructose in reducing power. Either the $> \overset{17}{C}H—\overset{20}{CO}—\overset{21}{CH_2OH}$ or $> \overset{17}{C}HOH—\overset{20}{CO}—\overset{21}{CH_2OH}$ group reduces ammoniacal silver solutions, cupric ion in alkaline solution, or phosphomolybdic acid. Diminished physiologic activity is associated with higher homologs formed by lengthening the α-ketol side chain and by spatial isomers of the C-17 side chain. Reduced activity also results upon reduction of the C-20 ketone group and the introduction of a C-17 tertiary hydroxyl group.

Evaluation of physiologic activity. As was pointed out by Reichstein and Shoppee (68), great difficulty is associated with the determination of cortical activity. Although the final result of cortical ablation is death, the use of this single criterion in bioassay methods is not desirable because it is important to evaluate the disturbances in the various biochemical processes in their relation to the death of the animal.

The biochemical disturbances that contribute to the eventual death of the adrenalectomized animal were classified by Reichstein (68) as follows: (*a*) increased excretion of Na^+, Cl^-, and water; retention of K^+; (*b*) increased blood urea; (*c*) muscle weakness (asthenia); (*d*) decreased liver glycogen, lowered resistance to insulin; and (*e*) decreased resistance to shock (cold, mechanical, chemical).

Methods used for the evaluation of the physiologic activity of cortical preparations depend upon the alleviation of one or more of the above disturbances.

Although a large number of crystalline compounds has been isolated from extracts of the adrenal gland (29,69), seven of these account for the greater part of the activity of the gland. The biologic activity of the various steroids has been studied by many investigators (70) in a wide variety of test systems. From these studies, it is clear that although the various steroids exhibit greater or less activity in any one test system, most steroids possess all types of activity to some degree (71). In addition to evaluating activity on the basis of steroid ability to maintain the life of an adrenalectomized animal, one or more of the following have been used as a criterion of activity: recovery of fatigued muscle (68), K^+, Na^+ and Cl^- retention (71), work performance (67), antiinsulin activity (72), diabetogenic activity (73), glycogen deposition activity (74), etc. In many studies on the effects of the hormones upon physiologic processes, there has been a great variation in the amount of the preparation administered. In certain cases, the qualitative effects of the preparation differ. This fact adds to the difficulty of assigning a specific physiologic potency to each of the preparations. In general, however, the lack of an alcoholic or ketonic oxygen function at C_{11} causes the compound to have predominately electrolyte effects, and the presence of an oxygen function at C_{11} causes the compounds to affect reactions of intermediary metabolism. Aldosterone may be an exception to this role, but it is to be remembered that the C_{19}—CH_3 of this compound has been replaced with a —CHO function and that this function is spacially adjacent to the carbon 11 hydroxyl group and easily forms a hemiacetal. The presence of a C_{14} hydroxyl appears to enhance the C_{11} oxygen effect. The effects of a number of steroids have been modified by the introduction of halogens in the 9α position; these and other structural changes may greatly enhance the pharmacological action and use of the steroids.

It is of considerable clinical importance that from adrenal extracts both male and female sex hormones have been isolated. Four androgenically active steroids have been isolated from cortical extracts incidental to other work (75). Estrone alone of the estrogens has been isolated from adrenal extracts (76,77). Two progestationally related compounds, progesterone and allopregnanol-3(β)one-20, also have been isolated, the latter compound being inactive.

The relation of these sex hormones of the adrenal to normal sex function is not understood. Since certain tumors of the male adrenal may have profound feminizing effects and certain tumors of the female may cause characteristic masculinization, it is possible that the adrenal may play a role in normal sex function.

The adrenal sterols had been used in medical therapy for some time, but it was not until ACTH and cortisone were shown to be beneficial in the treatment of certain rheumatic disorders that widespread use of these substances was initiated. It is beyond the scope of this text to discuss therapy with ACTH and cortisone in any detail. Although certain conditions respond favorably to therapy (71,78), our knowledge of the mechanisms involved is fragmentary. Treatment with ACTH, when functional adrenal tissue is present, generally gives results similar to mixed cortical therapy.

Of early interest were the effects of cortical compounds upon electrolyte and water balances. Treatment of deranged electrolyte balance as seen in Addison's disease, the nephrotic syndrome and related disorders is possible with ACTH and cortical compounds.

Large or continued dosage with ACTH or cortisone may have a diabetogenic action and will intensify preexisting diabetes. The hyperglycemia and glucosuria often seen in these conditions may not be related, suggesting again the multiple actions of these compounds.

ACTH and cortical compounds exert pronounced effects upon nitrogen metabolism. Increases in urinary nitrogen (some amino acids, uric acid, etc.) occur during treatment, suggesting increased protein catabolism, but this may be localized in certain tissues.

Effects on fat metabolism are yet limited to observations on serum cholesterol and ketone bodies and upon body fat stores, making it difficult to assign a specific role to the adrenal cortical compounds.

As further stated by Sprague (78), lymphoid tissue exhibits a great sensitivity to cortical hormones. Neoplastic lymphoid tissue appears to be inhibited by cortical administration. The marked reduction in blood eosinophils after treatment has been used as a test of the adequacy of ACTH therapy. A striking effect of cortical therapy is the relief of various conditions associated with tissue inflammation and sensitivity of the collagen tissues. Since a variety of causes may result in such collagen disorders, it is likely that the cortical substances modify not the agent but the tissue reactivity to the agents. This appears also to be the case in the relief of allergic reactions.

Metabolism of the adrenal steroids. With the advent of isotopically labeled substrates, the biosynthesis and the catabolism of the steroids have received a great deal of attention (29,71). It is beyond the scope of this book to consider these reactions in detail, but the following points highlight this work.

The perfused adrenal gland and adrenal slices can synthesize a number of steroids and this synthesis is stimulated by ACTH. Acetate is converted to cholesterol and cholesterol, in turn, is converted to various corticoids. Acetate, however, may form the corticoids directly. ACTH appears to stimulate the conversion of cholesterol to corticoids rather than to increase acetate incorporation into corticoids. The reactions involved in the conversion of cholesterol to active corticoids involve most of the following: (a) shortening of the isooctyl side chain, (b) formation of the C_3 ketone on an unsaturated ring (A), (c) formation of an OH group at C_{11}, (d) C_{21} hydroxylation, and (e) C_{17} hydroxylation.

The studies (69) on the catabolism of the corticosteroids have involved not only the isolation of steroid intermediates and final excretory products, but have also allowed the isolation of a number of the enzymes concerned with steroid metabolism. Two of the most important reactions concerned in the catabolic phase of steroid metabolism are: (a) the reduction of both the ketone at C_3 and the double bond at C_{4-5} and (b) the removal of the two carbon side chain to produce a C_{17} ketone.

THE TESTES

The testes in the adult human male are paired ovoid organs located in the scrotum. Weighing about 25 g, the testes are around 3 to 5 cm in length,

2 to 3 cm in width, and 1 to 2 cm in thickness (56). Histologically, the testes consist of the seminiferous tubules between which is interspersed interstitial tissue. Certain cells of the epithelium of the tubules are transformed successively into spermatogonia, spermatocytes, spermatids, and spermatozoa. In addition to being the source of germ cells, the testes, through their interstitial cells (cells of Leydig), are a source of hormonal material.

As previously discussed, FSH is responsible for tubular development and germ cell production. ICSH of the anterior pituitary is credited with interstitial cell stimulation and the consequent production of male hormone (androgen) (75, 79).

If the gonads are removed before puberty, the accessory sex organs and sex characteristics fail to develop. Castration after puberty results in atrophy of the accessory sex organs, seminal vesicles, prostate, and prepubital glands. Changes in bone development and metabolic processes also occur (79).

An androgen is defined as a substance capable of stimulating male secondary sex characteristics (80). The stimulation of fowl comb growth is one of the most sensitive and specific indications of androgenic activity.

Testosterone (III), was first isolated in pure form from bull testes [see (75) and (79) for historical development]. The first androgens isolated, however, were androsterone (I) and dehydroisoandrosterone (II), found by Butenandt in normal male urine, 15 mg being obtained from 25,000 l of urine. Androgenically active material has been demonstrated in the urine of women as well as children of both sexes:

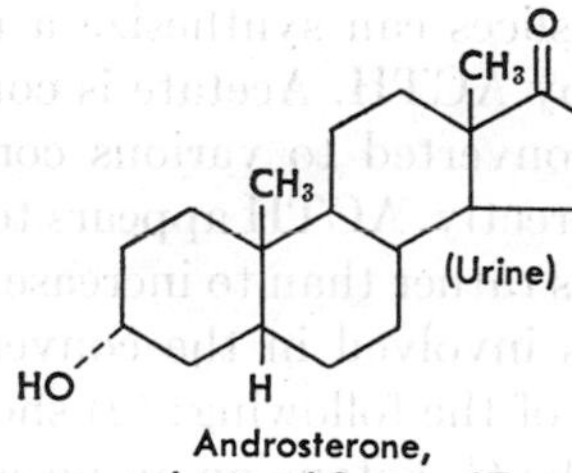

Androsterone,
androstanol-3α-one-17
I

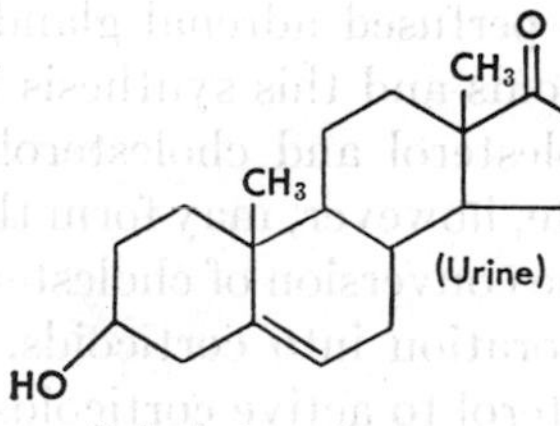

Dehydroisoandrosterone,
Δ⁵-androstenol-3β-one-17
II

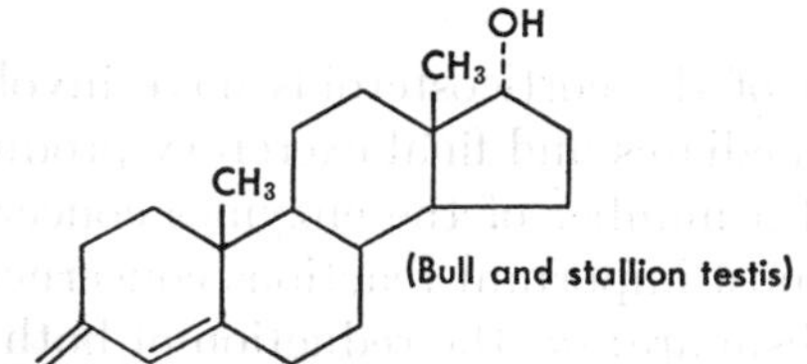

Testosterone,
Δ⁴-androstenol-17α-one-3
III

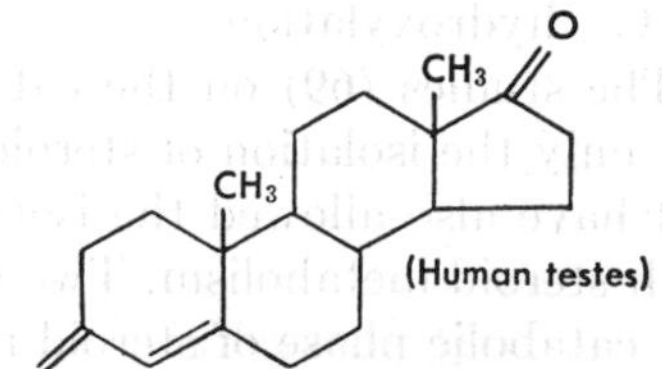

Δ⁴-Androstene-3,17-dione
IV

Additional compounds have been isolated from testes, adrenals, and urine (80), but most of these fail to have androgenic activity.

Androgens are also formed by adrenal tissue, such as Δ⁴-androstene-3,17 dione, adrenosterone, 11β-hydroxy-Δ^4-androstene-3,17-dione, and 11β-hydroxyepiandrosterone, which have been isolated from it (69).

It has been reported that the ovary synthesizes androgenic material as well as estrogenic hormones. If ovaries are transplanted into the ears of castrate mice, thus exteriorizing the organs (75), such ovaries are capable of synthesizing androgens at an increased rate. Ovaries transplanted to the abdomen of castrate males are unable to do this. These findings may bear a distinct relationship to the failure of testicular function in the case of undescended testes. The placenta also may elaborate androgens.

Testosterone production by the testes is necessary for the normal development of the male reproductive organs and stimulation of the seminal vesicles for germ cell formation. In addition, the male type voice, facial and body hair pattern, and growth and skeletal muscular development are attributed to testicular hormone action.

Although specific information on the mode of action of the androgens is not available, such materials cause growth stimulation of a rather specific nature. Associated with growth is a positive nitrogen balance. That the androgens cause nitrogen retention and favor protein anabolism is evident from many studies (80). A sensitive assay method for androgens is the growth of the comb of the two- or three-day-old chick. Androgens painted on the surface of the immature comb cause growth proportional to the amount of hormone used. Since an early response of this growth phenomenon is an increase in the vascularity of the comb, a further role of increasing blood flow to certain regions of the body through increased vascularity may be attributed to the androgens.

Although the metabolic effects of the androgens have been extensively studied (69,80,81) and various enzymic reactions are known to be influenced by these compounds, clear-cut metabolic roles are not yet established.

Of great interest clinically is the determination of the 17-ketosteroids (nonphenolic) in urine. At least seven urinary 17-ketosteroids are thought to arise almost entirely from the adrenal cortex in the normal female, and mainly from the cortex in the male (66). These cortical metabolites are related to the adrenal cortex-pituitary system under stress, and their urinary values vary widely. The 17-ketosteroid values studied over longer periods of time may give an index of urinary androgen excretion (75). Up to about 18 years of age both boys and girls excrete approximately the same amounts of these compounds, excretion showing a rapid increase at 6 to 7 years of age.

Normal adult female androgen and 17-ketosteroid values are approximately two-thirds those of the male (75). Until more is known about androgen secretion of female and male adrenals, as well as possible androgen secretion by the ovary, the significance of normal 17-ketosteroid levels will not be known. Such determinations are, however, of considerable importance in the diagnosis of deranged cortex and gonad function.

Biosynthesis and catabolism of the androgens. Acetate has been shown to be a precursor of the androgens, just as it is of the adrenal and ovarian steroids. Chorionic gonadotropin, although enhancing the formation of testosterone by perfused testes, does not increase the incorporation of acetate into testosterone. The cholesterol isolated in these studies does not appear to be an obligatory precursor of the androgens.

Although some 12 steroids have been isolated in studies on androgen catabolism, the three androgens testosterone, Δ^4-androstene-3,17-dione, and dehydroepiandrosterone seem to be converted primarily to the two 17-ketosteroids androsterone and etiocholanolone. Dehydroepiandrosterone is excreted largely unchanged (69). An important metabolic reaction here is the reduction of the 4–5 double bond to the androsterone (5α) or etiocholane (5β) form.

THE OVARIES

In the early 1900's it became obvious that the ovary is a gland of internal secretion and its secretion is important in regulating sex functions. Research on the endocrine function of the ovary was established on a quantitative basis with the development of a convenient bioassay method by Allen and Doisy in 1923 (82). Cornification of the vaginal epithelium after treatment with extracts of follicular fluid gives a sensitive index of estrogenic potency. Corner and Allen (82) subsequently developed a bioassay method based upon progestational reactions in the rabbit which enabled investigators to evaluate extracts containing the active principle of the corpus luteum (progesterone).

Estrogenic hormones. The cortex of the human ovary contains as many as 500,000 follicles, only a small number of which mature and produce ova. Growth of the follicle, maturation, and expulsion of the ovum are associated with FSH and ICSH stimulation, as pointed out in a previous section. The hormone (estrogen) synthesized by the maturing follicle is estradiol-17β (α-estradiol) (II), first isolated from sow ovaries by McCorquodale, Thayer, and Doisy (82). These workers fractionated four tons of sow ovaries and recovered 50 per cent of the activity in the form of about 12 mg of estradiol-17β (α-estradiol).

The first estrogen isolated, estrone or theelin (I), was obtained from pregnancy urine by Doisy and associates. The discovery by Aschheim and Zondek that pregnancy urine contains large amounts of estrogenic material made it possible for many workers to utilize this abundant cheap source rather than the tissues previously used. It is of interest that stallion urine may contain over 100 times as much estrogenic material as human pregnancy urine, and that horse testes are the richest tissue source of estrogens.

Estrogens subsequently have been isolated from a number of sources including adrenal glands, testes, placenta, and mare, human, and stallion urine (83). In addition, some plant materials contain appreciable quantities of estrogens (82). It has been estimated (84) that the normal woman produces about 10 mg of estrogens per menstrual cycle.

Estrogen secretion by the follicle is largely responsible for the development of the sex organs at puberty. It is also responsible for the development of the secondary sex characteristics: texture and distribution of hair, texture of the skin, character of the voice, and distribution of body fat. These effects, under

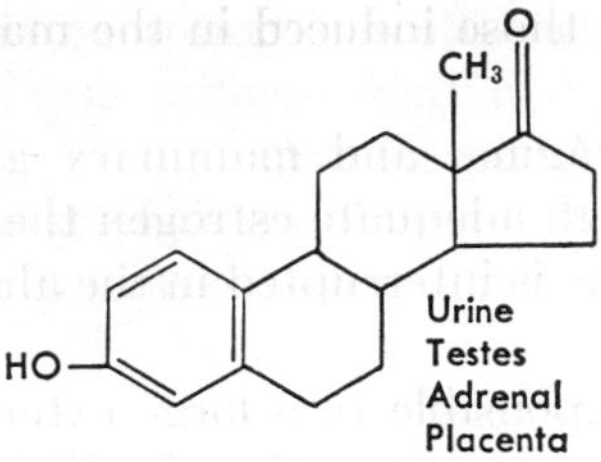

Urine
Testes
Adrenal
Placenta

Estrone (theelin),
$\Delta^{1,3,5}$-estratrieneol-3-one-17

I

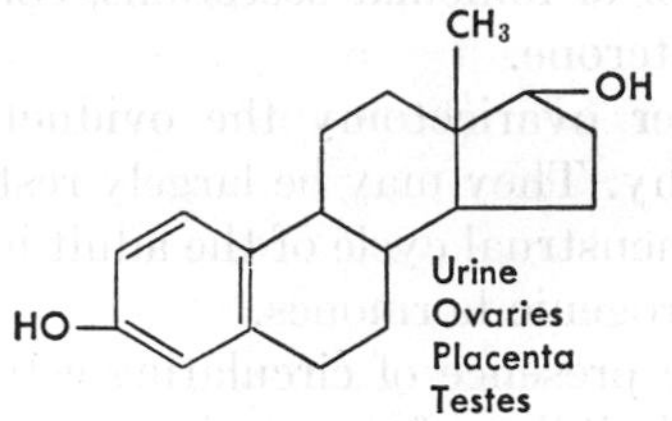

Urine
Ovaries
Placenta
Testes

α-estradiol (dihydrotheelin),
$\Delta^{1,3,5}$-estratrienediol-3,17,
estradiol-17β

II

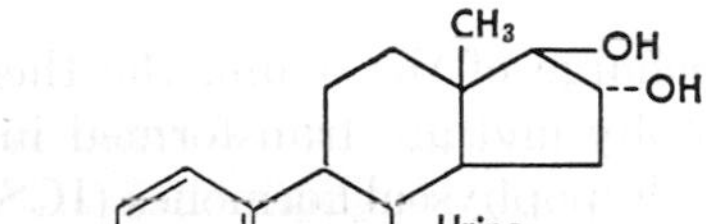

Urine
Placenta

Estriol (theelol),
$\Delta^{1,3,5}$-estratrienetriol-3,16,17

III

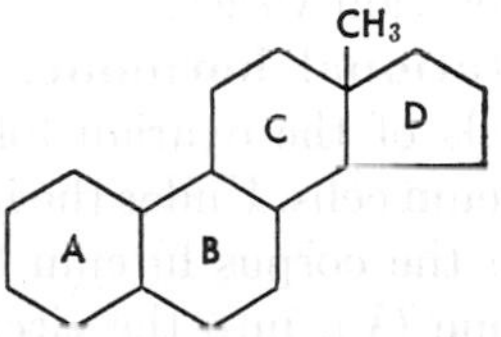

Estrane (parent substance)

IV

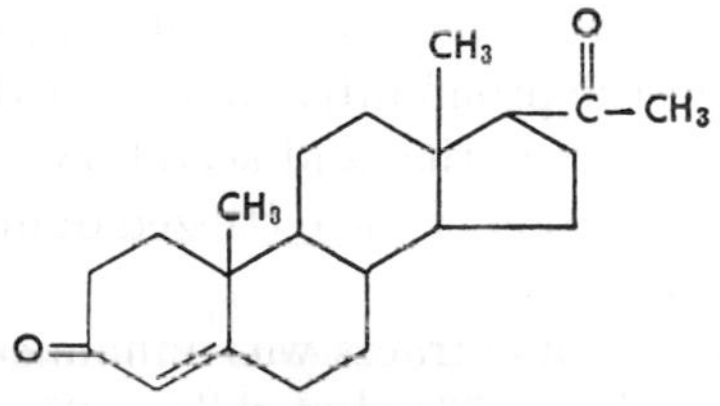

Progesterone
Δ^4-pregnenedione-3,20

V

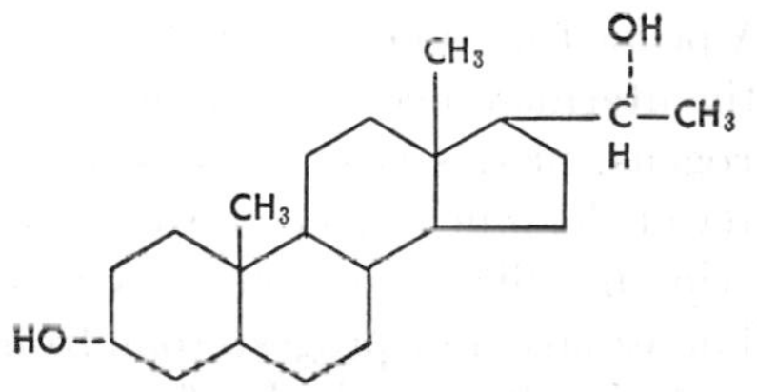

Pregnanediol
pregnanediol-3α,20α

VI

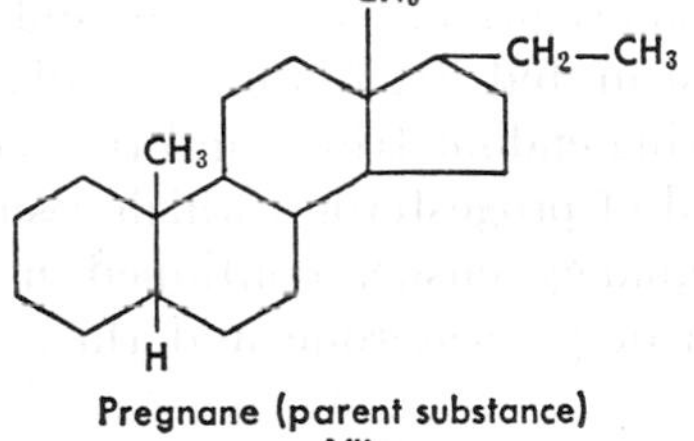

Pregnane (parent substance)

VII

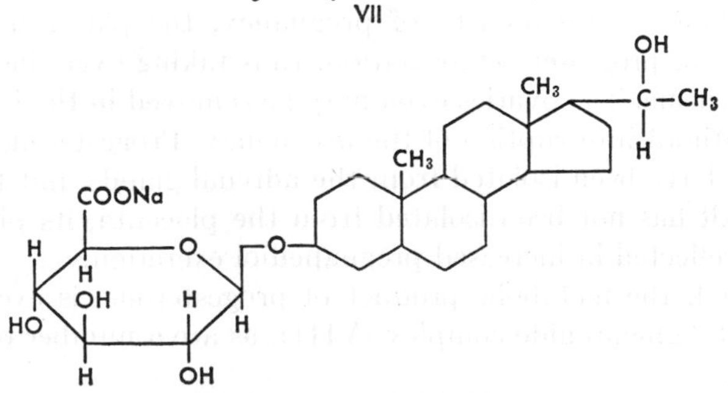

Sodium pregnanediol-3α,20α
glucuronidate

VIII

control of follicular secretions, correspond to those induced in the male by testosterone.

After ovariectomy the oviduct, uterus, vagina, and mammary glands atrophy. They may be largely restored through adequate estrogen therapy. The menstrual cycle of the adult human female is interrupted in the absence of estrogenic hormones.

The presence of circulating estrogens is responsible to a large extent for the rebuilding of the uterine endometrium after menstruation. Proliferation of the uterine mucosa to the premenstrual stage can be accomplished by estradiol, estrone, and estriol, but the potency of these compounds in causing this proliferation varies.

Progestational hormone. After the discharge of the ovum, the theca interna cells of the ovarian follicle hypertrophy and are transformed into corpus luteum cells. Under the influence of the hypophyseal hormones (ICSH and LTH) the corpus luteum becomes secretory and releases its hormone, progesterone (V), into the circulation. This secretion continues during the second half of the menstrual cycle but stops rather abruptly several days before the onset of menstruation.

A prime function of progesterone is induction of the progestational changes of the uterine mucosa. Exerting its effect after the proliferative action of the estrogens, progesterone causes an increase in vascularity and secretory activity of the mucosa, a condition essential for nidation of the fertilized ovum. Uterine motility is inhibited by progesterone.

The isolation of progesterone from corpora lutea extracts was announced almost simultaneously by four groups of workers (83), but Allen (85) is credited with developing basic principles of extraction and purification. Prior to the isolation of progesterone, Marrian (83,86) had isolated pregnanediol (VI) from human pregnancy urine. This compound is a metabolic product of progesterone metabolism, but itself is biologically inactive.

The sloughing of uterine endometrium and the bleeding of menstruation is due to the withdrawal of progesterone which results with corpus luteum regression. Should pregnancy ensue, continued hypophyseal stimulation maintains the secretion of progesterone and thus retains the uterus in a functional state.

After the first several months of pregnancy, the placenta becomes an important site of progesterone formation, thus taking over the functions of luteal progesterone. The ovaries even may be removed in the later stages of pregnancy without interruption of the pregnancy. Progesterone and related C-21 steroids have been isolated from the adrenal glands, but thus far progesterone itself has not been isolated from the placenta, its placental synthesis being reflected in increased pregnanediol excretion.

Pregnanediol, the metabolic product of progesterone, is excreted in the urine as a 3-β-d-glucuronide complex (VIII), as are a number of other C-21 steroids (83).

Metabolism of the estrogens. As in the case of the androgens and adrenal cortical hormones, little is known of the metabolism of the estrogens,

All these substances are steroids and contain the same fundamental ring structure as cholesterol. The fact that pregnanediol containing deuterium has been isolated from the urine of a pregnant woman after the administration of deuterized cholesterol indicates cholesterol to be the precursor of the hormone.

The estrogens have been shown to be formed from acetate, as is the case with the adrenal and testicular steroids. Cholesterol does not appear to be an intermediate in the formation of estrogens from acetate. The estrogenic compounds Equilin and Equilenin differ from human estrogens in being unsaturated in ring B. Studies have shown that it is likely that there are two independent pathways of synthesis for the compounds saturated and unsaturated in ring B (69).

Studies on the metabolism of the estrogens are complicated by the fact that 80 to 90 per cent of administered estrogen is converted to unknown metabolic products (84). The 10 to 20 per cent of the estrogen excreted in such experiments is often converted to another estrogenically active form. Since such interconversions vary with the species of animal studied, it is difficult to present the entire picture of estrogen metabolism at this time. In man, estradiol-17β (α-estradiol) and estrone appear to be interconvertible, at least to a small degree. Both estradiol-17β and estrone give rise to estriol when administered to man, but estriol administration causes the excretion of only unchanged estriol. Thus estriol may be an important end product of estrogen metabolism in the human. In the rabbit, upon administration of estrone or estradiol-17β, estradiol-17α (β-estradiol) appears in the urine as the chief metabolite. This epimerization of the 17-hydroxyl group may require the preliminary formation of estrone from estradiol-17β.

Estriol is excreted in human urine as the glucuronide, while estrone is found in mare urine as the sulfuric acid ester, such conjugation probably being related to the excretory phases of hormone metabolism. The bile is important in the excretion of estrogens and their catabolic products.

Perfusion studies and liver slice experiments indicate that the liver is an important site of estrogen catabolism and interconversion. The gonads and accessory sex tissue, however, may also be involved in *in vivo* hormone metabolism.

Fusion of estrone or estradiol-17β with KOH leads to rupture of the five-membered D ring, with the formation of a carboxyl group on C-17. Doisynolic acid, the compound so formed, possesses high biologic activity, particularly in pituitary inhibition assays. Marrianolic acid from the KOH fusion of estriol is only slightly active biologically.

Stilbestrol. Several unnatural synthetic substances which possess estrogenic activity have been prepared, the most important of which is stilbestrol:

$$\text{HO} - \underset{}{\bigcirc} - \underset{\underset{C_2H_5}{|}}{C} = \underset{\underset{C_2H_5}{|}}{C} - \underset{}{\bigcirc} - \text{OH}$$

Stilbestrol

Stilbestrol possesses a high degree of estrogenic potency, and is used clinically in place of natural estrogens. It possesses the advantages of low cost and of being active when administered orally. Stilbestrol is eliminated in the urine to some extent as the glucuronide and very slightly as the ethereal sulfate. Other synthetic estrogens are related to stilbestrol through modifications in its structure (hexestrol, benzestrol, dienestrol).

Pregnancy tests. Aschheim and Zondek developed an assay method for the detection of the increased amounts of urinary gonadotropin associated with early pregnancy. The urine sample is injected six times over a two-day period into infantile female mice. The animals are killed 96 hours after the first injection, and the ovaries are examined for hemorrhagic follicles (blutpunkte) and for developed corpora lutea (yellow protrusions).

In the Friedman test, 10 ml of urine are injected into the marginal ear vein of a mature female rabbit that has previously been isolated for three weeks. Twenty-four hours later the ovaries are examined for the appearance of ruptured or hemorrhagic follicles.

Urinary gonadotropins injected subcutaneously into the back of the female South African clawed toad (*Xenopus laevis*) cause the deposition of one to several thousand eggs in from 8 to 36 hours. After a rest period the animals may be reused.

THE PANCREAS

Insulin. In 1890 von Mering and Minkowski demonstrated the relation between pancreatic hypofunction and diabetes mellitus. Many attempts were made to isolate the pancreatic principle, but it was not until 1922 that Banting and Best announced the preparation of potent extracts. About the same time Macleod definitely established the fact that the hormonal principle is elaborated by pancreatic islet rather than acinar tissue.

The normal human adult pancreas contains on the average some 500,000 islets, this tissue comprising 1 to 3 per cent of the total tissue (87). The β-islet cell is thought to be responsible for the bulk of insulin production.

Insulin at present is obtained commercially from minced beef or pig pancreas by extraction with a variety of solvents, followed by selective precipitation procedures. The isolation of crystalline insulin was accomplished in 1926 by Abel and associates, this being the first instance of a crystalline protein with specific biologic properties. The presence of zinc, cobalt, nickel, or cadmium facilitates insulin crystallization. Pure insulin preparations from several species are immunologically identical and have the same biologic potency, although the amino acid sequences differ (87,88).

Crystalline zinc insulin contains on the average 0.3 to 0.6 per cent zinc and a high (3.3 per cent) content of sulfur. The sulfur is accounted for entirely as the disulfide linkages (—S—S—) of cystine. Irreversible inactivation of insulin occurs after reduction of about one-third of its disulfide linkages (87,88). No loss of activity occurs when up to two-thirds of the initially available carboxyl groups are esterified. Up to 12 mols of methoxy groups per molecular unit of 12,000 can be added. Other derivates of insulin have been prepared with variable effects upon the biologic activity.

Determination of the molecular weight of insulin has been difficult because of the apparent dependence of the measurements upon pH, ionic strength, and association with Zn (18). Although a number of workers have obtained values of 6000–6500, others have obtained values two to eight times this large. A possible reason for these widely spaced values is the finding (18,88) that insulin contains one mole of Zn per 12,000 molecular weight and that only when the conditions are such that allow for the removal of the Zn, are there obtained weights around 6000 (18). A molecular weight value of 12,000 is usually used in calculations involving molecular structure.

The brilliant investigations of Sanger and others (88) on the numbers and sequential arrangement of the amino acids in insulin has resulted in the elucidation of its structure. Insulin of molecular weight 6000 consists of one A chain of amino acids, terminating in glycine, and one B chain, terminating in phenylalanine. These two chains are linked to each other by disulfide bridges between half-cystine residues. The complete order of amino acids present in the A and B chains is given in Chapter 8 (p. 303). A final picture of the three-dimensional structure of insulin cannot be drawn at this time, although rod-like structures, left- and right-hand helices, and folded sheet structures have been suggested (18,88).

Insulin usually is standardized by determination of the quantity required to produce convulsions or to lower the blood sugar to a certain level in rabbits.

Glucagon. Shortly after the discovery of the hypoglycemic activity of insulin, it was found that certain preparations contained a factor that caused a transient hyperglycemia. This hyperglycemic factor (HGF) is now called "glucagon" and has been purified and crystallized (89), and its structure determined (18,90). It has been shown that glucagon contains 29 amino acid residues and a minimum molecular weight of 3550. Histidine is the N-terminal residue and threonine the C-terminal residue. The amino acid sequence is:

His. Ser. Glu.—(NH$_2$). Gly. Thr. Phe. Thr. Ser. Asp. Tyr. Ser. Lys. Tyr. Leu. Asp. Ser. Arg. Arg. Ala. Glu.—(NH$_2$) Asp. Phe. Val. Glu.—(NH$_2$). Tyr. Leu. Met. Asp.—(NH$_2$). Thr.

The amino acid sequence is very different from that of insulin, and there are no disulfide bridges as in insulin. The α cells of the islets of Langerhans appear to be the source of glucagon, but there are some data which suggest that other tissues elaborate a similar factor (18).

Glucagon causes an increase in intracellular concentrations of both glucose-1-PO$_4$ and glucose-6-PO$_4$, apparently by increasing the activity of the phosphorylase enzyme responsible for breakdown of glycogen to glucose-1-PO$_4$. The hyperglycemia resulting from injection of glucagon in vivo results from the action of glucose-6-phosphatase upon the glucose-6-PO$_4$ newly made available. Glucagon may exert its phosphorylase stimulating effect by protecting the enzyme from inactivation. Glucagon appears to have effects similar to those of epinephrine but as yet glucagon has not been shown to affect *muscle* phosphorylase as does epinephrine. This and other points of difference indicate that glucagon and epinephrine may play independent rolls in metabolic reactions.

Physiologic functions of insulin. Insulin is secreted by the islet cells largely in response to high blood sugar levels. The hypophysis apparently does not control islet function in a dynamic fashion as in case of the gonads. However, a relation does exist between the pancreas and the pituitary, as is evident from the following facts: (a) Hypophysectomy renders the animal more sensitive to insulin. (b) Hypophysectomy relieves the symptoms of diabetes that follow pancreatectomy. (c) Injection of pituitary extracts over a period of time may cause the development of diabetes.

The effects of pancreatectomy and the diabetic syndrome that results are discussed in Chapter 24. It should be pointed out, however, that the depancreatized experimental animal may not be an exact prototype of the human with diabetes. Since pituitary, adrenal, thyroid, and dietary factors may grossly affect the diabetic syndrome, it appears that in some cases of diabetes deficient insulin secretion is not the primary factor (87).

In the absence of an adequate insulin supply the following disturbances result: (a) hyperglycemia and glucosuria, (b) decreased liver and muscle glycogen stores, (c) decreased oxidation of glucose, (d) increased glucose formation from protein (gluconeogenesis), and (e) increased catabolism of fat, with resulting ketosis due to acetoacetic and β-hydroxybutyric acids.

Mechanism of action of insulin. Although many studies have sought to elucidate the mechanism of action of insulin, a complete explanation is lacking. Cellular utilization of glucose is dependent upon a number of factors—i.e., availability of glucose to the cell membranes, translocation of glucose to the intracellular spaces, availability of cofactors such as ATP, and finally activation of glucose (phosphorylation). Studies designed to determine the prime factor controlling glucose utilization have often failed to control or have been unable to control some other factor. It appears clear (82,90) that membrane passage of glucose and cellular activation may both be rate-limiting. Insulin may exert its activating effects by releasing the hexokinase reaction from anterior pituitary protein inhibition.

Recent studies on the effects of insulin upon membrane transport of carbohydrates are presented in the chapter on carbohydrate metabolism and should be consulted.

An important approach to the study of insulin action was afforded by the introduction of alloxan as an agent to destroy β-islet cells. With this substance it is possible to effect pancreatectomy chemically without the hazards of surgery usually associated with this operation. This technique has been particularly valuable with certain species, such as the rat, in which the pancreatic tissue is diffuse and difficult to remove surgically.

GASTROINTESTINAL HORMONES

A number of substances, secretin, cholecystokinin, gastrin, pancreozymin, and enterogastrone have been postulated to be hormones concerned with gastrointestinal function. Available evidence, however, permits the assignment of a true hormonal role to only the first two substances (91).

Secretin. "Secretin" is the name proposed by Bayliss and Starling in 1902 for a substance released from the upper intestinal mucosa which stimulates the secretion of pancreatic juice, the acidity of the duodenal contents being the controlling factor in the release of secretin. That an acid pH alone might not be the only stimulus has been repeatedly suggested.

Crystalline picrolonate derivatives of secretin have been prepared and studied chemically. Secretin activity is associated with a polypeptide structure having a molecular weight around 5000. It is of interest that some ten amino acid residues may be removed from this purified secretin by the enzyme aminopolypeptidase without loss of potency (91). Since the crystalline picrolonates can be further fractionated, it is likely that the pure hormone has not as yet been isolated.

Stimulation of a transplanted or denervated pancreas, in the dog, by as little as 0.005 mg of purified secretin preparations causes the secretion of pancreatic juice. Such stimulated juice is often low in enzyme content. Secretin also stimulates the flow of bile, and the bile may be low in bile salt and pigment (91).

Cholecystokinin. Contraction of the muscular wall of the gall bladder causes the contents to empty via the cystic duct, and the principal regulator of this contraction is the hormone cholecystokinin. This hormone is apparently formed in the mucosa of the upper part of the small intestine. Fat, fatty acids, dilute HCl, and peptone cause the release of the hormone.

Cholecystokinin has not been isolated in pure form, and its activity usually is associated with secretin in fractionation procedures.

Pancreozymin. Pancreozymin preparations from intestinal mucosa have been shown to have a high level of activity on the pancreas and to be free of secretin action. Entirely pure preparations, however, have not been made. Pancreatic stimulation by pancreozymin causes the secretion of pancreatic juice rich in enzymes. The secretion of pancreatic juice thus appears to be influenced by both secretin and pancreozymin.

Gastrin. The pyloric mucosa secretes a substance which in turn stimulates the secretion of acid by the gastric glands. Considerable controversy over the possible identity of this hormone-like secretion with histamine has failed to indicate clearly the nature of the gastric hormone. Although many workers feel that histamine (see Chapter 12) answers all the requirements for this type of stimulation, recent work has reopened the question. Komarov and also Uvnas (91) have been able to prepare pyloric mucosa fractions apparently free from histamine activity. These fractions were not inactivated by histaminase, resisted heating at 100° C in 0.1 N HCl, but were inactivated by 0.1 N NaOH. The activity was not destroyed by pepsin. The products exerted a selective action on HCl secretion, the pepsin concentration of the stimulated gastric juice being low. Further confirmation of these results may clarify the function of the suggested hormone, gastrin.

Enterogastrone. Soaps, fatty acids, fat, and certain sugars in contact with the mucosa of the upper small intestine cause the release of a hormone-like material enterogastrone. This material inhibits motor and secretory activity of the stomach, which is demonstrable in one to seven minutes after the introduction of fat into the intestine.

Little real progress has been made on the chemical isolation of enterogastrone. Active concentrates contain amino acids, but apparently the molecular size of the principle is too small to precipitate with trichloroacetic acid.

Urogastrone. It is possible to prepare extracts of normal urine which, when given parenterally, inhibit gastric acid secretion. The relation of this material to normal gastric function and enterogastrone action is not clear.

Enterocrinin. Enterocrinin is another poorly defined entity thought to be involved in intestinal function. Suitably prepared extracts increase the rate of succus entericus secretion by the jejunum and ileum, and also increase the enzyme content of the succus entericus. Although rather potent fractions with enterocrinin activity have been prepared, little is known of the chemical nature of the principle.

Additional substances related to the gastrointestinal tract such as anthelone, duocrinin, and villikinin have been described, but are not as yet well-defined entities.

SPECIAL REFERENCES

1. Selye, H.: *Textbook of Endocrinology*. Acta Endocrinologica, Montreal, 1949.
2. Li, C. H., in *The Proteins*, by H. Neurath and K. Bailey, Academic Press, New York, 1954, p. 595.
3. Li, C. H., and Evans, H. M., in *The Hormones*, by G. Pincus and K. V. Thimann. Academic Press, Inc., New York, 1948, p. 631.
4. Li, C. H.: *Advances in Protein Chemistry*, 12, 270, 1957.
5. Evans, H. M.; Simpson, M. E.; Marx, W.; and Kibrick, E. A.: *Endocrinology*, 32, 13, 1943.
6. Teel, H. M., and Watkins, O.: *Am. J. Physiol.*, 89, 662, 1929.
7. Li, C. H., and Evans, H. M.: *Recent Progress in Hormone Research*, 3, 3, 1948.
8. Saffran, M., and Saffran, J.: *Ann. Rev. Physiol.*, 21, 403, 1959.
9. De Bodo, R. C., and Altszuler, N.: *Vitamins and Hormones*, 15, 205, 1957. De Bodo, R. C., and Altszuler, N., in *Hypophysical Growth Hormone, Nature and Actions*, by R. W. Smith, O. H. Gaebler, and C. N. H. Long. McGraw-Hill Book Co., Inc., New York, 1955, p. 293.
10. Marx, W., and Evans, H. M., in *The Chemistry and Physiology of Hormones*. American Association for the Advancement of Science, Washington, D.C., 1944, p. 47.
11. Li, C. H., and Harris, J. I.: *Ann. Rev. Biochem.*, 21, 603, 1952.
12. White, A., in *The Chemistry and Physiology of Hormones*. American Association for the Advancement of Science, Washington, D.C., 1944, p. 1.
13. Hays, E. E., and Steelman, S. L., in *The Hormones*, by G. Pincus and K. V. Thimann. Academic Press, Inc., New York, Vol. III, 1955, p. 201.
14. Rawson, R. W., and Money, W. L.: *Recent Progress in Hormone Research*, 4, 397, 1949.
15. Albert, A.: *Ann. N. Y. Acad. Sci.*, 50, 466, 1949.
16. Rawson, R. W.: *Ann. N. Y. Acad. Sci.*, 50, 491, 1949.
17. White, A.: *Vitamins and Hormones*, 7, 253, 1949.
18. Behrens, O. K., and Bromer, W. W.: *Ann. Rev. Biochem.*, 27, 57, 1958.
19. Peterson, W. E.: *Recent Progress in Hormone Research*, 2, 133, 1948.
20. Nelson, W. O.: *Physiol. Revs.*, 16, 488, 1936.
21. Turner, C. W., in *Sex and Internal Secretions*, by E. Allen. Williams & Wilkins Co., Baltimore, 1939.
22. Smith, P. E.: *Am. J. Anat.*, 45, 205, 1930.
23. Smith, P. E., in *Sex and Internal Secretions*, by E. Allen. Williams & Wilkins Co., Baltimore, 1939. Van Dyke, H. B.: *The Physiology and Pharmacology of the Pituitary Body*, Vol. I., 1936; Vol. II, 1939. University of Chicago Press, Chicago.

24. Fevold, H. L., in *The Chemistry and Physiology of Hormones*. American Association for the Advancement of Science, Washington, D.C., 1944, p. 152.
25. Heller, C. G., and Nelson, W. O.: *Recent Progress in Hormone Research*, 3, 229, 1948.
26. Levin, L., in *Chemistry and Physiology of Hormones*. American Association for the Advancement of Science, Washington, D.C., 1944, p. 152.
27. Li, C. H.: *Vitamins and Hormones*, 7, 223, 1949.
28. Li, C. H.: *Advances in Protein Chemistry*, 11, 101, 1956.
29. Hechter, O., and Pincus, G.: *Physiol. Rev.*, 34, 459, 1954.
30. Astwood, E. B., in *The Hormones*, by G. Pincus and K. V. Thimann. Academic Press, Inc., New York, Vol. III, 1955, p. 235.
31. Sayers, G. and Sayers, M. A.: *Recent Progress in Hormone Research*, 2, 81, 1948.
32. Long, C. N. H.: *Recent Progress in Hormone Research*, 7, 75, 1952.
33. Lerner, A. B., and Takahashi, Y.: *Recent Progress in Hormone Research*, 12, 303, 1956.
34. Harris, J. I., and Lerner, A. B.: *Nature*, 179, 1346, 1957.
35. Irving, G. W., Jr., and du Vigneaud, V.: *Ann. N. Y. Acad. Sci.*, 43, 273, 1943.
    Irving, G. W., Jr., in *Chemistry and Physiology of Hormones*. American Association for the Advancement of Science, Washington, D.C., 1944, p. 28.
36. Stehle, R. L.: *Vitamins and Hormones*, 7, 383, 429, 1949.
37. Landgrebe, F. W.; Ketterer, B.; and Waring, H. In *The Hormones*, by G. Pincus and K. V. Thimann. Academic Press, Inc., New York, Vol. III, 1955, p. 309.
38. Stehle, R. L.: *Vitamins and Hormones*, 8, 215, 1950.
39. Greep, R. O., and Kenny, A. D. In *The Hormones*, by G. Pincus and K. V. Thimann, Academic Press, Inc., New York, Vol. III, 1955, p. 153.
40. Dempsey, E. W.: *Ann. N. Y. Acad. Sci.*, 50, 336, 1949.
41. Kendall, E. C.: *Thyroxine*. Chemical Catalog Co., 1929.
42. Harington, C. R.: *The Thyroid Gland, Its Chemistry and Physiology*. Oxford University Press, London, 1933.
43. Pitt-Rivers, R., and Tata, J. R.: *The Thyroid Hormones*. Pergamon Press, London, 1959.
44. Frieden, E., and Winzler, R. J.: *J. Biol. Chem.*, 176, 155, 1948.
45. Rawson, R. W.; Roll, J. E.; and Sonenberg, M. In *The Hormones*, by G. Pincus and K. V. Thimann. Academic Press, Inc., New York, Vol. III, 1955, p. 433.
46. Gross, J., and Pitt-Rivers, R.: *Biochem. J.*, 53, 645, 1953.
47. Taurog, A., and Chaikoff, I. L.: *J. Biol. Chem.*, 165, 217, 1946.
48. Chaikoff, I. L., and Taurog, A.: *Ann. N. Y. Acad. Sci.*, 50, 377, 1949.
49. Leblond, C. P., and Gross, J.: *J. Clin. Endocrinol.*, 9, 149, 1949.
50. Williams, R. H., and Whittenberger, J. L.: *Am. J. Med.*, 214, 193, 1947.
51. Salter, W. T.: *Western J. Surg. Obstet. Gynecol.*, 55, 15, 1947.
52. Taurog, A., and Chaikoff, I. L.: *J. Biol. Chem.*, 176, 639, 1948.
53. De Robertis, E., and Nowinski, W. W.: *J. Clin. Endocrinol.*, 6, 235, 1946.
54. Astwood, E. B.: *Ann. N. Y. Acad. Sci.*, 50, 419, 1949.
55. Chaipper, H. A., and Gordon, A. S.: *Vitamins and Hormones*, 5, 274, 1947.
56. Grollman, A.: *Essentials of Endocrinology* J. B. Lippincott Co., Philadelphia, 1941.
57. Winkler, A. W., in *Diseases of Metabolism*, 2nd ed., by G. G. Duncan. W. B. Saunders Co., Philadelphia, 1947.
58. Greep, R. O., in *The Hormones*, by G. Pincus and K. V. Thimann. Academic Press, Inc., New York, 1948, p. 255.
59. Ross, W. F., and Wood, T. R.: *J. Biol. Chem.*, 146, 49, 1942.
60. L'Heureux, M. V.; Tepperman, H. M.; and Wilhelmi, A. E.: *J. Biol. Chem.*, 168, 167, 1947.
61. Gaddum, J. H., and Holzbauer, M.: *Vitamins and Hormones*, 15, 151, 1957.
62. Euler, U. S. von: *Noradrenaline*. Charles C Thomas, Publisher, Springfield, Ill., 1956.
63. Ingle, D. J., in *The Chemistry and Physiology of Hormones*. American Association for the Advancement of Science, Washington, D.C., 1944, p. 83.
64. Hartman, F. A., and Brownell, K. A.: *Science*, 72, 76, 1930.
65. Swingle, W. D., and Pfiffner, J.: *J. Science*, 72, 75, 1930.
66. Heard, R. D. H., in *The Hormones*, by G. Pincus and K. V. Thimann. Academic Press, Inc., New York, 1948, p. 550.
67. Kuizenga, M. H., in *The Chemistry and Physiology of Hormones*. American Association for the Advancement of Science, Washington, D.C., 1944, p. 57.
68. Reichstein, T., and Shoppee, C. W.: *Vitamins and Hormones*, 1, 346, 1943.

69. Dorfman, R. I., in *The Hormones*, by G. Pincus and K. V. Thimann. Academic Press, Inc., New York, Vol. III, 1955, p. 589.
70. Noble, R. L., in *The Hormones*, by G. Pincus and K. V. Thimann. Academic Press, Inc., New York, Vol. III, 1955, p. 685.
71. Thorn, G. W.; Engle, L. L.; and Lewis, R. A.: *Science*, **94**, 348, 1941.
72. Grattan, J. F., and Jensen, H.: *J. Biol. Chem.*, **135**, 511, 1940.
73. Long, C. N. H.; Katzin, B.; and Fry, E. L.: *Endocrinology*, **26**, 309, 1940.
74. Olson, R. E.; Thayer, S. A.; and Kopp, L. H.: *Endocrinology*, **35**, 464, 1944.
75. Dorfman, R. I., in *The Hormones*, by G. Pincus and K. V. Thimann. Academic Press, Inc., New York, 1948, p. 467.
76. Beall, D.: *Nature*, **144**, 76, 1939.
77. Fieser, L. F., and Fieser, M.: *Natural Products Related to Phenanthrene*, 3rd ed. Reinhold, New York, 1949.
78. Sprague, R. G.: *Vitamins and Hormones*, **9**, 264, 1951.
79. Hooker, C. W.: *Recent Progress in Hormone Research*, **3**, 173, 1948.
80. Kochakian, C. D.: *Vitamins and Hormones*, **4**, 256, 1946.
81. Pincus, G., in *The Hormones*, by G. Pincus and K. V. Thimann. Academic Press, Inc., New York, 1955, p. 665.
82. Doisy, E. A., in *Sex and Internal Secretions*, by F. Allen. Williams & Wilkins Co., Baltimore, 1939, p. 846.
83. Pincus, G., and Pearlman, W. H.: *Vitamins and Hormones*, **1**, 294, 1943.
84. Doisy, E. A.; Thayer, S. A.; and Van Bruggen, J. T.: *Federation Proc.*, **1**, 202, 1942.
85. Allen, W. M.: *Am. J. Physiol. (London)*, **92**, 174, 612, 1930; **100**, 650, 1932.
86. Pearlman, W. H., in *The Hormones*, by G. Pincus and K. V. Thimann. Academic Press, Inc., New York, 1948, pp. 351, 407.
87. Jensen, H., in *The Hormones*, by G. Pincus and K. V. Thimann. Academic Press, Inc., New York, 1948, p. 301.
88. *Ciba Foundation Colloquia on Endocrinology, Internal Secretions of the Pancreas*, by G. E. W. Wolstenholme and C. M. O'Connor, J. & A. Churchill Ltd., London, 1956.
89. Staub, A.; Sinn, L.; and Behrens, O. K.: *Science*, **117**, 628, 1953.
90. Stetten, D., and Bloom, B., in *The Hormones*, by G. Pincus and K. V. Thimann. Academic Press, Inc., New York, 1955, p. 175.
91. Grossman, M. I.: *Physiol. Revs.*, **30**, 33, 1950.

Appendix

ANSWERS TO PROBLEMS

In the cases where more than one problem involving calculation is given in an exercise, the answers are listed in sequence corresponding to the sequence of the problems.

Chapter 2 (p. 18). Ex. 1: 17.8 M; 35.6 N; 174.8. Ex. 3: 9.095 g. Ex. 4: 0.0796; 43. Ex. 5: 6.4.

Chapter 3 (p. 69). Ex. 7: 12.3 at ordinary temperature. Ex. 8: 1.59×10^{-8}. Ex. 10: 4.64.; 0.111. Ex. 14: 7.1. Ex. 16: 0.025 M; 0.0125 M. Ex. 20: 0.5708 v. Ex. 21: 4.15.

Chapter 4 (p. 82). Ex. 1: 7.85. Ex. 2: 1.237 M; 31.5 atm. Ex. 3: 5.4. Ex. 6: 0.125 g.

Chapter 5 (p. 124). Ex. 10: 1.656. Ex. 12: 0.355 M

ABBREVIATED FORMS OF SOME BIOCHEMICAL TERMS

AAD	alloxazine adenine dinucleotide (FAD)	Dopa	dioxy-, or dihydroxyphenylalanine
ACTH	adrenocorticotrophic hormone	DPN⁺ or DPN	diphosphopyridine nucleotide, oxidized form (NAD*)

AAD — alloxazine adenine dinucleotide (FAD)

ACTH — adrenocorticotrophic hormone

AcCoA — acyl coenzyme A

ADH — alcohol dehydrogenase

ADP — adenosine diphosphate

AHG — antihemophilic globulin

AI or AIR — 5-aminoimidazole ribotide

AICA — 5-amino-4-imidazolecarboxylic acid ribotide

AMP — adenosine monophosphate

APF — animal protein factor

ATP — adenosine triphosphate

ATPase — adenosine triphosphatase

AT-10 — anti-tetany preparation No. 10 (dihydrotachysterol)

BAL — British anti-Lewisite

CDP — cytidine diphosphate

CDPC — cytidine diphosphate choline

CF — citrovorum factor (folinic acid or leucovorin)

CIF — Castle's intrinsic factor

CMP — cytidine monophosphate

CoA — coenzyme A

CoI — coenzyme I, diphosphopyridine nucleotide (DPN or NAD*)

CoII — coenzyme II, triphosphopyridine nucleotide (TPN or NADP*)

CTP — cytidine triphosphate

DDT — dichlorodiphenyl trichloroethane

DFP — diisopropylfluorophosphate or diisopropyl phosphofluorinate

D:N — dextrose-nitrogen ratio (glucose-nitrogen ratio, G:N)

DNA — deoxyribose nucleic acid

DNase — deoxyribonuclease

DNP — dinitrophenol

Dopa — dioxy-, or dihydroxyphenylalanine

DPN⁺ or DPN — diphosphopyridine nucleotide, oxidized form (NAD*)

DPNH — diphosphopyridine nucleotide, reduced form

2,4-D — 2,4-dichlorophenoxyacetic acid

EAA — essential amino acids

EAA index — essential amino acids index

EDTA — ethylenediamine tetraacetic acid

EFA — essential fatty acids

ETP — electron transport particles

FA — folic acid

FAD — flavinadenine dinucleotide, oxidized form

FADH₂ — flavinadenine dinucleotide, reduced form

FADN — flavinadenine dinucleotide

FFA — free fatty acids

FH₄ — tetrahydrofolic acid

f⁵-FH₄ — N⁵-formyltetrahydrofolic acid

f⁵,¹⁰-FH₄ — N⁵,¹⁰-methylenetetrahydrofolic acid

f¹⁰-FH₄ — N¹⁰-formyltetrahydrofolic acid

FIGLU — formiminoglutamic acid

FMN — flavinmononucleotide (riboflavin phosphate)

FSH — follicle stimulating hormone

GDP — guanosine diphosphate

GH — growth hormone

GMP — guanosine monophosphate

G:N — glucose-nitrogen ratio (dextrose-nitrogen ratio, D:N)

GSH — glutathione, reduced form

GSSG — glutathione, oxidized form

GTP — guanosine triphosphate

HCG — human chorionic gonadotropin

HGF	hyperglycemic factor	PR enzyme	prosthetic group removing enzyme
HMP shunt	hexose monophosphate shunt	PRPP	phosphoribose pyrophosphate (5-phosphoribosyl-1-pyrophosphate)
IAA	indole acetic acid		
ICSH	intersticial cell stimulating hormone	PTH	parathyroid hormone
IDP	inosine diphosphate		
IMP	inosine monophosphate	Q_{10} value	enzyme activity in relation to temperature
INH	isonicotinic acid hydrazide	Q_{10},Q_9,Q_8,Q_7	different forms of coenzyme Q
IR	infra red		
ITP	inosine triphosphate	Q-275	a form of coenzyme Q
LBF	lactobacillus factor	R5P	ribose-5-phosphate
LH	luteinizing hormone	RNA	ribose nucleic acid
L/P	lactate-pyruvate ratio	RNase	ribonuclease
LTH	leuteotrophic hormone	RQ	respiratory quotient
LTPP	lipothiamide pyrophosphate		
		SPCA	serum prothrombin conversion accelerator
MSH	melanocyte stimulating hormone	TCA	trichloracetic acid, also tricarboxylic acid cycle
NAD	nicotinamide adenine dinucleotide* (DPN or CoI)	TEPP	tetraethyl pyrophosphate
		THFA	tetrahydrofolic acid
NADP	nicotinamide adenine dinucleotide phosphate* (TPN or CoII)	TPN	triphosphopyridine nucleotide (CoII)*
		TPP	thiamine pyrophosphate
NEFA	non-esterified fatty acids	Tris	tris (hydroxymethyl)-aminomethane
N^5-fTHFA	N^5-formyltetrahydrofolic acid	TSH	thyroid stimulating hormone
N^{10}-fTHFA	N^{10}-formyltetrahydrofolic acid	UDP	uridine diphosphate
NMN	nicotinamide mononucleotide	UDPG	uridine diphosphoglucose
NPN	non-protein nitrogen	UDPGA	uridine diphosphoglucuronic acid
PAB or PABA	p-aminobenzoic acid	UDPGal	uridine diphosphogalactose
PGA	pteroyl glutamic acid		
P_i or P_{in}	inorganic phosphate	UDP glucuronic acid	uridine diphosphoglucuronic acid
PMSG	pregnant mare serum gonadotropin	UMP	uridine monophosphate
PNA	pentose nucleic acid	USP	United States Pharmacopoeia
P:O	moles ATP formed per atom oxygen consumed	UTP	uridine triphosphate
		UV	ultra violet
PP or PP_i	pyrophosphate, inorganic	VDM	vasodepressor material

* On the basis of objections cited in a footnote page 378 and others, DPN and TPN are unfortunate choices as names for coenzyme I and coenzyme II. For some years the Enzyme Commission of the International Union of Biochemists has given careful consideration to the nomenclature of coenzymes in an effort to reach a generally acceptable solution. Recommendations have been made by the Commission and include NAD for nicotinamide-adenine dinucleotide (DPN or coenzyme I or CoI) and NADP for nicotinamide-adenine dinucleotide phosphate (TPN or coenzyme II or CoII). The biological Chemistry Nomenclature Commission of the International Union of Pure and Applied Chemistry has likewise recommended NAD and NADP. For discussion of this matter see Dixon, M., Science, 132, 1548 (1960).

HGF	hypoglycemic factor	PR enzyme	prosthetic group removing enzyme
HMP shunt	hexose monophosphate shunt	PRPP	phosphoribose pyrophosphate-5-phosphate (phosphoribosyl-1-pyrophosphate)
IAA	indole acetic acid	PTH	parathyroid hormone
ICSH	interstitial cell stimulating hormone	Q_{10} value	enzyme activity in relation to temperature
IDP	inosine diphosphate	Q, Q_6, Q_7, Q_{10}	different forms of coenzyme Q
IMP	inosine monophosphate	Q-275	a form of coenzyme Q
INH	isonicotinic acid hydrazide		
IR	infra red		
ITP	inosine triphosphate		

LIF	lactobacillus factor	R5P	ribose-5-phosphate
LH	luteinizing hormone	RNA	ribose nucleic acid
L/P	lactate-pyruvate ratio	RNase	ribonuclease
LTH	luteotrophic hormone	RQ	respiratory quotient
LTPP	lipothiamide pyrophosphate	SPCA	serum prothrombin conversion accelerator
MSH	melanocyte stimulating hormone	TCA	trichloroacetic acid, also tricarboxylic acid cycle
NAD	nicotinamide adenine dinucleotide (DPN) or (CoI)	TEPP	tetraethyl pyrophosphate
NADP	nicotinamide adenine dinucleotide phosphate (TPN or CoII)	THFA	tetrahydrofolic acid
		TPN	triphosphopyridine nucleotide (CoII)*
NEFA	non-esterified fatty acids	TPP	thiamine pyrophosphate
N^5-f THFA	N^5-formyltetrahydro folic acid	Tris	tris (hydroxymethyl) aminomethane
N^{10}-f THFA	N^{10}-formyltetrahydro folic acid	TSH	thyroid stimulating hormone
NMN	nicotinamide mononucleotide	UDP	uridine diphosphate
NPN	non-protein nitrogen	UDPG	uridine diphosphoglucose
PAB or PABA	p-aminobenzoic acid	UDPGA	uridine diphosphoglucuronic acid
PGA	pteroyl glutamic acid	UDPGal	uridine diphosphogalactose
P_i or P_a	inorganic phosphate	UDP glucuronic acid	uridine diphosphoglucuronic acid
PMSG	pregnant mare serum gonadotropin	UMP	uridine monophosphate
PNA	pentose nucleic acid	USP	United States Pharmacopeia
P:O	moles ATP formed per atom oxygen consumed	UTP	uridine triphosphate
		UV	ultra violet
PP or PP$_i$	pyrophosphate, inorganic	VDM	vasodepressor material

* On the basis of discussions cited in a footnote page 375 and others, DPN and TPN are unfortunate choices as names for coenzyme I and coenzyme II. For some years the Enzyme Commission of the International Union of Biochemistry has given careful consideration to the nomenclature of coenzymes in an effort to reach a generally acceptable solution. Recommendations have been made by the Commission and include NAD for nicotinamide-adenine dinucleotide (DPN at coenzyme I or CoI) and NADP for nicotinamide-adenine dinucleotide phosphate (TPN at coenzyme II or CoII). The biology of Chemistry, Nomenclature Committee of the International Union of Pure and Applied Chemistry, has likewise recommended NAD and NADP. For discussion of this matter see Dixon, M., Science, 132, 1548 (1960).

Index

LOGARITHMS

Natural Numbers	0	1	2	3	4	5	6	7	8	9	PROPORTIONAL PARTS								
											1	2	3	4	5	6	7	8	9
10	0000	0043	0086	0128	0170	0212	0253	0294	0334	0374	4	8	12	17	21	25	29	33	37
11	0414	0453	0492	0531	0569	0607	0645	0682	0719	0755	4	8	11	15	19	23	26	30	34
12	0792	0828	0864	0899	0934	0969	1004	1038	1072	1106	3	7	10	14	17	21	24	28	31
13	1139	1173	1206	1239	1271	1303	1335	1367	1399	1430	3	6	10	13	16	19	23	26	29
14	1461	1492	1523	1553	1584	1614	1644	1673	1703	1732	3	6	9	12	15	18	21	24	27
15	1761	1790	1818	1847	1875	1903	1931	1959	1987	2014	3	6	8	11	14	17	20	22	25
16	2041	2068	2095	2122	2148	2175	2201	2227	2253	2279	3	5	8	11	13	16	18	21	24
17	2304	2330	2355	2380	2405	2430	2455	2480	2504	2529	2	5	7	10	12	15	17	20	22
18	2553	2577	2601	2625	2648	2672	2695	2718	2742	2765	2	5	7	9	12	14	16	19	21
19	2788	2810	2833	2856	2878	2900	2923	2945	2967	2989	2	4	7	9	11	13	16	18	20
20	3010	3032	3054	3075	3096	3118	3139	3160	3181	3201	2	4	6	8	11	13	15	17	19
21	3222	3243	3263	3284	3304	3324	3345	3365	3385	3404	2	4	6	8	10	12	14	16	18
22	3424	3444	3464	3483	3502	3522	3541	3560	3579	3598	2	4	6	8	10	12	14	15	17
23	3617	3636	3655	3674	3692	3711	3729	3747	3766	3784	2	4	6	7	9	11	13	15	17
24	3802	3820	3838	3856	3874	3892	3909	3927	3945	3962	2	4	5	7	9	11	12	14	16
25	3979	3997	4014	4031	4048	4065	4082	4099	4116	4133	2	3	5	7	9	10	12	14	15
26	4150	4166	4183	4200	4216	4232	4249	4265	4281	4298	2	3	5	7	8	10	11	13	15
27	4314	4330	4346	4362	4378	4393	4409	4425	4440	4456	2	3	5	6	8	9	11	13	14
28	4472	4487	4502	4518	4533	4548	4564	4579	4594	4609	2	3	5	6	8	9	11	12	14
29	4624	4639	4654	4669	4683	4698	4713	4728	4742	4757	1	3	4	6	7	9	10	12	13
30	4771	4786	4800	4814	4829	4843	4857	4871	4886	4900	1	3	4	6	7	9	10	11	13
31	4914	4928	4942	4955	4969	4983	4997	5011	5024	5038	1	3	4	6	7	8	10	11	12
32	5051	5065	5079	5092	5105	5119	5132	5145	5159	5172	1	3	4	5	7	8	9	11	12
33	5185	5198	5211	5224	5237	5250	5263	5276	5289	5302	1	3	4	5	6	8	9	10	12
34	5315	5328	5340	5353	5366	5378	5391	5403	5416	5428	1	3	4	5	6	8	9	10	11
35	5441	5453	5465	5478	5490	5502	5514	5527	5539	5551	1	2	4	5	6	7	9	10	11
36	5563	5575	5587	5599	5611	5623	5635	5647	5658	5670	1	2	4	5	6	7	8	10	11
37	5682	5694	5705	5717	5729	5740	5752	5763	5775	5786	1	2	3	5	6	7	8	9	10
38	5798	5809	5821	5832	5843	5855	5866	5877	5888	5899	1	2	3	5	6	7	8	9	10
39	5911	5922	5933	5944	5955	5966	5977	5988	5999	6010	1	2	3	4	5	7	8	9	10
40	6021	6031	6042	6053	6064	6075	6085	6096	6107	6117	1	2	3	4	5	6	8	9	10
41	6128	6138	6149	6160	6170	6180	6191	6201	6212	6222	1	2	3	4	5	6	7	8	9
42	6232	6243	6253	6263	6274	6284	6294	6304	6314	6325	1	2	3	4	5	6	7	8	9
43	6335	6345	6355	6365	6375	6385	6395	6405	6415	6425	1	2	3	4	5	6	7	8	9
44	6435	6444	6454	6464	6474	6484	6493	6503	6513	6522	1	2	3	4	5	6	7	8	9
45	6532	6542	6551	6561	6571	6580	6590	6599	6609	6618	1	2	3	4	5	6	7	8	9
46	6628	6637	6646	6656	6665	6675	6684	6693	6702	6712	1	2	3	4	5	6	7	7	8
47	6721	6730	6739	6749	6758	6767	6776	6785	6794	6803	1	2	3	4	5	5	6	7	8
48	6812	6821	6830	6839	6848	6857	6866	6875	6884	6893	1	2	3	4	4	5	6	7	8
49	6902	6911	6920	6928	6937	6946	6955	6964	6972	6981	1	2	3	4	4	5	6	7	8
50	6990	6998	7007	7016	7024	7033	7042	7050	7059	7067	1	2	3	3	4	5	6	7	8
51	7076	7084	7093	7101	7110	7118	7126	7135	7143	7152	1	2	3	3	4	5	6	7	8
52	7160	7168	7177	7185	7193	7202	7210	7218	7226	7235	1	2	2	3	4	5	6	7	7
53	7243	7251	7259	7267	7275	7284	7292	7300	7308	7316	1	2	2	3	4	5	6	6	7
54	7324	7332	7340	7348	7356	7364	7372	7380	7388	7396	1	2	2	3	4	5	6	6	7